Stanley Gibbons
Stamp Catalogue

Commonwealth and British Empire Stamps 1840 – 1952

109th edition 2007

Stanley Gibbons Ltd
London and Ringwood

By Appointment to Her Majesty The Queen
Stanley Gibbons Ltd, London
Philatelists

Published by Stanley Gibbons Ltd
Editorial, Publications Sales Offices
and Distribution Centre:
Parkside, Christchurch Road, Ringwood,
Hants BH24 3SH

ISBN: 0-85259-626-X

Item No. 2813 (07)

Printed and bound by
Polestar Wheatons Ltd, Exeter

Preface to the 2007 Edition

An Interesting Year

The 12 months since I sat down to write these notes for the 2006 edition of this catalogue have been interesting ones for philately. On the negative side, a stamp investment scandal in Europe led some to believe that the current upsurge in interest in our hobby might be short-lived. However, the continuing trend of record-breaking auction realisations, the growth of the internet as a medium for buying and selling stamps and the success of national and international stamp exhibitions has confounded the doom-mongers. As a result, half way through Stanley Gibbons' 150th anniversary year we continue to look forward to a bright future for stamp collecting.

The year has also been a busy one in the Stanley Gibbons catalogue department. The most obvious development in this catalogue will be the significant increase in the number of colour illustrations, not only as part of the on-going process of converting the old black and white pictures into colour, but also the reintroduction of illustrations that were taken out many years ago in order to conserve space. This has rendered the 2007 edition a much more colourful catalogue than any of its predecessors, a fact which we hope collectors will enjoy. Once again, I should like to thank the stamp department at Spink for their help in this process.

We have also been pressing on with the Commonwealth Countries series of catalogues, listing individual countries or groups of territories from SG1 to date in handy single volumes. New editions of three of these have appeared in the past year, together with four new titles, bringing the total to 14 different catalogues, with more on the way. Collectors of Queen Elizabeth stamps are therefore welcome to provide us with details of their research and discoveries with a view to them being included in the next edition of the relevant 'yellow' catalogue. Those who are using these catalogues will be aware that in some areas interest in modern stamps remains high and that prices have risen substantially since the publication of the last 'full' British Commonwealth catalogue in 2001. However, the reintroduction of this catalogue becomes less and less feasible as postal administrations continue to issue ever greater numbers of stamps which would need to be listed in it.

In the last full 'Part 1' and in the new 'yellow' volumes, countries are listed according to their current names, but in this catalogue we continue to arrange them under the names current in 1952. Thus, British Solomon Islands is used rather than Solomon Islands and Virgin Islands, rather than British Virgin Islands. Colonies that amalgamated into larger territories or dominions are grouped together before the united country, while dependent territories appear after the main listings. Thus the Australian states appear before Australia itself, with Nauru, New Guinea and Papua after it.

PRICES

Regular readers of *Gibbons Stamp Monthly* will know that the SG100™ Stamp Price Index for the hundred most frequently traded stamps continues to rise, and at the end of June 2006 showed an increase of 7.3 per cent for the first six months of the year, compared to a rise of 6.0 per cent over the same period in 2005. Many of the stamps which make up the SG100 are listed in this catalogue, so it will not come as a surprise that there are even more price increases in this year's catalogue than there were last time.

Australia and states have once again been reviewed with the help of Simon Dunkerley, to whom we are grateful for his on-the-spot advice on this very active market. Victoria, Western Australia and the later issues of New South Wales have received particular attention this time, while, in Australia itself, postage dues, booklets, official stamps, varieties and, most especially, inverted watermarks see significant increases.

Looking at other major countries; Canada has been relatively quiet for the past few years, but there are further rises for the provinces and for Canada itself,

especially the 19th century issues. India continues to be popular, with a huge number of increases to the Convention and Feudatory states. Price rises continue in Malaya and in New Zealand there are increases for the postal fiscals, officials, Life Insurance Department stamps and most issues prior to 1936. In South Africa, although activity is widespread, main interest is bound to centre on Transvaal, where the sale of Dr. Alan Drysdall's collection has allowed extensive revision, with many previously listed but unpriced varieties now being given a valuation.

Elsewhere, several African countries and Caribbean Islands have seen notable advances. In the former group particular mention should be made of Gambia, Gold Coast, British East Africa, Rhodesia, Sierra Leone and Zanzibar (especially the postage dues), while in the West Indies we note Antigua, Barbados (to 1885), British Honduras, British Guiana, Leeward Islands, St. Lucia and St. Vincent, where, following the sale of the Peter Jaffé collection, a much more detailed table of on-cover multipliers has now been provided for issues up to 1882.

Asian territories continue to rise in value also, with Hong Kong, Iraq (especially Baghdad), North Borneo and Pakistan standing out, while, although the Pacific area continues to lag somewhat, Fiji, New Guinea and Papua have all done well this year.

Stamps of one country used in another also continue to receive attention. This time we note in particular Great Britain used in Ascension, Gibraltar, Malta and the Niger Company Territories, India used in Bahrain, Falkland Islands used in the Dependencies, New Zealand used on Pitcairn and, predictably, Hong Kong stamps with Treaty Port cancellations.

Varieties and errors, irrespective of their country of origin also continue to move up in price and plate flaws and watermark varieties throughout the catalogue see further increases.

In addition to these more general trends there are sharp rises for individual rarities which have fetched high prices at auction over the past year. The sale of Sir Gawaine Baillie's Commonwealth collection has led to increases in African territories, British North America and New Zealand, while important sales of Australia and states and Great Britain have influenced prices in these areas.

Users of the Stanley Gibbons *Great Britain Concise Catalogue* are aware that this country continues to increase in popularity and that prices, especially for rare stamps in fine condition continue to rise accordingly, with *Gibbons Stamp Monthly* (July 2006) reporting that the GB30 Index had risen by 11.4 per cent in the past year.

Once again, I should remind readers that newsworthy auction realisations are achieved by stamps in fine condition or better and that in this increasingly condition-conscious age, whether we are buying on the internet, at stamp fairs, from dealers or at one of the major international auction houses, prices for stamps of lower grade should be significantly less expensive than quoted here. The Information and Guidelines section of this catalogue gives advice on this aspect of the hobby which we recommend that all collectors consider very carefully before making any purchase.

REVISIONS TO THIS EDITION

Mention has already been made of the increased use of colour. This is particularly true in the case of illustrations showing varieties, where Richard Lockyer has resubmitted many of the stamps which provided the black-and-white images in earlier catalogues, so that they may now be illustrated in colour. We have also taken the opportunity to show one or two varieties which have not been illustrated before, such as **New Guinea** SG210a, while new King George VI varieties provided by Mr. Lockyer include the **Ceylon** 2c. 'comma' flaw and the **Gibraltar** 2s. 'Bird on Memorial'.

Inverted and reversed watermarks continue to be discovered and reported to us by individual collectors

and members of the trade, to whom we are extremely grateful. Surprisingly, over 60 new varieties of this type have been added to this edition alone, with my personal favourite being the **Aden** 1937 2½a. Coronation with inverted watermark, reported by Ken Pitkethly; this is now listed as 14w.

Apart from his pricing advice, Simon Dunkerley has made a number of suggestions for the **Australia** and states listings and has provided illustrations of Australia 123a for scanning as well as the newly listed roller flaws on the 1s. Lyre bird and £2 Arms designs.

Brian Hurst of the **Bechuanalands** and Botswana Society has assisted with expanding the listings of varieties on the Cape of Good Hope overprints and, even more importantly, has provided illustrations of the "curved foot to '2'" and "small figure '1'" varieties, both listed here for many years. Hopefully the provision of these illustrations will be of assistance to collectors, dealers and auction houses in correctly identifying these in the years to come.

Five varieties of surcharge on the "C.E.F." overprints of **Cameroon** have also been listed without illustrations for some years. Four of these are now shown.

In **Fiji** the "Void corner" on Nos. 28 and 31, is now illustrated, thanks to John Ray, and Mr. Ray has also provided an illustration of the "Bold 'TA'" on the 1915-19 War stamps.

No less than six new additions have been made to the listings of **Hong Kong** stamps used in the British post offices in China and further varieties have been added to **Iraq**, thanks once again to Freddy Khalastchy.

In **Malaya**, the section covering the Siamese Posts in Northern Malaya (formerly Z2/392) has now been transferred to the respective states in which they were used (Kedah, Kelantan and Perlis). On the closure of the Siamese offices, stamps of the Federated Malay States went on sale in the three states. Thanks to Rob Holley, assisted by other members of the Malaya Study Group, a priced listing is now provided for Federated Malay States stamps bearing Kedah, Kelantan and Perlis cancellations of this period. A number of new and improved variety illustrations have been added to the Malaya section, thanks, particularly to Keith Elliot.

New Zealand includes new notes, an additional listing and revised prices for the 'long' postal fiscals, following research by Robin Gwynn, published in the *New Zealand Stamp Collector*, while in **Niger Coast Protectorate**, **North Borneo** and **Labuan**, several new perforation combinations have been added to the Waterlow printed stamps, in the latter two countries thanks, particularly, to Andrew Dixon.

Derek Barker of the **Sudan** Study Circle has provided a previously unknown inverted watermark on the 1924-41 definitives and further improvements to the accuracy of the issue dates of the shades on the 1951 set.

Judging from the *Gibbons Stamp Monthly* postbag, the **Togo** overprints on Gold Coast have long been a problem for many collectors. Now, following the publication of his book *Togo Overprints on Stamps of the Gold Coast 1915-1920*, Peter Duggan has provided new illustrations and extended notes which should make those problems a thing of the past.

Finally, Vince Cordell has reviewed the listings of **Great Britain used abroad**, making a number of changes and revising the prices.

Many other additions and amendments have been made throughout the catalogue and, once again, we are grateful to many collectors, study circles and members of the trade for their advice and assistance. We look forward to further cooperation as we commence work on the 2008 edition.

I would again like to add my personal thanks to my colleagues in Ringwood and London for their continued help and support. Without them this catalogue could not have been published. My thanks to you all.

Hugh Jefferies,
Catalogue Editor.

Stanley Gibbons Holdings Plc

Stanley Gibbons Limited, Stanley Gibbons Auctions
399 Strand, London WC2R OLX
Telephone 020 7836 8444, Fax 020 7836 7342,
E-mail: *enquiries@stanleygibbons.co.uk*
Internet: *www.stanleygibbons.com*
for all departments,
Auction and Specialist Stamp Departments.
Open Monday–Friday 9.30 a.m. to 5 p.m.
Shop. Open Monday–Friday 9 a.m. to 5.30 p.m. and Saturday
9.30 a.m. to 5.30 p.m.

Stanley Gibbons Publications
Parkside, Christchurch Road, Ringwood,
Hampshire BH24 3SH.
Telephone 01425 472363 (24 hour answer phone service), Fax
01425 470247,
E-mail: *info@stanley gibbons.co.uk*
Publications Mail Order. FREEPHONE 0800 611622
Monday–Friday 8.30 a.m. to 5 p.m.

Gibbons Stamp Monthly
Parkside, Christchurch Road, Ringwood,
Hampshire BH24 3SH.
Subscriptions. 01425 472363, Fax 01425 470247
E-mail: *gsm@stanleygibbons.co.uk*

Fraser's
(a division of Stanley Gibbons Ltd)

399 Strand, London WC2R OLX
Autographs, photographs, letters and documents
Telephone 020 7836 8444, Fax 020 7836 7342,
E-mail: *info@frasersautographs.co.uk*
Internet: *www.frasersautographs.com*
Monday–Friday 9 a.m. to 5.30 p.m. and
Saturday 10 a.m. to 4 p.m.

**Stanley Gibbons
Publications Overseas
Representation**

Stanley Gibbons Publications
are represented overseas by
the following
sole distributors (*),
distributors (**)
or licensees (***).

Australia
*Lighthouse Philatelic (Aust.)
Pty. Ltd.* *
Locked Bag 5900
Botany DC,
New South Wales, 2019.

*Stanley Gibbons (Australia)
Pty. Ltd.* ***
Level 6,
36 Clarence Street, Sydney,
New South Wales 2000,

Belgium and Luxembourg
Davo c/o Philac, Rue du
Midi 48, Bruxelles, 1000.

Canada
Unitrade,
99 Floral Parkway, Toronto,
Ontario M6L 264

Denmark
Samlerforum/Davo,
Ostergade 3,
DK 7470 Karup, Denmark.

Finland
*Davo
c/o Kapylan Merkkiky*
Pohjolankatu 00610
Helsinki.

France *
Davo France (Casteilla),
10, Rue Leon Foucault,
78184 St. Quentin Yvelines
Cesex.

Hong Kong
Po-on Stamp Service,
GPO Box 2498,
Hong Kong.

Israel
Capital Stamps,
P.O. Box 3769,
Jerusalem 91036. Israel.

Italy *
Ernesto Marini Sri,
Via Struppa 300, I-16165,
Genova GE.

Japan
Japan Philatelic Co. Ltd.,
P.O. Box 2,
Suginami-Minami, Tokyo.

Netherlands *
Davo Publications,
P.O. Box 411,
7400 AK Deventer.

New Zealand ***
Mowbray Collectables.
P.O. Box 80, Wellington.

Norway
Davo Norge A/S,
P.O. Box 738 Sentrum,
N-0105, Oslo.

Saudi Arabia
Arabian Stamps Centre,
P. O. Box 54645,
Riyadh 11524.

Singapore
*Stamp Inc Collectibles
Pte Ltd.,*
10 Ubi Cresent, #01-43 Ubi
Tech Park, Singapore 408564.

Sweden *
Chr Winther Soerensen AB,
Box 43, S-310 Knaered,
Sweden.

Switzerland
Phila Service, Burgstrasse
160, CH 4125, Riehen.

United States
Filatco Inc,
P. O. Box 520, McLean,
VA 22101-0520.

Stanley Gibbons Stamp Catalogue
Complete list of parts

1 ***Commonwealth & British Empire Stamps 1840–1952*** (formerly Part 1) (Annual)

Foreign Countries

2 ***Austria & Hungary*** (6th edition, 2002)
  • Austria • U.N. (Vienna) • Hungary

3 ***Balkans*** (4th edition, 1998) • Albania • Bosnia & Herzegovina
  • Bulgaria • Croatia • Greece & Islands • Macedonia • Romania
  • Slovenia • Yugoslavia

4 ***Benelux*** (5th edition 2003)
  • Belgium & Colonies • Luxembourg
  • Netherlands & Colonies

5 ***Czechoslovakia & Poland*** (6th edition, 2002)
  • Czechoslovakia • Czech Republic • Slovakia
  • Poland

6 ***France*** (5th edition, 2001)
  • France • Colonies • Post Offices •Andorra • Monaco

7 ***Germany*** (7th edition, 2005)
  • Germany • States • Colonies • Post Offices

8 ***Italy & Switzerland*** (6th edition, 2003)
  • Italy & Colonies • Liechtenstein • San Marino
  • Switzerland • U.N. (Geneva) • Vatican City

9 ***Portugal & Spain*** (5th edition, 2004)
  • Andorra • Portugal & Colonies • Spain & Colonies

10 ***Russia*** (5th edition, 1999)
  • Russia • Armenia • Azerbaijan • Belarus
  • Estonia • Georgia • Kazakhstan • Kyrgyzstan
  • Latvia • Lithuania • Moldova • Tajikistan
  • Turkmenistan • Ukraine • Uzbekistan • Mongolia

11 ***Scandinavia*** (5th edition, 2001)
  • Aland Islands • Denmark • Faroe Islands
  • Finland • Greenland • Iceland • Norway
  • Sweden

12 ***Africa since Independence A-E*** (2nd edition 1983)
  • Algeria • Angola • Benin • Burundi • Cameroun • Cape Verde
  • Central African Republic • Chad • Comoro Islands
  • Congo • Djibouti • Equatorial Guinea • Ethiopia

13 ***Africa since Independence F-M*** (1st edition, 1981)
  • Gabon • Guinea • Guinea-Bissau
  • Ivory Coast • Liberia • Libya • Malagasy Republic • Mali •
  Mauritania • Morocco • Mozambique

14 ***Africa since Independence N-Z*** (1st edition, 1981)
  • Niger Republic • Rwanda • St. Thomas & Prince • Senegal
  • Somalia • Sudan • Togo • Tunisia • Upper Volta • Zaire

15 ***Central America*** (2nd edition, 1984)
  • Costa Rica • Cuba • Dominican Republic • El Salvador
  • Guatemala • Haiti - Honduras • Mexico • Nicaragua • Panama

16 ***Central Asia*** (4th edition, 2006)
  • Afghanistan • Iran • Turkey

17 ***China*** (6th edition, 1998)
  • China • Taiwan • Tibet • Foreign P.O.s • Hong Kong • Macao

18 ***Japan & Korea*** (4th edition, 1997)
  • Japan • Korean Empire • South Korea • North Korea

19 ***Middle East*** (6th edition, 2005)
  • Aden • Bahrain • Egypt • Iraq .• Israel • Jordan • Kuwait
  • Lebanon • Oman • Qatar • Saudi Arabia • Syria
  • U.A.E. • Yemen

20 ***South America*** (3rd edition, 1989)
  • Argentina • Bolivia • Brazil • Chile • Colombia • Ecuador
  • Paraguay • Peru • Surinam • Uruguay • Venezuela

21 ***South-East Asia*** (4th edition, 2004)
  • Bhutan • Cambodia • Indo-China • Indonesia • Laos • Myanmar
  • Nepal • Philippines • Thailand • Timor • Vietnam

22 ***United States*** (6th edition, 2005)
  • U.S. & Possessions • Marshall Islands
  • Micronesia • Palau • U.N. (New York, Geneva, Vienna)

Great Britain Specialised Catalogues

Volume 1 ***Queen Victoria*** (13th edition, 2004)
Volume 2 ***King Edward VII to King George VI***
  (12th edition, 2005)
Volume 3 ***Queen Elizabeth II Pre-decimal Issues***
  (11th edition, 2005)
Volume 4 ***Queen Elizabeth II Decimal Definitive Issues***
  (9th edition, 2000)
Volume 5 ***Queen Elizabeth II Decimal Special Issues*** (3rd edition,
  1998 with 1998–99 and 2000/1 Supplements)

Thematic Catalogues

Stanley Gibbons Catalogues for use
with ***Stamps of the World.***
Collect Aircraft on Stamps (out of print)
Collect Birds on Stamps (5th edition, 2003)
Collect Chess on Stamps (2nd edition, 1999)
Collect Fish on Stamps (1st edition, 1999)
Collect Fungi on Stamps (2nd edition, 1997)
Collect Motor Vehicles on Stamps (1st edition 2004)
Collect Railways on Stamps (3rd edition, 1999)
Collect Shells on Stamps (Out of Print)
Collect Ships on Stamps (3rd edition, 2001)

Stamps Added

Great Britain 418c, O9ca
Aden 14w
   Kathiri State of Seiyun 13b
Antigua Z6a
Australia
   New South Wales 313b, 335c, 352a
   Queensland 234ba, 285a
   South Australia 293b, 293ba, 299c, 300b, 303c
   Tasmania 245ee, 250eb, 250gh
   Victoria 137d, 401ba, 419a, 427aa, 427ab, 427b, 427c, 453a
   W Australia 71by, 83w, 115w, 116w, 161a
   Commonwealth of Australia 47k, 192a, 224da, 230db
   Nauru 18sa
Bahamas 60x, 106a, 109a, 110b, 144i
Barbados 24b, 208wb, 231ax, 264b, 264eb
Bechuanaland 30a, 30ab, 30ba, 30bb, 38f
Bermuda 25x, 59y, 63x, 70w, 76x, 121ba, 121ca
British Guiana 126w, 170x
British Occupation of Italian Colonies MD2w, ED1a
Brunei 57d
Canada 17a, 25b, 188a
Ceylon 55ax, 63ay, 64aw, 66bx, 148w, 279w, 306aw, 335w, 337y, 359h/hf, 386aa, 386ab
Falkland Island Dependencies Z6, PH3, PH4, Z87a, G9b, G10a/16a
Fiji 138e, 139e
Gibraltar 128bb
Gold Coast 12w
Grenada 163ea

Hong Kong 28w, 32x, 134e, Z221, Z233, Z524, Z807a, Z1030, Z1077
India 155w, 221a, 311w, 314w, C30a
Indian Convention States
   Chamba 61a
   Gwalior 28ca, O38a, O51a
   Patiala O44a
Indian Feudatory States
   Bundi O30ba, O41
   Duttia 2b, 3b, 8bb, 39c
   Sirmoor 75d
   Travancore-Cochin O10fi
Iraq 106a, 107d, 108a
Ireland 1w, 31w, 48w, 72bw, 146w, D2y
Jamaica 83x
Kenya, Uganda and Tanganyika
   British East Africa 49e, 50d, 53g
   Kenya, Uganda and Tanganyika 49w
Kuwait 22w
Malaya
   Straits Settlements 68w, 226b, F1
   Federated Malay States 49y
   British Military Administration 13ac
   Kedah Z231/82, 30ax
   Kelantan Z367/96
   Negri Sembilan – Sungei Ujong 22a
   Negri Sembilan 15b
   Perlis Z441/5
   Trengganu 21b, 21c
   Japanese Occupation J107b, J133a
Maldive Islands 21a
Mauritius 120w

Morocco Agencies 5ca
New Zealand 152y, 195bh, 208a, 216baa, 218m, 228c, 237d, 333x, 410xa, 424aa, 430aa, 430cba, 446bxa, 584ca, O100d, F6a
Nigeria
   Niger Coast Protectorate 49c, 58c, 58d, 64b, 64c, 67f, 70c
   Nigeria SB3
North Borneo 68c, 70aa, 75c, 78b, 94e, 101b, 108d, 113b, 231a, 313a
Labuan 86d, 89ab, 118aa
Northern Rhodesia D2a
Nyasaland 133ab
St. Helena 97d
St. Vincent 55x
Somaliland Protectorate 1b
South Africa
   Griqualand West 10cw, 10dw, 25w
   Natal 62x, 63w, 97aw
   New Republic 79e
   Orange Free State 113p, 124p
   Transvaal 263aw
   Union of South Africa 113a, 127b
South West Africa 93a, 136a, D4b
Sudan 43aw, 53ay, 57bx, 77ax
Tanganyika M42a
Togo H51a
Tonga 37Bc
Trinidad D3w, O10w
Turks Islands 15b
Zanzibar 15l, 26m

Catalogue Numbers Altered

The table below is a cross-reference of those catalogue numbers which have been altered in this edition.

		Old	New
Australia			
	New South Wales	336da	336a
		336db	336b
	Victoria	396	384c
		397	deleted
		397a	deleted
		416a	deleted
		426a	416a
		426b	416b
		426ba	416ba
		417ba	417c
		417c	417d
		419a	419b
		454b	454ac
		454c	454a
		454a	454ab
	Nauru	2b	2c
		2bb	2cb
Barbados		43a	deleted
		231a	231b
		264b	264c
		264c	264d
		264d	264e
		264da	264ea
		264db	264ec
		264dc	264ed
Bechuanaland		38f	38g
British Honduras		59a	deleted
Canada			
	Newfoundland	33a	deleted

		Old	New
Ceylon		359/f	359h/hf
		SB6	SB6a
		SB6a	SB6b
Hong Kong		Z807a	Z807b
		Z807b	Z807c
Indian Convention States			
	Gwalior	O51a/ca	O51b/da
Indian Feudatory States			
	Bundi	O41	O41a
		O41a	O41b
		O41ab	O41ba
	Duttia	8bb	8bc
Malaya			
	Kelantan	Z237/347	Z301/62
	Negri Sembilan	24	24a
		24a	24
	Pahang	31	31a
		31a	31
	Perlis	Z349/92	Z401/38
	Selangor	71	71a
		71a	71
	Siamese Posts in Northern Malaya relisted under respective states		

		Old	New
South Africa			
	New Republic	72a	deleted
		79a	deleted
		89a	deleted
		92a	deleted
		93a	deleted
	Transvaal	263a	263b
Sudan		43a	43b
		77a	77b
Togo		H56b	deleted

Contents

General Philatelic Information and Guidelines to the Scope of Stanley Gibbons Commonwealth Catalogues

The notes which follow seek to reflect current practice in compiling the Stanley Gibbons Commonwealth Catalogues.

It scarcely needs emphasising that the Stanley Gibbons Stamp Catalogue has a very long history and that the vast quantity of information it contains has been carefully built up by successive generations through the work of countless individuals. Philately is never static and the Catalogue has evolved and developed over the years. These notes relate to the current criteria upon which a stamp may be listed or priced. It should be recognised that these criteria have developed over time and may have differed somewhat in the early years of this catalogue. These notes are not intended to suggest that we plan to make wholesale changes to the listing of classic issues in order to bring them into line with today's listing policy, they are designed to inform catalogue users as to the policies currently in operation.

PRICES

The prices quoted in this Catalogue are the estimated selling prices of Stanley Gibbons Ltd at the time of publication. They are, unless it is specifically stated otherwise, for examples in fine condition for the issue concerned. Superb examples are worth more; those of a lower quality considerably less.

All prices are subject to change without prior notice and Stanley Gibbons Ltd may from time to time offer stamps below catalogue price. Individual low value stamps sold at 399 Strand are liable to an additional handling charge. Purchasers of new issues are asked to note the prices charged for them contain an element for the service rendered and so may exceed the prices shown when the stamps are subsequently catalogued. Postage and handling charges are extra.

No guarantee is given to supply all stamps priced, since it is not possible to keep every catalogued item in stock. Commemorative issues may, at times, only be available in complete sets and not as individual values.

Quotation of prices. The prices in the left-hand column are for unused stamps and those in the right-hand column are for used.

A dagger (†) denotes that the item listed does not exist in that condition and a blank, or dash, that it exists, or may exist, but we are unable to quote a price.

Prices are expressed in pounds and pence sterling. One pound comprises 100 pence (£1 = 100p).

The method of notation is as follows: pence in numerals (e.g. 10 denotes ten pence); pounds and pence, up to £100, in numerals (e.g. 4.25 denotes four pounds and twenty-five pence); prices above £100 are expressed in whole pounds with the '£' sign shown.

Unused stamps. Great Britain and Commonwealth: the prices for unused stamps of Queen Victoria to King George V are for lightly hinged examples. Unused prices for King Edward VIII and King George VI issues are for unmounted mint.

Some stamps from the King George VI period are often difficult to find in unmounted mint condition. In such instances we would expect that collectors would need to pay a high proportion of the price quoted to obtain mounted mint examples. Generally speaking lightly mounted mint stamps from this reign, issued before 1945, are in considerable demand.

Used stamps. The used prices are normally for stamps postally used but may be for stamps cancelled-to-order where this practice exists.

A pen-cancellation on early issues can sometimes correctly denote postal use. Instances are individually noted in the Catalogue in explanation of the used price given.

Prices quoted for bisects on cover or large piece are for those dated during the period officially authorised.

Stamps not sold unused to the public (e.g. some official stamps) are priced used only.

The use of 'unified' designs, that is stamps inscribed for both postal and fiscal purposes, results in a number of stamps of very high face value. In some instances these may not have been primarily intended for postal purposes, but if they are so inscribed we include them. We only price such items used, however, where there is evidence of normal postal usage.

Cover prices. To assist collectors, cover prices are quoted for issues up to 1945 at the beginning of each country.

The system gives a general guide in the form of a factor by which the corresponding used price of the basic loose stamp should be multiplied when found in fine average condition on cover.

Care is needed in applying the factors and they relate to a cover which bears a single of the denomination listed; if more than one denomination is present the most highly priced attracts the multiplier and the remainder are priced at the simple figure for used singles in arriving at a total.

The cover should be of non-philatelic origin; bearing the correct postal rate for the period and distance involved and cancelled with the markings normal to the offices concerned. Purely philatelic items have a cover value only slightly greater than the catalogue value for the corresponding used stamp. This applies generally to those high-value stamps used philatelically rather than in the normal course of commerce. Low-value stamps, e.g. ¼d. and ½d., are desirable when used as a single rate on cover and merit an increase in 'multiplier' value.

First day covers in the period up to 1945 are not within the scope of the system and the multiplier should not be used. As a special category of philatelic usage, with wide variations in valuation according to scarcity, they require separate treatment.

Oversized covers, difficult to accommodate on an album page, should be reckoned as worth little more than the corresponding value of the used stamps. The condition of a cover also affects its value. Except for 'wreck covers', serious damage or soiling reduce the value where the postal markings and stamps are ordinary ones. Conversely, visual appeal adds to the value and this can include freshness of appearance, important addresses, old-fashioned but legible hand-writing, historic town-names, etc.

The multipliers are a base on which further value would be added to take account of the cover's postal historical importance in demonstrating such things as unusual, scarce or emergency cancels, interesting routes, significant postal markings, combination usage, the development of postal rates, and so on.

Minimum price. The minimum catalogue price quoted is 10p. For individual stamps prices between 10p. and 95p. are provided as a guide for catalogue users. The lowest price charged for individual stamps or sets purchased from Stanley Gibbons Ltd is £1

Set prices. Set prices are generally for one of each value, excluding shades and varieties, but including major colour changes. Where there are alternative shades, etc., the cheapest is usually included. The number of stamps in the set is always stated for clarity. The mint prices for sets containing *se-tenant* pieces are based on the prices quoted for such combinations, and not on those for the individual stamps.

Varieties. Where plate or cylinder varieties are priced in a used condition the price quoted is for a fine used example with the cancellation well clear of the listed flaw.

Specimen stamps. The pricing of these items is explained under that heading.

Stamp booklets. Prices are for complete assembled booklets in fine condition with those issued before 1945 showing normal wear and tear. Incomplete

booklets and those which have been 'exploded' will, in general, be worth less than the figure quoted.

Repricing. Collectors will be aware that the market factors of supply and demand directly influence the prices quoted in this Catalogue. Whatever the scarcity of a particular stamp, if there is no one in the market who wishes to buy it cannot be expected to achieve a high price. Conversely, the same item actively sought by numerous potential buyers may cause the price to rise.

All the prices in this Catalogue are examined during the preparation of each new edition by the expert staff of Stanley Gibbons and repriced as necessary. They take many factors into account, including supply and demand, and are in close touch with the international stamp market and the auction world.

Commonwealth cover prices and advice on postal history material originally provided by Edward B Proud.

GUARANTEE

All stamps are guaranteed originals in the following terms:

If not as described, and returned by the purchaser, we undertake to refund the price paid to us in the original transaction. If any stamp is certified as genuine by the Expert Committee of the Royal Philatelic Society, London, or by BPA Expertising Ltd, the purchaser shall not be entitled to make any claim against us for any error, omission or mistake in such certificate.

Consumers' statutory rights are not affected by the above guarantee.

The recognised Expert Committees in this country are those of the Royal Philatelic Society, 41 Devonshire Place, London W1G, 6JY, and BPA Expertising Ltd, PO Box 137, Leatherhead, Surrey KT22 0RG. They do not undertake valuations under any circumstances and fees are payable for their services.

CONDITION GUIDE

To assist collectors in assessing the true value of items they are considering buying or in reviewing stamps already in their collections, we now offer a more detailed guide to the condition of stamps on which this catalogue's prices are based.

For a stamp to be described as 'Fine', it should be sound in all respects, without creases, bends, wrinkles, pin holes, thins or tears. If perforated, all perforation 'teeth' should be intact, it should not suffer from fading, rubbing or toning and it should be of clean, fresh appearance.

Margins on imperforate stamps: These should be even on all sides and should be at least as wide as half the distance between that stamp and the next. To have one or more margins of less than this width, would normally preclude a stamp from being described as 'Fine'. It should be remembered that some early stamps were positioned very close together on the printing plate and in such cases 'Fine' margins would necessarily be narrow. On the other hand, some plates were laid down to give a substantial gap between individual stamps and in such cases margins would be expected to be much wider.

An 'average' four-margin example would have a narrower margin on one or more sides and should be priced accordingly, while a stamp with wider, yet even, margins than 'Fine' would merit the description 'Very Fine' or 'Superb' and, if available, would command a price in excess of that quoted in the catalogue.

Gum: Since the prices for stamps of King Edward VIII, and King George VI are for 'unmounted' or 'never hinged' mint, it should be anticipated that even stamps from these reigns which have been very lightly mounted should be available at a discount from catalogue price, the more obvious the hinge marks, the greater the discount.

Catalogue prices for stamps issued prior to King Edward VIII's reign are for mounted mint, so unmounted examples would be worth a premium. Hinge marks on 20th century stamps should not be too obtrusive, and should be at least in the lightly mounted category. For 19th century stamps more obvious hinging would be acceptable, but stamps should still carry a large part of their original gum—'Large part o.g.'—in order to be described as 'Fine'.

Centring: Ideally, the stamp's image should appear in the exact centre of the perforated area, giving equal margins on all sides. 'Fine' centring would be close to this ideal with any deviation having an effect on the value of the stamp. As in the case of the margins on imperforate stamps, it should be borne in mind that the space between some early stamps was very narrow, so it was very difficult to achieve accurate perforation, especially when the technology was in its infancy. Thus, poor centring would have a less damaging effect on the value of a 19th century stamp than on a 20th century example, but the premium put on a perfectly centred specimen would be greater.

Cancellations: Early cancellation devices were designed to 'obliterate' the stamp in order to prevent it being reused and this is still an important objective for today's postal administrations. Stamp collectors, on the other hand, prefer postmarks to be lightly applied, clear, and to leave as much as possible of the design visible. Dated, circular cancellations have long been 'the postmark of choice', but the definition of a 'Fine' cancellation will depend upon the types of cancellation in use at the time a stamp was current—it is clearly illogical to seek a circular datestamp on a Penny Black.

'Fine', by definition, will be superior to 'Average', so, in terms of cancellation quality, if one begins by identifying what 'Average' looks like, then one will be half way to identifying 'Fine'. The illustrations will give some guidance on mid-19th century and mid-20th century cancellations of Great Britain, but types of cancellation in general use in each country and in each period will determine the appearance of 'Fine'.

As for the factors discussed above, anything less than 'Fine' will result in a downgrading of the stamp concerned, while a very fine or superb cancellation will be worth a premium.

Combining the factors: To merit the description 'Fine', a stamp should be fine in every respect, but a small deficiency in one area might be made up for in another by a factor meriting an 'Extremely Fine' description.

Some early issues are so seldom found in what would normally be considered to be 'Fine' condition, the catalogue prices are for a slightly lower grade, with 'Fine' examples being worth a premium. In such cases a note to this effect is given in the catalogue, while elsewhere premiums are given for well-centred, lightly cancelled examples.

It should be emphasised that stamps graded at less than fine remain collectable and, in the case of more highly priced stamps will continue to hold a value. Nevertheless, buyers should always bear condition in mind.

MARGINS ON IMPERFORATE STAMPS

Superb — Very fine — Fine — Average — Poor

GUM

Unmounted — Very lightly mounted — Lightly mounted — Mounted/large part original gum (o.g.). — Heavily mounted small part o.g

CENTRING

Superb — Very fine — Fine — Average — Poor

CANCELLATIONS

Superb — Very fine — Fine — Average — Poor

Superb — Very fine

Fine — Average — Poor

THE CATALOGUE IN GENERAL

Contents. The Catalogue is confined to adhesive postage stamps, including miniature sheets. For particular categories the rules are:

(a) Revenue (fiscal) stamps or telegraph stamps are listed only where they have been expressly authorised for postal duty.

(b) Stamps issued only precancelled are included, but normally issued stamps available additionally with precancel have no separate precancel listing unless the face value is changed.

(c) Stamps prepared for use but not issued, hitherto accorded full listing, are nowadays foot-noted with a price (where possible).

(d) Bisects (trisects, etc.) are only listed where such usage was officially authorised.

(e) Stamps issued only on first day covers or in presentation packs and not available separately are not listed but may be priced in a footnote.

(f) New printings are only included in this Catalogue where they show a major philatelic variety, such as a change in shade, watermark or paper. Stamps which exist with or without imprint dates are listed separately; changes in imprint dates are mentioned in footnotes.

(g) Official and unofficial reprints are dealt with by footnote.

(h) Stamps from imperforate printings of modern issues which occur perforated are covered by footnotes, but are listed where widely available for postal use.

Exclusions. The following are excluded:

(a) non-postal revenue or fiscal stamps;

(b) postage stamps used fiscally;

(c) local carriage labels and private local issues;

(d) bogus or phantom stamps;

(e) railway or airline letter fee stamps, bus or road transport company labels;

(f) cut-outs;

(g) all types of non-postal labels and souvenirs;

(h) documentary labels for the postal service, e.g. registration, recorded delivery, air-mail etiquettes, etc.;

(i) privately applied embellishments to official issues and privately commissioned items generally;

(j) stamps for training postal officers.

Full listing. 'Full listing' confers our recognition and implies allotting a catalogue number and (wherever possible) a price quotation.

In judging status for inclusion in the catalogue broad considerations are applied to stamps. They must be issued by a legitimate postal authority, recognised by the government concerned, and must be adhesives valid for proper postal use in the class of service for which they are inscribed. Stamps, with the exception of such categories as postage dues and officials, must be available to the general public, at face value, in reasonable quantities without any artificial restrictions being imposed on their distribution.

For errors and varieties the criterion is legitimate (albeit inadvertent) sale through a postal administration in the normal course of business. Details of provenance are always important; printers' waste and deliberately manufactured material are excluded.

Certificates. In assessing unlisted items due weight is given to Certificates from recognised Expert Committees and, where appropriate, we will usually ask to see them.

Date of issue. Where local issue dates differ from dates of release by agencies, 'date of issue' is the local date. Fortuitous stray usage before the officially intended date is disregarded in listing.

Catalogue numbers. Stamps of each country are catalogued chronologically by date of issue. Subsidiary classes are placed at the end of the country, as separate lists, with a distinguishing letter prefix to the catalogue number, e.g. D for postage due, O for official and E for express delivery stamps.

The catalogue number appears in the extreme left-column. The boldface Type numbers in the next column are merely cross-references to illustrations.

Once published in the Catalogue, numbers are changed as little as possible; really serious renumbering is reserved for the occasions when a complete country or an entire issue is being rewritten. The edition first affected includes cross-reference tables of old and new numbers.

Our catalogue numbers are universally recognised in specifying stamps and as a hallmark of status.

Illustrations. Stamps are illustrated at three-quarters linear size. Stamps not illustrated are the same size and format as the value shown, unless otherwise indicated. Stamps issued only as miniature sheets have the stamp alone illustrated but sheet size is also quoted. Overprints, surcharges, watermarks and postmarks are normally actual size. Illustrations of varieties are often enlarged to show the detail. Stamp booklet covers are illustrated half-size, unless otherwise indicated.

Designers. Designers' names are quoted where known, though space precludes naming every individual concerned in the production of a set. In particular, photographers supplying material are usually named only where they also make an active contribution in the design stage; posed photographs of reigning monarchs are, however, an exception to this rule.

CONTACTING THE CATALOGUE EDITOR

The editor is always interested in hearing from people who have new information which will improve or correct the Catalogue. As a general rule he must see and examine the actual stamps before they can be considered for listing; photographs or photocopies are insufficient evidence.

Submissions should be made in writing to the Catalogue Editor, Stanley Gibbons Publications at the Ringwood office. The cost of return postage for items submitted is appreciated, and this should include the registration fee if required.

Where information is solicited purely for the benefit of the enquirer, the editor cannot undertake to reply if the answer is already contained in these published notes or if return postage is omitted. Written communications are greatly preferred to enquiries by telephone or e-mail and the editor regrets that he or his staff cannot see personal callers without a prior appointment being made. Correspondence may be subject to delay during the production period of each new edition.

The editor welcomes close contact with study circles and is interested, too, in finding reliable local correspondents who will verify and supplement official information in countries where this is deficient.

We regret we do not give opinions as to the genuineness of stamps, nor do we identify stamps or number them by our Catalogue.

TECHNICAL MATTERS

The meanings of the technical terms used in the catalogue will be found in our *Philatelic Terms Illustrated.*

References below to (more specialised) listings are to be taken to indicate, as appropriate, the Stanley Gibbons *Great Britain Specialised Catalogue* in five volumes or the *Great Britain Concise Catalogue.*

1. Printing

Printing errors. Errors in printing are of major interest to the Catalogue. Authenticated items meriting consideration would include: background, centre or frame inverted or omitted; centre or subject transposed; error of colour; error or omission of value; double prints and impressions; printed both sides; and so on. Designs *tête-bêche*, whether intentionally or by accident, are listable. *Se-tenant* arrangements of stamps are recognised in the listings or footnotes. Gutter pairs (a pair of stamps separated by blank margin) are not included in this volume. Colours only partially omitted are not listed. Stamps with embossing omitted are reserved for our more specialised listings.

Printing varieties. Listing is accorded to major changes in the printing base which lead to completely new types. In recess-printing this could be a design re-engraved; in photogravure or photolithography a screen altered in whole or in part. It can also encompass flat-bed and rotary printing if the results are readily distinguishable.

To be considered at all, varieties must be constant.

Early stamps, produced by primitive methods, were prone to numerous imperfections; the lists reflect this, recognising re-entries, retouches, broken frames, misshapen letters, and so on. Printing technology has, however, radically improved over the years, during which time photogravure and lithography have

become predominant. Varieties nowadays are more in the nature of flaws and these, being too specialised for this general catalogue, are almost always outside the scope.

In no catalogue, however, do we list such items as: dry prints, kiss prints, doctor-blade flaws, colour shifts or registration flaws (unless they lead to the complete omission of a colour from an individual stamp), lithographic ring flaws, and so on. Neither do we recognise fortuitous happenings like paper creases or confetti flaws.

Overprints (and surcharges). Overprints of different types qualify for separate listing. These include overprints in different colours; overprints from different printing processes such as litho and typo; overprints in totally different typefaces, etc. Major errors in machine-printed overprints are important and listable. They include: overprint inverted or omitted; overprint double (treble, etc.); overprint diagonal; overprint double, one inverted; pairs with one overprint omitted, e.g. from a radical shift to an adjoining stamp; error of colour; error of type fount; letters inverted or omitted, etc. If the overprint is handstamped, few of these would qualify and a distinction is drawn. We continue, however, to list pairs of stamps where one has a handstamped overprint and the other has not.

Varieties occurring in overprints will often take the form of broken letters, slight differences in spacing, rising spaces, etc. Only the most important would be considered for listing or footnote mention.

Sheet positions. If space permits we quote sheet positions of listed varieties and authenticated data is solicited for this purpose.

De La Rue plates. The Catalogue classifies the general plates used by De La Rue for printing British Colonial stamps as follows:

VICTORIAN KEY TYPE

Die I

1. The ball of decoration on the second point of the crown appears as a dark mass of lines.

2. Dark vertical shading separates the front hair from the bun.

3. The vertical line of colour outlining the front of the throat stops at the sixth line of shading on the neck.

4. The white space in the coil of the hair above the curl is roughly the shape of a pin's head.

Die II

1. There are very few lines of colour in the ball and it appears almost white.

2. A white vertical strand of hair appears in place of the dark shading.

3. The line stops at the eighth line of shading.

4. The white space is oblong, with a line of colour partially dividing it at the left end.

Plates numbered 1 and 2 are both Die I. Plates 3 and 4 are Die II.

GEORGIAN KEY TYPE

Die I

A. The second (thick) line below the name of the country is cut slanting, conforming roughly to the shape of the crown on each side.

B. The labels of solid colour bearing the words "POSTAGE" and "& REVENUE" are square at the inner top corners.

C. There is a projecting "bud" on the outer spiral of the ornament in each of the lower corners.

Die II

A. The second line is cut vertically on each side of the crown.

B. The labels curve inwards at the top.

C. There is no "bud" in this position.

Unless otherwise stated in the lists, all stamps with watermark Multiple Crown CA (w **8**) are Die I while those with watermark Multiple Crown Script CA (w **9**) are Die II. The Georgian Die II was introduced in April 1921 and was used for Plates 10 to 22 and 26 to 28. Plates 23 to 25 were made from Die I by mistake.

2. Paper

All stamps listed are deemed to be on (ordinary) paper of the wove type and white in colour; only departures from this are normally mentioned.

Types. Where classification so requires we distinguish such other types of paper as, for example, vertically and horizontally laid; wove and laid bâtonné; card(board); carton; cartridge; glazed; granite; native; pelure; porous; quadrillé; ribbed; rice; and silk thread.

Wove paper   Laid paper

Granite paper   Quadrillé paper

Burelé band

The various makeshifts for normal paper are listed as appropriate. The varieties of double paper and joined paper are recognised. The security device of a printed burelé band on the back of a stamp, as in early Queensland, qualifies for listing.

Descriptive terms. The fact that a paper is handmade (and thus probably of uneven thickness) is mentioned where necessary. Such descriptive terms as "hard" and "soft"; "smooth" and "rough"; "thick", "medium" and "thin" are applied where there is philatelic merit in classifying papers.

Coloured, very white and toned papers. A coloured paper is one that is coloured right through (front and back of the stamp). In the Catalogue the colour of the paper is given in italics, thus:
black/*rose* = black design on rose paper.

Papers have been made specially white in recent years by, for example, a very heavy coating of chalk. We do not classify shades of whiteness of paper as distinct varieties. There does exist, however, a type of paper from early days called toned. This is off-white, often brownish or buffish, but it cannot be assigned any definite colour. A toning effect brought on by climate, incorrect storage or gum staining is disregarded here, as this was not the state of the paper when issued.

"Ordinary" and "Chalk-surfaced" papers. The availability of many postage stamps for revenue purposes made necessary some safeguard against the illegitimate re-use of stamps with removable cancellations. This was at first secured by using fugitive inks and later by printing on paper surfaced by coatings containing either chalk or china clay, both of which made it difficult to remove any form of obliteration without damaging the stamp design.

This catalogue lists these chalk-surfaced paper varieties from their introduction in 1905. Where no indication is given, the paper is "ordinary".

Our chalk-surfaced paper is specifically one which shows a black mark when touched with a silver wire. The paper used during the Second World War for high values, as in Bermuda, the Leeward Islands, etc., was thinly coated with some kind of surfacing which does not react to silver and is therefore regarded (and listed) as "ordinary". Stamps on chalk-surfaced paper can easily lose this coating through immersion in water.

Another paper introduced during the War as a substitute for chalk-surfaced is rather thick, very white and glossy and shows little or no watermark, nor does it show a black line when touched with silver. In the Bahamas high values this paper might be mistaken for the chalk-surfaced (which is thinner and poorer-looking) but for the silver test.

Some modern coated papers show little or no reaction to the silver test and, therefore, cannot be classed as chalk-surfaced.

Green and yellow papers. Issues of the First World War and immediate postwar period occur on green and yellow papers and these are given separate Catalogue listing. The original coloured papers (coloured throughout) gave way to surface-coloured papers, the stamps having "white backs"; other stamps show one colour on the front and a different one at the back. Because of the numerous variations a grouping of colours is adopted as follows:

Yellow papers

(1) The original *yellow* paper (throughout), usually bright in colour. The gum is often sparse, of harsh consistency and dull-looking. Used 1912–1920.

(2) The *white-backs*. Used 1913–1914.

(3) A bright lemon paper. The colour must have a pronounced greenish tinge, different from the "yellow" in (1). As a rule, the gum on stamps using this lemon paper is plentiful, smooth and shiny, and the watermark shows distinctly. Care is needed with stamps printed in green on yellow paper (1) as it may appear that the paper is this lemon. Used 1914–1916.

(4) An experimental *orange-buff* paper. The colour must have a distinct brownish tinge. It is not to be confused with a muddy yellow (1) nor the misleading appearance (on the surface) of stamps printed in red on yellow paper where an engraved plate has been insufficiently wiped. Used 1918–1921.

(5) An experimental *buff* paper. This lacks the brownish tinge of (4) and the brightness of the yellow shades. The gum is shiny when compared with the matt type used on (4). Used 1919–1920.

(6) A *pale yellow* paper that has a creamy tone to the yellow. Used from 1920 onwards.

Green papers

(7) The original "green" paper, varying considerably through shades of blue-green and yellow-green, the front and back sometimes differing. Used 1912–1916.

(8) The *white backs*. Used 1913–1914.

(9) A paper blue-green on the surface with *pale olive* back. The back must be markedly paler than the front and this and the pronounced olive tinge to the back distinguish it from (7). Used 1916–1920.

(10) Paper with a vivid green surface, commonly called *emerald-green*; it has the olive back of (9). Used 1920.

(11) Paper with *emerald-green* both back and front. Used from 1920 onwards.

3. Perforation and Rouletting

Perforation gauge. The gauge of a perforation is the number of holes in a length of 2 cm. For correct classification the size of the holes (large or small) may need to be distinguished; in a few cases the actual number of holes on each edge of the stamp needs to be quoted.

Measurement. The Gibbons *Instanta* gauge is the standard for measuring perforations. The stamp is viewed against a dark background with the transparent gauge put on top of it. Though the gauge measures to decimal accuracy, perforations read from it are generally quoted in the Catalogue to the nearest half. For example:

Just over perf 12¾ to just under 13¼ = perf 13
Perf 13¼ exactly, rounded up = perf 13½
Just over perf 13¼ to just under 13¾ = perf 13½
Perf 13¾ exactly, rounded up = perf 14

However, where classification depends on it, actual quarter-perforations are quoted.

Notation. Where no perforation is quoted for an issue it is imperforate. Perforations are usually abbreviated (and spoken) as follows, though sometimes they may be spelled out for clarity. This notation for rectangular stamps (the majority) applies to diamond shapes if "top" is read as the edge to the top right.

P 14: perforated alike on all sides (read: "perf 14").

P 14×15: the first figure refers to top and bottom, the second to left and right sides (read: "perf 14 by 15"). This is a compound perforation. For an upright triangular stamp the first figure refers to the two sloping sides and second to the base. In inverted triangulars the base is first and the second figure to the sloping sides.

P 14–15: perforation measuring anything between 14 and 15: the holes are irregularly spaced, thus the gauge may vary along a single line or even along a single edge of the stamp (read: "perf 14 to 15").

P 14 *irregular*: perforated 14 from a worn perforator, giving badly aligned holes irregularly spaced (read: "irregular perf 14").

P *comp(ound)* 14×15: two gauges in use but not necessarily on opposite sides of the stamp. It could be one side in one gauge and three in the other; or two adjacent sides with the same gauge. (Read: "perf compound of 14 and 15".) For three gauges or more, abbreviated as "P 12, 14½, 15 *or compound*" for example.

P 14, 14½: perforated approximately 14¼ (read: "perf 14 or 14½"). It does *not* mean two stamps, one perf 14 and the other perf 14½. This obsolescent notation is gradually being replaced in the Catalogue.

Imperf: imperforate (not perforated)

Imperf×P 14: imperforate at top ad bottom and perf 14 at sides.

P 14×*imperf*: perf 14 at top and bottom and imperforate at sides.

Such headings as "P 13×14 (*vert*) and P 14×13 (*horiz*)"

indicate which perforations apply to which stamp format—vertical or horizontal.

Some stamps are additionally perforated so that a label or tab is detachable; others have been perforated for use as two halves. Listings are normally for whole stamps, unless stated otherwise.

Imperf×perf

Other terms. Perforation almost always gives circular holes; where other shapes have been used they are specified, e.g. square holes; lozenge perf. Interrupted perfs are brought about by the omission of pins at regular intervals. Perforations merely simulated by being printed as part of the design are of course ignored. With few exceptions, privately applied perforations are not listed.

In the 19th century perforations are often described as clean cut (clean, sharply incised holes), intermediate or rough (rough holes, imperfectly cut, often the result of blunt pins).

Perforation errors and varieties. Authenticated errors, where a stamp normally perforated is accidentally issued imperforate, are listed provided no traces of perforation (blind holes or indentations) remain. They must be provided as pairs, both stamps wholly imperforate, and are only priced in that form.

Stamps imperforate between stamp and sheet margin are not listed in this catalogue, but such errors on Great Britain stamps will be found in the *Great Britain Specialised Catalogue*.

Pairs described as "imperforate between" have the line of perforations between the two stamps omitted.

Imperf between (horiz pair): a horizontal pair of stamps with perfs all around the edges but none between the stamps.

Imperf between (vert pair): a vertical pair of stamps with perfs all around the edges but none between the stamps.

Imperf between
(vertical pair)

Imperf horizontally
vertical pair)

Where several of the rows have escaped perforation the resulting varieties are listable. Thus:

Imperf vert (horiz pair): a horizontal pair of stamps perforated top and bottom; all three vertical directions are imperf—the two outer edges and between the stamps.

Imperf horiz (vert pair): a vertical pair perforated at left and right edges; all three horizontal directions are imperf—the top, bottom and between the stamps.

Straight edges. Large sheets cut up before issue to post offices can cause stamps with straight edges, i.e. imperf on one side or on two sides at right angles. They are not usually listable in this condition and are worth less than corresponding stamps properly perforated all round. This does not, however, apply to certain stamps, mainly from coils and booklets, where straight edges on various sides are the manufacturing norm affecting every stamp. The listings and notes make clear which sides are correctly imperf.

Malfunction. Varieties of double, misplaced or partial perforation caused by error or machine malfunction are not listable, neither are freaks, such as perforations placed diagonally from paper folds, nor missing holes caused by broken pins.

Types of perforating. Where necessary for classification, perforation types are distinguished. These include:

Line perforation from one line of pins punching single rows of holes at a time.

Comb perforation from pins disposed across the sheet in comb formation, punching out holes at three sides of the stamp a row at a time.

Harrow perforation applied to a whole pane or sheet at one stroke.

Rotary perforation from toothed wheels operating across a sheet, then crosswise.

Sewing machine perforation. The resultant condition, clean-cut or rough, is distinguished where required.

Pin-perforation is the commonly applied term for pin-roulette in which, instead of being punched out, round holes are pricked by sharp-pointed pins and no paper is removed.

Mixed perforation occurs when stamps with defective perforations are re-perforated in a different gauge.

Punctured stamps. Perforation holes can be punched into the face of the stamp. Patterns of small holes, often in the shape of initial letters, are privately applied devices against pilferage. These (perfins) are outside the scope except for Australia, Canada, Cape of Good Hope, Papua and Sudan where they were used as official stamps by the national administration. Identification devices, when officially inspired, are listed or noted; they can be shapes, or letters or words formed from holes, sometimes converting one class of stamp into another.

Rouletting. In rouletting the paper is cut, for ease of separation, but none is removed. The gauge is measured, when needed, as for perforations. Traditional French terms descriptive of the type of cut are often used and types include:

Arc roulette (percé en arc). Cuts are minute, spaced arcs, each roughly a semicircle.

Cross roulette (percé en croix). Cuts are tiny diagonal crosses.

Line roulette (percé en ligne or en ligne droite). Short straight cuts parallel to the frame of the stamp. The commonest basic roulette. Where not further described, "roulette" means this type.

Rouletted in colour or coloured roulette (percé en lignes colorées or en lignes de coleur). Cuts with coloured edges, arising from notched rule inked simultaneously with the printing plate.

Saw-tooth roulette (percé en scie). Cuts applied zigzag fashion to resemble the teeth of a saw.

Serpentine roulette (percé en serpentin). Cuts as sharply wavy lines.

Zigzag roulette (percé en zigzags). Short straight cuts at angles in alternate directions, producing sharp points on separation. US usage favours "serrate(d) roulette" for this type.

Pin-roulette (originally percé en points and now perforés trous d'epingle) is commonly called pin-perforation in English.

4. Gum

All stamps listed are assumed to have gum of some kind; if they were issued without gum this is stated. Original gum (o.g.) means that which was present on the stamp as issued to the public. Deleterious climates and the presence of certain chemicals can cause gum to crack and, with early stamps, even make the paper deteriorate. Unscrupulous fakers are adept in removing it and regumming the stamp to meet the unreasoning demand often made for "full o.g." in cases where such a thing is virtually impossible.

5. Watermarks

Stamps are on unwatermarked paper except where the heading on the set says otherwise.

Detection. Watermarks are detected for Catalogue description by one of four methods: (1) holding stamps to the light; (2) laying stamps face down on a dark

background; (3) adding a few drops of petroleum ether 40/60 to the stamp laid face down in a watermark tray; (4) by use of the Stanley Gibbons Detectamark, or other equipment, which work by revealing the thinning of the paper at the watermark. (Note that petroleum ether is highly inflammable in use and can damage photogravure stamps.)

Listable types. Stamps occurring on both watermarked and unwatermarked papers are different types and both receive full listing.

Single watermarks (devices occurring once on every stamp) can be modified in size and shape as between different issues; the types are noted but not usually separately listed. Fortuitous absence of watermark from a single stamp or its gross displacement would not be listable.

To overcome registration difficulties the device may be repeated at close intervals *(a multiple watermark),* single stamps thus showing parts of several devices. Similarly, a *large sheet watermark* (or *all-over watermark*) covering numerous stamps can be used. We give informative notes and illustrations for them. The designs may be such that numbers of stamps in the sheet automatically lack watermark: this is not a listable variety. Multiple and all-over watermarks sometimes undergo modifications, but if the various types are difficult to distinguish from single stamps notes are given but not separate listings.

Papermakers' watermarks are noted where known but not listed separately, since most stamps in the sheet will lack them. Sheet watermarks which are nothing more than officially adopted papermakers' watermarks are, however, given normal listing.

Marginal watermarks, falling outside the pane of stamps, are ignored except where misplacement caused the adjoining row to be affected, in which case they may be footnoted.

Watermark errors and varieties. Watermark errors are recognised as of major importance. They comprise stamps intended to be on unwatermarked paper but issued watermarked by mistake, or stamps printed on paper with the wrong watermark. Varieties showing letters omitted from the watermark are also included, but broken or deformed bits on the dandy roll are not listed unless they represent repairs.

Watermark positions. The diagram shows how watermark position is described in the Catalogue. Paper has a side intended for printing and watermarks are usually impressed so that they read normally when looked through from that printed side. However, since philatelists customarily detect watermarks by looking at the back of the stamp the watermark diagram also makes clear what is actually seen.

AS DESCRIBED (Read through front of stamp)		AS SEEN DURING WATERMARK DETECTION (Stamp face down and back examined
GvR	Normal	ЯvꓛG
ЯvꓛG	Inverted	ꓛvЯ
ЯvꓛG	Reversed	GvR
ꓛvЯ	Reversed and Inverted	ЯvꓛG
GvR	Sideways	ꓛvЯ
ꓛvꓛR	Sideways Inverted	Яvꓛꓛ

Illustrations in the Catalogue are of watermarks in normal positions (from the front of the stamps) and are actual size where possible.

Differences in watermark position are collectable varieties. This Catalogue now lists inverted, sideways inverted and reversed watermark varieties on Commonwealth stamps from the 1860s onwards except where the watermark position is completely haphazard.

Great Britain inverted and sideways inverted watermarks can be found in the *Great Britain Specialised Catalogue* and the *Great Britain Concise Catalogue*.

Where a watermark comes indiscriminately in various positions our policy is to cover this by a general note: we do not give separate listings because the watermark position in these circumstances has no particular philatelic importance.

Standard types of watermark. Some watermarks have been used generally for various British possessions rather than exclusively for a single colony. To avoid repetition the Catalogue classifies 11 general types, as under, with references in the headings throughout the listings being given either in words or in the form ("W w **9**") (meaning "watermark type w **9**"). In those cases where watermark illustrations appear in the listings themselves, the respective reference reads, for example, W **153**, thus indicating that the watermark will be found in the normal sequence of illustrations as (type) **153**.

The general types are as follows, with an example of each quoted.

W	Description	Example
w **1**	Large Star	St. Helena No. 1
w **2**	Small Star	Turks Is. No. 4
w **3**	Broad (pointed) Star	Grenada No. 24
w **4**	Crown (over) CC, small stamp	Antigua No. 13
w **5**	Crown (over) CC, large stamp	Antigua No. 31
w **6**	Crown (over) CA, small stamp	Antigua No. 21
w **7**	Crown CA (CA over Crown), large stamp	Sierra Leone No. 54
w **8**	Multiple Crown CA	Antigua No. 41
w **9**	Multiple Script CA	Seychelles No. 158
w **9**a	do. Error	Seychelles No. 158a
w **9**b	do. Error	Seychelles No. 158b
w **10**	V over Crown	N.S.W. No. 327
w **11**	Crown over A	N.S.W. No. 347

CC in these watermarks is an abbreviation for "Crown Colonies" and CA for "Crown Agents". Watermarks w **1**, w **2** and w **3** are on stamps printed by Perkins, Bacon; w **4** onwards on stamps from De La Rue and other printers.

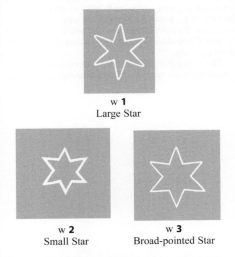

w **1**
Large Star

w **2**
Small Star

w **3**
Broad-pointed Star

Watermark w **1**, *Large Star*, measures 15 to 16 mm across the star from point to point and about 27 mm from centre to centre vertically between stars in the sheet. It was made for long stamps like Ceylon 1857 and St. Helena 1856.

Watermark w **2**, *Small Star* is of similar design but measures 12 to 13½mm from point to point and 24 mm from centre to centre vertically. It was for use with ordinary-size stamps such as Grenada 1863–71.

When the Large Star watermark was used with the smaller stamps it only occasionally comes in the centre of the paper. It is frequently so misplaced as

to show portions of two stars above and below and this eccentricity will very often help in determining the watermark.

Watermark w **3**, *Broad-pointed Star*, resembles w **1** but the points are broader.

w **4**
Crown (over) CC

w **5**
Crown (over) CC

Two *Crown (over) CC* watermarks were used: w **4** was for stamps of ordinary size and w **5** for those of larger size.

w **6**
Crown (over) CA

w **7**
CA over Crown

Two watermarks of *Crown CA* type were used, w **6** being for stamps of ordinary size. The other, w **7**, is properly described as *CA over Crown*. It was specially made for paper on which it was intended to print long fiscal stamps: that some were used postally accounts for the appearance of w **7** in the Catalogue. The watermark occupies twice the space of the ordinary Crown CA watermark, w **6**. Stamps of normal size printed on paper with w **7** watermark show it *sideways*; it takes a horizontal pair of stamps to show the entire watermark.

w **8**
Multiple Crown CA

w **9**
Multiple Script CA

Multiple watermarks began in 1904 with w **8**, *Multiple Crown CA*, changed from 1921 to w **9**, *Multiple Script CA*. On stamps of ordinary size portions of two or three watermarks appear and on the large-sized stamps a greater number can be observed. The change to letters in script character with w **9** was accompanied by a Crown of distinctly different shape.

It seems likely that there were at least two dandy rolls for each Crown Agents watermark in use at any one time with a reserve roll being employed when the normal one was withdrawn for maintenance or repair.

Both the Mult Crown CA and the Mult Script CA types exist with one or other of the letters omitted from individual impressions. It is possible that most of these occur from the reserve rolls as they have only been found on certain issues. The MCA watermark experienced such problems during the early 1920s and the Script over a longer period from the early 1940s until 1951.

During the 1920s damage must also have occurred on one of the Crowns as a substituted Crown has been found on certain issues. This is smaller than the normal and consists of an oval base joined to two upright ovals with a circle positioned between their upper ends. The

upper line of the Crown's base is omitted, as are the left and right-hand circles at the top and also the cross over the centre circle.

Substituted Crown

The *Multiple Script CA* watermark, w **9**, is known with two errors, recurring among the 1950–52 printings of several territories. In the first a crown has fallen away from the dandy-roll that impresses the watermark into the paper pulp. It gives w **9**a, *Crown missing*, but this omission has been found in both "Crown only" (*illustrated*) and "Crown CA" rows. The resulting faulty paper was used for Bahamas, Johore, Seychelles and the postage due stamps of nine colonies

w **9**a: Error, Crown missing

w **9**b: Error, St. Edward's Crown

When the omission was noticed a second mishap occurred, which was to insert a wrong crown in the space, giving w **9**b, St. Edward's Crown. This produced varieties in Bahamas, Perlis, St. Kitts-Nevis and Singapore and the incorrect crown likewise occurs in (Crown only) and (Crown CA) rows.

w **10**
V over Crown

w **11**
Crown over A

Resuming the general types, two watermarks found in issues of several Australian States are: w **10**, *V over Crown*, and w **11**, *Crown over A*.

6. Colours

Stamps in two or three colours have these named in order of appearance, from the centre moving outwards. Four colours or more are usually listed as multicoloured.

In compound colour names the second is the predominant one, thus:

orange-red = a red tending towards orange;

red-orange = an orange containing more red than usual.

Standard colours used. The 200 colours most used for stamp identification are given in the Stanley Gibbons Stamp Colour Key. The Catalogue has used the Stamp Colour Key as standard for describing new issues for some years. The names are also introduced as lists are rewritten, though exceptions are made for those early issues where traditional names have become universally established.

Determining colours. When comparing actual stamps with colour samples in the Stamp Colour Key, view in a good north daylight (or its best substitute; fluorescent "colour matching" light). Sunshine is not recommended. Choose a solid portion of the stamp design; if available, marginal markings such as solid bars of colour or colour check dots are helpful. Shading lines in the design can be misleading as they appear lighter than solid colour. Postmarked portions of a stamp appear darker than normal. If more than one colour is present, mask off the extraneous ones as the eye tends to mix them.

Errors of colour. Major colour errors in stamps or overprints which qualify for listing are: wrong colours; one colour inverted in relation to the rest; albinos (colourless impressions), where these have Expert Committee certificates; colours completely omitted, but only on unused stamps (if found on used stamps the information is footnoted) and with good credentials, missing colours being frequently faked.

Colours only partially omitted are not recognised, Colour shifts, however spectacular, are not listed.

Shades. Shades in philately refer to variations in the intensity of a colour or the presence of differing amounts of other colours. They are particularly significant when they can be linked to specific printings. In general, shades need to be quite marked to fall within the scope of this Catalogue; it does not favour nowadays listing the often numerous shades of a stamp, but chooses a single applicable colour name which will indicate particular groups of outstanding shades. Furthermore, the listings refer to colours as issued; they may deteriorate into something different through the passage of time.

Modern colour printing by lithography is prone to marked differences of shade, even within a single run, and variations can occur within the same sheet. Such shades are not listed.

Aniline colours. An aniline colour meant originally one derived from coal-tar; it now refers more widely to colour of a particular brightness suffused on the surface of a stamp and showing through clearly on the back.

Colours of overprints and surcharges. All overprints and surcharges are in black unless stated otherwise in the heading or after the description of the stamp.

7. Specimen Stamps

Originally, stamps overprinted SPECIMEN were circulated to postmasters or kept in official records, but after the establishment of the Universal Postal Union supplies were sent to Berne for distribution to the postal administrations of member countries.

SPECIMEN   SPECIMEN
De La Rue & Co. Ltd.

SPECIMEN.   SPECIMEN.
Bradbury, Wilkinson & Co. Ltd.

SPECIMEN   SPECIMEN
Waterlow & Sons Ltd.

SPECIMEN   SPECIMEN   SPECIMEN
Great Britain overprints

During the period 1884 to 1928 most of the stamps of British Crown Colonies required for this purpose were overprinted SPECIMEN in various shapes and sizes by their printers from typeset formes. Some locally produced provisionals were handstamped locally, as were sets prepared for presentation. From 1928 stamps were punched with holes forming

the word SPECIMEN, each firm of printers using a different machine or machines. From 1948 the stamps supplied for UPU distribution were no longer punctured.

Stamps of some other Commonwealth territories were overprinted or handstamped locally, while stamps of Great Britain and those overprinted for use in overseas postal agencies (mostly the higher denominations) bore SPECIMEN overprints and handstamps applied by the Inland Revenue or the Post Office.

Some of the commoner types of overprints or punctures are illustrated here. Collectors are warned that dangerous forgeries of the punctured type exist.

The *Stanley Gibbons Commonwealth Catalogues* record those Specimen overprints or perforations intended for distribution by the UPU to member countries. In addition the Specimen overprints of Australia and its dependent territories, which were sold to collectors by the Post Office, are also included.

Various Perkins Bacon issues exist obliterated with a "CANCELLED" within an oval of bars handstamp.

Perkins Bacon "CANCELLED" Handstamp

This was applied to six examples of those issues available in 1861 which were then given to members of Sir Rowland Hill's family. 75 different stamps (including four from Chile) are recorded with this handstamp although others may possibly exist. The unauthorised gift of these "CANCELLED" stamps to the Hill family was a major factor in the loss of the Agent General for the Crown Colonies (the forerunner of the Crown Agents) contracts by Perkins Bacon in the following year. Where examples of these scarce items are known to be in private hands the catalogue provides a price.

For full details of these stamps see *CANCELLED by Perkins Bacon* by Peter Jaffé (published by Spink in 1998).

All other Specimens are outside the scope of this volume.

Specimens are not quoted in Great Britain as they are fully listed in the Stanley Gibbons *Great Britain Specialised Catalogue*.

In specifying type of specimen for individual high-value stamps, "H/S" means handstamped, "Optd" is overprinted and "Perf" is punctured. Some sets occur mixed, e.g. "Optd/Perf". If unspecified, the type is apparent from the date or it is the same as for the lower values quoted as a set.

Prices. Prices for stamps up to £1 are quoted in sets; higher values are priced singly. Where specimens exist in more than one type the price quoted is for the cheapest. Specimen stamps have rarely survived even as pairs; these and strips of three, four or five are worth considerably more than singles.

8. Coil Stamps

Stamps issued only in coil form are given full listing. If stamps are issued in both sheets and coils the coil stamps are listed separately only where there is some feature (e.g. perforation or watermark sideways) by which singles can be distinguished. Coil stamps containing different stamps *se-tenant* are also listed.

Coil join pairs are too random and too easily faked to permit of listing; similarly ignored are coil stamps which have accidentally suffered an extra row of perforations from the claw mechanism in a malfunctioning vending machine.

9. Stamp Booklets

Stamp booklets (with the exception of those from Great Britain for which the current edition of the *Great Britain Concise Catalogue*) are now listed in this catalogue.

Single stamps from booklets are listed if they are distinguishable in some way (such as watermark or perforation) from similar sheet stamps.

Booklet panes are listed where they contain stamps of different denominations *se-tenant*, where stamp-size labels are included, or where such panes are otherwise identifiable. Booklet panes are placed in the listing under the lowest denomination present.

Particular perforations (straight edges) are covered by appropriate notes.

10. Miniature Sheets and Sheetlets

We distinguish between "miniature sheets" and "sheetlets" and this affects the catalogue numbering. An item in sheet form that is postally valid, containing a single stamp, pair, block or set of stamps, with wide, inscribed and/or decorative margins, is a miniature sheet if it is sold at post offices as an indivisible entity. As such the Catalogue allots a single **MS** number and describes what stamps make it up. The sheetlet or small sheet differs in that the individual stamps are intended to be purchased separately for postal purposes. For sheetlets, all the component postage stamps are numbered individually and the composition explained in a footnote. Note that the definitions refer to post office sale—not how items may be subsequently offered by stamp dealers.

11. Forgeries and Fakes

Forgeries. Where space permits, notes are considered if they can give a concise description that will permit unequivocal detection of a forgery. Generalised warnings, lacking detail, are not nowadays inserted, since their value to the collector is problematic.

Forged cancellations have also been applied to genuine stamps. This catalogue includes notes regarding those manufactured by "Madame Joseph", together with the cancellation dates known to exist. It should be remembered that these dates also exist as genuine cancellations.

For full details of these see *Madame Joseph Forged Postmarks* by Derick Worboys (published by the Royal Philatelic Society London and the British Philatelic Trust in 1994) or *Madame Joseph Revisited* by Brian Cartwright (published by the Royal Philatelic Society London in 2005).

Fakes. Unwitting fakes are numerous, particularly "new shades" which are colour changelings brought about by exposure to sunlight, soaking in water contaminated with dyes from adherent paper, contact with oil and dirt from a pocketbook, and so on. Fraudulent operators, in addition, can offer to arrange: removal of hinge marks; repairs of thins on white or coloured papers; replacement of missing margins or perforations; reperforating in true or false gauges; removal of fiscal cancellations; rejoining of severed pairs, strips and blocks; and (a major hazard) regumming. Collectors can only be urged to purchase from reputable sources and to insist upon Expert Committee certification where there is any kind of doubt.

The Catalogue can consider footnotes about fakes where these are specific enough to assist in detection.

Abbreviations

Printers

A.B.N. Co.	American Bank Note Co, New York.
B.A.B.N.	British American Bank Note Co. Ottawa
B.W.	Bradbury Wilkinson & Co, Ltd.
C.B.N.	Canadian Bank Note Co, Ottawa.
Continental B.N. Co.	Continental Bank Note Co.
Courvoisier	Imprimerie Courvoisier S.A., La-Chaux-de-Fonds, Switzerland.
D.L.R.	De La Rue & Co, Ltd, London.
Enschedé	Joh. Enschedé en Zonen, Haarlem, Netherlands.
Harrison	Harrison & Sons, Ltd. London
P.B.	Perkins Bacon Ltd, London.
Waterlow	Waterlow & Sons, Ltd, London.

General Abbreviations

Alph	Alphabet
Anniv	Anniversary
Comp	Compound (perforation)
Des	Designer; designed
Diag	Diagonal; diagonally
Eng	Engraver; engraved
F.C.	Fiscal Cancellation
H/S	Handstamped
Horiz	Horizontal; horizontally

Imp, Imperf	Imperforate
Inscr	Inscribed
L	Left
Litho	Lithographed
mm	Millimetres
MS	Miniature sheet
N.Y.	New York
Opt(d)	Overprint(ed)
P or P-c	Pen-cancelled
P, Pf or Perf	Perforated
Photo	Photogravure
Pl	Plate
Pr	Pair
Ptd	Printed
Ptg	Printing
R	Right
R.	Row
Recess	Recess-printed
Roto	Rotogravure
Roul	Rouletted
S	Specimen (overprint)
Surch	Surcharge(d)
T.C.	Telegraph Cancellation
T	Type
Typo	Typographed
Un	Unused
Us	Used
Vert	Vertical; vertically
W or wmk	Watermark
Wmk s	Watermark sideways

(†) = Does not exist
(–) (or blank price column) = Exists, or may exist, but no market price is known.

/ between colours means "on" and the colour following is that of the paper on which the stamp is printed.

Colours of Stamps

Bl (blue); blk (black); brn (brown); car, carm (carmine); choc (chocolate); clar (claret); emer (emerald); grn (green); ind (indigo); mag (magenta); mar (maroon); mult (multicoloured); mve (mauve); ol (olive); orge (orange); pk (pink); pur (purple); scar (scarlet); sep (sepia); turq (turquoise); ultram (ultramarine); verm (vermilion); vio (violet); yell (yellow).

Colour of Overprints and Surcharges

(B.) = blue, (Blk.) = black, (Br.) = brown, (C.) = carmine, (G.) = green, (Mag.) = magenta, (Mve.) = mauve, (Ol.) = olive, (O.) = orange, (P.) = purple, (Pk.) = pink, (R.) = red, (Sil.) = silver, (V.) = violet, (Vm.) or (Verm.) = vermilion, (W.) = white, (Y.) = yellow.

Arabic Numerals

As in the case of European figures, the details of the Arabic numerals vary in different stamp designs, but they should be readily recognised with the aid of this illustration.

٠	١	٢	٣	٤	٥	٦	٧	٨	٩
0	1	2	3	4	5	6	7	8	9

International Philatelic Glossary

English	French	German	Spanish	Italian
Agate	Agate	Achat	Agata	Agata
Air stamp	Timbre de la poste aérienne	Flugpostmarke	Sello de correo aéreo	Francobollo per posta aerea
Apple Green	Vert-pomme	Apfelgrün	Verde manzana	Verde mela
Barred	Annulé par barres	Balkenentwertung	Anulado con barras	Sbarrato
Bisected	Timbre coupé	Halbiert	Partido en dos	Frazionato
Bistre	Bistre	Bister	Bistre	Bistro
Bistre-brown	Brun-bistre	Bisterbraun	Castaño bistre	Bruno-bistro
Black	Noir	Schwarz	Negro	Nero
Blackish Brown	Brun-noir	Schwärzlichbraun	Castaño negruzco	Bruno nerastro
Blackish Green	Vert foncé	Schwärzlichgrün	Verde negruzco	Verde nerastro
Blackish Olive	Olive foncé	Schwärzlicholiv	Oliva negruzco	Oliva nerastro
Block of four	Bloc de quatre	Viererblock	Bloque de cuatro	Bloco di quattro
Blue	Bleu	Blau	Azul	Azzurro
Blue-green	Vert-bleu	Blaugrün	Verde azul	Verde azzurro
Bluish Violet	Violet bleuâtre	Bläulichviolett	Violeta azulado	Violtto azzurrastro
Booklet	Carnet	Heft	Cuadernillo	Libretto
Bright Blue	Bleu vif	Lebhaftblau	Azul vivo	Azzurro vivo
Bright Green	Vert vif	Lebhaftgrün	Verde vivo	Verde vivo
Bright Purple	Mauve vif	Lebhaftpurpur	Púrpura vivo	Porpora vivo
Bronze Green	Vert-bronze	Bronzegrün	Verde bronce	Verde bronzo
Brown	Brun	Braun	Castaño	Bruno
Brown-lake	Carmin-brun	Braunlack	Laca castaño	Lacca bruno
Brown-purple	Pourpre-brun	Braunpurpur	Púrpura castaño	Porpora bruno
Brown-red	Rouge-brun	Braunrot	Rojo castaño	Rosso bruno
Buff	Chamois	Sämisch	Anteado	Camoscio
Cancellation	Oblitération	Entwertung	Cancelación	Annullamento
Cancelled	Annulé	Gestempelt	Cancelado	Annullato
Carmine	Carmin	Karmin	Carmín	Carminio
Carmine-red	Rouge-carmin	Karminrot	Rojo carmín	Rosso carminio
Centred	Centré	Zentriert	Centrado	Centrato
Cerise	Rouge-cerise	Kirschrot	Color de ceresa	Color Ciliegia
Chalk-surfaced paper	Papier couché	Kreidepapier	Papel estucado	Carta gessata
Chalky Blue	Bleu terne	Kreideblau	Azul turbio	Azzurro smorto
Charity stamp	Timbre de bienfaisance	Wohltätigkeitsmarke	Sello de beneficenza	Francobollo di beneficenza
Chestnut	Marron	Kastanienbraun	Castaño rojo	Marrone
Chocolate	Chocolat	Schokolade	Chocolate	Cioccolato
Cinnamon	Cannelle	Zimtbraun	Canela	Cannella
Claret	Grenat	Weinrot	Rojo vinoso	Vinaccia
Cobalt	Cobalt	Kobalt	Cobalto	Cobalto
Colour	Couleur	Farbe	Color	Colore
Comb-perforation	Dentelure en peigne	Kammzähnung, Reihenzähnung	Dentado de peine	Dentellatura e pettine
Commemorative stamp	Timbre commémoratif	Gedenkmarke	Sello conmemorativo	Francobollo commemorativo
Crimson	Cramoisi	Karmesin	Carmesí	Cremisi
Deep Blue	Blue foncé	Dunkelblau	Azul oscuro	Azzurro scuro
Deep bluish Green	Vert-bleu foncé	Dunkelbläulichgrün	Verde azulado oscuro	Verde azzurro scuro
Design	Dessin	Markenbild	Diseño	Disegno
Die	Matrice	Urstempel. Type, Platte	Cuño	Conio, Matrice
Double	Double	Doppelt	Doble	Doppio
Drab	Olive terne	Trüboliv	Oliva turbio	Oliva smorto
Dull Green	Vert terne	Trübgrün	Verde turbio	Verde smorto
Dull purple	Mauve terne	Trübpurpur	Púrpura turbio	Porpora smorto
Embossing	Impression en relief	Prägedruck	Impresión en relieve	Impressione a relievo
Emerald	Vert-eméraude	Smaragdgrün	Esmeralda	Smeraldo
Engraved	Gravé	Graviert	Grabado	Inciso
Error	Erreur	Fehler, Fehldruck	Error	Errore
Essay	Essai	Probedruck	Ensayo	Saggio
Express letter stamp	Timbre pour lettres par exprès	Eilmarke	Sello de urgencia	Francobollo per espresso
Fiscal stamp	Timbre fiscal	Stempelmarke	Sello fiscal	Francobollo fiscale
Flesh	Chair	Fleischfarben	Carne	Carnicino
Forgery	Faux, Falsification	Fälschung	Falsificación	Falso, Falsificazione
Frame	Cadre	Rahmen	Marco	Cornice
Granite paper	Papier avec fragments de fils de soie	Faserpapier	Papel con filamentos	Carto con fili di seta
Green	Vert	Grün	Verde	Verde

English	French	German	Spanish	Italian
Greenish Blue	Bleu verdâtre	Grünlichblau	Azul verdoso	Azzurro verdastro
Greenish Yellow	Jaune-vert	Grünlichgelb	Amarillo verdoso	Giallo verdastro
Grey	Gris	Grau	Gris	Grigio
Grey-blue	Bleu-gris	Graublau	Azul gris	Azzurro grigio
Grey-green	Vert gris	Graugrün	Verde gris	Verde grigio
Gum	Gomme	Gummi	Goma	Gomma
Gutter	Interpanneau	Zwischensteg	Espacio blanco entre dos grupos	Ponte
Imperforate	Non-dentelé	Geschnitten	Sin dentar	Non dentellato
Indigo	Indigo	Indigo	Azul indigo	Indaco
Inscription	Inscription	Inschrift	Inscripción	Dicitura
Inverted	Renversé	Kopfstehend	Invertido	Capovolto
Issue	Émission	Ausgabe	Emisión	Emissione
Laid	Vergé	Gestreift	Listado	Vergato
Lake	Lie de vin	Lackfarbe	Laca	Lacca
Lake-brown	Brun-carmin	Lackbraun	Castaño laca	Bruno lacca
Lavender	Bleu-lavande	Lavendel	Color de alhucema	Lavanda
Lemon	Jaune-citron	Zitrongelb	Limón	Limone
Light Blue	Bleu clair	Hellblau	Azul claro	Azzurro chiaro
Lilac	Lilas	Lila	Lila	Lilla
Line perforation	Dentelure en lignes	Linienzähnung	Dentado en linea	Dentellatura lineare
Lithography	Lithographie	Steindruck	Litografía	Litografia
Local	Timbre de poste locale	Lokalpostmarke	Emisión local	Emissione locale
Lozenge roulette	Percé en losanges	Rautenförmiger Durchstich	Picadura en rombos	Perforazione a losanghe
Magenta	Magenta	Magentarot	Magenta	Magenta
Margin	Marge	Rand	Borde	Margine
Maroon	Marron pourpré	Dunkelrotpurpur	Púrpura rojo oscuro	Marrone rossastro
Mauve	Mauve	Malvenfarbe	Malva	Malva
Multicoloured	Polychrome	Mehrfarbig	Multicolores	Policromo
Myrtle Green	Vert myrte	Myrtengrün	Verde mirto	Verde mirto
New Blue	Bleu ciel vif	Neublau	Azul nuevo	Azzurro nuovo
Newspaper stamp	Timbre pour journaux	Zeitungsmarke	Sello para periódicos	Francobollo per giornali
Obliteration	Oblitération	Abstempelung	Matasello	Annullamento
Obsolete	Hors (de) cours	Ausser Kurs	Fuera de curso	Fuori corso
Ochre	Ocre	Ocker	Ocre	Ocra
Official stamp	Timbre de service	Dienstmarke	Sello de servicio	Francobollo di
Olive-brown	Brun-olive	Olivbraun	Castaño oliva	Bruno oliva
Olive-green	Vert-olive	Olivgrün	Verde oliva	Verde oliva
Olive-grey	Gris-olive	Olivgrau	Gris oliva	Grigio oliva
Olive-yellow	Jaune-olive	Olivgelb	Amarillo oliva	Giallo oliva
Orange	Orange	Orange	Naranja	Arancio
Orange-brown	Brun-orange	Orangebraun	Castaño naranja	Bruno arancio
Orange-red	Rouge-orange	Orangerot	Rojo naranja	Rosso arancio
Orange-yellow	Jaune-orange	Orangegelb	Amarillo naranja	Giallo arancio
Overprint	Surcharge	Aufdruck	Sobrecarga	Soprastampa
Pair	Paire	Paar	Pareja	Coppia
Pale	Pâle	Blass	Pálido	Pallido
Pane	Panneau	Gruppe	Grupo	Gruppo
Paper	Papier	Papier	Papel	Carta
Parcel post stamp	Timbre pour colis postaux	Paketmarke	Sello para paquete postal	Francobollo per pacchi postali
Pen-cancelled	Oblitéré à plume	Federzugentwertung	Cancelado a pluma	Annullato a penna
Percé en arc	Percé en arc	Bogenförmiger Durchstich	Picadura en forma de arco	Perforazione ad arco
Percé en scie	Percé en scie	Bogenförmiger Durchstich	Picado en sierra	Foratura a sega
Perforated	Dentelé	Gezähnt	Dentado	Dentellato
Perforation	Dentelure	Zähnung	Dentar	Dentellatura
Photogravure	Photogravure, Heliogravure	Rastertiefdruck	Fotograbado	Rotocalco
Pin perforation	Percé en points	In Punkten durchstochen	Horadado con alfileres	Perforato a punti
Plate	Planche	Platte	Plancha	Lastra, Tavola
Plum	Prune	Pflaumenfarbe	Color de ciruela	Prugna
Postage Due stamp	Timbre-taxe	Portomarke	Sello de tasa	Segnatasse
Postage stamp	Timbre-poste	Briefmarke, Freimarke, Postmarke	Sello de correos	Francobollo postale
Postal fiscal stamp	Timbre fiscal-postal	Stempelmarke als Postmarke verwendet	Sello fiscal-postal	Fiscale postale
Postmark	Oblitération postale	Poststempel	Matasello	Bollo
Printing	Impression, Tirage	Druck	Impresión	Stampa, Tiratura
Proof	Épreuve	Druckprobe	Prueba de impresión	Prova
Provisionals	Timbres provisoires	Provisorische Marken. Provisorien	Provisionales	Provvisori
Prussian Blue	Bleu de Prusse	Preussischblau	Azul de Prusia	Azzurro di Prussia
Purple	Pourpre	Purpur	Púrpura	Porpora
Purple-brown	Brun-pourpre	Purpurbraun	Castaño púrpura	Bruno porpora
Recess-printing	Impression en taille douce	Tiefdruck	Grabado	Incisione
Red	Rouge	Rot	Rojo	Rosso
Red-brown	Brun-rouge	Rotbraun	Castaño rojizo	Bruno rosso

English	French	German	Spanish	Italian
Reddish Lilac	Lilas rougeâtre	Rötlichlila	Lila rojizo	Lilla rossastro
Reddish Purple	Poupre-rouge	Rötlichpurpur	Púrpura rojizo	Porpora rossastro
Reddish Violet	Violet rougeâtre	Rötlichviolett	Violeta rojizo	Violetto rossastro
Red-orange	Orange rougeâtre	Rotorange	Naranja rojizo	Arancio rosso
Registration stamp	Timbre pour lettre chargée (recommandée)	Einschreibemarke	Sello de certificado lettere	Francobollo per raccomandate
Reprint	Réimpression	Neudruck	Reimpresión	Ristampa
Reversed	Retourné	Umgekehrt	Invertido	Rovesciato
Rose	Rose	Rosa	Rosa	Rosa
Rose-red	Rouge rosé	Rosarot	Rojo rosado	Rosso rosa
Rosine	Rose vif	Lebhaftrosa	Rosa vivo	Rosa vivo
Roulette	Percage	Durchstich	Picadura	Foratura
Rouletted	Percé	Durchstochen	Picado	Forato
Royal Blue	Bleu-roi	Königblau	Azul real	Azzurro reale
Sage green	Vert-sauge	Salbeigrün	Verde salvia	Verde salvia
Salmon	Saumon	Lachs	Salmón	Salmone
Scarlet	Écarlate	Scharlach	Escarlata	Scarlatto
Sepia	Sépia	Sepia	Sepia	Seppia
Serpentine roulette	Percé en serpentin	Schlangenliniger Durchstich	Picado a serpentina	Perforazione a serpentina
Shade	Nuance	Tönung	Tono	Gradazione de colore
Sheet	Feuille	Bogen	Hoja	Foglio
Slate	Ardoise	Schiefer	Pizarra	Ardesia
Slate-blue	Bleu-ardoise	Schieferblau	Azul pizarra	Azzurro ardesia
Slate-green	Vert-ardoise	Schiefergrün	Verde pizarra	Verde ardesia
Slate-lilac	Lilas-gris	Schierferlila	Lila pizarra	Lilla ardesia
Slate-purple	Mauve-gris	Schieferpurpur	Púrpura pizarra	Porpora ardesia
Slate-violet	Violet-gris	Schieferviolett	Violeta pizarra	Violetto ardesia
Special delivery stamp	Timbre pour exprès	Eilmarke	Sello de urgencia	Francobollo per espressi
Specimen	Spécimen	Muster	Muestra	Saggio
Steel Blue	Bleu acier	Stahlblau	Azul acero	Azzurro acciaio
Strip	Bande	Streifen	Tira	Striscia
Surcharge	Surcharge	Aufdruck	Sobrecarga	Soprastampa
Tête-bêche	Tête-bêche	Kehrdruck	Tête-bêche	Tête-bêche
Tinted paper	Papier teinté	Getöntes Papier	Papel coloreado	Carta tinta
Too-late stamp	Timbre pour lettres en retard	Verspätungsmarke	Sello para cartas retardadas	Francobollo per le lettere in ritardo
Turquoise-blue	Bleu-turquoise	Türkisblau	Azul turquesa	Azzurro turchese
Turquoise-green	Vert-turquoise	Türkisgrün	Verde turquesa	Verde turchese
Typography	Typographie	Buchdruck	Tipografía	Tipografia
Ultramarine	Outremer	Ultramarin	Ultramar	Oltremare
Unused	Neuf	Ungebraucht	Nuevo	Nuovo
Used	Oblitéré, Usé	Gebraucht	Usado	Usato
Venetian Red	Rouge-brun terne	Venezianischrot	Rojo veneciano	Rosso veneziano
Vermilion	Vermillon	Zinnober	Cinabrio	Vermiglione
Violet	Violet	Violett	Violeta	Violetto
Violet-blue	Bleu-violet	Violettblau	Azul violeta	Azzurro violetto
Watermark	Filigrane	Wasserzeichen	Filigrana	Filigrana
Watermark sideways	Filigrane couché liegend	Wasserzeichen	Filigrana acostado	Filigrana coricata
Wove paper	Papier ordinaire, Papier uni	Einfaches Papier	Papel avitelado	Carta unita
Yellow	Jaune	Gelb	Amarillo	Giallo
Yellow-brown	Brun-jaune	Gelbbraun	Castaño amarillo	Bruno giallo
Yellow-green	Vert-jaune	Gelbgrün	Verde amarillo	Verde giallo
Yellow-olive	Olive-jaunâtre	Gelboliv	Oliva amarillo	Oliva giallastro
Yellow-orange	Orange jaunâtre	Gelborange	Naranja amarillo	Arancio giallastro
Zig-zag roulette	Percé en zigzag	Sägezahnartiger Durchstich	Picado en zigzag	Perforazione a zigzag

Specialist Philatelic Societies

Requests for inclusion on this page should be sent to the Catalogue Editor.

Great Britain Philatelic Society
Membership Secretary – Mr P. Tanner,
"High Standings" 13 Hubeerts Close,
Gerards Cross, Bucks SL9 7EN

Great Britain Collectors' Club
Secretary – Mr Parker A. Bailey Jr
13 Greenwood Road, Merrimack,
NH03054 U.S.A.

Channel Islands Specialists Society
Membership Secretary – Sheila Marshall,
3 La Marette, St. Anne, Alderney
GY9 3UQ

GB Overprints Society
Secretary – Mr A. Stanford,
P. O. Box 2675, Maidenhead, SL6 9ZN.

Aden & Somaliland Study Group
UK Representative – Mr M. Lacey
P.O. Box 9, Winchester, Hampshire
SO22 5RF

Ascension Study Circle
Secretary – Dr. R.C.F. Baker
Greys, Tower Road, Whitstable,
Kent CT5 3ER

Australian States Study Circle
Royal Sydney Philatelic Club
Honorary Secretary – Mr. B. Palmer
G.P.O. Box 1751, Sydney
N.S.W. 1043 Australia

British Society of Australian Philately
Secretary – Mr. A.J. Griffiths
c/o The British Philatelic Centre,
107 Charterhouse Street, London EC1M 6PT

Society of Australasian Specialists/Oceania
Secretary – Mr. S. Leven
P.O. Box 24764, San Jose, CA 95154-4764
U.S.A.

Bechuanalands and Bostwana Society
Membership Secretary – Mr. N. Midwood
69 Porlock Lane, Furzton,
Milton Keynes MK4 1JY

Bermuda Collectors Society
Secretary – Mr. T.J. McMahon
P.O. Box 1949, Stuart, FL 34995 U.S.A.

British Caribbean Philatelic Study Group
Overseas Director – Mr. D.N. Druett
Pennymead Auctions, 1 Brewerton Street,
Knaresborough, North Yorkshire HG5 8AZ

British West Indies Study Circle
Membership Secretary – Mr. P.G. Boulton
84 Tangier Road, Richmond,
Surrey TW10 5DN

Burma (Myanmar) Philatelic Study Circle
Secretary – Mr. D. Taylor Smith,
30 Seabrook Court,
Norwich NR5 9NQ

Canadian Philatelic Society of Great Britain
Secretary – Mr. J.M. Wright,
12 Milchester House, Staveley Road
Meads, Eastbourne, East Sussex BN20 7JX

Ceylon Study Circle
Secretary – Mr. R.W.P. Frost
42 Lonsdale Road, Cannington, Bridgewater,
Somerset TA5 2JS

Cyprus Study Circle
Membership Secretary – Mr J. Wigmore
19 Riversmeet, Appledore, Bideford,
North Devon EX39 1RE

East Africa Study Circle
Honorary secretary – Mr. J.P. A. Smalley
1 Lincoln Close, Tewkesbury, Glos
GL20 5TY

Egypt Study Circle
Secretary – Mr M. Murphy,
109 Chadwick Road, Peckham, London SE15 4PY

Falklands Islands Study Group
Membership Secretary – Mr. H.A. Osbourne
6 Russet Gardens,
Camberley, Surrey GU15 2LG

Gibraltar Study Circle
Membership Secretary – Mr E. D. Holmes,
29 Highgate Road, Woodley, Reading RG5 3ND

Hong Kong Study Circle
Membership Secretary -- Mr. P.V. Ball
37 Harcourt, Newcastle-under-Lyne,
Staffordshire ST5 2AL

Indian Ocean Study Circle
Secretary – Mrs S. Hopson
Field Acre, Hoe Benham, Newbury,
Berkshire RG20 8PD

India Study Circle
Secretary – Mr B. Allcock
9 Golspie Croft, Hodge Lea,
Milton Keynes MK12 6JU

Irish Philatelic Circle
General Secretary – Mr. F. McDonald
63 Rafters Road, Drimnagh, Dublin 12,
Ireland

King George V Silver Jubilee Study Circle
Secretary – Mr. N. Levinge
80 Towcaster Road, Northampton NN4 8LQ

King George VI Collectors Society
Secretary – Mr. J.L. Shaw MBE
17 Balcaskie Road, Eltham
London SE9 1HQ

Kiribati and Tuvalu Philatelic Society
Honorary Secretary – Mr. M.J. Shaw
88 Stoneleigh Avenue, Worcester Park,
Surrey KT4 8XY

Malaya Study Group
Membership Secretary – Mr. K. Elliot
78 Howard Road. Queens Park,
Bournemouth, Dorset BH8 9ED

Malta Study Circle
Honorary Secretary – Mr. D. Crookes
9a Church Street,
Durham DH1 3DG

Natal and Zululand Study Circle
Secretary – Mr. J. Dickson, Lismore House,
Great Lane, Shepton Beauchamp,
Somerset TA19 0LJ

New Zealand Society of Great Britain
General Secretary – Mr. K.C. Collins
13 Briton Crescent Sanderstead
Surrey CR2 0JN

Orange Free State Study Circle
Secrretary – Mr. J.R. Stroud
28 Oxford Street, Burnham-on-Sea,
Somerset TA8 1LQ

Pacific Islands Study Circle
Honorary Secretary – Mr. J.D. Ray
24 Woodvale Avenue, London SE25 4AE

Papua Philatelic Society
Secretary – Mr. D.C. Ashton
71 Lowerside, Ham, Plymouth
Devon PL2 2HU

Pitcairn Islands Study Group (U.K.)
Honorary Secretary – Mr. D. Sleep
6 Palace Gardens, 100 Court Road, Eltham,
London SE9 5NS

Rhodesian Study Circle
Membership Secretary – Mr. R.G. Barnett
2 Cox Ley, Hatfield Heath,
Bishop's Stortford CM22 7ER

Royal Philatelic Society of New Zealand
Secretary – Mr. W.T.C. Kitching
P.O. Box 1269, Wellington,
New Zealand

St. Helena, Ascension and Tristan da Cunha
Philatelic Society
Secretary – Mr. J. Havill
205 N. Murray Blvd., #221, Colorado Springs,
CO 80916 U.S.A.

Sarawak Specialists Society
(also Brunei, North Borneo and Labuan)
Secretary – Dr. J. Higgins
31 Grimston Road, Kings Lynn,
Norfolk PE30 3HT

South African Collectors' Society
General Secretary – Mr. C. Oliver
Telephone 020 8940 9833

Philatelic Society of Sri Lanka
Secretary – Mr. H. Goonawardena, J.P.
44A Hena Road, Mt. Lavinia 10370,
Sri Lanka

Sudan Study Group
Secretary – Mr B.A. Gardner, Chimneys,
Mapledurwell, Basingstoke, Hants
RG25 2LH

Transvaal Study Circle
Secretary – Mr. J. Woolgar
132 Dale Street, Chatham, Kent
ME4 6QH

West Africa Study Circle
Secretary – Mr. J. Powell
23 Brook Street, Edlesborough, Dunstable,
Bedfordshire LU6 2LG IBAR

Select Bibliography

The literature on British Commonwealth stamps is vast, but works are often difficult to obtain once they are out of print. The selection of books below has been made on the basis of authority together with availability to the general reader, either as new or secondhand. Very specialised studies, and those covering aspects of postal history to which there are no references in the catalogue, have been excluded.

The following abbreviations are used to denote publishers:

CRL   Christie's Robson Lowe;
HH   Harry Hayes;
PB   Proud Bailey Co. Ltd. and Postal History Publications Co.;
PC   Philip Cockrill;
RPSL   Royal Philatelic Society, London;
SG   Stanley Gibbons Ltd.

Where no publisher is quoted, the book is published by its author.

GENERAL
Encylopaedia of British Empire Postage Stamps. Vols 1-6. Edited Robson Lowe. (CRL, 1951--1991)
Specimen Stamps of the Crown Colonies 1857-1948. Marcus Samuel. (RPSL, 1976 and 1984 Supplement)
Cancelled by Perkins Bacon. P. Jaffé. (Spink & Son Ltd., 1998)
U.P.U. Specimen Stamps. J. Bendon. (1988)
King George V Key Plates of the Imperium Postage and Revenue Design. P. Fernbank. (West Africa Study Circle, 1997)
Silver Jubilee of King George V Stamps Handbook. A.J. Ainscough. (Ainweel Developments, 1985)
The Commemorative Stamps of the British Commonwealth. H.D.S. Haverbeck. (Faber, 1955)
The Printings of King George VI Colonial Stamps. W.J.W. Potter & Lt-Col R.C.M. Shelton. (1952 and later facsimile edition)
King George VI Large Key Type Stamps of Bermuda, Leeward Islands, Nyasaland. R.W. Dickgiesser and E.P. Yendall. (Triad Publications, 1985)
Madame Joseph Forged Postmarks. D. Worboys. (RPSL, 1994)
Madame Joseph Revisted. B.M. Cartwright. (RPSL, 2005)
G.B. Used Abroad: Cancellations and Postal Markings. J. Parmenter. (The Postal History Society, 1993)

GREAT BRITAIN
For extensive bibliographies see *G.B. Specialised Catalogues. Vols 1-5*.
Stamps and Postal History of the Channel Islands. W. Newport. (Heineman, 1972)

ADEN
The Postal History of British Aden 1839-1967. Major R.W. Pratt. (PB, 1985)

ASCENSION
Ascension. The Stamps and Postal History. J.H. Attwood. (CRL, 1981)

AUSTRALIA
The Postal History of New South Wales 1788-1901. Edited J.S. White. (Philatelic Association of New South Wales, 1988)
South Australia. The Long Stamps 1902-12. J.R.W. Purves. (Royal Philatelic Society of Victoria, 1978)
The Departmental Stamps of South Australia. A.R. Butler. (RPSL, 1978)
A Priced Listing of the Departmental Stamps of South Australia. A.D. Presgrave. (2nd edition, 1999)
Stamps and Postal History of Tasmania. W.E. Tinsley. (RPSL, 1986)
The Pictorial Stamps of Tasmania 1899-1912. K.E. Lancaster. (Royal Philatelic Society of Victoria, 1986)
The Stamps of Victoria. G. Kellow. (B. & K. Philatelic Publishing, 1990)
Western Australia. The Stamps and Postal History. Edited M. Hamilton and B. Pope. (W. Australian Study Group, 1979)
Postage Stamps and Postal History of Western Australia. Vols 1-3. M. Juhl. (1981-83)
The Chapman Collection of Australian Commonwealth Stamps. R. Chapman. (Royal Philatelic Society of Victoria, 1999)
Nauru 1915--1923. K. Buckingham. (The British Philatelic Association Expertising Educational Charity, 2004)
The Postal History of British New Guinea and Papua 1885-1942. R. Lee. (CRL, 1983)
Norfolk Island. A Postal and Philatelic History, 1788-1969. P. Collas & R. Breckon. (B. & K. Philatelic Publishing, 1997)

BAHAMAS
The Postage Stamps and Postal History of the Bahamas. H.G.D. Gisburn, (SG, 1950 and later facsimile edition)

BARBADOS
The Stamps of Barbados. E.A. Bayley. (1989)
Advanced Barbados Philately. H.F. Deakin. (B.W.I. Study Circle, 1997)

BASUTOLAND
The Cancellations and Postal Markings of Basutoland/Lesotho Post Offices. A. H. Scott. (Collectors Mail Auctions (Pty) Ltd., 1980)

BATUM
British Occupation of Batum. P.T. Ashford. (1989)

BECHUANALAND
The Postage Stamps, Postal Stationery and Postmarks of the Bechuanalands. H.R. Holmes. (RPSL, 1971)

BERMUDA
The Postal History and Stamps of Bermuda. M.H. Ludington. (Quarterman Publications Inc., 1978)
The King George V High-value Stamps of Bermuda, 1917-1938. M. Glazer. (Calaby Publishers, 1994)
The Postal History of Bermuda. E.B. Proud. (PB, 2003)

BRITISH GUIANA
The Postage Stamps and Postal History of British Guiana. W.A. Townsend & F.G. Howe. (RPSL, 1970)

BRITISH HONDURAS
The Postal History of British Honduras. E.B. Proud. (PB, 1999)

BRITISH OCCUPATION OF GERMAN COLONIES
G.R.I. R.M. Gibbs. (CRL, 1989)

BRITISH POSTAL AGENCIES IN EASTERN ARABIA
The Postal Agencies in Eastern Arabia and the Gulf. N. Donaldson. (HH, 1975) and Supplement (Bridger & Kay Guernsey Ltd., 1994)

BRITISH SOLOMON ISLANDS
British Solomon Islands Protectorate. Its Postage Stamps and Postal History. H.G.D. Gisburn. (T. Sanders (Philatelist) Ltd., 1956)

BRITISH WEST AFRICA
The Postal History and Handstamps of British West Africa. C. McCaig. (CRL, 1978)

BURMA
Burma Postal History. G. Davis and D Martin. (CRL, 1971 and 1987 Supplement).
The Postal History of Burma. E.B. Proud. (PB, 2002)

CAMEROONS
The Postal Arrangements of the Anglo-French Cameroons Expeditionary Force 1914-1916. R.J. Maddocks. (1996)

CANADA
The Postage Stamps and Postal History of Newfoundland. W.S. Boggs. (Quarterman Publications Inc., 1975)
Stamps of British North America. F. Jarrett. (Quarterman Publications Inc., 1975)
The Postage Stamps and Postal History of Canada. W.S. Boggs. (Quarterman Publications Inc., 1974)
The First Decimal Issue of Canada 1859-68. G. Whitworth. (RPSL, 1966)
The Five Cents Beaver Stamp of Canada. G. Whitworth. (RPSL, 1985)
The Small Queens of Canada. J. Hillson. (CRL, 1989)
Canada Small Queens Re-Appraised. J. Hillson. (Canadian Philatelic Society of Great Britain, 1999)
The Edward VII Issue of Canada, G.C. Marler, (National Postal Museum, Canada, 1975)
The Admiral Issue of Canada. G.C. Marler. (American Philatelic Society, 1982)

CEYLON
The Postal History of Ceylon. E. B. Proud (PB, 2006)

CYPRUS
Cyprus 1353-1986. W. Castle. (CRL 3rd edition, 1987)

DOMINICA
Dominica Postal History, Stamps and Postal Stationery to 1935. E.V. Toeg. (B.W.I. Study Circle, 1994)

EGYPT
Egypt Stamps & Postal History. P.A.S. Smith. (James Bendon, 1999)
The Nile Post. J. H. Chalhoub. (2003)

FALKLAND ISLANDS
The Postage Stamps of the Falkland Islands and Dependencies. B.S.H. Grant. (SG, 1952 and later facsimile edition)
The Falkland Islands Philatelic Digest. Nos. 1 & 2. M. Barton and R Spafford. (HH, 1975 and 1979)
The De La Rue Definitives of the Falkland Islands 1901-1929. J.P. Bunt. (1986 and 1996 Supplement)
The Falkland Islands. The 1891 Provisionals. M. Barton. (BPA Expertising Educational Trust, 2002)
The War Stamp Overprints of the Falkland Islands 1918-1920. J.P. Bunt. (1981)
The Falkland Islands. Printings of the Pictorial Issue of 1938-49. C.E. Glass. (CRL, 1979)

FIJI
Fiji Philatelics. D.E.F. Alford. (Pacific Islands Study Circle, 1994)
Fiji Queen Victoria One Shilling and Five Shillings Postage Stamps 1881-1902. R.F. Duberal. (Pacific Islands Study Circle, 2003)
The Postal History of Fiji 1911-1952. J.G. Rodger. (Pacific Islands Study Circle, 1991)

GAMBIA
The Stamps and Postal History of the Gambia. Edited J.O. Andrew. (CRL, 1985)
The Postal History of the Gambia. E.B. Proud. (PB, 1994)

GIBRALTAR
Posted in Gibraltar. W. Hine-Haycock. (CRL, 1978 and 1983 Supplement)
Gibraltar. The Postal History and Postage Stamps. Vol 1 to 1885). G. Osborn. (Gibraltar Study Circle, 1995)
The Postal History of Gibraltar. R.J.M. Garcia & E.B. Proud. (PB, 1998)
Gibraltar, Collecting King George VI. E. Chambers. (The Gibraltar Study Circle, 2003)

GOLD COAST
The Postal History of the Gold Coast. E.B. Proud. (PB, 1995)
The Postal Services of the Gold Coast, 1901-1957. Edited M. Ensor. (West Africa Study Circle, 1998)
The Postal Services of the Gold Coast to 1901. Edited J. Sacher. (RPSL, 2003)

HONG KONG
The Philatelic History of Hong Kong. Vol 1. (Hong Kong Study Circle, 1984)
Hong Kong Postage Stamps of the Queen Victoria Period. R.N. Gurevitch. (1993)
Hong Kong. The 1898 10c. on 30c. Provisional Issue. A.M. Chu. (1998)
The Postal History History of Hong Kong. E.B. Proud (PB, 2004)
British Post Offices in the Far East. E.B. Proud. (PB, 1991)
Cancellations of the Treaty Ports of Hong Kong. H. Schoenfield. (1988)
The Crown Colony of Wei Haiwei. M.Goldsmith and C.W. Goodwyn. (RPSL, 1985)

INDIA
C.E.F. The China Expeditionary force 1900-1923. D.S. Virk, J.C. Hume, G. Sattin. (Philatelic Congress of India, 1992)
India Used Abroad. V.S. Dastur. (Mysore Philatelics, 1982)
The Indian Postal Agencies in the Persian Gulf Area. A. Parsons. (Sahara Publications Ltd., 2001)
A Handbook on Gwalior Postal History and Stamps. V.K. Gupta. (1980)
The Stamps of Jammu & Kashmir. F. Staal. (The Collectors Club, 1983)
Sorath Stamps and Postal History. R.A. Malaviya. (Ravi Prakashan, 1999)

IRAQ
The Postal History of Iraq. P.C. Pearson and E.B. Proud. (PB, 1996)

IRELAND
Irish Stamp Booklets 1931-1991. C.J. Dulin. (1998)

JAMAICA
Encyclopaedia of Jamaican Philately. Vol 1. D.Sutcliffe & S. Jarvis. (1997); *Vol 6.* S. Jarvis. (2001) (B.W.I. Study Circle)
Jamaica, the Definitive and Commemorative Stamps and Postal Stationery of the Reign of King George VI. H.A.H. James. (The King George VI Collectors Society, 1999)

KENYA
British East Africa. The Stamps and Postal Stationery. J. Minns. (RPSL, 1982 and 1990 Supplement) (New edition, revised and updated, George T. Krieger, 2006)
The Postal History of Kenya. E.B. Proud. (PB, 1992)

LEEWARD ISLANDS
The Leeward Islands – Notes for Philatelists. M.N. Oliver. (B.W.I. Study Circle, 2000)

MALAYA
The Postal History of British Malaya. Vols 1-3. E.B. Proud. (PB, 2nd edition, 2000)
The Postage Stamps of Federated Malay States. W.A. Reeves. (Malaya Study Group, 1978)

Kedah and Perlis. D.R.M. Holley. (Malaya Study Group, 1995)
Kelantan. Its Stamps and Postal History. W.A. Reeves and B.E. Dexter. (Malaya Study Group, 1992)
The Postal History of the Occupation of Malaya and British Borneo 1941-1945. E.B. Proud and M.D. Rowell. (PB, 1992)

MALTA
Malta. The Postal History and Postage Stamps. Edited R.E. Martin. (CRL, 1980 and 1985 Supplement)

MAURITIUS
The Postal History and Stamps of Mauritius. P. Ibbotson. (RPSL, 1991); Revisions and additions Supplement (Indian Ocean Study Circle, 1995)
The Postal History of Mauritius. E.B. Proud. (PB, 2001)

MONTSERRAT
Montserrat to 1965. L.E. Britnor. (B.W.I. Study Circle. 2nd edition, 1998)

MOROCCO AGENCIES
British Post Offices and Agencies in Morocco 1857-1907 and Local Posts 1891-1914. R.K. Clough. (Gibraltar Study Circle, 1984)

NEW ZEALAND
The Postage Stamps of New Zealand. Vols I-VII. (Royal Philatelic Society of New Zealand. 1939—98)
The Early Cook Islands Post Office. A.R. Burge (Hawthorn Pres, 1978)
The Postal History and Postage Stamps of the Tokelau/Union Islands. A.H. Burgess. (Pacific Island Study Circle, 2nd edition, 1998)
A Postal History of the Samoan Islands (Parts I and II). Edited R. Burge. (Royal Philatelic Society of New Zealand, 1987-89)
The Stamps and Postal History of Nineteenth Century Samoa. R.P. Odenweller. (RPSL and The Royal Philatelic Society of New Zealand, 2004)

NIGERIA
The Postal Services of the British Nigeria Region. J. Ince and J. Sacher. (RPSL, 1992)
The Postal History of Nigeria. E.B. Proud (PB, 1995)

NORTH BORNEO
A Concise Guide to the Queen Issues of Labuan. R. Price. (Sarawak Specialists Society, 1991)
The Stamps and Postal History of North Borneo. Parts 1-3. L.H. Shipman and P.K. Cassells. (Sarawak Specialists Society, 1976-88)
The Postal History of British Borneo. E.B. Proud. (PB, 2003)

NORTHERN RHODESIA
Northern Rhodesia – The Mkushi Postage Dues and the renamed Old Mkushi Post Office Otto Peetoom (2005)
The King George VI Postage and Revenue Stamps of Northern Rhodesia Alan Drysdall, Ian Lane and Jean Cheston (Rhodesia Study Circle, 2006)

NYASALAND
The Postal History of Nyasaland. E.B. Proud. (PB, 1997)

PALESTINE
The Stamps & Postal Stationery of Palestine Mandate 1918-1948. D. Dorfman. (Edward G. Rosen, 2001)

PITCAIRN ISLANDS
Pitcairn Islands Philately. D.E. Hume. (2nd edition, 1999)

RHODESIA
Mashonaland. A Postal History 1890—96. Dr. A.R. Drysdall and D. Collis. (CRL, 1990)
Rhodesia. A Postal History. R.C. Smith. (1967 and 1970 Supplement)
The Rhodesia Philatelist. (Ormskirk Stamps)

ST. HELENA
St. Helena, Postal History and Stamps. E. Hibbert. (CRL, 1979)

ST. KITTS-NEVIS
A Study of the King George VI Stamps of St. Kitts-Nevis. P.L. Baldwin. (Murray Payne Ltd., 2nd edition, 1997)
The Philately of Nevis. F. Borromeo. (British West Indies Study Circle, 2001)

SARAWAK
The Stamps and Postal History of Sarawak. W.A. Forrester-Wood. (Sarawak Specialists Society, 1959 and 1970 Supplement)
Sarawak: The Issues of 1871 and 1875. W. Batty-Smith and W.E.Watterson. (1990)

SEYCHELLES
Seychelles Postal History and Postage Stamps to 1976. S. Hopson & B.M. McCloy. (Indian Ocean Study Circle, 2002)

SIERRA LEONE
The Postal Service of Sierra Leone. P.O. Beale. (RPSL, 1988)
The Postal History of Sierra Leone. E.B. Proud. (PB, 1994)
Sierra Leone King George VI Definitive Stamps. F. Walton. (West Africa Study Circle, 2001)

SOUTH AFRICA
Postmarks of the Cape of Good Hope. R. Goldblatt. (Reijger Publishers (Pty) Ltd., 1984)
Stamps of the Orange Free State. Parts 1-3. G.D. Buckley & W.B. Marriott. (O.F.S. Study Circle, 1967—80)
Transvaal Philately. Edited I.B. Mathews. (Reijer Publishers (Pty) Ltd., 1986)
Transvaal. The Provisional Issues of the First British Occupation. Dr. A.R. Drysdall. (James Bendon, 1994)
The Wherewithal of Wolmaransstad. H. Birkhead and J. Groenewald. (Philatelic Foundation of Southern Africa, 1999)

SOUTH WEST AFRICA
The Overprinted Stamps of South West Africa to 1930. N. Becker. (Philatelic Holdings (Pty) Ltd., 1990)

SUDAN
Sudan. The Stamps and Postal Stationery of 1867 to 1970. E.C.W. Stagg. (HH, 1977) *The Camel Postman 1898-1998.* R. Stock. (Sudan Study Group, 2001)
The Postal History of Sudan. E. B Proud (PB, 2006)

TANGANYIKA
The Postal History of Tanganyika. 1915-1961. E.B. Proud. (PB, 1989)

TOGO
Togo-The Postal History of the Anglo-French Occupation 1914-22. J. Martin and F. Walton. (West Africa S.C., 1995)
Togo Overprints on Stamps of the Gold Coast 1915–1920. P. Duggan. (West Africa S.C. 2005)

TRANSJORDAN
The Stamps of Jordan 1920—1965. A.H. Najjar. (Sahara Publications Ltd., 1998)

TRINIDAD AND TOBAGO
The Postal History of Trinidad and Tobago. J.C. Aleong and E.B. Proud. (PB, 1997)

TRISTAN DA CUNHA
The History and Postal History of Tristan da Cunha. G. Crabb. (1980)

TURKS AND CAICOS ISLANDS
Turks Islands and Caicos Islands to 1950. J.J. Challis. (Roses Caribbean Philatelic Society, 1983)

UGANDA
The Postal History of Uganda and Zanzibar. E.B. Proud. (PB, 1993)

ZANZIBAR
Zanzibar 1895 – 1904. T.W. Hall. (Reprint, East Africa Study Circle, 2002)

Great Britain

STAMPS ON COVER. Prices are quoted, as a third price column, for those Victorian and Edwardian issues usually found used on cover. In general these prices refer to the cheapest version of each basic stamp with other shades, plates or varieties, together with unusual frankings and postmarks, being worth more.

UNITED KINGDOM OF GREAT BRITAIN
AND IRELAND

QUEEN VICTORIA
20 June 1837–22 January 1901

MULREADY ENVELOPES AND LETTER SHEETS, so called from the name of the designer, William Mulready, were issued concurrently with the first British adhesive stamps.

1d. black	Envelopes:	£250 unused;	£350 used.
	Letter Sheets:	£225 unused;	£325 used.
2d. blue	Envelopes:	£325 unused;	£1200 used.
	Letter Sheets:	£300 unused;	£1400 used.

LINE-ENGRAVED ISSUES
GENERAL NOTES

Brief notes on some aspects of the line-engraved stamps follow, but for further information and a full specialist treatment of these issues collectors are recommended to consult Volume 1 of the Stanley Gibbons *Great Britain Specialised Catalogue*.

Alphabet I   Alphabet II

Alphabet III   Alphabet IV

Typical Corner Letters of the four Alphabets

Alphabets. Four different styles were used for the corner letters on stamps prior to the issue with letters in all four corners, these being known to collectors as:

Alphabet I. Used for all plates made from 1840 to the end of 1851. Letters small.

Alphabet II. Plates from 1852 to mid-1855. Letters larger, heavier and broader.

Alphabet III. Plates from mid-1855 to end of period. Letters tall and more slender.

Alphabet IV. 1861. 1d. Die II, Plates 50 and 51 only. Letters were hand-engraved instead of being punched on the plate. They are therefore inconsistent in shape and size but generally larger and outstanding.

While the general descriptions and the illustrations of typical letters given above may be of some assistance, only long experience and published aids can enable every stamp to be allocated to its particular Alphabet without hesitation, as certain letters in each are similar to those in one of the others.

Blued Paper. The blueing of the paper of the earlier issues is believed to be due to the presence of prussiate of potash in the printing ink, or in the paper, which, under certain conditions, tended to colour the paper when the sheets were damped for printing. An alternative term is bleuté paper.

Corner Letters. The corner letters on the early British stamps were intended as a safeguard against forgery, each stamp in the sheet having a different combination of letters. Taking the first 1d. stamp, printed in 20 horizontal rows of 12, as an example, the lettering is as follows:

Row 1.   A A, A B, A C, etc. to A L.

Row 2.   B A, B B, B C, etc. to B L.

and so on to

Row 20   T A, T B, T C, etc. to T L.

On the stamps with four corner letters, those in the upper corners are in the reverse positions to those in the lower corners.

Thus in a sheet of 240 (12 × 20) the sequence is:

Row 1.	A A	B A	C A		L A
			etc. to		
	A A	A B	A C		A L
Row 2.	A B	B B	C B		L B
			etc. to		
	B A	B B	B C		B L
and so on to					
	A T	B T	C T		L T
Row 20.			etc. to		
	T A	T B	T C		T L

Placing letters in all four corners was not only an added precaution against forgery but was meant to deter unmarked parts of used stamps being pieced together and passed off as an unused whole.

Dies. The first die of the 1d. was used for making the original die of the 2d., both the No Lines and White Lines issues. In 1855 the 1d. Die I was amended by retouching the head and deepening the lines on a transferred impression of the original. This later version, known to collectors as Die II, was used for making the dies for the 1d. and 2d. with letters in all four corners and also for the 1½d.

The two dies are illustrated above No. 17 in the catalogue.

Double letter   Guide line in
corner

Guide line through value

Double Corner Letters. These are due to the workman placing his letter-punch in the wrong position at the first attempt, when lettering the plate, and then correcting the mistake; or to a slight shifting of the punch when struck. If a wrong letter was struck in the first instance, traces of a wrong letter may appear in a corner in addition to the correct one. A typical example is illustrated.

Guide Lines and Dots. When laying down the impressions of the design on the early plates, fine vertical and horizontal guidelines were marked on the plates to assist the operative. These were usually removed from the gutter margins, but could not be removed from the stamp impressions without damage to the plate, so that in such cases they appear on the printed stamps, sometimes in the corners, sometimes through "POSTAGE" or the value. Typical examples are illustrated.

Guide dots or cuts were similarly made to indicate the spacing of the guide lines. These too sometimes appear on the stamps.

Ivory Head

"Ivory Head." The so-called "ivory head" variety is one in which the Queen's Head shows white on the back of the stamp. It arises from the comparative absence of ink in the head portion of the design, with consequent absence of blueing. (*See* "Blued Paper" note above.)

Line-engraving. In this context "line-engraved" is synonymous with recess-printing, in which the engraver cuts recesses in a plate and printing (the coloured areas) is from these recesses. "Line-engraved" is the traditional philatelic description for these stamps; other equivalent terms found are "engraving in *taille-douce*" (French) or in "*intaglio*" (Italian).

Plates. Until the introduction of the stamps with letters in all four corners, the number of the plate was not indicated in the design of the stamp, but was printed on the sheet margin. By long study of identifiable blocks and the minor variations in the design, coupled with the position of the corner letters, philatelists are now able to allot many of these stamps to their respective plates. Specialist collectors often endeavour to obtain examples of a given stamp printed from its different plates and our catalogue accordingly reflects this depth of detail.

Example of 1844 type postmark

Postmarks. The so-called "Maltese Cross" design was the first employed for obliterating British postage stamps and was in use from 1840 to 1844. Being hand-cut, the obliterating stamps varied greatly in detail and some distinctive types can be allotted to particular towns or offices. Local types, such as those used at Manchester, Norwich, Leeds, etc., are keenly sought. A red ink was first employed, but was superseded by black, after some earlier experiments, in February 1841. Maltese Cross obliterations in other colours are rare.

Obliterations of this type, numbered 1 to 12 in the centre, were used at the London Chief Office in 1843 and 1844.

Some straight-line cancellations were in use in 1840 at the Penny Post receiving offices, normally applied on the envelope, the adhesives then being obliterated at the Head Office. They are nevertheless known, with or without Maltese Cross, on the early postage stamps.

In 1842 some offices in S.W. England used dated postmarks in place of the Maltese Cross, usually on the back of the letter since they were not originally intended as obliterators. These town postmarks have likewise been found on adhesives.

In 1844 the Maltese Cross design was superseded by numbered obliterators of varied type, one of which is illustrated. They are naturally comparatively scarce on the first 1d. and 2d. stamps. Like the Maltese Cross they are found in various colours, some of which are rare.

Re-entry

"Union Jack" re-entry

Re-entries. Re-entries on the plate show as a doubling of part of the design of the stamp generally at top or bottom. Many re-entries are very slight while others are most marked. A typical one is illustrated.

The "*Union Jack*" re-entry, so called owing to the effect of the re-entry on the appearance of the corner stars (*see* illustration) occurs on stamp L K of Plate 75 of the 1d. red, Die I.

T A (T L)   M A (M L)

Varieties of Large Crown Watermark

I   II

Two states of Large Crown Watermark

Watermarks. Two watermark varieties, as illustrated, consisting of crowns of entirely different shape, are found in sheets of the Large Crown paper and fall on stamps lettered M A and T A (or M L and T L) when the paper is printed on the wrong side). Both varieties are found on the 1d. rose-red of 1857, while the M A (M L) variety comes also on some plates of the 1d. of 1864 (Nos. 43, 44) up to about Plate 96. On the 2d. the T A (T L) variety is known on plates 8 and 9, and the M A (M L) on later prints of plate 9. These varieties may exist inverted, or inverted reversed, on stamps lettered A A and A L and H A and H L, and some are known.

In 1861 a minor alteration was made in the Large Crown watermark by the removal of the two vertical strokes, representing *fleurs-de-lis*, which projected upwards from the uppermost of the three horizontal curves at the base of the Crown. Hence two states are distinguishable, as illustrated.

CONDITION—IMPERFORATE
LINE-ENGRAVED ISSUES

The prices quoted for the 1840 and 1841 imperforate Line-engraved issues are for "fine" examples. As condition is most important in assessing the value of a stamp, the following definitions will assist collectors in the evaluation of individual examples.

Four main factors are relevant when considering quality.

(a) **Impression.** This should be clean and the surface free of any rubbing or unnatural blurring which would detract from the appearance.

(b) **Margins.** This is perhaps the most difficult factor to evaluate. Stamps described as "fine", the standard adopted in this catalogue for pricing purposes, should have margins of the recognised width, defined as approximately one half of the distance between two adjoining unsevered stamps. Stamps described as "very fine" or "superb" should have margins which are proportionately larger than those of a "fine" stamp. Examples with close margins should not, generally, be classified as "fine".

Maltese Cross   Type of Town postmark

Type of Penny Post cancellation

The Essential Guide
To The Line Engraved 1840 To 1864
1d & 2d Stars

For each plate used, Dr Statham analyses its HISTORY, ALIGNMENT, CHARACTERISTICS, CHECK LETTERS, DESCRIPTION, DATES, QUANTITIES, IMPRIMATURS and gives detailed listings of its VARIETIES and an aid to PLATING. The impetus for this book came from the frustration in his early plating days with the information then published. The availability and access to the new information, material and original documents has enabled previous data to be checked and amended where necessary. Many THOUSANDS of NEW VARIETIES have been listed for the first time, following Dr. Statham's meticulous research and process of double-checking. It is intended that virtually EVERY VARIETY is ILLUSTRATED - all drawn by Dr. Statham, who hopes that his publication will enable other collectors, both specialist and beginners alike, to derive the same pleasure that he has had over the years in collecting these issues.

* Publication date September 2006 *

Sets of Volumes 5&6, Volumes 9&10, Volumes 11&12, 13&14 each in an attractive Presentation Box available individually, £100 each, Volumes 15, 16, 17 £150, plus postage and packing.
Set of Volumes 5 to 18, each section in presentation box, £750 plus postage and packing, a few only.

We specialize in the Line Engraved 1840 To 1864 1d & 2d SG1 to SG42

We have good stocks of IMPERFS, PERFS & PLATES, both UNPLATED and PLATED including the RARE PLATES 175. 176 and 177 IMPERF with R.RS. certificates as well as The GARDINER-HILL Collection of the First Perforated Issue and INVERTED WMKS from the whole range.

LISTS   Reflecting our COMPREHENSIVE stocks of GB, QV to KGVI   **LISTS**
They include our specialist areas mentioned above as well as:-
1) SG 43/44 Id RED PLATES with CDS postmarks
2) Queen Victoria Surface-Printed to KGVI CDs & mint 3) GREAT BRITAIN USED ABROAD
4) INDIVIDUALLY PLATED 1d RED IMPERFS & STARS 5) A RARE, UNUSUAL and DIFFICULT-To-Find section
ALL STAMPS ARE ILLUSTRATED

(c) Cancellation. On a "fine" stamp this should be reasonably clear and not noticeably smudged. A stamp described as "superb" should have a neat cancellation, preferably centrally placed or to the right.

(d) Appearance. Stamps, at the prices quoted, should always be without any tears, creases, bends or thins and should not be toned on either the front or back. Stamps with such defects are worth only a proportion of the catalogue price.

Good

Fine

Very Fine

Superb

The above actual size illustrations of 1840 1d. blacks show the various grades of quality. When comparing these illustrations it should be assumed that they are all from the same plate and that they are free of any hidden defects.

PRINTERS. Nos. 1/53a were recess-printed by Perkins, Bacon & Petch, known from 1852 as Perkins, Bacon & Co.

1

1a

Small Crown

(Eng Charles and Frederick Heath)

1840 (6 May). *Letters in lower corners.* Wmk Small Crown. W **2**. Imperf.

			Un	Used	Used on Cover
1	**1**	1d. intense black	£7500	£350	
2		1d. black	£6000	£275	£475
3		1d. grey-black (worn plate)	£7000	£350	
4	**1a**	2d. deep full blue	£20000	£825	
5		2d. blue	£15000	£650	£1700
6		2d. pale blue	£20000	£700	

The 1d. stamp in black was printed from Plates 1 to 11. Plate 1 exists in two states (known to collectors as 1a and 1b), the latter being the result of extensive repairs.

Repairs were also made to Plates 2, 5, 6, 8, 9, 10 and 11, and certain impressions exist in two or more states.

The so-called "Royal reprint" of the 1d. black was made in 1864, from Plate 66, Die II, on paper with Large Crown watermark. A printing was also made in carmine, on paper with the same watermark, normal.

For 1d. black with "VR" in upper corners *see* No. V1 under Official Stamps.

The 2d. stamps were printed from Plates 1 and 2.

Plates of 1d. black

	Un	Used
1a	£8000	£300
1b	£6000	£275
2	£6000	£275
3	£8750	£325
4	£6000	£300
5	£6000	£275
6	£6500	£275
7	£6750	£300
8	£8500	£350
9	£9000	£420
10	£12000	£600
11	£11000	£3800

Varieties of 1d. black

		Un	Used
a.	On *bleuté* paper (Plates 1 to 8) ....*from*	—	£500
b.	Double letter in corner ....*from*	£6250	£300
bb.	Re-entry ....*from*	£6500	£325
bc.	"PB" re-entry (Plate 5, 3rd state)	—	£5500
c.	Guide line in corner ....*from*	£6250	£300
cc.	Large letters in each corner (E J, I L, J C and P A) (Plate 1b) ....*from*	£6250	£425
d.	Guide line through value ....*from*	£6250	£325
e.	Wmk inverted	£15000	£1400
g.	Obliterated by Maltese Cross		
	In red	—	£300
	In black	—	£275
	In blue	—	£5000
	In magenta	—	£2000
	In yellow	—	—
h.	Obliterated by Maltese Cross with number in centre ....*from*	—	£6000
	No. 1	—	£6000
	No. 2	—	£6000
	No. 3	—	£6000
	No. 5	—	£6000
	No. 6	—	£6000
	No. 7	—	£6000

		Un	Used
	No. 8	—	£6000
	No. 9	—	£6000
	No. 10	—	£6000
	No. 11	—	£6000
	No. 12	—	£6000
i.	Obliterated "Penny Post" in black (without Maltese Cross) ....*from*	—	£2500
j.	Obliterated by town postmark (without Maltese Cross)		
	In black ....*from*	—	£4000
	In yellow ....*from*	—	£22000
	In red ....*from*	—	£4000
k	Obliterated by 1844 type postmark in black ....*from*	—	£950

Plates of 2d. blue

Plate		Un	Used
1	*Shades from*	£15000	£650
2	*Shades from*	£20000	£700

Varieties of 2d. blue

		Un	Used
a.	Double letter in corner	—	£700
aa.	Re-entry	—	£750
b.	Guide line in corner	—	£675
c.	Guide line through value	—	£675
e.	Obliterated by Maltese Cross		
	In red	—	£700
	In black	—	£650
	In blue	—	£7500
	In magenta	—	£6500
f.	Obliterated by Maltese Cross with number in centre ....*from*		
	No. 1	—	£6000
	No. 2	—	£6000
	No. 3	—	£6000
	No. 4	—	£6000
	No. 5	—	£6000
	No. 6	—	£6000
	No. 7	—	£6000
	No. 8	—	£6000
	No. 9	—	£6000
	No. 10	—	£6000
	No. 11	—	£6000
	No. 12	—	£5500
g.	Obliterated "Penny Post" in black (without Maltese Cross) ....*from*	—	£4500
h.	Obliterated by town postmark (without Maltese Cross) in black ....*from*	—	£3500
i.	Obliterated by 1844 type postmark		
	In black ....*from*	—	£1500
	In blue ....*from*	—	£9000

1841 (10 Feb). *Printed from "black" plates.* Wmk W **2**. Paper more or less blued. Imperf.

			Un	Used	Used on Cover
7	**1**	1d. red-brown (*shades*)	£1250	75·00	£175
		a. "PB" re-entry (Plate 5, 3rd state)	—	£1500	

The first printings of the 1d. in red-brown were made from Plates 1b, 2, 5 and 8 to 11 used for the 1d. black.

1d. red-brown from "black" plates

Plate	Un	Used
1b	£8000	£275
2	£5500	£225
5	£2000	£125
8	£2000	£110
9	£2000	£110
10	£1500	£110
11	£1500	90·00

1841 (late Feb). *Plate 12 onwards.* Wmk W **2**. Paper more or less blued. Imperf.

			Un	Used	Used on Cover
8	**1**	1d. red-brown	£400	15·00	25·00
8a		1d. red-brown on very blue paper	£450	15·00	
9		1d. pale red-brown (worn plates)	£500	25·00	
10		1d. deep red-brown	£600	30·00	
11		1d. lake-red	£3500	£600	
12		1d. orange-brown	£1200	£150	

Error. No letter "A" in right lower corner (Stamp B(A), *Plate 77)*

			Un	Used
12a	**1**	1d. red-brown	—	£8500

The error "No letter A in right corner" was due to the omission to insert this letter on stamp B A of Plate 77. The error was discovered some months after the plate was registered and was then corrected.

There are innumerable variations in the colour and shade of the 1d. "red" and those given in the above list represent colour groups each covering a wide range.

Varieties of 1d. red-brown, etc.

		Un	Used
b.	Re-entry from	—	60·00
c.	Double letter in corner from	—	25·00
d.	Double Star (Plate 75) "Union Jack" re-entry	£15000	£2200
e.	Guide line in corner	—	18·00
f.	Guide line through value	—	22·00
g.	Thick outer frame to stamp	—	22·00
h.	Ivory head	£400	22·00
j.	Left corner letter "S" inverted (Plates 78, 105, 107) ....*from*	—	£120
k.	P converted to R (Plates 30/1, 33, 83, 86) .... *from*	—	60·00
l.	Obliterated by Maltese Cross		
	In red	—	£3500
	In black	—	45·00
	In blue	—	£500
m.	Obliterated by Maltese Cross with number in centre		
	No. 1	—	£135
	No. 2	—	£135
	No. 3	—	£160
	No. 4	—	£400

	Un	Used
No. 5	—	£135
No. 6	—	£110
No. 7	—	£110
No. 8	—	£110
No. 9	—	£135
No. 10	—	£225
No. 11	—	£225
No. 12	—	£225
n. Obliterated "Penny Post" in black (without Maltese Cross)	—	£550
o. Obliterated by town postmark (without Maltese Cross)		
In black ....*from*	—	£500
In blue ....*from*	—	£1200
In green ....*from*	—	£2200
In yellow ....*from*	—	—
In red ....*from*	—	£6500
p. Obliterated by 1844 type postmark		
In blue ....*from*	—	£175
In red ....*from*	—	£5000
In green ....*from*	—	£1750
In violet ....*from*	—	£2500
In black ....*from*	—	15·00

Stamps with thick outer frame to the design are from plates on which the frame-lines have been strengthened or recut, particularly Plates 76 and 90.

For "Union Jack" re-entry *see* General Notes to Line-engraved Issues.

In "P converted to R" the corner letter "R" is formed from the "P", the distinctive long tail having been hand-cut.

KEY TO LINE-ENGRAVED ISSUES

S.G Nos.	Description	Date	Wmk	Perf	Die	Alphabet
	THE IMPERFORATE ISSUES					
1/3	1d. black	6.5.40	SC	Imp	I	I
4/6	2d. no lines	8.5.40	SC	Imp	I	I
	PAPER MORE OR LESS BLUED					
7	1d. red-brown	Feb 1841	SC	Imp	I	I
8/12	1d. red-brown	Feb 1841	SC	Imp	I	I
8/12	1d. red-brown	6.2.52	SC	Imp	I	II
13/15	2d. white lines	13.3.41	SC	Imp	I	I
	THE PERFORATED ISSUES					
	ONE PENNY VALUE					
16a	1d. red-brown	1848	SC	Roul	I	I
16b	1d. red-brown	1850	SC	16	I	I
16c	1d. red-brown	1853	SC	16	I	II
17/18	1d. red-brown	Feb 1854	SC	16	I	II
22	1d. red-brown	Jan 1855	SC	14	I	II
24/5	1d. red-brown	28.2.55	SC	14	II	II
21	1d. red-brown	1.3.55	SC	16	II	II
26	1d. red-brown	15.5.55	LC	16	II	II
29/33	1d. red-brown	Aug 1855	LC	14	II	III
	NEW COLOURS ON WHITE PAPER					
37/41	1d. rose-red	Nov 1856	LC	14	II	III
36	1d. rose-red	26.12.57	LC	16	II	III
42	1d. rose-red	1861	LC	14	II	IV
	TWO PENCE VALUE					
19, 20	2d. blue	1.3.54	SC	16	I	I
23	2d. blue	22.2.55	SC	14	I	I
23a	2d. blue	5.7.55	SC	14	I	II
20a	2d. blue	18.8.55	SC	16	I	II
27	2d. blue	20.7.55	SC	16	I	II
34	2d. blue	20.7.55	LC	14	I	II
35	2d. blue	2.7.57	LC	14	I	III
36a	2d. blue	1.2.58	LC	16	I	III
	LETTERS IN ALL FOUR CORNERS					
48/9	½d. rose-red	1.10.70	W9	14	—	
43/4	1d. rose-red	1.4.64	LC	14		II
53a	1½d. rosy mauve	1860	LC	14		II
51/3	1½d. rose-red	1.10.70	LC	14		II
45	2d. blue	July 1858	LC	14		II
46/7	2d. thinner lines	7.7.69	LC	14		II

Watermarks: SC = Small Crown, T **2**.

LC = Large Crown, T **4**.

Dies: See notes above No. 17 in the catalogue.

Alphabets: See General Notes to this section.

3 White lines added

1841 (13 Mar)–**51**. *White lines added.* Wmk W **2**. Paper more or less blued. Imperf.

			Un	Used	Used on Cover
13	**3**	2d. pale blue	£3500	85·00	
14		2d. blue	£3000	75·00	£250
15		2d. deep full blue	£4000	85·00	
15aa		2d. violet-blue (1851)	£14000	£1000	

The 2d. stamp with white lines was printed from Plates 3 and 4.

No. 15aa came from Plate 4 and the price quoted is for examples on thicker, lavender tinted paper.

Plates of 2d. blue

Plate		Un	Used
3	shades ....*from*	£3000	85·00
4	shades ....*from*	£3500	75·00

Varieties of 2d. blue

		Un	Used
a.	Guide line in corner	—	90·00
b.	Guide line through value	£3250	90·00
bb.	Double letter in corner	—	90·00
be.	Re-entry	£4250	£140
c.	Ivory head	£3250	85·00
e.	Obliterated by Maltese Cross		
	In red	—	£15000
	In black	—	£200
	In blue	—	£3000
f.	Obliterated by Maltese Cross with number in centre		
	No. 1	—	£450
	No. 2	—	£450
	No. 3	—	£450
	No. 4	—	£425
	No. 5	—	£550
	No. 6	—	£425
	No. 7	—	£750
	No. 8	—	£600
	No. 9	—	£750
	No. 10	—	£875
	No. 11	—	£550
	No. 12	—	£350
g.	Obliterated by town postmark (without Maltese Cross)		
	In black ....*from*	—	£1250
	In blue ....*from*	—	£2000
h.	Obliterated by 1844 type postmark		
	In black ....*from*	—	75·00
	In blue ....*from*	—	£650
	In red ....*from*	—	£12000
	In green ....*from*	—	£2500

1841 (Apr). *Trial printing (unissued) on Dickinson silk-thread paper. No wmk. Imperf.*

16	1	1d. red-brown (Plate 11)	£4000

Eight sheets were printed on this paper, six being gummed, two ungummed, but we have only seen examples without gum.

1848. Wmk Small Crown, W **2**. *Rouletted approx 11½ by Henry Archer.*

16a	1	1d. red-brown (Plates 70, 71)	£8500

1850. Wmk Small Crown, W **2**. P 16 by Henry Archer.

			Un	Used	Used on Cover
16b	1	1d. red-brown (Alph 1) (from Plates 90-101) ......*from*	£1500	£475	£1000

Stamps on cover dated prior to February 1854 are worth a premium of 50% over the price on cover quoted above.

1853. *Government Trial Perforation.* Wmk Small Crown. W **2**.

			Un	Used
16c	1	1d. red-brown (P 16) (Alph II) (on cover)	†	£12000

SEPARATION TRIALS. Although the various trials of machines for rouletting and perforating were unofficial, Archer had the consent of the authorities in making his experiments, and sheets so experimented upon were afterwards used by the Post Office.

As Archer ended his experiments in 1850 and plates with corner letters Alphabet II did not come into issue until 1852, perforated stamps with corner letters of Alphabet I may safely be assumed to be Archer productions, if genuine.

The Government trial perforation is believed to have been done on Archer's machines after they had been purchased in 1853. As Alphabet II was by that time in use, the trials can only be distinguished from the perforated stamps listed below by being dated prior to 24 February 1854, the date when the perforated stamps were officially issued.

Die I Alphabet I, stamps from plates 74 and 113 perforated 14 have been recorded for many years, but it is now generally recognised that the type of comb machine used, producing one extension hole in the side margins, cannot be contemporary with other trials of this period.

Die I   Die II   Large Crown

Die I: The features of the portrait are lightly shaded and consequently lack emphasis.

Die II (Die I retouched): The lines of the features have been deepened and appear stronger.

The eye is deeply shaded and made more lifelike. The nostril and lips are more clearly defined, the latter appearing much thicker. A strong downward stroke of colour marks the corner of the mouth. There is a deep indentation of colour between lower lip and chin. The band running from the back of the ear to the chignon has a bolder horizontal line below it than in Die I.

The original die (Die I) was used to provide roller dies for the laying down of all the line-engraved stamps from 1840 to 1855. In that year a new master die was laid down (by means of a Die I roller die) and the impression was retouched by hand engraving by William Humphrys. This retouched die, always known to philatelists as Die II, was from that time used for preparing all new roller dies.

One Penny. The numbering of the 1d. plates recommenced at 1 on the introduction of Die II. Plates 1 to 21 were Alphabet II from which a scarce plum shade exists. Corner letters of Alphabet III appear on Plate 22 and onwards.

As an experiment, the corner letters were engraved by hand on Plates 50 and 51 in 1856, instead of being punched (Alphabet IV), but punching was again resorted to from Plate 52 onwards. Plates 50 and 51 were not put into use until 1861.

Two Pence. Unlike the 1d. the old sequence of plate numbers continued. Plates 3 and 4 of the 2d. had corner letters of Alphabet I, Plate 5 Alphabet II and Plate 6 Alphabet III. In Plate 6 the white lines are thinner than before.

1854–57. *Paper more or less blued.*

(a) Wmk Small Crown, W **2**. P 16.

			Un	Used*	Used on Cover
17	1	1d. red-brown (Die I) (24.2.54)....	£275	20·00	40·00
		a. Imperf three sides (horiz pair)	†		
18		1d. yellow brown (Die I)	£325	40·00	
19	3	2d. deep blue (Plate 4) (12.3.54)..	£2750	85·00	£130
		a. Imperf three sides (horiz pair)	†		
20		2d. pale blue (Plate 4)	£2750	90·00	
20a		2d. blue (Plate 5) (18.8.55)..........	£5000	£275	£425
21	1	1d. red-brown (Die II) (22.2.55)....	£300	50·00	90·00
		a. Imperf			

(b) Wmk Small Crown, W **2**. P 14.

22	1	1d. red-brown (Die I) (1.55)	£500	70·00	£125
23	3	2d. blue (Plate 4) (22.2.55)...........	£5000	£200	£300
23a		2d. blue (Plate 5) (4.7.55)............	£6000	£275	£400
		b. Imperf (Plate 5)			
24	1	1d. red-brown (Die II) (27.2.55).....	£450	45·00	75·00
24a		1d. deep red-brown (very blue paper) (Die II).......................	£525	70·00	
25		1d. orange-brown (Die II)............	£1400	£140	

(c) Wmk Large Crown, W **4**. P 16.

26	1	1d. red-brown (Die II) (15.5.55)...	£800	80·00	£180
		a. Imperf (Plate 7)			
27	3	2d. blue (Plate 5) (20.7.55)	£6500	£350	£450
		a. Imperf	—	£5500	

(d) Wmk Large Crown, W **4**. P 14.

29	1	1d. red-brown (Die II) (6.55).........	£200	15·00	30·00
		a. Imperf (*shades*) (Plates 22, 24, 25, 32, 43)........................	£2250	£2200	
30		1d. brick-red (Die II)	£275	35·00	
31		1d. plum (Die II) (2.56).................	£1800	£500	
32		1d. brown-rose (Die II)	£275	35·00	
33		1d. orange-brown (Die II) (3.57)..	£425	40·00	
34	3	2d. blue (Plate 5) (20.7.55)	£1900	50·00	£130
35		2d. blue (Plate 6) (2.7.57)............	£2200	50·00	£130
		a. Imperf	—	£5500	
		b. Imperf horiz (vert pair)...........	†	—	

*17/35a For well-centred, lightly used +125%.

1856–58. Wmk Large Crown, W **4**. Paper no longer blued.

(a) P 16.

36	1	1d. rose-red (Die II) (26.12.57)....	£1500	60·00	£130
36a	3	2d. blue (Plate 6) (1.2.58)............	£6750	£325	£450

(b) Die II. P 14.

37	1	1d. red-brown (11.56)..................	£800	£225	£500
38		1d. pale red (9.4.57)....................	75·00	15·00	
		a. Imperf	£1800	£1500	
39		1d. pale rose (3.57)	75·00	25·00	
40		1d. rose-red (9.57)......................	40·00	9·00	20·00
		a. Imperf	£1800	£1500	
		b. Imperf vert (horiz pair)	†	—	
41		1d. deep rose-red (7.57)..............	90·00	12·00	

1861. *Letters engraved on plate instead of punched (Alphabet IV).*

42	1	1d. rose-red (Die II) (Plates 50 and 51).......................................	£200	30·00	50·00
		a. Imperf...................................	—	£3250	

*36/42a For well-centred, lightly used +125%.

In both values, varieties may be found as described in the preceding issues—ivory heads, inverted watermarks, re-entries, and double letters in corners.

The change of perforation from 16 to 14 was decided upon late in 1854 since the closer holes of the former gauge tended to cause the sheets of stamps to break up when handled, but for a time both gauges were in concurrent use. Owing to faulty alignment of the impressions on the plates and to shrinkage of the paper when damped, badly perforated stamps are plentiful in the line-engraved issues.

5   **6**   Showing position of the plate number on the 1d. and 2d. values. (Plate 170 shown)

1858–79. *Letters in all four corners. Wmk Large Crown, W **4**. Die II (1d. and 2d.). P 14.*

43	5	1d. rose-red (1.4.64)...................	15·00	2·00	6·00
44		1d. lake-red	15·00	2·00	
		a. Imperf from.............................	£5000	£2500	

*43/4a For well-centred, lightly used +125%.

Plate		Un	Used	Plate		Un	Used
71............		35·00	3·00	150............		15·00	2·00
72............		40·00	4·00	151............		60·00	9·00
73............		40·00	3·00	152............		60·00	5·50
74............		40·00	2·00	153............		£100	9·00
76............		35·00	3·00	154............		50·00	2·00
77............		—	£120000	155............		50·00	2·25
78............		90·00	2·00	156............		45·00	2·00
79............		30·00	2·00	157............		50·00	2·00
80............		45·00	2·00	158............		30·00	2·00
81............		45·00	2·20	159............		30·00	2·00
82............		90·00	4·00	160............		30·00	2·00
83............		£110	7·00	161............		60·00	7·00
84............		40·00	2·25	162............		50·00	7·00
85............		40·00	2·25	163............		50·00	3·00
86............		50·00	4·00	164............		50·00	3·00
87............		30·00	2·00	165............		45·00	2·00
88............		£130	8·00	166............		45·00	6·00
89............		40·00	2·00	167............		45·00	2·00
90............		40·00	2·00	168............		50·00	8·00
91............		55·00	6·00	169............		60·00	7·00
92............		35·00	2·00	170............		35·00	2·00
93............		50·00	2·00	171............		15·00	2·00
94............		45·00	5·00	172............		30·00	2·00
95............		40·00	2·00	173............		70·00	9·00
96............		45·00	2·00	174............		30·00	2·00
97............		40·00	3·50	175............		60·00	3·50
98............		50·00	6·00	176............		60·00	2·25
99............		55·00	5·00	177............		40·00	2·00
100............		60·00	2·25	178............		60·00	3·50
101............		60·00	9·00	179............		50·00	2·25
102............		45·00	2·00	180............		50·00	5·00
103............		50·00	3·50	181............		45·00	2·00
104............		75·00	5·00	182............		90·00	5·00
105............		90·00	7·00	183............		55·00	3·00
106............		55·00	2·00	184............		30·00	2·25
107............		60·00	7·00	185............		50·00	3·00
108............		80·00	2·25	186............		65·00	2·25
109............		85·00	3·50	187............		50·00	2·00
110............		60·00	9·00	188............		70·00	10·00
111............		50·00	2·25	189............		70·00	7·00
112............		70·00	2·25	190............		50·00	6·00
113............		50·00	12·00	191............		30·00	7·00
114............		£250	12·00	192............		30·00	2·00
115............		90·00	2·25	193............		30·00	2·00
116............		75·00	9·00	194............		50·00	8·00
117............		45·00	2·00	195............		50·00	8·00
118............		50·00	2·00	196............		50·00	5·00
119............		45·00	2·00	197............		55·00	9·00
120............		15·00	2·00	198............		40·00	6·00
121............		40·00	9·50	199............		55·00	6·00
122............		15·00	2·00	200............		60·00	2·00
123............		40·00	2·00	201............		50·00	2·00
124............		28·00	2·00	202............		60·00	8·00
125............		40·00	2·00	203............		30·00	16·00
127............		55·00	2·25	204............		55·00	2·25
129............		40·00	8·00	205............		55·00	3·00
130............		55·00	2·25	206............		55·00	9·00
131............		65·00	16·00	207............		60·00	9·00
132............		£130	22·00	208............		55·00	16·00
133............		£110	9·00	209............		50·00	9·00
134............		15·00	2·00	210............		65·00	12·00
135............		95·00	26·00	211............		70·00	20·00
136............		90·00	20·00	212............		60·00	11·00
137............		28·00	2·25	213............		60·00	11·00
138............		18·00	2·00	214............		60·00	18·00
139............		60·00	16·00	215............		65·00	18·00
140............		18·00	2·00	216............		70·00	18·00
141............		£110	9·00	217............		70·00	7·00
142............		70·00	24·00	218............		65·00	8·00
143............		60·00	15·00	219............		90·00	7·00
144............		95·00	20·00	220............		40·00	7·00
145............		30·00	2·25	221............		70·00	16·00
146............		40·00	6·00	222............		80·00	40·00
147............		50·00	3·00	223............		90·00	60·00
148............		40·00	3·00	224............		£125	50·00
149............		60·00	6·00	225............		£2200	£650

The following plate numbers are also known imperf and used (No. 44a); 72, 79, 80, 81, 82, 83, 84, 85, 86, 87, 88, 90, 91, 92, 93, 96, 97, 98, 100, 101, 102, 103, 104, 105, 107, 108, 109, 112, 113, 114, 116, 117, 120, 121, 122, 136, 137, 142, 146, 148, 158, 162, 164, 166, 171, 174, 191 and 202.

The numbering of this series of 1d. red plates follows after that of the previous 1d. stamp, last printed from Plate 68.

Plates 69, 70, 75, 126 and 128 were prepared for this issue but rejected owing to defects, and stamps from these plates do not exist, so that specimens which appear to be from these plates (like many of those which optimistic collectors believe to be from Plate 77) bear other plate numbers. Owing to faulty engraving or printing it is not always easy to identify the plate number. Plate 77 was also rejected but some stamps printed from it were used. One specimen is in the Tapling Collection and six or seven others are known. Plates 226 to 228 were made but not used.

Specimens from most of the plates are known with inverted watermark. The variety of watermark described in the General Notes to this section occurs on stamp M A (or M L) on plates up to about 96 (*Prices from £110 used*).

Re-entries in this issue are few, the best being on stamps M K and T K of Plate 71 and on S L and T L, Plate 83.

			Un	Used*	Used on Cover
45	6	2d. blue (thick lines) (7.58)............................	£300	10·00	35·00
		a. Imperf (Plate 9)..........	—	£5000	
		Plate			
		7.............................	£1200	45·00	
		8.............................	£1100	32·00	
		9.............................	£300	10·00	
		12............................	£1800	£120	
46		2d. blue (thin lines)	£325	20·00	50·00
47		2d. deep blue (thin lines)..	£325	20·00	
		a. Imperf (Plate 13)	£6000		
		Plate			
		13............................	£325	20·00	
		14............................	£425	25·00	
		15............................	£400	25·00	

*45/7 For well-centred, lightly used +125%.

Plates 10 and 11 of the 2d. were prepared but rejected. Plates 13 to 15 were laid down from a new roller impression on which the white lines were thinner.

There are some marked re-entries and repairs, particularly on Plates 7, 8, 9 and 12.

Stamps with inverted watermark may be found and also the T A (T L) and M A (M L) watermark varieties (see General Notes to this section).

Though the paper is normally white, some printings showed blueing and stamps showing the "ivory head" may therefore be found.

7   Showing the plate number (9)

9

1870 (1 Oct). Wmk W **9**, extending over three stamps. P 14.

48	7	½d. rose-red	90·00	15·00	55·00
49		½d. rose	90·00	15·00	
		a. Imperf (Plates 1, 4, 5, 6, 8, 14) from	£2750	£1800	
		Plate			
		1	£225	70·00	
		3	£150	35·00	
		4	£130	25·00	
		5	90·00	15·00	
		6	£100	15·00	
		8	£300	95·00	
		9	£4500	£700	
		10	£110	15·00	
		11	£100	15·00	
		12	£100	15·00	
		13	£100	15·00	
		14	£100	15·00	
		15	£150	35·00	
		19	£175	50·00	
		20	£250	70·00	

*49/9a For well-centred, lightly used +200%

The ½d. was printed in sheets of 480 (24 × 20) so that the check letters run from

AA   XT
to
AA   TX

Plates 2, 7, 16, 17 and 18 were not completed while Plates 21 and 22, though made, were not used.

Owing to the method of perforating, the outer side of stamps in either the A or X row (ie the left or right side of the sheet) is imperf.

Stamps may be found with watermark inverted or reversed, or without watermark, the latter due to misplacement of the paper when printing.

8   Position of plate Number

1870 (1 Oct). Wmk W **4**. P 14.

51	8	1½d. rose-red	£375	50·00	£200
52		1½d. lake-red	£375	50·00	
		a. Imperf (Plates 1 and 3) from	£4000	†	
		Plate			
		(1)	£550	70·00	
		3	£375	50·00	

Error of lettering. OP–PC for CP–PC (Plate 1).

53	8	1½d. rose-red	£12000	£1200

Prepared for use in 1860 but not issued; blued paper.

53a	8	1½d. rosy mauve (Plate 1)	£5000	
		b. Error of lettering, OP–PC for CP–PC	—	†

*51/3 For well-centred, lightly used +125%.

Owing to a proposed change in the postal rates, 1½d. stamps were first printed in 1860, in rosy mauve, No. 53a, but the change was not approved and the greater part of the stock was destroyed, although three or four postally used examples have been recorded.

In 1870 a 1½d. stamp was required and was issued in rose-red.

Plate 1 did not have the plate number in the design of the stamps, but on stamps from Plate 3 the number will be found in the frame as shown above.

Plate 2 was defective and was not used.

The error of lettering OP–PC on Plate 1 was apparently not noticed by the printers, and therefore not corrected.

EMBOSSED ISSUES

Volume 1 of the Stanley Gibbons *Great Britain Specialised Catalogue* gives further detailed information on the embossed issues.

PRICES. The prices quoted are for cut-square stamps with average to fine embossing. Stamps with exceptionally clear embossing are worth more.

---

10   11

12   13

Position of die number

(Primary die engraved at the Royal Mint by William Wyon. Stamps printed at Somerset House)

1847–54. Imperf. (*For paper and wmk see footnote.*)

			Un	Used	Used on Cover
54	10	1s. pale green (11.9.47)	£8250	£750	£1000
55		1s. green	£8250	£800	
56		1s. deep green	£9000	£800	
		Die 1 (1847)	£8250	£750	
		Die 2 (1854)	£9000	£825	
57	11	10d. brown (6.11.48)	£5500	£1000	£1900
		Die 1 (1848)	£6000	£1000	
		Die 2 (1850)	£5500	£1000	
		Die 3 1853	£5500	£1000	
		Die 4 (1854)	£6000	£1000	
		Die 5			
58	12	6d. mauve (1.3.54)	£6500	£800	
59		6d. dull lilac	£6500	£800	£1250
60		6d. purple	£6500	£800	
61		6d. violet	£9000	£2200	

The 1s. and 10d. are on "Dickinson" paper with "silk" threads (actually a pale blue twisted cotton yarn). The 6d. is on paper watermarked V R in single-lined letters, W **13**, which may be found in four ways—upright, inverted, upright reversed, and inverted reversed, upright reversed being the most common.

The die numbers are indicated on the base of the bust. Only Die 1 was used for the 6d. The 10d. is from Die 1 (W.W.1 on stamps), and Dies 2 to 5 (2 W.W., 3 W.W., 4 W.W. and 5 W.W.) but the number and letters on stamps from Die 1 are seldom clear and many specimens are known without any trace of them. Because of this the stamp we previously listed as "No die number" has been deleted. That they are from Die 1 is proved by the existence of blocks showing stamps with and without the die number. The 1s. is from Dies 1 and 2 (W.W.1, W.W.2).

The normal arrangement of the "silk" threads in the paper was in pairs running down each vertical row of the sheet, the space between the threads of each pair being approximately 5 mm and between pairs of threads 20 mm. Varieties due to misplacement of the paper in printing show a single thread on the first stamp from the sheet margin and two threads 20 mm apart on the other stamps of the row. Faulty manufacture is the cause of stamps with a single thread in the middle.

Through bad spacing of the impressions, which were handstruck, all values may be found with two impressions more or less overlapping. Owing to the small margin allowed for variation of spacing, specimens with good margins on all sides are not common.

Double impressions are known of all values.

Later printings of the 6d. had the gum tinted green to enable the printer to distinguish the gummed side of the paper.

SURFACE-PRINTED ISSUES

GENERAL NOTES

Volume 1 of the Stanley Gibbons *Great Britain Specialised Catalogue* gives further detailed information on the surface-printed issues.

"Abnormals". The majority of the great rarities in the surface-printed group of issues are the so-called "abnormals", whose existence is due to the practice of printing six sheets from every plate as soon as made, one of which was kept for record purposes at Somerset House, while the others were perforated and usually issued. If such plates were not used for general production or if, before they came into full use, a change of watermark or colour took place, the six sheets originally printed would differ from the main issue in plate, colour or watermark and, if issued, would be extremely rare.

The abnormal stamps of this class listed in this Catalogue and distinguished, where not priced, by an asterisk (*), are:

No.
78   3d. Plate 3 (with white dots)
152   4d. vermilion, Plate 16
153   4d. sage-green, Plate 17
109   6d. mauve, Plate 10
124/a   6d. pale chestnut & 6d. chestnut, Plate 12
145   6d. pale buff, Plate 13
88   9d. straw (hair lines)
98   9d. Plate 5 (see footnote to No. 98)
113   10d. Plate 2
91   1s. Plate 3 ("Plate 2")
148/50   1s. green, Plate 14
120   2s. blue, Plate 3

Those which may have been issued, but of which no specimens are known, are 2½d. Anchor, Plates 4 and 5; 3d. wmk Emblems, Plate 5; 3d. wmk Spray, Plate 21; 6d. grey, wmk Spray, Plate 18; 8d. orange, Plate 2; 1s. wmk Emblems, Plate 4; 5s. wmk Maltese Cross, Plate 4.

The 10d. Plate 1, wmk Emblems (No. 99), is sometimes reckoned among the abnormals, but was an error, due to the use of the wrong paper.

Corner Letters. With the exception of the 4d., 6d. and 1s. of 1855–57, the ½d., 1½d., 2d. and 5d. of 1880, the 1d. lilac of 1881 and the £5 (which had letters in lower corners only, and in the reverse order to the normal), all the surface-printed stamps issued prior to 1887 had letters in all four corners, as in the later line-engraved stamps. The arrangement is the same, the letters running in sequence right across and down the sheets, whether these were divided into ones or not. The corner letters existing naturally depend on the number of stamps in the sheet and their arrangement.

Imprimaturs and Imperforate Stamps. The Post Office retained in their records (now in the National Postal Museum) one imperforate sheet from each plate, known as the Imprimatur (or officially approved) sheet. Some stamps were removed from time to time for presentation purposes and have come on to the market, but these tmperforates are not listed as they were not issued. Full details can be found in Volume I of the *Great Britain Specialised Catalogue*.

However, other imperforate stamps are known to have been issued and these are listed where it has been possible to prove that they do not come from the Imprimatur sheets. It is therefore advisable to purchase these only when acccompanied by an Expert Committee certificate of genuineness.

Plate Numbers. All stamps from No. 75 to No. 163 bear in their designs either the plate number or, in one or two earlier instances, some other indication by which one plate can be distinguished from another. With the aid of these and of the corner letters it is thus possible to "reconstruct" a sheet of stamps from any plate of any issue or denomination.

Surface-printing. In this context the traditional designation "surface-printing" is synonymous with typo(graphy)—a philatelic term—or letterpress—the printers' term—as meaning printing from (the surface of) raised type. It is also called relief-printing, as the image is in relief (in French, *en épargne*), unwanted parts of the design having been cut away. Duplicate impressions can be electrotyped or stereotyped from an original die, the resulting *clichés* being locked together to form the printing plate.

Wing Margins. As the vertical gutters (spaces) between the panes, into which sheets of stamps of most values were divided until the introduction of the Imperial Crown watermark, were perforated through the centre with a single row of holes, instead of each vertical row of stamps on the inner side of the panes having its own line of perforation as is now usual, a proportion of the stamps in each sheet have what is called a "wing margin" about 5 mm wide on one or other side.

The stamps with "wing margins" are the watermark Emblems and Spray of Rose series (3d., 6d., 9d., 10d., 1s. and 2s.) with letters D, E, H or I in S.E. corner, and the watermark Garter series (4d. and 8d.) with letters F or G in S.E. corner. Knowledge of this lettering will enable collectors to guard against stamps with wing margin cut down and reperforated, but note that wing margin stamps of Nos. 62 to 73 are also to be found re-perforated.

PRINTERS. The issues of Queen Victoria, Nos. 62/214, were typo by Thomas De La Rue & Co.

PERFORATIONS. All the surface-printed issues of Queen Victoria are Perf 14, with the exception of Nos. 126/9.

KEY TO SURFACE-PRINTED ISSUES 1855–83

S.G. Nos.	Description	Watermark	Date of Issue
		NO CORNER LETTERS	
62	4d. carmine	Small Garter	31.7.55
63/5	4d. carmine	Medium Garter	25.2.56
66/a	4d. carmine	Large Garter	Jan 1857
69/70	6d. lilac	Emblems	21.10.56
71/3	1s. green	Emblems	1.11.56
		SMALL WHITE CORNER LETTERS	
75/7	3d. carmine	Emblems	1.5.62
78	3d. carmine (dots)	Emblems	Aug 1862
79/82	4d. red	Large Garter	15.1.62
83/5	6d. lilac	Emblems	1.12.62
86/8	9d. bistre	Emblems	15.1.62
89/91	1s. green	Emblems	1.12.62
		LARGE WHITE CORNER LETTERS	
92	3d. rose	Emblems	1.3.65
102/3	3d. rose	Spray	July 1867
93/4	4d. vermilion	Large Garter	4.7.65
96/7	6d. lilac	Emblems	7.3.65
104/7	6d. lilac	Spray	21.6.67
108/9	6d. lilac	Spray	8.3.69
122/4	6d. chestnut	Spray	12.4.72
125	6d. grey	Spray	24.4.73
98	9d. straw	Emblems	30.10.65
110/11	9d. straw	Spray	3.10.67
99	10d. brown	Emblems	11.11.67
112/14	10d. brown	Spray	1.7.67
101	1s. green	Emblems	19.1.65
115/17	1s. green	Spray	13.7.67
118/20b	2s. blue	Spray	1.7.67
121	2s. brown	Spray	27·2.80
126/7	5s. rose	Cross	1.7.67
128	10s. grey	Cross	26.9.78
129	£1 brown-lilac	Cross	26.9.78
130, 134	5s. rose	Anchor	25.11.82
131, 135	10s. grey-green	Anchor	Feb 1883
132, 136	£1 brown-lilac	Anchor	Dec 1882
133, 137	£5 orange	Anchor	21.3.82
		LARGE COLOURED CORNER LETTERS	
138/9	2½d. rosy mauve	Anchor	1.7.75
141	2½d. rosy mauve	Orb	1.5.76
142	2½d. blue	Orb	5·2.80
157	2½d. blue	Crown	23.3.81
143/4	3d. rose	Spray	5.7.73
158	3d. rose	Crown	Jan 1881
159	3d. on 3d. lilac	Crown	1.1.83
152	4d. vermilion	Large Garter	1.3.76

S.G. Nos.	Description	Watermark	Date of Issue
153	4d. sage-green	Large Garter	12.3.77
154	4d. brown	Large Garter	15.8.80
160	4d. brown	Crown	9.12.80
145	6d. buff	Spray	15.3.73
146/7	6d. grey	Spray	20.3.74
161	6d. grey	Crown	1.1.81
162	6d. on 6d. lilac	Crown	1.1.83
156a	8d. purple-brown	Large Garter	July 1876
156	8d. orange	Large Garter	11.9.76
148/50	1s. green	Spray	1.9.73
151	1s. brown	Spray	14.10.80
163	1s. brown	Crown	24.5.81

Watermarks:		
	Anchor	**W 40, 47**
	Cross	**W 39**
	Crown	**W 49**
	Emblems	**W 20**
	Large Garter	**W 17**
	Medium Garter	**W 16**
	Orb	**W 48**
	Small Garter	**W 15**
	Spray	**W 33**

14   15 Small Garter

16 Medium Garter   17 Large Garter

1855–57. *No corner letters.*

(a) Wmk Small Garter, W **15**. *Highly glazed, deeply blued paper* (31 July 1855).

62	14	4d. carmine (*shades*).........	£5000	£375	£650
		a. Paper slightly blued	£5250	£375	
		b. White paper.................		£750	

(b) Wmk Medium Garter, W **16**.

(i) Thick, blued highly glazed paper (25 February 1856).

63	14	4d. carmine (*shades*).........	£5750	£425	£650
		a. White paper.................	£4750		

(ii) Ordinary thin white paper (September 1856).

64	14	4d. pale carmine	£4500	£350	£550
		a. Stamp printed double..	†		

(iii) Ordinary white paper, specially prepared ink (1 November 1856).

65	14	4d. rose or deep rose	£4250	£350	£500

(c) Wmk Large Garter, W **17**. *Ordinary white paper* (January 1857).

66	14	4d. rose-carmine................	£1400	£100	£175
		a. *Rose*..........................	£1100	£100	
		b. Thick glazed paper.......	£3000	£275	

*62/6b For well-centred, lightly used +125%.

18   19   20 Emblems wmk (normal)

20a Wmk error, three roses and shamrock   20b Wmk error, three roses and thistle

(d) Wmk Emblems, W **20**.

69	18	6d. deep lilac (21.10.56)...	£1100	£120	
70		6d. pale lilac.....................	£900	95·00	£175
		a. Azure paper.................	£4500	£700	
		b. Thick paper.................	£2200	£275	
		c. Error. Wmk W **20a**			
71	19	1s. deep green (1.11.56)...	£2200	£375	
72		1s. green..........................	£1250	£260	£350
73		1s. pale green...................	£1250	£260	
		a. Azure paper.................	—	£1500	
		b. Thick paper.................		£300	
		c. Imperf.........................	†	—	

*69/73b For well-centred, lightly used +125%.

21   22

23   24   25 Plate 2

A. White dots added

B. Hair lines

1862–64. *A small uncoloured letter in each corner, the 4d. wmk Large Garter,* W **17**, *the others Emblems,* W **20**.

75	21	3d. deep carmine-rose (Plate 2) (1.5.62)........	£3250	£400	
76		3d. bright carmine-rose.....	£1500	£250	£450
77		3d. pale carmine-rose........	£1500	£250	
		b. Thick paper..................	—	£350	
78		3d. rose (with white dots, Type A, Plate 3) (8.62)	£20000	£8000	
		a. Imperf (Plate 3)...........	£4000		
79	22	4d. bright red (Plate 3) (15.1.62)..................	£1350	£110	
80		4d. pale red......................	£1100	90·00	£200
81		4d. bright red (Hair lines, Type B, Plate 4) (16.10.63)..................	£1500	£110	
82		4d. pale red (Hair lines, Type B, Plate 4)........	£1350	90·00	£200
		a. Imperf (Plate 4)...........	£3000		
83	23	6d. deep lilac (Plate 3) (1.12.62)...................	£1450	£110	
84		6d. lilac...........................	£1400	90·00	£170
		a. Azure paper.................	—	£900	
		b. Thick paper.................	—	£225	
		c. Error. Shamrock missing from wmk (stamp TF)..............			
		d. Error. Wmk W **20b** (stamp TF)...............	—	£6000	
85		6d. lilac (Hair lines, Plate 4) (20.4.64)..............	£1800	£180	£275
		a. Imperf........................	£3000		
		c. Thick paper.................	£2200	£225	
		d. Error. Wmk W **20b** (stamp TF)...............			
86	24	9d. bistre (Plate 2) (15.1.62)...................	£3250	£400	£575
87		9d. straw.........................	£2750	£350	
		a. On azure paper............			
		b. Thick paper.................	£3500	£425	
		c. Error. Watermark W **20b** (stamp TF).....	†	—	
88		9d. bistre (Hair lines, Plate 3) (5.62).................	£13500	£7500	
89	25	1s. deep green (Plate No. 1 = Plate 2) (1.12.62)...................	£2500	£350	
90		1s. green (Plate No. 1 = Plate 2)....................	£1700	£175	£275
		a. "K" in lower left corner in white circle (stamp KD).............	£5500	£950	
		aa. "K" normal (stamp KD).............................	—	£1250	
		b. On azure paper............			
		c. Error. Wmk **20b** (stamp TF)...............			
		d. Thick paper.................		£275	
		da. Thick paper, "K" in circle as No. 90a........	—	£2100	
91		1s. deep green (Plate No. 2 = Plate 3).........	£20000		
		a. Imperf........................		£3800	

*75/91 For well-centred, lightly used +125%.

The 3d. as Type **21**, but with network background in the spandrels which is found overprinted SPECIMEN, was never issued.

The plates of this issue may be distinguished as follows:

3d.   Plate 2.   No white dots.
      Plate 3.   White dots as Illustration A.
4d.   Plate 3.   No hair lines. Roman I next to lower corner letters.
      Plate 4.   Hair lines in corners. (Illustration B). Roman II.
6d.   Plate 3.   No hair lines.
      Plate 4.   Hair lines in corners.
9d.   Plate 2.   No hair lines.
      Plate 3.   Hair lines in corners. Beware of faked lines.
1s.   Plate 2.   Numbered 1 on stamps.
      Plate 3.   Numbered 2 on stamps and with hair lines.

The 9d. on azure paper (No. 87a) is very rare, only one confirmed example being known.

The variety "K" in circle, No. 90a, is believed to be due to a damaged letter having been cut out and replaced. It is probable that the punch was driven in too deeply, causing the flange to penetrate the surface, producing an indentation showing as an uncoloured circle.

The watermark variety "three roses and a shamrock" illustrated in W **20a** was evidently due to the substitution of an extra rose for the thistle in a faulty watermark bit. It is found on stamp TA of Plate 4 of

the 3d., Plates 1 (No. 70c), 3, 5 and 6 of the 6d., Plate 4 of the 9d. and Plate 4 of the 1s.

Similar problems occurred on stamp TF of the 6d. and 9d. Here the shamrock emblem became detached and a used example of the 6d. (No. 84) is known showing it omitted. It was replaced by a third rose (W **20b**) and this variety exists on the 6d. (Nos. 84/5 and 97) and 9d. (Nos. 87 and 98).

26   27

28 (with hyphen)   28a (without hyphen)

29   30   31

1865–67. *Large uncoloured corner letters. Wmk Large Garter (4d.); others Emblems.*

92	26	3d. rose (Plate 4) (1.3.65).	£1350	£180	£275
		a. Error. Wmk W **20a**	£2750	£900	
		b. Thick paper.................	£1350	£200	
93	27	4d. dull vermilion (4.7.65)	£525	85·00	
94		4d. vermilion....................	£450	55·00	£125
		a. Imperf (Plates 11, 12).	£1750		
		Plate			
		7 (1865).....................	£550	£100	
		8 (1866).....................	£500	60·00	
		9 (1867).....................	£500	60·00	
		10 (1868).....................	£550	£110	
		11 (1869).....................	£500	60·00	
		12 (1870).....................	£475	55·00	
		13 (1872).....................	£500	55·00	
		14 (1873).....................	£550	85·00	
96	28	6d. deep lilac (with hyphen) (7.3.65).......	£1100	£130	
97		6d. lilac (with hyphen).....	£725	80·00	£120
		a. Thick paper.................	£825	£110	
		b. Stamp doubly printed (Pl 6)........................	—	£12000	
		c. Error. Wmk W **20a** (Pl 5, 6).................. *from*	—	£750	
		d. Error. Wmk W **20b** (Plate 5)...................			
		Plate			
		5 (1865).....................	£725	80·00	
		6 (1867).....................	£2200	£150	
98	29	9d. straw (Plate 4) (30.10.65).................	£2200	£500	£800
		a. Thick paper.................	£2500	£625	
		b. Error. Wmk W **20a**	—	£1200	
		c. Error. Wmk W **20b** (stamp TF)...............			
99	30	10d. red-brown (Pl 1) (11.11.67).................	*	£25000	
101	31	1s. green (Plate 4) (19.1.65)..................	£1450	£170	£250
		a. Error. Wmk W**20a**	—	£1100	
		b. Thick paper.................	£1600	£250	
		c. Imperf between (vert pair)........................	—	£9000	

*92/101c For well-centred, lightly used +100%.

From mid-1866 to about the end of 1871 4d. stamps of this issue appeared generally with watermark inverted.

Unused examples of No. 98 from Plate 5 exist, but this was never put to press and all evidence points to such stamps originating from a portion of the Imprimatur sheet which was perforated by De La Rue in 1887 for insertion in albums to be presented to members of the Stamp Committee (*Price* £18000 *un*).

The 10d. stamps, No. 99, were printed in *error* on paper watermarked "Emblems" instead of on "Spray of Rose".

32   33 Spray of Rose   34

1867–80. *Wmk Spray of Rose,* W **33**.

102	26	3d. deep rose (12.7.67)	£800	85·00	
103		3d. rose............................	£450	55·00	90·00
		a. Imperf (Plates 5, 6, 8) *from*	£2750		
		Plate			
		4 (1867).....................	£825	£190	
		5 (1868).....................	£450	55·00	
		6 (1870).....................	£475	55·00	
		7 (1871).....................	£550	60·00	
		8 (1872).....................	£525	55·00	
		9 (1872).....................	£525	60·00	
		10 (1873).....................	£650	£110	
104	28	6d. lilac (with hyphen) (Plate 6) (21.6.67)............	£1100	80·00	£160
		a. Imperf.........................			
105		6d. deep lilac (with hyphen) (Plate 6)...................	£1100	80·00	

			Un	Used	
106		6d. purple (with hyphen) (Pl 6)	£1100	£110	
107		6d. right violet (with hyphen) (Plate 6) (22.7.68)	£950	90·00	
108	28a	6d. dull violet (without hyphen) (8.3.69)	£550	80·00	
109		6d. mauve (without hyphen)	£500	80·00	£120
		a. Imperf (Plate Nos. 8 and 9)	£4750	£3250	
		Plate			
		8 (1869, mauve)	£500	£110	
		9 (1870, mauve)	£500	80·00	
		10 (1869, mauve)	*	£22000	
110	29	9d. straw (Plate No. 4) (3.10.67)	£1700	£275	£425
111		9d. pale straw (Plate No. 4)	£1600	£250	
		a. Imperf (Plate 4)	£5000		
112	30	10d. red-brown (1.7.67)	£2300	£300	£700
113		10d. pale red-brown	£2300	£325	
114		10d. deep red-brown	£3250	£475	
		a. Imperf (Plate 1)	£5000		
		Plate			
		1 (1867)	£2300	£300	
		2 (1867)	£22000	£8500	
115	31	1s. deep green (13.7.67)	£725	38·00	
117		1s. green	£650	35·00	55·00
		a. Imperf between (horiz pair) (Plate 7)			
		b. Imperf (Plate 4)	£3250	£1800	
		Plate			
		4 (1867)	£825	50·00	
		5 (1871)	£650	35·00	
		6 (1871)	£1000	35·00	
		7 (1873)	£1000	60·00	
118	32	2s. dull blue (1.7.67)	£2200	£175	£675
119		2s. deep blue	£2750	£175	
		a. Imperf (Plate 1)	£7000		
120		2s. pale blue	£2750	£200	
		aa. Imperf (Plate 1)	£7000		
120a		2s. cobalt	£11000	£2200	
120b		2s. milky blue	£9250	£1400	
		Plate			
		1 (1867)	£2200	£175	
		3 (1868)	*	£7000	
121		2s. brown (Plate No. 1) (27.2.80)	£15000	£28000	
		a. Imperf	£15000		
		b. No watermark	†	—	

*102/21 **For well-centred, lightly used +75%.**

Examples of the 1s. from Plates 5 and 6 *without* watermark are postal forgeries used at the Stock Exchange Post Office in the early 1870's.

1872–73. *Uncoloured letters in corners.* Wmk Spray, W 33.

122	34	6d. deep chestnut (Plate II) (12.4.72)	£875	90·00	
122a		6d. chestnut (Plate II) (22.5.72)	£650	50·00	90·00
122b		6d. pale chestnut (Plate II) (1872)	£550	50·00	
123		6d. pale buff (19.10.72)	£600	85·00	£200
		Plate			
		11 (1872, pale buff)	£600	85·00	
		12 (1872, pale buff)	£2000	£250	
124		6d. chestnut (Plate 12) (1872)	*	£2750	
124a		6d. pale chestnut (Plate 12) (1872)	*	£2750	
125		6d. grey (Plate 12) (24.4.73)	£1400	£200	£250
		a. Imperf	£3800		

*122/5 **For well-centred, lightly used +50%.**

35.   **36.**

37

38

39 Maltese Cross   **40** Large Anchor

1867–83. *Uncoloured letters in corners.*
(a) Wmk Maltese Cross, W 39. P 15½ × 15.

			Un	Used
126	35	5s. rose (1.7.67)	£5000	£600
127		5s. pale rose	£5000	£600
		a. Imperf (Plate 1)	£10000	
		Plate		
		1 (1867)	£5000	£600
		2 (1874)	£7500	£950
128	36	10s. greenish grey (Plate 1) (26.9.78)	£38000	£2500
129	37	£1 brown-lilac (Plate 1) (26.9.78)	£50000	£3750

(b) Wmk Anchor, W 40. P 14.
(i) Blued paper.

130	35	5s. rose (Plate 4) (25.11.82)	£18000	£3750
131	36	10s. grey-green (Plate 1) (2.83)	£60000	£4500
132	37	£1 brown-lilac (Plate 1) (12.82)	£80000	£8000
133	38	£5 orange (Plate 1) (21.3.82)	£40000	£11000

(ii) White paper.

134	35	5s. rose (Plate 4)	£14000	£2700
135	36	10s. greenish grey (Plate 1)	£60000	£3500
136	37	£1 brown-lilac (Plate 1)	£85000	£7000
137	38	£5 orange (Plate 1)	£9000	£4000

*126/37 **For well-centred, lightly used +75%.**

41   **42**   **43**
44   **45**   **46**

47 Small Anchor   **48** Orb

1873–80. *Large coloured letters in the corners.*
(a) Wmk Anchor, W 47.

			Un	Used*	Used on Cover
138	41	2½d. rosy mauve (*blued paper*) (1.7.75)	£700	£120	
		a. Imperf			
		Plate			
		1 (*blued paper*) (1875)	£700	£120	
		2 (*blued paper*) (1875)	£5500	£1250	
		3 (*blued paper*) (1875)	—	£4250	
139		2½d. rosy mauve (*white paper*)	£500	80·00	£140
		Plate			
		1 (*white paper*) (1875)	£500	80·00	
		2 (*white paper*) (1875)	£500	80·00	
		3 (*white paper*) (1875)	£775	£120	

Error of Lettering L H—F L for L H—H L (Plate 2).

140	41	2½d. rosy mauve	£14000	£1900

(b) Wmk Orb, W 48.

141	41	2½d. rosy mauve (1.5.76)	£425	50·00	80·00
		Plate			
		3 (1876)	£925	£100	
		4 (1876)	£425	50·00	
		5 (1876)	£425	50·00	
		6 (1876)	£425	50·00	
		7 (1877)	£425	50·00	
		8 (1877)	£425	50·00	
		9 (1877)	£425	50·00	
		10 (1878)	£475	65·00	
		11 (1878)	£425	50·00	
		12 (1878)	£425	50·00	
		13 (1878)	£425	50·00	
		14 (1879)	£425	50·00	
		15 (1879)	£425	50·00	
		16 (1879)	£425	50·00	
		17 (1880)	£1250	£240	
142		2½d. blue (5.2.80)	£375	40·00	75·00
		Plate			
		17 (1880)	£375	55·00	
		18 (1880)	£400	40·00	
		19 (1880)	£375	40·00	
		20 (1880)	£375	40·00	

(c) Wmk Spray, W 33.

143	42	3d. rose (5.7.73)	£350	45·00	60·00
144		3d. pale rose	£400	45·00	
		Plate			
		11 (1873)	£350	45·00	
		12 (1873)	£400	45·00	
		14 (1874)	£425	45·00	
		15 (1874)	£350	45·00	
		16 (1875)	£350	45·00	
		17 (1875)	£400	45·00	
		18 (1875)	£400	45·00	
		19 (1876)	£350	45·00	
		20 (1879)	£480	85·00	
145	43	6d. pale buff (Plate 13) (15.3.73)	*	£15000	

			Un	Used	Cover
146		6d. deep grey (20.3.74)	£400	60·00	£100
147		6d. grey	£400	60·00	
		Plate			
		13 (1874)	£400	60·00	
		14 (1875)	£400	60·00	
		15 (1876)	£400	60·00	
		16 (1878)	£400	60·00	
		17 (1880)	£675	£140	
148	44	1s. deep green (1.9.73)	£650	£120	
150		1s. green	£500	£100	£170
		Plate			
		8 (1873)	£575	£120	
		9 (1874)	£575	£120	
		10 (1874)	£575	£120	
		11 (1875)	£575	£120	
		12 (1875)	£500	£100	
		13 (1876)	£500	£100	
		14 (—)	*	£22000	
151		1s. orange-brown (Plate 13) (14.10.80)	£3250	£575	£1100

(d) Wmk Large Garter, W 17.

152	45	4d. vermilion (1.3.76)	£1750	£425	£850
		Plate			
		15 (1876)	£1750	£425	
		16 (1877)	*	£22000	
153		4d. sage-green (12.3.77)	£900	£250	£450
		Plate			
		15 (1877)	£1000	£275	
		16 (1877)	£900	£250	
		17 (1877)	*	£15000	
154		4d. grey-brown (Plate 17) (15.8.80)	£1500	£450	£1100
		a. Imperf	£7000		
156	46	8d. orange (Plate 1) (11.9.76)	£1100	£300	£450

*138/56 **For well-centred, lightly used +100%.**

1876 (July). *Prepared for use but not issued.*

156a	46	8d. purple-brown (Plate 1)	£6000	

49 Imperial Crown   **(50)**   **3ᵈ**

1880–83. Wmk Imperial Crown. W 49.

157	41	2½d. blue (23.3.81)	£350	28·00	45·00
		21 (1881)	£350	35·00	
		22 (1881)	£350	35·00	
		23 (1881)	£350	28·00	
158	42	3d. rose (1.3.81)	£400	80·00	£140
		Plate			
		20 (1881)	£550	£130	
		21 (1881)	£400	80·00	
159	50	3d. on lilac (C.) (Plate 21) 3d. (1.1.83)	£450	£130	£350
160	45	4d. grey-brown (8.12.80)	£350	60·00	£140
		Plate			
		17 (1880)	£350	60·00	
		18 (1882)	£350	60·00	
161	43	6d. grey (1.1.81)	£350	65·00	£120
		Plate			
		17 (1880)	£400	65·00	
		18 (1882)	£350	65·00	
162	50	6d. on lilac (C.) (Plate 18) 6d. (1.1.83)	£500	£130	£350
		a. Slanting dots (various) *from*	£950	£350	
		b. Opt double	—	£9000	
163	44	1s. orange-brown (24.5.81)	£500	£140	£450
		Plate			
		13 (1881)	£625	£140	
		14 (1881)	£500	£140	

*157/63 **For well-centred, lightly used +75%.**

The 1s. Plate 14 (line perf 14) exists in purple, but was not issued in this shade (*Price £7000 unused*). Examples were included in a few of the Souvenir Albums prepared for members of the "Stamp Committee of 1884".

52   **53**
54   **55**   **56**

1880–81. Wmk Imperial Crown. W 49.

164	52	½d. deep green (14.10.80)	45·00	10·00	20·00
		a. Imperf	£1800		
		b. No watermark	£5500		
165		½d. pale green	45·00	15·00	
166	53	1d. Venetian red (1.1.80)	22·00	10·00	18·00
		a. Imperf	£1800		
167	54	1½d. Venetian red (14.10.80)	£175	45·00	£130
168	55	2d. pale rose (8.12.80)	£225	90·00	£225
168a		2d. deep rose	£250	90·00	
169	56	5d. indigo (15.3.81)	£625	£110	£225
		a. Imperf	£3250	£2750	

*164/9 **For well-centred, lightly used +75%.**

Two used examples of the 1d. value have been reported on the Orb (fiscal) watermark.

Die I   57   Die II

1881. Wmk Imperial Crown. W **49.**

(a) 14 dots in each corner, Die I (12 July).

| 170 | 57 | 1d. lilac | £200 | 30·00 | 50·00 |
| 171 | | 1d. pale lilac | £200 | 30·00 | |

(b) 16 dots in each corner, Die II (13 December).

172	57	1d. lilac	2·50	2·00	3·00
172a		1d. bluish lilac	£375	£125	
173		1d. deep purple	2·50	2·00	
		a. Printed both sides	£750	†	
		b. Frame broken at bottom	£800	£300	
		c. Printed on gummed side	£700	†	
		d. Imperf three sides (pair)	£5000	†	
		e. Printed both sides but impression on back inverted	£800	†	
		f. No watermark	£3250	†	
		g. Blued paper	£4000		
174		1d. mauve	2·50	1·50	
		a. Imperf (pair)	£2750		

*170/4 **For well-centred, lightly used +50%.**

1d. stamps with the words "PEARS SOAP" printed on the back in *orange*, *blue* or *mauve* price *from* £500, *unused*.

The variety "frame broken at bottom" (No. 173b) shows a white space just inside the bottom frame-line from between the "N" and "E" of "ONE" to below the first "N" of "PENNY", breaking the pearls and cutting into the lower part of the oval below "PEN".

KEY TO SURFACE-PRINTED ISSUES 1880–1900

S.G. Nos.	Description	Date of Issue
164/5	½d. green	14.10.80
187	½d. slate-blue	1.4.84
197/e	½d. vermilion	1.1.87
213	½d. blue-green	17.4.1900
166	1d. Venetian red	1.1.80
170/1	1d. lilac, Die I	12.7.81
172/4	1d. lilac, Die II	12.12.81
167	1½d. Venetian red	14.10.80
188	1½d. lilac	1.4.84
198	1½d. purple & green	1.1.87
168/a	2d. rose	8.12.80
189	2d. lilac	1.4.84
199/200	2d. green & red	1.1.87
190	2½d. lilac	1.4.84
201	2½d. purple on blue paper	1.1.87
191	3d. lilac	1.4.84
202/4	3d. purple on yellow paper	1.1.87
192	4d. dull green	1.4.84
205/a	4d. green & brown	1.1.87
206	4½d. green and carmine	15.9.92
169	5d. indigo	15.3.81
193	5d. dull green	1.4.84
207	5d. purple & blue, Die I	1.1.87
207a	5d. purple & blue, Die II	1888
194	6d. dull green	1.4.84
208/a	6d. purple on rose-red paper	1.1.87
195	9d. dull green	1.8.83
209	9d. purple & blue	1.1.87
210/b	10d. purple & carmine	24.2.90
196	1s. dull green	1.4.84
211	1s. green	1.1.87
214	1s. green & carmine	11.7.1900
175	2s.6d.lilac on blued paper	2.7.83
178/9	2s.6d. lilac	1884
176	5s. rose on blued paper	1.4.84
180/1	5s. rose	1884
177/a	10s. ultramarine on blued paper	1.4.84
182/3a	10s. ultramarine	1884
185	£1 brown-lilac, wmk Crowns	1.4.84
186	£1 brown-lilac, wmk Orbs	6.1.88
212	£1 green	28.1.91

Note that the £5 value used with the above series is listed as Nos. 133 and 137.

58   59

60

1883–84. *Coloured letters in the corners.* Wmk Anchor, W **40.**

(a) Blued paper.

			Un	Used
175	58	2s.6d. lilac (2.7.83)	£4000	£1200
176	59	5s. rose (1.4.84)	£10000	£3500
177	60	10s. ultramarine (1.4.84)	£32000	£7500
177a		10s. cobalt (5.84)	£38000	£11000

(b) White paper.

178	58	2s.6d. lilac	£450	£140
179		2s.6d. deep lilac	£550	£175
		a. Error. On blued paper	£6000	£2500
180	59	5s. rose	£875	£200
181		5s. crimson	£775	£200
182	60	10s. cobalt	£25000	£6500
183		10s. ultramarine	£1700	£475
183a		10s. pale ultramarine	£1900	£475

*175/83a **For well-centred, lightly used +50%.**

For No. 180 perf 12 *see* second note below No. 196.

61

Broken frames, Plate 2

1884 (1 April). Wmk Three Imperial Crowns, W **49.**

| 185 | 61 | £1 brown-lilac | £22000 | £2200 |
| | | a. Frame broken | £35000 | £3800 |

1888 (Jan). Wmk Three Orbs, W **48.**

| 186 | 61 | £1 brown-lilac | £50000 | £3500 |
| | | a. Frame broken | £60000 | £6000 |

*185/6a **For well-centred, lightly used +50%.**

The December 1887 printing of the £1 brown-lilac was produced on paper watermarked Three Orbs in error. The decision was taken to issue date stamps for normal postal use and the earliest recorded postmark is 6 January 1888 at Leadenhall Street, London EC.

The broken-frame varieties, Nos. 185a and 186a, are on Plate 2 stamps JC and TA, as illustrated. *See also* No. 212a.

62   63   64

65   66

1883 (1 Aug.). *(9d.) or* **1884** (1 April) *(others).* Wmk Imperial Crown, W **49** (sideways on horiz designs).

			Un	Used	Used on Cover
187	52	½d. slate-blue	20·00	7·00	12·00
		a. Imperf	£2000		
188	62	1½d. lilac	95·00	38·00	£100
		a. Imperf	£2000		
189	63	2d. lilac	£175	70·00	£110
		a. Imperf	£2200		
190	64	2½d. lilac	75·00	12·00	25·00
		a. Imperf	£2200		
191	65	3d. lilac	£190	85·00	£125
		a. Imperf	£2200		
192	66	4d. dull green	£425	£175	£250
		a. Imperf	£2500		
193	62	5d. dull green	£425	£175	£250
		a. Imperf	£2700		
194	63	6d. dull green	£450	£200	£275
		a. Imperf	£2700		
195	64	9d. dull green (1.8.83)	£875	£375	£1800
		a. Imperf	£2200		
196	65	1s. dull green	£950	£200	£475
		a. Imperf	£4250		

*187/96 **For well-centred, lightly used +100%.**

The above prices are for stamps in the true dull green colour. Stamps which have been soaked, causing the colour to run, are virtually worthless.

Stamps of the above set and No. 180 are also found perf 12; these are official perforations, but were never issued. A second variety of the 5d. is known with a line instead of a stop under the "d" in the value; this was never issued and is therefore only known *unused* (Price £12000).

71   72   73

74   75   76

77   78   79

80   81   82

Die I   Die II

Die I: Square dots to right of "d".
Die II: Thin vertical lines to right of "d".

1887 (1 Jan)–**92.** *"Jubilee" issue. New types. The bicoloured stamps have the value tablets, or the frames including the value tablets, in the second colour.* Wmk Imperial Crown, W **49** (Three Crowns on £1).

197	71	½d. vermilion	1·50	1·00	6·00
		a. Printed on gummed side	£1400		†
		b. Printed both sides	£12000		
		c. Doubly printed	£12000		
		d. Imperf	£2200		
197e		½d. orange-vermilion	1·50	1·00	
198	72	1½d. dull purple and pale green	15·00	7·00	22·00
		a. Purple part of design double	—	£6500	
199	73	2d. green and scarlet	£350	£225	
200		2d. grey-green and carmine	8·00	12·00	24·00
201	74	2½d. purple/*blue*	22·00	3·00	6·00
		a. Printed on gummed side	£4500		
		b. Imperf three sides	£3500		
		c. Imperf	£4000		
202	75	3d. purple/*yellow*	22·00	3·25	30·00
		a. Imperf	£5500		
203		3d. deep purple/*yellow*	22·00	3·25	
204		3d. purple/*orange* (1890)	£500		
205	76	4d. green and purple-brown	30·00	13·00	35·00
		aa. Imperf	£6000		
205a		4d. green and deep brown	30·00	13·00	
206	77	4½d. green and carmine (15.9.92)	10·00	40·00	75·00
206a		4½d. green and deep bright carmine	£500	£400	
207	78	5d. dull purple and blue (Die I)	£500	85·00	£150
207a		5d. dull pur and blue (Die II) (1888)	35·00	11·00	40·00
208	79	6d. purple/*rose-red*	30·00	10·00	75·00
208a		6d. deep purple/*rose-red*	30·00	11·00	
209	80	9d. dull purple and blue	60·00	40·00	£200
210	81	10d. dull purple and carmine (*shades*) (24.2.90)	45·00	38·00	£225
		aa. Imperf	£6000		
210a		10d. dull purple and deep dull carm	£400	£200	
210b		10d. dull purple and scarlet	60·00	45·00	
211	82	1s. dull green	£200	60·00	£125
212	61	£1 green (28.1.91)	£3000	£650	
		a. Frame broken	£6000	£1750	

*197/212a **For well-centred, lightly used +50%.**

The broken-frame varieties, No. 212a, are on Plate 2 stamps JC or TA, as illustrated above No. 185.

½d. stamps with "PEARS SOAP" printed on the back in *orange*, *blue* or *mauve*, price *from* £475 each.

No used price is quoted for No. 204 as it is not possible to authenticate the paper colour on stamps in used condition.

1900. *Colours changed.* Wmk Imperial Crown, W **49.**

213	71	½d. blue-green (17.4.)	1·75	2·00	6·00
		a. Printed on gummed side	—		
		b. Imperf	£4000		
214	82	1s. green and carmine (11.7)	50·00	£125	£850
197/214		Set of 14	£500	£325	

*213/14 **For well-centred, lightly used +50%.**

The ½d., No. 213, in bright blue, is a colour changeling caused by a constituent of the ink used for some months in 1900.

KING EDWARD VII
22 January 1901–6 May 1910

PRINTINGS. Distinguishing De La Rue printings from the provisional printings of the same values made by Harrison & Sons Ltd. or at Somerset House may prove difficult in some cases. For very full guidance Volume 2 of the Stanley Gibbons *Great Britain Specialised Catalogue* should prove helpful.

Note that stamps perforated 15×14 must be Harrison; the 2½d., 3d. and 4d. in this perforation are useful reference material, their shades and appearance in most cases matching the Harrison perf 14 printings.

Except for the 6d. value, all stamps on chalk-surfaced paper were printed by De La Rue.

Of the stamps on ordinary paper, the De La Rue impressions are usually clearer and of a higher finish than those of the other printers. The shades are markedly different except in some printings of the 4d., 6d. and 7d. and in the 5s., 10s. and £1.

Used stamps in good, clean, unrubbed condition and with dated postmarks can form the basis of a useful reference collection, the dates often assisting in the assignment to the printers.

USED STAMPS. For well-centred, lightly used examples of King Edward VII stamps, add the following percentages to the used prices quoted below:

De La Rue printings (Nos. 215/66)—3d. values +35%, 4d. orange + 100%, 6d. +75%, 7d. and 1s. +25%, all other values + 50%.

Harrison printings (Nos. 267/86)—all values and perforations +75%.

Somerset House printings (Nos. 287/320)—1s. values +25%, all other values +50%.

83	84	85
86	87	88
89	90	91

92	93	94
95	96	

97

(Des E. Fuchs)

1902 (1 Jan)–**10.** *Printed by De La Rue & Co.* Wmk Imperial Crown (½d. to 1s.): Anchor (2s.6d. to 10s.); Three Crowns (£1). *Ordinary paper.* P 14.

215	83	½d. dull blue-green (1.1.02)	2·00	1·50	2·50
216		½d. blue-green	2·00	1·50	
217		½d. pale yellowish green (26.11.04)	2·00	1·50	2·50
218		½d. yellowish green	2·00	1·50	
		a. Booklet pane. Five stamps plus St. Andrew's Cross label (6.06)	£350		
		b. Doubly printed (bottom row on one pane) (Control H9)	£20000		
219		1d. scarlet (1.1.02)	2·00	1·50	2·50

220		1d. bright scarlet	2·00	1·50	
		a. Imperf (pair)	£20000		
221	84	1½d. dull purple and green (21.3.02)	35·00	18·00	
222		1½d. slate-purple and green.	38·00	18·00	30·00
223		1½d. pale dull pur & green (*chalk-surfaced paper*) (8.05)	40·00	18·00	
224		1½d. slate-purple & bluish green (*chalk-surfaced paper*)	40·00	15·00	
225	85	2d. yellowish green and carmine-red (25.3.02) .	45·00	18·00	32·00
226		2d. grey-grn & carm-red (1904)	50·00	24·00	
227		2d. pale grey-green and carm-red (*chalk-surfaced paper*) (4.06)	40·00	24·00	
228		2d. pale grey-green and scar (*chalk-surfaced paper*) (1909)	40·00	24·00	
229		2d. dull blue-green and carm (*chalk-surfaced paper*) (1907)	70·00	45·00	
230	86	2½d. ultramarine (1.1.02)	20·00	10·00	22·00
231		2½d. pale ultramarine	20·00	10·00	
232	87	3d. dull pur/orge-yell (20.3.02)	40·00	12·00	30·00
		a. Chalk-surfaced paper (3.06)	£150	70·00	
232b		3d. deep purple/orange-yellow	40·00	12·00	
232c		3d. pale reddish pur/orge-yell (*chalk-surfaced paper*) (3.06)	£150	60·00	
233		3d. dull reddish pur/yell (lemon back) (*chalk-surfaced paper*)	£150	75·00	
233b		3d. pale purple/lemon (*chalk-surfaced paper*)	35·00	15·00	
234		3d. pur/lemon (*chalk-surfaced paper*)	35·00	15·00	
235	88	4d. green and grey-brn (27.3.02)	50·00	30·00	
236		4d. green and chocolate-brown	50·00	30·00	
		a. Chalk-surfaced paper (1.06)	40·00	18·00	40·00
238		4d. dp green & choc-brn (*chalk-surfaced paper*) (1.06)	40·00	18·00	
239		4d. brown-orange (1.11.09)	£150	£130	
240		4d. pale orange (12.09)	20·00	15·00	35·00
241		4d. orange-red (12.09)	20·00	15·00	
242	89	5d. dull pur and ultram (14.5.02)	55·00	20·00	50·00
		a. Chalk-surfaced paper (5.06)	50·00	20·00	
244		5d. slate-pur and ultram (*chalk-surfaced paper*) (5.06)	50·00	20·00	
245	83	6d. pale dull purple (1.1.02)	35·00	18·00	50·00
		a. Chalk-surfaced paper (1.06)	35·00	18·00	
246		6d. slate-purple	35·00	18·00	
248		6d. dull purple (*chalk-surfaced paper*) (1.06)	35·00	18·00	
249	90	7d. grey-black (4.5.10)	10·00	18·00	£195
249a		7d. deep grey-black	£110	£100	
250	91	9d. dull pur and ultram (7.4.02)	80·00	60·00	£200
		a. Chalk-surfaced paper (6.05)	80·00	60·00	
251		9d. slate-purple and ultramarine	80·00	60·00	
		a. Chalk-surfaced paper (6.05)	80·00	60·00	
254	92	10d. dull purple and carm (3.7.02)	80·00	60·00	£225
		a. No cross on crown	£300	£200	
		b. Chalk-surfaced paper (9.06)	80·00	60·00	
255		10d. slate-purple and carm (*chalk-surfaced paper*) (9.06)	80·00	60·00	
		a. No cross on crown	£300	£200	
256		10d. dull purple & scarlet (*chalk-surfaced paper*) (9.10)	80·00	60·00	
		a. No cross on crown	£300	£200	
257	93	1s. dull green and carm (24.3.02)	80·00	35·00	£150
		a. Chalk-surfaced paper (9.05)	80·00	35·00	
259		1s. dull green and scarlet (*chalk-surfaced paper*) (9.10)	80·00	50·00	
260	94	2s.6d. lilac (5.4.02)	£220	£140	£700
261		2s.6d. pale dull purple (*chalk-surfaced paper*) (7.10.05)	£225	£150	
262		2s.6d. dull pur (*chalk-surfaced paper*)	£225	£150	
263	95	5s. bright carmine (5.4.02)	£350	£200	£950
264		5s. deep bright carmine	£350	£200	
265	96	10s. ultramarine (5.4.02)	£650	£450	
266	97	£1 dull blue-green (16.6.02)	£1600	£650	

97a

1910 (May). *Prepared for use by De La Rue but not issued.* Wmk Imperial Crown, W 49. P 14.

266a	97a	2d. Tyrian plum	£60000	

One example of this stamp is known used, but it was never issued to the public.

1911. *Printed by Harrison & Sons. Ordinary paper.* Wmk Imperial Crown.

(a) P 14.

267	83	½d. dull yellow-green (3.5.11)	2·75	1·50	4·00
268		½d. dull green	3·00	1·50	
269		½d. deep dull green	11·00	6·00	
270		½d. pale bluish green	40·00	40·00	
		a. Booklet pane. Five stamps plus St. Andrew's Cross label	£500		
		b. Wmk sideways	†	£22000	
		c. Imperf (pair)	£22000	†	
271		½d. brt green (fine impression) (6.11)	£250	£150	
272		1d. rose-red (3.5.11)	8·00	12·00	18·00
		a. No wmk (brick red)	40·00	45·00	
273		1d. deep rose-red	8·00	12·00	
274		1d. rose-carmine	55·00	30·00	
275		1d. aniline pink (5.11)	£550	£300	
275a		1d. aniline rose	£180	£140	
276	86	2½d. bright blue (10.7.11)	55·00	30·00	50·00
277	87	3d. purple/lemon (12.9.11)	65·00	£180	£550
277a		3d. grey/lemon	£3000		
278	88	4d. bright orange (12.7.11)	65·00	50·00	£175

(b) P 15×14.

279	83	½d. dull green (30.10.11)	40·00	45·00	£100
279a		½d. deep dull green	40·00	45·00	
280		1d. rose-red (4.10.11)	38·00	25·00	
281		1d. rose-carmine	15·00	15·00	30·00
282		1d. pale rose-carmine	22·00	15·00	
283	86	2½d. bright blue (14.10.11)	22·00	15·00	35·00
284		2½d. dull blue	22·00	15·00	
285	87	3d. purple/lemon (22.9.11)	45·00	15·00	40·00
285a		3d. grey/lemon	£2250		
286	88	4d. bright orange (11.11.11)	30·00	15·00	65·00
279/86 Set of 5			£130	90·00	

No. 272a was probably a trial printing.

1911–13. *Printed at Somerset House. Ordinary paper.* Wmk as 1902–1910. P 14.

287	84	1½d. reddish purple and bright green (13.7.11)	40·00	35·00	
288		1½d. dull purple and green..	25·00	28·00	50·00
289		1½d. slate-purple and grn (9.12)	28·00	28·00	
290	85	2d. dp dull green and red (8.8.11)	25·00	20·00	50·00
291		2d. deep dull green and carmine	25·00	20·00	
292		2d. grey-green and bright carmine (carmine shows clearly on back) (11.3.12)	25·00	25·00	
293	89	5d. dull reddish purple and bright blue (7.8.11)	30·00	20·00	65·00
294		5d. deep dull reddish purple and bright blue	30·00	20·00	
295	83	6d. royal purple (31.10.11)	50·00	85·00	
296		6d. bright magenta (*chalk-surfaced paper*) (31.10.11)	£7500		
297		6d. dull purple	30·00	20·00	85·00
298		6d. reddish purple (11.11)	30·00	25·00	
299		6d. very dp reddish pur (11.11)	40·00	40·00	
300		6d. dark purple (3.12)	30·00	35·00	
301		6d. dull purple ("Dickinson" coated paper) (3.13)	£170	£170	
303		6d. deep plum (7.13)	28·00	70·00	
		a. No cross on crown	£800		
305	90	7d. slate-grey (1.8.12)	15·00	22·00	£195
306	91	9d. reddish purple and light blue (24.7.11)	80·00	75·00	
306a		9d. deep dull reddish purple and deep bright blue (9.11)	80·00	75·00	
307		9d. dull reddish purple and blue (10.11)	60·00	60·00	£190
307a		9d. deep plum and blue (7.13)	60·00	60·00	
308		9d. slate-pur and cobalt-bl (3.12)	95·00	£100	
309	92	10d. dull purple and scar (9.10.11)	80·00	75·00	
310		10d. dull reddish pur and aniline pink	£275	£225	
311		10d. dull reddish purple and carm (5.12)	70·00	60·00	£225
		a. No cross on crown	£1250		
312	93	1s. dark green and scar (13.7.11)	£100	60·00	
313		1s. dp green and scar (9.10.11)	70·00	35·00	
314		1s. green & carmine (15.4.12)	55·00	35·00	£160
315	94	2s.6d. dull greyish purple (15.9.11)	£600	£350	
316		2s.6d. dull reddish purple	£220	£150	£950
317		2s.6d. dark purple	£220	£150	
318	95	5s. carmine (29.2.12)	£350	£180	£950
319	96	10s. blue (14.1.12)	£700	£500	
320	97	£1 deep green (3.9.11)	£1600	£700	

*No. 301 was on an experimental coated paper which does not respond to the silver test.

KING GEORGE V
6 May 1910–20 January 1936

Further detailed information on the issues of King George V will be found in Volume 2 of the Stanley Gibbons *Great Britain Specialised Catalogue*.

PRINTERS. Types **98** to **102** were typographed by Harrison & Sons Ltd, with the exception of certain preliminary printings made at Somerset House and distinguishable by the controls "A.11", "B.11" or "B.12" (the Harrison printings do not have a full stop after the letter). The booklet stamps, Nos. 334/7 and 344/5 were printed by Harrisons only.

WATERMARK VARIETIES. Many British stamps to 1967 exist without watermark owing to misplacement of the paper, and with either inverted, reversed, or inverted and reversed watermarks. A proportion of the low-value stamps issued in booklets have the watermark inverted in the normal course of printing.

Low values with *watermark sideways* are normally from stamp rolls used in machines with sideways delivery or, from June 1940, certain booklets.

STAMPS WITHOUT WATERMARK. Stamps found without watermark, due to misplacement of the sheet in relation to the dandy roll, are not listed here, but will be found in the *Great Britain Specialised Catalogue*.

The 1½d. and 5d. 1912–22, and 2d. and 2½d., 1924–26, listed here, are from *whole* sheets completely without watermark.

98	**99**

For type differences with T **101**/2 *see* notes below the latter.

Die A	Die B

Dies of Halfpenny

Die A. The three upper scales on the body of the right hand dolphin form a triangle; the centre jewel of the cross inside the crown is suggested by a comma.

Die B. The three upper scales are incomplete; the centre jewel is suggested by a crescent.

Die A	Die B

Dies of One Penny

Die A. The second line of shading on the ribbon to the right of the crown extends right across the wreath; the line nearest to the crown on the right hand ribbon shows as a short line at the bottom of the ribbon.

Die B. The second line of shading is broken in the middle; the first line is little more than a dot.

(Des Bertram Mackennal and G. W. Eve. Head from photograph by W. & D. Downey. Die eng J. A. C. Harrison)

1911–12. Wmk Imperial Crown, W **49**. P 15 × 14.

				Un	Used
321	**98**	½d. pale green (Die A) (22.6.11)		5·00	4·00
322		½d. green (Die A) (22.6.11)		4·00	4·00
		a. Error. Perf 14 (8.11)		£14000	£700
323		½d. bluish green (Die A)		£300	£180
324		½d. yellow-green (Die B)		12·00	1·50
325		½d. bright green (Die B)		8·00	1·50
		a. Wmk sideways		—	£3500
326		½d. bluish green (Die B)		£160	£100
327	**99**	1d. carmine-red (Die A) (22.6.11)		4·50	2·50
		c. Wmk sideways		†	—
328		1d. pale carmine (Die A) (22.6.11)		14·00	3·00
		a. No cross on crown		£425	£275
329		1d. carmine (Die B)		7·00	3·00
330		1d. pale carmine (Die B)		12·00	4·00
		a. No cross on crown		£550	£350
331		1d. rose-pink (Die B)		£110	40·00
332		1d. scarlet (Die B) (6.12)		45·00	18·00
333		1d. aniline scarlet (Die B)		£200	£110

For note on the aniline scarlet No. 333 *see* below No. 343.

100 Simple Cypher

1912 (Aug). *Booklet stamps.* Wmk Royal Cypher ("Simple"), W **100**. P 15×14.

334	**98**	½d. pale green (Die B)		40·00	40·00
335		½d. green (Die B)		40·00	40·00

336	**99**	1d. scarlet (Die B)		30·00	30·00
337		1d. bright scarlet (Die B)		30·00	30·00

101	**102**	**103** Multiple Cypher

Type differences

½d. In T **98** the ornament above "P" of "HALFPENNY" has two thin lines of colour and the beard is undefined. In T **101** the ornament has one thick line and the beard is well defined.

1d. In T **99** the body of the lion is unshaded and in T **102** it is shaded.

1912 (1 Jan). Wmk Imperial Crown, W **49**. P 15 × 14.

338	**101**	½d. deep green		15·00	8·00
339		½d. green		8·00	4·00
340		½d. yellow-green		8·00	4·00
		a. No cross on crown		£100	50·00
341	**102**	1d. bright scarlet		5·00	2·00
		a. No cross on crown		80·00	50·00
		b. Printed double, one albino		£180	
342		1d. scarlet		5·00	2·00
343		1d. aniline scarlet*		£175	£100
		a. No cross on crown			£1000

*Our prices for the aniline scarlet 1d. stamps, Nos. 333 and 343, are for specimens in which the colour is suffused on the surface of the stamp and shows through clearly on the back. Specimens without these characteristics but which show "aniline" reactions under the quartz lamp are relatively common.

1912 (Aug). Wmk Royal Cypher ("Simple"), W **100**. P 15×14.

344	**101**	½d. green		7·00	4·00
		a. No cross on crown		£100	50·00
345	**102**	1d. scarlet		8·00	4·50
		a. No cross on crown		£100	3·00

1912 (Sept–Oct). Wmk Royal Cypher ("Multiple"), W **103**. P 15×14.

346	**101**	½d. green (Oct)		12·00	8·00
		a. No cross on crown		£100	60·00
		b. Imperf		£130	
		c. Wmk sideways		†	£2750
		d. Printed on gummed side		—	†
347		½d. yellow-green		15·00	8·00
348		½d. pale green		15·00	8·00
349	**102**	1d. bright scarlet		18·00	10·00
350		1d. scarlet		18·00	10·00
		a. No cross on crown		£120	50·00
		b. Imperf		£130	
		c. Wmk sideways		£130	£150
		d. Wmk sideways. No cross on crown			£750

104	**105**	**106**

No. 357a
No. 357ac

No. 357ab/ac

107	**108**

Die I

Die II

Dies of 2d.

Die I.— Inner frame-line at top and sides close to solid of background. *Four* complete lines of shading between top of head and oval frame-line. These four lines do *not* extend to the oval itself. White line round "TWOPENCE" thin.

Die II.— Inner frame-line farther from solid of background. *Three* lines between top of head and extending to the oval. White line round "TWOPENCE" thicker.

(Des Bertram Mackennal (heads) and G. W. Eve (frames). Coinage head (½, 1½, 2 and 4d.); large medal head (1d., 2½d.); intermediate medal head (5d. to 1s.); small medal head used for fiscal stamps. Dies eng J. A. C. Harrison)

(Typo by Harrison & Sons Ltd., except the 6d. printed by the Stamping Department of the Board of Inland Revenue, Somerset House. The latter also made printings of the following which can only be distinguished by the controls: ½d. B.13; 1½d. A.12; 2d. C.13; 2½d. A.12; 3d. A.12, B.13, C.13; 4d. B.13; 5d. B.13; 7d. C.13; 8d. C.13; 9d. agate B.13; 10d. C.13; 1s. C.13)

1912–24. Wmk Royal Cypher, W **100**. *Chalk-surfaced paper* (6d.). P 15×14.

351	**105**	½d. green (16.1.13)		1·00	1·00
		a. Partial double print (half of bottom row from Control G15)		£16000	†
		b. Gummed both sides			
352		½d. bright green		1·00	1·00
353		½d. deep green		5·00	2·00
354		½d. yellow-green		6·00	3·00
355		½d. very yellow (Cyprus) green (1914)		£5000	†
356		½d. blue-green		40·00	25·00
357	**104**	1d. bright scarlet (8.10.12)		1·00	1·00
		a. "Q" for "O" (R. 1/4) (Control E14)		£150	£140
		ab. "Q" for "O" (R. 4/11) (Control T22)		£350	£175
		ac. Reversed "Q" for "O" (R. 15/9) (Control T22)		£300	£225
		ad. Inverted "Q" for "O" (R. 20/3)		£375	£225
		b. *Tête-bêche* (pair)		£55000	†
358		1d. vermilion		5·00	2·50
359		1d. pale rose-red		15·00	2·50
360		1d. carmine-red		11·00	5·00
361		1d. scarlet-vermilion		£125	50·00
		a. Printed on back †		£275	†
362	**105**	1½d. red-brown (15.10.12)		4·00	1·50
		a. "PENCF" (R. 15/12)		£200	£150
		b. Booklet pane. Four stamps plus two printed labels (2.24)		£450	
363		1½d. chocolate-brown		11·00	2·00
		a. Without wmk		£180	£110
364		1½d. chestnut		5·00	1·00
		a. "PENCF" (R. 15/12)		£100	80·00
365		1½d. yellow-brown		20·00	16·00
366	**106**	2d. orange-yellow (Die I) (20.8.12)		8·00	3·00
367		2d. reddish orange (Die I) (11.13)		6·00	3·00
368		2d. orange (Die I)		4·00	3·00
369		2d. bright orange (Die I)		5·00	3·00
370		2d. orange (Die II) (9.21)		5·00	3·50
371	**104**	2½d. cobalt-blue (18.10.12)		12·00	4·00
371a		2½d. bright blue (1914)		12·00	4·00
372		2½d. blue		12·00	4·00
373		2½d. indigo-blue* (1920)		£2000	£1200
373a		2½d. dull Prussian blue* (1921)		£700	£600
374	**106**	3d. dull reddish violet (9.10.12)		12·00	3·00
375		3d. violet		5·00	3·00
376		3d. bluish violet (11.13)		9·00	3·00
377		3d. pale violet		10·00	3·00
378		4d. deep grey-green (15.1.13)		35·00	10·00
379		4d. grey-green		15·00	2·00
380		4d. pale grey-green		25·00	5·00
381	**107**	5d. brown (30.6.13)		15·00	5·00
382		5d. yellow-brown		15·00	5·00
		a. Without wmk		£700	
383		5d. bistre-brown		£110	60·00
384		6d. dull purple (1.8.13)		25·00	10·00
385		6d. reddish purple (8.13)		15·00	7·00
		a. Perf 14 (9.20)		90·00	£110
386		6d. deep reddish purple		27·00	5·00
387		7d. olive (1.8.13)		20·00	10·00
388		7d. bronze-green (1915)		60·00	25·00
389		7d. sage-green (1917)		70·00	18·00
390		8d. black/*yellow* (1.8.13)		32·00	11·00
391		8d. black/*yellow-buff* (granite) (5.17)		40·00	15·00
392	**108**	9d. agate (30.6.13)		15·00	6·00
		a. Printed double, one albino			
393		9d. deep agate		25·00	6·00
393a		9d. olive-green (9.22)		£110	30·00
393b		9d. pale olive-green		£120	40·00
394		10d. turquoise-blue (1.8.13)		22·00	20·00
394a		10d. deep turquoise-blue		90·00	30·00
395		1s. bistre (1.8.13)		20·00	4·00
396		1s. bistre-brown		35·00	12·00
		351/95 Set of 15		£250	95·00

Imperf stamps of this issue exist but may be war-time colour trials.

†The impression of No. 361a is set sideways and is very pale.

Nos. 362a and 364a occur on Plates 12 and 29 and are known from Controls L18, M18, M19, O19 and Q21. The flaws were corrected by 1921.

*No. 373 comes from Control O20 and also exists on toned paper. No. 373a comes from Control R21 and also exists on toned paper, but both are unlike the rare Prussian blue shade of the 1935 2½d. Jubilee issue.

See also Nos. 418/29.

For the 2d., T **106** bisected, see note under Guernsey, War Occupation Issues.

1913 (1 Aug). Wmk Royal Cypher ("Multiple"). W **103**. P 15×14.

397	**105**	½d. bright green		£150	£180
		a. Wmk sideways		†	£18000
398	**104**	1d. dull scarlet		£225	£225

Both these stamps were originally issued in rolls only. Subsequently sheets were found, so that horizontal pairs and blocks are known but are of considerable rarity.

109

A   110 Single Cypher

Major Re-entries on 2s.6d.

Nos. 400a and 408a

No. 415b

(Des Bertram Mackennal. Dies eng J. A. C. Harrison. Recess)

High values, so-called "Sea Horses" design: T 109. Background around portrait consists of horizontal lines, Type A. Wmk Single Cypher, W **110**. P 11×12.

1913 (30 June–Aug). *Printed by Waterlow Bros & Layton.*
399	2s.6d. deep sepia-brown	£250	£160
400	2s.6d. sepia-brown	£225	£140
	a. Re-entry (R. 2/1)	£1200	£600
401	5s. rose-carmine	£400	£275
402	10s. indigo-blue (1 Aug)	£700	£425
403	£1 green (1 Aug)	£2200	£1200
404	£1 dull blue-green (1 Aug)	£2200	£1400

*399/404 For well-centred, lightly used +35%.

1915 (Oct–Dec). *Printed by De La Rue & Co.*
405	2s.6d. deep yellow-brown	£250	£200
406	2s.6d. yellow-brown	£225	£190
	a. Re-entry (R. 2/1)	£1250	£600
407	2s.6d. pale brown	£225	£190
	a. Re-entry (R. 2/1)	£1250	£600
408	2s.6d. sepia (seal-brown)	£225	£190
409	5s. bright carmine	£375	£300
410	5s. pale carmine	£450	£280
411	10s. deep blue (Dec)	£2250	£875
412	10s. blue	£1800	£700
413	10s. pale blue	£2000	£700

*405/13 For well-centred, lightly used + 45%. Nos. 406/7 were produced from the original Waterlow plates as were all De La Rue 5s. and 10s. printings. Examples of Nos. 406/7, 410 and 411 occur showing degrees of plate wear.

1918 (Dec)–**19**. *Printed by Bradbury, Wilkinson & Co. Ltd.*
413a	2s.6d. olive-brown	£100	65·00
414	2s.6d. chocolate-brown	£125	70·00
415	2s.6d. reddish brown	£125	70·00
415a	2s.6d. pale brown	£110	65·00
	b. Major re-entry (R. 1/2)	£650	£400
416	5s. rose-red (1.19)	£250	£110
417	10s. dull grey-blue (1.19)	£375	£160
399/417 Set of 4		£2500	£1400

*413a/17 For well-centred, lightly used +35%.

DISTINGUISHING PRINTINGS. Note that the £1 value was only printed by Waterlow.

Waterlow and De La Rue stamps measure exactly 22 mm vertically. In the De La Rue printings the gum is usually patchy and yellowish, and the colour of the stamp, particularly in the 5s., tends to show through the back. The holes of the perforation are smaller than those of the other two printers, but there is a thick perforation tooth at the top of each vertical row.

In the Bradbury Wilkinson printings the height of the stamp is 22¾ or 23 mm due to the use of curved plates. On most of the 22¾ mm high stamps a minute coloured guide dot appears in the margin just above the middle of the upper frame-line.

For (1934) re-engraved Waterlow printings *see* Nos. 450/2.

UNITED KINGDOM OF GREAT BRITAIN AND NORTHERN IRELAND

111   111a

Block Cypher

The watermark Type **111a**, as compared with Type **111**, differs as follows: Closer spacing of horizontal rows (12½ mm instead of 14½ mm). Letters shorter and rounder. Watermark thicker.

(Typo by Waterlow & Sons, Ltd (all values except 6d.) and later, 1934–35, by Harrison & Sons, Ltd (all values). Until 1934 the 6d. was printed at Somerset House where a printing of the 1½d. was also made in 1926 (identifiable only by control E.26). Printings by Harrisons in 1934–35 can be identified, when in mint condition, by the fact that the gum shows a streaky appearance vertically, the Waterlow gum being uniformly applied, but Harrisons also used up the balance of the Waterlow "smooth gum" paper)

1924 (Feb)–**26**. Wmk Block Cypher, W **111**. P 15×14.
418	105	½d. green	1·00	1·00
		a. Wmk sideways (5.24)	9·00	3·25
		b. Doubly printed	£8000	†
		c. No watermark	£3000	
419	104	1d. scarlet	1·00	1·00
		a. Wmk sideways	20·00	15·00
		b. Experimental paper, W **111a** (10.24)	22·00	
		c. Partial double print, one inverted	£7500	
		d. Inverted "Q" for "O" (R. 20/3)	£375	
420	105	1½d. red-brown	1·00	1·00
		a. *Tête-bêche* (pair)	£500	£800
		b. Wmk sideways (8.24)	19·00	3·50
		c. Printed on the gummed side	£400	†
		d. Booklet pane. Four stamps plus two printed labels (3.24)	£150	
		e. Ditto. Wmk sideways	£6000	
		f. Experimental paper, W **111a** (10.24)	60·00	70·00
		g. Double impression	£14000	†
421	106	2d. orange (Die II) (7.24)	2·50	2·50
		a. No wmk	£800	
		b. Wmk sideways (7.26)	£100	£100
		c. Partial double print	£18000	†
422	104	2½d. blue (10.10.24)	5·00	3·00
		a. No wmk	†	£6000
		b. Wmk sideways	†	£6000
423	106	3d. violet (10.10.24)	10·00	2·50
424		4d. grey-green (23.10.24)	12·00	2·50
		a. Printed on the gummed side	220·00	†
425	107	5d. brown (17.10.24)	20·00	3·00
426		6d. reddish purple (*chalk-surfaced paper*) (9.24)	12·00	2·50
426a		6d. purple (6.26)	3·00	1·50
427	108	9d. olive-green (11.11.24)	12·00	3·50
428		10d. turquoise-blue (28.11.24)	40·00	40·00
429		1s. bistre-brown (10.24)	22·00	3·00
418/29 Set of 12			£110	60·00

There are numerous shades in this issue.

The 6d. on both chalk-surfaced and ordinary papers was printed by both Somerset House and Harrisons. The Harrisons printings have streaky gum, differ slightly in shade, and that on chalk-surfaced paper is printed in a highly fugitive ink. The prices quoted are for the commonest (Harrison) printing in each case.

The dandy roll to produce watermark Type **111a** was provided by Somerset House in connection with experiments in paper composition undertaken during 1924–25. These resulted in a change from rag only paper to that made from a mixture including esparto and sulphite.

112

(Des H. Nelson. Eng J. A. C. Harrison, Recess Waterlow)

1924–25. *British Empire Exhibition.* W **111**. P 14.

(a) Dated "1924" (23.4.24).
430	112	1d. scarlet	10·00	11·00
431		1½d. brown	15·00	15·00

(b) Dated "1925" (9.5.25).
432	112	1d. scarlet	15·00	30·00
433		1½d. brown	40·00	70·00

113   114   115

116 St. George and the Dragon

117

(Des J. Farleigh (T **113** and **115**), E. Linzell (T **114**) and H. Nelson (T **116**). Eng C. G. Lewis (T **113**), T. E. Storey (T **115**), both at the Royal Mint; J. A. C. Harrison, of Waterlow (T **114** and **116**). Typo by Waterlow from plates made at the Royal Mint, except T **116**, recess by Bradbury, Wilkinson from die and plate of their own manufacture)

1929 (10 May). *Ninth U.P.U. Congress, London.*

(a) W **11**. P 15×14.
434	113	½d. green	2·25	2·25
		a. Wmk sideways	35·00	35·00
435	114	1d. scarlet	2·25	2·25
		a. Wmk sideways	60·00	60·00
436		1½d. purple-brown	2·25	1·75
		a. Wmk sideways	35·00	35·00
		b. Booklet pane. Four stamps plus two printed labels	£225	
437	115	2½d. blue	10·00	10·00

(b) W **117**. P 12.
438	116	£1 black	£750	£550
434/7 Set of 4 (to 2½d.)			15·00	14·50

PRINTERS. All subsequent issues were printed in photogravure by Harrison and Sons Ltd *except where otherwise stated.*

118   119   120

121   122

1934–36. W **111**. P 15 × 14.
439	118	½d. green (17.11.34)	50	50
		a. Wmk sideways	8·00	3·50
		b. Imperf three sides	£2500	
440	119	1d. scarlet (24.9.34)	50	50
		a. Imperf (pair)	£2000	
		b. Printed on the gummed side	£550	†
		c. Wmk sideways (30.4.35)	15·00	6·00
		d. Double impression	†	£17000
		e. Imperf between (pair)	£3000	
		f. Imperf three sides (pair)	£2000	
441	118	1½d. red-brown (20.8.34)	50	50
		a. Imperf (pair)	£600	
		b. Imperf three sides (lower stamp in vert pair)	£1200	
		c. Imperf between (horiz pair)		
		d. Wmk sideways	8·00	4·00
		e. Booklet pane. Four stamps plus two printed labels (1.35)	£100	
442	120	2d. orange (19.1.35)	75	75
		a. Imperf (pair)	£4000	
		b. Wmk sideways (30.4.35)	£110	75·00
443	119	2½d. ultramarine (18.3.35)	1·50	1·25
444	120	3d. violet (18.3.35)	1·50	1·25
445		4d. deep grey-green (2.12.35)	2·00	1·25
446	121	5d. yellow-brown (17.2.36)	6·50	2·75
447	122	9d. deep olive-green (2.12.35)	12·00	2·25
448		10d. turquoise-blue (24.2.36)	15·00	10·00
449		1s. bistre-brown (24.2.36)	15·00	1·25
		a. Double impression	—	†
439/49 Set of 11			50·00	20·00

Owing to the need for wider space for the perforations the size of the designs of the ½d. and 2d. were once, and the 1d. and 1½d. twice, reduced from that of the first printings.

There are also numerous minor variations, due to the photographic element in the process.

The ½d. imperf three sides, No. 439b, is known in a block of four, from a sheet, to which the bottom pair is imperf at top and sides.

For No. 442 bisected, see Guernsey, War Occupation Issues.

B   123

(Eng J. A. C. Harrison. Recess Waterlow)

1934 (16 Oct). T **109** (re-engraved). *Background around portrait consists of horizontal and diagonal lines. Type B.* W **110**. P 11×12.
450	109	2s.6d. chocolate-brown	70·00	40·00

451		5s. bright rose-red	£160	85·00
452		10s. indigo	£340	80·00
450/2	*Set of 3*		£525	£190

There are numerous other minor differences in the design of this issue.

(Des B. Freedman)

1935 (7 May). *Silver Jubilee.* W 111. P 15 × 14.

453	**123**	½d. green	1·00	1·00
454		1d. scarlet	1·50	2·00
455		1½d. red-brown	1·00	1·00
456		2½d. blue	5·00	6·00
456*a*		2½d. Prussian blue	£7000	£8000
453/6	*Set of 4*		8·50	9·25

The 1½d. and 2½d. values differ from T **123** in the emblem in the panel at right.

Four sheets of No. 456*a*, printed in the wrong shade, were issued in error by the Post Office Stores Department on 25 June 1935. It is known that three of the sheets were sold from the sub-office at 134 Fore Street, Upper Edmonton, London, between that date and 4 July.

KING EDWARD VIII
20 January–10 December 1936

Further detailed information on the stamps of King Edward VIII will be found in Volume 2 of the Stanley Gibbons *Great Britain Specialised Catalogue*.

124   **125**

(Des H. Brown, adapted Harrison using a photo by Hugh Cecil)

1936. W **125.** P 15×14.

457	**124**	1d. green (1.9.36)	30	30
		a. Double impression		
458		1d. scarlet (14.9.36)	60	50
459		1½d. red-brown (1.9.36)	30	30
		a. Booklet pane. Four stamps plus two printed labels (10.36)	75·00	
460		2½d. bright blue (1.9.36)	30	85
457/60	*Set of 4*		1·25	1·75

KING GEORGE VI
11 December 1936–6 February 1952

Further detailed information on the stamps of King George VI will be found in Volume 2 of the Stanley Gibbons *Great Britain Specialised Catalogue*.

126 King George VI and Queen Elizabeth   Colon flaw (Cyl. 7 No dot, R. 10/1, later corrected)

(Des E. Dulac)

1937 (13 May). *Coronation.* W **127.** P 15 × 14.

461	**126**	1½d. maroon	30	30
		a. colon flaw	15·00	

127   **128**

129   **130**

King George VI and National Emblems (Des T **128/9**, E. Dulac (head) and E. Gill (frames). T **130**, E. Dulac (whole stamp))

1937–47. W **127.** P 15 × 14.

462	**128**	½d. green (10.5.37)	30	25
		a. Wmk sideways (1.38)	50	50
		ab. Booklet pane of 4 (6.40)	50·00	
463		1d. scarlet (10.5.37)	30	25
		a. Wmk sideways (2.38)	20·00	9·00
		ab. Booklet pane of 4 (6.40)	£100	
464		1½d. red-brown (30.7.37)	30	25
		a. Wmk sideways (2.38)	1·00	1·25
		b. Booklet pane. Four stamps plus two printed labels (8.37)	£100	
		c. Imperf three sides (pair)	£3500	
465		2d. orange (31.1.38)	1·25	50
		a. Wmk sideways (2.38)	70·00	38·00
		b. Bisected (on cover)	†	40·00
466		2½d. ultramarine (10.5.37)	40	25
		a. Wmk sideways (6.40)	70·00	32·00

		b. *Tête-bêche* (horiz pair)	£2000	
467		3d. violet (31.1.38)	5·00	1·00
468	**129**	4d. grey-green (21.11.38)	60	75
		a. Imperf (pair)	£5000	
		b. Imperf three sides (horiz pair)	£5250	
469		5d. brown (21.11.38)	3·50	85
		a. Imperf (pair)	£6000	
		b. Imperf three sides (horiz pair)	£5250	
470		6d. purple (30.1.39)	1·50	60
471	**130**	7d. emerald-green (27.2.39)	5·00	60
		a. Imperf three sides (horiz pair)	£5000	
472		8d. bright carmine (27.2.39)	7·50	80
473		9d. deep olive-green (1.5.39)	6·50	80
474		10d. turquoise-blue (1.5.39)	7·00	80
		aa. Imperf (pair)	£6000	
474*a*		11d. plum (29.12.47)	3·00	2·75
475		1s. bistre-brown (1.5.39)	9·00	75
462/75	*Set of 15*		45·00	10·00

For later printings of the lower values in apparently lighter shades and different colours, see Nos. 485/90 and 503/8.

No. 465b was authorised for use in Guernsey. See notes on War Occupation Issues.

Nos. 468b and 469b are perforated at foot only and each occurs in the same sheet as Nos. 468a and 469a.

No. 471a is also perforated at foot only, but occurs on the top row of a sheet.

131 King George VI   **132** King George VI

133

(Des E. Dulac (T **131**) and Hon. G. R. Bellew (T **132**). Eng J. A. C. Harrison. Recess Waterlow)

1939–48. W **133.** P 14.

476	**131**	2s.6d. brown (4.9.39)	35·00	6·00
476*a*		2s.6d. yellow-green (9.3.42)	11·00	1·50
477		5s. red (21.8.39)	20·00	2·00
478	**132**	10s. dark blue (30.10.39)	£225	20·00
478*a*		10s. ultramarine (30.11.42)	20·00	5·00
478*b*		£1 brown (1.10.48)	20·00	26·00
476/8*b*	*Set of 6*		£300	55·00

134 Queen Victoria and King George VI.

(Des H. L. Palmer)

1940 (6 May). *Centenary of First Adhesive Postage Stamps.* W **127.** P 14½×14.

479	**134**	½d. green	30	75
480		1d. scarlet	1·00	75
481		1½d. red-brown	50	1·50
482		2d. orange	1·00	75
		a. Bisected (on cover)	†	30·00
483		2½d. ultramarine	2·25	50
484		3d. violet	3·00	3·50
479/84	*Set of 6*		8·75	5·25

No. 482a was authorised for use in Guernsey. See notes on War Occupation Issues.

1941–42. *Head as Nos. 462/7, but with lighter background to provide a more economic use of the printing ink.* W **127.** P 15×14.

485	**128**	½d. pale green (1.9.41)	30	30
		a. *Tête-bêche* (horiz pair)	£15000	
		b. Imperf (pair)	£5000	
486		1d. pale scarlet (11.8.41)	40	30
		a. Wmk sideways (10.42)	5·00	4·50
		b. Imperf (pair)	£6000	
		c. Imperf three sides (horiz pair)	£6000	
487		1½d. pale red-brown (28.9.42)	60	80
488		2d. pale orange (6.10.41)	50	50
		a. Wmk sideways (6.42)	28·00	19·00
		b. *Tête-bêche* (horiz pair)	£15000	
		c. Imperf (pair)	£5000	
		d. Imperf pane*	£15000	
489		2½d. light ultramarine (21.7.41)	30	30
		a. Wmk sideways (8.42)	15·00	12·00
		b. *Tête-bêche* (horiz pair)	£15000	
		c. Imperf (pair)	£4000	
		d. Imperf pane*	£10000	
		e. Imperf three sides (horiz pair)	£6000	
490		3d. pale violet (3.11.41)	2·50	1·00
485/90	*Set of 6*		3·50	2·75

The *tête-bêche* varieties are from defectively made-up stamp

booklets.

Nos. 486c and 489e are perforated at foot only and occur in the same sheets as Nos. 486b and 489c.

*BOOKLET ERRORS. Those listed as "imperf panes" show one row of perforations either at the top or at the bottom of the pane of 6.

WATERMARK VARIETIES. Please note that *inverted watermarks* are outside the scope of this listing but are fully listed in the *Great Britain Specialised* and *Great Britain Concise Catalogues.* See also the notes about watermarks at the beginning of the King George V section.

135   **136** Symbols of Peace and Reconstruction

Extra porthole aft (Cyl. 11 No dot, R. 16/1)   Extra porthole fore (Cyl. 8 Dot, R. 5/6)   Seven berries (Cyl. 4 No dot, R. 12/5)

(Des H. L. Palmer (T **135**) and R. Stone (T **136**))

1946 (11 June). *Victory.* W **127.** P 15×14.

491	**135**	2½d. ultramarine	20	20
		a. Extra porthole aft	45·00	
		b. Extra porthole fore	65·00	
492	**136**	3d. violet	20	50
		a. Seven berries	20·00	

137   **138** King George VI and Queen Elizabeth

(Des G. Knipe and Joan Hassall from photographs by Dorothy Wilding)

1948 (26 Apr). *Royal Silver Wedding.* W **127.** P 15×14 (2½d.) or 14×15 (£1).

493	**137**	2½d. ultramarine	35	20
494	**138**	£1 blue	40·00	40·00

1948 (10 May). Stamps of 1d. and 2½d. showing seaweed-gathering were on sale at eight Head Post Offices in Great Britain, but were primarily for use in the Channel Islands and are listed there (see after Great Britain Postal Fiscals).

139 Globe and Laurel Wreath   **140** "Speed"

141 Olympic Symbol   **142** Winged Victory

Crown Flaw (Cyl. 1 No dot, R. 20/2, later retouched)

(Des P. Metcalfe (T **139**), A. Games (T **140**), S. D. Scott (T **141**) and E. Dulac (T **142**))

1948 (29 July). *Olympic Games.* W **127.** P 15×14.

495	**139**	2½d. ultramarine	35	10
496	**140**	3d. violet	35	50
		a. Crown flaw	20·00	
497	**141**	6d. bright purple	70	40
498	**142**	1s. brown	1·50	1·50
495/8	*Set of 4*		2·25	2·00

143 Two Hemispheres   **144** U.P.U. Monument, Berne

145 Goddess Concordia, Globe and Points of Compass   **146** Posthorn and Globe

Lake in Asia (Cyl. 3 Dot, R. 14/1)   Lake in India (Cyl. 2 No Dot, R. 18/2)

(Des Mary Adshead (T **143**), P. Metcalfe (T **144**), H. Fleury (T **145**) and Hon. G. R. Bellew (T **146**))

1949 (10 Oct). *75th Anniv of Universal Postal Union.* W **127**. P 15×14.

499	**143**	2½d. ultramarine	25	10
		a. Lake in Asia	30·00	
		b. Lake in India	25·00	
500	**144**	3d. violet	25	50
501	**145**	6d. bright purple	50	75
502	**146**	1s. brown	1·00	1·25
499/502		*Set of 4*	1·50	2·50

1950–52. *4d. as Nos. 468 and others as Nos. 485/9, but colours changed.* W **127**. P 15×14.

503	**128**	½d. pale orange (3.5.51)	30	30
		a. Imperf (pair)	£4000	
		b. Tête-bêche (horiz pair)	£15000	
		c. Imperf pane	£12000	
504		1d. light ultramarine (3.5.51)	30	30
		a. Wmk sideways (5.51)	1·10	1·25
		b. Imperf (pair)	£4000	
		c. Imperf three sides (horiz pair)	£5000	
		d. Booklet pane. Three stamps plus three printed labels (3.52)	18·00	
		e. Ditto. Partial tête-bêche pane	£6000	
505		1½d. pale green (3.5.51)	65	60
		a. Wmk sideways (9.51)	3·25	5·00
506		2d. pale red-brown (3.5.51)	75	40
		a. Wmk sideways (5.51)	1·75	2·00
		b. Tête-bêche (horiz pair)	£15000	
		c. Imperf three sides (horiz pair)	£5000	
507		2½d. pale scarlet (3.5.51)	60	40
		a. Wmk sideways (5.51)	1·75	1·75
		b. Tête-bêche (hoiz pair)		
508	**129**	4d. light ultramarine (2.10.50)	2·00	1·75
		a. Double impression	†	£7000
503/8		*Set of 6*	4·00	3·25

No. 504c is perforated at foot only and occurs in the same sheet as No. 504b.

No. 506c is also perforated at foot only.

*BOOKLET ERRORS. Those listed as "imperf panes" show one row of perforations either at the top or at the bottom of the pane of 6.

147 H.M.S. *Victory*   **148** White Cliffs of Dover

149 St. George and the Dragon   **150** Royal Coat of Arms

(Des Mary Adshead (T **147/8**), P. Metcalfe (T **149/50**). Recess Waterlow)

1951 (3 May). W **133**. P 11×12.

509	**147**	2s.6d. yellow-green	2·00	1·00
510	**148**	5s. red	40·00	4·00
511	**149**	10s. ultramarine	10·00	7·50
512	**150**	£1 brown	48·00	18·00
509/12		*Set of 4*	95·00	25·00

151 "Commerce and Prosperity"   **152** Festival Symbol

(Des E. Dulac (T **151**), A. Games (T **152**))

1951 (3 May). *Festival of Britain.* W **127**. P 15×14.

513	**151**	2½d. scarlet	20	15
514	**152**	4d. ultramarine	30	35

STAMP BOOKLETS

For a full listing of Great Britain stamp booklets see the *Great Britain Concise Catalogue* published each Spring.

POSTAGE DUE STAMPS

PERFORATIONS. All postage due stamps to No. D39 are perf 14×15.

D 1   D 2

(Des G. Eve. Typo Somerset House (early trial printings of ½d., 1d., 2d. and 5d.; all printings of 1s.) or Harrison (later printings of all values except 1s.).

1914 (20 Apr)–**22**. W **100** (Simple Cypher) sideways.

D1	D **1**	½d. emerald	50	25
D2		1d. carmine	50	25
		a. Pale carmine	75	50
D3		1½d. chestnut (1922)	48·00	20·00
D4		2d. agate	50	25
D5		3d. violet (1918)	5·00	75
		a. Bluish violet	6·00	2·75
D6		4d. dull grey-green (12.20)	18·00	5·00
D7		5d. brownish cinnamon	7·00	3·50
D8		1s. bright blue (1915)	40·00	4·75
		a. Deep bright blue	40·00	5·00
D1/8		*Set of 8*	£100	32·00

The 1d. is known bisected from various offices between 1914 and 1924, the 2d. bisected for use as a 1d. between 1918 and 1923, the 3d. bisected for use as a 1½d. in 1922 at Warminster and trisected for use as a 1d. in 1921 at Malvern.

(Typo Waterlow)

1924. *As 1914–22, but on thick chalk-surfaced paper.*

D9	D **1**	1d. carmine	6·00	6·00

(Typo Waterlow and (from 1934) Harrison)

1924–31. W **111** (Block Cypher) sideways.

D10	D **1**	½d. emerald (6.25)	1·25	75
D11		1d. carmine (4.25)	60	25
D12		1½d. chestnut (10.24)	47·00	22·00
D13		2d. agate (7.24)	1·00	25
D14		3d. dull violet (10.24)	1·50	25
		a. Printed on gummed side	75·00	†
		b. Experimental paper W 111a	40·00	35·00
D15		4d. dull grey-green (10.24)	15·00	4·25
D16		5d. brownish cinnamon (1.31)	65·00	45·00
D17		1s. deep blue (9.24)	8·50	50
D18	D **2**	2s.6d. purple/yellow (5.24)	85·00	1·75
D10/18		*Set of 9*	£200	65·00

The 1d. is known bisected from various offices between 1925 and 1932 and the 2d. exists bisected to make up the 2½d. rate at Perranwell Station, Cornwall, in 1932.

1936–37. W **125** (E 8 R) sideways.

D19	D **1**	½d. emerald (6.37)	12·00	10·50
D20		1d. carmine (5.37)	2·00	1·75
D21		2d. agate (5.37)	12·00	12·00
D22		3d. dull violet (3.37)	2·00	2·00
D23		4d. dull grey-green (12.36)	40·00	34·00
D24		5d. brownish cinnamon (11.36)	65·00	30·00
		a. Yellow-brown (1937)	28·00	28·00
D25		1s. deep blue (12.36)	11·00	8·50
D26	D **2**	2s.6d. purple/yellow (5.37)	£320	12·00
D19/26		*Set of 8 (cheapest)*	£390	90·00

The 1d. is known bisected at Solihull in 1937.

1937–38. W **127** (G VI R) sideways.

D27	D **1**	½d. emerald (5.38)	13·00	8·75
D28		1d. carmine	3·00	50
D29		2d. agate (5.38)	2·75	30
D30		3d. violet (12.37)	10·50	30
D31		4d. dull grey-green (11.38)	£110	10·00
D32		5d. yellow-brown (11.38)	16·50	75
D33		1s. deep blue (10.37)	78·00	75
D34	D **2**	2s.6d. purple/yellow (9.38)	85·00	1·25
D27/34		*Set of 8*	£260	18·00

The 2d. is known bisected at various offices between 1951 and 1954.

DATES OF ISSUE. The dates for Nos. D35/9 are those on which stamps were first issued by the Supplies Department to postmasters.

1951–52. *Colours changed and new value (1½d.).* W **127** (G VI R) sideways.

D35	D **1**	½d. yellow-orange (18.9.51)	3·50	3·50
		a. Bright orange	25·00	
D36		1d. violet-blue (6.6.51)	1·50	75
D37		1½d. green (11.2.52)	2·00	
D38		4d. blue (14.8.51)	50·00	22·00
D39		1s. ochre (6.12.51)	28·00	5·25
D35/9		*Set of 5*	75·00	28·00

The 1d. is known bisected at Capel, Dorking in 1952 and at Camberley in 1954.

OFFICIAL STAMPS

In 1840 the 1d. black (Type **1**), with "V R" in the upper corners, was prepared for official use, but never issued for postal purposes. Obliterated specimens are those which were used for experimental trials of obliterating inks, or those that passed through the post by oversight.

V 1

1840. *Prepared for use but not issued; "V" "R" in upper corners.* Imperf.

			Un	Used	Used on Cover
V1	V **1**	1d. black	£12000	£18000	

The following Official stamps would be more correctly termed Departmental stamps as they were exclusively for the use of certain government departments. Until 1882 official mail used ordinary postage stamps purchased at post offices, the cash being refunded once a quarter. Later the government departments obtained Official stamps by requisition.

Official stamps were on sale to the public for a short time at Somerset House but they were not sold from post offices. The system of only supplying the Government departments was open to abuse so that all Official stamps were withdrawn on 13 May 1904.

OVERPRINTS, PERFORATIONS, WATERMARKS. All Official stamps were overprinted by Thomas De La Rue & Co. and are perf 14. They are on Crown watermarked paper unless otherwise stated.

INLAND REVENUE

These stamps were used by revenue officials in the provinces, mail to and from Head Office passing without a stamp. The London Office used these stamps only for foreign mail.

I.R.	I. R.
OFFICIAL	**OFFICIAL**
(O **1**)	(O **2**)

Optd with Types O **1** (½d. to 1s.) or O **2** (others)

1882–1901. *Stamps of Queen Victoria.*

(a) Issues of 1880–81.

			Un	Used*	Used on Cover
O1		½d. deep green (1.11.82)	80·00	30·00	75·00
O2		½d. pale green	65·00	25·00	
O3		1d. lilac (Die II) (1.10.82)	4·00	2·00	20·00
		a. Optd in blue-black	£190	70·00	
		b. "OFFICIAL" omitted	—	£7000	
O4		6d. grey (Plate 18) (3.11.82)	£400	85·00	

No. O3 with the lines of the overprint transposed is an essay.

(b) Issues of 1884–1888.

			Un	Used*	Used on Cover
O5		½d. slate-blue (8.5.85)	65·00	22·00	90·00
O6		2½d. lilac (12.3.85)	£300	£100	£950
O7		1s. dull green (12.3.85)	£4000	£1200	
O8		5s. rose (blued paper) (12.3.85)	£7500	£2800	
O9		5s. rose (wmk Anchor) (3.90)	£3500	£1200	
		a. Raised stop after "R"	£4000	£1500	
		b. Optd in blue-black	£4500	£1500	
O9c		10s. cobalt (blued paper) (wmk Anchor) (12.3.85)	£16000	£4500	
		a. Raised stop after "R"			
O9d		10s. ultramarine (blued paper) (wmk Anchor) (12.3.85)	£12000	£3500	
O10		10s. ultram (wmk Anchor) (3.90)	£5000	£1750	
		a. Raised stop after "R"	£5750	£2500	
		b. Optd in blue-black	£5750	£2500	
O11		£1 brown-lilac (wmk Crowns) (12.3.85)	£35000	£18000	
		a. Frame broken	£40000		
		b. Optd in blue-black			
O12		£1 brown-lilac (wmk Orbs) (3.90)	£55000	£25000	
		a. Frame broken	£65000		

(c) Issues of 1887–92.

			Un	Used*	Used on Cover
O13		½d. vermilion (15.5.88)	8·00	3·00	60·00
		a. Without "I.R."	£3500		
		b. Imperf	£2600		
		c. Opt double (imperf)	£3500		
O14		2½d. purple/blue (2.92)	£100	10·00	£300
O15		1s. dull green (9.89)	£550	£175	£2250
O16		£1 green (6.92)	£7500	£1750	
		a. No stop after "R"	—	£2500	
		b. Frame broken	£11000	£2800	

Nos. O3, O13, O15 and O16 may be found showing worn impressions of the overprints with thicker letters.

(d) Issues of 1887 and 1900.

			Un	Used*	Used on Cover
O17		½d. blue-green (4.01)	10·00	6·00	£200
O18		6d. purple/rose-red (1.7.01)	£300	80·00	
O19		1s. green and carmine (12.01)	£2400	£850	

*O1/19 For well-centred, lightly used +35%.

1902–04. *Stamps of King Edward VII. Ordinary paper.*

			Un	Used*	Used on Cover
O20		½d. blue-green (4.2.02)	22·00	3·00	£110
O21		1d. scarlet (4.2.02)	15·00	2·00	75·00
O22		2½d. ultramarine (19.2.02)	£700	£175	
O23		6d. pale dull purple (14.3.04)	£135000	£80000	
O24		1s. dull green and carmine (29.4.02)	£2250	£500	
O25		5s. bright carmine (29.4.02)	£10000	£6500	
		a. Raised stop after "R"	£11000	£6500	
O26		10s. ultramarine (29.4.02)	£55000	£25000	
		a. Raised stop after "R"	£60000	£28000	
O27		£1 dull blue-green (29.4.02)	£37000	£18000	

OFFICE OF WORKS

These were issued to Head and Branch (local) offices in London and to Branch (local) offices at Birmingham, Bristol, Edinburgh, Glasgow, Leeds, Liverpool, Manchester and Southampton. The overprints on stamps of value 2d. and upwards were created later in 1902, the 2d. for registration fees and the rest for overseas mail.

O.W.

OFFICIAL

(O 3)

Optd with Type O 3

1896 (24 Mar)–02. *Stamps of Queen Victoria.*

O31	½d. vermilion	£200	£100	£500
O32	½d. blue-green (2.02)	£300	£150	
O33	1d. lilac (Die II)	£350	£100	£550
O34	5d. dull purple and blue (II) (29.4.02)	£2000	£750	
O35	10d. dull purple and carmine (28.5.02)	£3500	£1000	

1902 (11 Feb)–03. *Stamps of King Edward VII. Ordinary paper.*

O36	½d. blue-green (2.02)	£500	£150	£1500
O37	1d. scarlet	£500	£150	£350
O38	2d. yellowish green and carmine-red (27.4.02)	£1500	£375	£2400
O39	2½d. ultramarine (29.4.02)	£2000	£550	£3750
O40	10d. dull purple and carmine (28.5.03)	£20000	£4750	

*O31/40 **For well-centred, lightly used +25%.**

ARMY

Letters to and from the War Office in London passed without postage. The overprinted stamps were distributed to District and Station Paymasters nationwide, including Cox and Co., the Army Agents, who were paymasters to the Household Division.

ARMY   **ARMY**   **ARMY**

OFFICIAL   **OFFICIAL**   **OFFICIAL**

(O 4)   (O 5)   (O 6)

1896 (1 Sept)–01. *Stamps of Queen Victoria optd with Type O 4 (½d., 1d.) or O 5 (2½d., 6d.).*

O41	½d. vermilion	3·50	1·50	40·00
	a. "OFFICIAI" (R. 13/7)	£200	90·00	
	b. Lines of opt transposed	£2000		
O42	½d. blue-green (6.00)	4·00	7·00	
O43	1d. lilac (Die II)	3·50	2·50	65·00
	a. "OFFICIAI" (R. 13/7)	£150	85·00	
O44	2½d. purple/*blue*	30·00	20·00	£450
O45	6d. purple/*rose-red* (20.9.01)	75·00	90·00	£975

Nos. O41a and O43a occur on sheets overprinted by Forme 1.

1902–03. *Stamps of King Edward VII optd with Type O 4 (Nos. O48/50) or Type O 6 (No. O52). Ordinary paper.*

O48	½d. blue-green (11.2.02)	5·00	2·00	90·00
O49	1d. scarlet (11.2.02)	5·00	2·00	90·00
	a. "ARMY" omitted	†	—	
O50	6d. pale dull purple (23.8.02)	£150	70·00	
O52	6d. pale dull purple (12.03)	£1800	£750	

GOVERNMENT PARCELS

These stamps were issued to all departments, including the Head Office, for use on parcels weighing over 3 lb. Below this weight government parcels were sent by letter post to avoid the 55% of the postage paid from accruing to the railway companies, as laid down by parcel-post regulations. Most government parcels stamps suffered heavy postmarks in use.

GOVᵀ PARCELS

(O 7)

Optd as Type O 7

1883 (1 Aug)–86. *Stamps of Queen Victoria.*

		Un	Used*
O61	1½d. lilac (1.5.86)	£300	60·00
	a. No dot under "T"	£450	£110
	b. Dot to left of "T"	£450	£110
O62	6d. dull green (1.5.86)	£1750	£750
O63	9d. dull green	£1500	£600
O64	1s. orange-brown (wmk Crown, Pl 13)	£850	£200
	a. No dot under "T"	£1200	£250
	b. Dot to left of "T"	£1200	£250
O64c	1s. orange-brown (Pl 14)	£1800	£300
	ca. No dot under "T"	£2200	£400
	cb. Dot to left of "T"		

1887–90. *Stamps of Queen Victoria.*

O65	1½d. dull purple and pale green (29.10.87)	80·00	7·00
	a. No dot under "T"	£120	18·00
	b. Dot to right of "T"	£120	18·00
	c. Dot to left of "T"	£120	18·00
O66	6d. purple/*rose-red* (19.12.87)	£150	30·00
	a. No dot under "T"	£150	30·00
	b. Dot to right of "T"	£200	35·00
	c. Dot to left of "T"	£200	35·00
O67	9d. dull purple and blue (21.8.88)	£225	40·00
O68	1s. dull green (25.3.90)	£400	£175
	a. No dot under "T"	£475	—
	b. Dot to right of "T"	£475	£250
	c. Dot to left of "T"	£500	£250
	d. Optd in blue-black		

1891–1900. *Stamps of Queen Victoria.*

O69	1d. lilac (Die II) (18.6.97)	70·00	15·00
	a. No dot under "T"	£100	38·00
	b. Dot to left of "T"	£100	38·00
	c. Opt inverted	£3750	£1700
	d. Ditto. Dot to left of "T"	£4000	£2000
O70	2d. grey-green and carmine (24.10.91)	£150	20·00
	a. No dot under "T"	£250	45·00
	b. Dot to left of "T"	£250	45·00
O71	4½d. green and carmine (29.9.92)	£250	£180
	b. Dot to right of "T"		
O72	1s. green and carmine (11.00)	£425	£160
	a. Opt inverted †	†	£9000

*O61/72 **For well-centred, lightly used +100%.**

The "no dot under T" variety occurred on R. 12/3 and 20/2. The "dot to left of T" comes four times in the sheet on R. 2/7, 6/7, 7/9 and 12/9. The best example of the "dot to right of T" is on R. 20/1. All three varieties were corrected around 1897.

1902. *Stamps of King Edward VII. Ordinary paper.*

O74	1d. scarlet (30.10.02)	30·00	12·00
O75	2d. yellowish green and carmine-red (29.4.02)	£140	35·00
O76	6d. pale dull purple (19.2.02)	£240	35·00
	a. Opt double, one albino	£10000	
O77	9d. dull purple and ultramarine (28.8.02)	£480	£150
O78	1s. dull green and carmine (17.12.02)	£800	£225

BOARD OF EDUCATION

BOARD OF EDUCATION

(O 8)

Optd with Type O 8

1902 (19 Feb). *Stamps of Queen Victoria.*

		Un	Used*	Used on cover
O81	5d. dull purple and blue (II)	£2000	£550	
O82	1s. green and carmine	£5500	£3500	

1902 (19 Feb)–04. *Stamps of King Edward VII. Ordinary paper.*

O83	½d. blue-green	£150	35·00	£350
O84	1d. scarlet	£150	35·00	£375
O85	2½d. ultramarine	£3000	£250	
O86	5d. dull purple and ultramarine (6.2.04)	£15000	£4000	
O87	1s. dull green and carmine (23.12.02)	£75000		

ROYAL HOUSEHOLD

R.H.

OFFICIAL

(O 9)

1902. *Stamps of King Edward VII optd with Type O 9. Ordinary paper.*

O91	½d. blue-green (29.4.02)	£350	£180	£1000
O92	1d. scarlet (19.2.02)	£300	£150	£900

ADMIRALTY

ADMIRALTY   **ADMIRALTY**

OFFICIAL   **OFFICIAL**

(O 10)   (O 11) (with different "M")

1903 (1 Apr). *Stamps of King Edward VII optd with Type O 10. Ordinary paper.*

O101	½d. blue-green	25·00	12·00
O102	1d. scarlet	15·00	6·00	£275
O103	1½d. dull purple and green	£225	£110
O104	2d. yellowish green and carmine-red	£250	£125
O105	2½d. ultramarine	£375	£110
O106	3d. purple/*yellow*	£300	£120

1903–04. *Stamps of King Edward VII optd with Type O 11. Ordinary paper.*

O107	½d. blue-green (9.03)	50·00	20·00	£450
O108	1d. scarlet (12.03)	50·00	20·00	£125
O109	1½d. dull purple and green (2.04)	£700	£450
O110	2d. yellowish green and carmine-red (3.04)	£1100	£500
O111	2½d. ultramarine (3.04)	£1200	£700
O112	3d. dull purple/*orange-yellow* (12.03)	£1000	£250

Stamps of various issues perforated with a Crown and initials ("H.M.O.W.", "O.W.", "B.T." or "S.O.") or with initials only ("H.M.S.O." or "D.S.I.R.") have also been used for official purposes, but these are outside the scope of the catalogue.

POSTAL FISCAL STAMPS

PRICES. Prices in the used column are for stamps with genuine postal cancellations dated from the time when they were authorised for use as postage stamps. Beware of stamps with fiscal cancellations removed and fraudulent postmarks applied.

VALIDITY. The 1d. Surface-printed stamps were authorised for postal use from 1 June 1881 and at the same time the 1d. postage issue, No. 166, was declared valid for fiscal purposes. The 3d. and 6d. values, together with the Embossed issues were declared valid for postal purposes by another Act effective from 1 January 1883.

SURFACE-PRINTED ISSUES

(Typo Thomas De La Rue & Co)

F 1 Rectangular Buckle

F 2

F 3 Octagonal Buckle

F 4

F 5 Double-lined Anchor   F 6 Single-lined Anchor

1853–57. P 15½×15.

		(a) Wmk F 5 (inverted) (1853–55)			
F1	F 1	1d. light blue (10.10.53)	35·00	45·00	£170
F2	F 2	1d. ochre (10.53)	£100	£120	£475
		a. *Tête-bêche* (in block of four)	£16000		
F3	F 3	1d. pale turquoise-blue (12.53)	27·00	42·00	£250
F4		1d. light blue/*blue* (12.53)	70·00	70·00	£400
F5	F 4	1d. reddish lilac/*blue glazed paper* (25.3.55)	£100	£110	£350

Only one example is known of No. F2a outside the National Postal Museum and the Royal Collection.

		(b) Wmk F 6 (1856–57)			
F6	F 4	1d. reddish lilac (*shades*)	9·25	7·75	£140
F7		1d. reddish lilac/*bluish* (*shades*) (1857)	9·25	7·75	£140

INLAND REVENUE

(F 7)

1860 (3 Apr). *No. F7 optd with Type F 7, in red.*

F8	F 4	1d. dull reddish lilac/*blue*	£700	£550	£1100

BLUE PAPER. In the following issues we no longer distinguish between bluish and white paper. There is a range of papers from white or greyish to bluish.

F 8

F 9

F 10

1860–67. *Bluish to white Paper.* P 15½×15.

		(a) Wmk F **6** *(1860)*.			
F9	F **8**	1d. reddish lilac (May)......	11·00	11·00	£140
F10	F **9**	3d. reddish lilac (June)......	£350	£225	£400
F11	F **10**	6d. reddish lilac (Oct).......	£160	£140	£350
		(b) W **40**. (Anchor 16 mm high) *(1864)*.			
F12	F **8**	1d. reddish lilac (Nov)............	9·25	9·25	£140
F13	F **9**	3d. pale reddish lilac.........	£200	£140	£400
F14	F **10**	6d. pale reddish lilac.........	£160	£140	£350
		(c) W **40** (Anchor 18 mm high) *(1867)*.			
F15	F **8**	1d. reddish lilac................	18·00	18·00	£200
F16	F **9**	3d. reddish lilac................	90·00	90·00	£350
F17	F **10**	6d. reddish lilac................	80·00	65·00	£225

For stamps perf 14, see Nos. F24/7.

F 11	F 12

Four Dies of Type F 12

Nos. F19/21 show "O" of "ONE" circular. No. F22 (Die 4) shows a horizontal oval

Die 1. Four lines of shading in left band of ribbon opposite "Y" of "PENNY", small ornaments and heavy shading under chin

Die 2. Two lines of shading in left band of ribbon. Clear line of shading under chin. Small ornaments

Die 3. Ornaments larger and joined; line of shading under chin extended half way down neck

Die 4. Ornaments much larger; straight line of shading continued to bottom of neck

1867–81. *White to bluish paper.* P 14.

		(a) W **47** (Small Anchor).			
F18	F **11**	1d. purple (1.9.67)	16·00	16·00	£110
F19	F **12**	1d. purple (Die 1) (6.68)...	5·00	5·50	£110
F20		1d. purple (Die 2) (6.76)...	20·00	14·00	£250
F21		1d. purple (Die 3) (3.77)...	10·00	10·00	£160
F22		1d. purple (Die 4) (7.78)...	6·50	6·50	£100
		(b) W **48** (Orb).			
F23	F **12**	1d. purple (Die 4) (1.81)...	6·50	3·25	90·00

1881. *White to bluish paper.* P 14.

		(a) W **40** (Anchor 18 mm high) (Jan).			
F24	F **9**	3d. reddish lilac................	£650	£350	£750
F25	F **10**	6d. reddish lilac................	£300	£140	£350

		(b) **W40** (Anchor 20 mm high) (May).			
F26	F **9**	3d. reddish lilac................	£500	£275	£550
F27	F **10**	6d. reddish lilac................	£275	£140	£350

ISSUES EMBOSSED IN COLOUR
(Made at Somerset House)

The embossed stamps were struck from dies not appropriated to any special purpose on paper which had the words "INLAND REVENUE" previously printed, and thus became available for payment of any duties for which no special stamps had been provided.

The die letters are included in the embossed designs and holes were drilled for the insertion of plugs showing figures indicating dates of striking.

F 13	F 14

INLAND REVENUE
(F 15)

INLAND REVENUE
(F 16)

1860 (3 Apr)–**71.** *Types F* **13/14** *and similar types embossed on bluish paper. Underprint Type F* **15***. No wmk. Imperf.*

			Un	Used
F28		2d. pink (Die A) (1.1.71)........................	£550	
F29		3d. pink (Die C)................................	£140	
		a. Tête-bêche (vert pair)........................	£1100	
F30		3d. pink (Die D)................................	£550	
F31		6d. pink (Die T)................................		
F32		6d. pink (Die U)................................	£275	
		a. Tête-bêche (vert pair)........................		
F33		9d. pink (Die C) (1.1.71)........................	£700	
F34		1s. pink (Die E) (28.6.61).......................	£550	
		a. Tête-bêche (vert pair)........................		
F35		1s. pink (Die F) (28.6.61).......................	£200	
		a. Tête-bêche (vert pair)........................	£800	
F36		2s. pink (Die K) (6.8.61)........................	£550	
F37		2s.6d. pink (Die N) (28.6.61)...................		
F38		2s.6d. pink (Die O) (28.6.61)...................	£275	

1871 (Aug). *As last but perf 12½.*

F39		2d. pink (Die A)................................	£350	
F42		9d. pink (Die C)................................	£800	
F43		1s. pink (Die E)................................	£550	
F44		1s. pink (Die F)................................	£475	
F45		2s.6d. pink (Die O).............................	£275	

1874 (Nov). *Types as before embossed on white paper. Underprint Type F* **16***, in green.* W **47** (Small Anchor). P 12½.

F46		2d. pink (Die A)................................		
F47		9d. pink (Die C)................................		
F48		1s. pink (Die F)................................	£550	
F49		2s.6d. pink (Die O).............................		

It is possible that the 2d., 9d. and 2s.6d. may not exist with the thin underprint, Type F **16**, in this shade.

1875 (Nov)–**80.** *As last but colour changed and on white or bluish paper.*

F50		2d. vermilion (Die A) (1880)...................	£400	
F51		9d. vermilion (Die C) (1876)...................	£550	
F52		1s. vermilion (Die E)..........................	£350	
F53		1s. vermilion (Die F)..........................	£800	
F54		2s.6d. vermilion (Die O) (1878)	£350	

1882 (Oct). *As last but* W **48** (Orbs).

F55		2d. vermilion (Die A)..........................		
F56		9d. vermilion (Die C)..........................		
F57		1s. vermilion (Die E)..........................		
F58		2s.6d. vermilion (Die O).......................	£700	£550

Although specimen overprints of Nos. F55/7 are known there is some doubt if these values were issued.

The sale of Inland Revenue stamps up to the 2s. value ceased from 30 December 1882 and stocks were called in and destroyed. The 2s.6d. value remained on sale until 2 July 1883 when it was replaced by the 2s.6d. "Postage & Revenue" stamp. Inland Revenue stamps still in the hands of the public continued to be accepted for revenue and postal purposes.

TELEGRAPH STAMPS. A priced listing of the Post Office telegraph stamps appears in Volume 1 of the Stanley Gibbons *Great Britain Specialised Catalogue.* The last listing for the private telegraph companies in the Part 1 Catalogue was in the 1940 edition and for military telegraphs the 1941 edition.

CHANNEL ISLANDS

GENERAL ISSUE

C 1 Gathering Vraic	C 2 Islanders gathering Vraic

Broken Wheel (R. 20/5)

(Des J. R. R. Stobie (1d.) or from drawing by E. Blampied (2½d.). Photo Harrison)

1948 (10 May). *Third Anniv of Liberation.* W **127** of Great Britain. P 15×14.

C1	C **1**	1d. scarlet	25	30
		a. Broken Wheel	15·00	
C2	C **2**	2½d. ultramarine	25	30

Supplies of these stamps were also available from eight head post offices on the mainland of Great Britain.

GUERNSEY

WAR OCCUPATION ISSUES

Stamps issued under the authority of the Guernsey States during the German Occupation

BISECTS. On 24 December 1940 authority was given, by Post Office notice, that prepayment of penny postage could be effected by using half a British 2d. stamp, diagonally bisected. Such stamps were first used on 27 December 1940.

The 2d. stamps generally available were those of the Postal Centenary issue, 1940 (S.G. 482) and the first colour of the King George VI issue (S.G. 465). These are listed under Nos. 482a and 465b. A number of the 2d. King George V, 1912–22, and of the King George V photogravure stamp (S.G. 442) which were in the hands of philatelists, were also bisected and used.

1

1a Loops (*half actual size*)

(Des E. W. Vaudin. Typo Guernsey Press Co Ltd)

1941–44. *Rouletted.*

		(a) White paper. No wmk.		
1	**1**	½d. light green (7.4.41)	5·25	2·50
		a. Emerald-green (6.41)................	6·00	2·00
		b. Bluish green (11.41)................	32·00	13·00
		c. Bright green (2.42)	22·00	10·00
		d. Dull green (9.42)	4·00	2·00
		e. Olive-green (2.43)....................	32·00	16·00
		f. Pale yellowish green (7.43 and later) (shades)	3·00	2·00
		g. Imperf (pair)....................	£200	
		h. Imperf between (horiz pair)........	£700	
		i. Imperf between (vert pair)........	£800	
2		1d. scarlet (18.2.41)	2·25	1·25
		a. Pale vermilion (7.43) (etc.)	3·50	1·25
		b. Carmine (1943)....................	2·00	1·50
		c. Imperf (pair)....................	£150	75·00
		d. Imperf between (horiz pair)........	£700	
		da. Imperf vert (centre stamp of horiz strip of 3)........................	£800	
		e. Imperf between (vert pair)........	£100	
		f. Printed double (scarlet shade) ...		
3		2½d. ultramarine (12.4.44)	9·75	10·00
		a. Pale ultramarine (7.44)	6·00	5·00
		b. Imperf (pair)....................	£500	
		c. Imperf between (horiz pair)........	£1000	
		(b) Bluish French bank-note paper. W **1a** (sideways).		
4	**1**	½d. bright green (11.3.42)	27·00	21·00
5		1d. scarlet (9.4.42)	14·00	21·00

The dates given for the shades of Nos. 1/3 are the months in which they were printed as indicated on the printer's imprints. Others are issue dates.

JERSEY

WAR OCCUPATION ISSUES

Stamps issued under the authority of the Jersey States during the German Occupation

1

(Des Major N. V. L. Rybot. Typo Jersey Evening Post, St. Helier)

1941–43. *White paper (thin to thick).* No wmk. P 11.

1	**1**	½d. bright green (29.1.42)	5·25	3·75
		a. Imperf between (vert pair)........	£800	
		b. Imperf between (horiz pair).......	£700	

2

c. Imperf (pair)............................	£250	
d. On greyish paper (1.43)	5·50	5·50
1d. scarlet (1.4.41)	6·25	3·50
a. Imperf between (vert pair).........	£800	
b. Imperf between (horiz pair).......	£700	
c. Imperf (pair)............................	£275	
d. On chalk-surfaced paper............	42·00	38·00
e. On greyish paper (1.43)	5·50	5·75

2 Old Jersey Farm

3 Portelet Bay

4 Corbière Lighthouse

5 Elizabeth Castle

6 Mont Orgueil Castle

7 Gathering Vraic (seaweed)

(Des E. Blampied. Eng H. Cortot. Typo French Govt Works, Paris)

1943–44. No wmk. P 13½.

3	**2**	½d. green (1 June)	9·75	10·00
		a. Rough, grey paper (6.10.43)......	9·00	6·50
4	**3**	1d. scarlet (1 June)	2·25	50
		a. On newsprint (28.2.44)...............	2·50	75
5	**4**	1½d. brown (8 June)	7·00	5·75
6	**5**	2d. orange-yellow (8 June).............	6·50	2·00
7	**6**	2½d. blue (29 June)	2·00	1·00
		a. On newsprint (25.2.44)...............	1·00	1·75
		ba. Thin paper*	£225	
8	**7**	3d. violet (29 June)	1·25	2·75
3/8		Set of 6	22·00	15·00

*On No. 7ba the design shows clearly through the back of the stamp.

British Post Offices Abroad

The origins of the network of Post Offices, Postal Agencies and Packet Agents can be recognised from the 18th century, but the system did not become established until the expansion of trade, following the end of the Napoleonic Wars in 1815.

Many offices were provided in newly acquired dependent territories, and were then, eventually, transferred from the control of the British Post Office to the evolving local administrations.

Those in foreign countries, nearly always based on existing British Consular appointments, were mostly connected to the network of British Packet lines which had been re-established in 1814. They tended to survive until the country in which they were situated established its own efficient postal service or joined the U.P.U. The term "Post Office Agent" was employed by the British G.P.O. and "Packet Agent" by the shipping lines to describe similar functions.

Listed in this section are the Crowned-circle handstamps and G.B. stamps used in the Post Offices and Agencies situated in foreign countries. Those for the territories within the scope of this catalogue will be found under the following headings:

Prices. Catalogue prices quoted in this section, and throughout the volume, covering Crowned-circle handstamps and stamps of Great Britain used abroad are for used examples with the cancellation or handstamp clearly legible. Poor impressions of the cancellations and handstamps are worth much less than the prices quoted.

They also take into account the fact that many identifiable cancellations of the post offices abroad render the stamps they obliterate in less than 'fine' condition. As a result, some stamps listed in this section are priced at less than the same items used in Great Britain, where the prices are for fine examples. Lightly cancelled stamps used in offices abroad would be worth a premium over the prices quoted.

CROWNED-CIRCLE HANDSTAMPS

Following the introduction, in 1840, of adhesive stamps in Great Britain there was considerable pressure from a number of the dependent territories for the British Post Office to provide something similar for their use.

Such suggestions were resisted, however, because of supposed operational problems, but the decision was taken, in connection with an expansion of the Packet Service, to issue a uniform series of handstamps and date stamps to the offices abroad, both in the dependent territories and in foreign countries.

Under the regulations circulated in December 1841, letters and packets forwarded through these offices to the United Kingdom or any of its territories were to be sent unpaid, the postage being collected on delivery. Where this was not possible, for example from a British colony to a foreign country or between two foreign ports, then a *crowned-circle handstamp* was to be applied with the postage, paid in advance, noted alongside in manuscript.

Examples of these handstamps were supplied over twenty years from 1842, but many continued to fulfil other functions long after the introduction of adhesive stamps in the colony.

Our listings cover the use of these handstamps for their initial purpose and the prices quoted are for examples used on cover during the pre-adhesive period.

In most instances the dates quoted are those on which the handstamp appears in the G.P.O. Record Books, but it seems to have been normal for the handstamps to be sent to the office concerned immediately following this registration. The only known examples of certain handstamps are those in The Record Books; these include St. Michaels (Azores), Cobija (Bolivia), St Vincent (Cape Verde Islands), Cartagena (CC1) and Chagres (Colombia), Cap Haitien (Haiti), Greytown (Nicaragua), Corunna (Spain), and Charleston, Mobile, New Orleans and Savannah (United States of America).

Many of the handstamps were individually cut by hand, so that each has its own characteristics, but for the purposes of the listing they have been grouped into nine Types as shown in the adjacent column. No attempt has been made to identify them by anything but the most major differences, so that minor differences in size and in the type of the crown have been ignored.

DOUBLE CIRCLE

CC 1 Curved "PAID"

CC 1a

CC 1b Curved "PAID"

CC 1c

CC 2 Straight "PAID"

SINGLE CIRCLE

CC 3 Straight "PAID"

CC 5 Curved "PAID"

CC 6 Straight "PAID"

CC 7 Curved "PAID"

GREAT BRITAIN STAMPS USED ABROAD

Prices quoted are for single stamps not on cover unless otherwise stated. Stamps on cover are worth considerably more in most cases.

In many instances obliterators allocated to post offices abroad were, at a later date re-allocated to offices at home. Postmarks on issues later than those included in our lists can therefore safely be regarded as *not* having been "used abroad".

INDEX

TYPES OF OBLITERATOR FOR GREAT BRITAIN STAMPS USED ABROAD

HORIZONTAL OVAL

(1)   (2)

(3)

(4)

VERTICAL OVAL

(5)   (6)

(7)

(8)   (9)

(10)

(11)

(11A)

(12)

(13)

(14)

(14A)

(14B)

(15)

(16)   (16A)

(17)   (17A)

(17B)   (18)

(19)   (20)

(21)

Late fee

(22)

ARGENTINE REPUBLIC

BUENOS AYRES

The first regular monthly British mail packet service was introduced in 1824, replacing a private arrangement which had previously existed for some years.

Great Britain stamps were used from 1860 until the office closed at the end of June 1873. Until 1878 the British Consul continued to sell stamps which were used in combination with an Argentine value prepaying the internal rate. The British stamps on such covers were cancelled on arrival in England.

CROWNED-CIRCLE HANDSTAMPS

CC1   CC 7 BUENOS AYRES (Black or R.)
(5.1.1851).............................. *Price on cover* £775

Stamps of GREAT BRITAIN *cancelled* "B 32" *as Types* **2**, **12** *or* **13** *in black or blue.*

1860–73.
Z1	1d. rose-red (1857)..		45·00
Z2	1d. rose-red (1864)................................ *From*		38·00
	Plate Nos. 71, 72, 73, 74, 76, 78, 79, 80, 81,		
	82, 85, 87, 89, 90, 91, 92, 93, 94, 95, 96, 97,		
	99, 101, 103, 104, 107, 108, 110, 112, 113, 114,		
	117, 118, 119, 120, 121, 123, 125, 127, 129,		
	130, 131, 135, 136, 138, 139, 140, 142, 143,		
	145, 147, 149, 150, 151, 155, 159, 163, 164,		
	166, 169, 172.		
Z3	2d. blue (1858–69)................................ *From*		45·00
	Plate Nos. 8, 9, 12, 13, 14.		
Z4	3d. carmine-rose (1862)............................		£270
Z5	3d. rose (1865) (Plate No. 4)......................		£110
Z6	3d. rose (1867–73)................................ *From*		45·00
	Plate Nos. 4, 5, 6, 7, 8, 9, 10.		
Z7	4d. rose (1857)....................................		£110
Z8	4d. red (1862) (Plate Nos. 3, 4)...................		£100
Z9	4d. vermilion (1865–73)........................... *From*		50·00
	Plate Nos. 7, 8, 9, 10, 11, 12, 13.		
Z10	6d. lilac (1856)...................................		£100
Z11	6d. lilac (1862) (Plate Nos. 3, 4)................		
Z12	6d. lilac (1865–67) (Plate Nos. 5, 6).......... *From*		80·00
Z13	6d. lilac (1867) (Plate No. 6)....................		90·00

Z14	6d. violet (1867–70) (Plate Nos. 6, 8, 9)	From	70·00
Z15	6d. buff (1872) (Plate No. 11)...........		85·00
Z16	6d. chestnut (1872) (Plate No. 11)		45·00
Z17	9d. bistre (1862)............		£325
Z18	9d. straw (1862)............		£300
Z19	9d. straw (1865)............		£475
Z20	9d. straw (1867)............		£300
Z21	10d. red-brown (1867).........		£325
Z22	1s. green (1856)............		£275
Z23	1s. green (1862)............		£170
Z24	1s. green (1865) (Plate No. 4)........		£160
Z25	1s. green (1867–73) (Plate Nos. 4, 5, 6, 7)	From	45·00
Z26	1s. green (1873–77) (Plate No. 8).......		
Z27	2s. blue (1867)............		£150
Z28	5s. rose (1867) (Plate No. 1).......		£450

A "B 32' obliteration was later used by Mauritius on its own stamps.

AZORES

ST. MICHAELS (SAN MIGUEL)

A British Postal Agency existed at Ponta Delgada, the chief port of the island, to operate with the services of the Royal Mail Steam Packet Company.

CROWNED-CIRCLE HANDSTAMPS

CC1   CC 1b ST. MICHAELS (27.5.1842).....................

Although recorded in the G.P.O. Proof Books, no example of No. CC1 is known on cover.

BOLIVIA

COBIJA

It is believed that the British Postal Agency opened in 1862. The stamps of Great Britain were used between 1865 and 1878. They can be found used in combination with Bolivia adhesive stamps paying the local postage. The Agency closed in 1881, the town having been occupied by Chile in 1879

CROWNED-CIRCLE HANDSTAMPS

CC1   CC 4 COBIJA (29.3.1862).....................

Although recorded in the G.P.O. Proof Books, no example of No. CC1 is known on cover.

Stamps of GREAT BRITAIN cancelled "C 39" as Types 4, 8 or 12.

1865–78.

Z1	1d. rose-red (Plate Nos. 93, 95)...........		
Z2	2d. blue (1858–69) (Plate No. 14).........		
Z3	3d. rose (1867–73) (Plate No. 6)........		
Z4	3d. rose (1873–76) (Plate Nos. 16, 19)......		
Z5	4d. sage-green (1877) (Plate No. 15).......		£500
Z6	6d. violet (1867–70) (Plate No. 9).......		£475
Z7	6d. buff (1872) (Plate No. 11)........		
Z8	6d. lilac (1874–76) (Plate Nos. 13, 14, 15, 16)		£375
Z9	1s. green (1867–73) (Plate Nos. 4, 5).......		£375
Z10	1s. green (1873–77) (Plate Nos. 10, 11, 12, 13)...		£375
Z11	2s. blue (1867)............		£375
Z12	5s. rose (1867–74) (Plate No. 2).........		£750

BRAZIL

The first packets ran to Brazil in 1808 when the Portuguese royal family went into exile at Rio de Janeiro. The Agencies at Bahia and Pernambuco did not open until 1851. All three agencies used the stamps of Great Britain from 1866 and these can be found used in combination with Brazil adhesive stamps paying the local postage. The agencies closed on 30 June 1874

BAHIA

CROWNED-CIRCLE HANDSTAMPS

CC1   CC 7 BAHIA (Black, B. or R.) (6.1.1851)
.... Price on cover £2750

Stamps of GREAT BRITAIN cancelled "C 81" as Type 12.

1866–74.

Z1	1d. rose-red (1864–79)...........	From	45·00
	Plate Nos. 90, 93, 96, 108, 113, 117, 135, 140, 147, 155.		
Z2	1½d. lake-red (1870–74) (Plate No. 3)		£110
Z3	2d. blue (1858–59) (Plate Nos. 9, 12, 13, 14)......		65·00
Z4	3d. rose (1865) (Plate No. 4)........		
Z5	3d. rose (1867–73) (Plate Nos. 4, 6, 8, 9, 10)......		55·00
Z6	3d. rose (1873–79) (Plate No. 11)......		
Z7	4d. vermilion (1865–73)...........	From	50·00
	Plate Nos. 8, 9, 10, 11, 12, 13.		
Z8	6d. lilac (1865–67) (Plate No. 5)........		
Z9	6d. lilac (1867) (Plate No. 6)........		90·00
Z10	6d. violet (1867–70) (Plate Nos. 6, 8, 9)		70·00
Z11	6d. buff (1872–73) (Plate Nos. 11, 12)........	From	£100
Z12	6d. chestnut (1872) (Plate No. 11)........		£100
Z13	6d. grey (1873) (Plate No. 12)........		
Z14	6d. grey (1874–76) (Plate No. 13)......		
Z15	9d. straw (1865)..........		£425
Z16	9d. straw (1867)..........		£250
Z17	1s. green (1865) (Plate No. 4)........		£170
Z18	1s. green (1867–73) (Plate Nos. 4, 5, 6, 7)..	From	50·00
Z19	1s. green (1873–77) (Plate Nos. 8, 9).......		85·00
Z20	2s. blue (1867)............		£275
Z21	5s. rose (1867) (Plate No. 1).......		£450

PERNAMBUCO

CROWNED-CIRCLE HANDSTAMPS

CC2   CC 7 PERNAMBUCO (Black or R.) (6.1.1851)
.... Price on cover £2750

Stamps of GREAT BRITAIN cancelled "C 82" as Type 12 or with circular date stamp as Type 16.

1866–74.

Z22	1d. rose-red (1864–79)............	From	45·00
	Plate Nos. 85, 108, 111, 130, 131, 132, 149, 157, 159, 160, 187.		
Z23	2d. blue (1858–69)...........	From	55·00
	Plate Nos. 9, 12, 13, 14.		
Z23a	3d. rose (1865) (Plate No. 4)........		£110
Z24	3d. rose (1867–73) (Plate Nos. 4, 5, 6, 7, 10)...		55·00
Z25	3d. rose (1873–77) (Plate No. 11)......		
Z26	4d. vermilion (1865–73)...........	From	50·00
	Plate Nos. 9, 10, 11, 12, 13, 14.		
Z27	6d. lilac (1865–67) (Plate Nos. 5, 6)......		
Z28	6d. lilac (1867) (Plate No. 6)........		80·00
Z29	6d. violet (1867–70) (Plate No. 6).........	From	70·00
Z30	6d. buff (1872–73) (Plate Nos. 11, 12)........	From	75·00
Z31	6d. chestnut (1872) (Plate No. 11).......		55·00
Z32	6d. grey (1873) (Plate No. 12)........		
Z33	9d. straw (1865)...........		£425
Z34	9d. straw (1867)...........		£225
Z35	10d. red-brown (1867)........		£300
Z36	1s. green (1865) (Plate No. 4)........		£170
Z37	1s. green (1867–73) (Plate Nos. 4, 5, 6, 7)..		50·00
Z38	2s. blue (1867)............		£250
Z39	5s. rose (1867–74) (Plate Nos. 1, 2)...........	From	£475

RIO DE JANEIRO

CROWNED-CIRCLE HANDSTAMPS

CC3	CC 7 RIO DE JANEIRO (Black, B., G. or R.) (6.1.1851)................	Price on cover	£500

Stamps of GREAT BRITAIN cancelled "C 83" as Type 12.

1866–74.

Z40	1d. rose-red (1857)...........		45·00
Z41	1d. rose-red (1864–79)...........	From	38·00
	Plate Nos. 71, 76, 80, 82, 86, 94, 103, 113, 117, 119, 123, 130, 132, 134, 135, 146, 148, 159, 161, 166, 185, 200, 204.		
Z42	2d. blue (1858–69)..........	From	38·00
	Plate Nos. 9, 12, 13, 14.		
Z43	3d. rose (1867–73)...........	From	45·00
	Plate Nos. 4, 5, 6, 7, 8, 9.		
Z44	3d. rose (1873–77) (Plate No. 11)......		
Z45	4d. vermilion (1865–73)...........	From	50·00
	Plate Nos. 8, 9, 10, 11, 12, 13, 14.		
Z46	6d. lilac (1865–67) (Plate No. 5)........		£100
Z47	6d. lilac (1867) (Plate No. 6)........		75·00
Z48	6d. violet (1867–70) (Plate Nos. 6, 8, 9)	From	70·00
Z49	6d. buff (1872) (Plate No. 11)........		75·00
Z50	6d. chestnut (1872) (Plate No. 11)........		45·00
Z51	6d. grey (1873) (Plate No. 12)........		
Z52	9d. straw (1865)...........		£400
Z53	9d. straw (1867)...........		£200
Z54	10d. red-brown (1867)........		£275
Z55	1s. green (1865) (Plate No. 4)........		£140
Z56	1s. green (1867–73) (Plate Nos. 4, 5, 6, 7)	From	45·00
Z57	1s. green (1873–77) (Plate Nos. 8, 9).		70·00
Z58	2s. blue (1867)...........		£130
Z59	5s. rose (1867–74) (Plate Nos. 1, 2).......		£425

CAPE VERDE ISLANDS

The British Packet Agency at St. Vincent opened in 1851 as part of the revised service to South America. The agency was closed by 1860.

CROWNED-CIRCLE HANDSTAMPS

CC1   CC 6 ST. VINCENT C.DE.V. (6.1.1851)

Although recorded in the G.P.O. Proof Books, no example of No. CC1 is known on cover.

CHILE

The British Postal Agency at Valparaiso opened on 7 May 1846, to be followed by further offices at Caldera (1858) and Coquimbo (1863). The stamps of Great Britain were introduced in 1865 and can be found used in combination with Chile adhesives paying the local postage. All three offices closed on 31 March 1881 when Chile joined the U.P.U.

CALDERA

Stamps of GREAT BRITAIN cancelled "C 37" as in Type 4 in black and blue.

1865–81.

Z1	1d. rose-red (1864–79)...........	From	55·00
	Plate Nos. 71, 72, 88, 90, 95, 160, 195.		
Z2	1½d. lake-red (1870–74) (Plate No. 3)......		
Z3	2d. blue (1858–69) (Plate No. 9).......		60·00
Z4	3d. rose (1865) (Plate No. 4).......		90·00
Z5	3d. rose (1867–73) (Plate Nos. 5, 7).......		65·00
Z6	3d. rose (1873–76)...........	From	55·00
	Plate Nos. 11, 12, 16, 17, 18, 19.		
Z7	4d. red (1862) (Plate No. 4)........		
Z8	4d. vermilion (1865–73)...........	From	55·00
	Plate Nos. 8, 11, 12, 13, 14.		
Z9	4d. sage-green (1877) (Plate No. 16)......		
Z10	6d. lilac (1862) (Plate No. 4)........		£100
Z11	6d. lilac (1865–67) (Plate Nos. 5, 6)......	From	£130
Z12	6d. violet (1867–70) (Plate Nos. 6, 8, 9) ...	From	90·00
Z13	6d. buff (1872) (Plate No. 11)......		
Z14	6d. chestnut (1872) (Plate No. 11)......		
Z15	6d. grey (1873) (Plate No. 12)......		
Z16	6d. grey (1874–80)...........	From	55·00
	Plate Nos. 13, 14, 15, 16, 17.		
Z17	8d. orange (1876)...........		£350
Z18	9d. straw (1867)..........		£250
Z19	10d. red-brown (1867)........		£275
Z20	1s. green (1865) (Plate No. 4)........		
Z21	1s. green 1867–73 (Plate Nos. 4, 5, 6)	From	55·00
Z22	1s. green (1873–77)...........		85·00
	Plate Nos. 8, 10, 11, 12, 13.		
Z23	2s. blue (1867)...........		£225
Z23a	2s. cobalt (1867)............		£1900
Z24	2s. brown (1880)...........		£1900
Z25	5s. rose (1867–74) (Plate No. 2).......		£475

COQUIMBO

Stamps of GREAT BRITAIN cancelled "C 40" as in Type 4 or with circular date stamp as Type 16.

1865–81.

Z26	½d. rose-red (1870–79) (Plate No. 14)......		
Z27	1d. rose-red (1857)............		
Z28	1d. rose-red (1864–79) (Plate Nos. 85, 204).........		
Z29	2d. blue (1858–69) (Plate Nos. 9, 14).........		
Z30	3d. rose (1865)............		
Z31	3d. rose (1865)............		
Z32	3d. rose (1873–76) (Plate Nos. 18, 19)...	From	55·00
Z33	4d. red (1863) (Plate No. 4) (Hair lines)......		
Z34	4d. vermilion (1865–73) (Plate Nos. 12, 14)......		60·00
Z35	4d. sage-green (1877) (Plate Nos. 15, 16) ...	From	£200
Z36	6d. lilac (1862) (Plate Nos. 3, 4)......	From	85·00
Z37	6d. lilac (1865–67) (Plate No. 5)........		
Z38	6d. lilac (1867) (Plate No. 6)........		75·00
Z39	6d. violet (1867–70) (Plate Nos. 6, 8, 9) ...	From	70·00
Z40	6d. buff (1872–73) (Plate Nos. 11, 12).......		75·00
Z41	6d. chestnut (1872) (Plate No. 11)......		
Z42	6d. grey (1873) (Plate No. 12)........		£210
Z43	6d. grey (1874–76)...........	From	55·00
	Plate Nos. 13, 14, 15, 16.		
Z44	8d. orange (1876)...........		
Z45	9d. straw (1862)...........		£300
Z46	9d. straw (1867)...........		£225
Z47	10d. red-brown (1867)........		£325
Z48	1s. green (1865) (Plate No. 4)........		£170
Z49	1s. green (1867–73) (Plate Nos. 4, 5, 6)......		55·00
Z50	1s. green (1873–77)...........	From	80·00
	Plate Nos. 8, 10, 11, 12, 13.		
Z51	2s. blue (1867)...........		£190
Z51a	2s. cobalt (1867)............		
Z52	2s. brown (1880)...........		£1900
Z53	5s. rose (1867–74) (Plate Nos. 1, 2)...........	From	£475

VALPARAISO

CROWNED-CIRCLE HANDSTAMPS

CC1	CC 1 VALPARAISO (R.) (without stop) (13.1.1846)...........................	Price on cover	£400
CC2	VALPARAISO. (R.) (with stop) (16.7.1846)...........................	Price on cover	£450

Stamps of GREAT BRITAIN cancelled "C 30", as in Types 12, 14 and 14a (without "PAID" before 1870) or with circular date stamp as Type 16.

1865–81.

Z54	½d. rose-red (1870–79)...........	From	65·00
	Plate Nos. 6,11, 12, 13, 14.		
Z55	1d. rose-red (1864–79)...........	From	32·00
	Plate Nos. 80, 84, 85, 89, 91, 101, 106, 113, 116, 122, 123, 138, 140, 141, 146, 148, 149, 152, 157, 158, 162, 167, 175, 178, 181, 185, 186, 187, 189, 190, 195, 197, 198, 199, 200, 201, 207, 209, 210, 211, 212, 213, 214, 215, 217.		
Z56	1½d. lake-red (1870–74) (Plate Nos. 1, 3)......	From	65·00
Z57	2d. blue (1858–69) (Plate Nos. 9, 13, 14, 15)......		45·00
Z58	2½d. rosy mauve (1875), white paper......		£200
	Plate No. 2.		
Z59	2½d. rosy mauve (1876) (Plate Nos. 4, 8).......		£165
Z60	3d. carmine-rose (1862)........		
Z61	3d. rose (1865) (Plate No. 4)......		
Z62	3d. rose (1867–73)...........	From	50·00
	Plate Nos. 5, 6, 7, 8, 9, 10.		
Z63	3d. rose (1873–76)...........	From	38·00
	Plate Nos. 11, 12, 14, 16, 17, 18, 19.		
Z63a	4d. red (1862) (Plate Nos. 3, 4)......		
Z64	4d. vermilion (1865–73)...........	From	50·00
	Plate Nos. 9, 10, 11, 12, 13, 14.		
Z65	4d. vermilion (1876) (Plate No. 15).......		£300
Z66	4d. sage-green (1877) (Plate Nos. 15, 16) ...	From	£200
Z67	4d. grey-brown (1880) wmk Large Garter......		
	Plate No. 17.		
Z68	6d. lilac (1862) (Plate Nos. 3, 4)......	From	£100
Z69	6d. lilac (1865) (Plate Nos. 5, 6)......		
Z70	6d. lilac (1867) (Plate No. 6)........		
Z71	6d. violet (1867–70) (Plate Nos. 6, 8, 9) ...	From	70·00
Z72	6d. buff (1872–73) (Plate Nos. 11, 12).......	From	80·00
Z73	6d. chestnut (1872) (Plate No. 11).......		45·00
Z74	6d. grey (1873) (Plate No. 12)........		£210
Z75	6d. grey (1874–80)...........	From	45·00
	Plate Nos. 13, 14, 15, 16, 17.		
Z76	6d. grey (1881) (Plate No. 17)......		
Z77	8d. orange (1876)...........		£300
Z78	9d. straw (1862)...........		
Z79	9d. straw (1865)...........		
Z80	9d. straw (1867)...........		£200
Z81	10d. red-brown (1867)........		£275
Z82	1s. green (1865) (Plate No. 4)......		
Z83	1s. green (1867–73)...........	From	38·00
	Plate Nos. 4, 5, 6, 7.		
Z84	1s. green (1873–77)...........	From	65·00
	Plate Nos. 8, 9, 10, 11, 12, 13.		
Z85	1s. orange-brown (1880) (Plate No. 13).......		£375
Z86	2s. blue (1867)...........		£120
Z86a	2s. cobalt (1867)............		£1500
Z87	2s. brown (1880)...........		£1900
Z88	5s. rose (1867–74) (Plate Nos. 1, 2).......	From	£400
Z89	10s. grey-green (1878) (wmk Cross).......		£2750
Z90	£1 brown-lilac (1878) (wmk Cross).......		£3750

1880.

Z91	1d. Venetian red............		90·00
Z92	1½d. Venetian red............		£130

COLOMBIA

The system of British Postal Agencies in the area was inaugurated by the opening of the Carthagena office in 1825. In 1842 agencies at Chagres, Panama and Santa Martha were added to the system. A further office opened at Colon in 1852, this port also being known as Aspinwall. During 1872 the system was further enlarged by an office at Savanilla, although this agency was later, 1878, transferred to Barranquilla.

Stamps of Great Britain were supplied to Carthagena, Panama and Santa Martha in 1865, Colon in 1870 and Savanilla in 1872. Combination covers with Colombia stamps paying the local postage are known from Santa Martha and Savanilla as are similar covers from Panama showing Costa Rica and El Salvador stamps.

All offices, except Chagres which had ceased to operate in 1855, closed for public business on 30 June 1881. Colon and Panama continued to exist as transit offices to deal with the mail across the isthmus. Both finally closed on 31 March 1921.

CARTHAGENA

CROWNED-CIRCLE HANDSTAMPS

CC1	CC **1b** CARTHAGENA (R.) (15.1.1841)	
CC2	CC **1** CARTHAGENA (1.7.1846).... *Price on cover*	£1000

Although recorded in the G.P.O. Proof Books, no example of No. CC1 is known on cover.

Stamps of GREAT BRITAIN cancelled "C 56" *as in Type* **4**.
1865–81.

Z1	½d. rose-red (1870–79) (Plate No. 10)		
Z2	1d. rose-red (1864–79) .... *From*	55·00	
	Plate Nos. 78, 87, 100, 111, 113, 117, 119, 125, 172, 189, 217.		
Z3	2d. blue (1858–69) (Plate Nos. 9, 14)......... *From*	55·00	
Z4	3d. rose (1865) (Plate No. 4)		
Z5	3d. rose (1865–68) (Plate Nos. 4, 5)		
Z6	3d. rose (1873–79) (Plate Nos. 12, 17, 18).. *From*	55·00	
Z7	4d. vermilion (1865–73) .... *From*	55·00	
	Plate Nos. 7, 8, 9, 10, 11, 12, 13, 14.		
Z8	4d. vermilion (1876) (Plate No. 15)	£300	
Z9	4d. sage-green (1877) (Plate Nos. 15, 16) .. *From*	£200	
Z10	6d. lilac (1865–67) (Plate Nos. 5, 6)		
Z11	6d. violet (1867–70) (Plate Nos. 6, 8)......... *From*	75·00	
Z12	6d. grey (1873) (Plate No. 12)	£210	
Z13	6d. grey (1874–76)	55·00	
	Plate Nos. 13, 14, 15, 16.		
Z14	8d. orange (1876)	£325	
Z15	9d. straw (1865)		
Z16	1s. green (1865)		
Z17	1s. green (1867–73) (Plate Nos. 4, 5, 7)...... *From*	60·00	
Z18	1s. green (1873–77) .... *From*	70·00	
	Plate Nos. 8, 9, 10, 11, 12, 13.		
Z19	1s. orange-brown (1880)		
Z20	2s. blue (1867)	£275	
Z21	5s. rose (1867) (Plate No. 1)	£500	

Cancelled "C 65" *(incorrect handstamp, supplied in error) as Type* **12**.
1866–81.

Z22	½d. rose-red (1870–79) (Plate No. 10)		
Z23	1d. rose-red (1864–79) .... *From*	75·00	
	Plate Nos. 100, 106, 111, 123.		
Z23a	1½d. lake-red (1870) (Plate No. 3)		
Z24	2d. blue (1858–69) (Plate No. 9)	75·00	
Z25	2d. rose (1880)		
Z26	2½d. blue (1880) (Plate No. 19)		
Z27	3d. rose (1867–73) (Plate No. 9)		
Z28	3d. rose (1873–79) (Plate Nos. 14, 17, 19, 20).....		
Z29	4d. vermilion (1865–73) .... *From*	60·00	
	Plate Nos. 7, 8, 9, 11, 12, 13 14.		
Z30	4d. vermilion (1876) (Plate No. 15)	£300	
Z31	4d. sage-green (1877) (Plate Nos. 15, 16) ... *From*	£200	
Z32	6d. violet (1867–70) (Plate Nos. 6, 8)	90·00	
Z33	6d. pale buff (1872) (Plate No. 11)		
Z34	6d. grey (1873) (Plate No. 12)	£210	
Z35	6d. grey (1874–80) .... *From*	60·00	
	Plate Nos. 13, 14, 15, 16, 17.		
Z36	8d. orange (1876)	£400	
Z37	9d. straw (1865)	£450	
Z38	1s. green (1867) (Plate No. 4)	£130	
Z39	1s. green (1867) (Plate Nos. 4, 5, 6, 7)....... *From*	65·00	
Z40	1s. green (1873–77) .... *From*	75·00	
	Plate Nos. 8, 11, 12, 13.		
Z41	1s. orange-brown (1880)		
Z42	2s. blue (1867)	£650	
Z43	2s. brown (1880)	£2250	
Z44	5s. rose (1867) (Plate Nos. 1, 2) .... *From*	£525	

CHAGRES

CROWNED-CIRCLE HANDSTAMPS

CC3	CC **1** CHAGRES (16.9.1846)	

Although recorded in the G.P.O. Proof Books, no example of No. CC3 is known on cover.

COLON

CROWNED-CIRCLE HANDSTAMPS

CC4	CC **5** COLON (R.) (21.6.1854) .... *Price on cover*	£4750	

Stamps of GREAT BRITAIN cancelled "E 88" *as in Type* **12** *or circular date stamp as Type* **16, 16a** *and* **17a**.
1870–81.

Z45	1d. rose-red (1864–79) .... *From*	50·00	
	Plate Nos. 107, 121, 122, 123, 125, 127, 130, 131, 133, 136, 138, 142, 150, 151, 152, 153, 155, 156, 157, 158, 160, 169, 170, 171, 174, 176, 178, 179, 184, 187, 188, 194, 195, 201, 209, 213, 214, 217.		
Z46	1d. Venetian red (1880)	£110	
Z47	1½d. lake-red (1870–74) (Plate No. 3)	£100	
Z48	2d. blue (1858–69) (Plate Nos. 14, 15)	50·00	
Z49	2d. pale rose (1880)		
Z50	3d. rose (1867–73) (Plate Nos. 6, 9)		
Z51	3d. rose (1873–76) .... *From*	55·00	
	Plate Nos. 11, 12, 16, 18, 19, 20.		
Z52	4d. vermilion (1865–73) .... *From*	55·00	
	Plate Nos. 10, 11, 12 13 14.		
Z53	4d. vermilion (1876) (Plate No. 15)		
Z54	4d. sage-green (1877) (Plate Nos. 15, 16) ... *From*	£200	
Z55	4d. grey-brown (1880) wmk Large Garter	£325	
	Plate No. 17.		
Z56	4d. grey-brown (1880) wmk Crown	75·00	
	Plate No. 17.		

Z57	6d. violet (1867–70) (Plate No. 6, 8, 9)		
Z58	6d. buff (1872) (Plate No. 11)		
Z59	6d. chestnut (1872) (Plate No. 11)	65·00	
Z60	6d. grey (1873) (Plate No. 12)		
Z61	6d. grey (1874–80)	55·00	
	Plate Nos. 13, 14, 15, 16, 17.		
Z62	8d. orange (1876)		
Z63	9d. straw (1867)	£225	
Z63a	10d. red-brown (1867)		
Z64	1s. green (1867–73) .... *From*	50·00	
	Plate Nos. 4, 5, 6, 7.		
Z65	1s. green (1873–77) .... *From*	65·00	
	Plate Nos. 8, 9, 10, 11, 12, 13.		
Z66	1s. orange-brown (1880) (Plate 13)	£375	
Z67	1s. orange-brown (1881) (Plate 13)	£140	
Z68	2s. blue (1867)	£150	
Z69	2s. brown (1880)	£1900	
Z70	5s. rose (1867) (Plate Nos. 1, 2) .... *From*	£500	

PANAMA

CROWNED-CIRCLE HANDSTAMPS

CC5	CC **1** PANAMA (R.) (24.8.1846) .... *Price on cover*	£1900	

Stamps of GREAT BRITAIN cancelled "C 35" *as in Type* **4, 11a, 14b** *or as* **21**.
1865–81.

Z71	½d. rose-red (1870–79)............... *From*	50·00	
	Plate Nos. 10, 11, 12, 13, 14, 15, 19.		
Z72	1d. rose-red (1864–79)................. *From*	32·00	
	Plate Nos. 71, 72, 76, 81, 85, 87, 88, 89, 93, 95, 96, 101, 104, 114, 122, 124, 130, 138, 139, 142, 159, 168, 171, 172, 174, 177, 179, 180, 182, 184, 185, 187, 189, 191, 192, 193, 196, 197, 200, 203, 204, 205, 207, 208, 209, 210, 211, 213, 214, 215, 218, 224.		
Z73	1½d. lake-red (1870–74) (Plate No. 3)	65·00	
Z74	2d. blue (1858–69)...................... *From*	38·00	
	Plate Nos. 9, 12, 13, 14, 15.		
Z75	2½d. rosy mauve (1875) (Plate No. 1)	£200	
Z76	2½d. rosy mauve (1876–80) (Plate Nos. 4, 12, 16).	£170	
Z77	2½d. blue (1880) (Plate No. 19)		
Z78	2½d. blue (1881) (Plate Nos. 22, 23)		
Z79	3d. carmine-rose (1862)	£250	
Z80	3d. rose (1865) (Plate No. 4)		
Z81	3d. rose (1867–73)....................... *From*	50·00	
	Plate Nos. 4, 5, 6, 7, 8, 9.		
Z82	3d. rose (1873–76)....................... *From*	38·00	
	Plate Nos. 12, 14, 15, 16, 17, 18, 19, 20.		
Z83	3d. rose (1881) (Plate Nos. 20, 21)		
Z84	4d. red (1863) (Plate No. 4) (*Hair lines*)	£110	
Z85	4d. vermilion (1865–73) .... *From*	50·00	
	Plate Nos. 7, 8, 9, 10, 11, 12, 13, 14.		
Z86	4d. vermilion (1876) (Plate No. 15)	£300	
Z87	4d. sage-green (1877) (Plate Nos. 15, 16) ... *From*	£300	
Z88	4d. grey-brown (1880) *wmk* Crown ...... *From*	55·00	
	Plate Nos. 17 18.		
Z89	6d. lilac (1862) (Plate Nos. 3, 4)........ *From*	95·00	
Z90	6d. lilac (1865–67) (Plate Nos. 5, 6)..... *From*	75·00	
Z91	6d. lilac (1867) (Plate No. 6)		
Z92	6d. violet (1867–70) (Plate Nos. 6, 8, 9)	70·00	
Z93	6d. buff (1872–73) (Plate Nos. 11, 12)...... *From*	75·00	
Z94	6d. chestnut (Plate No. 11)	50·00	
Z95	6d. grey (1873) (Plate No. 12)	£210	
Z96	6d. grey (1874–80)	50·00	
	Plate Nos. 13, 14, 15, 16, 17.		
Z97	6d. grey (1881) (Plate No. 17)	70·00	
Z98	8d. orange (1876)	£300	
Z99	9d. straw (1862)	£350	
Z100	9d. straw (1867)	£250	
Z101	10d. red-brown (1867)	£275	
Z102	1s. green (1865) (Plate No. 4)	£140	
Z103	1s. green (1867–73)....................... *From*	45·00	
	Plate Nos. 4, 5, 6, 7.		
Z104	1s. green (1873–77)....................... *From*	60·00	
	Plate Nos. 8, 9, 10, 11, 12, 13.		
Z105	1s. orange-brown (1880) (Plate No. 13)	£400	
Z106	1s. orange-brown (1881) (Plate No. 13)	£110	
Z107	2s. blue (1867)	£130	
Z108	2s. brown (1880)	£1900	
Z109	5s. rose (1867–74) (Plate Nos. 1, 2)...... *From*	£450	

1880.

Z110	1d. Venetian red	55·00	
Z111	2d. rose	£110	
Z112	2d. indigo	£190	

Later stamps cancelled "C 35" are believed to originate from sailors' letters or other forms of maritime mail.

SANTA MARTHA

CROWNED-CIRCLE HANDSTAMPS

CC6	CC **1b** SANTA MARTHA (R.) (15.12.1841) .... *Price on cover*	£1900	

Stamps of GREAT BRITAIN cancelled "C 62" *as in Type* **4**.
1865–81.

Z113	½d. rose-red (1870–79) (Plate No. 6)	90·00	
Z114	1d. rose-red (1864–79) (Plate No. 106)	65·00	
Z115	2d. blue (1858–69) (Plate Nos. 9, 13)	90·00	
Z116	4d. vermilion (1865–73) .... *From*	60·00	
	Plate Nos. 7, 8, 9, 11, 12, 13, 14.		
Z117	4d. sage-green (1877) (Plate No. 15)	£200	
Z118	4d. grey-brown (1880) wmk Large Garter	£325	
	Plate No. 17.		
Z119	4d. grey-brown (1880) wmk Crown	75·00	
	Plate No. 17.		
Z120	6d. lilac (1865–67) (Plate No. 5)	£100	
Z121	6d. grey (1873) (Plate No. 12)		
Z122	6d. grey (1874–76) (Plate No. 14)		
Z123	8d. orange (1876)	£350	
Z123a	9d. bistre (1862)		
Z124	1s. green (1865) (Plate No. 4)	£160	
Z125	1s. green (1867–73) (Plate Nos. 5, 7)...... *From*	75·00	
Z126	1s. green (1873–77) (Plate No. 8)		
Z127	2s. blue (1867)	£300	
Z128	5s. rose (1867) (Plate No. 2)	£525	

SAVANILLA (BARRANQUILLA)

Stamps of GREAT BRITAIN cancelled "F 69" *as in Type* **12**.
1872–81.

Z129	½d. rose-red (1870–79) (Plate No. 6)	90·00	
Z130	1d. rose-red (1864–79) (Plate Nos. 122, 171)	65·00	
Z131	1½d. lake-red (1870–74) (Plate No. 3)	£110	
Z132	3d. rose (1867–73) (Plate No. 7)		
Z133	3d. rose (1873–76) (Plate No. 20)	£100	
Z134	3d. rose (1881) (Plate No. 20)	£100	
Z135	4d. verm (1865–73) .... *From*	60·00	
	Plate Nos. 12, 13, 14.		
Z136	4d. vermilion (1876) (Plate No. 15)	£300	
Z137	4d. sage-green (1877) (Plate Nos. 15, 16) .. *From*	£225	
Z138	4d. grey-brown (1880) wmk Large Garter	£375	
	Plate No. 17.		
Z139	4d. grey-brown (1880) wmk Crown	75·00	
	Plate No. 17.		
Z140	6d. buff (1872) (Plate No. 11)		
Z141	6d. grey (1878) (Plate Nos. 16, 17)........ *From*	80·00	
Z142	8d. orange (1876)	£350	
Z143	1s. green (1867–73) (Plate Nos. 5, 7)	75·00	
Z144	1s. green (1873–77) (Plate Nos. 8, 11, 12, 13).	80·00	
Z145	1s. orange-brown (1880)	£400	
Z146	2s. blue (1867)	£225	
Z147	5s. rose (1867–74) (Plate No. 2)	£525	

CUBA

The British Postal Agency at Havana opened in 1762, the island then being part of the Spanish Empire. A further office, at St. Jago de Cuba, was added in 1841.

Great Britain stamps were supplied to Havana in 1865 and to St. Jago de Cuba in 1866. They continued in use until the offices closed on 30 May 1877.

HAVANA

CROWNED-CIRCLE HANDSTAMPS

1890.

CC1	CC **1b** HAVANA (13.11.1841).......... *Price on cover*	£1000	
CC2	CC **1c** HAVANA (1848).................. *Price on cover*	£1000	
CC3	CC **2** HAVANA (14.7.1848)............. *Price on cover*	£825	

Stamps of GREAT BRITAIN cancelled "C 58" *as in Type* **4**, *or as Type* **14, 14b**.
1865–77.

Z1	½d. rose-red (1870) (Plate Nos. 6, 12)	75·00	
Z2	1d. rose-red (1864–79)	60·00	
	Plate Nos. 86, 90, 93, 115, 120, 123, 144, 146, 171, 174, 208.		
Z3	2d. blue (1858–69) (Plate Nos. 9, 14, 15)	75·00	
Z4	3d. rose (1867–73) (Plate No. 4)	£140	
Z5	3d. rose (1873–76) (Plate Nos. 18, 19)		
Z6	4d. vermilion (1865–73) .... *From*	65·00	
	Plate Nos. 7, 8, 10, 11, 12, 13, 14.		
Z7	4d. vermilion (1876) (Plate No. 15)	£300	
Z8	6d. lilac (1865) (with hyphen) (Plate No. 5)		
Z9	6d. grey (1874–76) (Plate No. 15)		
Z10	8d. orange (1876)		
Z11	9d. straw (1867)	£275	
Z12	10d. red-brown (1867)	£300	
Z13	1s. green (1865) (Plate No. 4)	£160	
Z14	1s. green (1867–73) (Plate Nos. 4, 5, 7).... *From*	65·00	
Z15	1s. green (1873–77) (Plate Nos. 10, 12, 13) *From*	90·00	
Z16	2s. blue (1867)	£225	
Z17	5s. rose (1867–74) (Plate Nos. 1, 2) ..... *From*	£475	

ST. JAGO DE CUBA

CROWNED-CIRCLE HANDSTAMPS

CC4	CC **1b** ST JAGO-DE-CUBA (R.) (15.12.1841) .... *Price on cover*	£6000	

Stamps of GREAT BRITAIN cancelled "C 88" *as Type* **12**.
1866–77.

Z18	½d. rose-red (1870–79) (Plate Nos. 4, 6, 14)		
Z19	1d. rose-red (1864–79) .... *From*	£130	
	Plate Nos. 100, 105, 106, 109, 111, 120, 123, 138, 144, 146, 147, 148, 171, 208.		
Z20	1½d. lake-red (1870–74) (Plate No. 3)		
Z21	2d. blue (1858–69) (Plate Nos. 9, 12, 13, 14)	£130	
Z22	3d. rose (1867) (Plate No. 5)		
Z23	4d. vermilion (1865–73) .... *From*	£130	
	Plate Nos. 9, 10, 11, 12, 13, 14.		
Z24	4d. vermilion (1876) (Plate No. 15)	£500	
Z25	6d. violet (1867–70) (Plate Nos. 6, 8, 9) .... *From*	£325	
Z26	6d. buff (Plate No. 11)		
Z27	9d. straw (1865)		
Z27a	9d. straw (1867)		
Z28	10d. red-brown (1867)	£475	
Z29	1s. green (1867–73) (Plate Nos. 4, 5, 6).... *From*	£300	
Z30	1s. green (1873–77) (Plate Nos. 9, 10, 12, 13).....		
Z31	2s. blue (1867)		
Z32	5s. rose (1867) (Plate 1)		

DANISH WEST INDIES

ST. THOMAS

The British Postal Agency at St. Thomas opened in January 1809 and by 1825 was the office around which many of the packet routes were organised.

Great Britain stamps were introduced on 3 July 1865 and can be found used with Danish West Indies adhesives paying the local postage.

Following a hurricane in October 1867 the main British packet office was moved to Colon in Colombia.

The British Post Office at St. Thomas closed to the public on 1 September 1877, but continued to operate as a transit office for a further two years

CROWNED-CIRCLE HANDSTAMPS

CC1	CC **1** ST. THOMAS (R.) (20.2.49).. *Price on cover*	£500	
CC2	CC **6** ST. THOMAS (R.) (1.5.1855) *Price on cover*	£1650	

Stamps of GREAT BRITAIN *cancelled "C 51" as in Types* **4**, **12** *or* **14**.
1865–79.

Z1	½d. rose-red (1870–79)	38·00
	Plate Nos. 5, 6, 8, 10, 11, 12.	
Z2	1d. rose-red (1857)	
Z3	1d. rose-red (1864–79) *From*	27·00
	Plate Nos. 71, 72, 79, 81, 84, 85, 86, 87, 88, 89, 90, 93, 94, 95, 96, 97, 98, 99, 100, 101, 102, 105, 106, 107, 108, 109, 110, 111, 112, 113, 114, 116, 117, 118, 119, 120, 121, 122, 123, 124, 125, 127, 129, 130, 131, 133, 134, 136, 137, 138, 139, 140, 141, 142, 144, 145, 146, 147, 148, 149, 150, 151, 152, 154, 155, 156, 157, 158, 159, 160, 161, 162, 163, 164, 165, 166, 167, 169, 170, 171, 172, 173, 174, 175, 176, 177, 178, 179, 180, 181, 182, 184, 185, 186, 187, 189, 190, 197.	
Z4	1½d. lake-red (1870–74) (Plate Nos. 1, 3)	65·00
Z5	2d. blue (1858–69) *From*	32·00
	Plate Nos. 9, 12, 13, 14, 15.	
Z6	3d. rose (1865) (Plate No. 4)	90·00
Z7	3d. rose (1867–73) *From*	45·00
	Plate Nos. 4, 5, 6, 7, 8, 9, 10.	
Z8	3d. rose (1873–76) *From*	32·00
	Plate Nos. 11, 12, 14, 15, 16, 17, 18, 19.	
Z9	4d. red (1862) (Plate Nos. 3, 4)	75·00
Z10	4d. vermilion (1865–73) *From*	50·00
	Plate Nos. 7, 8, 9, 10, 11, 12, 13, 14.	
Z11	4d. vermilion (1876) (Plate No. 15)	£300
Z12	4d. sage-green (1877) (Plate Nos. 15, 16) .. *From*	200
Z14	6d. lilac (1864) (Plate No. 4)	150
Z15	6d. lilac (1865–67) (Plate Nos. 5, 6)	75·00
Z16	6d. lilac (1867) (Plate No. 6)	75·00
Z17	6d. violet (1867–70) (Plate No. 6, 8, 9) .... *From*	70·00
Z18	6d. buff (1872–73) (Plate Nos. 11, 12) .... *From*	75·00
Z19	6d. chestnut (1872) (Plate No. 11)	45·00
Z20	6d. grey (1873) (Plate No. 12)	210
Z21	6d. grey (1874–76) *From*	45·00
	Plate Nos. 13, 14, 15, 16.	
Z22	8d. orange (1876)	£275
Z23	9d. straw (1862)	£275
Z24	9d. bistre (1862)	£300
Z25	9d. straw (1865)	£375
Z26	9d. straw (1867)	£200
Z27	10d. red-brown (1867)	£275
Z28	1s. green (1865) (Plate No. 4)	£140
Z29	1s. green (1867–73) (Plate Nos. 4, 5, 6, 7) *From*	32·00
Z30	1s. green (1873–77) *From*	60·00
	Plate Nos. 8, 9, 10, 11, 12, 13.	
Z31	2s. blue (1867)	£130
Z32	5s. rose (1867–74) (Plate Nos. 1, 2) .... *From*	£450

DOMINICAN REPUBLIC

British Postal Agencies may have existed in the area before 1867, but it is only from that year that details can be found concerning offices at Porto Plata and St. Domingo. Both were closed in 1871, but re-opened in 1876.

Although postmarks were supplied in 1866 it seems likely that Great Britain stamps were not sent until the offices re-opened in 1876.

Covers exist showing Great Britain stamps used in combination with those of Dominican Republic with the latter paying the local postage. Both agencies finally closed in 1881.

PORTO PLATA

Stamps of GREAT BRITAIN *cancelled "C 86" or circular date stamp as in Types* **8** *or* **17**.
1876–81.

Z1	½d. rose-red (1870–79) *From*	75·00
	Plate Nos. 10, 12, 14.	
Z2	1d. rose-red (1864–79) *From*	60·00
	Plate Nos. 123, 130, 136, 146, 151, 178, 199, 200, 205, 217.	
Z3	1½d. lake-red (1870–74) (Plate No. 3)	£110
Z4	2d. blue (1858–69) (Plate Nos. 14, 15)	75·00
Z5	2½d. rosy mauve (1876–79) *From*	200
	Plate Nos. 13, 14.	
Z6	3d. rose (1873–76) (Plate No. 18)	90·00
Z7	4d. vermilion (1873) (Plate No. 14)	90·00
Z8	4d. vermilion (1876) (Plate No. 15)	£325
Z9	4d. sage-green (1877) (Plate No. 15)	£250
Z10	6d. violet (1867–70) (Plate No. 8)	
Z11	6d. grey (1874–76) (Plate No. 15)	75·00
Z12	8d. orange (1876)	£400
Z13	1s. green (1867–73) (Plate Nos. 4, 7) .... *From*	65·00
Z14	1s. green (1873–77) *From*	75·00
	Plate Nos. 11, 12, 13.	
Z15	2s. blue (1867)	£275
Z15a	5s. rose (1867–83) (Plate No. 2)	

ST. DOMINGO

Stamps of GREAT BRITAIN *cancelled "C 87" or circular date stamp as in Types* **12** *or* **16**.
1876–81.

Z16	½d. rose-red (1870–79) *From*	90·00
	Plate Nos. 5, 6, 8, 10, 11, 13.	
Z17	1d. rose-red (1864–79) *From*	65·00
	Plate Nos. 146, 154, 171, 173, 174, 176, 178, 186, 190, 197, 220.	
Z18	1½d. lake-red (1870–74) (Plate No. 3)	£110
Z19	2d. blue (1858–69) (Plate Nos. 13, 14)	£100
Z20	3d. rose (1873–76) (Plate No. 18)	
Z21	4d. vermilion (1865–73) *From*	£100
	Plate Nos. 11, 12, 14.	
Z22	4d. vermilion (1876) (Plate No. 15)	£400
Z23	4d. sage-green (1877) (Plate No. 15)	£250
Z24	6d. grey (1874–76) (Plate No. 15)	
Z25	9d. straw (1867)	
Z26	1s. green (1867) (Plate No. 4)	
Z27	1s. green (1873–77) *From*	90·00
	Plate Nos. 10, 11, 12, 13.	
Z28	2s. blue (1867)	

ECUADOR

GUAYAQUIL

The first British Postal Agent in Guayaquil was appointed in 1848. Great Britain stamps were supplied in 1865 and continued to be used until the agency closed on 30 June 1880. They can be found used in combination with stamps of Ecuador with the latter paying the local postage.

Stamps of GREAT BRITAIN *cancelled "C 41" as Type* **4**.
1865–80.

Z1	½d. rose-red (1870–79) (Plate Nos. 5, 6)	60·00
Z2	1d. rose-red (1857)	
Z3	1d. rose-red (1864–79) *From*	45·00
	Plate Nos. 74, 78, 85, 92, 94, 105, 110, 115, 133, 140, 145, 166, 174, 180, 216.	
Z4	1½d. lake-red (1870–74) (Plate No. 3)	90·00
Z5	2d. blue (1858–69) (Plate Nos. 9, 13, 14)... *From*	45·00
Z6	3d. carmine-rose (1862)	£250
Z7	3d. rose (1865) (Plate No. 4)	£120
Z8	3d. rose (1867–73) (Plate Nos. 6, 7, 9, 10).. *From*	50·00
Z9	3d. rose (1873–76) *From*	50·00
	Plate Nos. 11, 12, 15, 16, 17, 18, 19, 20.	
Z10	4d. red (1862) (Plate Nos. 3, 4)	£120
Z11	4d. vermilion (1865–73) *From*	50·00
	Plate Nos. 7, 8, 9, 10, 11, 12, 13, 14.	
Z12	4d. vermilion (1876) (Plate No. 15)	£300
Z13	4d. sage-green (1877) (Plate Nos. 15, 16) .. *From*	200
Z14	6d. lilac (1864) (Plate No. 4)	£150
Z15	6d. lilac (1865–67) (Plate Nos. 5, 6)	75·00
Z16	6d. lilac (1867) (Plate No. 6)	
Z17	6d. violet (1867–70) (Plate Nos. 6, 8, 9)	70·00
Z18	6d. buff (1872–73) (Plate Nos. 11,12)	80·00
Z19	6d. chestnut (1872) (Plate No. 11)	
Z20	6d. grey (1873) (Plate No. 12)	
Z21	6d. grey (1874–76) *From*	50·00
	Plate Nos. 13, 14, 15, 16.	
Z22	8d. orange (1876)	£325
Z23	9d. straw (1862)	£275
Z24	9d. straw (1867)	£200
Z25	10d. red-brown (1867)	£300
Z26	1s. green (1865) (Plate No. 4)	£160
Z27	1s. green (1867–73) (Plate Nos. 4, 5, 6, 7).. *From*	45·00
Z28	1s. green (1873–77) *From*	75·00
	Plate Nos. 8, 9, 10, 11, 12, 13.	
Z29	2s. blue (1867)	£150
Z30	2s. brown (1880)	£2250
Z31	5s. rose (1867–74) (Plate Nos. 1, 2) *From*	£450

FERNANDO PO

The British government leased naval facilities on this Spanish island from 1827 until 1834. A British Consul was appointed in 1849 and a postal agency was opened on 1 April 1858.

The use of Great Britain stamps was authorised in 1858, but a cancellation was not supplied until 1874. The office remained open until 1877.

CROWNED-CIRCLE HANDSTAMPS

CC1	CC **4** FERNANDO-PO (R.)		
	(19.2.1859)	*Price on cover*	£5500

Stamps of GREAT BRITAIN *cancelled "247" as Type* **9**.
1874–77.

Z1	4d. vermilion (1865–72) (Plate Nos. 13, 14)	
Z2	4d. vermilion (1876) (Plate No. 15)	
Z3	6d. grey (1874–76) (Plate Nos. 13, 14, 15, 16)	

GUADELOUPE

A British Packet Agency was established on Guadeloupe on 1 October 1848 and continued to function until 1874.

No. CC1 is often found used in conjunction with French Colonies (General Issues) adhesive stamps.

A similar packet agency existed on Martinique from 1 October 1848 until 1879, but no crowned-circle handstamp was issued for it.

CROWNED-CIRCLE HANDSTAMPS

CC1	CC **1** GUADALOUPE (R., B. or Black)		
	(9.3.1849)	*Price on cover*	£2000

HAITI

The original British Postal Agencies in Haiti date from 1830 when it is known a Packet Agency was established at Jacmel. An office at Port-au-Prince followed in 1842, both these agencies remaining in operation until 30 June 1881.

During this period short-lived agencies also operated in the following Haitian towns: Aux Cayes (1848 to 1863), Cap Haitien (1842 to 1863), Gonaives (1849 to 1857) and St. Marc (1854 to 1861). A further agency may have operated at Le Mole around the year 1841.

Great Britain stamps were supplied to Jacmel in 1865 and to Port-au-Prince in 1869.

CAP HAITIEN

CROWNED-CIRCLE HANDSTAMPS

CC1	CC **1b** CAPE-HAITIEN (R.) (31.12.1841)	

Although recorded in the G.P.O. Proof Books, no example of No. CC1 is known on cover.

JACMEL

CROWNED-CIRCLE HANDSTAMPS

CC2	CC **1b** JACMEL (R.) (29.6.1843)	*Price on cover*	£900

Stamps of GREAT BRITAIN *cancelled "C 59" as Type* **4** *or with circular date stamp as Type* **16a**.
1865–81.

Z1	½d. rose-red (1870–79) *From*	60·00
	Plate Nos. 4, 5, 6, 10, 11, 12, 14, 15.	

Z2	1d. rose-red (1864–79) *From*	45·00
	Plate Nos. 74, 81, 84, 87, 95, 106, 107, 109, 122, 136, 137, 139, 146, 148, 150, 151, 152, 156, 157, 159, 160, 162, 164, 166, 167, 170, 171, 179, 181, 183, 184, 186, 187, 189, 192, 194, 198, 200, 204, 206, 215, 219.	
Z3	1½d. lake-red (1870–74) (Plate No. 3)	65·00
Z4	2d. blue (1858–69) (Plate Nos. 9, 13, 14, 15)	45·00
Z5	2½d. rosy mauve (1876) (Plate No. 4)	
Z6	3d. rose (1867–73) *From*	50·00
	Plate Nos. 5, 6, 7, 8, 9, 10.	
Z7	3d. rose (1873–76) *From*	50·00
	Plate Nos. 11, 12, 14, 16, 17, 18, 19.	
Z8	4d. red (1863) (Plate No. 4) (*Hair lines*)	£120
Z9	4d. vermilion (1865–73) *From*	50·00
	Plate Nos. 7, 8, 9, 10, 11, 12, 13, 14.	
Z10	4d. vermilion (1876) (Plate No. 15)	£300
Z11	4d. sage-green (1877) (Plate Nos. 15, 16) ... *From*	200
Z12	4d. grey-brown (1880) *wmk* Large Garter.	£325
	Plate No. 17.	
Z13	4d. grey-brown (1880) *wmk* Crown	55·00
	Plate No. 17.	
Z14	6d. lilac (1867) (Plate Nos. 5, 6)	80·00
Z15	6d. violet (1867–70) (Plate Nos. 8, 9)	75·00
Z16	6d. buff (1872–73) (Plate Nos. 11, 12) .... *From*	80·00
Z17	6d. chestnut (1872) (Plate No. 11)	
Z18	6d. grey (1873) (Plate No. 12)	
Z19	6d. grey (1874–76) *From*	55·00
	Plate Nos. 13, 14, 15, 16, 17.	
Z20	8d. orange (1876)	£325
Z21	9d. straw (1862)	£275
Z22	9d. straw (1867)	£200
Z23	10d. red-brown (1867)	£300
Z24	1s. green (1865) (Plate No. 4)	£140
Z25	1s. green (1867–73) (Plate Nos. 4, 5, 6, 7) *From*	45·00
Z26	1s. green (1873–77) *From*	65·00
	Plate Nos. 8, 9, 10, 11, 12, 13.	
Z27	1s. orange-brown (1880) (Plate No. 13)	£375
Z28	2s. blue (1867)	£130
Z29	2s. brown (1880)	£2250
Z30	5s. rose (1867–74) (Plate Nos. 1, 2) *From*	£450

1880.

Z31	½d. green (1880)	55·00
Z32	1d. Venetian red	55·00
Z33	1½d. Venetian red	75·00
Z34	2d. rose	£110

PORT-AU-PRINCE

CROWNED-CIRCLE HANDSTAMPS

CC3	CC **1b** PORT-AU-PRINCE (R.)		
	(29.6.1843)	*Price on cover*	£2250

Stamps of GREAT BRITAIN *cancelled "E 53" as in Types* **8**, **12** *or* **16**.
1869–81.

Z35	½d. rose-red (1870–79) *From*	60·00
	Plate Nos. 5, 6, 10, 11, 12, 13, 14.	
Z36	1d. rose-red (1864–79) *From*	45·00
	Plate Nos. 87, 134, 154,146, 159, 167, 171, 173, 174, 177, 181, 183, 187, 189, 193, 199, 200, 201, 202, 206, 209, 210, 218, 219.	
Z37	1½d. lake-red (1870–74) (Plate No. 3)	80·00
Z38	2d. blue (1858–69) (Plate Nos. 9, 14, 15)	50·00
Z40	2½d. rosy mauve (1876–79) (Plate Nos. 3, 9) *From*	£150
Z41	3d. rose (1867–73) (Plate Nos. 6, 7)	50·00
Z42	3d. rose (1873–76) (Plate Nos. 17, 18, 20).. *From*	50·00
Z43	4d. vermilion (1865–73) *From*	50·00
	Plate Nos. 11, 12, 13, 14.	
Z44	4d. vermilion (1876) (Plate No. 15)	£300
Z45	4d. sage-green (1877) (Plate Nos. 15, 16) ... *From*	200
Z46	4d. grey-brown (1880) *wmk.*	£325
	Large Garter Plate No. 17.	
Z47	4d. grey-brown (1880) *wmk* Crown	55·00
	Plate No. 17.	
Z48	6d. grey (1874–76) (Plate Nos. 15, 16).	
Z49	8d. orange (1876)	£325
Z50	1s. green (1867–73) (Plate Nos. 4, 5, 6, 7).. *From*	45·00
Z51	1s. green (1873–77) *From*	65·00
	Plate Nos. 8, 9, 10, 11, 12, 13.	
Z52	1s. orange-brown (1880) (Plate No. 13)	£375
Z53	1s. orange-brown (1880) (Plate No. 13)	£120
Z54	2s. blue (1867).	£160
Z55	2s. brown (1880)	£2250
Z56	5s. rose (1867–74) (Plate Nos. 1, 2) *From*	£450
Z57	10s. greenish grey (1878)	£3250

1880.

Z58	½d. green.	55·00
Z59	1d. Venetian red	55·00
Z60	1½d. Venetian red	75·00
Z61	2d. rose	£110

MACAO

A British Consular Post Office opened in 1841. It had been preceded by the Macao Boat Office, possibly a private venture, which operated in the 1830s. The office closed when the consulate closed on 30 September 1845, but was back in operation by 1854.

The Agency continued to function, in conjunction with the Hong Kong Post Office, until 28 February 1884 when Portugal joined the U.P.U.

CROWNED-CIRCLE HANDSTAMPS

Z 2

CC1	– PAID AT MACAO (crowned-oval 20 mm wide)		
	(R.) (1844)	*Price on cover*	£32500

CC2   Z **2** Crown and Macao (1881)................................

No. CC2 with the Crown removed was used by the Portuguese post office in Macao as a cancellation until 1890.

A locally-cut mark, as Type CC **2**, inscribed "PAGO EM MACAO" is known on covers between 1870 and 1877. It was probably used by the Portuguese postmaster to send letters via the British Post Office (*Price* £10000).

MADEIRA

The British Packet Agency on this Portuguese island was opened in 1767 and was of increased importance from 1808 following the exile of the Portuguese royal family to Brazil. The South American packets ceased to call in 1858. It appears to have closed sometime around 1860.

CROWN-CIRCLE HANDSTAMPS
CC1   CC **1b** MADEIRA (R). (28.2.1842)... *Price on cover* £17500

MEXICO

The British Postal Agency at Vera Cruz opened in 1825, following the introduction of the Mexican Packet service. No handstamps were supplied, however, until 1842, when a similar agency at Tampico was set up.

Great Britain stamps were used at Tampico from 1867, but, apparently, were never sent to the Vera Cruz office. Combination covers exist showing the local postage paid by Mexican adhesives. The Agency at Vera Cruz closed in 1874 and that at Tampico in 1876.

TAMPICO

CROWNED-CIRCLE HANDSTAMPS
CC1   CC **1b** TAMPICO (R). (13.11.1841)... *Price on cover* £1750

No. CC1 may be found on cover, used in conjunction with Mexico adhesive stamps.

Stamps of GREAT BRITAIN *cancelled* "C 63" *as Type* **4**.
1867–76.
Z1	1d. rose-red (1864–79)................................ *From*	£110
	Plate Nos. 81, 89, 103, 117, 139, 147.	
Z2	2d. blue (1858–69) (Plate Nos. 9, 14)...................	£150
Z3	4d. vermilion (1865–73)................................	90·00
	Plate Nos. 7, 8, 10, 11, 12, 13, 14.	
Z4	1s. green (1867–73) (Plate Nos. 4, 5, 7, 8)..........	£130
Z5	2s. blue (1867)................................	£400

VERA CRUZ

CROWNED-CIRCLE HANDSTAMPS
CC2	CC **1b** VERA CRUZ (R.)		
	(13.11.1841) .... *Price on cover*	£1750
CC3	VERA CRUZ (Black)		
	(*circa* 1845) .... *Price on cover*	£900

NICARAGUA

GREYTOWN

British involvement on the Mosquito Coast of Nicaragua dates from 1655 when contacts were first made with the indigenous Misquito Indians. A formal alliance was signed in 1740 and the area was considered as a British dependency until the Spanish authorities negotiated a withdrawal in 1786.

The Misquitos remained under British protection, however, and, following the revolutionary period in the Spanish dominions, this eventually led to the appropriation, by the Misquitos with British backing, of the town of San Juan del Norte, later renamed Greytown.

The port was included in the Royal West Indian Mail Steam Packet Company's mail network from January 1842, forming part of the Jamaica District. This arrangement only lasted until September of that year, however, although packets were once again calling at Greytown by November 1844. Following the discovery of gold in California the office increased in importance, owing to the overland traffic, although the first distinctive postmark is not recorded in use until February 1856.

A subsidiary agency, without its own postmark, operated at Bluefields from 1857 to 1863.

The British Protectorate over the Misquitos ended in 1860, but the British Post Office at Greytown continued to operate, being supplied with Great Britain stamps in 1865. These are occasionally found used in combination with Nicaragua issues, which had only internal validity.

The British Post Office at Greytown closed on 1 May 1882 when the Republic of Nicaragua joined the U.P.U.

CROWNED-CIRCLE HANDSTAMPS
CC1   C **4** GREYTOWN (R.) (14.4.1859) ....

Although recorded in the G.P.O. Proof Books, no example of No. CC1 is known on cover.

Stamps of GREAT BRITAIN *cancelled* "C 57" *as in Types* **4** (*issued* 1865), **14a** (*issued* 1875), *or with circular postmark as Type* **16** (*issued* 1864).
1865–82.
Z1	½d. rose-red (1870–79) (Plate Nos. 5, 10, 11).......	80·00
Z2	1d. rose-red (1864–79)................................	50·00
	Plate Nos. 180, 197, 210.	
Z3	1½d. lake-red (1870) (Plate No. 3)...................	75·00
Z4	2d. blue (1858–69) (Plate Nos. 9, 14, 15)............	
Z5	3d. rose (1873–76) (Plate Nos. 17, 18, 19, 20).....	55·00
Z6	3d. rose (1881) (Plate No. 20)........................	
Z7	4d. vermilion (1865–73)................................ *From*	55·00
	Plate Nos. 8, 10, 11, 12, 13, 14.	
Z8	4d. vermilion (1876) (Plate No. 15)...................	£300
Z9	4d. sage-green (1877) (Plate Nos. 15, 16) ... *From*	£200
Z10	4d. grey-brown (1880) wmk Large Garter............	£325
	Plate No. 17.	
Z11	4d. grey-brown (1880) wmk Crown....................	90·00
	Plate No. 17.	
Z12	6d. grey (1874–76) (Plate Nos. 14, 15, 16, 17).....	95·00
Z13	8d. orange (1876)................................	£300
Z14	1s. green (1865) (Plate No. 4)........................	
Z15	1s. green (1867–73) (Plate Nos. 6, 7).................	
Z16	1s. green (1873–77)................................ *From*	65·00
	Plate Nos. 8, 10, 12, 13.	

Z17	1s. orange-brown (1880) (Plate No. 13)...............	£375
Z18	1s. orange-brown (1881) (Plate No. 13)...............	£110
Z19	2s. blue (1867)................................	£160
Z20	2s. brown (1880)................................	£2250
Z21	5s. rose (1867–74) (Plate Nos. 1, 2).................	£450
Z22	5s. rose (1882) (Plate No. 4), *blue paper*.........	£2250
Z23	10s. greenish grey (1878)........................	£3250

1880.
Z24	1d. Venetian red................................	75·00
Z25	1½d. Venetian red................................	75·00

PERU

British Agencies in Peru date from 1846 when offices were established at Arica and Callao. The network was later expanded to include agencies at Paita (1848), Pisco (1868) and Iquique and Islay (both 1869). This last office was transferred to Mollendo in 1877.

It is believed that a further agency existed at Pisagua, but no details exist.

Great Britain stamps were supplied from 1865 and are often found in combination with Peru adhesives which paid the local postal tax.

The Postal Agency at Pisco closed in 1870 and the remainder in 1879, the towns of Arica, Iquique and Pisagua passing to Chile by treaty in 1883.

ARICA

CROWNED-CIRCLE HANDSTAMPS
CC1	CC **1** ARICA (Black or R.)		
	(5.11.1850) .... *Price on cover*	£4250

Stamps of Great Britain *cancelled* "C 36" *as Types* **4**, **12**, **14b** *and* **16a** *in black and blue*.
1865–79.
Z1	½d. rose-red (1870–79)........................ *From*	75·00
	Plate Nos. 5, 6, 10, 11, 13.	
Z2	1d. rose-red (1864–79)........................ *From*	55·00
	Plate Nos. 102, 139, 140, 163, 167.	
Z3	1½d. lake-red (1870–74) (Plate No. 3)	
Z4	2d. blue (1858–69) (Plate Nos. 5, 9).................	75·00
Z5	3d. rose (1867–73) (Plate Nos. 5, 9)	
Z6	3d. rose (1873–76)........................ *From*	55·00
	Plate Nos. 11, 12, 17, 18, 19.	
Z7	4d. vermilion (1865–73)........................ *From*	55·00
	Plate Nos. 10, 11, 12, 13, 14.	
Z8	4d. vermilion (1876) (Plate No. 15)	
Z9	4d. sage-green (1877) (Plate Nos. 15, 16)...........	£225
Z10	6d. lilac (1862) (Plate Nos. 3, 4)...................	
Z11	6d. lilac (1865–67) (Plate No. 5)...................	
Z12	6d. violet (1867–70) (Plate Nos. 6, 8, 9) ..... *From*	80·00
Z13	6d. buff (1872) (Plate No. 11)........................	£100
Z14	6d. chestnut (1872) (Plate No. 11)...................	£100
Z15	6d. grey (1873) (Plate No. 12)........................	£210
Z16	6d. grey (1874–76)........................ *From*	55·00
	Plate Nos. 13, 14, 15, 16.	
Z17	8d. orange (1876)................................	
Z18	9d. straw (1862)................................	
Z19	9d. straw (1865)................................	
Z20	9d. straw (1867)................................	£225
Z21	10d. red-brown (1867)................................	
Z22	1s. green (1862)................................	
Z23	1s. green (1865)................................	
Z24	1s. green (1867–73) (Plate Nos. 4, 5, 6, 7).. *From*	55·00
Z25	1s. green (1873–77)........................ *From*	70·00
	Plate Nos. 8, 9, 10, 11, 12, 13.	
Z26	2s. blue (1867)................................	£175
Z27	5s. rose (1867–74) (Plate Nos. 1, 2)........... *From*	£450

CALLAO

CROWNED-CIRCLE HANDSTAMPS
CC2	CC **1** CALLAO (R.) (13.1.1846)..... *Price on cover*	£650

A second version of No. CC 2, showing "PAID" more curved, was supplied in July 1847.

No. CC2 can be found used on covers from 1865 showing the local postage paid by a Peru adhesive.

Stamps of GREAT BRITAIN *cancelled* "C 38" *as in Types* **4**, **12** *and* **14b**, *with circular date stamp as* **16a** *or with boxed handstamp Type* **22**.
1865–79.
Z28	½d. rose-red (1870–79)........................ *From*	45·00
	Plate Nos. 5, 6, 10, 11, 12, 13, 14.	
Z29	1d. rose-red (1864–79)........................ *From*	32·00
	Plate Nos. 74, 88, 89, 93, 94, 97, 108, 123, 127,	
	128, 130, 134, 137, 139, 140, 141, 143, 144,	
	145, 146, 148, 149, 156, 157, 160, 163, 167,	
	171, 172, 173, 175, 176, 180, 181, 182, 183,	
	185, 187, 190, 193, 195, 198, 199, 200, 201,	
	204, 206, 209, 210, 212, 213, 215.	
Z30	1½d. lake-red (1870–74) (Plate No. 3)	
Z31	2d. blue (1858–69)........................ *From*	32·00
	Plate Nos. 9, 12, 13, 14, 15.	
Z32	3d. carmine-rose (1862)........................	
Z33	3d. rose (1865) (Plate No. 4)........................	£100
Z34	3d. rose (1867–73)........................ *From*	45·00
	Plate Nos. 5, 6, 7, 8, 9, 10.	
Z35	3d. rose (1873–76)........................ *From*	45·00
	Plate Nos. 11, 12, 14, 15, 16, 17, 18, 19.	
Z36	4d. red (1862) (Plate Nos. 3, 4)...................	
Z37	4d. vermilion (1865–73)........................ *From*	38·00
	Plate Nos. 8, 10, 11, 12, 13, 14.	
Z38	4d. vermilion (1876) (Plate No. 15)...................	£300
Z39	4d. sage-green (1877) (Plate Nos. 15, 16)...........	£200
Z40	6d. lilac (1862) (Plate Nos. 3, 4)...................	
Z40a	6d. lilac (1865) (Plate No. 5)........................	
Z41	6d. lilac (1867)................................	
Z42	6d. violet (1867–70)........................ *From*	70·00
	Plate Nos. 6, 8, 9.	
Z43	6d. buff (1872–73) (Plate Nos. 11, 12) .... *From*	70·00
Z44	6d. chestnut (1872) (Plate No. 11)...................	50·00
Z45	6d. grey (1873) (Plate No. 12)........................	£210
Z46	6d. grey (1874–80)........................ *From*	50·00
	Plate Nos. 13, 14, 15, 16.	
Z47	8d. orange (1876)................................	£275
Z48	9d. straw (1862)................................	
Z49	9d. straw (1865)................................	£400
Z50	9d. straw (1867)................................	£200

Z51	10d. red-brown (1867)................................	£275
Z52	1s. green (1865)................................	
Z53	1s. green (1867–73)........................ *From*	38·00
	Plate Nos. 4, 5, 6, 7.	
254	1s. green (1873–77)........................ *From*	55·00
	Plate Nos. 8, 9, 10, 11, 12, 13.	
Z55	2s. blue (1867)................................	£120
Z56	5s. rose (1867–74) (Plate Nos. 1, 2)........... *From*	£450

IQUIQUE

Stamps of GREAT BRITAIN *cancelled* "D 87" *as Type* **12**.
1865–79.
Z57	½d. rose-red (1870–79) (Plate Nos. 5, 6, 13, 14)..	75·00
Z58	1d. rose-red (1864–79)................................	50·00
	Plate Nos. 76, 179, 185, 205.	
Z59	2d. blue (1858–69) (Plate Nos. 9, 12, 13, 14).......	50·00
Z60	3d. rose (1867–73) (Plate Nos. 5, 6, 7, 8, 9) *From*	60·00
Z61	3d. rose (1873–76) (Plate Nos. 12, 18, 19).........	75·00
Z62	4d. vermilion (1865–73)........................ *From*	65·00
	Plate Nos. 12, 13, 14.	
Z63	4d. vermilion (1876) (Plate No. 15)...................	£300
Z64	4d. sage-green (1877) (Plate Nos. 15, 16) ... *From*	£200
Z65	6d. mauve (1869) (Plate Nos. 8, 9)...................	
Z66	6d. buff (1872–73) (Plate Nos. 11, 12)...............	£110
Z67	6d. chestnut (1872) (Plate No. 11)...................	
Z68	6d. grey (1873) (Plate No. 12)........................	£210
Z69	6d. grey (1874–76) (Plate Nos. 13, 14, 15, 16).....	80·00
Z70	8d. orange (1876)................................	£325
Z71	9d. straw (1867)................................	£200
Z72	10d. red-brown (1867)................................	
Z73	1s. green (1867–73) (Plate Nos. 4, 6, 7)..... *From*	60·00
Z74	1s. green (1873–77)........................ *From*	80·00
	Plate Nos. 8, 9, 10, 11, 12, 13.	
Z75	2s. blue (1867)................................	£225

ISLAY (*later* MOLLENDO)

CROWNED-CIRCLE HANDSTAMPS
CC4	CC **1** ISLAY (Black or R.)		
	(23.10.1850) .... *Price on cover*	£5000

Stamps of GREAT BRITAIN *cancelled* "C 42" *as Type* **4** *or with circular date stamp as Type* **16**.
1865–79.
Z76	1d. rose-red (1864–79)........................ *From*	55·00
	Plate Nos. 78, 84, 87, 88, 96, 103, 125, 134.	
Z77	1½d. lake-red (1870–74) (Plate No. 3)...............	
Z78	2d. blue (1858–69) (Plate Nos. 9, 13, 15)...........	55·00
Z79	3d. carmine-rose (1862)........................	
Z80	3d. rose (1865)................................	£110
Z81	3d. rose (1867–73) (Plate Nos. 4, 5, 6, 10).. *From*	60·00
Z82	4d. red (1862) (Plate Nos. 3, 4)...................	£130
Z83	4d. vermilion (1865–73)................................	60·00
	Plate Nos. 9, 10, 11, 12, 13.	
Z84	4d. vermilion (1876) (Plate No. 15)...................	
Z85	4d. sage-green (1877) (Plate Nos. 15, 16) ... *From*	£200
Z86	6d. lilac (1862) (Plate Nos. 3, 4)............... *From*	90·00
Z87	6d. lilac (1865) (Plate No. 5)........................	80·00
Z88	6d. violet (1867–70) (Plate Nos. 6, 8, 9) ... *From*	80·00
Z88a	6d. chestnut (1872) (Plate No. 11)...................	
Z89	6d. buff (1873) (Plate No. 12)........................	
Z90	6d. grey (1873) (Plate No. 12)........................	
Z91	6d. grey (1874–76)........................ *From*	65·00
	Plate Nos. 13, 14, 15, 16.	
Z92	9d. straw (1867)................................	£375
Z93	9d. straw (1865)................................	£200
Z94	10d. red-brown (1867)................................	£275
Z95	1s. green (1865) (Plate No. 4)........................	
Z96	1s. green (1867–73) (Plate Nos. 4, 5, 6, 7).. *From*	60·00
Z97	1s. green (1873–77)........................ *From*	80·00
	Plate Nos. 8, 10, 12, 13.	
Z98	2s. blue (1867)................................	
Z99	5s. rose (1867) (Plate No. 1)........................	

PAITA

CROWNED-CIRCLE HANDSTAMPS
CC5	CC **1** PAITA (Black or R.)		
	(5.11.1850) .... *Price on cover*	£6500

Stamps of GREAT BRITAIN *cancelled* "C 43" *as Type* **4** *or with circular date stamp as Type* **16a** *in black or blue*.
1865–79.
Z100	1d. rose-red (1864–79) (Plate Nos. 127, 147).......	65·00
Z101	2d. blue (1858–69) (Plate Nos. 9, 14)...............	65·00
Z102	3d. rose (1867–73) (Plate Nos. 5, 6).................	75·00
Z103	3d. rose (1876) (Plate Nos. 17, 18, 19).............	75·00
Z104	4d. vermilion (1865–73)........................ *From*	75·00
	Plate Nos. 10, 11, 12, 13, 14.	
Z105	4d. sage-green (1877) (Plate No. 15)	
Z106	6d. lilac (1862) (Plate No. 3)........................	£110
Z107	6d. lilac (1865–67) (Plate Nos. 5, 6)........... *From*	£100
Z108	6d. violet (1867–70) (Plate Nos. 6, 8, 9) ... *From*	90·00
Z109	6d. buff (1872–73) (Plate Nos. 11, 12) .... *From*	£100
Z110	6d. chestnut (Plate No. 11)........................	75·00
Z111	6d. grey (1873)................................	
Z112	6d. grey (1874–76) (Plate Nos. 13, 14, 15).........	
Z113	9d. straw (1862)................................	
Z114	10d. red-brown (1867)................................	£375
Z115	1s. green (1865) (Plate No. 4)........................	
Z116	1s. green (1867–73) (Plate No. 4)...................	75·00
Z117	1s. green (1873–77) (Plate Nos. 8, 9, 10, 13).....	90·00
Z118	2s. blue (1867)................................	£300
Z119	5s. rose (1867) (Plate No. 1)........................	£650

PISAGUA(?)

Stamps of GREAT BRITAIN *cancelled* "D 65" *as Type* **12**.
Z119a	1d. rose-red (1864–79)................................	
Z119b	2d. blue (1858–69)................................	
Z120	2s. blue (1867)................................	

There is no record of an office opening at Pisagua. The few known examples of "D 65" in red are on loose stamps. The 2s. blue listing, based on a single cover cancelled "D 65" in black, is without any datestamp confirming its origin.

We continue to list this office pending further research.

PISCO AND CHINCHA ISLANDS

Stamps of GREAT BRITAIN cancelled "D 74" as Type **12**.
1865–70.

Z121	2d. blue (1858–69) (Plate No. 9)............................	
Z122	4d. vermilion (1865–73) (Plate Nos. 10, 12)........	£550
Z123	6d. violet (1868) (Plate No. 6)	£1100
Z124	1s. green (1867) (Plate No. 4)..............................	
Z125	2s. blue (1867)..	£1300

PORTO RICO

A British Postal Agency operated at San Juan from 1844. On 24 October 1872 further offices were opened at Aguadilla, Arroyo, Mayaguez and Ponce, with Naguabo added three years later.

Great Britain stamps were used from 1865 to 1877, but few letters appear to have used the San Juan postal agency between 1866 and 1873 due to various natural disasters and the hostile attitude of the local authorities. All the British Agencies closed on 1 May 1877.

AGUADILLA

Stamps of GREAT BRITAIN cancelled "F 84" as Type **8**.
1873–77.

Z1	½d. rose-red (1870) (Plate No. 6)	90·00
Z2	1d. rose-red (1864–79)...	55·00
	Plate Nos. 119, 122, 139, 149, 156, 160.	
Z3	2d. blue (1858–69) (Plate No. 14).........................	
Z4	3d. rose (1867–73) (Plate Nos. 7, 8, 9)................	
Z5	3d. rose (1873–76) (Plate No. 12).........................	
Z6	4d. vermilion (1865–73)........................... From	65·00
	Plate Nos. 12, 13, 14.	
Z7	4d. vermilion (1876) (Plate No. 15)......................	£300
Z7a	6d. pale buff (1872–73) (Plate No. 11)	
Z8	6d. grey (1874–76) (Plate Nos. 13, 14)................	
Z9	9d. straw (1867)	£350
Z10	10d. red-brown (1867)	£350
Z11	1s. green (1867–73) (Plate Nos. 4, 5, 6, 7).. From	60·00
Z12	1s. green (1873–77).................................... From	70·00
	Plate Nos. 8, 9, 10, 11, 12.	
Z13	2s. blue (1867)..	£275

ARROYO

Stamps of GREAT BRITAIN cancelled "F 83" as Type **8** (black or red) or with circular date stamps as Types **17** and **17b**.
1873–77.

Z14	½d. rose-red 1870 (Plate No. 5)............................	60·00
Z15	1d. rose-red (1864–79)...	55·00
	Plate Nos. 149, 150, 151, 156, 164, 174, 175.	
Z16	1½d. lake-red (1870) (Plate Nos. 1, 3)...................	
Z17	2d. blue (1858–69) (Plate No. 9)...........................	
Z18	3d. rose (1867–73) (Plate Nos. 5, 7, 10)...... From	60·00
Z19	3d. rose 1873–76...................................... From	65·00
	Plate Nos. 11, 12, 14, 16, 18.	
Z20	4d. verm (1865–73) (Plate Nos. 12, 13, 14) From	55·00
Z21	4d. vermilion (1876) (Plate No. 15)......................	£300
Z22	6d. chestnut (1872) (Plate No. 11)........................	65·00
Z23	6d. pale buff (1872) (Plate No. 11)	80·00
Z23a	6d. grey (1873) (Plate No. 12)	
Z24	6d. grey (1874–76) (Plate Nos. 13, 14, 15)	60·00
Z25	9d. straw (1867)	£300
Z26	10d. red-brown (1867)	£300
Z27	1s. green (1865) (Plate No. 4)..............................	
Z28	1s. green (1867–73) (Plate Nos. 4, 5, 6, 7).. From	60·00
Z29	1s. green (1873–77).................................... From	70·00
	Plate Nos. 8, 9, 10, 11, 12, 13.	
Z30	2s. blue (1867)..	£225
Z31	5s. rose (1867–74) (Plate No. 2)...........................	

MAYAGUEZ

Stamps of GREAT BRITAIN cancelled "F 85" as Type **8** in black or blue.
1873–77.

Z32	½d. rose-red (1870).................................... From	55·00
	Plate Nos. 4, 5, 6, 8, 10, 11.	
Z33	1d. rose-red (1864–79)............................. From	38·00
	Plate Nos. 76, 120, 121, 122, 124, 134, 137, 140, 146, 149, 150, 151, 154, 155, 156, 157, 160, 167, 170, 171, 174, 175, 176, 178, 180, 182, 185, 186, 189.	
Z34	1½d. lake-red (1870–74) (Plate Nos. 1, 3).............	50·00
Z35	2d. blue (1858–69) (Plate Nos. 13, 14, 15).........	50·00
Z36	3d. rose (1867–73) (Plate Nos. 7, 8, 9, 10).. From	55·00
Z37	3d. rose (1873–76).................................... From	50·00
	Plate Nos. 11, 12, 14, 15, 16, 17, 18, 19.	
Z38	4d. vermilion (1865–73)........................... From	50·00
	Plate Nos. 11, 12, 13, 14.	
Z39	4d. vermilion (1876) (Plate No. 15)......................	£300
Z40	4d. sage-green (1877) (Plate No. 15)....................	
Z41	6d. mauve (1870) (Plate No. 9)	
Z42	6d. buff (1872) (Plate No. 11)..............................	80·00
Z43	6d. chestnut (1872) (Plate No. 11)........................	70·00
Z44	6d. grey (1873) (Plate No. 12)	£200
Z45	6d. grey (1874–76).................................... From	50·00
	Plate Nos. 13, 14, 15, 16.	
Z46	8d. orange (1876)...	£300
Z47	9d. straw (1867)	£225
Z48	10d. red-brown (1867)	£300
Z49	1s. green (1867–73) (Plate Nos. 4, 5, 6, 7).. From	45·00
Z50	1s. green (1873–77).................................... From	60·00
	Plate Nos. 8, 9, 10, 11, 12.	
Z51	2s. blue (1867)..	£180
Z52	5s. rose (1867–74) (Plate Nos. 1, 2).....................	

NAGUABO

Stamps of GREAT BRITAIN cancelled "582" as Type **9**.
1875–77.

Z53	½d. rose-red (1870–79) (Plate Nos. 5. 12, 14)	
Z54	1d. rose-red (1864–79) (Plate Nos. 150, 159, 165) .	£300
Z55	3d. rose (1873–76) (Plate Nos. 17, 18)..................	£500
Z56	4d. vermilion (1872–73) (Plate Nos. 13, 14). From	£475
Z57	4d. vermilion (1876) (Plate No. 15)......................	
Z58	6d. grey (1874–76) (Plate Nos. 14, 15)................	
Z59	9d. straw (1867)	
Z60	10d. red-brown (1867)	£900
Z61	1s. green (1873–77) (Plate Nos. 11, 12)	
Z62	2s. dull blue (1867) (Plate No. 1)	£650

PONCE

Stamps of GREAT BRITAIN cancelled "F 88" as Type **8**.
1873–77.

Z63	½d. rose-red (1870) (Plate Nos. 5, 10, 12)	55·00
Z64	1d. rose-red (1864–79)............................. From	45·00
	Plate Nos. 120, 121, 122, 123, 124, 146, 148, 154, 156, 157, 158, 160, 167, 171, 174, 175, 179, 186, 187.	
Z65	1½d. lake-red (1870–74) (Plate No. 3)	£110
Z66	2d. blue (1858–69) (Plate Nos. 13, 14)................	55·00
Z67	3d. rose (1867–73) (Plate Nos. 7, 8, 9)................	
Z68	3d. rose (1873–76)	50·00
	Plate Nos. 12, 16, 17, 18, 19.	
Z69	4d. vermilion (1865–73)........................... From	55·00
	Plate Nos. 8, 9, 12, 13, 14.	
Z70	4d. vermilion (1876) (Plate No. 15)......................	£300
Z71	4d. sage-green (1877) (Plate Nos. 15, 16) .. From	£200
Z72	6d. buff (1872–73) (Plate Nos. 11, 12)	75·00
Z73	6d. chestnut (1872) (Plate No. 11)........................	65·00
Z74	6d. grey (1873) (Plate No. 12)	
Z75	6d. grey (1874–76) (Plate Nos. 13, 14, 15) . From	55·00
Z76	9d. straw (1867)	£275
Z77	10d. red-brown (1867)	£300
Z78	1s. green (1867–73) (Plate Nos. 4, 6, 7)..............	50·00
Z79	1s. green (1873–77).................................... From	60·00
	Plate Nos. 8, 9. 10, 11, 12, 13.	
Z80	2s. blue (1867)..	
Z81	5s. rose (1867–74) (Plate Nos. 1, 2)........... From	£375

SAN JUAN

CROWNED-CIRCLE HANDSTAMPS

CC1	CC **1** SAN JUAN PÒRTO RICO (R. or Black)	
	(25.5.1844)............................ Price on cover	£650

No. CC1 may be found on cover, used in conjunction with Spanish colonial adhesive stamps paying the local postage.

Stamps of GREAT BRITAIN cancelled "C 61" as in Types **4**, **8**, **12** or **14a**.
1865–77.

Z82	½d. rose-red (1870) (Plate Nos. 5, 10, 15) .. From	50·00
Z83	1d. rose-red (1857)..	
Z84	1d. rose-red (1864–79)............................. From	38·00
	Plate Nos. 73, 74, 81, 84, 90, 94, 100, 101, 102, 107, 117, 122, 124, 125, 127, 130, 137, 138, 139, 140, 145, 146, 149, 153, 156, 159, 160, 162, 163, 169, 171, 172, 173, 174, 175, 179, 180, 182, 186.	
Z85	1½d. lake-red (1870–74) (Plate Nos. 1, 3).... From	65·00
Z86	2d. blue (1858–69) (Plate Nos. 9, 13, 14).... From	38·00
Z87	3d. rose (1865) (Plate No. 4)...............................	90·00
Z88	3d. rose (1867–73).................................... From	50·00
	Plate Nos. 5, 6, 7, 8, 9, 10.	
Z89	3d. rose (1873–76).................................... From	45·00
	Plate Nos. 11, 12, 14, 15, 16, 17, 18.	
Z90	4d. vermilion (1865–73)........................... From	50·00
	Plate Nos. 7, 8, 9, 10, 11, 12, 13, 14.	
Z91	4d. vermilion (1876) (Plate No. 15)......................	£300
Z92	6d. lilac (1865–67) (Plate Nos. 5, 6)......... From	75·00
Z93	6d. lilac (1867) (Plate No. 6)...............................	75·00
Z94	6d. violet (1867–70) (Plate Nos. 6, 8, 9) ... From	70·00
Z95	6d. buff (1872–73) (Plate Nos. 11, 12) .... From	75·00
Z96	6d. chestnut (1872) (Plate No. 11)........................	50·00
Z97	6d. grey (1873) (Plate No. 12)	
Z98	6d. grey (1874–76) (Plate Nos. 13, 14, 15) . From	50·00
Z99	9d. straw (1862)...	£300
Z100	9d. straw (1865)...	£375
Z101	9d. straw (1867)	£200
Z102	10d. red-brown (1867)	£275
Z103	1s. green (1865) (Plate No. 4)..............................	£140
Z104	1s. green (1867–73) (Plate Nos. 4, 5, 6, 7).. From	45·00
Z105	1s. green (1873–77).................................... From	60·00
	Plate Nos. 8, 9, 10, 11, 12, 13.	
Z106	2s. blue (1867)..	£130
Z107	5s. rose (1867) (Plate Nos. 1, 2)................ From	£450

RUSSIA

ARMY FIELD OFFICES IN THE CRIMEA
1854–57.

Crown between Stars.

Z1	1d. red-brown (1841), imperf................................	£700
Z2	1d. red-brown (1854), Die I, wmk Small Crown, perf 16..	
Z3	1d. red-brown (1855), Die II, wmk Small Crown, perf 16..	£200
Z4	1d. red-brown, Die I, wmk Small Crown, perf 14	
Z5	1d. red-brown (1855), Die II, Small Crown, perf 14..	
Z6	2d. blue (1841) imperf...	£1200
Z7	2d. blue, Small Crown (1854), perf 16 (Plate No. 4)..	
Z8	1s. green (1847), embossed...................................	£2000

Star between Cyphers.

Z9	1d. red-brown (1841), imperf................................	
Z10	1d. red-brown (1854), Die I, wmk Small Crown, perf 16..	75·00
Z11	1d. red-brown (1855), Die II, wmk Small Crown, perf 16..	75·00
Z12	1d. red-brown (1855), Die I, wmk Small Crown, perf 14..	75·00
Z13	1d. red-brown (1855), Die II, wmk Small Crown, perf 14..	75·00
Z14	1d. red-brown (1855), Die II, wmk Large Crown, perf 16..	£100

Z15	1d. red-brown (1855), Die II, wmk Large Crown, perf 14..	45·00
Z16	2d. blue (1841), imperf...	£1400
Z17	2d. blue (1854), wmk Small Crown, perf 16. ...... From	£140
	Plate Nos. 4, 5.	
Z18	2d. blue (1855), wmk Small Crown, perf 14. ...... Plate No. 4.	£200
Z19	2d. blue (1855), wmk Large Crown, perf 16. ...... Plate No. 5.	£225
Z20	2d. blue (1855), wmk Large Crown, perf 14. ...... Plate No. 5.	£130
Z21	4d. rose (1857)..	£900
Z22	6d. violet (1854), embossed.................................	£1600
Z23	1s. green (1847), embossed.................................	£1600

SPAIN

Little is known about the operation of British Packet Agencies in Spain, other than the dates recorded for the various postal markings in the G.P.O. Proof Books. The Agency at Corunna is said to date from the late 17th century when the Spanish packets for South America were based there. No. CC1 was probably issued in connection with the inauguration of the P. & O. service to Spain in 1843. The Spanish port of call was changed to Vigo in 1846 and the office at Corunna was then closed. Teneriffe became a port-of-call for the South American packets in 1817 and this arrangement continued until 1858.

CORUNNA

CROWNED-CIRCLE HANDSTAMPS

CC1	CC **1b** CORUNNA (28.2.1842)........................	

Although recorded in the G.P.O. Proof Books no example of No. CC1 on cover is known.

TENERIFFE (CANARY ISLANDS)

CROWNED-CIRCLE HANDSTAMPS

CC2	CC **7** TENERIFFE (6.1.1851).......... Price on cover	£3750
CC3	CC **4** TENERIFFE (23.10.1857)...... Price on cover	£3750

No. CC2/3 can be found used on covers from Spain to South America with the rate from Spain to Teneriffe paid in Spanish adhesive stamps.

UNITED STATES OF AMERICA

The network of British Packet Agencies, to operate the trans-Atlantic Packet system, was re-established in 1814 after the War of 1812.

The New York Agency opened in that year to be followed by further offices at Boston, Charleston (South Carolina), New Orleans, Savannah (Georgia) (all in 1842), Mobile (Alabama) (1848) and San Francisco (1860). Of these agencies Charleston and Savannah closed the same year (1842) as did New Orleans, although the latter was re-activated from 1848 to 1850. Mobile closed 1850, Boston in 1865, New York in 1882 and San Francisco, for which no postal markings have been recorded, in 1883.

Although recorded in the G.P.O. Proof Books no actual examples of the Crowned-circle handstamps for Charleston, Mobile, New Orleans and Savannah are known on cover.

The G.P.O. Proof Books record, in error, a Crowned-circle handstamp for St. Michaels, Maryland. This handstamp was intended for the agency on San Miguel in the Azores.

CHARLESTON

CROWNED-CIRCLE HANDSTAMPS

CC1	CC **1b** CHARLESTON (15.12.1841)	

MOBILE

CROWNED-CIRCLE HANDSTAMPS

CC2	CC **1b** MOBILE (15.12.1841)	

NEW ORLEANS

CROWNED-CIRCLE HANDSTAMPS

CC3	CC **1b** NEW ORLEANS (15.12.1841)	
CC4	CC **1** NEW ORLEANS (27.4.1848)	

NEW YORK

CROWNED-CIRCLE HANDSTAMPS

CC5	CC **1b** NEW YORK (R.)	
	(15.12.1841) .... Price on cover	£27500

SAVANNAH

CROWNED-CIRCLE HANDSTAMPS

CC6	CC **1b** SAVANNAH (15.12.1841)	

Although recorded in the G.P.O. Proof Books, no examples of Nos. CC1/4 or CC6 are known on cover.

URUGUAY

MONTEVIDEO

British packets commenced calling at Montevideo in 1824 on passage to and from Buenos Aires.

Great Britain stamps were in use from 1864. Combination covers exist with the local postage paid by Uruguay adhesive stamps. The agency was closed on 31 July 1873.

CROWNED-CIRCLE HANDSTAMPS

CC1	CC **5** MONTEVIDEO (Black or R.)	
	(6.1.1851) .... Price on cover	£1000

Stamps of GREAT BRITAIN cancelled "C 28" as Type **4**.
1864–73.

Z1	1d. rose-red (1864)..	55·00
	Plate Nos. 73, 92, 93, 94, 119, 148, 154, 157, 171.	
Z2	2d. blue (1858–69) (Plate Nos. 9, 13).................	55·00
Z3	3d. rose (1865) (Plate No. 4)...............................	

Z4	3d. rose (1867–71) (Plate Nos. 4, 5, 7)....... *From*	50·00
Z6	4d. rose (1857)...	
Z7	4d. red (1862) (Plate No. 4)	
Z8	4d. vermilion (1865–70) .... *From*	50·00
	Plate Nos. 7, 8, 9, 10, 11, 12.	
Z9	6d. lilac (1856)..	
Z10	6d. lilac (1862) (Plate No. 4).......................	£160
Z11	6d. lilac (1865–67) (Plate Nos. 5, 6).......... *From*	90·00
Z12	6d. lilac (1867) (Plate No. 6).......................	
Z13	6d. violet (1867–70) (Plate Nos. 8, 9)........	80·00
Z14	6d. buff (1872)...	
Z15	6d. chestnut (1872)	
Z16	9d. straw (1862)	
Z17	9d. straw (1865)	
Z18	9d. straw (1867)	£275
Z19	10d. red-brown (1867)	£325
Z20	1s. green (1862)	£160
Z21	1s. green (1865) (Plate No. 4).....................	£140
Z22	1s. green (1867–73) (Plate Nos. 4, 5)........ *From*	60·00
Z23	2s. blue (1867)	£200
Z24	5s. rose (1867) (Plate No. 1)	£450

VENEZUELA

British Postal Agencies were initially opened at La Guayra and Porto Cabello on 1 January 1842. Further offices were added at Maracaibo in 1842 and Ciudad Bolivar during January 1858. Porto Cabello closed in 1858 and Maracaibo was also short-lived. The remaining offices closed at the end of 1879 when Venezuela joined the U.P.U.

Great Britain stamps were used at La Guayra from 1865 and at Ciudad Bolivar from its establishment in 1868. They can be found used in combination with Venezuela adhesives paying the local postage.

CIUDAD BOLIVAR

Stamps of GREAT BRITAIN *cancelled* "D 22" *as Type* **12**, *or circular date stamps as Types* **16** (black) *or* **17** (red).
1868–79.

Z1	1d. rose-red (1864–79) (Plate No. 133)	£130
Z2	2d. blue (1858–69) (Plate No. 13)................	
Z3	3d. rose (1865)	
Z4	3d. rose (1867–73) (Plate No. 5)..................	
Z5	3d. rose (1873–79) (Plate No. 11)................	£160
Z6	4d. vermilion (1865–73) .... *From*	£140
	Plate Nos. 9, 11, 12, 14.	
Z7	4d. sage-green (1877) (Plate Nos. 15, 16) ... *From*	£350
Z8	4d. grey-brown (1880) wmk Crown (Plate No. 17)...................................	£650
Z9	10d. red-brown (1867)	
Z10	1s. green (1867–73) (Plate Nos. 4, 5, 7)...... *From*	£200
Z11	1s. green (1873–77) (Plate Nos. 10, 12, 13) *From*	£275
Z12	2s. blue (1867)	£650
Z13	5s. rose (1867–74) (Plate Nos. 1, 2).......... *From*	£1100

LA GUAYRA

CROWNED-CIRCLE HANDSTAMPS

CC1	CC **1b** LA GUAYRA (R.)	
	(15.12.1841) .... *Price on cover*	£1300

Stamps of GREAT BRITAIN *cancelled* "C 60" *as Type* **4**, *circular date stamp as Types* **16** *and* **17** *or with No.* CC1.
1865–80.

Z14	½d. rose-red (1870) Plate No. 6).................	
Z15	1d. rose-red (1864–79)........................... *From*	55·00
	Plate Nos. 81, 92, 96, 98, 111, 113, 115, 131, 138, 144, 145, 154, 177, 178, 180, 196.	
Z16	1½d. lake-red (1870–74) (Plate No. 3)	
Z17	2d. blue (1858–69) (Plate Nos. 13, 14).......	55·00
Z18	3d. rose (1873–76) .... *From*	60·00
	Plate Nos. 14, 15, 17, 18, 19.	
Z19	4d. vermilion (1865–73) .... *From*	55·00
	Plate Nos. 7, 9, 11, 12, 13, 14.	
Z20	4d. vermilion (1876) (Plate No. 15).............	£300
Z21	4d. sage-green (1877) (Plate Nos. 15, 16) .. *From*	£225
Z22	6d. lilac (1865) (Plate No. 5)......................	
Z23	6d. violet (1867–70) (Plate Nos. 6, 8).........	
Z24	6d. buff (1872–73) (Plate Nos. 11, 12) .... *From*	£100
Z25	6d. grey (1873) (Plate No. 12).....................	£210
Z26	6d. grey (1874–76) (Plate Nos. 13, 14, 15, 16)	60·00
Z27	8d. orange (1876).......................................	£300
Z28	9d. straw (1862)	
Z29	9d. straw (1867)	
Z30	10d. red-brown (1867)	£160
Z31	1s. green (1865) (Plate No. 4).....................	
Z32	1s. green (1867–73) (Plate Nos. 4, 7).........	
Z33	1s. green (1873–77) .... *From*	55·00
	Plate Nos. 8, 9, 10, 11, 12, 13.	
Z34	2s. blue (1867)	£225
Z35	5s. rose (1867–74) (Plate Nos. 1, 2)..........	£450

MARACAIBO

CROWNED-CIRCLE HANDSTAMPS

CC2	CC **1b** MARACAIBO (31.12.1841)	

No examples of No. CC2 on cover have been recorded.

PORTO CABELLO

CROWNED-CIRCLE HANDSTAMPS

CC3	CC **1b** PORTO-CABELLO (R.)	
	(15.12.1841) .... *Price on cover*	£3250

MAIL BOAT OBLITERATIONS

The following cancellations were supplied to G.P.O. sorters operating on ships holding mail contracts from the British Post Office. They were for use on mail posted on board, but most examples occur on letters from soldiers and sailors serving overseas which were forwarded to the mailboats without postmarks.

P. & O. MEDITERRANEAN AND FAR EAST MAILBOATS

The first such cancellation, "A 17" as Type **2**, was issued to the Southampton–Alexandria packet in April 1858, but no examples have

been recorded.

The G.P.O. Proof Book also records "B 16", in Type **2**, as being issued for marine sorting in November 1859, but this postmark was subsequently used by the Plymouth and Bristol Sorting Carriage.

Sorting on board P. & O. packets ceased in June 1870 and many of the cancellation numbers were subsequently reallocated using Types **9**, **11** or **12**.

Stamps of GREAT BRITAIN *cancelled* "A 80" *as Type* **2**.
1859 (Mar)–70.

Z1	1d. rose-red (1857). Die II, wmk Large Crown, perf 14	40·00
Z2	6d. lilac (1856)	£160

Stamps of GREAT BRITAIN *cancelled* "A 81" *as Type* **2**.
1859 (Mar)–70.

Z3	1d. rose-red (1857), Die II, wmk Large Crown, perf 14	40·00
Z4	1d. rose-red (1864–79) .... *From*	35·00
	Plate Nos. 84, 85, 86, 91, 97.	
Z5	2d. blue (1858–69) (Plate No. 9)..................	50·00
Z6	4d. red (1862) (Plate No. 4)	£120
Z7	4d. vermilion (1865–73) (Plate No. 8)	60·00
Z8	6d. lilac (1856)..	£160
Z9	6d. lilac (1862) (Plate No. 3).......................	£120
Z10	6d. lilac (1865–67) (Plate Nos. 5, 6).......... *From*	£100
Z11	6d. lilac (1867) (Plate No. 6).......................	£100
Z12	6d. violet (1867–70) (Plate Nos. 6, 8).........	75·00
Z13	10d. red-brown (1867)	£500
Z14	1s. red-brown (1856)	£275

Stamps of GREAT BRITAIN *cancelled* "A 82" *as Type* **2**.
1859 (Mar)–

Z15	1d. rose-red (1857), Die II, wmk Large Crown, perf 14	50·00
Z16	2d. blue (1858) (Plate No. 7).......................	55·00
Z17	4d. rose (1856)	£225
Z18	6d. lilac (1856)..	£200
Z19	6d. lilac (1865–67) (Plate Nos. 5, 6).......... *From*	£130
Z20	6d. lilac (1867) (Plate No. 6).......................	£110

Stamps of GREAT BRITAIN *cancelled* "A 83" *as Type* **2**.
1859 (Apr)–70.

Z21	1d. rose-red (1857), Die II, wmk Large Crown, perf 14	40·00
Z22	1d. rose-red (1864–79) .... *From*	35·00
	Plate Nos. 73, 74, 84, 91, 109.	
Z23	3d. carmine-rose (1862)	£275
Z24	4d. rose (1857)..	£200
Z25	4d. red (1862)	£110
Z26	4d. vermilion (1865–73) (Plate Nos. 9, 10). *From*	60·00
Z27	6d. lilac (1856)..	£160
Z28	6d. lilac (1862)	£125
Z29	6d. lilac (1865–67) (Plate Nos. 5, 6).......... *From*	£100
Z30	6d. violet (1867–70) (Plate Nos. 6, 8).........	75·00
Z31	10d. red-brown (1867)	£500
Z32	1s. green (1862)	£275

Stamps of GREAT BRITAIN *cancelled* "A 84" *as Type* **2**.
1859 (Apr)–70.

Z33	1d. rose-red (1857), Die II, wmk Large Crown, perf 14	£110

Stamps of GREAT BRITAIN *cancelled* "A 85" *as Type* **2**.
1859 (Apr)–70.

Z34	1d. rose-red (1857), Die II, wmk Large Crown, perf 14	40·00
Z35	1d. rose-red (1864–79) .... *From*	35·00
	Plate Nos. 79, 97, 103.	
Z36	3d. carmine-rose (1862)	£275
Z37	4d. red (1862)	£110
Z38	6d. lilac (1856)..	£160
Z39	6d. lilac (1862) (Plate Nos. 3, 4) .... *From*	£120
Z40	6d. lilac (1865–67) (Plate No. 5).................	£120
Z41	6d. lilac (1867) (Plate No. 6).......................	90·00
Z42	1s. green (1862)	£300

Stamps of GREAT BRITAIN *cancelled* "A 86" *as Type* **2**.
1859 (Apr)–70.

Z43	1d. rose-red (1857), Die II, wmk Large Crown, perf 14	40·00
Z44	1d. rose-red (1864–79) .... *From*	35·00
	Plate Nos. 73, 84, 94, 97, 114, 118.	
Z45	3d. rose (1865)	£250
Z46	3d. rose (1867–73) (Plate Nos. 4, 5)...........	75·00
Z47	4d. rose (1857)..	£200
Z48	4d. red (1862) (Plate No. 4)	£110
Z49	4d. vermilion (1865–73) (Plate No. 10)........	80·00
Z50	6d. lilac (1856)..	£160
Z51	6d. lilac (1862) (Plate Nos. 3, 4) .... *From*	£120
Z52	6d. lilac (1865–67) (Plate Nos. 5, 6).......... *From*	£100
Z53	6d. lilac (1867) (Plate Nos. 6, 8) .... *From*	75·00
Z54	10d. red-brown (1867)	£450
Z55	1s. green (1862)	£275

Stamps of GREAT BRITAIN *cancelled* "A 87" *as Type* **2**.
1859 (Apr)–70.

Z56	1d. rose-red (1857), Die II, wmk Large Crown, perf 14	55·00
Z57	4d. rose (1856)	£250
Z58	6d. lilac (1867) (Plate No. 6).......................	£120

Stamps of GREAT BRITAIN *cancelled* "A 88" *as Type* **2**.
1859 (Apr)–70.

Z59	1d. rose-red (1857), Die II, wmk Large Crown, perf 14	40·00
Z60	1d. rose-red (1864–79) .... *From*	35·00
	Plate Nos. 74, 80, 85.	
Z61	4d. rose (1857)..	£225
Z62	4d. red (1862)	£200
Z63	4d. vermilion (1865–73) (Plate No. 8)	60·00
Z64	6d. lilac (1856)..	
Z65	6d. lilac (1862) (Plate No. 4).......................	£160
Z66	6d. lilac (1865–67) (Plate No. 5).................	£120
Z67	6d. lilac (1867) (Plate No. 6).......................	£100
Z68	6d. violet (1867–70) (Plate No. 8)	75·00
Z69	10d. red-brown (1867)	£525
Z70	1s. green (1856)	£300

Stamps of GREAT BRITAIN *cancelled* "A 89" *as Type* **2**.
1859 (Apr)–70.

Z71	1d. rose-red (1857), Die II, wmk Large Crown, perf 14	£110
Z72	6d. lilac (1856)	£300

Stamps of GREAT BRITAIN *cancelled* "A 90" *as Type* **2**.
1859 (June)–70.

Z73	1d. rose-red (1857), Die II, wmk Large Crown, perf 14	65·00
Z74	4d. rose (1856)	
Z75	6d. lilac (1856)..	£250
Z76	6d. lilac (1865–67) (Plate Nos. 5, 6).......... *From*	£160
Z77	9d. straw (1867)	

Stamps of GREAT BRITAIN *cancelled* "A 99" *as Type* **2**.
1859 (June)–70.

Z78	1d. rose-red (1857), Die II, wmk Large Crown, perf 14	40·00
Z79	1d. rose-red (1864–79) .... *From*	35·00
	Plate Nos. 93, 97, 99, 118.	
Z80	4d. rose (1857)..	£200
Z81	4d. red (1862)	£110
Z82	4d. vermilion (1865–73) (Plate No. 11)........	60·00
Z83	6d. lilac (1856)..	
Z84	6d. lilac (1862)	£160
Z85	6d. lilac (1865–67) (Plate Nos. 5, 6).......... *From*	£120
Z86	10d. red-brown (1867)	£500

Stamps of GREAT BRITAIN *cancelled* "B 03" *as Type* **2**.
1859 (Aug)–70.

Z87	1d. rose-red (1857), Die II, wmk Large Crown, perf 14	55·00
Z88	1d. rose-red (1864–79) (Plate Nos. 109, 116) . *From*	40·00
Z89	3d. rose (1865) (Plate No. 4).......................	£100
Z90	6d. lilac (1856)..	£170
Z91	6d. lilac (1867) (Plate No. 6).......................	£140
Z92	6d. violet (1867–70) (Plate Nos. 6, 8).......... *From*	£100
Z93	10d. red-brown (1867)	£550

Stamps of GREAT BRITAIN *cancelled* "B 12" *as Type* **2**.
1859 (Oct)–70.

Z94	1d. rose-red (1857), Die II, wmk Large Crown, perf 14	55·00
Z95	1d. rose-red (1864–79) (Plate No. 94)..........	40·00
Z96	3d. rose (1865) (Plate No. 4).......................	£100
Z97	4d. red (1862)	£120
Z98	4d. vermilion (1865–73) (Plate No. 8)	75·00
Z99	6d. lilac (1856)..	
Z100	6d. lilac (1862)	£170
Z101	6d. lilac (1865–67) (Plate Nos. 5, 6).......... *From*	£140
Z102	6d. violet (1867–70) (Plate No. 8)	95·00

Stamps of GREAT BRITAIN *cancelled* "B 56" *as Type* **2**.
1861 (July)–70.

Z103	1d. rose-red (1864–70) (Plate No. 84)..........	40·00
Z104	2d. blue (1858–69) (Plate No. 9)..................	60·00
Z105	4d. red (1862) (Plate No. 4)	£120
Z106	4d. vermilion (1865–73) (Plate Nos. 7, 8).....	65·00
Z107	6d. lilac (1862) (Plate Nos. 3, 4) .... *From*	£140
Z108	6d. lilac (1865–67) (Plate Nos. 5, 6).......... *From*	£120
Z109	6d. violet (1867–71) (Plate Nos. 6, 8)......... *From*	£100

Stamps of GREAT BRITAIN *cancelled* "B 57" *as Type* **2**.
1861 (July)–70.

Z110	1d. rose-red (1857), Die II, wmk Large Crown, perf 14	50·00
Z111	1d. rose-red (1864–79) (Plate No. 81)..........	40·00
Z112	2d. blue (1858–69) (Plate No. 9)..................	60·00
Z113	4d. red (1862).	£120
Z114	4d. vermilion (1865–73) (Plate No. 8)	65·00
Z115	6d. lilac (1865–67) (Plate Nos. 5, 6).......... *From*	£120

Stamps of GREAT BRITAIN *cancelled* "C 79" *as Type* **12**.
1866 (June)–70.

Z116	6d. violet (1867–70) (Plate Nos. 6, 8).......... *From*	95·00
Z117	10d. red-brown (1867)	£450

CUNARD LINE ATLANTIC MAILBOATS

These were all issued in June 1859. No examples are known used after August 1868. "B 61" is recorded as being issued in March 1862, but no examples are known. Cancellation numbers were subsequently reallocated to offices in Great Britain or, in the case of "A 91", the British Virgin Islands.

Stamps of GREAT BRITAIN *cancelled* "A 91" *as Type* **2**.
1859 (June)–68.

Z130	1d. rose-red (1857), Die II, wmk Large Crown, perf 14	70·00
Z131	1d. rose-red (1864–79) (Plate No. 121)	60·00
Z132	2d. blue (1855), wmk Small Crown, perf 14	
Z133	2d. blue (1858–69) (Plate Nos. 8, 9)............	95·00
Z134	4d. rose (1857)..	£250
Z135	4d. red (1862)	£130
Z136	6d. lilac (1856)..	£175
Z137	6d. lilac (1862)	£150
Z138	6d. lilac (1865–67)	£120
Z139	9d. straw (1862)	
Z140	1s. green (1856)	£325

Stamps of GREAT BRITAIN *cancelled* "A 92" *as Type* **2**.
1859 (June)–68.

Z141	1d. rose-red (1857), Die II, wmk Large Crown, perf 14	70·00
Z142	1d. rose-red (1864–79) (Plate Nos. 93, 97).. *From*	60·00
Z143	6d. lilac (1856)..	£175
Z144	6d. lilac (1862) (Plate No. 3).......................	£160
Z145	6d. lilac (1865–67) (Plate Nos. 5, 6).......... *From*	£120

Stamps of GREAT BRITAIN *cancelled* "A 93" *as Type* **2**.

1859 (June)–68.

Z146	1d. rose-red (1857), Die II, wmk Large Crown, perf 14	70·00

Z147	1d. rose-red (1864–79) (Plate No. 85)	60·00
Z148	6d. lilac (1856)...	£175
Z149	6d. lilac (1865–67) (Plate No. 6)..........................	£160
Z150	10d. red-brown (1867)...	£525

Stamps of GREAT BRITAIN *cancelled* "A 94" *as Type* **2**.
1859 (June)–**68**.

Z151	1d. rose-red (1857), Die II, wmk Large Crown, perf 14..	95·00
Z152	1d. rose-red (1864–79) (Plate Nos. 74, 97)...........	70·00
Z153	4d. vermilion (1865–73) (Plate No. 7)..................	£100
Z154	6d. lilac (1856)...	£200
Z155	6d. lilac (1862)...	£160
Z156	6d. lilac (1865–67) (Plate Nos. 5, 6)............ *From*	£140

Stamps of GREAT BRITAIN *cancelled* "A 95" *as Type* **2**.
1859 (June)–**68**.

Z157	1d. rose-red (1857), Die II, wmk Large Crown, perf 14..	65·00
Z158	1d. rose-red (1864–79).......................... *From* Plate Nos. 72, 89, 97.	55·00
Z159	3d. rose (1867–73) (Plate No. 5)..........................	95·00
Z160	4d. red (1862)...	£130
Z161	4d. vermilion (1865–73) (Plate No. 8)..................	70·00
Z162	6d. lilac (1862)...	£190
Z163	6d. lilac (1865–67) (Plate No. 5)..........................	£160
Z164	6d. lilac (1867) (Plate No. 6)...............................	£130
Z165	1s. green (1856)..	£275

Stamps of GREAT BRITAIN *cancelled* "A 96" *as Type* **2**.
1859 (June)–**68**.

Z166	1d. rose-red (1857), Die II, wmk Large Crown, perf 14..	70·00
Z167	4d. vermilion (1865–73) (Plate No. 7)..................	£100
Z168	6d. lilac (1856)...	£180
Z169	1s. green (1856)..	£300

Stamps of GREAT BRITAIN *cancelled* "A 97" *as Type* **2**.
1859 (June)–**68**.

Z170	1d. rose-red (1857), Die II, wmk Large Crown, perf 14..	70·00
Z171	1d. rose-red (1864–79) (Plate No. 71)	60·00
Z172	4d. Ted (1862) (Plate No. 3).................................	£140

Stamps of GREAT BRITAIN *cancelled* "A 98" *as Type* **2**.
1859 (June)–**68**.

Z173	1d. rose-red (1857), Die II, wmk Large Crown, perf 14..	70·00
Z174	4d. red (1862)...	£140
Z175	6d. lilac (1856)...	£200
Z176	6d. lilac (1862) (Plate No. 4)...............................	£160
Z177	6d. lilac (1865–67) (Plate Nos. 5, 6)............ *From*	£120

ALLAN LINE ATLANTIC MAILBOATS

British G.P.O. sorters worked on these Canadian ships between November 1859 and April 1860. Cancellations as Type **2** numbered "B 17", "B 18", "B 27", "B 28", "B 29" and "B 30" were issued to them, but have not been reported used on Great Britain stamps during this period. All were subsequently reallocated to British post offices.

SPANISH WEST INDIES MAILBOATS

"D 26" was supplied for use by British mail clerks employed on ships of the Herrara Line operating between St. Thomas (Danish West Indies), Cuba, Dominican Republic and Porto Rico.

Stamps of GREAT BRITAIN *cancelled* "D 26" *as Type* **12**.
1868–71.

Z190	1d. rose-red (1864–79) (Plate Nos. 98, 125).........	
Z191	4d. vermilion (1865–73) (Plate Nos. 9, 10, 11)	£825
Z192	6d. violet (1867–70) (Plate No. 8)	
Z193	1s. green (1867) (Plate No. 4)..............................	

Aden

The first post office in Aden opened during January 1839, situated in what became known as the Crater district. No stamps were initially available, but, after the office was placed under the Bombay Postal Circle, stocks of the 1854 ½a. and 1a. stamps were placed on sale in Aden from 10 October 1854. Supplies of the 2a. and 4a. values did not arrive until December. Most Indian issues from the 1854 lithographs up to 1935 Silver Jubilee set can be found with Aden postmarks.

During January 1858 a further office, Aden Steamer Point, was opened in the harbour area and much of the business was transferred to it by 1869. The original Aden post office, in Crater, was renamed Aden Cantonment, later to be changed again to Aden Camp.

The first cancellation used with the Indian stamps was a plain diamond of dots. This type was also used elsewhere so that attribution to Aden is only possible when on cover. Aden was assigned "124" in the Indian postal number system, with the sub-office at Aden Steamer Point being "132". After a short period "124" was used at both offices, cancellations being identifiable by the spacing and shape of the numerals. It is possible that "132" was also used at an office in India.

1858 "124" Cancellation

1870 Aden Duplex

1872 Aden Steamer Point Duplex

Both post offices used "124" until 1871 when Aden Cantonment was assigned "125", only to have this swiftly amended to "124A" in the same year.

1871 Aden Cantonment "125" Cancellation

1871 Aden Cantonment "124A" Cancellation

Cancellations inscribed "Aden Steamer Point" disappear after 1874 and this office was then known simply as Aden. Following this change the office was given number "B-22" under the revised Indian P.O. scheme and this number appears as a major part of the cancellations from 1875 to 1886, either on its own or as part of a duplex, Aden Camp, the alternative name for the Cantonment office, became "B-22/1".

1875 Aden Duplex

Squared-circle types for Aden and Aden Cantonment were introduced in 1884 and 1888 to be in turn replaced by standard Indian double and single circle from 1895 onwards.

A number of other post offices were opened between 1891 and 1937:

Dthali (opened 1903, initially using "EXPERIMENTAL P.O. B-84" postmark; closed 1907)

Kamaran (opened c 1915, but no civilian postmarks known before 1925)

Khormaksar (opened 1892; closed 1915; reopened 1925)

Maalla (opened 1923; closed 1931)

Nobat-Dakim (opened 1904, initially using "EXPERIMENTAL P.O. B-84" postmark; closed 1905)

Perim (opened 1915; closed 1936)

Sheikh Othman (opened 1891; closed 1915; reopened 1922; closed 1937)

(Currency. 12 pies = 1 anna; 16 annas = 1 rupee)

1 Dhow

(Recess D.L.R.)

1937 (1 Apr). Wmk Mult Script CA sideways. P 13×12.

1	1	½a. yellow-green	3·75	2·50
2		9p. deep green	3·75	2·75
3		1a. sepia	3·75	1·25
4		2a. scarlet	3·75	2·75
5		2½a. bright blue	4·00	1·50
6		3a. carmine	10·00	8·00
7		3½a. grey-blue	7·50	4·00
8		8a. pale purple	24·00	7·50
9		1r. brown	42·00	8·50
10		2r. yellow	65·00	23·00
11		5r. deep purple	£120	80·00
12		10r. olive-green	£375	£400
1/12 Set of 12			£600	£475
1s/12s Perf "Specimen" Set of 12			£400	

1937 (12 May). Coronation. As Nos. 95/7 of Antigua, but ptd by D.L.R. P 14.

13		1a. sepia	65	1·25
14		2½a. light blue	75	1·40
		w. Wmk inverted	£650	
15		3½a. grey-blue	1·00	2·75
13/15 Set of 3			2·25	4·75
13s/15s Perf "Specimen" Set of 3			90·00	

3 Aidrus Mosque, Crater

4 Adenese Camel Corps

5 The Harbour

6 Adenese Dhow

7 Mukalla

8 "Capture of Aden, 1839" (Captain Rundle)

(Recess Waterlow)

1939 (19 Jan)–**48**. Wmk Mult Script CA. P 12½.

16	3	½a. yellowish green	70	60
		a. Bluish green (13.9.48)	2·75	4·00
17	4	¾a. red-brown	1·75	1·25
18	4	1a. pale blue	20	40
19	6	1½a. scarlet	1·00	60
20	3	2a. sepia	20	25
21	7	2½a. deep ultramarine	50	30
22	8	3a. sepia and carmine	60	25
23	3	8a. red-orange	75	40
23a	8	14a. sepia and light blue (15.1.45)	2·50	1·00
24	6	1r. emerald-green	2·50	2·00
25	5	2r. deep blue and magenta	5·50	2·25
26	4	5r. red-brown and olive-green	17·00	11·00
27	8	10r. sepia and violet	30·00	12·00
16/27 Set of 13			55·00	29·00
16s/27s Perf "Specimen" Set of 13			£200	

Accent over "D" (R. 7/1, later corrected)

1946 (15 Oct). Victory. As Nos. 110/11 of Antigua.

28		1½a. carmine	15	1·40
		a. Accent over "D"	27·00	
29		2½a. blue	15	60
		w. Wmk inverted	£650	
28s/9s Perf "Specimen" Set of 2			70·00	

1949 (17 Jan). Royal Silver Wedding. As Nos. 112/13 of Antigua.

30		1½a. scarlet (P 14×15)	40	1·75
31		10r. mauve (P 11½×11)	28·00	38·00

1949 (10 Oct). 75th Anniv of U.P.U. As Nos. 114/17 of Antigua, surch with new values by Waterlow.

32		2½a. on 20c. ultramarine	50	1·50
33		3a. on 30c. carmine-red	1·75	1·50
34		8a. on 50c. orange	1·10	1·50
35		1r. on 1s. blue	1·60	2·75
32/5 Set of 4			4·50	6·50

(New Currency. 100 cents = 1 shilling)

5 CENTS
(12)

1951 (1 Oct). Nos. 18 and 20/7 surch with new values, in cents or shillings, as T 12, or in one line between bars (30c.) by Waterlow.

36	5	5c. on 1a. pale blue	15	40
37		10c. on 2a. sepia	15	45
38	7	15c. on 2½a. deep ultramarine	20	1·25
		a. Surch double	£900	
39	8	20c. on 3a. sepia and carmine	30	40
40	7	30c. on 8a. red-orange (R.)	30	65
41		50c. on 8a. red-orange	30	35
42	8	70c. on 14a. sepia and light blue	2·00	1·50
43	6	1s. on 1r. emerald-green	35	30
44	5	2s. on 2r. deep blue and magenta	9·50	2·75
		a. Surch albino	£600	
45	4	5s. on 5r. red-brown and olive-green	18·00	10·00
46	8	10s. on 10r. sepia and violet	26·00	11·00
36/46 Set of 11			50·00	26·00

ADEN PROTECTORATE STATES

KATHIRI STATE OF SEIYUN

The stamps of ADEN were used in Kathiri State of Seiyun from 22 May 1937 until 1942. A further office was opened at Tarim on 11 December 1940.

1 Sultan of Seiyun

2 Seiyun

3 Tarim

4 Mosque, Seiyun

5 Fortress, Tarim

6 Mosque, Seiyun

7 South Gate, Tarim

8 Kathiri House

9 Mosque Entrance, Tarim

VICTORY ISSUE 8TH JUNE 1946
(10)

(Recess D.L.R.)

1942 (July–Oct). Wmk Mult Script CA. T 1, perf 14; others, perf 12×13 (vert) or 13×12 (horiz).

1	1	½a. blue-green	20	80
2		¾a. brown	40	2·00
3		1a. blue	80	70
4	2	1½a. carmine	70	1·50
5	3	2a. sepia	40	1·25
6	4	2½a. blue	1·25	1·25
7	5	3a. sepia and carmine	1·75	2·75
8	6	8a. red	1·25	60
9	7	1r. green	3·75	2·50

1

10	8	2r. blue and purple	7·00	12·00
11	9	5r. brown and green	22·00	20·00
1/11 Set of 11			35·00	40·00
1s/11s Perf "Specimen" Set of 11			£170	

1946 (15 Oct). *Victory.* No. 4 optd with T **10**, and No. 6 optd similarly but in four lines, by De La Rue.

12	2	1½a. carmine	10	65
13	4	2½a. blue (R.)	10	10
		a. Opt inverted	£600	
		b. Opt double	£750	
12s/13s Perf "Specimen" Set of 2			70·00	

1949 (17 Jan). *Royal Silver Wedding.* As Nos. 112/13 of Antigua.

14	1½a. scarlet	30	3·00
15	5r. green	16·00	9·00

1949 (10 Oct). *75th Anniv of U.P.U.* As Nos. 114/17 of Antigua, surch with new values by Waterlow.

16	2½a. on 20c. ultramarine	15	50
17	3a. on 30c. carmine-red	1·25	1·00
18	8a. on 50c. orange	25	1·00
19	1r. on 1s. blue	30	1·00
16/19 Set of 4		1·75	3·25

5 CTS **50 CENTS** **5/-**
(11) (12) (13)

1951 (1 Oct). *Currency changed.* Nos. 3 and 5/11 surch as T **11** (5c.), **12** (10c. ("CTS"), 15c. ("CTS"), 20c. and 50c.) or **13** (1s. to 5s.), by Waterlow.

20	1	5c. on 1a. blue (R.)	15	1·25
21	3	10c. on 2a. sepia	30	75
22	4	15c. on 2½a. blue	15	1·50
23	5	20c. on 3a. sepia and carmine	20	2·50
24	6	50c. on 8a. red	20	80
25	7	1s. on 1r. green	50	2·75
26	8	2s. on 2r. blue and purple	4·50	29·00
27	9	5s. on 5r. brown and green	23·00	40·00
20/27 Set of 8			26·00	70·00

QU'AITI STATE IN HADHRAMAUT

The stamps of ADEN were used in Qu'aiti State in Hadhramaut from 22 April 1937 until 1942. The main post office was at Mukalla. Other offices existed at Du'an (*opened* 1940), Gheil Ba Wazir (*opened* 1942), Haura (*opened* 1940), Shibam (*opened* 1940) and Shihr (*opened* 1939).

PRICES FOR STAMPS ON COVER TO 1945

Nos. 1/11	*from* × 6

I. ISSUES INSCR "SHIHR AND MUKALLA".

1 Sultan of Shihr and Mukalla

2 Mukalla Harbour

3 Gateway of Shihr

4 Shibam

5 Outpost of Mukalla

6 'Einat

7 Du'an

8 Mosque in Hureidha

9 Meshhed

VICTORY ISSUE 8TH JUNE 1946
(10)

(Recess D.L.R.)

1942 (July)–**46**. Wmk Mult Script CA. P 14 (½ to 1a.), 12×13 (1½, 2, 3a. and 1r.) or 13×12 (others).

1	1	½a. blue-green	1·00	50
		a. Olive-green (12.46)	26·00	35·00
2		¾a. brown	1·75	30
3		1a. blue	1·00	1·00
4	2	1½a. carmine	1·50	50
5	3	2a. sepia	1·50	1·75
6	4	2½a. blue	50	30
7	5	3a. sepia and carmine	1·00	75
8	6	8a. red	50	40
9	7	1r. green	4·50	3·75
		a. "A" of "CA" missing from wmk.	†	£800
10	8	2r. blue and purple	12·00	8·50
11	9	5r. brown and green	16·00	11·00
1/11 Set of 11			38·00	25·00
1s/11s Perf "Specimen" Set of 11			£170	

1946 (15 Oct). *Victory.* No. 4 optd. with T **10** and No. 6 optd similarly, but to three lines, by De La Rue.

12	2	1½a. carmine	15	1·00
13	4	2½a. blue (R.)	15	15
12s/13s Perf "Specimen" Set of 2			70·00	

1949 (17 Jan). *Royal Silver Wedding.* As Nos. 112/13 of Antigua.

14	1½a. scarlet	50	3·75
15	5r. green	16·00	9·50

1949 (10 Oct). *75th Anniv of U.P.U.* As Nos. 114/17 of Antigua, surch with new values by Waterlow.

16	2½a. on 20c. ultramarine	15	20
17	3a. on 30c. carmine-red	1·10	40
18	8a. on 50c. orange	25	60
19	1r. on 1s. blue	30	50
	a. Surch omitted	£1800	
16/19 Set of 4		1·60	1·60

1951 (1 Oct). *Currency changed.* Surch with new values in cents or shillings as T **11**(5c.), **12** (10c. ("CTS"), 15c., 20c. and 50c.) or **13** (1s. to 5s.) of Seiyun, by Waterlow.

20	1	5c. on 1a. blue (R.)	15	20
21	3	10c. on 2a. sepia	15	20
22	4	15c. on 2½a. blue	15	20
23	5	20c. on 3a. sepia and carmine	30	60
		a. Surch double, one albino	£275	
24	6	50c. on 8a. red	50	2·00
25	7	1s. on 1r. green	2·00	40
26	8	2s. on 2r. blue and purple	8·00	16·00
27	9	5s. on 5r. brown and green	13·00	26·00
20/27 Set of 8			22·00	40·00

Aitutaki *see after* New Zealand

Antigua

It is believed that the first postmaster for Antigua was appointed under Edward Dummer's scheme in 1706. After the failure of his service, control of the overseas mails passed to the British G.P.O. Mail services before 1850 were somewhat haphazard, until St. John's was made a branch office of the British G.P.O. in 1850. A second office, at English Harbour, opened in 1857.

The stamps of Great Britain were used between May 1858 and the end of April 1860, when the island postal service became the responsibility of the local colonial authorities. In the interim period, between the take-over and the appearance of Antiguan stamps, the crowned-circle handstamps were again utilised and No. CC1 can be found used as late as 1869.

For illustrations of the handstamp and postmark types see BRITISH POST OFFICES ABROAD notes, following GREAT BRITAIN.

ST. JOHN'S

CROWNED-CIRCLE HANDSTAMPS

CC1	CC **1** ANTIGUA (St. John's) (9.3.1850) (R.)	
	Price on cover	£650

Stamps of GREAT BRITAIN *cancelled* "A 02" *as Type* **2**.
1858–60.

Z1	1d. rose-red (1857), P 14	£550
Z2	2d. blue (1855), P 14 (Plate No. 6)	£950
Z3	2d. blue (1858) (Plate Nos. 7, 8, 9)	£650
Z4	4d. rose (1857)	£550
Z5	6d. lilac (1856)	£170
Z6	1s. green (1856)	£1900

ENGLISH HARBOUR

CROWNED-CIRCLE HANDSTAMPS

CC2	CC **3** ENGLISH HARBOUR (10.12.1857)	
	Price on cover	£5500

Stamps of GREAT BRITAIN *cancelled* "A 18" *as Type* **2**.
1858–60.

Z6a	1d. rose-red (1857)	
Z7	2d. blue (1858) (Plate No. 7)	£5500
Z8	4d. rose (1857)	£5500
Z9	6d. lilac (1856)	£2000
Z10	1s. green (1856)	

PRICES FOR STAMPS ON COVER TO 1945

No. 1	*from* × 10
Nos. 2/4	†
Nos. 5/10	*from* × 20
Nos. 13/14	*from* × 30
No. 15	*from* × 60
Nos. 16/18	*from* × 50
Nos. 19/23	*from* × 12
No. 24	*from* × 50
Nos. 25/30	*from* × 10
Nos. 31/51	*from* × 4
Nos. 52/4	*from* × 4
Nos. 55/61	*from* × 4
Nos. 62/80	*from* × 3
Nos. 81/90	*from* × 4
Nos. 91/4	*from* × 5
Nos. 95/7	*from* × 4
Nos. 98/109	*from* × 3

CROWN COLONY

1 3

(Eng C. Jeens after drawing by Edward Corbould. Recess P.B.)

1862 (Aug). No wmk.

		(a) Rough perf 14 to 16.		
1	1	6d. blue-green	£800	£500
		(b) P 11 to 12½.		
2	1	6d. blue-green	£5500	
		(c) P 14 to 16×11 to 12½.		
3	1	6d. blue-green	£3000	
		(d) P 14 to 16 compound with 11 to 12½.		
4	1	6d. blue-green	£3000	

Nos. 2/4 may be trial perforations. They are not known used.

1863 (Jan)–**67**. Wmk Small Star. W w **2** (sideways on 6d.). Rough perf 14 to 16.

5	1	1d. rosy mauve	£130	55·00
6		1d. dull rose (1864)	£100	42·00
		a. Imperf between (vert pair)	£21000	
7		1d. vermilion (1867)	£200	25·00
		a. Imperf between (horiz pair)	£21000	
		b. Wmk sideways	£250	38·00
8		6d. green (*shades*)	£500	25·00
		a. Wmk upright	—	£120
9		6d. dark green	£600	25·00
10		6d. yellow-green	£3500	80·00

Caution is needed in buying No. 10 as some of the shades of No. 8 verge on yellow-green.

The 1d. rosy mauve exists showing trial perforations of 11 to 12½ and 14 to 16 (*Price*, £8000 *unused*).

(Recess D.L.R. from P.B. plates)

1872. Wmk Crown CC. P 12½.

13	1	1d. lake	£140	15·00
		w. Wmk inverted		
		x. Wmk reversed	£140	15·00
		y. Wmk inverted and reversed		
14		1d. scarlet	£190	20·00
		w. Wmk inverted	£200	50·00
		x. Wmk reversed	—	30·00
15		6d. blue-green	£500	10·00
		w. Wmk inverted	—	70·00
		x. Wmk reversed	£500	12·00
		y. Wmk inverted and reversed	—	80·00

1876. Wmk Crown CC. P 14.

16	1	1d. lake	£150	9·50
		a. Bisected (½d.) (1883) (on cover)	†	£4500
		x. Wmk reversed		
17		1d. lake-rose	£150	9·50
		w. Wmk inverted	£190	65·00
		x. Wmk reversed	—	30·00
		y. Wmk inverted and reversed		
18		6d. blue-green	£350	14·00
		w. Wmk inverted	†	90·00
		x. Wmk reversed	£350	15·00
		y. Wmk inverted and reversed	£450	60·00

(Recess (T **1**); typo (T **3**) De La Rue & Co).

1879. Wmk Crown CC. P 14.

19	3	2½d. red-brown	£600	£170
		a. Large "2" in "2½" with slanting foot	£9000	£2500
20		4d. blue	£250	15·00

Top left triangle detached (Pl 2 R. 3/3 of right panel)

1882. Wmk Crown CA. P 14.

21	3	½d. dull green	3·00	16·00
		a. Top left triangle detached	£300	£450

22		2½d. red-brown	£190	55·00
		a. Top left triangle detached		
		b. Large "2" in "2½" with slanting foot	£3250	£1200
23		4d. blue	£275	15·00
		a. Top left triangle detached	—	£600

1884. Wmk Crown CA. P 12.

24	1	1d. carmine-red	50·00	15·00
		w. Wmk inverted		
		y. Wmk inverted and reversed		

The 1d. scarlet is a colour changeling.

1884–87. Wmk Crown CA. P 14.

25	1	1d. carmine-red	2·25	3·75
		x. Wmk reversed	—	20·00
		y. Wmk inverted and reversed		
26		1d. rose	55·00	12·00
27	3	2½d. ultramarine (1887)	7·00	14·00
		a. Large "2" in "2½" with slanting foot	£160	£250
		b. Top left triangle detached	£375	£325
28		4d. chestnut (1887)	2·25	3·00
29	1	6d. deep green	60·00	£120
30	3	1s. mauve (1886)	£160	£130
		a. Top left triangle detached	£1400	
25/30 Set of 5			£200	£225
27s, 28s, 30s Optd "Specimen" Set of 3			£150	

Nos. 25 and 26 postmarked "A 12" in place of "A 02" were used in St. Christopher.

2½ 2½ 2½
A   B   C

The variety "Large '2' in '2½' with slanting foot" occurs on R. 7/1 of the duty plate on all printings. At this position the "NN" of "PENNY" also sustained damage in about 1882, leaving three vertical strokes shortened. A and B (above) represent two states of the flaw at R. 7/1. Head plate 2, first used for Antigua in 1886, was a double-pane plate of 120, but the same 60-set duty plate remained in use, the variety thus occuring on R. 7/1 of each pane. A very similar flaw (C above) appeared at R. 3/1 of the duty plate (on which the "NN" was undamaged) early in the life of No. 27 and thus occurs on both panes of that stamp.

From 31 October 1890 until July 1903 Leeward Islands general issues were used. Subsequently both general issues and the following separate issues were in concurrent use until July 1956, when the general Leewards Island stamps were withdrawn.

4   5

(Typo D.L.R.)

1903 (July)–**07.** Wmk Crown CC. *Ordinary paper.* P 14.

31	4	½d. grey-black and grey-green	3·75	6·50
32		1d. grey-black and rose-red	6·50	1·25
33		2d. dull purple and brown	7·50	24·00
34		2½d. grey-black and blue	9·50	15·00
		a. Chalk-surfaced paper (1907)	28·00	60·00
35		3d. grey-green and orange-brown	11·00	20·00
36		6d. purple and black	32·00	50·00
		w. Wmk inverted	£130	
37		1s. blue and dull purple	45·00	55·00
		a. Chalk-surfaced paper (1907)	55·00	£120
38		2s. grey-green and pale violet	75·00	95·00
39		2s.6d. grey-black and purple	20·00	55·00
40	5	5s. grey-green and violet	70·00	£100
		a. Chalk-surfaced paper (1907)	£120	£160
31/40 Set of 10			£250	£350
31s/40s Optd "Specimen" Set of 10			£150	

1908–17. Wmk Mult Crown CA. *Chalk-surfaced paper* (2d., 3d. to 2s.). P 14.

41	4	½d. green	2·75	4·50
		w. Wmk inverted		
42		½d. blue-green (1917)	4·00	6·50
43		1d. red (1909)	7·00	2·25
44		1d. scarlet (5.8.15)	7·00	3·25
		w. Wmk inverted		
45		2d. dull purple and brown (1912)	4·75	30·00
46		2½d. ultramarine	14·00	16·00
		a. Blue	20·00	21·00
47		3d. grey-green and orange-brown (1912)	6·50	19·00
48		6d. purple and black (1911)	7·50	40·00
49		1s. blue and dull purple	17·00	70·00
50		2s. grey-green and violet (1912)	85·00	95·00
41/50 Set of 8			£130	£250
41s, 43s, 46s Optd "Specimen" Set of 3			65·00	

1913. As T **5**, but portrait of George V. Wmk Mult Crown CA. *Chalk-surfaced paper.* P 14.

51		5s. grey-green and violet	70·00	£110
		s. Optd "Specimen"	65·00	

WAR STAMP

(7)   8

1916 (Sept)–**17.** *No. 41 optd in London with T* **7**.

52	4	½d. green (Bk.)	2·50	2·50
53		½d. green (R.) (1.10.17)	1·50	2·50

1918 (July). *Optd with T* **7**. Wmk Mult Crown CA. P 14.

54	4	1½d. orange	1·00	1·25
52s/4s Optd "Specimen" Set of 3			75·00	

(Typo D.L.R.)

1921–29. P 14.

(a) Wmk Mult Crown CA. *Chalk-surfaced paper.*

55	8	3d. purple/*pale yellow*	4·50	12·00
56		4d. grey-black and red/*pale yellow* (1922)	2·25	5·50
57		1s. black/*emerald*	4·25	9·00
58		2s. purple and blue/*blue*	13·00	21·00
59		2s.6d. black and red/*blue*	17·00	50·00
60		5s. green and red/*pale yellow* (1922)	8·50	50·00
61		£1 purple and black/*red* (1922)	£225	£325
55/61 Set of 7			£250	£425
55s/61s Optd "Specimen" Set of 7			£180	

(b) Wmk Mult Script CA. *Chalk-surfaced paper* (3d. to 4s.).

62	8	½d. dull green	2·50	50
63		1d. carmine-red	3·25	50
64		1d. bright violet (1923)	4·75	1·50
		a. Mauve	14·00	7·00
65		1d. bright scarlet (1929)	23·00	3·75
67		1½d. dull orange (1922)	4·25	7·00
68		1½d. carmine-red (1926)	6·50	1·75
69		1½d. pale red-brown (1929)	3·00	60
70		2d. grey (1922)	3·25	75
		a. Wmk sideways	†	£1800
71		2½d. bright blue (1922)	6·50	17·00
72		2½d. orange-yellow (1923)	2·50	17·00
73		2½d. ultramarine (1927)	7·00	5·50
74		3d. purple/*pale yellow* (1925)	6·00	8·50
75		6d. dull and bright purple (1922)	4·75	6·50
76		1s. black/*emerald* (1929)	6·00	7·00
77		2s. purple and blue/*blue* (1927)	10·00	55·00
78		2s.6d. black and red/*blue* (1927)	30·00	28·00
79		3s. green and violet (1922)	40·00	90·00
80		4s. grey-black and red (1922)	48·00	65·00
62/80 Set of 16			£160	£275
62s/80s Optd or Perf (Nos. 65, 69, 76) "Specimen" Set of 18			£350	

9 Old Dockyard, English Harbour

10 Government House, St. John's

11 Nelson's *Victory*   12 Sir Thomas Warner's *Concepcion*

(Des Mrs. J. Goodwin (5s.), Waterlow (others). Recess Waterlow)

1932 (27 Jan). *Tercentenary.* Wmk Mult Script CA. P 12½.

81	9	½d. green	3·25	7·50
82		1d. scarlet	3·75	7·50
83		1½d. brown	3·25	4·75
84	10	2d. grey	4·50	20·00
85		2½d. deep blue	4·50	8·50
86		3d. orange	4·50	12·00
87	11	6d. violet	15·00	12·00
88		1s. olive-green	19·00	27·00
89		2s.6d. claret	45·00	65·00
90	12	5s. black and chocolate	£100	£130
81/90 Set of 10			£180	£250
81s/90s Perf "Specimen" Set of 10			£200	

Examples of all values are known showing a forged St. Johns postmark dated "MY 18 1932".

13 Windsor Castle

(Des H. Fleury. Recess D.L.R.)

1935 (6 May). *Silver Jubilee.* Wmk Mult Script CA. P 13½×14.

91	13	1d. deep blue and carmine	2·00	3·25
		f. Diagonal line by turret	75·00	
92		1½d. ultramarine and grey	2·75	55
93		2½d. brown and deep blue	6·50	1·25
		g. Dot to left of chapel	£180	
94		1s. slate and purple	8·50	13·00
		a. Frame printed double, one albino		
		g. Dot by flagstaff	£250	
		h. Dot by flagstaff		
91/4 Set of 4			18·00	16·00
91s/4s Perf "Specimen" Set of 4			90·00	

For illustrations of plate varieties see Omnibus section following Zanzibar.

---

14 King George VI and Queen Elizabeth

(Des D.L.R. Recess B.W.)

1937 (12 May). *Coronation.* Wmk Mult Script CA. P 11×11½.

95	14	1d. carmine	60	1·75
96		1½d. yellow-brown	60	2·00
97		2½d. blue	1·75	2·25
95/7 Set of 3			2·75	5·50
95s/7s Perf "Specimen" Set of 3			70·00	

15 English Harbour   16 Nelson's Dockyard

16a Fort James   16b St. John's Harbour

(Recess Waterlow)

1938 (15 Nov)–**51.** Wmk Mult Script CA. P 12½.

98	15	½d. green	40	1·25
99	16	1d. scarlet	3·00	2·00
		a. Red (8.42 and 11.47)	4·00	2·75
100		1½d. chocolate-brown	6·50	1·50
		a. Dull reddish brown (12.43)	2·75	2·25
		b. Lake-brown (7.49)	32·00	13·00
101	15	2d. grey	1·00	80
		a. Slate-grey (6.51)	8·50	5·00
102	16	2½d. deep ultramarine	1·00	80
103	16a	3d. orange	1·00	1·00
104	16b	6d. violet	3·25	1·25
105		1s. black and brown	6·00	2·00
		a. Black and red-brown (7.49)	32·00	11·00
		ab. Frame ptd double, one albino	£4000	
106	16a	2s.6d. brown-purple	48·00	14·00
		a. Maroon (8.42)	26·00	14·00
107	16b	5s. olive-green	14·00	7·50
108	16	10s. magenta (1.4.48)	16·00	28·00
109	1ba	£1 slate-green (1.4.48)	25·00	40·00
98/109 Set of 12			85·00	90·00
98s/109s Perf "Specimen" Set of 12			£180	

17 Houses of Parliament, London

(Des and recess D.L.R.)

1946 (1 Nov). *Victory.* Wmk Mult Script CA. P 13½×14.

110	17	1½d. brown	20	10
111		3d. red-orange	20	50
110s/11s Perf "Specimen" Set of 2			65·00	

18 King George VI and Queen Elizabeth   19

(Des and photo Waterlow (T **18**). Design recess; name typo B.W. (T **19**))

1949 (3 Jan). *Royal Silver Wedding.* Wmk Mult Script CA.

112	18	2½d. ultramarine (P 14×15)	50	2·50
113	19	5s. grey-olive (P 11½×11)	10·00	10·00

20 Hermes, Globe and Forms of Transport   21 Hemispheres, Jet-powered Vickers Viking Airliner and Steamer

22 Hermes and Globe   **23** U.P.U. Monument

(Recess Waterlow (T **20**, **23**). Designs recess, name typo B.W.
(T **21**/2))

1949 (10 Oct). *75th Anniv of Universal Postal Union.* Wmk Mult
Script CA.
114	**20**	2½d. ultramarine (P 13½–14)	40	50
115	**21**	3d. orange (P 11×11½)	1·75	2·25
116	**22**	6d. purple (P 11×11½)	45	1·75
117	**23**	1s. re-brown (P 13½–14)	45	1·25
114/17 Set of 4			2·75	5·25

(New Currency. 100 cents = 1 West Indian,
later Eastern Caribbean, dollar)

24 Arms of University   **25** Princess Alice

(Recess Waterlow)

1951 (16 Feb). *Inauguration of B.W.I. University College.* Wmk
Mult Script CA. P 14×14½.
118	**24**	3c. black and brown	45	1·25
119	**25**	12c. black and violet	80	1·50

BARBUDA

DEPENDENCY OF ANTIGUA

PRICES FOR STAMPS ON COVER TO 1945

Nos. 1/11   *from* × 5

BARBUDA
(1)

1922 (13 July). *Stamps of Leeward Islands optd with T* **1**. *All
Die II. Chalk-surfaced paper (3d. to 5s.).*

(a) Wmk Mult Script CA.
1	**11**	½d. deep green	1·50	9·50
2		1d. bright scarlet	1·50	9·50
		x. Wmk reversed	£700	£800
3	**10**	2d. slate-grey	1·50	7·00
		x. Wmk reversed	70·00	
4	**11**	2½d. bright blue	1·50	7·50
		w. Wmk inverted	30·00	90·00
5		6d. dull and bright purple	2·00	18·00
6	**10**	2s. purple and blue/*blue*	14·00	48·00
7		3s. bright green and violet	32·00	75·00
8		4s. black and red (R.)	40·00	75·00

(b) Wmk Mult Crown CA.
9	**10**	3d. purple/*pale yellow*	1·75	12·00
10	**12**	1s. black/*emerald* (R.)	1·50	8·00
11		5s. green and red/*pale yellow*	65·00	£130
1/11 Set of 11			£140	£350
1s/11s Optd "Specimen" Set of 11			£225	

Examples of all values are known showing a forged Barbuda postmark of "JU 1 23".

Stocks of the overprinted stamps were exhausted by October 1925 and issues of Antigua were then used in Barbuda until 1968.

Ascension
DEPENDENCY OF ST. HELENA

Ascension, first occupied in 1815, was retained as a Royal Navy establishment from 1816 until 20 October 1922 when it became a dependency of St. Helena by Letters Patent.

Under Post Office regulations of 1850 (ratings) and 1854 (officers) mail from men of the Royal Navy serving abroad had the postage repaid in Great Britain stamps, supplies of which were issued to each ship. Great Britain stamps used on Ascension before 1860 may have been provided by the naval officer in charge of the postal service.

The British G.P.O. assumed responsibility for such matters in 1860, but failed to send any stamps to the island until January 1867.

Until about 1880 naval mail, which made up most early correspondence, did not have the stamps cancelled until arrival in England. The prices quoted for Nos. Z1/3 and Z6 are for examples on cover showing the Great Britain stamps cancelled on arrival and an Ascension postmark struck elsewhere on the front of the envelope.

The use of British stamps ceased in December 1922.

The following postmarks were used on Great Britain stamps from Ascension:

Z 1   Z 2

Z 3   Z 4

Z 5

Postmark Type	Approx Period of Use	Diameter	Index Letter
Z 1	1862	20 mm	A
Z 2	1864–1872	20 mm	A
	1872–1878	21½ mm	A
	1879–1889	19½mm	A
	1891–1894	21½ mm	C
	1894–1902	22 mm	A
	1903–1907	20½ mm	A
	1908–1920	21 mm	A or none
	1909–1920	23 mm	C sideways (1909), none (1910–11), B (1911–20)
Z 3	1920–1922	24 mm	none
Z 4	1897–1903 Reg'd	23 mm	none
Z 5	1900–1902 Reg'd	28 mm	C
	1903–1904 Reg'd	29 mm	A

Postmark Type Z **1** appears in the G.P.O. proof book for 1858, but the first recorded use is 3 November 1862.

Forged postmarks exist. Those found most frequently are genuine postmarks of the post-1922 period with earlier date slugs fraudulently inserted, namely a 20 mm postmark as Type Z **2** (because of the shape of the "O" in "ASCENSION" this is often known as the Square O postmark) and a 24 mm postmark as Type Z **3** but with the index letter A.

Stamps of GREAT BRITAIN *cancelled with Types* Z **2/5**. *Prices quoted for Nos. Z* 1/6 *are for complete covers.*
Line-engraved issues.
Z1	1d. red-brown (1855)	£4500
Z2	1d. rose-red (1864–79)	*From* £2000
	Plate Nos. 71, 74, 76, 83, 85, 96, 100, 102, 103, 104, 122, 134, 138, 154, 155, 157, 160, 168, 178	

Surface-printed issues (1856–1883).
Z2a	6d. lilac (1856)	
Z3	6d. lilac (1865) (Plate No. 5)	£4500
Z4	1s. green (1865) (Plate No. 4)	
Z5	1s. green (1867) (Plate No. 7)	
Z6	6d. grey (1874) (Plate Nos. 15, 16)	£3750
Z6a	6d. on 6d. lilac (1883)	
Z7	1d. lilac (1881) (16 dots)	48·00

1887–92
Z8	½d. vermilion	75·00
Z9	1½d. purple and green	£350
Z10	2d. green and carmine	£160
Z11	2½d. purple/*blue*	75·00
Z12	3d. purple/*yellow*	£325
Z13	4d. green and brown	£250
Z14	4½d. green and carmine	£600
Z15	5d. dull purple and blue	£250
Z16	6d. purple/*rose-red*	£190
Z17	9d. purple and blue	£500
Z17a	10d. dull purple and carmine	£650
Z18	1s. green	£550

1900.
Z19	½d. blue-green	75·00
Z20	1s. green and carmine	£600

1902–11. *King Edward VII issues.*
Z21	½d. green	48·00
Z22	1d. red	22·00
Z23	1½d. purple and green	£170
Z24	2d. green and carmine	£110
Z25	2½d. blue	£110
Z26	3d. purple/*yellow*	£170
Z27	4d. green and brown	£500
Z28	4d. orange (1909)	£190
Z29	5d. purple and ultramarine	£180
Z30	6d. purple	£170
Z31	7d. grey-black (1910)	£300
Z32	9d. purple and violet (1910)	£300
Z32a	10d. dull purple and scarlet	£400
Z33	1s. green and carmine	£110
Z33a	2s.6d. dull reddish purple (1911)	£700
Z34	5s. carmine	£950
Z35	10s. ultramarine	£1500
Z35a	£1 green	£3750

1911–12. *T 98/9 of Great Britain.*
Z36	½d. green (Die A)	95·00
Z37	½d. yellow-green (Die B)	48·00
Z38	1d. scarlet (Die B)	£550

1912. *T 101/2 of Great Britain.*
Z38a	½d. green	55·00
Z38b	1d. scarlet	55·00

1912–22.
Z39	½d. green (1913)	42·00
Z40	1d. scarlet	24·00
Z41	1½d. red-brown	60·00
Z42	2d. orange (Die I)	50·00
Z42a	2d. orange (Die II) (1921)	£450
Z43	2½d. blue	70·00
Z44	3d. violet	90·00
Z45	4d. grey-green (1913)	£120
Z46	5d. brown (1913)	£120
Z47	6d. purple (1913)	£100
Z47a	7d. green (1913)	£400
Z47b	8d. black/*yellow* (1913)	£425
Z48	9d. agate (1913)	£375
Z49	9d. olive-green (1922)	£850
Z50	10d. turquoise-blue (1913)	£375
Z51	1s. bistre (1913)	£140
Z52	2s.6d. brown (1918)	£1000
Z53	5s. rose-red (1919)	£1600

Supplies of some values do not appear to have been sent to the island and known examples originate from maritime or, in the case of high values, philatelic mail.

PRICES FOR STAMPS ON COVER
Nos. 1/34	*from* × 5
Nos. 35/7	*from* × 10
Nos. 38/47	*from* × 6

ASCENSION
(1)

Line through "P" of "POSTAGE" (R. 3/6)

Blot on scroll (R. 3/10)

1922 (2 Nov). *Stamps of St. Helena, showing Government House or the Wharf, optd with T* **1** *by D.L.R.*

(a) Wmk Mult Script CA.
1		½d. black and green	4·50	19·00
		x. Wmk reversed	£750	
2		1d. green	4·50	18·00
3		1½d. rose-scarlet	16·00	48·00
4		2d. black and grey	17·00	13·00
		a. Line through "P" of "POSTAGE"	£300	£300
		b. Blot on scroll	£275	£275
5		3d. bright blue	13·00	19·00
6		8d. black and dull purple	26·00	48·00
7		2s. black and blue/*blue*	90·00	£120
8		3s. black and violet	£130	£160

(b) Wmk Mult Crown CA.
9		1s. black/*green* (R.)	28·00	48·00
1/9 Set of 9			£300	£425
1s/9s Set of 9			£700	

Nos. 1, 4 and 6/8 are on special printings which were not issued without overprint.

Examples of all values are known showing a forged Ascension postmark dated "MY 24 23".

PLATE FLAWS ON THE 1924–33 ISSUE. Many constant plate varieties exist on both the vignette and duty plates of this issue.

The three major varieties are illustrated and listed below.

This issue utilised the same vignette plate as the St. Helena 1922–37 set so that these flaws occur there also.

2 Badge of St. Helena

Broken mainmast. Occurs on R. 2/1 of all values.

Torn flag. Occurs on R. 4/6 of all values except the 5d. Retouched on sheets of ½d. and 1d. printed after 1927.

Cleft rock. Occurs on R. 5/1 of all values.

Broken scroll. Occurs on R. 1/4 of 1½d. only

(Typo D.L.R.)

1924 (20 Aug)–**33**. Wmk Mult Script CA. *Chalk-surfaced paper*. P 14.

10	**2**	½d. grey-black and black	3·50	14·00
		a. Broken mainmast	80·00	£160
		b. Torn flag	£130	£190
		c. Cleft rock	65·00	£150
11		1d. grey-black and deep blue-green	5·50	9·50
		a. Broken mainmast	90·00	£150
		b. Torn flag	£110	£170
		c. Cleft rock	80·00	£140
11d		1d. grey-black & brt blue-green (1933)	£100	£475
		da. Broken mainmast	£475	
		dc. Cleft rock	£475	
12		1½d. rose-red	7·50	28·00
		a. Broken mainmast	95·00	£190
		b. Torn flag	£100	£190
		c. Cleft rock	85·00	£170
		d. Broken scroll	£120	£200
13		2d. grey-black and grey	16·00	9·00
		a. Broken mainmast	£130	£150
		b. Torn flag	£160	£180
		c. Cleft rock	£110	£140
14		3d. blue	8·00	15·00
		a. Broken mainmast	£110	£160
		b. Torn flag	£110	£160
		c. Cleft rock	90·00	£150
15		4d. grey-black and black/*yellow*	48·00	80·00
		a. Broken mainmast	£300	£425
		b. Torn flag	£300	£425
		c. Cleft rock	£250	£350
15d		5d. purple and olive-green (8.27)	10·00	22·00
		da. Broken mainmast	£170	£275
		dc. Cleft rock	£150	£250
16		6d. grey-black and bright purple	50·00	£100
		a. Broken mainmast	£350	£475
		b. Torn flag	£350	£475
		c. Cleft rock	£300	£425
17		8d. grey-black and bright violet	15·00	42·00
		a. Broken mainmast	£170	£300
		b. Torn flag	£170	£300
		c. Cleft rock	£140	£275
18		1s. grey-black and brown	20·00	50·00
		a. Broken mainmast	£200	£325
		b. Torn flag	£200	£325
		c. Cleft rock	£180	£300
19		2s. grey-black and blue/*blue*	55·00	85·00
		a. Broken mainmast	£375	£475
		b. Torn flag	£375	£475
		c. Cleft rock	£325	£425
20		3s. grey-black and black/*blue*	80·00	90·00
		a. Broken mainmast	£500	£650
		b. Torn flag	£500	£650
		c. Cleft rock	£450	£550
10/20	*Set of 12*		£275	£475
10s/20s Optd "Specimen" *Set of 12*			£650	

3 Georgetown

4 Ascension Island

"Teardrops" flaw (R. 4/5)

(Des and recess D.L.R.)

1934 (2 July). *T* **3/4** *and similar designs*. Wmk Mult Script CA. P 14.

21	**3**	½d. black and violet	90	80
22	**4**	1d. black and emerald	1·75	1·25
		a. Teardrops flaw	80·00	80·00
23	–	1½d. black and scarlet	1·75	2·25
24	**4**	2d. black and orange	1·75	2·50
		a. Teardrops flaw	£100	£120
25	–	3d. black and ultramarine	1·75	1·50
26	–	5d. black and blue	2·25	3·25
27	**4**	8d. black and sepia	4·25	4·75
		a. Teardrops flaw	£200	£250
28	–	1s. black and carmine	18·00	8·00
29	**4**	2s.6d. black and bright purple	45·00	35·00
		a. Teardrops flaw	£650	£650
30	–	5s. black and brown	50·00	55·00
21/30 *Set of 10*			£110	£100
21s/30s Perf "Specimen" *Set of 10*			£375	

Designs: *Horiz*—1½d. The Pier; 3d. Long Beach; 5d. Three Sisters; 1s. Sooty Tern and Wideawake Fair; 5s. Green Mountain.

1935 (6 May). *Silver Jubilee. As Nos. 91/4 of Antigua, but ptd by Waterlow*. P 11×12.

31		1½d. deep blue and scarlet	3·50	8·00
		l. Kite and horizontal log	£225	
32		2d. ultramarine and grey	11·00	24·00
		l. Kite and horizontal log	£350	
33		5d. green and indigo	17·00	26·00
		k. Kite and vertical log	£250	£325
		l. Kite and horizontal log	£425	
34		1s. slate and purple	23·00	29·00
		l. Kite and horizontal log	£500	£550
31/4 *Set of 4*			48·00	80·00
31s/4s Perf "Specimen" *Set of 4*			£275	

For illustrations of plate varieties see Omnibus section following Zanzibar.

1937 (19 May). *Coronation. As Nos. 95/7 of Antigua, but printed by D.L.R*. P 14.

35		1d. green	50	1·40
36		2d. orange	1·00	60
37		3d. bright blue	1·00	50
35/7 *Set of 3*			2·25	2·25
35s/7s Perf "Specimen" *Set of 3*			£250	

10 The Pier

Long centre bar to "E" in "GEORGETOWN" (R. 2/3)

"Mountaineer" flaw (R. 4/4)

"Davit" flaw (R. 5/1) (all ptgs of 1½d. and 2s.6d.)

(Recess D.L.R.)

1938 (12 May)–**53**. *Horiz designs as King George V issue, but modified and with portrait of King George VI as in T* **10**. Wmk Mult Script CA. P 13½.

38	**3**	½d. black and violet	3·50	1·50
		a. Long centre bar to E	£170	£130
		b. Perf 13. *Black and bluish violet* (17.5.44)	80	1·75
		ba. Long centre bar to E	75·00	
39	–	1d. black and green	42·00	8·50
39a	–	1d. black and yellow-orange (8.7.40)	14·00	9·00
		b. Perf 13 (5.42)	45	60
		ba. Mountaineer flaw	90·00	
		c. Perf 14 (17.2.49)	70	16·00
		ca. Mountaineer flaw	90·00	
39d	–	1d. black and green, P 13 (1.6.49)	60	1·50
40	**10**	1½d. black and vermilion	4·50	1·40
		a. Davit flaw	£300	£140
		b. Perf 13 (17.5.44)	85	80
		ba. Davit flaw	£130	£120
		c. Perf 14 (17.2.49)	1·25	13·00
		ca. Davit flaw	£160	
40d		1½d. black and rose-carmine, P 14 (1.6.49)	55	80
		da. Davit flaw	£120	£130
		db. Black and carmine	8·00	5·00
		dba. Davit flaw	£300	£225
		e. Perf 13 (25.2.53)	45	6·50
		ea. Davit flaw	£110	
41	–	2d. black and red-orange	4·00	1·00
		a. Perf 13 (17.5.44)	80	40
		aa. Mountaineer flaw	£130	
		b. Perf 14 (17.2.49)	1·25	35·00
		ba. Mountaineer flaw	£130	
41c	–	2d. black and scarlet, P 14 (1.6.49)	1·00	1·75
		ca. Mountaineer flaw	£120	
42	–	3d. black and ultramarine	£100	27·00
42a	–	3d. black and grey (8.7.40)	18·00	1·25
		b. Perf 13 (17.5.44)	70	80
42c	–	4d. black and ultramarine (8.7.40)	16·00	3·25
		d. Perf 13 (17.5.44)	4·50	3·00
		da. Mountaineer flaw	£250	
43	–	6d. black and blue	9·00	2·25
		a. Perf 13 (17.5.44)	9·00	5·00
44	**3**	1s. black and sepia	17·00	1·90
		a. Perf 13 (17.5.44)	4·75	2·00
45	**10**	2s.6d. black and deep carmine	42·00	9·50
		a. Frame printed double, one albino	£3500	
		b. Davit flaw	£900	£400
		c. Perf 13 (17.5.44)	27·00	32·00
		ca. Davit flaw	£800	£900
46	–	5s. black and yellow-brown	95·00	8·50
		a. Perf 13 (17.5.44)	38·00	28·00
47	–	10s. black and bright purple	£110	42·00
		a. Perf 13 (17.5.44)	42·00	55·00
38/47a *Set of 16*			£250	£100
38s/47s Perf "Specimen" *Set of 13*			£700	

Designs: *Horiz*—1d. (Nos. 39/c), 2d., 4d. Green Mountain; 1d. (No. 39d), 6d., 10s. Three Sisters; 3d., 5s. Long Beach.

1946 (21 Oct). *Victory. As Nos. 110/11 of Antigua*.

48		2d. red-orange	40	1·00
49		4d. blue	40	60
48s/9s Perf "Specimen" *Set of 2*			£225	

1948 (20 Oct). *Royal Silver Wedding. As Nos. 112/13 of Antigua*.

50		3d. black	50	30
51		10s. bright purple	45·00	42·00

1949 (10 Oct). *75th Anniv of Universal Postal Union. As Nos. 114/17 of Antigua*.

52		3d. carmine	1·00	2·00
53		4d. deep blue	3·50	1·50
54		6d. olive	2·00	3·50
55		1s. blue-black	2·00	1·50
52/5 *Set of 4*			7·50	7·75

Australia

The Australian colonies of New South Wales, Queensland, South Australia, Tasmania, Victoria and Western Australia produced their own issues before federation in 1901. Stamps inscribed for the individual states continued in use after federation until the end of December 1912.

INVERTED WATERMARKS. The stamp printers in the various Australian colonies paid little attention to the position of the watermark in the sheets they produced so that some entire printings had the watermark inverted, some 50% upright and 50% inverted while on others the inverted watermarks were restricted to odd sheets. In such circumstances it is impossible to provide adequate prices for such items so only those inverted watermarks occurring on stamps printed in Great Britain are included in the following listings.

NEW SOUTH WALES

PRICES FOR STAMPS ON COVER	
Nos. 1/83	from × 2
Nos. 84/7	from × 3
No. 88	—
Nos. 89/96	from × 2
Nos. 97/8	—
Nos. 99/101	from × 2
Nos. 102/13	from × 3
No. 114	from × 10
Nos. 115/17	from × 2
Nos. 118/27	from × 3
Nos. 131/53	from × 2
Nos. 154/70	from × 3
Nos. 171/81	—
Nos. 186/202	from × 2
Nos. 203/6	from × 10
Nos. 207/21	from × 5
Nos. 222/37	from × 6
Nos. 238/42	—
Nos. 243/4	from × 6
Nos. 253/64	from × 10
Nos. 265/8	from × 15
Nos. 269/70	from × 2
Nos. 271/3	from × 10
Nos. 280/1	from × 2
Nos. 288/97	from × 10
Nos. 298/312	from × 12
Nos. 313/31	from × 10
No. 332	—
Nos. 333/49	from × 12
No. 350	—
Nos. 351/63	from × 12
No. O1	—
Nos. O2/12	from × 4
Nos. O13/18	—
Nos. O19/34	from × 20
Nos. O35/8	—
Nos. O39/47	from × 40
Nos. O48/53	—
Nos. O54/8	from × 20
No. O59	—
Nos. D1/7	from × 50
Nos. D8/10	—
Nos. D11/15	from × 50

EMBOSSED LETTER SHEETS AND ENVELOPES. From 1 November 1838 the Sydney G.P.O. supplied letter sheets pre-stamped with an albino embossing, as illustrated, at 1½d. each or 1s.3d. per dozen. From January 1841 the price was reduced to 1s. per dozen. The public were also able to present their own stationery for embossing. The circular design measures approximately 29 mm in diameter, and examples are known on laid or wove paper of varying colours. Embossing continued until 1 May 1852 after which the Post Office refused to carry mail which was not franked with postage stamps. The die was used for reprints in 1870 and 1898 before it was destroyed later the same year.

A 1

PRINTERS. The early issues of New South Wales were printed on a press supervised by the Inspector of Stamps. On 1 January 1857 this responsibility passed to the Government printer who produced all subsequent issues, *unless otherwise stated*.

SPECIMEN OVERPRINTS. Those listed are from U.P.U. distributions between 1892 and 1903. Further "Specimen" overprints exist, but these were used for other purposes. From 1891 examples of some of these Specimens, together with cancelled stamps, were sold to collectors by the N.S.W. Post Office.

NEW SOUTH WALES USED IN NEW CALEDONIA. From October 1859 mail for Europe from New Caledonia was routed via Sydney and franked with New South Wales stamps in combination with local issues. Such N.S.W. stamps were cancelled on arrival in Sydney.

1

2

(Eng Robert Clayton, Sydney)

1850 (1 Jan). *T* **1**. *Plate I. No clouds.*

(a) Soft yellowish paper.

1	1d. crimson-lake	£6500	£450
2	1d. carmine	£6000	£400
3	1d. reddish rose	£5500	£375
4	1d. brownish red	£6000	£400

(b) Hard bluish paper.

5	1d. pale red	£5500	£375
6	1d. dull lake	£6000	£400

1850 (Aug). *T* **2**. *Plate I re-engraved by H. C. Jervis, commonly termed Plate II. With clouds.*

(a) Hard toned white to yellowish paper.

7	1d. vermilion	£3750	£300
8	1d. dull carmine	£3750	£300
	a. No trees on hill (R. 2/2)	£6500	£475
	b. Hill unshaded (R. 2/3)	£6500	£475
	c. Without clouds (R. 3/5)	£6500	£475

(b) Hard greyish or bluish paper.

9	1d. crimson-lake	£3750	£300
10	1d. gooseberry-red	£4250	£475
11	1d. dull carmine	£3250	£275
12	1d. brownish red	£3500	£275
	a. No trees on hill (R. 2/2)	£6000	£475
	b. Hill unshaded (R. 2/3)	£6000	£475
	c. Without clouds (R. 3/5)	£6000	£475

(c) Laid paper.

13	1d. carmine	£6000	£475
14	1d. vermilion	£6500	£450
	a. No trees on hill (R. 2/2)	—	£800
	b. Hill unshaded (R. 2/3)	—	£800
	c. Without clouds (R. 3/5)	—	£800

The varieties quoted with the letters "a", "b", "c" of course exist in each shade; the prices quoted are for the commonest shade, and the same applies to the following portions of this list.

Nos. 1/14 were printed in sheets of 25 (5×5).

LAID PAPER. Nos. 13/14, 34/5, 38 and 43*d/e* can be found showing parts of the papermaker's watermark (T. H. SAUNDERS 1847 in double-lined capitals and the figure of Britannia seated in an oval beneath a crown).

3

4

A (Pl I)

Illustrations A, B, C and D are sketches of the lower part of the inner circular frame, showing the characteristic variations of each plate.

(Eng John Carmichael)

1850 (1 Jan). *Plate I. Vertical-lined background. T* **3**.

(a) Early impressions, full details of clouds, etc.

15	2d. greyish blue	£7000	£400
16	2d. deep blue		£450
	a. Double lines on bale (R. 2/7)	—	£650

(b) Intermediate impressions.

16b	2d. greyish blue	£4500	£275
16c	2d. deep blue	£4750	£325

(c) Later impressions, clouds, etc., mostly gone, T **4**.

17	2d. greyish blue	£3250	£150
18	2d. dull blue	£2750	£140

(d) Stamps in the lower row partially retouched (end Jan).

19	2d. greyish blue	£4000	£225
20	2d. dull blue	£4250	£275

5   B (Pl II)   C (Pl III)

(Plate entirely re-engraved by H. C. Jervis.)

1850 (Apr). *T* **5**. *Plate III. Horizontal-lined background. Bale on left side supporting the seated figure, dated. Dot in centre of the star In each corner.*

(a) Early impressions.

21	2d. indigo	£5000	£275
22	2d. lilac-blue	—	£1200
23	2d. grey-blue	£5000	£225
24	2d. bright blue	£5000	£225
	a. Fan in Pl III, but with shading outside (R. 1/1)	—	£375
	b. Fan in Pl III, but without shading, and inner circle intersects the fan (R. 1/2)	—	£375
	c. Fan as B, but inner circle intersects fan (R. 1/3)	—	£375
	d. No whip and inner circle intersects fan (R. 1/4)	—	£375
	e. No whip (R. 1/8, 2/8)	—	£300
	f. Pick and shovel omitted (R. 1/10)	—	£375
	g. "CREVIT" omitted (R. 2/1)	—	£600

(b) Worn impressions.

25	2d. dull blue	£2750	£130
26	2d. Prussian blue	£2750	£170
	a. Fan as in Pl III, but with shading outside (R. 1/1)	—	£300
	b. Fan as in Pl III, but without shading, and inner circle intersects the fan (R. 1/2)	—	£300

---

	c. Fan as B, but inner circle intersects fan (R. 1/3)	—	£300
	d. No whip and inner circle intersects fan (R. 1/4)	—	£300
	e. No whip (R. 1/8, 2/8)	£3750	£225
	f. Pick and shovel omitted (R. 1/10)	—	£300
	g. "CREVIT" omitted (R. 2/1)	—	£400

(c) Bottom row retouched with dots and dashes in lower spandrels (from July).

27	2d. Prussian blue	£4000	£225
28	2d. dull blue	£3750	£150
	e. No whip (R. 2/8)		£250
	g. "CREVIT" omitted (R. 2/1)		£375

(Plate re-engraved a second time by H. C. Jervis)

1850 (Sept). *Plate III. Bale not dated and single-lined, except on No. 30c which is doubled-lined. No dots in stars.*

29	2d. ultramarine	£3250	£170
30	2d. deep blue	£3250	£170
	a. No whip (R. 2/3, 2/7)		£250
	b. Fan with 6 segments (R. 2/8)		£375
	c. Double lines on bale (R. 1/7, 1/10, 1/12)		£225

(Plate re-engraved a third time by H. C. Jervis)

1851 (Jan). *Plate IV. Double-lined bale, and circle in centre of each star.*

(a) Hard bluish grey wove paper.

31	2d. ultramarine	£4000	£160
32	2d. Prussian blue	£3250	£130
33	2d. bright blue	£3500	£150
	a. Hill not shaded (R. 1/12)	—	£225
	b. Fan with 6 segments (R. 2/8)	—	£225
	c. No clouds (R. 2/10)	—	£225
	d. Retouch (R. 2/1)	—	£300
	e. No waves (R. 1/9, 2/5)	—	£190

(b) Stout yellowish vertically laid paper.

34	2d. ultramarine	£4500	£170
35	2d. Prussian blue	£4750	£180
	a. Hill not shaded (R. 1/12)	—	£250
	b. Fan with 6 segments (R. 2/8)	—	£250
	c. No clouds (R. 2/10)	—	£250
	d. Retouch (R. 2/1)	—	£325
	e. No waves (R. 1/9, 2/5)	—	£200
	f. "PENOE" (R. 1/10, 2/12)	—	£250

The retouch, Nos. 33d and 35d., occurs outside the left margin line on R. 2/1.

6   D (Pl V)   7

(Plate re-engraved a fourth time by H. C. Jervis)

1851 (Apr). *T* **6**. *Plate V. Pearl in fan.*

(a) Hard greyish wove paper.

36	2d. ultramarine	£3500	£140
37	2d. dull blue	£3500	£140
	a. Pick and shovel omitted (R. 2/5)	—	£250
	b. Fan with 6 segments (R. 2/8)	—	£250

(b) Stout yellowish vertically laid paper.

38	2d. dull ultramarine	£5500	£300
	a. Pick and shovel omitted (R. 2/5)	—	£425
	b. Fan with 6 segments (R. 2/8)	—	£425

Nos. 15/38 were printed in sheets of 24 (12×2), although the existence of an inter-panneau *tête-bêche* pair from Plate II indicates that the printer applied two impressions of the plate to each sheet of paper. The two panes were normally separated before issue. The original plate I was re-cut four times to form Plates II to V. An interesting variety occurs on R. 1/9-11 and 2/7 in all five plates. It consists of ten loops of the engine-turning on each side of the design instead of the normal nine loops.

(Eng H. C. Jervis)

1850. *T* **7**.

(a) Soft yellowish wove paper.

39	3d. yellow-green	£4500	£250
40	3d. myrtle green	£13000	£1000
41	3d. emerald-green	£5000	£275
	a. No whip (R. 4/3–4)	—	£375
	b. "SIGIIIUM" for "SIGILLUM" (R. 5/3)		£450

(b) Bluish to grey wove paper.

42	3d. yellow-green	£4000	£225
43	3d. emerald-green	£4750	£225
	b. No whip (R. 4/3–4)		£300
	c. "SIGIIIUM" for "SIGILLUM" (R. 5/3)		£375

(c) Yellowish to bluish laid paper.

43d	3d. bright green	£7500	£500
43e	3d. deep yellowish green	£7000	£450
	f. No whip (R. 4/3–4)		£650
	g. "SIGIIIUM" for "SIGILLUM" (R. 5/3)		£750

Nos. 39/43e were printed in sheets of 25 (5×5).
A used example of No. 42 is known printed double, one albino.

8

9

(Des A. W. Manning from sketch by W. T. Levine; eng on steel by John Carmichael, Sydney)

1851 (18 Dec)–**52**. Imperf.

(a) Thick yellowish paper.

44	**8**	1d. carmine	£2000	£225
		a. No leaves right of "SOUTH" (R. 1/7, 3/1)	—	£400
		b. Two leaves right of "SOUTH" (R. 2/5)	—	£550
		c. "WALE" (R. 1/9)	—	£550

(b) Bluish medium wove paper (1852).

45	**8**	1d. carmine	£1100	£140
46	**8**	1d. scarlet	£1100	£140
47	**8**	1d. vermilion	£1000	£120
48	**8**	1d. brick-red	£1000	£120
		a. No leaves right of "SOUTH" (R. 1/7, 3/1)	£2250	£250
		b. Two leaves right of "SOUTH" (R. 2/5)	—	£325
		c. "WALE" (R. 1/9)	—	£325

(c) Thick vertically laid bluish paper (1852?).

49	**8**	1d. orange-brown	£3500	£375
50	**8**	1d. claret	£3500	£400
		a. No leaves right of "SOUTH" (R. 1/7, 3/1)	—	£650
		b. Two leaves right of "SOUTH" (R. 2/5)	—	£800
		c. "WALE" (R. 1/9)	—	£800

Nos. 44/50 were printed in sheets of 50 (10×5).

(Eng John Carmichael (Nos. 51/9), H. C. Jervis (Nos. 60/4))

1851 (24 July)–**55**. Imperf.

(a) Plate I.

(i) Thick yellowish wove paper.

51	**8**	2d. ultramarine	£900	85·00

(ii) Fine impressions, blue to greyish medium paper.

52	**8**	2d. ultramarine	£800	30·00
53		2d. chalky blue	£700	30·00
54		2d. dark blue	£700	30·00
55		2d. greyish blue	£700	30·00

(iii) Worn plate, blue to greyish medium paper.

56	**8**	2d. ultramarine	£475	30·00
57		2d. Prussian blue	£475	30·00

(iv) Worn plate, blue wove medium paper.

58	**8**	2d. ultramarine	£375	30·00
59		2d. Prussian blue	£350	30·00

(b) Plate II. Stars in corners (Oct 1853).

(i) Bluish medium to thick wove paper.

60	**9**	2d. deep ultramarine	£1100	£110
61		2d. indigo	£1200	90·00
		a. "WAEES" (R. 3/3)	—	£375

(ii) Worn plate, hard blue wove paper.

62	**9**	2d. deep Prussian blue	£1100	£100
		a. "WAEES" (R. 3/3)	—	£375

*(c) Plate III, being Plate I (T **8**) re-engraved by H. C. Jervis. Background of crossed lines (Sept 1855).*

(i) Medium bluish wove paper.

63	—	2d. Prussian blue	£500	60·00
		a. "WALES" partly covered with wavy lines (R. 1/3)	—	£190

(ii) Stout white wove paper.

64	—	2d. Prussian blue	£500	60·00
		a. "WALES" partly covered with wavy lines (R. 1/3)	—	£190

Nos. 51/64 were printed in sheets of 50 (10×5).

(Eng John Carmichael)

1852 (3 Dec). Imperf.

(a) Medium greyish blue wove paper.

65	**8**	3d. deep green	£2000	£200
66		3d. green	£1600	£140
67		3d. dull yellow-green	£1500	£100
		a. "WAEES" with centre bar of first "E" missing (R. 4/7)	—	£350

(b) Thick blue wove paper.

69	**8**	3d. emerald-green	£1900	£225
71		3d. blue-green	£1900	£225
		a. "WAEES" with centre bar of first "E" missing (R. 4/7)	—	£600

Nos. 65/71 were printed in sheets of 50 (10×5).

1852 (Apr)–**53**. Imperf.

(a) Plate I.

(i) Medium white wove paper.

72	**8**	6d. vandyke-brown	—	£900
		a. "WALLS" (R. 2/3)	—	£1600

(ii) Medium bluish grey wove paper.

73	**8**	6d. vandyke-brown	£1900	£250
74		6d. yellow-brown	£2000	£275
75		6d. chocolate-brown	£1900	£250
76		6d. grey-brown	£1800	£275
		a. "WALLS" (R. 2/3)	—	£600

(b) Plate I re-engraved by H. C. Jervis. Coarse background (June 1853).

77	—	6d. brown	£2000	£300
78	—	6d. grey-brown	£1900	£300

Examples of the 6d. in vandyke-brown on thick yellowish paper are proofs.

Nos. 72/6 and 77/8 were printed in sheets of 25 (5×5).

(Eng H. C. Jervis)

1853 (May). Imperf. *Medium bluish paper.*

79		8d. dull yellow	£4750	£600
80		8d. orange-yellow	£4750	£600
81		8d. orange	£5000	£650
		a. No bow at back of head (R. 1/9)	—	£1400
		b. No leaves right of "SOUTH" (R. 3/1)	—	£1400
		c. No lines in spandrel (R. 2/2, 3/2, 4/2)	—	£850

Nos. 79/81 were issued in sheets of 50 (10×5).

10

NOTE. All watermarked stamps from No. 82 to No. 172 have double-lined figures, as T **10**.

1854 (Jan–Mar). *Yellowish wove paper.* Wmk "**1**", "**2**", or "**3**" as T **10**, to match face value. Imperf.

82	**8**	1d. red-orange (Feb)	£225	20·00
83		1d. orange-vermilion	£225	20·00
		a. No leaves right of "SOUTH" (R. 1/7, 3/1)	£450	90·00
		b. Two leaves right of "SOUTH" (R. 2/5)	£600	£130
		c. "WALE" (R. 1/9)	£600	£130
84	—	2d. ultramarine (Pl III) (Jan)	£150	12·00
85	—	2d. Prussian blue (Pl III)	£150	12·00
86	—	2d. chalky blue (Pl III)	£150	9·50
		a. "WALES" partly covered by wavy lines (R. 1/3)	£500	55·00
87	**8**	3d. yellow-green (Mar)	£275	32·00
		a. "WAEES" with centre bar of first "E" missing (R. 4/7)	£900	£130
		b. Error. Wmk "2"	£3250	£1600

Nos. 82/7 were printed in sheets of 50 (10×5).

11	12
13	14

(6d. and 1s. des E. H. Corbould after sketches by T. W. Levinge. Printed by New South Wales Govt Ptg Dept from Perkins Bacon plates)

1854 (1 Feb)–**59**. Wmk "**5**", "**6**", "**8**" or "**12**" to match face value. Imperf.

88	**11**	5d. dull green (1.12.55)	£1000	£650
89	**12**	6d. deep slate	£750	35·00
		a. Wmk sideways	†	£850
90		6d. greenish grey	£600	35·00
91		6d. slate-green	£600	35·00
		a. Printed both sides	—	£850
92		6d. bluish grey	£650	35·00
93		6d. fawn	£700	95·00
		a. Wmk "8" (15.8.59)	£2500	£110
94		6d. grey	£650	35·00
95		6d. olive-grey	£650	35·00
96		6d. greyish brown	£650	35·00
		a. Wmk "8" (15.8.59)	£2500	£110
		ab. Wmk sideways	—	£375
97	**13**	8d. golden yellow (1.12.55)	£5500	£1200
98		8d. dull yellow-orange	£5000	£1100
99	**14**	1s. rosy vermilion (2.54)	£1200	70·00
		a. Wmk "8" (20.6.57)	£3250	£180
100		1s. pale red	£1200	70·00
101		1s. brownish red	£1300	80·00

Nos. 93a, 96a and 99a come from printings made when supplies of the correct numeral watermarks were unavailable.

Plate proofs of the 6d. in red-brown and of the 1s. in deep blue on unwatermarked paper exist handstamped "CANCELLED" in oval of bars (see note on Perkins Bacon "CANCELLED" in Catalogue introduction) (*Price* £10000 each).

For further examples of Types **11/14** on different watermarks see Nos. 141/53, 160/70, 215, 218, 231/3, 236 and 329.

15	16

(Eng John Carmichael)

1856 (1 Jan)–**59**. *For Registered Letters.* No wmk. Imperf.

(a) Soft medium yellowish paper.

102	**15**	(6d.) vermilion and Prussian blue	£900	£170
		a. Frame printed on back	£4000	£2250
103		(6d.) salmon and indigo	£900	£190

104		(6d.) orange and Prussian blue	£900	£225
105		(6d.) orange and indigo	£900	£200

(b) Hard medium bluish wove paper, with manufacturer's wmk in sans-serif, double-lined capitals across sheet and only showing portions of letters on a few stamps in a sheet.

106	**15**	(6d.) orange and Prussian blue (4.59)	£1000	£180

For further examples of Type **15** on different watermarks see Nos. 119/27.

(Printed by New South Wales Govt Ptg Dept from plates engraved by Perkins, Bacon & Co)

1856 (7 Jan)–**60**. Wmk "**1**", "**2**" or "**3**" to match face value. Imperf.

(a) Recess.

107	**16**	1d. orange-vermilion (6.4.56)	£170	23·00
		a. Error. Wmk "2"	†	£5500
108		1d. carmine-vermilion	£170	23·00
109		1d. orange-red	£170	23·00
		a. Printed on both sides	£1800	£1800
110		2d. deep turquoise-blue (Pl I)	£160	10·00
111		2d. ultramarine (Pl I)	£150	10·00
112		2d. blue (Pl I)	£150	10·00
		a. Major retouch (1858)	£1800	£450
		b. Error. Wmk "1"	†	£5500
		c. Wmk "5" (3.57)	£500	65·00
		d. Error. Wmk "8"	—	£5500
113		2d. pale blue (Pl I)	£150	10·00
114		2d. blue (Pl II) (1.60)	£550	55·00
115		3d. yellow-green (10.10.56)	£800	80·00
116		3d. bluish green	£850	85·00
117		3d. dull green	£850	85·00
		a. Error. Wmk "2"	—	£3250

(b) Lithographic transfer of Plate I.

118	**16**	2d. pale blue (3.8.59)	—	£750
		a. Retouched	—	£2500

For further examples of Type **16** on different watermarks see Nos. 131/40, 154/8, 171/2, 211/12, 226/8 and 327/8.

Two plates were used for the 2d. The 2d. Plate I was retouched, on a total of ten positions, several times as No. 112a. Stamps from Plate II are wider apart and are more regularly spaced. There is also a white patch between "A" of "WALES" and the back of the Queen's head.

On the 3d. the value is in block letters on a white background. No. 112c comes from a printing made when supplies of the "2" paper were unavailable. Of the errors there are only two known of both Nos. 112b and 112d, all used. One example of each is in the Royal Collection.

The 1d. exists privately rouletted 10, a used pair of which is known postmarked 15 May 1861.

No. 114 was mainly used at post offices in Queensland.

STAMPS WITH STRAIGHT EDGES. Stamps between Nos. 119 and 243 can be found with one or two sides imperforate. These come from the outside rows which were not perforated between the stamps and the sheet margins.

1860 (Feb)–**63**. *For Registered Letters.*

(a) P 12.

(i) Hard medium bluish wove paper with manufacturer's wmk in sans-serif, double-lined capitals across sheet, showing portions of letters on a few stamps.

119	**15**	(6d.) orange and Prussian blue	£450	60·00
120		(6d.) orange and indigo	£425	60·00

(ii) Coarse, yellowish wove paper with manufacturer's wmk in Roman capitals (Feb 1860).

121	**15**	(6d.) rose-red and Prussian blue	£350	42·00
122		(6d.) rose-red and indigo	£425	90·00
123		(6d.) salmon and indigo		

(b) P 13. (i) Coarse, yellowish wove paper with manufacturer's wmk in Roman capitals (1862).

124	**15**	(6d.) rose-red and Prussian blue	£350	60·00

(ii) Yellowish wove paper. Wmk "6" (May 1863).

125	**15**	(6d.) rose-red and Prussian blue	£130	22·00
126		(6d.) rose-red and indigo	£190	29·00
127		(6d.) rose-red and pale blue	£100	20·00
		a. Double impression of frame	—	£500

1860 (14 Feb)–**72**. Wmk double-lined figure of value.

(a) P 12.

131	**16**	1d. orange-red	£200	16·00
		a. Imperf between (pair)		
		b. Double impression		
132		1d. scarlet	£140	16·00
133		2d. pale blue (Pl I)	£550	£140
		a. Retouched	—	£1300
134		2d. greenish blue (Pl II)	£120	10·00
136		2d. Prussian blue (Pl II)	£120	11·00
		a. Error. Wmk "1"	—	£3000
		b. Retouched (shades)	—	£400
137		2d. Prussian blue (Pl I) (3.61)	£150	12·00
138		2d. dull blue (Pl I)	£140	11·00
139		3d. yellow-green (1860)	£1200	55·00
140		3d. blue-green	£650	42·00
141	**11**	5d. dull green (1863)	£200	65·00
142		5d. yellowish green (1863)	£200	65·00
143	**12**	6d. grey-brown	£400	48·00
144		6d. olive-brown	£400	55·00
145		6d. greenish grey	£475	45·00
146		6d. fawn	£450	65·00
147		6d. mauve	£425	35·00
148		6d. violet	£400	16·00
		a. Imperf between (pair)		
149	**13**	8d. lemon-yellow	—	£1700
150		8d. orange	£3500	£950
151		8d. red-orange	£3500	£950
152	**14**	1s. brownish red	£700	48·00
153		1s. rose-carmine	£700	48·00
		a. Imperf between (pair)		

(b) P 13.

154	**16**	1d. scarlet (1862)	85·00	11·00
155		1d. dull red	85·00	11·00
156		3d. blue-green (12.62)	50·00	11·00
157		3d. yellow-green	65·00	8·50
		a. Wmk "6" (7.72)	£120	12·00
158		3d. dull green	65·00	8·00
		a. Wmk "6" (7.72)	£120	15·00
160	**11**	5d. bluish green (12.63)	70·00	18·00

161		5d. bright yellow-green (8.65)	£120	45·00
162		5d. sea-green (1866)	70·00	21·00
162a		5d. dark bluish green (11.70)	50·00	21·00
163	12	6d. reddish purple (Pl I) (7.62)	£110	6·00
164		6d. mauve	£110	6·00
165		6d. purple (Pl II) (1864)	75·00	4·75
		a. Wmk "5" (7.66)	£500	25·00
		ab. Wmk "5" sideways	†	£1000
		b. Wmk "12" (12.66 and 1868)	£450	20·00
166		6d. violet	75·00	6·50
		a. Wmk "5" (7.66)	—	30·00
167		6d. aniline mauve	£1000	£120
167a	13	8d. red-orange (1862)	£200	55·00
167b		8d. yellow-orange	£225	42·00
167c		8d. bright yellow	£200	42·00
168	14	1s. rose-carmine (1862)	£120	7·50
169		1s. carmine	£110	8·00
170		1s. crimson-lake	£100	8·00

(c) Perf compound 12×13.

171	16	1d. scarlet (1862)	—	£1700
172		2d. dull blue (1.62)	£2250	£180

No. 133 was made by perforating a small remaining stock of No. 113. Nos. 137/8 were printed from the original plate after its return from London, where it had been repaired.

Nos. 157a, 158a and 165a/b come from printings made when supplies of paper with the correct face value were unavailable.

For later printings in these types, with different watermarks and perforations, see Nos. 195, 211/2, 215, 218, 226/8, 231/3, 236, 269/70 and 327/9.

24	25

(Des E. H. Corbould, R.I.)

1861–88. W **25.** Various perfs.

174	24	5s. dull violet, P 12 (1861)	£1400	£325
		a. Perf 13 (1861)	£250	35·00
175		5s. royal purple, P 13 (1872)	£425	60·00
176		5s. deep rose-lilac, P 13 (1875)	£140	35·00
177		5s. deep purple, P 13 (1880)	£225	50·00
		a. Perf 10 (1882)	£225	60·00
178		5s. rose-lilac, P 10 (1883)	£160	50·00
		a. Perf 10×12 (1885)	—	£150
179		5s. purple, P 12 (1885)	—	60·00
180		5s. reddish purple, P 10 (1886)	£160	50·00
		a. Perf 12×10 (1887)	£350	60·00
181		5s. rose-lilac, P 11 (1888)	—	£140

This value was replaced by Nos. 261, etc. in 1888 but reissued in 1897, *see* Nos. 297c/e.

26	27	28

(Printed by De La Rue & Co, Ltd, London and perf at Somerset House, London)

1862–65. *Surfaced paper.* P 14.

(i) W **27.**

186	26	1d. dull red (Pl I) (1.4.64)	£120	55·00

(ii) No wmk.

187	26	1d. dull red (Pl II) (1.65)	90·00	42·00
188	28	2d. pale blue (25.3.62)	95·00	55·00

(Printed from the De La Rue plates in the Colony)

1862 (12 Apr). Wmk double-lined "2" (No. 189) or "5" (No. 190). P 13.

189	28	2d. blue	70·00	12·00
		a. Perf 12	£150	32·00
		b. Perf 12×13	£450	£200
190		2d. dull blue (9.62)	75·00	13·00

29

1863–69. W **29.** P 13.

191	26	1d. pale red (3.69)	£120	18·00
192	28	2d. pale blue (4.63)	19·00	1·50
		a. Perf 12		
193		2d. cobalt-blue	19·00	1·50
194		2d. Prussian blue	30·00	3·75

1864–65. W **27.** P 13.

195	16	1d. pale red (6.64)	55·00	21·00
196	26	1d. dark red-brown (Pl I)	£170	22·00
197		1d. brownish red (Pl II)	30·00	3·75
		a. Imperf between (horiz pair)	†	£850
198		1d. brick-red (Pl II)	30·00	3·75
		a. Highly surfaced paper (1865)	£225	
199	28	2d. pale blue	£150	4·50

Plates I and II were made from the same die; they can only be distinguished by the colour or by the marginal inscription.

1865–66. *Thin to very thin wove paper.* No wmk. P 13.

200	26	1d. brick-red	£130	25·00
201		1d. brownish red	£130	25·00
202	28	2d. pale blue (11.65)	75·00	4·50

32	34

33	35

1867 (Sept)–**93.** W **33** and **35.**

203	32	4d. red-brown, P 13	60·00	4·50
204		4d. pale red-brown, P 13	60·00	4·50
205	34	10d. lilac, P 13	17·00	5·00
		a. Imperf between (horiz pair)	£1000	
		s. Optd "Specimen"	25·00	
206		10d. lilac, P 11 (1893)	15·00	5·00
		a. Perf 10	16·00	6·50
		b. Perf 10×11 or 11×10	21·00	8·00
		c. Perf 12×11	£110	15·00

36	37	38

NINEPENCE
(39)

From 1871 to 1903 the 9d. is formed from the 10d. by a black surch. (T **39**), 15 mm long on Nos. 219 to 220g, and 13½ mm long on subsequent issues.

1871–1902. W **36.**

207	26	1d. dull red, P 13 (8.71)	10·00	1·25
		a. Imperf vert (horiz pair)	†	£1100
208		1d. salmon, P 13 (1878)	10·00	1·25
		a. Perf 10 (6.80)	£250	30·00
		b. Perf 10×13 (6.80)	50·00	6·50
		ba. Perf 13×10	22·00	1·00
		c. Scarlet. Perf 10 (4.82)	—	£180
209	28	2d. Prussian-blue, P 13 (11.71)	15·00	1·00
		a. Perf 11×12, comb (11.84)	£250	40·00
		b. Imperf between (vert pair)	†	
210		2d. pale blue, P 13 (1876)	15·00	1·00
		a. Perf 10 (6.80)	£250	22·00
		b. Perf 10×13 (6.80)	£100	16·00
		ba. Perf 13×10	15·00	1·00
		c. Surfaced paper. Perf 13		
211	16	3d. yellow-green, P 13 (3.74)	30·00	3·75
		a. Perf 10 (6.80)	65·00	8·00
		b. Perf 11 (1902)	£150	£100
		c. Perf 12 (5.85)	—	£150
		d. Perf 10×12 or 12×10 (5.85)	£150	32·00
		e. Perf 11×12 (1902)	£120	32·00
212		3d. bright green, P 10 (6.80)	£120	14·00
		a. Perf 13×10 (6.80)	£110	18·00
		b. Perf 13		
213	32	4d. pale red-brown, P 13 (8.77)	70·00	10·00
214		4d. red-brown, P 13	70·00	9·00
		a. Perf 10 (6.80)	£190	50·00
		b. Perf 10×13 (6.80)	£110	22·00
		ba. Perf 13×10	80·00	5·00
215	11	5d. bluish green, P 10 (8.84)	20·00	16·00
		a. Perf 12 (5.85)	£250	£100
		b. Perf 10×13 or 13×10		
		c. Perf 10×12 (5.85)	£120	48·00
		ca. Perf 12×10	38·00	17·00
216	37	6d. bright mauve, P 13 (1.1.72)	60·00	1·75
		a. Imperf between (horiz pair)	†	£1000
217		6d. pale lilac, P 13 (1878)	60·00	1·75
		a. Perf 10 (6.80)	£180	12·00
		b. Perf 10×13 (6.80)	85·00	15·00
		ba. Perf 13×10	65·00	2·00
		c. Imperf between (horiz pair). Perf 13×10	†	£1000
218	13	8d. yellow, P 13 (3.77)	£130	17·00
		a. Perf 10 (6.80)	£300	26·00
		b. Perf 13×10 (6.80)	£200	24·00
219	34	9d. on 10d. pale red-brown, P 13 (8.71)	35·00	4·75
220		9d. on 10d. red-brown, P 13 (1878)	35·00	9·00
		a. Perf 10 (6.80)	12·00	7·50
		b. Perf 12 (5.85)	12·00	7·50
		c. Perf 11 (12.85)	35·00	8·00
		ca. Surch in both black and blue (12.85)	£180	
		d. Perf 12×10 (5.85)	£250	£160
		e. Perf 10×11 or 11×10 (12.85)	50·00	13·00
		f. Perf 12×11 (12.85)	14·00	5·50
		g. Perf 12×11, comb (1.84)	14·00	5·50
		gs. Optd "Specimen"	25·00	
221	38	1s. black, P 13 (1.4.76)	85·00	5·00
		a. Perf 10 (6.80)	£200	15·00
		b. Perf 10×13 (6.80)	£240	25·00

		ba. Perf 13×10	£170	7·50
		c. Perf 11		
		d. Imperf between (vert pair)	†	£1200
		e. Imperf (pair)	†	£1100

Collectors should note that the classification of perforations is that adopted by the Royal Philatelic Society, London. "Perf 12" denotes the perforation formerly called "11½, 12" and "perf 13" that formerly called "12½, 13".

BISECTS. Between 1887 and 1913 various 1d. and 2d. stamps can be found vertically or diagonally bisected. This was unauthorised.

40

1882 (Apr)–**97.** W **40.**

222	26	1d. salmon, P 10	20·00	80
		a. Perf 13		
		b. Perf 10×13		
		ba. Perf 13×10	45·00	1·75
223		1d. orange *to* scarlet, P 13	£800	£400
		a. Perf 10	12·00	60
		ab. Imperf between (horiz pair)		
		b. Perf 10×13	£120	7·50
		c. Perf 10×12 or 12×10 (4.85)	£250	65·00
		d. Perf 11×10 (12.85)	£450	£120
		e. Perf 12×11 (12.85)	—	£120
		f. Perf 11×12, comb (1.84)	6·00	50
		h. Perf 11 (12.85)	—	£130
224	28	2d. pale blue, P 13	£450	90·00
		a. Perf 10	24·00	50
		b. Perf 10×13	65·00	2·75
		ba. Perf 13×10		
225		2d. Prussian blue, P 10	32·00	50
		b. Perf 12 (4.85)	—	£225
		c. Perf 11 (12.85)	—	£100
		d. Perf 12×11 (12.85)	£400	£100
		e. Perf 10×12 (4.85)	£225	65·00
		ca. Perf 12×10	£400	£100
		f. Perf 10×11 or 11×10 (12.85)	£450	£150
		g. Perf 11×12, comb (1.84)	13·00	50
		ga. Printed double	†	£550
226	16	3d. yellow-green, P 10 (1886)	11·00	5·50
		a. Double impression	†	£1100
		b. Wmk sideways		
		bs. Optd "Specimen"	25·00	
		c. Perf 12×10	£160	35·00
		ca. Perf 12×10	£120	15·00
		d. Perf 11	6·50	1·00
		da. Imperf vert (horiz pair)	£350	
		e. Perf 11×12 or 12×11	6·00	1·00
		f. Perf 12	10·00	1·50
		g. Imperf (pair)	£250	
227		3d. bluish green, P 10	10·00	1·25
		a. Wmk sideways	50·00	10·00
		b. Perf 11	10·00	1·50
		c. Perf 10×11	21·00	2·25
		ca. Perf 11×10	£100	35·00
		d. Perf 11×12 or 12×11	8·50	2·00
		e. Perf 10×12 or 12×10	35·00	3·50
228		3d. emerald-green, P 10 (1893)	55·00	8·00
		a. Wmk sideways	—	16·00
		b. Perf 11	55·00	4·00
		ba. Perf 11×10	£120	38·00
		c. Perf 10×12	50·00	4·00
		ca. Perf 12×10	75·00	6·50
		d. Perf 12×11	—	11·00
229	32	4d. red-brown, P 10	60·00	3·50
		a. Perf 10×12 (4.85)	—	£160
		b. Perf 11×12, comb (1.84)	60·00	2·00
230		4d. dark brown, P 10	60·00	3·00
		a. Perf 12 (4.85)	£300	£180
		b. Perf 10×12 (4.85)	£200	60·00
		ba. Perf 12×10	£300	£150
		c. Perf 11×12, comb (1.84)	42·00	1·75
231	11	5d. dull green, P 10 (1890)	20·00	1·75
		as. Optd "Specimen"	25·00	
		b. Perf 11×10	50·00	
		c. Perf 10×12 (4.85)	80·00	4·25
232		5d. bright green, P 10	45·00	5·50
		b. Perf 10×11 (12.85)	50·00	5·50
		ba. Perf 11×10	50·00	6·50
		c. Perf 10×12 (4.85)	£150	32·00
		ca. Perf 12×10	£100	70·00
233		5d. blue-green, P 10	14·00	1·25
		a. Perf 12 (4.85)	17·00	1·25
		ab. Wmk sideways	55·00	
		b. Perf 11 (12.85)	9·50	1·00
		c. Perf 10×11 (12.85)	38·00	2·00
		d. Perf 11×12 or 12×11 (12.85)	9·00	1·00
		da. Wmk sideways (P 11×12)	60·00	20·00
		e. Imperf (pair)	£350	
234	37	6d. pale lilac, P 10	55·00	1·25
		a. Perf 10×13 or 13×10	—	£300
		b. Perf 10×12 or 12×10 (4.85)	60·00	1·50
235		6d. mauve, P 10	55·00	1·25
		a. Perf 12 (4.85)	80·00	10·00
		b. Perf 11 (12.85)	80·00	8·00
		c. Perf 10×11 (12.85)	60·00	8·00
		ca. Perf 12×10	55·00	2·25
		cb. Imperf between (horiz pair)	†	£1000
		d. Perf 11×12 (12.85)	80·00	12·00
		da. Perf 11×10	55·00	1·60
		e. Perf 11×10 (12.85)	65·00	2·25
236	13	8d. yellow, P 10 (1883)	£120	16·00
		a. Perf 12 (4.85)	£190	28·00
		b. Perf 11 (12.85)	£120	22·00
		c. Perf 10×12 (4.85)	£150	45·00
		ca. Perf 12×10	£120	38·00
236d	34	9d. on 10d. red-brn, P 11×12 (28.2.97)	8·00	9·00
		das. Optd "Specimen"	25·00	
		db. Perf 12	11·00	11·00
		dc. Perf 11	11·00	12·00

236e		dca. Surch double	£250	£225
		10d. violet, P 11×12 (1897)	14·00	8·50
		eas. Optd "Specimen"	25·00	
		eb. Perf 12×11½	12·00	8·50
		ec. Perf 12	15·00	9·50
		ed. Perf 11	22·00	11·00
237	38	1s. black, P 10	75·00	4·00
		a. Perf 11 (12.85)	£200	11·00
		b. Perf 10×12	—	£250
		c. Perf 10×13		4·00
		ca. Perf 13×10	£200	22·00
		d. Perf 11×12, comb (1.84)	75·00	4·00

41   **42**

1885–86. W 41 (sideways).

(i) Optd "POSTAGE", in black.

238	42	5s. lilac and green, P 13 (15.10.85)		90·00
		b. Perf 12×10	£425	90·00
239		10s. lilac and claret, P 13 (17.5.86) ..		
		a. Perf 12	£950	£200
240		£1 lilac and claret, P 13 (17.5.86) ..	—	£3500
		a. Perf 12	£3750	

(ii) Overprinted in blue.

241	42	10s. mauve and claret, P 10	£750	£200
		as. Optd "Specimen"	60·00	
		b. Perf 12	£225	65·00
		c. Perf 12×11		
242		£1 rose-lilac and claret, P 12×10	£3500	£2250

1886–87. W 41.

243	26	1d. scarlet, P 10 (12.86)	21·00	6·50
		a. Perf 11×12, comb.	7·00	3·00
244	28	2d. deep blue, P 10 (12.87)	55·00	8·50
		a. Perf 11×12, comb.	18·00	3·00
		b. Imperf.		

45 View of Sydney   **46** Emu   **47** Captain Cook

48 Queen Victoria and Arms of Colony   **49** Superb Lyrebird   **50** Eastern Grey Kangaroo

51 Map of Australia   **52** Capt. Arthur Phillip, first Governor and Lord Carrington, Governor in 1888

(Des M. Tannenberg (1d., 6d.), Miss Devine (2d., 8d.), H. Barraclough (4d.), Govt Ptg Office (1s.), C. Turner (5s.), Mrs. F. Stoddard (20s.). Eng W. Bell).

1888 (1 May)–89. *Centenary of New South Wales.*

(a) W 40. P 11×12.

253	45	1d. lilac (9.7.88)	5·50	80
		a. Perf 12×11½	18·00	1·00
		b. Perf 12	7·50	30
		c. Imperf (pair)		
		d. Mauve	6·00	30
		da. Imperf between (pair)		
		db. Perf 12×11½	8·50	50
		dc. Perf 12	8·50	50
254	46	2d. Prussian blue (1.9.88)	10·00	30
		a. Imperf (pair)	£160	£275
		b. Imperf between (pair)	£600	
		c. Perf 12×11½	13·00	30
		d. Perf 12	12·00	30
		e. Chalk blue	8·50	30
		ea. Perf 12×11½	11·00	50
		eb. Perf 12	11·00	50
255	47	4d. purple-brown (8.10.88)	14·00	3·50
		a. Perf 12×11½	38·00	8·00
		b. Perf 12	32·00	3·50
		c. Perf 11	£300	95·00
		d. Red-brown	12·00	3·50
		da. Perf 12×11½	14·00	2·75
		db. Perf 12	14·00	2·75
		e. Orange-brown, P 12×11½	18·00	3·50

256	48	6d. carmine (26.11.88)	24·00	3·50
		a. Perf 12×11½	28·00	4·00
		b. Perf 12	24·00	8·50
257	49	8d. lilac-rose (17.1.89)	20·00	4·25
		a. Perf 12×11½	42·00	12·00
		b. Perf 12	20·00	4·75
		c. Magenta	75·00	10·00
		ca. Perf 12×11½	20·00	4·50
		cb. Perf 12	20·00	4·75
258	50	1s. maroon (21.2.89)	30·00	2·00
		a. Perf 12×11½	32·00	2·00
		b. Perf 12	35·00	2·00
		c. Violet-brown	30·00	2·25
		ca. Imperf (pair)	£700	
		cb. Perf 12×11½	50·00	2·75
		cc. Perf 12	50·00	2·25
		253s/8s Optd "Specimen" Set of 6	£170	

(b) W 41. P 11×12.

259	45	1d. lilac (1888)	23·00	
		a. Mauve	20·00	2·75
260	46	2d. Prussian blue (1888)	70·00	3·50

(c) W 25 (sideways on 5s.) P 10.

261	51	5s. deep purple (13.3.89)	£200	48·00
		a. Deep violet	£200	48·00
262	52	20s. cobalt-blue (27.4.88)	£300	£130

Nos. 255c and 261/2 are line perforated, the remainder are comb.

A postal forgery exists of the 2d. on unwatermarked paper and perforated 11.

53   **54**

1890. W 53 (5s.). or 54 (20s.). P 10.

263	51	5s. lilac	£150	29·00
		a. Perf 11	£200	42·00
		ab. Imperf between (horiz pair)		
		b. Perf 12	£300	48·00
		c. Perf 10×11 or 11×10	£225	29·00
		d. Mauve	£190	29·00
		da. Perf 11	£190	42·00
264	52	20s. cobalt-blue	£325	£140
		a. Perf 11	£275	75·00
		b. Perf 10×11		
		c. Ultramarine, P 11	£225	75·00
		ca. Perf 12	£275	£130
		cb. Perf 11×12 or 12×11	£180	75·00
		263s/4s Optd "Specimen" Set of 2	£180	

55 Allegorical figure of Australia

Halfpenny (56)   **SEVEN-PENCE HALFPENNY** (57)

1890 (22 Dec). W 40.

265	55	2½d. ultramarine, P 11×12 comb	5·00	50
		as. Optd "Specimen"	25·00	
		b. Perf 12×11½, comb.	48·00	48·00
		c. Perf 12, comb.	9·00	50

1891 (5 Jan). Surch as T 56 and 57. W 40.

266	26	½d. on 1d. grey, P 11×12 comb	3·00	4·00
		a. Surch omitted		
		b. Surch double	£300	
267	37	7½d. on 6d. brown, P 10	5·50	4·00
		a. Perf 11	5·00	3·00
		b. Perf 12	7·00	3·50
		c. Perf 11×12 or 12×11..	5·50	3·50
		d. Perf 10×12	6·00	3·50
268	38	12½d. on 1s. red, P 10	12·00	14·00
		a. "HALFPENNY" omitted		
		b. Perf 11	13·00	13·00
		c. Perf 11×12, comb.	12·00	11·00
		d. Perf 12×11½, comb.	12·00	11·00
		e. Perf 12, comb.	15·00	11·00
		266/8s Optd "Specimen" Set of 3	70·00	

1891 (1 July). Wmk "10" as W 35. P 10.

269	16	3d. green	12·00	80·00
270		3d. dark green	5·00	17·00

58   Type I. Narrow "H" in "HALF"

1892 (21 Mar)–99. *Type I.* W 40.

271	58	½d. grey, P 10	30·00	1·50
		a. Perf 11	75·00	6·00
		b. Perf 10×12 or 12×10	70·00	8·50

		c. Perf 11×12	2·50	20
		cs. Optd "Specimen"	20·00	
		d. Perf 12	2·75	30
272		½d. slate, P 11×12 (1897)	2·25	20
		a. Perf 12×11½	2·50	20
		b. Perf 12	2·50	20
		c. Imperf between (horiz pair).		
		Perf 11×12	£600	
273		½d. bluish green, P 11×12 (1.99)	4·00	30
		a. Perf 12×11½	2·00	30
		b. Perf 12	3·75	30

The perforations 11×12, 12×11½, 12, are from comb machines.

The die for Type **58** was constructed from an electro taken from the die of the De La Rue 1d., Type **26**, with "ONE" replaced by "HALF" and two "½" plugs added to the bottom corners. These alterations proved to be less hard-wearing than the remainder of the die and defects were visible on the 1905 plate of No. 333. It seems likely that repairs were undertaken before printing from the next plate in late 1907 which produced stamps as Type II.

59

1894–1904. *Optd "POSTAGE" in blue. W 59 (sideways).*

274	42	10s. mauve and claret, P 10	£375	£150
275		10s. violet and claret, P 12	£180	50·00
		a. Perf 11	£325	90·00
		b. Perf 12×11	£200	60·00
276		10s. violet and aniline crimson, P 12×11	£200	55·00
		a. Chalk-surfaced paper (1903)	£200	55·00
		b. Perf 12	£300	85·00
277		10s. violet and rosine (*chalk-surfaced paper*), P 12 (1904) ..	£200	80·00
		a. Perf 11	£250	85·00
		b. Perf 12×11	£200	50·00
278		10s. violet and claret (*chalk-surfaced paper*), P 12×11 (1904)	£250	90·00
279		£1 violet and claret, P 12×11		

60

61

(Des C. Turner. Litho Govt Printing Office, Sydney)

1897. *Diamond Jubilee and Hospital Charity.* T **60/1**. W **40**. P 12×11 (1d.) or 11 (2½d.).

280	60	1d. (1s.) green and brown (22.6)	40·00	40·00
281	61	2½d. (2s.6d.), gold, carmine and blue (28.6)	£170	£170
		280s/1s Optd "Specimen" Set of 2	£200	

These stamps, sold at 1s. and 2s.6d. respectively, paid postage of 1d. and 2½d. only, the difference being given to a Consumptives' Home.

62   **63**   **64**

Dies of the 1d.

Die I   Die II

1d. Die I. The first pearl on the crown on the left side is merged into the arch, the shading under the fleur-de-lis is indistinct, the "S" of "WALES" is open.

1d. Die II. The first pearl is circular, the vertical shading under the fleur-de-lis clear, the "S" of "WALES" not so open.

Dies of the 2½d.

Die I   Die II

2½d. Die I. There are 12 radiating lines in the star on the Queen's breast.

Die II. There are 16 radiating lines in the star and the eye is nearly full of colour.

(Des D. Souter (2d., 2½d.). Eng W. Amor)

1897 (22 June)–**99**. W **40** (sideways on 2½d.). P 12×11 (2½d.) or 11×12 (others)

288	62	1d. carmine (Die I)	2·50	10
		a. Perf 12×11½	2·50	10
		s. Optd "Specimen"	20·00	
289		1d. scarlet (Die I)	3·25	10
		a. Perf 12×11½	4·75	40
		b. Perf 12	4·75	50
		ba. Imperf horiz (vert pair)	£350	
290		1d. rose-carmine (Die II) (10.97)	2·50	10
		a. Perf 12×11½	2·00	10
		b. Perf 12	2·75	10
		c. Imperf between (pair)	£500	
291		1d. salmon-red (Die II) (P 12×11½)	2·75	10
		a. Perf 12	4·00	40
292	63	2d. deep dull blue	4·50	40
		a. Perf 12×11½	4·50	40
		b. Perf 12	6·50	40
		s. Optd "Specimen"	20·00	
293		2d. cobalt-blue	6·50	40
		a. Perf 12×11½	4·00	40
		b. Perf 12	6·00	40
294		2d. ultramarine (1.12.97)	4·50	20
		a. Perf 12×11½	2·75	20
		b. Perf 12	2·75	20
		c. Imperf between (pair)		
		s. Optd "Specimen"	22·00	
295	64	2½d. purple (Die I)	12·00	1·75
		a. Perf 11½×12	14·00	1·75
		b. Perf 11	14·00	2·75
		s. Optd "Specimen"	20·00	
296		2½d. deep violet (Die II) (11.97)	11·00	1·25
		a. Perf 11½×12	14·00	1·25
		b. Perf 12	10·00	1·25
297		2½d. Prussian blue (17.1.99)	11·00	2·00
		a. Perf 11½×12	4·50	2·00
		b. Perf 12	4·00	2·00

The perforations 11×12, 12×11½ and 12 are from comb machines, the perforation 11 is from a single-line machine.

1897. Reissue of T **24**. W **25**. P 11.

297c		5s. reddish purple (shades)	48·00	13·00
		ca. Imperf between (horiz pair)	£7000	
		d. Perf 12	65·00	24·00
		e. Perf 11×12 or 12×11	50·00	19·00

1898–99. W **40**. P 11×12.

297f	48	6d. emerald-green	32·00	3·00
		fa. Perf 12×11½	25·00	9·50
		fb. Perf 12	23·00	9·50
		fs. Optd "Specimen"	22·00	
297g		6d. orange-yellow (1899)	17·00	5·50
		ga. Perf 12×11½	15·00	4·50
		gb. Perf 12	25·00	6·50
		gc. Yellow, P 12×11½	17·00	3·25

1899 (Oct). Chalk-surfaced paper. W **40** (sideways on 2½d.). P 12×11½ or 11½×12 (2½d.), comb.

298	58	½d. blue-green (Type I)	1·50	60
		a. Imperf (pair)	£120	£140
299	62	1d. carmine (Die II)	2·75	10
		a. Imperf horiz (vert pair)	£450	
		b. Perf 11		
300		1d. scarlet (Die II)	1·75	10
		a. Perf 11		
301		1d. salmon-red (Die II)	3·75	10
		a. Imperf (pair)	£130	£150
302	63	2d. cobalt-blue	3·00	20
		a. Imperf (pair)	£130	
		b. Imperf horiz (pair)	£700	
303	64	2½d. Prussian blue (Die II)	4·00	70
		a. Imperf (pair)	£160	
303b	47	4d. red-brown	15·00	6·00
		c. Imperf (pair)	£375	
304		4d. orange-brown	10·00	5·00
305	48	6d. deep orange	14·00	3·25
		a. Imperf (pair)	£300	
306		6d. orange-yellow	12·00	3·25
307		6d. emerald-green	75·00	22·00
		a. Imperf (pair)	£375	
308	49	8d. magenta	21·00	3·75
309	34	9d. on 10d. dull brown	8·00	9·00
		a. Surcharge double	£160	£180
		b. Without surcharge	£170	
310		10d. violet	15·00	8·00
311	50	1s. maroon	24·00	2·50
312		1s. purple-brown	24·00	3·00
		a. Imperf (pair)	£325	

65 The spacing between the Crown and "NSW" is 1 mm in T **65** as against 2 mm in T **40**.

66 Superb Lyrebird

67

1902–03. Chalk-surfaced paper. W **65** (sideways on 2½d.). P 12×11½ or 11½×12 (2½d.), comb

313	58	½d. blue-green (Type I)	4·25	40
		a. Perf 12×11	4·25	40
		b. Mixed perfs 12×11½	£550	
314	62	1d. carmine (Die II)	2·50	20
		a. Perf 11	†	£1000
315	63	2d. cobalt-blue	3·50	50
		a. Perf 11	—	
316	64	2½d. dark blue (Die II)	7·50	50
317	47	4d. orange-brown	38·00	9·00
318	48	6d. yellow-orange	18·00	3·00
319		6d. orange	18·00	3·00
320		6d. orange-buff	30·00	3·00
321	49	8d. magenta	21·00	3·75
322	34	9d. on 10d. brownish orange	9·50	4·00
323		10d. violet	18·00	8·00
324	50	1s. maroon	35·00	2·25
325		1s. purple-brown	35·00	2·25
326	66	2s.6d. green (1903)	42·00	19·00
		s. Optd "Specimen"	60·00	

1903–08. W **65**.

327	16	3d. yellow-green, P 11	9·50	1·25
		b. Perf 12	9·00	1·00
		ba. Imperf between (horiz pair)		
		c. Perf 11×12 or 12×11	9·00	1·00
328		3d. dull green, P 12	27·00	2·75
		a. Perf 11×12 or 12×11	11·00	1·75
		b. Perf 11	11·00	1·75
329	11	5d. dark blue-green, P 11×12 or 12	9·50	1·25
		a. Wmk sideways	24·00	7·00
		b. Perf 11	20·00	1·25
		ba. Wmk sideways	—	50·00
		c. Perf 12	30·00	4·00
		ca. Wmk sideways	£100	50·00
		d. Imperf (pair)	£190	

Stamps from this series without watermark are from the edge of the sheet.

(Typo Victoria Govt Printer, Melbourne)

1903 (18 July). Wmk double-lined V over Crown. W w **10**.

330	67	9d. brown & ultram, P 12¼×12½, comb	15·00	3·25
		s. Optd "Specimen"	40·00	
331		9d. brown & dp blue, P 12¼×12½, comb	15·00	3·25
332		9d. brown and blue, P 11	£2500	£1300

Type II. Broad "H" in "HALF"   **68**

1905 (1 Oct)–**10**. W **68** (sideways on 2½d.). Chalk-surfaced paper. P 12×11½ or 11½×12 (2½d.), comb, unless otherwise stated.

333	58	½d. blue-green (Type I)	2·75	30
		a. Perf 11½×11	11·00	1·50
		b. Type II (1908)	2·50	30
		ba. Perf 11½×11	2·75	30
334	62	1d. rose-carmine (Die II)	2·00	10
		a. Double impression	£350	£400
		b. Perf 11½×11	2·50	20
335	63	2d. deep ultramarine	2·00	20
		a. Perf 11½×11	2·50	20
		c. Perf 11		
336		2d. milky blue (1910)	2·50	10
		a. Perf 11	60·00	70·00
		b. Perf 11½×11	2·50	20
337	64	2½d. Prussian blue (Die II)	4·00	2·00
338	47	4d. orange-brown	10·00	3·50
339		4d. red-brown	12·00	3·50
		a. Perf 11½×11	22·00	3·50
340	48	6d. dull yellow	13·00	2·25
341		6d. orange-yellow	14·00	2·25
		a. Perf 11	28·00	3·50
342		6d. deep orange	13·00	2·25
		a. Perf 11	£250	
343		6d. orange-buff	14·00	2·25
		a. Perf 11½×11	24·00	3·50
344	49	8d. magenta	22·00	4·50
345		8d. lilac-rose	22·00	5·00
346	34	10d. violet	14·00	4·50
		a. Perf 11½×11	13·00	4·00
		b. Perf 11	13·00	4·00
347	50	1s. maroon	27·00	1·75
348		1s. purple-brown (1908)	27·00	1·75
349	66	2s.6d. blue-green	55·00	27·00
		a. Perf 11½×11	35·00	18·00
		b. Perf 11	35·00	22·00

69

1905 (Dec). W **69**. Chalk-surfaced paper. P 11.

350	52	20s. cobalt-blue	£190	65·00
		a. Perf 12	£225	75·00
		b. Perf 11½×12 or 12×11	£190	60·00

(Typo Victoria Govt Printer, Melbourne)

1905 (Dec). Wmk double-lined "A" and Crown, W w **11**. P 12×12½ comb.

351	67	9d. brown and ultramarine	13·00	1·75
		a. Perf 11	75·00	60·00
		b. Mixed perfs 12×12½ and 11	£1200	
352		9d. yellow-brown and ultramarine	13·00	1·75
		a. Perf 11	75·00	60·00

1907 (July). W w **11** (sideways on 2½d.). P 12×11½ or 11½×12 (2½d.), comb, unless otherwise stated

353	58	½d. blue-green (Type I)	4·25	1·75
354	62	1d. dull rose (Die II)	7·50	7·50
355	63	2d. cobalt-blue	7·50	1·50
		a. Wmk sideways	—	£250
356	64	2½d. Prussian blue (Die II)	65·00	£110
357	47	4d. orange-brown	16·00	15·00
358	48	6d. orange-buff	35·00	22·00
359		6d. dull yellow	32·00	22·00
360	49	8d. magenta	19·00	22·00
361	34	10d. violet, P 11 (12.07)	32·00	45·00
362	50	1s. purple-brown	42·00	8·50
		a. Perf 11	†	£1200
363	66	2s.6d. blue-green	65·00	65·00

Stamps from this series without watermark are from the edge of the sheet.

STAMP BOOKLETS.

There are very few surviving examples of Nos. SB1/4. Listings are provided for those believed to have been issued with prices quoted for those known to still exist.

1904 (May)–**19**. Black on red cover with map of Australia on front and picture of one of six different State G.P.O's on back. Stapled.

SB1	£1 booklet containing two hundred and forty 1d. in four blocks of 30 and two blocks of 60	
	a. Red on pink cover (1909)	
	b. Blue on pink cover	

1904 (May). Black on grey cover as No. SB1. Stapled.

SB2	£1 booklet containing one hundred and twenty 2d. in four blocks of 30	

1910 (May). Black on cream. cover inscribed "COMMONWEALTH OF AUSTRALIA/POSTMASTER-GENERAL'S DEPARTMENT". Stapled.

SB3	2s. booklet containing eleven ½d. (No. 333), either in block of 6 plus block of 5 or block of 11, and eighteen 1d. (No.334), either in three blocks of 6 or block of 6 plus block of 12	£4250

Unsold stock of No. SB3 was uprated with one additional ½d. in May 1911.

1911 (Aug). Red on pink cover as No. SB3. Stapled.

SB4	2s. booklet containing twelve ½d. (No. 333), either in two blocks of 6 and block of 12, and eighteen 1d. (No. 334) either in three blocks of 6 or 1 block of 6 plus block of 12	£3750

OFFICIAL STAMPS

O S   O S   O S

(O 1)   (O 2)   (O 3)

The space between the letters is normally 7 mm as illustrated, except on the 5d. and 8d. (11–11½ mm), 5s. (12 mm) and 20s. (14 mm). Later printings of the 3d., W **40**, are 5½ mm, and these are listed. Varieties in the settings are known on the 1d. (8 and 8½ mm), 2d. (8½ mm) and 3d. (9 mm).

Varieties of Type O 1 exist with "O" sideways.

Nos. O1/35 overprinted with Type O 1

1879. Wmk double-lined "6". P 13.

O1	16	3d. dull green	—	£475

1879 (Oct)–**85**. W **36**. P 13.

O2	26	1d. salmon	18·00	2·50
		a. Perf 10 (5.81)	£180	32·00
		b. Perf 13×10 (1881)	35·00	4·00
O3	28	2d. blue	22·00	2·00
		a. magenta	£225	32·00
		b. Perf 10 (7.81)	£225	32·00
		b. Perf 10×13 (1881)	50·00	25·00
		ba. Perf 13×10	35·00	3·00
		d. Perf 11×12 (11.84?)	—	£225
O4	16	3d. dull green (R.) (12.79)	£500	£275
O5		3d. dull green (3.80)	£250	55·00
		a. Perf 10 (1881)	£150	50·00
		b. Yellow-green. Perf 10 (10.81)	£150	27·00
		ba. Perf 13×10 (1881)	£150	27·00
		bb. Perf 12 (4.85)	£200	50·00
		be. Perf 10×12 or 12×10 (4.85)	£200	50·00
O6	32	4d. red-brown	£180	8·00
		a. Perf 10 (1881)	—	£225
		b. Perf 10×13 (1881)	£225	90·00
		ba. Perf 13×10	£170	12·00
O7	11	5d. green, P 10 (8.84)	18·00	18·00
O8	37	6d. pale lilac	£250	7·00
		a. Perf 10 (1881)	£375	42·00
		b. Perf 13×10 (1881)	£180	42·00
O9	13	8d. yellow (R.) (12.79)	—	£275
O10		8d. yellow (1880)	—	26·00
		a. Perf 10 (1881)	£325	75·00
O11	34	9d. on 10d. brown, P 10 (30.5.80)	£500	
		s. Optd "Specimen"	60·00	
O12	38	1s. black (R.)	£275	11·00
		a. Perf 10 (1881)	—	20·00
		b. Perf 10×13 (1881)	—	32·00
		ba. Perf 13×10	—	12·00

Other stamps are known with red overprint but their status is in doubt.

1880–88. W 25.

(a) P 13.

O13	24	5s. deep purple (15.2.80)	£500	95·00
		a. Royal purple	—	£300
		b. Deep rose-lilac	£500	95·00

(b) P 10.

O14	24	5s. deep purple (9.82)	£500	£170
		a. Opt double	£2750	£1500
		b. Rose-lilac (1883)	£375	£110

(c) P 10×12.

O15	24	5s. purple (10.86)		

(d) P 12×10.

O16	24	5s. reddish purple (1886)	£475	£110

(e) P 12.

O17	24	5s. purple	†	£500

(f) P 11.

O18	24	5s. rose-lilac (1888)	£225	85·00

1880 (31 May). W 35. P 13.

O18a	34	10d. lilac	£180	£100
		ab. Perf 10 and 11, compound	£250	£200
		ac. Perf 10	£250	
		aca. Opt double, one albino	£350	
		as. Optd "Specimen"	60·00	

1882–85. W 40. P 10.

O19	26	1d. salmon	21·00	3·00
		a. Perf 13×10	—	£130
O20		1d. orange to scarlet	12·00	1·75
		a. Perf 10×13	—	£130
		b. Perf 11×12, comb (1.84)	9·00	1·40
		c. Perf 10×12 or 12×10 (4.85)	—	£110
		d. Perf 12×11 (12.85)		
O21	28	2d. blue	12·00	1·00
		a. Perf 10×13 or 13×10	£190	75·00
		b. Perf 11×12, comb (1.84)	8·50	1·00
		ca. Opt double	—	£275
		e. Perf 12×11 (12.85)		
O22	16	3d. yellow-green (7 mm)	8·50	3·50
		a. Wmk sideways		
		b. Perf 12 (4.85)	£120	80·00
		c. Perf 12×10 (4.85)	—	5·00
		ca. Opt double	†	£500
		d. Perf 12×11		
O23		3d. bluish green (7 mm)	11·00	4·00
		a. Perf 12 (4.85)	£120	80·00
		b. Perf 12×10 (4.85)		
		c. Perf 10×11 (12.85)		
O24		3d. yellow-green (5½ mm)	35·00	23·00
		a. Wmk sideways	35·00	
		as. Optd "Specimen"	35·00	
		b. Perf 10×12 or 12×10 (4.85)	13·00	4·25
		c. Perf 10×11 or 11×10 (12.85)	—	5·00
O25		3d. bluish green (5½ mm)	7·50	4·50
		a. Wmk sideways		
		b. Perf 10×12 or 12×10 (4.85)	7·50	5·00
		c. Perf 10×11 or 11×10 (12.85)	5·00	3·75
O26	32	4d. red-brown	32·00	4·00
		a. Perf 11×12, comb (1.84)	12·00	3·50
		b. Perf 10×12 (4.85)	—	70·00
O27		4d. dark brown	16·00	3·50
		a. Perf 11×12, comb (1.84)	13·00	3·50
		b. Perf 12 (4.85)	£200	£150
		c. Perf 10×12 (4.85)	£200	90·00
O28	11	5d. dull green	14·00	15·00
		a. Perf 11×12, comb		
		s. Optd "Specimen"	35·00	
O29		5d. blue-green	14·00	18·00
		a. Perf 12 (4.85)	£100	£100
		b. Perf 10×11	14·00	16·00
		c. Perf 11	—	£150
O30	37	6d. pale lilac	20·00	5·50
		a. Perf 12 (12.85)	24·00	5·50
O31		6d. mauve	20·00	6·00
		a. Perf 12 (4.85)	—	45·00
		b. Perf 10×12 or 12×10 (4.85)	20·00	5·50
		d. Perf 11×10 (12.85)	20·00	6·00
		e. Perf 11×12		
		ea. Perf 12×11 (12.85)	55·00	16·00
O32	13	8d. yellow	22·00	11·00
		a. Perf 12 (4.85)	£130	38·00
		b. Perf 10×12 or 12×10 (4.85)	22·00	10·00
		ba. Opt double	†	—
		d. Perf 12×11 (12.85)	22·00	15·00
		da. Opt double		
		db. Opt treble	†	—
O33	38	1s. black (R.)	25·00	8·50
		a. Perf 10×13	—	55·00
		b. Perf 11×12, comb (1.84)	25·00	8·00
		ba. Opt double	—	£275

1886–87. W 41. P 10.

O34	26	1d. scarlet	50·00	4·50
O35	28	2d. deep blue	25·00	
		a. Perf 11×12, comb		

1887–90. *Nos. 241/2 optd in black.*

(a) With Type O 1.

O36	42	10s. mauve and claret, P 12 (1890)	—	£2000

(b) With Type O 2 (30 April 1889).

O37	42	10s. mauve and claret P 12	£2500	£1000
		as. Optd "Specimen"	80·00	
		b. Perf 10	£4000	£2000

(c) With Type O 3 (7 Jan 1887).

O38	42	£1 mauve and claret, P 12×10	£11000	£6500

Only nine examples of No. O38 are recorded, three of which are mint. One of the used stamps, in the Royal Collection, shows overprint Type O 3 double.

1888 (17 July)–90. *Optd as Type O 1.*

(a) W 40. P 11×12.

O39	45	1d. lilac	3·50	75
		a. Perf 12	3·00	75
		b. Mauve	3·00	75
			3·00	75
O40	46	2d. Prussian blue (15.10.88)	4·50	40
		a. Perf 12	5·50	1·00
O41	47	4d. purple-brown (10.10.89)	11·00	3·75
		a. Perf 12	15·00	4·50
		b. Perf 11		
		c. Red-brown	12·00	3·75
		ca. Opt double	†	£750
		cb. Perf 12	15·00	4·00
O42	48	6d. carmine (16.1.89)	8·50	5·50
		a. Perf 12	13·00	5·50
O43	49	8d. lilac-rose (1890)	21·00	12·00
		a. Perf 12	30·00	15·00
O44	50	1s. maroon (9.1.90)	22·00	4·00
		a. Perf 12	22·00	4·00
		b. Purple-brown	22·00	4·00
		ba. Opt double		
		bb. Perf 12	22·00	4·00
O39s/44s		Optd "Specimen" Set of 6	£200	

(b) W 41. P 11×12 (1889).

O45	45	1d. mauve		
O46	46	2d. blue		

(c) W 25. P 10.

O47	51	5s. deep purple (R.) (9.1.90)	£800	£500
O48	52	20s. cobalt-blue (10.3.90)	£2000	£800

1890 (15 Feb)–91. *Optd as Type O 1. W 53 (5s.) or 54 (20s.). P 10.*

O49	51	5s. lilac	£350	£120
		a. Mauve	£190	70·00
		b. Dull lilac, P 12	£500	£130
O50	52	20s. cobalt-blue (3.91)	£2000	£600
O49s/50s		Optd "Specimen" Set of 2	£200	

1891 (Jan). *Optd as Type O 1. W 40.*

(a) On No. 265. P 11×12.

O54	55	2½d. ultramarine	11·00	9·50

(b) On Nos. 266/8.

O55	26	½d. on 1d. grey, P 11×12	55·00	55·00
		a. Opt double	—	†
O56	37	7½d. on 6d. brown, P 10	35·00	45·00
O57	38	12½d. on 1s. red, P 11×12	60·00	75·00
O54s/7s		Optd "Specimen" Set of 4	£140	

1892 (May). *No. 271 optd as Type O 1. P 10.*

O58	58	½d. grey	7·00	16·00
		a. Perf 11×12	5·00	11·00
		as. Optd "Specimen"	30·00	
		b. Perf 12	6·50	11·00
		c. Perf 12×11½	17·00	13·00

Official stamps were withdrawn from the government departments on 31 December 1894.

POSTAGE DUE STAMPS

D 1

(Dies eng by A. Collingridge. Typo Govt Printing Office, Sydney)

1891 (1 Jan)–92. W 40. P 10.

D1	D 1	½d. green (21.1.92)	5·00	4·00
D2		1d. green	12·00	1·75
		a. Imperf vert (horiz pair)	†	
		b. Perf 11	9·50	1·75
		c. Perf 12	21·00	3·50
		d. Perf 12×10	27·00	2·75
		e. Perf 10×11	14·00	2·25
		f. Perf 11×12 or 12×11	9·50	1·75
D3		2d. green	14·00	2·25
		a. Perf 11	14·00	2·25
		b. Perf 12	—	12·00
		c. Perf 12×10	25·00	4·00
		d. Perf 10×11	15·00	2·50
		e. Perf 11×12 or 12×11	14·00	2·00
		f. Wmk sideways	23·00	10·00
D4		3d. green	27·00	5·50
		a. Perf 10×11	27·00	5·50
D5		4d. green	18·00	2·25
		a. Perf 11	19·00	2·25
		b. Perf 10×11	18·00	2·25
D6		6d. green	27·00	7·00
D7		8d. green	85·00	20·00
D8		5s. green	£140	48·00
		a. Perf 11	£300	85·00
		b. Perf 11×12	—	£275
D9		10s. green (early 1891)	£300	65·00
		a. Perf 12×10	£300	£150
D10		20s. green (early 1891)	£450	£100
		a. Perf 12	£500	
		b. Perf 12×10	£300	£200
D1s/10s		Optd "Specimen" Set of 10	£200	

Used prices for 10s. and 20s. are for cancelled-to-order stamps. Postally used examples are rare.

1900. *Chalk-surfaced paper. W 40. P 11.*

D11	D 1	½d. emerald-green		
D12		1d. emerald-green	12·00	3·75
		a. Perf 12	27·00	8·50
		b. Perf 11×12 or 12×11	12·00	2·75
D13		2d. emerald-green	14·00	4·25
		a. Perf 12	—	35·00
		b. Perf 11×12 or 12×11	12·00	4·25
D14		3d. emerald-green, P 11×12 or 12×11	42·00	12·00
D15		4d. emerald-green (7.00)	22·00	5·00

New South Wales became part of the Commonwealth of Australia on 1 January 1901.

QUEENSLAND

The area which later became Queensland was previously part of New South Wales known as the Moreton Bay District. The first post office, at Brisbane, was opened in 1834 and the use of New South Wales stamps from the District became compulsory from 1 May 1854.

Queensland was proclaimed a separate colony on 10 December 1859, but continued to use New South Wales issues until 1 November 1860.

Post Offices opened in the Moreton Bay District before 10 December 1859, and using New South Wales stamps, were

Office	Opened	Numeral Cancellation
Brisbane	1834	95
Burnett's Inn/ Goode's Inn/ Nanango	1850	108
Callandoon	1850	74
Condamine	1856	151
Dalby	1854	133
Drayton	1846	85
Gayndah	1850	86
Gladstone	1854	131
Goode's Inn	1858	108
Ipswich	1846	87
Maryborough	1849	96
Rockhampton	1858	201
Surat	1852	110
Taroom	1856	152
Toowoomba	1858	214
Warwick	1848	81

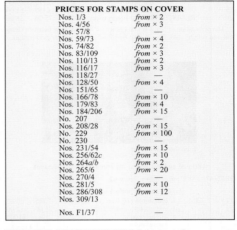

PRICES FOR STAMPS ON COVER

Nos. 1/3	from × 2
Nos. 4/56	from × 3
Nos. 57/8	
Nos. 59/73	from × 4
Nos. 74/82	from × 2
Nos. 83/109	from × 3
Nos. 110/13	from × 2
Nos. 116/17	from × 3
Nos. 118/27	
Nos. 128/50	from × 4
Nos. 151/65	
Nos. 166/78	from × 10
Nos. 179/83	from × 4
Nos. 184/206	from × 15
No. 207	
Nos. 208/28	from × 15
No. 229	from × 100
No. 230	
Nos. 231/54	from × 15
Nos. 256/62c	from × 10
Nos. 264a/b	from × 2
Nos. 265/6	from × 20
Nos. 270/4	
Nos. 281/5	from × 10
Nos. 286/308	from × 12
Nos. 309/13	—
Nos. F1/37	—

PERKINS BACON "CANCELLED". For notes on these handstamps, showing "CANCELLED" between horizontal bars forming an oval, see Catalogue Introduction.

1 / 2 Large Star / 3 Small Star

(Dies eng W. Humphrys. Recess P.B.)

1860. W 2

(a) Imperf.

1	1	1d. carmine-rose	£2750	£800
2		2d. blue	£7000	£1700
3		6d. green	£4250	£800

(b) Clean-cut perf 14–16.

4	1	1d. carmine-rose	£1500	£300
5		2d. blue	£600	£110
		a. Imperf between (horiz pair)	†	
6		6d. green (15 Nov)	£650	70·00

3d. re-entry / 3d. retouch (R.2/8)

The 3d. re-entry which occurs on one stamp in the second row, shows doubling of the left-hand arabesque and the retouch has redrawn spandrel dots under "EN" of "PENCE", a single dot in the centre of the circle under "E" and the bottom outer frame line closer to the spandrel's frame line.

1860–61. W 3.

(a) Clean-cut perf 14–16.

7	1	2d. blue	£550	£110
		a. Imperf between (horiz pair)	†	£2000
8		3d. brown (15.4.61)	£350	70·00
		a. Re-entry	—	£250
		b. Retouch	—	£250
9		6d. green	£650	75·00

10		1s. violet (15.11.60) (H/S "CANCELLED" in oval £9000)	£650	95·00
11		"REGISTERED" (6d.) olive-yellow (1.61) (H/S "CANCELLED" in oval £9000)	£425	85·00
		a. Imperf between (pair)..	£5000	

(b) Clean-cut perf 14 at Somerset House (7.61).

12	1	1d. carmine-rose (H/S "CANCELLED" in oval £9000)	£150	42·00
13		2d. blue (H/S "CANCELLED" in oval £9000)	£400	55·00

(c) Rough perf 14–16 (9.61).

14	1	1d. carmine-rose	80·00	32·00
15		2d. blue	£130	28·00
		a. Imperf between (horiz pair)	£3500	
16		3d. brown (H/S "CANCELLED" in oval £10000)	60·00	32·00
		a. Imperf vert (horiz pair)	£3500	
		b. Re-entry	£275	£130
		c. Retouch (R. 2/8)	—	£130
17		6d. deep green (H/S "CANCELLED" in oval £9000)	£180	27·00
18		6d. yellow-green	£275	27·00
19		1s. violet	£450	85·00
20		"REGISTERED" (6d.) orange-yellow	75·00	38·00

The perforation of No. 8 is that known as "intermediate between clean-cut and rough", No. 20 can also be found with a similar perforation.

Line through design

(Printed and perforated by Thomas Ham, Brisbane)

1862–67. *Thick toned paper. No wmk.*

(a) P 13 rough perforations (1862–63).

21	1	1d. Indian red (16.12.62)	£325	60·00
22		1d. orange-vermilion (2.63)	75·00	12·00
		a. Imperf (pair)	—	£1000
		b. Imperf between (horiz pair)	†	
23		2d. pale blue (16.12.62)	£100	27·00
24		2d. blue	50·00	9·00
		a. Imperf (pair)	—	£1000
		b. Imperf between (horiz pair)	†	£1700
		c. Imperf between (vert pair)	£3000	
25		3d. brown	75·00	32·00
		a. Re-entry	—	£130
		b. Retouch (R. 2/8)	—	£130
26		6d. apple green (17.4.63)	£120	15·00
		a. Line through design at right	—	85·00
		b. Line through design at left	—	85·00
27		6d. yellow-green	£110	12·00
		a. Imperf between (horiz pair)	†	£1600
		b. Line through design at right	—	75·00
		c. Line through design at left	—	75·00
28		6d. pale bluish green	£170	14·00
		a. Imperf (pair)	—	£1100
		b. Line through design at right	—	£130
		c. Line through design at left	—	£130
29		1s. grey (14.7.63)	£180	22·00
		a. Imperf between (horiz pair)	†	£2250
		b. Imperf between (vert pair)	†	—
		s. Handstamped "Specimen"	40·00	

The top or bottom row of perforations was sometimes omitted from the sheet, resulting in stamps perforated on three sides only.

Prior to the plates being printed from in Brisbane, damage occurred to the 6d. plate in the form of a scratch across two adjoining stamps. The position of the pair in the plate is not yet recorded. One joined pair is known.

This flaw was not corrected until around 1869 when, after plate cleaning, only faint traces remain. These are hard to see.

(b) P 12½×13 rough (1863–67).

30	1	1d. orange-vermilion	75·00	27·00
31		2d. blue	65·00	20·00
32		3d. brown	80·00	25·00
		a. Re-entry	—	£120
		b. Retouch (R. 2/8)	—	£120
33		6d. apple green	£120	40·00
		a. Line through design at right	—	£170
		b. Line through design at left	—	£170
34		6d. yellow-green	£120	40·00
		a. Line through design at right	—	£170
		b. Line through design at left	—	£170
35		6d. pale bluish green		
		a. Line through design at right	—	
		b. Line through design at left	—	
36		1s. grey	£250	38·00
		a. Imperf between (horiz pair)		

This paper was used again for a very limited printing in 1867 which can be properly regarded as the First Government Printing. The perforations were now clean-cut, the designs and the background to the head are very well defined, the plates having been cleaned when transferred to the Government Printing Office.

(c) P 13 Clean-cut (1867).

37		1d. orange-vermilion	75·00	20·00
38		2d. blue	55·00	9·00
40		6d. apple green	£130	16·00
41		6d. yellow-green	£130	19·00
42		6d. deep green		

Previously listed and then removed, the significance of this issue has been reassessed and it is now re-listed under this paper.
Copies of the 3d. and 1s. have been identified with these characteristics but there are no records of them being printed at this time.

1864–65. W **3**.

(a) P 13.

44	1	1d. orange-vermilion (1.65)	70·00	26·00
		a. Imperf between (horiz pair)	£850	
45		2d. pale blue (1.65)	75·00	16·00
46		2d. deep blue (1.65)	75·00	16·00
		a. Imperf between (vert pair)	£1600	
		b. Bisected (1d.) (on cover)	†	£2750
47		6d. yellow-green (1.65)	£130	22·00
		a. Line through design at right	—	£110
		b. Line through design at left	—	£110
48		6d. deep green	£150	22·00
		a. Line through design at right	—	£110
		b. Line through design at left	—	£110
49		"REGISTERED" (6d.) orge-yell (21.6.64)	95·00	35·00
		a. Double printed	£1500	£1500
		b. Imperf		

(b) P 12½×13.

50	1	1d. orange-vermilion	95·00	48·00
50a		2d. deep blue	£120	48·00

The "REGISTERED" stamp was reprinted in 1895. See note below No. 82.

1866 (24 Jan). Wmk "QUEENSLAND/POSTAGE—POSTAGE/STAMPS—STAMPS" in three lines in script capitals with double wavy lines above and below the wmk and single wavy lines with projecting sprays between each line of words. There are ornaments ("fleurons") between "POSTAGE" "POSTAGE" and between "STAMPS" "STAMPS". Single stamps only show a portion of one or two letters of this wmk.

(a) P 13.

51	1	1d. orange-vermilion	£140	27·00
52		2d. blue	55·00	17·00

(b) P 12½×13.

52a	1	1d. orange-vermilion	£170	48·00
52b		2d. blue	£170	48·00

1866. *Lithographed on thick paper. No wmk. P 13.*
The 4d. was lithographed from two separate transfers from the 3d. plate and the 5s. was taken from the 1s. plate.

First transfer   Double transfer

First Transfer (Sept 1866) "FOUR" in taller thin letters.

53		4d. reddish lilac (*shades*)	£200	20·00
		a. Re-entry	—	£110
		b. Double transfer	—	£150
54		4d. grey-lilac (*shades*)	£200	20·00
		a. Re-entry	—	£110
		b. Double transfer	—	£150

Second transfer

Second Transfer (Feb 1867) "FOUR" in shorter letters.

55		4d. lilac (*shades*)	£170	18·00
		a. Retouch (R. 2/8)	—	95·00
		b. "FOUR" missing	—	£250
56		4d. grey-lilac (*shades*)	£170	18·00
		a. Retouch (R. 2/8)	—	95·00
		b. "FOUR" missing	—	£250
		s. Handstamped "Specimen"	45·00	
57		5s. bright rose	£450	£120
58		5s. pale rose	£375	85·00
		a. Imperf between (vert pair)	†	£2250
		s. Handstamped "Specimen"	55·00	

The alterations in values were made by hand on the stones and there are minor varieties in the shape and position of the letters.

4

2d. Pl II. Dot by "U"   2d. Pl II. Dots near arabesque

1868–74. *Wmk small truncated Star, W **4** on each stamp, and the word "QUEENSLAND" in single-lined Roman capitals four times in each sheet. A second plate of the 2d. denomination was sent by Perkins, Bacon to the Colony in 1872 and it was first printed from in August of that year. The new plate is helpful in separating many of the 2d. printings up to 1879. P 13.*

59	1	1d. orange-vermilion (18.1.71)	45·00	4·50
60		2d. pale blue (3.4.68) (Pl I)	45·00	4·50
61		2d. blue (18.1.71) (Pl I)	40·00	2·75
62		2d. bright blue (Pl I)	50·00	2·75
63		2d. greenish blue (Pl I)	85·00	2·50
64		2d. dark blue (Pl I)	45·00	2·50
		a. Imperf		
65		3d. olive-green (27.2.71)	85·00	6·00
		a. Re-entry	—	42·00
		b. Retouch (R. 2/8)	—	42·00
66		3d. greenish grey	£100	5·50
		a. Re-entry	—	40·00
		b. Retouch (R. 2/8)	—	40·00
67		3d. brown	80·00	5·50
		a. Re-entry	—	40·00
		b. Retouch (R. 2/8)	—	40·00
68		6d. yellow-green (10.11.71)	£140	7·00
69		6d. green	£130	10·00
70		6d. deep green	£170	17·00
71		1s. greenish grey (13.11.72)	£375	40·00
72		1s. brownish grey	£375	40·00
73		1s. mauve (19.2.74)	£225	22·00
		59s/73s H/S "Specimen" *Set of 5*	£180	

(b) P 12 (about Feb 1874).

74	1	1d. orange-vermilion	£325	24·00
75		2d. blue (Pl II)	£750	48·00
76		3d. greenish grey	—	£170
		b. Retouch (R. 2/8)	—	£170
77		3d. brown	£450	£170
		a. Re-entry		
		b. Retouch (R. 2/8)		
78		6d. green	£1200	42·00
79		1s. mauve	£475	45·00

(c) P 13×12.

80	1	1d. orange-vermilion	—	£170
81		2d. blue (Pl II)	£1000	40·00
82		3d. greenish grey	—	£275

Plate II of the 2d. may be identified by a smudged dot to the left of "U" in "QUEEN" and tiny dots near the lower curl of the right arabesque.

Reprints were made in 1895 of all five values on Wmk W **4**, and perforated 13; the colours are:—1d. orange and brownish orange, 2d. deep dull blue (Pl II), 3d. brown, 6d green, 1s. red-violet and dull violet. The "Registered" was also reprinted with these on the same paper, but perforated 12. One sheet of the 2d. reprint is known to have had the perforations missing between the fourth and fifth vertical rows.

5   6

4d. First transfer   4d. Second transfer

The first transfer of the 4d. was taken from the 3d. plate, identified by the lack of the curl at the foot of the arabesque, the second was from Plate II of the 2d.

(4d., litho. Other values recess)

1868–78. Wmk Crown and Q. W **5**.

(a) P 13 (1868–75).

83	1	1d. orange-vermilion (10.11.68)	60·00	4·50
		a. Imperf (pair)	£375	
84		1d. pale rose-red (4.11.74)	55·00	9·00
85		1d. deep rose-red	95·00	9·50
86		2d. pale blue (20.11.68) (Pl I)	50·00	1·75
87		2d. deep blue (4.11.74) (Pl II)	45·00	4·50
		a. Imperf (pair)	£475	
		b. Imperf between (vert pair)	†	
88		3d. brown (11.6.75)	80·00	12·00
		a. Re-entry	—	70·00
		b. Retouch (R. 2/8)	—	70·00

89		4d. yellow (*shades*) (1st transfer) (1.1.75)	£850	60·00
		s. Handstamped "Specimen"	65·00	
90		6d. deep green (9.4.69)	£120	9·00
91		6d. yellow-green	£100	6·50
92		6d. pale apple-green (1.1.75)	£130	9·00
		a. Imperf (pair)	£4250	
93		1s. mauve	£200	45·00

(b) P 12 (1876–78).

94	I	1d. deep orange-vermilion	38·00	5·00
95		1d. pale orange-vermilion	40·00	5·00
		a. Imperf between (vert pair)	†	—
96		1d. rose-red	48·00	10·00
97		1d. flesh	65·00	10·00
98		2d. pale blue (Pl II)	85·00	15·00
99		2d. bright blue (Pl II)	38·00	1·00
100		2d. deep blue (Pl II)	40·00	1·50
101		3d. brown	75·00	9·00
		a. Re-entry	—	50·00
		b. Retouch (R. 2/8)	—	50·00
102		4d. yellow (*shades*) (1st transfer)	£700	25·00
103		4d. buff-yellow (*shades*) (2nd transfer)	£700	24·00
104		6d. deep green	£140	8·00
105		6d. green	£130	4·25
106		6d. yellow-green	£140	4·50
107		6d. apple-green	£150	7·00
108		1s. mauve	50·00	9·00
109		1s. purple	£140	5·00
		a. Imperf between (vert pair)	†	—

(c) P 13×12 or 12×13.

110	I	1d. orange-vermilion	—	£150
110a		1d. rose-red	—	£180
111		2d. deep blue (Pl II)	£1100	£250
112		4d. yellow	—	£300
113		6d. deep green	—	£300

(d) P 12½×13 (1868).

114	I	1d. orange-vermilion	—	£350
115		2d. deep blue (Pl I)	—	£350
115a		6d. yellow-green		

(e) P 12½ (1868).

115b	I	2d. deep blue (Pl I)		

Reprints of the above were made in 1895 on thicker paper, Wmk W 6, perf 12. The colours are:—1d. vermilion-red, 2d. deep dull blue and pale ultramarine, 3d. brown, 6d. dull yellow-green and 1s. lilac-grey.

1879. No wmk. P 12.

116	1	6d. pale emerald-green	£250	27·00
		a. Imperf between (horiz pair)	†	£1400
117		1s. mauve (*fiscal cancel £5*)	£130	65·00

No. 117 has a very indistinct lilac *burelé* band at back.
Nos. 116/17 can be found showing portions of a papermaker's watermark, either T. H. Saunders & Co or A. Pirie & Sons.

1880. *Lithographed from transfers from the 1s. die.* Wmk Crown and Q. W 6. P 12.

118	1	2s. pale blue	£100	32·00
119		2s. blue (*fiscal cancel £4*)	£100	32·00
		a. Imperf vert (horiz pair)		
120		2s. deep blue (*fiscal cancel £4*)	£120	32·00
121		2s.6d. dull scarlet	£160	60·00
122		2s.6d. bright scarlet (*fiscal cancel £4*)	£190	60·00
123		5s. pale yellow-ochre	£225	90·00
124		5s. yellow-ochre (*fiscal cancel £5*)	£225	90·00
125		10s. reddish brown	£450	£160
		a. Imperf	£500	
126		10s. bistre-brown	£450	£160
127		20s. rose (*fiscal cancel £7*)	£1100	£190

Of the 2s. and 20s. stamps there are five types of each, and of the other values ten types of each.
Beware of fiscally used copies that have been cleaned and provided with forged postmarks.

7   Die I   Die II

Dies I and II often occur in the same sheet.
Die I. The white horizontal inner line of the triangle in the upper right-hand corner merges into the outer white line of the oval above the "L".
Die II. The same line is short and does not touch the inner oval.

1879–80. *Typo*. P 12.

(a) Wmk Crown and Q. W 5.

128	7	1d. reddish brown (Die I) (15.5.79)	85·00	24·00
		a. Die II	£130	24·00
		ab. Imperf between (horiz pair)		
		ac. "QOEENSLAND"	£1100	£200
129		1d. orange-brown (Die I)	£130	24·00
130		2d. blue (Die I) (10.4.79)	75·00	11·00
		a. "PENGE" (R. 12/6)	£700	£110
		b. "QUEENSbAND" (R. 5/6)	—	£110
		c. "QU" joined		£110
131		4d. orange-yellow (6.6.79)	£475	50·00

(b) No wmk, with lilac burelé band on back.

132	7	1d. reddish brown (Die I) (21.10.79)	£375	50·00
		a. Die II	£400	80·00
		ab. "QOEENSLAND"	—	£1500
133		2d. blue (Die I) (21.10.79)	£450	30·00
		a. "PENGE" (R. 12/6)	£3500	£650
		b. "QUEENSbAND" (R. 5/6)		

(c) Wmk Crown and Q. W 6.

134	7	1d. reddish brown (Die I) (31.10.79)	45·00	6·00
		a. Imperf between (pair)	†	£650
		b. Die II	60·00	6·00
		ba. "QOEENSLAND"	£275	45·00
		bb. Imperf between (pair)	†	£750
135		1d. dull orange (Die I)	26·00	4·50
		a. Die II	29·00	4·50
		ab. "QOEENSLAND"	85·00	24·00
136		1d. scarlet (Die I) (7.3.81)	23·00	2·75
		a. Die II	25·00	3·25
		ab. "QOEENSLAND"	£110	27·00
137		2d. blue (Die I) (10.4.79)	40·00	1·50
		a. "PENGE"	£150	40·00
		b. "QUEENSbAND"	£150	40·00
		c. Die II	45·00	3·25
138		2d. grey-blue (Die I)	40·00	1·25
		a. "PENGE"	£150	40·00
		b. "QUEENSbAND"	£150	40·00
		c. Die II	45·00	3·00
139		2d. bright blue (Die I)	45·00	1·25
		a. "PENGE"	£160	40·00
		b. "QUEENSbAND"	£160	40·00
		c. Imperf between (pair)	£950	
		d. Die II	48·00	3·25
140		2d. deep blue (Die I)	48·00	1·25
		a. "PENGE"	£170	40·00
		b. "QUEENSbAND"	£170	40·00
		c. Die II	40·00	4·75
141		4d. orange-yellow	£160	10·00
		a. Imperf between (pair)	†	
142		6d. deep green	85·00	4·50
143		6d. yellow-green	90·00	4·50
		a. Imperf between (pair)		
144		1s. deep violet (3.80)	85·00	5·50
145		1s. pale lilac	75·00	7·00

The variety "QO" is No. 48 in the first arrangement, and No. 44 in a later arrangement on the sheets.
All these values have been seen imperf and unused, but we have no evidence that any of them were used in this condition.
The above were printed in sheets of 120, from plates made up of 30 groups of four electrotypes. There are four different types in each group, and two such groups of four are known of the 1d. and 2d., thus giving eight varieties of these two values. There was some resetting of the first plate of the 1d., and there are several plates of the 2d.; the value in the first plate of the latter value is in thinner letters, and in the last plate three types in each group of four have the "TW" of "TWO" joined, the letters of "PENCE" are larger and therefore much closer together, and in one type the "O" of "TWO" is oval, that letter being circular in the other types.

Half-penny

(8)   9   10

1880 (21 Feb). *Surch with T 8.*

151	7	½d. on 1d. (No. 134) (Die I)	£250	£150
		a. Die II	£600	£425
		ab. "QOEENSLAND"	£1500	£1000

Examples with "Half-penny" reading downwards are forged surcharges.

£1 Re-entry (R. 1/2)   £1 Retouch (R. 6/8)

(Eng H. Bourne. Recess Govt Printing Office, Brisbane, from plates made by B.W.)

1882 (13 Apr)–95. P 12.

(a) W 5 (twice sideways). Thin paper.

152	9	2s. bright blue (14.4.82)	£120	32·00
153		2s.6d. vermilion (7.12.82)	85·00	21·00
154		5s. rose	80·00	23·00
155		10s. brown (12.7.82)	£150	42·00
156		£1 deep green (30.5.83)	£350	£140
		a. Re-entry	—	£275
		b. Retouch (R. 6/4)	—	£275
152s/6s		(*ex 2s. 6d.*) H/S "Specimen" Set of 4	£170	

(b) W 10. Thick paper (10.11.86).

157	9	2s. bright blue	£140	32·00
158		2s.6d. vermilion	45·00	23·00
159		5s. rose	42·00	32·00
160	9	10s. brown	£100	45·00
161		£1 deep green	£225	65·00
		a. Re-entry (R. 1/2)	£600	£140
		b. Retouch (R. 6/4)	£600	£140

(c) W 6 (twice sideways). Thin paper (1895).

162	9	2s.6d. vermilion	60·00	35·00
163		5s. rose	55·00	22·00
164		10s. brown	£350	90·00
165		£1 deep green	£250	90·00
		a. Re-entry (R. 1/2)	£600	£170
		b. Retouch (R. 6/4)	£600	£170

The re-entry on the £1 shows as a double bottom frame line and the retouch occurs alongside the bottom right numeral.
See also Nos. 270/1, 272/4 and 309/12.

11   12

In T 12 the shading lines do not extend entirely across, as in T 11, thus leaving a white line down the front of the throat and point of the bust.

4d. "PENGE" for "PENCE" (R. 8/1)   4d. "EN" joined in "PENCE" (R. 4/6)

1882 (1 Aug)–91. W 6.

(a) P 12.

166	11	1d. pale vermilion-red (23.11.82)	4·50	60
		a. Double impression		
167		1d. deep vermilion-red	4·50	60
168		2d. blue	7·50	60
		a. Imperf between (horiz pair)		
169		4d. pale yellow (18.4.83)	20·00	2·25
		a. "PENGE" for "PENCE"	£160	45·00
		b. "EN" joined in "PENCE"	£110	30·00
		c. Imperf (11.91)		
170		6d. green (6.11.82)	12·00	1·50
171		1s. violet (6.2.83)	23·00	3·75
172		1s. lilac	11·00	3·25
173		1s. deep mauve	11·00	3·00
174		1s. pale mauve	12·00	3·00
		a. Imperf	†	

(b) P 9½×12 (1884).

176	11	1d. pale red	£130	40·00
177		2d. blue	£425	60·00
178		1s. blue	£225	50·00

The above were printed from plates made up of groups of four electrotypes as previously. In the 1d. the words of value are followed by a full stop. There are four types of the 4d., 6d. and 1s., eight types of the 1d., and twelve types of the 2d.
No. 169c is from a sheet used at Roma post office and comes cancelled with the "46" numeral postmark.

1887 (5 May)–91. W 6.

(a) P 12.

179	12	1d. vermilion-red	4·50	80
180		2d. blue	7·00	80
		a. Oval white flaw on Queen's head behind diadem (R. 12/5)	28·00	7·50
181		2s. deep brown (12.3.89)	70·00	40·00
182		2s. pale brown	60·00	32·00

(b) P 9½×12.

183	12	2d. blue	£375	60·00

These are from new plates; four types of each value grouped as before. The 1d. is without stop. In all values No. 2 in each group of four has the "L" and "A" of "QUEENSLAND" joined at the foot, and No. 3 of the 2d. has "P" of word "PENCE" with a long downstroke.
The 2d. is known bisected and used as a 1d. value.

13   14

1890–94. W 6 (sideways on ½d.). P 12½, 13 (comb machine).

184	13	½d. pale green	6·00	1·50
185		½d. deep green	5·00	1·50
186		½d. deep blue-green	4·50	1·50
187	12	1d. vermilion-red	3·75	30
		a. Imperf (pair)	£180	£180
		b. Oval broken by tip of bust (R. 10/3)	28·00	5·00
		c. Double impression	†	£400
188		2d. blue (old plate)	6·50	30
189		2d. pale blue (old plate)	6·50	30
190		2d. pale blue (retouched plate)	6·50	60
		a. "FWO" for "TWO" (R. 8/7)	—	22·00
191	14	2½d. carmine	13·00	1·50
192	12	3d. brown	9·00	3·25
193	11	4d. yellow	13·00	2·50
		a. "PENGE" for "PENCE"	65·00	22·00
		b. "EN" joined in "PENCE"	48·00	16·00
194		4d. orange	19·00	2·75
		a. "PENGE" for "PENCE"	85·00	22·00
		b. "EN" joined in "PENCE"	65·00	16·00
195		4d. lemon	22·00	2·75
		a. "PENGE" for "PENCE"	95·00	28·00
		b. "EN" joined in "PENCE"	75·00	20·00
196		6d. green	11·00	1·50
197	12	2s. red-brown	42·00	22·00
198		2s. pale brown	48·00	24·00

This issue is perforated by a new vertical comb machine, gauging about 12¾×12¾. The 3d. is from a plate similar to those of the last issue, No. 2 in each group of four types having "L" and "A" joined at the foot. The ½d. and 2½d. are likewise in groups of four types, but the differences are very minute. In the retouched plate of the 2d. the letters "L" and "A" no longer touch in No. 2 of each group and the "P" in No. 3 is normal.

1895. A. Thick paper. W 10.

(a) P 12½, 13.

202	12	1d. vermilion-red (16.1.95)	4·00	30
		a. Oval broken by tip of bust (R. 10/3)	32·00	5·00
203		1d. red-orange	4·00	30
		a. Oval broken by tip of bust (R. 10/3)	32·00	5·00
204		2d. blue (retouched plate) (16.1.95)	4·00	30
		a. "FWO" for "TWO" (R. 8/7)	65·00	22·00

(b) P 12.

205	11	1s. mauve (8.95)	15·00	6·00

B. Unwmkd paper; with blue burelé band at back. P 12½, 13.

206	12	1d. vermilion-red (19.2.95)............	2·50	40
		a. Oval broken by tip of bust (R. 10/3)............	22·00	5·00
		b. "PE" of "PENNY" omitted (R. 1/2)............	£180	£150
206c		1d. red-orange............	2·50	40

C. Thin paper. Crown and Q faintly impressed.P 12½, 13.

207	12	2d. blue (retouched plate) (6.95).....	12·00	£150
		a. "FWO" for "TWO" (R. 8/7)......	£110	

15   16

17   18

1895–96. A. W 6 (sideways on ½d.).

(a) P 12½, 13.

208	15	½d. green (11.5.95)............	1·90	75
		a. Double impression............	†	—
209		½d. deep green............	1·90	75
		a. Printed both sides............	£150	
210	16	1d. orange-red (28.2.95)............	3·50	20
211		1d. pale red............	5·50	20
212		2d. blue (19.6.95)............	13·00	50
213	17	2½d. carmine (8.95)............	16·00	3·75
214		2½d. rose............	17·00	3·75
215	18	5d. purple-brown (10.95)............	20·00	3·75

(b) P 12.

217	16	1d. red (8.95)............	50·00	18·00
218		2d. blue (8.95)............	50·00	18·00

B. Thick paper. W **10** (sideways) (part only on each stamp).

(a) P 12½, 13.

219	15	½d. green (6.8.95)............	2·75	2·50
220		½d. deep green............	2·75	2·50

(b) P 12.

221	15	½d. green............	22·00
222		½d. deep green............	22·00

C. No wmk; with blue burelé band at back.

(a) P 12½, 13.

223	15	½d. green (1.8.95)............	5·50	3·00
		a. Without *burelé* band............	55·00	
224		½d. deep green............	5·50	

(b) P 12.

225	15	½d. green............	20·00
		a. Without *burelé* band............	£100

Nos. 223a and 225a are from the margins of the sheet.

D. Thin paper, with Crown and Q faintly impressed. P 12½, 13.

227	15	½d. green............	2·00	3·00
228	16	1d. orange-red............	3·25	2·00

19

1896–1902. W 6. P 12½, 13.

229	19	1d. vermilion............	12·00	50
230		6d. green (1902)............	†	£15000

Only used examples of No. 230 are known, mostly with readable postmarks from 1902. It is suggested that an electrotype of this unissued design was inadvertently entered in a plate of No. 249.

20   21   22

23   24   25

"Cracked plate"

Die I   Die II

Two Dies of 4d.:

Die I. Serif of horizontal bar on lower right 4d. is clear of vertical frame line.

Die II. Serif joins vertical frame line.

1897–08. *Figures in all corners.* W **6** (sideways on ½d.). P 12½, 13 (comb).

231	20	½d. deep green............	3·75	5·50
		a. Perf 12............	—	£130
232	21	1d. orange-vermilion............	2·50	25
233		1d. vermilion............	2·50	25
		a. Perf 12 (1899)............	8·00	3·00
234		2d. blue............	3·25	25
		a. Cracked plate............	70·00	24·00
		b. Perf 12 (1905)............	£1000	7·00
		ba. Cracked plate............	£1000	
235		2d. deep blue............	3·25	25
		a. Cracked plate............	70·00	24·00
236	22	2½d. rose (10.98)............	17·00	22·00
237		2½d. purple/*blue* (20.1.99)............	9·50	2·50
238		2½d. brown-purple/*blue*............	9·50	2·50
239		2½d. slate/*blue* (5.08)............	14·00	4·50
240	21	3d. brown (10.98)............	10·00	2·50
241		3d. deep brown............	8·00	2·50
242		3d. reddish brown (1906)............	8·00	2·50
243		3d. grey-brown (1907)............	12·00	2·50
244		4d. yellow (Die I) (10.98)............	9·00	2·50
		a. Die II............	24·00	5·00
245		4d. yellow-buff (Die I)............	9·00	2·50
		a. Die II............	22·00	5·00
246	23	5d. purple-brown............	8·50	2·50
247		5d. dull brown (1906)............	9·50	3·25
248		5d. black-brown (1907)............	11·00	3·50
249	21	6d. green (1.4.98)............	8·00	2·50
250		6d. yellow-green............	7·00	2·50
251	24	1s. pale mauve (1.7.99)............	13·00	3·00
252		1s. dull mauve............	13·00	3·00
253		1s. bright mauve............	15·00	4·00
254	25	2s. turquoise-green............	30·00	25·00

Stamps of this issue also exist with the irregular line perforation 12½, 13.

The 1d. perf 12×9½ exists used and unused but their status has not yet been established (*price* £100 *unused*).

The cracked plate variety on the 2d. developed during 1901 and shows as a white break on the Queen's head and neck. The electro was later replaced.

1897–98. W 6.

(a) Zigzag roulette in black.

(b) The same but plain.

(c) Roulette *(a)* and also *(b)*.

(d) Roulette *(b)* and perf 12½, 13.

(e) Roulette *(a)* and perf 12½, 13.

(f) Compound of *(a)*, *(b)*, and perf 12½, 13.

256	21	1d. vermilion *(a)*............	14·00	9·50
257		1d. vermilion *(b)*............	7·00	4·00
258		1d. vermilion *(c)*............	15·00	17·00
259		1d. vermilion *(d)*............	9·00	6·00
260		1d. vermilion *(e)*............	65·00	85·00
261		1d. vermilion *(f)*............	85·00	90·00

26   27

(Des M. Kellar)

1899 (Sept.)–1906. W 6. P 12½, 13 (comb).

262	26	½d. deep green............	3·00	1·75
		a. Grey-green............	2·50	1·75
		b. Green (P 12) (1905)............	£100	50·00
		c. Pale green (1906)............	3·00	1·75

Stamps of T 26 without wmk, are proofs.

Stamps of this issue also exist with the irregular line perforation 12½, 12.

(Des F. Elliott)

1900 (19 June). *Charity.* T **27** and horiz design showing *Queen Victoria in medallion inscr* "PATRIOTIC FUND 1900". W **6**. P 12.

264a		1d. (6d.) claret............	£120	£110
264b		2d. (1s.) violet............	£300	£275

These stamps, sold at 6d. and 1s. respectively, paid postage of 1d. and 2d. only, the difference being contributed to a Patriotic Fund.

28   A   B

TWO TYPES OF "QUEENSLAND". Three different duty plates, each 120 (12 x 10), were produced for Type **28**. The first contained country inscriptions as Type A and was only used for No. 265. The second duty plate used for Nos. 265/6 and 282/4 contained 117 examples as Type A and 3 as Type B occurring on R. 1/6, R. 2/6 and R. 3/6. The third plate, used for Nos. 266, 283, 284 and 285 had all inscriptions as Type B.

(Typo Victoria Govt Printer, Melbourne)

1903 (4 July)–05. W w 10. P 12½.

265	28	9d. brown and ultramarine (A)........	23·00	3·75
266		9d. brown and ultramarine (B) (1905)............	23·00	3·75

1903 (Oct). *As Nos. 162 and 165.* W **6** (twice sideways). P 12½, 13 (irregular line).

270	9	2s.6d. vermilion............	£110	45·00
271		£1 deep green............	£1600	£600
		a. Re-entry (R. 1/2)............	£2750	£1100
		b. Retouch (R. 6/4)............	£2750	£1100

(Litho Govt Ptg Office, Brisbane, from transfers of the recess plates).

1905 (Nov)–06. W 6 (twice sideways).

(a) P 12½, 13 (irregular line).

272	9	£1 deep green............	£850	£140
		a. Re-entry (R. 1/2)............	£1500	£275
		b. Retouch (R. 6/4)............	£1500	£275

(b) P 12.

273	9	5s. rose (7.06)............	95·00	75·00
274		£1 deep green (7.06)............	£375	£110
		a. Re-entry (R. 1/2)............	£700	£200
		b. Retouch (R. 6/4)............	£700	£200

30   32

Redrawn types of T 21

T **30**. The head is redrawn, the top of the crown is higher and touches the frame, as do also the back of the chignon and the point of the bust. The forehead is filled in with lines of shading, and the figures in the corners appear to have been redrawn also.

T **32**. The forehead is plain (white instead of shaded), and though the top of the crown is made higher, it does not touch the frame; but the point of the bust and the chignon still touch. The figure in the right lower corner does not touch the line below, and has not the battered appearance of that in the first redrawn type. The stamps are very clearly printed, the lines of shading being distinct.

1906 (Sept). W 6. P 12½, 13 (comb).

281	30	2d. dull blue (*shades*)............	10·00	4·00

(Typo Victoria Govt Printer, Melbourne)

1906 (Sept)–10. Wmk Crown and double-lined A, W w 11.

(a) P 12×12½.

282	28	9d. brown and ultramarine (A)........	48·00	5·00
283		9d. brown and ultramarine (B)............	13·00	4·00
283a		9d. pale brown and blue (A)............	48·00	5·00
284		9d. pale brown and blue (B)............	13·00	4·00

(b) P 11 (1910).

285	28	9d. brown and blue (B)............	£4500	£600

(c) Compound perf 12×12½ and 11.

285a		9d. brown and ultramarine (B)............	†	£1200

33

1907–11. W 33.

(a) P 12½, 13 (comb).

286	26	½d. deep green............	1·75	2·75
287		½d. deep blue-green............	1·75	2·75
288	21	1d. vermilion............	3·00	30
		a. Imperf (pair)............	£275	
289	30	2d. dull blue............	9·00	1·25
289a		2d. bright blue (3.08)............	16·00	7·50
290	32	2d. bright blue (4.08)............	3·50	30

291	21	3d. pale brown (8.08)......................	13·00	2·50
292		3d. bistre-brown...........................	12·00	3·00
293		4d. yellow (Die I).........................	11·00	3·25
		a. Die II................................	35·00	7·00
294		4d. grey-black (Die I) (4.09).........	19·00	4·50
		a. Die II................................	40·00	9·50
295	23	5d. dull brown............................	14·00	7·00
295a		5d. sepia (12.09).........................	16·00	8·00
296	21	6d. yellow-green..........................	14·00	4·25
297		6d. bright green...........................	14·00	4·50
298	24	1s. violet (1908).........................	14·00	3·00
299		1s. bright mauve..........................	14·00	3·00
300	25	2s. turquoise-green (8.08)..............	35·00	24·00

Stamps of this issue also exist with the irregular line perforation 12½, 13. This was used when the comb perforator was under repair.

(b) P 13×11 to 12½ (May 1911).

301	26	½d. deep green.............................	6·00	7·50
302	21	1d. vermilion...............................	7·50	4·00
303	32	2d. blue.....................................	10·00	7·50
304	21	3d. bistre-brown...........................	18·00	12·00
305		4d. grey-black.............................	55·00	48·00
		a. Die II................................	£120	85·00
306	23	5d. dull brown............................	26·00	38·00
307	21	6d. yellow-green..........................	27·00	38·00
308	23	1s. violet....................................	38·00	38·00

The perforation (b) is from a machine introduced to help cope with the demands caused by the introduction of penny postage. The three rows at top (or bottom) of the sheet show varieties gauging 13×11½, 13×11, and 13×12, respectively, these are obtainable in strips of three showing the three variations.

(Litho Govt Ptg Office, Brisbane)

1907 (Oct)–**11**. W **33** (twice sideways). P 12½, 13 (irregular line).

309	9	2s.6d. vermilion.............................	42·00	40·00
		a. Dull orange (1911)..................	70·00	65·00
		b. Reddish orange (1912).............	£170	£200
310		5s. rose (12.07)..........................	65·00	45·00
		a. Deep rose (1910)....................	75·00	65·00
		b. Carmine-red (1911).................	£180	£250
311		10s. blackish brown......................	£120	65·00
		a. Sepia (1911) (12.07)..............	£375	£275
312		£1 bluish green...........................	£250	£110
		a. Re-entry (R. 1/2)...................	£600	£200
		b. Retouch (R. 6/4)...................	£600	£200
		c. Deep bluish green (1910).........	£450	£300
		ca. Re-entry (R. 1/2)..................	—	£500
		cb. Retouch (R. 6/4).................	—	£500
		d. Deep yellowish green (1911).....	£1600	£1800
		da. Re-entry (R. 1/2)..................	£3500	£1800
		db. Retouch (R. 6/4).................	£3500	£1800

The 1912 printings are on thinner, whiter paper.

The lithographic stone used for Nos. 272/4 and 309/12 took the full sheet of 30 so the varieties on the £1 recess-printed version also appear on the stamps printed by lithography.

1911. W **33**. Perf irregular compound, 10½ to 12½.

313	21	1d. vermilion..................................	£850	£550

This was from another converted machine, formerly used for perforating Railway stamps. The perforation was very unsatisfactory.

STAMP BOOKLETS

There are very few surviving examples of Nos. SB1/4. Listings are provided for those believed to have been issued with prices quoted for those known to still exist.

1904 (1 Jan)–**09**. *Black on a red cover as No. SB1 of New South Wales. Stapled.*

SB1	£1 booklet containing two hundred and forty 1d. in four blocks of 30 and two blocks of 60......	
	a. Red on pink cover (1909).............................	
	b. Blue on pink cover	£13000

1904 (1 Jan). *Black on grey cover as No. SB1. Stapled.*

SB2	£1 booklet containing one hundred and twenty 2d. in four blocks of 30	

1910 (May). *Black on cream cover as No. SB3 of New South Wales. Stapled.*

SB3	2s. booklet containing eleven ½d. (No. 301), either in block of 6 plus block of 5 or block of 11 and eighteen 1d. (No 302), either in three blocks of 6 or block of 6 plus block of 12..	

Unsold stock of No. SB3 was uprated with one additional ½d. in May 1911.

1911 (Aug). *Red on pink cover as No. SB3. Stapled.*

SB4	2s. booklet containing twelve ½d. (No. 301), either in two blocks of 6 or block of 12, and eighteen 1d. (No. 302), either in three blocks of 6 or block of 6 plus block of 12................	£3750
	a. Red on white.............................	£3750

POSTAL FISCALS

Authorised for use from 1 January 1880 until 1 July 1892

CANCELLATIONS. Beware of stamps which have had pen-cancellations cleaned off and then had faked postmarks applied. Used prices quoted are for postally used examples between the above dates.

F **1** F **2**

1866–68.

A. No wmk. P 13.

F1	F **1**	1d. blue...................................	50·00	13·00
F2		6d. deep violet...........................	60·00	60·00
F3		1s. blue-green...........................	70·00	32·00
F4		2s. brown................................	£140	90·00
F5		2s.6d. dull red...........................	£140	75·00
F6		5s. yellow................................	£325	£100
F6a		6s. light brown..........................	£650	
F7		10s. green................................	£500	£190
F8		20s. rose.................................	£700	£300

B. Wmk F 2. P 13.

F9	F **1**	1d. blue...................................	28·00	30·00
F10		6d. deep violet...........................	60·00	60·00
F11		6d. blue...................................	£130	90·00
F12		1s. blue-green...........................	70·00	48·00
F13		2s. brown................................	£140	70·00
F13a		5s. yellow................................	£325	£110
F14		10s. green................................	£500	£190
F15		20s. rose.................................	£700	£300

F **3** F **3a**

1871–72. P 12 or 13.

A. Wmk Large Crown and Q, Wmk F 3a.

F16	F **3**	1d. mauve................................	22·00	10·00
F17		6d. red-brown...........................	48·00	26·00
F18		1s. green.................................	60·00	26·00
F19		2s. blue..................................	80·00	32·00
F20		2s.6d. brick-red.........................	£120	65·00
F21		5s. orange-brown.......................	£160	75·00
F22		10s. brown...............................	£350	£130
F23		20s. rose.................................	£600	£190

B. No wmk. Blue burelé band at back.

F24	F **3**	1d. mauve................................	26·00	12·00
F25		6d. red-brown...........................	48·00	26·00
F26		6d. mauve................................	£110	50·00
F27		1s. green.................................	60·00	26·00
F28		2s. blue..................................	95·00	75·00
F29		2s.6d. vermilion.........................	£150	70·00
F30		5s. yellow-brown........................	£200	80·00
F31		10s. brown...............................	£375	£150
F32		20s. rose.................................	£600	£190

F **4** F **5**

1878–79.

A. No wmk. Lilac burelé band at back. P 12.

F33	F **4**	1d. violet.................................	75·00	28·00

B. Wmk Crown and Q, W 5. P 12.

F34	F **4**	1d. violet.................................	30·00	21·00

Stamps as Type F **5** may not have been issued until after 1 July 1892 when the proper use of duty stamps for postal service was terminated but there are several examples which appear to have genuinely passed through the post during the 1890's. Unless they are dated during 1892 their postal use was certainly unauthorised although they may have been accepted.

Queensland became part of the Commonwealth of Australia on 1 January 1901.

SOUTH AUSTRALIA

PRICES FOR STAMPS ON COVER		
Nos. 1/3	*from* × 3	
No. 4	†	
Nos. 5/12	*from* × 2	
Nos. 13/18	*from* × 3	
Nos. 19/43	*from* × 4	
Nos. 44/9b	—	
Nos. 50/110	*from* × 3	
No. 111	—	
Nos. 112/34	*from* × 6	
Nos. 135/45	*from* × 3	
Nos. 146/66	*from* × 5	
Nos. 167/70a	*from* × 10	
No. 171/2a	—	
Nos. 173/94a	*from* × 12	
Nos. 195/208	—	
Nos. 229/31	*from* × 12	
No. 232	—	
Nos. 233/42	*from* × 12	
Nos. 268/75	*from* × 30	
Nos. 276/9	—	
Nos. 280/8	*from* × 30	
Nos. 289/92	—	
Nos. 293/304	*from* × 15	
No. 305	—	
Nos. O1/13	—	
Nos. O14/36	*from* × 20	
Nos. O37/42	*from* × 5	
Nos. O43/4	*from* × 50	
Nos. O45/7	—	
Nos. O48/52	*from* × 30	
No. O53	—	
Nos. O54/85	*from* × 50	
Nos. O86/7	—	

SPECIMEN OVERPRINTS. Those listed are from U.P.U. distributions between 1889 and 1895. Further "Specimen" overprints exist, but these were used for other purposes.

PERKINS BACON "CANCELLED". For notes on these handstamps, showing "CANCELLED" between horizontal bars forming an oval, see Catalogue Introduction.

1 2 Large Star

(Eng Wm Humphrys. Recess P.B.)

1855 (1 Jan–Oct). *Printed in London.* W **2**. Imperf.

1	**1**	1d. dark green (H/S "CANCELLED" in oval £10000)......................	£3750	£475
2		2d. rose-carmine (*shades*) (H/S "CANCELLED" in oval £10000)	£550	80·00
3		6d. deep blue (Oct 1855) (H/S "CANCELLED" in oval £10000)......................	£2250	£160

Prepared and sent to the Colony, but not issued.

4	**1**	1s. Violet (H/S "CANCELLED" in oval £14000)......................	£6500	

A printing of 500,000 of these 1s. stamps was delivered, but, as the colour was liable to be confused with that of the 6d. stamp, this stock was destroyed on 5 June 1857. It is believed that surviving examples of No. 4 come from Perkins Bacon remainders which came on to the market in the late 1890s.

Proofs of the 1d. and 6d. without wmk exist, and these are found with forged star watermarks added, and are sometimes offered as originals. For reprints of the above and later issues, see note after No. 194.

1856–58. *Printed by Printer of Stamps, Adelaide, from Perkins, Bacon plates.* W **2**. Imperf.

5	**1**	1d. deep yellow-green (15.6.58)......	£6000	£550
6		1d. yellow-green (11.10.58).........	£5000	£650
7		2d. orange-red (23.4.56)	£1500	80·00
8		2d. blood-red (14.11.56)	£1300	60·00
		a. Printed on both sides	†	£850
9		2d. red (shades) (29.10.57)	£650	40·00
		a. Printed on both sides	†	£650
10		6d. slate-blue (7.57).................	£2500	£170
11		1s. red-orange (8.7.57)	†	£500
12		1s. orange (11.6.58).................	£4500	£400

1858–59. *Rouletted.* (This first rouletted issue has the same colours as the local imperf issue). W **2**.

13	**1**	1d. yellow-green (8.1.59).............	£650	60·00
14		1d. light yellow-green (18.3.59)......	£650	65·00
		a. Imperf between (pair).............		
15		2d. red (17.2.59)....................	£130	21·00
		a. Printed on both sides	†	£650
17		6d. slate-blue (12.12.58)	£475	38·00
18		1s. orange (18.3.59).................	£1000	42·00
		a. Printed on both sides	†	£1200

3 4 (5)

1860–69. Second rouletted issue, *printed (with the exception of No. 24) in colours only found rouletted or perforated. Surch with T 5 (Nos. 35/7). W 2.*

19	1	1d. bright yellow-green (22.4.61)....	60·00	32·00
20		1d. dull blue-green (17.12.63).....	55·00	30·00
21		1d. sage-green	75·00	40·00
22		1d. Pale sage-green (27.5.65)	60·00	
23		1d. deep green (1864)	£300	75·00
24		1d. deep yellow-green (1869)	£120	
24a		2d. pale red	85·00	4·00
	b.	Printed on both sides	†	£400
25		2d. pale vermilion (3.2.63)..........	70·00	4·00
26		2d. bright vermilion (19.8.64)	65·00	3·25
	a.	Imperf between (horiz pair)	£1500	£450
27	3	4d. dull violet (24.1.67)............	75·00	22·00
28	1	6d. violet-blue (19.3.60)............	£170	7·00
29		6d. greenish blue (11.2.63).........	85·00	4·00
30		6d. dull ultramarine (25.4.64)......	80·00	4·00
	a.	Imperf between (horiz pair)	†	£425
31		6d. violet-ultramarine (11.4.68)	£160	6·00
32		6d. dull blue (26.8.65)	£120	6·50
	a.	Imperf between (pair)	†	£850
33		6d. Prussian blue (7.9.69)..........	£600	50·00
33a		6d. indigo	—	55·00
34	4	9d. grey-lilac (24.12.60)............	65·00	9·00
	a.	Imperf between (horiz pair).........	†	£1500
35		10d. on 9d. orange-red (B.) (20.7.66)..	£225	35·00
36		10d. on 9d. yellow (B.) (29.7.67)......	£350	27·00
37		10d. on 9d. yellow (Blk.) (14.8.69)....	£1800	45·00
	a.	Surch inverted at the top	†	£3500
	b.	Printed on both sides	†	£900
	c.	Roul × perf 10		
38	1	1s. yellow (25.10.61)...............	£500	28·00
	a.	Imperf between (vert pair)........	†	£1600
39		1s. grey-brown (10.4.63)............	£170	19·00
40		1s. dark grey-brown (26.5.63)......	£150	19·00
41		1s. chestnut (25.8.63)	£160	11·00
42		1s. lake-brown (27.3.65)	£120	12·00
	a.	Imperf between (horiz pair)......	†	£550
43	3	2s. rose-carmine (24.1.67)	£190	29·00
	a.	Imperf between (vert pair)........	†	£1000

1868–71. *Remainders of old stock subsequently perforated by the 11½–12½ machine.*

(a) Imperf stamps. P 11½–12½.

44	1	2d. pale vermilion (Feb 1868)	—	£900
45		2d. vermilion (18.3.68)	—	£1000

(b) Rouletted stamps. P 11½–12½.

46	1	1d. bright green (9.11.69)...........	—	£550
47		2d. pale vermilion (15.8.68)	£1500	£425
48		6d. Prussian blue (8.11.69)	—	£250
	aa.	Horiz pair perf all round, roul between ...		
48a		6d. indigo	—	£325
49	4	9d. grey-lilac (29.3.71)	£1600	£180
	a.	Perf × roulette	—	£200
49b	1	1s. lake-brown (23.5.70)		

1867–70. W 2. P 11½–12½ × roulette.

50	1	1d. pale bright green (2.11.67).......	£180	23·00
51		1d. bright green (1868)..............	£160	23·00
52		1d. grey-green (26.1.70).............	£180	25·00
	a.	Imperf between (horiz pair).........		
53		1d. blue-green (29.11.67)............	£250	42·00
54	3	4d. dull violet (July 1868)	£1600	£150
55		4d. dull purple (1869)	—	£100
56	1	6d. bright pale blue (29.5.67).......	£475	19·00
57		6d. Prussian blue (30.7.67)	£425	19·00
	a.	Printed on both sides		
58		6d. indigo (1.8.69)	£550	25·00
59	4	10d. on 9d. yellow (B.) (2.2.69)......	£700	35·00
	a.	Printed on both sides	—	£700
60	1	1s. chestnut (April 1868)	£275	18·00
61		1s. lake-brown (3.3.69)	£275	18·00

NOTE. The stamps perf 11½, 12½, or compound of the two, are here combined in one list, as both perforations are on the one machine, and all the varieties may be found in each sheet of stamps. This method of classifying the perforations by the machines is by far the most simple and convenient.

3-PENCE

(6)   7 (=Victoria W 19)

1868–79. *Surch with T 6 (Nos. 66/8). W 2. P 11½–12½.*

62	1	1d. pale bright green (8.2.68)	£170	32·00
63		1d. grey-green (18.2.68).............	£140	50·00
64		1d. dark green (20.3.68).............	80·00	22·00
	a.	Printed on both sides	†	£750
65		1d. deep yellow-green (28.6.72)......	75·00	22·00
	a.	Imperf between (horiz pair).......	†	£1600
66	3	3d. on 4d. Prussian blue (Blk.) (7.2.71)..	—	£850
67		3d. on 4d. sky-blue (Blk.) (12.8.70)..	£300	13·00
	a.	Imperf		
	b.	Rouletted	†	£750
68		3d. on 4d. deep ultramarine (Blk.) (9.72)..	80·00	9·00
	a.	Surch double	†	£3500
	b.	Additional surch on back	†	£2750
	c.	Surch omitted	£20000	£11000
70		4d. dull purple (1.2.68).............	70·00	15·00
	a.	Imperf between (horiz pair).......	†	—
71		4d. dull violet (1868)..............	65·00	8·00
72	1	6d. bright pale blue (23.2.68)	£325	11·00
73		6d. Prussian blue (29.9.69).........	£110	7·00
	a.	Perf 11½×imperf (horiz pair)	†	£1100
74		6d. indigo (1869)...................	£140	17·00
75	4	9d. claret (7.72)...................	£110	8·00
76		9d. bright mauve (1.11.72)..........	£110	8·00
	a.	Printed on both sides	†	£650
77		9d. red-purple (15.1.74)............	70·00	8·00
78		10d. on 9d. yellow (B.) (15.8.68)....	£1200	35·00

	a.	Wmk Crown and S A (W 10) (1868)......	—	£1000
79		10d. on 9d. yellow (Blk.) (13.9.69)..	£250	40·00
80	1	1s. lake-brown (9.68)...............	£160	11·00
81		1s. chestnut (8.10.72)..............	£130	11·00
82		1s. dark red-brown	£100	11·00
83		1s. red-brown (6.1.69)..............	£110	11·00
84	3	2s. pale rose-pink (10.10.69).......	£1100	£170
85		2s. deep rose-pink (8.69)..........	—	£110
86		2s. crimson-carmine (16.10.69)......	£100	19·00
87		2s. carmine (1869).................	90·00	13·00
	a.	Printed on both sides	†	£375

No. 68c comes from two sheets on which it is believed, some stamps showed the surcharge omitted and others the surcharge double. One of the used examples of No. 68c is known postmarked in 1875 and many of the others in 1879.

No. 78a was a trial printing made to test the perforating machine on the new D.L.R. paper.

1870–71. W 2. P 10.

88	1	1d. grey-green (6.70)	£150	17·00
89		1d. pale bright green (9.8.70).......	£150	17·00
90		1d. bright green (1871)..............	£130	17·00
91	3	3d. on 4d. dull ultramarine (R.) (6.8.70)...	£500	80·00
92		3d. on 4d. pale ultram (Blk.) (14.2.71)..	£325	21·00
93		3d. on 4d. ultramarine (Blk.) (14.8.71)..	£140	23·00
93a		3d. on 4d. Prussian blue (Blk.) (16.12.71).	—	£1000
94		4d. dull lilac (1870)...............	£120	11·00
95		4d. dull purple (1871)..............	£110	11·00
96	1	6d. bright blue (19.6.70)...........	£180	17·00
97		6d. indigo (11.10.71)...............	£250	16·00
98		1s. chestnut (4.1.71)...............	£160	25·00

1870–73. W 2. P 10×11½–12½, 11½–12½×10, or compound.

99	1	1d. pale bright green (11.10.70)......	£170	14·00
	a.	Printed on both sides		
100		1d. grey-green	£160	15·00
101		1d. deep green (19.6.71)...........	90·00	10·00
102	3	3d. on 4d. pale ultram (9.11.70)...	£250	55·00
103		4d. dull lilac (11.5.72)..........	—	20·00
104		4d. slate-lilac (5.3.73)..........	£130	18·00
105	1	6d. Prussian blue (2.3.70)........	£150	8·00
106		6d. bright Prussian blue (26.10.70).	£160	10·00
107	4	10d. on 9d. yellow (Blk.) (1.70)...	£140	30·00
108	1	1s. chestnut (17.6.71).............	£225	50·00
109	3	2s. rose-pink (24.4.71)............	—	£190
110		2s. carmine (2.3.72)..............	£150	38·00

1871 (17 July). W 7. P 10.

111	3	4d. dull lilac	£2250	£225
	a.	Printed on both sides	†	£3000

8 Broad Star   (9)

8 PENCE

1876–1900. *Surch with T 9 (Nos. 118/21). W 8.*

(a) P 11½–12½.

112	3	3d. on 4d. ultramarine (1.6.79) ...	85·00	20·00
	a.	Surch double	†	£1500
113		4d. violet-slate (15.3.79)........	£110	14·00
114		4d. plum (16.4.80)................	60·00	6·50
115		4d. deep mauve (8.6.82)...........	60·00	5·50
116	1	6d. indigo (2.12.76)..............	£110	4·50
	a.	Imperf between (horiz pair)......	†	
117		6d. Prussian blue (7.78)..........	75·00	4·00
118	4	8d. on 9d. brown-orange (7.76).....	95·00	7·00
119		8d. on 9d. burnt umber (1880)......	£100	7·00
120		8d. on 9d. brown (9.3.80)..........	£100	7·00
	a.	Imperf between (vert pair)........	£750	
121		8d. on 9d. grey-brown (10.5.81)....	85·00	7·00
	a.	Surch double	—	£1400
122		9d. purple (9.3.80)...............	60·00	8·50
	a.	Printed on both sides	—	£400
123		9d. rose-lilac (21.8.80)..........	16·00	3·25
124		9d. rose-lilac (large holes) (26.5.00)	10·00	3·50
125	1	1s. red-brown (3.11.77)...........	50·00	2·75
	a.	Imperf between (horiz pair)......	†	£475
126		1s. reddish lake-brown (1880).....	50·00	3·00
127		1s. lake-brown (9.1.83)...........	55·00	2·75
	a.	Printed double		
128		1s. Vandyke brown (1891)..........	65·00	8·00
129		1s. dull brown (1891).............	45·00	3·00
130		1s. chocolate (large holes) (6.5.97)..	25·00	3·00
	a.	Imperf vert (horiz pair)...........	£225	
131		1s. sepia (large holes) (22.5.00)..	25·00	3·00
	a.	Imperf between (vert pair)........	£250	
132	3	2s. carmine (15.2.77).............	38·00	5·00
	a.	Imperf between (horiz pair)......	†	£1200
	b.	Imperf (pair).....................		
133		2s. rose-carmine (1885)...........	42·00	6·50
134		2s. rose-carmine (*large holes*) (6.12.98)	30·00	6·50

The perforation with larger, clean-cut holes resulted from the fitting of new pins to the machine.

(b) P 10.

135	1	6d. Prussian blue (11.11.79)	£110	15·00
136		6d. bright blue (1879)............	£130	15·00
136a		1s. reddish lake-brown	£300	

(c) P 10×11½–12½, 11½–12½×10, or compound.

137	3	4d. violet-slate (21.5.79)........	£110	17·00
138		4d. dull purple (4.10.79).........	45·00	2·75
139	1	6d. Prussian blue (29.12.77)......	65·00	2·50
140		6d. bright blue	85·00	5·00
141		6d. bright ultramarine	55·00	2·00
142		6d. reddish lake-brown (9.2.85)...	90·00	10·00
143		1s. dull brown (29.6.86)..........	£120	12·00
144	3	2s. carmine (27.12.77)............	60·00	6·00
145		2s. rose-carmine (1887)..........	55·00	5·00
	a.	Imperf between (horiz pair)......	†	£900

10   11   12

1901–02. Wmk Crown SA (wide). W 10. P 11½–12½ (large holes).

146	4	9d. claret (1.2.02)...............	16·00	16·00
147		1s. dark brown (12.6.01)..........	22·00	12·00
148		1s. dark reddish brown (1902).....	24·00	13·00
	a.	Imperf horiz (vert pair).........	£1300	£1300
149		1s. red-brown (aniline) (18.7.02)..	22·00	15·00
150	3	2s. crimson (29.8.01).............	30·00	15·00
151		2s. carmine	25·00	11·00

(Plates and electrotypes by D.L.R. Printed in Adelaide)

1868–76. W 10.

(a) Rouletted.

152	12	2d. deep brick-red (8.68).........	75·00	4·50
153		2d. pale orange-red (10.68).......	70·00	2·75
	a.	Printed on both sides	†	£425
	b.	Imperf between (horiz pair).......	†	£700
	c.	Imperf horiz (vert pair).........	†	£1000

(b) P 11½–12½.

154	11	1d. blue-green (10.1.75)..........	85·00	17·00
155	12	2d. pale orange-red (5.5.69)......	£900	£200

(c) P 11½–12½ × roulette.

156	12	2d. pale orange-red (20.8.69).....	—	£140

(d) P 10 × roulette.

157	12	2d. pale orange-red (7.5.70)......	£275	27·00

(e) P 10.

158	11	1d. blue-green (4.75).............	45·00	5·50
159	12	2d. brick-red (4.70)..............	22·00	1·00
160		2d. orange-red (1.7.70)...........	13·00	1·00
	a.	Printed on both sides	†	£325

(f) P 10×11½–12½, 11½–12½×10, or compound.

161	11	1d. blue-green (27.8.75)..........	75·00	19·00
162	12	2d. brick-red (19.1.71)...........	£450	14·00
163		2d. orange-red (3.2.71)...........	£120	15·00
	a.	Imperf (8.76).....................	£1000	£1000

1869. Wmk Large Star W 2.

(a) Rouletted.

164	12	2d. orange-red (13.3.69)..........	80·00	18·00

(b) P 11½–12½ × roulette.

165	12	2d. orange-red (1.8.69)...........	—	£100

(c) P 11½–12½.

165a	12	2d. orange-red (7.69).............	—	£850

1871 (15 July). Wmk V and Crown, W 7. P 10.

166	12	2d. brick-red	80·00	23·00

13   HALF-PENNY

     (14)

1876–1904. Wmk Crown SA (close). W 13.

(a) P 10 (1876–85).

167	11	1d. blue-green (9.2.76)...........	15·00	40
	a.	*Yellowish green* (11.78).........	16·00	40
	b.	*Deep green* (11.79).............	16·00	30
	ba.	Imperf between (horiz pair)......		
	bb.	Printed double	†	—
168	12	2d. orange-red (8.76).............	16·00	30
	a.	*Dull brick-red* (21.5.77).......	17·00	30
	b.	*Blood-red* (31.10.79)...........	£225	3·25
	c.	*Pale red* (4.85)................	11·00	30

(b) P 10×11½–12½, 11½–12½×10 or compound (1877–80).

169	11	1d. deep green (11.2.80)..........	45·00	4·50
	a.	*Blue-green* (2.3.80)............	25·00	3·50
170	12	2d. orange-red (4.9.77)...........	£130	5·00
	a.	*Dull brick-red* (6.80)..........	£130	5·00

(c) P 11½–12½ (1877–84).

171	11	1d. blue-green (2.84).............	—	£130
172	12	2d. orange-red (14.9.77)..........	—	£130
	a.	*Blood-red* (1.4.80).............	—	£130

(d) P 15 (1893).

173	11	1d. green (8.5.93)................	13·00	1·00
174	12	2d. pale orange (9.2.93)..........	13·00	75
	a.	*Orange-red*	13·00	75
	b.	Imperf between (vert pair).......	£400	

(e) P 13 (1895–1903).

175	11	1d. pale green (11.1.95)..........	7·50	20
	a.	*Green*	7·50	20
	b.	Imperf between (vert pair).......		
176		1d. rosine (8.8.99)...............	4·75	20
	a.	*Scarlet* (23.12.03).............	4·50	30
	b.	*Deep red*	4·50	30
177	12	2d. pale orange (19.1.95).........	6·50	10
	a.	*Orange-red* (9.5.95)............	9·00	10
178		2d. bright violet (10.10.99)......	4·25	10

(f) P 12×11½ (comb) (1904).

179	11	1d. rosine (2.2.04)	8·00	50
180	12	2d. bright violet (11.10.04)	6·50	70
		a. Scarlet (25.7.04)	6·00	20

Examples of the 1d. pale green with thicker lettering come from a worn plate.

1882 (1 Jan). No. 167 surch with T **14**.

| 181 | 11 | ½d. on 1d. blue-green | 12·00 | 8·00 |

| 15 | 16 |

| 17 | 18 |

1883–99. W **13** (sideways on ½d.).

(a) P 10 (1883–95).

182	15	½d. chocolate (1.3.83)	6·00	1·25
		a. Imperf between (horiz pair)	†	£850
		b. Red-brown (4.4.89)	5·00	1·25
		c. Brown (1895)	4·25	1·25
183	16	3d. sage-green (12.86)	15·00	2·25
		a. Olive-green (6.6.90)	13·00	2·75
		b. Deep green (12.4.93)	9·00	2·75
		s. Optd "Specimen"	30·00	
184	17	4d. pale violet (3.90)	20·00	2·75
		a. Aniline violet (3.1.93)	21·00	3·25
		s. Optd "Specimen"	35·00	
185	18	6d. pale blue (4.87)	18·00	2·25
		a. Blue (5.5.87)	19·00	1·00
		s. Optd "Specimen"	30·00	

(b) P 10×11½–12½, 11½–12½×10 or compound (1891).

| 186 | 15 | ½d. red-brown (25.9.91) | 13·00 | 4·75 |
| | | a. Imperf between (horiz pair) | £160 | |

(c) P 11½–12½ (1890).

| 187 | 15 | ½d. red-brown (12.10.90) | 14·00 | 2·25 |

(d) P 15 (1893–94).

188	15	½d. pale brown (1.93)	5·00	1·00
		a. Deep brown	5·00	1·00
		b. Imperf between (horiz pair)	£160	
		c. Perf 12½ between (pair)	£180	42·00
189	17	4d. purple (1.1.94)	22·00	3·25
		a. Slate-violet	22·00	3·25
190	18	6d. blue (20.11.93)	38·00	3·50

(e) P 13 (1895–99).

191	15	½d. pale brown (9.95)	2·75	30
		a. Deep brown (19.3.97)	3·75	30
192	16	3d. pale olive-green (26.7.97)	8·00	2·00
		a. Deep olive-green (27.11.99)	5·00	1·75
193	17	4d. violet (21.1.96)	6·00	50
194	18	6d. pale blue (3.96)	7·00	1·50
		a. Blue	7·00	1·50

REPRINTS. In 1884, and in later years, reprints on paper wmkd Crown SA, W **10**, were made of Nos. 1, 2, 3, 4, 12, 13, 14, 15, 19, 24, 27, 28, 32, 33, 34, 35, 36, 37, 38, 40, 43, 44, 49a, 53, 65, 67, 67 with surcharge in red, 70, 71, 72, 73, 78, 79, 81, 83, 86, 90, 118, 119, 120, 121, 122, 155, 158, 159, 164, 181, 182. They are overprinted "REPRINT".

In 1889 examples of the reprints for Nos. 1/3, 12, 15, 19, 27, 32/8, 44, 67, 67 surcharged in red, 70/1, 73, 83, 86, 118, 121/2, 158/9, 164 and 181/2, together with No. 141 overprinted "Specimen", were supplied to the U.P.U. for distribution.

| 19 | (20) | (21) |

(Plates and electrotypes by D.L.R. Printed in Adelaide)

1886 (20 Dec)–**96**. T **19** (inscr "POSTAGE & REVENUE"). W **13**. Parts of two or more wmks, on each stamp, sometimes sideways. P 10.

195		2s.6d. mauve	50·00	9·50
		a. Perf 11½–12½. Dull violet	40·00	7·00
		bb. Bright aniline violet	42·00	9·00
196		5s. rose-pink	70·00	17·00
		a. Perf 11½–12½	50·00	17·00
		ab. Rose-carmine	50·00	19·00
197		10s. green	£150	50·00
		a. Perf 11½–12½	£130	48·00
198		15s. brownish yellow	£375	£275
		a. Perf 11½–12½	£425	£180
199		£1 blue	£325	£140
		a. Perf 11½–12½	£275	£130
200		£2 Venetian red	£1300	£425
		a. Perf 11½–12½	£1200	£375
201		50s. dull pink	£1800	£550
		a. Perf 11½–12½	£1700	£450
202		£3 sage green	£2000	£500
		a. Perf 11½–12½	£1900	£450

203		£4 lemon	£3750	
		a. Perf 11½–12½	£3250	£800
204		£5 grey	£3250	
		a. Perf 11½–12½	£3250	
205		£5 brown (P 11½–12½) (1896)	£2500	£800
206		£10 bronze	£3750	£1000
		a. Perf 11½–12½	£3000	£900
207		£15 silver	£10000	
		a. Perf 11½–12½	£9000	£1500
208		£20 claret	£12000	
		a. Perf 11½–12½	£11000	£1600
195s/208s		Optd "Specimen" Set of 14	£700	

Variations exist in the length of the words and shape of the letters of the value inscription.

The 2s.6d. dull violet, 5s. rose-pink, 10s., £1 and £5 brown exist perf 11½–12½ with either large or small holes; the 2s.6d. aniline, 5s. rose-carmine, 15s., £2 and 50s. with large holes only and the remainder only with small holes.

Stamps perforated 11½–12½ small holes are, generally speaking, rather rarer than those with the 1895 (large holes) gauge.

Stamps perf 10 were issued on 20 Dec 1886. Stamps perf 11½–12½ (small holes) are known with earliest dates covering the period from June 1890 to Feb 1896. Earliest dates of stamps with large holes range from July 1896 to May 1902.

1891 (1 Jan)–**93**. T **17**/18 surch with T **20**/1. W **13**.

(a) P 10.

229	17	2½d. on 4d. pale green (Br.)	7·50	2·50
		a. Fraction bar omitted	95·00	75·00
		b. Deep green	8·00	1·75
		ba. Fraction bar omitted	95·00	70·00
		bb. "2" and "½" closer together	26·00	18·00
		bc. Imperf between (horiz pair)		
		bd. Imperf between (vert pair)	†	£1200
		s. Optd "Specimen"	30·00	
230	18	5d. on 6d. pale brn (C.)	16·00	5·00
		a. Deep brown	16·00	4·75
		b. No stop after "5D"	£160	
		s. Optd "Specimen"	30·00	

(b) P 10×11½–12½ or 11½–12½×10.

| 231 | 17 | 2½d. on 4d. pale green (Br.) | 25·00 | 4·00 |
| | | a. Deep green | 25·00 | 4·00 |

(c) P 11½–12½.

| 232 | 17 | 2½d. on 4d. deep green | 38·00 | 50·00 |

(d) P 15.

233	17	2½d. on 4d. green (14.10.93)	25·00	2·75
		a. Fraction bar omitted		
		b. "2" and "½d." closer	70·00	22·00

| 22 Red Kangaroo | 23 | 24 G.P.O., Adelaide |

(Des M. Tannenberg, plates by D.L.R.)

1894 (1 Mar)–**1906**. W **13**.

(a) P 15.

234	22	2½d. violet-blue	23·00	2·75
235	23	5d. brown-purple	26·00	3·50
234s/5s		Optd "Specimen" Set of 2	60·00	

(b) P 13.

236	22	2½d. violet-blue (11.2.95)	19·00	70
237		2½d. indigo (25.3.98)	6·00	1·75
238	23	5d. Brown-purple (1.96)	6·50	1·00
		a. Purple	6·50	75

(c) P 12×11½ (comb).

| 239 | 22 | 2½d. indigo (4.7.06) | 8·00 | 2·50 |
| 240 | 23 | 5d. dull purple (1.05) | 15·00 | 2·00 |

(Typo D.L.R.)

1899 (27 Dec)–**1905**. W **13**.

(a) P 13.

| 241 | 24 | ½d. yellow-green | 2·25 | 50 |

(b) P 12×11½ (comb).

| 242 | 24 | ½d. yellow-green (7.05) | 3·50 | 1·25 |

| 25 |

The measurements given indicate the length of the value inscription in the bottom label. The dates are those of the earliest known postmarks.

1902–04. As T **19**, but top tablet as T **25** (thin "POSTAGE"). W **13**.

(a) P 11½–12½.

268		3d. olive-green (18½ mm) (1.8.02)	7·00	2·00
		a. Wmk sideways	†	£1600
269		4d. red-orange (17 mm) (29.11.02)	13·00	2·00
270		6d. blue-green (16–16½ mm) (29.11.02)	7·50	2·00
271		8d. ultramarine (19 mm) (25.4.02)	8·50	8·00
272		8d. ultramarine (16½ mm) (22.3.04)	12·00	8·00
		a. "EIGNT" (R.2/9)	£1400	£2500
273		9d. rosy lake (19.9.02)	9·00	4·75
		a. Imperf between (vert pair)	£900	
		b. Imperf between (horiz pair)	£900	
274		10d. dull yellow (29.11.02)	13·00	8·50
275		1s. brown (18.8.02)	17·00	4·50
		a. Imperf between (horiz pair)	£1000	
		b. Imperf between (horiz pair)	£1000	
		c. "POSTAGE" and value in red-brown	£900	£900

276		2s.6d. pale violet (19.9.02)	45·00	23·00
		a. Bright violet (2.2.03)	25·00	13·00
277		5s. rose (17.10.02)	70·00	45·00
278		10s. green (1.11.02)	£120	70·00
279		£1 blue (1.11.02)	£300	£170

(b) P 12.

280		3d. olive-green (20 mm) (15.4.04)	14·00	2·50
		a. "POSTAGE" omitted; value below "AUSTRALIA"	£1600	
281		4d. orange-red (17½–18 mm) (18.2.03)	13·00	2·25
282		6d. blue-green (15 mm) (14.11.03)	24·00	6·00
283		9d. rosy lake (2.12.03)	70·00	12·00

No. 280a comes from the bottom row of the sheet. Other stamps show the value below "AUSTRALIA" with "POSTAGE" over the bottom frame (Price £500, unused).

PRINTER. Stamp printing in Adelaide ceased in 1909 when the Printer of Stamps, J. B. Cooke, was appointed head of the Commonwealth Stamp Printing Branch in Melbourne. From 9 March 1909 further printings of current South Australia stamps were made in Melbourne.

| 26 |

 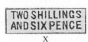

| V | X |

In Type X the letters in the bottom line are slightly larger than in Type V, especially the "A", "S" and "P".

| Y | Z |

In Type Z the letters "S" and "G" are more open than in Type Y.

Nos. 196/a and 277 are similar to Type Y with all letters thick and regular and the last "S" has the top curve rounded instead of being slightly flattened.

1904–11. As T **19**, but top tablet as T **26** (thick "POSTAGE"). W **13**. P 12.

284		6d. blue-green (27.4.04)	15·00	3·00
		a. Imperf between (vert pair)	£2500	
285		8d. bright ultramarine (4.7.05)	10·00	8·00
		a. Value closer (15¼ mm)	30·00	18·00
		b. Dull ultramarine (2.4.08)	20·00	5·00
		ba. Ditto. Value closer (15¼ mm)	60·00	14·00
286		9d. rosy lake (17–17¼ mm) (18.7.04)	15·00	4·75
		a. Value 16½–16¾ mm (2.06)	35·00	6·50
		b. Brown-lake. Perf 12½ small holes (11.3.11)	14·00	13·00
287		10d. dull yellow (8.07)	16·00	13·00
		a. Imperf between (horiz pair)	£1100	£1200
		b. Imperf between (vert pair)	£2000	
288		1s. brown (12.4.04)	21·00	3·00
		a. Imperf between (vert pair)	£900	
		b. Imperf between (horiz pair)	£1100	
289		2s.6d. bright violet (V.) (14.7.05)	55·00	17·00
		a. Dull violet (X) (8.06)	55·00	17·00
290		5s. rose-scarlet (Y) (8.04)	50·00	32·00
		a. Scarlet (Z) (8.06)	50·00	32·00
		b. Pale rose. Perf 12½ (small holes) (Z) (6.10)	75·00	40·00
291		10s. green (26.8.08)	£130	£140
292		£1 blue (29.12.04)	£250	£140
		a. Perf 12½ (small holes) (6.10)	£150	£130

The "value closer" variety on the 8d. occurs six times in the sheet of 60. The value normally measures 16½ mm but in the variety it is 15¼ mm.

The 9d., 5s. and £1, perf 12½ (small holes), are late printings made in 1910–11 to use up the Crown SA paper.

No. 286b has the value as Type C of the 9d. on Crown over A paper.

| 27 |

1905–11. W **27**. P 12×11½ (new comb machine).

293	24	½d. pale green (4.07)	5·50	1·00
		a. Yellow-green	5·50	1·00
		b. Thin ready gummed paper (1912)	8·00	2·00
		ba. Mixed perf 12×11½ and 12½	£750	
294	11	1d. rosine (2.12.05)	5·00	20
		a. Scarlet (8.06)	4·00	1·25
295	12	2d. bright violet (2.2.06)	9·00	20
		aa. Imperf three sides (horiz pair)	£1300	
		a. Mauve (4.08)	5·00	20
296	22	2½d. indigo-blue (14.9.10)	9·00	7·50
297	23	5d. brown-purple (11.3.08)	18·00	4·00

No. 295aa is perforated at foot.

Three types of the 9d., perf 12½, distinguished by the distance between "NINE" and "PENCE".
A. Distance 1¾ mm. B. Distance 2¼ mm. C. Distance 2½ mm.

1906–12. T **19** ("POSTAGE" thick as T **26**). W **27**. P 12 or 12½ (small holes).

| 298 | | 3d. sage-green (19 mm) (26.6.06) | 8·00 | 3·00 |
| | | a. Imperf between (horiz pair) | † | £3750 |

b. Perf 12½. *Sage-green* (17 mm)
(9.12.09)...................... 8·00 3·00
c. Perf 12½. *Deep olive* (20 mm)
(7.10)........................ 45·00 11·00
d. Perf 12½. *Yellow-olive* (19 mm)
(16.12.11)................... 50·00 20·00
da. Perf 12½. *Bright olive-green* (19–
19¾ mm) Thin ready gummed paper
(8.9.11)..................... 12·00 14·00
e. Perf 11 (17 mm) (1910)........ £900 £650
299 4d. orange-red (10.9.06)...... 12·00 2·50
a. Orange...................... 12·00 2·50
b. Perf 12½. *Orange*............ 11·00 4·25
c. Thin ready gummed paper (19.8.12). 12·00 14·00
300 6d. blue-green (1.9.06)........ 8·00 2·25
a. Perf 12½ (21.4.10)........... 8·00 4·00
ab. Perf 12½. Imperf between (vert pair) £900 £1000
b. Thin ready gummed paper (3.12).. 8·00 9·00
301 8d. bright ultramarine (P 12½) (8.09).. 10·00 13·00
a. Value closer (8.09)........... 42·00 50·00
302 9d. brown-lake (3.2.06)......... 11·00 3·50
a. Imperf between (vert pair)...... £850
aa. Imperf between (horiz strip of three) £2250
b. Deep lake (9.5.08).......... 42·00 6·50
c. Perf 12½. *Lake* (A) (5.9.09)... 11·00 4·75
d. Perf 12½. *Lake* (B) ((7.09)... 23·00 5·00
e. Perf 12½. *Brown-lake*........ 23·00 6·50
ea. Perf 12½. *Deep lake*. Thin paper (C) 23·00 6·00
f. Perf 11 (1909)............... † £1500
303 1s. brown (30.5.06)............ 12·00 4·75
a. Imperf between (horiz pair)...... £1600
aa. Imperf between (vert pair)...... £1300
b. Perf 12½ (10.3.10).......... 10·00 5·50
c. Thin ready gummed paper (4.8.11).. 10·00 6·00
304 2s.6d. bright violet (X) (10.6.09) 55·00 14·00
a. Perf 12½. *Pale violet* (X) (6.10). 55·00 17·00
ab. Perf 12½. *Deep purple* (X) Thin
ready gummed paper (15.11.12).. 65·00 42·00
305 5s. bright rose (P 12½) (Z) Thin
gummed paper (24.4.11)........ 80·00 7·00

The "value closer" variety of the 8d. occurred 11 times in the sheet of 60 in the later printing only. On No. 301 the value measures 16½ mm while on No. 301a it is 15¼ mm.

The 1s. brown, perf compound of 11½ and 12½, formerly listed is now omitted, as it must have been perforated by the 12 machine, which in places varied from 11½ to 13. The 4d. has also been reported with a similar perforation.

STAMP BOOKLETS

There are very few surviving examples of Nos. SB1/4. Listings are provided for those believed to have been issued with prices quoted for those known still to exist.

1904 (1 Jan)–**09**. *Black on red cover as No. SB1 of New South Wales. Stapled.*
SB1 £1 booklet containing two hundred and forty 1d.
in four blocks of 30 and two blocks of 60.....
a. Red on pink cover (1909).......................
b. Blue on pink cover........................... £13000

1904 (1 Jan). *Black on grey cover as No. SB1. Stapled.*
SB2 £1 booklet containing one hundred and twenty
2d. in four blocks of 30................................

1910 (May). *Black on cream cover as No. SB3 of New South Wales. Stapled.*
SB3 2s. booklet containing eleven ½d. (No. 262A),
either in block of 6 plus block of 5 or block
of 11, and eighteen 1d. (No. 264A), either in
three blocks of 6 or block of 6 plus block of
12.......................................

Unsold stock of No. SB3 was uprated with one additional ½d. in May 1911.

1911 (Aug). *Red on pink cover as No. SB3. Stapled.*
SB4 2s. Booklet containing twelve 12d. (No. 262A),
either in two blocks of 6 or block of 12 and
eighteen 1d. (No. 264A), either in three
blocks of 6 or block of 6 plus block of 12 .... £5000

OFFICIAL STAMPS
A. Departmentals

Following suspected abuses involving stamps supplied for official use it was decided by the South Australian authorities that such supplies were to be overprinted with a letter, or letters, indicating the department of the administration to which the stamps had been invoiced.

The system was introduced on 1 April 1868 using overprints struck in red. Later in the same year the colour of the overprints was amended blue, and, during the latter months of 1869, to black.

In 1874 the Postmaster-General recommended that this some-what cumbersome system be replaced by a general series of "O.S." overprints with the result that the separate accounting for the Departmentals ceased on 30 June of that year. Existing stocks continued to be used, however, and it is believed that much of the residue was passed to the Government Printer to pay postage on copies of the *Government Gazette*.

We are now able to provide a check list of these most interesting issues based on the definitive work. *The Departmental Stamps of South Australia* by A. R. Butler, FRPSL, RDP, published by the Royal Philatelic Society, London in 1978.

No attempt has been made to assign the various overprints to the catalogue numbers of the basic stamps, but each is clearly identified by both watermark and perforation. the colours are similar to those of the contemporary postage stamps, but there can be shade variations. Errors of overprint are recorded in footnotes, but not errors occurring on the basic stamps used.

Most departmental overprints are considered to be scarce to rare in used condition, with unused examples, used multiples and covers being regarded as considerable rarities.

Forgeries of a few items do exist, but most can be readily identified by comparison with genuine examples. A number of forged overprints on stamps not used for the genuine issues also occur.

A. (Architect)
Optd in red with stop. W **2**. 2d. (Roul), 4d. (P 11½–12½), 6d. (Roul),
1s. (Roul)
Optd in red without stop W **2**. Roul. 1d., 2d., 6d., 1s.
Optd in black. (*a*) W **2**. 4d. (P 10×11½–12½), 6d. (P 11½–12½), 2s.
(Roul)
(*b*) W **10**. 2d. D.L.R. (Roul), 2d. D.L.R. (P 10)

A.G. (Attorney-General)
Optd in red. W **2**. Roul. 1d., 2d., 6d., 1s.
Optd in blue. (*a*) W **2**. Roul. 6d.
(*b*) W **10**. Roul. 2d. D.L.R.
Optd in black. (*a*) W **2**. 1d (P 11½–12½×Roul), 4d.
(P 10), 6d. (P 11½–12½×Roul), 6d. (P 11½–12½), 1s.
(P 11½–12½×Roul) 1s. (P 11½–12½) 1s. (P 10)
(*b*) W **10**. 2d. D.L.R. (P 10)

A.O. (Audit Office)
Optd in red. W **2**. 2d. (Roul), 4d. (P 11½–12½), 6d. (Roul)
Optd in blue. (*a*) W **2**. P 11½–12½. 1d., 6d.
(*b*) W **10**. Roul. 2d. D.L.R.
Optd in black. (*a*) W **2**. 1d (P 11½–12½), 1d. (P 10), 2d. D.L.R.
(Roul), 4d. (P 11½–12½) 4d. (P 10), 4d. (P 10×11½–12½), 6d.
(Roul), 6d. (P 11½–12½), 1s. (P 11½–12½), 1s. (P 11½–
12½×Roul)
(*b*) W **7**. P 10. 4d.
(*c*) W **10**. 2d. D.L.R. (Roul), 2d. D.L.R. (P 10)

B.D. (Barracks Department)
Optd in red. W **2**. Roul. 2d., 6d., 1s.

B.G. (Botanic Garden)
Optd in black. (*a*) W **2**. 1d (P 11½–12½×R), 1d. (P 11½–12½), 1d.
(P 10×11½–12½), 2d. D.L.R. (Roul), 6d. (Roul), 6d.
(P 11½–12½×Roul), 6d. (P 11½–12½), 1s. (P 11½–12½×Roul),
1s. (P 11½–12½), 1s. (P 10), 1s. (P 10×11½–12½)
(*b*) W **7**. P 10. 2d. D.L.R.
(*c*) W **10**. 2d. D.L.R. (Roul), 2d. D.L.R. (P 10)
The 6d. (W **2**. Roul) is known without stamp after "B".

B.M. (Bench of Magistrates)
Optd in red. W **2**. Roul. 2d.
Optd in black. W **10**. Roul. 2d. D.L.R.

C. (Customs)
Optd in red. W **2**. 1d. (Roul), 4d. (P 11½–12½), 6d.
(Roul), 1s. (Roul)
Optd in blue (*a*) W **2**. Roul. 1d., 4d., 6d., 1s., 2s.
(*b*) W **10**. Roul. 2d. D.L.R.
Optd in black. (*a*) W **2**. 1d. (Roul), 1d. (P 10), 1d. (P 10×11½–12½),
4d. (P 11½–12½), 4d. (P 10), 4d. (P 10×11½–12½), 6d. (Roul),
6d. (P 11½–12½), 6d. (P 10), 6d. (P 10×11½–12½), 1s.
(P 11½–12½), 2s. (Roul)
(*b*) W **7**. P 10. 2d. D.L.R.
(*c*) W **10**. 2d. D.L.R. (Roul), 2d. D.L.R. (P 10×Roul), 2d. D.L.R.
(P 10), 2d. D.L.R. (P 10×11½–12½)
The 2d. (W **10**. (Roul) is known showing the error "G" for "C".

C.D. (Convict Department)
Optd in black. (*a*) W **2**. 2d. (Roul), 4d. (P 11½–12½), 6d. (Roul), 1s. (Roul).
4d. (P 11½–12½), 6d. (Roul), 6d. (P 11½–12½×Roul, 1s.
(P 11½–12½×Roul)
(*b*) W **10**. 2d. D.L.R. (Roul), 2d. D.L.R. (P 10), 2d.
D.L.R. (P 11½–12½×Roul)

C.L. (Crown Lands)
Optd in red. W **2**. 2d. (Roul), 4d. (P 11½–12½), 6d. (Roul), 1s. (Roul)
Optd in blue. (*a*) W **2**. Roul. 4d., 6d.
(*b*) W **10**. Roul. 2d. D.L.R.
Optd in black. (*a*) W **2**. 2d. D.L.R. (Roul), 4d. (P 11½–12½), 4d.
(P 10), 4d. (P 10×11½–12½), 6d. (Roul), 6d. (P 11½–12½), 1s.
(P 11½–12½×Roul), 2s. (Roul), 2s. (P 11½–12½)
(*b*) W **7**. P 10. 2d. D.L.R., 4d.
(*c*) W **10**. 2d. D.L.R. (Roul), 2d. D.L.R. (P 10), 2d. D.L.R.
(P 10×11½–12½)
The 2s. (W **2**. P 11½–12½) with black overprint is known showing the stop omitted after "L".

C.O. (Commissariat Office)
Optd in red. W **2**. (Roul), 4d. (P 11½–12½) 6d. (Roul), 1s. (Roul)
Optd in black. (*a*) W **2**. 2d. (P 10), 4d. (P 10×11½–12½), 6d. (P 11½–
12½), 1s. (P 11½–12½), 2s. (Roul), 2s. (P 11½–12½)
(*b*) W **10**. 2d. D.L.R. (Roul), 2d. D.L.R. (P 10)
The 6d. (W **2**. Roul) with red overprint is known showing the error "O" for "C", and the 2s. (W **2**. P 11½–12½) with black overprint with the stop omitted after "O".

C.P. (Commissioner of Police)
Optd in red. W **2**. 2d. (Roul), 4d. (P 11½–12½), 6d.

C.S. (Chief Secretary)
Optd in red. W **2**. 2d. (Roul), 4d. (P 11½–12½), 6d. (Roul), 1s. (Roul)
Optd in blue. (*a*) W **2**. Roul. 4d., 6d.
(*b*) W **10**. Roul. 2d. D.L.R.
Optd in black. (*a*) W **2**. 2d. D.L.R. (Roul), 4d. (Roul), 4d. (P 11½–
12½×Roul), 4d. (P 11½–12½), 4d. (P 10), 4d. (P 10×11½–12½),
6d. (P 11½–12½×Roul), 6d. (Roul), 6d. (P 10), 6d. (Roul),
(P 10×11½–12½), 1s. (P 11½–12½), 1s. (P 10×11½–12½), 1s.
(P 10), 1s. (P 10×11½–12½), 2s. (P 10×11½–12½)
(*b*) W **7**. P 10. 2d.
(*c*) W **10**. 2d. D.L.R. (Roul), 2d. D.L.R. (P 10)
The 6d. and 1s. (W **2**. Roul) with red overprint are known showing the error "G" for "C".

C.Sgn. (Colonial Surgeon)
Optd in red. W **2**. 2d. (Roul), 4d. (P 11½–12½), 6d. (Roul)
Optd in black. (*a*) W **2**. 2d. D.L.R. (Roul), 4d. (P 10), 4d.
(P 10×11½–12½), 2d. D.L.R. (Roul), 4d. (P 10), 4d.
(P 11½–12½)
(*b*) W **10**. 2d. D.L.R. (Roul), 2d. D.L.R. (P 11½–12½×Roul), 2d.
(P 10×Roul), 2d. D.L.R. (P 10)
Two types of overprint exist on the 2d. D.L.R., the second type having block capitals instead of the serifed type used for the other values.

D.B. (Destitute Board)
Optd in red. W **2**. 1d. (Roul), 2d. (Roul), 4d. (P 11½–12½), 6d.
(Roul), 1s. (Roul)
Optd in blue. (*a*) W **2**. 2d. (Roul), 4d. (P 11½–12½), 6d.
(Roul)

(from right column)
(*b*) W **10**. Roul. 2d. D.L.R.
Optd in black. (*a*) W **2**. 1d. (P 11½–12½), 4d. (P 11½–12½), 4d.
(P 10), 6d. (P 10×11½–12½) 1s. (P 10)
(*b*) W **10**. 2d. D.L.R. (Roul), 2d. D.L.R. (P 11½–12½), 2d.
D.L.R. (P 10), 2d. D.L.R. (P 10×11½–12½) 1s. (P 10)
The 2d. D.L.R. (W **10**. P 10) with black overprint is known showing the stop omitted after "D".

D.R. (Deeds Registration)
Optd in red. W **2**. Roul. 2d., (Roul)

E. (Engineer)
Optd in red. W **2**. 2d. (Roul), 4d. (P 11½–12½), 6d. (Roul), 1s. (Roul)
Optd in blue. (*a*) W **2**. Roul. 1s.
(*b*) W **10**. Roul. 2d. D.L.R.
Optd in black. (*a*) W **2**. 4d. (P 11½–12½), 4d. (P 10), 4d.
(P 10×11½–12½), 6d. (P 11½–12½), 1s. (P 11½–12½×Roul), 1s.
(P 11½–12½), 1s. (P 10×11½–12½)
(*b*) W **7**. P 10. 4d.
(*c*) W **10**. P 10. 2d. D.L.R.

E.B. (Education Board)
Optd in red. W **2**. 2d. (Roul), 4d. (P 11½–12½), 6d. (Roul)
Optd in blue. (*a*) W **2**. Roul. 4d., 6d.
(*b*) W **10**. Roul. 2d. D.L.R.
Optd in black. (*a*) W **2**. 2d. D.L.R. (Roul), 4d (Roul), 4d. (P 11½–
12½), 4d. (P 10), 6d. (P 11½–12½×Roul), 6d. (P 11½12½)
(*b*) W **7**. P 10. 2d. D.L.R.
(*c*) W **10**. 2d. D.L.R. (Roul), 2d. D.L.R. (P 10), 2d. D.L.R.
(P 10×11½–12½)

G.F. (Gold Fields)
Optd in black. (*a*) W **2**. Roul. 6d.
(*b*) W **10**. 2d. D.L.R. (P 10×Roul), 2d. D.L.R. (P 10)
G.P. (Government Printer)Optd in red. W **2**. Roul. 1d., 2d., 6d., 1s.
Optd in black. (*a*) W **2**. 1d., 6d., 1s., 2s.
(*b*) W **10**. 2d. D.L.R.
Optd in black. (*a*) W **2**. 1d. (Roul), 1d. (P 11½–12½×Roul), 1d.
(P 11½–12½) 1d. (P 10) 1d (P 10×11½–12½), 6d. (P 11½–
12½×Roul), 1s. (P 10×11½–12½), 2s. (Roul), 2s. (P 11½–12½),
2s. (P 10×11½–12½)
(*b*) W **10**. 2d. D.L.R. (Roul), 2d. D.L.R.(P 10)
The 1d. and 1s. (W **2**. Roul) with red overprint are known showing "C.P." instead of "G.P.".

G.S. (Government Storekeeper)
Optd in red. W **2**. Roul. 2d.

G.T. (Goolwa Tramway)
Optd in red. W **2**. 1d. (Roul), 2d. (Roul), 4d. (P 11½–12½), 6d.
(Roul), 1s. (Roul)
Optd in black. (*a*) W **2**. 2d. D.L.R. (Roul), 4d. (P 11½–12½)
(*b*) W **10**. Roul. 2d. D.L.R.
The 2d. and 6d. (both W **2**. Roul) with red overprint are known showing the stop omitted after "T". The 6d, and 1s. (W **2**. Roul) with red overprint are known showing "C.T.", instead of "G.T.".

H. (Hospitals)
Optd in black. (*a*) W **2**. Roul. 4d.
(*b*) W **7**. P 10. 2d. D.L.R.
(*c*) W **10**. 2d. D.L.R. (P 10), 2d. D.L.R. (P 10×11½–12½)
H.A. (House of Assembly)Optd in red. W **2**. 1d. (Roul), 2d. (Roul), 6d.
(Roul)
Optd in black. (*a*) W **2**. 1d. (Roul), 1d. (P 11½–12½), 1d. (P 10) 1d. (P 10×11½–12½),
4d. (P 11½–12½), 4d. (P 10), 6d. (Roul), 6d. (P 11½–12½×Roul),
1s. (P 11½–12½×Roul), 1s. (P 11½–12½)
(*b*) W **10**. 2d. D.L.R. (Roul), 2d. D.L.R. (P 10)

I.A. (Immigration Agent)
Optd in red. W **2**. 1d. (Roul), 2d. (Roul), 4d. (P 11½–12½), 6d. (Roul)

I.E. (Intestate Estates)
Optd in black. W **10**. P 10. 2d. D.L.R.

I.S. (Inspector of Sheep)
Optd in red. W **2**. Roul. 2d., 6d.
Optd in blue. W **2**. P 11½–12½. 6d.
Optd in black. (*a*) W **2**. 2d. D.L.R. (Roul), 6d. (P 11½–12½×Roul)
(*b*) W **10**. 2d. D.L.R. (Roul), 2d. D.L.R. (P 10)

L.A. (Lunatic Asylum)
Optd in red. W **2**. 1d. (Roul), 2d. (Roul), 4d. (P 11½–12½), 6d.
(Roul), 1s. (Roul)
Optd in black. (*a*) W **2**. 4d. (P 11½–12½), 4d. (P 10), 4d. (P 10×11½–
12½), 6d. (P 11½–12½), 1s. (P 11½–12½), 2s. (Roul)
(*b*) W **10**. 2d. D.L.R. (Roul), 2d. D.L.R. (P 10)

L.C. (Legislative Council)
Optd in red. W **2**. Roul. 2d., 6d.
Optd in black. (*a*) W **2**. Roul. 6d.
(*b*) W **10**. 2d. D.L.R. (Roul), 2d. D.L.R. (P 10×Roul)
The 2d. and 6d. (both W **2**. Roul) with red overprint are known showing the stop omitted after "C".

L.L. (Legislative Librarian)
Optd in red. W **2**. 2d. (Roul), 4d. (P 11½–12½), 6d. (Roul)
Optd in black. (*a*) W **2**. P 11½–12½. 6d. (Roul)
(*b*) W **10**. P 10. 2d. D.L.R.
The 2d. and 6d. (both W **2**. Roul) with red overprint are known showing the stop omitted from between the two letters.

L.T. (Land Titles)
Optd in red. W **2**. 2d. (Roul), 4d. (P 11½–12½), 6d. (Roul), 1s. (Roul)
Optd in blue. W **10**. Roul. 2d. D.L.R.
Optd in black. (*a*) W **2**. 4d. (P 11½–12½), 4d. (P 10), 4d. (P 10×11½–
12½), 6d. (P 11½–12½×Roul), 6d. (P 11½–12½), 6d. (P 10), 6d.
(P 10×11½–12½)
(*b*) W **7**. P 10. 2d. D.L.R.
(*c*) W **10**. 2d. D.L.R. (Roul), 2d. D.L.R. (P 10)
The 2d. and 6d. (both W **2**. Roul) with red overprint are known showing the stop omitted after "T".

M. (Military)

Optd in red. W **2**. Roul. 2d., 6d., 1s.

Optd in black. W **2**. 6d. (P 11½–12½×Roul), 1s. (P 11½–12½×Roul), 2s. (Roul)

M.B. (Marine Board)

Optd in red. W **2**. 1d. (Roul), 2d. (Roul), 4d. (Roul), 4d. (P 11½–12½), 6d. (Roul), 1s. (Roul)

Optd in black. (*a*) W **2**. 1d. (Roul), 1d. (P 11½–12½), 2d. D.L.R. (Roul), 4d. (Roul), 4d. (P 11½–12½×Roul), 4d. (P 10), 4d. (P 10×11½–12½), 6d. (Roul), 6d. (P 11½–12½×Roul), 1s. (P 11½–12½×Roul), 1s. (P 10), 1s. (P 10×11½–12½)

(*b*) W **7**. P 10. 4d.

(*c*) W **10**. Roul. 2d. D.L.R.

M.R. (Manager of Railways)

Optd in red. W **2**. Roul. 2d., 6d.

Optd in black. (*a*) W **2**. 1d. (P 11½–12½), 1d. (P 10), 2d. D.L.R. (Roul), 4d. (Roul), 4d. (P 11½–12½), 6d. (P 11½–12½×Roul), 1s. (P 11½–12½), 2s. (P 10×11½–12½)

(*b*) W **10**. 2d. D.L.R. (Roul), 2d. D.L.R. (P 10), 2d. D.L.R. (P 10×11½–12½)

M.R.G. (Main Roads Gambierton)

Optd in red without stops. W **2**. Roul. 2d., 6d.

Optd in blue without stops. W **10**. Roul. 2d. D.L.R.

Optd in black without stops. W **10**. 2d. D.L.R. (Roul), 2d. D.L.R. (Roul 10)

Optd in black with stops. W **10**. 2d. D.L.R. (Roul), 2d. D.L.R. (Roul 10)

The 2d. D.L.R. (W **10**. P 10) with black overprint is known showing the stops omitted after "M" and "R".

N.T. (Northern Territory)

Optd in black (*a*) W **2**. P 11½–12½. 1d., 3d. on 4d., 6d., 1s.

(*b*) W **10**. 2d. D.L.R. (Roul), 2d. D.L.R. (P 10)

O.A. (Official Assignee)

Optd in red. W **2**. 2d. (Roul), 4d. (P 11½–12½)

Optd in blue. W **10**. Roul. 2d. D.L.R.

Optd in black. (*a*) W **2**. P 10. 4d.

(*b*) W **7**. P 10. 2d. D.L.R.

(*c*) W **10**. 2d. D.L.R. (Roul), 2d. D.L.R. (P 10×roul), 2d. D.L.R. (P 10)

P. (Police)

Optd in blue. (*a*) W **2**. Roul. 6d.

(*b*) W **10**. Roul. 2d. D.L.R.

Optd in black. (*a*) W **2**. 6d. (P 11½–12½×Roul), 6d. (P 11½–12½), 6d. (P 10)

(*b*) W **7**. P 10. 2d. D.L.R.

(*c*) W **10**. 2d. D.L.R. (Roul), 2d. D.L.R. (P 11½–12½), 2d. D.L.R. (P 11½–12½×Roul), 2d. D.L.R. (P 10×Roul), 2d. D.L.R. (P 10), 2d. D.L.R. (P 10×11½–12½)

P.A. (Protector of Aborigines)

Optd in red. W **2**. Roul. 2d., 6d.

Optd in black. (*a*) W **2**. 2d. D.L.R., 6d.

(*b*) W **10**. 2d. D.L.R. (Roul), 2d. D.L.R. (P 10)

P.O. (Post Office)

Optd in red. W **2**. 1d., 2d., 6d., 1s.

Optd in blue. (*a*) W **2**. Roul. 2d.

(*b*) W **10**. Roul. 2d. D.L.R.

Optd in black. (*a*) W **2**. 1d. (P 10×11½–12½), 2d. D.L.R. (Roul), 2d. D.L.R. (P 11½–12½×Roul), 4d. (P 11½–12½), 6d. (Roul), 6d. (P 11½–12½), 6d. (P 11½–12½×Roul), 1s. (P 11½–12½) 1s. (P 10) 1s. (P 10×11½–12½)

(*b*) W **10**. 2d. D.L.R. (Roul), 2d. D.L.R. (P 11½–12½×Roul), 2d. D.L.R. (P 10×Roul), 2d. D.L.R. (P 10)

The 4d. (W **2**. P 11½–12½) with black overprint is known showing the stop omitted after "O".

P.S. (Private Secretary)

Optd in red. W **2**. 1d. (Roul), 2d. (Roul), 4d. (Roul), 6d. (Roul), 1s. (Roul)

Optd in black. (*a*) W **2**. 1d. (P 11½–12½×Roul), 1d. (P 10), 1d. (P 10), 2d. D.L.R. (in black) on 4d. (P 11½–12½), 3d. (in red) on 4d. (P 10), 3d. (in black) on 4d. (P 10), 4d. (P 11½–12½×Roul), 4d. (P 10), 4d. (P 11½–12½×Roul), 6d. (Roul), 6d. (P 11½–12½×Roul), 6d. (P 11½–12½), 6d. (P 10), 9d. (Roul), 9d. (P 11½–12½) 10d. on 9d. (P 10), 10d. on 9d. (P 10×11½–12½), 1s. (P 11½–12½×Roul)

(*b*) W **7**. P 10. 2d. D.L.R.

(*c*) W **10**. 2d. D.L.R. (Roul), 2d. D.L.R. (P 10)

P.W. (Public Works)

Optd in red without stop after "W". W **2**. Roul. 2d., 6d., 1s.

Optd in black. (*a*) W **2**. 2d. D.L.R. (Roul), 4d. (P 10), 6d. (Roul), 6d. (P 11½–12½), 1s. (P 11½–12½×Roul)

(*b*) W **10**. 2d. D.L.R. (Roul), 2d. D.L.R. (P 10)

R.B. (Road Board)

Optd in red. W **2**. 1d. (Roul), 2d. (Roul), 4d. (P 11½–12½), 6d. (Roul), 1s. (Roul)

Optd in blue without stops. W **10**. Roul. 2d D.L.R

Optd in black. (*a*) W **2**. 1d. (P 11½–12½×Roul), 1d. (P 10), 4d. (Roul), 4d. (P 10), 6d. (P 10), 2s. (Roul)

(*b*) W **7**. P 10. 2d. D.L.R.

(*c*) W **10**. 2d. D.L.R. (Roul), 2d. (D.L.R.) (P 10×Roul), 2d. D.L.R. (P 10)

The 6d. (W **2**. Roul) with red overprint is known showing the stop omitted after "B".

R.G. (Registrar-General)

Optd in red. W **2**. Roul. 2d., 6d., 1s.

Optd in blue. (*a*) W **2**. Roul×P 11½–12½×Roul. 6d.

(*b*) W **10**. 2d. D.L.R. (P 11½–12½), 2d. D.L.R. (P 11½–12½×Roul)

Optd in black. (*a*) W **2**. 2d. D.L.R. (Roul), 6d. (P 10), 6d. (P 10×11½–12½), 1s. (P 11½–12½ x Roul), 1s. (P 10)

(*b*) W **7**. P 10. 2d. D.L.R.

(*c*) W **10**. 2d. D.L.R. (Roul), 2d. D.L.R. (P 10), 2d. D.L.R. (P 10×11½–12½)

The 2d. (W **2**. Roul) with red overprint is known showing "C" for "G".

S. (Sheriff)

Optd in red. W **2**. Roul. 2d., 6d.

Optd in blue. W **10**. Roul. 2d. D.L.R.

Optd in black. (*a*) W **2**. 6d. (Roul), 6d. (P 11½–12½×Roul), 6d. (P 11½–12½), 6d. (P 10)

(*b*) W **10**. 2d. D.L.R. (Roul), 2d. D.L.R. (P 10×Roul), 2d. D.L.R. (P 10)

S.C. (Supreme Court)

Optd in red. W **2**. Roul. 2d. 6d.

Optd in black. W **10**. P 10. 2d. D.L.R.

S.G. (Surveyor-General)

Optd in red. W **2**. 2d. (Roul), 4d. (P 11½–12½), 6d. (Roul)

Optd in blue. (*a*) W **2**. Roul. 4d.

(*b*) W **10**. Roul. 2d. D.L.R.

Optd in black. (*a*) W **2**. 2d. D.L.R. (Roul), 4d. (P 11½–12½), 4d. (P 10) 4d. (P 10×11½–12½), 6d. (P 11½–12½×Roul), 6d. (P 11½–12½), 6d. (P 10), 6d. (P 10×11½–12½)

(*b*) W **7**. P 10. 2d. D.L.R.

(*c*) W **10**. 2d. D.L.R. (Roul), 2d. D.L.R. (P 11½–12½), 2d. D.L.R. (P 10×Roul), 2d. D.L.R. (P 10), 2d. D.L R (P 10)

The 2d. (W **7** and W **10**. P 10) with black overprint are known showing "C" for "G".

S.M. (Stipendiary Magistrate)

Optd in red. W **2**. Roul. 1d., 2d., 4d., 1s.

Optd in blue. (*a*) W **2**. Roul. 2d., 4d., 6d.

(*b*) W **10**. Roul. 2d. D.L.R.

Optd in black. (*a*) W **2**. 1d. (P 11½–12½), 1d. (P 10), 2d. D.L.R. (Roul), 4d. (Roul), 4d. (P 11½–12½×Roul), 4d. (P 11½–12½), 4d. (P 10), 4d. (P 10×11½–12½), 6d. (P 11½–12½×Roul), 6d. (P 11½–12½), 6d. (P 10), 6d. (P 10×11½–12½), 1s. (P 11½–12½×Roul)

(*b*) W **7**. P 10. 2d. D.L.R.

(*c*) W **10**. 2d. D.L.R. (Roul), 2d. D.L.R. (P 11½–12½), 2d. D.L.R. (P 10×Roul) 2d. D.L.R. (P 10), 2d. D.L.R. (P 10×11½–12½)

The 2d. and 4d. (both W **2**. Roul) with red overprint are known showing the stop omitted after "M".

S.T. (Superintendent of Telegraphs)

Optd in red. W **2**. Roul. 2d. D.L.R., 6d.

Optd in blue. W **10**. Roul. 2d. D.L.R.

Optd in black. (*a*) W **2**. Roul. 2d. D.L.R., 6d.

(*b*) W **7**. P 10. 2d. D.L.R.

(*c*) W **10**. 2d. D.L.R. (Roul), 2d. D.L.R. (P 10×Roul), 2d. D.L.R. (P 10)

The 2d. and 6d. (both W **2**. Roul) with red overprint are known showing the stop omitted after "T".

T. (Treasury)

Optd in red. W **2**. 1d. (Roul), 2d. (Roul), 4d. (P 11½–12½×Roul), 6d. (Roul), 1s. (Roul)

Optd in blue. (*a*) W **2**. Roul. 1d., 4d., 6d.

(*b*) W **10**. Roul. 2d. D.L.R.

Optd in black. (*a*) W **2**. 1d. (P 10), 2d. D.L.R. (Roul), 4d. (Roul), 4d. (P 11½–12½), 4d. (P 10), 6d. (Roul), 6d. (P 11½–12½), 1s. (P 11½–12½×Roul), 1s. (P 10×11½–12½), 2s. (Roul), 2s. (P 11½–12½), 2s. (P 10×11½–12½)

(*b*) W **7**. P 10. 2d. D.L.R.

(*c*) W **10**. 2d. D.L.R. (Roul), 2d. D.L.R. (P 10)

T.R. (Titles Registration)

Optd in black. (*a*) W **2**. 4d. (P 11½–12½), 4d. (P 10×11½–12½), 6d. (P 11½–12½), 1s. (P 11½–12½)

(*b*) W **10**. P 10. 2d. D.L.R.

V. (Volunteers)

Optd in black. (*a*) W **2**. 4d. (P 10×11½–12½), 6d. (P 11½–12½), 1s. (P 11½–12½)

(*b*) W **10**. P 10. 2d. D.L.R.

(*c*) W **10**. 2d. D.L.R. (Roul), 2d. D.L.R. (P 10×Roul), 2d. D.L.R. (P 10)

The 2d. (W **10**. P 10×Roul) overprinted in black is only known showing the stop omitted after "V".

VA. (Valuator of Runs)

Optd in black without stop after "V". (*a*) W **2**. Roul. 4d.

(*b*) W **10**. P 10. 2d. D.L.R.

VN. (Vaccination)

Optd in black without stop after "V". W **2**. 4d. (P 10), 4d. (P 10×11½–12½)

W. (Waterworks)

Optd in red. W **2**. Roul. 2d.

Optd in black. W **10**. 2d. D.L.R. (Roul), 2d. D.L.R. (P 10)

The 2d. (W **2**. Roul) with red overprint is known showing the stop omitted after "W".

B. General

O.S. **O.S.**

(O **1**) (O **2**)

1874–77. *Optd with Type* O **1**. W **2**.

		(a) P 10.		
O1	3	4d. dull purple (18.2.74)	£1200	£300
		(b) P 11½–12½×10.		
O2	1	1d. green (2.1.74)	—	£275
O3	3	4d. dull violet (12.2.75)	70·00	5·00
O4	1	6d. Prussian blue (20.10.75)	85·00	9·50
O4a	3	2s. rose-pink		
O5		2s. carmine (3.12.76)	—	£110

		(c) P 11½–12½.		
O6	1	1d. deep yellow-green (30.1.74)	£1300	£250
		a. Printed on both sides	—	£800
O7	3	3d. on 4d. ultramarine (26.6.77)	£2750	£1300
		a. No stop after "S"	—	£1800
O8		4d. dull violet (13.7.74)	50·00	6·50
		a. No stop after "S"	—	42·00
O9	1	6d. bright blue (31.8.75)	£100	13·00
		a. No stop after "S"	—	£120
O10		6d. Prussian blue (27.3.74)	90·00	7·50
		a. No stop after "S"	—	50·00
O11	4	9d. red-purple (22.3.76)	£1400	£750
		a. No stop after "S"	£2000	£1100
O12	1	1s. red-brown (5.8.74)	70·00	6·00
		a. No stop after "S"	—	£120
		b. "O.S." double	£180	50·00
O13	3	2s. crimson-carmine (13.7.75)	£150	22·00
		a. No stop after "S"	—	80·00
		b. No stops	—	95·00
		c. Stops at top of letters		

1876–85. *Optd with Type* O **1**. W **8**.

		(a) P 10.		
O14	1	6d. bright blue (1879)	90·00	13·00
		(b) P 10×11½–12½, 11½–12½×10, or compound.		
O15	3	4d. violet-slate (24.1.78)	70·00	6·50
O16		4d. plum (29.11.81)	38·00	2·75
O17		4d. deep mauve	38·00	2·50
		a. No stop after "S"	£120	32·00
		b. No stop after "O"		
		c. "O.S." double		
		d. "O.S." inverted	—	£150
O18	1	6d. bright blue (1877)	75·00	4·75
		a. "O.S." inverted		
		b. No stop after "S"		
O19		6d. bright ultramarine (27.3.85)	70·00	4·50
		a. "O.S." inverted		
		b. No stop after "S"		
		c. "O.S." double, one inverted	—	£325
		d. No stop after "S"	—	42·00
		e. No stops after "O" & "S"		
O20	1	1s. red-brown (27.3.83)	55·00	7·00
		a. "O.S." inverted		
		b. No stop after "S"	—	48·00
O21	3	2s. carmine (16.3.81)	£120	8·00
		a. "O.S." double	—	£200
		b. No stop after "S"	—	65·00
		(c) P 11½–12½.		
O22	3	3d. on 4d. ultramarine	£2750	
O23		4d. violet-slate (14.3.76)	£140	13·00
O24		4d. deep mauve (19.8.79)	55·00	4·75
		a. "O.S." inverted		
		b. "O.S." double, one inverted		
		c. No stop after "S"	—	38·00
O25	1	6d. Prussian blue (6.77)	75·00	7·00
		a. "O.S." double	—	85·00
		b. "O.S." inverted		
O26	4	8d. on 9d. brown (9.11.76)	£1900	£900
		a. "O.S." double	£2500	
		b. "O" only	—	£1100
O26c		9d. purple	£3500	
O27	1	1s. red-brown (12.2.78)	35·00	8·50
		a. "O.S." inverted	£275	
		b. No stop after "S"	£200	48·00
O28		1s. lake-brown (8.11.83)	42·00	3·50
O29	3	2s. rose-carmine (12.8.85)	£120	8·50
		a. "O.S." double	—	£120
		b. "O.S." inverted	—	£130
		c. No stop after "S"	—	50·00

1891–1903. *Optd with Type* O **2**.

		(a) W **8**. P 11½–12½.		
O30	1	1s. lake-brown (18.4.91)	50·00	10·00
O31		1s. Vandyke brown	60·00	7·00
O32		1s. dull brown (2.7.96)	42·00	5·50
		a. No stop after "S"	—	65·00
O33		1s. sepia (large holes) (4.1.02)	35·00	5·50
		a. "O.S." double	—	£225
O34	3	2s. carmine (26.6.00)	85·00	15·00
		a. No stop after "S"		
		(b) W **8**. P 10×11½–12½.		
O35	3	2s. rose-carmine (9.11.95)	75·00	10·00
		a. "O.S." double	£160	
		b. "O.S." double		
		(c) W **10**. P 11½–12½.		
O36	1	1s. dull brown (1902)	55·00	15·00

1874–76. *Optd with Type* O **1**. W **10**.

		(a) P 10.		
O37	11	1d. blue-green (30.9.75)	90·00	23·00
		a. "O.S." inverted		
		b. No stop after "S"		
O38	12	2d. orange-red (18.2.74)	22·00	3·50
		a. No stop after "S"	—	30·00
		b. "O.S." double		
		(b) P 10×11½–12½, 11½–12½×10, or compound.		
O39	11	1d. blue-green (16.9.75)	—	£275
		a. No stop after "S"		
O40	12	2d. orange-red (27.9.76)	—	12·00
		(c) P 11½–12½		
O41	11	1d. blue-green (13.8.75)	—	30·00
		a. "O.S." inverted		
O42	12	2d. orange-red (20.5.74)	—	£100

1876–80. *Optd with Type* O **1**. W **13**.

		(a) P 10.		
O43	11	1d. blue-green (2.10.76)	15·00	1·00
		a. "O.S." inverted	—	50·00
		b. "O.S." double	80·00	45·00
		c. "O.S." double, one inverted		

		d. No stops	—	30·00
		e. No stop after "O"	—	14·00
		f. No stop after "S"	—	14·00
		g. *Deep green*	20·00	1·00
		ga. No stop after "S"	—	50·00
O44	**12**	2d. orange-red (21.9.77)	9·00	1·00
		a. "O.S." inverted	—	24·00
		b. "O.S." double	85·00	40·00
		c. "O.S." double, one inverted......		
		d. "O.S." double, both inverted	£130	
		e. No stops	—	60·00
		f. No stop after "O"	—	20·00
		g. No stop after "S"		
		h. *Dull brick-red*.	40·00	1·00

(b) P 10×11½–12½, 11½–12½×10 or compound.

O45	**11**	1d. deep green (14.8.80)	—	35·00
		a. "O.S." inverted		
O46	**12**	2d. orange-red (6.4.78)	60·00	12·00
		a. "O.S." inverted	—	£120
		b. No stop after "S"	—	55·00

(c) P 11½–12½.

| O47 | **12** | 2d. orange-red (15.7.80) .... | — | 70·00 |

1882 (20 Feb). *No. 181 optd with Type O* **1**.

| O48 | **11** | ½d. on 1d. blue-green .... | 65·00 | 17·00 |
| | | a. "O.S." inverted .... | | |

1888 (15 Nov)–**91**. *Nos. 184 and 185a optd with Type O* **1**. *P 10.*

O49	**17**	4d. pale violet (24.1.91)	70·00	5·00
O50	**18**	6d. blue	27·00	1·25
		a. "O.S." double		
		b. No stop after "S"		

1891. *Nos. 229b and 231a/2 optd with Type O* **1**.

(a) P 10.

O51	**17**	2½d. on 4d. deep green (Br.) (1 Aug)	70·00	10·00
		a. "2" and "½" closer together	—	45·00
		b. "O.S." inverted		
		c. "O.S." double		
		d. "OS." omitted (in vert pair with normal)		
		e. No stop after "S"		

(b) P 10×11½–12½ or 11½–12½×10.

| O52 | **17** | 2½d. on 4d. deep green (Br.) (1 Oct) .... | 75·00 | 17·00 |

(c) P 11½–12½.

| O53 | **17** | 2½d. on 4d. deep green (Br.) (1 June)......... | £140 | 70·00 |

1891–96. *Optd with Type O* **2**. *W* **13**.

(a) P 10.

O54	**11**	1d. deep green (22.4.91)	26·00	2·00
		a. "O.S." double	75·00	40·00
		b. "O.S." double, one inverted......	48·00	11·00
		c. No stop after "S"	—	4·25
		d. Blackish blue opt	£200	
O55	**12**	2d. orange-red (22.4.91)	26·00	1·75
		a. "O.S." double		
		b. "O.S." double, both inverted		
		c. No stop after "S"	—	13·00

(b) P 15.

O56	**11**	1d. green (8.9.94)	14·00	1·25
		a. "O.S." double		
		b. No stop after "S"		
O57	**12**	2d. orange-red (16.6.94)	14·00	60
		a. "O.S." double	—	30·00
		b. "O.S." inverted	—	23·00

(c) P 13.

O58	**11**	1d. green (20.5.95)	23·00	60
		a. No stop after "S"	70·00	10·00
O59	**12**	2d. orange-red (11.2.96)	23·00	50
		a. "O.S." double	£110	
		b. No stop after "S"	65·00	10·00

1891–99. *Optd with Type O* **2**. *W* **13** *(sideways on ½d.).*

(a) P 10.

O60	**15**	½d. brown (2.5.94)	24·00	5·50
		a. No stop after "S"	60·00	30·00
O61	**17**	4d. pale violet (13.2.91)	50·00	3·50
		a. "O.S." double		
		b. "S." omitted	—	75·00
		d. *Aniline violet* (31.8.93)	50·00	4·50
		da. "O.S." double		
		dc. No stop after "S"		
O62	**18**	6d. blue (4.4.93)	22·00	2·50
		a. No stop after "S"		
		b. Blackish blue opt		

(b) P 10×11½–12½.

| O63 | **15** | ½d. brown (26.3.95) .... | 20·00 | 7·50 |

(c) P 11½–12½.

| O64 | **15** | ½d. red-brown (13.6.91) .... | 48·00 | 11·00 |

(d) P 15.

O65	**15**	½d. pale brown (8.6.95)	35·00	10·00
O66	**17**	4d. slate-violet (4.4.95)	65·00	4·50
		a. "O.S." double	£200	40·00
O67	**18**	6d. blue (20.9.93)	29·00	4·00

(e) P 13.

O68	**15**	½d. deep brown (17.5.98)	22·00	6·00
		a. Opt triple, twice sideways	£180	
O69	**17**	4d. violet (12.96)	70·00	3·00
		a. "O.S." double	£160	38·00
		b. No stop after "S"	£160	28·00
O70	**18**	6d. blue (13.9.99)	35·00	2·00
		a. No stop after "S"	£100	55·00

1891–95. *Nos. 229b, 230a and 231a optd with Type O* **2**.

| O71 | **17** | 2½d. on 4d. deep green (Br.) (18.8.94) | 40·00 | 15·00 |
| | | a. Fraction bar omitted .... | | |

		b. "2" and "½" closer together	95·00	40·00
		c. "O.S." inverted	£225	
		d. No stop after "S"	—	45·00
O72	**18**	5d. on 6d. deep brown (C.) (2.12.91)	45·00	18·00
		a. No stop after "5D"	£200	
		b. No stop after "S"	£110	45·00

(b) P 10×11½–12½.

| O73 | **17** | 2½d. on 4d. deep green (Br.) (17.9.95) .... | — | 55·00 |
| | | a. "O.S." double .... | | |

1897–1901. *Nos. 235/6 and 238a optd with Type O* **2**.

(a) P 15.

| O74 | **23** | 5d. brown-purple (29.3.01) .... | 70·00 | 12·00 |

(b) P 13

O75	**22**	2½d. violet-blue (5.7.97)	50·00	7·00
		a. No stop after "s"	—	38·00
O76	**23**	5d. purple (29.9.01)	70·00	16·00
		a. No stop after "S"		

O. S.

(O **3**)

1899–1901. *Optd with Type O* **3**. *W* **13**. *P 13.*

O80	**24**	½d. yellow-green (12.2.00)	16·00	6·00
		a. "O.S." inverted	70·00	
		b. No stop after "S"	42·00	
O81	**11**	1d. rosine (22.9.99)	15·00	1·60
		a. "O.S." inverted	60·00	40·00
		b. "O.S." double	†	£250
		c. No stop after "S"	48·00	16·00
O82	**12**	2d. bright violet (1.6.00)	19·00	80
		a. "O.S." inverted	50·00	25·00
		b. "O.S." double		
		c. No stop after "S"	40·00	15·00
O83	**22**	2½d. indigo (2.10.01)	55·00	19·00
		a. "O.S." inverted	—	80·00
		b. No stop after "S"	£160	
O84	**17**	4d. violet (18.11.00)	50·00	5·50
		a. "O.S." inverted	£200	
		b. No stop after "S"	£140	
O85	**18**	6d. blue (8.10.00)	24·00	5·50
		a. No stop after "S"	70·00	

1891 (May). *Optd as Type O* **3** *but wider. W* **13**. *P 10.*

| O86 | **19** | 2s.6d. pale violet .... | £3750 | £3250 |
| O87 | | 5s. pale rose .... | £3750 | £3250 |

Only one sheet (60) of each of these stamps was printed.

The use of stamps overprinted "O S" was made invalid by the Posts and Telegraph Act of 1 November 1902.

South Australia became part of the Commonwealth of Australia on 1 January 1901.

TASMANIA

SPECIMEN OVERPRINTS. Those listed are from U.P.U. distributions between 1892 and 1904. Further "Specimen" overprints exist, but these were used for other purposes.

| 1 | 2 | 3 |

(Eng C.W. Coard. Recess H. and C. Best at the *Courier* newspaper, Hobart)

1853 (1 Nov). *Twenty-four varieties in four rows of six each. No wmk. Imperf.*

(a) Medium soft yellowish paper with all lines clear and distinct.

| 1 | **1** | 1d. pale blue .... | £5000 | £1000 |
| 2 | | 1d. blue .... | £5000 | £1000 |

(b) Thin hard white paper with lines of the engraving blurred and worn.

| 3 | **1** | 1d. pale blue .... | £4750 | £900 |
| 4 | | 1d. blue .... | £4750 | £900 |

1853 (1 Nov)–**54**. *No wmk. Imperf. In each plate there are twenty-four varieties in four rows of six each.*

(a) Plate I. Finely engraved. All lines in network and background thin, clear, and well defined. (1853).

(i) First state of the plate, brilliant colours.

5	**2**	4d. bright red-orange	£4000	£700
		a. Double impression		
6		4d. bright brownish orange............	—	£850

(ii) Second state of plate, with blurred lines and worn condition of the central background.

7	**2**	4d. red-orange	£3000	£450
8		4d. orange	£2750	£425
9		4d. pale orange	£2750	£425

(b) Plate II. Coarse engraving, lines in network and background thicker and blurred (Dec. 1854).

10	**2**	4d. orange	£2750	£400
		a. Double print, one albino		
11		4d. dull orange	£2750	£350
12		4d. yellowish orange	£2750	£350

In the 4d. Plate I, the outer frame-line is thin all round. In Plate II it is, by comparison with other parts, thicker in the lower left angle.

The 4d. is known on vertically laid paper from proof sheets. Examples from Plate I have the lines close together and those from Plate II wide apart (Price £5000 *unused*).

In 1879 reprints were made of the 1d. in blue and the 4d., Plate I, in brownish yellow, on thin, tough, white wove paper, and perforated 11½. In 1887, a reprint from the other plate of the 4d. was made was made in reddish brown and black on thick white paper, imperforate, and in 1889 of the 1d. in blue and in black, and of the 4d. (both plates) in yellow and in black on white card, imperforate. As these three plates were defaced after the stamps had been superseded, all these reprints show two, or three thick strokes across the Queen's head.

All three plates were destroyed in July 1950.

PERKINS BACON "CANCELLED". For notes on these handstamps, showing "CANCELLED" between horizontal bars forming an oval, see Catalogue Introduction.

(Eng W. Humphrys, after water-colour sketch by E. Corbould. Recess P.B.)

1855 (17 Aug–16 Sept). *Wmk Large Star. W w* **1**. *Imperf.*

14	**3**	1d. carmine (16.9) (H/S "CANCELLED" in oval £10000)	£5500	£800
15		2d. deep green (16.9)	£2500	£500
16		2d. green (16.9) (H/S "CANCELLED" in oval £11000)	£2500	£450
17		4d. deep blue	£1800	£100
18		4d. blue (H/S "CANCELLED" in oval £10000)	£1800	£120

Proofs of the 1d. and 4d. on thick paper, *without watermark*, are sometimes offered as the issued stamps. The 6d. dull lilac on this watermark was prepared, but not issued. Examples exist from a creased proof sheet (*Price £750 unused*).

(Recess H. and C. Best, Hobart, from P.B. plates)

1856 (Apr)–**57**. *No wmk. Imperf.*

(a) Thin white paper.

19	**3**	1d. pale brick-red (4.56)	£6500	£600
20		2d. dull emerald-green (1.57)	£7500	£900
21		4d. deep blue (5.57)	£850	£110
22		4d. blue (5.57)	£750	£110
23		4d. pale blue (5.57)	—	£140

(b) Pelure paper.

| 24 | **3** | 1d. deep red-brown (11.56) .... | £5000 | £750 |

| 4 | 7 | 8 |

(Recess H. Best (August 1857–May 1859), J. Davies (August 1859–March 1862), J. Birchall (March 1863), M. Hood (October 1863–April 1864), Govt Printer (from July 1864), all from P.B. plates)

1857 (Aug)–**69**. *Wmk double-lined numerals "1", "2" or "4" as W* **4** *on appropriate value. Imperf.*

25	**3**	1d. deep red-brown	£500	38·00
26		1d. pale red-brown	£350	28·00
27		1d. brick-red (1863)	£170	25·00
28		1d. dull vermilion (1865)	£110	23·00
29		1d. carmine (1867)	£120	23·00
		a. Double print	—	£140
		b. Error. Wmkd "2" (1869)		
30		2d. dull emerald-green	—	£110
31		2d. green	—	50·00
		a. double print	—	£170
32		2d. yellow-green	£400	95·00
33		2d. deep green (1858)	£350	£650
34		2d. slate-green (1860)	£190	75·00
35		4d. deep blue	—	80·00
		a. Double print	—	£170
36		4d. pale blue	£160	24·00
37		4d. blue	£160	26·00
		a. Double print	—	£170
38		4d. bright blue	£160	26·00
		a. Printed on both sides	†	
		b. Double print	—	£140
39		4d. cobalt-blue	—	85·00

Printings before July 1864 were all carried out at the *Courier* printing works which changed hands several times during this period.

CANCELLATIONS. Beware of early Tasmanian stamps with pen-cancellations cleaned off and faked postmarks applied.

(Recess P.B.)

1858. Wmk double-lined numerals "6" or "12" as W **4**. Imperf.

40	**7**	6d. dull lilac (H/S "CANCELLED" in oval £9000)	£700	85·00
41	**8**	1s. verm (shades) (H/S "CANCELLED" in oval £7500)	£550	75·00

(Recess J. Davies (March 1860), J. Birchall (April 1863), Govt Printer (from February 1865), all from P.B. plates)

1860 (Mar)–**67**. Wmk double-lined "6" as W **4**. Imperf.

44	**7**	6d. dull slate-grey	£300	65·00
45		6d. grey		70·00
46		6d. grey-violet (4.63)	£200	65·00
		a. Double print		£300
47		6d. dull cobalt (2.65)	£450	£100
48		6d. slate-violet (2.65)	£325	55·00
49		6d. reddish mauve (4.67)	£700	£150

In 1871 reprints were made of the 6d. (in mauve) and the 1s. on white wove paper, and perforated 11½. They are found with or without "REPRINT". In 1889 they were again reprinted on white card, imperforate. These later impressions are also found overprinted "REPRINT" and perforated 11½.

PERFORATED ISSUES. From 1 October 1857 the Tasmania Post Office only supplied purchasers requiring five or more complete sheets of stamps. The public obtained their requirements, at face value, from licensed stamp vendors, who obtained their stocks at a discount from the Post Office.

From 1863 onwards a number of the stamp vendors applied their own roulettes or perforations. The Hobart firm of J. Walch & Sons achieved this so successfully that they were given an official contract in July 1869 to perforate sheets for the Post Office. The Government did not obtain a perforating machine until late in 1871.

1863–**71**. Double-lined numeral watermarks. Various unofficial roulettes and perforations.

(a) By J. Walch & Sons, Hobart.

(i) Roulette about 8, often imperf × roul (1863–68).

50	**3**	1d. brick-red		£250
51		1d. carmine	£425	£150
52		2d. yellow-green		£650
53		2d. slate green		
54		4d. pale blue		£225
55	**7**	6d. dull lilac		£275
56	**8**	1s. vermilion		£750

(ii) P 10 (1864–69).

57	**3**	1d. brick-red	80·00	30·00
58		1d. dull vermilion	80·00	£308
		a. Double print	†	
59		1d. carmine	70·00	28·00
60		2d. yellow-green	£425	£120
61		2d. slate-green	£425	£180
62		4d. pale blue	£150	15·00
63		4d. blue	£150	15·00
		a. Double print		£130
64	**7**	6d. grey-violet	£225	22·00
65		6d. dull cobalt	£325	80·00
66		6d. slate-violet		29·00
67		6d. reddish mauve	£400	80·00
68	**8**	1s. vermilion	£170	28·00
		Imperf vert (horiz pair)		

(iii) P 12 (1865–71—from July 1869 under contract to the Post Office).

69	**3**	1d. dull vermilion	75·00	
		a. Double print	£750	—
70		1d. carmine	60·00	12·00
		a. Error. Wmkd "2" (pen cancel £110)		£1500
71		2d. yellow-green	£225	65·00
72		4d. deep blue	£120	20·00
73		4d. blue	£120	22·00
74		4d. cobalt-blue		50·00
75	**7**	6d. slate-violet	£170	28·00
		Imperf between (vert pair)		
76		6d. reddish mauve	90·00	40·00
		a. Imperf between (vert or horiz pair) (pen cancel £200)		
77	**8**	1s. vermilion	£170	38·00
		a. Double print	—	£170
		b. Imperf between (horiz pair) (pen cancel £200)		

(iv) Perf compound 10×12 (1865–69).

78	**3**	1d. carmine		£1800
79		4d. blue		£1400

(b) P 12½ by R. Harris, Launceston (1864–68).

80	**3**	1d. brick-red	85·00	35·00
81		1d. dull vermilion	80·00	28·00
82		1d. carmine	48·00	13·00
83		2d. yellow-green	£400	£130
84		2d. slate-green	£325	£150
85		4d. blue	£190	50·00
86		4d. bright blue	£190	50·00
87	**7**	6d. dull cobalt	£350	95·00
88		6d. slate-violet	£250	55·00
89		6d. reddish mauve	£425	£120
90	**8**	1s. vermilion	£325	£100

(c) Imperf×oblique roulette 11½ at Oatlands (1866).

91	**3**	4d. blue	—	£600
91a	**7**	6d. dull cobalt	†	

(d) Oblique roulette 10–10½, possibly at Deloraine (1867).

92	**3**	1d. brick-red	—	£500
93		1d. carmine	£1400	£425
94		2d. yellow-green	—	£650
95		4d. bright blue	—	£600
96	**7**	6d. grey-violet	—	£900

(e) Oblique roulette 14–15, probably at Cleveland (1867–69).

97	**3**	1d. brick-red	—	£600
98		1d. dull vermilion	—	£600
99		1d. carmine	—	£600

100		2d. yellow-green	—	£700
101		4d. pale blue	—	£550
102	**7**	6d. grey-violet	—	£900
103	**8**	1s. vermilion	—	£1100

(f) Pin-perf 5½ to 9½ at Longford (1867).

104	**3**	1d. carmine	£550	£140
105		2d. yellow-green		
106		4d. bright blue		£275
107	**7**	6d. grey-violet		£250
108		6d. reddish mauve		£650
109	**8**	1s. vermilion		

(g) Pin-perf 12 at Oatlands (1867).

110	**3**	4d. blue		

(h) Pin-perf 13½ to 14½ (1867).

111	**3**	1d. brick-red		£350
112		1d. dull vermilion		£350
113		1d. carmine		
114		2d. yellow-green		£500
115		4d. pale blue		£300
116	**7**	6d. grey-violet		£600
117	**8**	1s. vermilion		

(j) Serrated perf 19 at Hobart (1868–69).

118	**3**	1d. carmine (pen-cancel £9)	£400	£150
119		2d. yellow-green		£425
120		4d. deep blue	£950	£140
121		4d. cobalt-blue		£140
122	**7**	6d. slate-violet		£600
123	**8**	1s. vermilion		

(k) Roul 4½, possibly at Macquarie River (1868).

124	**3**	4d. blue		
125	**7**	6d. reddish mauve		
126	**8**	1s. vermilion		

An example of the 1d. carmine is known perforated 10 on three sides and serrated 19 on the fourth.

For stamps perforated 11½ or 12 by the Post Office see Nos. 134a/43.

(Typo Govt Printer, Hobart, from plates made by D.L.R.)

1870 (1 Nov)–**71**. Wmk single-lined numerals W **12** (2d.), **13** (1d., 4d.) or **14** (1d., 10d.).

(a) P 12 by J. Walch & Sons.

127	**11**	1d. rose-red (wmk "10")	55·00	10·00
		a. Imperf (pair)	£750	£750
		b. Deep rose-red	65·00	8·00
128		1d. rose-red (wmk "4") (3.71)	65·00	18·00
		a. Imperf (pair)	—	£700
129		2d. yellow-green	80·00	7·00
		a. Imperf (pair)		
		b. Blue-green	85·00	7·00
130		4d. blue	£750	£425
131		10d. black	24·00	28·00
		a. Imperf (pair)	£350	

(b) P 11½ by the Post Office (1871).

132	**11**	1d. rose-red (wmk "10")	£1100	
133		2d. yellow-green	£140	7·00
		a. Blue-green	75·00	5·00
		ab. Double print		
134		10d. black	28·00	28·00

The above were printed on paper obtained from New South Wales. See also Nos. 144/55, 156/8, 159/66, 170/4, 226/7, 242 and 255/6.

(Recess P.B.)

1871. Wmk double-lined numeral "12". P 11½ by the Post Office.

134a	**7**	1s. vermilion	

(Recess Govt Printer, Hobart)

1871–**91**. Double-lined numeral watermarks as W **4**. Perforated by the Post Office.

(a) P 11½.

135	**7**	6d. dull lilac	£110	22·00
136		6d. lilac	£100	22·00
		a. Imperf between (pair)		£800
137		6d. deep slate-lilac (3.75)	£100	22·00
		a. Imperf (pair)	—	£600
138		6d. bright violet (5.78)	£100	32·00
		a. Double print		£130
		b. Imperf between (horiz pair)	£1300	
139		6d. dull reddish lilac (10.79)	95·00	40·00
140	**8**	1s. brown-red (1.73)	£130	48·00
		a. Imperf between (horiz pair)		
141		1s. orange-red (3.75)	£120	48·00
141a		1s. orange (5.78)		

(b) P 12.

142	**7**	6d. reddish purple (1884)	95·00	20·00
		a. Imperf between (horiz pair)	£850	
143		6d. dull claret (7.91)	29·00	13·00

The perforation machine used on Nos. 142/3 was previously owned by J. Walch and Sons and passed to the ownership of the Government in 1884. It may have been used to perforate leftover sheets of previous printings.

15	**16**

"Wedge" flaw (Right pane R. 10/6)

(Typo Govt Printer, Hobart, from plates made by D.L.R.)

1871 (25 Mar)–**78**. W **15**.

(a) P 11½.

144	**11**	1d. rose (5.71)	8·00	1·00
		a. Imperf (pair) (pen cancel £40)	—	£800
		b. Bright rose	8·00	1·00
		c. Carmine	9·50	1·00
		d. Pink	11·00	2·25
		e. Vermilion (4.75)	£250	75·00
		f. Wedge flaw	£170	32·00
145		2d. deep green (11.72)	35·00	1·00
		a. Blue-green	32·00	1·00
		b. Yellow-green (12.75)	£170	2·75
146		3d. pale red-brown	48·00	4·00
		a. Imperf (pair)	£350	
		b. Imperf horiz (vert pair)	£1500	
		c. Deep red-brown	48·00	4·50
		ca. Purple-brown (1.78)	48·00	4·00
		cb. Imperf (pair)	—	£750
		da. Brownish purple	48·00	4·00
147		4d. pale yellow (8.8.76)	70·00	21·00
		a. Ochre (7.78)	70·00	9·00
		b. Buff	60·00	9·50
148		9d. blue (2.10.71)	18·00	6·50
		a. Imperf (pair)	£300	
		b. Double print		
149		5s. purple (pen cancel £3.75)	£225	60·00
		a. Imperf (pair)		
		b. Mauve	£200	60·00

(b) P 12.

150	**11**	1d. rose	90·00	9·50
		a. Carmine	95·00	11·00
		b. Wedge flaw		75·00
151		2d. green	£550	£140
		a. Imperf (pair)		£950
152		3d. red-brown	90·00	17·00
		a. Deep red-brown	90·00	17·00
153		4d. buff	£275	18·00
154		9d. pale blue	29·00	
		a. Imperf between (horiz pair)	£1400	
155		5s. purple	£375	
		a. Mauve	£275	

(Type D.L.R.)

1878 (28 Oct). W **16**. P 14.

156	**11**	1d. carmine	4·25	75
		a. Rose-carmine	4·25	75
		b. Scarlet	5·00	75
157		2d. pale green	5·50	75
		a. Green	5·50	75
158		8d. dull purple-brown	14·00	5·00

Plate scratch (Left pane R. 10/1)

(Typo Govt Printer, Hobart (some printings of 1d. in 1891 by *Mercury* Press) from plates made by Victoria Govt Printer, Melbourne (½d.) or D.L.R. (others)).

1880 (Apr)–**91**. W **16** (sideways on 1d.).

(a) P 11½.

159	**11**	½d. orange (8.3.89)	3·00	3·00
		a. Deep orange	3·00	3·00
160		1d. dull red (14.2.89)	7·00	2·50
		a. Vermilion-red	5·50	2·50
		b. Wedge flaw	60·00	24·00
161		3d. red-brown	14·00	4·00
		a. Imperf (pair)	£225	
162		4d. deep yellow (1.83)	38·00	14·00
		a. Chrome-yellow	38·00	15·00
		b. Olive-yellow	£110	23·00
		c. Buff	32·00	9·50

(b) P 12.

163	**11**	½d. orange	2·25	3·75
		a. Deep orange	2·25	3·75
		ab. Wmk sideways		
164		1d. pink (1891)	20·00	£225
		a. Imperf (pair)	£200	
		b. Rosine	16·00	3·50
		c. Dull rosine	40·00	4·50
		ca. Imperf (pair)	£190	

165		d. Wedge flaw	£100	30·00
		3d. red-brown	8·00	4·50
		a. Imperf between (horiz pair)	£1000	
		b. Plate scratch	70·00	40·00
166		4d. deep yellow	75·00	15·00
		a. Chrome-yellow	90·00	14·00
		ab. Printed both sides	£800	

SPECIMEN AND PRESENTATION REPRINTS OF TYPE 11.
In 1871 the 1d., 2d., 3d., 4d. blue, 9d., 10d. and 5s. were reprinted on soft white wove paper to be followed, in 1879, by the 4d. yellow and 8d. on rough white wove. Both these reprintings were perforated 11½. In 1886 it was decided to overprint remaining stocks with the word "REPRINT".

In 1889 Tasmania commenced sending sample stamps to the U.P.U. in Berne and a further printing of the 4d. blue was made, imperforate, on white card. This, together with the 5s. in mauve on white card, both perforated 11½ and overprinted "REPRINT", were included in presentation sets supplied to members of the states' legislatures in 1901.

Halfpenny
(17)

d.
2½
(18) (2¼ mm between "d" and "2")

d.
2½
(19) (3½ mm between "d" and "2")

1889 (1 Jan). *No. 156b surch locally with T 17.*

167	11	½d. on 1d. scarlet	9·50	15·00
		a. "al" in "Half" printed sideways (R. 1/2)	£1100	£900

No. 167a occurred in a second printing and was later corrected.
A reprint on white card, perforated 11½ or imperforate, overprinted "REPRINT" was produced in 1901.

1891 (1 Jan–June). *Surch locally. W 16.*

(a) With T 18. P 11½.

168	11	2½d. on 9d. pale blue	10·00	4·25
		a. Surch double, one inverted	£450	£500
		b. Deep blue (May)	9·00	4·75

(b) With T 19. P 12.

169	11	2½d. on 9d. pale blue (June)	5·00	3·50
		a. Blue surch		

A reprint, using a third setting, perforated 11½ and overprinted "REPRINT" was produced in 1901.

(Typo Govt Printer, Hobart)

1891 (Apr–Aug). *W 15.*

(a) P 11½.

170	11	½d. orange	32·00	15·00
		a. Brown-orange	25·00	14·00
171		1d. rosine	17·00	7·00
		a. Wedge flaw	£130	48·00

(b) P 12.

172	11	½d. orange	26·00	20·00
		a. Imperf (pair)	£150	
173		1d. dull rosine	22·00	17·00
		a. Rosine	35·00	19·00
		b. Wedge flaw	£150	85·00
174		4d. bistre (Aug)	18·00	13·00

20 **21** **21a**

(Typo D.L.R.)

1892 (12 Feb)–**99**. *W 16. P 14.*

216	20	½d. orange and mauve (11.92)	1·75	1·00
217	21	2½d. purple	2·50	1·50
218	20	5d. pale blue and brown	6·00	2·50
219		6d. violet and black (11.92)	8·00	3·25
220	21	10d. purple-lake and deep green (30.1.99)	9·00	11·00
221	20	1s. rose and green (11.92)	8·00	2·75
222		2s.6d. brown and blue (11.92)	22·00	18·00
223		5s. lilac and red (3.2.97)	55·00	20·00
224		10s. mauve and brown (11.92)	10·00	70·00
225		£1 green and yellow (2.97)	£350	£300
216/25	*Set of 10*		£500	£375
216s/25s	Optd "Specimen" *Set of 10*		£400	

See also Nos. 243 and 257/8.

(Typo Govt Printer, Hobart)

1896. *W 16. P 12.*

226	11	4d. pale bistre	12·00	7·00
227		9d. pale blue	8·00	2·75
		a. Blue	8·50	3·25

22 Lake Marion

23 Mount Wellington

---

24 Hobart

25 Tasman's Arch

26 Spring River, Port Davey

27 Russell Falls

28 Mount Gould, Lake St. Clair

29 Dilston Fall

30

(Eng L. Phillips. Recess D.L.R.)

1899 (Dec)–**1900**. *W 30. P 14.*

229	22	½d. deep green (31.3.00)	8·50	6·50
230	23	1d. bright lake (13.12.99)*	5·50	1·75
231	24	2d. deep violet (15.12.99)*	14·00	1·75
232	25	2½d. indigo (1900)	20·00	3·75
233	26	3d. sepia (1900)	11·00	4·75
234	27	4d. deep orange-buff (1900)	17·00	7·50
235	28	5d. bright blue (31.3.00)	25·00	11·00
236	29	6d. lake (31.3.00)	25·00	22·00
229/36	*Set of 8*		£110	55·00
229s/36s	Optd "Specimen" *Set of 8*		£400	

*Earliest known postmark dates.
See also Nos. 237/9, 240/1, 245/8, 249/54, 259 and 261/2.

DIFFERENCES BETWEEN LITHOGRAPHED AND TYPOGRAPHED PRINTINGS OF TYPES 22/9

Lithographed *General appearance fine.*	Typographed *Comparatively crude and coarse appearance.*
½d. All "V over Crown" wmk.	All "Crown over A" wmk.
1d. The shading on the path on the right bank of the river consists of very fine dots. In printings from worn stones the dots hardly show. The shading on the white mountain is fine (or almost absent in many stamps).	The shading on the path is coarser, consisting of large dots and small patches of colour. The shading on the mountain is coarse, and clearly defined.
2d. Three rows of windows in large building on shore, at extreme left, against inner frame.	Two rows of windows.
3d. Clouds very white. Stars in corner ornaments have long points. Shading of corner ornaments is defined by a coloured outer line.	Clouds dark. Stars have short points. Shading of ornaments terminates against white background.
4d. Lithographed only.	
6d. No coloured dots at base of waterfall. Outer frame of value tablets is formed by outer line of design.	Coloured dots at base of waterfall. Thick line of colour between value tablets and outer line. Small break in inner frame below second "A" of "TASMANIA".

(Litho, using transfers from D.L.R. plates, Victoria Government Printing Office, Melbourne)

1902 (Jan)–**04**. *Wmk V over Crown, W w 10 (sideways on ½d., 2d.). P 12½.*

237	22	½d. green (2.03)	4·25	1·50
		a. Wmk upright	22·00	22·00
		b. Perf 11 (1904)	5·00	6·00
		c. Perf comp of 12½ and 11	£110	85·00
		d. Perf comp of 12½ and 12	£325	
		s. Optd "Specimen"	80·00	
238	23	1d. carmine-red	8·00	1·50
239	24	2d. deep reddish violet	7·50	70
		a. Perf 11	7·00	4·50
		c. Wmk upright (2.04)	45·00	11·00
		d. Deep rose-lilac (4.05)	14·00	50
		da. Perf 11	9·00	2·25
		db. Perf comp of 12½ and 11	£130	70·00
		s. Optd "Specimen"	80·00	

As the V and Crown paper was originally prepared for stamps of smaller size, portions of two or more watermarks appear on each stamp.

We only list the main groups of shades in this and the following issues. There are variations of shade in all values, particularly in the 2d. where there is a wide range, also in the 1d. in some issues.

(Typo, using electrotyped plates, Victoria Govt Ptg Office, Melbourne)

1902 (Oct)–**04**. *Wmk V over Crown, W w 10. P 12½.*

240	23	1d. pale red (wmk sideways)	13·00	1·75
		a. Perf 11	28·00	3·75
		b. Perf comp of 12½ and 11	£250	60·00
		c. Wmk upright (1.03)	27·00	8·00
		ca. Perf 11	38·00	10·00
		d. Rose-red (wmk upright) (4.03)	8·00	2·00
		db. Perf comp of 12½ and 11	£250	60·00
		ds. Optd "Specimen"	80·00	
241		1d. scarlet (wmk upright) (9.03)	6·50	1·50
		a. Perf 11	10·00	1·75
		b. Perf comp of 12½ and 11		
		c. Rose-scarlet (1904)	6·00	1·50
		ca. Perf 11	6·00	1·75
		cb. Perf comp of 12½ and 11	85·00	30·00

The 1d. scarlet of September 1903 was from new electrotyped plates which show less intense shading.

(Typo Victoria Govt Ptg Office, Melbourne)

1903 (Apr–Dec). *Wmk V over Crown, W w 10. P 12½.*

242	11	9d. blue (Apr)	9·00	3·50
		a. Perf 11	8·00	9·00
		b. Perf comp of 12½ and 11	£650	£650
		c. Wmk sideways	90·00	32·00
		d. Pale blue	11·00	6·50
		e. Bright blue	11·00	7·00
		f. Ultramarine	£400	
		g. Indigo	£170	
243	20	1s. rose and green (Dec)	20·00	5·50
		a. Perf 11	45·00	45·00
242s/3s	Optd "Specimen" *Set of 2*		£160	

1¹d.
½
(31)

ONE PENNY
(32)

1904 (29 Dec). *No. 218 surch with T 31.*

244	20	1½d. on 5d. pale blue and brown	1·25	1·00
		s. Optd "Specimen"	48·00	

Stamps with inverted surcharge or without surcharge *se-tenant* with stamps with normal surcharge were obtained irregularly and were not issued for postal use.

PRINTER. The Victoria Govt Ptg Office became the Commonwealth Stamp Printing Branch in March 1909.

(Litho, using transfers from D.L.R. plates, Victoria Govt Ptg Office, Melbourne)

1905 (Sep)–**12**. *Wmk Crown over A, W w 11 (sideways on horiz stamps). P 12½.*

245	24	2d. deep purple	6·00	55
		a. Perf 11	23·00	1·00
		b. Perf comp of 12½ and 11	22·00	5·00
		c. Perf comp of 12½ and 12	95·00	75·00
		d. Perf comp of 11 and 12	£160	£120
		e. Slate-lilac (1906)	7·50	55
		ea. Perf 11	27·00	1·00
		ed. Perf comp of 11 and 12	£160	£120
		ee. Perf comp of 12½ and 12		
		f. Reddish lilac (1907)	18·00	1·50
		fa. Perf 11	27·00	2·75
		fb. Perf comp of 12½ and 11	90·00	
246	26	3d. brown (1906)	8·50	4·25
		a. Perf 11 (9.05)	17·00	13·00
		b. Perf comp of 12½ and 11	£130	£140
247	27	4d. pale yellow-brown (3.07)	13·00	4·00
		a. Perf 11	30·00	9·00
		b. Orange-buff (5.09)	23·00	4·00
		ba. Perf 11	30·00	14·00
		bb. Perf comp of 12½ and 11	£275	£325
		c. Brown-ochre (wmk sideways). Perf 11 (6.11)	30·00	38·00
		ca. Perf comp of 12½ and 11	—	£450
		d. Orange-yellow (3.12)	15·00	22·00
		da. Perf 11	40·00	40·00
		db. Perf comp of 12½ and 11	£275	£325
248	29	6d. lake (7.08)	45·00	7·00
		a. Perf 11	70·00	7·50
		b. Perf comp of 12½ and 11	£250	£275

Stamps with perf compound of 12½ and 12 or 11 and 12 are found on sheets which were sent from Melbourne incompletely perforated along the outside edge of the pane or sheet. The missing perforations were applied in Hobart using a line machine measuring 12 (11.8 is the exact gauge). This perforation can only occur on one side of a stamp.

(Typo, using electrotyped plates, Victoria Govt Ptg Office, Melbourne)

1905 (Aug)–**11**. *Wmk Crown over A, W w 11 (sideways on horiz designs). P 12½.*

249	22	½d. yellow-green (10.12.08)	1·75	60
		a. Perf 11	1·75	60
		b. Perf comp of 12½ and 11	65·00	20·00
		c. Perf comp of 11 and 12	£140	
		d. Wmk upright (1909)	12·00	5·00
		da. Perf 11	85·00	
250	23	1d. rose-red	1·75	30
		a. Perf 11	4·25	30
		b. Perf comp of 12½ and 11	4·50	3·50
		c. Perf comp of 12½ and 12	80·00	35·00
		d. Perf comp of 11 and 12	95·00	35·00
		e. Wmk sideways (1907)	11·00	2·00
		ea. Perf 11	12·00	3·00
		eb. Perf comp of 12½ and 11	50·00	20·00
		f. Imperf (pair)	£350	£350
250g		1d. carmine-red (3.10)	6·50	1·75
		ga. Perf 11	8·00	2·00
		gb. Perf comp of 12½ and 11	9·50	5·50
		gc. Perf comp of 12½ and 12	85·00	30·00
		gd. Perf comp of 11 and 12	£100	35·00

		ge. Imperf (pair)..........................	£350	
		gf. Wmk sideways........................	6·50	1·75
		gg. Perf 11	7·50	1·75
		gh. Perf comp of 12½ and 11	9·50	5·50
		h. Carmine-vermilion (1911)	12·00	4·50
		ha. Perf 11	15·00	4·75
		hb. Perf comp of 12½ and 11	35·00	7·00
		hc. Perf comp of 12½ and 12.........		
		hd. Perf comp of 11 and 12		
251	24	2d. plum (8.07)...........................	11·00	60
		a. Wmk upright	18·00	3·00
		b. Perf 11	2·00	20
		ba. Wmk upright (12.07)..............	17·00	2·75
		c. Perf comp of 12½ and 11	25·00	9·50
		d. Perf comp of 12½ and 12	£225	80·00
		e. Perf comp of 11 and 12	£130	60·00
		f. Bright reddish violet (1910)	5·50	2·25
		fa. Perf 11	5·50	1·75
		fb. Perf comp of 12½ and 11	28·00	16·00
		fc. Perf comp of 12½ and 12.........	£225	80·00
253	26	3d. brown (3.09)	10·00	5·50
		b. Perf 11	16·00	6·00
		c. Perf comp of 12½ and 11	£250	£275
254	29	6d. carmine-lake (12.10)...............	19·00	26·00
		b. Perf 11	20·00	35·00
		b. Perf comp of 12½ and 11	£250	
		c. Dull carmine-red (3.11)	23·00	35·00
		ca. Wmk upright	38·00	40·00
		cb. Perf 11	25·00	40·00
		cc. Perf comp of 12½ and 11	£275	£300

The note after No. 248 re perfs compound with perf 12 also applies here.

Nos. 250/f were printed from the same plates as Nos. 241/cb. Nos. 250/gh/hd are from a further pair of new plates and the images are sharper.

(Typo Victoria Govt Printing Office, Melbourne).

1906–13. Wmk Crown over A, W w **11.** P 12½.

255	11	8d. purple-brown (1907)...............	20·00	9·00
		a. Perf 11	16·00	5·00
256		9d. blue (1907)............................	7·00	4·25
		a. Perf 11	7·00	4·25
		b. Perf comp of 12½ and 11 (1909)	65·00	
		c. Perf comp of 12½ and 12 (1909)	£225	
		d. Perf comp of 11 and 12	£300	
257	20	1s. rose and green (1907).............	13·00	5·00
		a. Perf 11 (1907)	26·00	21·00
		b. Perf comp of 12½ and 11	23·00	28·00
		c. Perf comp of 12½ and 12	£140	
258		10s. mauve and brown (1906)........	£180	£190
		a. Perf 11	£300	£325
		b. Perf comp of 12½ and 12	£400	

The note after No. 248 re perfs compound with perf 12, also applies here.

(Typo, using stereotyped plates, Commonwealth Stamp Ptg Branch, Melbourne)

1911 (Jan). Wmk Crown over A, W w **11** (sideways). P 12½.

259	24	2d. bright violet...........................	8·50	4·00
		a. Wmk upright	26·00	5·50
		b. Perf 11	8·50	4·00
		ba. Wmk upright	26·00	5·50
		c. Perf comp of 12½ and 11	75·00	25·00
		d. Perf comp of 12½ and 12	£275	

Stamps from this stereotyped plate differ from No. 251 in the width of the design (33 to 33¾ mm, against just over 32 mm), in the taller, bolder letters of "TASMANIA", in the slope of the mountain in the left background, which is clearly outlined in white, and in the outer vertical frame-line at left, which appears "wavy". Compare Nos. 260, etc, which are always from this plate.

1912 (Oct). No. 259 surch with T **32.** P 12½.

260	24	1d. on 2d. bright violet (R.)	1·00	1·00
		a. Perf 11	1·50	1·50
		b. Perf comp of 12½ and 11	£130	£140

(Typo, using electrotyped plates, Commonwealth Stamp Ptg Branch, Melbourne).

1912 (Dec). Thin ready gummed paper, white gum (as Victoria, 1912). W w **11** (sideways on 3d.). P 12½.

261	23	1d. carmine-vermilion	19·00	12·00
		a. Perf 11	19·00	12·00
		b. Perf comp of 12½ and 11	†	£325
262	26	3d. brown	65·00	85·00

STAMP BOOKLETS

There are very few surviving examples of Nos. SB1/4. Listings are provided for those believed to have been issued with prices quoted for those known to still exist.

1904 (1 Jan)–**09.** Black on red cover as No. SB1 of New South Wales.

SB1	£1 booklet containing two hundred and forty 1d. in twelve blocks of 20 (5×4)	
	a. Red on pink cover (1909)	
	b. Blue on pink cover	

1904 (1 Jan). Black on grey cover No. SB1. Stapled.

SB2	£1 booklet containing two hundred and twenty 2d. in four blocks of 30

1910 (1 May). Black on white cover as No. SB3. of New South Wales. Stapled.

SB3	2s. booklet containing eleven ½d. (No. 249), either in block of 6 plus block of 5 or block of 11, and eighteen 1d. (No. 250), either in three blocks of 6 or block of 6 plus block of 12	£4750

Unsold stock No. SB3 was uprated with one additional ½d. in May 1911.

1911 (Aug). Red on pink cover as No. SB3. Stapled.

SB4	2s. booklet containing twelve ½d. (No. 249), either in two blocks of 6 or block of 12, and eighteen 1d. (No. 250), either in three blocks of 6 or block of 6 plus block of 12	£4000

POSTAL FISCAL STAMPS

VALIDITY. Nos. F1/29 were authorised for postal purposes on 1 November 1882.

CLEANED STAMPS. Beware of postal fiscal stamps with pen-cancellations removed.

F 1   F 2

F 3   F 4

(Recess Alfred Bock, Hobart)

1863–80. Wmk double-lined "1". W **4.**

(a) Imperf.

F1	F 1	3d. green (1.65)	£225	£120
F2	F 2	2s.6d. carmine (11.63)	£225	£120
F3		2s.6d. lake (5.80)	£275	
F4	F 3	5s. brown (1.64)	£475	£400
F5		5s. sage-green (1880)	£275	£160
F6	F 4	10s. orange (1.64)	£700	40·00
F7		10s. salmon (5.80)	£475	£400

(b) P 10.

F8	F 1	3d. green	£100	55·00
F9	F 2	2s.6d. carmine	£120	
F10	F 3	5s. brown	£180	
F11	F 4	10s. orange	£140	

(c) P 12.

F12	F 1	3d. green	£100	75·00
F13	F 2	2s.6d. carmine	£100	85·00
F14	F 3	5s. brown	£200	
F15		5s. sage-green	95·00	75·00
F16	F 4	10s. orange	£130	95·00
F17		10s. salmon	95·00	75·00

(d) P 12½.

F18	F 1	3d. green	£200	
F19	F 2	2s.6d. carmine	£190	
F20	F 3	5s. brown	£300	
F21	F 4	10s. orange-brown	£190	

(e) P 11½.

F22	F 1	3d. green	£275	
F23	F 2	2s.6d. lake	£100	90·00
F24	F 3	5s. sage-green	95·00	75·00
F25	F 4	10s. salmon	£160	£120

See also No. F30.

In 1879, the 3d., 2s.6d., 5s. (brown), and 10s. (orange) were reprinted on thin, tough, white paper, and are found with or without "REPRINT". In 1889 another reprint was made on white card, imperforate and perforated 12. These are also found with or without "REPRINT".

F 5 Duck-billed Platypus

REVENUE
(F 6)

(Typo D.L.R.)

1880 (19 Apr). W **16** (sideways). P 14.

F26	F 5	1d. slate	22·00	7·00
F27		3d. chestnut	20·00	3·50
F28		6d. mauve	85·00	2·25
F29		1s. rose-pink	£110	14·00
		a. Perf comp of 14 and 11		

All values are known imperf, but not used.

Reprints are known of the 1d. in deep blue and the 6d. in lilac. The former is on yellowish white, the latter on white card. Both values also exist on wove paper, perf 12, with the word "REPRINT".

1888. W **16.** P 12.

F30	F 2	2s.6d. lake	45·00	35·00
		a. Imperf between (horiz pair).......	£850	

1900 (15 Nov). Optd with Type F **6.**

(a) On Types F **2** and F **4**.

F32	F 2	2s.6d. lake (No. F30)	£275	
		a. "REVFNUE"	£375	
		b. Opt inverted	£550	
		c. Imperf	£300	
F33	F 4	10s. salmon (No. F17)	—	£400
		a. "REVFNUE"		

(b) On Nos. F27 and F29.

F34	F 5	3d. chestnut	25·00	25·00
		a. Double opt, one vertical	85·00	£120
F35		1s. rose-pink		

(c) On stamps as Nos. F26/9, but typo locally. W **16.** P 12.

F36	F 5	1d. blue	20·00	
		a. Imperf between (horiz pair)	£300	
		b. Imperf vert (horiz pair)............	£350	
		c. "REVENUE" inverted	£100	
		d. "REVENUE" double	£160	
		e. Pale blue	19·00	
F37		6d. mauve	60·00	
		a. Double print	£250	
F38		1s. pink	90·00	

(d) On No. 225.

F39	20	£1 green and yellow.....................	£140	£120
		a. Opt double, one vertical	£275	£275

It was not intended that stamps overprinted with Type F **6** should be used for postal purposes, but an ambiguity in regulations permitted such usage until all postal fiscal stamps were invalidated for postal purposes on 30 November 1900.

Printings of some of the above with different watermarks, together with a 2d. as Nos. F36/8, did not appear until after the stamps had become invalid for postal purposes.

Tasmania became part of the Commonwealth of Australia on 1 January 1901.

VICTORIA

During the expansion of the Australian settlements in the fourth decade of the nineteenth century the growing population of the Port Phillip District in the south of New South Wales led to a movement for its creation as a separate colony. This aspiration received the approval of the British Government in 1849, but the colony of Victoria, as it was to be called, was not to be created until 1 July 1851.

In the meantime the New South Wales Legislative Council voted for the introduction of postal reforms, including the use of postage stamps, from 1 January 1850, and this act was also to apply to the Port Phillip District where stamps inscribed "VICTORIA" would predate the creation of that colony by eighteen months.

Until the end of 1859 the stamps of Victoria, with the exception of Nos. 40 and 73, were produced by local contractors working under the supervision of the colonial administration.

SPECIMEN OVERPRINTS. Those listed are from U.P.U. distributions in 1892 and 1897. Further "Specimen" overprints exist, but these are used for other purposes.

HAM PRINTINGS. The first contractor was Thomas Ham of Melbourne. He was responsible for the initial printings of the "Half-Length" 1d., 2d. and 3d., together with the replacement "Queen on Throne" 2d. The first printings were produced from small sheets of 30 (5×6) laid down directly from the engraved die which showed a single example of each value. Subsequent printings, of which No. 4a was the first, were in sheets of 120 (two panes of 60) laid down using intermediate stones of various sizes. Impressions from the first printings were fine and clear, but the quality deteriorated when intermediate stones were used.

1 Queen Victoria
("Half Length")

(Lithographed by Thomas Ham, Melbourne)

1850 (3 Jan)–**53**. Imperf.

1d. Thin line at top

2d. Fine border and background

3d. White area to left of orb

(a) *Original state of dies:* 1d. (tops of letters of "VICTORIA" reach to top of stamp); 2d. (fine border and background); 3d. (thicker white outline around left of orb, central band of orb does not protrude at left). No frame-lines on dies.

1	1	1d. orange-vermilion....................	£25000	£3250
		a. Orange-brown	†	£1600
		b. Dull chocolate-brown	£9000	£1800
2		2d. lilac-mauve (shades) (Stone A)..	£6500	£750
3		2d. brown-lilac (shades) (Stone B)..	£5000	£400
		a. Grey-lilac	—	£400
4		3d. bright blue (shades)	£3750	£450
		a. Blue (shades)	£3750	£275
		ab. Retouched (between Queen's head and right border) (No. 11 in transfer group) (8 varieties)...	—	£425
		ac. Retouched (under "V") (No. 10 in transfer group)	£10000	£850

With the exception of No. 4a the above were printed from small stones of 30 (5×6) laid down directly from the engraved die which showed a single example of each value. There were two stones of the 2d. and one for each of the other values. No. 4a is the second printing of the 3d. for which the sheet size was increased to 120, the printing stone being constructed from an intermediate stone of 15 (5×3).

1d. Thick line at top

2d. Coarse background

3d. White area small and band protruding to left of orb

(b) *Second state of dies:* 1d. (more colour over top of letters of "VICTORIA"); 2d. (fine border as (a) but with coarse background); 3d. (thinner white outline around left of orb, central band of orb protrudes at left).

5	1	1d. red-brown (shades) (2.50)	£5500	£400
		a. Pale dull red-brown	£4500	£400
6		2d. grey-lilac (shades) (1.50)........	£1800	£140
		a. Dull grey	£1800	£150
7		3d. blue (shades) (6.51)	£1600	£150
		a. Retouched (22 varieties) from ...	£2750	£300

Printed in sheets of 120 (10×12) with the printing stones constructed from intermediate stones of 30 (5×6) for the 1d. and 2d. or 10 (5×2) for the 3d. It is believed that the use of the smaller intermediate stone for the latter resulted in the many retouches.

Frame-lines added

(c) *Third state of dies:* As in (b) but with frame-lines added, very close up, on all four sides.

8	1	1d. dull orange-vermilion (11.50)....	£2500	£550
		a. Dull red (shades)	£2000	£170
9		1d. deep red-brown (5.51)	—	£650
		a. Brownish red (shades)	£1100	£150

10		b. Dull rose (shades).................	£1100	£150
		2d. grey (shades) (8.50)...............	£1300	£170
		a. Olive-grey (shades).............	£1700	£170
11		3d. blue (shades) (12.52).............	£550	70·00
		a. Deep blue (shades)..............	£750	70·00
		b. Pale greenish blue (shades)......	£950	£140

Printed in sheets of 120 (12×10) produced from intermediate stones of 30 (6×5) for No. 8 and 12 (6×2) for the others.

White veil

(d) *As (c) but altered to give, for the 1d. and 3d., the so-called "white veils", and for the 2d., the effect of vertical drapes to the veil.*

12	1	1d. reddish brown (6.51).................	£1200	£140
		a. Bright pinky red (shades)	£850	£140
13		2d. drab (1.51)........................	£1700	£150
		a. Grey-drab (shades)................	£2000	£150
		b. Lilac-drab	—	£150
		c. Red-lilac	—	£700
		d. Void lower left corner...............	†	£20000
14		3d. blue (shades) (1.53)..............	£550	60·00
		a. Deep blue (shades)	£550	60·00
		b. Greenish blue (shades)	£750	65·00
		c. Retouched (9 varieties).........	£1200	£150

Printed in sheets of 120 (12×10) produced from intermediate stones of 12 (6×2) on which the details of the veil were amended as described above.

The "void corner" error occurred on the printing stone. It is believed that only four examples still exist.

2d. Coarse border and background

(e) *Fourth state of 2d. die only:* Coarse border and background. Veil details as in original die.

15	1	2d. red-lilac (shades) (5.50)............	£1000	£275
		a. Lilac	£1000	£275
		b. Grey	—	£375
		c. Dull brownish lilac	£750	£140
		d. Retouched lower label—value omitted .... from	†	£10000
		e. Other retouches (17 varieties) .... from	£1600	£300

Printed in sheets of 120 (12×10) produced from an intermediate stone of 30 (6×5).

(f) *2d. as (e), but with veils altered to give effect of vertical drapes.*

16	1	2d. lilac-grey (1.51)	£1200	£150
		a. Deep grey	£1500	£150
		b. Brown-lilac	£1100	80·00
17		2d. cinnamon (shades) (2.51)	£950	£140
		a. Drab (shades)	£1000	80·00
		b. Pale dull brown (shades)...........	£1100	90·00
		c. Greenish grey	£950	80·00
		d. Olive-drab (shades)	£1100	£160
		e. Buff	†	£170

Printed in sheets of 120 (12×10) produced from two successive intermediate stones of 30 (6×5) on which the details of the veil were amended as described above.

This was the final printing of the 2d. "Half Length" as the die for this value had been damaged. A replacement 2d. design was ordered from Thomas Ham.

For the later printings of the 1d. and 3d. in this design see Nos. 23/4, 26/31, 48/9 and 78/9.

2 Queen on Throne **3**

(Recess-printed by Thomas Ham)

1852 (27 Dec). Imperf.

18	2	2d. reddish brown	£250	22·00
		a. Chestnut	—	£120
		b. Purple-brown	£325	22·00

Printed in sheets of 50 (10×5) from a hand-engraved plate of the same size. Each stamp in the sheet had individual corner letters made-up of various combinations, none of which contained the letter "J".

Reprints were made in 1891 using the original plate, on paper wmk V over Crown, both imperf and perf 12½.

For later printings of this design see Nos. 19/22 and 36/9.

CAMPBELL & CO PRINTINGS. In May 1853 the Victoria postal authorities placed an order for 1d. and 6d. stamps in the "Queen on Throne" design with Perkins, Bacon in London. These would not arrive for some time, however, and supplies of Ham's printings were rapidly becoming exhausted. Local tenders were, therefore, solicited for further supplies of the 1d. and 3d. "Half Lengths" and the 2d. "Queen on Throne". That received from J. S. Campbell & Co was accepted. The stamps were produced by lithography, using transfers from either the "Half Length" engraved die or the 2d. "Queen on Throne" engraved plate of 50. Stamps from the Campbell & Co printings can be distinguished from later printings in lithography by the good quality paper used.

(Lithographed by J. S. Campbell & Co, Melbourne, using transfers taken from Ham's engraved plate.)

1854 (Jan–July). *Good quality white or toned paper.* Imperf.

(a) *Clear impressions with details around back of throne generally complete.*

19	2	2d. brownish purple	£225	30·00
		a. Grey-brown	£325	30·00
		b. Purple-black	—	30·00
		c. Dull lilac-brown (toned paper only)	£375	42·00

(b) *Poor impressions with details around back of throne not fully defined.*

20	2	2d. violet-black (2.54).............	£325	30·00
		a. Grey-black	£425	30·00
		b. Grey-lilac	£325	30·00
		c. Dull brown (on toned)	£325	30·00
		ca. Substituted transfer (in pair)......	—	£2000

(c) *Weak impressions with background generally white without details. Toned paper only.*

21	2	2d. grey-purple (7.54).............	£180	26·00
		a. Purple-black......................	£180	26·00

(d) *Printings using an intermediate stone. Impression flat and blurred. Background details usually complete. Toned paper only.*

22	2	2d. grey-drab (shades) (5.54)	£300	26·00
		a. Black	—	£120

Nos. 19/21 were produced using transfers taken directly from the original Ham engraved plate. It is believed that the different strengths of the impressions were caused by the amount of pressure exerted when the transfers were taken. The stamps were printed in sheets of 100 (2 panes 10×5). On one stone a block of four at bottom left, lettered "FL GM" over "QV RW", was damaged and the stone was repaired by using a block of four substituted transfers. These were lettered "VZ WA" over "FL GM". No. 20ca covers any one of these substituted transfers in pair with normal. As horizontal pairs these are lettered "WA HN" or "GM SX" and as vertical "VZ" over "VZ" or "WA" over "WA".

For No. 22 an intermediate stone was used to produce a printing stone of 300 (6 panes 10×5). The insertion of a further stage into the process caused the blurred appearance of stamps from this printing. No. 22a is believed to come from proof sheets issued to post offices for normal use. Examples are usually cancelled with Barred Oval 108 and Barred Numerals 1 and 2.

(Lithographed by J.S. Campbell & Co, Melbourne)

1854 (Feb–June). *Good quality wove paper.* Imperf.

23	1	1d. orange-red (shades)	£600	£120
		a. Rose	£3000	£450
24		3d. blue (shades) (6.54)..............	£600	40·00
		a. Retouched under "C" of "VICTORIA"	—	£130

The 1d. was produced in sheets of 192 (two panes of 96 (12×8)) and the 3d. in sheets of 320 (two panes of 160 (18×9)). Both printing stones were constructed from transfers taken from intermediate stones of 24 (6×4). The spacing between stamps is far wider than on the Ham printings. The 3d. panes of 160 were constructed using six complete transfers of 24 and three of 6 with the final impression in the bottom two rows removed.

The 1d. Campbell printings have the frame lines almost completely absent due to lack of pressure when taking transfers.

The 3d. retouch, No. 24a, occurs on R. 3/5 of the intermediate stone.

CAMPBELL AND FERGUSSON PRINTINGS. Increased postal rates in early 1854 led to a requirement for a 1s. value and in April a contract for this stamp was awarded to Campbell and Fergusson (the new corporate style of J. S. Campbell & Co). Further contracts to print the 1d. and 3d. "Half Lengths" and the 2d. "Queen on Throne" followed. All were produced by lithography with the two "Half Lengths" using transfers from the original engraved die and the 2d. "Queen on Throne" transfers from Ham's original engraved plate.

All Campbell and Fergusson printings were on paper of a poorer quality than that used for the earlier contract.

(Lithographed by Campbell & Fergusson)

1854 (6 July). *Poorer quality paper.* Imperf.

25	3	1s. blue (shades)	£700	24·00
		a. Greenish blue (shades)	£800	24·00
		b. Indigo-blue	—	£130

No. 25 was produced in sheets of 100 (8×12 with an additional stamp appearing at the end of rows 6 to 9). The printing stones used each contained four such sheets. They were constructed from an intermediate stone of 40 (8×5) taken from a single engraved die. Each pane of 100 showed two complete transfers of 40, one of 20, and one of a vertical strip of 4.

For this stamp rouletted or perforated see Nos. 54 and 81.

(Lithographed by Campbell & Fergusson)

1854 (July)–**57**. *Poorer quality paper.* Imperf.

26	1	1d. brown (shades)...................	£600	£100
		a. Brick-red (shades)	£700	80·00
		b. Dull red (shades)	£750	80·00
27		1d. Orange-brown (shades) (8.55)..	£475	£110
		a. Dull rose-red (shades)	£475	65·00
		b. Bright rose-pink	£600	£110
		c. Retouched (6 varieties)	£1500	£400
28		1d. pink (shades) (2.55)............	£450	38·00
		a. Rose (shades)	£450	38·00
		b. Lilac-rose (shades)	£500	38·00
		c. Dull brown-red (shades)	—	£110
		d. Retouched (8 varieties)	£850	£325
29		3d. bright blue (shades) (7.57)	£500	55·00
		a. Greenish blue (shades)	£450	45·00
		b. Retouch under "C" of "VICTORIA"	—	£110
30		3d. Prussian blue (shades) (11.56)..	£600	75·00
		a. Milky blue	£1100	£120
		b. Retouch under "C" of "VICTORIA"	—	£250
31		3d. steel-blue (shades) (heavier impression) (5.55)..............	—	50·00
		a. Greenish blue (shades)	£425	40·00
		b. Blue (shades)	£425	40·00
		c. Deep blue (shades)	£425	40·00
			—	42·00

The 1d. was produced in sheets of 400 (2 panes 20×10) constructed from transfers originating from the J. S. Campbell & Co intermediate stone. Each pane contained six complete transfers of 24, three of 12, two of 8 and one of 4.

The 3d. was produced in sheets of 320 (2 panes of 160) (No. 29), 200 (No. 30) or 400 (2 panes of 200) (No. 31.) The stone for No. 29 was constructed from transfers taken from the J. S. Campbell intermediate stone with the retouch on R. 3/5 still present. The panes of 160 contained six transfers of 24 and three of 6 with the last impression in both rows 8 and 9 removed. Quality of impression is generally poor. The stone for No. 30, once again taken from the Campbell intermediate stone, was laid down in the same combination of transfers as the 1d. value. Impressions from it were, however, so poor that transfers from a new intermediate stone were used for No. 31. Impressions from this stone, on which the panes of 200 were in a similar layout to the 1d. were much further apart than those on the stones used to produce Nos. 29/30.

The Campbell and Ferguson printings of the "Half Lengths" are listed in the order in which they were printed.

CALVERT PRINTINGS. Contracts for the provision of other values required by the postal rate changes in 1853 were placed with Samuel Calvert of Melbourne who used typography as the printing process. Calvert continued to print, and later roulette, stamps for the Victoria Post Office until March 1858 when it was discovered that he had placed some of the stock in pawn.

| 4 | 5 | 6 |

(Typographed from woodblocks by Samuel Calvert)

1854 (1 Sep)–**55**. Imperf.
32	4	6d. reddish brown (13.9.54)............	£350	45·00
		a. Dull orange.............................	£190	18·00
		b. Orange-yellow........................	£190	19·00
33	5	6d. ("TOO LATE") lilac and green		
		(1.1.55).......................................	£1100	£180
34	6	1s. ("REGISTERED") rose-pink		
		and blue (1.12.54).....................	£1400	£150
35	4	2s. dull bluish green/pale yellow.....	£1500	£160

No. 33 was provided to pay the additional fee on letters posted after the normal closure of the mails. This service was only available in the larger towns; examples are usually postmarked Castlemaine, Geelong or Melbourne. The service was withdrawn on 30 June 1857 and remaining stocks of the "TOO LATE" stamps were used for normal postal purposes.

No. 34 was issued to pay the registration fee and was so used until 5 January 1858 after which remaining stocks were used for normal postage.

These four values were produced from individually-engraved boxwood woodblocks. The 6d. was in sheets of 100 printed by two impressions from two plates of 25. The 2s. was in sheets of 50 from a single plate of 25. The bicoloured "TOO LATE" and "REGISTERED" stamps are unusual in that Calvert used a common woodblock "key" plate of 25 for both values combined with "duty" plates made up from metal stereos. Both values were originally in sheets of 50, but the "REGISTERED" later appeared in sheets of 100 for which a second "key" plate of 25 was utilised.

For these stamps roulette or perforated see Nos. 53, 55/8, 60/1 and 82.

(Lithographed by Campbell & Ferguson)

1855 (Mar)–**56**. Poorer quality paper. Imperf.

(a) Printings from stones which were not over-used; background around top of throne generally full and detail good.
36	2	2d. lilac (shades) (7.55)...................	£180	26·00
		a. Purple (shades).......................	£180	26·00
		b. "TVO" for "TWO"......................	£6500	£950

(b) Early printings from stones which were over-used. Similar characteristics to those above, though detail is not quite so full. Distinctive shades.
37	2	2d. brown...................................	—	70·00
		a. Brown-purple........................	£200	24·00
		b. Warm purple........................		24·00
		c. Rose-lilac..............................		24·00
		d. Substituted transfer (pair)........		£600

(c) Later printings from the same stones used for No. 37 when in a worn condition. Impressions heavy, coarse and overcoloured; details blurred; generally white background around top of throne.
38	2	2d. dull lilac-mauve (1856)............	£200	28·00
		a. Dull mauve...........................	£200	28·00
		b. Grey-violet............................		28·00
		c. Red-lilac................................		29·00
		d. Substituted transfer (pair)........		£600

(d) Printings from a stone giving blotchy and unpleasing results, with poor definition. Mainly shows in extra colour patches found on most stamps.
39	2	2d. dull purple (7.55)....................	—	48·00
		a. Dull grey-lilac.......................	£225	48·00
		b. On thick card paper................		£550

The Campbell and Ferguson 2d. "Queen on Throne" printings were in sheets of 200 (4 panes 10×5) constructed from transfers taken from the original Ham engraved plate.

Four separate stones were used. On Stone A a creased transfer running through R. 4/8, 4/9 and 5/8 caused the "TVO" variety on the stamp from the bottom row of one pane. On Stone C the impression in the first vertical row of one pane were found to be so faulty that they were replaced by substituted transfers taken from elsewhere on the sheet causing abnormal horizontal pairs lettered "UY BF", "TX MQ", "DI WA", "SW GM" and "CH RW". The vertical pairs from the substituted transfers are lettered "UY" over "TX" and "DI" over "SW".

PERKINS BACON "CANCELLED". For notes on these handstamps, showing "CANCELLED" between horizontal bars forming an oval, see Catalogue Introduction.

7 Queen on Throne   8 "Emblems"

(Recess Perkins, Bacon & Co, London)

1856 (23 Oct). Wmk Large Star. Imperf.
40	7	1d. yellow-green (H/S		
		"CANCELLED" in oval		
		(£6500))	£160	24·00

Supplies of this stamp, and the accompanying 6d. which was only issued roulette (see No. 73), arrived in the colony at the end of 1854, but the 1d. was not placed on sale until almost two years later.

No. 40 was reprinted from the original plate in 1891. Examples, in either dull yellow-green or bright blue-green, are imperforate and on V over Crown watermarked paper.

(Typographed from electrotypes by Calvert)

1857 (26 Jan–6 Sept). Imperf.

(a) Wmk Large Star, W w 1.
41	8	1d. yellow-green (18 Feb)............	£110	16·00
		a. Deep green.............................	£130	30·00
		b. Printed on both sides...............	†	£1300
42		4d. vermilion.............................	£275	16·00
		a. Brown-vermilion.....................	£250	9·00
		b. Printed on both sides...............	†	£1300
43		4d. dull red (20 July)..................	£170	7·50
44		4d. dull rose (6 Sept).................	£250	7·50

(b) No wmk. Good quality medium wove paper.
45		2d. pale lilac (25 May)................	£250	11·00
		a. Grey-lilac..............................	£250	11·00

Nos. 41/5 were produced in sheets of 120, arranged as four panes of 30 (6×5) (1d. and 4d.) or twelve panes of 10 (2×5) (2d.), using electrotypes taken from a single engraved die of each value. The setting of the 4d. was rearranged before the printing of Nos. 43/4.

Only two examples of No. 41b and No. 42b have been recorded.

For this printing roulette or perforated see Nos. 46/7, 50/2, 59, 74 and 77.

ROULETTES AND PERFORATIONS. In August 1857 a rouletting machine was provided at the G.P.O., Melbourne, to enable the counter clerks to separate stamp stocks before sale to the public. This machine produced roulettes of 7½–9 in one direction across six rows at a time. There was also a single wheel device which gauged 7–7½. Both were in use between the earliest known date of 12 August and the end of 1857.

Calvert was granted a separate contract in October 1857 to roulette the stamps he printed, but only Nos. 57/61 had been produced when it was found, in April 1858, that he had pawned a quantity of the sheets. His contracts were terminated and his successor, F. W. Robinson, used a roulette machine of a different gauge before switching to a gauge 12 perforating machine in January 1859.

1857 (12 Aug–Sept). Rouletted 7–9 by counter clerks at G.P.O., Melbourne.
46	8	1d. yellow-green (No. 41)............	£400	80·00
47		2d. pale lilac (No. 45)..................	—	30·00
		a. Grey-lilac..............................	—	30·00
48	1	3d. blue (shades) (No. 24)............	—	£190
		a. Retouch under "C" of		
		"VICTORIA"...............................		
49		3d. bright blue (shades) (No. 29)..	—	£200
		a. Greenish blue (shades)............	£1100	£180
		b. Retouch under "C" of		
		"VICTORIA"..............................		
50	8	4d. vermilion (No. 42).................	—	£100
51		4d. dull red (No. 43)..................	—	38·00
52		4d. dull rose (No. 44) (Sept)........	—	26·00
53	4	6d. reddish brown (No. 32).........	—	65·00
		a. Dull orange............................	—	42·00
		b. Orange-yellow........................	—	50·00
54	3	1s. blue (shades) (No. 25)............	—	90·00
		a. Greenish blue.........................	—	90·00
55	6	1s. ("REGISTERED") rose-pink		
		and blue (No.34)........................	£5500	£275
56	4	2s. dull bluish green/pale yellow		
		(No. 35).....................................	£4500	£425

With the exception of the 1s., Nos. 54/a, these stamps are normally found rouletted on one or two sides only.

1857 (Oct). Rouletted by Calvert.

(a) Rouletted 7–9 on all four sides and with finer points than No. 53b.
57	4	6d. orange-yellow (No. 32b)...........	—	60·00

(b) Serpentine roulette 10–10½.
58	4	6d. orange-yellow (No. 32b)...........	—	80·00

(c) Serrated 18–19.
59	8	2d. grey-lilac (No. 45a)................	£700	£425
60	4	6d. orange-yellow (No. 32b)...........	—	85·00

(d) Compound of serrated 18–19 and serpentine 10–10½.
61	4	6d. orange-yellow (No. 32b)...........	—	£130

No. 59 was not covered by the contract given to Calvert, but it is believed to be a test run for the rouletting machine. No. 61 always shows serrated 18–19 on three sides and the serpentine roulette at the top or bottom of the stamp.

(Typo from electrotypes by Calvert)

1858 (14 Jan–Apr). Good quality white wove paper. No wmk.

(a) Rouletted 7–9 on all four sides.
62	8	1d. pale emerald........................	£325	21·00
		a. Emerald-green........................	£325	21·00
63		4d. rose-pink (18 Jan)..................	£225	6·00
		a. Bright rose.............................	£225	6·00
		b. Reddish pink..........................		11·00
		c. Imperf horiz (vert pair)............	†	£475

(b) Imperf (Apr).
64	8	1d. pale emerald........................	£200	11·00
		a. Emerald-green........................	—	14·00
65		4d. rose-pink..............................	£275	23·00
		a. Bright rose.............................	—	23·00
		b. Reddish pink..........................	—	30·00

Nos. 62/5 were produced in sheets of 120, arranged as four panes of 30 (6×5).

The Royal Collection contains a used horizontal pair of the 4d. showing the vertical roulettes omitted.

The majority of Nos. 64/5 were issued in April after Calvert's contracts had been terminated, although there is some evidence that imperforate sheets of the 4d., at least, were issued earlier.

For the 1d. of this issue perforated see No. 75.

ROBINSON PRINTINGS. Calvert's contracts were cancelled in April 1858 and the work was then placed with F. W. Robinson, who had unsuccessfully tendered in 1856. The same electrotypes were used, but a perforating machine was introduced from January 1859. Robinson continued to print and perforate stamps under contract until the end of 1859 when the Victoria Post Office purchased his equipment to set up a Stamp Printing Branch and appointed him Printer of Postage Stamps.

(Typo from electrotypes by Robinson)

1858 (May–Dec).*(a)* Imperf.

(i) Coarse quality wove paper.
66	8	4d. dull rose (oily ink)...............	—	60·00

(ii) Smooth vertically-laid paper.
67	8	4d. dull rose (oily ink)...............	—	38·00
		a. Dull rose-red.........................	—	38·00
68		4d. dull rose-red (normal ink) (20		
		May)..	£425	20·00

(b) Rouletted 5½–6½.

(i) Smooth-laid paper.
69	8	2d. brown-lilac (shades) (horiz		
		laid) (June)...............................	£130	8·50
		a. Vert laid paper (21 Sept)........	£200	10·00
70		2d. violet (horiz laid) (27 Nov)......	£160	6·00
		a. Dull violet.............................	£190	18·00
71		4d. pale dull rose (vert laid) (1		
		June)..	£160	3·75
		a. Horiz laid paper.....................	†	£850
		b. Dull rose-red.........................	£130	3·75
		c. Rose-red...............................	£130	3·50
		ca. Serrated 19..........................	†	£475

(ii) Good quality wove paper.
72	8	1d. yellow-green (24 Dec)............	£300	26·00

Nos. 66/72 were produced in sheets of 120, arranged as four panes of 30 (6×5).

For stamps of this issue perforated see Nos. 76 and 80.

(Recess Perkins, Bacon & Co, London)

1858 (1 Nov). Wmk Large Star, W w 1. Rouletted 5½–6½.
73	7	6d. bright blue............................	£190	14·00
		a. Light blue..............................	£250	25·00

No. 73 was received from London at the same time as the 1d., No. 40, but was kept in store until November 1858 when the stock was rouletted by Robinson. When issued the gum was in a poor state.

Imperforate examples exist from Perkins Bacon remainders. Examples are known handstamped "CANCELLED" in oval of bars. Price £6500.

Imperforate reprints, in shades of indigo, were made from the original plate in 1891 on V over Crown watermarked paper.

1859 (Jan–May). P 12 by Robinson.
74	8	1d. yellow-green (No. 41)............	—	£275
75		1d. emerald-green (No. 64a).........	—	£275
		a. Imperf between (horiz pair)......		
76		1d. yellow-green (as No. 72) (11		
		Jan)...	£190	14·00
		a. Imperf horiz (vert pair)...........	—	£325
		b. Thin, glazed ("Bordeaux")		
		paper.......................................	†	£150
77		2d. pale lilac (No. 45).................	—	£250
		a. Grey-lilac..............................	—	£250
78	1	3d. blue (No. 24) (2 Feb)............	£750	£110
		a. Retouch under "C" of		
		"VICTORIA"...............................	—	£350
79		3d. greenish blue (shades) (No.29a)	†	£350
		a. Retouch under "C" of		
		"VICTORIA"...............................	†	£1000
80	8	4d. dull rose-red (No. 68)............	—	£300
81	3	1s. blue (No. 25) (4 Feb)............	£150	15·00
		a. Greenish blue.........................	£170	12·00
		b. Indigo-blue............................	—	30·00
82	4	2s. dull bluish green/pale yellow		
		(No. 35) (May)..........................	£300	38·00

The 1s. was reprinted in 1891 using transfers taken from the original die. These reprints were on V over Crown watermarked paper and perforated 12½.

For perforated 6d. black and 2s. blue both as Type **4** see Nos. 102 and 129/30.

(Typo from electrotypes by Robinson)

1859 (17 May–23 Dec). P 12.

(a) Good quality wove paper.
83	8	4d. dull rose.............................	£160	4·50
		a. Roul 5½–6½...........................	†	£800

(b) Poorer quality wove paper.
84	8	1d. dull green (July)....................	£130	13·00
		a. Green (11 Nov)......................	£130	13·00
85		4d. rose-carmine (16 July)............	£160	5·00
		a. Rose-pink (thick paper) (30		
		Nov)..		10·00

(c) Horizontally laid paper with the lines wide apart.
86	8	1d. dull green (18 July)................	—	25·00
		a. Laid lines close together...........	£140	14·00
		b. Green (Oct)............................		14·00
87		4d. rose-pink (shades) (23 Dec)......	£130	7·50
		a. Laid lines close together...........	—	10·00

STAMP PRINTING BRANCH. On 1 January 1860 F. W. Robinson was appointed Printer of Postage Stamps and his equipment purchased by the Post Office to establish the Stamp Printing Branch. All later Victoria issues were printed by the Branch which became part of the Victoria Government Printing Office in December 1885. In 1909 the Commonwealth Stamp Printing Office under J. B. Cooke was established in Melbourne and produced stamps for both the states and Commonwealth until 1918.

9

	10		11		

(Des and eng F. Grosse. Typo from electrotypes)

1860 (31 Jan)–66. P 12.

(a) No wmk.

88	9	3d. deep blue (horiz laid paper)......	£350	40·00
		a. Light blue................................		
89		4d. rose-pink (thin glazed Bordeaux paper) (21.4.60)........................	—	14·00
		a. Rose..	£325	17·00
		ab. Thick coarse paper (7.60)........	£325	14·00

(b) On paper made by T. H. Saunders of London wmkd with the appropriate value in words as W 10.

90	9	3d. pale blue (1.61)........................	£140	7·00
		a. Bright blue (10.61).....................	£140	8·50
		b. Blue (4.63)................................	£150	6·00
		c. Deep blue (4.64)........................	£150	6·00
		d. "TRREE" for "THREE" in wmk...	—	£450
91		3d. maroon (13.2.66)....................	£130	25·00
		a. Perf 13....................................	£150	28·00
92		4d. rose-pink (1.8.60)....................		8·50
		a. Rose-red..................................	90·00	4·25
		b. Rose-carmine............................		9·00
		c. Dull rose..................................	90·00	4·25
		d. Printed on "FIVE SHILLINGS" diagonal wmk paper (11.9.62)...	£1700	20·00
93		6d. orange (25.10.60)....................	£4000	£275
94		6d. black (20.8.61)........................	£130	5·50
		a. Grey-black................................	£130	5·50

(c) On paper made by De La Rue wmkd with the appropriate value as a single-lined numeral as W 11.

95	9	4d. dull rose-pink (9.10.62)............	£100	5·00
		a. Dull rose..................................	£110	5·50
		b. Rose-red..................................	—	5·00
		c. Roul 8 (28.7.63)........................	—	£250
		d. Imperf (31.7.63)........................	—	75·00
		e. Perf 13×12................................		

All three values were produced in sheets of 120, initially as four panes of 30 (6×5). Printings of the 3d. from 1864 were in a changed format of six panes of 20 (4×5).

The "TRREE" watermark error comes from early printings of No. 90 on R. 10/7.

Two examples of the 4d. on Saunders paper are known bisected in 1863, but such use was unauthorised.

Nos. 95c/e were issued during July and August 1863 when the normal perforating machine had broken down.

Reprints, from new plates, were made of the 3d. and 4d. in 1891 on "V over Crown" paper and perforated 12½.

1860 (Apr)–63. P 12.

(a) No wmk.

| 96 | 8 | 1d. bright green (horiz laid paper).. | | |
| 97 | | 1d. bright green (thin, glazed Bordeaux paper) (25.5.60) .... | — | 38·00 |

(b) On paper made by T. H. Saunders of London wmkd with the appropriate value in words as W 10.

98	8	1d. pale yellowish green (8.7.60)...	75·00	4·50
		a. Yellow-green.............................	85·00	4·75
		b. Error. Wmkd "FOUR PENCE".	†	£6000
99		2d. brown-lilac (7.7.61)		29·00
100		2d. bluish slate (8.61)	£120	5·50
		a. Greyish lilac (9.61)....................	£130	5·50
		b. Slate-grey (1.62).......................		5·50
		c. Printed on "THREE PENCE" wmkd paper. Pale slate (27.12.62)	£130	13·00
		ca. Bluish grey (2.63)	£140	16·00

(c) On paper made by De La Rue wmkd single-lined "2", W 11.

101	8	2d. dull reddish lilac (24.4.63)	£180	9·50
		a. Grey-lilac (10.63).......................	£170	15·00
		ab. Error. Wmkd "6"....................	†	£4750
		b. Grey-violet (11.63).....................	£120	12·00
		c. Slate (12.63).............................	£170	21·00

Only two examples of No. 98b have been recorded, one of which is in the Royal Collection.

1861 (22 Jun). On paper made by T. H. Saunders of London wmkd "SIX PENCE" as W 10. P 12.

| 102 | 4 | 6d. black................................... | £180 | 45·00 |

No. 102 was produced as an emergency measure after the decision had been taken to change the colour of the current 6d. from orange (No. 93) to black (No. 94). During the changeover the old Calvert "woodblock" plates were pressed into service to provide two months' supply.

	12		13		

(Des, eng and electrotyped De Gruchy & Leigh, Melbourne. Typo)

1861 (1 Oct)–64. P 12.

(a) On paper made by T. H. Saunders of London. Wmk "ONE PENNY" as W 10.

| 103 | 12 | 1d. pale green.............................. | 90·00 | 9·00 |
| | | a. Olive-green............................... | — | 10·00 |

(b) On paper made by De La Rue. Wmk single-lined "1" as W 11.

104	12	1d. olive-green (1.2.63).................	70·00	12·00
		a. Pale green (9.63).......................	70·00	6·50
		b. Apple-green (4.64).....................	70·00	6·00

(c) On paper supplied to Tasmania by Perkins, Bacon. Wmk double-lined "1", W 4 of Tasmania.

105	12	1d. yellow-green (10.12.63)...........	£130	10·00
		a. Dull green................................		10·00
		b. Imperf between (pair)	†	

All printings were in sheets of 120 containing four panes of 30 (6×5).

Reprints from new plates were made in 1891 on paper watermarked "V over Crown" and perforated 12½.

(Frame die eng F. Grosse. Typo from electrotypes)

1862 (26 Apr)–64. Centre vignette cut from T 9 with a new frame as T 13.

(a) On paper made by T. H. Saunders of London. Wmk "SIX PENCE" as W 10. P 12.

106	13	6d. grey.....................................	95·00	8·00
		a. Grey-black................................	95·00	9·50
		b. Jet-black..................................	£100	11·00

(b) On paper made by De La Rue. Wmk single-lined "6" as W 11.

107	13	6d. grey (p 12) (18.6.63)...............	85·00	5·50
		a. Jet-black..................................	—	7·50
		b. Grey-black................................	85·00	6·00
		c. Perf 13. Jet-black.......................	95·00	7·50
		ca. Grey-black...............................	95·00	7·50

Printings before August 1863 were in sheets of 120 containing four panes of 30 (6×5). For subsequent printings of No. 107 the format was changed to six panes of 20 (4×5).

Reprints from new plates were made in 1891 on paper watermarked "V over Crown" and perforated 12½.

SINGLE-LINED NUMERAL WATERMARK PAPERS. The first consignment of this paper, showing watermarks as W 11, arrived in Victoria during October 1862. Five further consignments followed, all but the last supplied by De La Rue.

The complexity of the scheme for different watermarks for each value, together with the time required to obtain further supplies from Great Britain, resulted in the emergency use of paper obtained from Tasmania and of the wrong numeral watermark on certain printings.

The final order for this paper was placed, in error within the firm of T. H. Saunders of London. Although the actual watermarks are the same (the dandy rolls were the property of the Victoria Government and supplied to each firm in turn) there are considerable differences between the two types of paper. That manufactured by Saunders is of a more even quality and is smoother, thicker, less brittle and less white than the De La Rue type.

De La Rue supplied white paper watermarked "1", "2", "4", "6" and "8", blue paper watermarked "1" and green paper watermarked "2".

The Saunders consignment of October 1865 contained white paper watermarked "1", "4" and "6", blue paper watermarked "1", green paper watermarked "2" and pink paper watermarked "10".

It is helpful for comparison purposes to note that all white paper watermarked "2" or "8" can only be De La Rue and all pink paper watermarked "10" can only be Saunders.

	14		15		16

(Des and eng F. Grosse. Typo from electrotypes)

1863–74. "Laureated" series.

(a) On paper made by De La Rue wmkd with the appropriate value in single-lined numerals as W 11.

108	14	1d. pale green (P 12) (9.9.64).........	75·00	8·50
		a. Perf 12½×12 (9.64).....................		
		b. Perf 13 (10.10.64)......................	70·00	5·00
		c. Bluish green (P 13)......................	65·00	4·25
		ca. Printed double..........................	†	£900
		d. Green (P 12) (7.65)....................	70·00	4·25
		da. Perf 13....................................	65·00	4·50
		e. Deep green (P 12) (12.65)............	85·00	4·50
		ea. Perf 13....................................	—	4·50
		eb. Perf 12×13..............................	—	9·00
		f. Bright yellow-green (P 13).............	—	18·00
109		2d. violet (1.4.64)........................	75·00	8·00
		a. Dull violet (P 12) (10.64).............	80·00	8·00
		ab. Perf 12½×12............................		
		ac. Perf 12½.................................		
		ad. Perf 12½×12............................	80·00	6·50
		b. Dull lilac (P 13) (4.65).................	65·00	6·50
		ba. Perf 12 (7.66)..........................	—	11·00
		bb. Perf 12×13 (7.66)......................	—	12·00
		c. Reddish mauve (P 13) (11.65)......	70·00	9·00
		d. Rose-lilac (P 13) (1.66)...............	65·00	8·00
		da. Perf 12×13 or 13×12 (1.66).........	65·00	8·00
		e. Grey (P 12) (7.66)......................	£100	10·00
		ea. Perf 13....................................	65·00	4·25
110		4d. deep rose (P 12) (11.9.63)	£130	4·25
		a. Printed double..........................	†	£900
		b. Rose-pink (P 12) (9.63)...............	£100	2·50
		c. Pink (P 13) (5.64)......................	£100	2·50
		ca. Error. Wmkd single-lined "8"......	†	£6500
		cb. Perf 12½×12 (9.64)...................		
		d. Dull rose (P 13) (10.64)..............	90·00	2·50
		e. Dull rose-red (P 13)...................	90·00	2·50
		ea. Perf 12 (8.65)..........................	£140	75·00
111	16	6d. blue (P 12) (13.2.66)...............	55·00	6·00

112	14	8d. orange (P 13) (22.2.65)...........	£375	60·00
113	17	1s. blue/blue (P 13) (10.4.65)........	£130	4·00
		a. Perf 12×13 (4.66).......................	£130	4·00
		ab. Imperf between (vert pair).........	†	£3000
		b. Bright blue/blue (P 13) (6.67).......	£100	3·50
		c. Indigo-blue/blue (P 13) (3.68).......	—	3·50
		d. Dull blue/blue (P 12) (6.74).........	—	3·75

(b) Emergency printings on Perkins, Bacon paper borrowed from Tasmania. Wmk double-lined "4" as W 4 of Tasmania.

114	14	4d. deep rose (P 12) (7.1.64).........	£140	5·00
		a. Pale rose (P 12)........................	—	4·50
		b. Dull reddish rose (P 13) (11.8.65)...................................	£140	4·75
		ba. Perf 12....................................	—	4·75
		bb. Perf 12×13...............................	—	13·00
		bc. Perf 12½, 12 and 13 compound		
		c. Red (P 13) (4.12.65)...................	£150	4·75

(c) Emergency printings on De La Rue paper as W 11, but showing incorrect single-lined numeral. P 13.

115	14	1d. brt yellow-grn (wmkd "8") (27.12.66).................................	£150	16·00
116		1d. brt yellow-green (wmkd "6") (6.67)..	—	27·00
117		2d. grey (wmkd "8") (18.1.67)........	£140	5·00
118	15	3d. lilac (wmkd "8") (29.9.66)........	£140	28·00
119	16	10d. grey (wmkd "8") (21.10.65)......	£550	£110
		a. Grey-black................................	£550	£120

(d) On paper made by T. H. Saunders wmkd with the appropriate value in single-lined numerals as W 11.

120	14	1d. deep yellow-green (P 12×13) (1.66)..	£120	12·00
		a. Perf 13 (3.66)............................	65·00	5·00
		b. Perf 12 (7.66)............................	—	13·00
121		4d. rose-red (P 13) (12.12.65).........	85·00	3·25
		a. Perf 12×13 or 13×12 (2.66).........	£130	6·50
		b. Perf 12 (4.66)............................	—	6·50
122	16	6d. blue (P 13) (28.5.66)...............	50·00	1·50
		a. Perf 12....................................	55·00	3·75
		b. Perf 12×13................................	50·00	2·25
		ba. Imperf between (horiz pair)........	†	£1400
123		10d. dull purple/pink (P 13) (22.3.66).	£100	5·00
		a. Perf 12×13................................	£140	6·50
		b. Blackish brown/pink (P 13) (12.69)..	£110	5·50
		c. Purple-brown/pink (P 13) (12.69)..		
124	17	1s. bright blue/blue (P 13) (5.12.70).	70·00	3·00
		a. Pale dull blue/blue (P 12) (1.73)...	£140	4·00
		ab. Perf 13...................................	—	9·50
		b. Indigo-blue/blue (P 13) (9.73).......	—	6·50
		ba. Perf 13...................................	70·00	4·00

(e) Emergency printings on Saunders paper as W 11, but showing incorrect single-lined numeral. P 13.

125	14	1d. brt yellow-green (wmkd "4") (6.3.67)......................................	£110	16·00
126		1d. brt yellow-green (wmkd "6") (6.67)..	£160	23·00
127		2d. grey (wmkd "4") (21.2.67)........	£110	5·50
128		2d. grey (wmkd "6") (13.5.67)........	£180	6·00

The 1d., 2d., 4d. and 8d. were originally produced in sheets of 120 containing eight panes of 15 (3×5). The 3d. and 6d. were in sheets of 120 (12×10) and the 1d. (from February 1866), 2d. (from July 1866) and 4d. (from April 1866) subsequently changed to this format. The 10d. was in sheets of 120 containing twenty panes of 6 (2×3). The 1s. was originally in sheets of 60 containing three panes of 20 (4×5), but this changed to 120 (12×10) in April 1866.

Only single examples are thought to exist of Nos. 110a, 110ca, 113ab, and 122ba and two of No. 108ca.

For later emergency printings on these papers see Nos. 153/66.

(Typo from composite woodblock and electrotype plate)

(a) On De La Rue paper. Wmk single-lined "2" as W 11.

129	4	2s. light blue/green (P 13) (22.11.64)................................	£170	7·00
		a. Dark blue/green (P 12) (9.65)...	£190	13·00
		ab. Perf 13 (6.66).........................	£170	7·50
		b. Blue/green (P 13) (6.68).............	£160	5·00
		c. Greenish blue/green (P 13) (7.73)..	£160	7·00
		ca. Perf 12....................................	£180	8·00
		d. Deep greenish blue/green (P 12½)..	£160	6·50

(b) On Saunders paper. Wmk single-lined "2" as W 11.

130	4	2s. dark blue/green (P 13) (23.11.67)................................	£180	7·00
		a. Blue/green (P 13) (10.71)............	£180	6·50
		ab. Perf 12 (8.74)..........................	£200	7·50
		c. Deep greenish blue/green (P 12½) (7.80)................................	£160	5·50

Nos. 129/30 were produced in sheets of 30 containing two panes of 15 (3×5). The plate contained eighteen of the original woodblock impressions and twelve electrotypes taken from them.

	19		20

V OVER CROWN WATERMARKS. The changeover from the numeral watermarks to a general type to be used for all values was first suggested at the end of 1865, but the first supplies did not reach Melbourne until April 1867. Five different versions were used before the V over Crown watermark was superseded by the Commonwealth type in 1905. The five versions are listed as follows:

Type **19** De La Rue paper supplied 1867 to 1882. Shows four points at the top of the crown with the left and right ornaments diamond-shaped

Type **33** De La Rue paper supplied 1882 to 1895 No points at the top of the crown with the left and right ornaments oval-shaped

Type **82** Waterlow paper supplied 1896 to 1899. Wide base to crown

Type **85** Waterlow paper used for postal issues 1899 to 1905. Wide top to crown

Type **104** James Spicer and Sons paper used for postal issues August and September 1912. Narrow crown

(Type from electrotypes)

1867–81. Wmk. V over Crown. W **19**.

(a) P 13.

131	14	1d. bright yellow-green (10.8.67)....	65·00	3·25
		a. Bright olive-green (1.69)	95·00	19·00
		b. Yellow-green (4.69)	65·00	3·00
		c. Dull green (3.70)	65·00	3·00
		d. Pale green (10.70)	60·00	3·00
		e. Grass-green (1871)	60·00	3·25
		f. Bluish green (shades) (7.72)......	60·00	3·25
		g. Green (shades) (9.72)	60·00	3·00
132		2d. slate-grey (26.8.67)..............	70·00	3·50
		a. Grey-lilac (29.1.68).................	70·00	5·00
		b. Lilac (26.8.68)........................	50·00	3·25
		c. Dull mauve (shades) (10.68)....	50·00	3·00
		d. Lilac-grey (1.69)	—	3·50
		e. Lilac-rose (2.69)	55·00	3·00
		f. Mauve (4.69)	70·00	3·25
		g. Red-lilac (1871)	55·00	3·00
		h. Dull lilac (6.69)	55·00	2·50
		i. Silver-grey (9.69)	£110	7·50
133	15	3d. lilac (28.8.67)......................	£200	35·00
		a. Grey-lilac (6.68)	£225	38·00
134		3d. yellow-orange (12.6.69)..........	28·00	4·00
		a. Dull orange (6.70)	26·00	3·75
		b. Orange (3.73)		3·75
		c. Bright orange (3.73)................	30·00	3·75
		d. Orange-brown (glazed paper) (10.78)...................................	29·00	9·50
135	14	4d. dull rose (28.11.67)...............	75·00	6·00
		a. Wmk sideways........................	†	65·00
		b. Aniline red (shades) (21.4.69)...	—	7·50
		c. Rose-pink (11.69)...................	—	5·00
		d. Rose (shades) (8.71)...............	70·00	3·25
		e. Dull rose (glazed paper) (5.3.79)...................................	70·00	3·50
		f. Dull rose-red (glazed paper) (11.79)...................................	—	5·00
		g. Bright lilac-rose (aniline) (glazed paper) (2.80)................	80·00	3·75
		h. Rosine (aniline) (glazed paper) (9.80).....................................	£200	5·50
136	16	6d. deep blue (15.1.68)..............	—	3·75
		a. Blue (21.12.68)	35·00	2·50
		b. Indigo-blue (10.69).................	35·00	2·50
		c. Prussian blue (9.72)...............	32·00	3·00
		d. Indigo (4.73)	35·00	3·00
		e. Dull blue (worn plate) (3.74)....	—	2·50
		f. Dull ultramarine (2.12.75)........	45·00	2·50
		g. Light Prussian blue (12.75).......	65·00	2·50
		h. Dull violet-blue (7.77).............	—	9·00
		i. Blue (glazed paper) (6.78)........	48·00	2·50
		j. Dull milky-blue (glazed paper) (9.79).....................................	45·00	2·50
		k. Prussian blue (glazed paper) (4.80).....................................	—	2·50
		l. Light blue (glazed paper) (4.81).....................................	48·00	2·50
		m. Deep blue (glazed paper) (10.81)...................................	45·00	2·50
137	14	8d. lilac-brown/pink (24.1.77)	85·00	5·50
		a. Purple-brown/pink (2.78)	85·00	5·50
		b. Chocolate/pink (8.78)	90·00	6·00
		ba. Compound perf 13×12	†	£325
		c. Red-brown/pink (12.78)	85·00	6·00
		d. Wmk sideways........................	†	£375
138	17	1s. light blue (11.5.75)................	£120	9·50
139	18	5s. blue/yellow (26.12.67)............	£2000	£300
		a. Wmk reversed	—	£500
140		5s. indigo-blue and carmine (I) (8.10.68)...............................	£275	28·00
		a. Blue and carmine (4.69)	£225	18·00
		b. Pale bright blue and carmine (glazed paper) (24.7.77).........	—	24·00
		c. Grey-blue and carmine (glazed paper) (4.78)........................	£225	20·00
		d. Wmk sideways. Deep lavender-blue and carmine (4.6.80).........	£225	24·00
141		5s. bright blue and red (II) (glazed paper) (12.5.81)......................	£200	19·00
		a. Indigo-blue and red (glazed paper)...................................	—	25·00

(b) P 12.

142	14	1d. pale green (10.71)	70·00	4·25
		a. Grass-green (1871)	60·00	4·25
		b. Bluish green (shades) (7.72)......	—	4·25
		c. Green (shades) (9.72).............	60·00	4·00
143	15	3d. dull orange (5.72)	28·00	2·50
		a. Orange (3.73)	—	2·10
		b. Bright orange (3.73)	—	2·50
		c. Dull orange-yellow (glazed paper) (12.80)........................	—	
144	14	4d. rose (shades) (8.71)...............	70·00	3·00
		a. Compound perf 12×13	—	£400
		b. Dull rose (glazed paper) (3.79)..	—	3·25
		c. Dull rose-red (glazed paper) (11.79)...................................	—	3·75
		d. Bright lilac-rose (aniline) (glazed paper) (2.80)................	—	9·00
		e. Rosine (aniline) (glazed paper) (9.80).....................................	80·00	6·50
145	16	6d. deep blue (2.2.72)	—	3·00
		a. Prussian blue (9.72)................	35·00	3·00
		b. Indigo (4.73)	45·00	3·25
		c. Dull blue (worn plate)..............	—	
		d. Blue (glazed paper) (6.78)........	—	3·00
		e. Dull milky-blue (glazed paper)...	—	3·00
		f. Light blue (glazed paper) (4.81)	—	4·00
146	14	8d. red-brn/pink (glazed paper) (11.80)...................................	80·00	9·00

147	17	1s. light blue/blue (5.75)................	—	9·00
148	18	5s. bright blue and red (II) (glazed paper) (5.81)...........................	£200	14·00
		a. Indigo-blue and red................	£300	18·00

(c) P 12½.

149	15	3d. dull orange-yellow (glazed paper) (12.80)........................	45·00	5·00
150	14	4d. rosine (aniline) (glazed paper) (9.80).....................................		
151	16	6d. Prussian blue (glazed paper) (4.80).....................................		
		a. Light blue (glazed paper) (4.81).....................................		
		b. Deep blue (glazed paper) (10.81)...................................	45·00	3·50
152	14	8d. lilac-brown/pink (8.77)	80·00	9·00
		a. Red-brown/pink (glazed paper) (11.80)...................................	†	£500

The same electrotypes as the previous issues were used for this series with the exception of the 5s. which was a new value. The 1d., 2d., 3d., 4d., 6d. and 1s. plates were arranged to print sheets of 120 (12×10) and the 8d. conformed to this when reintroduced in 1877. New plates for the 1d. (1868), 2d. (1869) and 6d. (1875) were constructed by Robinson's successor, J. P. Atkinson, using the improved facilities then available.

Atkinson was also responsible for the printing of the 5s. value. The original printings in blue on yellow paper were produced in sheets of 25, or possibly 50, using a vertical strip of five electrotypes. Due to its size the 5s. did not exactly fit the watermarked paper and, to avoid a preprinted sheet number, a proportion of the printing was made on the back of the paper creating the reversed watermark variety, No. 139a. These varieties occur in the first printing only as Atkinson created a plate of 25 for the second printing in March 1868. Printings of the 5s. bicoloured to April 1880 were made from electrotypes taken from the monocoloured plate. These showed a blue line beneath the crown (Type I). In early 1881 this plate was found to be too worn for further use and a new die was made from which a plate of 100 was constructed. Stamps from this plate are without the blue line beneath the crown (Type II).

PERFORATIONS. Various perforating machines were in use during this period. The use of line machines gauging 12 ceased around 1883. Of the line machines gauging 13 two were converted to comb types in 1873 and were eventually replaced by the 12½ gauge line and comb machines first used in 1876.

(Typo from electrotypes)

1867–70. *Emergency printings on various papers due to shortages of V over Crown paper.* P 13.

(a) Perkins, Bacon paper borrowed from Tasmania. Wmkd double-lined numerals as W **4** of Tasmania.

153	14	1d. pale yellowish green (wmkd "1") (24.9.67).......................	70·00	4·00
		a. Deep yellow-green (10.67)	70·00	4·00
154		1d. pale yellow-green (wmkd "4") (27.5.68)...............................	£1500	90·00
155		2d. grey-lilac (wmkd "4") (3.2.68)..	£130	4·25
		a. Slate (4.68)..........................	£130	3·50
		b. Mauve (7.68)........................	—	4·50
		c. Imperf (pair).........................	†	£3750
156		2d. mauve (wmkd "1") (30.6.68)....	£130	5·50
157	15	3d. grey-lilac (wmkd "1") (8.68)....	£170	50·00
158	14	4d. dull rose-red (wmkd "4") (5.68)	£130	5·00
159	16	6d. blue (wmkd "4") (20.6.68)......	£170	18·00
		a. Indigo-blue	—	20·00
160		6d. blue (wmkd "1") (28.7.68)......	65·00	4·50
161		6d. dull blue (wmkd "2") (1870).....	†	£2500

(b) Saunders paper. Wmkd in words as W **10**.

162	14	1d. pale yellow-green (wmkd "SIX PENCE") (23.3.68).................	£600	30·00
163		2d. slate-grey (wmkd "SIX PENCE") (6.68)......................	†	£5000
164	16	6d. blue (wmkd "SIX PENCE") (20.5.68)...............................	£425	24·00
		a. Indigo-blue	—	26·00
165		6d. dull blue (wmkd "THREE PENCE") (6.12.69)..................	£250	9·50
		a. Deep blue	—	10·00
166		6d. dull blue (wmkd "FOUR PENCE") (21.5.70)...................	£425	29·00
		a. Deep blue	—	30·00

*(c) V over Crown, W **19**, coloured paper.*

167	14	2d. mauve/lilac (7.68)..................	70·00	6·50
		a. Lilac/lilac	70·00	6·50

*(d) Saunders single-lined numeral "4" as W **11**.*

168	16	6d. dull blue (21.5.70)	†	£1600

The supply of paper was so short during 1868 that many odds and ends were utilised. Nos. 161 (five known), 163 (one known) and 168 (ten known) are the rarest of these emergency printings.

(Printed in Melbourne from a double electrotyped plate of 240 supplied by D.L.R.)

1870 (28 Jan)–**73.** Wmk V over Crown. W **19**.

169	20	2d. brown-lilac (P 13)	75·00	1·50
		a. Dull lilac-mauve (9.70)..............	65·00	1·00
		b. Mauve (worn plate) (3.73)........	65·00	1·25
170		2d. dull lilac-mauve (p 12) (28.7.71).................................	70·00	2·50
		a. Mauve (worn plate) (3.73)........	70·00	2·25

NINEPENCE

(21)

1871 (22 Apr). No. 123c surch with T **21** in blue.

171	16	9d. on 10d. purple-brown/pink...........	£325	10·00
		a. Blackish brown/pink..........	£400	12·00
		b. Surch double	†	£1300

22	23	24

25	26	27

(Des and eng W. Bell. Typo from electrotyped plates)

1873 (25 Mar)–**74.** *Saunders paper.* Wmk single-lined "10" as W **11**.

172	25	9d. pale brown/pink (P 13)	80·00	17·00
		a. Red-brown/pink (7.74)............	75·00	16·00
173		9d. pale brown/pink (P 12)	85·00	17·00

½ ½

HALF

(28)

1873 (25 Jun). No. 131g surch with T **28** in red.

174	14	½d. on 1d. green (P 13)...................	50·00	14·00
		a. Grass-green	55·00	14·00
		b. Short "1" at right (R. 1/3)	—	70·00
175		½d. on 1d. green (P 12)...................	70·00	14·00
		a. Grass-green	70·00	14·00
		b. Short "1" at right (R. 1/3)	—	75·00

Die I	Die II

Two Dies of 2d.:
  Die I. Single-lined outer oval
  Die II. Double-lined outer oval

(Des and eng W. Bell. Typo from electrotyped plates)

1873–87. Wmk V over Crown, W **19** (sideways on ½d.).

(a) P 13.

176	22	½d. rose-red (10.2.74)...................	14·00	1·00
		a. Lilac-rose (1874)	15·00	1·50
		b. Rosine (shades) (glazed paper) (12.80)...................................	13·00	1·00
		c. Pale red (glazed paper) (1882).	14·00	1·00
		d. Mixed perf 13 and 12	†	£400
177	23	1d. dull bluish green (14.12.75)......	28·00	1·75
		a. Green (shades) (1877)	28·00	1·75
		b. Yellow-green (glazed paper)....	28·00	1·50
		c. Mixed perf 13 and 12..............		
178	24	2d. deep lilac-mauve (I) (1.10.73)...	42·00	65
		a. Dull violet-mauve	42·00	65
		b. Dull mauve	42·00	65
		c. Pale mauve (worn plate) (glazed paper) (1.79)...............	42·00	80
		d. Mixed perf 13 and 12	£375	£275
179		2d. lilac-mauve (II) (glazed paper) (17.12.78)...............................	42·00	65
		a. Grey-mauve (1.80)..................	—	70
		b. Pale mauve (6.80)..................	50·00	70
		c. Vert pair, lower stamp imperf horiz	†	£1900
180	26	1s. indigo-blue/blue (16.8.76).........	75·00	3·50
		a. Wmk sideways.......................	†	£750
		b. Deep blue/blue (7.77).............	80·00	3·50
		c. Pale blue/blue (3.80)..............	85·00	3·50
		d. Bright blue/blue (9.80)...........	90·00	7·50
		e. Bright blue/blue (glazed paper) (21.11.83)...............................	90·00	5·00
		f. Pale blue/blue (glazed paper) ...		
		g. Mixed perf 13 and 12	†	

(b) P 12.

181	22	½d. rose-red (1874)......................	14·00	2·50
		a. Lilac-rose (1874)	14·00	2·50
		b. Rosine (shades) (glazed paper).	14·00	2·25
		c. Pale red (glazed paper) (1882).	14·00	2·50
182	23	1d. dull bluish green (1875)	35·00	6·50
		a. Green (shades) (1877)	32·00	6·50
		b. Yellow-green (glazed paper)......	—	4·00
183	24	2d. deep lilac-mauve (I) (1873)......	—	5·00
		a. Dull violet-mauve	—	5·00
		b. Dull mauve	55·00	2·75
		c. Pale mauve (worn plate) (glazed paper) (1879)...............	—	3·00
184		2d. lilac-mauve (II) (glazed paper) (1878)....................................	60·00	2·50
		a. Grey-mauve (glazed paper) (1880)...................................	—	2·50
		b. Pale mauve (glazed paper) (1880)...................................	—	3·50
185	25	9d. lilac-brown/pink (1.12.75)	£120	14·00
186	26	1s. deep blue/blue (1880)	—	7·50
		a. Bright blue/blue (1880)	—	7·50

(c) P 12½.

187	22	½d. rosine (shades) (glazed paper) (1880)...................................		
		a. Pale red (glazed paper) (1882).		

188	23	1d. yellow-green (*glazed paper*) (1880)		
189	24	2d. grey-mauve (II) (*glazed paper*) (1880)		
		a. *Pale mauve* (1880)		
190	27	2s. deep blue/*green* (*glazed paper*) (8.7.81)	£130	19·00
		a. *Light blue/green (glazed paper)* (4.83)	£140	22·00
		ab. Wmk sideways		
		b. *Ultramarine/green (glazed paper)* (6.84)	—	28·00
		ba. Wmk sideways	—	50·00

8ᵈ 8ᵈ

EIGHTPENCE
(29)

1876 (1 July). No. 185 *surch with T* **29** *in blue*.

191	25	8d. on 9d. lilac-brown/*pink*	£200	17·00
		a. "F.IGHTPENCE"	—	£250

No. 191a was caused by a broken "E" and it occurred once in each sheet of 120.

1877. *Saunders paper.* Wmk "10" as W **11**.

192	14	8d. lilac-brown/*pink* (P 13)	—	£500
		a. *Purple-brown/pink* (2.78)	£110	10·00
		b. *Chocolate/pink* (8.78)	†	£600
		c. *Red-brown/pink* (8.79)	90·00	5·50
193		8d. red-brown (P 12) (8.79)	£200	16·00
194		8d. red-brown/*pink* (P 12½) (8.79)	—	50·00

Nos. 192/4 occur amongst the V over Crown printings, the two types of pink paper having become mixed.

1878. *Emergency printings on coloured papers.* Wmk V over Crown, W **19** (sideways on ½d.). P 13.

195	22	½d. rose-red/*pink* (1.3.78)	38·00	23·00
196	23	1d. yellow-green/*yellow* (5.3.78)	95·00	16·00
197		1d. yellow-green/*drab* (5.4.78)	£140	60·00
198	24	2d. dull violet-mauve/*lilac* (21.2.78)	—	£750
199		2d. dull violet-mauve/*green* (23.2.78)	£180	22·00
200		2d. dull violet-mauve/*brown* (21.3.78)	£170	22·00

There was a shortage of white V over Crown, W **19**, watermarked paper in the early months of 1878 and various coloured papers were used for printings of the ½d., 1d. and 2d. values until fresh stocks of white paper were received.

No. 198 is often misidentified. It can be confused with discoloured examples of Nos. 178/b, and has often been faked.

30 31 32

(Des and eng C. Naish. Typo from electrotyped plates)

1880 (3 Nov)–**84**. Wmk V over Crown. W **19**.

201	30	1d. green (P 12½) (2.84)	£100	14·00
202	31	2d. sepia (P 12½)	29·00	80
		a. *Sepia-brown* (2.81)	27·00	80
		b. *Brown (aniline)* (5.81)	30·00	80
		c. *Dull black-brown* (10.81)	—	80
		d. *Dull grey-brown* (3.82)	26·00	80
203		2d. sepia (P 13)		
		a. *Mixed perf 13 and 12*	†	£650
204		2d. sepia (P 12)	—	£120
		a. *Sepia-brown* (2.81)	—	£120
		b. *Brown (aniline)* (5.81)	—	£120
205		2d. mauve (*worn plate*) (P 12½) (2.84)	£225	7·50
206	32	4d. rose-carmine (P 12½) (10.81)	65·00	5·50
		a. *Rosine* (7.82)	65·00	5·00

Nos. 201 and 205 are subsequent printings of stamps first produced on watermark W **33**.

33

1882–84. Wmk V over Crown W **33** (sideways on ½d.). P 12½.

207	22	½d. rosine (3.83)	19·00	6·00
		a. *Perf 12*	—	21·00
208	23	1d. yellow-green (9.82)	30·00	2·75
		a. *Perf 12*		
209	30	1d. yellow-green (29.10.83)	28·00	1·75
		a. *Green* (1.84)	26·00	1·75
		b. *Pale green* (5.84)	26·00	1·50
210	31	2d. dull grey-brown (15.8.82)	25·00	1·25
		a. *Chocolate* (3.83)	25·00	1·25
		ab. *Perf 12*	†	£375
211		2d. mauve (20.12.83)	23·00	1·25
		a. *Worn plate* (2.84)	23·00	1·25
		b. *Perf 12*	†	£750
		c. *Mixed perf 12 and 12½*	†	£750
212	15	3d. yellow-orange (13.4.83)	50·00	12·00
		a. *Dull brownish orange*	50·00	14·00
213	32	4d. rose-red (3.83)	60·00	9·00
214	16	6d. dull violet-blue (10.11.82)	30·00	2·00
		a. *Indigo-blue* (11.83)	30·00	2·00
		b. *Light ultramarine* (8.84)	30·00	2·00

Reprints were made in 1891 of the "Laureated" 1d., 2d., 3d. (in yellow), 4d., 6d., 8d. (in orange-yellow), 10d. (in greenish slate) and 5s. (in blue and red), of the Bell ½d., 1d., 2d. (Die II), 9d. and 1s. and of the Naish 2d. With the exception of the Bell 9d., which was watermarked W **19**, all were watermarked W **33** and perforated 12½. Some were from new plates.

THE POST OFFICE ACT OF 1883. Following official concern as to the number of different series of adhesive stamps, both fiscal and postal, used in Victoria it was decided that the system should be unified to the extent that the postage stamps, Stamp Statute fiscals and Stamp Duty fiscals should be replaced by a single series valid for all three purposes. As the Stamp Duty series contained the largest number of values it was adopted as the basis of the new range.

The regulations for the changeover were detailed in the Post Office Act of 1883 which came into force on 1 January 1884. From that date all existing Stamp Statute (first produced in 1871) and Stamp Duty (first produced in 1879) issues became valid for postal purposes, and the previous postage stamps could be used for fiscal fees.

Until matters could be organised printings of some of the existing postage values continued and these will be found included in the listings above.

Printing of the Stamp Statute series was discontinued in early 1884. The existing Stamp Duty range was initially supplemented by postage stamps overprinted "STAMP DUTY" for those values where the available fiscal design was considered to be too large to be easily used on mail. These overprints were replaced by smaller designs inscribed "STAMP DUTY".

Stamp Statute and Stamp Duty values which became valid for postal purposes on 1 January 1884 have previously been listed in this catalogue as Postal Fiscals. Under the circumstances this distinction appears somewhat arbitrary and all such stamps are now shown in the main listing. In some instances prices quoted are for examples with postal cancellations. Used prices are also provided for fiscally used and these are marked "F.C.".

34 35 36

37

(Des and dies eng J. Turner (3d., 2s.6d.), W. Bell (others). Typo from electrotypes)

1884 (1 Jan*). *Stamp Statute series. Vert designs as T* **34/6**, *and others showing Queen Victoria, and T* **37**. P 13.

(a) Wmk single-lined numerals according to face value, as W **11**, (sideways). *Paper manufactured by T. H. Saunders unless otherwise stated.*

215		1s. blue/*blue*	80·00	24·00
		a. *Perf 12*	95·00	30·00
216		2s. blue/*green (D.L.R. paper)*	£130	80·00
		a. *Perf 12*	£130	80·00
217		2s. deep blue/*green*	£130	
		a. *Perf 12*	—	80·00
		b. *Wmk upright*		
218		10s. brown-olive/*pink*		
219		10s. red-brown/*pink*	£950	£250
		a. *Wmk upright Perf 12*		

(b) Wmk V over Crown W **19** (sideways). P 13.

220		1d. pale green	50·00	38·00
		a. *Green (wmk upright)* (P 12½)	85·00	65·00
221		3d. mauve	£650	£350
222		4d. rose	£550	£275
		a. *Wmk upright*	£650	
223		6d. blue	75·00	24·00
		a. *Ultramarine*	65·00	21·00
		ab. *Perf 12*	75·00	22·00
224		1s. blue/*blue*	75·00	24·00
		a. *Perf 12*	80·00	28·00
		b. *Ultramarine/blue* (P 12½)	—	50·00
		ba. *Perf 12*	—	35·00
		c. *Deep blue/blue* (P 12½)	75·00	24·00
		ca. *Perf 12*	80·00	24·00
225		2s. blue/*green*	£120	75·00
		a. *Perf 12*	£120	
		b. *Deep blue/blue-green (glazed paper)*	£120	80·00
		ba. *Perf 12*	£120	85·00
226		2s.6d. orange	—	£140
		a. *Perf 12*		
		b. *Yellow (glazed paper)*	£350	
		ba. *Perf 12*	£350	£140
		c. *Orange-yellow (glazed paper)* (P 12½)	—	£150
		ca. *Perf 12*		
227		5s. blue/*yellow*	£325	80·00
		a. *Perf 12*	£325	
		b. *Wmk upright*	£325	
		ba. *Perf 12*		
		c. *Ultram/lemon (glazed paper)* (P 12½)	£325	80·00
		ca. *Wmk upright*		
228		10s. brown/*pink*	£950	£250
		a. *Purple-brown/pink*	£950	£250

229		£1 slate-violet/*yellow*	£700	£190
		a. *Wmk upright*		
		b. *Mauve/yellow*		
		ba. *Perf 12*	£700	£190
		bb. *Perf 12½*	£700	£190
230		£5 black and yellow-green	£4250	£950
		a. *Perf 12*		
		b. *Wmk upright. Perf 12½*	£4250	£950

(c) Wmk V over Crown (sideways) W **33**

231		1d. yellowish green (P 12½)	65·00	65·00
232		2s.6d. pale orange-yellow (P 12)	£325	£140
233		£5 black & yellow-grn (wmk upright) (P 12)	—	£900

½d

HALF
(38)

1884 (1 Jan*). *No.* 220 *surch with T* **38** *in red*.

234		½d. on 1d. pale green	65·00	65·00

*The dates quoted are those on which the stamps became valid for postal purposes. The ½d., 1d., 4d., 6d., 1s., 5s. and £1 were issued for fiscal purposes on 26 April 1871. The 10s. was added to the series in June 1871, the £5 in September 1871, the 2s.6d. in July 1876 and the 3d. in October 1879.

All values of the Stamp Statute series were reprinted in 1891 on paper watermarked W **19** (5s., 10s., £1) or W **33** (others). The £5 was pulled from the original plate, but the others were produced from new electrotypes taken from the original dies.

39 40 41

42 43 44

45 46 47

48 49 50

51 52 53

54 55

56   57

58   59

60

61

(Des H. Samson and F. Oxenbould (T **39**), C. Jackson and L. Lang (all others except T **40**). Dies eng C. Jackson, J. Turner, J. Whipple, A. Williams and other employees of Sands & MacDougall. T **40** die eng C. Naish)

1884 (1 Jan*)–**96**. *Existing Stamp Duty series.*

(a) Litho. Wmk V over Crown. W **19** (sideways). P 13.

235	**39**	1d. blue-green	75·00	25·00
		a. Perf 12	75·00	25·00
		b. Perf 12½		
236	**43**	1s.6d. rosine	£180	27·00
		a. Perf 12	—	35·00
		b. Perf 12½		
237	**45**	3s. purple/*blue*	£450	45·00
		a. Perf 12	£500	50·00
		b. Perf 12½		
238	**46**	4s. orange-red	95·00	19·00
		a. Perf 12	95·00	19·00
		b. Perf 12½		
239	**48**	6s. apple-green	£300	38·00
240	**49**	10s. brown/*rose* (glazed paper)	£475	85·00
		a. Perf 12		
		b. Perf 12½		
		c. Wmk upright		
		cb. Perf 12½		
241	**50**	15s. mauve	£1300	£225
242	**51**	£1 red-orange	£475	80·00
		a. Perf 12½	£475	80·00
243	**52**	£1.5s. dull rose (wmk upright)........	£1300	£250
244	**53**	£1.10s. deep grey-olive	£1300	£150
		a. Wmk upright		£180
245	—	35s. grey-violet (wmk upright) (F.C. £225)	£6000	
246	**54**	£2 blue	—	£130
247	**55**	45s. dull brown-lilac	£2750	£225
248	**56**	£5 rose-red (wmk upright) (F.C. £65)	£3500	£500
249	**57**	£6 blue/*pink* (wmk upright) (glazed paper) (F.C. £120)	—	£800
250	**58**	£7 violet/*blue* (wmk upright) (F.C. £120)	—	£800
251	**59**	£8 brownish red/*yellow* (wmk upright) (glazed paper) (F.C. £120)	—	£950
252	**60**	£9 yellow-green/*green* (wmk upright) (glazed paper) (F.C. £120)	—	£950

(b) Typo from electrotypes.

(i) Wmk V over Crown. W **19** (sideways). P 13.

253	**39**	1d. yellowish green	60·00	25·00
		a. Perf 12	60·00	25·00
		b. Perf 12½		
254	**40**	1d. pale bistre	23·00	4·00
		a. Perf 12	23·00	4·75
		b. Perf 12½		
255	**41**	6d. dull blue	75·00	12·00
		a. Perf 12	80·00	20·00
		b. Perf 12½		
256	**42**	1s. deep blue/*blue*	85·00	5·50
		a. Perf 12	85·00	7·00
		b. Perf 12½		
		c. Brt blue/*blue* (glazed paper) (P 12½)	85·00	6·50
		ca. Perf 12		7·00
		d. Ultramarine/*blue* (glazed paper) (P 12½) (11.84)	£130	7·00
257		1s. chalky blue/*lemon* (glazed paper) (P 12½) (3.3.85)...	£100	24·00
258	**44**	2s. deep blue/*green* (glazed paper).	£160	24·00
		a. Perf 12	—	26·00
		b. Perf 12½	£160	28·00
		c. Indigo/*green*	£140	28·00
		ca. Perf 12	£180	29·00
		cb. Perf 12½		
259	**45**	3s. mar/*bl* (glazed paper) (P 12½) (8.8.84)	£375	35·00
260	**47**	5s. claret/*yellow* (glazed paper)	55·00	6·00
		a. Perf 12	70·00	12·00
		b. Perf 12½		
		c. Pale claret/*yellow* (P 12½)	55·00	13·00
		ca. Perf 12	75·00	13·00
		d. Reddish purple/*lemon* (P 12½) (6.87)	50·00	12·00
		e. Brown-red/*yellow* (P 12½) (5.93)	80·00	32·00
261	**49**	10s. chocolate/*rose* (glazed paper) ...	—	80·00
		a. Perf 12		
		b. Perf 12½		
		c. Wmk upright		
262	**51**	£1 yellow-orange/*yellow* (P 12)......	£600	75·00
		a. Orange/*yellow* (P 12½) (8.84)...	£550	55·00
		b. Reddish orange/*yellow* (P 12½) (9.88)	£350	55·00
263	**54**	£2 deep blue (P 12)	—	£120
264	**61**	£10 dull mauve (P 12)	£3250	£180
		a. Deep red-lilac (P 12)		

(ii) Wmk V over Crown W **33** (sideways). P 12½.

265	**40**	1d. ochre	35·00	6·00
		a. Perf 12	35·00	6·00
266	**41**	6d. ultramarine	80·00	11·00
		a. Perf 12	80·00	11·00
267	**43**	1s.6d. pink (1.85)	£140	26·00
		a. Bright rose-carmine (4.86)..	£160	23·00
268	**45**	3s. drab (20.10.85)	75·00	16·00
		a. Olive-drab (1.93)	70·00	16·00
269	**46**	4s. red-orange (5.86)	80·00	15·00
		a. Yellow-orange (12.94)..........	£100	13·00
		ab. Wmk upright		
270	**47**	5s. rosine (8.5.96)	75·00	19·00
271	**48**	6s. pea-green (12.11.91)	£110	42·00
		a. Apple-green (wmk upright) .	£180	40·00
272	**49**	10s. dull bluish green (10.85)	£190	40·00
		a. Grey-green (5.86)	£150	30·00
273	**50**	15s. purple-brown (12.85)............	£700	80·00
		a. Brown (wmk upright) (5.95) ..	£700	85·00
274	**52**	£1.5s. pink (wmk upright) (6.8.90)	£1300	95·00
275	**53**	£1.10s. pale olive (6.88)..............	£900	85·00
276	**54**	£2 bright blue	—	80·00
		a. Blue (7.88)	£800	80·00
277	**55**	45s. lilac (15.8.90)	£3000	£110
278	**56**	£5 rose-pink (P 12)	—	£450
		a. Pink (P 12½)	—	£600
279	**61**	£10 mauve (3.84)	£3250	£120
		a. Lilac (6.85)		£130

*This is the date on which the stamps became valid for postal use. The 1d., 6d., 1s., 1s.6d., 2s., 3s., 4s., 5s., 10s., 15s., £1, £1 10s., £2, £5 and £10 were issued for fiscal purposes on 18 December 1879 with the £1 5s., 35s., 45s., £6 and £9 added to the range later the same month and the 6s., £7 and £8 in January 1880.

Used prices for the £1 5s., £1 10s., £2 (No. 276a), 45s. and £10 watermarked W **33** are for examples from the cancelled-to-order sets sold to collectors by the Victoria postal authorities between September 1900 and 30 June 1902.

Similar Stamp Duty designs were prepared for 7s., 8s., 9s., 11s., 12s., 13s., 14s., 16s., 17s., 18s., and 19s., but were never issued.

The two different 1d. designs were reprinted in 1891 on W **33** paper. For these designs with later watermarks see Nos. 345/50 and 369/71.

62

(Des C. Jackson and L. Lang. Dies eng C. Jackson)

1884 (1 Jan*)–**00**. *High value Stamp Duty series.*

(a) Recess-printed direct from the die.

(i) Wmk V over Crown W **19** (sideways). P 12½.

280	**62**	£25 yellow-green (F.C. £80)............		
		a. Wmk upright		
		b. Perf 13		
		c. Deep green (F.C. £80)		
		ca. Wmk upright		
281		£50 bright mauve (F.C. £110)........		
		a. Wmk upright		
		b. Perf 13		
282		£100 crimson-lake (F.C. £160)........		
		a. Wmk upright		
		b. Perf 13		

(ii) Wmk V over Crown W **33** (sideways).P 12½.

283	**62**	£25 yellow-green		
		a. Perf 12		
		b. Deep green (1.85) (F.C. £80)	—	£600
		c. Bright blue-green (10.90) (F.C £80)		
		ca. Wmk upright		
284		£50 dull lilac-mauve (wmk upright) (F.C. £110)		
		a. Black-violet (10.90) (F.C £90)...	—	£600
		ab. Wmk upright		
285		£100 crimson (F.C. £160)		
		a. Wmk upright		
		b. Perf 12 (F.C. £160)		
		c. Aniline crimson (wmk upright) (2.85) (F.C. £160)	—	£750
		d. Scarlet-red (5.95)	—	£750
		da. Wmk upright	—	£600

(b) Litho. Wmk V over Crown W **33** (sideways). P 12½.

286	**62**	£25 dull yellowish green (1.86) (F.C. £60)		
		a. Wmk upright (11.87).		
		b. Dull blue-green (9.88) (F.C £60)		
		ba. Wmk upright		
287		£50 dull purple (1.86) (F.C. £80)		
		a. Wmk upright		
		b. Bright violet (11.89) (F.C. £80)..		
		ba. Wmk upright		
288		£100 rosine (1.86) (F.C. £130)...........		
		a. Wmk upright		

(c) Typo from electrotyped plates. Wmk V over Crown. W **33**. P 12½.

289	**62**	£25 dull blue-green (12.97)	—	£180
290		£50 bright mauve (10.97)	—	£275
291		£100 pink-red (10.19.00)	—	£350

*This is the date on which the stamps became valid for postal use. All three values were issued for fiscal purposes on 18 December 1879.

Used prices for Nos. 283b, 284a, 285c/d and 289/91 are for examples from the cancelled-to-order sets described beneath No. 279a. "F.C." indicates that the price quoted is for a stamp with a fiscal cancellation.

For the £25 and £50 with watermark W **82** see Nos. 351/2.

63

(Des and die eng C. Naish. Typo from electrotyped plates)

1884 (23 Apr)–**92**. *New design inscr* "STAMP DUTY". Wmk V over Crown, W **33** (sideways). P 12½.

292	**63**	2s.6d. brown-orange	85·00	14·00
		a. Yellow (8.85)	80·00	11·00
		b. Lemon-yellow (2.92)	80·00	12·00

For this design on later watermarks see Nos. 344 and 370.

64   65   66

67   68

(Des and dies eng C. Naish. Typo from electrotyped plates)

1885 (1 Jan)–**95**. *New designs inscr* "STAMP DUTY". P 12½.

(a) W **19**.

293	**68**	8d. rose/*pink*	30·00	7·00
		a. Rose-red/*pink* (2.88)	32·00	7·00
294	**66**	1s. deep dull blue/*lemon* (11.85)....	85·00	9·00
		a. Dull blue/*yellow* (6.86)	85·00	9·50
295	**68**	2s. olive/*bluish green* (12.85).........	75·00	3·25

(b) W **33**.

296	**64**	½d. pale rosine	11·00	1·25
		a. Deep rosine (7.85)	14·00	1·50
		b. Salmon (9.85)	14·00	1·50
297	**65**	1d. yellowish green (1.85)	16·00	1·25
		a. Dull pea-green (2.85)	18·00	1·75
298	**66**	2d. lilac	15·00	40
		a. Mauve (1886)	15·00	40
		b. Rosy-mauve (1886)	17·00	60
299	**65**	3d. yellowish brown	19·00	1·25
		a. Pale ochre (9.86)	11·00	1·25
		b. Bistre-yellow (9.92)	11·00	1·25
300	**67**	4d. magenta	60·00	3·25
		a. Bright mauve-rose (12.86)........	60·00	3·75
		b. Error. Lilac (12.86)	£4000	£800
301	**65**	6d. chalky blue (1.85)	80·00	2·75
		a. Bright blue (3.85)	50·00	2·40
		b. Cobalt (7.85)	50·00	2·40
302	**68**	8d. bright scarlet/*pink* (3.95)........	30·00	9·00
303		2s. olive-green/*pale green* (1.90)	32·00	5·50
304		2s. apple-green (12.8.95)	25·00	50·00
		a. Blue-green (29.10.95)	18·00	12·00

The plates for the 1d., 6d., 1s. and 2s. were derived from the dies of the 2d. (1s.), 3d. (1d. and 6d.) and 8d. (2s.). In each instance lead moulds of six impressions were taken from the original die and the face values altered by hand creating six slightly different versions.

Two states of the 2d. die exist with the second showing a break in the top frame line near the right-hand corner. This damaged die was used for seven impressions on Plate 1 and all 120 on Plate 2.

No. 300b occurred during the December 1886 printing of the 4d. when about fifty sheets were printed in the colour of the 2d. by mistake. The sheets were issued to Melbourne post offices and used examples are known postmarked between 21 December 1886 and 4 March 1887. Nine unused are also believed to exist.

Reprints of the ½d., 1d., 2d., 4d., 6d. and 1s. values were made in 1891 from the existing plates. The 1s. was watermarked W **19** and the remainder W **33**.

For some of these values used with later watermarks see Nos. 336, 343, 361 and 369.

(69)

1885 (Feb–Nov). *Optd with T* **69**. P 12½.

(a) W **19**.

305	**15**	3d. dull orge-yell (*glazed paper*) (B.) (Nov)	—	£140
306	**26**	1s. pale blue/*blue* (*glazed paper*) (P 13)	95·00	21·00
		a. Deep blue/*blue*	—	23·00
		b. Blue opt (F.C. £14)	£1700	£900
307	**27**	2s. ultramarine/*grn* (*glazed paper*) (Mar)	95·00	18·00
		a. Wmk sideways	£110	24·00

(b) W **33**.

308	**15**	3d. yellow-orange (B.) (Nov)	60·00	26·00
		a. Dull brownish orange (B.)	65·00	28·00
309	**32**	4d. rose-red (B.) (Nov)	55·00	40·00

Unauthorised reprints of the 4d. and 1s. values were made in 1895–96, both with blue overprints and watermarked W **33**. The 4d. reprint, which is in pale red, also exists without the overprint.

70	**71**	**72**

| **73** | **74** | **75** |

| **76** | **77** | **78** |

79 **80**

(Des S. Reading (1d.) (No. 313), M. Tannenberg (2½d., 5d.), C. Naish (1s.6d.), P. Astley (others). Dies eng C. Naish (2d. (both existing dies with lines added behind Queen's head) and 1s.6d.), S. Reading (originally an employee of Fergusson & Mitchell) (others). Typo from electrotyped plates).

1886 (26 July)–**96**. W **33** (sideways on ½d., 1s., £5, £7 to £9). P 12½.

310	**70**	½d. lilac-grey (28.8.86)	22·00	6·00
		a. Grey-black	—	35·00
311		½d. pink (15.2.87)	13·00	60
		a. Rosine (aniline) (1889)	7·50	30
		b. Rose-red (1891)	7·50	30
		c. Vermilion (1896)	8·00	35
312	**71**	1d. green	10·00	80
		a. Yellow-green (1887)	10·00	80
313	**72**	1d. dull chestnut (1.1.90)	11·00	50
		a. Deep red-brown (1890)	11·00	30
		b. Orange-brown (1890)	11·00	30
		c. Brown-red (1890)	11·00	30
		d. Yellow-brown (1891)	11·00	30
		e. Bright yellow-orange	50·00	12·00
		f. Brownish orange (1894)	6·50	30
314	**73**	2d. pale lilac (17.12.86)	13·00	20
		a. Pale mauve (1887)	14·00	20
		b. Deep lilac (1888, 1892)	8·00	20
		c. Purple (1894)	5·50	25
		d. Violet (1895)	5·50	20
		e. Imperf.		£800
315	**74**	2½d. red-brown/*lemon* (1.1.91)	23·00	3·25
		a. Brown-red/*yellow* (1892)	17·00	80
		b. Red/*yellow* (1893)	14·00	70
316	**75**	4d. rose-red (1.4.87)	23·00	1·00

317	**76**	a. Red (1893)	13·00	90
		5d. purple-brown (1.1.91)	11·00	2·25
		a. Pale reddish brown (1893)	8·50	2·25
318	**77**	6d. bright ultramarine (27.8.86)	23·00	1·75
		a. Pale ultramarine (1887)	20·00	50
		b. Dull blue (1891)	19·00	50
319	**25**	9d. apple-green (18.10.92)	27·00	9·50
320		9d. carmine-rose (15.10.95)	35·00	9·50
		a. Rosine (aniline) (1896)	38·00	8·50
321	**78**	1s. dull purple-brown (14.3.87)	60·00	2·25
		a. Lake (1890)	48·00	3·00
		b. Carmine-lake (1892)	24·00	1·50
		c. Brownish red (1896)	25·00	1·60
322	**79**	1s.6d. pale blue (9.88)	£140	70·00
323		1s.6d. orange (19.9.89)	20·00	8·50
		a. Red-orange (1893)	20·00	2·25
324	**80**	£5 pale blue and maroon (7.2.88)†	£2000	95·00
325		£6 yellow and pale blue (1.10.87)†	£2500	£130
326		£7 rosine and black (17.10.89)†	£2750	£140
327		£8 mauve and brown-orange (2.8.90)†	£3000	£170
328		£9 apple-green and rosine (21.8.88)†	£3250	£180

†The used prices provided for these stamps are for cancelled-to-order examples.

Unauthorised reprints of the ½d. lilac-grey and 1s.6d. pale blue were made in 1894–95 on W **33** paper and perforated 12½. These differ in shade from the originals and have rougher perforations. It should be noted that the original printing of No. 322 does not occur with inverted watermark, but the reprint does.

A single example of No. 314e is known postmarked "737" (Foster). A second, postmarked "249" (Mortlake), was reported in 1892. It is known that an imperforate sheet was sold at Mortlake P.O. in 1890. Other examples are believed to be clandestine.

Later printings of the £5 to £9 values, as No. 324/8 but on W **85** paper perforated 12½ or 11, were not valid for postal use (*Unused prices*, £275 *for £5 value, from £375 for £6 to £9 values*).

A £10 value as Type **80** was prepared, but not issued.

1891 (17 June). W **19**. P 12½.

329	**72**	1d. orange-brown/*pink*	7·00	2·75

No. 329 was an emergency printing during a shortage of white W **33** paper.

81 **82**

(Die eng A. Williams (1½d.). Typo from electrotyped plates).

1896 (11 Jun)–**99**. W **82** (sideways on ½d., 1½d., 1s., 2s.6d. to 15s.). P 12½.

330	**70**	½d. light scarlet (1.7.96)	4·50	80
		a. Carmine-rose (1897)	4·50	80
		b. Dp carmine-red (coarse impression) (1899)	—	2·25
		c. Wmk upright	£100	65·00
331		½d. emerald (1.8.99)	15·00	3·25
		a. Wmk upright	—	
332	**72**	1d. brown-red (13.6.96)	6·50	10
		a. Brownish orange (1897)	6·50	10
		b. Wmk sideways		
333	**81**	1½d. apple-green (7.10.97)	3·00	4·00
334	**73**	2d. violet (9.96)	11·00	10
		a. Wmk sideways	†	80·00
335	**74**	2½d. blue (1.8.99)	9·00	8·00
336	**65**	3d. ochre (11.96)	9·00	65
		a. Buff (1898)	8·00	65
		b. Wmk sideways		
337	**75**	4d. red (6.97)	17·00	3·00
338	**76**	5d. red-brown (7.97)	18·00	1·50
339	**77**	6d. dull blue (9.96)	16·00	80
340	**25**	9d. rosine (9.96)	30·00	9·50
		a. Rose-carmine (1898)	—	3·50
		b. Dull rose (1898)	26·00	3·50
		c. Wmk sideways		
341	**78**	1s. brownish red (3.97)	16·00	2·25
		a. Wmk sideways		
342	**79**	1s.6d. brown-orange (8.98)	42·00	24·00
343	**68**	2s. blue-green (4.97)	40·00	7·00
344	**63**	2s.6d. yellow (9.96)	90·00	14·00
		a. Wmk upright (1898)	£100	14·00
345	**45**	3s. olive-drab (12.96)	55·00	19·00
		a. Wmk upright (1898)	55·00	19·00
346	**46**	4s. orange (9.97)	85·00	14·00
347	**47**	5s. rosine (2.97)	85·00	14·00
		a. Rose-carmine (1897)	85·00	14·00
		b. Wmk upright. Rosine (1899)	85·00	15·00
348	**48**	6s. pale yellow-green (4.99)†	85·00	24·00
349	**49**	10s. grey-green (4.97)	£160	19·00
		a. Blue-green (1898)	£160	19·00
350	**50**	15s. brown (4.97)†	£450	60·00
351	**62**	£25 dull bluish green (1897)†	—	£160
352		£50 dull purple (1897)†	—	£225

†The used prices provided for these stamps are for cancelled-to-order examples.

83 **84**

(Des M. Tannenberg. Dies eng A. Mitchelhill. Typo from electrotyped plates)

1897 (22 Oct). *Hospital Charity Fund.* W **82** (sideways). P 12½.

353	**83**	1d. (1s.) blue	18·00	19·00
354	**84**	2½d. (2s.6d) red-brown	90·00	75·00
353s/4s		Optd "Specimen" Set of 2		£150

These stamps were sold at 1s. and 2s.6d., but only had postal validity for 1d. and 2½d. with the difference going to the Fund.

1899 (1 Aug). W **33** (sideways). P 12½.

355	**81**	1½d. brown-red/*yellow*	3·00	1·75

85

1899 (1 Aug)–**1901**. W **85** (sideways on ½d., 1s. and 2s.6d. to 10s.). P 12½.

356	**70**	½d. emerald (12.99)	4·75	40
		a. Deep blue-green	5·00	40
		b. Wmk upright	—	10·00
357	**72**	1d. rose-red	7·50	20
		a. Rosine (1900)	4·50	10
		b. Wmk sideways		
358		1d. olive (6.6.01)	6·50	4·00
359	**73**	2d. violet	14·00	10
		a. Wmk sideways		†
360	**74**	2½d. blue (10.99)	17·00	1·50
361	**65**	3d. bistre-yellow (9.99)	7·00	2·50
		a. Wmk sideways		
362		3d. slate-green (20.6.01)	23·00	11·00
363	**75**	4d. rose-red (10.99)	10·00	2·50
364	**76**	5d. red-brown (10.99)	18·00	2·50
365	**77**	6d. dull ultramarine (1.00)	11·00	2·25
366	**25**	9d. rose-red (9.99)	18·00	1·75
		a. Wmk sideways		
367	**78**	1s. brown-red (5.00)	21·00	3·00
368	**79**	1s.6d. orange (9.99)	22·00	17·00
369	**68**	2s. blue-green (6.00)	22·00	9·50
370	**63**	2s.6d. yellow (1.00)	£300	20·00
371	**45**	3s. pale olive (4.00)†	£130	24·00
372	**47**	5s. rose-red (4.00)	£100	24·00
373	**49**	10s. green (3.00)†	£170	24·00

†The used prices provided for these stamps are for cancelled-to-order examples.

From 1 July 1901 stamps inscribed "STAMP DUTY" could only be used for fiscal purposes.

86 Victoria Cross   **87** Australian Troops in South Africa

(Des Sands and MacDougall (1d.), J. Sutherland (2d.). Dies eng S. Reading. Typo from electrotyped plates)

1900 (22 May). *Empire Patriotic Fund.* W **85** (sideways). P 12½.

374	**86**	1d. (1s.) olive-brown	80·00	48·00
375	**87**	2d. (2s.) emerald-green	£150	£160

These stamps were sold at 1s. and 2s., but only had postal validity for 1d. and 2d. with the difference going to the Fund.

FEDERATION. The six Australian colonies were federated as the Commonwealth of Australia on 1 January 1901. Under the terms of the Post and Telegraph Act their postal services were amalgamated on 1 March 1901, but other clauses to safeguard the financial position of the individual States provided them with a large degree of independence until 13 October 1910 when issues of each state could be used throughout Australia. Postage stamps for the Commonwealth of Australia did not appear until January 1913.

It was agreed in 1901 that stamp printing should be centralised at Melbourne under J. B. Cooke of South Australia who was appointed Commonwealth Stamp Printer. By 1909 the Commonwealth Stamp Printing Branch in Melbourne was producing stamps for Papua, South Australia, Tasmania and Western Australia in addition to those of Victoria.

On federation it was decided to separate postal and fiscal stamp issues so Victoria needed urgent replacements for the current Stamp Duty series which reverted to fiscal use only on 30 June 1901.

1901 (29 Jan). *Re-use of previous designs without "POSTAGE" inscr.* W **82** (2s.) or W **85** (others) (sideways on ½d.). P 12×12½.

376	**22**	½d. bluish green	2·00	1·75
		a. "VICTCRIA" (R. 7/19)	35·00	40·00
377	**31**	2d. reddish violet	8·00	1·75
378	**15**	3d. dull orange	15·00	2·75
379	**32**	4d. bistre-yellow	25·00	15·00
380	**16**	6d. emerald	9·00	7·50
381	**26**	1s. yellow	50·00	38·00
382	**27**	2s. blue/*pink*	42·00	27·00
383	**18**	5s. pale red and deep blue	48·00	42·00

88 **89** **90**

91 92 93

94 95 96

97 98 99

100 101 102

I   II   III

Three die states of ½d.:

I. Outer vertical line of colour to left of "V" continuous except for a break opposite the top of "V". Triangles either end of "VICTORIA" are more or less solid colour.
II. Die re-engraved. Three breaks in outer line of colour left of "V". White lines added to left triangle.
III. Die re-engraved. As II, but equivalent triangle at right also contains white lines.

I

II

III

Three die states of 1d.:

I. Thick lines fill top of oval above Queen's head.
II. Die re-engraved. Lines thinner, showing white space between.
III. Die re-engraved. As II, but with bottom left value table recut to show full point separated from both "1" and the circular frame.

I and II   III

Two die states of 2d.:

I. Frame line complete at top right corner. Bottom right corner comes to a point.
II. Break in right frame line just below the top corner. Bottom right corner is blunted.

Two types of 1s.:

A. "POSTAGE" 6 mm long (produced by a hand punch applied twice to each impression on the previous 1s. electrotyped plate. Slight variations in position occur).
B. "POSTAGE" 7 mm long (produced from new electrotyped plates incorporating the "POSTAGE" inscriptions).

(Eng S. Reading after photo by W. Stuart (£1, £2))

1901 (29 Jan)–**10**. Previous issues with "POSTAGE" added and new designs (£1, £2). W **85** (sideways on ½d., 1½d., £1, £2).

(a) P 12×12½ (½ to 2s.) or 12½ (5s. to £2).

384	88	½d. blue-green (I) (26.6.01)	3·25	70
		a. Wmk upright (1903)	3·25	70
		b. Die state II (6.04)	4·50	70
		ba. Wmk upright	4·50	30
		c. Die state III (6.05)	10·00	1·00
385	89	1d. rose (I)	7·50	20
		a. Dull red (12.02)	7·00	20
		ab. Wmk sideways	†	75·00
		b. Die state II (4.01)	2·75	15
		ba. Dull red (12.02)	2·50	15
		c. Die state III. Pale rose-red	5·00	1·75
		ca. Wmk sideways	60·00	60·00
386	90	1½d. maroon/yellow (9.7.01)	10·00	6·00
		a. Wmk upright. Brn-red/yell (9.01)	2·40	55
		b. Dull red-brown/yellow (1906)	2·10	55
		ba. On yellow-buff back (1908)	3·75	1·25
387	91	2d. lilac (I) (26.6.01)	12·00	30
		a. Die state II	28·00	1·50
		b. Reddish violet (1902)	11·00	30
		ba. Die state II	28·00	1·50
		c. Bright purple (II) (1905)	7·00	30
		d. Rosy mauve (II) (1905)		
		e. Wmk sideways	30·00	
388	92	2½d. dull blue	12·00	35
		a. Deep blue (1902)	12·00	35
		b. Wmk sideways	†	£900
389	93	3d. dull orange-brown (5.7.01)	9·00	1·25
		a. Chestnut (1901)	9·00	70
		b. Yellowish brown (1903)	9·00	70
		ba. Wmk sideways	12·00	20·00
390	94	4d. bistre-yellow (26.6.01)	7·00	65
		a. Brownish bistre (1905)	10·00	1·25
391	95	5d. reddish brown	11·00	40
		a. Purple-brown (1903)	10·00	55
392	96	6d. emerald (5.7.01)	12·00	1·00
		a. Dull green (1904)	14·00	1·00
393	97	9d. dull rose-red (5.7.01)	16·00	2·50
		a. Wmk sideways (1901)	28·00	11·00
		b. Pale red (1901)	16·00	1·25
		c. Dull brownish red (1905)	20·00	2·75
394	98	1s. yellow-orange (A) (5.7.01)	18·00	2·00
		a. Yellow (1902)	18·00	2·00
		b. Type B (4.03)	19·00	3·00
		ba. Orange (1904)	18·00	2·50
		bb. Wmk sideways (1905)	35·00	14·00
395	99	2s. blue/rose (5.7.01)	23·00	2·00
		a. Wmk sideways	†	£850
398	100	5s. rose-red and pale blue (5.7.01)	60·00	16·00
		a. Scarlet and deep blue	70·00	14·00
		b. Rosine and blue (12.04)	70·00	14·00
399	101	£1 carmine-rose (18.11.01)	£250	£120
400	102	£2 deep blue (2.6.02)	£500	£300

(b) P 11.

401	88	½d. blue-green (I) (9.02)	8·00	3·50
		a. Wmk upright (1903)	3·25	1·75
		b. Die state II (6.04)	7·00	1·75
		ba. Wmk upright	9·00	2·50
		c. Die state III (6.05)	8·50	2·00
402	89	1d. dull red (I) (12.02)	55·00	40·00
		a. Die state II	45·00	18·00
		ab. Pale red (aniline) (3.03)	9·50	2·25
		ac. Pale rose (aniline) (1904)	28·00	6·00
		b. Die state III. Pale rose-red (7.05)	45·00	40·00
403	90	1½d. dull red-brown/yellow (1910)	70·00	70·00
404	91	2d. bright purple (II) (1905)	£600	£250
		a. Rosy mauve (II) (1905)	†	£200
405	93	3d. yellowish brown (1903)	5·50	7·50
		a. Wmk sideways	16·00	32·00
406	96	6d. emerald (2.03)	12·00	20·00
		a. Dull green (1905)	£600	£250
407	101	£1 rose (5.05)	£375	£150
408	102	£2 deep blue (1905)	£1500	£1100

(c) Compound or mixed perfs of 12×12½ or 12½ and 11.

409	88	½d. blue-green (I) (1901)	35·00	13·00
		a. Wmk upright (1903)	35·00	13·00
		b. Die state II (1904)	32·00	26·00
		ba. Wmk upright	45·00	32·00
410	89	1d. dull red (I) (1902)	—	£275
		a. Die state II	†	£550
411	90	1½d. maroon/yellow (1903)	£650	£325
412	91	2d. reddish violet (I) (1903)	†	£425
413	93	3d. dull orange-brown (1902)	—	£800
414	96	6d. emerald (1903)	†	£750
415	100	5s. rosine and blue (12.04)	£1500	

Examples of the 1d. Die state II perforated 12×12½ exist with two black lines printed across the face of the stamp. These were prepared in connection with stamp-vending machine trials.

1905–13. Wmk Crown over A, W w **11** (sideways on ½d., £1, £2).

(a) P 12×12½. (½d. to 1s.) or 12½ (5s. to £2).

416	88	½d. blue-green (shades) (III) (21.10.05)	2·50	30
		a. Wmk upright	15·00	4·00
		b. Thin, ready gummed paper (6.12)	5·00	5·00
		ba. Wmk upright	4·00	6·00
417	89	1d. rose-red (III) (16.7.05)	2·00	10
		a. Pale rose (1907)	1·25	10
		b. Rose-carmine (1911)	14·00	2·50
		c. Wmk sideways	14·00	7·50
		d. Thin, ready gummed paper (10.12)	4·50	2·25
418	91	2d. dull mauve (II) (13.9.05)	6·00	30
		a. Lilac (1906)	6·00	25
		b. Reddish violet (1907)	6·00	25

		c. Bright mauve (1910)	5·50	1·00
		ca. Thin, ready gummed paper (8.12)	28·00	6·50
419	92	2½d. deep dull blue (10.08)	5·00	1·25
		a. Dull blue (11.09)	3·00	40
		b. Indigo (7.09)	16·00	2·75
420	93	3d. orange-brown (11.11.05)	9·00	1·25
		a. Yellow-orange (1908)	9·00	1·25
		b. Dull orange-buff (1909)	8·00	1·25
		c. Ochre (1912)	8·00	5·00
421	94	4d. yellow-bistre (1.06)	8·00	65
		a. Olive-bistre (1908)	7·00	65
		b. Yellow-olive (1912)	7·00	3·25
422	95	5d. chocolate (14.8.06)	7·00	2·75
		a. Dull reddish brown (1908)	7·00	2·75
		b. Wmk sideways	†	£550
		c. Thin, ready gummed paper (19.10.12)	13·00	15·00
423	96	6d. dull green (25.10.05)	14·00	80
		a. Dull yellow-green (1907)	13·00	80
		b. Emerald (1909)	13·00	1·10
		c. Yellowish green (1911)	13·00	2·75
		d. Emerald. Thin, ready gummed paper (11.12)	22·00	22·00
424	97	9d. brown-red (11.12.05)	22·00	2·75
		a. Orange-brown (1906)	15·00	2·50
		b. Red-brown (1908)	16·00	2·50
		c. Pale dull rose (1909)	16·00	3·75
		d. Rose-carmine (1910)	9·50	1·25
		e. Wmk sideways	£200	75·00
425	98	1s. orange (B) (13.2.06)	8·00	2·00
		a. Yellow-orange (1906)	11·00	2·00
		b. Yellow (1908)	13·00	2·00
		ba. Thin, ready gummed paper (11.12)	30·00	25·00
		c. Pale orange. Thin, ready gummed paper (1913)	30·00	28·00
430	100	5s. rose-red and ultramarine (12.07)	70·00	17·00
		a. Rose-red and blue (1911)	80·00	22·00
		ab. Wmk sideways	90·00	25·00
431	101	£1 salmon (12.2.07)	£250	£130
		a. Dull rose (1910)	£250	£130
		ab. Wmk upright (1911)	£300	£150
432	102	£2 dull blue (18.7.06)	£550	£375

(b) P 11.

433	88	½d. blue-green (shades) (III) (1905)	1·60	30
		a. Wmk upright. Thin, ready gummed paper (1912)	17·00	21·00
434	89	1d. rose-red (III) (1905)	4·00	1·50
		a. Pale rose (1907)	4·00	1·50
		b. Rose-carmine (1911)	7·00	4·00
		ba. Wmk sideways	20·00	14·00
		c. Thin, ready gummed paper (10.12)	10·00	4·75
435	91	2d. lilac (II) (1906)	†	£250
		a. Reddish violet (1907)	65·00	20·00
		b. Bright mauve (1910)	29·00	16·00
436	92	2½d. blue (1908)	60·00	16·00
		a. Indigo (1909)	15·00	9·50
437	93	3d. orange-brown (1905)	10·00	13·00
		a. Yellow-orange (1908)	†	£130
		b. Dull orange-buff (1909)	15·00	21·00
		c. Ochre (1912)	9·00	8·00
		d. Wmk sideways		
438	94	4d. yellow-bistre (1906)	10·00	18·00
		a. Olive-bistre (1909)		
		b. Yellow-olive (1912)	8·50	18·00
439	95	5d. chocolate (1906)	†	£750
		a. Dull reddish brown (1908)	†	£750
440	96	6d. emerald (1909)	10·00	19·00
		a. Yellowish green (1911)	16·00	16·00
441	97	9d. rose-carmine (1910)	†	£650
442	98	1s. yellow-orange (B) (1906)	†	£275
		a. Orange (1910)	£650	
443	100	5s. rose-red and ultramarine (12.07)	75·00	9·50
444	101	£1 salmon (12.2.07)	£400	£140
445	102	£2 dull blue (1.07)	£850	£450

(c) Compound or mixed perfs of 12×12½ or 12½ and 11.

446	88	½d. blue-green (shades) (III) (1905)	21·00	16·00
		a. Wmk upright. Thin, ready gummed paper (1912)	£110	80·00
447	89	1d. rose-red (III) (1905)	50·00	50·00
		a. Pale rose (1907)	—	60·00
		b. Rose-carmine (1911)	—	60·00
448	91	2d. reddish violet (II) (1907)	£475	£325
449	93	3d. orange-brown (1905)	†	£400
		a. Ochre (1912)	£400	
450	94	4d. bistre (1908)	†	£500
451	96	6d. emerald (1909)	†	£600
		a. Yellowish green (1911)	†	£400
452	97	9d. orange-brown (1906)	†	£700
		a. Red-brown (1908)	†	£700
453	98	1s. yellow-orange (1906)	£950	
453a		£1 dull rose	†	£2500

(d) Rotary comb perf 11½×12¼.

454	89	1d. scarlet-red	4·00	1·00
		a. Thin, ready gummed paper (Rose-carmine)	2·75	3·00
		ab. Rose-red	2·75	3·00
		ac. Wmk sideways	35·00	25·00
455	91	2d. lilac (II) (1910)	15·00	1·50

The original Crown over A watermark paper used by Victoria was of medium thickness and had toned gum applied after printing. Stocks of this paper lasted until 1912 when further supplies were ordered from a new papermakers, Cowan and Sons. This paper was much thinner and was supplied with white gum already applied. The first delivery arrived in June 1912 and a second in September of the same year.

The rotary comb perforating machine gauging 11½×12¼ was transferred from South Australia in 1909 when J. B. Cooke moved to Melbourne.

Examples of the 1d. perforated 12½ or 11 exist with two black lines across the face of the stamp. These were prepared in connection with stamp-vending machine trials.

ONE PENNY

(103)   104

1912 (29 June). No. 455 surch with T **103** in red.
| 456 | 91 | 1d. on 2d. lilac (II) | 70 | 50 |

1912 (1 Aug). W **104**.

(a) P 12½ (½d.) or 12×12½.
457	88	½d. bluish green (III)	3·00	4·50
458	89	1d. rose-carmine (III)	5·00	3·75
		a. Wmk sideways	50·00	
459	91	2d. reddish violet (II) (Sept)	3·00	4·25
		a. Lilac	5·50	7·00
460	97	9d. rose-carmine	19·00	20·00

(b) P 11.
461	88	½d. bluish green (III)	20·00	25·00
462	89	1d. rose-carmine (III)	40·00	23·00
		a. Wmk sideways		
463	97	9d. rose-carmine	35·00	40·00

(c) Compound perfs of 12×12½ or 12½ and 11.
| 464 | 97 | 9d. rose-carmine | † | £700 |

Nos. 457/64 were emergency printings caused by the non-arrival of stocks of the Cowan thin, ready gummed Crown over A watermarked paper. Paper watermarked W **104** had been introduced in 1911 and was normally used for Victoria fiscal stamps. This watermark can be easily distinguished from the previous W **85** by its narrow crown.

STAMP BOOKLETS

There are very few surviving examples of Nos. SB1/4. Listings are provided for those believed to have been issued with prices quoted for those known to still exist.

1904 (Mar)–**09**. Black on red cover as No. SB1 of New South Wales. Stapled.
SB1   £1 booklet containing two hundred and forty 1d. in four blocks of 30 and two blocks of 60......
| | a. Red on pink cover (1909) | £20000 |
| | b. Blue on pink cover | £18000 |

1904 (Mar). Black on grey cover as No. SB1. Stapled.
SB2   £1 booklet containing one hundred and twenty 2d. in four blocks of 30

1910 (May). Black on white cover as No. SB3 of New South Wales. Stapled.
SB3   2s. booklet containing eleven ½d. (No. 426), either in block of 6 plus block of 5 or block of 11, and eighteen 1d. (No. 427), either in three blocks of 6 or block of 6 plus block of 12
| | | £3750 |
| | a. Black on pale green cover | £4000 |

Unsold stock of No. SB3 was uprated with one additional ½d. in May 1911.

1911 (1 Aug). Red on pink cover as No. SB3. Stapled.
SB4   2s. Booklet containing twelve ½d. (No.426), either in two blocks of 6 or block of 12, and eighteen 1d. (No.427), either in three blocks of 6 or block of 6 plus block of 12 ... £4250

POSTAGE DUE STAMPS

D 1

(Dies eng A. Williams (values) and J. McWilliams (frame). Typo)

1890 (12 Oct)–**94**. Wmk V over Crown, W 33. P 12×12½.
D1	D 1	½d. dull blue and brown-lake (24.12.90)	4·50	3·75
		a. Dull blue and deep claret	3·00	4·00
D2		1d. dull blue and brown-lake	6·00	1·40
		a. Dull blue and brownish red (1.93)	8·50	1·50
D3		2d. dull blue and brown-lake	10·00	1·75
		a. Dull blue and brownish red (3.93)	15·00	1·00
D4		4d. dull blue and brown-lake	15·00	2·50
		a. Dull blue and pale claret (5.94)	17·00	6·00
D5		5d. dull blue and brown-lake	14·00	2·00
D6		6d. dull blue and brown-lake	15·00	3·50
D7		10d. dull blue and brown-lake	75·00	48·00
D8		1s. dull blue and brown-lake	48·00	7·50
D9		2s. dull blue and brown-lake	£110	50·00
D10		5s. dull blue and brown-lake	£160	90·00
D1/10 Set of 10			£400	£170
D1as/10s Optd "Specimen" Set of 10			£300	

A used example of the 6d. showing compound perforation of 12×12½ and 11 exists in the Royal Collection.

1895 (17 Jan)–**96**. Colours changed. Wmk V over Crown, W 33. P 12×12½.
D11	D 1	½d. rosine and bluish green	5·00	1·60
		a. Pale scarlet and yellow-green (3.96)	3·75	1·75
D12		1d. rosine and bluish green	5·00	1·50
		a. Pale scarlet and yellow-green (3.96)	5·50	1·50
D13		2d. rosine and bluish green	11·00	2·00

		a. Pale scarlet and yellow-green (3.96)	11·00	1·50
D14		4d. rosine and bluish green	11·00	1·50
		a. Pale scarlet and yellow-green (3.96)	9·50	2·00
D15		5d. rosine and bluish green	14·00	14·00
		a. Pale scarlet and yellow-green (3.96)	11·00	8·50
D16		6d. rosine and bluish green	11·00	7·50
D17		10d. rosine and bluish green	24·00	10·00
D18		1s. rosine and bluish green	16·00	3·25
D19		2s. pale red and yellowish green (28.3.95)	60·00	20·00
D20		5s. pale red and yellowish green (28.3.95)	£100	40·00
D11/20 Set of 10			£225	85·00

1897 (1 July)–**99**. Wmk V over Crown. W 82. P 12×12½.
D21	D 1	1d. pale scarlet and yellow-green	7·50	1·25
		a. Dull red and bluish green (8.99)	8·00	1·25
D22		2d. pale scarlet and yellow-green	11·00	1·25
		a. Dull red and bluish green (6.99)	12·00	1·00
D23		4d. pale scarlet and yellow-green	23·00	2·25
		a. Dull red and bluish green (8.99)	23·00	2·00
D24		5d. pale scarlet and yellow-green	23·00	4·00
D25		6d. pale scarlet and yellow-green	10·00	4·25
D21/5 Set of 5			65·00	11·50

1900 (1 June)–**04**. Wmk V over Crown. W 85. P 12×12½.
D26	D 1	½d. rose-red and pale green	10·00	5·50
		a. Pale red and deep green (8.01)	5·00	5·00
		b. Scarlet and deep green (1.03)		26·00
		c. Aniline rosine and green (6.04)	8·50	8·50
D27		1d. rose-red and pale green	11·00	1·25
		a. Pale red and deep green (9.01)	10·00	45
		b. Scarlet and deep green (2.02)	11·00	70
		c. Aniline rosine and green (9.03)	11·00	1·25
D28		2d. rose-red and pale green (7.00)	13·00	1·75
		a. Pale red and deep green (9.01)	13·00	1·75
		b. Scarlet and deep green (2.02)	13·00	1·00
		c. Aniline rosine and green (9.03)	13·00	1·75
D29		4d. rose-red and pale green (5.01)	23·00	6·50
		a. Pale red and deep green (9.01)	22·00	2·75
		b. Scarlet and deep green (6.03)	22·00	3·50
		c. Aniline rosine and green (6.04)	£232	42·00
D30		5d. scarlet and deep green (1.03)	19·00	8·00
D31		1s. scarlet and deep green (3.02)	21·00	7·50
D32		2s. scarlet and deep green (1.03)	£120	70·00
D33		5s. scarlet and deep green (1.03)	£140	70·00
D26/33 Set of 8			£300	£140

1905 (Dec)–**09**. Wmk Crown over A, W w **11**. P 12×12½.
D34	D 1	½d. aniline rosine and pale green (1.06)	14·00	13·00
		a. Scarlet & pale yellow-green (7.07)	5·50	7·00
		b. Dull scarlet and pea-green (3.09)	6·50	8·00
		ba. Compound perf 12×12½ and 11	£375	£250
D35		1d. aniline rosine and pale green	50·00	6·00
		a. Scarlet and pale yellow-green (5.06)	6·50	2·50
		b. Dull scarlet and pea-green (1.07)	10·00	2·50
D36		2d. aniline scarlet and dp yell-grn (5.06)	18·00	2·75
		a. Dull scarlet and pea-green (11.07)	12·00	2·50
D37		4d. dull scarlet and pea-green (1908)	22·00	11·00
D34/7 Set of 4			35·00	20·00

A printing of the 5d. in dull scarlet and pea-green on this paper was prepared in 1907–08, but not put into use. A few examples have survived, either mint or cancelled-to-order from presentation sets (Price £1400 mint, £1000 cancelled-to-order).

WESTERN AUSTRALIA

PRICES FOR STAMPS ON COVER	
Nos. 1/6	from × 6
Nos. 15/32	from × 4
Nos. 33/46	from × 5
Nos. 49/51	from × 6
Nos. 52/62	from × 10
Nos. 63/a	from × 8
No. 67	—
Nos. 68/92a	from × 10
Nos. 94/102	from × 40
Nos. 103/5	from × 8
Nos. 107/10a	from × 12
Nos. 111a/b	—
Nos. 112/16	from × 25
Nos. 117/25	from × 10
Nos. 126/8	—
Nos. 129/34	from × 8
Nos. 135/6	—
Nos. 138/48	from × 12
Nos. 151/63	from × 5
Nos. 168/9	from × 20
Nos. 170/1	from × 4
Nos. 172/3	from × 40
Nos. F11/22	from × 10
Nos. T1/2	—

SPECIMEN OVERPRINTS. Those listed are from U.P.U. distributions between 1889 and 1892. Further "Specimen" overprints exist, but those were used for other purposes.

1   2

3   4

GUM. The 1854 and 1857–59 issues are hardly ever seen with gum, so the unused prices quoted are for examples without gum.

(Eng W. Humphrys. Recess P.B.)

1854 (1 Aug). W **4** (sideways).

(a) Imperf.
| 1 | 1 | 1d. black | £900 | £200 |

(b) Rouletted 7½ to 14 and compound.
| 2 | 1 | 1d. black | £2000 | £500 |

In addition to the supplies received from London a further printing, using the original plate and watermarked paper from Perkins, Bacon, was made in the colony before the date of issue. The 1d. is also known pin-perforated.

(Litho H. Samson (later A. Hillman), Government Lithographer)

1854 (1 Aug)–**55**. W **4** (sideways).

(a) Imperf.
3	2	4d. pale blue	£300	£180
		a. Blue	£300	£180
		b. Deep dull blue	£2000	£750
		c. Slate-blue (1855)	£2250	£950
		d. "T" of "POSTAGE" shaved off to a point at foot (R. 7/5, 7/10, 7/15, 7/20)	£1200	£800
		e. Top of letters of "AUSTRALIA" cut off so that they are barely 1 mm high	†	£13000
		f. "PEICE" instead of "PENCE"	†	£13000
		g. "CE" of "Pence" close together (R. 8/1, 8/6, 8/11, 8/16)	†	£16000
		h. Frame inverted (R. 8/1, 8/6, 8/11, 8/16)	†	£75000
		i. Tilted border (R. 7/4, 7/9, 7/14, 7/19)	£1400	£950
		j. "WEST" in squeezed-down letters and "F" of "FOUR" with pointed foot (R. 2/17)	£1500	£1000
		k. "ESTERN" in squeezed-down letters and "U" of "FOUR" squeezed up (R. 3/17)	£2750	£1700
		l. Small "S" in "POSTAGE" (R. 4/17)	£1500	£1000
		m. "EN" of "PENCE" shorter (R. 6/4)	£1300	£900
		n. "N" of "PENCE" tilted to right with thin first downstroke (R. 6/16)	£1300	£900
		o. Swan and water above "ENCE" damaged (R. 6/20)	£1300	£900
		p. "F" of "FOUR" slanting to left (R. 7/17)	£1300	£900
		q. "WESTERN" in squeezed-down letters only 1½ mm high (R. 8/17)	£1600	£1100
		r. "P" of "PENCE" with small head (R. 9/15)	£1300	£900
		s. "RALIA" in squeezed-down letters only 1½ mm high (R. 9/16)	£1500	£950
		t. "PE" of "PENCE" close together (R. 10/15)	£1300	£900
		u. "N" of "PENCE" narrow (R. 10/16)	£1300	£900
		v. Part of right cross-stroke and downstroke of "T" of "POSTAGE" cut off (R. 11/15)	£1300	£900
		w. "A" in "POSTAGE" with thin right limb (R. 11/16)	£1300	£900
		x. Coloured line above "AGE" of "POSTAGE" (R. 8/6)	£1400	£950
		y. No outer line above "GE" of "POSTAGE" and coloured line under "FOU" of "FOUR" (R. 8/11)	£1400	£1000
4	3	1s. salmon	£15000	£2750
		a. Deep red-brown	£1500	£750
		b. Grey-brown (1.55)	£550	£375
		c. Pale brown (10.55)	£400	£300

(b) Rouletted 7½ to 14 and compound.
5	2	4d. pale blue	£1600	£475
		a. Blue	—	£475
		b. Slate-blue (1855)	£1600	
6	3	1s. grey-brown (1.55)	£3500	£900
		a. Pale brown (10.55)	£3250	£750

The 1s. is also known pin-perforated.
The 4d. value was prepared from the Perkins, Bacon 1d. plate. A block of 60 (5×12) was taken as a transfer from this plate, the frames painted out and then individually replaced by transfers taken from a single impression master plate of the frame. Four transfers were then taken from this completed intermediate stone to construct the printing stone of 240 impressions. This first printing stone was used by H. Samson to print the initial supplies in July 1854.
The intermediate stone had carried several transfer errors, the most prominent of which was the "T" of "POSTAGE" sliced at foot, which appeared on four positions of the printing stone (Nos. 3d).
The original printing stone also contained three scarce creased transfers, whose exact positions in the sheet have yet to be established (Nos. 3e/g). These were corrected during the first printing.

Further supplies were required in January 1855 and A. Hillman, Samson's successor, found, after printing three further sheets from the first printing stone, that two of the impressions on the intermediate stone were defective giving one inverted and one tilted frame (Nos. 3h/i), was then prepared on which the four positions of the inverted frame were individually corrected.

None of the creased transfers from the first printing stone appear on the second, which exhibits its own range of similar varieties (Nos. 3j/w).

For the third printing in October 1855 the impressions showing the inverted frame were replaced on the printing stone with fresh individual transfers of the frame. On two of the positions traces of the original frame transfer remained visible (Nos. 3x/y).

The same stone was used for a further printing in December 1855 and it is believed that the slate-blue shade occurred from one of the 1855 printings.

The above varieties, with the exception of Nos. 3e/g, also occur on the rouletted stamps.

The 1s. value was produced in much the same way, based on a transfer from the Perkins, Bacon 1d. plate.

5

(Litho A. Hillman, Government Lithographer)

1857 (7 Aug)–**59**. W **4** (sideways).

(a) Imperf.

15	5	2d. brown-black/*red* (26.2.58)	£2500	£550
		a. Printed both sides	£3250	£800
16		2d. brown-black/*Indian red* (26.2.58)	£2750	£800
		a. Printed both sides	£3250	£850
17		6d. golden bronze	£10000	£1600
18		6d. black-bronze	£4000	£650
19		6d. grey-black (1859)	£4000	£550

(b) Rouletted 7½ to 14 and compound.

20	5	2d. brown-black/*red*	£7000	£1600
		a. Printed both sides	—	£2000
21		2d. brown-black/*Indian red*		£1700
22		6d. black-bronze	£7000	£950
23		6d. grey-black	—	£1000

The 2d. and 6d. are known pin-perforated.

Prices quoted for Nos. 15/23 are for "cut-square" examples. Collectors are warned against "cut-round" copies with corners added.

(Recess in the colony from P.B. plates)

1860 (11 Aug)–**64**. W **4** (sideways).

(a) Imperf.

24	1	2d. pale orange	80·00	75·00
25		2d. orange-vermilion	80·00	75·00
		a. Wmk upright		
25b		2d. deep vermilion	£1300	£750
26		4d. blue (Wmk upright) (21.6.64)	£250	£1800
		a. Wmk sideways		
27		4d. deep blue (Wmk upright)	£250	£1700
28		6d. sage-green (27.7.61)	£1600	£400
28a		6d. deep sage-green	—	£550

(b) Rouletted 7½ to 14.

29	1	2d. pale orange	£475	£190
30		2d. orange-vermilion	£550	£200
31		4d. deep blue (Wmk upright)	£3500	
32		6d. sage-green	£3250	£600

PERKINS BACON "CANCELLED". For notes on these handstamps, showing "CANCELLED" between horizontal bars forming an oval, see Catalogue Introduction.

(Recess P.B.)

1861. W **4** (sideways).

(a) Intermediate perf 14–16.

33	1	1d. rose	£425	£130
34		2d. blue	£150	40·00
35		4d. vermilion	£750	£1700
36		6d. purple-brown	£475	90·00
37		1s. yellow-green	£600	£180

(b) P 14 at Somerset House.

38	1	1d. rose	£225	60·00
39		2d. blue	£100	40·00
40		4d. vermilion	£275	£170

(c) Perf clean-cut 14–16.

41	1	2d. blue	80·00	24·00
		a. Imperf between (pair)		
42		6d. purple-brown	£275	50·00
43		1s. yellow-green	£450	75·00
		a. Wmk upright	—	75·00

(d) P 14–16 very rough (July).

44	1	1d. rose-carmine (H/S "CANCELLED" in oval £17000)	£225	50·00
45		6d. purple/*blued* (H/S "CANCELLED" in oval £11000)	£2500	£400
46		1s. deep green (H/S "CANCELLED" in oval £10000)	£1400	£300

Perkins, Bacon experienced considerable problems with their perforating machine during the production of these stamps.

The initial printing showed intermediate perforation 14–16. Further supplies were then sent, in late December 1860, to Somerset House to be perforated on their comb 14 machine. The Inland Revenue Board were only able to process the three lower values, although the 6d. purple-brown and 1s. yellow-green are known from this perforation overprinted "SPECIMEN".

The Perkins, Bacon machine was repaired the following month and the 6d., 1s. and a further supply of the 2d. were perforated on it to give a clean-cut 14–16 gauge.

A final printing was produced in July 1861, but by this time the machine had deteriorated so that it produced a very rough 14–16.

(Recess D.L.R. from P.B. plates)

1863 (16 Dec)–**64**. No wmk. P 13.

49	1	1d. carmine-rose	65·00	3·50
50		1d. lake	65·00	3·50
51		6d. deep lilac (15.4.64)	£140	40·00
51a		6d. dull violet (15.4.64)	£200	45·00

Both values exist on thin and on thick papers, the former being the scarcer.

Both grades of paper show a marginal sheet watermark, "T H SAUNDERS 1860" in double-lined large and small capitals, but parts of this watermark rarely occur on the stamps.

(Recess D.L.R. from P.B. plates)

1864 (27 Dec)–**79**. Wmk Crown CC (sideways* on 1d.). P 12½.

52	1	1d. bistre	60·00	5·50
		w. Wmk Crown to right of CC	60·00	5·50
		x. Wmk sideways reversed	60·00	6·00
53		1d. yellow-ochre (16.10.74)	75·00	8·00
		w. Wmk Crown to right of CC	75·00	8·00
54		2d. chrome-yellow (18.1.65)	70·00	2·75
55		2d. yellow	70·00	2·75
		a. Wmk sideways (5.79)	—	20·00
		aw. Wmk Crown to right of CC	—	20·00
		b. Error. Mauve (1879)	£12000	£11000
		x. Wmk reversed	70·00	2·75
56		4d. carmine (18.1.65)	75·00	5·00
		a. Doubly printed	£6500	
		w. Wmk inverted		26·00
57		6d. violet (18.1.65)	95·00	6·00
		a. Doubly printed	†	£8500
		b. Wmk sideways		£225
		x. Wmk reversed		6·00
58		6d. indigo-violet	£350	32·00
		x. Wmk reversed		32·00
59		6d. lilac (1872)	£170	6·00
60		6d. mauve (12.5.75)	£160	6·00
		x. Wmk reversed		6·00
61		1s. bright green (18.1.65)	£120	13·00
		s. Handstamped "Specimen"	£140	
62		1s. sage-green (10.68)	£300	26·00

*The normal sideways watermark shows Crown to left of CC, *as seen from the back of the stamp.*

Beware of fakes of No. 55b made by altering the value tablet of No. 60.

7

ONE PENNY

(8)

(Typo D.L.R.)

1871 (29 Oct)–**73**. Wmk Crown CC (sideways). P 14.

63	7	3d. pale brown	40·00	4·50
		a. Cinnamon (1873)	40·00	4·00
		s. Handstamped "Specimen"	£110	

1874 (10 Dec). No. 55 *surch with T* **8** *by Govt Printer.*

67	1	1d. on 2d. yellow (G.)	£425	55·00
		a. Pair, one without surch		
		b. Surch triple	†	£4000
		c. "O" of "ONE" omitted		

Forged surcharges of T **8** are known on stamps wmk Crown CC perf 14, and on Crown CA, perf 12 and 14.

(Recess D.L.R. from P.B. plates)

1876–81. Wmk Crown CC (sideways*). P 14.

68	1	1d. ochre	60·00	3·25
		w. Wmk Crown to right of CC	60·00	3·25
69		1d. bistre (1878)	£100	4·25
70		1d. yellow-ochre (1879)	70·00	2·00
71		2d. chrome-yellow	70·00	1·50
		a. Wmk upright (1877)	90·00	2·50
		by. Wmk Crown to right of CC and reversed		
74		4d. carmine (1881)	£400	90·00
75		6d. lilac (1877)	£120	3·75
		a. Wmk upright (1879)	£500	15·00
		bw. Wmk Crown to right of CC		3·75
75c		6d. reddish lilac (1879)	£120	5·50

*The normal sideways watermark shows Crown to left of CC, *as seen from the back of the stamp.*

(Recess D.L.R. from P.B. plates)

1882 (Mar)–**85**. Wmk Crown CA (sideways*).

(a) P 14.

76	1	1d. yellow-ochre	25·00	1·75
		w. Wmk Crown to right of CA	25·00	1·75
		x. Wmk sideways reversed		
77		2d. chrome-yellow	28·00	1·75
		a. Wmk upright	†	
78		4d. carmine (8.82)	£100	7·50
		a. Wmk upright (1885)		75·00
		w. Wmk Crown to right of CA	£100	7·50
79		6d. reddish lilac (1882)	90·00	3·00
80		6d. lilac (1884)	90·00	4·00
		s. Handstamped "Specimen"	£120	
		w. Wmk Crown to right of CA		5·00
		y. Wmk sideways inverted and reversed		27·00

(b) P 12×14.

81	1	1d. yellow-ochre (2.83)	£1600	£150

(c) P 12.

82	1	1d. yellow-ochre (2.83)	70·00	4·75
83		2d. chrome-yellow (6.83)	95·00	4·50
		a. Imperf between (pair)		
		w. Wmk Crown to right of CA		
84		4d. carmine (5.83)	£160	35·00
		w. Wmk Crown to right of CA	—	35·00
85		6d. lilac (6.83)	£325	35·00
		w. Wmk Crown to right of CA	—	35·00

*The normal sideways watermark shows Crown to left of CA, *as seen from the back of the stamp.*

(Typo D.L.R.)

1882 (July)–**95**. Wmk Crown CA (sideways). P 14.

86	7	3d. pale brown	16·00	2·50
87		3d. red-brown (12.95)	8·50	2·50

The 3d. stamps in other colours, watermark Crown CA and perforated 12, are colour trials dating from 1883.

½	1d.	1d.
(9)	(10)	(11)

1884 (19 Feb). Surch with T **9**, in red, by Govt Printer.

89	1	½d. on 1d. yellow-ochre (No.76)	17·00	24·00
		a. Thin bar	80·00	95·00
90		½d. on 1d. yellow-ochre (No.82)	11·00	19·00

Inverted or double surcharges are forgeries made in London about 1886.

The "Thin bar" varieties occur on R. 12/3, R. 12/8, R. 12/13 and R. 12/18, and show the bar only 0.2 mm thick.

1885 (May). Nos. 63/a surch, in green, by Govt Printer.

(a) Thick "1" with slanting top, T **10** *(Horizontal Rows 1/5).*

91		1d. on 3d. pale brown	60·00	16·00
		a. Cinnamon	50·00	15·00
		b. Vert pair. Nos. 91/2	£200	

(b) Thin "1" with straight top, T **11** *(Horizontal Row 6).*

92		1d. on 3d. pale brown	£160	45·00
		a. Cinnamon	£130	45·00

12

13

14

15

(Typo D.L.R.)

1885 (May)–**93**. Wmk Crown CA (sideways). P 14.

94	12	½d. yellow-green	4·25	70
94a		½d. green	4·00	70
95	13	1d. carmine (2.90)	22·00	50
96	14	2d. bluish grey (6.90)	27·00	1·50
96a		2d. grey	25·00	1·50
97	15	2½d. deep blue (1.5.92)	14·00	1·75
97a		2½d. blue	13·00	1·75
98		4d. chestnut (7.90)	10·00	1·50
99		5d. bistre (1.5.92)	9·50	3·25
100		6d. bright violet (1.93)	15·00	1·25
101		1s. pale olive-green (4.90)	28·00	4·50
102		1s. olive-green	19·00	4·25

94s/101s (ex 1d., 6d.) Handstamped (Nos. 96, 98, 101) or optd "Specimen" Set of 6 ... £375

(Recess D.L.R. from P.B. plates)

1888 (Mar–Apr). Wmk Crown CA (sideways). P 14.

103	1	1d. carmine-pink	20·00	3·25
104		2d. grey	48·00	1·25
105		4d. red-brown (April)	75·00	21·00

103s/5s H/S "Specimen" Set of 3 ... £200

ONE PENNY   **Half-penny**

(16)   (17)

1893 (Feb). Surch with T **16**, in green, by Govt Printer.

107	7	1d. on 3d. pale brown (No. 63)	12·00	4·00
108		1d. on 3d. cinnamon (No. 63a)	12·00	4·00
		a. Double surcharge	£1100	
109		1d. on 3d. pale brown (No. 86)	50·00	5·50

1895 (21 Nov). Surch with T **17** by Govt Printer.

(a) In green.

110	7	½d. on 3d. pale brown (No. 63)	8·50	25·00
110a		½d. on 3d. cinnamon (No. 63a)	6·50	25·00
		b. Surcharge double	£800	

(b) In red and in green.

111a	7	½d. on 3d. cinnamon (No.63a)	85·00	£225
111b		½d. on 3d. red-brown (No.87)	65·00	£150

Green was the adopted surcharge colour but a trial had earlier been made in red on stamps watermarked Crown CC. As they proved unsatisfactory they were given another surcharge in green. The trial stamps were inadvertently issued and, to prevent speculation, a further printing of the duplicated surcharge was made, but on both papers, Crown CC (No. 111a) and Crown CA (No. 111b).

18

19

20   21

(Typo D.L.R.)

1898 (Dec)–**1907**. Wmk W Crown A, W **18**. P 14.

112	**13**	1d. carmine	5·50	10
113	**14**	2d. bright yellow (1.99)	17·00	2·00
114	**19**	2½d. blue (1.01)	11·00	1·00
115	**20**	6d. bright violet (10.06)	24·00	1·75
		w. Wmk inverted	—	£110
116	**21**	1s. olive-green (4.07)	28·00	3·75
		w. Wmk inverted	—	65·00

22   23   24

25   26   27

28   29   30

31   32   33

(Typo Victoria Govt Printer, Melbourne, Commonwealth Stamp Ptg Branch from March 1909)

1902 (Oct)–**12**. Wmk V and Crown, W **33** (sideways on horiz designs).

(a) P 12½ or 12½×12 (horiz), 12×12½ (vert).

117	**22**	1d. carmine-rose (1.03)	13·00	50
		a. Wmk upright (10.02)	17·00	60
118	**23**	2d. yellow (4.1.03)	14·00	2·75
		a. Wmk upright (1903)	27·00	3·50
119	**24**	4d. chestnut (4.03)	16·00	2·25
		a. Wmk upright	£325	
120	**15**	5d. bistre (4.9.05)	£100	70·00
121	**25**	8d. apple-green (3.03)	18·00	2·75
122	**26**	9d. yellow-orange (5.03)	27·00	10·00
		a. Wmk upright (11.03)	65·00	27·00
123	**27**	10d. red (3.03)	32·00	7·50
124	**28**	2s. bright red/*yellow*	85·00	23·00
		a. Wmk sideways	£190	17·00
		b. *Orange*/*yellow* (7.06)	45·00	10·00
		c. *Brown-red*/*yellow* (5.11)	45·00	10·00
125	**29**	2s.6d. deep blue/*rose*	45·00	8·00
126	**30**	5s. emerald-green	70·00	26·00
127	**31**	10s. deep mauve	£160	75·00
		a. *Bright purple* (1910)	£550	£300
128	**32**	£1 orange-brown (1.11.02)	£325	£170
		a. *Orange* (10.7.09)	£600	£325

(b) P 11.

129	**22**	1d. carmine-rose	£225	21·00
		a. Wmk upright	†	£325
130	**23**	2d. yellow	£250	35·00
		a. Wmk upright	†	£325
131	**24**	4d. chestnut	£800	£325
132	**15**	5d. bistre	48·00	55·00
133	**26**	9d. yellow-orange	£100	£110
134	**28**	2s. bright red/*yellow*	£180	£120
		a. *Orange*/*yellow*	£300	£150

(c) Perf compound of 12½ or 12½×12 and 11.

135	**22**	1d. carmine-rose	£750	£400
136	**23**	2d. yellow	£1000	£650
137	**24**	4d. chestnut		

Type **22** is similar to Type **13** but larger.

34   35

1905–**12**. Wmk Crown and A, W **34** (sideways).

(a) P 12½ or 12½×12 (horiz), 12×12½ (vert).

138	**12**	½d. green (6.10)	4·25	5·50
139	**22**	1d. rose-pink (10.05)	10·00	70
		a. Wmk upright (1.06)	9·00	70
		b. *Carmine* (1909)	12·00	70
		c. *Carmine-red* (1912)	12·00	7·50
140	**23**	2d. yellow (15.11.05)	7·00	1·75
		a. Wmk upright (4.10)	†	£200
141	**7**	3d. brown (2.06)	22·00	2·25
142	**24**	4d. bistre-brown (12.06)	23·00	7·50
		a. *Pale chestnut* (1908)	22·00	7·00
		b. *Bright brown-red* (14.10.10)	11·00	3·00
143	**15**	5d. pale olive-bistre (8.05)	17·00	9·00
		a. *Olive-green* (1.09)	17·00	9·00
		b. *Pale greenish yellow* (5.12)	55·00	80·00
144	**25**	8d. apple-green (22.4.12)	18·00	50·00
145	**26**	9d. orange (11.5.06)	26·00	5·00
		a. *Red-orange* (6.10)	42·00	5·00
		b. Wmk upright (7.12)	55·00	28·00
146	**27**	10d. rose-orange (16.2.10)	23·00	18·00
148	**30**	5s. emerald-green (wmk upright) (9.07)	£140	£100

(b) P 11.

150	**12**	½d. green	£1500	
151	**22**	1d. rose-pink	32·00	14·00
		a. *Carmine-red*	40·00	13·00
		b. Wmk upright	60·00	17·00
152	**23**	2d. yellow	35·00	19·00
153	**7**	3d. brown	17·00	5·50
154	**24**	4d. yellow-brown	£650	£225
		a. *Pale chestnut*		£325
155	**15**	5d. pale olive-bistre	32·00	10·00
		a. *Olive-green*	18·00	13·00
157	**26**	9d. orange	£120	£140
		a. *Red-orange*	—	£150
		b. Wmk upright (1912)	†	£700

(c) Perf compound of 12½ or 12½×12 and 11.

161	**22**	1d. rose-pink (wmk upright)	£600	£300
		a. Wmk sideways		£500
162	**23**	2d. yellow	£550	£325
163	**7**	3d. brown		£750
164	**26**	9d. red-orange		

The prices provided for Nos. 154/*a* are for examples perforated "OS".

1912 (Mar). Wmk Crown and A W **35** (sideways). P 11½×12.

168	**20**	6d. bright violet	12·00	10·00
169	**21**	1s. sage-green	27·00	17·00
		a. Perf 12½ (single line)	—	£850

1912 (7 Aug). *Thin, ready gummed paper with white gum (as Victoria)*. W **34** (sideways).

170	**7**	3d. brown (P 12½)	55·00	60·00
		a. Wmk upright	£110	£110
171		3d. brown (P 11)		
		a. Wmk upright		

ONE PENNY
(36)

1912 (6 Nov). Nos. 140 *and* 162 surch with T **36** *in Melbourne*.

(a) P 12½ ×12.

172	**23**	1d. on 2d. yellow	1·25	1·25
		a. Wmk upright	4·00	7·00

(b) Perf compound of 12½×12 and 11.

173	**23**	1d. on 2d. yellow	£450	£300

STAMP BOOKLETS

There are very few surviving examples of Nos. SB1/4. Listings are provided for those believed to have been issued with prices quoted for those known to still exist.

1904 (1 Jan)–**09**. *Black on red cover as* No. SB1 *of New South Wales. Stapled.*

SB1   £1 booklet containing two hundred and forty 1d. in four blocks of 30 and two blocks of 60.

     a. Red on pink cover (1909) ... £18000
     b. blue on pink cover ...

1904 (1 Jan). *Black on grey cover as* No. SB1. *Stapled.*

SB2   £1 Booklet containing one hundred and twenty 2d. in four blocks of 30 ...

1910 (May). *Black on cream cover as* No. SB3 *of New South Wales. Stapled.*

SB3   2s. booklet containing eleven ½d. (No. 138), either in block of 6 plus block of 5 or block of 11, and eighteen 1d. (No. 139) either in three blocks of 6 or block of 6 plus block of 12 ... £4750

Unsold stock of No. SB3 was uprated with one additional ½d. in May 1911.

1911 (1 Aug). *Red on pink cover as* No. SB3. *Stapled.*

SB4   2s. Booklet containing twelve ½d. (No. 138), either in two blocks of 6 or block of 12, and eighteen 1d. either in three blocks of 6 or block of 6 plus block of 12 ... £4250

POSTAL FISCAL STAMPS

By the Post and Telegraph Act of 5 September 1893 the current issue of fiscal stamps up to and including the 1s. value, Nos. F11/15, was authorised for postal use.

These stamps had been initially supplied, for fiscal purposes, in February 1882 and had been preceded by a series of "I R" surcharges and overprints on postage stamps which were in use for a period of about six months. Examples of these 1881–82 provisionals can be found postally used under the terms of the 1893 Act but, as they had not been current for fiscal purposes for over eleven years, we no longer list them.

F 3

(Typo D.L.R.)

1893 (5 Sep). *Definitive fiscal stamps of Feb 1882.* Wmk CA over Crown. P 14.

F11	F **3**	1d. dull purple	16·00	2·75
F12		2d. dull purple	£160	50·00
F13		3d. dull purple	55·00	3·75
F14		6d. dull purple	65·00	5·00
F15		1s. dull purple	£110	10·00

The 1s. value is as Type F **3** but with rectangular outer frame and circular frame surrounding swan.

Higher values in this series were not validated by the Act for postal use.

Two varieties of watermark exist on these stamps. Initial supplies showed an indistinct watermark with the base of the "A" 4 mm wide. From 1896 the paper showed a clearer watermark on which the base of the "A" was 5 mm wide.

1897. Wmk W Crown A, W **18**. P 14.

F19	F **3**	1d. dull purple	12·00	2·75
F20		3d. dull purple	48·00	3·75
F21		6d. dull purple	48·00	4·00
F22		1s. dull purple	£110	13·00

The above were invalidated for postal purposes from 1 January 1901.

TELEGRAPH STAMPS USED FOR POSTAGE

The 1d. Telegraph stamps were authorised for postal purposes from 25 October 1886.

T 1

1886 (25 Oct). Wmk Crown CC.

T1	T **1**	1d. bistre (P 12½)	42·00	5·00
T2		1d. bistre (P 14)	42·00	6·00

Copies of a similar 6d. value are known postally used, but such use was unauthorised.

OFFICIAL STAMPS

Stamps of the various issues from 1854–85 are found with a circular hole punched out, the earlier size being about 3 mm. in diameter and the later 4 mm. These were used on official correspondence by the Commissariat and Convict Department, branches of the Imperial administration separate from the colonial government. This system of punching ceased by 1886. Subsequently many stamps between Nos. 94 and 148 may be found punctured, "PWD", "WA" or "OS".

Western Australia became part of the Commonwealth of Australia on 1 January 1901.

COMMONWEALTH OF AUSTRALIA

On 1 March 1901 control of the postal service passed to the federal administration although it was not until 13 October 1910 that the issues of the various states became valid for use throughout Australia. Postal rates were standardised on 1 May 1911.

The first national postage due stamps appeared in July 1902, but it was not until January 1913 that postage stamps inscribed "AUSTRALIA" were issued.

PRICES FOR STAMPS ON COVER		
Nos. 1/6	*from* × 6	
Nos. 15/32	*from* × 4	
Nos. 33/46	*from* × 5	
Nos. 49/51	*from* × 6	
Nos. 52/62	*from* × 10	
Nos. 63/*a*	*from* × 8	
No. 67	—	
Nos. 68/92*a*	*from* × 10	
Nos. 94/102	*from* × 40	
Nos. 103/5	*from* × 8	
Nos. 107/10*a*	*from* × 12	
Nos. 111*a*/*b*	—	
Nos. 112/16	*from* × 25	
Nos. 126/8	*from* × 10	
Nos. 129/34	*from* × 8	
Nos. 135/6		
Nos. 138/48	*from* × 12	
Nos. 151/63	*from* × 5	
Nos. 168/9	*from* × 20	
Nos. 170/1	*from* × 4	
Nos. 172/3	*from* × 40	
Nos. F11/22	*from* × 10	
Nos. T1/2		

PRINTERS. Except where otherwise stated, all Commonwealth stamps to No. 581 were printed under Government authority at Melbourne. Until 1918 there were two establishments (both of the Treasury Dept)—the Note Printing Branch and the Stamp Printing Branch. The former printed T **3** and **4**.

In 1918 the Stamp Printing Branch was closed and all stamps were printed by the Note Printing Branch. In 1926 control was transferred from the Treasury to the Commonwealth Bank of Australia, and on 14 January 1960 the branch was attached to the newly established Reserve Bank of Australia.

Until 1942 stamps bore in the sheet margin the initials or names of successive managers and from 1942 to March 1952 the imprint "Printed by the Authority of the Government of the Commonwealth of Australia". After November 1952 (or Nos. D129/31 for Postage Dues) imprints were discontinued.

SPECIMEN OVERPRINTS. These come from Specimen sets, first made available to the public on 15 December 1913. In these sets the lower values were cancelled-to-order, but stamps with a face value of 7s.6d. or 75c. were overprinted "Specimen" in different types. These overprints are listed as they could be purchased from the Australian Post Office.

It is, however, believed that examples of No. 112 overprinted "Specimen" were distributed by the U.P.U. in 1929. Supplies of the 1902 and 1902–04 postage due stamps overprinted "Specimen" were supplied to the U.P.U. by some of the states.

1   2

Die I   Die II

Dies of Type 1 (mono-coloured values only):—
Die I. Break in inner frame line at lower left level with top of words of value.
Die II. Die repaired showing no break.

Die I was only used for the ½d., 1d., 2d. and 3d. Several plates were produced for each except the 3d. When the second plate of the 3d. was being prepared the damage became aggravated after making 105 out of 120 units when the die was returned for repair. This gave rise to the se-tenant pairs showing the two states of the die.

Die II was used until 1945 and deteriorated progressively with damage to the frame lines and rounding of the corners.

Specialists recognise seven states of this die, but we only list the two most major of the later versions.

Die IIA. This state is as Die II, but, in addition, shows a break in the inner left-hand frame line, 9 mm from the top of the design (occurs on 1d., 2d. and 6d.).

Die IIB. As Die IIA, but now also showing break in outer frame line above "ST", and (not illustrated) an incomplete corner to the inner frame line at top right (occurs on 3d., 6d., 9d., 1s. and £1 (No. 75)).

(Des B. Young. Eng S. Reading. Typo J. B. Cooke)

1913 (2 Jan)–14. W **2**. P 12.

1	**1**	½d. green (Die I) (14.1.13)	6·00	3·75
		bw. Wmk inverted	42·00	12·00
		c. Wmk sideways	†	£10000
		cw. Wmk sideways inverted	†	£13000
2		1d. red (Die I)	9·00	1·00
		a. Wmk sideways	£950	£225
		aw. Wmk sideways inverted	£1000	£250
		b. Carmine	9·00	1·00
		cw. Wmk inverted	35·00	8·00
		d. Die II Red (16.1.13)	9·00	1·00
		da. Wmk sideways	£1000	£250
		daw. Wmk sideways inverted	£1000	£250
		db. Carmine	8·50	1·25
		dw. Wmk inverted	35·00	12·00
		e. Die IIA. Red (4.14)	15·00	1·25
		eb. Carmine	15·00	1·25
		ew. Wmk inverted	50·00	9·00
3		2d. grey (Die I) (15.1.13)	35·00	5·50
		w. Wmk inverted	75·00	20·00
4		2½d. indigo (Die II) (27.1.13)	30·00	13·00
5		3d. olive (Die I) (28.1.13)	50·00	9·00
		a. imperf three sides (horiz pair)	£35000	
		b. in pair with Die II	£550	£250
		c. Yellow-olive	50·00	9·50

Dot before "1" (Plate 3 right pane R. 4/3)

1d. Die II   Thin "1" in fraction at right (Plate 5 right pane R. 8/1)

"Secret mark" (Plate 4 left pane R. 1/1)

---

	ca. In pair with Die II	£550	£275
	dw. Wmk inverted	£140	50·00
	e. Die II Olive	£200	65·00
	ea. Yellow-olive	£200	65·00
	ew. Wmk inverted	£500	£180
6	4d. orange (Die II) (19.2.13)	50·00	22·00
	a. Orange-yellow	£250	60·00
8	5d. chestnut (Die II) (18.1.13)	45·00	32·00
9	6d. ultramarine (Die II) (18.1.13)	48·00	20·00
	a. Retouched "E"	£2000	£700
	b. Die IIA (substituted cliché) (11.13)	£2250	£750
	w. Wmk inverted	£500	£225
10	9d. violet (Die II) (1.2.13)	50·00	24·00
11	1s. emerald (Die II) (25.1.13)	60·00	17·00
	a. Blue-green	60·00	17·00
	w. Wmk inverted	£750	70·00
12	2s. brown (Die II) (28.1.13)	£160	75·00
13	5s. grey and yellow (Die II) (20.3.13)	£300	£160
14	10s. grey and pink (Die II) (20.3.13)	£650	£500
15	£1 brown and ultram (Die II) (20.3.13)	£1600	£1700
16	£2 black and rose (Die II) (8.4.13)	£3500	£2250
1/16 Set of 15		£6000	£4250
14s/16s Optd "Specimen" Set of 3			£750

The watermark on Nos. 1c, 2a and 2da shows the Crown pointing to the left and on Nos. 1cw, 2aw and 2daw pointing to the right, as seen from the back of the stamp. Two examples of 1c and one example of 1cw are known, all used.

The 3d. was printed from two plates, one of which contained 105 stamps as Die I and 15 as Die II. The other plate contained Die I stamps only.

No. 5a. shows the stamp perforated at foot only. Examples are known from the top or bottom rows of different sheets.

No. 9a shows a badly distorted second "E" in "PENCE", which is unmistakable. It occurs on the upper plate right pane R. 10/6 and was replaced by a substitute cliché in Die IIA (No. 9b) in the November 1913 printing.

See also Nos. 24/30 (W **5**), 35/45b (W **6**), 73/5 (W **6**, new colours), 107/14 (W **7**), 132/8 (W **15**), 212 (2s. re-engraved).

3   4 Laughing Kookaburra

(Des R. A. Harrison. Eng and recess T. S. Harrison)

1913 (9 Dec)–14. No wmk. P 11.

17	**3**	1d. red	2·50	4·50
		a. Imperf between (horiz pair)	£1800	
		b. Imperf horiz (vert pair)	£1800	
		c. Pale rose-red	7·00	12·00
		ca. Imperf between (vert pair)	£2250	
		cb. Imperf between (horiz pair)	£3000	
19	**4**	6d. claret (26.8.14)	65·00	45·00

All printings from Plate 1 of the 1d. were in the shade of No. 17c. This plate shows many retouches.

Flaw under neck (Plate 4 left pane R. 7/1)

"RA" joined (Plate 4 left pane R. 10/6)

1d. Die II. The flaw distinguishing the so-called Die II, a white upward spur to the right of the base of the "1" in the left value tablet, is now known to be due to a defective roller-die. It occurred on all stamps in the second and third vertical rows of upper left plate, right pane. Each of the twenty defective impressions differs slightly; a typical example is illustrated above.

(Dies eng P.B. Typo J. B. Cooke until May 1918, then T. S. Harrison)

1914 (17 July)–20. W **5**. P 14¼×14 (comb).

20	**5a**	½d. bright green (22.2.15)	3·75	1·00
		a. Perf 14¼ (line) (12.15)	£5000	£450
		b. Green (1916)	3·75	1·00
		c. Yellow-green (1916)	23·00	10·00
		d. Thin "1" in fraction at right	£12000	£3250
		w. Wmk inverted	13·00	4·00
21		1d. carmine-red (shades) (Die I) (P 14¼ (line))	25·00	4·00
		a. Die II	£6500	£1300
		bw. Wmk inverted	†	£10000
		c. Perf 14¼×14 (comb)	7·50	60
		ca. Rusted cliché (Pl 2 rt pane R. 6/4 and 6/5) (9.16)	£7500	£375
		cb. Substituted cliché (Pl 2 rt pane R. 6/5) (2.18)	£1100	60·00
		cc. Pale carmine (shades) (1917)	10·00	60
		cd. Rose-red (1917)	11·00	2·50
		ce. Carmine-pink (1918)	£120	11·00
		cf. Carmine (aniline) (1920)	16·00	3·25
		cg. Dot before "1"	50·00	7·50
		ch. "Secret mark"	50·00	7·50
		ci. Flaw under neck	50·00	7·50
		cj. "RA" joined	50·00	7·50
		cw. Wmk inverted	13·00	2·00
		d. Die II Carmine-red (shades)	£325	6·00
		db. Substituted cliché (Pl 2 right pane R. 6/4) (2.18)	£1100	60·00
		dc. Pale carmine (shades)	£375	7·00
		dw. Wmk inverted	£600	30·00
22		4d. orange (6.1.15)	27·00	2·50
		a. Yellow-orange (1915)	27·00	3·25
		b. Lemon-yellow (3.16)	75·00	14·00
		c. Pale orange-yellow (1.17)	80·00	12·00
		d. Dull orange (1920)	42·00	3·25
		e. Line through "FOUR PENCE" (Pl 2 right pane R. 2/6) (all shades) .... From	£300	95·00
		w. Wmk inverted	40·00	12·00
23		5d. brown (P 14¼ (line)) (22.2.15)	25·00	4·00
		aw. Wmk inverted	£325	£120
		b. Perf 14¼×14 (comb)	18·00	5·00
		ba. Yellow-brown (1920)	25·00	2·75
		bw. Wmk inverted	£250	90·00

The variety No. 20d was caused by the engraving of a new fraction in a defective electro in 1918.

No. 21ca was caused by rusting on two positions of the steel plate 2 and shows as white patches on the back of the King's neck and on, and beside, the top of the right frame (right pane R. 6/4) and on the left frame, wattles, head and ears of kangaroo (right pane R. 6/5). These were noticed in December 1916 when the damaged impressions were removed and replaced by a pair of copper electros (Die II for R. 6/4 and Die I for R. 6/5), showing rounded corners and some frame damage, the former also showing a white spot under tail of emu. In time the tops of the crown quickly wore away.

Most of Nos. 20/3 were perforated 14 by a comb machine (exact gauge 14.25×14), but printings of the ½d. in December 1915, of the 1d. in July and August 1914 and of the 5d. until June 1917 were perforated by a line machine measuring 14.2.

See also Nos. 47/fa (W **5**, rough paper), 48/52 (W **6a**), 53/ba (1d. Die III), 56/66b and 76/81 (W **5**, new colours), 82 (W **6a**), 83/4 (no wmk), 85/104 (W **7**), 124/31 (W **15**).

(Typo J. B. Cooke)

1915 (15 Jan–Aug). W **5**. P 12.

24	**1**	2d. grey (Die I)	60·00	12·00
		w. Wmk inverted	†	£5000
25		2½d. indigo (Die II) (July)	60·00	40·00
26		6d. ultramarine (Die II) (April)	£140	22·00
		a. Bright blue	£250	60·00
		b. Die IIA. Ultramarine (substituted cliché) (Upper plate rt pane R. 10/6)	£2500	£750
		ba. Bright blue	£3000	£1000
		w. Wmk inverted	†	£8000
27		9d. violet (Die II) (9 July)	£160	40·00
		w. Wmk inverted	£2500	£1500
28		1s. blue-green (Die II) (Apr)	£150	24·00
29		2s. brown (Die II) (March)	£425	90·00
30		5s. grey and yellow (Die II) (12 Feb)	£650	£275
		a. Yellow portion doubly printed	£12000	£3250
		w. Wmk inverted	£750	£325
24/30 Set of 7			£1500	£450

6	6a

No. 35a (Upper plate left pane R. 10/1)

Nos. 38da and 73a (Upper plate left pane R. 1/6)

(Typo J. B. Cooke (to May 1918), T. S. Harrison (to February 1926), A. J. Mullett (to June 1927) and thereafter J. Ash).

1915 (8 Oct)–**28**. W **6** (narrow Crown). P 12.

35	**1**	2d. grey (Die I) (11.15)	30·00	6·50
		a. Die IIA substituted cliché (Upper plate left pane R. 10/1)*	£3000	£1000
		bw. Wmk inverted	42·00	14·00
		c. Silver-grey (shiny paper)	32·00	12·00
		d. Die IIA. Silver-grey (shiny paper) (3.18)	48·00	13·00
		daw. Wmk inverted	†	£8000
		dba. Grey (1920)	50·00	13·00
36		2½d. deep blue (Die II) (9.17)	23·00	10·00
		aw. Wmk inverted	65·00	35·00
		b. Deep indigo (1919)	32·00	8·50
		ba. "1" of fraction omitted (Lower plate left pane R. 6/3)	£22000	£6000
37		3d. yellow-olive (Die I)	28·00	4·50
		a. In pair with Die II	£250	£130
		b. Olive-green (1917)	30·00	4·50
		ba. In pair with Die II	£250	£130
		cw. Wmk inverted	60·00	30·00
		d. Die II Yellow-olive	80·00	27·00
		da. Olive-green	85·00	27·00
		dw. Wmk inverted	£250	£150
		e. Die IIB. Light olive (1.23)	40·00	12·00
38		6d. ultramarine (Die II) (15.12.15)	55·00	7·50
		a. Die IIA (substituted cliché) (Upper plate rt pane R. 10/6)	£1800	£600
		b. Dull blue (6.18)	65·00	11·00
		ba. Die IIA (substituted cliché)	£1900	£650
		cw. Wmk inverted	£275	65·00
		d. Die IIB. Bright ultramarine (23.7.21)	55·00	10·00
		da. Leg of kangaroo broken	£2250	£550
		dw. Wmk inverted	—	£150
39		9d. violet (Die II) (29.7.16)	38·00	11·00
		aw. Wmk inverted	£180	55·00
		b. Die IIB. Violet (16.4.19)	45·00	8·00
		bw. Wmk inverted	£110	40·00
		c. Die II (substituted cliché in pair with Die IIB)	£300	£180
40		1s. blue-green (Die II) (6.16)	35·00	3·75
		aw. Wmk inverted	£140	45·00
		b. Die IIB (9.12.20)	48·00	3·75
		ba. Wmk sideways (13.12.27)	60·00	£300
		bw. Wmk inverted	£140	45·00
41		2s. brown (Die II) (6.16)	£190	13·00
		a. Imperf three sides (horiz pair)	£42000	
		b. Red-brown (aniline)	£750	£225
		c. "Dollar" flaw	£850	90·00
		w. Wmk inverted	£180	75·00
42		5s. grey and yellow (Die II) (4.18)	£180	75·00
		a. Grey and orange (1920)	£225	90·00
		b. Grey and deep yellow	£200	85·00
		ba. Wmk sideways	†	£20000
		c. Grey and pale yellow	£180	75·00
		w. Wmk inverted	£650	£400
43		10s. grey and pink (Die II) (5.2.17)	£450	£250
		a. Grey and bright aniline pink (10.18)	£400	£225
		ab. Wmk sideways	£16000	£8000
		aw. Wmk inverted	£1500	£900
		b. Grey and pale aniline pink (1922)	£500	£250
44		£1 chocolate and dull blue (Die II) (7.16)	£1900	£1100
		a. Chestnut and bright blue (6.17)	£2000	£1100
		ab. Wmk sideways	†	£25000
		aw. Wmk inverted	£2750	£1500
		b. Bistre-brown and bright blue (7.19)	£2000	£1200
		ba. Frame printed double, one albino	£5000	
45		£2 black and rose (Die II) (12.19)	£3000	£2000
		a. Grey and crimson (1921)	£2750	£1800
		b. Purple-black and pale rose (6.24)	£2250	£1400
35/45b	Set of 11		£4500	£2500
43s/5s	Optd "Specimen" Set of 3		£500	

*The Die IIA of No. 35a is a substituted cliché introduced to repair a crack which occurred on R. 10/1 of the upper plate left pane. Its Die IIA characteristics are more pronounced than on the sheet stamps from this die, with the break at left extending to the outer, in addition to the inner, frame line.

One plate of the 3d. contained mixed Die I and Die II stamps as described.

No. 39c. comes from six substituted clichés taken from plate 2 (Die II) and inserted in plate 4 (Die IIB) at positions left pane R. 1/3-4, 2/3-4 and 8/6 and right pane R. 2/1 This substitution took place towards the end of the printings on W **6**. The variety can also be found on stamps with W **7** and W **15**, see Nos. 108a and 133a.

All values were printed by both Cooke and Harrison, and the 9d., 1s. and 5s. were also printed by Mullett and Ash.

The watermark on No. 40ba shows the Crown printing to the right, that on Nos. 42ba and 43ab shows the Crown pointing to the left as seen from the back of the stamp.

1916 (Nov)–**18**. Rough, unsurfaced paper, locally gummed. W **5**. P 14.

47	**5a**	1d. scarlet (Die I)	18·00	2·50
		a. Deep red (1917)	18·00	2·50
		b. Rose-red (1918)	28·00	2·75
		ba. Substituted cliché (Pl 2 rt pane R. 6/5)	£1000	60·00
		c. Rosine (1918)	£160	13·00
		ca. Substituted cliché (Pl 2 rt pane R. 6/5)	£1700	£250
		d. Dot before "1"	65·00	13·00
		e. Secret mark	65·00	13·00
		f. Flaw under neck	65·00	13·00
		g. "RA" joined	65·00	13·00
		hw. Wmk inverted	45·00	5·50
		i. Die II Rose-red (1918)	£325	23·00
		ia. Substituted cliché (Pl 2 rt pane R. 6/4)	£1000	60·00
		iw. Wmk inverted	£500	50·00
		j. Die II Rosine (1918)	£500	80·00
		ja. Substituted cliché (Pl 2 rt pane R. 6/4)	£1700	£250
		k. No wmk		£1200

All examples of the 5d. on this paper were perforated "OS" and will be found listed as No. O60.

(Typo J. B. Cooke to May 1918 thereafter T. S. Harrison)

1918 (4 Jan)–**20**. W **6a** (Mult). P 14.

48	**5a**	½d. green (shades)	5·00	2·50
		a. Thin 1 in fraction at right	£100	£110
		b. Wmk sideways	†	£11000
		bw. Wmk sideways inverted	†	£11000
		w. Wmk inverted	20·00	11·00
49		1d. carmine-pink (Die I) (23.1.18)	£170	£120
		aw. Wmk inverted	†	£7500
		b. Deep red (1918)	£3500	£2000
		c. Dot before "1"	£650	£325
		d. Secret mark	£650	£325
		e. Flaw under neck	£650	£325
		f. "RA" joined	£650	£325
50		1d. carmine (10.12.19)	30·00	9·00
		aw. Wmk inverted	£800	£2000
		b. Deep red (aniline) (1920)	£500	£180
		c. Dot before "1"	£120	60·00
		d. Secret mark	£120	60·00
		e. Flaw under neck	£120	60·00
		f. "RA" joined	£120	60·00
51		1½d. black-brown (30.1.19)	4·00	3·50
		a. Very thin paper (2.19)	20·00	13·00
		w. Wmk inverted	20·00	10·00
52		1½d. red-brown (4.19)	10·00	2·25
		a. Chocolate (1920)	10·00	2·25
		w. Wmk inverted	48·00	13·00

No. 48 was printed by Cooke and Harrison, Nos. 49/b by Cooke only and Nos. 50/2a by Harrison only. Nos. 49/b have rather yellowish gum, that of No. 50 being pure white.

The watermark on No. 48b shows the Crown pointing to the left and on No. 48bw pointing to the right, as seen from the back of the stamp. One example of each is known.

1d. Die III

1d. Die III. In 1917 a printing (in sheets of 120) was made on paper originally prepared for printing War Savings Stamps, with watermark T **5**. A special plate was made for this printing, differing in detail from those previously used. The shading round the head is even; the solid background of the words "ONE PENNY" is bounded at each end by a white vertical line; and there is a horizontal white line cutting the vertical shading lines at left on the King's neck.

(Typo J. B. Cooke)

1918 (15 July). Printed from a new Die III plate on white unsurfaced paper, locally gummed. W **5**. P 14.

53	**5a**	1d. rose-red	60·00	30·00
		a. Rose-carmine	60·00	30·00
		w. Wmk inverted	£100	50·00

(Typo T. S. Harrison or A. J. Mullett (1s.4d. from March 1926))

1918 (9 Nov)–**23**. W **5**. P 14.

56	**5a**	½d. orange (8.11.23)	2·50	2·75
		w. Wmk inverted	6·00	7·00
57		1d. violet (shades) (12.2.22)	3·50	1·50
		a. Imperf three sides (horiz pair)	£35000	
		b. Red-violet	6·50	2·25
		c. Dot before "1"	35·00	13·00
		d. Secret mark	35·00	13·00
		e. Flaw under neck	35·00	13·00
		f. "RA" joined	35·00	13·00
58		1½d. black-brown	8·50	1·50
		w. Wmk inverted	19·00	5·00
59		1½d. deep red-brown (4.19)	6·50	70
		a. Chocolate (1920)	6·50	60
		w. Wmk inverted	17·00	4·75
60		1½d. bright red-brown (20.1.22)	17·00	3·75
61		1½d. green (7.3.23)	4·00	80
		a. Coarse unsurfaced paper (1923)	£150	60·00
		w. Wmk inverted	†	£6000
62		2d. brown-orange (9.20)	12·00	1·00
		a. Dull orange (1921)	14·00	1·00
		w. Wmk inverted	†	£5000
63		2d. bright rose-scarlet (19.1.22)	9·00	1·50
		a. Dull rose-scarlet	9·00	1·50

		w. Wmk inverted	£10000	
64		4d. violet (21.6.21)	13·00	15·00
		a. Line through "FOUR PENCE" (Pl 2 rt pane R. 2/6)	£13000	£3250
		b. "FOUR PENCE" in thinner letters (Pl 2 rt pane R. 2/6)	£425	£275
65		4d. ultramarine (shades) (23.3.22)	48·00	8·50
		a. "FOUR PENCE" in thinner letters (Pl 2 rt pane R. 2/6)	£400	£150
		b. Pale milky blue	75·00	13·00
		w. Wmk inverted	75·00	£180
66		1s.4d. pale blue (2.12.20)	55·00	26·00
		a. Dull greenish blue	60·00	24·00
		b. Deep turquoise (1922)	£2000	£1600
56/66	Set of 11		£160	50·00

In addition to a number of mint pairs from two sheets purchased at Gumeracha, South Australia, with the bottom row imperforate on three sides, a single used example of No. 57 imperforate on three sides is known.

No. 61a was printed on a batch of coarse unsurfaced paper during 1923. Examples may be indentified by a mesh effect in the paper, with mint stamps having a yellowish gum.

The 4d. ultramarine was originally printed from the Cooke plates but the plates were worn in mid-1923 and Harrison prepared a new pair of plates. Stamps from these plates can only be distinguished by the minor flaws which are peculiar to them.

The variety of Nos. 64 and 65 with "FOUR PENCE" thinner, was caused by the correction of the line through "FOUR PENCE" flaw early in the printing of No. 64.

(Typo T. S. Harrison (to February 1926), A. J. Mullett (to June 1927), thereafter J. Ash)

1923 (6 Dec)–**24**. W **6**. P 12.

73	**1**	6d. chestnut (Die IIB)	24·00	1·75
		a. Leg of kangaroo broken (Upper plate left pane R. 1/6)	75·00	£110
		w. Wmk inverted	†	£12000
74		2s. maroon (Die II) (1.5.24)	55·00	28·00
		w. Wmk inverted	£700	£325
75		£1 grey (Die IIB) (1.5.24)	£475	£250
		s. Optd "Specimen"	75·00	

The 6d. and 2s. were printed by all three printers, but the £1 only by Harrison.

No. 73a was corrected during the Ash printing.

(Typo T. S. Harrison (to February 1926), thereafter A. J. Mullett)

1924 (1 May–18 Aug). P 14.

(a) W **5**.

76	**5a**	1d. sage-green	3·00	1·50
		a. Dot before "1"	30·00	10·00
		b. Secret mark	30·00	10·00
		c. Flaw under neck	30·00	10·00
		d. "RA" joined	30·00	10·00
		w. Wmk inverted	13·00	6·50
77		1½d. scarlet (shades)	2·25	40
		a. Very thin paper	40·00	20·00
		b. "HALEPENCE" (Pl 22 left pane R. 4/4)	30·00	25·00
		c. "RAL of AUSTRALIA" thin (Pl 22 Left pane R. 5/4)	30·00	25·00
		d. Curved "1" and thin fraction at left (Pl 24 rt pane R. 7/5)	30·00	25·00
		w. Wmk inverted	35·00	10·00
78		2d. red-brown	17·00	7·00
		a. Bright red-brown	22·00	8·00
		w. Wmk inverted	†	£7500
79		3d. dull ultramarine	26·00	2·00
		a. Imperf three sides (horiz pair)	£6500	
80		4d. olive-yellow	29·00	5·00
		a. Olive-green	29·00	6·00
		w. Wmk inverted	†	£4500
81		4½d. violet	23·00	3·50

(b) W **6a**.

82	**5a**	1d. sage-green (20 May)	8·50	8·50
		a. Dot before "1"	48·00	55·00
		b. Secret mark	48·00	55·00
		c. Flaw under neck	48·00	55·00
		d. "RA" joined	48·00	55·00
		w. Wmk inverted	†	£5000

(c) No wmk.

83	**5a**	1d. sage-green (18 August)	5·50	9·50
		a. Dot before "1"	32·00	55·00
		b. Secret mark	32·00	55·00
		c. Flaw under neck	32·00	55·00
		d. "RA" joined	32·00	55·00
84		1½d. scarlet (14 August)	13·00	9·50
76/84	Set of 9		£110	42·00

Nos. 78/a and 82/4 were printed by Harrison only but the remainder were printed by both Harrison and Mullett.

In the semi-transparent paper of Nos. 54a and 77a the watermark is almost indistinguishable.

Nos. 77b, 77c and 77d are typical examples of retouching of which there are many others in these issues. In No. 77c the letters "RAL" differ markedly from the normal. There is a white stroke cutting the oval frame-line above the "L", and the right-hand outer line of the Crown does not cut the white frame-line above the "A".

It is believed that No. 79a occurs on the bottom row of at least four sheets purchased from post offices in Victoria during 1926.

7

1

II
New Dies

1d.   For differences see note above No. 20.
1½d. From new steel plates made from a new die. Nos. 87a and 96a are the Ash printings, the ink of which is shiny.
2d.   Die I. Height of frame 25.6 mm. Left-hand frame-line thick and uneven behind Kangaroo. Pearls in Crown vary in size.
       Die II. Height of frame 25.6 mm. Left-hand frame-line thin and even. Pearls in Crown are all the same size.
       Die III. Height 25.1 mm; lettering and figures of value bolder than Die I.
3d.   Die II has bolder letters and figures than Die I, as illustrated above.
5d.   Die II has bolder figure "5" with flat top compared with Die I of the earlier issues.

(Typo A. J. Mullett or J. Ash (from June 1927))

1926–30. W 7.

(a) P 14.

85	5a	½d. orange (10.3.27)	6·00	7·50
		w. Wmk inverted	75·00	55·00
86		1d. sage-green (23.10.26)	3·25	1·00
		a. Dot before "1"	48·00	16·00
		b. Secret mark	48·00	16·00
		c. Flaw under neck	70·00	27·00
		d. "RA" joined	70·00	27·00
		w. Wmk inverted	16·00	4·75
87		1½d. scarlet (5.11.26)	7·50	2·00
		a. Golden scarlet (1927)	12·00	2·50
		w. Wmk inverted	16·00	4·50
89		2d. red-brown (Die I) (17.8.27)	30·00	40·00
90		3d. dull ultramarine (12.26)	24·00	5·00
		w. Wmk inverted	†	£5500
91		4d. yellow-olive (17.1.28)	48·00	40·00
92		4½d. violet (26.10.27)	18·00	3·75
93		1s.4d. pale greenish blue (6.9.27)	90·00	80·00
		w. Wmk inverted	†	£6500
85/93 *Set of 8*			£200	£160

(b) P 13½×12½.

94	5a	½d. orange (21.11.28)	2·25	1·40
95		1d. sage-green (Die I) (23.12.26)	2·25	70
		aa. Dot before "1"	80·00	38·00
		ab. Secret mark	90·00	42·00
		ac. Flaw under neck	90·00	42·00
		ad. "RA" joined	90·00	42·00
		aw. Wmk inverted	12·00	4·50
		b. Die II (6.28)	50·00	80·00
		bw. Wmk inverted	£750	£750
96		1½d. scarlet (14.1.27)	2·25	1·00
		a. Golden scarlet (1927)	2·25	1·00
		w. Wmk inverted	12·00	2·50
97		1½d. red-brown (16.9.30)	5·50	5·50
98		2d. red-brown (Die II) (28.4.28)	8·00	9·00
99		2d. golden scarlet (Die II) (2.8.30)	12·00	2·25
		a. Die II (9.9.30)	7·50	85
		ab. No wmk	£1000	£2000
		ac. Tête-bêche (pair)	£110000	
		aw. Wmk inverted (from booklets)	9·00	1·40
100		3d. dull ultramarine (Die I) (28.2.28)	38·00	6·50
		aw. Wmk inverted	£140	£2750
		b. Die II *Deep ultramarine* (28.9.29)	20·00	1·40
		bw. Wmk inverted	†	£4500
102		4d. yellow-olive (19.4.29)	23·00	3·25
		w. Wmk inverted	†	£4500
103		4½d. violet (11.28)	48·00	24·00
103a		5d. orange-brown Die II (27.8.30)	25·00	7·00
104		1s.4d. turquoise (30.9.28)	80·00	26·00
		w. Wmk inverted	†	£8500
94/104 *Set of 11*			£200	£200

Owing to defective manufacture, part of the sheet of the 2d. (Die III), discovered in July 1931, escaped unwatermarked; while the watermark in other parts of the same sheet was faint or normal.

Only one example of No. 99ac is known.

8 Parliament House, Canberra   **9** "DH66" Biplane and Pastoral Scene

(Des R. A. Harrison. Die eng J. A. C. Harrison (Waterlow, London). Plates and printing by A. J. Mullett)

1927 (9 May). *Opening of Parliament House, Canberra.* No wmk. P 11.

105	8	1½d. brownish lake	50	50
		a. Imperf between (vert pair)	£2750	
		b. Imperf between (horiz pair)	£4000	£4000

(Eng H. W. Bell. Recess J. Ash)

1928 (29 Oct–2 Nov). *4th National Stamp Exhibition, Melbourne. As T* **4**. No wmk. P 11.

106	3d. blue (2 Nov)		4·25	5·50
MS106a 65×70 mm. No. 106×4			£110	£200
	ab. Imperf (pane of four)		£60000	

No. MS106a comes from special sheets of 60 stamps divided into 15 blocks of 4 (5×3) and separated by wide gutters perforated down the middle, printed and sold at the Exhibition.

(Typo J. Ash)

1929 (Feb)–**30. W 7.** P 12.

107	1	6d. chestnut (Die IIB) (25.9.29)	23·00	4·50
108		9d. violet (Die IIB)	30·00	19·00

---

		a. Die II (substituted cliché) in pair with Die IIB	£250	£180
109		1s. blue-green (Die IIB) (12.6.29)	40·00	6·00
		w. Wmk inverted	†	£6000
110		2s. maroon (Die II) (3.29)	50·00	15·00
111		5s. grey and yellow (Die II) (30.11.29)	£190	80·00
112		10s. grey and pink (Die II)	£375	£450
114		£2 black and rose (Die II) (11.30)	£2750	£550
107/14 *Set of 7*			£3000	£1000
112s/14s Optd "Specimen" *Set of 2*			£325	

(Des R. A. Harrison and H. Herbert. Eng A. Taylor. Recess J. Ash)

1929 (20 May). *Air.* No wmk. P 11.

115	9	3d. green (*shades*)	8·00	4·00

Variations of up to ¾mm in the design size of No. 115 are due to paper shrinkage on the printings produced by the "wet" process. The last printing, in 1935, was printed by the "dry" method.

10 Black Swan   **11** "Capt. Charles Sturt" (J. H. Crossland)

(Des G. Pitt Morrison. Eng F. D. Manley. Recess J. Ash)

1929 (28 Sep). *Centenary of Western Australia.* No wmk. P 11.

116	10	1½d. dull scarlet	1·25	1·60
		a. Re-entry ("T" of "AUSTRALIA" clearly double) (Pl 2 R. 7/4)	55·00	60·00

(Des R. A. Harrison. Eng F. D. Manley. Recess J. Ash)

1930 (2 June). *Centenary of Exploration of River Murray by Capt. Sturt.* No wmk. P 11.

117	11	1½d. scarlet	1·00	1·00
118		3d. blue	3·50	7·50

No. 117 with manuscript surcharge of "2d. paid P M L H I" was issued by the Postmaster of Lord Howe Island during a shortage of 2d. stamps between 23 August and 17 October 1930 (*Price* £650 *un. or used*). A few copies of the 1½d. value No. 96a were also endorsed (*Price* £1400 *un. or used*). These provisionals are not recognized by the Australian postal authorities.

TWO

PENCE

(12)

13 Fokker F. VIIa/3m *Southern Cross* above Hemispheres

1930 (28 July–2 Aug). *T* **5a** *surch as T* **12**. W **7**. P 13½×12½.

119		2d. on 1½d. golden scarlet	1·50	1·00
120		5d. on 4½d. violet (2 Aug)	6·00	10·00

No. 120 is from a redrawn die in which the words "FOURPENCE HALFPENNY" are noticeably thicker than in the original die and the figure "4" has square instead of tapering serifs. The redrawn die also shows thin white lines to the left and right of the tablet carrying "FOURPENCE HALFPENNY".

Stamps from the redrawn die without the surcharge were printed, but not issued thus. Some stamps, *cancelled to order*, were included in sets supplied by the post office. A few mint copies, which escaped the cancellation were found and some may have been used postally (*Price* £2500 *unused*, £35 *used c.t.o.*).

Re-entry ("FO" and "LD" double) (Pl 1 R. 5/5)

(Des and eng F. D. Manley. Recess John Ash)

1931 (19 Mar). *Kingsford Smith's Flights.* No wmk. P 11.

(a) Postage.

121	13	2d. rose-red	1·00	1·00
122		3d. blue	4·50	5·00

(b) Air. Inscr "AIR MAIL SERVICE" at sides.

123	13	6d. violet	5·50	14·00
		a. Re-entry	50·00	85·00
121/3 *Set of 3*			10·00	18·00

15   **17** Superb Lyrebird

(Typo John Ash).

1931–36. W 15.

(a) P 13½×12½.

124	5a	½d. orange (2.33)	4·75	6·00
125		1d. green (Die I) (10.31)	1·75	20
		w. Wmk inverted	17·00	3·50
		x. Wmk reversed	£650	£450
		y. Wmk inverted and reversed	£1000	£750
126		1½d. red-brown (10.36)	6·00	10·00
127		2d. golden scarlet (Die III) (18.12.31)	1·75	10
		w. Wmk inverted (from booklets)	2·25	50
128		3d. ultramarine (30.9.32)	18·00	1·25
		w. Wmk inverted	£5000	£5000
129		4d. yellow-olive (2.33)	18·00	1·25
		w. Wmk inverted	†	£5000
130		5d. orange-brown (Die II) (25.2.32)	15·00	20
		w. Wmk inverted	†	£5000
131		1s.4d. turquoise (18.8.32)	50·00	3·50
		w. Wmk inverted	†	£6000
124/31 *Set of 8*			£100	20·00

(b) P 12.

132	1	6d. chestnut (Die IIB) (20.4.32)	22·00	27·00
133		9d. violet (Die IIB) (20.4.32)	28·00	1·25
		a. Die II (substituted cliché) in pair with Die IIB	£225	£120
134		2s. maroon (Die II) (6.8.35)	5·00	60
135		5s. grey and yellow (Die II) (12.32)	£130	12·00
136		10s. grey and pink (Die II) (31.7.32)	£300	£120
137		£1 grey (Die IIB) (11.35)	£475	£190
138		£2 black and rose (Die II) (6.34)	£2250	£400
132/8 *Set of 7*			£2750	£700
136s/8s Optd "Specimen" *Set of 3*			75·00	

Stamps as No. 127, but without watermark and perforated 11, are forgeries made in 1932 to defraud the P.O. (*Price* £300, *unused*).
For re-engraved type of No. 134, see No. 212.
For 133a/ab see note below No. 114.

(Des and eng F. D. Manley. Recess John Ash)

1931 (4 Nov). *Air Stamp. As T* **13** *but inscr* "AIR MAIL SERVICE" *in bottom tablet.* No wmk. P 11.

139		6d. sepia	13·00	12·00

1931 (17 Nov). *Air.* No. 139 optd with Type O **4**.

139a		6d. sepia	35·00	55·00

This stamp was not restricted to official use but was on general sale to the public.

(Des and eng F. D. Manley. Recess John Ash)

1932 (15 Feb). No wmk. P 11.

140	17	1s. green	42·00	2·00
		a. Yellow-green	48·00	2·75

18 Sydney Harbour Bridge   **19** Laughing Kookaburra

(Des R. A. Harrison. Eng F. D. Manley. Printed John Ash)

1932 (14 Mar). *Opening of Sydney Harbour Bridge.*

(a) Recess. No wmk. P 11.

141	18	2d. scarlet	2·75	3·25
142		3d. blue	4·75	7·00
143		5s. blue-green	£400	£190

(b) Typo. W **15**. P 10½.

144	18	2d. scarlet	2·50	1·40
141/4 *Set of 4*			£400	£190

Stamps as No. 144 without wmk and perf 11 are forgeries made in 1932 to defraud the P.O. (*Price* £500, *unused*).

(Des and eng F. D. Manley. Recess John Ash)

1932 (1 June). W **15**. P 13½×12½.

146	19	6d. red-brown	25·00	55
		w. Wmk inverted	†	£1800

20 Melbourne and R. Yarra   **21** Merino Ram

(Des and eng F. D. Manley. Recess John Ash)

1934 (2 July–Aug). *Centenary of Victoria.* W **15**. P 10½.

147	20	2d. orange-vermilion	2·50	1·75
		a. Perf 11½ (Aug)	7·00	1·75
148		3d. blue	4·00	5·50
		a. Perf 11½ (Aug)	4·00	8·00
149		1s. black	50·00	20·00
		a. Perf 11½ (Aug)	55·00	22·00
147/9 *Set of 3*			50·00	25·00
147a/9a *Set of 3*			60·00	28·00

Stamps were originally issued perforated 10½, but the gauge was subsequently changed to 11½ in August 1934 due to difficulties in separating stamps in the first perforation.

(Des and eng F. D. Manley. Recess John Ash)

1934 (1–26 Nov). *Death Centenary of Capt. John Macarthur (founder of Australian sheep farming).* W **15**. P 11½.

150	21	2d. carmine-red (A)	5·00	1·50
150a		2d. carmine-red (B) (26 Nov)	25·00	3·25

40

151		3d. blue	10·00	12·00
152		9d. bright purple	27·00	45·00
150/2		Set of 3	38·00	50·00

Type A of the 2d. shows shading on the hill in the background varying from light to dark (as illustrated). Type B has the shading almost uniformly dark.

22 Hermes   **23** Cenotaph, Whitehall

(Des F. D. Manley. Eng E. Broad and F. D. Manley. Recess John Ash until April 1940; W. C. G. McCracken thereafter)

1934 (1 Dec)–48.

(a) No wmk. P 11.

153	22	1s.6d. dull purple	38·00	1·00

(b) W **15**. *Chalk-surfaced paper.* P 13½×14.

153a	22	1s.6d. dull purple (22.10.37)	9·00	45
		b. Thin rough ordinary paper (12.2.48)	2·00	1·40

(Des B. Cottier; adapted and eng F. D. Manley. Recess John Ash)

1935 (18 Mar). *20th Anniv of Gallipoli Landing.* W **15**. P 13½×12½ or 11 (1s.).

154	23	2d. scarlet	1·50	30
155		1s. black (chalk-surfaced)	42·00	38·00

The 1s. perforated 13½×12½ is a plate proof (*Price £1500, unused*).

24 King George V on "Anzac"   **25** Amphitrite and Telephone Cable

(Des and eng F. D. Manley. Recess John Ash)

1935 (2 May). *Silver Jubilee. Chalk-surfaced paper.* W **15** (sideways). P 11½.

156	24	2d. scarlet	1·50	30
157		3d. blue	5·00	9·00
158		2s. bright violet	27·00	45·00
156/8		Set of 3	30·00	48·00

(Des and eng F. D. Manley. Recess John Ash)

1936 (1 Apr). *Opening of Submarine Telephone Link to Tasmania.* W **15**. P 11½.

159	25	2d. scarlet	75	50
160		3d. blue	2·75	2·75

26 Site of Adelaide, 1836; Old Gum Tree, Glenelg; King William St, Adelaide

(Des and eng F. D. Manley. Recess John Ash)

1936 (3 Aug). *Centenary of South Australia.* W **15**. P 11½.

161	26	2d. carmine	1·50	40
162		3d. blue	4·50	3·50
163		1s. green	11·00	8·50
161/3		Set of 3	15·00	11·00

27 Wallaroo   **28** Queen Elizabeth   **28a** Queen Elizabeth

29   **30** King George VI   **30a**

31 King George VI   **32** Koala   **33** Merino Ram

34 Laughing Kookaburra   **35** Platypus   **36** Superb Lyrebird

38 Queen Elizabeth   **39** King George VI

40 King George VI and Queen Elizabeth

Dies of 3d.:

Die I   Die Ia   Die II

Die I. The letters "TA" of "POSTAGE" at right are joined by a white flaw; the outline of the chin consists of separate strokes.

No. 168a is a preliminary printing made with unsuitable ink and may be detected by the absence of finer details; the King's face appears whitish and the wattles are blank. The greater part of this printing was distributed to the Press with advance notices of the issue.

Die Ia. As Die I, but "T" and "A" have been clearly separated by individual retouches made on the plates.

Die II. A completely new die. "T" and "A" are separate and a continuous line has been added to the chin. The outline of the cheek extends to about 1 mm above the lobe of the King's right ear.

Die III. Differs from Dies I and II in the King's left eyebrow which is shaded downwards from left to right instead of from right to left.

Line to Kangaroo's ear (Right pane R. 6/8)

Medal flaw (Right pane R. 2/5)

Top hat flaw (Lower plate, right pane R. 3/3)

Roller flaw over "o" of "one" (upper plate, right pane R. 1/6-6/6)

(Des R. A. Harrison (T **28/30**), F. D. Manley (T **27**, **31/6**), H. Barr (T **38/9**), H. Barr and F. D. Manley (T **40**). Eng F. D. Manley and T. C. Duffell (T **34**), T. C. Duffell (revised lettering for T **28a**, **30a**), F. D. Manley (others). All recess with John Ash, W. C. G. McCracken or "By Authority ..." imprints)

1937–49. *Chalk-surfaced paper (3d.* (No. 168), *5s., 10s., £1).* W **15** (sideways on 5d., 9d., 5s. and 10s.).

(a) P 13½×14 (vert designs) or 14×13½ (horiz).

164	27	½d. orange (3.10.38)	2·50	50
165	28	1d. emerald-green (10.5.37)	80	50
166	29	1½d. maroon (20.4.38)	9·00	4·50
167	30	2d. scarlet (10.5.37)	80	40
168	31	3d. blue (Die I) (2.8.37)	60·00	16·00
		a. "White wattles" (from 1st ptg)	£120	75·00
		b. Die Ia	£140	7·00
		c. Die II (3.38)	60·00	4·75

		ca. *Bright blue* (ordinary thin paper) (20.12.38)	60·00	3·75
170	32	4d. green (1.2.38)	9·00	2·25
171	33	5d. purple (1.12.38)	1·50	60
172	34	6d. purple-brown (2.8.37)	20·00	1·50
173	35	9d. chocolate (1.9.38)	4·50	1·50
174	36	1s. grey-green (2.8.37)	48·00	2·50
175	31	1s. 4d. pale magenta (3.10.38)	2·00	2·50
		a. *Deep magenta* (1943)	3·25	2·50

(b) P 13½.

176	38	5s. claret (1.4.38)	18·00	2·00
		a. Thin rough ordinary paper (4.2.48)	3·75	2·50
177	39	10s. dull purple (1.4.38)	38·00	16·00
		a. Thin rough ordinary paper (11.48)	42·00	32·00
178	40	£1 bluish slate (1.11.38)	55·00	32·00
		a. Thin rough ordinary paper (4.4.49)	55·00	60·00
		s. Optd "Specimen"	£425	
164/78		Set of 14	£225	60·00

(c) P 15×14 (vert designs) or 14×15 (horiz) (1d. and 2d. redrawn with background evenly shaded and lettering strengthened).

179	27	½d. orange (28.1.42)	55	10
		a. Line to kangaroo's ear	16·00	
		b. Coil pair (1942)	17·00	24·00
		c. Coil block of four (1943)	£500	
180	28a	1d. emerald-green (1.8.38)	3·75	60
181		1d. maroon (10.12.41)	1·50	50
		a. Coil pair (1942)	14·00	24·00
182	29	1½d. maroon (21.11.41)	4·75	9·50
183		1½d. emerald-green (10.12.41)	1·00	1·50
184	30a	2d. scarlet (11.7.38)	3·25	20
		a. Coil pair (10.41)	£350	£400
		b. Medal flaw	£160	50·00
		w. Wmk inverted (*from booklets*)	7·00	65
185		2d. bright purple (10.12.41)	50	1·50
		a. Coil pair (1942)	42·00	60·00
		b. Medal flaw	50·00	55·00
		w. Wmk inverted (*from coils*)	£120	55·00
186	31	3d. bright blue (Die III) (11.40)	45·00	3·75
187		3d. purple-brown (Die III) (10.12.41)	40	10
188	32	4d. green (10.42)	1·00	10
		w. Wmk inverted	†	£1500
189	33	5d. purple (17.12.45)	50	10
190	34	6d. red-brown (6.42)	2·25	10
		a. Purple-brown (1944)	1·75	10
		b. "top hat" flaw	£275	£150
191	35	9d. chocolate (12.9.43)	1·00	30
192	36	1s. grey-green (29.3.41)	1·25	10
		a. Roller flaw	20·00	10·00
		w. Wmk inverted	£1800	£1300
179/92		Set of 14	60·00	18·00

For unwmkd issue, see Nos. 228/30d.

Thin paper. Nos. 176a, 177a, 178a. In these varieties the watermark is more clearly visible on the back and the design is much less sharp. On early printings of No. 176a the paper appears tinted.

SPECIAL COIL PERFORATION. This special perforation of large and small holes on the narrow sides of the stamps was introduced after 1939 for stamps issued in coils and was intended to facilitate separation. Where they exist they are listed as "Coil pairs".

The following with "special coil" perforation were placed on sale in *sheets*: Nos. 179, 205, 222a (1952), 228, 230, 237, 262 (1953), 309, 311, and 314. These are listed as "Coil blocks of four". Coils with "normal" perforations also exist for Nos. 180 and 184.

41 "Governor Phillip at Sydney Cove" (J. Alcott)   "Tail" flaw (Left pane R. 7/1. Later retouched)

(Des and eng E. Broad and F. D. Manley. Recess J. Ash)

1937 (1 Oct). *150th Anniv of Foundation of New South Wales.* W **15**. P 13½×14.

193	41	2d. scarlet	2·25	30
		a. "Tail" flaw	£375	95·00
194		3d. bright blue	6·00	2·25
195		9d. purple	16·00	10·00
193/5		Set of 3	22·00	11·00

42 A.I.F. and Nurse

(Des and eng F. D. Manley from drawing by Virgil Reilly. Recess W. C. G. McCracken)

1940 (15 Jul). *Australian Imperial Forces.* W **15** (sideways). P 14×13½.

196	**42**	1d. green	1·75	2·50
197		2d. scarlet	1·75	1·50
198		3d. blue	12·00	9·50
199		6d. brown-purple	22·00	18·00
196/9		Set of 4	35·00	28·00

(43)   (44)   (45)

(Opts designed by F. D. Manley)

1941 (10 Dec). Nos. 184, 186 *and* 171 surch with T **43/5**.

200	**30a**	2½d. on 2d. scarlet (V.)	75	70
		a. Pair, one without surcharge	£7000	
		b. Medal flaw	£200	£130
201	**31**	3½d. on 3d. bright blue (Y. on Black)	1·00	2·25
202	**33**	5½d. on 5d. purple (V.)	4·00	5·50
200/2		Set of 3	5·25	7·50

Nos. 200/2 were prepared in connection with the imposition of a ½d. "war tax" increase on most postage rates.

One sheet of the 2½d. on 2d. was discovered showing the surcharge omitted on R. 1/4 and R. 1/5.

46 Queen Elizabeth	**46a** Queen Elizabeth	**47** King George VI
48 King George VI	**49** King George VI	**50** Emu

(Des F. D. Manley. Eng F. D. Manley and T. C. Duffell (T **46/a**) or F. D. Manley (others))

1942–50. *Recess.* W **15**. P 15×14.

203	**46**	1d. brown-purple (2.1.43)	1·25	10
		a. Coil pair (1944)	22·00	32·00
204	**46a**	1½d. green (1.12.42)	1·25	10
205	**47**	2d. bright purple (4.12.44)	65	10
		b. Coil pair (1.49)	90·00	£110
		ba. Coil block of four (5.50)	£1000	
206	**48**	2½d. scarlet (7.1.42)	40	10
		a. Imperf (pair)*	£4000	
		w. Wmk inverted (from booklets)	4·50	80
207	**49**	3½d. bright blue (3.42)	70	60
		a. Deep blue	1·25	60
208	**50**	5½d. slate-blue (12.2.42)	1·00	20
203/8		Set of 6	4·75	2·10

*No. 206a comes in horizontal pair with the right-hand stamp completely imperforate and the left-hand stamp imperforate at right only.

Coils with normal perforations exist for 1d.

For stamps as Nos. 204/5 but without watermark see Nos. 229/30.

The following items are understood to have been the subject of unauthorised leakages from the Commonwealth Note and Stamp Printing Branch and are therefore not listed by us.

It is certain that none of this material was distributed to post offices for issue to the public.

Imperforate all round. 1d. Princess Elizabeth; 1½d. Queen; 2½d. King; 4d. Koala; 6d. Kookaburra; 9d. Platypus; 1s. Lyrebird (small) (also imperf three sides); 1s.6d. Air Mail (Type **22**); 2½d. Mitchell; 2½d. Newcastle (also imperf three sides or imperf vertically).

Also 2½d. Peace, unwatermarked; 2½d. King, *tête-bêche*; 3½d. Newcastle, in dull ultramarine; 2½d. King on "toned" paper.

---

52 Duke and Duchess of Gloucester

(Des F. D. Manley. Eng F. D. Manley and T. C. Duffell. Recess)

1945 (19 Feb). *Arrival of Duke and Duchess of Gloucester in Australia.* W **15**. P 14½.

209	**52**	2½d. lake	10	10
210		3½d. ultramarine	15	90
211		5½d. indigo	20	90
209/11		Set of 3	40	1·75

A   B

1945 (24 Dec). *Kangaroo type, as No. 134, but re-engraved as B.* W **15**. P 12.

212	**1**	2s. maroon	2·25	4·75
		w. Wmk inverted	†	£6500

No. 134 has two background lines between the value circle and "TWO SHILLINGS"; No. 212 has only one line in this position. There are also differences in the shape of the letters.

53 Star and Wreath   **56** Sir Thomas Mitchell and Queensland

(Des F. D. Manley (2½d.), F. D. Manley and G. Lissenden (3½d.), G. Lissenden (5½d.). Eng F. D. Manley. Recess)

1946 (18 Feb). *Victory Commemoration.* T **53** and similar designs. W **15** (sideways on 5½d.). P 14½.

213		2½d. scarlet	10	10
214		3½d. blue	30	1·25
215		5½d. green	35	75
213/15		Set of 3	70	1·75

Designs: Horiz—3½d. Flag and dove. Vert—5½d. Angel.

These designs were re-issued in 1995 with face values in decimal currency.

(Des F. D. Manley. Eng F. D. Manley and T. C. Duffell. Recess)

1946 (14 Oct). *Centenary of Mitchell's Exploration of Central Queensland.* W **15**. P 14½.

216	**56**	2½d. scarlet	10	10
217		3½d. brown	40	1·25
218		1s. grey-olive	40	50
216/18		Set of 3	80	1·60

57 Lt. John Shortland R.N. **58** Steel Foundry **59** Coal Carrier Cranes

(Des and eng G. Lissenden (5½d.), F. D. Manley (others). Recess)

1947 (8 Sep). *150th Anniv of City of Newcastle, New South Wales.* W **15** (sideways on 3½d.). P 14½ or 15×14 (2½d.).

219	**57**	2½d. lake	10	10
220	**58**	3½d. blue	40	1·00
221	**59**	5½d. green	40	55
219/21		Set of 3	80	1·50

60 Queen Elizabeth II when Princess

(Des R. A. Harrison. Eng F. D. Manley. Recess)

1947 (20 Nov)–**52**. *Marriage of Princess Elizabeth.* P 14×15.

(a) W **15** (sideways).

222	**60**	1d. purple	15	30

(b) No wmk.

222a	**60**	1d. purple (8.48)	10	10
		b. Coil pair (1.50)	2·25	5·00
		c. Coil block of four (9.52)	4·75	

61 Hereford Bull   **61a** Hermes and Globe

62 Aboriginal Art   **62a** Commonwealth Coat of Arms

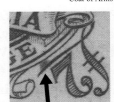

Roller flaw below "E" of "POSTAGE" (R. 4/1 and 5/1). Later retouched.

(Des G. Sellheim (T **62**), F. D. Manley (others). Eng G. Lissenden (T **62**), F. D. Manley (1s.3d., 1s.6d., 5s.), F. D. Manley and R. J. Becker (10s., £1, £2). Recess)

1948 (16 Feb)–**56**. W **15** (sideways).

(a) P 14½.

223	**61**	1s.3d. brown-purple	1·75	1·10
223a	**61a**	1s.6d. blackish brown (1.9.49)	70	10
224	**62**	2s. chocolate	1·50	10

(b) P 14½×13½.

224a	**62a**	5s. claret (11.4.49)	2·75	20
		ab. Thin paper (1951)	38·00	24·00
224b		10s. purple (3.10.49)	14·00	85
224c		£1 blue (28.11.49)	30·00	3·50
224d		£2 green (16.1.50)	80·00	14·00
		da. Roller flaw	£120	70·00
223/24d		Set of 7	£120	17·00
224bs/ds		Optd "Specimen" Set of 3	£140	

(c) No wmk. P 14½.

224e	**61a**	1s.6d. blackish brown (2.12.56)	7·00	1·50
224f		2s. chocolate (27.6.56)	7·00	60

No. 224ab is an emergency printing on white Harrison paper instead of the toned paper used for No. 224a.

No. 224b exists with watermark inverted and overprinted "SPECIMEN".

63 William J. Farrer **64** F. von Mueller **65** Boy Scout

(Des and eng F. D. Manley. Recess)

1948 (12 July). *William J. Farrer (wheat research) Commemoration.* W **15**. P 15×14.

225	**63**	2½d. scarlet	20	10

(Des and eng F. D. Manley. Recess)

1948 (13 Sep). *Sir Ferdinand von Mueller (botanist) Commemoration.* W **15**. P 15×14.

226	**64**	2½d. lake	20	10

(Des and eng F. D. Manley. Recess)

1948 (15 Nov). *Pan-Pacific Scout Jamboree, Wonga Park.* W **15** (sideways). P 14×15.

227	**65**	2½d. lake	20	10

See also No. 254.

Sky retouch (normally unshaded near hill) (Rt pane R.6/8) (No. 228a retouched in 1951)

"Green mist" retouch. A large area to the left of the bird's feathers is recut. (upper plate left pane R.9/3)

1948–56. No wmk. P 15×14 or 14×15 (9d.).

228	**27**	½d. orange (15.9.49)	20	10
		a. Line to kangaroo's ear	22·00	
		b. Sky retouch	32·00	
		c. Coil pair (1950)	75	2·75
		ca. Line to kangaroo's ear	55·00	
		cb. Sky retouch (in pair)	£160	
		d. Coil block of four (1953)	2·75	
229	**46a**	1½d. green (17.8.49)	1·00	1·25
230	**47**	2d. bright purple (20.12.48)	80	1·75
		aa. Coil pair	3·00	7·50
230a	**32**	4d. green (18.8.56)	2·00	2·25
230b	**34**	6d. purple-brown (18.8.56)	5·50	1·00
230c	**35**	9d. chocolate (13.12.56)	22·00	3·75
230d	**36**	1s. grey-green (13.12.56)	4·00	1·25
		da. "Green mist" retouch	£1400	
		db. Roller flaw	30·00	18·00
228/30d		Set of 7	32·00	10·00

66 "Henry Lawson" (Sir Lionel Lindsay)   **67** Mounted Postman and Convair CV 240 Aircraft

(Des F. D. Manley. Eng. E. R. M. Jones. Recess)

1949 (17 June). *Henry Lawson (poet) Commemoration.* P 15×14.
231   **66**   2½d. maroon 20   10

(Des Sir Daryl Lindsay and F. D. Manley. Eng F. D. Manley. Recess)

1949 (10 Oct). *75th Anniv of Founding of U.P.U.* P 15×14.
232   **67**   3½d. ultramarine 30   60

68 John, Lord Forrest of Bunbury   **69** Queen Elizabeth   **70** King George VI

(Des and eng F. D. Manley. Recess)

1949 (28 Nov). *John, Lord Forrest of Bunbury (explorer and politician) Commemoration.* W **15**. P 15×14.
233   **68**   2½d. lake 20   10

(Des and eng F. D. Manley. Recess)

1950 (12 Apr)–52.

(a) W **15**. P 15×14.
234   **70**   2½d. scarlet (12.4.50) 10   10
235   3d. scarlet (28.2.51) 15   25
       aa. Coil pair (4.51) .... 17·00   32·00

(b) No wmk.
236   **69**   1½d. green (19.6.50) 40   40
237   2d. yellow-green (28.3.51) 15   10
       b. Coil pair .... 6·00   9·50
       b. Coil block of four (11.52) .... 12·00
237c **70**   2½d. purple-brown (23.5.51) 15   35
237d   3d. grey-green (14.11.51) 15   10
       da. Coil pair (12.51) .... 24·00   32·00
234/7d Set of 6 .... 1·00   1·00

On 14 October 1951 No. 235 was placed on sale in sheets of 144 originally intended for use in stamp booklets. These sheets contain 3 panes of 48 (16×3) with horizontal gutter margin between.

71 Aborigine   **72** Reproduction of First Stamps of New South Wales   **73** Reproduction of First Stamps of Victoria

(Des and eng F. D. Manley. Recess)

1950 (14 Aug). W **15**. P 15×14.
238   **71**   8½d. brown 20   1·00
For T **71** in a larger size, see Nos. 253/b.

(Des and eng G. Lissenden (T **72**), E. R. M. Jones (T **73**). Recess)

1950 (27 Sep). *Centenary of First Adhesive Postage Stamps in Australia.* P 15×14.
239   **72**   2½d. maroon 25   10
       a. Horiz pair. Nos. 239/40 50   70
240   **73**   2½d. maroon 25   10
Nos. 239/40 were printed alternately in vertical columns throughout the sheet.

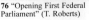

74 Sir Edmund Barton   **75** Sir Henry Parkes

76 "Opening First Federal Parliament" (T. Roberts)   **77** Federal Parliament House, Canberra

(Des and eng F. D. Manley. Recess)

1951 (1 May). *50th Anniv of Commonwealth of Australia.* P 15×14.
241   **74**   3d. lake 40   10
       a. Horiz pair. Nos. 241/2 .... 2·00   2·50
242   **75**   3d. lake 40   10
243   **76**   5½d. blue 20   2·25
244   **77**   1s.6d. purple-brown 35   50
241/4 Set of 4 .... 2·25   2·75
Nos. 241/2 were printed alternately in vertical columns throughout the sheet.

78 E. H. Hargraves   **79** C. J. Latrobe

(Des and eng F. D. Manley. Recess)

1951 (2 July). *Centenaries of Discovery of Gold in Australia and of Responsible Government in Victoria.* P 15×14.
245   **78**   3d. maroon 30   10
       a. Horiz pair. Nos. 245/6 .... 1·00   2·00
246   **79**   3d. maroon 30   10
Nos. 245/6 were printed alternately in vertical columns throughout the sheet.

80   **81** King George VI   **82**

(Des E. R. M. Jones (7½d.), F. D. Manley (others) Eng. F. D. Manley. Recess)

1951–52. W **15** (sideways on 1s.0½d.) P 14½ (1s.0½d.) or 15×14 (others).
247   **80**   3½d. brown-purple (28.11.51) 10   10
       a. Imperf between (horiz pair) £8500
248   4½d. scarlet (20.2.52) 15   1·25
249   6½d. brown (20.2.52) 15   1·00
250   6½d. emerald-green (9.4.52) 10   25
251   **81**   7½d. blue (31.10.51) 15   80
       a. Imperf three sides (vert pair) £11000
252   **82**   1s.0½d. indigo (19.3.52) 60   60
247/52 Set of 6 .... 1·10   3·50
No. 251a occurs on the left-hand vertical row of one sheet.

(Des F. D. Manley. Eng E. R. M. Jones. Recess)

1952 (19 Mar)–65. P 14½.

(a) W **15** (sideways*).
253   2s.6d. deep brown .... 1·50   70
       aw. Wmk Crown to left of C of A .... †   £1000

(b) No wmk.
253b   2s.6d. deep brown (30.1.57) .... 4·00   75
       ba. Sepia (10.65) .... 13·00   13·00
Design:—2s.6d. As T **71** but larger (21×25½ mm).
*The normal sideways watermark on No. 253 shows Crown to right of C of A, *as seen from the back of the stamp.*
No. 253ba was an emergency printing and can easily be distinguished from No. 253b as it is on white Harrison paper, No. 253b being on toned paper.

(Des and eng F. D. Manley. Recess)

1952 (19 Nov). *Pan-Pacific Scout Jamboree, Greystanes. As T* **65**, *but inscr* "1952–53". W **15** (sideways). P 14×15.
254   3½d. brown-lake 20   10

STAMP BOOKLETS

Illustrations of booklet covers are reduced to ½ size, *unless otherwise stated.*
All booklets from 1913 to 1949 were stapled.

1913 (17 Jan). *Red on pink cover (SB1) or blue on pink cover with map of Australia on front and picture of State G.P.O. on back (SB2).*
SB1   2s. booklet containing twelve ½d. and eighteen 1d. (Nos. 1/2) in blocks of 6 .... £1500
SB2   £1 booklet containing two hundred and forty 1d. (No. 2) in blocks of 30 .... £15000

1914 (6 Oct)–18. *Red on pink cover (Nos. SB2a/3), black on red cover (No. SB4) or blue on pink cover with map of Australia on front and picture of State G.P.O. on back (No. SB5).*
SB2a   2s. booklet containing twelve ½d. and eighteen 1d. (Nos. 1, 21c) in blocks of 6 .... £3250
SB3   2s. booklet containing twelve ½d. and eighteen 1d. (Nos. 20, 21c) in blocks of 6 (1915) £2750
SB4   2s. booklet containing twenty-four 1d. (No. 21c) in blocks of 6 (10.5.17) £2750
       a. Black on green cover £3250
       b. Red on green cover £3000
SB5   £1 booklet containing two hundred and forty 1d. (No. 21c) in blocks of 30 .... £15000
       a. Back cover without G.P.O. picture (1918) £17000
Records show that a £1 booklet containing one hundred and twenty 2d. stamps was issued in very limited quantities during 1914. No examples are known to have survived.

1919 (Jan–Apr). *Black on pink (Nos. SB6/7) or black on green (Nos. SB8/9c) covers.*
SB6   2s.3d. booklet containing eighteen 1½d. (No. 58) in blocks of 6 .... £2250
       a. Black on green cover £2250
SB7   2s.3d. booklet containing eighteen 1½d. (No. 51) in blocks of 6 .... £2250
       a. Black on green cover £2250
SB8   2s.3d. booklet containing eighteen 1½d. (No. 59) in blocks of 6 (Apr) £2250
       a. Black on pink cover £2250
SB9   2s.3d. booklet containing eighteen 1½d. (No. 52) in blocks of 6 (Apr) £2250
       a. Black on pink cover £2250
       b. Black on blue cover £2250
SB9c   £1 booklet containing one hundred and sixty 1½d. (No. 51) in blocks of 20 .... £17000
SB9d   £1 booklet containing one hundred and sixty 1½d. (No. 52) in blocks of 20 (Apr) £15000

1920 (Dec)–22. *Black on blue (Nos. SB10, SB12), black on white (No. SB11) or black on brown (No. SB14) covers.*
SB10   2s. booklet containing twelve 2d. (No. 62) in blocks of 6 .... £2750
       a. Black on pink cover £2750
       b. Black on orange cover (3.22) £3250
SB11   2s. booklet containing twelve 2d. (No. 63) in blocks of 6 (3.22) £3500

       a. Black on orange cover (7.22) £3000
       b. Black on pink cover £2750
       c. Brown on buff cover £3000
       d. Brown on pink cover £3000
SB12   £1 booklet containing one hundred and twenty 2d. (No. 62) in blocks of 15 (1.21) £16000
SB13   £1 booklet containing ninety 2d. and fifteen 4d. (Nos. 63, 65) in blocks of 15 (3.22) £15000
SB14   £1 booklet containing one hundred and twenty 2d. (No. 63) in blocks of 15 (8.22) £15000

1923 (Oct)–24. *Black on rose (No. SB15), or green on pale green (Nos. SB16/18) covers.*
SB15   2s.3d. booklet containing eighteen 1½d. (No. 61) in blocks of 6 .... £2250
       a. Black on pale green cover £2250
SB16   2s.3d. booklet containing eighteen 1½d. (No. 77) in blocks of 6 (5.24) £1800
SB17   £1 booklet containing one hundred and sixty 1½d. (No. 61) in blocks of 20 (3.24) £13000
SB18   £1 booklet containing one hundred and sixty 1½d. (No. 77) in blocks of 20 (5.24) £13000

1927 (Jan–June). *Green on pale green covers.*
SB19   2s.3d. booklet containing eighteen 1½d. (No. 87) in blocks of 6 .... £1200
SB20   2s.3d. booklet containing eighteen 1½d. (No. 96) in blocks of 6 .... £1200
SB21   £1 booklet containing one hundred and sixty 1½d.(No. 96) in blocks of 20 (June) £10000

1927 (9 May). *Opening of Parliament House, Canberra. Green on pale green cover with picture of H.M.S. Renown on back (2s.).*
SB22   2s. booklet containing sixteen 1½d. (No. 105) in blocks of 6 .... £85·00
Examples of a 10s. booklet containing eighty 1½d. (No. 105) are known without a front cover and with the back cover blank. There is no record that this was an official issue.

1928 (Nov). *Green on pale green cover.*
SB23   2s.3d. booklet containing eighteen 1½d. (No. 96a or 96w) in blocks of 6 .... £350

1930 (July)–35. *Air. Black on blue cover inscr* "AIR MAIL. SAVES TIME" *and biplane.*
SB24   3s. booklet containing twelve 3d. (No. 115) in blocks of 4 plus two panes of air mail labels £750
       a. Black on pale green cover inscr "USE THE AIR MAIL" and monoplane (5.35) £1200

1930 (9 Sep)–33. *Green on pale green covers inscr* "USE THE AIR MAIL" *on the back (2s).*
SB25   2s. booklet containing twelve 2d. (No. 99a or 99aw) in blocks of 6 .... £300
SB25a   2s. booklet containing twelve 2d. (No. 127 or 127w) in blocks of 6 (1.32) £300
       ab. Cover with parcel rates on back (1933) £425
SB26   £1 booklet containing one hundred and twenty 2d. (No. 99) in blocks of 20 .... £8500
SB26a   £1 booklet containing one hundred and twenty 2d. (No. 99a) in blocks of 20 .... £8500

1934 (June). *Black on cream cover inscr* "Address your mail fully..." *on front.*
SB26b   2s. booklet containing twelve 2d. (No. 127 or 127w) in blocks of 6 .... £500

1935–38. *Black on green cover with Commonwealth Savings Bank advertisement on front inscr* "WHEREVER THERE IS A MONEY ORDER POST OFFICE".
SB26c   2s. booklet containing twelve 2d. (No. 127 or 127w) in blocks of 6 .... £375
       ca. Front cover inscr "IN MOST MONEY ORDER OFFICES" (1936) £350
       cb. Ditto with waxed interleaves (1938) £425

1938 (Dec). *Black on green cover as No. SB26c. Postal rates on interleaves.*
SB27   2s. booklet containing twelve 2d. (No. 184 or 184w) in blocks of 6 .... £400
       a. With waxed interleaves. Postal rates on back cover £500
       b. Black on buff cover £500

1942 (Aug). *Black on buff cover, size 73×47½ mm. Postal rates on interleaves.*
SB28   2s.6d. booklet containing twelve 2½d. (No. 206 or 206w) in blocks of 6, upright within the booklet £110
       a. With waxed interleaves. Postal rates on back cover £225

1949 (Sept). *Black on buff cover, size 79½×42½ mm including figure of Hermes.*
SB29   2s.6d. booklet containing twelve 2½d. (No. 206) in blocks of 6, sideways within the booklet .... 80·00

B 1

1952 (24 June). *Vermilion and deep blue on green cover as Type* **B 1**.
SB30   3s.6d. booklet containing twelve 3½d. (No. 247) in blocks of 6 .... 17·00
       a. With waxed interleaves .... 90·00

POSTAGE DUE STAMPS

POSTAGE DUE PRINTERS. Nos. D1/62 were typographed at the New South Wales Government Printing Office, Sydney. They were not used in Victoria.

D 1   D 2   D 3

Type D **1** adapted from plates of New South Wales Type D **1**. No letters at foot.

1902 (1 Jul). *Chalk-surfaced paper.* Wmk Type D **2** (inverted on 1d., 3d. and 4d.).

(a) P 11½, 12.

D1	D **1**	½d. emerald-green *or* dull green......	3·25	4·50
D2		1d. emerald-green	12·00	8·00
D3		w. Wmk upright	32·00	21·00
		2d. emerald-green	40·00	9·00
D4		w. Wmk inverted	£100	
		3d. emerald-green	32·00	23·00
D5		w. Wmk upright	38·00	27·00
		4d. emerald-green	42·00	12·00
D6		w. Wmk upright	50·00	22·00
		6d. emerald-green	55·00	9·50
D7		w. Wmk inverted	55·00	9·50
		8d. emerald-green *or* dull green	95·00	75·00
D8		5s. emerald-green *or* dull green	180	70·00
D1/8 *Set of 8*			£400	£180
D1s/7s Opt "Specimen" *Set of 7*			£275	

(b) P 11½, 12, compound with 11.

D9	D **1**	1d. emerald-green	£250	£140
		w. Wmk upright	£275	£130
D10		2d. emerald-green	£375	£140
		w. Wmk inverted	£425	£160

(c) P 11.

D12	D **1**	1d. emerald-green (*wmk upright*)	£1100	£450

Stamps may be found showing portions of the marginal watermark "NEW SOUTH WALES POSTAGE".

1902 (July)–**04**. *Type D* **3** (*with space at foot filled in*). *Chalk-surfaced paper.* Wmk Type D **2** (inverted on 3d., 4d., 6d., 8d. and 5s.).

(a) P 11½, 12.

D13	D **3**	1d. emerald-green (10.02)................	£180	95·00
D14		2d. emerald-green (3.03).................	—	£110
D15		3d. emerald-green (3.03).................	£225	80·00
D17		5d. emerald-green	50·00	10·00
D18		10d. emerald-green *or* dull green	75·00	17·00
D19		1s. emerald-green *or* dull green	55·00	14·00
D20		2s. emerald-green	£100	18·00

(b) P 11½, 12, compound with 11.

D22	D **3**	½d. emerald-green *or* dull green (3.04)..............................	9·00	8·00
		w. Wmk inverted	10·00	8·00
D23		1d. emerald-green *or* dull grn (10.02)	8·50	3·00
		w. Wmk inverted	8·50	3·00
D24		2d. emerald-green *or* dull green (3.03).................................	25·00	3·00
		w. Wmk inverted	25·00	3·00
D25		3d. emerald-green *or* dull green (3.03).................................	65·00	16·00
		w. Wmk upright	85·00	27·00
D26		4d. emerald-green *or* dull green (5.03).................................	55·00	11·00
		w. Wmk upright	55·00	12·00
D27		5d. emerald-green	55·00	23·00
D28		6d. emerald-green (3.04)	55·00	10·00
D29		8d. emerald-green (3.04)	£120	50·00
D30		10d. emerald-green *or* dull green	95·00	18·00
D31		1s. emerald-green	90·00	18·00
D32		2s. emerald-green	£130	27·00
D33		5s. emerald-green *or* dull green (5.03).................................	£225	22·00

(c) P 11.

D34	D **3**	½d. emerald-green *or* dull green (wmk inverted) (3.04)...............	£300	£180
D35		1d. emerald-green *or* dull green (10.02)................................	90·00	27·00
		w. Wmk inverted	£120	40·00
D36		2d. emerald-green (3.03).................	£130	29·00
		w. Wmk inverted	£130	29·00
D37		3d. emerald-green *or* dull green (3.03).................................	70·00	40·00
		w. Wmk upright	70·00	40·00
D38		4d. emerald-green *or* dull green (5.03).................................	£150	55·00
		w. Wmk upright	£150	55·00
D39		5d. emerald-green	£225	48·00
D40		6d. emerald-green (3.04)	85·00	16·00
D41		1s. emerald-green	£275	38·00
D42		5s. emerald-green (5.03)	£700	£130
D43		10s. dull green (10.03).....................	£1600	£1600
D44		20s. dull green (10.03).....................	£3750	£2250
D13/44 Opt "Specimen" *Set of 14*			£5500	£3750
D13s/44s *Set of 14*			£850	

The 10s. and 20s. values were only issued in New South Wales.

D 4   D 6

1906 (Jan)–**08**. *Chalk-surfaced paper.* Wmk Type D **4**.

(a) P 11½, 12, compound with 11.

D45	D **3**	½d. green (1.07).............................	9·50	11·00
		w. Wmk inverted	9·50	11·00
D46		1d. green	16·00	3·75
		w. Wmk inverted	16·00	3·75
D47		2d. green	38·00	5·50
		w. Wmk inverted	38·00	5·50
D48		3d. green (7.08).............................	£500	£250
D49		4d. green (4.07).............................	60·00	23·00
		w. Wmk inverted	60·00	23·00
D50		6d. green (3.08).............................	180	25·00
		w. Wmk inverted	180	25·00
D45/50 *Set of 6*			£700	£275

(b) P 11.

D51	D **3**	1d. dull green	£1500	£600
		aw. Wmk inverted	—	£600
D51*b*		2d. green	†	£1500
D52		4d. dull green (4.07)	£2250	£1300

No. D51*b* is only known pen-cancelled.
Shades exist.

1907 (July–Sept). *Chalk-surfaced paper.* Wmk Type w **11** (Crown over double lined A) (inverted on ½d.). P 11½×11.

D53	D **3**	½d. dull green	25·00	60·00
		w. Wmk upright	42·00	85·00
D54		1d. dull green (August)	65·00	40·00
		w. Wmk upright	65·00	40·00
D55		2d. dull green (Sept)	£120	95·00
		w. Wmk inverted	£140	95·00
D56		4d. dull green (Sept)	180	90·00
		w. Wmk inverted	180	90·00
		y. Wmk inverted and reversed.......	£400	
D57		6d. dull green (Sept)	£200	£120
		w. Wmk inverted	—	£225
D53/7 *Set of 5*			£550	£375

1908 (Sept)–**09**. *Stroke after figure of value. Chalk-surfaced paper.* Wmk Type D **4** (inverted on 10s.).

(a) P 11½×11.

D58	D **6**	1s. dull green (1909)	75·00	9·00
D59		5s. dull green (1909)	£225	48·00

(b) P 11.

D60	D **6**	2s. dull green (1909)	£1000	£5000
D61		10s. dull green (1909)	£2500	£15000
D62		20s. dull green (1909)	£6000	£30000
D58/62 *Set of 5*			£9000	£45000

Nos. D61/2 were only issued in New South Wales.

D 7

Die I   Die II

1d.

Die I   Die II

2d.

(Typo J. B. Cooke, Melbourne)

1909 (1 July)–**10**. Wmk Crown over A, Type w **11**.

(a) P 12×12½ (comb).

D63	D **7**	½d. rosine and yellow-green (8.09)..	14·00	26·00
D64		1d. rosine and yellow-green (I)	14·00	4·00
		b. Die II (7.10)...........................	20·00	1·75
D65		2d. rosine and yellow-green (I)	27·00	3·75
		a. Die II (8.10)...........................	29·00	1·75
		aw. Wmk inverted		
D66		3d. rosine and yellow-green (9.09)..	28·00	14·00
D67		4d. rosine and yellow-green (8.09)..	28·00	5·00
D68		6d. rosine and yellow-green (8.09)..	27·00	3·25
D69		1s. rosine and yellow-green (8.09)..	30·00	2·75
D70		2s. rosine and yellow-green (8.09)..	70·00	9·50
D71		5s. rosine and yellow-green (10.09)	90·00	13·00
D72		10s. rosine and yellow-green (11.09)	£250	£150
D73		£1 rosine and yellow-green (11.09)	£475	£275
D63/73 *Set of 11*			£900	£450

(b) P 11.

D74	D **7**	1d. rose and yellow-green (II).........	£1800	£750
D74*a*		2d. rose and yellow-green (II).........	£10000	£4000
D75		2d. rose and yellow-green (8.09).....	£11000	£11000

Only one unused example, without gum, and another pen-cancelled are known of No. D74*a*.

The 1d. of this printing is distinguishable from No. D78 by the colours, the green being very yellow and the rose having less of a carmine tone. The paper is thicker and slightly toned, that of No D78 being pure white; the gum is thick and yellowish, No. D78 having thin white gum.

All later issues of the 1d. and 2d. are Die II.

(Typo J. B. Cooke (later ptgs by T. S. Harrison))

1912 (Dec)–**23**. *Thin paper. White gum.* W w **11**.

(a) P 12½ (line).

D76	D **7**	½d. scarlet and pale yellow-green (7.13)..................................	23·00	26·00
		w. Wmk inverted	38·00	32·00

(b) P 11.

D77	D **7**	½d. rosine and bright apple-green (10.14)...............................	11·00	17·00
		a. Wmk sideways	6·50	8·50
D78		1d. rosine & brt apple-green (8.14)..	9·00	2·25
		a. Wmk sideways	14·00	2·25
		w. Wmk inverted	42·00	16·00

(c) P 14.

D79	D **7**	½d. rosine and bright apple-green (11.14)...............................	80·00	£100
		a. Carmine and apple-green (Harrison) (1919)	9·00	16·00
D80		1d. rosine and bright apple-green (9.14).................................	55·00	14·00
		a. Scarlet and pale yellow-green (2.18).................................	20·00	6·00
		aw. Wmk inverted	†	£450
		b. Carmine and apple-green (Harrison) (1919)	12·00	3·75
D81		2d. scarlet and pale yellow-green (1.18).................................	17·00	9·00
		a. Carmine and pale yellow-green (Harrison) (10.18)...................	18·00	4·25
D82		3d. rosine and apple-green (5.16)....	75·00	32·00
		a. Wmk sideways	£4000	£2500
D83		4d. carmine and apple-green (Harrison) (5.21).....................	90·00	55·00
		b. Carmine and pale yellow-grn (5.21).................................	65·00	50·00
		ba. Wmk sideways	£700	£375
D85		1s. scarlet and pale yellow-green (6.23).................................	25·00	13·00
D86		10s. scarlet and pale yellow-green (5.21).................................	£1000	
D87		£1 scarlet and pale yellow-green (5.21).................................	£800	£1200

(d) Perf 14 compound with 11.

D88	D **7**	1d. carmine and apple-green..........	£4000	
D76/88 *Set of 8*			£1800	

(Typo T. S. Harrison (to Feb 1926), A. J. Mullett (to June 1927) and J. Ash (thereafter))

1922 (1 May)–**30**. W **6**.

(a) P 14.

D91	D **7**	½d. carmine and yellow-green (17.5.23)...............................	2·50	6·50
D92		1d. carmine and yellow-green	4·00	1·00
D93		1½d. carmine and yellow-green (3.25).................................	1·50	9·00
D94		2d. carmine and yellow-green (3.3.22).................................	3·50	2·25
D95		3d. carmine and yellow-green (7.2.22).................................	9·50	3·50
D96		4d. carmine and yellow-green (7.2.22).................................	35·00	14·00
D97		6d. carmine and yellow-green (8.22).................................	26·00	13·00

(b) P 11.

D98	D **7**	4d. carmine and yellow-green (22.9.30)..............................	6·50	4·50
D91/8 *Set of 8*			75·00	45·00

All values perforated 14 were printed by Harrison and all but the 1d. by Mullett and Ash. The 4d. perforated 11 was produced by J. Ash. There is a wide variation of shades in this issue.

(Typo J. Ash)

1931 (Oct)–**36**. W **15**.

(a) P 14.

D100	D **7**	1d. carmine and yellow-green (10.31)................................	7·00	11·00
		a. Imperf between (horiz pair)......	†	£10000
D102		2d. carmine and yellow-green (19.10.31)..............................	7·00	11·00

(b) P 11.

D105	D **7**	½d. carmine and yellow-green (4.34).................................	12·00	14·00
D106		1d. carmine and yellow-green (21.11.32)..............................	7·50	2·25
D107		2d. carmine and yellow-green (1933).................................	9·50	75
D108		3d. carmine and yellow-green (5.36).................................	70·00	70·00
D109		4d. carmine and yellow-green (23.5.34)..............................	6·50	3·25
D110		6d. carmine and yellow-green (4.36).................................	£325	£300
D111		1s. carmine and yellow-green (8.34).................................	48·00	35·00
D105/11 *Set of 7*			£425	£375

D 8   D 9

A   B   C

Type A. Solid rectangle inside "D" (ptgs of ½d., 1d., 2d., 4d. and 6d. from 1909 to 1945)

Type B. Shaded area inside "D" (ptgs of 3d. from 1909 to 1945)

Type C. Solid segment of circle inside "D" (ptgs of all values below 1s. from 1946)

D   E

Type D. Six lines of shading above numeral and four below (ptgs of 1s. from 1909 to 1945)

Type E. Larger "1" with only three background lines above; hyphen more upright (ptgs of 1s. from 1946 to 1953)

(Frame recess. Value typo J. Ash to 1940, then W. C. G. McCracken)).

1938 (1 July). W **15**. P 14½×14.

D112	D **8**	½d. carmine and green (A) (Sept)....	3·00	2·75
D113		1d. carmine and green (A)..........	10·00	60
D114		2d. carmine and green (A)..........	13·00	2·00
D115		3d. carmine and green (B) (Aug)...	32·00	17·00
D116		4d. carmine and green (A) (Aug)...	13·00	60
D117		6d. carmine and green (A) (Aug)...	70·00	45·00
D118		1s. carmine and green (D) (Aug)...	50·00	12·00
D112/18 Set of 7			£170	70·00

Shades exist.

1946–57. Redrawn as Type C and E (1s). W **15**. P 14½×14.

D119	D **9**	½d. carmine and green (9.56)..........	1·25	3·25
D120		1d. carmine and green (17.6.46)....	1·25	80
		w. Wmk inverted		
D121		2d. carmine and green (9.46)..........	4·50	1·25
D122		3d. carmine and green (6.8.46).......	4·50	1·25
D123		4d. carmine and green (30.7.52).....	8·00	2·50
D124		5d. carmine and green (16.12.48)...	11·00	4·00
D125		6d. carmine and green (9.47)..........	9·00	2·00
D126		7d. carmine and green (26.8.53).....	2·25	4·50
D127		8d. carmine and green (24.4.57).....	5·00	20·00
D128		1s. carmine and green (9.47)..........	15·00	1·75
D119/28 Set of 10			55·00	38·00

There are many shades in this issue.

OFFICIAL STAMPS

From 1902 the departments of the Commonwealth government were issued with stamps of the various Australian States perforated "OS" to denote official use. These were replaced in 1913 by Commonwealth of Australia issues with similar perforated initials as listed below.

During the same period the administrations of the Australian States used their own stamps and those of the Commonwealth perforated with other initials for the same purpose. These States issues are outside the scope of this catalogue.

Most shades listed under the postage issues also exist perforated "OS". Only those which are worth more than the basic colours are included below.

(O **1**)   (O **2**) (11 holes in   (O **3**)
             "S". Examples with
             12 holes in "S"
             are N.S.W. state
             issues

1913 (Jan–Apr). Nos. 1/16 punctured as Type O **1**. W **2**. P 12.

O1	**1**	½d. green (Die I).....................	16·00	9·50
		w. Wmk inverted	†	80·00
O2		1d. red (Die I).......................	15·00	3·50
		cw. Wmk inverted	80·00	10·00
		d. Die II...................	20·00	6·50
		da. Wmk sideways	†	£500
		dw. Wmk inverted	80·00	15·00
O3		2d. grey (Die I)......................	29·00	12·00
O4		2½d. indigo (Die II)................	£275	£120
O5		3d. olive (Die I).....................	£100	42·00
		ca. In pair with Die II.............	£700	
		dw. Wmk inverted	£150	55·00
		e. Die II...................	£300	£100
		ew. Wmk inverted	£500	£150
O6		4d. orange (Die II).................	£160	21·00
		a. Orange–yellow	£250	85·00
O7		5d. chestnut (Die II)...............	£140	32·00
O8		6d. ultramarine (Die II)...........	£110	19·00
		w. Wmk inverted	£500	£120
O9		9d. violet (Die II)...................	£120	45·00
		w. Wmk inverted	†	£4000
O10		1s. emerald (Die II)................	£160	25·00
		w. Wmk inverted	£700	£325
O11		2s. brown (Die II)...................	£275	£120
		a. Double print	†	£3000
O12		5s. grey and yellow	£650	£375
O13		10s. grey and pink	£2000	£1200
O14		£1 brown and ultramarine	£3000	£2000
O15		£2 black and rose	£6500	£3750
O1/15 Set of 15			£12000	£7000

1914. Nos. 1/16 punctured as Type O **2**. W **2**. P 12.

O16	**1**	½d. green (Die I).....................	15·00	10·00
		w. Wmk inverted	†	50·00
O17		1d. red (Die I).......................	16·00	6·50
		d. Die II...................	23·00	3·50
		e. Die IIA................	18·00	2·25
O18		2d. grey (Die I)......................	60·00	4·50
		w. Wmk inverted	£100	16·00
O19		2½d. indigo (Die II)................	£250	£120
O20		3d. olive (Die I).....................	90·00	15·00
		dw. Wmk inverted	£150	35·00
		e. Die II...................	£225	60·00
		ew. Wmk inverted	£375	£150
O21		4d. orange (Die II).................	£180	75·00
		a. Orange–yellow	£250	£100
O22		5d. chestnut (Die II)...............	£160	45·00
O23		6d. ultramarine (Die II)...........	£100	13·00
			£200	75·00

O24		9d. violet (Die II)...................	£110	27·00
O25		1s. emerald (Die II)................	£110	22·00
O26		2s. brown (Die II)...................	£350	90·00
O27		5s. grey and yellow		
O28		10s. grey and pink		
O29		£1 brown and ultramarine	£3500	£2250
O30		£2 black and rose	£7000	

1915. Nos. 24 and 26/30 punctured as Type O **2**. W **5**. P 12.

O31	**1**	2d. grey (Die I)......................	£100	11·00
O33		6d. ultramarine (Die II)...........	£150	15·00
		b. Die IIA................	£1800	£550
O34		9d. violet (Die II)...................	£250	70·00
O35		1s. blue-green (Die II)............	£250	60·00
O36		2s. brown (Die II)...................	£800	£110
O37		5s. grey and yellow	£850	£140
		a. Yellow portion doubly printed...	†	£3000
		w. Wmk inverted	£950	£180

1914–21. Nos. 20/3 punctured as Type O **2**. W **5**. P 14¼×14 (comb).

O38	**5a**	½d. bright green	11·00	2·75
		a. Perf 14¼ (line).................	†	£1200
		w. Wmk inverted	18·00	7·50
O39		1d. carmine-red (I) (No. 21c).....	12·00	1·00
		gw. Wmk inverted	19·00	2·75
		h. Die II...................	£325	15·00
O41		4d. orange	45·00	3·50
		a. Yellow-orange	60·00	7·50
		b. Pale orange-yellow	£100	16·00
		c. Lemon-yellow	£275	50·00
		w. Wmk inverted	55·00	19·00
O42		5d. brown (P 14¼ (line)...........	55·00	3·25
		aw. Wmk inverted	£225	£100
		b. Printed on the gummed side		
		(wmk inverted).................	£1800	
		c. Perf 14¼×14 (comb)...........	55·00	3·25
		cw. Wmk inverted	£190	45·00

1915–28. Nos. 35/45 punctured as Type O **2**. W **6**. P 12.

O43	**1**	2d. grey (Die I)......................	24·00	6·00
		bw. Wmk inverted	42·00	3·00
		d. Die IIA................	38·00	17·00
		da. Printed double	†	£2000
O44		2½d. deep blue (Die II)............	60·00	14·00
		w. Wmk inverted	†	40·00
O45		3d. yellow-olive (Die I)...........	32·00	5·50
		cw. Wmk inverted	50·00	30·00
		d. Die II...................	£110	55·00
		dw. Wmk inverted	£180	£110
		e. Die IIB................	28·00	18·00
		ew. Wmk inverted	60·00	40·00
O46		6d. ultramarine (Die II)...........	40·00	6·50
		a. Die IIA................	£1300	£500
		d. Die IIB................	65·00	22·00
		dw. Wmk inverted	£130	40·00
O47		9d. violet (Die II)...................	35·00	16·00
		b. Die IIB................	50·00	17·00
		bw. Wmk inverted	†	40·00
O48		1s. blue-green (Die II)............	25·00	3·00
		aw. Wmk inverted	£750	£500
		b. Die IIB................	25·00	3·50
O49		2s. brown (Die II)...................	£225	17·00
		b. Red-brown (aniline).............	£550	£100
		w. Wmk inverted	£850	£200
O50		5s. grey and yellow	£250	45·00
		w. Wmk inverted	£550	£350
O51		10s. grey and pink	£500	60·00
O52		£1 chocolate and dull blue	£2750	£1600
		ab. Wmk sideways. Chestnut and bright blue.................	£30000	
		aw. Wmk inverted	£3250	£2250
O53		£2 black and rose	£2250	£1200
O43/53 Set of 11			£5500	£2750

1916–20. Nos. 47/f and 5d. as No. 23 punctured as Type O **2**. Rough paper. W **5**. P 14.

O54	**5a**	1d. scarlet (I).......................	22·00	7·00
		a. Deep red	22·00	7·00
		b. Rose-red	22·00	7·00
		c. Rosine............................	60·00	13·00
		dw. Wmk inverted	26·00	8·50
		e. Die II. Rose-red	£225	15·00
		f. Die II. Rosine..................	£425	42·00
		fw. Wmk inverted		
O60		5d. bright chestnut (9.20)........	£2000	£150

All examples of the 5d. on this paper were perforated "OS".

1918–20. Nos. 48/52 punctured as Type O **2**. W **6a**. P 14.

O61	**5a**	½d. green	16·00	2·00
		w. Wmk inverted	23·00	10·00
O62		1d. carmine-pink (I)...............	†	£650
O63		1d. carmine (I)......................	£150	55·00
O64		1½d. black-brown	18·00	3·50
		a. Very thin paper.................	55·00	22·00
		w. Wmk inverted	50·00	10·00
O65		1½d. red-brown	23·00	2·25
		w. Wmk inverted	42·00	9·00
O61/5 Set of 4			£190	55·00

1918–23. Nos. 56/9 and 61/6 punctured as Type O **2**. W **5**. P 14.

O66	**5a**	½d. orange	17·00	10·00
O67		1d. violet	24·00	14·00
		w. Wmk inverted	†	£8000
O68		1½d. black-brown	26·00	2·75
		w. Wmk inverted	40·00	7·50
O69		1½d. deep red-brown	22·00	2·50
		w. Wmk inverted	38·00	7·50
O69b		1½d. bright red-brown	†	50·00
O70		1½d. green...........................	15·00	1·50
O71		2d. brown-orange	13·00	1·25
		w. Wmk inverted	£225	55·00
O72		2d. bright rose-scarlet	18·00	4·00
		w. Wmk inverted	£250	55·00
O73		4d. violet	45·00	13·00
O74		4d. ultramarine	65·00	11·00
O75		1s.4d. pale blue....................	55·00	17·00
		b. Deep turquoise	£1600	£1200
O66/75 Set of 10			£275	65·00

1923–24. Nos. 73/5 punctured as Type O **2**. W **6**. P 12.

O76	**1**	1d. chestnut (Die IIB).............	23·00	2·50
O77		2s. maroon (Die II).................	85·00	12·00
O78		£1 grey (Die IIB)...................	£700	£400
O76/8 Set of 3			£750	£400

1924. Nos. 76/84 punctured as Type O **2**. P 14.

(a) W **5**.

O79	**5a**	1d. sage-green	9·00	2·25
O80		1½d. scarlet	7·00	70
		w. Wmk inverted	60·00	10·00
		wa. Printed on the gummed side	£275	
O81		2d. red-brown	20·00	17·00
		a. Bright red-brown	38·00	23·00
O82		3d. dull ultramarine	32·00	6·00
O83		4d. olive-yellow	42·00	6·00
O84		4½d. violet	75·00	14·00
		w. Wmk inverted	†	£4000

(b) W **6a**.

O85	**5a**	1d. sage-green	16·00	16·00

(c) No wmk.

O86		1d. sage-green	70·00	65·00
O87		1½d. scarlet	75·00	65·00
O79/87 Set of 9			£300	£170

1926–30. Nos. 85/104 punctured as Type O **2**. W **7**.

(a) P 14.

O88	**5a**	½d. orange	£190	85·00
O89		1d. sage-green	10·00	1·50
O90		1½d. scarlet	22·00	2·50
		a. Golden scarlet	24·00	4·75
		w. Wmk inverted	24·00	3·75
O92		2d. red-brown (Die I)..............	£140	45·00
O93		3d. dull ultramarine	70·00	13·00
		w. Wmk inverted	70·00	13·00
O94		4d. yellow-olive	£150	40·00
O95		4½d. violet	£150	35·00
O96		1s.4d. pale greenish blue	£350	£140
O88/96 Set of 8			£950	£325

(b) P 13½×12½.

O97	**5a**	½d. orange	4·50	1·25
O98		1d. sage-green (Die I).............	4·50	1·50
		b. Die II...................	£100	£120
O100		1½d. scarlet	8·50	2·50
		a. Golden scarlet	5·00	2·75
		w. Wmk inverted	7·00	3·25
O102		1½d. red-brown	17·00	5·00
O103		2d. red-brown (Die II).............	28·00	16·00
O104		2d. golden scarlet (Die II)........	16·00	4·00
		a. Die III.................	13·00	3·25
		aw. Wmk inverted	22·00	7·50
O106		3d. dull ultramarine (Die I).......	28·00	5·00
		aw. Wmk inverted	55·00	25·00
		b. Die II. Deep ultramarine	£10000	£7000
		bw. Wmk inverted		
O108		4d. yellow-olive	22·00	3·75
O109		4½d. violet	£130	£130
O110		5d. orange-brown (Die II).........	55·00	7·00
O111		1s.4d. turquoise....................	£275	27·00
O97/111 Set of 11			£500	£180

1927 (9 May). Opening of Parliament House, Canberra. No. 105 punctured as Type O **3**.

O112	**8**	1½d. brownish lake	16·00	7·50

1928 (29 Oct). National Stamp Exhibition, Melbourne. No. 106 punctured as Type O **2**.

O113		3d. blue..............................	13·00	9·00

1929–30. Nos. 107/14 punctured as Type O **2**. W **7**. P 12.

O114	**1**	6d. chestnut (Die IIB).............	24·00	4·25
O115		9d. violet (Die IIB).................	55·00	5·50
O116		1s. blue-green (Die IIB)...........	23·00	4·50
O117		2s. maroon (Die II).................	£110	8·00
O118		5s. grey and yellow	£275	40·00
O118a		10s. grey and pink	£2250	
O118b		£2 black and rose	£4000	£3000

1929 (20 May). Air. No. 115 punctured as Type O **3**.

O119	**9**	3d. green	24·00	12·00

1929 (28 Sep). Centenary of Western Australia. No. 116 punctured as Type O **3**.

O120	**10**	1½d. dull scarlet....................	17·00	12·00

1930 (2 Jun). Centenary of Exploration of River Murray by Capt. Sturt. Nos. 117/18 punctured as Type O **2**.

O121	**11**	1½d. scarlet	12·00	7·50
O122		3d. blue..............................	15·00	8·00

O S

(O **4**)

1931 (4 May). Nos. 121/2 optd with Type O **4**.

O123	**13**	2d. rose-red	55·00	18·00
O124		3d. blue..............................	£200	32·00

For No. 139 overprinted with Type O **4**, see No. 139a.

1932 (Feb)–33. Optd as Type O **4**.

(a) W **7**.

(i) P 13½×12½.

O125	**5a**	2d. golden scarlet (Die III).......	12·00	1·50
		a. Opt inverted	†	£25000
		w. Wmk inverted	£3000	£2250
O126		4d. yellow-olive (3.32)............	16·00	3·75

(ii) P 12.

O127	**1**	6d. chestnut (3.32)	48·00	50·00

(b) W **15**.

(i) P 13½×12½.

O128	**5a**	½d. orange (11.7.32)	4·75	1·50
		a. Opt inverted	£10000	£5500
O129		1d. green (3.32)	3·25	45
		w. Wmk inverted	£1000	£500
		x. Wmk reversed	£1400	£750
O130		2d. golden scarlet (Die III)	10·00	55
		a. Opt inverted	†	£20000
O131		3d. ultramarine (Die II) (2.33)	7·50	4·00
O132		5d. orange-brown (7.32)	35·00	27·00

(ii) P 12.

O133	**1**	6d. chestnut (9.32)	22·00	20·00
		a. Opt inverted	†	£30000

(c) Recess. No wmk. P 11.

O134	**18**	2d. scarlet (3.32)	5·00	2·00
O135		3d. blue (3.32)	14·00	5·00
O136	**17**	1s. green (3.32)	40·00	27·00

No. O128a and probably the other inverted overprints were caused by the insertion of a stamp upside down into sheets repaired before surcharging.

Issue of overprinted official stamps ceased in February 1933 and thereafter mail from the federal administration was carried free.

BRITISH COMMONWEALTH OCCUPATION FORCE (JAPAN)

Nos. J1/7 were used by the Australian forces occupying Japan after the Second World War. Initially their military post offices supplied unoverprinted Australian stamps, but it was decided to introduce the overprinted issue to prevent currency speculation.

B.C.O.F.
JAPAN
1946
(1)

B.C.O.F.
JAPAN
1946
(2)

Ɔ.F. Ɔ.F.
1946 AN AN

Wrong fount "6"
(left pane R. 9/4)

Normal

Narrow "N"
(right pane R. 1/8)

1946 (11 Oct)–**48**. *Stamps of Australia optd as T* **1** *(1d., 3d.) or T* **2** *(others) at Hiroshima Printing Co, Japan.*

J1	**27**	½d. orange (No. 179)	4·00	7·00
		a. Wrong fount "6"	£100	£120
		b. Narrow "N"	£100	£120
		c. Stop after "JAPAN" (right pane R.5/5)	£100	£120
J2	**46**	1d. brown-purple (No. 203)	3·25	3·75
		a. Blue-black overprint	55·00	95·00
J3	**31**	3d. purple-brown (No. 187)	2·75	3·00
		a. Opt double	£750	
J4	**34**	6d. purple-brown (No. 189a) (8.5.47)	17·00	13·00
		a. Wrong fount "6"	£200	£190
		b. Stop after "JAPAN" (right pane R. 5/5)	£200	£190
		c. Narrow "N"	£200	£190
J5	**36**	1s. grey-green (No. 191) (8.5.47)	16·00	15·00
		a. Wrong fount "6"	£250	£225
		b. Stop after "JAPAN" (right pane R. 5/5)	£250	£225
		c. Narrow "N"	£250	£225
J6	**1**	2s. maroon (No. 212) (8.5.47)	42·00	50·00
J7	**38**	5s. claret (No. 176) (8.5.47)	£100	£130
		a. Thin rough paper (No. 176a)	80·00	£130
J1/7 Set of 7			£140	£190

The ½d., 1d. and 3d. values were first issued on 11 October 1946, and withdrawn two days later, but were re-issued together with the other values on 8 May 1947.

The following values with T **2** in the colours given were from proof sheets which, however, were used for postage: ½d. (red) 1d. (red or black) and 3d. (gold, red or black). (*Prices for black opts* £100, *each, and for red or gold from* £300 *each, all un*).

The use of B.C.O.F. stamps ceased on 12 February 1949.

NAURU

Stamps of MARSHALL ISLANDS were used in Nauru from the opening of the German Colonial Post Office on 14 July 1908 until 8 September 1914.

Following the occupation by Australian forces on 6 November 1914 the "N.W. PACIFIC ISLANDS" overprints on Australia (see NEW GUINEA) were used from 2 January 1915.

PRICES FOR STAMPS ON COVER TO 1945

Nos. 1/12	from × 10
Nos. 13/16	from × 4
Nos. 17/25	
Nos. 26/39	from × 6
Nos. 40/3	from × 10
Nos. 44/7	from × 15

BRITISH MANDATE

NAURU **NAURU** **NAURU**
(1)   (2)   (3)

1916 (2 Sept)–**23**. *Stamps of Great Britain (1912–22) overprinted at Somerset House.*

(a) With T **1** *(12½ mm long) at foot.*

1		½d. yellow-green	2·25	8·00

		a. "NAUP.U"	£425	
		b. Double opt, one albino	60·00	
		c. Triple opt, two albino	£300	
2		1d. bright scarlet	1·75	6·50
		a. "NAUP.U"	£650	£850
		b. Double opt, one albino	£300	
2c		1d. carmine-red	12·00	55
		cb. Double opt, one albino	£225	
3		1½d. red-brown (1923)	55·00	80·00
4		2d. orange (Die I)	2·00	13·00
		a. "NAUP.U"	£375	£650
		b. Double opt, one albino	£110	
		c. Triple opt, two albino	£275	
		y. Wmk inverted and reversed	£110	
5		2d. orange (Die II) (1923)	70·00	£100
6		2½d. blue	2·75	7·00
		a. "NAUP.U"	£425	£700
		b. Double opt, one albino	£225	
7		3d. bluish violet	2·00	4·50
		a. "NAUP.U"	£450	£750
		b. Double opt, one albino	£300	
8		4d. slate-green	2·00	8·50
		a. "NAUP.U"	£600	£1000
		b. Double opt, one albino	£225	
9		5d. yellow-brown	2·25	10·00
		a. "NAUP.U"	£1300	
		b. Double opt, one albino	£150	
10		6d. purple (*chalk-surfaced paper*)	5·00	10·00
		a. "NAUP.U"	£1000	
		b. Double opt, one albino	£325	
11		9d. agate	8·50	23·00
		a. Double opt, one albino	£300	
12		1s. bistre-brown	7·00	19·00
		a. Double opt, one albino	£350	
		s. Optd "Specimen"	£130	
1/12 Set of 11			80·00	£170

(b) With T **2** *(13½ mm long) at centre (1923).*

13		½d. green	4·50	42·00
14		1d. scarlet	19·00	32·00
15		1½d. red-brown	25·00	42·00
		a. Double opt, one albino	£160	
16		2d. orange (Die II)	30·00	60·00
13/16 Set of 4			70·00	£160

The "NAUP.U" errors occur on R.6/2 from Control I 16 only. The ink used on this batch of overprints was shiny jet-black.

There is a constant variety consisting of short left stroke to "N" which occurs at R. 1/8 on Nos. 1, 2, 4 (£30 *each*); 2c (£75); 3 (£175); 5 (£200); 6, 7 (£40 *each*); 8, 9, 10 (£60 *each*); 11, 12 (£85 *each*). All unused prices.

(c) With T **3**.

(i) Waterlow printing.

17		5s. rose-carmine	£2500	£2000
		s. Optd "Specimen"	£1600	
18		10s. indigo-blue (R.)	£9000	£5000
		a. Double opt, one albino	£11000	£7000
		s. Optd "Specimen"	£1000	
		sa. Ditto "NAURU" double, one albino.	£2000	

(ii) De La Rue printing.

19		2s.6d. sepia-brown (*shades*)	£600	£1500
		a. Double opt, one albino	£1600	
		b. Treble opt, two albino	£1600	
		s. Optd "Specimen"	£300	
20		2s.6d. yellow-brown (*shades*)	65·00	£100
21		2s.6d. brown (*shades*)	70·00	£100
		a. Re-entry (R. 2/1)	£6000	
22		5s. bright carmine (*shades*)	£100	£140
		a. Treble opt, two albino	£1200	
		s. Optd "Specimen"	£275	
23		10s. pale blue (R.)	£250	£325
		a. Treble opt (Blk.+R.+albino)	£3000	
		b. Double opt, one albino	£1200	
23c		10s. deep bright blue (R.)	£500	£550

(iii) Bradbury, Wilkinson printing (1919).

24		2s.6d. chocolate-brown	90·00	£140
		a. Double opt, one albino	£450	
25		2s.6d. pale brown	80·00	£120
		b. Double opt, one albino	£450	

The initial printing of the 2s.6d. to 10s. values, made in Sept 1915 but not known to have been issued before 2 Sept 1916, comprised 1½ sheets each of the 2s.6d. (No. 19) and 10s. (No. 18) and 3 sheets of the 5s. (No. 17), as well as the supply of "Specimens", where the 5s. value was mostly from the De La Rue printing (No. 22).

The original supply of the 2s.6d. value (No. 19) included distinct shade variants, covered by "sepia-brown (*shades*)". The "Specimens" are mostly in a deeper shade than the issued stamp. One half-sheet of 20 was quite deep, and only appears to exist cancelled "SE 2 16", apart from a mint block of 4 in the Royal Collection. The full sheet of 40 was in a slightly paler shade and included 12 double, one albino and 8 treble, two albino varieties. A few sheets in sepia-brown shades were also included in later supplies of the 2s.6d. value, but these were mostly in shades of yellow-brown (No. 20) and brown (No. 21).

Examples of most values between Nos. 1 and 25 are known showing a forged P.O. Pleasant Island postmark dated "NO 2 21".

AUSTRALIAN MANDATE

4 *Century (freighter)*

(Des R. A. Harrison. Eng T. S. Harrison. Recess Note Printing Branch of the Treasury, Melbourne and from 1926 by the Commonwealth Bank of Australia)

1924–48. No wmk. P 11.

A. Rough surfaced, greyish paper (1924–34).

26A	**4**	½d. chestnut	1·75	2·75
27A		1d. green	3·50	2·75
28A		1½d. scarlet	4·00	4·00
29A		2d. orange	4·00	11·00
30A		2½d. slate-blue	6·00	25·00
		c. Greenish blue (1934)	18·00	19·00

31A		3d. pale blue	4·00	13·00
32A		4d. olive-green	7·50	19·00
33A		5d. brown	4·25	7·00
34A		6d. dull violet	4·75	12·00
35A		9d. olive-brown	9·50	19·00
36A		1s. brown-lake	6·50	13·00
37A		2s.6d. grey-green	28·00	50·00
38A		5s. claret	50·00	£100
39A		10s. yellow	£130	£180
26A/39A Set of 14			£225	£400

B. Shiny surfaced, white paper (1937–48).

26B	**4**	½d. chestnut	5·00	13·00
		c. Perf 14 (1947)	1·40	10·00
27B		1d. green	2·50	3·00
28B		1½d. scarlet	1·00	1·50
29B		2d. orange	2·25	8·00
30B		2½d. dull blue (1948)	3·00	4·00
		a. Imperf between (vert pair)	£10000	£15000
		b. Imperf between (horiz pair)	£10000	£15000
31B		3d. greenish grey (1947)	3·50	14·00
32B		4d. olive-green	4·25	13·00
33B		5d. brown	4·75	4·00
34B		6d. dull violet	4·50	5·00
35B		9d. olive-brown	7·50	21·00
36B		1s. brown-lake	7·00	2·75
37B		2s.6d. grey-green	29·00	35·00
38B		5s. claret	38·00	50·00
39B		10s. yellow	85·00	£100
26B/39B Set of 14			£170	£225

HIS MAJESTY'S JUBILEE.

1910 - 1935
(5)

6

1935 (12 July). *Silver Jubilee. T* **4** *(shiny surfaced, white paper) optd with T* **5**.

40		1½d. scarlet	75	80
41		2d. orange	1·50	4·25
42		2½d. dull blue	1·50	1·50
43		1s. brown-lake	5·00	3·50
40/3 Set of 4			8·00	9·00

(Recess John Ash, Melbourne)

1937 (10 May). *Coronation.* P 11.

44	**6**	1½d. scarlet	45	1·75
45		2d. orange	45	2·75
46		2½d. purple	45	1·75
47		1s. purple	65	1·75
44/7 Set of 4			1·75	7·25

Japanese forces invaded Nauru on 26 August 1942 and virtually all the inhabitants were removed to Truk in the Caroline Islands.

The Australian army liberated Nauru on 13 September 1945. After an initial period without stamps Australian issues were supplied during October 1945 and were used from Nauru until further supplies of Nos. 26/39 became available. The deportees did not return until early in 1946.

NEW GUINEA

Stamps of Germany and later of GERMAN NEW GUINEA were used in New Guinea from 1888 until 1914.

During the interim period between the "G.R.I." surcharges and the "N.W. PACIFIC ISLANDS" overprints, stamps of AUSTRALIA perforated "OS" were utilised.

PRICES FOR STAMPS ON COVER

Nos. 1/30	from × 3
Nos. 31/2	—
Nos. 33/49	from × 3
Nos. 50/9	from × 3
Nos. 60/2	—
Nos. 63/4	from × 2
Nos. 64c/q	
Nos. 65/81	from × 5
Nos. 83/5	—
Nos. 86/97	from × 5
No. 99	—
Nos. 100/16	from × 4
Nos. 117/18	—
Nos. 119/24	from × 4
Nos. 125/203	from × 2
Nos. 204/5	—
Nos. 206/11	from × 8
Nos. 212/25	from × 2
Nos. O1/33	from × 8

AUSTRALIAN OCCUPATION

Stamps of German New Guinea surcharged

G.R.I.   **G.R.I.**

2d.   **1s.**   **1**
(1)   (2)   (3)

SETTINGS. The "G.R.I" issues of New Guinea were surcharged on a small hand press which could only accommodate one horizontal row of stamps at a time. In addition to complete sheets the surcharges were also applied to multiples and individual stamps which were first lightly affixed to plain paper backing sheets. Such backing sheets could contain a mixture of denominations, some of which required different surcharges.

Specialists recognise twelve settings of the low value surcharges (1d. to 8d.):

Setting 1 (Nos. 1/4 7/11) shows the bottom of the "R" 6 mm from the top of the "d"

Setting 2 (Nos. 16/19, 22/6) shows the bottom of the "R" 5 mm from the top of the "d"

Setting 3 was used for the Official stamps (Nos. O1/2)

Setting 4, which included the 2½d. value for the first time, and Setting 5 showed individual stamps with either 6 mm or 5 mm spacing.

These five settings were for rows of ten stamps, but the remaining seven, used on odd stamps handed in for surcharging, were applied as strips of five only. One has, so far, not been reconstructed, but of the remainder three show the 6 mm spacing, two the 5 mm and one both.

On the shilling values the surcharges were applied as horizontal rows of four and the various settings divide into two groups, one with 3½ to 4½ mm between the bottom of the "R" and the top of numeral, and the second with 5½ mm between the "R" and numeral. The first group includes the very rare initial setting on which the space is 4 to 4½ mm.

	G.R.I.	G.R.I.	G.R.I.
	2d.	**1d.**	**1s.**
	"1" for "I" (Setting 1)	Short "1" (Setting 1)	Large "S" (Setting 1)

1914 (17 Oct)–**15.** *Stamps of 1901 surch.*

(a) As T **1.** *"G.R.I." and value 6 mm apart.*

1	1d. on 3pf. brown	£425	£475
	a. "1" for "I"	£1000	
	b. Short "1"	£1000	
	c. "1" with straight top serif (Setting 6)	£1000	
	d. "I" for "1" (Setting 12)	£1300	
2	1d. on 5pf. green	50·00	65·00
	a. "1" for "I"	£200	£275
	b. Short "1"	£200	£275
	c. "1" with straight top serif (Settings 6 and 9)	£325	£375
3	2d. on 10pf. carmine	55·00	80·00
	a. "1" for "I"	£250	£325
4	2d. on 20pf. ultramarine	55·00	65·00
	a. "1" for "I"	£225	£275
	e. Surch double, one "G.R.I." albino	£2750	
	f. Surch inverted	£6000	
5	2½d. on 10pf. carmine (27.2.15)	65·00	£140
	a. Fraction bar omitted (Setting 9)	£1500	£1600
6	2½d. on 20pf. ultramarine (27.2.15)	75·00	£150
	a. Fraction bar omitted (Setting 9)		
7	3d. on 25pf. black and red/*yellow*	£190	£275
	a. "1" for "I"	£700	£800
8	3d. on 30pf. black and orange/*buff*	£250	£300
	a. "1" for "I"	£750	£850
	e. Surch double	£5500	£5500
9	4d. on 40pf. black and carmine	£250	£325
	a. "1" for "I"	£850	
	e. Surch double	£1400	£1900
	f. Surch inverted	£6000	
10	5d. on 50pf. black and purple/*buff*	£450	£700
	a. "1" for "I"	£1300	£1600
	e. Surch double	£6000	
11	8d. on 80pf. black and carmine/*rose*	£650	£900
	a. "1" for "I"	£1800	£2250
	d. No stop after "d"	£2250	
	e. Error. Surch "G.R.I. 4d."	£5500	

(b) As T **2.** *"G.R.I." and value 3½ to 4 mm apart.*

12	1s. on 1m. carmine	£1600	£2500
	a. Large "s"	£5500	£5500
13	2s. on 2m. blue	£1700	£2500
	a. Large "s"	£5500	£7000
	c. Error. Surch "G.R.I. 5s."	£20000	
	d. Error. Surch "G.R.I. 2d." corrected by handstamped "S"	£25000	
14	3s. on 3m. violet-black	£3250	£4250
	a. Large "s"	£7500	£7500
	b. No stop after "I" (Setting 3)	£7500	£7500
15	5s. on 5m. carmine and black	£8000	£9500
	a. Large "s"	£16000	
	b. No stop after "I" (Setting 3)	£10000	£12000
	c. Error. Surch "G.R.I. 1s."	£45000	

	G.R.I.	G.R.I.
	3d.	**5d.**
	Thick "3" (Setting 2)	Thin "5" (Setting 2)

1914 (16 Dec)–**15.** *Stamps of 1901 surch.*

(a) As T **1.** *"G.R.I." and value 5 mm apart.*

16	1d. on 3pf. brown	45·00	55·00
	a. "I" for "1" (Setting 11)	£425	
	b. Short "1" (Setting 2)	£200	
	c. "1" with straight top serif (Settings 2 and 6)	75·00	90·00
	e. Surch double	£550	£800
	f. Surch double, one inverted	£3000	
	g. Surch inverted	£2000	
	h. Error. Surch "G.R.I. 4d."	£6500	
17	1d. on 5pf. green	18·00	32·00
	b. Short "1" (Setting 2)	£110	£160
	c. "1" with straight top serif (Setting 2)	35·00	60·00
	e. "d" inverted	†	£1200
	f. "1d" inverted	†	£4500
	g. "G.R.I." without stops or spaces	£4500	
	ga. "G.R.I." without stops, but with normal spaces		£4500
	h. "G.I.R." instead of "G.R.I."	£5500	£6000
	i. Surch double	£2000	
18	2d. on 10pf. carmine	24·00	40·00
	e. No stop after "d" (Setting 2)	£130	£180

	f. Stop before, instead of after, "G" (Settings 4 and 5)	£4500	
	g. Surch double	£7500	£7500
	h. Surch double, one inverted		£6000
	i. In vert pair with No. 20	£15000	
	j. In horiz pair with No. 20	£15000	
	k. Error. Surch ".G.R.I. 1d."	£5000	£4500
	l. Error. Surch "G.I.R. 3d."	£6000	
19	2d. on 20pf. ultramarine	28·00	45·00
	e. No stop after "d" (Setting 2)	95·00	£130
	f. No stop after "I" (Setting 11)	£850	
	g. "R" inverted (Settings 4 and 5)	—	£3750
	h. Surch double	£1200	£2000
	i. Surch double, one inverted	£2000	£2500
	j. Surch inverted	£4500	
	k. Albino surch (in horiz pair with normal)	£12000	
	l. In vert pair with No. 21	£10000	£12000
	m. Error. Surch "G.R.I. 1d."	£5500	£6000
20	2½d. on 10pf. carmine (27.2.15)	£160	£250
21	2½d. on 20pf. ultramarine (27.2.15)	£1500	£1800
	a. Error. Surch "G.R.I. 3d." (in vert pair with normal)	£24000	
22	3d. on 25pf. black and red/*yellow*	£110	£160
	e. Thick "3"	£500	£650
	f. Surch double	£4500	£5500
	g. Surch inverted	£4500	£5500
	h. Surch omitted (in horiz pair with normal)	£11000	
	i. Error. Surch "G.R.I. 1d."	£11000	
23	3d. on 30pf. black and orange/*buff*	90·00	£140
	e. No stop after "d" (Setting 2)	£550	
	f. Thick "3"	£475	
	g. Surch double	£1400	£2000
	h. Surch double, one inverted	£2250	£2250
	i. Surch double, both inverted	£5000	£6000
	j. Surch inverted	£4000	
	k. Albino surch	£8000	
	l. Surch omitted (in vert pair with normal)	£6500	
	m. Error. Surch "G.R.I. 1d."	£5000	£6000
24	4d. on 40pf. black and carmine	£100	£170
	e. Surch double	£1200	
	f. Surch double, one inverted	£2250	
	g. Surch double, both inverted	£5500	
	h. Surch inverted	£4000	
	i. Error. Surch "G.R.I. 1d."	£3500	
	ia. Surch "G.R.I. 1d." inverted	£7500	
	j. Error. Surch "G.R.I. 3d." double	£15000	
	k. No stop after "I" (Setting 11)	£2000	
25	5d. on 50pf. black and purple/*buff*	£160	£200
	e. Thin "5"	£900	£2250
	f. Surch double	£1700	
	g. Surch double, one inverted	£4500	£5500
	h. Surch double, both inverted	£5000	£5500
	i. Surch inverted	£4000	
	j. Error. Surch "G.I.R. 3d."	£10000	
26	8d. on 80pf. black and carmine/*rose*	£325	£400
	e. Surch double	£3000	£3750
	f. Surch double, one inverted	£3000	£3750
	g. Surch triple	£3500	£4000
	h. Surch inverted	£5500	
	i. Error. Surch "G.R.I. 3d."	£10000	

(b) As T **2.** *"G.R.I." and value 5½ mm apart.*

27	1s. on 1m. carmine	£2750	£4000
	a. No stop after "I" (Setting 7)	£5500	
28	2s. on 2m. blue	£2750	£4500
	a. No stop after "I" (Setting 7)	£5500	
29	3s. on 3m. violet-black	£5000	£8000
	a. "G.R.I." double	£20000	
30	5s. on 5m. carmine and black	£19000	£22000

1915 (1 Jan). *Nos. 18 and 19 further surch with T* **3.**

31	1d. on 2d. on 10pf.	£15000	£15000
32	1d. on 2d. on 20pf.	£15000	£9500

German New Guinea Registration Labels surcharged

	G.R.I. Kieta (Deutsch-Neuguinea) 3d. N° 929		G.R.I. Käwieng (Deutsch Neuguinea) 3d. N° 171
	4		4a

	G.R.I.
	3d.
	Sans serif "G" and different "3"

1915 (Jan). *Registration Labels surch "G.R.I. 3d." in settings of five or ten and used for postage. Each black and red on buff. Inscr "Deutsch Neuguinea)" spelt in various ways as indicated.* P 14 (No. 43) or 11½ (others).

I. With name of town in sans-serif letters as T **4.**

33	**Rabaul** "(Deutsch Neuguinea)"	£180	£200
	a. "G.R.I. 3d." double	£2500	£3250
	b. No bracket before "Deutsch"	£700	£900
	ba. No bracket and surch double	£6500	
	d. "(Deutsch-Neuguinea)"	£250	£375
	da. "G.R.I. 3d." double	£6500	£6500
	db. No stop after "I"	£650	
	dc. "G.R.I. 3d" inverted	£6500	
	dd. No bracket before "Deutsch"	£1000	£1400
	de. No bracket after "Neuguinea"	£1000	£1400
34	**Deulon** "(Deutsch Neuguinea)"	£13000	£15000
35	**Friedrich-Wilhelmshafen** "(Deutsch Neuguinea)"	£170	£550
	a. No stop after "d"	£325	
	b. "G" omitted	£3750	
	c. Sans-serif "G"	£7000	
	d. Sans-serif "G" and different "3"	£6500	

	e. Surch inverted	†	£6500
	f. "(Deutsch-Neuguinea)"	£180	£550
	fa. No stop after "d"	£375	
36	**Herbertshohe** "(Deutsch Neuguinea)"	£190	£500
	a. No stop after "d"	£400	
	b. No stop after "I"	£700	
	c. "G" omitted	£4000	
	d. Surch omitted (in horiz pair with normal)	£8500	
	e. "(Deutsch Neu-Guinea)"	£350	£700
37	**Kawieng** "(Deutsch-Neuguinea)"	£650	
	a. No bracket after "Neuguinea"	£2750	
	b. "Deutsch Neu-Guinea"	£250	£475
	ba. No stop after "I"	£425	
	bb. "G.R.I." double	£3500	
	be. "3d." double	£3500	
	bd. "G" omitted	£4500	
38	**Kieta** "(Deutsch-Neuguinea)"	£350	£600
	a. No bracket before "Deutsch"	£1200	£1800
	b. No stop after "d"	£650	
	c. Surch omitted (right hand stamp of horiz pair)	£7000	
	e. No stop after "I"	£950	
	f. "G" omitted	£4250	
39	**Manus** "(Deutsch Neuguinea)"	£200	£650
	a. "G.R.I. 3d." double	£4000	
	b. No stop after "I"	£900	£1600
40	**Stephansort** "(Deutsch Neu-Guinea)"	†	£1800
	a. No stop after "d"	†	£4000

II. With name of town in letters with serifs as T **4a.**

41	**Friedrich Wilhelmshafen** "(Deutsch-Neuguinea)"	£160	£500
	b. No stop after "d"	£325	£750
	c. No stop after "I"	£650	£1100
	d. No bracket before "Deutsch"	£1000	£1600
	e. No bracket after "Neuguinea"	£1000	£1600
42	**Kawieng** "(Deutsch Neuguinea)"	£150	£450
	a. No stop after "d"	£375	
	b. No stop after "I"		
43	**Manus** "(Deutsch Neuguinea)"	£2000	£3000
	a. No stop after "d"	£4000	£3750

Examples of Nos. 33db, 36b, 38e, 41c and 43a also show the stop after "R" either very faint or missing completely.

Stamps of Marshall Islands surcharged

SETTINGS. The initial supply of Marshall Islands stamps, obtained from Nauru, was surcharged with Setting 2 (5 mm between "R" and "d") on the penny values and with the 3½ to 4 setting on the shilling stamps.

Small quantities subsequently handed in were surcharged, often on the same backing sheet as German New Guinea values, with Settings 6, 7 or 12 (all 6 mm between "R" and "d") for the penny values and with a 5½ mm setting for the shilling stamps.

1914 (16 Dec). *Stamps of 1901 surch.*

(a) As T **1.** *"G.R.I." and value 5 mm apart.*

50	1d. on 3pf. brown	50·00	85·00
	c. "1" with straight top serif (Setting 2)	£110	£180
	d. ".G.R.I." and "1" with straight top serif (Settings 4 and 5)	†	£5500
	e. Surch inverted	£3750	
51	1d. on 5pf. green	50·00	55·00
	c. "1" with straight top serif (Settings 2 and 11)	£100	£120
	d. "I" for "1" (Setting 11)	£700	
	e. "1" and "d" spaced	£275	£300
	f. Surch double	£1400	£2000
	g. Surch inverted	£2000	
52	2d. on 10pf. carmine	17·00	26·00
	e. No stop after "G" (Setting 2)	£550	
	f. Surch double	£1400	
	g. Surch double, one inverted	£2000	
	h. Surch inverted	£3000	
	i. Surch sideways	£4750	
53	2d. on 20pf. ultramarine	18·00	30·00
	e. No stop after "d" (Setting 2)	48·00	80·00
	g. Surch double	£1600	£2250
	h. Surch double, one inverted	£4000	£4500
	i. Surch inverted	£4750	£4750
54	3d. on 25pf. black and red/*yellow*	£275	£375
	e. No stop after "d" (Settings 2 and 11)	£500	£700
	f. Thick "3"	£750	£1000
	g. Surch double	£1600	£2250
	h. Surch double, one inverted	£1600	
	i. Surch inverted	£4750	
55	3d. on 30pf. black and orange/*buff*	£300	£400
	e. No stop after "d" (Setting 2)	£550	£750
	f. Thick "3"	£800	
	g. Surch inverted	£3500	£4000
	h. Surch double	£3000	
56	4d. on 40pf. black and carmine	£100	£140
	e. No stop after "d" (Setting 2)	£250	£400
	f. "d" omitted (Setting 2)	†	£3750
	g. Surch double	£3000	£3500
	h. Surch triple	£5500	
	i. Surch inverted	£4250	
	j. Error. Surch "G.R.I. 1d."	£8000	
	k. Error. Surch "G.R.I. 3d."	£8000	
57	5d. on 50pf. black and purple/*buff*	£140	£190
	e. Thin "5"	£2750	
	f. "d" omitted (Setting 2)	£1400	
	g. Surch double	£4550	
	h. Surch inverted	£7500	
58	8d. on 80pf. black and carmine/*rose*	£400	£500
	e. Surch double	£4000	
	f. Surch double, both inverted	£5000	£6000
	g. Surch triple	£6000	
	h. Surch inverted	£4750	

(b) As T **2.** *"G.R.I." and value 3½–4 mm apart.*

59	1s. on 1m. carmine	£2000	£3250
	e. No stop after "I"	£3750	£5000
	e. Surch double	£18000	
	f. Error. Additional surch "1d."	£20000	
60	2s. on 2m. blue	£1200	£2500
	d. No stop after "I"	£2500	£4000
	e. Surch double	£18000	

	f. Surch double, one inverted	£18000	£18000
61	3s. on 3m. violet-black	£3750	£5500
	b. No stop after "I"	£5000	
	e. Surch double	£16000	£20000
62	5s. on 5m. carmine and black	£7500	£9500
	e. Surch double, one inverted	† £30000	

1915 (Jan). *Nos. 52 and 53 further surch with T* **3**.

63	1d. on 2d. on 10pf. carmine	£140	£170
	a. "1" double	£8000	
	b. "1" inverted	£9000	£9000
	c. Small "1"	£350	
64	1d. on 2d. on 20pf. ultramarine	£3000	£2250
	a. On No. 53e	£5000	£3000
	b. "1" inverted	£9000	£9000

The surcharged "1" on No. 63c is just over 4 mm tall. Type **3** is 6 mm tall.

1915. *Stamps of 1901 surch.*

(a) As T **1**. *"G.R.I." and value 6 mm apart.*

64c	1d. on 3pf. brown	£1200
	cc. "1" with straight top serif (Setting 6)	
	cd. "I" for "1" (Setting 12)	£1600
	ce. Surch inverted	£6000
64d	1d. on 5pf. green	£1200
	dc. "1" with straight top serif (Setting 6)	
	dd. "I" for "1" (Setting 12)	£1600
	de. Surch inverted	£6000
	df. Surch double	£6000
64e	2d. on 10pf. carmine	£1800
	ea. Surch sideways	£6500
64f	2d. on 20pf. ultramarine	£1500
	fe. Surch inverted	£6000
64g	2½d. on 10pf. carmine	£10000
64h	2½d. on 20pf. ultramarine	£15000
64i	3d. on 25pf. black and red/*yellow*	£2000
64j	3d. on 30pf. black and orange/*buff*	£2000
	je. Error. Surch "G.R.I. 1d."	£8000
64k	4d. on 40pf. black and carmine	£2000
	ke. Surch double	£6500
	kf. Surch inverted	£6500
64l	5d. on 50pf. black and purple/*buff*	£1800
	le. Surch double	£6500
64m	8d. on 80pf. black and carmine/*rose*	£2500
	me. Surch inverted	£7000

(b) As T **2**. *"G.R.I." and value 5½ mm apart.*

64n	1s. on 1m. carmine	£7000
	na. Large "s" (Setting 5)	£9500
	nb. No stop after "I" (Setting 7)	£9500
64o	2s. on 2m. blue	£5500
	as. Large "s" (Setting 5)	£8500
	as. Surch double, one inverted	£25000
64p	3s. on 3m. violet-black	£11000
	pa. Large "s" (Setting 5)	£15000
	ph. No stop after "I" (Setting 7)	£15000
	pe. Surch inverted	£25000
64q	5s. on 5m. carmine and black	£20000
	qa. Large "s" (Setting 5)	£23000

Stamps of Australia overprinted

N. W. PACIFIC ISLANDS. (a)	N. W. PACIFIC ISLANDS. (b)	N. W. PACIFIC ISLANDS. (c)

(6)

1915–16. *Stamps of Australia optd in black as T* **6** *(a), (b) or (c).*

(i) T **5a**. *W* **5** *of Australia.P* 14¼×14 (*4 Jan–15 Mar 1915*).

65	½d. green	2·75	8·50
	a. Bright green	3·00	9·50
	aw. Wmk inverted	90·00	
67	1d. pale rose (Die I) (4.1)	7·00	6·50
	a. Dull red	7·00	6·50
	b. Carmine-red	7·00	6·50
	ba. Substituted cliché (Pl 2 rt pane R. 6/5)	£1200	£1000
	bb. Dot before "1"	60·00	65·00
	bc. "Secret mark"	60·00	65·00
	bd. Flaw under neck	60·00	65·00
	be. "RA" joined	60·00	65·00
	c. Die II. Carmine-red	£100	£140
	ca. Substituted cliché (Pl 2 rt pane R. 6/4)	£1200	£1000
70	4d. yellow-orange	4·00	15·00
	a. Pale orange-yellow	17·00	32·00
	b. Chrome-yellow	£250	£275
	c. Line through "FOUR PENCE" (Pl 2 rt pane R. 2/6) (all shades) from	£350	£550
72	5d. brown (P 14¼ (line))	2·25	16·00

(ii) T **1**. *W* **2** *of Australia. P* 12 (*4 Jan 1915–March 1916*).

73	2d. grey (Die I)	18·00	50·00
74	2½d. indigo (Die II) (4.1.15)	2·75	16·00
76	3d. yellow-olive (Die I)	21·00	50·00
	a. Die II	£300	£400
	ab. In pair with Die I	£600	£800
	c. Greenish olive	£190	£275
	ca. Die II	£1300	
	cb. In pair with Die I	£2250	
78	6d. ultramarine (Die II)	85·00	90·00
	a. Retouched "E"	£5000	£6000
	w. Wmk inverted	£130	£180
79	9d. violet (Die II)	48·00	55·00
81	1s. green (Die II)	50·00	55·00
83	5s. grey and yellow (Die II) (3.16)	£950	£1300
84	10s. grey and pink (Die II) (12.15)	£110	£160
85	£1 brown and ultramarine (Die II) (12.15)	£425	£600

(iii) T **1**. *W* **5** *of Australia. P* 12 (*Oct 1915–July 1916*).

86	2d. grey (Die I)	18·00	23·00
87	2½d. indigo (Die II) (7.16)	£11000	£11000
88	6d. ultramarine (Die II)	10·00	12·00
89	9d. violet (Die II) (12.15)	16·00	21·00
90	1s. emerald (Die II) (12.15)	11·00	24·00
91	2s. brown (Die II) (12.15)	90·00	£110
92	5s. grey and yellow (Die II) (12.15)	70·00	£100

(iv) T **1**. *W* **6** *of Australia. P* 12 (*Dec 1915–1916*).

94	2d. grey (Die I)	6·00	17·00
	a. Die IIA (substituted cliché)	£500	
96	3d. yellow-olive (Die I)	5·50	11·00
	a. Die II	85·00	£130
	ab. In pair with Die I	£180	
97	2s. brown (Die II) (8.16)	35·00	50·00
	w. Wmk inverted	30·00	70·00
99	£1 chocolate and dull blue (Die II) (8.16)	£250	£400

Dates for Nos. 67 and 74 are issue dates at Rabaul. The stamps were in use from 2 January 1915 on Nauru. All other dates are those of despatch. Nos. 65/6, 68/73, 76/81 were despatched on 15 March 1915. For Die IIA of 2d. see note below Australia No. 45.

SETTINGS. Type **6** exists in three slightly different versions, illustrated above as (a), (b), and (c). These differ in the letters "S" of "ISLANDS" as follows:

(a) Both "SS" normal.
(b) First "S" with small head and large tail and second "S" normal.
(c) Both "SS" with small head and large tail.

Type **11**, which also shows the examples of "S" as the normal version, can be identified from Type **6** (a) by the relative position of the second and third lines of the overprint. On Type **6** (a) the "P" of "PACIFIC" is exactly over the first "S" of "ISLANDS". On Type **11** the "F" appears over the space between "I" and "S".

It has been established, by the study of minor variations, that there are actually six settings of the "N.W. ISLANDS" overprint, including that represented by T **11**, but the following are the different arrangements of Type **6** (a), (b), and (c) which occur:
A. Horizontal rows 1 and 2 all Type (a). Row 3 all Type (b). Rows 4 and 5 all Type (c).
B. (½d. green only.) As A, except that the types in the bottom row run (c) (c) (c) (c) (b) (c).
C. As A, but bottom row now shows types (a) (c) (c) (c) (b) (c).
Horizontal strips and pairs showing varieties (a) and (c), or (b) and (c) *se-tenant* are scarce.

The earliest printing of the 1d. and 2½d. values was made on sheets with margin attached on two sides, the later printings being on sheets from which the margins had been removed. In this printing the vertical distances between the overprints are less than in later printings, so that in the lower horizontal rows of the sheet the overprint is near the top of the stamp.

The settings used on King George stamps and on the Kangaroo type are similar, but the latter stamps being smaller the overprints are closer together in the vertical rows.

PURPLE OVERPRINTS. We no longer differentiate between purple and black overprints in the above series. In our opinion the two colours are nowadays insufficiently distinct to warrant separation.

PRICES. The prices quoted for Nos. 65 to 101 apply to stamps with opts Types **6** (a) or **6** (c). Stamps with opt Type **6** (b) are worth a 25 per cent premium. Vertical strips of three, showing (a), (b) and (c), are worth from four times the prices quoted for singles as Types **6** (a) or **6** (c).

One Penny (10)	N. W. PACIFIC ISLANDS. (11)

1918 (23 May). *Nos. 72 and 81 surch locally with T* **10**.

100	1d. on 5d. brown	90·00	80·00
101	1d. on 1s. green	90·00	75·00

Types **6** (a), (b), (c) occur on these stamps also.

1918–23. *Stamps of Australia optd with T* **11** (*"P" of "PACIFIC" over space between "I" and "S" of "ISLANDS"*).

(i) T **5a**. *W* **5** *of Australia. P* 14¼×14.

102	½d. green	1·50	3·50
103	1d. carmine-red (Die I)	3·75	1·60
	a. Substituted cliché (Pl 2 rt pane R. 6/5)	£700	£425
	ab. Dot before "1"	42·00	32·00
	ac. "Secret mark"	42·00	32·00
	ad. Flaw under neck	42·00	32·00
	ae. "RA" joined	42·00	32·00
	b. Die II	£110	75·00
	ba. Substituted cliché (Pl 2 rt pane R. 6/4)	£700	£425
104	4d. yellow-orange (1919)	3·25	16·00
	a. Line through "FOUR PENCE" (Pl 2 rt pane R. 2/6)	£800	£1200
105	5d. brown (1919)	3·00	12·00

(ii) T **1**. *W* **6** *of Australia. P* 12.

106	2d. grey (Die I) (1919)	7·00	21·00
	a. Die II	11·00	42·00
107	2½d. indigo (Die II) (1919)	3·75	16·00
	a. "1" of "½" omitted	£5500	£7000
	b. Blue (1920)	7·50	29·00
109	3d. greenish olive (Die I) (1919)	23·00	26·00
	a. Die II	60·00	70·00
	ab. In pair with Die I	£375	£450
110	6d. ultramarine (Die II) (1919)	4·50	14·00
	a. Greyish ultramarine (1922)	42·00	65·00
112	9d. violet (Die IIB) (1919)	9·00	42·00
113	1s. emerald (Die II)	6·50	30·00
	a. Pale blue-green	14·00	30·00
115	2s. brown (Die II) (1919)	21·00	38·00
116	5s. grey and yellow (Die II) (1919)	60·00	65·00
117	10s. grey and bright pink (Die II) (1919)	£150	£200
118	£1 bistre-brown and grey-bl (Die II) (1922)	£2750	£4000

(iii) T **5a**. *W* **6a** *of Australia (Mult Crown A). P* 14.

119	½d. green (1919)	1·50	3·75
	w. Wmk inverted	60·00	

(iv) T **5a**. *W* **5** *of Australia. Colour changes and new value.*

120	1d. violet (*shades*) (1922)	1·75	6·50
	a. Dot before "1"	25·00	65·00
	b. "Secret mark"	25·00	65·00
	c. Flaw under neck	25·00	65·00
121	d. "RA" joined	25·00	65·00
122	2d. orange (1921)	7·00	2·75
123	2d. rose-scarlet (1922)	9·50	3·75
	4d. violet (1922)	20·00	40·00
	a. "FOUR PENCE" in thinner letters (Pl 2 rt pane R. 2/6)	£650	£1000
124	4d. ultramarine (1922)	11·00	60·00
	a. "FOUR PENCE" in thinner letters (Pl 2 rt pane R. 2/6)	£750	£1200
120/4	Set of 5	45·00	£100

Type **11** differs from Type **6** (a) in the position of the "P" of "PACIFIC", which is further to the left in Type **11**.
For 1d. rosine Dies I and II on rough unsurfaced paper see Nos. O16/b.

MANDATED TERRITORY OF NEW GUINEA

A civil administration for the Mandated Territory of New Guinea was established on 9 May 1921.

PRINTERS. See note at the beginning of Australia.

12 Native Village (13)

(Des R. Harrison. Eng T. Harrison. Recess Note Printing Branch, Treasury, Melbourne, from 1926 Note Ptg Branch, Commonwealth Bank of Australia, Melbourne)

1925 (23 Jan)–**28**. P 11.

125	12	½d. orange	2·50	7·00
126		1d. green	2·50	5·50
126a		1½d. orange-vermilion (1926)	3·25	2·75
127		2d. claret	2·50	4·50
128		3d. blue	4·50	4·00
129		4d. olive-green	13·00	21·00
130		6d. dull yellow-brown	20·00	48·00
		a. Olive-bistre (1927)	6·00	50·00
		b. Pale yellow-bistre (1928)	5·00	48·00
131		9d. dull purple (*to violet*)	13·00	45·00
132		1s. dull blue-green (6.4.25)	15·00	27·00
133		2s. brown-lake (6.4.25)	30·00	48·00
134		5s. olive-bistre (6.4.25)	48·00	65·00
135		10s. dull rose (6.4.25)	£100	£180
136		£1 dull olive-green (6.4.25)	£190	£300
125/36		Set of 13	£375	£600

1931 (8 June). *Air. Optd with T* **13**. P 11.

137	12	½d. orange	1·50	7·00
138		1d. green	1·60	5·00
139		1½d. orange-vermilion	1·25	5·00
140		2d. claret	1·25	7·00
141		3d. blue	1·75	13·00
142		4d. olive-green	1·25	9·00
143		6d. pale yellow-bistre	1·75	14·00
144		9d. violet	3·00	17·00
145		1s. dull blue-green	3·00	17·00
146		2s. brown-lake	7·00	42·00
147		5s. olive-bistre	20·00	65·00
148		10s. bright pink	75·00	£100
149		£1 olive-grey	£140	£250
137/49		Set of 13	£225	£500

14 Raggiana Bird of Paradise (Dates either side of value) (15)

(Recess John Ash, Melbourne)

1931 (2 Aug). *Tenth Anniv of Australian Administration. T* **14** (*with dates*). P 11.

150	14	1d. green	4·00	2·00
151		1½d. vermilion	5·00	10·00
152		2d. claret	5·00	2·25
153		3d. blue	5·00	4·75
154		4d. olive-green	6·50	21·00
155		5d. deep blue-green	5·00	21·00
156		6d. bistre-brown	5·00	19·00
157		9d. violet	8·50	19·00
158		1s. pale blue-green	6·00	15·00
159		2s. brown-lake	10·00	32·00
160		5s. olive-brown	42·00	55·00
161		10s. bright pink	85·00	£130
162		£1 olive-grey	£190	£250
150/62		Set of 13	£325	£500

1931 (2 Aug). *Air. Optd with T* **15**.

163	14	½d. orange	3·25	3·25
164		1d. green	4·00	4·75
165		1½d. vermilion	3·75	10·00
166		2d. claret	3·75	3·00
167		3d. blue	6·00	6·50
168		4d. olive-green	6·00	9·00
169		5d. deep blue-green	6·00	11·00
170		6d. bistre-brown	7·00	26·00
171		9d. violet	8·00	15·00
172		1s. pale blue-green	7·50	15·00
173		2s. dull lake	16·00	48·00
174		5s. olive-brown	42·00	70·00
175		10s. bright pink	60·00	£120
176		£1 olive-grey	£110	£250
163/76		Set of 14	£250	£500

1932 (30 June)–**34**. *T* **14** (*redrawn without dates*). P 11.

177		1d. green	2·50	20

178	1½d. claret..............................		2·50	11·00
179	2d. vermilion........................		2·50	20
179a	2½d. green (14.9.34)...............		6·50	21·00
180	3d. blue.................................		3·25	1·00
180a	3½d. aniline carmine (14.9.34).....		13·00	11·00
181	4d. olive-green.....................		3·25	6·00
182	5d. deep blue-green..............		3·50	70
183	6d. bistre-brown...................		4·50	3·25
184	9d. violet..............................		9·50	22·00
185	1s. blue-green......................		4·50	10·00
186	2s. dull lake.........................		4·00	17·00
187	5s. olive...............................		27·00	45·00
188	10s. pink................................		48·00	70·00
189	£1 olive-grey........................		95·00	£100
177/89 Set of 15			£200	£275

1932 (30 June)–34. *Air.* T **14** *(redrawn without dates), optd with* T **15**. P 11.

190	½d. orange............................		60	1·50
191	1d. green..............................		1·25	1·50
192	1½d. claret..............................		1·75	7·50
193	2d. vermilion........................		1·75	30
193a	2½d. green (14.9.34)...............		6·00	2·50
194	3d. blue.................................		3·25	6·00
194a	3½d. aniline carmine (14.9.34).....		4·50	3·25
195	4d. olive-green.....................		4·50	10·00
196	5d. deep blue-green..............		7·00	7·50
197	6d. bistre-brown...................		4·50	15·00
198	9d. violet..............................		6·00	9·00
199	1s. pale blue-green...............		6·00	9·00
200	2s. dull lake.........................		10·00	48·00
201	5s. olive-brown....................		48·00	60·00
202	10s. blue................................		80·00	80·00
203	£1 olive-grey........................		75·00	55·00
190/203 Set of 16			£225	£275

The ½d. orange redrawn without dates exists without overprint, but it is believed that this was not issued (*Price* £100 un).

16 Bulolo Goldfields

(Recess John Ash, Melbourne)

1935 (1 May). *Air.* P 11.

204	**16**	£2 bright violet......................	£225	£130
205		£5 emerald-green	£550	£400

HIS MAJESTY'S JUBILEE. 1910 — 1935

(17)   **18**

1935 (27 June). *Silver Jubilee. As Nos. 177 and 179, but shiny paper. Optd with* T **17**.

206	1d. green..............................		75	50
207	2d. vermilion........................		1·75	50

Re-entry (design completely duplicated) (Pl 2a R. 5/2)

(Recess John Ash, Melbourne)

1937 (18 May). *Coronation.* P 11.

208	**18**	2d. scarlet............................	50	1·00
209		3d. blue.................................	50	1·75
210		5d. green..............................	50	1·75
		a. Re-entry......................	60·00	90·00
211		1s. purple.............................	50	1·50
208/11 Set of 4			1·75	5·50

(Recess John Ash, Melbourne)

1939 (1 Mar). *Air. Inscr* "AIRMAIL POSTAGE" *at foot.* P 11.

212	**16**	½d. orange............................	3·75	7·00
213		1d. green..............................	3·25	4·00
214		1½d. claret..............................	4·00	9·50
215		2d. vermilion........................	8·00	3·50
216		3d. blue.................................	13·00	18·00
217		4d. yellow-olive...................	14·00	8·50
218		5d. deep green.....................	13·00	4·00
219		6d. bistre-brown...................	26·00	20·00
220		9d. violet..............................	26·00	26·00
221		1s. pale blue-green...............	26·00	21·00
222		2s. dull lake.........................	65·00	48·00
223		5s. olive-brown....................	£130	95·00
224		10s. pink................................	£400	£250
225		£1 olive-green.....................	£100	£110
212/25 Set of 14			£750	£550

OFFICIAL STAMPS

O. S.

G.R.I.

1d.   **O S   o   s**

(O 1)   (O 2)   (O 3)

1915 (27 Feb). *Stamps of 1901 surch as Type* O **1**. "G.R.I." *and*

value 3½ mm apart.

O1	1d. on 3pf. brown................		26·00	75·00
	a. "1" and "d" spaced..........		75·00	£170
	b. Surch double..................		£2500	
O2	1d. on 5pf. green.................		80·00	£140
	a. "1" and "d" spaced..........		£160	£300

1919–23. *Stamps of Australia optd with* T **11** *and punctured* "O S" *(8 × 15½ mm with eleven holes in the perforated* "S").

(i) T **5a**. *of Australia.* W **5**. P 14¼×14.

O3	1d. carmine-red (Die I)...........		£130	30·00
	b. Die II.............................		—	£250
O4	4d. yellow-orange...............		£140	55·00
	a. Line through "FOUR PENCE" (Pl 2 rt pane R. 2/6)....		£2750	
O5	5d. brown (1921).................		£200	45·00

(ii) T **1** *of Australia.* W **6**. P 12.

O6	2d. grey (Die I)....................		£200	42·00
O7	2½d. indigo (Die I).................		£350	£200
O8	3d. greenish olive (Die I) (1921)..		£400	85·00
O9	6d. ultramarine (Die II) (1921)....		£400	£140
	a. Greyish ultramarine.......		£350	£150
O10	9d. violet (Die IIB) (1921)......		£120	85·00
O11	1s. emerald (Die II) (1921).....		£200	£100
	a. Pale blue-green.............		£250	£100
O12	2s. brown (Die II) (1922).......		£200	£120
O13	5s. grey and yellow (Die II) (1922)...		—	£400
O14	10s. grey and bright pink (Die II) (1921).			

(iii) T **5a** *of Australia.* W **5**. *Rough unsurfaced paper, locally gummed.* P 14.

O16	1d. rosine (Die I) (1920)........		£500	£150
	b. Die II.............................		£1500	£500

(iv) T **5a** *of Australia.* W **5**. *Colour changes and new value.* P 14.

O17	1d. violet (*shades*) (1923)......		£200	£150
O18	2d. orange (1921).................		85·00	30·00
O19	2d. rose-scarlet (1923)..........		£200	23·00
O20	4d. violet (1921)..................		£140	70·00
	a. "FOUR PENCE" in thinner letters (Pl 2 rt pane R. 2/6).....		£200	
O21	4d. ultramarine (1922)..........		£180	85·00

Dates quoted for Nos. O3/21 are those of despatch from Australia. The earliest postmark date recorded is 2 April 1919 on No. O3. Their continued use on mail from government departments after the establishment of the civil administration is confirmed by a notice in the official *New Guinea Gazette* of 1 August 1921.

Australian postal archives indicate that nine sheets of the £1 Type **1** perforated "O S" were sent to New Guinea in September 1921. There is a pane of 30 of this stamp in the Royal Collection, but as no other examples are known it may not have been used for postal purposes.

1925 (6 Apr)–31. *Optd with Type* O **2**. P 11.

O22	**12**	1d. green..............................	1·00	4·50
O23		1½d. orange-vermilion (1931)...........	5·50	17·00
O24		2d. claret.............................	1·75	3·75
O25		3d. blue.................................	3·50	8·00
O26		4d. olive-green.....................	4·50	8·50
O27		6d. olive-bistre	20·00	35·00
		a. Pale yellow-bistre (1931) ..	7·00	35·00
O28		9d. violet..............................	4·00	35·00
O29		1s. dull blue-green...............	5·50	35·00
O30		2s. brown-lake.....................	28·00	60·00
O22/30 Set of 9			55·00	£180

1931 (2 Aug). *Optd with Type* O **3**. P 11.

O31	**14**	1d. green..............................	7·00	13·00
O32		1½d. vermilion........................	8·00	12·00
O33		2d. claret.............................	10·00	7·00
O34		3d. blue.................................	6·50	6·00
O35		4d. olive-green.....................	6·50	8·50
O36		5d. deep blue-green..............	10·00	12·00
O37		6d. bistre-brown...................	14·00	17·00
O38		9d. violet..............................	16·00	28·00
O39		1s. pale blue-green...............	16·00	28·00
O40		2s. brown-lake.....................	40·00	70·00
O41		5s. olive-brown....................	£100	£170
O31/41 Set of 11			£200	£350

1932 (30 June)–34. T **14** *(redrawn without dates), optd with Type* O **3**. P 11.

O42	1d. green..............................		9·00	10·00
O43	1½d. claret..............................		10·00	12·00
O44	2d. vermilion........................		10·00	3·25
O45	2½d. green (14.9.34)...............		3·75	6·00
O46	3d. blue.................................		9·00	27·00
	a. Double opt, one albino...		£1000	
O47	3½d. aniline carmine (14.9.34).....		3·75	9·00
O48	4d. olive-green.....................		10·00	21·00
O49	5d. deep blue-green..............		8·50	21·00
O50	6d. bistre-brown...................		15·00	42·00
O51	9d. violet..............................		14·00	42·00
O52	1s. pale blue-green...............		15·00	29·00
O53	2s. dull lake.........................		30·00	75·00
O54	5s. olive-brown....................		£110	£170
O42/54 Set of 13			£225	£400

Civil Administration in New Guinea was suspended in 1942, following the Japanese invasion.

Various New Guinea stamps exist overprinted with an anchor and three Japanese characters in a style similar to the Japanese Naval Control Area overprints found on the stamps of Netherlands Indies. These overprints on New Guinea are bogus. Two different versions are known, one produced in Japan during 1947 and the other in Australia during the late 1980s.

On resumption, after the Japanese defeat in 1945, Australian stamps were used until the appearance of the issue for the combined territories of Papua & New Guinea.

NORFOLK ISLAND

Norfolk Island, first settled in 1788 from New South Wales, was transferred to Tasmania on 29 September 1844. It became a separate settlement on 1 November 1856 under the control of the Governor of New South Wales. The island was declared an Australian Territory on 1 July 1914. Unlike the other External Territories it retains an independent postal administration.

A Post Office was opened on Norfolk Island in 1832. The stamps of TASMANIA were used on Norfolk Island from July 1854 until May 1855, such use being identified by the "72" numeral cancellation. Stamps of NEW SOUTH WALES were first used on the island in 1877, but were not regularly available until 1898. The first "NORFOLK ISLAND" cancellation was supplied in 1892, but not used until 1898. Stamps of AUSTRALIA were in use from 1913 to 1947.

1 Ball Bay

(Des and eng F. Manley. Recess Note Printing Branch, Reserve Bank of Australia)

1947 (10 June)–59. *Toned paper.* P 14.

1	**1**	½d. orange............................	85	60
		a. White paper (11.56)........	1·10	6·00
2		1d. bright violet..................	50	60
		a. White paper (8.57)..........	5·00	17·00
3		1½d. emerald-green................	50	70
		a. White paper (11.56)........	7·50	21·00
4		2d. reddish violet................	55	40
		a. White paper (11.56)........	90·00	£130
5		2½d. scarlet............................	80	30
6		3d. chestnut.........................	70	70
6a		3d. emerald-green (*white paper*) (6.7.59).....................	13·00	7·50
7		4d. claret.............................	1·75	40
8		5½d. indigo.............................	70	30
9		6d. purple-brown................	70	30
10		9d. magenta.........................	1·25	40
11		1s. grey-green......................	70	40
12		2s. yellow-bistre..................	1·00	1·00
12a		2s. deep blue (*white paper*) (6.7.59).....................	17·00	8·00
1/12a Set of 14			35·00	19·00

Stamps as Type **1**, some in different colours, perforated 11 were prepared in 1940 but never issued. Examples exist from sheets stolen prior to the destruction of these stocks.

PAPUA (BRITISH NEW GUINEA)

Stamps of QUEENSLAND were used in British New Guinea (Papua) from at least 1885 onwards. Post Offices were opened at Daru (1894), Kulumadau (Woodlarks) (1899), Nivani (1899), Port Moresby (1885), Samarai (1888), Sudest (1899) and Tamata (1899). Stamps were usually cancelled "N.G." (at Port Moresby from 1885) or "BNG" (without stops at Samarai or with stops at the other offices) from 1888. Queensland stamps were replaced in Papua by the issue of 1901.

PRICES FOR STAMPS ON COVER

Nos. 1/7	*from* × 15
No. 8	
Nos. 9/15	*from* × 20
No. 16	
Nos. 17/27	*from* × 6
No. 28	
Nos. 39/45a	*from* × 5
Nos. 47/71	*from* × 8
No. 72/4	
Nos. 75/92a	*from* × 8
Nos. 93/103	*from* × 6
Nos. 104/5	
Nos. 106/11	*from* × 10
Nos. 112/14	*from* × 6
No. 115	
Nos. 116/28	*from* × 5
Nos. 130/53	*from* × 4
No. 154/7	*from* × 12
Nos. 158/67	*from* × 4
No. 168	*from* × 3
Nos. O1/54	*from* × 10
Nos. O55/66a	*from* × 7

1 Lakatoi (trading canoe) with Hanuabada Village in Background

2 (Horizontal)

Deformed "d" at left (R. 4/3)

(Recess D.L.R.)

1901 (1 July)–**05**. Wmk Mult Rosettes, W **2**. P 14.

A. Wmk horizontal. Thick paper. Line perf.

1	1	½d. black and yellow-green	12·00	19·00
		a. Thin paper	£170	£140
2		1d. black and carmine	9·50	11·00
3		2d. black and violet	13·00	7·00
4		2½d. black and ultramarine	20·00	10·00
		a. Thin paper	£225	£160
		ab. Black and dull blue	£500	£350
5		4d. black and sepia	48·00	35·00
		a. Deformed "d" at left	£250	£200
6		6d. black and myrtle-green	45·00	35·00
7		1s. black and orange	60·00	65·00
8		2s.6d. black and brown (1.1.05)	£550	£500

B. Wmk vertical. Medium to thick paper. Line or comb perf.

9	1	½d. black and yellow-green	10·00	3·75
		a. Thin paper (*comb perf*) (1905)	16·00	24·00
10		1d. black and carmine	4·25	2·00
11		2d. black and violet	10·00	4·00
		a. Thin paper (*comb perf*) (1905)	50·00	16·00
12		2½d. black and ultramarine (*shades*)	15·00	12·00
13		4d. black and sepia	35·00	50·00
		a. Deformed "d" at left	£200	£275
		b. Deformed "d" at left (1905)	£190	
		ba. Deformed "d" at left	£900	
14		6d. black and myrtle-green	48·00	75·00
		a. Thin paper (*comb perf*) (1905)	£600	
15		1s. black and orange	55·00	85·00
		a. Thin paper (*comb perf*) (1905)	£550	
16		2s.6d. black and brown (1905)	£3000	£2250
		a. Thin paper (*comb perf*)	£500	£1000
1/16		Set of 8	£600	£1000

The paper used for Nos. 1/8 is white, of consistent thickness and rather opaque. The thin paper used for the horizontal watermark printings is of variable thickness, readily distinguishable from the thick paper by its greater transparency and by the gum which is thin and smooth.

Nos. 9/16 were initially printed on the same thick paper as the stamps with horizontal watermark and were line perforated. Values from ½d. to 2½d. were subsequently printed on medium paper on which the watermark was more visible. These were comb perforated. The thin paper with vertical watermark, produced in 1905, is much more transparent and has smooth gum. Printings were made on this paper for all values except the 2½d., but only the ½d. and 2d. were issued in Papua although used examples of the 2s.6d. are also known. The entire printing of the 1d. on thin paper with vertical watermark was used for subsequent overprints.

The sheets of the ½d., 2d. and 2½d. show a variety known as "white leaves" on R. 4/5, while the 2d. and 2½d. (both R. 6/2) and the ½d. and 1s. (both R. 6/3) show what is known as the "unshaded leaves" variety.

Papua.   **Papua.**
(3)   (4)

1906–07. I. Optd with T **3** (large opt), at Port Moresby (8 Nov 1906).

A. Wmk horizontal. Thick paper. Line perf.

17	1	4d. black and sepia	£190	£150
		a. Deformed "d" at left	£600	£500
18		6d. black and myrtle-green	48·00	48·00
19		1s. black and orange	20·00	38·00
20		2s.6d. black and brown	£140	£150

B. Wmk vertical. Thin paper (½d., 1d., 2d.) or medium to thick paper (others). Comb perf (½d. to 2½d.) or line perf (others).

21	1	½d. black and yellow-green	4·75	20·00
22		1d. black and carmine	14·00	18·00
23		2d. black and violet	5·50	3·00
24		2½d. black and ultramarine	3·75	15·00
25		4d. black and sepia	£170	£130
		a. Deformed "d" at left	£550	
26		6d. black and myrtle-green	28·00	55·00
27		1s. black and orange	£1200	£900
28		2s.6d. black and brown	£8000	£7000
17/28		Set of 8	£325	£375

II. Optd with T **4** (small opt), at Brisbane (May–June 1907).

A. Wmk horizontal. Thick paper. Line perf.

34	1	½d. black and yellow-green		
		a. Thin paper	60·00	80·00
35		2½d. black and ultramarine		
		a. Thin paper	42·00	60·00
		ac. Black and dull blue	£140	£150
36		1s. black and orange	£160	£225
37		2s.6d. black and brown	32·00	50·00
		a. Opt reading downwards	£4500	
		c. Opt double (horiz)	†	£3000
		d. Opt triple (horiz)	†	£2500

B. Wmk vertical. Thin paper (½d., 1d., 2d., 4d., 6d.) or medium to thick paper (2½d., 1s., 2s.6d.). Line perf (2½d.), comb perf (2½d.), line perf (1s., 2s.6d.) or comb perf (others).

38	1	½d. black and yellow-green	11·00	12·00
		a. Opt double	£2000	
39		1d. black and carmine	4·00	5·00
		a. Opt reading upwards	£3250	£1700
40		2d. black and violet	4·50	2·25
		a. Opt double	£2250	
41		2½d. black and ultramarine	9·50	18·00
42		4d. black and sepia	30·00	50·00
		a. Deformed "d" at left	£170	£275
43		6d. black and myrtle-green	32·00	42·00
		a. Opt double	£3500	£6000
44		1s. black and orange	60·00	75·00
		b. Thin paper (*comb perf*)	27·00	40·00
		ba. Opt double, one diagonal	£10000	£6000
45		2s.6d. black and brown	£6000	£4500
		a. Thin paper (*comb perf*)	38·00	48·00
34/45		(*cheapest*) Set of 8	£120	£190

In the setting of this overprint Nos. 10,16, and 21 have the "p" of "Papua" with a defective deformed or inverted "d" for "p", and in No. 17 the "pua" of "Papua" is a shade lower than the first "a".

No. 37a comes from a single sheet on which the overprints were sideways. Examples exist showing one, two or four complete or partial overprints.

PRINTERS. All the following issues were printed at Melbourne by the Stamp Ptg Branch (to 1928) or Note Ptg Branch.

WATERMARK VARIETIES. When printing the lithographed issues, Nos. 47/83, little attention was paid to the position of the watermark. Nos. 47, 49/58 and 75/83 all come either upright or inverted while Nos. 48 and 59/71 all occur with watermark sideways to left or right. Nos. 51/2 are known with watermark reversed and others may well exist.

5 Large "PAPUA"   B   C

Three types of the 2s.6d.:—

A. Thin top to "2" and small ball. Thin "6" and small ball. Thick uneven stroke.

B. Thin top to 2" and large, well shaped ball. Thin "6" and large ball. Very thick uneven stroke.

C. Thick top to "2" and large, badly shaped ball. Thick "6" and uneven ball. Thin even line.

Type A is not illustrated as the stamp is distinguishable by perf and watermark.

The litho stones were prepared from the engraved plates of the 1901 issue, value for value except the 2s.6d. for which the original plate was mislaid. No. 48 containing Type A was prepared from the original ½d. plate with the value inserted on the stone and later a fresh stone was prepared from the 1d. plate and this contained Type B. Finally, the original plate of the 2s.6d. was found and a third stone was prepared from this, and issued in 1911. These stamps show Type C.

6 Small "PAPUA"

(Litho Stamp Ptg Branch, Melbourne, from transfers taken from original engraved plates)

1907–10. A. Large "PAPUA". Wmk Crown over A, W w **11**.

(a) Wmk upright. P 11.

47	5	½d. black and yellow-green (11.07)	1·50	3·50

(b) Wmk sideways. P 11.

48	5	2s.6d. black and chocolate (12.09)	48·00	60·00
		a. "POSTAGE" at left (R.1/5)	£550	£650

B. Small "PAPUA" I. Wmk upright.

(a) P 11 (1907–8).

49	6	1d. black and rose (6.08)	4·75	5·00
50		2d. black and purple (10.08)	12·00	4·50
51		2½d. black and bright ultramarine (7.08)	20·00	28·00
		a. Black and pale ultramarine	6·50	6·50
52		4d. black and sepia (20.11.07)	4·25	11·00
		a. Deformed "d" at left	30·00	50·00
53		6d. black and myrtle-green (4.08)	11·00	16·00
54		1s. black and orange (10.08)	25·00	20·00

(b) P 12½ (1907–9).

55	6	2d. black and purple (10.08)	25·00	6·50
56		2½d. black and bright ultramarine (7.08)	£120	£130
		a. Black and pale ultramarine	50·00	75·00
57		4d. black and sepia (20.11.07)	8·00	8·00
		a. Deformed "d" at left	50·00	50·00
58		1s. black and orange (1.09)	60·00	85·00

II. Wmk sideways.

(a) P 11 (1909–10).

59	6	½d. black and yellow-green (12.09)	2·25	2·75
		a. Black and deep green (1910)	28·00	42·00
60		1d. black and carmine (1.10)	9·00	8·00
61		2d. black and purple (1.10)	13·00	9·00
62		2½d. black and dull blue (1.10)	4·25	22·00
63		4d. black and sepia (1.10)	4·75	9·00
		a. Deformed "d" at left	30·00	48·00
64		6d. black and myrtle-green (11.09)	10·00	19·00
65		1s. black and orange (3.10)	48·00	60·00

(b) P 12½ (1909–10).

66	6	½d. black and yellow-green (12.09)	1·75	3·75
		a. Black and deep green (1910)	30·00	38·00
67		1d. black and carmine (12.09)	7·50	12·00
68		2d. black and purple (1.10)	3·75	5·50
69		2½d. black and dull blue (1.10)	9·00	40·00
70		6d. black and myrtle-green (11.09)	£3000	£4000
71		1s. black and orange (3.10)	15·00	42·00

(c) Perf compound of 11 and 12½.

72	6	½d. black and yellow-green	£2250	£2250
73		2d. black and purple	£850	

(d) Mixed perfs 11 and 12½.

74	6	4d. black and sepia	£8500	

Compound perforations on the 4d. are fakes.

The only known examples of No. 74 come from the top row of a sheet perforated 11 and with an additional line perf 12½ in the top margin.

(Litho Stamp Ptg Branch, Melbourne, by J. B. Cooke, from new stones made by fresh transfers)

1910 (Sept)–**11**. Large "PAPUA". W w **11** (upright). P 12½.

75	5	½d. black and green (12.10)	3·50	11·00
76		1d. black and carmine	10·00	8·50
77		2d. black & dull purple (*shades*) (12.10)	5·50	5·00

		a. "C" for "O" in "POSTAGE" (R. 4/3)	65·00	65·00
78		2½d. black and blue-violet (10.10)	6·00	17·00
79		4d. black and sepia (10.10)	6·00	10·00
		a. Deformed "d" at left	28·00	50·00
80		6d. black and myrtle-green	8·50	7·50
81		1s. black and deep orange (12.10)	7·00	19·00
82		2s.6d. black and brown (B)	38·00	45·00
83		2s.6d. black and brown (C) (1911)	42·00	55·00
75/82		Set of 8	75·00	£110

A variety showing a white line or "rift" in clouds occurs on R. 5/3 in Nos. 49/83 and the "white leaves" variety mentioned below No. 16 occurs on the 2d. and 2½d. values in both issues. They are worth about three times the normal price.

8   **ONE PENNY**
                   (9)

(Eng S. Reading. Typo J. B. Cooke.)

1911–15. *Printed in one colour.* W **8** (sideways*).

(a) P 12½ (1911–12).

84	6	½d. yellow-green	1·25	3·75
		a. Green	50	2·25
		w. Wmk Crown to right of A	10·00	
85		1d. rose-pink	70	75
		w. Wmk Crown to right of A	20·00	20·00
86		2d. bright mauve	70	75
		w. Wmk Crown to right of A	60·00	40·00
87		2½d. bright ultramarine	4·75	8·50
		a. Dull ultramarine	5·50	8·50
		aw. Wmk Crown to right of A	50·00	
88		4d. pale olive-green	2·25	11·00
		w. Wmk Crown to right of A	—	40·00
89		6d. orange-brown	3·75	5·00
		w. Wmk Crown to right of A	75·00	
90		1s. yellow	9·00	15·00
		w. Wmk Crown to right of A	75·00	
91		2s.6d. rose-carmine	32·00	38·00
		w. Wmk Crown to right of A	£170	
84/91		Set of 8	48·00	70·00

(b) P 14.

92	6	1d. rose-pink (6.15)	22·00	6·00
		a. Pale scarlet	6·50	2·00
		w. Wmk Crown to right of A	—	40·00

*The normal sideways watermark shows Crown to left of A, *as seen from the back of the stamp.*

(Typo J. B. Cooke (1916–18), T. S. Harrison (1918–26), A. J. Mullett (No. 95b only) (1926–27), or John Ash (1927–31))

1916 (Aug)–**31**. *Printed in two colours.* W **8** (sideways*). P 14.

93	6	½d. myrtle and apple green (Harrison and Ash) (1919)	80	1·00
		a. Myrtle and pale olive-green (1927)	1·75	2·25
		w. Wmk Crown to right of A	5·00	7·00
94		1d. black and carmine-rose	1·40	1·25
		a. Grey-black and red (1918)	1·60	1·25
		aw. Wmk Crown to right of A	3·25	50
		b. Intense black and red (Harrison) (wmk Crown to right of A) (1926)	2·50	2·50
95		1½d. pale grey-blue (*shades*) and brown (1925)	1·50	80
		aw. Wmk Crown to right of A	15·00	5·00
		b. Cobalt and light brown (Mullett) (wmk Crown to right of A) (1927)	6·00	3·25
		c. Bright blue and bright brown (1929)	2·75	2·00
		d. "POSTACE" at right (R.1/1) (all printings)	*From* 32·00	32·00
96		2d. brown-purple and brown-lake (1919)	1·75	75
		a. Deep brown-purple and lake (1931)	25·00	1·75
		aw. Wmk Crown to right of A	30·00	2·50
		b. Brown-purple and claret (1931)	2·00	75
97		2½d. myrtle and ultramarine (1919)	4·75	12·00
98		3d. black and bright blue-green (12.16)	2·25	1·75
		a. Error. Black and deep greenish Prussian blue†	£500	£500
		b. Sepia-black & brt bl-grn (Harrison)	22·00	19·00
		c. Black and blue-green (1927)	4·50	8·00
99		4d. brown and orange (1919)	2·50	5·00
		a. Light brown and orange (1927)	9·00	16·00
		aw. Wmk Crown to right of A	8·00	16·00
100		5d. bluish slate and pale brown (1931)	4·25	16·00
101		6d. dull and pale purple (*wmk Crown to right of A*) (1919)	3·25	9·50
		aw. Wmk Crown to left of A	12·00	
		b. Dull purple and red-purple (wmk Crown to left of A) (1927)	14·00	16·00
		c. "POSTACE" at left (R. 6/2) (all printings)	*From* 70·00	£100
102		1s. sepia and olive (1919)	3·50	7·00
		a. Brown and yellow-olive (1927)	6·50	14·00
103		2s.6d. maroon and pale pink (1919)	21·00	40·00
		a. Maroon & brt pink (shades) (1927)	19·00	50·00
104		5s. black and deep green (12.16)	48·00	48·00
105		10s. green and pale ultramarine (1925)	£140	£160
93/105		Set of 13	£200	£275

*The normal sideways watermark shows Crown to left of A, *as seen from the back of the stamp.*

†Beware of similar shades produced by removal of yellow pigment. No 98a is a colour trial, prepared by Cooke, of which, it is believed, five sheets were sold in error.

The printers of various shades can be determined by their dates of issue. The Ash printings are on whiter paper.

For 9d. and 1s.3d. values, see Nos. 127/8.

1917 (Oct). *Nos. 84, 86/9 and 91 surch with T 9 by Govt Ptg Office, Melbourne.*

106	6	1d. on ½d. yellow-green	1·50	1·60
		a. Green	1·00	1·25
		w. Wmk Crown to right of A	4·25	4·75
107		1d. on 2d. bright mauve	12·00	15·00
108		1d. on 2½d. ultramarine	1·25	3·75
109		1d. on 4d. pale olive-green	1·75	4·50
		w. Wmk Crown to right of A	—	40·00
110		1d. on 6d. orange-brown	8·50	17·00
111		1d. on 2s.6d. rose-carmine	1·50	6·00
106/11 *Set of 6*			23·00	42·00

AIR MAIL

(10)   (11)

1929 (Oct)–**30**. *Air. Optd with T 10 by Govt Printer, Port Moresby.*

(a) Cooke printing. Yellowish paper.

112	6	3d. black and bright blue-green	1·25	12·00
		a. Opt omitted in vert pair with normal	£3750	

(b) Harrison printing. Yellowish paper.

113	6	3d. sepia-black and bright blue-green	50·00	65·00

(c) Ash printing. White paper.

114	6	3d. black and blue-green	1·00	7·00
		a. Opt omitted (in horiz pair with normal)	£4250	
		b. Ditto, but vert pair	£3750	
		c. Opt vertical, on back	£3500	
		d. Opts tête-bêche (vert pair)	£4000	

1930 (15 Sept). *Air. Optd with T 11, in carmine by Govt Printer, Port Moresby.*

(a) Harrison printings. Yellowish paper.

115	6	3d. sepia-black and bright blue-green	£1700	£2750
116		6d. dull and pale purple	3·00	16·00
		a. "POSTACE" at left (R. 6/2)	65·00	£110
117		1s. sepia and olive	8·00	23·00
		a. Opt inverted	£7000	

(b) Ash printings. White paper.

118	6	3d. black and blue-green	1·00	6·00
119		6d. dull purple and red-purple	7·00	10·00
		a. "POSTACE" at left (R. 6/2)	70·00	£100
120		1s. brown and yellow-olive	4·25	15·00
118/20 *Set of 3*			11·00	28·00

The rare Harrison printing with this overprint, No. 115, should not be confused with examples of the Ash printing, No. 118, which have been climatically toned.

5d.

TWO PENCE   FIVE PENCE
(12)   (13)

1931 (1 Jan). *Surch with T 12 by Govt Printer, Port Moresby.*

(a) Mullett printing.

121	6	2d. on 1½d. cobalt and light brown	12·00	24·00
		a. "POSTACE" at right (R. 1/1)	£140	£225

(b) Ash printing.

122	6	2d. on 1½d. bright blue and bright brown	1·00	2·00
		a. "POSTACE" at right (R. 1/1)	25·00	42·00

1931. *Surch as T 13 by Govt Printer, Port Moresby.*

(a) Cooke printing.

123	6	1s.3d. on 5s. black and deep green	4·25	9·00

(b) Harrison printing. Yellowish paper.

124	6	9d. on 2s.6d. maroon and pale pink (Dec)	6·00	23·00

(c) Ash printings. White paper.

125	6	5d. on 1s. brown and yellow-olive (26.7)	1·00	1·75
126		9d. on 2s.6d. maroon and bright pink	5·50	8·50

(Typo J. Ash)

1932. *W 15 of Australia (Mult "C of A"). P 11.*

127	5	9d. lilac and violet	4·50	32·00
128		1s.3d. lilac and pale greenish blue	7·50	32·00
127s/8s Optd "Specimen" *Set of 2*			£450	

15 Motuan girl

16 A Chieftain's son

17 Tree houses

18 Raggiana Bird of Paradise

19 Papuan dandy

20 Native mother and child

21 Masked dancer

22 Papuan motherhood

23 Papuan shooting fish

24 Dubu—or ceremonial platform

25 "Lakatoi"

26 Papuan art

27 Pottery making

28 Native policeman

29 Lighting a fire

30 Delta house

(Des F. E. Williams (2s., £1 and frames of other values), E. Whitehouse (2d., 4d., 6d., 1s., and 10s.); remaining centres from photos by Messrs F. E. Williams and Gibson. Recess J. Ash (all values) and W. C. G. McCracken (½d., 1d., 2d., 4d.))

1932 (14 Nov)–**40**. *T 15/30. No wmk. P 11.*

130	15	½d. black and orange	1·50	3·25
		a. Black and buff (McCracken) (1940)	13·00	22·00

131	16	1d. black and green	1·75	60
132	17	1½d. black and lake	1·50	8·00
133	18	2d. red	11·00	30
134	19	3d. black and blue	3·25	6·50
135	20	4d. olive-green	6·00	9·50
136	21	5d. black and slate-green	3·00	3·00
137	22	6d. bistre-brown	7·50	5·00
138	23	9d. black and violet	10·00	21·00
139	24	1s. dull blue-green	4·00	8·50
140	25	1s.3d. black and dull purple	15·00	27·00
141	26	2s. black and slate-green	15·00	24·00
142	27	2s.6d. black and rose-mauve	25·00	38·00
143	28	5s. black and olive-brown	55·00	55·00
144	29	10s. black	85·00	85·00
145	30	£1 black and olive-grey	£190	£150
130/145 *Set of 16*			£375	£375

31 Hoisting the Union Jack   32 Scene on H.M.S. *Nelson*

(Recess J. Ash)

1934 (6 Nov). *50th Anniv of Declaration of British Protectorate. P 11.*

146	31	1d. green	1·00	3·50
147	32	2d. scarlet	1·75	3·00
148	31	3d. blue	1·75	3·00
149	32	5d. purple	11·00	16·00
146/9 *Set of 4*			14·00	23·00

HIS MAJESTY'S JUBILEE.

HIS MAJESTY'S JUBILEE.
1910   1935   1910 — 1935
(33)   (34)

MAJESTY'S   MAJESTY'S

Normal   "Accent" flaw (R.5/4)

1935 (9 July). *Silver Jubilee. Nos. 131, 133/4 and 136 optd with T 33 or 34 (2d.).*

150		1d. black and green	75	3·00
		a. "Accent" flaw	27·00	50·00
151		2d. scarlet	2·50	3·00
152		3d. black and blue	1·75	3·00
		a. "Accent" flaw	45·00	70·00
153		5d. black and slate-green	2·50	3·00
		a. "Accent" flaw	60·00	80·00
150/3 *Set of 4*			6·75	11·00

35   36 Port Moresby

(Recess J. Ash)

1937 (14 May). *Coronation. P 11.*

154	35	1d. green	45	20
155		2d. scarlet	45	1·25
156		3d. blue	45	1·25
157		5d. purple	45	1·75
154/7 *Set of 4*			1·60	4·00

Some covers franked with these stamps and posted on 2 June 1937 were postmarked 2 April 1937 in error.

(Recess J. Ash)

1938 (6 Sept). *Air. 50th Anniv of Declaration of British Possession. P 11.*

158	36	2d. rose-red	3·00	2·50
159		3d. bright blue	3·00	2·25
160		5d. green	3·00	3·50
161		8d. brown-lake	6·00	15·00
162		1s. mauve	19·00	16·00
158/62 *Set of 5*			30·00	35·00

37 Natives poling Rafts

(Recess J. Ash)

1939 (6 Sept). *Air. P 11.*

163	37	2d. rose-red	3·00	4·50
164		3d. bright blue	3·00	8·50
165		5d. green	3·00	2·25
166		8d. brown-lake	8·00	3·25
167		1s. mauve	10·00	8·50

(Recess W. C. G. McCracken)

1941 (2 Jan). *Air. P 11½.*

168	37	1s.6d. olive-green	30·00	35·00
163/168 *Set of 6*			50·00	55·00

OFFICIAL STAMPS

1908 (Oct). *Punctured "OS".*

O1	**1**	2s.6d. black and brown (No. 37).........	£600	35·00
O2		2s.6d. black and brown (No. 45).........	£2500	£2250
		a. Thin paper (No. 45a)................	£700	£550

1908 (Dec)–**10**. *Nos. 49/71 punctured "OS".*

I. Wmk upright.

(a) P 11.

O4	**6**	1d. black and rose......................	17·00	6·00
O5		2d. black and purple......................	26·00	4·50
O6		2½d. black and bright ultramarine......	38·00	32·00
		a. Black and pale ultramarine......	18·00	4·25
O7		4d. black and sepia......................	18·00	4·50
		a. Deformed "d" at left................	85·00	27·00
O8		6d. black and myrtle-green.............	50·00	26·00
O9		1s. black and orange......................	50·00	18·00
O4/9 *Set of 6*................................			£150	55·00

(b) P 12½.

O10	**6**	2d. black and purple......................	45·00	11·00
O11		2½d. black and bright ultramarine......	£130	85·00
		a. Black and pale ultramarine......	75·00	60·00
O12		4d. black and sepia......................	45·00	9·00
		a. Deformed "d" at left................	£150	55·00
O13		1s. black and orange......................	£120	55·00
O10/13 *Set of 4*................................			£250	£120

II. Wmk sideways.

(a) P 11.

O14	**6**	½d. black and yellow-green.............	20·00	4·50
		a. Black and deep green	50·00	30·00
O15		1d. black and carmine....................	45·00	13·00
O16		2d. black and purple......................	15·00	2·00
O17		2½d. black and dull blue	26·00	5·00
O18		4d. black and sepia......................	22·00	10·00
		a. Deformed "d" at left................	95·00	50·00
O19		6d. black and myrtle-green.............	40·00	5·00
O20		1s. black and orange......................	£120	48·00
O14/20 *Set of 7*................................			£250	80·00

(b) P 12½.

O21	**6**	½d. black and yellow-green.............	15·00	1·50
		a. Black and deep green	50·00	30·00
O22		1d. black and carmine....................	40·00	4·00
O23		2d. black and purple......................	24·00	3·00
O24		2½d. black and dull blue	50·00	14·00
O25		6d. black and myrtle-green.............	—	£1100
O26		1s. black and orange......................	48·00	16·00

1910. *Nos. 47/8 punctured "OS".*

O27	**5**	½d. black & yellow-green (wmk upright)......................	18·00	13·00
O28		2s.6d. black & chocolate (wmk sideways)......................	£110	85·00

1910–11. *Nos. 75/83 punctured "OS".*

O29	**5**	½d. black and green......................	20·00	9·00
O30		1d. black and carmine....................	45·00	8·00
O31		2d. black and dull purple	17·00	10·00
		a. "C" for "O" in "POSTAGE"	£150	75·00
O32		2½d. black and blue-violet	24·00	6·50
O33		4d. black and sepia......................	29·00	6·00
		a. Deformed "d" at left................	£120	35·00
O34		6d. black and myrtle-green.............	29·00	6·00
O35		1s. black and deep orange.............	45·00	9·00
O36		2s.6d. black and brown (B)................	80·00	30·00
O37		2s.6d. black and brown (C)............	95·00	65·00
O29/36 *Set of 8*................................			£225	75·00

1911–12. *Nos. 84/91 punctured "OS".*

O38	**6**	½d. yellow-green	10·00	2·00
O39		1d. rose-pink	15·00	1·25
O40		2d. bright mauve	15·00	1·25
		w. Wmk Crown to right of A	—	22·00
O41		2½d. bright ultramarine	19·00	8·00
O42		4d. pale olive-green	24·00	16·00
O43		6d. orange-brown	23·00	6·00
O44		1s. yellow....................................	35·00	11·00
O45		2s.6d. rose-carmine	65·00	70·00
O38/45 *Set of 8*................................			£180	£100

1930. *Nos. 93/6a and 98c/103 punctured "OS".*

O46	**6**	½d. myrtle and apple green	9·00	14·00
O47		1d. intense black and red	16·00	3·25
O48		1½d. bright blue and bright brown.....	11·00	16·00
		a. "POSTACE" at right................	90·00	£120
O49		2d. deep brown-purple and lake	22·00	32·00
O50		3d. black and blue-green.................	55·00	70·00
O51		4d. light brown and orange.............	32·00	35·00
O52		6d. dull purple and pale purple.......	17·00	32·00
		a. "POSTACE" at left................	£160	£225
O53		1s. brown and yellow-olive.............	35·00	50·00
O54		2s.6d. maroon and pale pink	85·00	£110
O46/54 *Set of 9*..			£225	£300

O   S

(O **1**)

(Typo T. S. Harrison (1d. and 2s.6d.) and J. Ash)

1931 (29 July)–**32**. *Optd with Type O* **1**. *W* **8** *or W* **15** *of Australia (9d., 1s.3d.). P 14 or 11 (9d., 1s.3d.).*

O55	**6**	½d. myrtle and apple-green.............	2·25	4·75
O56		1d. grey black and red		
		a. Intense black and red................	4·00	9·00
O57		1½d. bright blue and bright brown.....	1·60	12·00
		a. "POSTACE" at right................	45·00	£130
O58		2d. brown-purple and claret............	3·75	11·00
O59		3d. black and blue-green.................	2·50	22·00
O60		4d. light brown and orange (No. 99aw)........................	2·50	18·00
O61		5d. bluish slate and pale brown	6·00	38·00
O62		6d. dull purple and red-purple.........	4·00	8·50
		a. "POSTACE" at left................	95·00	£180
O63		9d. lilac and violet (1932)...............	30·00	48·00

O64		1s. brown and yellow-olive............	9·00	30·00
O65		1s.3d. lilac and pale greenish blue (1932)........................	30·00	48·00
O66		2s.6d. maroon & pale pink (Harrison).	40·00	85·00
		a. Maroon and bright pink (Ash)..	40·00	85·00
O55/66 *Set of 12*			£120	£300

Civil Administration in Papua was suspended in 1942. On resumption, after the Japanese defeat in 1945, Australian stamps were used until the appearance of the issue of the combined territories of Papua & New Guinea.

Baghdad *see* Iraq

Bahamas

The British Post Office at Nassau was established during the early days of the West Indies packet system, and was certainly operating by 1733. The first known local postmark dates from 1802.

The crowned-circle handstamp No. CC1 was issued in 1846 and was generally replaced, for the public mails, by various stamps of Great Britain in 1858.

Local mail deliveries were rudimentary until 1859 when Nos. 1/2 were issued by the colonial authorities for interisland mails. Examples used for this purpose are usually cancelled in manuscript or with a "27" postmark. The "local" 1d. stamp became valid for overseas mails in May, 1860, when the colonial authorities took over this service from the British G.P.O.

For illustrations of the handstamp and postmark types see BRITISH POST OFFICES ABROAD notes, following GREAT BRITAIN.

NASSAU

CROWNED-CIRCLE HANDSTAMPS

CC1   CC 2 BAHAMAS (Nassau) (18.5.1846) (R.)
                                                    Price on cover   £2250

No. CC1 was later struck in black and used as an Offical Paid mark between July 1899 and September 1935. Handstamps as Types CC 1 and CC 3 (only three known) struck in black were used for the same purpose from 1933 until 1953; but it is believed that these were never employed during the pre-stamp period. *Price on cover from £50.*

Stamps of GREAT BRITAIN *cancelled* "A 05" *as Type* 2.

1858–60.
Z1		1d. rose-red (1857), perf 14	£2250
Z2		2d. blue (1858) (Plate Nos. 7, 8)	£1300
Z3		4d. rose (1857)	£450
Z3a		6d. purple (1854), embossed	£4000
Z4		6d. lilac (1856)	£350
Z5		1s. green (1856)	£2250

PRICES FOR STAMPS ON COVER TO 1945

No. 1	*from* × 8
No. 2	
Nos. 3/6	*from* × 8
No. 7	
Nos. 8/11	*from* × 10
Nos. 12/15	*from* × 4
Nos. 16/19a	*from* × 6
Nos. 20/5	*from* × 15
Nos. 26/8	*from* × 4
No. 29	
Nos. 30/2	*from* × 15
No. 33	*from* × 30
Nos. 35/7	*from* × 6
Nos. 38/9	*from* × 10
No. 39b	*from* × 30
No. 40	*from* × 50
No. 41	*from* × 6
No. 42	*from* × 15
No. 43	*from* × 5
No. 44/a	*from* × 10
No. 45	*from* × 40
Nos. 47/57	*from* × 4
Nos. 58/89	*from* × 2
Nos. 90/130	*from* × 3
Nos. 131/2	*from* × 10
Nos. 141/5	*from* × 4
Nos. 146/8	*from* × 4
Nos. 149/57	*from* × 3
Nos. 158/60	*from* × 4
No. 161	*from* × 8
Nos. 162/75	*from* × 5
Nos. S1/3	*from* × 20

CROWN COLONY

1   2   3

(Eng and recess P.B.)

1859 (10 June)–**60**. No wmk. Imperf.

(a) Thick, opaque paper.
1	1	1d. reddish lake (*shades*)	£4750	£2250

(b) Thin paper.
2	1	1d. dull lake (4.60)	60·00	£1500

No. 1, the printing on thick opaque paper, is very rare in unused condition. Unused remainders, on medium to thick, but slightly transparent, paper are worth about £250.

Collectors are warned against false postmarks upon the remainder stamps of 1d., imperf, on thin paper.

1860 (Oct). No wmk. Clean-cut perf 14 to 16.
3	1	1d. lake (H/S "CANCELLED" in oval £8000)	£5000	£700

For notes on "CANCELLED" examples see Catalogue Introduction. Examples with this handstamp on No. 3 are imperforate horizontally.

1861 (June)–**62**. No wmk.

(a) Rough perf 14 to 16.
4	1	1d. lake	£650	£325
5	2	4d. dull rose (Dec, 1861)	£1400	£400
		a. Imperf between (pair)	£28000	
6		6d. grey-lilac (Dec, 1861)	£4000	£600
		a. Pale dull lilac	£3000	£500

(b) P 11 to 12½ (1862).
7	1	1d. lake		£2250

No. 7 was a perforation trial on a new machine at Perkins, Bacon. It was not sent out to the Colony and is also known part perforated.

(Recess D.L.R.)

1862. No wmk.*

(a) P 11½, 12.
8	1	1d. carmine-lake	£1000	£180
9		1d. lake	£1500	£250
10	2	4d. dull rose	£3250	£400
11		6d. lavender-grey	£9500	£500

(b) P 11½, 12, compound with 11.
12	1	1d. carmine-lake	£2000	£850
13		1d. lake	£2250	£950
14	2	4d. dull rose	£18000	£1900
15		6d. lavender-grey	£18000	£1800

(c) P 13.
16	1	1d. lake	£900	£160
17		1d. brown-lake	£750	£130
18	2	4d. dull rose	£2750	£375
19		6d. lavender-grey	£3250	£475
		a. Lilac	£2750	£450

*Stamps exist with part of papermaker's sheet wmk ("T. H. SAUNDERS" and date).

1863–77. Wmk Crown CC.

(a) P 12½.
20	1	1d. brown-lake	90·00	60·00
		w. Wmk inverted	£140	95·00
		x. Wmk reversed		
		y. Wmk inverted and reversed	—	£150
21		1d. carmine-lake	£100	65·00
		w. Wmk inverted	£140	85·00
		x. Wmk reversed	£110	65·00
22		1d. carmine-lake (aniline)	£120	70·00
		w. Wmk inverted	£170	
23		1d. rose-red	60·00	42·00
		w. Wmk inverted	£100	
		x. Wmk reversed	60·00	42·00
24		1d. red	60·00	42·00
		w. Wmk inverted		
		x. Wmk reversed	—	42·00
25		1d. vermilion	65·00	42·00
		w. Wmk inverted	£100	75·00
		x. Wmk reversed	65·00	42·00
		y. Wmk inverted and reversed	£150	90·00
26	2	4d. bright rose	£300	60·00
		w. Wmk inverted	—	£190
		x. Wmk reversed		
27		4d. dull rose	£400	60·00
		w. Wmk inverted	—	£190
		x. Wmk reversed	£375	60·00
		y. Wmk inverted and reversed	£850	£190
28		4d. brownish rose (*wmk reversed*)	£450	80·00
		w. Wmk inverted	—	
29		6d. rose-lilac	—	£2250
30		6d. lilac (*shades*)	£375	70·00
		w. Wmk inverted	—	£190
		x. Wmk reversed		
31		6d. deep violet	£160	60·00
		w. Wmk inverted	£500	120·00
		x. Wmk reversed	£180	65·00
		y. Wmk inverted and reversed		
32		6d. violet (aniline)	£250	90·00
		x. Wmk reversed	£250	95·00

(b) P 14.
33	1	1d. scarlet-vermilion (1877)	50·00	15·00
		x. Wmk reversed	60·00	23·00
34		1d. scarlet (or scarlet-vermilion) (aniline)	£1000	
		x. Wmk reversed		
35	2	4d. bright rose (1876)	£375	40·00
		w. Wmk inverted	£750	£190
36		4d. dull rose	£1500	40·00
		w. Wmk inverted		
37		4d. dull rose	£425	40·00

No. 29 is believed to be the shade of the first printing only and should not be confused with other lilac shades of the 6d.

No. 34 is not known postally used, although manuscript fiscal cancellations on this shade do exist.

(Typo D.L.R.)

1863–80. Wmk Crown CC.

(a) P 12½.
38	3	1s. green (1865)	£2500	£300

(b) P 14.
39	3	1s. deep green	£250	38·00
		aw. Wmk inverted		
		b. Green	£120	25·00
		ba. Thick paper (1880)	8·00	7·50
		bw. Wmk inverted (thick paper)	—	£150

1882 (Mar). Wmk Crown CA.

(a) P 12.
40	1	1d. scarlet-vermilion	48·00	12·00
		x. Wmk reversed	—	60·00
41	2	4d. rose	£550	45·00

(b) P 14.
42	1	1d. scarlet-vermilion	£425	60·00
		x. Wmk reversed	£550	
43	2	4d. rose	£800	60·00
		x. Wmk reversed	£900	70·00

1882 (Mar)–**98**. Wmk Crown CA. P 14.
44	3	1s. green	38·00	14·00
44a		1s. blue-green (1898)	35·00	26·00

FOURPENCE
(4)   5

1883. *No. 31 surch with T* **4.**
45	2	4d. on 6d. deep violet	£550	£400
		a. Surch inverted	£14000	£8500
		x. Wmk reversed	£600	£450

Type **4** was applied by handstamp and occurs in various positions. Caution is needed in buying Nos. 45/x.

Sloping "2" (R. 10/6)   Malformed "E"

(Typo D.L.R.)

1884–90. Wmk Crown CA. P 14.
47	5	1d. pale rose	75·00	13·00
48		1d. carmine-rose	7·00	2·50
49		1d. bright rose (aniline)	2·75	6·50
50		2½d. dull blue (1888)	75·00	18·00
51		2½d. blue	42·00	7·50
		a. Sloping "2"	£425	£120
52		2½d. ultramarine	9·50	2·25
		a. Sloping "2"	£150	70·00
		s. Optd "Specimen"	65·00	
		w. Wmk inverted	£160	80·00
53		4d. deep yellow	9·50	4·00
54		6d. mauve (1890)	6·00	28·00
		a. Malformed "E" (R. 6/6)	£180	£325
		s. Optd "Specimen"	65·00	
56		5s. sage-green	65·00	75·00
57		£1 Venetian red	£275	£325
		47/57 Set of 6	£325	£300

Examples of Nos. 54/7 are known showing a forged Bahamas postmark dated "AU 29 94".

6 Queen's Staircase,   7   8
Nassau

(Recess D.L.R.)

1901 (23 Sept)–**03**. Wmk Crown CC. P 14.
58	6	1d. black and red	10·00	2·50
		w. Wmk inverted	£100	£100
59		5d. black and orange (1.03)	8·50	48·00
		y. Wmk inverted and reversed	£130	£180
60		2s. black and blue (1.03)	27·00	50·00
		x. Wmk reversed	£250	
61		3s. black and green (1.03)	38·00	60·00
		w. Wmk inverted	£110	£120
		y. Wmk inverted and reversed	£130	£140
		58/61 Set of 4	75·00	£140
		58s/61s Optd "Specimen" Set of 4	£130	

For stamps in this design, but with Mult Crown CA or Mult Script CA watermarks see Nos. 75/80 and 111/14.

(Typo D.L.R.)

1902 (18 Dec)–**10**. Wmk Crown CA. P 14.
62	7	1d. carmine	1·50	2·50
63		2½d. ultramarine	6·50	1·25
		a. Sloping "2"	£250	£120
64		4d. orange	15·00	60·00
65		4d. deep yellow (3.10)	23·00	70·00
66		6d. brown	3·50	22·00
		a. Malformed "E" (R. 6/6)	£150	£225
67		1s. grey-black and carmine	20·00	50·00
68		1s. brownish grey and carmine (6.07)	22·00	50·00
69		5s. dull purple and blue	65·00	80·00
70		£1 green and black	£250	£325
		62/70 Set of 7	£325	£475
		62s/70s Optd "Specimen" Set of 7	£275	

Examples of most values are known showing a forged Nassau postmark dated "2 MAR 10".

1906 (Apr)–**11**. Wmk Mult Crown CA. P 14.
71	7	½d. pale green (5.06)	5·00	3·00
		s. Optd "Specimen"	55·00	
72		1d. carmine-rose	25·00	1·25
73		2½d. ultramarine (4.07)	25·00	26·00
		a. Sloping "2"	£350	£400
		w. Wmk inverted	£140	£140
74		6d. bistre-brown (8.11)	17·00	48·00
		a. Malformed "E" (R. 6/6)	£275	£475
		71/4 Set of 4	65·00	70·00

1911 (Feb)–**19**. Wmk Mult Crown CA. P 14.
75	6	1d. black and red	17·00	2·75
		a. Grey-black and scarlet (1916)	4·75	2·50
		b. Grey-black & deep carmine-red (1919)	7·50	6·00
76		3d. purple/yellow (thin paper) (18.5.17)	4·75	30·00
		a. Reddish pur/buff (thick paper) (1.19)	5·50	5·00
		s. Optd "Specimen"	38·00	
		x. Wmk reversed	†	£325
77		3d. black and brown (23.3.19)	2·00	2·25

		s. Optd "Specimen"	38·00	
		w. Wmk inverted		£325
		x. Wmk reversed	†	£325
78		5d. black and mauve (18.5.17)	2·75	5·50
		s. Optd "Specimen"	38·00	
79		2s. black and blue (11.16)	29·00	55·00
		w. Wmk inverted		£300
80		3s. black and green (8.17)	65·00	55·00
		w. Wmk inverted	£170	£170
		y. Wmk inverted and reversed	£130	£130
75/80		Set of 6	95·00	£110

(Typo D.L.R.)

1912–19. Wmk Mult Crown CA. *Chalk-surfaced paper (1s. to £1).* P 14.

81	8	½d. green	80	9·50
		a. Yellow-green	2·50	15·00
82		1d. carmine (aniline)	3·50	30
		a. Deep rose	8·00	2·25
		b. Rose	11·00	3·00
		w. Wmk inverted	£190	85·00
83		2d. grey (1919)	2·25	3·00
84		2½d. ultramarine	4·75	28·00
		a. Deep dull blue	15·00	38·00
		b. Sloping "2"	—	£400
85		4d. orange-yellow	5·50	20·00
		a. Yellow	2·50	14·00
86		6d. bistre-brown	1·75	4·25
		a. Malformed "E" (R. 6/6)	£110	£150
87		1s. grey-black and carmine	1·75	9·00
		a. Jet-black and carmine	14·00	22·00
88		5s. dull purple and blue	40·00	70·00
		a. Pale dull purple and deep blue .	50·00	75·00
89		£1 dull green and black	£160	£300
		a. Green and black	£200	£325
81/9		Set of 9	£200	£400
81s/9s		Optd "Specimen" Set of 9	£300	

1.1.17.　**WAR TAX**
(9)　　　　(10)

1917 (18 May). No. 75b optd with T 9 in red by D.L.R.

90	6	1d. grey-black and deep carmine-red	40	2·00
		a. Long stroke to "7" (R. 4/6)	40·00	75·00
		s. Optd "Specimen"	65·00	

It was originally intended to issue No. 90 on 1 January 1917, but the stamps were not received in the Bahamas until May. Half the proceeds from their sale were donated to the British Red Cross Society.

1918 (21 Feb–10 July). Nos. 75/6, 81/2 and 87 optd at Nassau with T 10.

91	8	½d. green	9·00	42·00
		a. Opt double		
		b. Opt inverted		
92		1d. carmine (aniline)	1·00	50
		a. Opt double		
		b. Opt inverted		
		w. Wmk inverted	£250	
		x. Wmk reversed	£275	
93	6	1d. black and red (10 July)	3·50	4·75
		a. Opt double, one inverted	£850	
		b. Opt double	£1700	£1800
		c. Opt inverted	£1500	£1600
		x. Wmk reversed	£225	
94		3d. purple/yellow (thin paper)	2·25	2·25
		a. Opt double	£1600	£1700
		b. Opt inverted	£1100	£1200
		c. "W" of "WAR" inserted by hand	£2750	
95	8	1s. grey-black and carmine	£100	£140
		a. Opt double		
91/5		Set of 5	£110	£170

No. 93 was only on sale for ten days.

No. 94c occured on R. 1/1 of one sheet, the original "W" having been omitted as a result of a paper fold.

WAR TAX　**WAR TAX**　**WAR CHARITY 3.6.18.**
(11)　　　(12)　　　(13)

1918 (1 June–20 July). Optd by D.L.R. in London with T 11 or 12 (3d.).

96	8	½d. green	1·75	1·75
		w. Wmk inverted		
		x. Wmk reversed		
97		1d. carmine	1·50	35
		a. Wmk sideways	£300	
		w. Wmk inverted		
		y. Wmk inverted and reversed	£300	
98	6	3d. purple/yellow (20 July)	1·00	1·50
		w. Wmk inverted	95·00	
		x. Wmk reversed		
99	8	1s. grey-black and carmine (R.)	9·00	2·75
96/9		Set of 4	12·00	5·75
96s/9s		Optd "Specimen" Set of 4	£140	

1919 (21 Mar). No. 77 optd with T 12 by D.L.R.

100	6	3d. black and brown	60	4·00
		a. "C" and "A" missing from wmk	£1500	
		s. Optd "Specimen"	50·00	
		w. Wmk inverted	60·00	

No. 100a shows the "C" omitted from one impression and the "A" missing from the next one to the right (as seen from the front of the stamp). The "C" is badly distorted in the second watermark.

1919 (1 Jan). No. 75b optd with T 13 by D.L.R.

101	6	1d. grey-black and deep carmine-red (R.)	30	2·50
		a. Opt double	£1700	
		s. Optd "Specimen"	55·00	
		w. Wmk inverted	60·00	
		x. Wmk reversed	60·00	
		y. Wmk inverted and reversed	95·00	

The date is that originally fixed for the issue of the stamp. The year 1918 was also the bicentenary of the appointment of the first Royal governor.

WAR　**WAR**

TAX　**TAX**
(14)　　(15)

1919 (14 July).

(a) Optd with T 14 by D.L.R.

102	8	½d. green (R.)	30	1·25
103		1d. carmine	1·50	1·50
104	—	1s. grey-black and carmine (R.)	20·00	38·00

(b) No. 77 optd with T 15.

105	6	3d. black and brown	75	8·00
		w. Wmk inverted	60·00	
		ws. Ditto. Optd "Specimen"	50·00	
		x. Wmk reversed	65·00	
		y. Wmk inverted and reversed	75·00	
102/5		Set of 4	20·00	45·00
102s/5s		Optd "Specimen" Set of 4	£140	

16　　　17 Great Seal of the Bahamas.

(Recess D.L.R.)

1920 (1 Mar). Peace Celebration. Wmk Mult Crown CA (sideways*). P 14.

106	16	½d. green	1·00	5·50
		a. "A" of "CA" missing from wmk	£750	
		x. Wmk sideways reversed	£325	£325
107		1d. carmine	2·75	1·00
		x. Wmk sideways reversed	£375	
		y. Wmk Crown to right of CA and reversed	£375	
108		2d. slate-grey	2·75	7·50
		a. "C" of "CA" missing from wmk	£800	
109		3d. deep brown	2·75	9·00
		a. "C" of "CA" missing from wmk	£850	
		w. Wmk Crown to right of CA	£250	
110		1s. deep myrtle-green	12·00	35·00
		a. Substituted crown in wmk	£1300	
		b. "C" of "CA" missing from wmk	£1300	
		x. Wmk sideways reversed	£500	
106/10		Set of 5	19·00	50·00
106s/10s		Optd "Specimen" Set of 5	£160	

*The normal sideways watermark shows Crown to left of CA, *as seen from the back of the stamp.*

For illustration of the substituted watermark crown see Catalogue Introduction.

1921 (29 Mar)–29. Wmk Script CA. P 14.

111	6	1d. grey and rose-red	1·00	2·00
112		5d. black and purple (8.29)	3·75	45·00
113		2s. black and blue (11.22)	19·00	22·00
114		3s. black and green (9.24)	48·00	65·00
111/14		Set of 4	65·00	£120
111s/14s		Optd or Perf (5d.) "Specimen" Set of 4	£170	

Examples of all values are known showing a forged Nassau postmark dated "2 MAR 10".

Elongated "E" (left pane R. 9/6)

1921 (8 Sept)–37. Wmk Mult Script CA. *Chalk-surfaced paper (3d., 1s., 5s., £1).* P 14.

115	8	½d. green (1924)	50	40
		a. Elongated "E"	48·00	50·00
116		1d. carmine	1·00	15
117		1½d. brown-red (1934)	7·00	1·00
118		2d. grey (1927)	1·50	2·25
119		2½d. ultramarine (1922)	1·00	2·25
120		3d. purple/pale yellow (1931)	6·50	16·00
		a. Purple/orange-yellow (1937)	7·50	17·00
121		4d. orange-yellow (1924)	1·50	4·00
122		6d. bistre-brown (1922)	70	1·25
		a. Malformed "E" (R. 6/6)	90·00	£130
123		1s. black and carmine (1926)	2·75	5·50
124		5s. dull purple and blue (1924)	35·00	65·00
125		£1 green and black (1926)	£170	£325
115/25		Set of 11	£200	£375
115s/25s		Optd or Perf (1½d., 3d.) "Specimen" Set of 11	£400	

(Recess B.W.)

1930 (2 Jan). Tercentenary of Colony. Wmk Mult Script CA. P 12.

126	17	1d. black and scarlet	2·00	2·75
127		3d. black and deep brown	4·00	15·00
128		5d. black and deep purple	4·00	15·00
129		2s. black and deep blue	18·00	50·00
130		3s. black and green	42·00	85·00
126/30		Set of 5	65·00	£150
126s/30s		Perf "Specimen" Set of 5	£150	

18

(Recess B.W.)

1931 (14 July)–46. Wmk Mult Script CA. P 12.

131	18	2s. slate-purple and deep ultramarine	22·00	28·00
		a. Slate-purple and indigo (9.42) ..	85·00	40·00
		b. Brownish black and indigo (13.4.43)	10·00	4·25
		c. Brownish black and steel-blue (6.44)	14·00	2·25
132		3s. slate-purple and myrtle-green	28·00	26·00
		a. Brownish black and green (13.4.43)	8·50	3·00
		b. Brownish blk & myrtle-grn (1.10.46)	8·00	4·50
131s/2s		Perf "Specimen" Set of 2	80·00	

Most of the stamps from the September 1942 printing (No. 131a and further stocks of the 3s. similar to No. 132) were used for the 1942 "LANDFALL" overprints.

1935 (6 May). Silver Jubilee. As Nos. 91/4 of Antigua. P 13½×14.

141		1½d. deep blue and carmine	1·00	3·00
		h. Dot by flagstaff	95·00	£150
		i. Dash by turret	£160	
142		2½d. brown and deep blue	5·00	9·00
		f. Diagonal line by turret	£140	
		g. Dot to left of chapel	£225	
143		6d. light blue and olive-green	7·00	13·00
		g. Dot to left of chapel	£200	
		h. Dot by flagstaff	£250	
144		1s. slate and purple	7·00	11·00
		h. Dot by flagstaff	£250	£325
		i. Dash by turret	£275	
141/4		Set of 4	18·00	32·00
141s/4s		Perf "Specimen" Set of 4	£110	

For illustrations of plate varieties see Omnibus section following Zanzibar.

19 Greater Flamingos in flight　　20 King George VI

(Recess Waterlow)

1935 (22 May). Wmk Mult Script CA. P 12½.

145	19	8d. ultramarine and scarlet	6·00	3·25
		s. Perf "Specimen"	48·00	

1937 (12 May). Coronation. As Nos. 95/7 of Antigua, but printed by D.L.R. P 14.

146		½d. green	15	15
147		1½d. yellow-brown	30	1·10
148		2½d. bright blue	50	1·10
146/8		Set of 3	85	2·10
146s/8s		Perf "Specimen" Set of 3	75·00	

Accent flaw (right pane R. 1/5) (1938 ptg only)　　Short "T" in "TWO" (right pane R. 3/6) (Retouched on No. 152c, although bottom of letter is still pointed)

"RENCE" flaw (Right pane R. 9/3. Later corrected.)

(Typo D.L.R.)

1938 (11 Mar)–52. Wmk Mult Script CA. *Chalk-surfaced paper (1s. to £1).* P 14.

149	20	½d. green	1·00	1·25
		a. Elongated "E"	95·00	
		b. Accent flaw	£170	
		c. Bluish green (11.9.42)	1·75	2·25
		ca. Elongated "E"	£130	
		d. Myrtle-green (11.12.46)	7·00	7·00
		da. Elongated "E"	£275	
149e		½d. brown-purple (18.2.52)	1·00	2·50
		ea. Error. Crown missing	£8500	
		eb. Error. St Edward's Crown	£3750	
		ec. Elongated "E"	£120	

150		1d. carmine....................................	8·50	2·50
150a		1d. olive-grey (17.9.41)............	3·25	3·25
		ab. Pale slate (11.9.42)..............	60	70
151		1½d. red-brown (19.4.38)............	1·50	1·25
		a. Pale red-brown (19.4.48)........	6·50	2·50
152		2d. pale slate (19.4.38).............	18·00	4·00
		a. Short "T"................................	£650	
152b		2d. scarlet (17.9.41).................	1·00	65
		ba. Short "T"...............................	£100	
		bb. "TWO PENCE" printed double...	†	£8000
		bc. Dull rose-red (19.4.48)...........	3·25	3·25
152c		2d. green (1.5.51)......................	1·25	80
153		2½d. ultramarine......................	3·25	1·50
153a		2½d. violet (1.7.43)....................	1·25	1·25
		ab. "2½ PENNY" printed double....	£3250	
154		3d. violet (19.4.38)..................	16·00	3·00
154a		3d. blue (4.43).........................	60	1·25
		aa. "RENCE" flaw......................		
		ab. Bright ultramarine (19.4.48)....	4·25	4·75
154b		3d. scarlet (1.2.52)..................	60	3·25
154c		10d. yellow-orange (18.11.46)..........	2·50	20
155		1s. grey-black and carmine (*thick paper*) (15.9.38).................	23·00	6·00
		a. Brownish grey and scarlet (4.42)...................................	£400	70·00
		b. Ordinary paper. *Black and carmine* (9.42)....................	22·00	7·00
		c. Ordinary paper. *Grey-black and bright crimson* (6.3.44).............	13·00	75
		d. Pale brownish grey and crimson (19.4.48)...............	14·00	1·50
156		5s. lilac & blue (*thick paper*) (19.4.38).................	£170	£100
		a. Reddish lilac and blue (4.42) ...	£2000	£550
		b. Ordinary paper. *Purple & bl* (9.42)...................................	28·00	20·00
		c. Ordinary paper. *Dull mauve and deep blue* (11.46)..............	95·00	60·00
		d. Brown-purple & dp brt bl (19.4.48)............................	35·00	11·00
		e. Red-purple & dp bright blue (8.51)................................	24·00	15·00
157		£1 deep grey-green and black (*thick paper*) (15.9.38)..............	£250	£140
		a. Ordinary paper. *Blue-green and black* (13.4.43)....................	60·00	55·00
		b. Ordinary paper. *Grey-green and black* (3.44).........................	£150	90·00
	149/57a *Set of 17*		£140	80·00
	149s/57s Perf "Specimen" *Set of 14*		£500	

Nos. 149/50a exist in coils, constructed from normal sheets.

No. 149eb occurs on a row in the watermark in which the crowns and letters "CA" alternate.

The thick chalk-surfaced paper, used for the initial printing of the 1s., 5s. and £1, was usually toned and had streaky gum. The April 1942 printing for the 1s. and 5s., which was mostly used for the "LANDFALL" overprints, was on thin, white chalk-surfaced paper with clear gum. Printings of the three values between September 1942 and November 1946 were on a thick, smooth, opaque ordinary paper.

21 Sea Garden, Nassau 　 22 Fort Charlotte

23 Greater Flamingos in flight

3d.
(24)

(Recess Waterlow)

1938 (1 July). Wmk Mult Script CA. P 12½.

158	21	4d. light blue and red-orange..........	1·00	1·00
159	22	6d. olive-green and light blue..........	60	90
160	23	8d. ultramarine and scarlet............	7·50	2·25
	158/60 *Set of 3*		8·25	3·75
	158s/60s Perf "Specimen" *Set of 3*		£120	

1940 (28 Nov). No. 153 surcharged with T **24** by The Nassau Guardian.

161	20	3d. on 2½d. blue.................................	1·50	1·75

1492 LANDFALL OF COLUMBUS 1942
(25)

1942 (12 Oct). *450th Anniv of Landing of Columbus in New World. Optd as T **25** by The Nassau Guardian.*

162	20	½d. bluish green...................	30	60
		a. Elongated "E".....................	50·00	
		b. Opt double.........................	£1300	
163		1d. pale slate.......................	30	60
164		1½d. red-brown......................	40	60
165		2d. scarlet...........................	50	65
		a. Short "T"...........................	90·00	
166		2½d. ultramarine...................	50	65
167		3d. ultramarine.....................	30	65
		a. "RENCE" flaw.....................	£300	
168	21	4d. light blue and red-orange...........	40	90
		a. "COIUMBUS" (R. 5/2)............	£750	£850
169	22	6d. olive-green and light blue.........	40	1·75
		a. "COIUMBUS" (R. 5/2)............	£750	£900
170	23	8d. ultramarine and scarlet............	1·50	70
		a. "COIUMBUS" (R. 5/2)............	£6500	£2500
171	20	1s. brownish grey and scarlet.........	7·00	4·00

		a. Ordinary paper. *Black and carmine*...........................	7·00	7·50
		b. Ordinary paper. *Grey-black and bright crimson*..................	13·00	7·50
172	18	2s. slate-purple and indigo............	16·00	21·00
		a. Brownish black and indigo........	8·00	10·00
		b. Brownish black and steel-blue...	30·00	26·00
		c. Stop after "COLUMBUS" (R. 2/12)............................	£3250	
173		3s. slate-purple and myrtle-green....	8·00	6·50
		a. Brownish black and green..........	40·00	35·00
		b. Stop after "COLUMBUS" (R. 2/12)............................	£2000	
174	20	5s. reddish lilac and blue.............	48·00	17·00
		a. Ordinary paper. *Purple and blue*...............................	23·00	14·00
175		£1 deep grey-green & blk (*thick paper*)............................	80·00	80·00
		a. Ordinary paper. *Grey-green & black*...............................	30·00	25·00
	162/75a *Set of 14*		70·00	60·00
	162s/75s Perf "Specimen" *Set of 14*		£475	

These stamps replaced the definitive series for a period of six months. Initially stocks of existing printings were used, but when further supplies were required for overprinting a number of new printings were produced, some of which, including the new colour of the 3d., did not appear without overprint until much later.

1946 (11 Nov). *Victory. As Nos. 110/11 of Antigua.*

176		1½d. brown.............................	10	60
177		3d. blue................................	10	60
	176s/7s Perf "Specimen" *Set of 2*		70·00	

26 Infant Welfare Clinic

27 Agriculture (combine harvester)

28 Sisal

29 Straw work

30 Dairy farm

31 Fishing fleet

32 Hatchet Bay, Eleuthera

33 Tuna fishing

34 Paradise Beach

35 Modern hotels

36 Yacht racing

37 Water Sports—skiing

38 Shipbuilding

39 Transportation

40 Salt production

41 Parliament buildings

(Recess C.B.N.)

1948 (11 Oct). *Tercentenary of Settlement of Island of Eleuthera. T **26/41**. P 12.*

178	26	½d. orange...........................	30	1·25
179	27	1d. sage-green......................	30	35
180	28	1½d. yellow..........................	30	80
181	29	2d. scarlet...........................	30	40
182	30	2½d. brown-lake.....................	70	75
183	31	3d. ultramarine.....................	2·50	85
184	32	4d. black.............................	60	70
185	33	6d. emerald-green.................	2·25	80
186	34	8d. violet............................	1·00	70
187	35	10d. carmine........................	1·00	35
188	36	1s. sepia.............................	2·25	50
189	37	2s. magenta.........................	4·25	4·50
190	38	3s. blue..............................	9·00	8·50
191	39	5s. mauve...........................	15·00	4·50
192	40	10s. grey............................	12·00	10·00
193	41	£1 vermilion........................	11·00	15·00
	178/93 *Set of 16*		55·00	48·00

1948 (1 Dec). *Royal Silver Wedding. As Nos. 112/13 of Antigua.*

194		1½d. red-brown......................	20	25
195		£1 slate-green......................	35·00	32·00

1949 (10 Oct). *75th Anniv of Universal Postal Union. As Nos. 114/17 of Antigua.*

196		2½d. violet...........................	35	50
197		3d. deep blue.......................	2·25	2·75
198		6d. greenish blue.................	55	2·50
199		1s. carmine.........................	55	75
	196/9 *Set of 4*		3·25	6·00

STAMP BOOKLETS

1938. *Black on pink cover with map and "BAHAMAS ISLES OF JUNE" on reverse. Stapled.*
SB1   2s. booklet containing twelve 1d. (No. 150) in blocks of 6 and eight 1½d. (No. 151) in folded block of 8 .... £9500

SPECIAL DELIVERY STAMPS
SPECIAL DELIVERY
(S 1)

1916 (1 May). *No. 59 optd with Type* S **1** *by The Nassau Guardian.*
S1	6	5d. black and orange	6·00	38·00
		a. Opt double	£800	£1200
		b. Opt double, one inverted	£950	£1300
		c. Opt inverted	£1300	£1400
		d. Pair, one without opt	£24000	£35000
		x. Wmk reversed		£600

There were three printings from similar settings of 30, and each sheet had to pass through the press twice. The first printing of 600 was on sale from 1 May 1916 in Canada at Ottawa, Toronto, Westmount (Montreal) and Winnipeg; and under an agreement with the Canadian P.O. were used in combination with Canadian stamps and were cancelled in Canada. The second printing (number unknown) was made about the beginning of December 1916, and the third of 6000, issued probably on 1 March 1917, were on sale only in the Bahamas. These printings caused the revocation, in mid-December 1916, of the agreement by Canada, which no longer accepted the stamps as payment of the special delivery fee and left them to be cancelled in the Bahamas.

It is not possible to identify the printings of the normal stamps without plating both the basic stamp and the overprint, though, in general, the word "SPECIAL" is further to the right in relation to "DELIVERY" in the third printing than in the first or second. Our prices for No. S1 are for the third printing and any stamps which can be positively identified as being from the first or second printings would be worth about eight times as much unused, and any on cover are very rare. All the errors appear to be from the third printing.

SPECIAL DELIVERY (S 2)   SPECIAL DELIVERY (S 3)

1917 (2 July). *As No. 59, but Wmk Mult Crown CA. Optd with Type* S **2** *by D.L.R.*
S2	6	5d. black and orange	50	8·00
		s. Optd "Specimen"	65·00	

1918. *No. 78 optd with Type* S **3** *by D.L.R.*
S3	6	5d. black and mauve (R.)	30	2·75
		s. Optd "Specimen"	65·00	

Nos. S2/3 were only on sale in the Bahamas.

Bahawalpur *see after* Pakistan

Bahrain

An independent shaikhdom, with an Indian postal administration from 1884. A British postal administration operated from 1 April 1948 to 31 December 1965.

The first, and for 62 years the only, post office in Bahrain opened at the capital, Manama, on 1 August 1884 as a sub-office of the Indian Post Office at Bushire (Iran), both being part of the Bombay Postal Circle.

Unoverprinted postage stamps of India were supplied to the new office, continuing on sale there until 1933.

Z 1   Z 2

Stamps of INDIA *cancelled with Type* Z **1** (*this was normally struck elsewhere on the envelope with the stamps obliterated with "B" enclosed in a circular background of horizontal bars*) (1884–86)

1882–90. *Queen Victoria (Nos. 84/101).*
Z1	½a. deep blue-green		£250
Z2	2a. pale blue		£250

Stamps of INDIA *cancelled with Type* Z **2** (*squared-circle*) (1886–1909)

1882–90. *Queen Victoria (Nos. 84/101).*
Z5	½a. deep blue-green	8·00
Z5a	½a. blue-green	9·00
Z6	1a. brown-purple	10·00
Z6a	1a. plum	10·00
Z7	1a.6p. sepia	30·00
Z8	2a. pale blue	16·00
Z8a	2a. blue	16·00
Z9	3a. orange	30·00
Z9a	3a. brown-orange	14·00
Z10	4a. olive-green	28·00
Z11	8a. dull mauve	35·00

1891. *Surch on Queen Victoria (No. 102).*
Z12	2½a. on 4a.6p. yellow-green	19·00

1892–97. *Queen Victoria (Nos. 103/6).*
Z13	2a.6p. yellow-green	10·00
Z14	1r. green and aniline carmine	42·00

1900–02. *Queen Victoria (Nos. 112/18).*
Z15	½a. pale yellow-green	14·00
Z15a	½a. yellow-green	14·00
Z16	1a. carmine	14·00
Z17	2½a. ultramarine	26·00

OFFICIAL STAMPS

1883–99. *Queen Victoria (Nos. O37a/48).*
Z18	½a. blue-green	35·00
Z19	1a. brown-purple	40·00

Z 3   Z 4

Stamps of INDIA *cancelled with Type* Z **3** (*single circle, principally intended for use as a backstamp*) (1897–1920)

1882–90. *Queen Victoria (Nos. 84/101).*
Z21	½a. blue-green	19·00
Z22	3a. brown-orange	24·00

1892–97. *Queen Victoria (Nos. 103/6).*
Z23	1r. green and aniline carmine	48·00

1899. *Queen Victoria (No. 111).*
Z24	3p. aniline carmine	19·00

1900–02. *Queen Victoria (Nos. 112/18).*
Z25	½a. pale yellow-green	19·00
Z25a	½a. yellow-green	19·00
Z26	1a. carmine	19·00
Z27	2a.6p. ultramarine	30·00

1902–11. *King Edward VII (Nos. 119/47).*
Z28	½a. green	18·00
Z29	2a. mauve	18·00
Z30	2a.6p. ultramarine	15·00

1906–07. *King Edward VII (Nos. 149/50).*
Z31	½a. green	10·00
Z32	1a. carmine	12·00

1911–22. *King George V. Wmk Star (Nos. 151/91).*
Z33	3p. grey	15·00
Z34	½a. light green	10·00
Z35	2a. purple	22·00
Z36	2a.6p. ultramarine (No. 171)	24·00

Stamps of INDIA *cancelled with Type* Z **4** (*double circle with date band and black lines in centre*) (1902–24)

1876. *Queen Victoria (Nos. 80/2).*
Z40	6a. pale brown	40·00

1882–90. *Queen Victoria (Nos. 84/101).*
Z41	3a. brown-orange	24·00
Z42	4a. olive-green	29·00
Z43	8a. dull mauve	29·00
Z44	12a. purple/red	60·00

1895. *Queen Victoria (Nos. 107/9).*
Z45	2r. carmine and yellow-brown	£170
Z46	5r. ultramarine and violet	£200

1899. *Queen Victoria (No. 111).*
Z47	3p. aniline carmine	8·50

1900–02. *Queen Victoria (Nos. 112/18).*
Z48	½a. pale yellow-green	10·00
Z48a	½a. yellow-green	10·00
Z49	1a. carmine	13·00
Z50	2a. pale violet	32·00
Z51	2a.6p. ultramarine	28·00

1902–11. *King Edward VII (Nos. 119/47).*
Z52	3p. grey	8·00
Z52a	3p. slate-grey	9·00
Z53	½a. yellow-green	5·50
Z53a	½a. green	5·50
Z54	1a. carmine	6·50
Z55	2a. violet	14·00
Z55a	2a. mauve	14·00
Z56	2a.6p. ultramarine	8·00
Z57	3a. orange-brown	18·00
Z58	4a. olive	22·00
Z59	6a. olive-bistre	35·00
Z60	8a. purple	40·00
Z61	2r. rose-red and yellow-brown	£120

1905. *Surcharged on King Edward VII (No. 148).*
Z62	¼a. on ½a. green	19·00

1906–07. *King Edward VII (Nos. 149/50).*
Z63	½a. green	7·00
Z64	1a. carmine	8·00

1911–22. *King George V. Wmk Star (Nos. 151/91).*
Z65	3p. grey	13·00
Z66	½a. light green	5·50
Z67	1a. carmine	8·00
Z67a	1a. rose-carmine	8·00
Z68	1½a. chocolate (Type A)	24·00
Z69	2a. purple	15·00
Z70	2a.6p. ultramarine (No. 171)	11·00
Z71	3a. orange	19·00
Z72	6a. yellow-bistre	30·00

1922–26. *King George V. Wmk Star (Nos. 197/200).*
Z73	1a. chocolate	14·00

OFFICIAL STAMPS

1902–09. *King Edward VII (Nos. O54/65).*
Z74	2a. mauve	38·00

1906. *King Edward VII (Nos. O66/7).*
Z75	1a. carmine	35·00

Z 5

Stamps of INDIA *cancelled with type* Z **5** (*double circle without arc*) (*previously intended for use as a backstamp*) (1915–33)

1911–22. *King George V. Wmk Star (Nos. 151/91).*
Z79	3p. grey	15·00
Z80	½a. light green	9·00
Z80a	½a. emerald	10·00
Z81	1a. aniline carmine	12·00
Z81a	1a. pale rose-carmine	13·00
Z82	1½a. chocolate (Type A)	30·00
Z83	2a. purple	18·00
Z83a	2a. reddish purple	18·00
Z83b	2a. bright reddish violet	21·00
Z84	2a.6p. ultramarine (No. 171)	15·00
Z85	3a. orange	25·00
Z86	6a. yellow-bistre	38·00
Z87	1r. brown and green (*shades*)	48·00

1922–26. *King George V. Wmk Star (Nos. 197/200).*
Z88	1a. chocolate	17·00
Z89	3a. ultramarine	30·00

1926–33. *King George V. Wmk Multiple Star (Nos. 201/19).*
Z90	3p. slate	8·50
Z91	½a. green	8·00
Z92	1a. chocolate	7·00
Z93	2a. bright purple (No. 205)	32·00
Z94	2a. purple (No. 206)	14·00
Z95	3a. ultramarine	24·00
Z95a	3a. blue	24·00
Z96	4a. sage-green (No. 211)	18·00
Z97	8a. reddish purple	24·00
Z98	1r. chocolate and green	30·00
Z99	2r. carmine and orange	48·00
Z100	5r. ultramarine and purple	70·00

The 1a. is known with inverted watermark.

1929. *Air (Nos. 220/5).*
Z101	2a. deep blue-green	19·00
Z102	3a. blue	18·00
Z103	4a. olive-green	24·00
Z104	6a. bistre	30·00

1931. *Inauguration of New Delhi (Nos. 226/31).*
Z105	¼a. olive-green and orange-brown ..	30·00
Z106	1a. mauve and chocolate	17·00

Nos. Z101/6 come with watermark sideways to left or right.

OFFICIAL STAMPS

1902–09. *King Edward VII (Nos. O54/65).*
Z107	2a. mauve	38·00

1912–13. *King George V. Wmk Star (Nos. O73/96).*
Z108	½a. light green	24·00
Z109	1a. rose-carmine	24·00
Z110	2a. reddish purple	30·00

Z 6

Stamps of INDIA *cancelled with Type Z 6 (double circle with black arc in lower segment) (1924–33)*

1911–22. *King George V. Wmk Star (Nos. 151/91).*
Z115	3p. grey	13·00	
Z116	½a. light green	8·00	
Z117	1a. aniline carmine	9·50	
Z118	2a. purple	15·00	
Z119	6a. yellow-bistre	22·00	

1922–26. *King George V. Wmk Star (Nos. 197/200).*
Z120	1a. chocolate	9·00	
Z121	3a. ultramarine	18·00	

1926–33. *King George V. Wmk Multiple Star (Nos. 201/19).*
Z122	3p. slate	5·50	
Z123	½a. green	5·50	
Z124	1a. chocolate	5·50	
Z124a	Tête-Bêche (pair)	22·00	
Z125	1½a. rose-carmine	22·00	
Z126	2a. bright purple (No. 205)	22·00	
Z127	2a. purple (No. 206)	8·00	
Z128	3a. blue	9·00	
Z130	4a. sage-green (No. 211)	13·00	
Z131	8a. reddish purple	17·00	

The ½a. and 1a. are known with watermark inverted.

1929. *Air (Nos. 220/5).*
Z132	2a. deep blue-green	10·00	
Z133	3a. blue	10·00	
Z134	3a. olive-green	14·00	
Z135	6a. bistre	18·00	

1931. *Inauguration of New Delhi (Nos. 226/31).*
Z136	2a. violet and green	17·00	
Z137	2a. green and blue	21·00	

Nos. Z132/5 and Z136/7 exist with watermark showing stars pointing left or right.

1932–36. *King George V. Wmk Multiple Star (Nos. 232/9).*
Z138	1a. chocolate	9·50	
Z139	1a.3p. mauve	9·50	
Z140	2a. vermilion	15·00	
Z141	3a. carmine	17·00	

PRICES FOR STAMPS ON COVER TO 1945	
Nos. 1/14	from × 5
Nos. 15/19	from × 6
Nos. 20/37	from × 2
Nos. 38/50	from × 6

(Currency. 12 pies = 1 anna; 16 annas = 1 rupee)

BAHRAIN   **BAHRAIN**
(1)   (2)

Stamps of India overprinted with T 1 or T 2 (rupee values).

1933 (10 Aug)–37. *King George V. Wmk Mult Star, T 69.*
1	55	3p. slate (11.33)	3·50	45
2	56	½a. green	7·50	3·25
		w. Wmk inverted	42·00	23·00
3	80	9p. deep green (litho)	3·75	2·75
		a. Typo ptg (1937)	12·00	12·00
4	57	1a. chocolate	7·00	2·50
		w. Wmk inverted	27·00	9·00
5	82	1a.3p. mauve	8·00	2·25
		w. Wmk inverted	8·00	2·25
6	70	2a. vermilion	10·00	17·00
		w. Wmk inverted	15·00	17·00
7	62	3a. blue	19·00	55·00
8	83	3a.6p. ultramarine	3·75	30
		w. Wmk inverted	12·00	60
9	71	4a. sage-green	18·00	55·00
10	65	8a. reddish purple	6·00	30
		w. Wmk inverted	†	70·00
11	66	12a. claret	7·50	1·25
		w. Wmk inverted	†	65·00
12	67	1r. chocolate and green	16·00	9·00
13		2r. carmine and orange	28·00	35·00
14		5r. ultramarine and purple	£130	£140
		w. Wmk inverted	£100	£130
1/14w Set of 14			£200	£275

1934–37. *King George V. Wmk Mult Star. T 69.*
15	79	½a. green (1935)	4·50	1·75
		w. Wmk inverted	8·50	1·00
16	81	1a. chocolate	1·00	40
		w. Wmk inverted (from booklets)..	25·00	35·00
17	59	2a. vermilion (1935)	42·00	7·50
17a		2a. vermilion (small die) (1937)	75·00	25
18	62	3a. carmine	4·75	50
19	63	4a. sage-green (1935)	5·00	40
15/19 Set of 6			£130	9·00

1938–41. *King George VI.*
20	91	3p. slate (5.38)	16·00	4·25
21		½a. red-brown (5.38)	7·00	10
22		9p. green (5.38)	9·00	7·50
23		1a. carmine (5.38)	8·50	10
24	92	2a. vermilion (1939)	5·00	2·50
26	–	3a. yellow-green (1941)	12·00	6·50
27	–	3a.6p. bright blue (7.38)	6·00	4·00
28	–	4a. brown (1941)	£130	70·00
30	–	8a. slate-violet (1940)	£180	35·00
31	–	12a. lake (1940)	£120	45·00
32	93	1r. grey and red-brown (1940)	4·50	1·75
33		2r. purple and brown (1940)	13·00	8·00
34		5r. green and blue (1940)	15·00	13·00
35		10r. purple and claret (1941)	65·00	38·00
36		15r. brown and green (1941)	£150	£160
		w. Wmk inverted	60·00	65·00
37		25r. slate-violet and purple (1941)	£100	85·00
20/37 Set of 16			£650	£350

1942–45. *King George VI on white background.*
38	100	3p. slate	2·50	2·00
39		½a. purple	4·25	2·50
40		9p. green	13·00	17·00
41		1a. carmine	5·50	75
42	101	1a.3p. bistre	8·50	19·00
43		1½a. dull violet	6·00	7·00
44		2a. vermilion	6·00	1·50
45		3a. bright violet	18·00	6·50
46		3½a. bright blue	4·75	19·00
47	102	4a. brown	3·50	2·00
48		6a. turquoise-green	15·00	10·00
49		8a. slate-violet	5·50	3·50
50		12a. lake	8·50	5·00
38/50 Set of 13			90·00	85·00

Unoverprinted India Victory stamps, Nos. 278/81, were placed on sale in Bahrain during January 1946.

Although the stamps of Pakistan were never placed on sale in Bahrain examples of the 1947 "PAKISTAN" overprints on India can be found cancelled in Bahrain from air mail originating at Dubai or Sharjah.

Stamps of Great Britain surcharged

For similar surcharges without the name of the country, see BRITISH POSTAL AGENCIES IN EASTERN ARABIA.

BAHRAIN

BAHRAIN

1
ANNA
(3)

5 RUPEES
(4)

1948 (1 Apr)–49. *Surch as T 3, 4 (2r. and 5r.) or similar surch with bars at foot (10r.).*
51	128	½a. on ½d. pale green	50	1·25
52		1a. on 1d. pale scarlet	50	2·25
53		1½a. on 1½d. pale red-brown	50	3·00
54		2a. on 2d. pale orange	50	20
55		2½a. on 2½d. light ultramarine	50	3·75
56		3a. on 3d. pale violet	50	10
57	129	6a. on 6d. purple	50	10
58	130	1r. on 1s. bistre-brown	1·25	10
59	131	2r. on 2s.6d. yellow-green	5·50	4·75
60		5r. on 5s. red	5·50	4·75
60a	132	10r. on 10s. ultramarine (4.7.49)	70·00	50·00
51/60a Set of 11			75·00	65·00

BAHRAIN
2½
ANNAS
(5)

BAHRAIN
15
RUPEES
(6)

1948 (26 Apr). *Silver Wedding, surch as T 5 or 6.*
61	137	2½a. on 2½d. ultramarine	1·00	1·50
62	138	15r. on £1 blue	30·00	48·00

1948 (29 July). *Olympic Games, surch as T 5, but in one line (6a.) or two lines (others); the 1r. also has a square of dots as T 7.*
63	139	2½a. on 2½d. ultramarine	1·00	3·50
		a. Surch double	£1500	£2250
64	140	3a. on 3d. violet	1·00	3·25
65	141	6a. on 6d. bright purple	1·50	3·25
66	142	1r. on 1s. brown	2·50	3·25
63/6 Set of 4			5·50	12·00

Fifteen used examples of No. 63a are known, of which thirteen, including a block of 4, were postmarked at Experimental P.O. K-121 (Muharraq), one on cover from F.P.O. 756 (Shaibah) on 25 October 1948 and one apparently cancelled-to-order at Bahrain on 10 October 1949.

BAHRAIN
3 ANNAS
(7)

1949 (10 Oct). *75th Anniv of U.P.U., surch as T 7, in one line (2½a.) or in two lines (others).*
67	143	2½a. on 2½d. ultramarine	60	2·25
		a. Lake in India	80·00	
68	144	3a. on 3d. violet	70	3·50
69	145	6a. on 6d. bright purple	60	3·00
70	146	1r. on 1s. brown	1·25	2·25
67/70 Set of 4			2·75	10·00

BAHRAIN   **BAHRAIN**

2 RUPEES   **2 RUPEES**
(7a)   Type II

BAHRAIN
Extra bar (R. 6/1)

Three Types of 2r.:

Type I. As Type **7a** showing "2" level with "RUPEES" and "BAHRAIN" sharp.

Type II. "2" raised. "BAHRAIN" worn. 15 mm between "BAHRAIN" and "2 RUPEES".

Type III. As Type II, but 16 mm between "BAHRAIN" and "2 RUPEES". Value is set more to the left of "BAHRAIN".

1950 (2 Oct)–55. *Surch as T 3 or 7a (rupee values).*
71	128	½a. on ½d. pale orange (3.5.51)	2·50	2·50
72		1a. on 1d. light ultramarine (3.5.51)	3·00	20
73		1½a. on 1½d. pale green (3.5.51)	3·00	13·00
74		2a. on 2d. pale red-brown (3.5.51)	1·50	30
75		2½a. on 2½d. pale scarlet (3.5.51)	3·00	13·00
76	129	4a. on 4d. light ultramarine (3.5.51)	3·25	1·50
77	147	2r. on 2s.6d. yellow-green (3.5.51)..	26·00	10·00
		a. Surch Type II (1953)	80·00	38·00
		b. Surch Type III (1955)..	£800	90·00
		ba. "I" inverted and raised (R. 2/1)	£6000	£750
78	148	5r. on 5s. red (3.5.51)	14·00	4·00
		a. Extra bar	£375	
79	149	10r. on 10s. ultramarine (3.5.51)	30·00	8·50
71/79 Set of 9			80·00	48·00

STAMP BOOKLETS

1934. *Red and black on tan cover. Mysore Sandal Soap advertisement on front.*
SB1	16a. booklet containing sixteen 1a. (Nos. 16 and/ or 16w) in blocks of 4		£1200

Bangkok *see* British Post Office in Siam

Barbados

Regular mails between Barbados and Great Britain were established at an early date in the island's development and it is believed that the British Mail Packet Agency at Bridgetown was opened in 1688 as part of the considerable expansion of the Packet Service in that year.

From 1 August 1851 the colonial authorities were responsible for the internal post system, but the British G.P.O. did not relinquish control of the overseas post until 1858.

For illustrations of the handstamp types see BRITISH POST OFFICES ABROAD notes, following GREAT BRITAIN.

CROWNED-CIRCLE HANDSTAMPS

CC1   CC 1 BARBADOES (3.10.1849) (R.)
          Price on cover £450

Combination covers exist with the local postage paid by a Barbados 1d. stamp and the overseas fee by an example of No. CC1.

During shortages of ½d. stamps in 1893 (17 February to 15 March) and of the ¼d. in 1896 (23 January to 4 May) No. CC1 was utilised, struck in black, on local mail. *Price on cover from* £90.

PRICES FOR STAMPS ON COVER TO 1945	
Nos. 1/35	from × 5
Nos. 43/63	from × 4
Nos. 64/6	from × 10
Nos. 67/83	from × 5
Nos. 86/8	from × 3
Nos. 89/103	from × 4
No. 104	from × 20
Nos. 105/15	from × 4
Nos. 116/24	from × 8
Nos. 125/33	from × 5
Nos. 135/44	from × 4
Nos. 145/52	from × 6
No. 153	from × 5
Nos. 158/62	from × 5
Nos. 163/9	from × 3
Nos. 170/96	from × 4
Nos. 197/8	from × 10
Nos. 199/212	from × 6
Nos. 213/39	from × 3
Nos. 240	from × 10
Nos. 241/4	from × 5
Nos. 245/7	from × 4
Nos. 248/56a	from × 4
Nos. 257/61	from × 5
Nos. D1/3	from × 25

PERKINS BACON "CANCELLED". For notes on these handstamps, showing "CANCELLED" between horizontal bars forming an oval, see Catalogue Introduction.

CROWN COLONY

1 Britannia   2 Britannia

(Recess Perkins, Bacon & Co)

1852 (15 April)–55. *Paper blued. No wmk. Imperf.*
1	1	(½d.) yellow-green (1855)	—	£700
2		(½d.) deep green	£110	£325
3		(1d.) blue	48·00	£190
4		(1d.) deep blue	29·00	70·00
4a		(2d.) greyish slate	£250	£1200
		b. Bisected (1d.) (on cover) (1854)	†	£7000
5		(1d.) brownish red (1855)	£100	£275

The bisect, No. 4b, was authorised for use between 4 August and 21 September 1854 during a shortage of 1d. stamps.

Prepared for use but not issued.

5a	1	(No value), slate-blue (shades)	25.00	
5b		(No value), deep slate	£225	

Nos. 5a/b were never sent to Barbados and come from the Perkins Bacon remainders sold in the 1880's.

Apart from the shade, which is distinctly paler, No. 4a can be distinguished from No. 5b by the smooth even gum, the gum of No. 5b being yellow and patchy, giving a mottled appearance to the back of the stamp. No. 5a also has the latter gum.

1855–58. *White paper.* No wmk. Imperf.

7	1	(½d.) yellow-green (1857)	£475	£110
8		(½d.) green (shades) (1858)	£150	£200
9		(1d.) pale blue	95.00	70.00
10		(1d.) dp blue (H/S "CANCELLED" in oval £8000)	38.00	60.00

No. 8 exists in a yellowish green shade which should not be confused with No. 7.

1858 (10 Nov). No wmk. Imperf.

11	2	6d. pale rose-red	£750	£120
11a		6d. deep rose-red	£750	£180
12		1s. brown-black	£250	£110
12a		1s. black	£225	75.00

BISECTS. The various 1d. bisects recorded between Nos. 14a and 73a were principally used for the ½d. inland rate, covering newspapers from 1854 onwards.

Prices for Nos. 24a, 52a, 66a and 73a are for examples on dated piece, undated pieces being worth considerably less. Nos. 14a, 15a and 19a are only known on undated piece and the prices for these bisects are for items in this condition.

1860. No wmk.

(a) Pin-perf 14.

13	1	(½d.) yellow-green	£2000	£425
14		(1d.) pale blue	£1800	£150
		a. Bisected (½d.) (on piece)	†	£1000
15		(1d.) deep blue	£1800	£170
		a. Bisected (½d.) (on piece)	†	£1000

(b) Pin-perf 12½.

16	1	(½d.) yellow-green	£7500	£650
16a		(1d.) blue	—	£1500

(c) Pin-perf 14×12½.

16b	1	(½d.) yellow-green	—	£7500

1861. No wmk. Clean-cut perf 14 to 16.

17	1	(½d.) deep green (H/S "CANCELLED" in oval £8000)	£120	12.00
18		(1d.) pale blue	£700	65.00
19		(1d.) blue	£800	70.00
		a. Bisected (½d.) (on piece)	†	£750

1861–70. No wmk.

(a) Rough perf 14 to 16.

20	1	(½d.) deep green	23.00	26.00
21		(½d.) green	18.00	17.00
21a		(½d.) blue-green	55.00	75.00
		b. Imperf (pair)	£600	
22		(½d.) grass-green	29.00	26.00
		a. Imperf (pair)	£700	
23		(1d.) blue (1861)	50.00	2.25
		a. Imperf (pair) (pale blue, worn plate)	£750	
24		(1d.) deep blue	40.00	3.75
		a. Bisected diag (½d.) (on piece) (1863)	†	£600
25		(4d.) dull rose-red (1861)	95.00	48.00
		a. Imperf (pair)	£800	
26		(4d.) dull brown-red (1865)	£140	55.00
		a. Imperf (pair)	£1200	
27		(4d.) lake-rose (1868)	£130	80.00
		a. Imperf (pair)	£1300	
28		(4d.) dull vermilion (1869)	£250	85.00
		a. Imperf (pair)	£1200	
29	2	6d. rose-red (1861) (Handstamped "CANCELLED" in oval £8000)	£325	15.00
30		6d. orange-red (1864)	£110	22.00
31		6d. bright orange-vermilion (1868)	95.00	23.00
32		6d. dull orange-vermilion (1870)	£110	19.00
		a. Imperf (pair)	£600	
33		6d. orange (1870)	£130	35.00
34		1s. brown-black (1863)	75.00	6.50
		a. Error. Blue	£17000	
35		1s. black (1866)	65.00	7.00
		a. Imperf between (horiz pair)	£6500	

(b) Prepared for use, but not issued. P 11 to 12.

36	1	(½d.) grass-green	£9500	
37		(1d.) blue	£2000	

The (1d.) deep blue, No. 24, also exists imperforate, from a new plate, but examples cannot readily be distinguished from No. 10.

The bisect, No. 24a, was first authorised for use in April 1863 and further examples have been reported up to January 1869 during shortages of ½d. stamps.

No. 34a was an error on the part of the printer who supplied the first requisition of the 1s. value in the colour of the 1d. The 1s. blue stamps were never placed on sale, but the Barbados Colonial Secretary circulated some samples which were defaced by a manuscript corner-to-corner cross. A number of these samples subsequently had the cross removed.

Nos. 36/7 were never sent to Barbados and come from the Perkins Bacon remainders. It is believed that the imperforate pairs came from the same source.

1870. Wmk Large Star, Type w **1.** Rough perf 14 to 16.

43	1	(½d.) green	£130	6.50
43b		(½d.) yellow-green	£170	45.00
44		(1d.) blue	£1800	55.00
		a. Blue paper	£3000	£100
45		(4d.) dull vermilion	£1000	£120
46	2	6d. orange-vermilion	£900	70.00
47		1s. black	£400	18.00

No. 43 exists imperforate (Price £1100).

1871. Wmk Small Star, Type w **2.** Rough perf 14 to 16.

48	1	(1d.) blue	£150	2.25
49		(4d.) dull rose-red	£1000	40.00

50	2	6d. orange-vermilion	£600	16.00
51		1s. black	£180	9.50

1872. Wmk Small Star, Type w **2.**

(a) Clean-cut perf 14½ to 15½.

52	1	(1d.) blue	£275	2.00
		a. Bisected diag (½d.) (on piece)	†	£1000
53	2	6d. orange-vermilion	£850	65.00
54		1s. black	£160	9.50

(b) P 11 to 13×14½ to 15½.

56	1	(½d.) green	£325	48.00
57		(4d.) dull vermilion	£750	£110

1873. Wmk Large Star, Type w **1.**

(a) Clean-cut perf 14½ to 15½.

58	1	(½d.) green	£325	17.00
59		(4d.) dull rose-red	£1100	£190
60	2	6d. orange-vermilion	£750	75.00
		a. Imperf between (horiz pair)	£7000	
		b. Imperf (pair)	90.00	
61		1s. black	£150	14.00
		a. Imperf between (horiz pair)	£6500	

(b) Prepared for use, but not issued. P 11 to 12.

62	2	6d. orange-vermilion	£7000	

Only eight mint examples, in two strips of four, are known of No. 62.

Two used singles of No. 60b have been seen.

1873 (June). Wmk Small Star, Type w **2** (sideways = two points upwards). P 14.

63	2	3d. brown-purple	£325	£110

BARBADOS

5 SHILLINGS

3

1873 (June). Wmk Small Star, Type w **2** (sideways). P 15½×15.

64	3	5s. dull rose	£950	£300
		s. Handstamped "Specimen"	£300	

1874 (May)**–75.** Wmk Large Star, Type w **1.**

(a) Perf 14.

65	2	½d. deep green	35.00	7.00
66		1d. deep blue	90.00	2.75
		a. Bisected (½d.) (on piece) (5.75)	†	£750

(b) Clean-cut perf 14½ to 15½.

66b	2	1d. deep blue	†	£8500
		c. Imperf (pair)		

(Recess D.L.R)

1875–80. Wmk Crown CC (sideways* on 6d., 1s.).

(a) P 12½.

67	2	½d. bright green	55.00	5.00
		x. Wmk reversed	—	12.00
68		4d. deep red	£275	14.00
		w. Wmk inverted	£375	35.00
		x. Wmk reversed	£275	16.00
69		6d. bright yellow (aniline)	£950	90.00
70		6d. chrome-yellow	£600	70.00
		v. Wmk upright	†	£2250
		w. Wmk Crown to right of CC	—	75.00
71		1s. violet (aniline)	£500	3.50
		x. Wmk sideways reversed	£500	3.00
		y. Wmk sideways inverted and reversed	—	10.00

(b) P 14.

72	2	½d. bright green (1876)	13.00	50
		s. Handstamped "Specimen" in red	90.00	
		sa. Handstamped "Specimen" in black	£120	
		w. Wmk inverted	—	14.00
		x. Wmk reversed	13.00	75
73		1d. dull blue	70.00	1.25
		a. Bisected (½d.) (on piece) (3.77)	†	£400
		s. Handstamped "Specimen" in red	90.00	
		sa. Handstamped "Specimen" in black	£120	
		w. Wmk inverted	—	14.00
		x. Wmk reversed		
74		1d. grey-blue	70.00	1.00
		a. Wmk sideways	†	£850
		w. Wmk inverted	£120	21.00
		x. Wmk reversed	85.00	1.25
		y. Wmk inverted and reversed	—	35.00
75		3d. mauve-lilac (1878)	£130	7.00
		s. Handstamped "Specimen" in black	£130	
		w. Wmk inverted	†	85.00
76		4d. red (1878)	£130	9.00
		s. Handstamped "Specimen" in black	£130	
		w. Wmk reversed		
77		4d. carmine	£190	2.50
		w. Wmk inverted	†	60.00
		x. Wmk reversed		5.50
78		4d. crimson-lake	£500	2.75
79		6d. chrome-yellow (1876)	£140	1.75
		s. Handstamped "Specimen" in black	£130	
		w. Wmk Crown to right of CC	£140	2.50
		x. Wmk sideways reversed	—	2.50

80		6d. yellow	£325	6.50
		w. Wmk Crown to right of CC	—	10.00
81		1s. purple (4.78)	£150	4.25
		s. Handstamped "Specimen" in red	£130	
		w. Wmk Crown to right of CC	£140	4.25
		x. Wmk sideways reversed	—	6.50
82		1s. violet (aniline) (6.77)	£3750	40.00
		w. Wmk Crown to right of CC	—	40.00
		x. Wmk sideways reversed		
83		1s. dull mauve (1879)	£475	3.75
		a. Bisected (6d.) (on piece) (1.80)	†	
		x. Wmk sideways reversed	—	11.00

(c) P 14×12½.

84	2	4d. red	£6000	

The normal sideways watermark shows Crown to left of CC, as seen from the back of the stamp.

Only two examples, both used, of No. 70a have been reported.

Nos. 72sa/3sa were from postal stationery and are without gum.

Very few examples of No. 84 have been found unused and only one used specimen is known.

1D.	1D.	1D.
(3a)	(3b)	(3c)

1878 (28 Mar). No. 64 surch by West Indian Press with T **3a/c** sideways twice on each stamp and then divided vertically by 11½ to 13 perforations. The lower label, showing the original face value, was removed before use.

*(a) With T **3a.** Large numeral "1", 7 mm high with curved serif, and large letter "D", 2¾ mm high.*

86	3	1d. on half 5s. dull rose	£4250	£650
		a. No stop after "D"	£13000	£1700
		b. Unsevered pair (both No. 86)	£18000	£2250
		c. Ditto, Nos. 86 and 87	—	£4000
		ca. Pair without dividing perf	†	£27000
		d. Ditto, Nos. 86 and 88	£27000	£6500

*(b) With T **3b.** As last, but numeral with straight serif.*

87	3	1d. on half 5s. dull rose	£5000	£800
		a. Unsevered pair	†	£3000

*(c) With T **3c.** Smaller numeral "1", 6 mm high and smaller "D", 2½ mm high.*

88	3	1d. on half 5s. dull rose	£6500	£900
		a. Unsevered pair	£22000	£4000

All types of the surcharge are found reading upwards as well as downwards, and there are minor varieties of the type.

BARBADOS

THREE PENCE

4

HALF·PENNY

(5)

(Typo D.L.R)

1882 (28 Aug)**–86.** Wmk Crown CA. P 14.

89	4	½d. dull green (1882)	18.00	1.50
		w. Wmk inverted		
90		½d. green	18.00	1.50
91		1d. rose (1882)	65.00	2.25
		a. Bisected (½d.) (on cover)	†	£1300
		w. Wmk inverted		
92		1d. carmine	23.00	1.00
93		2½d. ultramarine (1882)	90.00	1.50
		w. Wmk inverted	—	£110
94		2½d. deep blue	£110	1.50
95		3d. deep purple (1885)	£110	32.00
96		3d. reddish purple	4.25	19.00
97		4d. grey (1882)	£300	3.75
98		4d. pale brown (1885)	14.00	3.25
		w. Wmk inverted	—	85.00
		x. Wmk reversed	†	£140
		y. Wmk inverted and reversed	†	£275
99		4d. deep brown	6.00	1.50
100		6d. olive-black (1886)	75.00	45.00
102		1s. chestnut (1886)	29.00	21.00
103		5s. bistre (1886)	£150	£190
89/103		Set of 9	£600	£250
95s/103s		(ex 4d. grey) Optd "Specimen" Set of 5	£400	

1892 (July). No. 99 surch with T **5** by West Indian Press.

104	4	½d. on 4d. deep brown	2.25	5.50
		a. No hyphen	13.00	24.00
		b. Surch double (R.+Bk.)	£750	£900
		ba. Surch double (R.+Bk.) both without hyphen	£2000	£2500
		c. Surch double, one albino		
		d. Surch "PENNY HALF"	£350	£200

Nos. 104b/ba come from a sheet with a trial surcharge in red which was subsequently surcharged again in black and put back into stock.

No. 104c is known in a horizontal pair (Price, £2500, unused) with the left hand stamp showing the first two letters of the second impression inked. The right hand stamp shows a complete albino surcharge.

BARBADOS

VICTORIA·R·1

1837·1897

ONE FARTHING

ONE PENNY

6 Seal of Colony	**7**

(Typo D.L.R.)

1892 (July)–**1903**. Wmk Crown CA. P 14.

105	**6**	¼d. slate-grey and carmine (5.5.96).	2·50	10
		w. Wmk inverted	2·50	
106		½d. dull green	2·50	10
		w. Wmk inverted	—	85·00
107		1d. carmine	4·75	10
108		2d. slate-black and orange (5.99)	8·00	75
109		2½d. ultramarine	17·00	20
110		5d. grey-olive	7·00	4·50
111		6d. mauve and carmine	16·00	2·00
112		8d. orange and ultramarine	4·00	23·00
113		10d. dull blue-green and carmine	8·00	6·50
114		2s.6d. blue-black and orange	48·00	50·00
		w. Wmk inverted	£130	£140
115		2s.6d. violet and green (29.5.03)	£100	£180
105/15 *Set of 11*			£200	£225
105s/15s Optd "Specimen" *Set of 11*			£225	

See also Nos. 135/44 and 163/9.

(Typo D.L.R.)

1897 (16 Nov)–**98**. *Diamond Jubilee.* T **7**. Wmk Crown CC. P 14.

(a) White paper.

116		¼d. grey and carmine	5·00	60
117		½d. dull green	5·00	60
118		1d. rose	5·00	60
119		2½d. ultramarine	7·50	85
		w. Wmk inverted	—	£100
120		5d. olive-brown	20·00	18·00
121		6d. mauve and carmine	27·00	24·00
122		8d. orange and ultramarine	12·00	25·00
123		10d. blue-green and carmine	48·00	55·00
124		2s.6d. blue-black and orange	75·00	55·00
		w. Wmk inverted		
116/24 *Set of 9*			£180	£160
116s/24s Optd "Specimen" *Set of 9*			£170	

(b) Paper blued.

125		¼d. grey and carmine	28·00	30·00
126		½d. dull green	29·00	30·00
127		1d. carmine	38·00	40·00
128		2½d. ultramarine	40·00	45·00
129		5d. olive-brown	£225	£250
130		6d. mauve and carmine	£130	£140
131		8d. orange and ultramarine	£140	£150
132		10d. dull green and carmine	£190	£225
133		2s.6d. blue-black and orange	£120	£130

1905. Wmk Mult Crown CA. P 14.

135	**6**	¼d. slate-grey and carmine	9·50	2·75
136		½d. dull green	19·00	10
137		1d. carmine	19·00	10
139		2½d. blue	21·00	15
141		6d. mauve and carmine	19·00	19·00
142		8d. orange and ultramarine	50·00	£100
144		2s.6d. violet and green	55·00	£120
135/144 *Set of 7*			£170	£225

See also Nos. 163/9.

8 Nelson Monument

(Des Mrs. G. Goodman. Recess D.L.R.)

1906 (1 Mar). *Nelson Centenary.* Wmk Crown CC. P 14.

145	**8**	¼d. black and grey	9·50	1·75
		w. Wmk inverted	40·00	42·00
146		½d. black and pale green	10·00	15
		w. Wmk inverted		
		x. Wmk reversed	£150	75·00
147		1d. black and red	12·00	15
		w. Wmk inverted	55·00	
		x. Wmk reversed	†	7·50
148		2d. black and yellow	1·75	4·50
149		2½d. black and bright blue	3·75	1·25
		w. Wmk inverted		
150		6d. black and mauve	18·00	25·00
151		1s. black and rose	21·00	50·00
145/51 *Set of 7*			65·00	75·00
145s/51s Optd "Specimen" *Set of 7*			£160	

Two sets may be made of these: one on thick, opaque, creamy white paper; the other on thin, rather transparent, bluish white paper. See also Nos. 158/62a.

9 Olive Blossom, 1605

Kingston Relief Fund. 1d.

(10)

(Des Lady Carter. Recess D.L.R.)

1906 (15 Aug). *Tercentenary of Annexation.* Wmk Multiple Crown CA (sideways). P 14.

152	**9**	1d. black, blue and green	10·00	25
		s. Optd "Specimen"	65·00	

1907 (25 Jan–25 Feb). *Kingston Relief Fund. No. 108 surch with* T **10** *by T. E. King & Co., Barbados.*

153	**6**	1d. on 2d. slate-black and orange (R.)	3·25	8·00
		a. Surch inverted (25.2.07)	1·75	6·50
		b. Surch double	£850	£950
		c. Surch double, both inverted	£850	
		d. Surch tête-bêche (vert pair)	£1200	

		e. No stop after "1d."	50·00	85·00
		ea. Do., surch inverted (25.2.07)	40·00	95·00
		eb. Do., surch double	—	£1600
		f. Vert pair, one normal, one surch double	—	£1100

The above stamp was sold for 2d. of which 1d. was retained for the postal revenue, and the other 1d. given to a fund for the relief of the sufferers by the earthquake in Jamaica.

An entire printing as No. 153a was created after a sheet of inverted surcharges was found in the initial supply.

1907 (6 July). *Nelson Centenary.* Wmk Mult Crown CA. P 14.

158	**8**	¼d. black and grey	5·00	6·00
161		2d. black and yellow	29·00	30·00
162		2½d. black and bright blue	8·00	29·00
		a. Black and indigo	£700	£800
158/62 *Set of 3*			38·00	60·00

1909 (July)–**10**. Wmk Mult Crown CA. P 14.

163	**6**	¼d. brown	9·50	30
164		½d. blue-green	23·00	1·25
165		1d. red	22·00	10
166		2d. greyish slate (8.10)	7·50	13·00
167		2½d. bright blue (1910)	9·00	9·50
168		6d. dull and bright purple (1910)	13·00	17·00
169		1s. black/green (8.10)	11·00	14·00
163/9 *Set of 7*			£120	50·00
163s/9s (ex ½d., 2½d.) Optd "Specimen" *Set of 5* ...			£140	

11   **12**   **13**

(Typo D.L.R.)

1912 (23 July)–**16**. Wmk Mult Crown CA. P 14.

170	**11**	¼d. brown	1·50	1·50
		a. Pale brown (1916)	1·50	2·50
		aw. Wmk inverted		
171		½d. green	3·75	10
		a. Wmk sideways	†	—
172		1d. red (13.8.12)	11·00	10
		a. Scarlet (1915)	28·00	3·50
173		2d. greyish slate (13.8.12)	3·50	14·00
174		2½d. bright blue (13.8.12)	1·50	50
175	**12**	3d. purple/yellow (13.8.12)	1·50	14·00
176		4d. red and black/yellow (13.8.12) ..	2·25	18·00
177		6d. purple and dull purple (13.8.12)	12·00	12·00
178	**13**	1s. black/green (13.8.12)	8·50	16·00
179		2s. blue and purple/blue (13.8.12) ..	48·00	50·00
180		3s. violet and green (13.8.12)	95·00	£100
170/80 *Set of 11*			£170	£200
170s/80s Optd "Specimen" *Set of 11*			£150	

WAR TAX

14   **(15)**

(Recess D.L.R.)

1916 (16 June)–**19**. Wmk Mult Crown CA. P 14.

181	**14**	¼d. deep brown	75	40
		a. Chestnut-brown (9.17)	1·50	35
		b. Sepia-brown (4.18)	3·75	2·75
		w. Wmk inverted	17·00	18·00
		y. Wmk inverted and reversed	38·00	42·00
182		½d. green	1·60	15
		a. Deep green (9.17)	1·60	15
		b. Pale green (4.18)	2·25	80
		w. Wmk inverted	32·00	
		x. Wmk reversed	55·00	
183		1d. deep red	17·00	6·00
		a. Bright carmine-red (4.17)	2·50	15
		b. Pale carmine-red (9.17)	6·00	65
		w. Wmk inverted	32·00	
		x. Wmk reversed		
		y. Wmk inverted and reversed	32·00	
184		2d. grey	6·50	24·00
		a. Grey-black (9.19)	40·00	70·00
		w. Wmk inverted and reversed		
185		2½d. deep ultramarine	4·00	2·75
		a. Royal blue (11.17)	4·25	3·00
		w. Wmk inverted		
		y. Wmk inverted and reversed	38·00	38·00
186		3d. purple/yellow (thin paper)	3·00	8·00
		a. Dp purple/yell (thick paper) (9.19)	29·00	45·00
187		4d. red/yellow	1·00	14·00
188		6d. purple	5·00	5·00
189		1s. black/green	7·00	12·00
190		2s. purple/blue	16·00	7·50
		w. Wmk inverted and reversed	80·00	
191		3s. deep violet	55·00	£140
		w. Wmk inverted		
		y. Wmk inverted and reversed	£1100	
181/91 *Set of 11*			90·00	£190
181s/91s "Specimen" *Set of 11*			£200	

Dates quoted for shades are those of despatch from Great Britain. Examples of the ½d. and 1d. values can be found perforated either by line or by comb machines.
No. 191y is gummed on the printed side.
See also Nos. 199/200a.

1917 (10 Oct)–**18**. *War Tax. Optd in London with* T **15**.

197	**11**	1d. bright red	50	15
		s. Optd "Specimen"	55·00	
		w. Wmk inverted	—	£120
198		1d. pale red (thicker bluish paper) (4.18)	4·00	50

1918 (18 Feb)–**20**. *Colours changed.* Wmk Mult Crown CA. P 14.

199	**14**	4d. black and red	1·00	3·75
		w. Wmk reversed	£160	
200		3s. green and deep violet	21·00	80·00
		a. Green and bright violet (1920)..	£250	£375
199s/200s Optd "Specimen" *Set of 2*			£130	

The centres of these are from a new die having no circular border line.

16 Winged Victory from the Louvre   **17** Victory from Victoria Memorial, London

(Recess D.L.R.)

1920 (9 Sept)–**21**. *Victory.* P 14.

(a) Wmk Mult Crown CA (sideways* on T **17**).

201	**16**	¼d. black and bistre-brown	30	70
		a. "C" of "CA" missing from wmk	£275	
		c. Substituted crown in wmk	£325	
		w. Wmk inverted	95·00	
		x. Wmk reversed	40·00	
		y. Wmk inverted and reversed	45·00	
202		½d. black and bright yellow-green...	1·00	15
		a. "C" of "CA" missing from wmk	£300	£250
		b. "A" of "CA" missing from wmk	£300	
		c. Substituted crown in wmk	£425	
		w. Wmk inverted	—	£100
		x. Wmk reversed	95·00	
		y. Wmk inverted and reversed	95·00	95·00
203		1d. black and vermilion	4·00	10
		a. "A" of "CA" missing from wmk	†	£375
		c. Substituted crown in wmk	†	£375
		w. Wmk inverted	38·00	40·00
		y. Wmk inverted and reversed	95·00	
204		2d. black and grey	2·25	9·00
		a. "C" of "CA" missing from wmk	£350	
205		2½d. indigo and ultramarine	2·75	20·00
		a. "C" of "CA" missing from wmk	£375	
		w. Wmk inverted	—	£100
		y. Wmk inverted and reversed	95·00	£110
206		3d. black and purple	3·00	6·50
		w. Wmk inverted	30·00	42·00
207		4d. black and blue-green	3·25	7·00
208		6d. black and brown-orange	3·75	17·00
		w. Wmk inverted	65·00	£100
		wa. "C" of "CA" missing from wmk	£1100	
		wb. Substituted crown in wmk	£1100	
209	**17**	1s. black and bright green	11·00	32·00
		a. "C" of "CA" missing from wmk	£900	
		w. Wmk Crown to left of CA	£130	
		x. Wmk sideways reversed		
		y. Wmk sideways inverted and reversed	£140	
210		2s. black and brown	32·00	48·00
		w. Wmk Crown to left of CA	70·00	£100
		x. Wmk sideways reversed	£130	
		y. Wmk sideways inverted and reversed		
211		3s. black and dull orange	35·00	60·00
		a. "C" of "CA" missing from wmk	£850	
		w. Wmk Crown to left of CA	85·00	
		x. Wmk sideways reversed		
		y. Wmk sideways inverted and reversed		

(b) Wmk Mult Script CA.

212	**16**	1d. black and vermilion (22.8.21)	17·00	30
201/12 *Set of 12*			£100	£180
201s/12s Optd "Specimen" *Set of 12*			£225	

*The normal sideways watermark on Nos. 209/11 shows Crown to right of CA, *as seen from the back of the stamp.*

For illustration of the substituted watermark crown see Catalogue Introduction.

18   **19**

(Recess D.L.R.)

1921 (14 Nov)–**24**. P 14.

(a) Wmk Mult Crown CA.

213	**18**	3d. purple/pale yellow	2·00	7·00
		a. "A" of "CA" missing from wmk		
		x. Wmk reversed	†	£160
214		4d. red/pale yellow	1·75	17·00

215		1s. black/*emerald*	5·50	16·00
	w.	Wmk inverted	†	£250
	x.	Wmk reversed	†	£225

(b) Wmk Mult Script CA.

217	**18**	¼d. brown	25	10
	x.	Wmk reversed	30·00	
	y.	Wmk inverted and reversed	42·00	
219		½d. green	1·50	10
220		1d. red	80	10
	aw.	Wmk inverted	25·00	32·00
	ax.	Wmk inverted	—	£100
	ay.	Wmk inverted and reversed	—	£100
	b.	*Bright rose-carmine*	7·00	1·00
	bw.	Wmk inverted	25·00	
221		2d. grey	1·75	20
	y.	Wmk inverted and reversed		
222		2½d. ultramarine	1·50	9·00
225		6d. reddish purple	3·50	5·50
226		1s. black/*emerald* (18.9.24)	50·00	£120
227		2s. purple/*blue*	10·00	19·00
228		3s. deep violet	15·00	70·00
	y.	Wmk inverted and reversed		
213/28	*Set of 12*		85·00	£225
213s/28s	Optd "Specimen" *Set of 12*			£180

1925 (1 Apr)–**35**. Wmk Mult Script CA. P 14.

229	**19**	¼d. brown	25	10
230		½d. green	50	10
	a.	Perf 13½×12½ (2.32)	7·00	10
231		1d. scarlet	50	10
	ax.	Wmk reversed	†	£250
	b.	Perf 13½×12½ (2.32)	7·00	50
231*b*		1½d. orange (1933)	14·00	3·25
	ba.	Perf 13½×12½ (15.8.32)	2·00	1·00
232		2d. grey	50	3·25
233		2½d. blue	50	80
	a.	*Bright ultramarine* (1933)	16·00	2·25
	ab.	Perf 13½×12½ (2.32)	8·50	4·50
234		3d. purple/*pale yellow*	1·00	45
	a.	*Reddish purple/yellow* (1935)	6·00	6·00
235		4d. red/*pale yellow*	75	1·00
236		6d. purple	1·00	90
237		1s. black/*emerald*	2·00	6·50
	a.	Perf 13½×12½ (8.32)	60·00	35·00
	b.	*Brownish black/bright yellow-green* (1934)	4·50	10·00
238		2s. purple/*blue*	7·00	6·50
238*a*		2s.6d. carmine/*blue* (1.9.32)	23·00	29·00
239		3s. deep violet	11·00	14·00
229/39	*Set of 13*		45·00	55·00
229s/39s	Optd or Perf (1½d., 2s.6d.) "Specimen"			
Set of 13				£200

Nos. 230/1 exist in coils constructed from normal sheets.

20 King Charles I and King George V

21 Badge of the Colony

(Recess B.W.)

1927 (17 Feb). *Tercentenary of Settlement of Barbados.* Wmk Mult Script CA. P 12½.

240	**20**	1d. carmine	1·00	75
	s.	Optd "Specimen"	50·00	

1935 (6 May). *Silver Jubilee. As Nos. 91/4 of Antigua, but ptd by Waterlow.* P 11×12.

241	1d. deep blue and scarlet	60	20
	j. Damaged turret	£200	
242	1½d. ultramarine and grey	3·75	6·50
	j. Damaged turret	£250	
243	2½d. brown and deep blue	2·25	4·50
	m. "Bird" by turret	£225	
244	1s. slate and purple	17·00	19·00
	k. Kite and horizontal log	£375	
241/4 *Set of 4*		21·00	27·00
241s/4s Perf "Specimen" *Set of 4*		95·00	

For illustrations of plate varieties see Omnibus section following Zanzibar.

1937 (14 May). *Coronation. As Nos. 95/7 of Antigua, but printed by D.L.R.* P 14.

245	1d. scarlet	30	15
246	1½d. yellow-brown	40	65
247	2½d. bright blue	1·00	75
245/7 *Set of 3*		1·50	1·40
245s/7s Perf "Specimen" *Set of 3*		70·00	

Recut line (R. 10/6)

Extra frame line (R. 11/9)

Mark on central ornament (R. 1/3, 2/3, 3/3)

Vertical line over horse's head (R. 4/10) (corrected on Dec 1947 ptg)

"Flying mane" (R. 4/1) (corrected on Dec 1947 ptg)

Curved line at top right (R. 7/8) (corrected on Dec 1947 ptg)

Cracked plate (extends to top right ornament) (R. 6/10))

(Recess D.L.R.)

1938 (3 Jan)—**47**. Wmk Mult Script CA. P 13½×13.

248	**21**	½d. green	6·00	15
	a.	Recut line	£130	40·00
	b.	Perf 14 (8.42)	70·00	1·25
	ba.	Recut line	£375	75·00
248*c*		½d. yellow-bistre (16.10.42)	15	30
	ca.	"A" of "CA" missing from wmk	£1100	
	cb.	Recut line	22·00	26·00
249		1d. scarlet (12.40)	£275	4·00
	a.	Perf 14 (3.1.38)	16·00	10
249*b*		1d. blue-green (1943)	5·00	1·25
	c.	Perf 14 (16.10.42)	15	10
	ca.	"A" of "CA" missing from wmk	£1100	
250		1½d. orange	15	40
	a.	"A" of "CA" missing from wmk	£1100	
	b.	Perf 14 (11.41)	4·75	75
250*c*		2d. claret (3.6.41)	50	2·50
	ca.	Extra frame line	42·00	75·00
250*d*		2d. carmine (20.9.43)	20	70
	da.	Extra frame line	28·00	42·00
	db.	"A" of "CA" missing from wmk	†	—
	e.	Perf 14 (11.9.44)	60	1·75
	ea.	Extra frame line	35·00	60·00
251		2½d. ultramarine	50	60
	a.	Mark on central ornament	42·00	42·00
	b.	*Blue* (17.2.44)	1·75	5·00
	ba.	"A" of "CA" missing from wmk	£1000	
	bb.	Mark on central ornament	60·00	75·00
252		3d. brown	20	2·50
	a.	Vertical line over horse's head	80·00	£130
	b.	Perf 14 (4.41)	20	60
	ba.	Vertical line over horse's head	80·00	95·00
252*c*		3d. blue (1.4.47)	20	1·75
	ca.	Vertical line over horse's head	80·00	£110
253		4d. black	20	10
	a.	Flying mane	£100	60·00
	b.	Curved line at top right	85·00	50·00
	c.	Cracked plate	85·00	50·00
	d.	Perf 14 (11.9.44)	20	5·00
	da.	Flying mane	£100	£150
	db.	Curved line at top right	85·00	£130
	dc.	Cracked plate	85·00	£130
254		6d. violet	80	40
254*a*		8d. magenta (9.12.46)	55	2·00
255		1s. olive-green	16·00	2·50
	a.	*Deep brown-olive* (19.11.45)	1·00	10
256		2s.6d. purple	7·00	1·50
256*a*		5s. indigo (3.6.41)	3·25	8·00
	ab.	"A" of "CA" missing from wmk	£1800	
248/56*a*	*Set of 16*		32·00	16·00
248s/56as Perf "Specimen" *Set of 16*				

No. 249a was perforated by two machines, one gauging 13.8×14.1 line (1938), the other 14.1 comb (October 1940).
Nos. 248/*c* and 249/*c* exist in coils constructed from normal sheets.

22 Kings Charles I, George VI, Assembly Chamber and Mace

(Recess D.L.R.)

1939 (27 June). *Tercentenary of General Assembly.* Wmk Mult Script CA. P 13½×14.

257	**22**	½d. green	2·75	1·00
258		1d. scarlet	2·75	1·00
259		1½d. orange	2·75	60
260		2½d. bright ultramarine	2·75	5·50
261		3d. brown	2·75	4·00
257/61	*Set of 5*		12·00	11·00
257s/61s	Perf "Specimen" *Set of 5*			£160

Two flags on tug (R. 5/2)

1946 (18 Sept). *Victory. As Nos. 110/11 of Antigua.*

262	1½d. red-orange	15	20
	a. Two flags on tug	24·00	
263	3d. brown	15	20
262s/3s Perf "Specimen" *Set of 2*		60·00	

ONE PENNY
(23)

NY PEN

Short "Y" (R. 6/2)   Broken "E" (R. 7/4 and 11/4)

ONE PENNY

Broken "N"s (R. 2/8, later sheets only)

(Surch by Barbados Advocate Co.)

1947 (21 Apr). *Surch with T* **23**.

(a) P 14.

264	**21**	1d. on 2d. carmine (No. 250*e*)	1·75	2·75
	a.	Extra frame line	75·00	85·00
	b.	Broken "N"s	75·00	85·00
	c.	Short "Y"	75·00	85·00
	d.	Broken "E"	40·00	45·00

(b) P 13½×13.

264*e*	**21**	1d. on 2d. carmine (No. 250*d*)	3·00	5·00
	ea.	Extra frame line	£180	£225
	eb.	Broken "N"s	£180	£225
	ec.	Short "Y"	£180	£225
	ed.	Broken "E"	£110	£140

The relationship of the two words in the surcharge differs on each position of the sheet.

1948 (24 Nov). *Royal Silver Wedding. As Nos. 112/13 of Antigua.*

265	1½d. orange	30	50
266	5s. indigo	12·00	10·00

1949 (10 Oct). *75th Anniv of Universal Postal Union. As Nos. 114/17 of Antigua.*

267	1½d. red-orange	40	1·50
268	3d. deep blue	2·00	3·25
269	4d. grey	40	3·00
270	1s. olive	40	60
267/70 *Set of 4*		3·00	7·50

(New Currency. 100 cents = 1 West Indian, later Barbados, dollar)

24 Dover Fort

25 Sugar cane breeding

26 Public buildings

27 Statue of Nelson

28 Casting net

29 *Frances W. Smith* (schooner)

30 Four-winged Flying Fish

31 Old Main Guard Garrison

32 St. Michael's Cathedral

33 Careenage

34 Map of Barbados and wireless mast

35 Seal of Barbados

(Recess B.W.)

1950 (1 May). T **24/35**. Wmk Mult Script CA. P 11×11½ (horiz), 13½ (vert).

271	24	1c. indigo	35	3·25
272	25	2c. emerald-green	15	2·00
273	26	3c. reddish brown and blue-green	1·25	3·00
274	27	4c. carmine	15	40
275	28	6c. light blue	15	2·25
276	29	8c. bright blue and purple-brown	1·50	2·50
277	30	12c. greenish blue and brown-olive	1·00	1·25
278	31	24c. scarlet and black	1·00	50
279	32	48c. violet	9·00	6·50
280	33	60c. green and claret	10·00	10·00
281	34	$1.20 carmine and olive-green	10·00	4·00
282	35	$2.40 black	21·00	24·00
271/282 Set of 12			50·00	55·00

1951 (16 Feb). Inauguration of B.W.I. University College. As Nos. 118/19 of Antigua.

283		3c. brown and blue-green	30	40
284		12c. blue-green and brown-olive	55	2·25

36 King George VI and Stamp of 1852

(Recess Waterlow)

1952 (15 Apr). Barbados Stamp Centenary. Wmk Mult Script CA. P 13½.

285	36	3c. green and slate-green	25	40
286		4c. blue and carmine	25	1·00
287		12c. slate-green and bright green	30	1·00
288		24c. red-brown and brownish black	30	55
285/8 Set of 4			1·00	2·75

STAMP BOOKLETS

1906 (Feb).
SB1   2s.½d. booklet containing twenty-four 1d. (No. 137) in blocks of 6 ....

1909. Black on red cover. Stapled.
SB1a   1s.6d. booklet containing eighteen 1d. (No. 165) in blocks of 6 ....

1913 (June). Black on red cover. Stapled.
SB2   2s. booklet containing twelve ½d. and eighteen 1d. (Nos. 171/2) in blocks of 6 .... £2500

1916 (16 June). Black on red cover. Stapled.
SB3   2s. booklet containing twelve ½d. and eighteen 1d. (Nos. 182/3) in pairs.................................. £1000

1920 (Sept). Black on red cover. Stapled.
SB4   2s. booklet containing twelve ½d. and eighteen 1d. (Nos. 202/3) in pairs.................................. £2000

1932 (12 Nov). Black on pale green cover. Austin Cars and Post Office Guide advertisements on front. Stapled.
SB5   2s. booklet containing ½d. and 1d. (Nos. 230a, 231a) each in block of 10 and 1½d. (No. 231ba) in block of 6 .... £1800

1933 (4 Dec). Black on pale green cover. Advocate Co. Ltd. advertisement on front. Stapled.
SB6   2s. booklet containing ½d. and 1d. (Nos. 230/1) each in block of 10 and 1½d. (No. 231b) in block of 6 .... £2000

1938 (3 Jan). Black on light blue cover. Advocate Co. Ltd. advertisement on front. Stapled.
SB7   2s. booklet containing ½d. and 1d. (Nos. 248, 249a) each in block of 10 and 1½d. (No. 250) in block of 6 .... £2250

POSTAGE DUE STAMPS

D 1

(Typo D.L.R.)

1934 (2 Jan)–47. Wmk Mult Script CA. P 14.

D1	D 1	½d. green (10.2.35)	1·25	8·50
D2		1d. black	1·25	1·25
		a. Bisected (½d.) (on cover)	†	£1500
D3		3d. carmine (13.3.47)	20·00	21·00
D1/3 Set of 3			20·00	28·00
D1s/3s Perf "Specimen" Set of 3			85·00	

The bisected 1d. was officially authorised for use between March 1934 and February 1935. Some specimens had the value "½d." written across the half stamp in red or black ink (Price on cover £2000).

(Typo D.L.R.)

1950 (8 Dec)–53. Values in cents. Wmk Mult Script CA. Ordinary paper. P 14.

D4	D 1	1c. green	3·75	27·00
		a. Chalk-surfaced paper. Deep green (29.11.51)	30	3·00
		ab. Error. Crown missing, W **9a**	£550	
		ac. Error. St. Edward's Crown, W **9b**	£275	
D5		2c. black	7·00	16·00
		a. Chalk-surfaced paper (20.1.53)	1·00	6·50
		ac. Error. St. Edward's Crown, W **9b**	£500	
D6		6c. carmine	16·00	17·00
		a. Chalk-surfaced paper (20.1.53)	1·00	8·50
		ab. Error. Crown missing, W **9a**	£250	
		ac. Error. St. Edward's Crown, W **9b**	£180	
D4/6 Set of 3			24·00	55·00
D4a/6a Set of 3			2·10	16·00

The 1c. has no dot below "c".

Barbuda (see after Antigua)

Basutoland

Stamps of CAPE OF GOOD HOPE were used in Basutoland from about 1876, initially cancelled by upright oval with framed number type postmarks of that colony. Cancellation numbers known to have been used in Basutoland are 133 (Quthing), 156 (Mafeteng), 210 (Mohaleshoek), 277 (Morija), 281 (Maseru), 317 (Thlotse Heights) and 688 (Teyateyaneng).

From 1910 until 1933 the stamps of SOUTH AFRICA were in use. Stamps of the Union provinces are also known used in Basutoland during the early years of this period and can also be found cancelled-to-order during 1932–33.

The following post offices and postal agencies existed in Basutoland before December 1933. Stamps of Cape of Good Hope or South Africa with recognisable postmarks from them are worth a premium. For a few of the smaller offices or agencies there are, as yet, no actual examples recorded. Dates given are those generally accepted as the year in which the office was first opened.

Bokong (1931)	Motsekuoa (1915)
Butha Buthe (1907)	Mount Morosi (1918)
Jonathan's (1927)	Mphotos (1914)
Khabos (1927)	Peka (1908)
Khetisas (1930)	Phamong (1932)
Khukhune (1933)	Pitseng (1921)
Kolonyama (1914)	Qachasnek (1895)
Kueneng (1914)	Qalo (1923?)
Leribe (1890)	Quthing (1882)
Mafeteng (1874)	Rankakalas (1933)
Majara (1912)	Roma Mission (1913)
Makhoa (1932)	Sebapala (1930)
Makoalis (1927)	Seforong (1924)
Mamathes (1919)	Sehlabathebe (1921)
Mapoteng (1925)	Sekake (1931)
Marakabeis (1932)	Teyateyaneng (1886)
Maseru (1872)	Thaba Bosigo (1913)
Maseru Rail (1915?)	Thabana Morena (1922)
Mashai (1929)	Thabaneng (1914)
Matsaile (1930)	Thaba Tseka (1929)
Mekading (1914)	Thlotse Heights (1872)
Mofokas (1915)	Tsepo (1923)
Mohaleshoek (1873)	Tsoelike (1927)
Mokhotlong (1921)	Tsoloane (1918)
Morija (1884)	

For further details of the postal history of Basutoland see The Cancellations and Postal Markings of Basutoland/Lesotho by A. H. Scott, published by Collectors Mail Auctions (Pty) Ltd, Cape Town, from which the above has been, with permission, extracted.

PRICES FOR STAMPS ON COVER TO 1945	
Nos. 1/19	from × 5
Nos. 11/14	from × 6
Nos. 15/17	from × 10
Nos. 18/28	from × 6
Nos. 29/31	from × 10
Nos. O1/4	from × 4
Nos. D1/2	from × 25

CROWN COLONY

1 King George V, Nile Crocodile and Mountains

(Recess Waterlow)

1933 (1 Dec). Wmk Mult Script CA. P 12½.

1	1	½d. emerald	1·00	1·75
2		1d. scarlet	75	1·25
3		2d. bright purple	1·00	80
4		3d. bright blue	75	1·25
5		4d. grey	2·00	7·00
6		6d. orange-yellow	2·25	1·75
7		1s. red-orange	2·25	4·50
8		2s.6d. sepia	22·00	45·00
9		5s. violet	50·00	70·00
10		10s. olive-green	£130	£140
1/10 Set of 10			£190	£250
1s/10s Perf "Specimen" Set of 10			£300	

1935 (4 May). Silver Jubilee. As Nos. 91/4 of Antigua. P 13½×14.

11		1d. deep blue and carmine	55	1·75
		f. Diagonal line by turret	90·00	£120
12		2d. ultramarine and grey	65	1·75
		f. Diagonal line by turret	80·00	£130
13		3d. brown and deep blue	3·75	4·75
		g. Dot to left of chapel	£130	
		h. Dot by flagstaff	£170	
		i. Dash by turret	£190	
14		6d. slate and purple	3·75	4·75
		g. Dot to left of chapel	£225	
		h. Dot by flagstaff	£225	£275
		i. Dash by turret	£225	
11/14 Set of 4			8·00	11·50
11s/14s Perf "Specimen" Set of 4			£100	

For illustrations of plate varieties see Omnibus section following Zanzibar.

1937 (12 May). Coronation. As Nos. 95/7 of Antigua, but printed by D.L.R. P 14.

15		1d. scarlet	35	1·00
16		2d. bright purple	50	1·00
17		3d. bright blue	60	1·00
15/17 Set of 3			1·25	2·75
15s/17s Perf "Specimen" Set of 3			75·00	

2 King George VI, Nile Crocodile and Mountains

Tower flaw (R. 2/4)

(Recess Waterlow)

1938 (1 Apr). Wmk Mult Script CA. P 12½.

18	2	½d. green	30	1·25
19		1d. scarlet	50	70
		a. Tower flaw	£130	
20		1½d. light blue	40	50
21		2d. bright purple	30	60
22		3d. bright blue	30	1·25
23		4d. grey	1·50	3·50
24		6d. orange-yellow	80	1·50
25		1s. red-orange	1·00	1·00
26		2s.6d. sepia	10·00	8·50
27		5s. violet	27·00	9·50
28		10s. olive-green	27·00	17·00
18/28 Set of 11			60·00	40·00
18s/28s Perf "Specimen" Set of 11			£250	

Basutoland
(3)

1945 (3 Dec). Victory. Stamps of South Africa, optd with T **3**, inscr alternately in English and Afrikaans.

			Un. pair	Used pair	Used single
29	55	1d. brown and carmine	40	60	10
30	56	2d. slate-blue and violet	40	50	10
31	57	3d. deep blue and blue	40	70	15
29/31 Set of 3			1·10	1·75	30

4 King George VI

5 King George VI and Queen Elizabeth

6 Queen Elizabeth II as Princess, and Princess Margaret   **7** The Royal Family

(Recess Waterlow)

1947 (17 Feb). *Royal Visit.* Wmk Mult Script CA. P 12½.

32	4	1d. scarlet	10	10
33	5	2d. green	10	10
34	6	3d. ultramarine	10	10
35	7	1s. mauve	15	10
32/5 Set of 4			40	30
32s/5s Perf "Specimen" Set of 4			90·00	

1948 (1 Dec). *Royal Silver Wedding. As Nos. 112/13 of Antigua.*

36	1½d. ultramarine	20	10
37	10s. grey-olive	32·00	32·00

1949 (10 Oct). *75th Anniv of Universal Postal Union. As Nos. 114/17 of Antigua.*

38	1½d. blue	20	1·50
39	3d. deep blue	1·75	2·00
40	6d. orange	1·00	3·00
41	1s. red-brown	50	1·25
38/41 Set of 4		3·00	7·00

OFFICIAL STAMPS

OFFICIAL

(O 1)

1934 (Feb). *Nos. 1/3 and 6 optd with Type O 1 by Govt printer, Pretoria.*

O1	1	½d. emerald	£9000	£5500
O2		1d. scarlet	£2250	£2000
O3		2d. bright purple	£2500	£750
O4		6d. orange-yellow	£11000	£4750
O1/4 Set of 4			£23000	£12000

Collectors are advised to buy these stamps only from reliable sources. They were not sold to the public.

300 of each value were supplied in January 1934 for use by the Secretariat at Maseru. Limited usage is recorded between 28 Feb 1934 and 8 June 1934. The issue was then withdrawn and the remainders destroyed. Only the following numbers appear to have been issued: ½d. 24, 1d. 34, 2d. 54, 6d. 27, from which a maximum of ten mint sets exist.

POSTAGE DUE STAMPS

D 1

 Normal

 Large "d." (R. 9/6, 10/6)

(Typo D.L.R.)

1933 (1 Dec)–52. *Ordinary paper.* Wmk Mult Script CA. P 14.

D1	D 1	1d. carmine	1·75	8·50
		a. Scarlet (1938)	35·00	42·00
		b. Chalk-surfaced paper. *Deep carmine* (24.10.51)	1·50	2·50
		ba. Error. Crown missing, W 9a	£180	
		bb. Error. St. Edward's Crown, W 9b	85·00	
D2		2d. violet	7·50	17·00
		a. Chalk-surfaced paper (6.11.52)	30	14·00
		ab. Error. Crown missing, W 9a	£200	
		ac. Error. St. Edward's Crown, W 9b	90·00	
		ad. Large "d"	6·00	
D1s/2s Perf "Specimen" Set of 2			42·00	

Batum

Batum, the outlet port on the Black Sea for the Russian Transcaucasian oilfields, was occupied by the Turks on 15 April 1918.

Under the terms of the armistice signed at Mudros on 30 October 1918 the Turks were to withdraw and be replaced by an Allied occupation of Batum, the Baku oilfields and the connecting Transcaucasia Railway. British forces arrived off Batum in early December and the oblast, or district, was declared a British military governorship on 25 December 1918. The Turkish withdrawal was complete five days later.

The provision of a civilian postal service was initially the responsibility of the Batum Town Council. Some form of mail service was in operation by February 1919 with the postage prepaid in cash. Letters are known showing a framed oblong handstamp, in Russian, to this effect. The Town Council was responsible for the production of the first issue, Nos. 1/6,

but shortly after these stamps were placed on sale a strike by Council employees against the British military governor led to the postal service being placed under British Army control.

SURCHARGES. Types **2** and **4/8** were all applied by handstamp. Most values from No. 19 to 40 are known showing the surcharge inverted, surcharge double or in pairs with surcharge *tête-bêche*. Inverted surcharges are worth from 2×normal, *tête-bêche* pairs from four times the price of a single stamp.

BRITISH OCCUPATION

(Currency. 100 kopeks = 1 rouble)

PRICES FOR STAMPS ON COVER	
Nos. 1/6	*from* × 60
Nos. 7/10	*from* × 15
Nos. 11/28	*from* × 60
Nos. 19/20	*from* × 15
Nos. 21/44	—
Nos. 45/53	*from* × 200

1 Aloe Tree   **(2)**

1919 (4 Apr). Litho. *Imperf.*

1	1	5k. green	6·50	13·00
2		10k. ultramarine	6·50	13·00
3		50k. yellow	3·00	4·50
4		1r. chocolate	4·75	4·75
5		3r. violet	9·50	15·00
6		5r. brown	10·00	25·00
1/6 Set of 6			35·00	65·00

Nos. 1/6 were printed in sheets of 198 (18×11).

1919 (13 Apr). *Russian stamps (Arms types) handstamped with T* **2**.

7	10r. on 1k. orange (imperf)	50·00	60·00
8	10r. on 3k. carmine-red (imperf)	22·00	27·00
9	10r. on 5k. brown-lilac (perf)	£375	£400
10	10r. on 10 on 7k. deep blue (perf)	£375	£400

A similar handstamped surcharge, showing the capital letters without serifs, is bogus.

BRITISH OCCUPATION

(3)

1919 (10 Nov). *Colours changed and new values. Optd with T* **3**.

11	1	5k. yellow-green	16·00	13·00
12		10k. bright blue	14·00	13·00
13		25k. orange-yellow	16·00	13·00
14		1r. pale blue	4·50	13·00
15		2r. pink	1·00	4·50
16		3r. bright violet	1·00	4·50
17		5r. brown	1·25	4·50
		a. "CCUPATION" (R. 5/1)	£400	
18		7r. brownish red	4·25	7·50
11/18 Set of 8			50·00	65·00

Nos. 11/18 were printed in sheets of 432 (18×24).

(4)   **(5)**

1919 (27 Nov)–20. *Russian stamps (Arms types) handstamped with T* **4** *or* **5**. *Imperf.*

19	10r. on 3k. carmine-red	18·00	22·00
20	15r. on 1k. orange	60·00	65·00
	a. Red surch	45·00	50·00
	b. Violet surch (10.3.20)	60·00	75·00

Nos. 20a/b have the handstamp in soluble ink.

1920 (12 Jan). *Russian stamps (Arms types) handstamped as T* **4**.

(a) Imperf.

21	50r. on 1k. orange	£425	£450
22	50r. on 2k. yellow-green (R.)	£550	£700

(b) Perf.

23	50r. on 2k. yellow-green	£550	£600
24	50r. on 3k. carmine-red	£1100	£1200
25	50r. on 4k. red	£750	£800
26	50r. on 5k. brown-lilac	£425	£500
27	50r. on 10k. deep blue (R.)	£1600	£1700
28	50r. on 15k. blue and red-brown	£550	£650

(6)

1920 (30 Jan–21 Feb). *Russian stamps (Arms types) handstamped as T* **6**.

(a) Perf.

29	25r. on 5k. brown-lilac (21 Feb)	42·00	48·00
	a. Blue surch	42·00	48·00

30	25r. on 10 on 7k. blue (21 Feb)	£120	£140
	a. Blue surch	70·00	75·00
31	25r. on 20 on 14k. dp carmine & bl (21 Feb)	75·00	85·00
	a. Blue surch	75·00	85·00
32	25r. on 25k. deep violet & lt green (21 Feb)	£130	£140
	a. Blue surch	95·00	£110
33	25r. on 50k. green and copper-red (21 Feb)	80·00	85·00
	a. Blue surch	75·00	85·00
34	50r. on 2k. yellow-green	£100	£120
35	50r. on 3k. carmine-red	£100	£120
36	50r. on 4k. red	90·00	£100
37	50r. on 5k. brown-lilac	70·00	80·00

(b) Imperf.

38	50r. on 2k. yellow-green	£350	£425
39	50r. on 3k. carmine-red	£425	£500
40	50r. on 5k. brown-lilac	£1200	£1300

1920 (10 Mar). *Romanov issue, as T* **25** *of Russia, handstamped with T* **6**.

41	50r. on 4k. rose-carmine (B.)	60·00	80·00

(7)   **(8)**

1920 (1 Apr). *Nos. 3, 11 and 13 handstamped with T* **7** *(Nos. 42/3) or* **8** *(No. 44).*

42	25r. on 5k. yellow-green	32·00	35·00
	a. Blue surch	48·00	48·00
43	25r. on 25k. orange-yellow	25·00	26·00
	a. Blue surch	£110	£110
44	50r. on 50k. yellow-green	20·00	24·00
	a. "50" cut	16·00	17·00
	b. Blue surch	95·00	95·00
	ba. "50"cut	£180	£180

Nos. 44a and 44ba show the figures broken by intentional file cuts applied as a protection against forgery. The "5" is cut at the base and on the right side of the loop. The "0" is chipped at top and foot, and has both vertical lines severed.

1920 (19 June). *Colours changed and new values. Optd with T* **3**. *Imperf.*

45	1	1r. chestnut	1·50	9·00
		a. "BPITISH"	65·00	
46		2r. pale blue	1·50	9·00
		a. "BPITISH"	75·00	
47		3r. pink	1·50	9·00
		a. "BPITISH"	75·00	
48		5r. black-brown	1·50	9·00
		a. "BPITISH"	75·00	
49		7r. yellow	1·50	9·00
		a. "BPITISH"	75·00	
50		10r. myrtle-green	1·50	9·00
		a. "BPITISH"	75·00	
51		15r. violet	2·00	12·00
		a. "BPITISH"	£160	
52		25r. scarlet	1·60	11·00
		a. "BPITISH"	£140	
53		50r. deep blue	2·00	14·00
		a. "BPITISH"	£250	
45/53 Set of 9			13·00	80·00

Nos. 45/53 were printed in sheets of 308 (22×14). The "BPITISH" error occurs on R. 1/19 of the overprint.

POSTCARD STAMPS

When Nos. 7/10 were issued on 13 April 1919 a similar 35k. surcharge was applied to stocks of various Russian postcards held by the post office. The majority of these had stamp impressions printed directly on to the card, but there were also a few cards, originally intended for overseas mail, on which Russia 4k. stamps had been affixed.

PRICES. Those in the left-hand column are for unused examples on complete postcard; those on the right for used examples off card. Examples used on postcard are worth more.

1919 (13 Apr). *Russian stamps handstamped as T* **2**.

P1	35k. on 4k. red (Arms type)	£4500	£5000
P2	35k. on 4k. carmine-red (Romanov issue)	£10000	£10000

Batum was handed over to the National Republic of Georgia on 7 July 1920.

Bechuanaland

Before the 1880s the only Europeans in the area which became Bechuanaland were scattered hunters and traders, together with the missionaries who were established at Kuruman as early as 1816.

Tribal conflicts in the early years of the decade led to the intervention of Boers from the Transvaal who established the independent republics of Goshen and Stellaland.

STELLALAND

The Boer republic of Stellaland was proclaimed towards the end of 1882. A postal service was organised from the capital, Vryburg, and stamps were ordered from a firm in Cape Town. These were only valid within the republic. Until June 1885 mail to other parts of South Africa was sent through Christiana, in the Transvaal, and was franked with both Stellaland and Transvaal stamps.

No date stamps or obliterators were used by the Stellaland Post Office. Stamps were pen-cancelled with the initials of a postal official and the date.

PRICES FOR STAMPS ON COVER

The issues of Stellaland are very rare on cover.

1 Arms of the Republic

(Litho by Van der Sandt, de Villiers & Co., Cape Town)

1884 (29 Feb). P 12.

1	**1**	1d. red		£180	£325
		a. Imperf between (horiz pair)......		£3750	
		b. Imperf between (vert pair)........		£4000	
2		3d. orange		22·00	£325
		a. Imperf between (horiz pair)......		£750	
		b. Imperf between (vert pair)........		£1600	
		c. Imperf vert (horiz pair)............		£1000	
3		4d. olive-grey		21·00	£350
		a. Imperf between (horiz pair)......		£650	
		b. Imperf between (vert pair)........		£1700	
4		6d. lilac-mauve		22·00	£350
		a. Imperf between (horiz pair)......		£1200	
		b. Imperf between (vert pair)........		£1400	
5		1s. green		55·00	£650

In 1884 the British Government, following appeals from local chiefs for protection, decided to annex both Goshen and Stellaland. A force under Sir Charles Warren from the Cape reached Vryburg on 7 February 1885 and continued to Mafeking, the principal town of Goshen.

On 30 September 1885 Stellaland and other territory to the south of the Molopo River was constituted the Crown Colony of British Bechuanaland. A protectorate was also proclaimed over a vast tract of land to the north of the Molopo.

Stellaland stamps continued to be used until 2 December 1885 with external mail, franked with Stellaland and Cape of Good Hope stamps, postmarked at Barkly West and Kimberley in Griqualand West.

1885 (Oct). *Handstamped* **"Cott"** *sideways in violet-lake.*

6	**1**	2d. on 4d. olive-grey		£3500

On 2 December 1885 Cape of Good Hope stamps overprinted "British Bechuanaland" were placed on sale at the Vryburg post office.

BRITISH BECHUANALAND

CROWN COLONY

PRICES FOR STAMPS ON COVER

Nos. 1/8	*from × 12*
No. 9	*from × 80*
Nos. 10/21	*from × 8*
Nos. 22/8	*from × 10*
No. 29	*from × 10*
No. 30	*from × 10*
Nos. 31/2	*from × 12*
Nos. 33/7	*from × 20*
Nos. 38/9	*from × 25*

BRITISH

British

Bechuanaland   **BECHUANALAND**

(1)   **(2)**

1885 (2 Dec)–**87**. *Stamps of Cape of Good Hope ("Hope" seated) optd with T **1**, by W. A. Richards & Sons, Cape Town.*

(a) Wmk Crown CC (No. 3) or Crown CA (others).

1	½d. grey-black (No. 40a) (R.)		16·00	24·00
	a. Opt in lake		£3500	£4000
	b. Opt double (Lake+Black).................		£700	
2	3d. pale claret (No. 43)......................		35·00	48·00
	a. No dot to 1st "i" of "British"...........		£375	
3	4d. dull blue (No. 30) (12.86?)...........		60·00	70·00

*(b) Wmk Anchor (Cape of Good Hope. Type **13**).*

4	½d. grey-black (No. 48a) (3.87)..........		7·50	14·00
	a. Error. "ritish".................................		£2250	
	b. Opt double		£3250	
5	1d. rose-red (No. 49).........................		12·00	9·00
	a. Error. "ritish".................................		£3500	£2250
	b. No dot to 1st "i" of "British"		£160	£160
	c. Opt double		†	
6	2d. pale bistre (No. 50)......................		35·00	8·00
	a. Error. "ritish".................................		£6000	£3750
	b. No dot to 1st "i" of "British"		£375	£160
	c. Opt double		†	£1800
7	6d. reddish purple (No. 52).................		£110	38·00
	a. No dot to 1st "i" of "British"...........		£1100	£500
8	1s. green (No. 53) (11.86?).................		£275	£160
	a. Error. "ritish".................................		£17000	£12000

Nos. 1/8 were overprinted from settings of 120. The missing "B" errors are believed to have occurred on one position for one of these settings only. The 'No dot to 1st "i"' variety occurs on R. 10/3 of the left pane.

Overprints with stop after "Bechuanaland" are forged.

1887 (1 Nov). *No. 197 of Great Britain optd with T **2**, by D.L.R.*

9	½d. vermilion....................................		1·25	1·25
	a. Opt double		£2250	
	s. Handstamped "Specimen"		85·00	

---

3   **4**   **5**

(Typo D.L.R.)

1887 (1 Nov).

*(a) Wmk Orb (Great Britain Type **48**). P 14.*

10	**3**	1d. lilac and black...........................	15·00	1·75
11		2d. lilac and black...........................	75·00	1·75
		a. Pale dull lilac and black	60·00	23·00
12		3d. lilac and black...........................	3·75	5·50
		a. Pale reddish lilac and black	65·00	20·00
13		4d. lilac and black...........................	50·00	2·25
14		6d. lilac and black...........................	60·00	2·50

(b) Wmk Script "V R" (sideways, reading up). P 13½.

15	**4**	1s. green and black..........................	29·00	6·00
16		2s. green and black..........................	50·00	38·00
17		2s.6d. green and black......................	60·00	60·00
18		5s. green and black..........................	90·00	£150
19		10s. green and black........................	£180	£350

(c) Two Orbs (sideways). P 14×13½.

20	**5**	£1 lilac and black............................	£800	£750
21		£5 lilac and black............................	£3000	£1500
10s/21s H/S "Specimen" *Set of 12*			£900	

Nos. 10/21 were produced by overprinting a series of "Unappropriated Die" designs originally produced by the Board of Inland Revenue for use as Great Britain fiscal stamps.

Several values are known on blued paper. No. 11a is the first printing of the 2d. (on safety paper?) and has a faded appearance.

When purchasing Nos. 20/21 in used condition beware of copies with fiscal cancellations cleaned off and bearing forged postmarks.

For No. 15 surcharged "£5" see No. F2.

1d.   **1s.**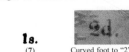

(6)   **(7)**   Curved foot to "2"

1888 (7 Aug). *Nos. 10/11 and 13/15 surch as T **6** or **7**, by P. Townshend & Co., Vryburg.*

22	**3**	1d. on 1d. lilac and black..................	7·50	6·50
23		2d. on 1d. lilac and black (R.)	25·00	3·00
		a. Pale dull lilac and black (No. 11a)........	90·00	48·00
		b. Curved foot to "2"......................	£250	£150
		c. Surch in green............................	†	£3500
25		4d. on 4d. lilac and black (R.)	£300	£400
26		6d. on 6d. lilac and black..................	£110	10·00
		a. Surch in blue..............................	†	£12000
28	**4**	1s. on 1s. green and black.................	£170	80·00

Nos. 23c and 26a are from two sheets of surcharge trials subsequently put into stock and used at Vryburg (2d.) or Mafeking (6d.) during 1888–89.

It should be noted that, in addition to its curved foot, the "2" on No. 23b is distinctly shorter than the "d".

One Half-Penny

(8)

1888 (Dec). *No. 12a surch with T **8**, by P. Townshend & Co, Vryburg.*

29	**3**	½d. on 3d. pale reddish lilac and black....................................	£160	£180
		a. Broken "f" in "Half"....................	£6500	

No. 29 was produced from a setting of 60 (12×5).

No. 29a shows the letter "f" almost completely missing and occurs on R. 5/11 of the setting. Five examples are known, one being in the Royal Collection.

Errors of spelling on this surcharge are bogus.

British

Bechuanaland.

(9)

British
Bechuanaland.

(10)

BRITISH
BECHUANALAND

(11)

1889 (Jan). *No. 48a of Cape of Good Hope (wmk Anchor) optd with T **9**, by P. Townshend & Co, Vryburg.*

30	½d. grey-black (G.).............................		3·25	26·00
	a. Opt "Bechuanaland British"			
	ab. "British" omitted			
	b. Opt double, one inverted			
	ba. Opt double, one inverted, inverted opt "Bechuanaland British"		£1600	
	bb. Opt double, one inverted, inverted "British" omitted		£3000	
	c. Opt double, one vertical		£750	
	ca. Se-tenant with stamp without opt......		£5000	

No. 30 was produced using a setting of 30 (6×5).

The overprint was misplaced upwards on at least one pane, giving the overprint "Bechuanaland British" (No. 30a) on rows 1 to 4 and "British" omitted on row 5 (No. 30ab). "British" was also omitted on R. 5/1 of the setting on some sheets only.

On one pane on which the overprint was applied double, one inverted, the inverted overprint was misplaced downwards, giving No. 30ba on rows 7 to 10 and "British" omitted (No. 30bb) on row 6.

n   **n**

Normal "n"   Inverted "u"

1891 (Nov). *Nos. 49/50 of Cape of Good Hope (wmk Anchor), optd with T **10**, reading upwards.*

31	1d. rose-red		10·00	9·00
	a. Horiz pair, one without opt			
	b. "British" omitted.............................		—	£2000
	c. "Bechuanaland" omitted.................		£2000	
	d. Inverted "u" for 2nd "n".................		£150	£150
32	2d. pale bistre		3·25	2·25
	a. No stop after "Bechuanaland"		£275	£325
	b. Inverted "u" for 2nd "n".................			
31s/2s H/S "Specimen" *Set of 2*			£130	

The overprint on Nos. 31 and 32 was of 120 impressions in two panes of 60 (6×10). That on No. 32 was applied both by a stereo plate and by a forme made up from loose type. No. 31 was overprinted only with the latter. No. 32a is from the stereo overprinting (left pane, R. 3/3), 31d and 32b are from the typeset overprinting (left pane, R. 10/4).

See also Nos. 38 and 39.

1891 (1 Dec)–**1904**. *Nos. 172, 200, 205, 208 and 211 of Great Britain optd with T **11**, by D.L.R.*

33	1d. lilac		6·00	1·50
34	2d. grey-green and carmine................		12·00	4·00
35	4d. green and purple-brown................		2·50	60
	a. Bisected (2d.) (on cover) (11.99)...		†	£2250
36	6d. purple/*rose-red*		3·50	2·00
37	1s. dull green (7.94)		13·00	16·00
	a. Bisected (6d.) (on cover) (12.04).....		†	
33/7 *Set of 5*			32·00	22·00
33s/6s H/S "Specimen" *Set of 4*			£170	

No. 35a was used at Palapye Station and No. 37a at Kanye, both in the Protectorate.

1893 (Dec)–**95**. *As Nos. 31/2, but T **10** reads downwards.*

38	1d. rose-red		2·25	2·25
	a. Pair, one without opt			
	b. "British" omitted.............................		£2750	
	c. Optd "Bechuanaland. British".........		£1300	£1400
	d. Inverted "u" for 2nd "n".................		£120	£130
	e. No dots to "i" of "British"..............		£120	£130
	f. "s" omitted		£250	£250
	g. Opt reading up, no dots to "i" of "British"..		£2500	
39	2d. pale bistre (12.3.95).....................		4·75	2·25
	a. Opt double		£1300	£650
	b. "British" omitted.............................		£650	£500
	c. "Bechuanaland" omitted.................		—	£500
	d. Optd "Bechuanaland. British".........		£400	£225
	e. Inverted "u" for 2nd "n".................		£160	£130
	f. No dots to "i" of "British"..............		£160	£130
	g. Opt reading up, no dots to "i" of "British"..			

The same typeset overprint was used for Nos. 38 and 39 as had been employed for Nos. 31 and 32 but applied the other way up; the inverted "u" thus falling on the right pane, R. 1/3. The no dots to "i" variety only occurs on this printing (right pane, R. 1/4). Some sheets of both values were overprinted the wrong way up, resulting in Nos. 38f. and 39g.

No. 38f. developed gradually on right pane R. 10/8. The variety is not known on Nos. 31, 32 or 39.

On 16 November 1895 British Bechuanaland was annexed to the Cape of Good Hope and ceased to have its own stamps, but they remained in use in the Protectorate until superseded in 1897. The Postmaster-General of Cape Colony had assumed control of the Bechuanaland postal service on 1 April 1893 and the Cape, and subsequently the South African, postal authorities continued to be responsible for the postal affairs of the Bechuanaland Protectorate until 1963.

BECHUANALAND PROTECTORATE

PRICES FOR STAMPS ON COVER TO 1945

Nos. 40/51	*from × 10*
Nos. 52/71	*from × 6*
Nos. 72/82	*from × 5*
Nos. 83/98	*from × 4*
Nos. 99/110	*from × 6*
Nos. 111/17	*from × 10*
Nos. 118/28	*from × 4*
Nos. 129/31	*from × 10*
Nos. D1/3	*from × 50*
Nos. D4/6	*from × 60*
No. F1	*from × 5*
No. F2	—
No. F3	*from × 5*

This large area north of the Molopo River was proclaimed a British Protectorate on 30 September 1885 at the request of the native chiefs.

A postal service using runners was inaugurated on 9 August 1888 and Nos. 40 to 55 were issued as a temporary measure with the object of assessing the cost of this service

Protectorate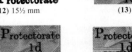

(12) 15½ mm   **(13)**

Protectorate
1d   **Protectorate**
                         1d

Small figure "1"   Small figure "1"
(R. 7/2)   **(R. 10/2)**

1888 (7 Aug). *No. 9 optd with T* **12** *and Nos. 10/19 surch or optd only as T* **13** *by P. Townshend & Co. Vryburg.*

40	–	½d. vermilion	4·75	30·00
		a. "Protectorate" double	£325	
		s. Handstamped "Specimen"	85·00	
41	3	1d. on 1d. lilac and black	8·00	14·00
		a. Small figure "1" (R. 7/2, 10/2)..	£425	£475
		b. Space between "1" and "d" (R. 10/9)	£550	
42		2d. on 2d. lilac and black	27·00	17·00
		b. Curved foot to "2"	£700	£475
43		3d. on 3d. pale reddish lilac and black	£130	£180
44		4d. on 4d. lilac and black	£350	£375
		a. Small figure "4"	£3750	£3750
45		6d. on 6d. lilac and black	70·00	42·00
46	4	1s. green and black	90·00	50·00
		a. First "o" omitted	£5000	£3000
		s. Handstamped "Specimen"	£110	
47		2s. green and black	£600	£900
		a. First "o" omitted	£15000	
48		2s.6d. green and black	£550	£800
		a. First "o" omitted	£12000	
49		5s. green and black	£1200	£2000
		a. First "o" omitted	£18000	
50		10s. green and black	£4000	£5500
		a. First "o" omitted	£25000	

Nos. 40/5 were produced from a basic setting of 120 (12×10) on which a faulty first "o" in "Protectorate" occurred on R. 5/12. For Nos. 46/50 the setting was reduced to 84 (12×7) and on many sheets the first "o" on R. 5/12 failed to print.

There are a number of slightly smaller than normal "1"s in the setting, but they all show the normal upper serif of the "1" which is pointed and slopes sharply downwards at the left. R. 7/2 and 10/2 are quite distinct and are as shown although the base of the "1" on R. 7/2 is not always aligned with the base of the "d".

The normal space between "1" and "d" measures 1 mm. On No. 41b it is 1.7 mm.

It should be noted that, like No. 23b, the "2" on No. 42b is distinctly shorter than the "d".

See also Nos. 54/5.

1888 (Dec). *No. 25 optd with T* **12** *by P. Townshend & Co., Vryburg.*

51	3	4d. on 4d. lilac and black	80·00	40·00

Bechuanaland

Protectorate

(14)

Protectorate. **Fourpence**

(14)　(15)

1889 (Jan). *No. 48a of Cape of Good Hope (wmk Anchor), optd with T* **14** *by P. Townshend & Co., Vryburg.*

52		½d. grey-black (G.)	2·75	45·00
		a. Opt double	£450	£650
		ab. Ditto, one reading "Protectorate Bechuanaland"	£1100	
		b. "Bechuanaland" omitted	£1600	
		c. Optd "Protectorate Bechuanaland"	£750	£850

1889 (1 Aug). *No. 9 surch with T* **15** *by P. Townshend & Co., Vryburg.*

53		4d. on ½d. vermilion	25·00	3·75
		a. "rpence" omitted (R. 9/2)	†	£6000
		b. "ourpence" omitted (R. 9/2)	£10000	
		c. Surch (T 15) inverted	†	£4000
		cb. Ditto. "ourpence" omitted	†	£14000
		s. Handstamped "Specimen"	£130	

The lines of the surcharge are normally 6 mm apart, but 5 mm and 4.5 mm spacings are known.
Examples of No. 53c are postmarked "679" (Tati).

Protectorate **Protectorate**

(16) 15 mm　(17)

1890. *No. 9 optd.*

54	16	½d. vermilion	£160	£170
		a. Type 16 inverted	75·00	95·00
		b. Type 16 double	£110	£160
		c. Type 16 double and inverted	£600	£600
		d. Optd "Portectorate" inverted	£16000	
		w. Wmk inverted		
55	17	½d. vermilion	£180	£325
		a. Type 17 double	£1500	
		b. Optd "Protectorrte"		
		c. Optd "Protectorrte" double	£16000	

These were trial printings made in 1888 which were subsequently issued.

In June 1890 the Bechuanaland Protectorate and the Colony of British Bechuanaland came under one postal administration and the stamps of British Bechuanaland were used in the Protectorate until 1897.

BRITISH

BECHUANALAND **BECHUANALAND PROTECTORATE**

(18)　(19)

1897. *No. 61 of Cape of Good Hope (wmk Anchor), optd as T* **18**.

(a) Lines 13 mm apart, bottom line 16 mm long, by Taylor & Marshall, Cape Town.

56		½d. yellow-green (July?)	2·50	12·00

(b) Lines 13½ mm apart, bottom line 15 mm long, by P. Townshend & Co., Vryburg.

57		½d. yellow-green (April)	21·00	75·00
		a. Opt double, one albino inverted	£225	

(c) Lines 10½ mm apart, bottom line 15 mm long, by W. A. Richards & Sons, Cape Govt Printers.

58		½d. yellow-green (July?)	9·00	48·00

Although issued only in the Protectorate, the above were presumably overprinted "BRITISH BECHUANALAND" because stamps bearing this inscription were in use there at the time.

1897 (Oct)–**1902**. *Nos. 172, 197, 200, 202, 205 and 208 of Great Britain (Queen Victoria) optd with T* **19** *by D.L.R.*

59		½d. vermilion	1·00	2·25
60		½d. blue-green (25.2.02)	1·40	3·50
61		1d. lilac	4·00	75
62		2d. grey-green and carmine	4·00	3·50
63		3d. purple/*yellow* (12.97)	5·50	8·50
64		4d. green and purple-brown	15·00	14·00
65		6d. purple/*rose-red*	23·00	11·00
		59/65 Set of 7	48·00	40·00
		59s/65s Optd or H/S (No. 60s) "Specimen" Set of 7	£225	

BECHUANALAND PROTECTORATE

(20)

BECHUANALAND PROTECTORATE

(21)

1904 (29 Nov)–**13**. *Nos. 216, 218/19, 230 and 313/14 (Somerset House ptgs) of Great Britain (King Edward VII) optd with T* **20**, *by D.L.R.*

66		½d. blue-green (3.06)	2·00	2·00
67		½d. yellowish green (11.08)	3·75	3·50
68		1d. scarlet (4.05)	7·50	30
		s. Optd "Specimen"	60·00	
69		2½d. ultramarine	7·50	5·00
		a. Stop after "P" in "PROTECTORATE"	£950	£1200
70		1s. deep green and scarlet (10.12)	40·00	£140
		a. Opt double, one albino	£200	
71		1s. green and carmine (1913)	42·00	£120
		s. Optd "Specimen"	95·00	

No. 69a occurs on R. 5/9 of the lower pane.

1912 (Sept)–**14**. *No. 342 of Great Britain (King George V, wmk Crown) optd with T* **20**.

72		1d. scarlet	2·00	60
		a. No cross on crown	£150	75·00
		b. *Aniline scarlet* (No. 343) (1914)	£140	80·00

1913 (1 July)–**24**. *Stamps of Great Britain (King George V) optd.*

(a) Nos. 351, 357, 362, 367, 370/1, 376, 379, 385 and 395 (wmk Simple Cypher, T **100**) *optd with T* **20**.

73		½d. green (*shades*)	1·25	1·75
74		1d. scarlet (*shades*) (4.15)	2·75	75
		a. *Carmine-red* (1922)	27·00	2·50
75		1½d. red-brown (12.20)	4·00	3·00
76		2d. reddish orange (Die I)	5·00	3·75
		a. *Orange* (Die I) (1921)	17·00	4·00
		aw. Wmk inverted		
77		2d. orange (Die II) (1924)	35·00	3·50
78		2½d. cobalt-blue	3·50	22·00
		a. *Blue* (1915)	11·00	23·00
79		3d. bluish violet	6·00	12·00
80		4d. grey-green	6·50	23·00
81		6d. reddish purple (*shades*)	7·00	17·00
		a. Opt double, one albino		
82		1s. bistre	10·00	22·00
		a. *Bistre-brown* (1923)	27·00	32·00
		s. Optd "Specimen"	75·00	
		73/82 Set of 9	42·00	95·00

(b) With T **21**.

(i) Waterlow printings (Nos. 399 and 401) (1914–15).

83		2s.6d. deep sepia-brown (1.15)	£130	£250
		a. Re-entry (R. 2/1)	£1100	£1600
		b. Opt double, one albino	£300	
84		5s. rose-carmine (1914)	£160	£375
		a. Opt double, one albino	£375	
		83s/4s Optd "Specimen" Set of 2	£275	

(ii) D.L.R. printings (Nos. 407/8 and 409) (1916–19).

85		2s.6d. pale brown (7.16)	£110	£250
		a. Re-entry (R. 2/1)	£1100	£1600
86		2s.6d. sepia (1917)	£130	£225
		a. Opt treble, two albino	£1200	
		b. Re-entry (R. 2/1)		
87		5s. bright carmine (8.19)	£300	£425
		a. Opt double, one albino	£450	

(iii) B.W. printings (Nos. 414 and 416) (1920–23).

88		2s.6d. chocolate-brown (7.23)	85·00	£160
		a. Major re-entry (R. 1/2)	£2000	
		b. Opt double, one albino	£550	
		c. Opt treble, two albino	£500	
89		5s. rose-red (7.20)	£110	£275
		a. Opt treble, two albino	£375	
		b. Opt double, one albino		

Examples of Nos. 83/9 are known showing a forged Lobatsi postmark dated "6 MAY 35" or "6 MAY 39".

1925 (July)–**27**. *Nos. 418/19, 421, 423/4, 426/a and 429 of Great Britain (wmk Block Cypher, T* **111**) *optd with T* **20**.

91		½d. green (1927)	1·50	1·75
92		1d. scarlet (8.25)	2·00	70
		w. Wmk inverted		
93		2d. orange (Die II)	1·75	1·00
94		3d. violet (10.26)	4·75	20·00
		a. Opt double, one albino	£200	
		w. Wmk inverted	£200	
95		4d. grey-green (10.26)	4·75	40·00
		a. Printed on the gummed side		
96		6d. reddish purple (*chalk-surfaced paper*) (12.25)	40·00	75·00
97		6d. purple (*ordinary paper*) (1926)	48·00	50·00
98		1s. bistre-brown (10.26)	9·00	24·00
		w. Wmk inverted	£325	£300
		91/8 Set of 8	£100	£190

No. 94w. also shows the variety, opt double, one albino.

22 King George V, Baobab Tree and Cattle drinking

23 King George VI, Baobab Tree and Cattle drinking

(Des from photo by Resident Commissioner, Ngamiland, Recess Waterlow)

1932 (12 Dec). *Wmk Mult Script CA. P* 12½.

99	22	½d. green	1·50	30
		a. Imperf between (horiz pair)	£18000	
100		1d. scarlet	1·00	25
101		2d. brown	1·00	30
102		3d. ultramarine	1·25	2·75
103		4d. orange	1·25	6·50
104		6d. purple	2·50	4·50
105		1s. black and olive-green	3·00	7·00
106		2s. black and orange	24·00	48·00
107		2s.6d. black and scarlet	19·00	32·00
108		3s. black and purple	35·00	45·00
109		5s. black and ultramarine	70·00	75·00
110		10s. black and brown	£140	£150
		99/110 Set of 12	£275	£325
		99s/110s Perf "Specimen" Set of 12	£275	

Examples of most values are known showing a forged Lobatsi postmark dated "6 MAY 35" or "6 MAY 39".

1935 (4 May). *Silver Jubilee. As Nos. 91/4 of Antigua but ptd by B.W. P* 11×12.

111		1d. deep blue and scarlet	30	3·75
		a. Extra flagstaff	£250	
		b. Short extra flagstaff	£375	
		c. Lightning conductor	£300	
		d. Flagstaff on right-hand turret	£325	
		e. Double flagstaff	£325	
112		2d. ultramarine and grey-black	1·00	3·75
		a. Extra flagstaff	£100	£160
		b. Short extra flagstaff	£130	
		c. Lightning conductor	£100	
113		3d. brown and deep blue	2·50	4·00
		a. Extra flagstaff	£140	
		b. Short extra flagstaff	£170	
		c. Lightning conductor	£140	
114		6d. slate and purple	4·75	4·00
		a. Extra flagstaff	£130	
		b. Short extra flagstaff	£150	
		c. Lightning conductor	£140	£150
		111/14 Set of 4	7·75	14·00
		111s/14s Perf "Specimen" Set of 4	95·00	

For illustrations of plate varieties see Omnibus section following Zanzibar.

1937 (12 May). *Coronation. As Nos. 95/7 of Antigua, but printed by D.L.R. P* 14.

115		1d. scarlet	45	40
116		2d. yellow-brown	60	1·00
117		3d. bright blue	60	1·25
		115/17 Set of 3	1·50	2·40
		115s/17s Perf "Specimen" Set of 3	75·00	

(Recess Waterlow)

1938 (1 Apr)–**52**. *Wmk Mult Script CA. P* 12½.

118	23	½d. green	2·00	2·75
		a. *Light yellowish green* (1941)	7·50	7·50
		b. *Yellowish green* (4.43)	6·50	4·00
		c. *Deep green* (4.49)	3·25	9·00
119		1d. scarlet	75	50
120		1½d. dull blue	9·00	2·00
		a. *Light blue* (4.43)	1·00	1·00
121		2d. chocolate-brown	75	50
122		3d. deep ultramarine	1·00	2·50
123		4d. orange	2·00	2·50
124		6d. reddish purple	4·75	3·00
		a. *Purple* (1944)	4·00	2·50
		ab. "A" of "CA" missing from wmk	†	—
125		1s. black and brown-olive	4·00	6·00
		a. *Grey-black & olive-green* (21.5.52)	16·00	24·00
126		2s.6d. black and scarlet	14·00	14·00
127		5s. black and deep ultramarine	30·00	19·00
		a. *Grey-black & dp ultram* (10.46)	75·00	50·00
128		10s. black and red-brown	15·00	22·00
		118/28 Set of 11	65·00	65·00
		118s/28s Perf "Specimen" Set of 11	£225	

Bechuanaland

(24)

1945 (3 Dec). *Victory. Stamps of South Africa optd with T* **24**. *Inscr alternately in English and Afrikaans.*

129	55	1d. brown and carmine	50	1·00
130	56	2d. slate-blue and violet	50	1·25
131	57	3d. deep blue and blue	50	1·25
		a. Opt omitted (in vert pair with normal)	£9000	
		129/31 Set of 3	1·40	3·25

No. 131a comes from a sheet on which the overprint was displaced downwards so that it is omitted from stamps in the top row and shown on the sheet margin at foot.

(Recess Waterlow)

1947 (17 Feb). *Royal Visit. As Nos. 32/5 of Basutoland. Wmk Mult Script CA. P* 12½.

132		1d. scarlet	10	10
133		2d. green	10	10
134		3d. ultramarine	10	10
135		1s. mauve	10	10
		132/5 Set of 4	35	30
		132s/5s Perf "Specimen" Set of 4	90·00	

1948 (1 Dec). *Royal Silver Wedding. As Nos. 112/13 of Antigua.*
136	1½d. ultramarine		30	10
137	10s. black		28·00	35·00

1949 (10 Oct). *75th Anniv of Universal Postal Union. As Nos. 114/17 of Antigua.*
138	1½d. blue		30	1·25
139	3d. deep blue		1·25	2·50
140	6d. magenta		45	2·00
141	1s. olive		45	1·50
138/41 *Set of 4*			2·25	6·50

POSTAGE DUE STAMPS

(D 1)   (D 2)

1926 (1 Jan). *Nos. D9/10 and D13 of Great Britain, optd with Types D 1 or D 2 (2d.).*
D1	½d. emerald (wmk sideways - inverted)..	6·00	85·00
D2	1d. carmine	6·00	50·00
D3	2d. agate	6·00	85·00
D1/3 *Set of 3*		16·00	£200

D 3   Normal   Large "d." (R. 9/6, 10/6)

Serif on "d" (R. 1/6)

(Typo D.L.R.)

1932 (12 Dec)–58. *Ordinary paper. Wmk Mult Script CA. P 14.*
D4	D 3	½d. sage-green	6·00	48·00
D5		1d. carmine	7·00	9·00
		a. Chalk-surfaced paper (27.11.58)	1·50	21·00
D6		2d. violet	9·00	50·00
		a. Large "d"	£110	
		b. Serif on "d"	£160	
		c. Chalk-surfaced paper (27.11.58)	1·75	20·00
		ca. Large "d"	35·00	
		cb. Serif on "d"	48·00	
D4/6b *Set of 3*			8·50	65·00
D4s/6s *Perf* "Specimen" *Set of 3*			70·00	

No. D6a first occurred on the 1947 printing.

POSTAL FISCAL STAMPS

The following stamps issued for fiscal purposes were each allowed to be used for postal purposes for a short time. No. F2 was used by the public because the word "POSTAGE" had not been obliterated and No. F3 because the overprint did not include the words "Revenue only" as did the contemporary fiscal overprints for Basutoland and Swaziland.

Bechuanaland
(F 1)   **£5** (F 2)   **Bechuanaland Protectorate.** (F 3)

1910 (July). *No. 266a of Transvaal optd with Type F 1 by Transvaal Govt Ptg Wks, Pretoria.*
F1		6d. black and brown-orange (BI-Blk)	£160	£325

No. F1 was supplied to Assistant Commissioners in January 1907 for revenue purposes. The "POSTAGE" inscription was not obliterated, however, and the stamp is known postally used for a period of a year from July 1910.

1918. *No. 15 surch with Type F 2 at top.*
F2	4	£5 on 1s. green and black (F.C.) £650)	£13000

1921. *No. 4b of South Africa optd with Type F 3, in varying positions.*
F3		1d. scarlet	42·00	£130
		a. Opt double, one albino	£160	

Bermuda

The first internal postal system for Bermuda was organised by Joseph Stockdale, the proprietor of the *Bermuda Gazette*, in January 1784. This service competed with that of the colonial post office, set up in May 1812, until 1818.
Control of the overseas postal services passed to the British G.P.O. in 1818. The internal delivery system was discontinued between 1821 and 1830. The overseas posts became a colonial responsibility in September 1859.

For illustrations of the handstamp types see BRITISH POST OFFICES ABROAD notes, following GREAT BRITAIN.

CROWNED-CIRCLE HANDSTAMPS
CC1	CC 1 ST. GEORGES BERMUDA (R.) (1.8.1845)	
		Price on cover £7000
CC2	IRELAND ISLE BERMUDA (R.) (1.8.1845)	
		Price on cover £7000
CC3	HAMILTON BERMUDA (R.) (13.11.1846)	
		Price on cover £3750

For Nos. CC1 and CC3 used as adhesive Postmasters' Stamps see Nos. O7 and O6.

PRICES FOR STAMPS ON COVER TO 1845
Nos. 1/11	*from* × 5
Nos. 12/17	*from* × 10
Nos. 19/29a	*from* × 8
Nos. 30/a	*from* × 10
Nos. 31/4	*from* × 4
Nos. 34a/55	*from* × 3
Nos. 56/8	*from* × 10
Nos. 59/76	*from* × 4
Nos. 76a/93	*from* × 3
Nos. 94/7	*from* × 4
Nos. 98/106	*from* × 3
Nos. 107/15	*from* × 4
Nos. 116/21	*from* × 5
No. 122	*from* × 20

COLONY

O 1   O 2

1848–61. *Postmasters' Stamps. Adhesives prepared and issued by the postmasters at Hamilton and St. Georges. Dated as given in brackets.*

(a) By W. B. Perot at Hamilton.
O1	O 1	1d. black/*bluish grey* (1848)	—	£130000
O2		1d. black/*bluish grey* (1849)	—	£150000
O3		1d. red/*thick white* (1853)	—	£110000
O4		1d. red/*bluish wove* (1854)	—	£275000
O5		1d. red/*bluish wove* (1856)	—	£170000
O6	O 2	(1d.) carmine-red/*bluish laid* (1861)	£100000	£80000

(b) By J. H. Thies at St. Georges. As Type O 2 but inscr "ST. GEORGES".
O7	(1d.) carmine-red/*buff* (1860)	†	£75000

Stamps of Type O 1 bear manuscript value and signature, the dates being those shown on the eleven known examples. The stamps are distributed between the dates as follows: 1848 three examples, 1849 two examples, 1853 three examples, 1854 two examples, 1856 one example.
It is believed that the franking value of Nos. O6/7 was 1d., although this is not shown on the actual stamps. Four examples are known of this type used from Hamilton, from March 1861 (and one unused), and five used from St. Georges between July 1860 and January 1863, both issues being cancelled by pen.
Prices shown reflect our estimation of value based on known copies. For instance of the two copies known of No. O4, one is in the Royal collection and the other is on entire.
It is possible that a fourth postmaster's provisional was used by Robert Ward at Hamilton in late 1862 when two examples of Type O 2 on laid paper are known cancelled by blue crayon.

1   2   3

4   5

(Typo D.L.R.)

1865–1903. *Wmk Crown CC.*

(a) P 14.
1	1	1d. rose-red (25.9.65)	90·00	1·25
		a. Imperf	£28000	£15000
		w. Wmk inverted	£350	£130
2		1d. pale rose	£130	7·00
		w. Wmk inverted	£375	£150
3	2	2d. dull blue (14.3.66)	£450	26·00
		w. Wmk inverted	—	£375
4		2d. bright blue (1877)	£475	19·00
		w. Wmk inverted	—	£375
5	3	3d. yellow-buff (10.3.73)	£475	65·00
		aw. Wmk inverted	£1100	£200
		ax. Wmk reversed		
5b		3d. orange (1875)	£1800	£150
6	4	6d. dull purple (25.9.65)	£1000	75·00
		w. Wmk inverted	£110	£140
7		6d. dull mauve (2.7.74)	23·00	12·00
		w. Wmk inverted	£110	£140
8	5	1s. green (25.9.65)	£325	55·00
		w. Wmk inverted	£650	£275

(b) P 14×12½.
10	3	3d. yellow-buff (12.81)	£170	60·00
10a	4	6d. bright mauve (1903)	13·00	22·00
		aw. Wmk inverted	£650	
11	5	1s. green (11.93)	11·00	£120
		a. Imperf between (vert strip of 3)	£12000	

No. 11a occurs from Rows 8, 9, and 10 of four panes, possibly from a single sheet. Some of the stamps have become partially separated. One *used* vertical pair is known (*Price* £12000).
Although they arrived in Bermuda in March 1880, stamps perforated 14×12½ were not issued until the dates given above.

THREE PENCE   THREE PENCE
(6)   (6a)

THREE PENCE   One Penny.
(7)   (8)

1874 (12 Mar–19 May). *Nos. 1 and 8 surch diagonally.*

(a) With T 6 ("P" and "R" different type).
12	1	3d. on 1d. rose-red	£18000
13	5	3d. on 1s. green	£2500 £850

(b) With T 6a ("P" same type as "R").
13b	5	3d. on 1s. green	£2000 £800

(c) With T 7 (19 May).
14	5	3d. on 1s. green	£1500 £650

The 3d. on 1d. was a trial surcharge which was not regularly issued, though a few specimens were postally used before 1879. Nos. 13, 13b and 14, being handstamped, are found with double or partial double surcharges.

(Surch by Queens Printer, Donald McPhee Lee)

1875 (March–May). *Surch with T 8.*
15	2	1d. on 2d. (No. 3) (23 Apr)	£700	£375
		a. No stop after "Penny"	£20000	£11000
16	3	1d. on 3d. (No. 5) (8 May)	£450	£350
17	5	1d. on 1s. (No. 8) (11 Mar)	£500	£250
		a. Surch inverted	†	£35000
		b. No stop after "Penny"	£22000	£14000

It is emphasised that the prices quoted for Nos. 12/17 are for fine examples. The many stamps from these provisional issues which are in inferior condition are worth much less.

9   10   11

(Typo D.L.R.)

1880 (25 Mar). *Wmk Crown CC. P 14.*
19	9	½d. stone	3·50	4·75
		w. Wmk inverted	85·00	£160
		y. Wmk inverted and reversed		
20	10	4d. orange-red	17·00	1·75
		w. Wmk inverted		
		x. Wmk reversed		

(Typo D.L.R.)

1883–1904. *Wmk Crown CA. P 14.*
21	9	½d. dull green (10.92)	3·75	3·00
21a		½d. deep grey-green (1893)	3·00	80
22	1	1d. dull rose (12.83)	£160	4·25
		w. Wmk inverted	—	£225
23		1d. rose-red	80·00	3·25
		w. Wmk inverted	—	£225
24		1d. carmine-rose (3.86)	50·00	1·00
24a		1d. aniline carmine (1889)	9·50	20
		aw. Wmk inverted	£250	£130
25	2	2d. blue (12.86)	60·00	4·00
		w. Wmk reversed	†	£700
26		2d. aniline purple (7.93)	14·00	4·00
26a		2d. brown purple (1898)	3·50	1·50
27	11	2½d. deep ultramarine (10.11.84)	15·00	2·75
		aw. Wmk inverted	£400	£160
27b		2½d. pale ultramarine	7·50	40
		bw. Wmk inverted	—	£140
28	3	3d. grey (20.1.86)	22·00	6·50
28a	10	4d. orange-brown (18.1.04)	35·00	60·00
		ax. Wmk reversed	£400	
29	5	1s. yellow-brown (1893)	19·00	17·00
		ax. Wmk reversed	—	£600
29b		1s. olive-brown	13·00	16·00
		bx. Wmk reversed		
21/9b *Set of 8*			£140	80·00
21s, 26s & 29s Optd "Specimen" *Set of 3*			£375	

1893 PROVISIONAL POSTCARD. Following the reduction of the overseas postcard rate to 1d. in 1893 existing stocks of postal stationery postcards, including some from the September 1880 issue franked with Nos. 19 and 22, were surcharged "One Penny". This surcharge was applied by the *Royal Gazette* press. It is generally believed that an individual in the Post Office acquired all the examples showing Nos. 19 and 22, but provisional postcards are known used to Europe or locally. *Price from* £550 *unused*, £1400 *used.*

ONE FARTHING
(12)   13 Dry Dock   14

1901. *As Nos. 29/a but colour changed, surch with T* **12** *by D.L.R.*

30	**5**	¼d. on 1s. dull grey (11.1.01)............	2·75	50
		as. Optd "Specimen".....................	80·00	
30b		¼d. on 1s. bluish grey (18.3.01)........	3·00	1·00
		ba. "F" in "FARTHING"		
		inserted by handstamp......	£6500	£7500

Eight examples of No. 30ba are known, six unused (one being in the Royal Collection) and two used (one on postcard). It would appear that the "F" in position one of an unspecified horizontal row was damaged and an additional impression of the letter was then inserted by a separate handstamp.

(Typo D.L.R.)

1902 (Nov)**–03**. Wmk Crown CA. P 14.

31	**13**	½d. black and green (12.03)............	12·00	2·75
32		1d. brown and carmine.................	8·00	10
33		3d. magenta and sage-green (9.03)..	3·25	2·00
31/3 *Set of 3*			21·00	4·25
31s/3s Optd "Specimen" *Set of 3*			£140	

1906–10. Wmk Mult Crown CA. P 14.

34	**13**	¼d. brown and violet (9.08)............	1·75	1·50
35		½d. black and green (12.06).........	19·00	65
36		½d. green (3.09)........................	14·00	2·75
37		1d. brown and carmine (4.06)........	29·00	20
		w. Wmk inverted	£450	£300
38		1d. red (5.08).............................	19·00	10
39		2d. grey and orange (10.07)...........	7·50	11·00
40		2½d. brown and ultramarine (12.06)..	19·00	7·00
41		2½d. blue (14.2.10).......................	12·00	6·50
42		4d. blue and chocolate (11.09)........	3·00	16·00
34/42 *Set of 9*			£110	40·00
34s, 36s, 38s/42s Optd "Specimen" *Set of 7*............			£375	

(Recess D.L.R.)

1910–25. Wmk Mult Crown CA. P 14.

44	**14**	¼d. brown (26.3.12)	1·75	2·50
		a. *Pale brown*.............................	60	1·50
45		½d. green (4.6.10).........................	1·50	25
		a. *Deep green* (1918).....................	8·50	1·25
		w. Wmk inverted		
		x. Wmk reversed...........................	£425	£325
		y. Wmk inverted and reversed.......		
46		1d. red (I) (15.10.10)....................	15·00	30
		a. *Rose-red* (1916)........................	22·00	30
		b. *Carmine* (12.19)........................	55·00	30
		w. Wmk inverted	£550	£450
		x. Wmk reversed...........................		
		y. Wmk inverted and reversed.......	£450	
47		2d. grey (1.13).............................	3·00	12·00
		x. Wmk reversed...........................		
48		2½d. blue (27.3.12)........................	3·50	60
		w. Wmk inverted		
		x. Wmk reversed...........................	—	£350
		y. Wmk inverted and reversed.......	£250	£180
49		3d. purple/*yellow* (1.13)..................	2·00	6·00
49a		4d. red/*yellow* (1.9.19)....................	6·00	12·00
50		6d. purple (26.3.12)......................	16·00	20·00
		a. *Pale claret* (2.6.24)...................	11·00	8·00
51		1s. black/*green* (26.3.12)................	4·25	4·00
		a. *Jet black/olive* (1925)................	4·75	16·00
44/51 *Set of 9*			42·00	40·00
44s/51s Optd "Specimen" *Set of 9*			£400	

Nos. 44 to 51a are comb-perforated 13.8×14 or 14. No. 45 exists also line-perforated 14 probably from the printing dispatched to Bermuda on 13 March 1911.

See also Nos. 76b/87a.

15

HIGH VALUE KEY TYPES. The reign of King Edward VII saw the appearance of the first in a new series of "key type" designs, initially for Nyasaland, to be used for high value denominations where a smaller design was felt to be inappropriate. The system was extended during the reign of King George V, using the portrait as Bermuda Type **15**, to cover Bermuda, Ceylon, Leeward Islands, Malaya — Straits Settlements, Malta and Nyasaland. A number of these territories continued to use the key type concept for high value King George VI stamps and one, Leeward Islands, for stamps of Queen Elizabeth II.

In each instance the King George V issues were printed in sheets of 60 (12×5) on various coloured papers. The system utilised a common "head" plate used with individual "duty" plates which printed the territory name and face value.

Many of the major plate flaws on the King George V head plate occur in different states, having been repaired and then damaged once again, perhaps on several occasions. Later printings of R. 1/12 show additional damage to the crown and upper scrolls. The prices quoted in the listings are for examples approximately as illustrated.

Break in scroll (R. 1/12)   Broken crown and scroll (R. 2/12)

Nick in top right scroll (R. 3/12) (Some printings from 1920 onwards show attempts at repair)   Break through scroll (R. 1/9. Ptgs from June 1929. Some show attempts at repair)

Break in lines below left scroll (R. 4/9. Ptgs from May 1920)   Damaged leaf at bottom right (R. 5/6. Ptgs from April 1918)

Gash in fruit and leaf (R. 5/12. Ptgs from November 1928)

(Typo D.L.R)

1918 (1 Apr)**–22**. Wmk Mult Crown CA. *Chalk-surfaced paper.* P 14.

51b	**15**	2s. purple and blue/*blue* (19.6.20) ..	19·00	50·00
		ba. Break in scroll.......................	£275	
		bb. Broken crown and scroll.........	£225	
		bc. Nick in top right scroll	£275	
		be. Break in lines below left scroll .	£275	£375
		bf. Damaged leaf at bottom right....	£275	
		bx. Wmk reversed........................	£1900	£2500
52		2s.6d. black and red/*blue*..................	30·00	80·00
		a. Break in scroll.........................	£325	
52b		4s. black and carmine (19.6.20)....	60·00	£160
		ba. Break in scroll.......................	£300	
		bb. Broken crown and scroll.........	£300	£600
		bc. Nick in top right scroll	£325	£600
		be. Break in lines below left scroll .	£350	
		bf. Damaged leaf at bottom right....	£350	
53		5s. deep green and deep red/*yellow*	65·00	£140
		a. Break in scroll.........................	£425	
		c. Nick in top right scroll	£425	
		d. *Green and carmine-red/pale*		
		yellow (1920)......................	50·00	£120
		da. Break in scroll......................	£375	£550
		db. Broken crown and scroll.........	£375	£550
		de. Break in lines below left scroll .	£400	
		df. Damaged leaf at bottom right....	£400	
		dw. Wmk inverted	£400	
		dx. Wmk reversed.......................	£3250	
		dy. Wmk inverted and reversed......	£3250	
54		10s. green and carmine/*pale bluish*		
		green....................................	£180	£350
		a. Break in scroll.........................	£750	
		c. *Green and red/pale bluish*		
		green (10.22)........................	£250	£400
		ca. Break in scroll......................	£850	
		cb. Broken crown and scroll.........	£850	
		ce. Break in lines below left scroll .	£900	
		cf. Damaged leaf at bottom right....	£900	
		cw. Wmk inverted	£1800	
55		£1 purple and black/*red*..................	£325	£550
		a. Break in scroll.........................	£850	
		b. Broken crown and scroll.........	£1000	
		c. Nick in top right scroll	£1000	
		d. Break through scroll	£1900	
		e. Break in lines below left scroll .	£1500	
		f. Damaged leaf at bottom right....	£1200	
		g. Gash in fruit and leaf...............	£1900	
		w. Wmk inverted	£1800	
51b/5 *Set of 6*			£600	£1100
51bs/5s Optd "Specimen" *Set of 6*			£800	

Beware of cleaned copies of the 10s. with faked postmarks. Examples of Nos. 51b/5 are known showing a forged Hamilton double ring postmark dated "22 JAN 13".

See also Nos. 88/93.

WAR TAX   **WAR TAX**
(16)   (17)

1918 (4 May). *Nos. 46 and 46a optd with T* **16** *by the Bermuda Press.*

56	**14**	1d. red	50	1·00
		a. *Rose-red*	50	1·25
		ay. Wmk inverted and reversed.......		

1920 (5 Feb). *No. 46b optd with T* **17** *by the Bermuda Press.*

| 58 | **14** | 1d. carmine .... | 1·50 | 2·25 |

The War Tax stamps represented a compulsory levy on letters to Great Britain and often Empire Countries in addition to normal postal fees until 31 Dec 1920. Subsequently they were valid for ordinary postage.

18   **19**

(Des by the Governor (Gen. Sir James Willcocks). Typo D.L.R.)

1920 (11 Nov)**–21**. *Tercentenary of Representative Institutions (1st issue). Chalk-surfaced paper (3d. to 1s.).* P 14.

(a) Wmk Mult Crown CA (sideways*) (19.1.21).

59	**18**	¼d. brown	3·25	21·00
		a. "C" of "CA" missing from		
		wmk...........................	£600	
		b. "A" of "CA" missing from		
		wmk...........................	£600	
		w. Wmk Crown to right of CA	£200	
		x. Wmk sideways reversed...........	£200	
		y. Wmk sideways inverted and		
		reversed...........................		
60		½d. green	4·50	12·00
		a. "C" of "CA" missing from		
		wmk...........................	£850	
		w. Wmk Crown to right of CA	£325	
		x. Wmk sideways reversed...........	£275	
		y. Wmk sideways inverted and		
		reversed...........................		
61		2d. grey	14·00	45·00
		a. "C" of "CA" missing from		
		wmk...........................	£850	
		w. Wmk Crown to right of CA	£425	
		y. Wmk sideways inverted and		
		reversed...........................	£475	
62		3d. dull and deep purple/*pale*		
		yellow...................................	12·00	42·00
		w. Wmk Crown to right of CA		
		x. Wmk sideways reversed...........		
63		4d. black and red/*pale yellow*.........	12·00	35·00
		a. "C" of "CA" missing from		
		wmk...........................	£1300	
		x. Wmk reversed.........................		
64		1s. black/*blue-green*....................	16·00	48·00

(b) Wmk Mult Script CA (sideways).

65	**18**	1d. carmine	4·00	30
66		2½d. bright blue	16·00	15·00
67		6d. dull and bright purple (19.1.21)	28·00	85·00
59/67 *Set of 9*			£100	£275
59s/67s Optd "Specimen" *Set of 9*			£375	

The normal sideways watermark shows Crown to left of CA, as seen from the back of the stamp.

(Des H. J. Dale. Recess D.L.R.)

1921 (12 May). *Tercentenary of Representative Institutions (2nd issue).* P 14.

(a) Wmk Mult Crown CA (sideways*).

68	**19**	2d. slate-grey	7·00	32·00
		a. "C" of "CA" missing from		
		wmk...........................	—	£700
		w. Wmk Crown to left of CA.......	£500	
69		2½d. bright ultramarine	9·00	3·00
		a. "C" of "CA" missing from		
		wmk...........................	£900	
		b. "A" of "CA" missing from		
		wmk...........................	£900	
		x. Wmk sideways reversed...........	—	£450
70		3d. purple/*pale yellow*	5·50	16·00
		w. Wmk Crown to left of CA.......		
71		4d. red/*pale yellow*	18·00	23·00
		x. Wmk sideways reversed...........	£250	
72		6d. purple	14·00	50·00
		a. "C" of "CA" missing from		
		wmk...........................	£1100	
		b. "A" of "CA" missing from		
		wmk...........................	£1200	
		c. Substituted crown in wmk........	†	£1700
73		1s. black/*green*.........................	23·00	50·00

(b) Wmk Mult Script CA (sideways*).

74	**19**	¼d. brown	2·00	3·75
		w. Wmk Crown to left of CA.......		
		x. Wmk sideways reversed...........		
75		½d. green	2·75	7·00
		w. Wmk Crown to left of CA.......	£180	£200
		y. Wmk sideways inverted and		
		reversed...........................	£350	
		ys. Optd "Specimen"..................	£100	
76		1d. deep carmine	3·25	35
		a. "C" of "CA" missing from		
		wmk...........................		
		w. Wmk Crown to left of CA.......	—	£425
		x. Wmk sideways reversed...........		
		y. Wmk sideways inverted and		
		reversed...........................	£850	

68/76 *Set of 9* .... 75·00 £170
68s/76s Optd "Specimen" *Set of 9* £325

*The normal sideways watermark shows Crown to right of CA, *as seen from the back of the stamp.*

For illustration of the substituted watermark crown see Catalogue Introduction.

Examples of most values of Nos. 59/76 are known showing part strikes of the forged Hamilton postmark mentioned below Nos. 51b/5.

Three Types of the 1d.

I. Scroll at top left very weak and figure "1" has pointed serifs.
II. Scroll weak. "1" has square serifs and "1d" is heavy.
III. Redrawn. Scroll is completed by a strong line and "1" is thinner with long square serifs.

Two Types of the 2½d.

I. Short, thick figures, especially of the "1", small "d".
II. Figures taller and thinner, "d" larger.

1922–34. Wmk Mult Script CA. P 14.

76b	14	¼d. brown (7.28)	1·50	3·00
77		½d. green (11.22)	1·50	15
		w. Wmk inverted		
		x. Wmk reversed		
78		1d. scarlet (I) (11.22)	17·00	60
		a. Carmine (7.24)	18·00	60
		bx. Wmk reversed		
78c		1d. carmine (II) (12.25)	42·00	6·00
		cx. Wmk reversed		
		d. Scarlet (8.27)	12·00	80
79		1d. scarlet (III) (10.28)	12·00	30
		a. Carmine-lake (1934)	25·00	2·25
79b		1½d. red-brown (27.3.34)	9·00	35
80		2d. grey (12.23)	1·50	1·50
		x. Wmk reversed	65·00	
81		2½d. pale sage-green (12.22)	2·25	1·50
		a. Deep sage-green (1924)	1·75	1·50
		aw. Wmk inverted		
		ax. Wmk reversed		
		ay. Wmk inverted and reversed......		
82		2½d. ultramarine (I) (1.12.26)	2·50	50
		aw. Wmk inverted	£170	
82b		2½d. ultramarine (II) (3.32)	1·75	70
83		3d. ultramarine (12.24)	16·00	26·00
		w. Wmk inverted	£130	
84		3d. purple/*yellow* (10.26)	4·00	1·00
85		4d. red/*yellow* (8.24)	2·00	1·00
		x. Wmk reversed		
86		6d. purple (8.24)	1·00	80
87		1s. black/*emerald* (10.27)	4·75	9·00
		a. Brownish black/*yellow-green* (1934)	35·00	50·00
		76b/87 *Set of 12*	50·00	40·00
		76bs/87s Optd or Perf (1½d.) "Specimen" *Set of 12*	£500	

Both comb and line perforations occur on Nos. 76b/87a.

Detailed gauges are as follows:

13.7×13.9 comb — Nos. 77, 78/a, 80, 81/a, 83, 84, 85, 86, 87
13.75 line — Nos. 76b, 77, 78c/d, 79/a, 79b, 80, 82, 82b, 84, 85, 86, 87/a13.
75×14 line — Nos. 77, 78c/d, 79b, 80, 82b, 86, 87a
14×13.75 line — Nos. 79/a
14 line — Nos. 81/a

Breaks in scrolls at right (R. 1/3. Ptgs of 12s.6d. from July 1932)

1924–32. Wmk Mult Script CA. *Chalk-surfaced paper.* P 14.

88	15	2s. purple and bright blue/*pale blue* (1.9.27)	45·00	75·00
		a. Break in scroll	£250	
		b. Broken crown and scroll.........	£250	

---

		e. Break in lines below left scroll...................................	£275	
		f. Damaged leaf at bottom right.	£275	
		g. Purple and blue/grey-blue (1931)	55·00	85·00
		ga. Break in scroll.....................	£300	
		gb. Broken crown and scroll.......	£300	
		gd. Break through scroll	£350	
		ge. Break in lines below left scroll...................................	£350	
		gf. Damaged leaf at bottom right.	£350	
		gg. Gash in fruit and leaf............	£350	
89		2s.6d. black and carmine/*pale blue* (4.27)	60·00	£100
		a. Break in scroll.....................	£300	
		b. Broken crown and scroll........	£300	
		e. Break in lines below left scroll...................................	£350	
		f. Damaged leaf at bottom right.	£350	
		g. Black and red/blue to deep blue (6.29)..............................	75·00	£110
		ga. Break in scroll.....................	£350	
		gb. Broken crown and scroll.......	£350	
		gd. Break through scroll	£400	
		ge. Break in lines below left scroll...................................	£400	
		gf. Damaged leaf at bottom right.	£400	
		gg. Gash in fruit and leaf............	£400	
		h. Grey-black and pale orange-vermilion/grey-blue (3.30)......	£2750	£2750
		ha. Break in scroll.....................	£5500	
		hb. Broken crown and scroll.......	£5500	
		hd. Break through scroll	£5500	
		he. Break in lines below left scroll...................................	£5500	
		hf. Damaged leaf at bottom right.	£5500	
		hg. Gash in fruit and leaf............	£5500	
		i. Black and carmine-red/deep grey-blue (8.30)......................	£100	£140
		ia. Break in scroll.....................	£500	
		ib. Broken crown and scroll.......	£500	
		id. Break through scroll	£600	
		ie. Break in lines below left scroll...................................	£600	
		if. Damaged leaf at bottom right.	£600	
		ig. Gash in fruit and leaf............	£600	
		j. Black and scarlet-vermilion/ dp bl (9.31)..............................	90·00	£130
		ja. Break in scroll.....................	£450	
		jb. Broken crown and scroll.......	£450	
		jc. Nick in top right scroll	£500	£600
		jd. Break through scroll	£550	
		je. Break in lines below left scroll...................................	£550	
		jf. Damaged leaf at bottom right.	£550	
		jg. Gash in fruit and leaf............	£550	
		k. Black & brt orange-vermilion/ deep blue (8.32).......................	£3000	£2750
		kb. Broken crown and scroll........	£5500	
		kc. Nick in top right scroll	£5500	
		kd. Break through scroll	£5500	
		ke. Break in lines below left scroll...................................	£5500	
		kf. Damaged leaf at bottom right.	£5500	
		kg. Gash in fruit and leaf............	£5500	
92		10s. green and red/*pale emerald* (12.24)	£130	£250
		a. Break in scroll.....................	£650	
		b. Broken crown and scroll........	£550	
		e. Break in lines below left scroll...................................	£650	
		f. Damaged leaf at bottom right.	£600	
		g. Green and red/deep emerald (1930)	£140	£275
		ga. Break in scroll.....................	£650	
		gb. Broken crown and scroll.......	£600	
		gc. Nick in top right scroll	£650	
		gd. Break through scroll	£700	
		ge. Break in lines below left scroll...................................	£700	
		gf. Damaged leaf at bottom right.	£650	
		gg. Gash in fruit and leaf............	£650	
93		12s.6d. grey and orange (8.32)...........	£250	£375
		a. Break in scroll.....................	£700	£900
		b. Broken crown and scroll........	£750	£950
		c. Nick in top right scroll	£800	
		d. Break through scroll	£900	
		e. Break in lines below left scroll...................................	£900	
		f. Damaged leaf at bottom right.	£800	
		g. Gash in fruit and leaf............	£800	
		h. Break in scrolls at right	£900	
		i. Error. Ordinary paper.............		
		88/93 *Set of 4*	£425	£700
		88s/93s Optd or Perf (12s.6d) "Specimen" *Set of 4* .	£500	

The true No. 89h is the only stamp on grey-blue paper, other deeper orange-vermilion shades exist on different papers. No. 89k was despatched to Bermuda in July/August 1932, but is not known used before 1937.

Beware fiscally used 2s.6d. 10s. and 12s.6d. stamps cleaned and bearing faked postmarks. Large quantities were used for a "head tax" levied on travellers leaving the country.

For 12s.6d. design inscribed "Revenue" at both sides see No. F1 under POSTAL FISCAL.

1935 (6 May). *Silver Jubilee. As Nos. 91/4 of Antigua, but ptd by Waterlow.* P 11×12.

94		1d. deep blue and scarlet	45	1·00
		j. Damaged turret	£250	
		m. "Bird" by turret	£130	£160
95		1½d. ultramarine and grey	70	2·75
		m. "Bird" by turret	£140	
96		2½d. brown and deep blue	1·40	1·75
		m. "Bird" by turret	£200	£225
97		1s. slate and purple	15·00	28·00
		k. Kite and vertical log.............	£190	£275
		l. Kite and horizontal log...........	£375	
		94/7 *Set of 4*	16·00	30·00
		94s/7s Perf "Specimen" *Set of 4*	£190	

For illustrations of plate varieties see Omnibus section following Zanzibar.

---

20 Red Hole, Paget   21 South Shore

22 *Lucie* (yacht)   23 Grape Bay, Paget Parish

24 Point House, Warwick Parish   25 Gardener's Cottage, Par-la-Ville, Hamilton

(Recess B.W.)

1936 (14 Apr)–**47**. *T* **20/25**. Wmk Mult Script CA (sideways on horiz designs).

98	20	½d. bright green	10	10
99	21	1d. black and scarlet	50	30
100		1½d. black and chocolate	1·00	50
101	22	2d. black and pale blue	5·00	1·50
102	23	2½d. light and deep blue	1·00	25
103	24	3d. black and scarlet	2·75	1·75
104	25	6d. carmine-lake and violet	80	10
		a. Claret and dull violet (6.47).....	3·50	1·75
105	23	1s. green	6·00	12·00
106	20	1s.6d. brown	50	10
		98/106 *Set of 9*	16·00	15·00
		98s/106s Perf "Specimen" *Set of 9*	£275	

All are line-perf 11.9, except printings of the 6d. from July 1951 onwards, which are comb-perf 11.9×11.75.

1937 (14 May). *Coronation. As Nos. 95/7 of Antigua, but printed by D.L.R.* P 14.

107		1d. scarlet	50	1·00
108		1½d. yellow-brown	60	1·50
109		2½d. bright blue	70	1·50
		107/9 *Set of 3*	1·60	3·50
		107s/9s Perf "Specimen" *Set of 3*	£150	

26 Ships in Hamilton Harbour   27 St. David's Lighthouse

28 White-tailed Tropic Bird, Arms of Bermuda and Native Flower   29 King George VI

(Des Miss Higginbotham (T **28**). Recess B.W.)

1938 (20 Jan)–**52**. *T* **22**, *T* **23** *(but with portrait of King George VI) and T* **26** *to* **28**. Wmk Mult Script CA. P 12.

110	26	1d. black and red (*a*) (*b*).................	85	20
111		1½d. deep blue and purple-brown (*a*) (*b*)	7·00	1·50
		a. Blue and brown (*a*) (3.43).........	8·00	3·25
		b. lt blue & purple-brn (*a*) (*b*) (9.45).......................................	2·25	1·00
		ba. "A" of "CA" missing from wmk...	£1500	
112	22	2d. light blue and sepia (*a*).............	50·00	8·50
112a		2d. ultramarine and scarlet (*a*) (*b*) (8.11.40)	1·50	1·00
113	23	2½d. light and deep blue (*a*).............	11·00	1·25
113a		2½d. lt blue & sepia-black (*a*) (18.12.41)	3·00	2·50
		b. Pale blue & sepia-black (*a*) (3.43)	2·75	2·50
		c. Bright blue and deep sepia-black (*b*) (23.9.52)..............	5·50	6·00
114	27	3d. black and rose-red (*a*)	22·00	3·50
114a		3d. black & deep blue (*a*) (*b*) (16.7.41)	1·75	40
114b	28	7½d. black, blue & brt grn (*a*) (18.12.41)	7·50	2·75

	c. Black, blue & yellow-grn (a) (3.43)		6·00	2·75
115	**23** 1s. green (a) (b)		2·00	50
	a. Bluish green (b) (20.6.52)		7·00	6·50

Perforations. Two different perforating machines were used on the various printings of these stamps: (a) the original 11.9 line perforation; (b) 11.9×11.75 comb perforation, introduced in July 1950. These perforations occur as indicated above.

Shading omitted from top right scroll (R. 1/1. March 1943 ptgs of 2s. and £1)

Lower right scroll with broken tail (R. 2/10. Line perforated printings only)

Broken top right scroll (R. 5/11. Line perforated ptgs only. A retouched state of the flaw is visible in later ptgs up to March 1943)

Broken lower right scroll (R. 5/12. Occurs on printings made between May 1941 and March 1943)

Gash in chin (R. 2/5. Ptgs between May 1941 and March 1943)

Missing pearl (R. 5/1, Nov 1945 ptg of 5s. only)

"ER" joined (R. 1/2. Occurs in its complete state on 1938 ptg only. Subsequent ptgs show it incomplete)

Damaged left value tablet (R. 1/11. Part of 1951 ptg only)

(Typo D.L.R.)

1938 (20 Jan)–**53**. *T* **29**. Wmk Mult Crown CA (£1) or Mult Script CA (others). *Chalk-surfaced paper.* P 14 (comb).

116	2s. deep purple and ultramarine/grey-blue	£110	12·00
	a. Deep reddish purple and ultram/ grey-blue (21.11.40)*	£350	27·00
	b. Perf 14¼ line. Deep purple and ultram/grey-blue (14.11.41)*	£300	85·00
	bc. Lower right scroll with broken tail	£2500	£900
	bd. Broken top right scroll	£1600	£650
	be. Broken lower right scroll	£1600	£650
	bf. Gash in chin	£1700	£750
	c. Ordinary paper. Pur and bl/dp bl (7.6.42)	8·00	1·50
	ce. Broken lower right scroll	£225	95·00
	cf. Gash in chin	£250	£100
	d. Ordinary paper. Purple and deep blue/blue (5.3.43)	12·00	1·50
	db. Shading omitted from top right scroll	£1500	£800
	de. Broken lower right scroll	£650	£375
	df. Gash in chin	£700	£400

	e. Perf 13. Ordinary paper. Dull purple and blue/pale blue (15.2.50)	14·00	15·00
	f. Perf 13. Ordinary paper. Reddish purple and blue/pale blue (10.10.50)	9·00	20·00
117	2s.6d. black and red/grey-blue	70·00	10·00
	a. Perf 14¼ line. Black and red/grey-blue (21.2.42)*	£550	£110
	ac. Lower right scroll with broken tail	£2750	£950
	ad. Broken top right scroll	£1800	£750
	ae. Broken lower right scroll	£1800	£750
	af. Gash in chin	£1900	£800
	b. Ordinary paper. Black and red/pale blue (5.3.43)	19·00	6·50
	be. Broken lower right scroll	£650	£325
	bf. Gash in chin	£700	£350
	c. Perf 13. Ordinary paper. Black and orange-red/pale blue (10.10.50)	17·00	11·00
	d. Perf 13. Ordinary paper. Black and red/ pale blue (18.6.52)	16·00	13·00
118	5s. green and red/yellow	£140	15·00
	a. Pale green & red/yellow (14.3.39)*	£325	75·00
	b. Perf 14¼ line. Dull yellow-green and red/yellow (5.1.43)*	£275	35·00
	bc. Lower right scroll with broken tail	£1900	£700
	bd. Broken top right scroll	£1000	£375
	be. Broken lower right scroll	£1000	£375
	bf. Gash in chin	£1100	£425
	c. Ordinary paper. Dull yellow-green & carmine-red/pale yellow (5.42)*	£800	£120
	ce. Broken lower right scroll	£5000	£1400
	cf. Gash in chin	£5000	£1400
	d. Ordinary paper. Pale bluish green and carmine-red/pale yellow (5.3.43)	£100	50·00
	de. Broken lower right scroll	£950	£500
	df. Gash in chin	£950	£500
	e. Ordinary paper. Green and red/pale yellow (11.45)*	50·00	21·00
	ea. Missing pearl	£800	
	f. Perf 13. Ordinary paper. Yellow-green and red/pale yellow (15.2.50)	26·00	22·00
	g. Perf 13. Green and scarlet/yellow (chalk-surfaced) (10.10.50)	45·00	55·00
119	10s. green and deep lake/pale emerald	£450	£325
	a. Bluish green and deep red/green (8.39)*	£225	£130
	b. Perf 14¼ line. Ordinary paper. Yellow green and carmine/green (1942)*	£475	£120
	bc. Lower right scroll with broken tail	£3000	£1200
	bd. Broken top right scroll	£1700	£800
	be. Broken lower right scroll	£1700	£800
	bf. Gash in chin	£1800	£850
	c. Ordinary paper. Yellowish green and deep carmine-red/green (5.3.43)	70·00	60·00
	ce. Broken lower right scroll	£2500	
	cf. Gash in chin	£2500	
	d. Ordinary paper. Deep green and dull red/green (emerald back) (11.12.46)..	80·00	60·00
	e. Perf 13. Ordinary paper. Green and vermilion/green (19.9.51)	38·00	42·00
	f. Perf 13. Ordinary paper. Green and dull red/green (16.4.53)	38·00	48·00
120	12s.6d. deep grey and brownish orange	£550	£425
	a. Grey and brownish orange (shades)	£200	75·00
	b. Grey and pale orange (9.11.40)*	95·00	50·00
	c. Ordinary paper (2.3.44)*	£110	65·00
	ce. Broken lower right scroll	£2250	£2500
	cf. Gash in chin	£2250	
	d. Ordinary paper. Grey and yell† (17.9.47)*	£700	£500
	e. Perf 13. Grey and pale orange (chalk surfaced) (10.10.50)	95·00	75·00
121	£1 purple and black/red	£275	£100
	a. "ER" joined	£800	£550
	b. Pale purple and black/pale red (13.5.43)*	80·00	65·00
	ba. "ER" joined	£550	£450
	bb. Shading omitted from top right scroll	£2750	
	be. Broken lower right scroll	£1600	£1100
	bf. Gash in chin	£1600	£1100
	c. Dp reddish pur and blk/pale red (5.3.43)*	60·00	65·00
	ca. "ER" joined	£550	£550
	ce. Broken lower right scroll	£1500	
	cf. Gash in chin	£1500	
	d. Perf 13. Violet & black/scarlet (7.12.51)	50·00	75·00
	da. Damaged left value tablet	£2750	
	e. Perf 13. Brt violet and blk/scar (10.12.52)	£160	£170
110/21d	Set of 16	£300	£180
110s/21s	Perf "Specimen" Set of 16	£1700	

Following extensive damage to their printing works on 29 December 1940 much of De La Rue's work was transferred to other firms operating under their supervision. It is understood that Williams Lea & Co produced those new printings ordered for the Bermuda high value stamps during 1941. The first batch of these printings showed the emergency use, by Williams Lea, of a 14¼ line perforating machine (exact gauge 14.15) instead of the comb perforation (exact gauge 13.9×13.8).

Dates marked * are those of earliest known use.

In No. 116c the coloured surfacing of the paper is mottled with white specks sometimes accompanied by very close horizontal lines. In Nos. 116d, 117b and 118c/d the surfacing is the same colour as the back, sometimes applied in widely spaced horizontal lines giving the appearance of laid paper.

†No. 120d is the so-called "lemon" shade.

HALF PENNY

X   X
30

31 Postmaster Perot's Stamp

1940 (20 Dec). *No. 110 surch with T* **30** *by Royal Gazette, Hamilton.*

122	**26** ½d. on 1d. black and red (shades)	40	1·50

The spacing between "PENNY" and "X" varies from 12½ mm to 14 mm.

1946 (6 Nov). *Victory. As Nos. 110/11 of Antigua.*

123	1½d. brown	15	15
124	3d. blue	15	15
123s/4s	Perf "Specimen" Set of 2	£100	

1948 (1 Dec). *Royal Silver Wedding. As Nos. 112/13 of Antigua.*

125	1½d. red-brown	30	50
126	£1 carmine	42·00	50·00

(Recess B.W.)

1949 (11 Apr). *Centenary of Postmaster Perot's Stamp.* Wmk Mult Script CA. P 13½.

127	**31** 2½d. blue and brown	15	25
128	3d. black and blue	15	15
129	6d. violet and green	15	15
127/9	Set of 3	40	50

1949 (10 Oct). *75th Anniv of Universal Postal Union. As Nos. 114/17 of Antigua.*

130	2½d. blue-black	30	1·75
131	3d. deep blue	1·40	1·25
132	6d. purple	40	75
133	1s. blue-green	40	1·50
130/3	Set of 4	2·25	4·75

STAMP BOOKLETS

1948 (5 Apr–10 May). *Pink (No. SB1), or light blue (No. SB2) covers. Stapled.*

SB1	5s. booklet containing six 1d., 1½d., 2d., 2½d. and 3d. (Nos. 110, 111b, 112a, 113b, 114a) in blocks of 6 (10 May)	£140
SB2	10s.6d. booklet containing six 3d. and eighteen 6d. (Nos. 114a, 104) in blocks of 6 with twelve air mail labels	£150

POSTAL FISCAL

1937 (1 Feb). *As T* **15**, *but inscr "REVENUE" at each side.* Wmk Mult Script CA. *Chalk-surfaced paper.* P 14

F1	12s.6d. grey and orange	£1000	£1300
	a. Break in scroll (R. 1/12)	£3750	£5500
	b. Broken crown and scroll (R. 2/12)	£3750	
	d. Break through scroll (R. 1/9)	£3750	
	e. Break in lines below left scroll	£3750	
	f. Damaged leaf at bottom right	£3750	
	g. Gash in fruit and leaf	£3750	
	h. Breaks in scrolls at right (R. 1/3)	£3750	

No. F1 was issued for fiscal purposes towards the end of 1936. Its use as a postage stamp was authorised from 1 February to April 1937. The used price quoted above is for examples postmarked during this period. Later in the same year postmarks with other dates were obtained by favour.

For illustration of No. F1a/h see above Nos. 51b and 88.

British Central Africa *see* **Nyasaland Protectorate**

British Columbia and Vancouver Island *see* **Canada**

British Commonwealth Occupation Force *see after* **Australia**

British East Africa *see* **Kenya, Uganda and Tanganyika**

British Forces in Egypt *see* **Egypt**

British Guiana

The postal service from what was to become British Guiana dates from 1796, being placed on a more regular basis after the final British occupation.

An inland postal system was organised in 1850, using the adhesive stamps of British Guiana, but, until 1 May 1860, overseas mails continued to be the province of the British G.P.O. The stamps of Great Britain were supplied for use on such letters from 11 May 1858 and examples of their use in combination with British Guiana issues have been recorded.

For illustration of the handstamp and postmark type see BRITISH POST OFFICES ABROAD notes, following GREAT BRITAIN.

CROWNED-CIRCLED HANDSTAMPS

The provision of a handstamp, probably as Type CC **1**, inscribed "DEMERARA", is recorded in the G.P.O. proof book under 1 March 1856. No examples have been reported. A further handstamp, as Type CC **6**, recorded in the proof book on 17 February 1866, is known used as a cancellation in at least two instances, *circa* 1868.

GEORGETOWN (DEMERARA)

Stamps of GREAT BRITAIN *cancelled* "A 03" *as Type* **2**.

1858–60.
Z1	1d. rose-red (1857), *perf* 14		£350
Z2	4d. rose (1857)		£170
Z3	6d. lilac (1856)		£120
	a. Azure paper		
Z4	1s. green (1856)		£1500

NEW AMSTERDAM (BERBICE)

Stamps of GREAT BRITAIN *cancelled* "A 04" *as Type* **2**.

1858–60.
Z5	1d. rose-red (1857), *perf* 14		£850
Z6	2d. blue (1858) (Plate Nos. 7, 8)		£950
Z7	4d. rose (1857)		£375
Z8	6d. lilac (1856)		£250
Z9	1s. green (1856)		£1800

PRICES FOR STAMPS ON COVER TO 1945

No. 1	*from* × 1
Nos. 2/8	*from* × 4
Nos. 9/21	*from* × 3
No. 23	†
Nos. 24/7	*from* × 5
Nos. 29/115	*from* × 5
Nos. 116/24	*from* × 8
Nos. 126/36	*from* × 7
Nos. 137/59	*from* × 8
Nos. 162/5	*from* × 10
Nos. 170/4	*from* × 8
Nos. 175/89	*from* × 10
No. 192	*from* × 30
Nos. 193/210	*from* × 5
Nos. 213/15	*from* × 8
Nos. 216/21	*from* × 5
Nos. 222/4	*from* × 10
Nos. 233/50	*from* × 4
No. 251	
Nos. 252/7	*from* × 4
Nos. 259/82	*from* × 8
Nos. 283/7	*from* × 8
Nos. 288/300	*from* × 5
Nos. 301/4	*from* × 6
Nos. 305/7	*from* × 5
Nos. 308/19	*from* × 5
Nos. D1/4	*from* × 15
Nos. O1/12	*from* × 15

CROWN COLONY
(Currency. 100 cents = 1 dollar)

1   2

(Set up and printed at the office of the *Royal Gazette*, Georgetown, British Guiana)

1850 (1 July)–**51**. *Type-set. Black impression.*

*(a) Medium wove paper. Prices are for—*I. Cut square. II. Cut round.
1	**1**	2c. *rose* (1.3.51)	—	£150000
2		4c. *orange*	£40000	£7000
3		4c. *lemon-yellow* (1851)	£65000	£10000
4		8c. *green*	£27000	£6000
5		12c. *blue*	£11000	£4000
6		12c. *indigo*	£16000	£5000
7		12c. *pale blue* (1851)	£16000	£5500
		a. "2" of "12" with straight foot	—	£12000
		b. "1" of "12" omitted	†	£75000

(b) Pelure paper (1851).
8	**1**	4c. *pale yellow*	£75000	£10000

These stamps were usually initialled by the postmaster, or the Post Office clerks, before they were issued. The initials are—E. T. E. D(alton), E. D. W(ight), J. B. S(mith), H. A. K(illikelley), and W. H. L(ortimer). There are several types of each value and it has been suggested that the setting contained one horizontal row of four slightly different impressions.

Ten examples of No. 1 have been recorded, including three pairs on separate covers.

(Litho Waterlow)

1852 (1 Jan). *Surface-coloured paper. Imperf.*
9	**2**	1c. black/*magenta*	£8500	£4250
10		4c. black/*deep blue*	£14000	£9000

There are two types of each value.

Reprints on thicker paper, and perf 12½, were made in 1865 (*Price £17 either value*).

Such reprints with the perforations removed are sometimes offered as genuine originals.

CONDITION. Prices for Nos. 9 to 21 are for fine copies. Poor to medium specimens can be supplied when in stock at much lower rates.

3   4   5

(Dies eng and stamps litho Waterlow)

1853–59. *Imperf.*

(a) Original printing.
11	**3**	1c. vermilion	£3250	£1000

This 1c. in *reddish brown* is probably a proof (*Price* £700).

A. "O" large and 1 mm from left corner.
B. "O" small and ¾ mm from left corner.
C. "O" small and ¾ mm from left corner. "NT" widely spaced.
D. "ONE" close together, "O" 1¼ mm from left corner.

(b) Fresh lithographic transfers from the 4c. with varying labels of value. White line above value (1857–59).
12	**3**	1c. dull red (A)	£3250	£1200
13		1c. brownish red (A)	£7000	£1600
14		1c. dull red (B)	£3750	£1300
15		1c. brownish red (B)	£7500	£1700
16		1c. dull red (C)	£4750	£1600
16a		1c. brownish red (C)	—	£2000
17		1c. dull red (D)	£17000	£7000

1853–55. *Imperf.*
18	**4**	4c. deep blue	£2500	£700
		a. Retouched	£3500	£950
19		4c. blue (1854)	£1400	£475
		a. Retouched	£2000	£650
20		4c. pale blue (1855)	£1000	£400
		a. Retouched	£1500	£550

The 4c. value was produced from transfers from the original 1c., with the bottom inscription removed, teamed with a new face value. The join often shows as a white line or traces of it above the label of value and lower corner figures. In some stamps on the sheet this line is missing, owing to having been retouched, and in these cases a line of colour usually appears in its place.

The 1c. and 4c. stamps were printed in 1865 from fresh transfers of five varieties. These are on thin paper and perf 12½ (*Price* £15 each unused).

1860 (May). *Figures in corners framed. Imperf*
21	**5**	4c. blue	£3750	£500

6

(Type-set and printed at the *Official Gazette* by Baum and Dallas, Georgetown).

1856.

(a) Surface-coloured paper.
23	**6**	1c. black/*magenta*	†	—
24		4c. black/*magenta* (Jan)	—	£7500
25		4c. black/*rose-carmine* (Aug)	£26000	£10000
26		4c. black/*blue* (Sept)	†	£55000

(b) Paper coloured through.
27	**6**	4c. black/*deep blue* (Aug)	†	£80000

Since only one example of No. 23 is known, no market price can be given. This celebrated stamp, frequently termed "the world's rarest", was last on the market in 1980. It is initialled by E. D. Wight and postmarked at Demerara on 4 April 1856.

These stamps, like those of the first issue, were initialled before being issued; the initials are—E.T.E.D (alton), E.D.W. (ight), C.A.W (atson), and W.H.L (ortimer). C.A.W. only appears on stamps postmarked between 14 March and 4 April and also 16–20 May. E.T.E.D. is only known on stamps between 1–5 July and on 1 August. All examples on the rose-carmine or blue papers show E.D.W.

Stamps as Type **6** were printed in sheets of 4 (2×2) each stamp differing slightly in the position of the inscriptions. There is evidence that the setting was re-arranged at some point before August, *possibly* to accommodate the production of the 1c.

PAPERMAKERS' WATERMARKS. Seven different papermakers' watermarks were used in the period 1860 to 1875 and stamps bearing portions of these are worth a premium.

7

A   B

C   D

E   F

(Dies eng and litho Waterlow)

1860 (July)–**63**. *Tablets of value as illustrated. Thick paper.* P 12.
29	**7**	1c. pale rose	£1500	£225
30		2c. deep orange (8.60)	£200	48·00
31		2c. pale orange	£225	50·00
32		4c. deep blue (8.60)	£450	85·00
33		4c. blue	£300	55·00
34		8c. brownish rose	£550	£100
35		8c. pink	£425	70·00
36		12c. lilac	£500	45·00
37		12c. grey-lilac	£425	42·00
38		24c. deep green (6.63)	£1400	£110
39		24c. green	£1000	65·00

The 1c. was reprinted in 1865 on *thin* paper, P 12½–13, and in a different shade. *Price* £17.

The 12c. in both shades is frequently found surcharged with a large "5d" in *red*; this is to denote the proportion of postage repayable by the colony to Great Britain for overseas letters.

1861 (3 Aug*). *Colour changed. Thick paper.* P 12.
40	**7**	1c. reddish brown	£325	95·00

*Earliest known postmark date.

1862–65.(a) Thin paper. P 12.
41	**7**	1c. brown	£475	£190
42		1c. black (1863)	£100	50·00
43		2c. orange	90·00	50·00
44		4c. blue	£110	45·00
45		4c. pale blue	95·00	32·00
46		8c. pink (1863)	£150	60·00
47		12c. dull purple (1863)	£180	28·00
48		12c. purple	£200	32·00
49		12c. lilac	£225	42·00
50		24c. green	£950	90·00

(b) Thin paper. P 12½–13 (1863).
51	**7**	1c. black	60·00	19·00
52		2c. orange	75·00	21·00
53		4c. blue	75·00	17·00
54		8c. pink	£225	80·00
55		12c. brownish lilac	£650	£110
56		24c. green	£650	65·00

Copies are found on *pelure* paper.

(c) Medium paper. P 12½–13.
57	**7**	1c. black (1864)	50·00	42·00
58		2c. deep orange (1864)	£100	26·00
59		2c. orange	70·00	24·00
60		4c. greyish blue (1864)	£300	20·00
61		4c. blue	95·00	26·00
62		8c. pink (1864)	£170	60·00
63		12c. brownish lilac (1865)	£550	£100
64		24c. green (1864)	£200	50·00
65		24c. deep green	£300	75·00

(d) Medium paper. P 10 (No. 1865).
65a	**7**	12c. grey-lilac	£550	80·00

8   9

G   H

I   K

New transfers for the 1c., 2c., 8c., and 12c. with the spaces between values and the word "CENTS" about 1 mm.

1863–76. *Medium paper.*

(a) P 12½–13 (1863–68).
66	**8**	1c. black (1866)	50·00	27·00
67		2c. orange-red (1865)	55·00	7·00
68		2c. orange	55·00	7·00
69	**9**	6c. blue (1865)	£140	60·00
70		6c. greenish blue	£150	65·00
71		6c. deep blue	£225	75·00
72		6c. milky blue	£140	60·00
73	**8**	8c. pink (1868)	£250	21·00
74		8c. carmine	£275	23·00
75		12c. grey-lilac (1867)	£475	35·00
76		12c. brownish purple	£600	45·00
77	**9**	24c. green (*perf* 12)	£275	20·00

78		24c. yellow-green (*perf* 12)	£180	12·00
79		24c. yellow-green (*perf* 12½–13)	£180	12·00
80		24c. green (*perf* 12½–13) (1864)	£180	12·00
81		24c. blue-green (*perf* 12½–13)	£225	20·00
82		48c. pale red	£275	60·00
83		48c. deep red	£300	60·00
84		48c. carmine-rose	£325	60·00

The 4c. corresponding to this issue can only be distinguished from that of the previous issue by minor plating flaws.

There is a variety of the 6c. with stop before "VICISSIM".

Varieties of most of the values of issues of 1863–64 and 1866 are to be found on both very thin and thick papers.

(b) P 10 (1866–71).

85	8	1c. black (1869)	13·00	5·50
86		1c. grey-black	15·00	13·00
87		2c. orange (1868)	30·00	4·00
88		2c. reddish orange	42·00	5·50
89		4c. slate-blue	£100	13·00
90		4c. blue	90·00	8·50
		a. Bisected (on cover)	†	£6000
		b. Ditto. Imperf (on cover)	—
91		4c. pale blue	85·00	15·00
92	9	6c. milky blue (1867)	£150	32·00
93		6c. ultramarine	£160	55·00
94		6c. dull blue	£150	35·00
95	8	8c. pink (5.71)	£150	27·00
96		8c. brownish pink	£180	29·00
96a		8c. carmine	£250	40·00
97		12c. pale lilac (1867)	£250	18·00
98		12c. grey-lilac	£200	17·00
99		12c. brownish grey	£200	19·00
100		12c. lilac	£200	19·00
101	9	24c. deep green	£275	9·50
102		24c. bluish green	£250	8·00
103		24c. yellow-green	£200	7·50
104		48c. crimson (1867)	£325	30·00
		s. Handstamped "Specimen"	£225
		as. Perf "Specimen"	£180
105		48c. red	£300	26·00

(c) P 15 (1875–76).

106	8	1c. black	48·00	7·50
107		2c. orange-red	£130	9·50
108		2c. orange	£130	9·50
109		4c. bright blue	£225	95·00
111	9	6c. ultramarine	£750	95·00
112	8	8c. deep rose (1876)	£250	85·00
113		12c. lilac	£600	65·00
114	9	24c. yellow-green	£650	35·00
115		24c. deep green	£1100	75·00

There is a variety of the 48c. with stop after "P" in "PETIMUSQUE".

Imperforate stamps of this and the previous issue are considered to be proofs, although examples of the 24c. imperforate from the 1869–73 period are known commercially used.

PRICES for stamps of the 1862 issue are for good average copies. Copies with roulettes on all sides very seldom occur and do not exist in marginal positions.

10   11   12
13   14   15

(Type-set and printed at the Office of the *Royal Gazette*, Georgetown)

1862 (Sept). Black on coloured paper. Roul 6.

116	10	1c. *rose*	£3250	£500
		a. Unsigned	£400
		b. Wrong ornament (as T 13) at left (R. 1/1)	—	£850
		c. "1" for "I" in "BRITISH" (R. 1/5)	—	£850
117	11	1c. *rose*	£4000	£700
		a. Unsigned	£450
		b. Narrow "T" in "CENTS" (R. 3/1)	—	£850
		c. Wrong ornament (as T 15) at top (R. 3/3)	—	£850
		d. "1" for "I" in "BRITISH" and italic "S" in "POSTAGE" (R. 3/5)	—	£850
118	12	1c. *rose*	£6000	£900
		a. Unsigned	£750
		b. "1" for "I" in "GUIANA" (R. 4/4)	—	£900
		c. Wrong ornament (as T 15) at left (R. 4/5)	—	£900
		d. "C" for "O" in "POSTAGE" (R. 4/6)	—	£900
119	10	2c. *yellow*	£3250	£325
		a. Unsigned	£1400
		b. Wrong ornament (as T 13) at left (R. 1/1)	—	£550
		c. "1" for "I" in "BRITISH" (R. 1/5)	—	£550
120	11	2c. *yellow*	£4000	£400
		a. Unsigned	£1500
		b. "C" for "O" in "TWO" and narrow "T" in "CENTS" (R. 3/1)	—	£550
		c. Wrong ornament (as T 15) at top (R. 3/3)	—	£550
		d. Italic "S" in "CENTS" (R. 3/4).	—	£550

		e. "1" for "I" in "BRITISH" and italic "S" in "POSTAGE" (R. 3/5)	—	£550
		f. Italic "T" in "TWO" (R. 3/6)	—	£550
121	12	2c. *yellow*	£6000	£650
		a. Unsigned	£1800
		b. "1" for "I" in "GUIANA" (R. 4/4)	—	£650
		c. Wrong ornament (as T 15) at left (R. 4/5)	—	£650
		d. "C" for "O" in "POSTAGE" (R. 4/6)	—	£650
122	13	4c. *blue*	£3500	£650
		a. Unsigned	£750
		b. Wrong ornament (as T 15) at left (R. 1/6)	£4750	£1100
		c. Wrong ornament (as T 15) at top and italic "S" in "CENTS" (R. 2/2)	—	£1100
		d. Ornament omitted at right (R. 2/4)	—	£1100
123	14	4c. *blue*	£4500	£900
		a. Unsigned	£800
		b. With inner frame lines (as in T 10/13) (R. 2/5–6)	£6500	£1500
		ba. "1" for "I" in "BRITISH" (R. 2/5)	£6500	£1500
		c. "1" for "I" in "BRITISH" and "GUIANA" (R. 4/1)	—	£1100
124	15	4c. *blue*	£4500	£900
		a. Unsigned	£850
		b. Wrong ornament (as T 12) at foot (R. 3/1)	—	£1100
		c. Italic "S" in "CENTS" (R. 3/2).	—	£1100
		d. Italic "S" in "BRITISH" (R. 3/3)	—	£1100

Stamps were initialled across the centre before use by the Acting Receiver-General, Robert Mather. Black was used on the 1c., red for the 2c. and an ink which appears white for the 4c.

The three values of this provisional were each printed in sheets of 24 (6×4). The 1c. and 2c. were produced from the same setting of the border ornaments which contained 12 examples as Type 10 (Rows 1 and 2), 8 as Type 11 (R. 3/1 to R. 4/2) and 4 as Type 12 (R. 4/3-6).

The setting of the 4c. contained 10 examples as Type 13 (R. 1/1 to R. 2/4), 8 as Type 14 (R. 2/5–6 and Row 4) and 6 as Type 15 (Row 3).

16   (17)

(Typo D.L.R.)

1876 (1 July)–79. Wmk Crown CC.

(a) P 14.

126	16	1c. slate	2·75	1·40
		w. Wmk inverted	£150
127		2c. orange	60·00	2·25
		w. Wmk inverted
128		4c. blue	£120	9·00
129		6c. brown	75·00	7·50
130		8c. rose	£110	75
		w. Wmk inverted
131		12c. pale violet	50·00	1·25
		w. Wmk inverted
132		24c. emerald-green	60·00	3·00
		w. Wmk inverted
133		48c. red-brown	£130	30·00
134		96c. olive-bistre	£475	£250
126/34		Set of 9	£950	£250
126s/32s, 134s Handstamped "Specimen" Set of 8 ..			£750
131sa/2sa Perf "Specimen" Set of 2			£200

(b) P 12½ (1877).

135	16	4c. blue	£1200	£200

(c) Perf compound of 14×12½ (1879).

136	16	1c. slate		£200

1878. Provisionals. Various stamps with old values ruled through with thick bars, in black ink, the bars varying in depth of colour.

(a) With two horiz bars (17 Apr).

137	16	(1c.) on 6c. brown	38·00	£110

(b) Official stamps with horiz bars across "OFFICIAL" (end Aug).

138	8	1c. black	£225	75·00
139	16	1c. slate	£170	65·00
140		2c. orange	£325	65·00

(c) With horiz and vert bars as T 17 (6 Nov).

141	9	(1c.) on 6c. ultramarine (93)	£180	75·00
142	16	(1c.) on 6c. brown	£300	£110
		a. Optd with vert bar only ..	†	£5000

(d) Official stamps with bars across "OFFICIAL" (23 Nov).

(i) With two horiz bars and one vert.

144	16	(1c.) on 4c. blue	£300	£100
145		(1c.) on 6c. brown	£450	£110
146	8	(2c.) on 8c. rose	£2500	£300

(ii) With one horiz bar and one vert.

147	16	(1c.) on 4c. blue	†	£3000
148		(2c.) on 8c. rose	£425	£120

1   **2**   **2**
(18)   (19)   (20)

1881 (21 Dec). No. 134 with old value ruled through with bar in black ink and surch.

149	18	1c. on 96c. olive-bistre	3·50	6·00
		a. Bar in red
		b. Bar omitted
150	19	2c. on 96c. olive-bistre	6·00	11·00
		a. Bar in red
151	20	2c. on 96c. olive-bistre	50·00	£100
		a. Bar in red

In the setting of 60 Type **19** occurs on the first five vertical rows and Type **20** on the sixth.

1   **2**   **2**
(21)   (23)   (24)

1881 (28 Dec). Various stamps with old value ruled with bar and surch.

(a) On No. 105.

152	21	1c. on 48c. red	45·00	5·00
		a. Bar omitted	—	£600

(b) On Official stamps (including unissued 48c. optd with Type O 2).

153	21	1 on 12c. brownish purple (O4)	£130	70·00
154		1 on 48c. red-brown	£170	£100
155	23	2 on 12c. pale violet (O11)	75·00	32·00
		a. Pair. Nos. 155/6	£1200	£1400
		b. Surch double	£800	£450
		c. Surch double (T 23 + 24)	£3750
		d. Extra bar through "OFFICIAL"
156	24	2 on 12c. pale violet (O11)	£550	£350
157	23	2 on 24c. emerald-green (O12)	85·00	48·00
		a. Pair. Nos. 157/8	£1500	£1600
		b. Surch double	£1100
158	24	2 on 24c. emerald-green (O12)	£700	£750
159	19	2 on 24c. green (O5)	£300	£150

On Nos. 149/59 the bar is found in various thicknesses ranging from 1 to 4 mm.

It is believed that the same composite surcharge setting of 60 (6×10) was used for Nos. 155/6 and 157/8. Type **24** occurs on R. 7/2, 4-6 and R. 8/1.

26   27

(Type-set, Baldwin & Co. Georgetown)

1882 (9 Jan). Black impression. P 12. Perforated with the word "SPECIMEN" diagonally.

162	26	1c. *magenta*	45·00	28·00
		a. Imperf between (horiz pair)	†
		b. Without "SPECIMEN"	£700	£400
		c. "1" with foot	£100	70·00
163		2c. *yellow*	80·00	50·00
		a. Without "SPECIMEN"	£600	£475
		b. Small "2"	80·00	50·00
164	27	1c. *magenta*	45·00	28·00
		a. Without "SPECIMEN"	£700	£400
		b. "1" with foot	£100	70·00
		c. Imperf between (horiz pair)	†	£5500
165		2c. *yellow*	75·00	50·00
		a. Bisected diagonally (1c.) (on cover)
		b. Without "SPECIMEN"	£600	£475
		c. Small "2"	£130	90·00

These stamps were perforated "SPECIMEN" as a precaution against fraud. Stamps are known with "SPECIMEN" double.

The 1c. and 2c. stamps were printed in separate sheets; but utilising the same clichés, these being altered according to the face value required. Two settings were used, common to both values:—

1st setting. Four rows of three, T **26** being Nos. 5, 6, 7, 8, 11 and 12, and T **27** the remainder.

From this setting there were two printings of the 2c., but only one of the 1c.

2nd setting. Six rows of two, T **26** being Nos. 3, 7, 8, 9, 11 and 12, and T **27** the remainder.

There were two printings of each value from this setting.

Se-tenant pairs are worth about 20% more.

The "1" with foot occurs on T **27** in the first setting and on T **26** on No. 7 in the first printing only of the second setting.

The small "2" appears on T **26** in the first setting on Nos. 6, 7 8 and 12 in the first printing and on Nos. 7, 8 and 12 in the second printing: in the second setting it comes on Nos. 3, 9 and 12 in the first printing and on Nos. 9, 11 and 12 in the second printing. On T **27** the variety occurs in the first setting on No. 9 of the second printing only and in the second setting on No. 10 in both printings.

(Typo D.L.R.)

1882. Wmk Crown C.A. P 14.

170	16	1c. slate (27 Jan)	8·50	30
		x. Wmk reversed	†	£150
171		2c. orange (27 Jan)	24·00	15
		a. Value doubly printed	†	£6000
		x. Wmk reversed
172		4c. blue	90·00	5·00
173		6c. brown	5·00	6·50
		w. Wmk inverted
174		8c. rose	90·00	40
		x. Wmk reversed
170/4		Set of 5	£190	11·00
170s/4s Perf "Specimen" Set of 5			£300

INLAND

2 CENTS
REVENUE
(28)

4 CENTS	4 CENTS
(a)	(b)

Two types of "4"

6	6
(c)	(d)

Two types of "6"

1888–89. *T* **16** *(without value in lower label) optd "INLAND REVENUE", and surch with value as T* **28**, *by D.L.R. Wmk Crown CA. P* 14.

175		1c. dull purple (8.89)	1·25	20
176		2c. dull purple (25.5.89)	1·25	55
177		3c. dull purple	1·00	20
178		4c. dull purple (a)	10·00	30
		a. Larger figure "4" (b)	20·00	6·00
179		6c. dull purple (c)	9·00	3·75
		a. Figure 6 with straight top (d)	19·00	4·50
180		8c. dull purple (8.89)	1·50	30
181		10c. dull purple	6·00	2·50
182		20c. dull purple	20·00	14·00
183		40c. dull purple	22·00	23·00
184		72c. dull purple (1.10.88)	45·00	60·00
185		$1 green (1.10.88)	£425	£550
186		$2 green (1.10.88)	£200	£250
187		$3 green (1.10.88)	£160	£200
188		$4 green (a) (1.10.88)	£475	£650
		a. Larger figure "4" (b)	£1600	£1900
189		$5 green (1.10.88)	£300	£325
175/89 Set of 15			£1500	£1800

Nos. 175/89 were surcharged in settings of 60 (6×10). No. 178a occurs on all stamps in the third vertical row, No. 179a in the fourth and sixth vertical rows and No. 188a in the second vertical row.

INLAND

One Cent	
1 DOLLAR (struck through)	
2	REVENUE
(29)	(31)
30	

1889 (6 June). *No. 176 surch with T* **29** *in red by Official Gazette.*

192		"2" on 2c. dull purple	2·50	15

The varieties with figure "2" *inverted* or *double* were made privately by a postal employee in Demerara.

1889 (Sept). *Wmk Crown CA. P* 14.

193	30	1c. dull purple and slate-grey	4·00	1·75
194		2c. dull purple and orange	2·50	10
		w. Wmk inverted		
195		4c. dull purple and ultramarine	4·50	2·25
196		4c. dull purple and cobalt	21·00	2·25
197		6c. dull purple and brown	35·00	18·00
198		6c. dull purple and maroon	7·00	14·00
199		8c. dull purple and rose	12·00	2·00
		w. Wmk inverted	—	80·00
200		12c. dull purple and bright purple	18·00	2·50
200a		12c. dull purple and mauve	8·50	2·50
201		24c. dull purple and green	6·00	2·50
202		48c. dull purple and orange-red	18·00	9·00
		x. Wmk reversed		
203		72c. dull purple and red-brown	28·00	38·00
204		72c. dull purple and yellow-brown	65·00	75·00
205		96c. dull purple and carmine	65·00	70·00
		x. Wmk reversed		
206		96c. dull purple and cosine	75·00	80·00
193/205 Set of 10			£140	£120
193s/205s Optd "Specimen" Set of 10			£140	

1890 (15 July). *Stamps of 1888-89 surch locally "One Cent", in red, as in T* **31**.

207		1c. on $1 (No. 185)	1·25	35
		a. Surch double	£180	£120
208		1c. on $2 (No. 186)	2·00	60
		a. Surch double	85·00	
209		1c. on $3 (No. 187)	2·00	1·25
		a. Surch double	£110	
210		1c. on $4 (No. 188)	2·00	7·00
		a. Surch double	95·00	
		b. Larger figure "4" (b)	12·00	30·00
207/10 Set of 4			6·50	8·50

1890–91. *Colours changed. Wmk Crown CA. P* 14

213	30	1c. sea-green (12.90)	75	10
214		5c. ultramarine (1.91)	2·75	10
215		8c. dull purple and greenish black (10.90)	2·75	1·10
213/15 Set of 3			5·50	1·10
213s/15s Optd "Specimen" Set of 3			60·00	

32 Mount Roraima

33 Kaieteur Falls

(Recess D.L.R.)

1898 (18 July). *Queen Victoria's Jubilee. Wmk Crown CC (sideways* on T* **32**). *P* 14.

216	32	1c. blue-black and carmine-red	5·00	1·25
		w. Wmk Crown to left of CC	6·00	1·40
		x. Wmk sideways reversed		
		y. Wmk sideways inverted and reversed		
217	33	2c. brown and indigo	25·00	3·00
		a. Imperf between (horiz pair)	£8000	
		x. Wmk reversed	—	£120
218		2c. brown and blue	27·00	3·00
219	32	5c. deep green and sepia	48·00	4·00
		a. Imperf between (horiz pair)		
		w. Wmk Crown to left of CC	45·00	3·75
220	33	10c. blue-black and brown-red	25·00	20·00
221	32	15c. red-brown and blue	30·00	17·00
216/21 Set of 5			£120	40·00
216s/21s Optd "Specimen" Set of 5			£110	

*The normal sideways watermark on Type **32** shows Crown to right of CC, *as seen from the back of the stamp.*

A second plate was later used for the 1c. on which the lines of shading on the mountains in the background are strengthened, and those along the ridge show distinct from each other, whereas, in the original, they are more or less blurred. In the second plate the shading of the sky is less pronounced.

TWO CENTS.	CE	
(34)	Shaved "E"	**35**

(Surch at Printing Office of the *Daily Chronicle*, Georgetown)

1899 (24 Feb–15 June). *Surch with T* **34**.

222	32	2c. on 5c. (No. 219) (15 June)	3·25	2·00
		a. No stop after "CENTS"	£130	85·00
		b. Comma after "CENTS" (R. 7/2)	65·00	
		c. "CINTS" (R. 4/1)	£140	
		d. Shaved "E" (R. 6/2)	42·00	
		w. Wmk Crown to left of CC	3·75	2·25
223	33	2c. on 10c. (No. 220)	2·25	2·25
		a. No stop after "CENTS" (R. 5/5 or 2/9)	20·00	50·00
		b. "GENTS" for "CENTS" (R. 5/7)	50·00	70·00
		c. Surch inverted	£500	£600
		ca. Surch inverted and stop omitted	£3750	
		d. Shaved "E" (R. 4/2 or 3/8)	27·00	
		x. Wmk reversed	£100	
224	32	2c. on 15c. (No. 221)	1·50	1·25
		a. No stop after "CENTS" (R. 9/2)	65·00	65·00
		b. Surch double	£750	£900
		ba. Surch double, one without stop		
		d. Surch inverted	£500	£700
		da. Surch inverted and stop omitted		
		f. Shaved "E" (R. 6/2)	38·00	
222/4 Set of 3			6·25	5·00

No. 222c was caused by damage to the first "E" of "CENTS" which developed during surcharging. The listing is for an example with only the upright stroke of the letter visible.

There were two settings of No. 223 with the no stop and shaved "E" varieties occurring on R. 5/5 and R. 4/2 of the first and on R. 2/9 and R. 3/8 of the second.

No. 224b occurred on the first five vertical columns of one sheet, the surcharges on the right hand vertical column being normal.

Only two examples of No. 224ba are known.

There is only one known example of No. 224da.

1900–03. *Wmk Crown CA. P* 14.

233	30	1c. grey-green (1902)	1·75	3·25
234		2c. dull purple and carmine	3·25	30
235		2c. dull purple and black/*red* (1901)	1·25	10
		w. Wmk inverted	—	80·00
236		6c. grey-black and ultramarine (1902)	6·50	11·00
237		48c. grey and purple-brown (1901)	50·00	35·00
		a. Brownish grey and brown	29·00	28·00
238		60c. green and rosine (1903)	60·00	£180
233/8 Set of 6			90·00	£200
233s/8s Optd "Specimen" Set of 6			95·00	

No. 233 is a reissue of No. 213 in non-fugitive ink.

1905–07. *Wmk Multiple Crown CA. Ordinary paper (1c. to 60c.) or chalk-surfaced paper (72, 96c.).*

240	30	1c. grey-green	4·25	30
		aw. Wmk inverted		
		b. Chalk-surfaced paper	5·50	30
241		2c. purple and black/*red*	9·50	10
		a. Chalk-surfaced paper	3·50	10
242		4c. dull purple and ultramarine	8·00	14·00
		a. Chalk-surfaced paper	6·00	12·00
243		5c. dull purple and blue/*blue* (1.5.05)	11·00	13·00
		a. Chalk-surfaced paper	3·50	6·50
		s. Optd "Specimen"	21·00	
244		6c. grey-black and ultramarine	16·00	45·00
		a. Chalk-surfaced paper	15·00	42·00
		aw. Wmk inverted		
245		12c. dull and bright purple	22·00	32·00
		a. Chalk-surfaced paper	22·00	42·00
246		24c. dull purple and green (1906)	11·00	12·00
		a. Chalk-surfaced paper	3·75	4·50
247		48c. grey and purple-brown	25·00	30·00
		a. Chalk-surfaced paper	14·00	20·00
248		60c. green and rosine	25·00	85·00
		a. Chalk-surfaced paper	14·00	85·00
249		72c. purple and orange-brown (1907)	32·00	65·00

250		96c. black & vermilion/*yellow* (20.11.05)	35·00	45·00
		s. Optd "Specimen"	32·00	
240/50 Set of 11			£140	£275

1905. *Optd "POSTAGE AND REVENUE". Wmk Multiple Crown CA. Chalk-surfaced paper. P* 14.

251	35	$2.40, green and violet	£160	£275
		s. Optd "Specimen"	75·00	

1907–10. *Colours changed. Wmk Mult Crown CA. P* 14

252	30	1c. blue-green	15·00	2·75
253		2c. rose-red	16·00	10
		a. Redrawn (1910)	8·50	10
254		4c. brown and purple	2·25	60
255		5c. ultramarine	14·00	3·00
256		6c. grey and black	13·00	7·00
257		12c. orange and mauve	4·00	4·00
252/7 Set of 6			50·00	15·00
253s/7s Optd "Specimen" Set of 5			75·00	

In No. 253a the flag at the main truck is close to the mast, whereas in the original type it appears to be flying loose from halyards. There are two background lines above the value "2 CENTS" instead of three and the "S" is further away from the end of the tablet.

34

37

War Tax

(38)

(Typo D.L.R.)

1913–21. *Wmk Mult Crown CA. Chalk-surfaced paper (4c. and 48c. to 96c.). P* 14.

259	37	1c. yellow-green	2·50	80
		a. Blue-green (1917)	1·50	25
		ay. Wmk inverted and reversed	†	£275
260		2c. carmine	1·25	10
		a. Scarlet (1916)	3·00	10
		b. Wmk sideways	†	£2000
261		4c. brown and bright purple (1914)	5·50	25
		aw. Wmk inverted		
		b. Deep brown and purple	3·75	25
262		5c. bright blue	1·75	10
263		6c. grey and black	2·75	1·25
264		12c. orange and violet	1·25	1·00
265		24c. dull purple and green (1915)	3·25	4·00
266		48c. grey and purple-brown (1914)	22·00	17·00
267		60c. green and rosine (1915)	15·00	50·00
268		72c. purple and orange-brown (1915)	42·00	75·00
269		96c. black and vermilion/*yellow* (1915)	30·00	60·00
		a. White back (1913)	20·00	48·00
		b. On lemon (1916)	19·00	48·00
		bs. Optd "Specimen"	32·00	
		c. On pale yellow (1921)	20·00	60·00
		cs. Optd "Specimen"	32·00	
259/69a Set of 11			£110	£180
259s/69as Optd "Specimen" Set of 11			£140	

Examples of Nos. 267/9c are known with part strikes of forged postmarks of Grove dated "29 OCT 1909" and of Georgetown dated "30 OCT 1909".

1918 (4 Jan). *No. 260a optd with T* **38**, *by D.L.R.*

271	37	2c. scarlet	1·25	15

The relative position of the words "WAR" and "TAX" vary considerably in the sheet.

1921–27. *Wmk Mult Script CA. Chalk-surfaced paper (24c. to 96c.). P* 14.

272	37	1c. green (1922)	4·75	30
273		2c. rose-carmine	4·25	20
		w. Wmk inverted	†	£150
274		2c. bright violet (1923)	2·50	10
275		4c. brown and bright purple (1922)	4·75	10
276		6c. bright blue (1922)	3·00	30
277		12c. orange and violet (1922)	2·75	1·50
278		24c. dull purple and green	2·00	4·50
279		48c. black and purple (1926)	9·50	3·50
280		60c. green and rosine (1926)	10·00	48·00
281		72c. dull purple & orange-brown (1923)	24·00	65·00
282		96c. black and red/*yellow* (1927)	20·00	45·00
272/82 Set of 11			80·00	£150
272s/82s Optd "Specimen" Set of 11			£160	

39 Ploughing a Rice Field

40 Indian shooting Fish

41 Kaieteur Falls

42 Public buildings, Georgetown

(Recess Waterlow)

1931 (21 July). *Centenary of County Union.* T **39/42**. Wmk Mult
Script CA. P 12½.

283	**39**	1c. emerald-green	2·50	1·25
284	**40**	2c. brown	2·00	10
285	**41**	4c. carmine	1·75	45
286	**42**	6c. blue	2·25	2·75
287	**41**	$1 violet	27·00	48·00
283/7 *Set of 5*			32·00	48·00
283s/7s Perf "Specimen" *Set of 5*			80·00	

\

43 Ploughing a Rice Field   **44** Gold Mining

45 Shooting logs over falls   **46** Stabroek Market

47 Sugar canes in punts   **48** Forest road

49 Victoria Regia Lilies   **50** Mount Roraima

51 Sir Walter Raleigh   **52** Botanical Gardens
and his son

(Recess Waterlow)

1934 (1 Oct)–**51**. T **40** (*without dates at top of frame*) *and* **43/52**.
Wmk Mult Script CA (*sideways on horiz designs*). P 12½.

288	**43**	1c. green	60	1·25
289	**40**	2c. red-brown	1·50	70
290	**44**	3c. scarlet	30	10
		aa. Wmk error. Crown missing	£2750	£1800
		a. Perf 12½×13½ (30.12.43)	60	80
		b. Perf 13×14 (28.4.49)	60	10
291	**45**	4c. slate-violet	2·00	2·00
		b. Imperf between (vert pair)	†	£20000
		b. Imperf horiz (vert pair)	£9000	£10000
292	**45**	6c. deep ultramarine	2·75	4·50
293	**46**	12c. red-orange	20	20
		a. Perf 14×13 (16.4.51)	50	1·00
294	**47**	24c. purple	3·50	8·00
295	**48**	48c. black	7·00	8·50
296	**41**	50c. green	10·00	17·00
297	**49**	60c. red-brown	26·00	27·00
298	**50**	72c. purple	1·25	2·25
299	**51**	96c. black	20·00	30·00
300	**52**	$1 bright violet	32·00	30·00
288/300 *Set of 13*			95·00	£110
288s/300s Perf "Specimen" *Set of 13*			£170	

Examples of Nos. 295/300 are known with forged
Georgetown postmarks dated "24 JY 31" or "6 MY 35".

1935 (6 May). *Silver Jubilee. As Nos. 91/4 of Antigua.*

301		2c. ultramarine and grey	20	10
		f. Diagonal line by turret	32·00	
		h. Dot by flagstaff	80·00	
302		6c. brown and deep blue	1·25	3·00
		f. Diagonal line by turret	75·00	
		g. Dot to left of chapel	£110	
		h. Dot by flagstaff	£110	
303		12c. green and indigo	4·50	8·00
		f. Diagonal line by turret	£110	
		h. Dot by flagstaff	£180	
		i. Dash by turret	£180	
304		24c. slate and purple	7·50	9·50
		h. Dot by flagstaff	£225	
		i. Dash by turret	£225	
301/4 *Set of 4*			12·00	18·00
301s/4s Perf "Specimen" *Set of 4*			95·00	

For illustrations of plate varieties see Omnibus section
following Zanzibar.

1937 (12 May). *Coronation. As Nos. 95/7 of Antigua, but ptd by
D.L.R.* P 14.

305	2c. yellow-brown	15	10
306	4c. grey-black	50	40
307	6c. bright blue	60	1·50
305/7 *Set of 3*		1·10	1·75
305s/7s Perf "Specimen" *Set of 3*		75·00	

53 South America   **54** Victoria Regia Lilies

(Recess Waterlow)

1938 (1 Feb)–**52**. *As earlier types but with portrait of King
George VI as in T* **53/4**. Wmk Mult Script CA. P 12½

308	**43**	1c. yellow-green	18·00	55
		a. Green (1940)	30	10
		ab. Perf 14×13 (1949)	30	80
309	**41**	2c. slate-violet	60	10
		a. Perf 13×14 (28.4.49)	30	10
310	**53**	4c. scarlet and black	70	30
		a. Imperf horiz (vert pair)	£20000	£15000
		b. Perf 13×14 (1952)	50	15
311	**40**	6c. deep ultramarine	40	10
		a. Perf 13×14 (24.10.49)	50	30
312	**47**	24c. blue-green	26·00	10·00
		a. Wmk sideways	1·25	10
313	**41**	36c. bright violet (7.3.38)	2·00	20
		a. Perf 13×14 (13.12.51)	3·00	30
314	**48**	48c. orange	60	50
		a. Perf 14×13 (8.5.51*)	1·50	15
315	**49**	60c. red-brown	15·00	6·50
316	**51**	96c. purple	3·75	2·50
		a. Perf 12½×13½ (1944)	6·00	8·50
		b. Perf 13×14 (8.2.51)	2·75	6·50
317	**52**	$1 bright violet	14·00	35
		a. Perf 14×13 (1951)	£400	£500
318	**50**	$2 purple (11.6.45)	6·50	18·00
		a. Perf 14×13 (9.8.50)	12·00	18·00
319	**54**	$3 red-brown (2.7.45)	28·00	27·00
		a. Bright red-brown (12.46)	29·00	28·00
		b. Perf 14×13. Red-brown (29.10.52)	26·00	45·00
308a/19 *Set of 12*			65·00	50·00
308s/19s Perf "Specimen" *Set of 12*			£250	

Designs: *Vert*—2c., 36c. Kaieteur Falls; 96c. Sir Walter
Raleigh and his son. *Horiz*—24c. Sugar cane in punts; 48c.
Forest road; 60c. Shooting logs over falls; $1 Botanical
Gardens; $2 Mount Roraima.

*Earliest known postmark date.

1946 (21 Oct). *Victory. As Nos. 110/11 of Antigua.*

320	3c. carmine	10	40
321	6c. blue	40	85
320s/1s Perf "Specimen" *Set of 2*		65·00	

1948 (20 Dec). *Royal Silver Wedding. As Nos. 112/13 of
Antigua, but $3 in recess.*

322	3c. scarlet	10	40
323	$3 red-brown	14·00	23·00

1949 (10 Oct). *75th Anniv of Universal Postal Union. As Nos.
114/17 of Antigua.*

324	4c. carmine	10	40
325	6c. deep blue	1·50	1·25
326	12c. orange	15	50
327	24c. blue-green	15	70
324/7 *Set of 4*		1·60	2·50

1951 (16 Feb). *University College of B.W.I. As Nos. 118/19 of
Antigua.*

328	3c. black and carmine	30	50
329	6c. black and blue	30	65

STAMP BOOKLETS

1909 (14 June). *Black on pink cover without face value. Stapled.*

SB1	49c. booklet containing twelve 1c. and eighteen 2c. (Nos. 252/3) in blocks of 6	£2000

1923. *Black on pink cover without face value. Stapled.*

SB2	30c. booklet containing six 1c. and twelve 2c. (Nos. 272, 274) in blocks of 6	

1923. *Black on pink without face value. Stapled.*

SB3	48c. booklet containing four 1c. and eighteen 2c. (Nos. 272, 274) in blocks of 6	£1600
	a. With face value on front cover	

1923. *Black on red cover without face value. Stapled.*

SB4	72c. booklet containing four 1c., six 2c. and twelve 4c. (Nos. 272, 274/5) in blocks of 6	£2500

1934. *Black on orange cover. Stitched.*

SB5	24c. booklet containing eight 1c. and 2c. (Nos. 288/9) in blocks of 4	

1934. *Black on orange cover. Stitched.*

SB6	36c. booklet containing four 1c., eight 2c. and four 4c. (Nos. 288/9, 291) in blocks of 4	

1938. *Black on orange cover. Stitched.*

SB7	36c. booklet containing four 1c., eight 2c. and four 4c. (Nos. 308/10) in blocks of 4	£425

1944. *Black on orange cover. Stitched.*

SB8	24c. booklet containing eight 1c. and eight 2c. (Nos. 308/9) in blocks of 4	£200

1945–49. *Black on red cover. Stitched.*

SB9	24c. booklet containing 1c., 2c. and 3c. (Nos. 290, 308, 309), each in block of 4		
	a. Containing Nos. 290, 308a, 309		65·00
	b. Containing Nos. 290, 308a, 309a		65·00
	c. Containing Nos. 290a, 308a, 309		65·00
	d. Containing Nos. 290b, 308a, 309		75·00
	e. Containing Nos. 290b, 308a, 309a		75·00
	f. Containing Nos. 290b, 308ab, 309a		75·00

POSTAGE DUE STAMPS

D 1

(Typo D.L.R.)

1940 (Mar)–**55**. Wmk Mult Script CA. *Chalk-surfaced paper (4c.)*.
P 14.

D1	**D 1**	1c. green	6·00	7·50
		a. Chalk-surfaced paper. Deep green, (30.4.52)	1·50	14·00
		ab. W **9a** (Crown missing)	£325	
		ac. W **9b** (St. Edward's Crown)	£120	
D2		2c. black	24·00	2·00
		a. Chalk-surfaced paper (30.4.52)	2·00	4·00
		ab. W **9a** (Crown missing)	£250	
		ac. W **9b** (St. Edward's Crown)	£100	
D3		4c. bright blue (1.5.52)	30	11·00
		a. W **9a** (Crown missing)	£225	
		b. W **9b** (St. Edward's Crown)	£100	
D4		12c. scarlet	30·00	4·50
		a. Chalk-surfaced paper (19.7.55)	16·00	27·00
D1a/4a *Set of 4*			18·00	50·00
D1s, D2s and D4s Perf "Specimen" *Set of 3*			65·00	

OFFICIAL STAMPS

OFFICIAL   OFFICIAL   OFFICIAL
(O 1)   (O 1a)   (O 2)

1875. *Optd with Type O* **1** (*1c.*) *or O* **1a** (*others*) *by litho.* P 10.

O1	**8**	1c. black (R.)	55·00	18·00
		a. Imperf between (horiz pair)	†	£12000
O2		2c. orange	£180	14·00
O3		8c. rose	£325	£120
O4	**7**	12c. brownish purple	£2500	£500
O5	**9**	24c. green	£1100	£225

Two types of the word "OFFICIAL" are found on each
value. On the 1c. the word is either 16 or 17 mm long. On
the other values the chief difference is in the shape and
position of the letter "o" in "OFFICIAL". In one case the "o"
is upright, in the other it slants to the left.

1877. *Optd with Type O* **2** *by typo.* Wmk Crown CC. P 14.

O6	**16**	1c. slate	£250	65·00
		a. Imperf between (vert pair)	†	£17000
O7		2c. orange	£120	15·00
O8		4c. blue	85·00	20·00
O9		6c. brown	£5500	£600
O10		8c. rose	£2000	£450

Prepared for use, but not issued.

O11	**16**	12c. pale violet	£1500
O12		24c. green	£1700

The "OFFICIAL" overprints have been extensively forged.

The use of Official stamps was discontinued in June 1878.

British Honduras

It is recorded that the first local post office was established
by the inhabitants in 1809, but Belize did not become a
regular packet port of call until December 1829. The post
office came under the control of the British G.P.O. in April
1844 and the stamps of Great Britain were supplied for use
on overseas mail from May 1858.

The colonial authorities took over the postal service on 1
April 1860, the Great Britain stamps being withdrawn at the
end of the month. There was no inland postal service until
1862.

For illustrations of the handstamp and postmark types see
BRITISH POST OFFICES ABROAD notes, following GREAT
BRITAIN.

BELIZE

CROWNED-CIRCLE HANDSTAMPS

CC1	CC **1** BELIZE (R.) (13.11.1841)		
		Price on cover	£4000

Stamps of GREAT BRITAIN *cancelled* "A 06" *as Type* **2**.

1858–60.

Z1	1d. rose-red (1857), *perf* 14		£900
Z2	4d. rose (1857)		£375
Z3	6d. lilac (1856)		£375
Z4	1s. green (1856)		£1600

PRICES FOR STAMPS ON COVER TO 1945

Nos. 1/4	*from* × 20
Nos. 5/16	*from* × 25
Nos. 17/22	*from* × 20
Nos. 23/6	*from* × 10
Nos. 27/30	*from* × 15
Nos. 35/42	*from* × 20
Nos. 43/4	*from* × 30
Nos. 49/50	*from* × 25

PRICES FOR STAMPS ON COVER TO 1945	
Nos. 51/69	*from* × 15
Nos. 80/100	*from* × 6
Nos. 101/10	*from* × 5
Nos. 111/20	*from* × 15
Nos. 121/2	*from* × 8
No. 123	*from* × 10
Nos. 124/37	*from* × 6
Nos. 138/42	*from* × 10
Nos. 143/9	*from* × 3
Nos. 150/61	*from* × 5
Nos. D1/3	*from* × 30

CROWN COLONY

1

(Typo D.L.R.)

1865 (1 Dec). No wmk. P 14.
1	**1**	1d. pale blue	60·00	60·00
		a. Imperf between (pair)		
2		1d. blue	80·00	70·00
3		6d. rose	£350	£160
4		1s. green	£325	£120
		a. In horiz pair with 6d.	£40000	
		b. In vert pair with 1d.	£50000	

In the first printing all three values were printed in the same sheet separated by horizontal and vertical gutter margins. The sheet comprised two panes of 60 of the 1s. at the top with a pane of 60 of the 1s. at bottom left and another of 6d. at bottom right. Copies of 1d. *se-tenant* with the 6d. are not known. There were two later printings of the 1d. but they were in sheets without the 6d. and 1s.

1872–79. Wmk Crown CC.

(a) P 12½.
5	**1**	1d. pale blue	85·00	19·00
		w. Wmk inverted	£250	
		y. Wmk inverted and reversed		
6		1d. deep blue (1874)	95·00	19·00
7		3d. red-brown	£150	75·00
8		3d. chocolate (1874)	£170	95·00
9		6d. rose	£325	45·00
9a		6d. bright rose-carmine (1874)	£500	60·00
10		1s. green	£475	29·00
10a		1s. deep green (1874)	£425	23·00
		b. Imperf between (horiz pair)	†	£20000
		w. Wmk inverted		

(b) P 14 (1877–79).
11	**1**	1d. pale blue (1878)	80·00	17·00
12		1d. blue	75·00	12·00
		a. Imperf between (horiz strip of 3)	£20000	
13		3d. chestnut	£140	19·00
14		4d. mauve (1879)	£200	8·50
		x. Wmk reversed		
15		6d. rose (1878)	£400	£190
		w. Wmk inverted	—	£400
16		1s. green	£275	11·00
		a. Imperf between (pair)		

1882–87. Wmk Crown CA. P 14.
17	**1**	1d. blue (4.84)	50·00	13·00
18		1d. rose (1884)	23·00	13·00
		a. Bisected (½d.) (on cover)	£200	
		s. Optd "Specimen"	£200	
19		1d. carmine (1887)	50·00	18·00
20		4d. mauve (7.82)	80·00	4·75
		w. Wmk inverted	—	£120
21		6d. yellow (1885)	£275	£200
22		1s. grey (1.87)	£250	£160
		s. Optd "Specimen"	75·00	

(New Currency. 100 cents = 1 British Honduras dollar)

2
CENTS
(2)

TWO
(3)

2
CENTS
(4)

1888 (1 Jan). Stamps of 1872–79 (wmk Crown CC), surch locally as T **2**.

(a) P 12½.
23	**1**	2c. on 6d. rose	£250	£180
24		3c. on 3d. chocolate	£15000	£5500

(b) P 14.
25	**1**	2c. on 6d. rose	£150	£140
		a. Surch double	£2000	
		b. Bisected (1c.) (on cover)	†	£250
		c. Slanting "2" with curved foot	£2500	
		w. Wmk inverted	—	£400
26		3c. on 3d. chestnut	90·00	95·00

There are very dangerous forgeries of these surcharges. No. 25c may be a trial.

1888. Stamps of 1882–87 (wmk Crown CA), surch locally as T **2**, P 14.
27	**1**	2c. on 1d. rose	8·50	24·00
		a. Surch inverted	£3000	£2750
		b. Surch double	£900	£900
		c. Bisected (1c.) (on cover)	†	£180
28		10c. on 4d. mauve	50·00	16·00
29		20c. on 6d. yellow	27·00	35·00
30		50c. on 1s. grey	£400	£600
		a. Error. "5" for "50"	£13000	

Various settings were used for the surcharges on Nos. 23/30, the most common of which was of 36 (6×6) impressions. For No. 29 this setting was so applied that an albino surcharge occurs in the margin above each stamp in the first horizontal row.

The same setting was subsequently amended, by altering the "2" to "1", to surcharge the 4d. value. As this was in sheets of 30 it was only necessary to alter the values on the bottom five rows of the setting. Albino surcharges once again occur in the top margin of the sheet, but, as the type in the first horizontal row remained unaltered, these read "20 CENTS" rather than the "10 CENTS" on the actual stamps.

1888 (Mar). No. 30 further surch locally with T **3**.
35	**1**	"TWO" on 50c. on 1s. grey (R.)	50·00	95·00
		a. Bisected (1c.) (on cover)	†	£275
		b. Surch in black	£14000	£12000
		c. Surch double (R.+Blk.)	£14000	£12000

1888 (July)–**91**. *Surch in London as T* **4**. Wmk Crown CA. P 14.
36	**1**	1c. on 1d. dull green (?12.91)	80	1·50
37		2c. on 1d. carmine	60	2·25
		a. Bisected (1c.) (on cover)	†	90·00
		w. Wmk inverted		
38		3c. on 3d. red-brown	3·25	1·40
39		6c. on 3d. ultramarine (?4.91)	2·75	18·00
40		10c. on 4d. mauve	13·00	50
		a. Surch double	£2750	
41		20c. on 6d. yellow (2.89)	12·00	14·00
42		50c. on 1s. grey (11.88)	29·00	85·00
36/42		*Set of* 7	55·00	£110
36s/42s		Optd "Specimen" *Set of* 7	£350	

6
10
CENTS
(5)

FIVE
(6)

15
(7)

1891. *Stamps of* 1888–9 *surch locally.*

(a) With T **5** *(May).*
43	**1**	6c. on 10c. on 4d. mauve (R.)	1·50	2·00
		a. "6" and bar inverted	£550	£550
		b. "6" only inverted	†	£5000
44		6c. on 10c. on 4d. mauve (Blk.)	1·25	1·50
		a. "6" and bar inverted	£3750	£950
		b. "6" only inverted	†	£5000

Of variety (b) only six copies of each can exist, as one of each of these errors came in the first six sheets, and the mistake was then corrected. Of variety (a) more copies exist.

Essays are known with "SIX" in place of "6" both with and without bars (*price* £120 *and* £500 *respectively*). Although not issued we mention them, as three contemporary covers franked with them are known.

(b) With T **6/7** *(23 Oct).*
49	**1**	5c. on 3c. on 3d. red-brown	1·25	1·40
		a. Wide space between "I" and "V"	60·00	75·00
		b. "FIVE" and bar inverted	£375	£425
50		15c. on 6c. on 3d. ultramarine (R.)	13·00	28·00
		a. Surch double		

8

9

10

11

(Typo D.L.R.)

1891 (July)–**1901**. Wmk Crown CA. P 14.
51	**8**	1c. dull green (4.95)	2·50	1·25
		a. Malformed "S"	£250	£140
		w. Wmk inverted		
52		2c. carmine-rose	2·50	20
		a. Malformed "S"	£250	95·00
		b. Repaired "S"	£225	95·00
53		3c. brown	6·50	4·00
		w. Wmk inverted	£170	
54		5c. ultramarine (4.95)	12·00	75
		a. Malformed "S"	£450	£170
55	**11**	5c. grey-black & ultram/*blue* (10.00)	16·00	2·50
56	**8**	6c. ultramarine	7·00	2·00
57	**9**	10c. mauve and green (4.95)	10·00	9·00
58	**10**	10c. dull purple and green (1901)	11·00	7·50
59	**9**	12c. reddish lilac and green	2·50	2·00
60		24c. yellow and blue	5·50	15·00
		a. *Orange and blue*	30·00	55·00
61		25c. red-brown and green (4.95)	80·00	£130
62	**10**	50c. green and carmine (12.99)	25·00	60·00
63	**11**	$1 green and carmine (12.99)	75·00	£130
64		$2 green and ultramarine (12.99)	£110	£170
65		$5 green and black (12.99)	£300	£400
51/65		*Set of* 15	£600	£850

51s/65s Optd "Specimen" *Set of* 15 .... £350

For illustrations of Nos. 51a, 52a/b and 54a see above Gambia No. 37.

Most values are known with a forged Belize postmark dated "OC 23 09".

1899 (1 July). *Optd* "REVENUE" 12 mm long.
66	**8**	5c. ultramarine	15·00	2·50
		a. "BEVENUE"	£110	£130
		b. Malformed "S" at right	£450	£325
		c. Repaired "S" at right	£450	
		d. Opt 11 mm long	23·00	8·50
67	**9**	10c. mauve and green	7·00	16·00
		a. "BEVENUE"	£200	£325
		b. "REVENU"	£550	
		c. Opt 11 mm long	19·00	45·00
		cb. "REVENU"	£650	£750
68		25c. red-brown and green	2·75	35·00
		a. "BEVENUE"	£130	£325
		b. "REVE UE"	£2000	
		c. Repaired "S" at right	£650	
		d. Opt 11 mm long	4·00	55·00
69	**1**	50c. on 1s. grey	£180	£350
		a. "BEVENUE"	£4250	
		c. Opt 11 mm long	£300	£450

Two minor varieties, a small "U" and a tall, narrow "U" are found in the word "REVENUE".

The overprint setting of 60 (6×10) contained 43 examples of the 12 mm size and 17 of the 11 mm. The smaller size overprints occur on R. 8/1, R. 8/3 to 6 and on all positions in Rows 9 and 10.

The "BEVENUE" error appears on R. 6/4 and, it is believed, "REVE UE" comes from R. 6/6. Both occur on parts of the printing only. The missing "E" developed during the overprinting and damage to this letter can be observed on at least eight positions in the setting.

14   **15**

(Typo D.L.R.)

1902 (10 Oct)–**04**. Wmk Crown CA. P 14.
80	**14**	1c. grey-green and green (28.4.04)	1·25	23·00
81		2c. purple and black/*red* (18.3.03)	75	25
		w. Wmk inverted	£120	75·00
82		5c. grey-black and blue/*blue*	8·00	30
		w. Wmk inverted		
83	**15**	20c. dull and bright purple (28.4.04)	6·00	17·00
80/3		*Set of* 4	14·50	35·00
80s/3s		Optd "Specimen" *Set of* 4	55·00	

1904 (Dec)–**07**. Wmk Mult Crown CA. *Ordinary paper (1, 2c.) or chalk-surfaced paper (others)*. P 14.
84	**14**	1c. grey-green and green (8.05)	10·00	13·00
		a. Chalk-surfaced paper (1906)	1·00	2·25
85		2c. purple and black/*red*	2·75	30
		a. Chalk-surfaced paper (1906)	75	20
86		5c. grey-black and blue/*blue* (5.2.06)	1·75	20
87	**15**	10c. dull purple & emerald-green (20.9.07)	4·00	11·00
89		25c. dull purple and orange (20.9.07)	7·00	48·00
90		50c. grey-green and carmine (20.9.07)	15·00	75·00
91	**14**	$1 grey-green and carmine (20.9.07)	55·00	85·00
92		$2 grey-green and blue (20 9 07)	£110	£170
93		$5 grey-green and black (20.9.07)	£275	£325
84/93		*Set of* 9	£425	£650
87s/93s		Optd "Specimen" *Set of* 6	£225	

Examples of most values are known showing a forged Belize postmark dated "OC 23 09".

1908 (7 Dec)–**11**. *Colours changed.* Wmk Mult Crown CA. *Chalk-surfaced paper (25c.)*. P 14.
95	**14**	1c. blue-green (1.7.10)	12·00	40
96		2c. carmine	12·00	10
		w. Wmk inverted		
97		5c. ultramarine (1.6.09)	1·75	10
100	**15**	25c. black/*green* (14.10.11)	3·25	45·00
95/100		*Set of* 4	26·00	45·00
96s/100s		Optd "Specimen" *Set of* 3	70·00	

16   **17**   **(18)**

1913–21. Wmk Mult Crown CA. *Chalk-surfaced paper (10c. to $5)*. P 14.
101	**16**	1c. blue-green	3·75	1·50
		a. Yellow-green (13.3.17)	7·00	2·50
		w. Wmk inverted		
102		2c. red	3·50	1·00
		a. Bright scarlet (1915)	6·00	1·00
		b. Dull scarlet (8.17)	3·00	1·50
		c. Red/bluish	12·00	8·00
		w. Wmk inverted		
103		3c. orange (16.4.17)	80	20
104		5c. bright blue	2·00	85
105	**17**	10c. dull purple and yellow-green	3·00	6·50
		a. Dull purple and bright green (1917)	16·00	25·00
106		25c. black/*green*	1·25	12·00
		a. On blue-green, olive back (8.17)	5·00	11·00

107		*b.* On emerald back (1921)...........	1·75	28·00
107		50c. purple and blue/*blue*	14·00	15·00
108	**16**	$1 black and carmine..................	19·00	50·00
109		$2 purple and green	65·00	80·00
110		$5 purple and black/*red*	£250	£275
101/10		*Set of 10*	£325	£400
101s/10s		Optd "Specimen" *Set of 10*	£225	

1915–16. *Optd with T* **18,** *in violet.*

111	**16**	1c. green (30.12.15).................	3·50	17·00
		a. Yellow-green (6.6.16).............	50	14·00
112		2c. scarlet (3.11.15)	3·50	50
113		5c. bright blue (29.7.15).............	30	6·00
111s/13s		Optd "Specimen" *Set of 3*	£100	

These stamps were shipped early in the 1914–18 war, and were thus overprinted, so that if seized by the enemy, they could be distinguished and rendered invalid.

WAR   WAR
(19)   (20)   21

1916 (23 Aug). *No. 111 optd locally with T* **19.**

114	**16**	1c. green.....................	10	1·50
		a. Opt inverted	£225	£275

1917–18. *Nos. 101 and 103 optd with T* **19.**

116	**16**	1c. blue-green (6.17).......................	1·50	4·00
		aw. Wmk inverted	£200	
		ax. Wmk reversed..............	£200	
		b. Yellow-green (3.3.17).............	20	2·25
118		3c. orange (12.3.18).............	4·25	6·00
		a. Opt double	£325	

1918. *Nos. 101 and 103 optd with T* **20.**

119	**16**	1c. blue-green (25.4.18).................	10	30
		a. Yellow-green	3·50	4·50
120		3c. orange (9.18).............	70	2·00
		y. Wmk inverted and reversed.......	£200	
119s/20s		Optd "Specimen" *Set of 2*	£100	

(Recess D.L.R.)

1921 (28 Apr). *Peace Commemoration. Wmk Mult Crown CA (sideways). P* 14.

121	**21**	2c. rose-red	3·75	50
		a. "C" of "CA" missing from wmk.........	£325	
		s. Optd "Specimen"..................	48·00	

1921 (26 Nov). *Wmk Mult Script CA. P* 14.

122	**16**	1c. green..................	3·75	12·00
		s. Optd "Specimen"..................	45·00	

1922 (4 Jan). *As T* **21** *but with words* "PEACE" *omitted. Wmk Mult Script CA (sideways). P* 14.

123		4c. slate	8·50	50
		s. Optd "Specimen"..................	48·00	

BELIZE

RELIEF   FUND

PLUS

3 CENTS

22   (23)

(Typo D.L.R.)

1922 (1 Aug)**–33.** *Ordinary paper (1c. to 5c.) or chalk-surfaced paper (others). P* 14.

(a) Wmk Mult Crown CA.

124	**22**	25c. black/*emerald*..................	6·50	42·00
125		$5 purple and black/*red* (1.10.24) ..	£200	£225

(b) Wmk Mult Script CA.

126	**22**	1c. green (2.1.29).............	8·00	6·50
127		2c. brown (1.3.23).............	1·50	1·50
128		2c. rose-carmine (10.12.26).............	3·25	1·50
129		3c. orange (1933).............	20·00	4·00
130		4c. grey (1.10.29).............	10·00	85
131		5c. ultramarine	1·50	55
		a. Milky blue (1923).............	4·75	3·75
132		10c. dull purple and sage-green (1.12.22).............	1·50	30
133		25c. black/*emerald* (1.10.24).............	1·25	8·50
134		50c. purple and blue/*blue* (1.11.23).............	4·75	16·00
136		$1 black and scarlet (2.1.25).............	8·00	24·00
137		$2 yellow-green and bright purple .	32·00	85·00
124/37		*Set of 13*	£275	£350
124s/37s		Optd or Perf (1c., 3c., 4c.) "Specimen" *Set of 13*	£275	

1932 (2 May). *Belize Relief Fund. Surch as T* **23.** *Wmk Mult Script CA. P* 14.

138	**22**	1c.+1c. green.............	1·00	9·00
139		2c.+2c. rose-carmine.............	1·00	9·00
140		3c.+3c. orange.............	1·00	21·00
141		4c.+4c. grey (R.).............	11·00	22·00
142		5c.+5c. ultramarine.............	6·50	14·00
138/42		*Set of 5*	18·00	65·00
138s/42s		Perf "Specimen" *Set of 5*	£110	

1935 (6 May). *Silver Jubilee. As Nos. 91/4 of Antigua, but ptd by B.W. & Co. P* 11×12.

143		3c. ultramarine and grey-black.............	2·00	50
		a. Extra flagstaff.............	55·00	75·00
		b. Short extra flagstaff.............	85·00	
		c. Lightning conductor.............	60·00	

144		*d.* Flagstaff on right-hand turret	£140	
144		4c. green and indigo.............	2·50	3·50
		a. Extra flagstaff.............	£180	
		c. Lightning conductor.............	£190	
		d. Flagstaff on right-hand turret.............	£250	
		e. Double flagstaff.............	£275	
145		5c. brown and deep blue.............	2·00	1·75
146		25c. slate and purple.............	4·25	4·50
		a. Extra flagstaff.............	£250	
		b. Short extra flagstaff.............	£375	
		c. Lightning conductor.............	£250	
		d. Flagstaff on right-hand turret.............	£350	
		e. Double flagstaff.............	£375	
143/6		*Set of 4*	9·75	9·25
143s/6s		Perf "Specimen" *Set of 4*	95·00	

For illustrations of plate varieties see Omnibus section following Zanzibar.

1937 (12 May). *Coronation. As Nos. 95/7 of Antigua, but printed by D.L.R. P* 14.

147		3c. orange.............	30	30
148		4c. grey-black.............	70	30
149		5c. bright blue.............	80	1·90
147/9		*Set of 3*	1·60	2·25
147s/9s		Perf "Specimen" *Set of 3*	70·00	

24 Maya Figures   **25** Chicle tapping

26 Cohune palm   **27** Local products

28 Grapefruit   **29** Mahogany logs in river

30 Sergeant's Cay   **31** Dorey

32 Chicle industry   **33** Court House, Belize

34 Mahogany felling   **35** Arms of Colony

(Recess B.W.)

1938 (10 Jan)**–47.** *T* **24/35.** *Wmk Mult Script CA (sideways on horizontal stamps). P* 11½×11 *(horiz designs) or* 11×11½ *(vert designs).*

150	**24**	1c. bright magenta and green (14.2.38).............	10	10
151	**25**	2c. black and scarlet (14.2.38)	20	1·00
		a. Perf 12 (1947).............	2·50	1·00
152	**26**	3c. purple and brown.............	65	80
153	**27**	4c. black and green.............	65	70

154	**28**	5c. mauve and dull blue	1·75	70
155	**29**	10c. green and reddish brown (14.2.38).............	1·75	60
156	**30**	15c. brown and light blue (14.2.38).......	3·75	70
157	**31**	25c. blue and green (14.2.38)........	3·00	1·25
158	**32**	50c. black and purple (14.2.38)........	13·00	3·50
159	**33**	$1 scarlet and olive (28.2.38)........	24·00	10·00
160	**34**	$2 deep blue and maroon (28.2.38)........	35·00	18·00
161	**35**	$5 scarlet and brown (28.2.38).......	38·00	28·00
150/61		*Set of 12*	£110	60·00
150s/61s		Perf "Specimen" *Set of 12*	£200	

1946 (9 Sept). *Victory. As Nos. 110/11 of Antigua.*

162		3c. brown.............	10	10
163		5c. blue.............	10	10
162s/3s		Perf "Specimen" *Set of 2*	65·00	

1948 (1 Oct). *Royal Silver Wedding. As Nos. 112/13 of Antigua.*

164		4c. green.............	15	60
165		$5 brown	18·00	48·00

36 Island of St. George's Cay   **37** H.M.S. *Merlin*

(Recess Waterlow)

1949 (10 Jan). *150th Anniv of Battle of St. George's Cay. Wmk Mult Script CA. P* 12½.

166	**36**	1c. ultramarine and green...............	10	1·00
167		3c. blue and yellow-brown.............	10	1·50
168		4c. olive and violet.............	10	1·00
169	**37**	5c. brown and deep blue...............	1·00	40
170		10c. green and red-brown.............	1·00	30
171		15c. emerald and ultramarine.............	1·00	30
166/71		*Set of 6*	2·75	4·00

1949 (10 Oct). *75th Anniv of U.P.U. As Nos. 114/17 of Antigua.*

172		4c. blue-green.............	30	30
173		5c. deep blue.............	1·50	50
174		10c. red-brown.............	40	3·00
175		25c. blue.............	35	50
172/5		*Set of 4*	2·25	3·75

1951 (16 Feb). *Inauguration of B.W.I. University College. As Nos. 118/19 of Antigua.*

176		4c. reddish violet and brown.............	45	1·50
177		10c. green and brown.............	45	30

STAMP BOOKLETS

1920. *Black on pink cover inscr* "British Honduras–100–Two Cent Stamps". *Stapled.*

SB1	$2 booklet containing one hundred 2c. (No. 102*b*) in blocks of 10 (5×2)		£3500

1920. *Grey-blue cover inscr* "British Honduras–100–Three Cent Stamps". *Stapled.*

SB2	$3 booklet containing one hundred 3c. (No. 103) in blocks of 10 (5×2)		

1923. *Black on pink cover inscr* "British Honduras–100–Two Cent Stamps". *Stapled.*

SB3	$2 booklet containing one hundred 2c. brown (No. 127) in blocks of 10 (5×2)		

1927. *Black on pink cover inscr* "British Honduras–100–Two Cent Stamps". *Stapled.*

SB4	$2 booklet containing one hundred 2c. rose-carmine (No. 128) in blocks of 10 (5×2)........		

POSTAGE DUE STAMPS

D 1

(Typo D.L.R.)

1923–64. *Wmk Mult Script CA. Ordinary paper. P* 14.

D1	D **1**	1c. black.............	2·25	13·00
		a. Chalk-surfaced paper (25.9.56).	50	22·00
		b. White uncoated paper (9.4.64)..	14·00	28·00
D2		2c. black.............	2·25	7·50
		a. Chalk-surfaced paper (25.9.56).	50	19·00
D3		4c. black.............	1·25	6·00
		a. Missing top serif on "C" (R. 6/6).............	26·00	
		b. Chalk-surfaced paper (25.9.56).	90	16·00
		ba. Missing top serif on "C" (R. 6/6).............	25·00	
		w. Wmk inverted.............	£225	
D1/3		*Set of 3*	5·25	24·00
D1a/3b		*Set of 3*	1·75	50·00
D1s/3s		Optd "Specimen" *Set of 3*	60·00	

The early ordinary paper printings were yellowish and quite distinct from No. D1*b*.

Stamps in this design, but with different watermark, were issued between 1965 and 1972.

British Levant

The term "British Levant" is used by stamp collectors to describe the issues made by various British Post Offices within the former Turkish Empire.

Arrangements for the first such service were included amongst the terms of a commercial treaty between the two countries in 1832, but the system did not start operations until September 1857 when a post office for civilian use was opened in Constantinople, replacing the Army Post Office which had existed there since June 1854.

Eventually the number of British Post Offices grew to five:

Beyrout (Beirut, Lebanon). Opened 1873, closed 30 September 1914.

Constantinople (Istanbul). Opened 1 September 1857, closed 30 September 1914, re-opened 4 February 1919, finally closed 27 September 1923.

Salonica (Thessalonika, Greece). Opened 1 May 1900, closed October 1914. The city was captured by Greek troops on 7 November 1912 and incorporated into Greece by the Treaty of London (July 1913).

Smyrna (Izmir). Opened 1872, closed 30 September 1914, re-opened 1 March 1919, finally closed September 1922. Between 15 May 1919 and 8 September 1922 the city was under Greek occupation.

Stamboul (a sub-office of Constantinople). Opened 1 April 1884, closed 25 August 1896, re-opened 10 February 1908, finally closed 30 September 1914.

Stamps from the two British Post Offices in Egypt still technically part of the Turkish Empire, are listed under EGYPT.

A. BRITISH POST OFFICES IN TURKISH EMPIRE, 1857–1914

For illustrations of the postmark types see BRITISH POST OFFICES ABROAD notes, following GREAT BRITAIN.

From 1 August 1885 letter and registered charges were prepaid with surcharged stamps (No. 1 onwards). Until 14 August 1905 postcards and parcels continued to be franked with unoverprinted Great Britain stamps. Only a limited range of values were stocked for this purpose and these are listed. Other values exist with Levant postmarks, but these stamps did not originate from the local post offices.

After 15 August 1905 the post offices were supplied with Great Britain stamps overprinted "LEVANT". Subsequent examples of unoverprinted stamps with Levant postmarks are omitted from the listing. The use of such stamps during 1919–22 at Constantinople and Smyrna is, however, covered by a later note.

BEYROUT (BEIRUT)

Between 1873 and 1876 much of the mail from the British Post Office in Beyrout sent to European addresses was forwarded through the French or Italian Post Offices at Alexandria. Such covers show Great Britain stamps used in combination with those of French or Italian P.O's in the Turkish Empire.

Stamps of GREAT BRITAIN cancelled "G 06" or circular postmark as in Types **8**, **18** or **20**.

1873.

Z1	½d. rose-red (1870–79)................ *From*	42·00	
	Plate Nos. 12, 13, 14, 19, 20.		
Z2	1d. rose-red (1864–79)................ *From*	17·00	
	Plate Nos. 107, 108, 130, 140, 145, 148, 155, 157, 162, 167, 177, 179, 180, 184, 185, 186, 187, 195, 198, 200, 203, 204, 211, 213, 215, 218, 220, 222.		
Z3	1½d. lake-red (1870–74) (Plate 3)...........	£275	
Z4	2d. blue (1858–69)................ *From*	24·00	
	Plate Nos. 13, 14, 15.		
Z5	2½d. rosy mauve (1875) (*blued paper*)............	75·00	
	Plate No. 1.		
Z6	2½d. rosy mauve (1875–76)................ *From*	32·00	
	Plate Nos. 1, 2, 3.		
Z7	2½d. rosy mauve (1876–79)................ *From*	25·00	
	Plate Nos. 3, 4, 5, 6, 7, 8, 9, 10, 11, 12, 13, 14, 15, 16, 17.		
Z8	2½d. blue (1880)................ *From*	15·00	
	Plate Nos. 17, 18, 19, 20.		
Z9	2½d. blue (1881)................ *From*	11·00	
	Plate Nos. 21, 22, 23.		
Z10	3d. rose (1867–73) (Plate No. 10)............		
Z11	3d. rose (1873–76)................	42·00	
	Plate Nos. 12, 15, 16, 18, 19, 20.		
Z12	3d. rose (1881) (Plate Nos. 20, 21).		
Z13	4d. vermilion (1865–73)................ *From*	38·00	
	Plate Nos. 11, 12, 13, 14.		
Z14	4d. vermilion (1876) (Plate No. 15).	£180	
Z15	4d. sage-green (1877)................	£120	
	Plate Nos. 15, 16.		
Z16	4d. grey-brown (1880) wmk Large Garter (Plate No. 17)............		
Z17	4d. grey-brown (1880) wmk Crown............	50·00	
	Plate Nos. 17, 18.		
Z18	6d. mauve (1870) (Plate Nos. 8, 9)............		
Z19	6d. buff (1872–73)................ *From*	85·00	
	Plate Nos. 11, 12.		
Z20	6d. chestnut (1872) (Plate No. 11)............	42·00	
Z21	6d. grey (1873) (Plate No. 12)............	£150	
Z22	6d. grey (1874–80)................ *From*	30·00	
	Plate Nos. 13, 14, 15, 16, 17.		
Z23	8d. orange (1876)............	£400	
Z24	10d. red-brown (1867)............	£160	
Z25	1s. green (1867–73)............	30·00	
	Plate Nos. 6, 7.		
Z26	1s. green (1873–77)................ *From*	42·00	
	Plate Nos. 8, 9, 10, 12, 13.		
Z27	1s. orange-brown (1880) (Plate No. 13).......		
Z28	1s. orange-brown (1881)............	60·00	
	Plate Nos. 13, 14.		
Z29	2s. blue (1867)............	£150	
Z30	5s. rose (1867) (Plate Nos. 1, 2)............ *From*	£600	

1880.

Z31	½d. deep green............	11·00	
Z32	½d. pale green............	12·00	

Z33	1d. Venetian red............	14·00	
Z34	1½d. Venetian red............	£170	
Z35	2d. pale rose............	55·00	
Z36	2d. deep rose............	55·00	
Z37	5d. indigo............	90·00	

1881.

Z38	1d. lilac (14 *dots*)............		
Z39	1d. lilac (16 *dots*)............	6·00	

1884.

Z40	½d. slate-blue............	18·00	
Z41	1½d. lilac............	85·00	
Z42	2d. lilac............	70·00	
Z43	2½d. lilac............	11·00	
Z44	4d. dull green............	£180	
Z45	5d. dull green............	£110	
Z46	1s. dull green............	£300	

1887–92.

Z47	½d. vermilion............	9·00	
Z54	6d. purple/*rose-red*............	25·00	
Z55	1s. dull green............	£140	

1900.

Z56	½d. blue-green............	12·00	
Z57	1s. green and carmine............	£170	

1902–04. *De La Rue ptgs.*

Z58	½d. blue-green............	4·75	
Z59	½d. yellowish green............	5·00	
Z60	1d. scarlet............	4·25	
Z64	1s. dull green and carmine............	30·00	

CONSTANTINOPLE

Stamps of GREAT BRITAIN cancelled "C" or circular postmark as in Types **1**, **10**, **18** or **19**.

1857.

Z68	½d. rose-red (1870–79)............ *From*	25·00	
	Plate Nos. 5, 6, 10, 11, 12, 13, 14, 15, 20.		
Z69	1d. red-brown (1854), Die I, wmk Small Crown, perf 16............		
Z70	1d. red-brown (1855), Die II, wmk Small Crown, perf 14............		
Z71	1d. red-brown, (1855), Die II, wmk Large Crown, perf 14............	20·00	
Z72	1d. rose-red (1857)............	7·00	
Z73	1d. rose-red (1861) Alphabet IV............		
Z74	1d. rose-red (1864–79)................ *From*	8·00	
	Plate Nos. 71, 72, 73, 74, 76, 78, 79, 80, 81, 83, 85, 87, 89, 90, 92, 93, 94, 95, 96, 97, 99, 101, 102, 105, 106, 108, 109, 110, 113, 116, 118, 119, 120, 121, 122, 123, 124, 125, 127, 129, 130, 131, 134, 135, 136, 137, 138, 140, 141, 143, 144, 145, 146, 147, 148, 149, 150, 151, 152, 155, 156, 157, 158, 159, 160, 161, 162, 163, 164, 165, 166, 167, 170, 171, 172, 173, 174, 175, 176, 177, 178, 179, 180, 191, 192, 193, 194, 195, 196, 197, 198, 200, 201, 203, 204, 205, 206, 207, 208, 210, 212, 214, 215, 216, 220, 222, 224.		
Z75	1½d. rose-red (1870) (Plate 1)............	£200	
Z76	2d. blue (1855), wmk Large Crown, perf 14. (Plate Nos. 5, 6)............		
Z77	2d. blue (1858–69)................ *From*	12·00	
	Plate Nos. 7, 8, 9, 12, 13, 14, 15.		
Z78	2½d. rosy mauve (1875–76) (*blued paper*) (Plate Nos. 1, 2)............	55·00	
Z79	2½d. rosy mauve (1875–76)................ *From*	30·00	
	Plate Nos. 1, 2, 3.		
Z80	2½d. rosy mauve (*Error of Lettering*)............		
Z81	2½d. rosy mauve (1876–79)................ *From*	23·00	
	Plate Nos. 3 to 17.		
Z82	2½d. blue (1880–81)................ *From*	11·00	
	Plate Nos. 17, 18, 19, 20.		
Z83	2½d. blue (1881) (Plate Nos. 21, 22, 23)........	7·50	
Z84	3d. carmine-rose (1862) (Plate No. 2)............	£130	
Z85	3d. rose (1865) (Plate No. 4)............	75·00	
Z86	3d. rose (1867–73) (Plate Nos. 4 to 10)........	70·00	
Z87	3d. rose (1873–76)................	22·00	
	Plate Nos. 11, 12, 15, 16, 17, 18, 19.		
Z88	3d. rose (1881) (Plate No. 21)............		
Z89	3d. on 3d. lilac (1883) (Plate No. 21)............		
Z90	4d. rose (1857)............	45·00	
	a. Rose-carmine............		
Z91	4d. red (1862) (Plate Nos. 3, 4)............ *From*	38·00	
Z92	4d. vermilion (1865–73)................ *From*	26·00	
	Plate Nos. 7 to 14.		
Z93	4d. vermilion (1876) (Plate No. 15)............	£150	
Z94	4d. sage-green (1877)................	£100	
	Plate Nos. 15, 16.		
Z95	4d. grey-brown (1880) wmk Large Garter (Plate No. 17)............		
Z96	4d. grey-brown (1880) wmk Crown (Plate Nos. 17, 18)............	40·00	
Z97	6d. lilac (1856)............	60·00	
Z98	6d. lilac (1862) (Plate Nos. 3, 4)........ *From*	38·00	
Z99	6d. lilac (1865–67)............	35·00	
	Plate Nos. 5, 6.		
Z100	6d. lilac (1867) (Plate No. 6)............	40·00	
Z101	6d. violet (1867–70)................ *From*	32·00	
	Plate Nos. 6, 8, 9.		
Z102	6d. buff (1872–73)................ *From*	55·00	
	Plate Nos. 11, 12.		
Z103	6d. chestnut (1872) (Plate No. 11)............	30·00	
Z104	6d. grey (1873) (Plate No. 12)............	75·00	
Z105	6d. grey (1874–76)................ *From*	25·00	
	Plate Nos. 13, 14, 15, 16.		
Z106	6d. grey (1881–82) (Plate Nos. 17, 18)............	27·00	
Z107	6d. on 6d. lilac (1883)............	80·00	
	a. Dots slanting (Letters MI or SJ)............	£140	
Z108	8d. orange (1876)............	£375	
Z109	10d. red-brown (1867), wmk Emblems............	£25000	
Z110	10d. red-brown (1867)............	£160	
Z111	1s. green (1856)............	£110	
Z112	1s. green (1862)............	60·00	

Z113	1s. green (1862) ("K" *variety*)............		
Z114	1s. green (1862) (*thick paper*)............		
Z115	1s. green (1865) (Plate No. 4)............	65·00	
Z116	1s. green (1867–73)................ *From*	16·00	
	Plate Nos. 4, 5, 6, 7.		
Z117	1s. green (1873–77)................ *From*	27·00	
	Plate Nos. 8, 9, 10, 11, 12, 13.		
Z118	1s. orange-brown (1880) (Plate No. 13).......	£180	
Z119	1s. orange-brown (1881)................ *From*	48·00	
	Plate Nos. 13, 14.		
Z120	2s. blue (1867)............	95·00	
Z121	5s. rose (1867–74)................ *From*	£250	
	Plate Nos. 1, 2.		
Z122	5s. rose (1882) (*white paper*)............	£850	
Z123	5s. rose (1882) (*blued paper*)............	£1100	

1880.

Z124	½d. deep green............	7·50	
Z125	½d. pale green............	10·00	
Z126	1d. Venetian red............	10·00	
Z127	2d. pale rose............	45·00	
Z128	2d. deep rose............	45·00	
Z129	5d. indigo............		

1881.

Z130	1d. lilac (14 *dots*)............		
Z131	1d. lilac (16 *dots*)............	2·50	

1883–84.

Z132	½d. slate-blue............	8·00	
Z133	1½d. lilac............		
Z134	2d. lilac............	55·00	
Z135	2½d. lilac............	7·00	
Z136	3d. lilac............		
Z137	4d. dull green............		
Z138	5d. dull green............	90·00	
Z139	6d. dull green............		
Z140	9d. dull green............		
Z141	1s. dull green............	£225	
Z142	2s.6d. lilac (*blued paper*)............	£600	
Z143	2s.6d. lilac (*white paper*)............	85·00	
Z144	5s. rose (*blued paper*)............		
Z145	5s. rose (*white paper*)............		

1887–92.

Z146	½d. vermilion............	3·25	
Z154	6d. purple/*rose-red*............	12·00	
Z157	1s. dull green............	85·00	

1900.

Z158	½d. blue-green............	6·00	
Z159	1s. green and carmine............	£140	

1902–04. *De La Rue ptgs.*

Z160	½d. blue-green............	3·00	
Z161	½d. yellowish green............	3·50	
Z162	1d. scarlet............	2·50	
Z169	6d. purple............	11·00	
Z172	1s. green and carmine............	18·00	
Z173	2s.6d. lilac............		
Z174	5s. carmine............		

POSTAL FISCALS

Z175	1d. purple (wmk Anchor) (1868)............		
Z176	1d. purple (wmk Orb) (1881)............	£600	

SALONICA

Stamps of GREAT BRITAIN cancelled with circular postmark as in Type **18** or double-circle datestamp.

1900.

Z202	½d. vermilion (1887)............	19·00	
Z203	½d. blue-green (1900)............	21·00	
Z204	1d. lilac (1881)............	21·00	
Z205	6d. purple/red (1887)............	28·00	
Z206	1s. green and carmine (1900)............	£180	
Z207	5s. rose (white paper) (1883)............	£900	

1902.

Z208	½d. blue-green............	24·00	
Z209	½d. yellow-green............	18·00	
Z209a	1d. scarlet............	18·00	
Z209c	1s. green and carmine............	48·00	

SMYRNA (IZMIR)

Stamps of GREAT BRITAIN cancelled "F 87" or circular postmark as in Type **8**, **16** or **18**.

1872.

Z210	½d. rose-red (1870–79)................ *From*	30·00	
	Plates 11, 12, 13, 14, 15.		
Z211	1d. rose-red (1864–79)................ *From*	14·00	
	Plate Nos. 120, 124, 134, 137, 138, 139, 140, 142, 143, 145, 146, 148, 149, 150, 151, 152, 153, 155, 156, 157, 158, 159, 160, 161, 162, 163, 164, 166, 167, 168, 169, 170, 171, 172, 173, 174, 175, 176, 177, 178, 183, 184, 185, 186, 187, 188, 191, 193, 195, 196, 198, 200, 201, 204, 210, 212, 215, 217, 218.		
Z212	1½d. lake-red (1870–74) (Plate Nos. 1, 3). *From*	£225	
Z213	2d. blue (1858) wmk Large Crown, perf 16......		
Z214	2d. blue (1858–69)................ *From*	16·00	
	Plate Nos. 13, 14, 15.		
Z215	2½d. rosy mauve (1875) (*blued paper*)............	60·00	
	Plate No. 1.		
Z216	2½d. rosy mauve (1875–76)................ *From*	27·00	
	Plate Nos. 1, 2, 3.		
Z217	2½d. rosy mauve (*Error of lettering*)............		
Z218	2½d. rosy mauve (1876–79)................ *From*	22·00	
	Plate Nos. 3, 4, 5, 6, 7, 8, 9, 10, 11, 12, 13, 14, 15, 16, 17.		
Z219	2½d. blue (1880)................ *From*	11·00	
	Plate Nos. 17, 18, 19, 20.		
Z220	2½d. blue (1881)................	9·00	
	Plate Nos. 21, 22, 23.		

Z221		3d. rose (1867–73)	38·00	
		Plate Nos. 5, 7, 9, 10.		
Z222		3d. rose (1873–76) (Plate 14)		
Z223		4d. vermilion (1865–73)	26·00	
		Plate Nos. 12, 13, 14.		
Z224		4d. vermilion (1876) (Plate No. 15)	£150	
Z225		4d. sage-green (1877)	95·00	
		Plate Nos. 15, 16.		
Z226		4d. grey-brown (1880) wmk Large Garter		
		(Plate No. 17)		
Z227		4d. grey-brown (1880) wmk Crown (Plate		
		Nos. 17, 18). .... *From*	38·00	
Z228		6d. buff (1872–73) .... *From*	70·00	
		Plate Nos. 11, 12.		
Z229		6d. chestnut (1872) (Plate No. 11)	75·00	
Z230		6d. grey (1873) (Plate No. 12)		
Z231		6d. grey (1874–80) .... *From*	27·00	
		Plate Nos. 13, 14, 15, 16, 17.		
Z232		6d. grey (1881–82) (Plate Nos. 17, 18). ...	50·00	
Z233		6d. on 6d. lilac (1883)	95·00	
Z234		8d. orange (1876)		
Z235		9d. straw (1867)	£275	
Z236		10d. red-brown (1867)	£130	
Z237		1s. green (1867–73) (Plate Nos. 6, 7).		
Z238		1s. green (1873–77) .... *From*	30·00	
		Plate Nos. 8, 9, 10, 11, 12, 13.		
Z239		1s. orange-brown (1880) (Plate No. 13) ...	£160	
Z240		1s. orange-brown (1881) (Plate Nos. 13, 14). ...	48·00	
Z241		5s. rose (1867–74) (Plate No. 2)		

1880.

Z242	½d. deep green	9·00	
Z243	½d. pale green	9·00	
Z244	1d. Venetian red	13·00	
Z245	1½d. Venetian red	£110	
Z246	2d. pale rose	42·00	
Z247	2d. deep rose	42·00	
Z248	5d. indigo	65·00	

1881.

Z249	1d. lilac (16 *dots*)	4·50	

1884.

Z250	½d. slate-blue	15·00	
Z251	2d. lilac	65·00	
Z252	2½d. lilac	10·00	
Z253	4d. dull green		
Z254	5d. dull green	£100	
Z255	1s. dull green	£275	

1887.

Z256	½d. vermilion	5·50	
Z263	6d. purple/*rose-red*	20·00	
Z264	1s. dull green	£110	

1900.

Z265	½d. blue-green	8·00	
Z266	1s. green and carmine		

1902–04. *De La Rue ptgs.*

Z267	½d. blue-green	4·50	
Z268	½d. yellowish green	5·00	
Z269	1d. scarlet	4·00	
Z276	6d. purple	14·00	
Z279	1s. green and carmine	25·00	
Z280	2s.6d. purple		
Z281	5s. carmine		

STAMBOUL (CONSTANTINOPLE)

Stamps of GREAT BRITAIN *cancelled* "S" *as Type* **10**, *or circular postmarks inscribed either* "BRITISH POST OFFICE CONSTANTINOPLE S" *or* "BRITISH POST OFFICE STAMBOUL" *as Type* **18**.

1884.

Z296	½d. slate-blue	25·00	
Z297	1d. lilac	12·00	
Z298	2d. lilac		
Z299	2½d. lilac	15·00	
Z300	5d. dull green	£150	

1887–92.

Z306	½d. vermilion	15·00	
Z314	6d. purple/*rose-red*	35·00	
Z317	1s. dull green		

The "S" cancellation was in use from 1885 to 1891 and the "Stamboul" mark from 1892 to 1896, when the office was closed, and from its reopening in 1908 to 1914. The "CONSTANTINOPLE S" handstamp was normally used as a back stamp, but can be found cancelling stamps in the period 1885 to 1892.

PRICES FOR STAMPS ON COVER	
Nos. 1/3a	*from* × 8
Nos. 4/6	*from* × 5
Nos. 7/40	*from* × 3
Nos. L1/10	*from* × 6
Nos. L11/17	*from* × 3

I. TURKISH CURRENCY

(40 paras = 1 piastre)

Following the depreciation of the Turkish piastre against sterling in 1884 it was decided to issue stamps surcharged in Turkish currency to avoid speculation. During the early period unsurcharged stamps of Great Britain remained on sale from the British Post Offices at the current rate of exchange until replaced by "LEVANT" overprints.

80 PARAS 4 PIASTRES 12 PIASTRES
(1)   **(2)**   **(3)**

PRINTERS. Nos. 1/24 were surcharged or overprinted by De La Rue, *unless otherwise stated.*

Stamps of Great Britain (Queen Victoria) surch as T 1 to 3

1885 (1 Aug)–88.

1	64	40pa. on 2½d. lilac	£100	1·25
2	62	80pa. on 5d. green	£190	9·50
3	58	12pi. on 2s.6d. lilac/*bluish* ..	£400	£250
		a. On white paper		
		(4.88)	45·00	22·00

Nos. 3, 11 and 33 were surcharged from a horizontal setting of eight clichés of which three showed a small final 'S'.

1887 (June)–96.

4	74	40pa. on 2½d. purple/*blue* ...	4·75	10
		a. Surch double	£1900	£2500
5	78	80pa. on 5d. purple and blue (7.90)	15·00	30
		a. Small "0" in "80"	£225	85·00
		w. Wmk inverted	†	£550
6	81	4pi. on 10d. dull purple & carm		
		(10.10.96)	42·00	8·00
		a. Dull purple and deep		
		bright carmine	42·00	11·00
		b. Large, wide "4" (R.		
		1/2, 1/4).	£180	65·00

No. 5a first appeared on the June 1895 printing when the size of the surcharge plate was increased from 60 to 120. On the Victorian stamp the variety comes on R. 4/1 and 4/7. The same setting was used for the first printing of the Edward VII surcharge, but here the sheet size was further increased to 240 so that No. 9a occurs on R. 4/1, 4/7, 14/1 and 14/7.

1893 (25 Feb). *Roughly handstamped at Constantinople, as T* **1**.

7	71	40pa. on ½d. vermilion	£425	£100

This provisional was in use for five days only at the Constantinople and Stamboul offices. As fraudulent copies were made with the original handstamp, and can be found "used" on piece cancelled by fraudulent use of the usual canceller, this stamp should only be purchased from undoubted sources.

The handstamp became damaged during use so that by 1 March the top of the "S" was broken. Used examples dated 25 or 26 February showing the broken "S" *must* be fraudulent. It is also known with genuine handstamp inverted (Price £850 unused, £325 used).

1902–05. *Stamps of King Edward VII surch as T* **1** *to* **3**.

8	86	40pa. on 2½d. ultramarine (3.02) ..	15·00	10
		a. Pale ultramarine	17·00	10
		ab. Surch double	†	£2250
9	89	80pa. on 5d. dull purple & ultram		
		(5.6.02)	9·00	2·50
		a. Small "0" in "80"	£250	£190
10	92	4pi. on 10d. dull purple & carmine		
		(6.9.02)	13·00	4·00
		a. No cross on crown	£130	90·00
		b. Chalk-surfaced paper ..	6·00	10·00
		ba. Chalk-surfaced paper.		
		No cross on crown ...	90·00	£110
11	94	12pi. on 2s.6d. lilac (29.8.03) ...	35·00	35·00
		a. Chalk-surfaced paper.		
		Pale dull purple	70·00	75·00
		b. Chalk-surfaced paper.		
		Dull purple	38·00	35·00
12	95	24pi. on 5s. bright carmine		
		(15.8.05)	32·00	40·00
8/12		*Set of 5*	85·00	70·00
9s/11s		Optd "Specimen" *Set of 3*	£150	

No. 9a only occurs on the first printing of 80pa. on 5d.

1 PIASTRE
(4)

1905–08. *Surch in* "PIASTRES" *instead of* "PARAS" *as T* **4** *and* **2**.

13	86	1pi. on 2½d. ultramarine (17.4.06) ..	16·00	10
		a. Surch double	†	£1600
		w. Wmk inverted	£750	£750
14	89	2pi. on 5d. dull purple & ultram		
		(11.11.05)	30·00	2·50
		a. Chalk-surfaced paper		
		(1.08)	25·00	3·00
		ab. Slate-purple and		
		ultramarine	30·00	7·00

ı Piastre   1 PIASTRE
(5)   10 PARAS
             (6)

1906 (2 July). *Issued at Beyrout. No. L4 surch with T* **5** *by American Press, Beyrout.*

15	85	1pi. on 2d. grey-green and carmine	£1300	£600

1909 (16 Nov–Dec). *Stamps of King Edward VII surch as T* **1** *(30pa.)* **6**, *and* **2** *(5 pi). Ordinary paper (No. 19) or chalk-surfaced paper (others).*

16	84	30pa. on 1½d. pale dull purple and		
		green	11·00	1·25
		a. Surch double, one		
		albino		
17	87	1pi.10pa. on 3d. dull purple/*orange-*		
		yell	12·00	35·00
18	88	1pi.30pa. on 4d. green & chocolate-		
		brn	5·00	17·00
19		1pi.30pa. on 4d. pale orange		
		(16.12.09)	17·00	60·00
20	83	2pi.20pa. on 6d. dull purple	21·00	60·00
21	93	5pi. on 1s. dull green and		
		carmine	4·25	10·00
		s. Optd "Specimen"	60·00	
16/21		*Set of 6*	60·00	£160

1³⁄₄ PIASTRE
(7)   **4**
           Normal "4"   Pointed "4"

1910 (24 Jan). *Stamps of King Edward VII surch as T* **7**. *Chalk-surfaced paper (Nos. 22 and 24).*

22	87	1¼pi. on 3d. dull purple/*orange-*		
		yellow	50	1·00
23	88	1¼pi. on 4d. pale orange	50	60
		a. Orange-red	5·50	6·00
		b. Thin, pointed "4" in		
		fraction	5·50	26·00
24	83	2½pi. on 6d. dull purple	1·40	65
22/4		*Set of 3*	2·25	2·00

No. 23b occurs in the first and seventh vertical rows of the sheet. The variety also occurs on No. 38, but not on No. 38b.

1 PIASTRE   1 PIASTRE
(8)   **(9)**

TYPE DIFFERENCES. In T **4** the letters are tall and narrow and the space enclosed by the upper part of the "A" is small.

In T **8** the opening of the "A" is similar but the letters are shorter and broader, the "P" and the "E" being particularly noticeable.

In T **9** the letters are short and broad, but the "A" is thin and open.

1911–13. *Stamps of King Edward VII, Harrison or Somerset House ptgs, surch at Somerset House.*

(a) Surch with T **4** *(20 July).*

25	86	1pi. on 2½d. bright blue (perf 14) ...	15·00	9·00
		a. Surch double, one albino ...	£225	
26		1pi. on 2½d. bright blue (perf 15×14)		
		(14.10.11)	18·00	2·50
		a. Dull blue	18·00	2·00

(b) Surch with T **8**.

27	86	1pi. on 2½d. bright blue (perf 15×14)		
		(3.12)	13·00	3·00
		a. Dull blue	22·00	3·50

(c) Surch with T **9** *(7.12).*

28	86	1pi. on 2½d. bright blue (perf 15×14)	65·00	75
		a. Dull blue	65·00	75

(d) Surch with T **1** *to* **3** *(1911–13).*

29	84	30pa. on 1½d. reddish purple and		
		bright green (22.8.11) ..	6·50	55
		a. Slate-purple and green	10·00	2·25
		b. Surch double, one		
		albino	55·00	
30	89	2pi. on 5d. dull reddish purple and		
		bright blue (13.5.12) ...	14·00	2·00
		a. Deep dull reddish		
		purple and bright blue.	17·00	2·25
31	92	4pi. on 10d. dull purple & scarlet		
		(26.6.12)	35·00	15·00
		a. Dull reddish purple &		
		aniline pink	£275	90·00
		b. Dull reddish purple		
		and carmine	13·00	11·00
		c. No cross on crown		
32	93	5pi. on 1s. green and carmine		
		(1913)	23·00	5·50
		a. Surch double, one		
		albino	£250	
33	94	12pi. on 2s.6d. dull reddish pur		
		(3.2.12)	55·00	38·00
		a. Dull greyish purple	55·00	38·00
34	95	24pi. on 5s. carmine (1913)	55·00	75·00
		a. Surch double, one		
		albino	£300	
29/34		*Set of 6*	£150	£120

1913 (Apr)–14. *Stamps of King George V, wmk Royal Cypher, surch as T* **1** *(30pa.),* **9** *(1pi.)* **7** *or* **2** *(4 and 5pi.).*

35	105	30pa. on 1½d. red-brown (4.13) ...	3·50	14·00
		a. Surch double, one		
		albino	£110	
36	104	1pi. on 2½d. cobalt-blue (6.13)...	8·50	10
		a. Bright blue	7·00	15
37	106	1¼pi. on 3d. dull reddish violet		
		(9.13)	4·75	4·25
		a. Violet	6·50	6·00
		b. Surch double, one		
		albino	£300	
38		1¾pi. on 4d. deep grey-green (7.13)	3·00	6·50
		a. Thin, pointed "4" in		
		fraction	45·00	80·00
		b. Grey-green	5·50	5·00
39	108	4pi. on 10d. turquoise-blue (12.13).	8·00	21·00
40		5pi. on 1s. bistre-brown (1.14) ...	40·00	60·00
35/40		*Set of 6*	60·00	95·00

II. BRITISH CURRENCY

Stamps overprinted "LEVANT" were for use on parcels, with the ½d. and 1d. principally used for printed paper and post cards. They replaced unoverprinted Great Britain stamps, Nos. Z58/64, Z160/74, Z208/9c and Z267/81, which had previously been used for these purposes.

From October 1907 the three lowest values were also used for certain other amended postal rates until Nos. 16/21 were introduced.

LEVANT
(L 1)

1905 (15 Aug)–12. *Stamps of King Edward VII optd with Type* L **1**.

(a) De La Rue ptgs.

L1	83	½d. pale yellowish green	8·50	15
		a. Yellowish green	8·50	15
L2		1d. scarlet	8·50	15
		a. Bright scarlet	8·50	90
L3	84	1½d. dull purple and green	6·00	2·00
		a. Chalk-surfaced paper. *Pale dull*		
		purple and green	14·00	3·00
L4	85	2d. grey-green and carmine-red.......	8·50	28·00
		a. Chalk-surfaced paper. *Pale*		
		grey-green and carmine-red	3·00	7·00
		ab. Dull blue-green and carmine.	3·00	8·00
L5	86	2½d. ultramarine	8·50	20·00
L6	87	3d. dull purple/*orange-yellow*	6·00	12·00
L7	88	4d. green and grey-brown	9·00	48·00
		a. Green and chocolate-brown	18·00	50·00

L8	89	5d. dull purple and ultramarine	16·00	29·00
L9	83	6d. pale dull purple	12·00	25·00
L10	93	1s. dull green and carmine	35·00	50·00
		a. Chalk-surfaced paper	35·00	50·00
L1/10	*Set of 10*			£100	£170

(b) Harrison ptgs optd at Somerset House.

L11	83	½d. dull yellow-green (p. 14) (2.12)	28·00	26·00
		a. *Dull green*.........................	28·00	26·00
		b. *Deep dull green*..................	38·00	32·00

On 28 December 1909 all values, except for the ½d. and 1d. were withdrawn from sale. A further consignment of the 2d, No. L4*ab*, probably ordered in error was however, received, and, as there was no requirement for this value, sold mainly to collectors. Subsequently dated cancellations on the withdrawn values are philatelic, being worth much less than the used prices quoted.

ANT

Distorted "N" (R. 2/10, 12/10)

1911–13. *Stamps of King George V optd with Type L 1 at Somerset House.*

(a) Die A. Wmk Crown.

L12	98	½d. green (No. 322) (12.9.11)..........	2·25	1·75
		a. Distorted "N"....................	35·00	
L13	99	1d. carmine-red (No. 327) (1.1.12) .	50	6·50
		a. No cross on crown....................	£150	
		b. Opt double, one albino	£100	
		c. Distorted "N"....................	18·00	

(b) Redrawn types. Wmk Crown.

L14	101	½d. green (No. 339) (19.3.12)........	1·00	20
		a. *Yellow-green*.......................	2·00	75
		b. Distorted "N"....................	20·00	
L15	102	1d. bright scarlet (No. 341)		
		(24.2.12)	1·00	1·60
		a. *Scarlet (No. 342)*	2·00	1·60
		b. Opt triple, two albino...............	42·00	
		c. Distorted "N"....................	20·00	

(c) New types. Wmk Royal Cypher (7.13).

L16	105	½d. green (No. 351)......................	60	1·50
		a. *Yellow-green*.......................	1·75	2·25
		b. Distorted "N"....................	18·00	
L17	104	1d. scarlet (No. 357)	30	5·50
		a. *Vermilion*.........................	9·50	10·00
		b. Distorted "N"....................	15·00	

Similar overprints were issued when the British Post Offices reopened in 1919, and are listed below.

B. BRITISH POST OFFICES IN CONSTANTINOPLE AND SMYRNA, 1919–1923

CONSTANTINOPLE

Following the occupation of Constantinople by Allied forces a British Military Post Office was opened for civilian use on 4 February 1919. During the period of its existence stamps of Great Britain with face values to 10s. were available and such use can be identified by the following cancellations:

"FIELD POST OFFICE H12" (4 February 1919 to 18 March 1919)
"ARMY POST OFFICE Y" (20 March 1919 to June 1920)
"ARMY POST OFFICE S.X.3" (March 1919 to April 1920)
"British A.P.O. CONSTANTINOPLE" (July 1919 to July 1920).

Of these four marks the first two types were also used for military mail.

The office reverted to civilian control on 29 July 1920, Nos. 41/50 and L18/24 being intended for its use.

Z 1   Z 2

Z 3   Z 4

1919–20. *Used at the Army Post Office. Stamps of GREAT BRITAIN cancelled with Types Z 1, Z 2, Z 3, Z 4.*

Z176		½d. green................................	2·00
Z177		1d. scarlet................................	2·00
Z178		1½d. brown................................	3·25
Z179		2d. orange (Die I)........................	2·50
Z180		2½d. blue................................	4·00
Z181		4d. grey-green............................	8·50
Z182		6d. purple................................	4·50
Z183		9d. agate................................	22·00
Z184		1s. bistre................................	5·50
Z185		2s.6d. brown..............................	38·00
Z186		5s. rose-red..............................	60·00
Z187		10s. dull grey-blue........................	£100

1920–21. *Used at the Civilian Post Office. Stamps of GREAT BRITAIN cancelled with Type 18 or double-circle datestamp.*

Z188		½d. green................................	2·00
Z189		1d. scarlet................................	2·00
Z190		1½d. brown................................	3·25
Z191		2d. orange (Die I)........................	2·50
Z192		2½d. blue................................	4·00
Z193		3d. violet................................	6·50
Z194		4d. grey-green............................	8·50
Z195		5d. brown................................	13·00
Z196		6d. purple................................	4·50
Z197		10d. turquoise-blue........................	22·00
Z198		1s. bistre................................	5·50
Z199		2s.6d. brown..............................	38·00
Z200		5s. rose-red..............................	60·00
Z201		10s. dull grey-blue........................	£100

PRICES FOR STAMPS ON COVER	
Nos. 41/50	*from* × 2
Nos. L18/24	*from* × 5

Stamps of Great Britain surch at Somerset House

I. TURKISH CURRENCY

1½ PIASTRES (10)   **15 PIASTRES** (11)

18¾ Short fraction bar (R. 4/12, 14/12)

1921 (Aug). *Stamps of King George V, wmk Royal Cypher, surch as T 1 (30pa.),* 10 *and* 11 (15 *and* 18¾*pi.*).

41	105	30pa. on ½d. green.......................	75	12·00
		a. *Yellow-green*.................	3·50	14·00
42	104	1½pi. on 1d. bright scarlet............	1·50	1·25
		a. *Vermilion*...................	10·00	3·75
		b. *Scarlet-vermilion*..........	8·00	4·25
43		3¾pi. on 2½d. blue.......................	1·25	25
		a. *Dull Prussian blue*.........	32·00	2·75
44	106	4½pi. on 3d. violet......................	2·00	3·75
		a. *Bluish violet*	3·00	3·00
45	107	7½pi. on 5d. brown......................	50	10
		a. *Yellow-brown*...............	2·25	20
46	108	15pi. on 10d. turquoise-blue	70	15
47		18¾pi. on 1s. bistre-brown.............	4·25	4·25
		a. Short fraction bar...........	55·00	
		b. *Olive-bistre*.................	6·00	4·75
		ba. Short fraction bar.........	70·00	

45 PIASTRES (12)   **45** Joined figures (second stamp in each horiz row)

1921. *Stamps of King George V (Bradbury, Wilkinson printing) surch as T 12.*

48	109	45pi. on 2s.6d. chocolate-brown........	20·00	45·00
		a. Joined figures...................	35·00	65·00
		b. *Olive-brown*	50·00	60·00
		ba. Joined figures.............	70·00	85·00
49		90pi. on 5s. rose-red	25·00	30·00
		a. Surch double, one		
		albino.....................	£250	
50		180pi. on 10s. dull grey-blue...........	45·00	40·00
		a. Surch double, one		
		albino.....................	£250	
41/50	*Set of 10*		90·00	£120
47s/50s Optd "Specimen" *Set of 4*			£275	

II. BRITISH CURRENCY

1921. *Stamps of King George V optd as Type L 1.*

L18	106	2d. reddish orange (Die I).............	1·25	30·00
		a. *Bright orange*..........................	2·25	30·00
L19		3d. bluish violet	7·50	10·00
L20		4d. grey-green	5·00	14·00
L21	107	5d. yellow-brown	12·00	28·00
L22		6d. dull purple (*chalk-surfaced paper*)	24·00	42·00
		a. *Reddish purple*	26·00	8·50
L23	108	1s. bistre-brown	13·00	8·50
		a. *Olive-bistre*	13·00	8·50
		s. Optd "Specimen"	65·00	
L24	109	2s.6d. chocolate-brown................	38·00	90·00
		a. *Olive-brown*	65·00	£120
		s. Optd "Specimen"	£140	
L18/24	*Set of 7*		85·00	£170

On No. L24 the letters of the overprint are shorter, being only 3 mm high.

Nos. 41/50 and L18/24 were used at the Constantinople office only.

SMYRNA

When the office re-opened on 1 March 1919 existing stocks of surcharged or overprinted issues were utilised until they were exhausted in mid-1920. During this period examples of Nos. 24, 29*a*, 30*a*, 33*b*/7, 39/40, L4*b*, L14/17 are known with commercial postmarks. These stamps were supplemented and finally replaced in mid-1920 by ordinary stamps of Great Britain.

1919–22. *Stamps of GREAT BRITAIN cancelled with circular postmark as Type 18 or with "REGISTERED" oval.*

Z282		½d. green................................	2·50
Z283		1d. scarlet................................	2·50

Z284		1½d. brown................................	3·50
Z285		2d. orange (Die I)........................	3·00
Z286		2d. orange (Die II).......................	26·00
Z287		2½d. blue (*shades*)......................	5·00
Z288		2½d. dull Prussian blue..................	£500
Z289		4d. grey-green............................	11·00
Z290		6d. purple................................	8·00
Z291		10d. turquoise-blue........................	30·00
Z292		1s. bistre................................	8·50
Z293		2s.6d. brown..............................	65·00
Z294		5s. rose-red..............................	95·00
Z295		10s. dull grey-blue........................	£160

C. BRITISH FIELD OFFICE IN SALONICA

These overprints were originally prepared for use by a civilian post office to be set up on Mt. Athos, Northern Greece. When the project was abandoned they were placed on sale at the Army Field Office in Salonica.

PRICES FOR STAMPS ON COVER	
Nos. S1/8	*from* × 6

Levant (S 1)

1916 (end Feb–9 Mar). *Stamps of Gt. Britain, optd with Type S 1 by Army Printing Office, Salonica.*

S1	105	½d. green................................	48·00	£250
		a. Opt double......................	£2500	£3250
		b. Vert pair, one without opt..........	£1300	£1700
S2	104	1d. scarlet................................	48·00	£225
		a. Opt double......................	£1600	£1900
S3	106	2d. reddish orange (Die I)..............	£150	£375
S4		3d. bluish violet	£120	£375
S5		4d. grey-green	£150	£375
S6	107	6d. reddish pur (*chalk-surfaced paper*)	85·00	£325
		a. Vert pair, one without opt..........	£1500	£1900
S7	108	9d. agate................................	£325	£600
		a. Opt double......................	£9500	£15000
S8		1s. bistre-brown..........................	£275	£500
S1/8	*Set of 8*		£1100	£2750

There are numerous forgeries of this overprint.

All values can be found with an additional albino overprint, inverted on the gummed side. These are worth a 25% premium.

British New Guinea *see* New Guinea *after* Australia

British Occupation of Iraq *see* Iraq

British Occupation of Italian Colonies

PRICES FOR STAMPS ON COVER TO 1945	
Nos. M1/21	*from* × 4
Nos. MD1/5	*from* × 10
Nos. S1/9	*from* × 6
The above prices refer to covers from the territories concerned, not examples used in Great Britain.	

MIDDLE EAST FORCES

For use in territory occupied by British Forces in Eritrea (1942), Italian Somaliland (from 13 April 1942), Cyrenaica (1943), Tripolitania (1943), and some of the Dodecanese Islands (1945).

PRICES. Our prices for used stamps with "M.E.F." overprints are for specimens with identifiable postmarks of the territories in which they were issued. These stamps were also used in the United Kingdom with official sanction, from the summer of 1950 onwards, and with U.K. postmarks are worth considerably less.

PRINTERS. Considerable research has been undertaken to discover the origins of Nos. M1/10. It is now suggested that Nos. M1/5, previously assigned to Harrison and Sons, were produced by the Army Printing Services, Cairo, and that the smaller printing, Nos. M6/10, previously identified as the work of the Army Printing Services, Cairo, was from an unidentified printer within the Middle East Forces area.

M.E.F. M.E.F.

(M 1) Opt. 14 mm long. Regular lettering and upright oblong stops.

(M 2) Opt. 13½ mm long. Regular lettering and square stops.

M.E.F.

(M 2a) Opt. 13½ mm long.
Rough lettering and round stops.

M.E.F.

Sliced "M" (R. 6/10)

(Illustrations twice actual size)

1942 (2 Mar). Stamps of Great Britain optd. W **127**. P 15×14.

(a) With Type M 1.

M1	128	1d. scarlet (No. 463)	1·75	2·50
		a. Sliced "M"	85·00	£100
M2		2d. orange (No. 465)	1·25	3·75
		a. Sliced "M"	65·00	
M3		2½d. ultramarine (No. 466)	1·00	1·25
		a. Sliced "M"	65·00	
M4		3d. violet (No. 467)	80	30
M5	129	5d. brown	70	30
		a. Sliced "M"	60·00	65·00

(b) With Type M 2.

M6	128	1d. scarlet (No. 463)	55·00	15·00
		a. Optd with Type M 2a	45·00	10·00
		b. Nos. M6/a se-tenant vert	£200	95·00
M7		2d. orange (No. 465)	75·00	£100
		a. Optd with Type M 2a	65·00	90·00
		b. Nos. M7/a se-tenant vert	£325	£375
M8		2½d. ultramarine (No. 466)	55·00	7·50
		a. Optd with Type M 2a	48·00	5·50
		b. Nos. M8/a se-tenant vert	£200	60·00
M9		3d. violet (No. 467)	£120	40·00
		a. Optd with Type M 2a	£110	38·00
		ab. Opt double	†	£4000
		b. Nos. M9/a se-tenant vert	£450	£190
M10	129	5d. brown	£400	90·00
		a. Optd with Type M 2a	£375	80·00
		b. Nos. M10/a se-tenant vert	£1200	£650

See note after No. M21.

Nos. M6/10 were issued in panes of 60 (6×10), rows 2, 3, and 7 being overprinted with Type M **2** and the other seven rows with Type M **2**a.

M.E.F.

(M **3**) Optd 13½ mm long. Regular lettering and upright oblong stops.

(Illustration twice actual size)

1943 (1 Jan)–*47. Stamps of Great Britain optd with Type M **3** by Harrison & Sons. W **127**, P 15×14 (1d. to 1s.); W **133**, P 14 (others).*

M11	128	1d. pale scarlet (No. 486)	1·50	10
M12		2d. pale orange (No. 488)	1·50	1·25
M13		2½d. light ultramarine (No. 489)	50	10
M14		3d. pale violet (No. 490)	1·50	10
M15	129	5d. brown	3·75	10
M16		6d. purple	40	10
M17	130	9d. deep olive-green	85	10
M18		1s. bistre-brown	50	10
M19	131	2s.6d. yellow-green	7·00	1·00
M20		5s. red (1947)	14·00	17·00
M21	132	10s. ultramarine (1947)	18·00	10·00
M11/21 Set of 11			45·00	27·00
M18s/21s Optd "Specimen" Set of 4			£550	

The overprint on No. M15 should not be confused with the other overprints on the 5d. value. It can be distinguished from No. M5 by the ½ mm difference in length; and from No. M10 by the more intense colour, thicker lettering and larger stops.

POSTAGE DUE STAMPS

M.E.F.

(MD **1**)

1942. *Postage Due stamps of Great Britain Nos. D27/30 and D33 optd with Type MD **1**, in blue-black.*

MD1	D **1**	½d. emerald	30	13·00
MD2		1d. carmine	30	1·75
		w. Wmk sideways inverted*	—	50·00
MD3		2d. agate	1·25	1·25
MD4		3d. violet	50	4·25
MD5		1s. deep blue	3·75	13·00
MD1/5 Set of 5			5·50	30·00
		s. Optd "Specimen"	£160	

*No. MD2w shows the Crown pointing to the left, *as seen from the back of the stamp.*

CYRENAICA

In June 1949 the British authorities recognised the leader of the Senussi, Amir Mohammed Idris Al-Senussi, as Amir of Cyrenaica with autonomy in internal affairs.

(Currency. 10 millièmes = 1 piastre, 100 piastres = 1 Egyptian pound)

24 Mounted Warrior

25 Mounted Warrior

(Recess Waterlow)

1950 (16 Jan). P 12½.

136	**24**	1m. brown	2·50	4·50
137		2m. carmine	2·50	4·50
138		3m. orange-yellow	2·50	4·50
139		4m. blue-green	2·50	4·50
140		5m. grey-black	2·50	3·00
141		8m. orange	2·50	2·25
142		10m. violet	2·50	1·75
143		12m. scarlet	2·50	1·75
144		20m. blue	2·50	1·75
145	**25**	50m. ultramarine and purple-brown	4·75	4·50
146		100m. carmine and black	10·00	9·00
147		200m. violet and deep blue	14·00	25·00
148		500m. orange-yellow and green	42·00	65·00
136/148 Set of 13			85·00	£120

POSTAGE DUE STAMPS

D **26**

(Recess Waterlow)

1950 (16 Jan). P 12½.

D149	D **26**	2m. brown	45·00	95·00
D150		4m. blue-green	45·00	95·00
D151		8m. scarlet	45·00	£100
D152		10m. orange	45·00	£100
D153		20m. orange-yellow	45·00	£110
D154		40m. blue	45·00	£150
D155		100m. grey-brown	45·00	£160
D149/155 Set of 7			£275	£700

On 24 December 1951 Cyrenaica united with Tripolitania, Fezzan and Ghadames to form the independent Kingdom of Libya, whose issues are listed in Part 13 (*Africa since Independence F—M*) of this catalogue.

ERITREA

From early 1950 examples of Nos. E1/32 exist precancelled in manuscript by a black or blue horizontal line for use by British troops on concession rate mail.

BRITISH MILITARY ADMINISTRATION

(Currency. 100 cents = 1 shilling)

B.M.A. ERITREA (E **1**)   **B.M.A. ERITREA** (E **2**)

10 CENTS (E **1**)   **5 SHILLINGS** (E **2**)

SH. 50 Normal   **SH .50** Misplaced Stop

1948–49. *Stamps of Great Britain surch as Types E **1** or E **2**.*

E1	128	5c. on ½d. pale green	1·25	65
E2		10c. on 1d. pale scarlet	1·25	2·50
E3		20c. on 2d. pale orange	50	2·25
E4		25c. on 2½d. light ultramarine	1·00	60
E5		30c. on 3d. pale violet	1·25	4·50
E6	129	40c. on 5d. brown	50	4·25
E7		50c. on 6d. purple	50	1·00
E7a	130	65c. on 8d. bright carmine (1.2.49)	7·00	2·00
E8		75c. on 9d. deep olive-green	70	75
E9		1s. on 1s. bistre-brown	70	50
E10	131	2s.50c. on 2s.6d. yellow-green	8·50	10·00
		a. Misplaced stop (R. 4/7)	£120	£140
E11		5s. on 5s. red	8·50	16·00
E12	132	10s. on 10s. ultramarine	22·00	22·00
E1/12 Set of 13			48·00	60·00

BRITISH ADMINISTRATION

1950 (6 Feb). *As Nos. E1/12, but surch "B.A. ERITREA" and new values instead of "B.M.A." etc.*

E13	128	5c. on ½d. pale green	1·50	8·00
E14		10c. on 1d. pale scarlet	30	3·00
E15		20c. on 2d. pale orange	30	80
E16		25c. on 2½d. light ultramarine	30	60
E17		30c. on 3d. pale violet	30	2·25
E18	129	40c. on 5d. brown	50	1·75
E19		50c. on 6d. purple	30	20
E20	130	65c. on 8d. bright carmine	2·50	1·50
E21		75c. on 9d. deep olive-green	30	25
E22		1s. on 1s. bistre-brown	30	15
E23	131	2s.50c. on 2s.6d. yellow-green	7·00	4·75
E24		5s. on 5s. red	7·00	12·00
E25	132	10s. on 10s. ultramarine	60·00	55·00
E13/25 Set of 13			70·00	80·00

1951 (28 May*). *Nos. 503/4, 506/7 and 509/11 of Great Britain surch "B.A. ERITREA" and new values.*

E26	128	5c. on ½d. pale orange	30	75
E27		10c. on 1d. light ultramarine	30	75
E28		20c. on 2d. pale red-brown	30	30
E29		25c. on 2½d. pale scarlet	30	30
E30	147	2s.50c. on 2s.6d. yellow-green	10·00	23·00
E31	148	5s. on 5s. red	21·00	23·00
E32		10s. on 10s. ultramarine	22·00	23·00
E26/32 Set of 7			50·00	65·00

---

*This is the local release date. The stamps were placed on sale in London on 3 May.

POSTAGE DUE STAMPS

B.M.A. ERITREA 10 CENTS (ED **1**)

1948. *Postage Due stamps of Great Britain Nos. D27/30 and D33 surch as Type ED **1**.*

ED1	D **1**	5c. on ½d. emerald	9·50	22·00
		a. No stop after "A"	—	£275
ED2		10c. on 1d. carmine	9·50	24·00
		a. No stop after "B"	£140	
ED3		20c. on 2d. agate	10·00	16·00
		a. No stop after "A"	60·00	
		b. No stop after "B" (R. 1/9)	£150	
ED4		30c. on 3d. violet	9·50	17·00
ED5		1s. on 1s. deep blue	18·00	32·00
ED1/5 Set of 5			50·00	£100

1950 (6 Feb). *As Nos. ED1/5, but surch "B.A. ERITREA" and new values instead of "B.M.A." etc.*

ED6	D **1**	5c. on ½d. emerald	11·00	48·00
ED7		10c. on 1d. carmine	11·00	16·00
		a. "C" of "CENTS" omitted	£2250	
		ab. "C" omitted and vertical oblong for "E" of "CENTS"	£4000	
ED8		20c. on 2d. agate	11·00	16·00
ED9		30c. on 3d. violet	15·00	25·00
		w. Wmk sideways-inverted*	—	55·00
ED10		1s. on 1s. deep blue	15·00	25·00
		a. Stop after "A" omitted (R. 2/13)	£375	
ED6/10 Set of 5			55·00	£110

No. ED7a, and probably No. ED7ab, occurred on R. 7/17, and the error was quickly corrected.

*No. ED9w shows the Crowns pointing to the left, *as seen from the back of the stamp.*

Stamps of Ethiopia were used in Eritrea after 15 September 1952 following federation with Ethiopia.

SOMALIA

BRITISH OCCUPATION

E.A.F.

(S **1** "East Africa Forces")

1943 (15 Jan)–*46. Stamps of Great Britain optd with Type S **1**, in blue.*

S1	128	1d. pale scarlet	60	60
S2		2d. pale orange	1·50	1·50
S3		2½d. light ultramarine	50	3·50
S4		3d. pale violet	1·00	15
S5	129	5d. brown	1·50	40
S6		6d. purple	50	1·25
S7	130	9d. deep olive-green	1·00	2·25
S8		1s. bistre-brown	2·50	15
S9	131	2s.6d. yellow-green (1946)	13·00	6·50
S1/9 Set of 9			20·00	14·50
S8s/9s Optd "Specimen" Set of 2			£275	

The note *re* used prices above Type M **1** of Middle East Forces also applies to the above issue.

BRITISH MILITARY ADMINISTRATION

(Currency. 100 cents = 1 shilling)

1948 (27 May). *Stamps of Great Britain surch "B.M.A./SOMALIA" and new values, as Types E **1** and E **2** of Eritrea.*

S10	128	5c. on ½d. pale green	1·25	1·75
S11		15c. on 1½d. pale red-brown	1·75	15·00
S12		20c. on 2d. pale orange	3·00	4·25
S13		25c. on 2½d. light ultramarine	2·25	4·50
S14		30c. on 3d. pale violet	2·25	9·00
S15	129	40c. on 5d. brown	1·25	20
S16		50c. on 6d. purple	50	20
S17	130	75c. on 9d. deep olive-green	2·00	18·00
S18		1s. on 1s. bistre-brown	1·25	20
S19	131	2s.50c. on 2s.6d. yellow-green	4·25	25·00
		a. Misplaced stop (R. 4/7)	95·00	£250
S20		5s. on 5s. red	9·50	40·00
S10/20 Set of 11			26·00	£110

For illustration of No. S19a, see previous column above No. E1 of Eritrea.

BRITISH ADMINISTRATION

1950 (2 Jan). *As Nos. S10/20, but surch "BA./SOMALIA" and new values, instead of "B.M.A." etc.*

S21	128	5c. on ½d. pale green	20	3·00
S22		15c. on 1½d. pale red-brown	75	17·00
S23		20c. on 2d. pale orange	75	7·50
S24		25c. on 2½d. light ultramarine	50	8·00
S25		30c. on 3d. pale violet	1·25	4·50
S26	129	40c. on 5d. brown	55	1·00
S27		50c. on 6d. purple	50	1·00
S28	130	75c. on 9d. deep olive-green	2·00	7·00
S29		1s. on 1s. bistre-brown	60	1·50
S30	131	2s.50c. on 2s.6d. yellow-green	4·00	24·00
S31		5s. on 5s. red	11·00	32·00
S21/31 Set of 11			20·00	95·00

Somalia reverted to Italian Administration on 1 April 1950 later becoming independent. Later issues will be found listed in Part 8 (*Italy and Switzerland*) of this catalogue.

TRIPOLITANIA

BRITISH MILITARY ADMINISTRATION

(Currency. 100 centesimi = 1 Military Administration lira)

4   4
M.A.L. M.A.L.

Normal	Misaligned surcharge (R. 8/8, 18/8)

1948 (1 July). *Stamps of Great Britain surch "B.M.A./ TRIPOLITANIA" and new values, as Types E 1 and E 2 of Eritrea, but expressed in M(ilitary) A(dministration) L(ire).*

T1	128	1l. on ½d. pale green	90	1·75
T2		2l. on 1d. pale scarlet	30	15
T3		3l. on 1½d. pale red-brown	30	50
		a. Misaligned surch	32·00	45·00
T4		4l. on 2d. pale orange	30	70
		a. Misaligned surch	32·00	55·00
T5		5l. on 2½d. light ultramarine	30	20
T6		6l. on 3d. pale violet	30	40
T7	129	10l. on 5d. brown	30	15
T8		12l. on 6d. purple	30	20
T9	130	18l. on 9d. deep olive-green	80	65
T10		24l. on 1s. bistre-brown	70	1·50
T11	131	60l. on 2s.6d. yellow-green	3·50	9·50
T12		120l. on 5s. red	15·00	21·00
T13	132	240l. on 10s. ultramarine	23·00	95·00
T1/13	Set of 13		42·00	£110

BRITISH ADMINISTRATION

1950 (6 Feb). *As Nos. T1/13, but surch "B.A. TRIPOLITANIA" and new values, instead of "B.M.A." etc.*

T14	128	1l. on ½d. pale green	2·75	13·00
T15		2l. on 1d. pale scarlet	2·50	40
T16		3l. on 1½d. pale red-brown	1·25	13·00
		a. Misaligned surch	55·00	£160
T17		4l. on 2d. pale orange	1·25	4·50
		a. Misaligned surch	55·00	£110
T18		5l. on 2½d. light ultramarine	70	70
T19		6l. on 3d. pale violet	1·75	3·25
T20	129	10l. on 5d. brown	50	4·00
T21		12l. on 6d. purple	2·00	50
T22	130	18l. on 9d. deep olive-green	2·25	2·75
T23		24l. on 1s. bistre-brown	2·75	3·75
T24	131	60l. on 2s.6d. yellow-green	8·00	12·00
T25		120l. on 5s. red	20·00	22·00
T26	132	240l. on 10s. ultramarine	35·00	65·00
T14/26	Set of 13		70·00	£130

1951 (3 May). *Nos. 503/7 and 509/11 of Great Britain surch "B.A. TRIPOLITANIA" and new values.*

T27	128	1l. on ½d. pale orange	20	6·00
T28		2l. on 1d. light ultramarine	20	1·00
T29		3l. on 1½d. pale green	30	8·00
T30		4l. on 2d. pale red-brown	20	1·25
T31		5l. on 2½d. pale scarlet	30	7·50
T32	147	60l. on 2s.6d. yellow-green	5·50	22·00
T33	148	120l. on 5s. red	9·00	27·00
T34	149	240l. on 10s. ultramarine	38·00	50·00
T27/34	Set of 8		48·00	£110

POSTAGE DUE STAMPS

1948. *Postage Due stamps of Great Britain Nos. D27/30 and D33 surch "B.M.A./TRIPOLITANIA" as Type ED 1 of Eritrea, but expressed in M(ilitary) A(dministration) L(ire).*

TD1	D 1	1l. on ½d. emerald	5·50	50·00
		a. No stop after "A"	70·00	
TD2		2l. on 1d. carmine	2·50	35·00
		a. No stop after "A"	45·00	
		b. No stop after "M" (R. 1/17)	£110	
TD3		4l. on 2d. agate	9·00	35·00
		a. No stop after "A"	£140	
		b. No stop after "M"	£180	
TD4		6l. on 3d. violet	7·50	21·00
TD5		24l. on 1s. deep blue	29·00	£100
TD1/5	Set of 5		48·00	£225

1950 (6 Feb). *As Nos. TD1/5, but surch "B.A. TRIPOLITANIA" and new values, instead of "B.M.A." etc.*

TD6	D 1	1l. on ½d. emerald	12·00	80·00
		a. No stop after "B"	£150	
TD7		2l. on 1d. carmine	3·50	27·00
		a. No stop after "B"	80·00	
TD8		4l. on 2d. agate	4·75	35·00
		a. No stop after "B"	85·00	
TD9		6l. on 3d. violet	18·00	60·00
		a. No stop after "B"	£225	
		w. Wmk sideways-inverted*	35·00	
TD10		24l. on 1s. deep blue	48·00	£140
		a. No stop after "A"	£475	
		b. No stop after "B"	£475	
TD6/10	Set of 5		75·00	£300

*No. TD9w shows the Crowns pointing to the left, *as seen from the back of the stamp.*

Tripolitania became part of the independent kingdom of Libya on 24 December 1951.

British P.Os in Crete

BRITISH ADMINISTRATION OF CANDIA PROVINCE HERAKLEION)

Crete, formerly part of the Turkish Empire, was made autonomous, under Turkish suzerainty, in November 1898 with British, French, Italian and Russian troops stationed in separate zones to keep the peace.

Overseas mail franked with Nos. B1/5 was forwarded through the Austrian post office at Canea, being additionally franked with stamps of the Austro-Hungarian Post Offices in the Turkish Empire.

(Currency. 40 pares = 1 piastre)

PRICES FOR STAMPS ON COVER	
No. B1	*from × 8*
Nos. B2/5	—

B 1	B 2

1898 (25 Nov). *Handstruck locally. Imperf.*

B1	B 1	20pa. bright violet	£425	£225

1898 (3 Dec). *Litho by M. Grundmann, Athens. P 11½.*

B2	B 2	10pa. blue	8·00	19·00
		a. Imperf (pair)	£250	
B3		20pa. green	14·00	17·00
		a. Imperf (pair)	£250	

1899. P 11½.

B4	B 2	10pa. brown	8·50	26·00
		a. Imperf (pair)	£250	
B5		20pa. rose	19·00	15·00
		a. Imperf (pair)	£250	

The British postal service closed at the end of 1899.

British P.O. in Siam

(Bangkok)

An overseas postal service for foreign residents was operated by the British Consulate at Bangkok from 1858. Mail was despatched by steamer to Singapore and from 1876 onwards was increasingly franked with Straits Settlements stamps. These were initially cancelled on arrival at Singapore, but later an oval postmark "BRITISH CONSULATE BANGKOK" was used. In 1883 a circular "BANGKOK" datestamp was introduced for use with Nos. 1/23. Both cancellations can also be found used on Hong Kong stamps between 1881 and 1885.

(Currency. 100 cents = 1 Straits dollar)

Stamps of Straits Settlements (see Malaysia) cancelled with oval postmark inscribed "BRITISH CONSULATE BANGKOK" around Royal Arms.

1882. Wmk Crown CC (Nos. 11/15, 33, 35).

Z1	2c. brown	£400
Z2	4c. rose	£400
Z3	6c. dull lilac	£450
Z4	8c. orange-yellow	£400
Z5	10c. on 30c. claret (thin "0") (No. 33)	£1000
Z6	10c. on 30c. claret (thick "10") (No. 34)	£1000
Z7	10c. on 30c. claret (thin "1", thick "0") (No. 35)	£1200
Z8	12c. blue	£600

Subsequent Straits Settlements values to 8c. watermarked Crown CA are known used at Bangkok in 1883 and 1884. During this period the stamps overprinted "B" were on sale at the British Post Office.

PRICES FOR STAMPS ON COVER
The issues of the British Post Offices in Siam are worth from × 100 the prices quoted for used stamps when on cover.

B
(1)

1882 (May)–**85**. *Stamps of Straits Settlements optd with T 1.*

(a) On No. 9 of 1867.

1	32c. on 2a. yellow (1885)	£35000

(b) On Nos. 11/13, 14a, 15/17 and 19 of 1867–72 and Nos. 48/9 of 1882. Wmk Crown CC.

2	2c. brown	£3500	£1500
3	4c. rose	£3250	£1300
	a. Opt double	—	£7500
4	5c. purple-brown	£350	£375
5	6c. lilac	£225	£120
6	8c. orange	£2500	£225
7	10c. slate	£400	£150
8	12c. blue	£950	£475
9	24c. green	£700	£150
10	30c. claret	£45000	£30000
11	96c. grey	£7500	£3000

(c) On Nos. 59/60 of April 1883.

12	2c. on 32c. pale red (*Wide "S"*)	£2750	£2750
13	2c. on 32c. pale red (*Wide "E"*)	£3500	£3500

(d) On Nos. 50/3 of 1882 and Nos. 63/7 of 1883–84. Wmk Crown CA.

14		2c. brown	£475	£350
15		2c. pale rose (1883)	55·00	45·00
		a. Opt inverted	—	£11000
		b. Opt double	£2750	£2750
		c. Opt treble	£10000	
16		4c. rose (1883)	£600	£325
17		4c. pale brown (1883)	80·00	70·00
		a. Opt double	£3500	
		b. Broken oval	£1100	£1100
18		5c. blue (1884)	£250	£170
19		6c. lilac (1884)	£180	£110
20		8c. orange (1883)	£160	65·00
		a. Opt inverted	£20000	£11000
21		10c. slate (1883)	£160	85·00
22		12c. brown-purple (1883)	£275	£150
23		24c. yellow-green (1884?)	£6000	£3000

The prices quoted for the overprint double errors, Nos. 3a, 15b and 17a, are for stamps showing two clear impressions of the overprint. Examples showing partial doubling, as these and other values, are worth a small premium over the price quoted for normal stamps.

No. 17b shows the edge of the central oval broken above the "O" of "POSTAGE". It occurs on R. 10/5 of the lower right pane.

The use of these stamps ceased on 30 June 1885. Siam joined the Universal Postal Union on 1 July 1885.

British Postal Agencies in Eastern Arabia

Certain Arab States in Eastern Arabia, whilst remaining independent, had British postal administrations replacing Bahrain, and subsequently Indian, post offices in the various states.

Bahrain and Kuwait (from 1948) and Qatar (from 1957) used British stamps overprinted and surcharged in local currency. Abu Dhabi (from 1964) and Trucial States (from 1961 and used only in Dubai) had definitive issues made under the auspices of the British Agencies.

In addition, British stamps were surcharged with value only for use in Muscat and certain other states. They were formerly listed under Muscat as they were first put on sale there, but in view of their more extended use, the list has been transferred here, retaining the same numbering.

The stamps were used in Muscat from 1 April 1948 to 29 April 1966; in Dubai from 1 April 1948 to 6 January 1961; in Qatar: Doha from August 1950, Umm Said from February 1956, to 31 March 1957; and in Abu Dhabi from 30 March 1963 (Das Island from December 1960) to 29 March 1964.

Nos. 21/2 were placed on sale in Kuwait Post Offices in April and May 1951 and from February to November 1953 due to shortages of stamps with "KUWAIT" overprint. Isolated examples of other values can be found commercially used from Bahrain or Kuwait.

(Currency. 12 pies = 1 anna; 16 annas = 1 rupee)

Stamps of Great Britain surcharged

I		2 RUPEES
ANNA		
(3)		(4)

1½	1½
I	II

Two types of 1½a. surcharge:

I. "1" 3¼ mm high and aligns with top of "2" in "½" (Rows 1 to 10).

II. "1" 3½ mm high with foot of figure below top of "2" (Rows 11 to 20).

1948 (1 Apr). *Surch with T 3 (½a. to 1r.) or 4 (2r.).*

16	128	½a. on ½d. pale green	2·75	7·50
17		1a. on 1d. pale scarlet	3·00	30
18		1½a. on 1½d. pale red-brown (I)	11·00	3·25
		a. Type II	11·00	3·25
		b. Vert pair. Nos. 18/a	65·00	
19		2a. on 2d. pale orange	2·00	3·25
20		2½a. on 2½d. light ultramarine	3·50	8·00
21		3a. on 3d. pale violet	3·50	10
22	129	6a. on 6d. purple	4·00	10
23	130	1r. on 1s. bistre-brown	4·50	60
24	131	2r. on 2s.6d. yellow-green	10·00	38·00
16/24	Set of 9		40·00	55·00

One example of No. 22 is known with the surcharge almost completely omitted from position R. 20/2 in the sheet.

2½		15
ANNAS		RUPEES
(5)		(6)

1948 (26 Apr). *Royal Silver Wedding. Nos. 493/4 surch with T 5 or 6.*

25	137	2½a. on 2½d. ultramarine	2·25	3·25
26	138	15r. on £1 blue	24·00	35·00

1948 (29 July). *Olympic Games. Nos. 495/8 surch with new values in "ANNAS" or "1 RUPEE", as T 5/6, but in one line on 2½a. (vert) or 6a. and 1r. (horiz) and grills obliterating former values of all except 2½a.*

27	139	2½a. on 2½d. ultramarine	35	2·50

28	**140**	3a. on 3d. violet		45	2·50
		a. Crown flaw........................		55·00	
29	**141**	6a. on 6d. bright purple............		45	2·75
30	**142**	1r. on 1s. brown		1·25	3·50
		a. Surch double		£1000	
27/30		Set of 4		2·25	10·00

1949 (10 Oct). *75th Anniv of Universal Postal Union. Nos. 499/ 502 surch with new values in "ANNAS" or "1 RUPEE" as T 3/4, but all in one line, with grills obliterating former values.*

31	**143**	2½a. on 2½d. ultramarine		50	3·00
		a. Lake in India........................		65·00	
32	**144**	3a. on 3d. violet		60	3·50
33	**145**	6a. on 6d. bright purple.............		60	2·75
34	**146**	1r. on 1s. brown		2·00	4·50
31/4		Set of 4		3·25	12·00

═ 2 RUPEES ═   2 RUPEES
(6a)   (6b)

Type **6a**. "2" and "RUPEES" level and in line with lower of the two bars.
Type **6b**. "2" raised in relation to "RUPEES" and whole surcharge below the lower bar.

1950 (2 Oct)–**55**. *Nos. 503/8 surch as T 3 and No. 509 with T 6a.*

35	**128**	½a. on ½d. pale orange (3.5.51)		70	9·00
36		1a. on 1d. light ultramarine (3.5.51).		30	7·50
37		1½a. on 1½d. pale green (I) (3.5.51)...		10·00	25·00
		a. Type II		10·00	25·00
		b. Vert pair. Nos. 37a		60·00	
38		2a. on 2d. pale red-brown (3.5.51)...		30	8·50
39		2½a. on 2½d. pale scarlet (3.5.51).....		30	16·00
40	**129**	4a. on 4d. light ultramarine		45	3·50
41	**147**	2r. on 2s.6d. yellow-green (3.5.51).....		29·00	7·00
		a. Surch with Type **6b**			
		(1955)		£200	65·00
35/41		Set of 7		38·00	70·00

British Solomon Islands

The first British Resident Commissioner, Charles Woodford, was appointed in 1896 and an administrative centre established at Tulagi.

Mail was initially sent unstamped by sealed bag to Sydney where New South Wales stamps were applied and cancelled. Later the Resident Commissioner kept a stock of New South Wales stamps which were still not cancelled until arrival at Sydney. From April 1906 Mr. Woodford used a vertical oblong "BRITISH SOLOMON ISLANDS PAID" handstamp in place of New South Wales stamps which were then added to many of the covers by the postal authorities in Sydney.

PRICES FOR STAMPS ON COVER TO 1945	
Nos. 1/7	*from* × 12
Nos. 8/17	*from* × 25
Nos. 18/36	*from* × 6
Nos. 37/8	
Nos. 39/51	*from* × 6
No. 52	
Nos. 53/6	*from* × 2
Nos. 57/9	*from* × 6
Nos. 60/72	*from* × 2
Nos. D1/8	*from* × 5

BRITISH PROTECTORATE

1   2

(Des C. M. Woodford. Litho W. E. Smith & Co. Sydney)

1907 (14 Feb). No wmk. P 11.

1	**1**	½d. ultramarine		9·00	14·00
2		1d. rose-carmine		23·00	25·00
3		2d. indigo		30·00	30·00
		a. Imperf between (horiz pair)......		£12000	
4		2½d. orange-yellow		32·00	42·00
		a. Imperf between (vert pair)......		£5000	
		b. Imperf between (horiz pair)......		£7000	£5000
5		5d. emerald-green		55·00	65·00
6		6d. chocolate		50·00	60·00
		a. Imperf between (vert pair)......		£4250	
7		1s. bright purple		70·00	75·00
1/7		Set of 7		£250	£275

Nos. 1/7 did not become valid for international postage until early September 1907. Overseas covers before that date show additional New South Wales values.

Three types exist of the ½d. and 2½d., and six each of the other values, differing in minor details.

Forgeries of Nos. 1/7 show different perforations and have the boat paddle touching the shore. Genuine stamps show a gap between the paddle and the shore.

(Recess D.L.R.)

1908 (1 Nov)–**11**. *Wmk Mult Crown CA (sideways). P 14.*

8	**2**	½d. green		1·50	1·00
9		1d. red		1·25	1·00
10		2d. greyish slate		1·25	1·00
11		2½d. ultramarine		3·75	2·00
11a		4d. red/*yellow* (6.3.11)...........		3·25	9·00
12		5d. olive		9·00	5·00
13		6d. claret		10·00	5·50
14		1s. black/*green*		8·50	5·00
15		2s. purple/*blue* (7.3.10)...........		40·00	55·00
16		2s.6d. red/*blue* (7.3.10)............		48·00	70·00

17		5s. green/*yellow* (7.3.10)		75·00	£100
8/17		Set of 11		£180	£225
8s/17s		Optd "Specimen" Set of 11		£250	

The ½d. and 1d. were issued in 1913 on rather thinner paper and with brownish gum.

3   4

(T **3** and **4**. Typo D.L.R.)

1913. *Inscribed "POSTAGE POSTAGE". Wmk Mult Crown CA. P 14.*

18	**3**	½d. green (1.4)......................		80	3·50
19		1d. red (1.4).......................		1·50	14·00
20		3d. purple (27.2)..................		80	4·00
		a. On orange-buff.................		8·00	24·00
21		11d. dull purple and scarlet (27.2)....		3·00	12·00
18/21		Set of 4		5·50	30·00
18s/21s		Optd "Specimen" Set of 4		70·00	

1914 (Mar)–**23**. *Inscribed "POSTAGE REVENUE". Chalk-surfaced paper (3d. to £1). Wmk Mult Crown CA. P 14.*

22	**4**	½d. green		80	12·00
23		½d. yellow-green (1917)		4·50	18·00
24		1d. carmine-red....................		1·50	1·25
25		1d. scarlet (1917).................		4·75	6·50
26		2d. grey (7.14)...................		3·00	9·00
27		2½d. ultramarine (7.14)............		2·25	5·00
28		3d. purple/*pale yellow* (3.23)...........		20·00	85·00
29		4d. black and red (7.14)..........		2·00	2·50
30		5d. dull purple and olive-green (7.14)........		20·00	30·00
31		5d. brown-purple and olive-green (7.14)........		20·00	30·00
32		6d. dull and bright purple (7.14)........		6·00	14·00
33		1s. black/*green* (7.14).............		4·75	7·00
		a. On blue-green, olive back (1923)		7·50	24·00
34		2s. purple and blue/*blue* (7.14).......		7·00	10·00
35		2s.6d. black and red/*blue* (7.14)......		9·50	24·00
36		5s. green and red/*yellow* (7.14).......		32·00	48·00
		a. On orange-buff (1920)		50·00	70·00
37		10s. green and red/*green* (7.14).......		85·00	65·00
38		£1 purple and black/*red* (7.14).......		£250	£120
22/38		Set of 14		£400	£375
22s/38s		Optd "Specimen" Set of 14		£400	

Variations in the coloured papers are mostly due to climate and do not indicate separate printings.

1922–31. *Chalk-surfaced paper (4d. and 5d. to 10s). Wmk Mult Script CA. P 14.*

39	**4**	½d. green (10.22)...................		30	3·50
40		1d. scarlet (4.23).................		9·00	11·00
41		1d. dull violet (2.27)		1·00	7·50
42	**3**	1½d. bright scarlet (7.24)..........		2·25	60
43	**4**	2d. slate-grey (4.23).............		4·50	15·00
44		3d. pale ultramarine (11.23).......		70	9·00
45		4d. black and red/*yellow* (7.27).......		3·50	23·00
45a		4½d. red-brown (1931)..............		3·00	20·00
46		5d. dull purple and olive-green (12.27)...........		3·00	27·00
47		6d. dull and bright purple (12.27)......		3·75	27·00
48		1s. black/*emerald* (12.27)...........		2·75	12·00
49		2s. purple and blue/*blue* (2.27)........		8·50	38·00
50		2s.6d. black and red/*blue* (2.27).......		7·50	45·00
51		5s. green and red/*pale yellow* (12.27)		26·00	55·00
52		10s. green and red/*emerald* (1.25)......		£100	95·00
39/52		Set of 15		£180	£325
39s/52s		Optd or Perf (4½d.) "Specimen" Set of 16..		£350	

1935 (6 May). *Silver Jubilee. As Nos. 91/4 of Antigua. P 13½×14.*

53		1½d. deep blue and carmine...........		1·00	1·00
		f. Diagonal line by turret.......		60·00	70·00
		h. Dot by flagstaff..............		£100	
54		3d. brown and deep blue..........		3·00	6·50
		f. Diagonal line by turret.......		£100	£140
		h. Dot by flagstaff..............		£190	
55		6d. light blue and olive-green.......		9·50	12·00
		a. Frame printed double, one albino		£1200	
		b. Frame printed triple, two albino		£1200	
		h. Dot by flagstaff..............		£275	£275
		i. Dash by turret................		£300	
56		1s. slate and purple..............		7·50	11·00
		a. Frame printed double, one albino......		£1500	
		f. Diagonal line by turret.......		£200	
		h. Dot by flagstaff..............		£275	
		i. Dash by turret................		£300	
53/6		Set of 4		19·00	27·00
53s/6s		Perf "Specimen" Set of 4		£100	

The second albino impression on No. 55b is sometimes almost co-incidental with the inked impression of the frame.

For illustrations of plate varieties see Omnibus section following Zanzibar.

1937 (13 May). *Coronation. As Nos. 95/7 of Antigua. P 11×11½.*

57		1d. violet		30	1·25
58		1½d. carmine		30	60
59		3d. blue		50	50
57/9		Set of 3		1·00	2·10
57s/9s		Perf "Specimen" Set of 3		80·00	

5 Spears and Shield   **6 Native Constable and Chief**

---

7 Artificial Island, Malaita   **8 Canoe House**

9 Roviana canoe   **10 Roviana canoes**

11 Native house, Reef Islands   **12 Coconut plantation**

13 Breadfruit   **14 Tinakula Volcano**

15 Bismarck Scrub Fowl   **16 Malaita canoe**

(Recess D.L.R. (2d., 3d., 2s. and 2s.6d.), Waterlow (others))

1939 (1 Feb)–**51**. *T 5/16. Wmk Mult Script CA. P 13½ (2d., 3d., 2s. and 2s.6d.) or 12½ (others).*

60	**5**	½d. blue and blue-green		15	1·00
61	**6**	1d. brown and deep violet		30	1·50
62	**7**	1½d. blue-green and carmine		70	1·25
63	**8**	2d. orange-brown and black		1·00	1·50
		a. Perf 12 (7.11.51).............		30	1·50
64	**9**	2½d. magenta and sage-green........		2·75	2·25
		a. Imperf horiz (vert pair)........		£11000	
65	**10**	3d. black and ultramarine		1·25	1·50
		a. Perf 12 (29.11.51)............		1·25	2·50
66	**11**	4½d. green and chocolate		4·00	13·00
67	**12**	6d. deep violet and reddish purple		75	1·00
68	**13**	1s. green and black		1·25	1·00
69	**14**	2s. black and orange.............		9·00	5·50
70	**15**	2s.6d. black and violet.............		28·00	6·50
71	**16**	5s. emerald-green and scarlet		32·00	11·00
72	**11**	10s. sage-green and magenta (27.4.42)		4·00	8·50
60/72		Set of 13		75·00	48·00
60s/72s		Perf "Specimen" Set of 13		£375	

Examples of No. 64a from the first two rows of the only known sheet are perforated between stamp and top margin.

1946 (15 Oct). *Victory. As Nos. 110/11 of Antigua.*

73		1½d. carmine........................		15	1·25
74		3d. blue............................		15	20
73s/4s		Perf "Specimen" Set of 2		70·00	

Pocket handkerchief flaw (R. 1/6)

1949 (14 Mar). *Royal Silver Wedding. As Nos. 112/13 of Antigua.*

75		2d. black...........................		50	50
		a. Pocket handkerchief flaw......		32·00	
76		10s. magenta........................		10·00	8·00

1949 (10 Oct). *75th Anniv of U.P.U. As Nos. 114/17 of Antigua.*

77		2d. red-brown		50	1·00
78		3d. deep blue		2·25	1·50
79		5d. deep blue-green		50	1·75

80	1s. blue-black..........................	50	1·75
77/80 *Set of 4*		3·25	5·50

POSTAGE DUE STAMPS

D 1

(Typo B.W.)

1940 (1 Sept). Wmk Mult Script CA. P 12.

D1	D 1	1d. emerald-green	6·50	7·00
D2		2d. scarlet	7·00	7·00
D3		3d. brown	7·00	11·00
D4		4d. blue	11·00	11·00
D5		5d. grey-green	12·00	21·00
D6		6d. purple	12·00	15·00
D7		1s. violet	14·00	26·00
D8		1s.6d. turquoise-green	29·00	48·00
D1/8 *Set of 8*			85·00	£130
D1s/8s Perf "*Specimen*" *Set of 8*			£160	

Brunei

Sultan Hashim Jalil-ul-alam Akamudin, 1885–1906

(Currency. 100 cents = 1 Straits, later Malayan and Brunei, dollar)

For many years the status of the 1895 issue remained uncertain to such an extent that the 1906 provisionals on Labuan were taken to be the first issue of Brunei.

The 1895 "Star and Crescent" design stamps were, from their first appearance, considered bogus or, at best, as an issue made purely for philatelic purposes. Research into the background of the events surrounding the set led to the publication, in 1933, of the original agreement between Sultan Hashim and J. C. Robertson, dated 20 August 1894, which made clear that the stamps fulfilled a genuine postal purpose. Although Robertson and his partners intended to exploit the philatelic sales for their own benefit, the agreement testifies, as does other evidence, to the use of the stamps by the Sultan for his postal service. As Brunei did not, at that time, belong to any local or international postal union, the stamps were only valid within the state or on mail to Labuan or Sarawak. Items for further afield required franking with Labuan stamps in addition. Although most covers surviving are addressed to Robertson's associates, enough commercial covers and cards exist to show that there was, indeed, a postal service.

PRICES FOR STAMPS ON COVER TO 1945	
Nos. 1/10	are rare used on cover.
Nos. 11/22	*from* × 30
Nos. 23/33	*from* × 25
Nos. 34/50	*from* × 10
Nos. 51/9	*from* × 12
Nos. 60/78	*from* × 8

The Sarawak Government maintained a post office at the coal mining centre of Brooketon, and the stamps of SARAWAK were used there from 1893 until the office was handed over to Brunei in February 1907.

1 Star and Local Scene

(Litho in Glasgow)

1895 (22 July). P 13–13½.

1	1	½c. brown	3·75	20·00
2		1c. brown-lake	3·25	15·00
3		2c. black	4·00	16·00
4		3c. deep blue	3·75	14·00
5		5c. deep blue-green	6·50	17·00
6		8c. plum	6·50	32·00
7		10c. orange-red	8·00	30·00
		a. Imperf (pair)	£1600	
8		25c. turquoise-green	75·00	90·00
9		50c. yellow-green	20·00	£100
10		$1 yellow-olive	22·00	£110
1/10 *Set of 10*			£140	£400

BRUNEI.   **BRUNEI.**

(2)   (3)

BRUNEI. TWO CENTS. 25 CENTS.

(2)   (3)   (4)

Line through "B" (R. 5/10)

(Optd by Govt Printer, Singapore)

1906 (1 Oct). *Nos. 117/26 of Labuan (see North Borneo), optd with T* **2**, *or surch as T* **3** *or* **4** *(25c.), in red. P 13½ or 14 (1c.).*

11		1c. black and purple....................	35·00	55·00
		a. Error. Opt in black	£2000	£2500
		b. Line through "B"	£450	
		c. Perf 13½–14, comp 12–13	£140	
12		2c. on 3c. black and sepia............	3·25	11·00
		a. "BRUNEI" double	£3750	£2500
		b. "TWO CENTS" double...........	£5000	
		c. Line through "B"	£150	
13		2c. on 8c. black and vermilion......	27·00	80·00
		a. "TWO CENTS" double............	£10000	
		b. "TWO CENTS" omitted (in vert pair with normal)............	£11000	
		c. Line through "B"	£425	
14		3c. black and sepia	32·00	85·00
		a. Line through "B"	£425	
15		4c. on 12c. black and yellow........	4·50	5·00
		a. Line through "B"	£160	
16		5c. on 16c. green and brown........	45·00	75·00
		a. Line through "B"	£475	
17		8c. black and vermilion...............	10·00	32·00
		a. Line through "B"	£275	
18		10c. on 16c. green and brown......	6·50	22·00
		a. Line through "B"	£225	
19		25c. on 16c. green and brown......	£100	£120
		a. Line through "B"	£900	
20		30c. on 16c. green and brown......	£100	£120
		a. Line through "B"	£900	
21		50c. on 16c. green and brown......	£100	£120
		a. Line through "B"	£900	
22		$1 on 8c. black and vermilion......	£100	£120
		a. Line through "B"	£900	
11/22 *Set of 12*			£475	£750

Only one sheet of the 1c. received the black overprint.

The surcharges were applied in settings of 50. Nos. 13a/b occur from one sheet on which the surcharge from the second impression of the setting was misplaced to give two surcharges on row five and none on row ten.

Examples of all values are known showing a forged Brunei postmark dated "13 JUL".

Sultan Mohamed Jemal-ul-Alam, 1906–1924

PRINTERS. All Brunei stamps from Nos. 23 to 113 were recess-printed by De La Rue.

5 View on Brunei River

1907 (26 Feb)–10. Wmk Mult Crown CA. P 14.

23	5	1c. grey-black and pale green.........	2·25	11·00
		x. Wmk reversed	15·00	
24		2c. grey-black and scarlet..............	2·50	4·50
		x. Wmk reversed	32·00	
25		3c. grey-black and chocolate.........	10·00	22·00
		x. Wmk reversed	38·00	
26		4c. grey-black and mauve.............	7·50	10·00
		a. *Grey-black and reddish purple* (1910)	60·00	50·00
		w. Wmk inverted	£170	
		x. Wmk reversed	65·00	
27		5c. grey-black and blue	50·00	90·00
		x. Wmk reversed	90·00	
		y. Wmk inverted and reversed......	£225	
28		8c. grey-black and orange.............	7·50	23·00
29		10c. grey-black and deep green.......	4·50	6·00
30		25c. pale blue and ochre-brown......	32·00	48·00
31		30c. violet and black.....................	24·00	22·00
32		50c. grey-black and deep brown.....	15·00	22·00
33		$1 red and grey.........................	60·00	90·00
23/33 *Set of 11*			£190	£300
23s/33s Optd "*Specimen*" *Set of 11*			£275	

I

II

I   Double plate. Lowest line of shading on water is dotted.

II   Single plate. Dotted line of shading removed.

Stamps printed in two colours are as I.

1908 (12 June)–**22**. *Colours changed. Double or single plates.* Wmk Mult Crown CA. P 14.

34	5	1c. green (I)	80	2·25
35		1c. green (II) (1911)	60	2·00
		a. "A" missing from wmk............	£225	
		b. "C" missing from wmk............	£225	
36		2c. black and brown (5.4.11)........	3·75	1·25
		w. Wmk inverted	75·00	
37		3c. scarlet (I)...............................	5·00	1·25
		a. Substituted crown in wmk........	£600	
38		3c. scarlet (II) (1916)...................	£100	38·00
39		4c. claret (II) (17.4.12).................	4·50	75
40		5c. black and orange (1916)..........	7·00	7·00
41		8c. blue and indigo-blue (10.08)....	7·00	11·00
42		10c. purple/*yellow* (II) (11.12).......	2·25	1·75
		a. *On pale yellow* (1922).............	1·50	4·00
		as. Optd "Specimen".................	48·00	
		w. Wmk inverted	£140	
		x. Wmk reversed	£100	
		y. Wmk inverted and reversed......	£275	£275
43		25c. deep lilac (II) (30.5.12)	4·00	17·00
		a. *Deep dull purple* (1920)...........	12·00	17·00
44		30c. purple and orange-yellow (18.3.12)	9·00	12·00
45		50c. black/*green* (II) (1912)..........	27·00	65·00
		a. *On blue-green* (1920)..............	8·50	35·00
46		$1 black and red/*blue* (18.3.12)...	21·00	48·00
47		$5 carmine/*green* (I) (1910)........	£150	£250
48		$25 black/*red* (I) (1910).............	£550	£1000
34/47 *Set of 12*			£200	£350
34s/48s Optd "*Specimen*" *Set of 13*			£550	

The used price for No. 48 is for a cancelled-by-favour example, dated before December 1941; there being no actual postal rate for which this value could be used. Examples dated after 1945 are worth much less.

For illustration of the substituted watermark crown see Catalogue Introduction.

MALAYA-BORNEO EXHIBITION, 1922.

Retouch   Normal

(6)

RETOUCHES. We list the very distinctive 5c. Retouch (top left value tablet, R. 1/8), but there are others of interest, notably in the clouds.

1916. *Colours changed. Single plates.* Wmk Mult Crown CA. P 14.

49	5	5c. orange....................................	16·00	20·00
		a. "5c." retouch	£475	£500
50		8c. ultramarine............................	6·00	27·00
49s/50s Optd "*Specimen*" *Set of 2*			£110	

MALAYA-BORNEO EXHIBITION OVERPRINTS. These were produced from a setting of 30 examples, applied twice to overprint the complete sheet of 60 stamps. Three prominent overprint flaws exist, each occurring on all the stamps in two vertical rows of the sheet.

HI	EX	NE
Short "I" (all stamps in 2nd and 8th vertical rows)	Broken "E" (all stamps in 4th and 10th vertical rows)	Broken "N" (all stamps in 6th and 12th vertical rows)

(Optd by Govt Printer, Singapore)

1922 (31 Mar). Optd with T **6**, in black.

51	5	1c. green (II)	5·00	30·00
		a. Short "I"	7·50	45·00
		b. Broken "E"	7·50	45·00
		c. Broken "N"	7·50	45·00
52		2c. black and brown....................	5·00	38·00
		a. Short "I"	10·00	50·00
		b. Broken "E"	10·00	50·00
		c. Broken "N"	10·00	50·00
53		3c. scarlet (II)	6·50	45·00
		a. Short "I"	12·00	65·00
		b. Broken "E"	12·00	65·00
		c. Broken "N"	12·00	65·00
54		4c. claret (II)	11·00	50·00
		a. Short "I"	16·00	75·00
		b. Broken "E"	16·00	75·00
		c. Broken "N"	16·00	75·00
55		5c. orange (II)	16·00	55·00
		a. "5c." retouch (and short "I")....	£425	£850
		b. Short "I"	21·00	85·00
		c. Broken "E"	21·00	85·00
		d. Broken "N"	21·00	85·00
56		10c. purple/*yellow* (II)	6·50	55·00
		a. Short "I"	14·00	85·00
		b. Broken "E"	14·00	85·00
		c. Broken "N"	14·00	85·00
57		25c. deep dull purple (II)...............	14·00	80·00
		a. Short "I"	30·00	£130
		b. Broken "E"	30·00	£130
		c. Broken "N"	30·00	£130
		d. "C" missing from wmk............	£1100	
		x. Wmk reversed	£300	
58		50c. black/*blue-green* (II).............	45·00	£150
		a. Short "I"	80·00	£225
		b. Broken "E"	80·00	£225
		c. Broken "N"	80·00	£225
59		$1 black and red/*blue*	70·00	£190
		a. Short "I"	£120	£275
		b. Broken "E"	£120	£275
		c. Broken "N"	£120	£275
51/9 *Set of 9*			£160	£600

Examples of all values are known showing a forged Brunei postmark dated "13 JUL".

Sultan Ahmed Tajudin Akhazul Khairi Wadin, 1924–1950

7 Native houses, Water Village

1924 (Feb)–**37**. *Printed from single plates as Type* II, *except* 30c. *and* $1 *as Type* I. Wmk Mult Script CA. P 14.

60	5	1c. black (9.26)............................	1·00	75
		a. "A" of "CA" missing from wmk	£750	
61		2c. brown (3.24)...........................	1·00	7·50
62		2c. green (3.33)............................	2·00	1·00
63		3c. green (3.24)............................	80	6·50
64		4c. maroon (3.24).........................	1·50	1·25
65		4c. orange (1929).........................	2·00	1·00
66		5c. orange-yellow* (3.24)............	5·50	1·50
		a. "5c." retouch........................	£250	£130
67		5c. grey (1931)............................	17·00	12·00
		a. "5c." retouch........................	£500	£425
68		5c. chocolate (1933)...................	16·00	70
69	7	6c. intense black** (3.24)...........	14·00	10·00
		x. Wmk reversed........................		
70		6c. scarlet (1931)........................	4·50	11·00
71	5	8c. ultramarine (9.27).................	6·00	5·00
72		8c. grey-black (1933)..................	15·00	75
73		10c. purple/*yellow* (3.37)..........	15·00	27·00
74	7	12c. blue......................................	4·50	9·00
		a. *Pale greenish blue* (1927).....	£130	£200
75	5	25c. slate-purple (1931)...............	9·00	13·00
76		30c. purple and orange-yellow (1931)	16·00	16·00
77		50c. black/*emerald* (1931)..........	9·00	15·00
78		$1 black and red/*blue* (1931).....	24·00	75·00
60/78 Set of 19...			£150	£190
60s/78s (ex 10c.) Optd (Nos. 60/1, 63/4, 66, 69, 71, 74) or Perf "Specimen" *Set of 18*............			£375	

*For 5 c, orange, see No. 82. No. 66 is a "Wet" printing and No. 82 a "Dry".

**For 6c. black, see No. 83. Apart from the difference in shade there is a variation in size, No. 69 being 37¾ mm long and No. 83 39 mm.

The 2c. orange and 3c. blue-green in Type **5**, and the 6c. greenish grey, 8c. red and 15c. ultramarine in Type **7** were not issued without the Japanese Occupation overprint, although unoverprinted examples exist. It is believed that these 1941 printings were produced and possibly perforated, by other firms in Great Britain following bomb damage to the De La Rue works at the end of 1940 (*Price for set of 5, £475 un*).

During the life of this issue De La Rue changed the method of production from a "Wet" to a "Dry" process. Initially the stamps were printed on ungummed paper which was dampened before being put on the press. Once the paper had dried, and contracted in the process, the gum was then applied. "Dry" printings, introduced around 1934, were on pre-gummed paper. The contraction of the "Wet" printings was considerable and usually involves a difference of between 0.5 mm and 1 mm when compared with the larger "Dry" printings. The following stamps occur from both "Wet" and "Dry" versions: 1c., 2c. green, 4c. orange, 5c. chocolate, 6c. scarlet, 8c. grey-black, 10c. and 25c.

Stamps of this issue can be found either line or comb perforated.

Brunei was occupied by the Japanese Army in January 1942 and remained under Japanese administration until liberated by the 9th Australian Division in June 1945.

> After the cessation of hostilities with the Japanese postal services were re-introduced by the British Military Administration. Post offices under B.M.A. control were opened at Brunei Town and Kuala Belait on 17 December 1945 where B.M.A. overprints on the stamps of NORTH BORNEO and SARAWAK were used until the reappearance of Brunei issues on 2 January 1947.

Redrawn clouds (R. 1/1 of No. 80*ab* only)

1947 (2 Jan)–**51**. *Colours changed and new values*. Wmk Mult Script CA. P 14.

79	5	1c. chocolate	50	2·00
		a. "A" of "CA" missing from wmk........	£1100	
80		2c. grey..	60	4·50
		a. Perf 14½×13½ (25.9.50).......	2·00	4·50
		ab. Black (27.6.51)......................	2·00	6·50
		ac. Redrawn clouds....................	75·00	
81	7	3c. green......................................	1·00	5·50
82	5	5c. orange*..................................	80	1·25
		a. "5c." retouch........................	65·00	85·00
		b. Perf 14½×13½ (25.9.50).......	4·00	13·00
		c. Ditto "5c." retouch...............	£130	£200
83	7	6c. black*....................................	1·00	4·25
84	5	8c. scarlet....................................	50	1·00
		a. Perf 13 (25.1.51)...................	55	8·50
85		10c. violet....................................	1·00	30
		a. Perf 14½×13½ (25.9.50).......	2·00	5·50
86		15c. ultramarine...........................	1·75	70
87		25c. deep claret..........................	2·75	1·00
		a. Perf 14½×13½ (25.1.51).......	1·75	8·00
88		30c. black and orange.................	2·25	1·00
		a. Perf 14½×13½ (25.1.51).......	2·00	11·00
89		50c. black....................................	4·00	80
		a. Perf 13 (25.9.50)...................	1·75	15·00
90		$1 black and scarlet	10·00	75

91		$5 green and red-orange (2.2.48) ...	17·00	18·00
92		$10 black and purple (2.2.48)..........	70·00	30·00
79/92 Set of 14			£100	65·00
79s/92s Perf "Specimen" *Set of 14*			£250	

*See also Nos. 66 and 69.

The 1, 2, 3, 5, 6, 10 and 25c. values utilised the plates of the pre-war issue and were line perforated until the introduction of the 14½×13½ comb machine for some values in 1950–51. The 8, 15, 50c., $1, $5 and $10 were from new plates with the sheets comb perforated. The 30c. was initially a pre-war plate, but it is believed that a new plate was introduced in 1951.

8 Sultan Ahmed Tajudin and Water Village

1949 (22 Sept). *Sultan's Silver Jubilee*. Wmk Mult Script CA. P 13.

93	8	8c. black and carmine....................	1·00	1·25
94		25c. purple and red-orange............	1·00	1·60
95		50c. black and blue........................	1·00	1·60
93/5 Set of 3			2·75	4·00

1949 (10 Oct). *75th Anniv of Universal Postal Union. As Nos. 114/17 of Antigua*.

96		8c. carmine.................................	1·00	1·25
97		15c. deep blue..............................	3·50	1·50
98		25c. magenta................................	1·00	1·50
99		50c. blue-black.............................	1·00	1·25
96/9 Set of 4			6·00	5·00

JAPANESE OCCUPATION OF BRUNEI

Japanese forces landed in Northern Borneo on 15 December 1941 and the whole of Brunei had been occupied by 6 January 1942.

Brunei, North Borneo, Sarawak and, after a short period, Labuan, were administered as a single territory by the Japanese. Until September-October 1942, previous stamp issues, without overprint, continued to be used in conjunction with existing postmarks. From the Autumn of 1942 onwards unoverprinted stamps of Japan were made available and examples can be found used from the area for much of the remainder of the War. Japanese Occupation issues for Brunei, North Borneo and Sarawak were equally valid throughout the combined territory but not, in practice, equally available.

PRICES FOR STAMPS ON COVER	
Nos. J1/16	*from* × 8
Nos. J17/20	

大日本

郵�— *(second character block)*

(1) ("Imperial Japanese Government") (2) ("Imperial Japanese Postal Service $3")

1942 (Oct)–**44**. *Stamps of Brunei handstamped with T* **1** *in violet to blue*. Wmk Mult Script CA (except Nos. J18/19, Mult Crown CA). P 14.

J1	5	1c. black.....................................	7·00	23·00
		a. Red opt...............................	80·00	£100
J2		2c. green....................................	50·00	£110
J3		2c. orange (1943)........................	4·00	9·00
J4		3c. blue-green............................	28·00	75·00
		a. Opt omitted (in pair with normal)..................................	£2250	
J5		4c. orange..................................	3·00	13·00
J6		5c. chocolate.............................	3·00	13·00
		a. "5c." retouch......................	£150	£375
J7	7	6c. greenish grey (P 14×11½) (1944)...............................	40·00	£225
J8		6c. scarlet..................................	£550	£550
J9	5	8c. grey-black............................	£650	£850
J10	7	8c. red.......................................	5·00	12·00
		a. Opt omitted (in pair with normal)..................................	£1800	
J11	5	10c. purple/*yellow*....................	9·00	26·00
J12	7	12c. blue.....................................	26·00	26·00
		a. Red opt...............................	£250	£350
J13		15c. ultramarine (1944)...............	17·00	26·00
J14	5	25c. slate-purple..........................	25·00	50·00
		a. Red opt...............................	£375	£450
J15		30c. purple and orange-yellow.....	95·00	£180
J16		50c. black/*emerald*....................	38·00	60·00
		a. Red opt...............................	£400	
J17		$1 black and red/*blue* (1944).....	55·00	70·00
		a. Red opt...............................	—	£850
J18		$5 carmine/*green* (1944)..........	£900	£2000
J19		$25 black/*red* (1944).................	£900	£2000

The overprint varies in shade from violet to blue, and being handstamped, exists inverted, double, double one inverted and treble. Nos. J3, J4, J7, J10 and J13 were not issued without the overprint. (See footnote below Brunei No. 78.)

1944 (11 May). *No. J1 surch with T* **2** *in orange-red*.

J20	5	$3 on 1c. black..........................	£6000	£6000
		a. Surch on No. 60 of Brunei...		£7500

Three separate handstamps were used to apply Type **2**, one for the top line, one for the bottom and the third for the two central characters.

Burma

(Currency. 12 pies = 1 anna; 16 annas = 1 rupee)

Stamps of India were used in Burma from 1854 and, after 1856, individual examples can be identified by the use of the concentric octagonal postmarks of the Bengal Postal Circle of which the following were supplied to Burmese post offices:

Type A No. B156 (Rangoon)   Type B No. B5 (Akyab)

B5	Akyab	B146	Pegu
B12*	Bassein	B150	Prome
B22	Nga Thine Khyoung	B156*	Rangoon
B56	Amherst	B159	Sandoway
B108	Kyouk Phyoo	B165	Sarawah (*to* 1860)
B111	Meeaday	B165	Henzada (*from* 1861)
B112	Mengyee	B171	Shoay Gyeen
B127	Moulmein	B173	Sittang
B128	Mergui	B179	Thayetmyo
B129	Tavoy	B181	Toungoo
B133	Myanoung	B227	Port Blair
B136	Namayan		

*Exists in black or blue. Remainder in black only.

Akyab, Moulmein and Rangoon used postmarks as both Type A and Type B, Port Blair as Type B only and the remainder as Type A only.

From 1860 various types of duplex cancellations were introduced and Burmese examples can be identified when sufficient of the left-hand portion is visible on the stamp. Such marks were issued for the following offices:

Akyab
Bassein
Mandalay
Moulmein
Port Blair
Prome

Rangoon
Rangoon C.R.H. (Cantonment Receiving House)
Thayetmyo
Toungoo

1862 Duplex from Toungoo

1865 Duplex from Akyab

During 1875, a further series of duplex marks was introduced in which the right-hand portion of the cancellation included the office code number, prefixed by the letter "R" for Rangoon:

R–1	Rangoon	R–9	Myanoung
R–1/1	Rangoon Cantonment	R–10	Port Blair
R–2	Akyab	1/R–10	Nancowry
R–3	Bassein	R–11	Prome
R–4	Henzada	R–12	Sandoway
R–5	Kyouk Phyoo	R–13	Shwegyeen
R–6	Mandalay	R–14	Tavoy
R–7	Mergui	R–15	Thayetmyo
R–8	Moulmein	R–16	Tounghoo
1/R–8	Amherst		

1875 type from Rangoon

1875 type from Rangoon Cantonment Receiving House

From 1886 the whole of Burma was united under the Crown and the post offices were supplied with circular date stamps giving the name of the town.

Most Indian stamps, both postage and official, issued during the period were supplied to post offices in Burma. None of the imperforates printed by De La Rue have been seen however, and from the later issues the following have not been recorded with Burma postmarks:

Nos. 39a, 66a, 68, 85a, 92a, 110a/b, 148a, 155a, 165, 192a/c, 195a/b, O15, O38, O40b, O50a/b, O76a, O101a, O102, O103/a, O104/5 and O142.

The value of most India stamps used in Burma coincides proportionately with the used prices quoted for India, but some, especially the provisional surcharges, are extremely rare with Burmese postmarks. Stamps of the face value of 2 r. and above from the reigns of Victoria and Edward VII are more common with telegraph cancellations than with those of the postal service.

PRICES FOR STAMPS ON COVER TO 1945

Nos. 1/18	from × 6
Nos. 18a/33	from × 4
No. 34	from × 5
Nos. 35/50	from × 8
Nos. O1/27	from × 15

BRITISH ADMINISTRATION

From 1 January 1886 Burma was a province of the Indian Empire but was separated from India and came under direct British administration on 1 April 1937.

BURMA BURMA
(1) **(1a)**

1937 (1 Apr). *Stamps of India. (King George V inscr* "INDIA POSTAGE") *optd with T* **1** *or* **1a** *(rupee values).* W **69**. P 14.

1		3p. slate	70	10
		w. Wmk inverted	2·50	85
2		½a. green	1·00	10
		w. Wmk inverted	2·75	85
3		9p. deep green (*typo*)	1·00	10
		w. Wmk inverted	2·50	85
4		1a. chocolate	1·75	10
		w. Wmk inverted	2·50	85
5		2a. vermilion (*small die*)	75	10
6		2½a. orange	60	10
		w. Wmk inverted	2·50	85
7		3a. carmine	1·50	30
		w. Wmk inverted	4·50	1·75
8		3½a. deep blue	2·75	10
		aw. Wmk inverted	3·25	30
		b. Dull blue	10·00	7·00
		bw. Wmk inverted	8·00	4·00
9		4a. sage-green	1·00	10
		w. Wmk inverted	—	50·00
10		6a. bistre	75	35
		w. Wmk inverted	—	50·00
11		8a. reddish purple	1·50	10
12		12a. claret	5·50	10
		w. Wmk inverted	14·00	2·50
13		1r. chocolate and green	28·00	3·25
14		2r. carmine and orange	30·00	10·00
		w. Wmk inverted	40·00	15·00
15		5r. ultramarine and purple	38·00	10·00
16		10r. green and scarlet	£100	65·00
17		15r. blue and olive (wmk inverted)	£375	£120
18		25r. orange and blue	£750	£300
		w. Wmk inverted	£750	£300
1/18 *Set of 18*			£1200	£475

The opt is at top on all values except the 3a.

The 1a. has been seen used from Yenangyaung on 22 Mar 1937.

2 King George VI and "Chinthes" **3** King George VI and "Nagas"

4 *Karaweik* (royal barge) **5** Burma teak

6 Burma rice **7** River Irrawaddy

8 King George VI and Peacock **9** King George VI and "Nats"

10 Elephants' Heads

Extra trees flaw (R. 11/8)

(Des Maung Kyi (2a.6p.), Maung Hline (3a.), Maung Ohn Pe (3a.6p.) and N. K. D. Naigamwalla (8a.). Litho Security Ptg Press, Nasik)

1938 (15 Nov)–**40**. T **2**/**9**. W **10**. P 14 (vert) or 13½ × 13 (horiz).

18a	**2**	1p. red-orange (1.8.40)	3·00	1·00
19		3p. bright violet	20	1·50
20		6p. bright blue	20	10
21		9p. yellow-green	1·00	1·25
22	**3**	1a. purple-brown	20	10
23		1½a. turquoise-green	20	1·75
24		2a. carmine	60	25
25	**4**	2a.6p. claret	14·00	2·00
26	**5**	3a. dull violet	14·00	2·50
27	**6**	3a.6p. light blue and blue	1·50	5·00
		a. Extra trees flaw	70·00	
28	**3**	4a. greenish blue	75	10
29	**7**	8a. myrtle-green	4·00	30
30	**8**	1r. purple and blue	4·00	30
31		2r. brown and purple	16·00	2·50
32	**9**	5r. violet and scarlet	50·00	28·00
33		10r. brown and myrtle	55·00	55·00
18a/33 *Set of 16*			£150	90·00

The 1a. exists lithographed or typographed, the latter having a "Jubilee" line in the sheet margin.

(11)

1940 (6 May). *Centenary of First Adhesive Postage Stamps. No. 25 surch with T* **11**.

34	**4**	1a. on 2a.6p. claret	4·00	2·00

For stamps issued in 1942–45 see under Japanese Occupation.

CHIN HILLS DISTRICT. This area, in the far north-west of the country, remained in British hands when the Japanese overran Burma in May 1942.

During the period July to December 1942 the local officials were authorised to produce provisional stamps and the letters "OHMS" are known overprinted by typewriter on Nos. 3, 20, 22/4, 28/9 and 31 of Burma or handstamped, in violet, on Nos. 25, 27 and 29. The two types can also occur together or in combination with a handstamped "SERVICE".

From early in 1943 ordinary postage stamps of India were used from the Chin Hills post offices of Falam, Haka, Fort White and Tiddim, this expedient continuing until the fall of Falam to the Japanese on 7 November 1943.

The provisional stamps should only be collected on Official cover (*Price, from* £2000) where dates and the sender's handwriting can be authenticated.

BRITISH MILITARY ADMINISTRATION

Preparations for the liberation of Burma commenced in February 1943 when the Civil Affairs Service (Burma) (CAS(B)) was set up at Delhi as part of the proposed military administration structure. One of the specific tasks assigned to CAS(B) was the operation of a postal service for the civilian population.

Operations against the Japanese intensified during the second half of 1944. The port of Akyab in the Arakan was reoccupied in January 1945. The 14th Army took Mandalay on 29 March and Rangoon was liberated from the sea on 3 May.

Postal services for the civilian population started in Akyab on 13 April 1945, while post offices in the Magwe Division around Meiktila were operating from 4 March. Mandalay post offices opened on 8 June and those in Rangoon on 16 June, but the full network was only completed in December 1945, just before the military administration was wound up.

MILY ADMN MILY ADMN
(12) **(13)**

1945 (from 11 Apr). *Nos. 18a to 33 optd with T* **12** (*small stamps*) *or* **13** (*others*) *by Security Printing Press, Nasik.*

35	**2**	1p. red-orange	10	10
		a. Opt omitted (in pair with normal)	£1600	
36		3p. bright violet	10	1·00
37		6p. bright blue	10	30
38		9p. yellow-green	30	1·00
39	**3**	1a. purple-brown (16.6)	10	10
40		1½a. turquoise-green (16.6)	10	15
41		2a. carmine	10	15
42	**4**	2a.6p. claret	2·00	1·75
43	**5**	3a. dull violet	1·50	40
44	**6**	3a.6p. light blue and blue	10	70
		a. Extra trees flaw	32·00	
45	**3**	4a. greenish blue	10	70
46	**7**	8a. myrtle-green	10	1·00
47	**8**	1r. purple and blue	40	50
48		2r. brown and purple	40	1·25
49	**9**	5r. violet and scarlet	40	1·25
50		10r. brown and myrtle	40	1·25
35/50 *Set of 16*			4·75	10·00

Only the typographed version of the 1a., No. 22, received this overprint.

The missing overprints on the 1p. occur on the stamps from the bottom row of one sheet. A further block with two examples of the variety caused by a paper fold also exists.

The exact dates of issue for Nos. 35/50 are difficult to establish.

The initial stock of overprints is known to have reached CAS(B) headquarters, Imphal, at the beginning of April 1945. Postal directives issued on 11 April refer to the use of the overprints in Akyab and in the Magwe Division where surcharged pre-war postal stationery envelopes had previously been in use. The 6p., 1a., 1½a. and 2a. values were placed on sale at Mandalay on 8 June and the 1a. and 2a. at Rangoon on 16 June. It has been suggested that only a limited service was initially available in Rangoon. All values were on sale by 9 August 1945.

BRITISH CIVIL ADMINISTRATION

1946 (1 Jan). *As Nos. 19/33, but colours changed.*

51	**2**	3p. brown	10	2·50
52		6p. deep violet	10	30
53		9p. green	15	3·50
54	**3**	1a. blue	15	20
55		1½a. orange	15	10
56		2a. claret	15	50
57	**4**	2a.6p. greenish blue	2·75	4·50
57a	**5**	3a. blue-violet	6·50	5·00
57b	**6**	3a.6p. black and ultramarine	70	2·50
		a. Extra trees flaw	55·00	
58	**3**	4a. purple	50	50
59	**7**	8a. maroon	1·75	3·75
60	**8**	1r. violet and maroon	1·25	1·50
61		2r. brown and orange	6·00	4·25
62	**9**	5r. brown and green	6·00	20·00
63		10r. claret and violet	11·00	25·00
51/63 *Set of 15*			32·00	65·00

No. 54 was printed in typography only.

14 Burman

(Des A. G. I. McGeogh. Litho Nasik)

1946 (2 May). *Victory. T* **14** *and similar vert designs.* W **10** (sideways). P 13.

64		9p. turquoise-green	20	20
65		1½a. violet	20	10
66		2a. carmine	20	20
67		3a.6p. ultramarine	50	20
64/7 *Set of 4*			1·00	50

Designs:—1½a. Burmese woman; 2a. Chinthe; 3a.6p. Elephant.

INTERIM BURMESE GOVERNMENT

ကြားဖြတ် ၁းဖြတ်ကြ တ်ကြ၁းဖြ
အစိုးရ။ အစိုးရ။ အစိုးရ။

(**18** *Trans.* **18a** **18b**
"Interim
Government")

Type 18a shows the first character transposed to the end of the top line (R. 6/15).

Type 18b shows the last two characters transposed to the front of the top line (R. 14/14).

Some sheets of the 3p. show both errors corrected by a handstamp as Type 18.

1947 (1 Oct). *Stamps of 1946 optd with T* **18** (*small stamps*) *or larger opt* (*others*).

68	**2**	3p. brown	70	70
		a. Opt Type 18a	50·00	
		ab. Corrected by handstamp as Type 18	£140	
		b. Opt Type 18b	50·00	
		ba. Corrected by handstamp as Type 18	£140	
69		6p. deep violet	10	30
		a. Opt Type 18a	30·00	
70		9p. green	10	30
		a. Opt inverted	22·00	27·00
71	**3**	1a. blue	10	30
		a. Vert pair, one with opt omitted	£850	
72		1½a. orange	1·00	10
73		2a. claret	30	15
		a. Horiz pair, one with opt omitted	£850	
		b. Opt Type 18a	45·00	
74	**4**	2a.6p. greenish blue	1·75	1·00
75	**5**	3a. blue-violet	2·50	1·75
76	**6**	3a.6p. black and ultramarine	50	2·00
		a. Extra trees flaw	50·00	
77	**3**	4a. purple	1·75	30
78	**7**	8a. maroon	1·75	2·25

79	8	1r. violet and maroon	4·50	1·50
80		2r. brown and orange	4·50	5·00
81	9	5r. green and brown	4·50	5·00
82		10r. claret and violet	3·25	5·00
68/82		Set of 15	24·00	23·00

The 3p., 6p., 2a., 2a.6p., 3a.6p. and 1r. are also known with overprint inverted.

OFFICIAL STAMPS

BURMA   **BURMA**

BURMA

SERVICE   **SERVICE**

(O 1)   (O 1a)

1937 (Apr–June). *Stamps of India.* (King George V inscr "INDIA POSTAGE") *optd with Type* O **1** *or* O **1a** *(rupee values).* W **69**. P 14.

O1	3p. slate	2·75	10
	w. Wmk inverted	—	25·00
O2	½a. green	11·00	10
	w. Wmk inverted	†	—
O3	9p. deep green	5·00	40
O4	1a. chocolate	6·00	10
O5	2a. vermilion (*small die*)	12·00	35
	w. Wmk inverted	—	25·00
O6	2½a. orange	6·00	2·25
O7	4a. sage-green	6·00	10
O8	6a. bistre	5·50	10·00
O9	8a. reddish purple (1.4.37)	5·50	1·75
O10	12a. claret (1.4.37)	5·00	8·00
O11	1r. chocolate and green (1.4.37)	17·00	5·00
O12	2r. carmine and orange	38·00	45·00
	w. Wmk inverted	40·00	48·00
O13	5r. ultramarine and purple	£110	50·00
O14	10r. green and scarlet	£325	£150
O1/14	Set of 14	£500	£250

For the above issue the stamps were either overprinted "BURMA" and "SERVICE" at one operation or had the two words applied separately. Research has yet to establish if all values exist with both forms of overprinting.

SERVICE   **SERVICE**

(O 2)   (O 3)

1939. *Nos. 19/24 and 28 optd with Type* O **2** *(typo) and Nos. 25 and 29/33 optd with Type* O **3** *(litho).*

O15	2	3p. bright violet	15	20
O16		6p. bright blue	15	20
O17		9p. yellow-green	4·00	4·50
O18	3	1a. purple-brown	15	15
O19		1½a. turquoise-green	3·50	2·00
O20		2a. carmine	1·25	20
O21	4	2a.6p. claret	18·00	16·00
O22	3	4a. greenish blue	4·50	70
O23	7	8a. myrtle-green	15·00	5·00
O24	8	1r. purple and blue	16·00	5·50
O25		2r. brown and purple	30·00	15·00
O26	9	5r. violet and scarlet	25·00	29·00
O27		10r. brown and myrtle	£130	38·00
O15/27		Set of 13	£225	£100

Both versions of the 1a. value exist with this overprint.

1946. *British Civil Administration. Nos. 51/6 and 58 optd with Type* O **2** *(typo) and Nos. 57 and 59/63 optd with Type* O **3** *(litho).*

O28	2	3p. brown	2·50	4·50
O29		6p. deep violet	2·25	2·25
O30		9p. green	50	3·75
O31	3	1a. blue	20	2·00
O32		1½a. orange	20	20
O33		2a. claret	20	2·00
O34	4	2a.6p. greenish blue	2·00	7·50
O35	3	4a. purple	20	70
O36	7	8a. maroon	3·75	4·00
O37	8	1r. violet and maroon	60	5·50
O38		2r. brown and orange	8·00	45·00
O39	9	5r. green and brown	11·00	50·00
O40		10r. claret and violet	17·00	60·00
O28/40		Set of 13	42·00	£170

1947. *Interim Burmese Government. Nos. O28/40 optd with T* **18** *(small stamps) or larger opt (others).*

O41	2	3p. brown	50	40
O42		6p. deep violet	3·00	10
O43		9p. green	4·00	90
O44	3	1a. blue	4·00	80
O45		1½a. orange	7·50	30
O46		2a. claret	4·25	15
O47	4	2a.6p. greenish blue	28·00	12·00
O48	3	4a. purple	15·00	40
O49	7	8a. maroon	15·00	4·00
O50	8	1r. violet and maroon	14·00	2·25
O51		2r. brown and orange	14·00	20·00
O52	9	5r. green and brown	14·00	20·00
O53		10r. claret and violet	14·00	30·00
O41/53		Set of 13	£120	80·00

Later stamp issues will be found listed in Part 21 (*South-East Asia*) of this catalogue.

JAPANESE OCCUPATION OF BURMA

PRICES FOR STAMPS ON COVER

Nos. J1/44	
Nos. J45/6	*from* × 6
Nos. J47/56	*from* × 8
No. J56g	
Nos. J57/72	*from* × 6
Nos. J73/5	*from* × 25

No. J76	*from* × 8
No. J77	*from* × 20
Nos. J78/81	*from* × 25
Nos. J82/4	*from* × 10
Nos. J85/7	*from* × 40
No. J88	*from* × 12
Nos. J89/97	*from* × 30
Nos. J98/104	*from* × 50
Nos. J105/111	*from* × 30

BURMA INDEPENDENCE ARMY ADMINISTRATION

The Burma Independence Army, formed by Aung San in 1941, took control of the Delta area of the Irrawaddy in May 1942. They reopened a postal service in the area and were authorised by the Japanese to overprint local stocks of stamps with the Burmese emblem of a peacock.

Postage and Official stamps with the peacock overprints or handstamps were used for ordinary postal purposes with the probable exception of No. J44.

DISTINGUISHING FEATURES. Type **1**. Body and head of Peacock always clearly outlined by broad uncoloured band. There are four slightly different sub-types of overprint Type **1**.

Type **2**. Peacock with slender neck and more delicately detailed tail. Clear spur on leg at right. Heavy fist-shaped blob of ink below and parallel to beak and neck.

Type **4**. No basic curve. Each feather separately outlined. Straight, short legs.

Type **5**. Much fine detail in wings and tail in clearly printed overprints. Thin, long legs ending in claws which, with the basic arc, enclose clear white spaces in well printed copies. Blob of colour below beak shows shaded detail and never has the heavy fist-like appearance of this portion in Type **2**.

Two sub-types may be distinguished in Type **5**, the basic arc of one having a chord of 14–15 mm and the other 12½–13 mm.

Type **6**. Similar to Type **5**, but with arc deeply curved and reaching nearly to the top of the wings. Single diagonal line parallel to neck below beak.

Collectors are warned against forgeries of these overprints, often in the wrong colours or on the wrong values.

(1)   (2)

(3)

1942 (May). *Stamps of Burma overprinted with the national device of a Peacock.*

I. Overprinted at Myaungmya.

*A. With Type **1** in black.*

On Postage Stamps of King George V.

J1		9p. deep green (No. 3)	£110	
J2		3½a. deep blue (No. 8)	60·00	

On Official Stamp of King George V.

J3		6a. bistre (No. O8)	80·00	

On Postage Stamps of King George VI.

J4	2	9p. yellow-green	£150	
J5	3	1a. purple-brown	£550	
J6		4a. greenish blue (opt black on red)	£160	
	a. Triple opt, black on double red	£450	

On Official Stamps of King George VI.

J7	2	3p. bright violet	28·00	90·00
J8		6p. bright blue	19·00	65·00
J9	3	1a. purple-brown	20·00	55·00
J9a		1½a. turquoise-green	£650	
J10		2a. carmine	26·00	£100
J11		4a. greenish blue	26·00	80·00

The overprint on No. J6 was apparently first done in red in error, and then corrected in black. Some stamps have the black overprint so accurately superimposed that the red hardly shows. These are rare.

Nos. J5 and J9 exist with the Peacock overprint on both the typographed and the litho printings of the original stamps.

*B. With Types **2** or **3** (rupee values), in black.*

On Postage Stamps of King George VI.

J12	2	3p. bright violet	18·00	75·00
J13		6p. bright blue	50·00	£110
J14		9p. yellow-green	21·00	70·00
J15	3	1a. purple-brown	14·00	65·00
J16		2a. carmine	23·00	85·00
J17		4a. greenish blue	45·00	£110
	a. Opt double		£700
	b. Opt inverted		£700
	c. Opt double, one inverted		£450
	d. Opt double, both inverted		£700
J18	8	1r. purple and blue		£275
J19		2r. brown and purple		£160

The Myaungmya overprints (including No. J44) are usually clearly printed.

(4)   (5)   (6)

Type **5** generally shows the details of the peacock much less clearly and, due to heavy inking, or careless impression, sometimes appears as almost solid colour.

Type **6** was officially applied only to postal stationery. However, the handstamp remained in the possession of a postal official who used it on postage stamps after the war. These stamps are no longer listed.

*II. Handstamped (at Pyapon?) with T **4**, in black (so-called experimental type).*

On Postage Stamps of King George VI.

J19a	2	6p. bright blue	85·00	
J19b	3	1a. purple-brown	£100	£250
J20		2a. carmine	£130	£300
J21		4a. greenish blue	£700	£700

Unused specimens of Nos. J20/1 are usually in poor condition.

*III. Overprinted at Henzada with T **5** in blue, or blue-black.*

On Postage Stamps of King George V.

J22		3p. slate (No. 1)	3·50	21·00
	a. Opt double	10·00	50·00
J23		9p. deep green (No. 3)	24·00	65·00
	a. Opt double	80·00	
J24		2a. vermilion (No. 5)	£100	£180

On Postage Stamps of King George VI.

J25	2	1p. red-orange	£225	£325
J26		3p. bright violet	38·00	80·00
J27		6p. bright blue	25·00	55·00
	a. Opt double	£100	£250
	b. Clear opt, on back and front	£300	
J28		9p. yellow-green	£900	
J29	3	1a. purple-brown	9·00	42·00
	a. Opt inverted	£1500	£800
J30		1½a. turquoise-green	21·00	70·00
	a. Opt omitted (in pair with normal)	£2750	
J31		2a. carmine	21·00	70·00
	a. Opt double	£1600	
J32		4a. greenish blue	42·00	£100
	a. Opt double	£250	
	b. Opt inverted	£2250	

On Official Stamps of King George VI.

J33	2	3p. bright violet	£130	£250
J34		6p. bright blue	£140	£250
J35	3	1½a. turquoise-green	£170	£300
J35a		2a. carmine	£350	£450
J36		4a. greenish blue	£1000	

(6a) "Yon Thon" = "Office use")

*V. Official Stamp of King George VI optd at Myaungmya with Type **6a** in black.*

J44	7	8a. myrtle-green	90·00	

No. J44 was probably for official use.

There are two types of T **6a**, one with base of peacock 8 mm long and the other with base about 5 mm long. The neck and other details also vary. The two types are found *se-tenant* in the sheet. Stocks of the peacock types were withdrawn when the Japanese Directorate-General took control of the postal services in the Delta in August 1942.

JAPANESE ARMY ADMINISTRATION

7   8 Farmer

1942 (1 June). *Impressed by hand. Thick yellowish paper. No gum.* P 12×11.

J45	7	(1a.) red	40·00	65·00

This device was the personal seal of Yano Sitza, the Japanese official in charge of the Posts and Telegraphs department of the Japanese Army Administration. It was impressed on paper already perforated by a line machine. Some stamps show part of the papermaker's watermark, either "ABSORBO DUPLICATOR" or "ELEPHANT BRAND", each with an elephant.

Other impressions of this seal on different papers, and showing signs of wear, were not valid for postal purposes.

(Des T. Kato. Typo *Rangoon Gazette* Press)

1942 (15 June). *Value in annas.* P 11 *or* 11×11½. *Laid bâtonné paper. No gum.*

J46	8	1a. scarlet	18·00	18·00

Some stamps show part of the papermaker's watermark, either "ELEPHANT BRAND" or "TITAGHUR SUPERFINE", each with an elephant.

½A. 1R.

(9) (10)

1942 (22 Sept). *(a) Nos. 314/17, 320/2, 325, 327 and 396 of Japan surch as T* **9/10**.

J47	**9**	¼a. on 1s. chestnut (Rice harvesting)	32·00	40·00
		a. Surch inverted..................	£110	£110
		b. Surch double, one inverted	£160	
J48		½a. on 2s. bright scarlet (General Nogi)	40·00	42·00
		a. Surch inverted..................	£100	£110
		b. Surch double, one inverted	£160	
J49		¾a. on 3s. green (Power station).......	65·00	70·00
		a. Surch inverted..................	£130	£130
		b. Surch double, one inverted	—	£170
J50		1a. on 5s. claret (Admiral Togo)......	60·00	55·00
		a. Surch inverted..................	£180	£180
		b. Surch double, one inverted	£200	£200
		c. Surch omitted (in pair with normal).	£325	£275
J51		3a. on 7s. green (Diamond Mts).......	95·00	£110
		a. Surch inverted..................	£180	
J52		4a. on 4s. emerald (Togo)...............	55·00	60·00
		a. Surch inverted..................	£180	
J53		8a. on 8s. violet (Meiji Shrine).......	£150	£150
		a. Surch inverted..................	£250	£250
		b. Surch double, one inverted	£375	
		c. Surch in red..................	£250	£275
		d. Red surch inverted...........	£375	
		e. Surch double (black and red)	£800	
J54	**10**	1r. on 10s. deep carmine (Yomei Gate).	21·00	25·00
		a. Surch inverted..................	85·00	95·00
		b. Surch double..................	80·00	£100
		c. Surch double (black and red)	£425	£425
		d. Surch omitted (in pair with normal).	£275	£275
		e. Surch omitted (in pair with inverted surch)........	£400	
J55		2r. on 20s. ultramarine (Mt Fuji)......	50·00	50·00
		a. Surch inverted..................	£120	£120
		b. Surch double, one inverted	£140	
		c. Surch omitted (in pair with normal black surch).	£180	£180
		d. Surch in red..................	50·00	50·00
		e. Red surch inverted...........	£120	£120
		f. Red surch double............	£120	£120
		g. Surch omitted (in pair with normal red surch)	£225	£225
		ga. Surch omitted (in pair with double red surch)..	£225	
		h. Surch double (black and red)	£375	
J56	**9**	5r. on 30s. turquoise (Torii Shrine) ...	12·00	27·00
		a. Surch inverted..................	85·00	
		b. Surch double..................	£110	
		c. Surch double, one inverted	£150	
		d. Surch omitted (in pair with normal surch).........	£200	£200
		e. Surch omitted (in pair with inverted black surch)	£300	
		f. Surch in red..................	26·00	32·00
		fa. Red surch inverted...........	90·00	90·00
		fb. J56a and J56fa *se-tenant*..	£450	£450
		fc. Surch omitted (in pair with normal red surch)	£200	£200

(b) No. 386 of Japan commemorating the fall of Singapore similarly surch.

J56g	**9**	4a. on 4+2s. green and red	£160	£170
		h. Surch omitted (in pair with normal).	£550	
		ha. Surch omitted (in pair with inverted surch).........	£600	
		i. Surch inverted................	£375	

(New Currency. 100 cents = 1 rupee)

15C. 15C. 15C.

(11) (12) (13)

1942 (15 Oct). *Previous issues, with "anna" surcharges obliterated, handstamped with new value in cents, as T* **11** *and* **12** *(No. J57 handstamped with new value only).*

(a) On No. J46.

J57		5c. on 1a. scarlet	16·00	20·00
		a. Surch omitted (in pair with normal).	£1400	

(b) On Nos. J47/53.

J58		1c. on ¼a. on 1s. chestnut	50·00	50·00
		a. "1 c." omitted (in pair with normal).	£800	
		b. "¼a." inverted..........	£275	
J59		2c. on ½a. on 2s. bright scarlet	50·00	50·00
J60		3c. on ¾a. on 3s. green........................	50·00	50·00
		a. Surch in blue..................	£180	
J61		5c. on 1a. on 5s. claret.........................	70·00	65·00
J62		10c. on 3a. on 7s. green........................	£120	£110
J63		15c. on 4a. on 4s. emerald......................	42·00	45·00

J64		20c. on 8a. on 8s. violet	£600	£500
		a. Surch on No. J53c (surch in red)................	£300	£160

The "anna" surcharges were obliterated by any means available, in some cases by a bar or bars, and in others by the butt of a pencil dipped in ink. In the case of the fractional surcharges, the letter "A" and one figure of the fraction, were sometimes barred out, leaving the remainder of the fraction to represent the new value, e.g. the "1" of "½" deleted to create the 2c. surcharge or the "4" of "¾" to create the 3c. surcharge.

1942. *Nos. 314/17, 320/1 and 396 of Japan surcharged in cents only as T* **13**.

J65		1c. on 1s. chestnut (Rice harvesting).......	26·00	20·00
		a. Surch inverted..........................	£120	£120
J66		2c. on 2s. brt scarlet (General Nogi)........	50·00	32·00
J67		3c. on 3s. green (Power station).............	70·00	55·00
		a. Pair, with and without surch....	—	£275
		b. Surch inverted..........................	£130	
		c. Surch in blue..........................	90·00	£100
		d. Surch in blue inverted..............	£225	£225
J68		5c. on 5s. claret (Admiral Togo).............	75·00	50·00
		a. Pair, with and without surch....	£325	
		b. Surch in violet..........................	£140	£160
		c. Surch double..........................	£375	
J69		10c. on 7s. green (Diamond Mts).............	90·00	65·00
J70		15c. on 4s. emerald (Togo)....................	20·00	22·00
		a. Surch inverted..........................	£130	£140
		b. Pair, with and without surch....	—	£250
J71		20c. on 8s. violet (Meiji Shrine).............	£170	85·00
		a. Surch double..........................	£350	

Nos. J67c and J68b were issued for use in the Shan States.

BURMESE GOVERNMENT

On 1 November 1942 the Japanese Army Administration handed over the control of the postal department to the Burmese Government. On 1 August 1943 Burma was declared by the Japanese to be independent.

14 Burma State Crest **15** Farmer

(Des U Tun Tin and Maung Tin from drawing by U Ba Than. Typo Rangoon)

1943 (15 Feb). *No gum.* P 11.

J72	**14**	5c. scarlet.......................................	20·00	24·00
		a. Imperf.......................................	21·00	24·00
		ab. Printed on both sides	90·00	

No. J72 was usually sold affixed to envelopes, particularly those with the embossed 1a. King George VI stamp, which it covered. Unused specimens off cover are not often seen and blocks are scarce.

1943. *Typo. No gum.* P 11½.

J73	**15**	1c. orange (22 March)	3·50	5·00
		a. Brown-orange	2·75	5·50
J74		2c. yellow-green (24 March)...........	60	1·00
		a. "3" for "2" in face value (R. 2/10).	£325	
		b. Blue-green............................	10·00	
J75		3c. light blue (25 March).................	3·25	1·00
		a. On laid paper	20·00	29·00
		b. Imperf between (horiz pair).......	—	£300
J76		5c. carmine (small "c") (17 March)	22·00	13·00
J77		5c. carmine (large "C")	3·25	4·50
		a. Imperf (pair)............................	£110	
		b. "G" for "C" (R. 2/6).................	£180	
J78		10c. grey-brown (25 March)	6·50	5·00
		a. Imperf (pair)............................	£110	
		b. Imperf between (horiz pair).......	—	£300
J79		15c. magenta (26 March)	30	2·50
		a. On laid paper	6·00	19·00
		ba. Inverted "C" in value (R. 2/3)..	£180	
J80		20c. grey-lilac (29 March).................	30	1·00
J81		30c. deep blue-green (29 March)......	30	1·25

The 1c., 2c. and 3c. have large "C" in value as illustrated. The 10c. and higher values have small "c". Nos. J73/81 had the face values inserted individually into the plate used for No. J46 with the original face value removed. There were a number of printings for each value, often showing differences such as missing stops, various founts of figures or "c", etc., in the value tablets.

The face value error, No. J74a, was later corrected.

Some sheets of No. J75a show a sheet watermark of Britannia seated within a crowned oval spread across fifteen stamps in each sheet. This paper was manufactured by T. Edmonds and the other half of the sheet carried the watermark inscription "FOOLSCAP LEDGER". No stamps have been reported showing letters from this inscription, but a block of 25 is known on laid paper showing a different sheet watermark "HERTFORDSHIRE LEDGER MADE IN ENGLAND". Examples showing parts of these sheet watermarks are rare.

There are marked varieties of shade in this issue.

16 Soldier carving word "Independence" **17** Rejoicing Peasant

18 Boy with National Flag

Normal Skyline flaw (R. 5/6)

(Des Maung Ba Thit (**16**), Naung Ohn Maung (**17**), and Maung Soi Yi (**18**). Typo State Press, Rangoon)

1943 (1 Aug). *Independence Day.*

(a) P 11.

J82	**16**	1c. orange	9·50	15·00
J83	**17**	3c. light blue	10·00	16·00
J84	**18**	5c. carmine	18·00	8·50
		a. Skyline flaw	90·00	
J82/4		*Set of 3*	35·00	35·00

(b) Rouletted.

J85	**16**	1c. orange	1·25	1·75
		b. Perf × roul	£110	£110
		c. Imperf (pair)	45·00	55·00
J86	**17**	3c. light blue	2·50	2·50
		b. Perf × roul	90·00	90·00
		c. Imperf (pair)	45·00	55·00
J87	**18**	5c. carmine	2·00	2·50
		b. Perf × roul	60·00	60·00
		c. Imperf (pair)	45·00	55·00
		d. Skyline flaw	18·00	22·00
J85/7		*Set of 3*	5·25	6·00

The stamps perf × rouletted may have one, two or three sides perforated.

The rouletted stamps often appear to be roughly perforated owing to failure to make clean cuts. These apparent perforations are very small and quite unlike the large, clean holes of the stamps perforated 11.

A few imperforate sets, mounted on a special card folder and cancelled with the commemorative postmark were presented to officials. These are rare.

19 Burmese Woman **20** Elephant carrying Log **21** Watch Tower, Mandalay

(Litho G. Kolff & Co, Batavia)

1943 (1 Oct). P 12½.

J88	**19**	1c. red-orange	20·00	15·00
J89		2c. yellow-green	50	2·00
J90		3c. deep violet	50	2·25
		a. Bright violet	1·75	4·00
J91	**20**	5c. carmine	65	6·00
J92		10c. blue	1·75	1·10
J93		15c. red-orange	1·00	3·00
J94		20c. yellow-green	1·00	1·75
J95		30c. olive-brown	1·00	2·00
J96	**21**	1r. red-orange	30	2·00
J97		2r. bright violet	30	2·25
J88/97		*Set of 10*	25·00	29·00

22 Bullock Cart **23** Shan Woman (**24** "Burma State" and value)

(Litho G. Kolff & Co, Batavia)

1943 (1 Oct). *Issue for Shan States.* P 12½.

J98	**22**	1c. olive-brown	28·00	35·00
J99		2c. yellow-green	30·00	35·00
J100		3c. bright violet	4·50	10·00
J101		5c. ultramarine	2·00	6·50
J102	**23**	10c. blue	14·00	17·00
J103		20c. carmine	30·00	17·00
J104		30c. olive-brown	19·00	48·00
J98/104		*Set of 7*	£110	£150

The Shan States, except for the frontier area around Keng Tung which was ceded to Thailand on 20 August 1943, were placed under the administration of the Burmese Government on 24 December 1943, and these stamps were later overprinted as T **24** for use throughout Burma.

1944 (1 Nov). *Optd as T* **24** *(the lower characters differ for each value).*

J105	**22**	1c. olive-brown	3·50	6·00
J106		2c. yellow-green	50	2·75
		a. Opt inverted	£425	£700
J107		3c. bright violet	2·25	4·00
J108		5c. ultramarine	1·00	1·75

J109	23	10c. blue..........................	3·25	2·00
J110		20c. carmine......................	50	1·50
J111		30c. olive-brown..................	50	1·75
J105/11 Set of 7			10·00	20·00

Bushire

BRITISH OCCUPATION

(Currency. 20 chahis = 1 kran; 10 kran = 1 toman)

Bushire, a seaport town of Persia, was occupied by the British on 8 August 1915. The Persian postal authorities resumed control on 18 October 1915. British forces returned to Bushire during 1916, but mail from this period was carried by Indian Army F.P.O. No. 319.

PRICES FOR STAMPS ON COVER	
Nos. 1/29	*from* × 5

Types of Iran (Persia) overprinted

57

66

67

68

BUSHIRE
Under British
Occupation.

(1)

1915 (15 Aug). *Nos. 361/3, 365, 367/70, 372, 374/6 and 378/9 of Iran optd with T* **1** *at the British Residency.*

1	**57**	1ch. orange and green......................	48·00	55·00
		a. No stop...................................	£140	£150
2		2ch. sepia and carmine	48·00	45·00
		a. No stop...................................	£140	£140
3		3ch. green and grey	60·00	60·00
		a. No stop...................................	£170	£190
4		5ch. carmine and brown	£350	£325
5		6ch. brown-lake and green	45·00	32·00
		a. No stop...................................	£140	£120
6		9ch. indigo-lilac and brown.............	45·00	55·00
		a. No stop...................................	£150	£170
		b. Opt double		
7		10ch. brown and carmine	45·00	50·00
		a. No stop...................................	£150	£160
8		12ch. blue and green........................	60·00	60·00
		a. No stop...................................	£180	£190
9		24ch. green and purple	£100	65·00
		a. No stop...................................	£300	£190
10		1kr. carmine and blue	95·00	38·00
		a. Double overprint........................	£7500	
		b. No stop...................................	£275	£120
11		2kr. claret and green......................	£275	£180
		a. No stop...................................	£850	£500
12		3kr. black and lilac........................	£200	£200
		a. No stop...................................	£650	£650
13		5kr. blue and red	£150	£130
		a. No stop...................................	£500	£450
14		10kr. rose and bistre-brown	£130	£110
		a. No stop...................................	£475	£425

Nos. 1/3 and 5/14 were overprinted in horizontal strips of 10 and No. 4 in horizontal strips of 5. Eight different settings are recognized with the "No stop" variety occurring on stamp 9 from four settings with 3 mm between "Under" and "British" and on stamp 10 from one setting where the gap is 2 mm.

1915 (Sept). *Nos. 426/40 and 441 of Iran optd with T* **1**.

15	**66**	1ch. deep blue and carmine..............	£425	£375
16		2ch. carmine and deep blue..............	£7500	£8000
17		3ch. deep green	£550	£500
18		5ch. vermilion	£6500	£6500
19		6ch. carmine and green....................	£5500	£5500
20		9ch. deep violet and brown	£800	£750
21		10ch. brown and deep green..............	£1200	£1200
22		12ch. ultramarine	£1500	£1500
23		24ch. sepia and brown	£550	£450
24	**67**	1kr. black, brown and silver	£550	£550
25		2kr. carmine, slate and silver...........	£550	£550
26		3kr. sepia, dull lilac and silver.........	£650	£650
27		5kr. slate, sepia and silver...............	£600	£650
		a. Opt inverted	—	£16000
28	**68**	1t. black, violet and gold...............	£550	£550
29		3t. red, crimson and gold	£4250	£4250

Nos. 15/29 were overprinted in strips of 5.

Examples of overprint Type **1** on Iran No. 414, 1ch. on 5ch. (previously No. 30), are now believed to be forged.

Cameroon

Allied operations against the German protectorate of Kamerun commenced in September 1914 and were completed in 18 February 1916. The territory was divided, under an Anglo-French agreement, on 31 March 1916, with the British administering the area in the west along the Nigerian border. League of Nations mandates were issued for the two sections of Cameroon, which were converted into United Nations trusteeships in 1946.

Supplies of Kamerun stamps were found on the German steamer *Professor Woermann*, captured at Freetown, and issued by the Cameroons Expeditionary Force at Duala in July 1915.

A French post office opened in Duala on 10 November 1915 using stamps of Gabon overprinted "Corps Expeditionnaire Franco Anglais Cameroun". Although under the overall control of the British combined force commander, this office remained part of the French postal system.

PRICES FOR STAMPS ON COVER
The stamps of British Occupation of Cameroons are rare used on cover.

CAMEROONS EXPEDITIONARY FORCE

A	B

C.E.F.	C.E.F.
1d.	1s.
(1)	(2)

SETTINGS. Nos. B1/3 were surcharged from a setting of 100 (10×10) with the face value changed for the 1d.

Nos. B4 and B6/9 were surcharged from a common setting of 50 (5×10) with the face value amended.

No. B5 was surcharged from a setting of 10 in a vertical strip repeated across the sheet. The figures of the surcharge on this are in a different style from the remainder of the pence stamps.

Nos. B10/13 were surcharged from a common setting of 20 (4×5) with the face value amended.

Different fount "d"	"1" with thin serifs
(R. 1/10, 6/9, 10/10)	(R. 5/1)

Short "4" (R. 10/2, 10/7)

5s.
"s" inverted (R. 3/4)

5s
"s" broken at top
(R. 3/1)

1915 (12 July). *Stamps of German Kamerun. Types A and B, surch as T* **1** *(Nos. B1/9) or* **2** *(Nos. B10/13) in black or blue.*

B1	A	½d. on 3pf. (No. K7) (B.)	13·00	38·00
		a. Different fount "d"	£140	£300
B2		½d. on 5pf. (No. K21 wmk lozenges) (B.)	3·25	9·50
		a. Different fount "d"	40·00	95·00
		b. Surch double	†	£850
		ba. Surch double, one albino		£225

B3		1d. on 10pf. (No. K22 wmk lozenges) (B.)	1·25	9·50
		a. "1" with thin serifs	13·00	65·00
		b. Surch double	£300	
		ba. Surch double, one albino	£100	
		c. "1d." only double	£1900	
		d. Surch triple, two albino	£250	
		e. Surch in black	14·00	55·00
		ea. "1" with thin serifs	£225	
B4		2d. on 20pf. (No. K23 wmk lozenges)	3·50	21·00
		a. Surch double, one albino	£225	
B5		2½d. on 25pf. (No. K11)	12·00	48·00
		a. Surch double	£8000	
		ab. Surch double, one albino		
B6		3d. on 30pf. (No. K12)	12·00	48·00
		a. Large "3" (R. 3/5, 3/10)	£850	
		b. Surch triple, two albino	£275	
B7		4d. on 40pf. (No. K13)	12·00	48·00
		a. Short "4"	£700	£1000
		b. Surch triple, two albino	£250	
		c. Surch quadruple, three albino	£1800	
B8		6d. on 50pf. (No. K4)	12·00	48·00
		a. Surch double, one albino	£200	
B9		8d. on 80pf. (No. K15)	12·00	48·00
		a. Surch triple, two albino	£1200	
B10	B	1s. on 1m. (No. K16)	£170	£700
		a. "s" inverted	£850	£2750
B11		2s. on 2m. (No. K17)	£170	£700
		a. "s" inverted	£850	£2750
		b. Surch double, one albino	£1600	
B12		3s. on 3m. (No. K18)	£170	£700
		a. "s" inverted	£850	£2750
		b. "s" broken at top	£600	
		c. Surch double	£9500	
		ca. Surch triple, two albino	£1600	
B13		5s. on 5m. (No. K25a wmk lozenges)	£225	£750
		a. "s" inverted	£1000	£3000
		b. "s" broken at top	£700	
B1/13		Set of 13	£750	£2750

The 1d. on 10pf. was previously listed with "C.E.F." omitted. This was due to misplacement, so that all stamps (except for a pair in the Royal Collection) from the bottom row show traces of the overprint on the top perforations.

Examples of all values exist showing a forged Duala, Kamerun postmark dated "11 10 15". Another forged cancel dated "16 11 15" is also known. This can be identified by the lack of a serif on the index letter "b".

The stamps of Nigeria were subsequently used in British Cameroons and the area was administered as part of Nigeria from February 1924.

For issues of Cameroon under French administration see Part 6 (*France*).

Canada

Separate stamp issues appeared for British Columbia and Vancouver Island, Canada, New Brunswick, Newfoundland, Nova Scotia and Prince Edward Island before these colonies joined the Dominion of Canada.

BRITISH COLUMBIA & VANCOUVER ISLAND

Vancouver Island was organised as a Crown Colony in 1849 and the mainland territory was proclaimed a separate colony as British Columbia in 1858. The two colonies combined, as British Columbia, on 19 November 1866.

PRICES FOR STAMPS ON COVER

Nos. 2/3	*from × 6*
Nos. 11/12	*from × 2*
Nos. 13/14	*from × 6*
Nos. 21/2	*from × 10*
Nos. 23/7	*from × 6*
Nos. 28/9	*from × 10*
No. 30	—
No. 31	*from × 10*
Nos. 32/3	—

1

(Typo D.L.R.)

1860. No wmk. P 14.

2	1	2½d. deep reddish rose	£350	£180
3		2½d. pale reddish rose	£350	£180

When Vancouver Island adopted the dollar currency in 1862 the 2½d. was sold at 5c. From 18 May until 1 November 1865 examples of Nos. 2/3 were used to prepay mail from Vancouver Island to British Columbia at the price of 15 cents a pair.

From 20 June 1864 to 1 November 1865, the 2½d. was sold in British Columbia for 3d. and was subsequently used for the same purpose during a shortage of 3d. stamps in 1867.

Imperforate plate proofs exist in pale dull red (*Price £3750 un*).

VANCOUVER ISLAND

(New Currency. 100 cents = 1 dollar)

2	3

(Typo D.L.R.)

1865 (19 Sept). Wmk Crown CC.

(a) Imperf (1866).

11	2	5c. rose	£30000	£9000
12	3	10c. blue	£1800	£850

(b) P 14.

13	2	5c. rose	£275	£160
		w. Wmk inverted	£1200	£700
		x. Wmk reversed	†	£700
14	3	10c. blue	£225	£140
		w. Wmk inverted	£800	£600

Medium or poor copies of Nos. 11 and 12 can be supplied at much lower prices, when in stock.

After the two colonies combined Nos. 13/14 were also used in British Columbia.

BRITISH COLUMBIA

4

(Typo D.L.R.)

1865 (1 Nov)–**67**. Wmk Crown CC. P 14.

21	4	3d. deep blue	85·00	65·00
22		3d. pale blue (19.7.67)	80·00	65·00
		w. Wmk inverted	£300	£200

British Columbia changed to the dollar currency on 1 January 1866. Remaining stocks of No. 21 and the supply of No. 22, when it finally arrived, were sold at 12½c. a pair.

(New Currency. 100 cents = 1 dollar)

TWO CENTS	5.CENTS.5
(5)	(6)

1868–71. T **4** *in various colours. Surch as T* **5** *or* **6**. *Wmk Crown CC.*

(a) P 12½ (3.69).

23		5c. red (Bk.)	£1200	£950
24		10c. lake (B.)	£850	£650
25		25c. yellow (V.)	£550	£550
26		50c. mauve (R.)	£700	£600
27		$1 green (G.)	£1100	£1200

(b) P 14.

28		2c. brown (Bk.) (1.68)	£150	£140
29		5c. pale red (Bk.) (5.69)	£190	£150
30		10c. lake (B.)	£1000	
31		25c. yellow (V.) (21.7.69)	£190	£150
32		50c. mauve (R.) (23.2.71)	£550	£1000
		w. Wmk inverted	£850	
33		$1 green (G.)	£900	

Nos. 30 and 33 were not issued.

British Columbia joined the Dominion of Canada on 20 July 1871.

COLONY OF CANADA

The first British post offices in what was to become the colony of Canada were opened at Quebec, Montreal and Trois Rivières during 1763. These, and subsequent, offices remained part of the British G.P.O. system until 6 April 1851.

The two provinces of Upper Canada (Ontario) and Lower Canada (Quebec) were united in 1840.

For illustration of the handstamp types see BRITISH POST OFFICES ABROAD notes, following GREAT BRITAIN.

NEW CARLISLE, GASPÉ

POSTMASTER'S PROVISIONAL ENVELOPE

1

1851 (7 April).

1	1	3d. black	

Only one example is known, addressed to Toronto, with the impression cancelled by the signature of the postmaster, R. W. Kelly.

QUEBEC

CROWNED-CIRCLE HANDSTAMPS

CC1	CC **1** QUEBEC L.C. (R.) (13.1.1842)		
		Price on cover	£150

PRICES FOR STAMPS ON COVER	
Nos. 1/23	*from* × 2
Nos. 25/8	*from* × 3
Nos. 29/43*a*	*from* × 3
Nos. 44/5	*from* × 8

1 American Beaver   **2** Prince Albert   **3**
(Designed by Sir
Sandford Fleming)

Major re-entry: Line though "EE PEN" (Upper pane R. 5/7)

(T **1**/6. Eng and recess Rawdon, Wright, Hatch and Edson, New
York)

1851. *Laid paper.* Imperf.

1	**1**	3d. red (23 April)	£15000	£750
1*a*		3d. orange-vermilion	£15000	£750
		b. Major re-entry	—	£1800
2	**2**	6d. slate-violet (15 May)	£20000	£950
3		6d. brown-purple	£22000	£1000
		a. Bisected (3d.) on cover	†	£25000
4	**3**	12d. black (14 June)	£120000	£45000

There are several re-entries on the plate of the 3d. in addition to the
major re-entry listed. All re-entries occur in this stamp on all papers.
Forgeries of the 3d. are known without the full stop after "PENCE".
They also omit the foliage in the corners, as do similar forgeries of
the 6d.

4   **5**   **6** Jacques Cartier

Re-entry (R. 10/12)

1852–57. Imperf.

A. Handmade wove paper, varying in thickness (1852–56).

5	**1**	3d. red	£1400	£160
		a. Bisected (1½d.) on cover (1856)	†	£25000
6		3d. deep red	£1600	£180
7		3d. scarlet-vermilion	£2000	£180
8		3d. brown-red	£1500	£180
		a. Bisected (1½d.) on cover (1856)	†	£25000
		b. Major re-entry (*all shades*)	from £3500	£650
9	**2**	6d. slate-violet	£18000	£950
		a. Bisected (3d.) on cover	†	£14000
10		6d. greenish grey	£18000	£1000
11		6d. brownish grey	£19000	£1200
12	**5**	7½d. yellow-green (*shades*) (2.6.57)	£8000	£1700
13	**6**	10d. bright blue (1.55)	£8000	£1300
14		10d. dull blue	£7500	£1200
15		10d. blue *to* deep blue	£8000	£1300
		a. Major re-entry (*all shades*)	—	£2000
16	**3**	12d. black	—	£70000

*B. Machine-made medium to thick wove paper of a more even hard
texture with more visible mesh. Clearer impressions (1857).*

17	**4**	½d. deep rose (1.8.57)	£800	£500
		a. Re-entry	£2000	£1000
18	**1**	3d. red	£1900	£450
		a. Bisected (1½d.) on cover	†	£25000
		b. Major re-entry	—	£1300
19	**2**	6d. grey-lilac	£22000	£2000
20	**6**	10d. blue *to* deep blue	£8500	£2000
		a. Major re-entry	£14000	£2500

C. Thin soft horizontally ribbed paper (1857).

21	**4**	½d. deep rose	£6500	£1700
		a. Vertically ribbed paper	£7000	£2500
22	**1**	3d. red	£3000	£400
		a. Major re-entry	—	£1200

D. Very thick soft wove paper (1857).

23	**2**	6d. reddish purple	£22000	£2750
		a. Bisected (3d.) on cover	†	£20000

Bisected examples of the 3d. value were used to make up the 7½d.
Canadian Packet rate to England from May 1856 until the introduction
of the 7½d. value on 2 June 1857.

The 7½d. and 10d. values can be found in wide and narrow versions.
These differences are due to shrinkage of the paper, which was wetted
before printing and then contracted unevenly during drying. The width
of these stamps varies between 17 and 18 mm.

The listed major re-entry on the 10d. occurs on R. 3/5 and shows
strong doubling of the top frame line and the left-hand "8d. stg."
with a line through the lower parts of "ANAD" and "ENCE". Smaller
re-entries occur on all values.

Examples of the 12d. on wove paper come from a proof sheet used
for postal purposes by the postal authorities.

The 3d. is known perforated 14 and also *percé en scie* 13. Both are
contemporary, but were unofficial.

1858–59. P 11¾.

*A. Machine-made medium to thick wove paper with a more even
hard texture.*

25	**4**	½d. deep rose (12.58)	£2500	£700
		a. Lilac-rose	£2500	£750
		b. Re-entry (R. 10/10)	£4500	£1500
26	**1**	3d. red (1.59)	£3250	£300
		a. Major re-entry	—	£1100
27	**2**	6d. brownish grey (1.59)	£10000	£3000
		a. Slate-violet	£10000	£2750

B. Thin soft horizontally ribbed paper.

27*b*	**4**	½d. deep rose-red	—	£3750
28	**1**	3d. red	—	£1400
		a. Major re-entry		

The re-entry on the imperforate and perforated sheets was the same,
but occurred on R. 10/10 of the perforated sheets because the two left-
hand vertical rows were removed prior to perforation.

(New Currency. 100 cents = 1 dollar)

7   **8** American Beaver

9 Prince Albert   **10**   **11** Jacques
Cartier

(Recess A.B.N. Co)

(On 1 May 1858, Messrs. Rawdon, Wright, Hatch and Edson joined
with eight other firms to form "The American Bank Note Co" and the
"imprint" on sheets of the following stamps has the new title of the firm
with "New York" added.)

1859 (1 July). P 12.

29	**7**	1c. pale rose (to rose-red)	£275	32·00
30		1c. deep rose (to carmine-rose)	£350	50·00
		a. Imperf (pair)	£3000	
		b. Imperf×perf		
31	**8**	5c. pale red	£300	13·00
32		5c. deep red	£300	13·00
		a. Re-entry* (R.3/8)	£2750	£450
		b. Imperf (pair)	£9000	
		c. Bisected (2½c.) with 10c. on cover	†	£4500
33	**9**	10c. black-brown	£8000	£1500
		a. Bisected (5c.), on cover	†	£6500
33*b*		10c. deep red-purple	£3000	£500
		ba. Bisected (5c.), on cover	†	£4250
34		10c. purple (*shades*)	£950	50·00
		a. Bisected (5c.), on cover	†	£4250
35		10c. brownish purple	£850	50·00
36		10c. brown (to pale)	£850	50·00
		a. Bisected (5c.), on cover	†	£5000
37		10c. dull violet	£950	55·00
38		10c. bright red-purple	£900	50·00
		a. Imperf (pair)	£8500	
39	**10**	12½c. deep yellow-green	£800	48·00
40		12½c. pale yellow-green	£750	48·00
41		12½c. blue-green	£900	60·00
		a. Imperf (pair)	£3500	
		b. Imperf between (vert pair)		
42	**11**	17c. deep blue	£1000	65·00
		a. Imperf (pair)	£3750	
43		17c. slate-blue	£1200	95·00
43*a*	**4**	17c. indigo	£1100	†

*The price of No. 32a is for the very marked re-entry showing oval
frame line doubled above "CANADA". Slighter re-entries are worth
from £30 upwards in used condition.

As there were numerous P.O. Dept. orders for the 10c., 12½c. and 17c.
and some of these were executed by more than one separate printing,
with no special care to ensure uniformity of colour, there is a wide range
of shade, especially in the 10c., and some shades recur at intervals after
periods during which other shades predominated. The colour-names
given in the above list therefore represent groups only.

It has been proved by leading Canadian specialists that the perforations
may be an aid to the approximate dating of a particular stamp, the gauge
used measuring 11¾×11¾ from mid-July 1859 to mid-1863, 12×11¾
from March 1863 to mid-1865 and 12×12 from April 1865 to 1868.
Exceptionally, in the 5c. value many sheets were perforated 12×12
between May and October, 1862, whilst the last printings of the 12½c.
and 17c. perf 11¾×11¾ were in July 1863, the perf 12×11¾ starting
towards the end of 1863.

12

(Recess A.B.N. Co)

1864 (1 Aug). P 12.

44	**12**	2c. rose-red	£475	£160
45		2c. bright rose	£475	£160
		a. Imperf (pair)	£1900	

The Colony of Canada became part of the Dominion of Canada on
1 July 1867.

NEW BRUNSWICK

New Brunswick, previously part of Nova Scotia, became a separate
colony in June 1784. The colony became responsible for its postal
service on 6 July 1851.

PRICES FOR STAMPS ON COVER	
Nos. 1/4	*from* × 2
Nos. 5/6	*from* × 3
Nos. 7/9	*from* × 10
Nos. 10/12	*from* × 30
No. 13	
Nos. 14/17	*from* × 2
No. 18	*from* × 5
No. 19	*from* × 100

1 Royal Crown and Heraldic
Flowers of the United Kingdom

(Recess P.B.)

1851 (5 Sept). *Blue paper.* Imperf.

1	**1**	3d. bright red	£2250	£350
2		3d. dull red	£2250	£325
		a. Bisected (1½d.) (on cover)	†	£2750
2*b*		6d. mustard-yellow	£6500	£1500
3		6d. yellow	£4500	£800
4		6d. olive-yellow	£4500	£700
		a. Bisected (3d.) (on cover)	†	£3000
		b. Quartered (1½d.) (on cover)	†	£42000
5		1s. reddish mauve	£15000	£4000
6		1s. dull mauve	£16000	£4500
		a. Bisected (6d.) (on cover)	†	£24000
		b. Quartered (3d.) (on cover)	†	£35000

Reprints of all three values were made in 1890 on thin, hard, white
paper. The 3d. is bright orange, the 6d. and 1s. violet-black.

Nos. 2a and 4b were to make up the 7½d. rate to Great Britain,
introduced on 1 August 1854.

(New Currency. 100 cents = 1 dollar)

2 Locomotive   **3**   **3a** Charles
Connell

4   **5**   **6** Paddle-steamer
Washington

7 King Edward
VII when Prince
of Wales

(Recess A.B.N. Co)

1860 (15 May)–**63**. No wmk. P 12.

7	**2**	1c. brown-purple	60·00	42·00
8		1c. purple	45·00	40·00
9		1c. dull claret	45·00	40·00
		a. Imperf vert (horiz pair)	£550	
10	**3**	2c. orange (1863)	23·00	21·00
11		2c. orange-yellow	27·00	21·00
12		2c. deep orange	28·00	21·00
		a. Imperf horiz (vert pair)	£450	
13	**3a**	5c. brown	£5500	
14	**4**	5c. yellow-green	20·00	15·00
15		5c. deep green	20·00	15·00
16		5c. sap-green (deep yellowish green)	£300	40·00
17	**5**	10c. red	42·00	45·00
		a. Bisected (5c.) (on cover) (1860)	†	£600
18	**6**	12½c. indigo	55·00	40·00
19	**7**	17c. black	38·00	50·00

Beware of forged cancellations.

No. 13 was not issued due to objections to the design showing Charles
Connell, the Postmaster-General. Most of the printing was destroyed.

New Brunswick joined the Dominion of Canada on 1 July 1867 and
its stamps were withdrawn in March of the following year.

NEWFOUNDLAND

Newfoundland became a self-governing colony in 1855 and a Dominion in 1917. In 1934 the adverse financial situation led to the suspension of the constitution.

The first local postmaster, at St. John's, was appointed in 1805, the overseas mails being routed via Halifax, Nova Scotia. A regular packet service was established between these two ports in 1840, the British G.P.O. assuming control of the overseas mails at the same time.

The responsibility for the overseas postal service reverted to the colonial administration on 1 July 1851.

For illustrations of the handstamp types see BRITISH POST OFFICES ABROAD notes, following GREAT BRITAIN.

ST. JOHN'S

CROWNED-CIRCLE HANDSTAMPS

CC1   CC **1** ST. JOHN'S NEWFOUNDLAND (R.)
        (27.6.1846)............................. *Price on cover*   £950

PRICES FOR STAMPS ON COVER TO 1945	
No. 1	*from* × 30
Nos. 2/4	*from* × 3
No. 5	*from* × 20
No. 6	*from* × 10
No. 7	*from* × 3
No. 8	*from* × 30
No. 9	*from* × 8
No. 10	
No. 11	*from* × 8
No. 12	*from* × 3
Nos. 13/14	*from* × 20
Nos. 15/17	
Nos. 18/20	*from* × 20
No. 21	*from* × 15
Nos. 22/3	
No. 25	*from* × 30
No. 26	*from* × 5
No. 27	*from* × 8
No. 28	*from* × 3
Nos. 29/30	*from* × 10
No. 31	*from* × 30
No. 32	*from* × 5
No. 33	*from* × 5
No. 33*a*	
Nos. 34/9	*from* × 8
Nos. 40/1	*from* × 5
Nos. 42/3	*from* × 30
Nos. 44/8	*from* × 8
No. 49	*from* × 50
Nos. 50/3	*from* × 10
No. 54	*from* × 4
Nos. 55/8*b*	*from* × 10
No. 59	*from* × 100
No. 59*a*	*from* × 10
Nos. 60/1	*from* × 4
Nos. 62/5	*from* × 8
Nos. 65*a*/79	*from* × 3
Nos. 83/90	*from* × 10
Nos. 91/3	*from* × 2
No. 94	*from* × 50
Nos. 95/141	*from* × 3
Nos. 142/*a*	*from* × 1½
No. 143	*from* × 8
Nos. 144/8*f*	*from* × 2
Nos. 149/62	*from* × 3
No. 163	—
Nos. 164/78	*from* × 3
Nos. 179/90	*from* × 3
No. 191	—
Nos. 192/220	*from* × 2
No. 221	—
Nos. 222/9	*from* × 3
Nos. 230/4	*from* × 2
No. 235	—
Nos. 236/91	*from* × 2
Nos. D1/6	*from* × 10

1   2   4

3   5

Royal Crown and Heraldic flowers of the United Kingdom

(Recess P.B.)

1857 (1 Jan)–**64**. *Thick, machine-made paper with a distinct mesh.*
No wmk. Imperf.

1	**1**	1d. brown-purple.............................	£110	£180
		a. Bisected (½d.) (1864) (on cover)...	†	£35000
2	**2**	2d. scarlet-vermilion (15 Feb).........	£14000	£5000
3	**3**	3d. yellowish green (H/S "CANCELLED" in oval £12000).........	£1000	£425
4	**4**	4d. scarlet-vermilion.......................	£8000	£2500
5	**1**	5d. brown-purple.............................	£200	£400
6	**4**	6d. scarlet-vermilion.......................	£16000	£3500
7	**5**	6½d. scarlet-vermilion.......................	£2750	£3000
8	**4**	8d. scarlet-vermilion.......................	£275	£500

---

		a. Bisected (4d.) (1859) (on cover)...	†	£4250
9	**2**	1s. scarlet-vermilion.......................	£16000	£5500
		a. Bisected (6d.) (1860) (on cover)...	†	£14000

The 6d. and 8d. differ from the 4d. in many details, as does also the 1s. from the 2d.

PERKINS BACON "CANCELLED". For notes on these handstamps, showing "CANCELLED" between horizontal bars forming an oval, see Catalogue Introduction.

1860 (15 Aug–Dec). *Medium, hand-made paper without mesh.* Imperf.

10	**2**	2d. orange-vermilion.......................	£375	£500
11	**3**	3d. grn *to* dp grn* (H/S "CANCELLED" in oval £10000)...........	80·00	£160
12	**4**	4d. orange-verm (H/S "CANCELLED" in oval £13000)...........	£2750	£850
		a. Bisected (2d.) (12.60) (on cover)...	†	£20000
13	**1**	5d. Venetian red (H/S "CANCELLED" in oval £12000)...........	£100	£350
14	**4**	6d. orange-vermilion.......................	£3250	£600
15	**2**	1s. orange-verm (H/S "CANCELLED" in oval £16000)...........	£25000	£8500
		a. Bisected (6d.) (12.60) (on cover)...	†	£42000

*No. 11 includes stamps from the July and November 1861 printings which are very difficult to distinguish.

The 1s. on horizontally or vertically *laid* paper is now considered to be a proof (*Price* £16000).

Stamps of this and the following issue may be found with part of the paper-maker's watermark "STACEY WISE 1858".

BISECTS. Collectors are warned against buying bisected stamps of these issues without a reliable guarantee.

1862–64. *New colours. Hand-made paper without mesh.* Imperf.

16	**1**	1d. chocolate-brown........................	£200	£350
		a. Red-brown	£5500	
17	**2**	2d. rose-lake	£200	£450
18	**4**	4d. rose-lake (H/S "CANCELLED" in oval £12000)........................	38·00	£100
		a. Bisected (2d.) (1864) (on cover) .	†	£35000
19	**1**	5d. chocolate-brown........................	80·00	£325
		a. Red-brown	65·00	£200
20	**4**	6d. rose-lake (H/S "CANCELLED" in oval £10000)........................	25·00	£100
		a. Bisected (3d.) (1863) (on cover) .	†	£9000
21	**5**	6½d. rose-lake (H/S "CANCELLED" in oval £10000)........................	80·00	£450
22	**4**	8d. rose-lake	90·00	£600
23	**2**	1s. rose-lake (H/S "CANCELLED" in oval £11000)........................	42·00	£300
		a. Bisected (6d.) (1863) (on cover) .	†	£22000

Nos. 16/23 come from printings made in July (2d., 4d., 6d., 6½d., and 1s. only) or November 1861 (all values). The paper used was from the same manufacturer as that for Nos. 11/15, but was of more variable thickness and texture, ranging from a relatively soft medium paper, which can be quite opaque, to a thin hard transparent paper. The rose-lake stamps also show a considerable variation in shade ranging from pale to deep. The extensive remainders of this issue were predominately in pale shades on thin hard paper, but it is not possible to distinguish between stamps from the two printings with any certainty. Deep shades of the 2d., 4d., 6½d. and 1s. on soft opaque paper do, however, command a considerable premium.

Beware of buying used specimens of the stamps which are worth much less in unused condition, as many unused stamps have been provided with faked postmarks. A guarantee should be obtained.

(New Currency. 100 cents = 1 dollar)

6 Atlantic Cod   7 Common Seal on Ice-floe

8 Prince Consort   9 Queen Victoria

10 Schooner   11 Queen Victoria

(Recess A.B.N. Co, New York)

1865 (15 Nov)–**71**. P 12.

(a) Thin yellowish paper.

25	**6**	2c. yellowish green	£130	60·00
		a. Bisected (1c.) (on cover) (1870)...	†	£6500
26	**7**	5c. brown	£550	£170
		a. Bisected (2½c.) (on cover)	†	£8000
27	**8**	10c. black	£300	90·00

---

		a. Bisected (5c.) (on cover) (1869)...	†	£5000
28	**9**	12c. red-brown	£450	£150
		a. Bisected (6c.) (on cover)	†	£3500
29	**10**	13c. orange-yellow	£110	85·00
30	**11**	24c. blue	38·00	38·00
		(b) Medium white paper.		
31	**6**	2c. red-brown (*to* deep) (1870)....	85·00	40·00
32	**8**	10c. black (1871)	£200	45·00
33	**9**	12c. chestnut (1870)	48·00	48·00

The inland postage rate was reduced to 3c. on 8 May, 1870. Until the 3c. value became available examples of No. 25 were bisected to provide 1c. stamps.

12 King Edward VII   14 Queen Victoria
when Prince of Wales

I

II

In Type II the white oval frame line is unbroken by the scroll containing the words "ONE CENT", the letters "N.F." are smaller and closer to the scroll, and there are other minor differences.

(Recess National Bank Note Co, New York)

1868 (Nov). P 12.

34	**12**	1c. dull purple (I)............................	65·00	55·00

(Recess A.B.N. Co)

1868 (Nov)–**73**. P 12.

35	**12**	1c. brown-purple (II) (5.71)	£100	65·00
36	**14**	3c. vermilion (7.70)	£300	£100
37		3c. blue (1.4.73)	£275	22·00
38	**7**	5c. black	£250	£110
39	**14**	6c. rose (7.70)	9·00	21·00

1876–79. Rouletted.

40	**12**	1c. lake-purple (II) (1877)	£100	50·00
41	**6**	2c. bluish green (1879)	£140	48·00
42	**14**	3c. blue (1877)	£300	4·75
43	**7**	5c. blue	£180	3·50
		a. Imperf (pair)...............................		

15 King Edward   16 Atlantic Cod
VII when Prince
of Wales

17   18 Common Seal on Ice-floe

(Recess British American Bank Note Co, Montreal)

1880–82. P 12.

44	**15**	1c. dull grey-brown	32·00	11·00
		a. Dull brown	30·00	11·00
		b. Red-brown	35·00	16·00
46	**16**	2c. yellow-green (1882)..................	50·00	26·00
47	**17**	3c. pale dull blue	90·00	7·00
		a. Bright blue	80·00	4·50
48	**18**	5c. pale dull blue	£275	10·00

19 Newfoundland   20 Atlantic Brigantine   21 Queen
Dog   Victoria

(Recess British American Bank Note Co, Montreal)

1887 (15 Feb)–**88**. *New colours and values.* P 12.

49	**19**	½c. rose-red	14·00	7·50
50	**15**	1c. blue-green (1.88)	12·00	8·00
		a. Green	6·00	3·50
		b. Yellow-green	11·00	9·50
51	**16**	2c. orange-vermilion (1.88)	20·00	6·00
		a. Imperf (pair)	£275	
52	**17**	3c. deep brown (1.88)	65·00	2·00
53	**18**	5c. deep blue (1.88)	£100	5·50
54	**20**	10c. black (1.88)	60·00	55·00
49/54 *Set of 6*			£225	70·00

For reissues of 1880/8 stamps in similar colours, see Nos. 62/5a.

(Recess B.A.B.N.)

1890 (Nov). P 12.

55	**21**	3c. deep slate	35·00	2·25
		a. Imperf (pair)		
56		3c. slate-grey (*to* grey)	35·00	2·25
		a. Imperf horiz (vert pair)	£425	
57		3c. slate-violet	45·00	4·50
58		3c. grey-lilac	45·00	2·25
58*a*		3c. brown-grey	45·00	6·00
58*b*		3c. purple-grey	48·00	6·00

There is a very wide range of shades in this stamp, and those given only cover the main groups.

Stamps on pink paper are from a consignment recovered from the sea and which were affected by the salt water.

(Recess British American Bank Note Co, Montreal)

1894 (Aug–Dec). *Changes of colour.* P 12.

59	**19**	½c. black (11.94)	9·50	5·00
59*a*	**18**	5c. bright blue (12.94)	70·00	4·25
60	**14**	6c. crimson-lake (12.94)	19·00	18·00
61	**9**	12c. deep brown	55·00	60·00

The 6c. is printed from the old American Bank Note Company's plates.

1896 (Jan)–**98**. *Reissues.* P 12.

62	**19**	½c. orange-vermilion	50·00	55·00
63	**15**	1c. deep brown	70·00	55·00
63*a*		1c. deep green (1898)	20·00	13·00
64	**16**	2c. green	£100	60·00
65	**17**	3c. deep blue	80·00	22·00
65*a*		3c. chocolate-brown	90·00	85·00
62/5a *Set of 6*			£375	£250

The above were *reissued* for postal purposes. The colours were generally brighter than those of the original stamps.

22 Queen Victoria **23** John Cabot **24** Cape Bonavista

 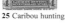

25 Caribou hunting **26** Mining

27 Logging **28** Fishing

29 *Matthew* (Cabot) **30** Willow Grouse

31 Group of Grey Seals **32** Salmon-fishing

33 Seal of the Colony **34** Iceberg off St. John's **35** Henry VII

(Des R. O. Smith. Recess A.B.N. Co)

1897 (24 June). *400th Anniv of Discovery of Newfoundland and 60th year of Queen Victoria's reign.* P 12.

66	**22**	1c. green	2·75	7·50
67	**23**	2c. bright rose	2·25	2·75

68	**24**	*a.* Bisected (1c.) on cover	†	£275
		3c. bright blue	3·50	1·00
		a. Bisected (1½c.) on cover	†	£275
69	**25**	4c. olive-green	9·50	5·00
70	**26**	5c. violet	14·00	3·00
71	**27**	6c. red-brown	9·50	3·25
		a. Bisected (3c.) on cover	†	£300
72	**28**	8c. orange	21·00	9·00
73	**29**	10c. sepia	42·00	8·50
74	**30**	12c. deep blue	35·00	7·50
75	**31**	15c. bright scarlet	20·00	18·00
76	**32**	24c. dull violet-blue	25·00	23·00
77	**33**	30c. slate-blue	48·00	75·00
78	**34**	35c. red	60·00	65·00
79	**35**	60c. black	19·00	13·00
66/79 *Set of 14*			£275	£225

The 60c. surcharged "TWO—2—CENTS" in three lines is an essay made in December 1918 (*Price* £375).

(36)   (37)

ONE CENT

(38)

1897 (19 Oct). *T* **21** *surch with T* **36/8** *by Royal Gazette, St. Johns, on stamps of various shades.*

80	**36**	1c. on 3c. grey-purple	55·00	24·00
		a. Surch double, one diagonal	£1200	
		d. Vert pair, one without lower bar and "ONE CENT"	£3750	
81	**37**	1c. on 3c. grey-purple	£120	90·00
82	**38**	1c. on 3c. grey-purple	£500	£450

Nos. 80/2 occur in the same setting of 50 (10×5) applied twice to each sheet. Type 36 appeared in the first four horizontal rows, Type 37 on R. 5/1–8 and Type 38 on R. 5/9 and 10.

Trial surcharges in red or red and black were not issued. (*Price*: Type 36 *in red* £850, *in red and black* £850: Type 37 *in red* £2500, *in red and black* £2750: Type 38 *in red* £6000, *in red and black* £7000).

These surcharges exist on stamps of various shades, but those on brown-grey are clandestine forgeries, having been produced by one of the printers at the *Royal Gazette*.

39 Prince Edward later Duke of Windsor **40** Queen Victoria **41** King Edward VII when Prince of Wales

42 Queen Alexandra when Princess of Wales **43** Queen Mary when Duchess of York **44** King George V when Duke of York

(Recess A.B.N. Co)

1897 (4 Dec)–**1918**. P 12.

83	**39**	½c. olive (8.98)	2·25	1·50
		a. Imperf (pair)	£450	
84	**40**	1c. carmine	3·25	3·50
85		1c. blue-green (6.98)	14·00	20
		a. Yellow-green	11·00	20
		b. Imperf horiz (vert pair)	£200	
86	**41**	2c. orange	5·00	5·50
		a. Imperf (pair)	—	£375
87		2c. scarlet (6.98)	17·00	40
		a. Imperf (pair)	£300	£300
		b. Imperf between (pair)	£400	
88	**42**	3c. orange (6.98)	22·00	30
		a. Imperf horiz (vert pair)	£375	
		b. Imperf (pair)	£300	£300
		c. Red-orange/bluish (6.18)	35·00	2·75
89	**43**	4c. violet (21.10.01)	26·00	4·75
		a. Imperf (pair)	£475	
90	**44**	5c. blue (6.99)	42·00	9·00
83/90 *Set of 8*			£110	16·00

No. 88c was an emergency war-time printing made by the American Bank Note Co from the old plate, pending receipt of the then current 3c. from England.

The imperforate errors of this issue are found used, but only as philatelic "by favour" items. It is possible that No. 86a only exists in this condition.

---

45 Map of Newfoundland

(Recess A.B.N. Co)

1908 (31 Aug). P 12.

94	**45**	2c. lake	27·00	1·00

46 King James I **47** Arms of Colonisation Co **48** John Guy

49 *Endeavour* (immigrant ship), 1610 **50** Cupids

51 Sir Francis Bacon **52** View of Mosquito

53 Logging Camp, Red Indian Lake **54** Paper Mills, Grand Falls

55 King Edward VII **56** King George V

6c. (A) "Z" in "COLONIZATION" reversed. (B) "Z" correct.

(Litho Whitehead, Morris & Co Ltd)

1910 (15 Aug).

(a) P 12.

95	**46**	1c. green	11·00	2·50
		a. "NFWFOUNDLAND" (Right pane R. 5/1)	70·00	£100
		b. "JAMRS" (Right pane R. 5/2)	70·00	£100
		c. Imperf between (horiz pair)	£325	£350
96	**47**	2c. rose-carmine	17·00	2·00
97	**48**	3c. olive	6·00	17·00
98	**49**	4c. violet	16·00	16·00
99	**50**	5c. bright blue	30·00	9·50
100	**51**	6c. claret (A)	45·00	£150
100*a*		6c. claret (B)	24·00	85·00
101	**52**	8c. bistre-brown	50·00	95·00
102	**53**	9c. olive-green	48·00	80·00
103	**54**	10c. purple-slate	55·00	£100
104	**55**	12c. pale red-brown	55·00	80·00
		a. Imperf (pair)	£325	
105	**56**	15c. black	65·00	£100
95/105 *Set of 11*			£325	£500

(b) P 12×14.

106	**46**	1c. green	5·00	9·00
		a. "NFWFOUNDLAND"	55·00	£150
		b. "JAMRS"	55·00	£150
		c. Imperf between (horiz pair)	£550	£600
107	**47**	2c. rose-carmine	5·50	40
		a. Imperf between (horiz pair)	£550	
108	**50**	5c. bright blue (P 14×12)	8·00	2·75

(c) P 12×11.

109	**46**	1c. green	2·00	30
		a. Imperf between (horiz pair)	£300	
		b. Imperf between (vert pair)	£350	
		c. "NFWFOUNDLAND"	27·00	55·00
		e. "JAMRS"	27·00	55·00

(d) P 12×11½.

110	**47**	2c. rose-carmine	£275	£200

(Dies eng Macdonald & Sons. Recess A. Alexander & Sons, Ltd)

1911 (7 Feb). *As T* **51** *to* **56**, *but recess printed.* P 14.

111		6c. claret (B)	18·00	48·00
112		8c. yellow-brown	50·00	75·00
		a. Imperf between (horiz pair)	£850	
		b. Imperf (pair)	£300	

113		9c. sage-green	48·00	£120
		a. Imperf between (horiz pair)..............		£850
114		10c. purple-black	90·00	£130
		a. Imperf between (horiz pair)...............		£850
		b. Imperf (pair).......................		£250
115		12c. red-brown	65·00	65·00
116		15c. slate-green	65·00	£120
111/16		Set of 6		£300	£475

The 9c. and 15c. exist with papermaker's watermark "E. TOWGOOD FINE".

 57 Queen Mary

 58 King George V

59 Duke of Windsor when Prince of Wales

 60 King George VI when Prince Albert

 61 Princess Mary, the Princess Royal

 62 Prince Henry, Duke of Gloucester

 63 Prince George, Duke of Kent

 64 Prince John

 65 Queen Alexandra

 66 Duke of Connaught

 67 Seal of Newfoundland

(1c. to 5c., 10c. eng and recess D.L.R.; others eng Macdonald & Co, recess A. Alexander & Sons.)

1911 (19 June)—16. *Coronation.* P 13½×14 (comb) (1c. to 5c., 10c.) or 14 (line) (others).

117	57	1c. yellow-green	10·00	30
		a. Blue-green (1915)..................	13·00	30
118	58	2c. carmine	6·00	20
		a. Rose-red (blurred impression). Perf 14 (1916)...................	12·00	55
119	59	3c. red-brown	21·00	35·00
120	60	4c. purple	19·00	27·00
121	61	5c. ultramarine	7·00	1·50
122	62	6c. slate-grey	13·00	25·00
123	63	8c. aniline blue	55·00	75·00
		a. Greenish blue	70·00	90·00
124	64	9c. violet-blue	22·00	48·00
125	65	10c. deep green	30·00	42·00
126	66	12c. plum	25·00	48·00
127	67	15c. lake	22·00	48·00
117/27		Set of 11	£200	£300

The 2c. rose-red, No. 118*a* is a poor war-time printing by Alexander & Sons.

Although No. 123 has a typical aniline appearance it is believed that the shade results from the thinning of non-aniline ink.

FIRST TRANS-ATLANTIC AIR POST April, 1919.

68 Caribou (69)

(Des J. H. Noonan. Recess D.L.R.)

1919 (2 Jan). *Newfoundland Contingent, 1914–1918.* P 14.

130	68	1c. green (a) (b)	3·75	20
131		2c. scarlet (a) (b)	3·75	85
		a. Carmine-red (a) (b)	15·00	45
132		3c. brown (a) (b)	8·00	20
		a. Red-brown (b)	10·00	30
133		4c. mauve (a)	9·50	80
		a. Purple (b)	15·00	30
134		5c. ultramarine (a) (b)	9·50	1·25
135		6c. slate-grey (a)	10·00	45·00
136		8c. bright magenta (a)	12·00	48·00
137		10c. deep grey-green (a)	7·00	4·50
138		12c. orange (a)	19·00	65·00
139		15c. indigo (a)	16·00	65·00
		a. Prussian blue (a)	90·00	£150
140		24c. bistre-brown (a)	22·00	28·00
141		36c. sage-green (a)	16·00	32·00
130/41		Set of 12	£150	£250

Each value bears with "Trail of the Caribou" the name of a different action: 1c. Suvla Bay; 3c. Gueudecourt; 4c. Beaumont Hamel; 6c. Monchy; 10c. Steenbeck; 15c. Langemarck; 24c. Cambrai; 36c. Combles; 2c., 5c., 8c., and 12c. inscribed "Royal Naval Reserve-Ubique".

Perforations. Two perforating heads were used: (a) comb 14×13.9; (b) line 14.1×14.1.

1919 (12 Apr). *Air. No. 132 optd with T **69**, by Robinson & Co Ltd, at the offices of the "Daily News".*

142	68	3c. brown	£16000	£8500

These stamps franked correspondence carried by Lieut. H. Hawker on his Atlantic flight. 18 were damaged and destroyed, 95 used on letters, 11 given as presentation copies, and the remaining 76 were sold in aid of the Marine Disasters Fund.

1919 (19 April). *Nos. 132 optd in MS. "Aerial Atlantic Mail. J.A.R."*

142a	68	3c. brown	£60000	£20000

This provisional was made by W. C. Campbell, the Secretary of the Postal Department, and the initials are those of the Postmaster, J. A. Robinson, for use on correspondence intended to be carried on the abortive Morgan-Raynham Trans-Atlantic flight. The mail was eventually delivered by sea.

In addition to the 25 to 30 used examples, one unused, no gum, copy of No. 142a is known.

Single examples of a similar overprint on the 2c., (No. 131) and 5c. (No. 134) are known used on cover, the former with an unoverprinted example of the same value.

Trans-Atlantic AIR POST, 1919. ONE DOLLAR. (70)

THREE CENTS (71)

1919 (9 June). *Air. No. 75 surch with T **70** by Royal Gazette, St. John's.*

143	31	$1 on 15c. bright scarlet	£110	£110
		a. No comma after "AIR POST"	£140	£150
		b. As var a and no stop after "1919"	£350	£400
		c. As var a and "A" of "AIR" under "a" of "Trans" ...	£350	£400

These stamps were issued for use on the mail carried on the first successful flight across the Atlantic by Capt. J. Alcock and Lieut. A. Brown, and on other projected Trans-Atlantic flights (Alcock flown cover, *Price* £3000).

The surcharge was applied in a setting of which 16 were normal, 7 as No. 143a, 1 as No. 143b and 1 as No. 143c.

1920 (Sept). *Nos. 75 and 77/8 surch as T **71**, by Royal Gazette (2c. with only one bar, at top of stamp).*

A. Bars of surch 10½ mm apart. B. Bars 13½ mm apart.

144	33	2c. on 30c. slate-blue (24 Sept)............	4·75	21·00
		a. Surch inverted..................	£850	£900
145	31	3c. on 15c. bright scarlet (A) (13 Sept)	£190	£200
		a. Surch inverted..................	£2000	
146		3c. on 15c. bright scarlet (B) (13 Sept)	24·00	20·00
147	34	3c. on 35c. red (15 Sept)	10·00	16·00
		a. Surch inverted..................	£1500	
		b. Lower bar omitted.................	£150	£190
		c. "THREE" omitted..............	£1200	

Our prices for Nos. 147b and 147c are for stamps with lower bar or "THREE" entirely missing. The bar may be found in all stages of incompleteness and stamps showing broken bar are not of much value.

On the other hand, stamps showing either only the top or bottom of the letters "THREE" are scarce, though not so rare as No. 147c.

The 6c. T **27** surcharged "THREE CENTS", in red or black, is an essay (*Price* £550). The 2c. on 30c. with red surcharge is a colour trial (*Price* £750).

AIR MAIL to Halifax, N.S. 1921. (72)

1921 (16 Nov). *Air. No. 78 optd with T **72** by Royal Gazette.*

I. 2¾ mm between "AIR" and "MAIL".

148	34	35c. red	£110	90·00
		a. No stop after "1921".................	95·00	80·00
		b. No stop and first "1" of 1921 below "f" of "Halifax"	£250	£190
		c. As No. 148, inverted.............	£4750	
		d. As No. 148a, inverted.............	£4000	
		e. As No. 148b, inverted.............	£14000	

II. 1½ mm between "AIR" and "MAIL".

148f	34	35c. red	£130	£100
		g. No stop after "1921"..............	£150	£120
		h. No stop and first "1" of "1921" below "f" of "Halifax"	£250	£190
		i. As No. 148f, inverted.............	£5750	
		k. As No. 148g, inverted.............	£8000	
		l. As No. 148h, inverted.............	£14000	

Type **72** was applied as a setting of 25 which contained ten stamps as No. 148a, seven as No. 148, four as No. 148f, two as No. 148g, one as No. 148b and one as No. 148h.

 73 Twin Hills, Tor's Cove

 74 South-West Arm, Trinity

 75 Statue of the Fighting Newfoundlander, St. John's

---

 76 Humber River

 77 Coast at Trinity

 78 Upper Steadies, Humber River

 79 Quidi Vidi, near St. John's

 80 Caribou crossing lake

 81 Humber River Cañon

 82 Shell Bird Island

 83 Mount Moriah, Bay of Islands

 84 Humber River nr. Little Rapids

 85 Placentia

 86 Topsail Falls

(Recess D.L.R.)

1923 (9 July)—24. *T **73/86**. P 14 (comb or line).*

149	73	1c. green	2·00	20
150	74	2c. carmine	1·00	10
		a. Imperf (pair)...............	£170	
151	75	3c. brown	1·50	10
152	76	4c. deep purple	1·00	30
153	77	5c. ultramarine	2·75	1·75
154	78	6c. slate	6·00	9·00
155	79	8c. purple	7·50	3·50
156	80	9c. slate-green	18·00	29·00
157	81	10c. violet	8·50	4·00
		a. Purple	10·00	2·75
158	82	11c. sage-green	3·75	19·00
159	83	12c. lake	3·50	11·00
160	84	15c. Prussian blue	3·50	22·00
161	85	20c. chestnut (28.4.24)	12·00	13·00
162	86	24c. sepia (22.4.24)	48·00	75·00
149/62		Set of 14	£110	£170

Perforations. Three perforating heads were used: comb 13.8×14 (all values); line 13.7 and 14, and combinations of these two (for all except 6, 8, 9 and 11c.).

Air Mail DE PINEDO 1927 (87)

1927 (18 May). *Air. No. 79 optd with T **87**, by Robinson & Co, Ltd.*

163	35	60c. black (R.)	£30000	£8500

For the mail carried by De Pinedo to Europe 300 stamps were overprinted, 230 used on correspondence, 66 presented to De Pinedo, Government Officials, etc., and 4 damaged and destroyed. Stamps without overprint were also used.

 88 Newfoundland and Labrador

 89 S.S. *Caribou*

90 King George V and Queen Mary

91 Duke of Windsor when Prince of Wales

92 Express Train

93 Newfoundland Hotel, St. John's

94 Heart's Content

95 Cabot Tower, St. John's

96 War Memorial, St. John's

97 G.P.O., St. John's

98 Vickers "Vimy" Aircraft

99 Parliament House, St. John's

100 Grand Falls, Labrador

(Recess D.L.R.)

1928 (3 Jan)–**29**. *Publicity issue.* P 14 (1c.) 13½×13 (2, 3, 5, 6, 10, 14, 20c.), 13×13½ (4c.) (all comb), or 14–13½* (line) (others).

164	88	1c. deep green	2·25	1·25
165	89	2c. carmine	3·25	50
166	90	3c. brown	6·50	1·25
		a. Perf 14–13½ (line)	2·25	1·25
167	91	4c. mauve	7·50	2·75
		a. Rose-purple (1929)	9·00	8·00
168	92	5c. slate-grey	13·00	6·50
		a. Perf 14–13½ (line)	27·00	13·00
169	93	6c. ultramarine	6·50	28·00
		a. Perf 14–13½ (line)	13·00	28·00
170	94	8c. red-brown	3·75	32·00
171	95	9c. deep green	2·00	17·00
172	96	10c. deep violet	18·00	16·00
		a. Perf 14–13½ (line)	6·00	21·00
173	97	12c. carmine-lake	2·00	22·00
174	95	14c. brown-purple (8.28)	15·00	12·00
		a. Perf 14–13½ (line)	30·00	8·50
175	98	15c. deep blue	4·50	30·00
176	99	20c. grey-black	18·00	18·00
		a. Perf 14–13½ (line)	3·00	7·00
177	97	28c. deep green (12.28)	28·00	50·00
178	100	30c. sepia	6·00	17·00
164/78	(cheapest)	Set of 15	85·00	£225

*Exact gauges for the various perforations are: 14 comb = 14×13.9; 13½×13 comb = 13.5×12.75; 14–13½ line = 14–13.75.

See also Nos. 179/87 and 198/208.

D 1c. P

D 2c. P

D 3c. P   D 4c. P

D 5c. P

D 6c. P   D 10c. P

D 15c. P

D 20c. P

D. De La Rue printing

P. Perkins, Bacon printing

1929 (10 Aug)–**31**. *Perkins, Bacon printing. Former types re-engraved.* No wmk. P 14 (comb) (1c.), 13½ (comb) (2, 6c.), 14–13½ (line) (20c.) or 13½×14 (comb) (others)*.

179	88	1c. green (26.9.29)	3·50	30
		a. Perf 14–13½ (line)	3·50	30
		b. Imperf between (vert pair)	£160	
		c. Imperf (pair)	£140	
180	89	2c. scarlet	1·75	40
		a. Imperf (pair)	£140	
		b. Perf 14–13½ (line)	3·25	1·00
181	90	3c. red-brown	1·00	20
		a. Imperf (pair)	£130	
182	91	4c. reddish purple (26.8.29)	2·75	80
		a. Imperf (pair)	£140	
183	92	5c. deep grey-green (14.9.29)	7·00	3·75
184	93	6c. ultramarine (8.11.29)	8·00	16·00
		a. Perf 14–13½ (line)	2·25	18·00
185	96	10c. violet (5.10.29)	4·25	3·75
186	98	15c. blue (1.30)	17·00	80·00
187	99	20c. black (1.1.31)	55·00	55·00
179/87		Set of 9	85·00	£140

*Exact gauges for the various perforations are: 14 comb = 14×13.9; 13½ comb = 13.6×13.5; 14–13½ line = 14–13.75; 13½ ×14 comb = 13.6×13.8.

Trans-Atlantic AIR MAIL By B. M. "Columbia" September 1930 Fifty Cents

THREE CENTS

(101)   (102)

(Surch by Messrs D. R. Thistle, St. John's)

1929 (23 Aug). *No. 154 surch with T* **101**.

188		3c. on 6c. slate (R.)	1·00	6·50
		a. Surch inverted	£700	£1000
		b. Surch in black	£800	

The issued surcharge shows 3 mm space between "CENTS" and the bar. The black surcharge also exists with 5 mm space, from a trial setting (*Price*, £650).

1930 (25 Sept). *Air. No. 141 surch with T* **102** *by Messrs D. R. Thistle.*

191	68	50c. on 36c. sage-green	£5500	£4750

103 Aeroplane and Dog-team   **104** Vickers-Vimy Biplane and early Sailing Packet

105 Routes of historic Transatlantic Flights

106

(Des A. B. Perlin. Recess P.B.)

1931. *Air*. P 14.

(a) Without wmk (2.1.31).

192	103	15c. chocolate	9·00	16·00
		a. Imperf between (horiz pair)	£800	
		b. Imperf between (vert pair)	£800	
		c. Imperf (pair)	£500	
193	104	50c. green	32·00	55·00
		a. Imperf between (horiz pair)	£850	£950
		b. Imperf between (vert pair)	£1100	
		c. Imperf (pair)	£700	
194	105	$1 deep blue	50·00	95·00
		a. Imperf between (horiz pair)	£900	
		b. Imperf between (vert pair)	£900	
		c. Imperf (pair)	£700	
192/4	*Set of 3*		80·00	£150

(b) Wmk W **106**, *(sideways*)* (13.3.31).

195	103	15c. chocolate	7·00	22·00
		a. Pair, with and without wmk	30·00	
		b. Imperf between (horiz pair)	£750	
		c. Imperf between (vert pair)	£800	
		ca. Ditto, one without wmk (vert pair)	£1200	
		d. Imperf (pair)	£500	
		e. Wmk Cross (pair)	£120	
196	104	50c. green	30·00	65·00
		a. Imperf between (horiz pair)	£850	
		b. Imperf between (vert pair)	£1000	
		c. Imperf (pair)	£325	
		d. Pair, with and without wmk	65·00	
		w. Wmk top of shield to right		
197	105	$1 deep blue	80·00	£140
		a. Imperf between (horiz pair)	£900	
		b. Imperf between (vert pair)	£850	
		c. Imperf horiz (vert pair)	£700	
		d. Pair, with and without wmk	£550	
		e. Imperf (pair)	£600	
195/7	*Set of 3*		£100	£200

The normal sideways wmk on this issue shows the top of the shield to right on the 15c., but top of the shield to left on the 50c. and $1.

"WITH AND WITHOUT WMK" PAIRS listed in the issues from No. 195a onwards must have one stamp *completely* without any trace of watermark.

1931 (25 March–July). *Perkins, Bacon printing (re-engraved types).* W **106** (sideways on 1c., 4c., 30c.). P 13½ (1c.) or 13½×14 (others), both comb*.

198	88	1c. green (7.31)	9·50	3·00
		a. Imperf between (horiz pair)	£550	
199	89	2c. scarlet (7.31)	6·00	5·00
		w. Wmk inverted	45·00	
200	90	3c. red-brown (7.31)	2·50	3·25
		w. Wmk inverted	45·00	
201	91	4c. reddish purple (7.31)	2·00	1·25
202	92	5c. deep grey-green (7.31)	7·00	15·00
203	93	6c. ultramarine (7.31)	7·00	27·00
		w. Wmk inverted	50·00	
204	94	8c. chestnut (1.4.31)	28·00	38·00
		w. Wmk inverted	60·00	
205	96	10c. violet (1.4.31)	16·00	15·00
206	98	15c. blue (1.7.31)	21·00	65·00
207	99	20c. black (1.7.31)	60·00	23·00
208	100	30c. sepia (1.7.31)	28·00	48·00
198/208	*Set of 11*		£160	£225

*Exact gauges for the two perforations are: 13½ = 13.6×13.5; 13½×14 = 13.6×13.8.

107 Atlantic Cod

108 King George V

109 Queen Mary

110 Duke of Windsor when Prince of Wales

111 Caribou

112 Queen Elizabeth II when Princess

113 Atlantic Salmon

114 Newfoundland Dog

115 Harp Seal   **116** Cape Race

117 Sealing Fleet   **118** Fishing Fleet

(Recess P.B.)

1932 (2 Jan). W **106** (sideways* on vert designs). P 13½ (comb).

209	**107**	1c. green	3·25	30
		a. Imperf (pair)........................	£140	
		b. Perf 13 (line)	19·00	30·00
		ba. Imperf between (vert pair)........	£130	
		w. Wmk top of shield to right........	45·00	
210	**108**	2c. carmine	1·50	20
		a. Imperf (pair)........................	£150	
		c. Perf 13 (line)	13·00	24·00
		w. Wmk top of shield to right........	45·00	
211	**109**	3c. orange-brown	1·50	20
		a. Imperf (pair)........................	90·00	
		c. Perf 13 (line)	18·00	30·00
		ca. Imperf between (vert pair)........	£250	
		d. Perf 14 (line). Small holes........	21·00	26·00
		w. Wmk top of shield to right........	45·00	
212	**110**	4c. bright violet	7·50	2·00
		w. Wmk top of shield to right........	45·00	
213	**111**	5c. maroon	6·50	2·75
		a. Imperf (pair)........................	£160	
		w. Wmk top of shield to right........		
214	**112**	6c. light blue	4·00	14·00
215	**113**	10c. black-brown	70	65
		a. Imperf (pair)........................	70·00	
		w. Wmk inverted	10·00	
216	**114**	14c. black	4·25	5·50
		a. Imperf (pair)........................	£150	
217	**115**	15c. claret	1·25	2·00
		a. Imperf (pair)........................	£180	
		b. Perf 14 (line)	8·00	10·00
218	**116**	20c. green	1·00	1·00
		a. Imperf (pair)........................	£150	
		b. Perf 14 (line)	90·00	90·00
		w. Wmk inverted	23·00	
219	**117**	25c. slate	2·00	2·25
		a. Imperf (pair)........................	£170	
		b. Perf 14 (line)	45·00	65·00
		ba. Imperf between (vert pair)........	£400	
220	**118**	30c. ultramarine	40·00	35·00
		a. Imperf (pair)........................	£425	
		b. Imperf between (vert pair)........	£900	
		c. Perf 14 (line)	£325	
209/20 Set of 12			60·00	60·00

*The normal sideways watermark shows the top of the shield to left, as seen from the back of the stamp.

Nos. 209b, 210c and 211c were only issued in stamp booklets.

For similar stamps in different perforations see Nos. 222/8c and 276/89.

TRANS-ATLANTIC WEST TO EAST
Per Dornier DO-X
May, 1932.
One Dollar and Fifty Cents

(119)

1932 (19 May). Air. No. 197 surch as T **119**, by Messrs. D. R. Thistle. P 14.

221	**105**	$1.50 on $1 deep blue (R.)	£225	£225
		a. Surch inverted	£13000	

120 Queen Mother, when Duchess of York   **121** Corner Brook Paper Mills

122 Loading Iron Ore, Bell Island

(Recess P.B.)

1932 (15 Aug)–**38**. W **106** (sideways* on vert designs). P 13½ (comb).

222	**107**	1c. grey	3·00	10
		a. Imperf (pair)........................	45·00	
		c. Perf 14 (line)	7·00	13·00
		d. Perf 14 (line). Small holes........	15·00	29·00
		e. Pair, with and without wmk........	55·00	
		w. Wmk top of shield to right........	50·00	
223	**108**	2c. green	2·25	10
		a. Imperf (pair)........................	35·00	
		b. Perf 14 (line)	8·00	13·00
		ca. Imperf between (horiz pair)........	£275	

---

		d. Perf 14 (line). Small holes........	19·00	30·00
		e. Pair, with and without wmk........	55·00	
		w. Wmk top of shield to right........	38·00	
224	**110**	4c. carmine (21.7.34).................	4·50	40
		a. Imperf (pair)........................	55·00	
		b. Perf 14 (line).....................	5·50	7·00
		ba. Imperf between (horiz pair)........	£170	
		bb. Imperf between (vert pair)........	£130	
		c. Pair, with and without wmk........	60·00	
		w. Wmk top of shield to right........	50·00	
225	**111**	5c. violet (Die I)	2·75	1·75
		a. Imperf (pair)........................	65·00	
		b. Perf 14 (line). Small holes........	25·00	28·00
		c. Die II	1·00	30
		ca. Imperf (pair)........................	65·00	
		cb. Perf 14 (line)	22·00	25·00
		cbw. Wmk top of shield to right........	45·00	
		cc. Imperf between (horiz pair)........	£200	
		cd. Pair, with and without wmk........	£130	
226	**120**	7c. red-brown	3·00	3·75
		b. Perf 14 (line)	£150	
		ba. Imperf between (horiz pair)........	£500	
		c. Imperf (pair)........................	£170	
		w. Wmk top of shield to right........		
227	**121**	8c. brownish red	3·50	2·00
		a. Imperf (pair)........................	90·00	
228	**122**	24c. bright blue	1·00	3·25
		a. Imperf (pair)........................	£300	
		b. Doubly printed	£1000	
		w. Wmk inverted	30·00	
228c	**118**	48c. red-brown (1.1.38)	9·00	10·00
		ca. Imperf (pair)........................	£110	
222/8c Set of 8			24·00	17·00

*The normal sideways watermark shows the top of the shield to left, as seen from the back of the stamp.

No. 223. Two dies exist of the 2c. Die I was used for No. 210 and both dies for No. 223. The differences, though numerous, are very slight.

No. 225. There are also two dies of the 5c., Die I only being used for No. 213 and both dies for the violet stamp. In Die II the antler pointing to the "T" of "POSTAGE" is taller than the one pointing to the "S" and the individual hairs on the underside of the caribou's tail are distinct.

For similar stamps in a slightly larger size and perforated 12½ or 13½ (5c.) see Nos. 276/89.

(123) "L.&S."—Land and Sea

1933 (9 Feb). No. 195 optd with T **123** for ordinary postal use, by Messrs. D. R. Thistle. W **106** (sideways top of shield to right from back). P 14.

229	**103**	15c. chocolate	4·25	14·00
		a. Pair, one without wmk..............	25·00	
		b. Opt reading up	£3000	
		c. Vertical pair, one without opt	£5000	

124 Put to Flight   **125** Land of Heart's Delight

126 Spotting the herd   **127** News from home

128 Labrador

(Des J. Scott. Recess P.B.)

1933 (9 June). Air. T **124/8** and similar horiz designs. W **106** (sideways). P 14 (5c., 30c., 75c.) or 11½ (10c., 60c.).

230		5c. red-brown	19·00	20·00
		a. Imperf (pair)........................	£160	
		b. Imperf between (horiz pair)........	£1000	
		c. Imperf between (vert pair)........	£1000	
231		10c. orange-yellow	14·00	35·00
		a. Imperf (pair)........................	£130	
232		30c. light blue	32·00	48·00
		a. Imperf (pair)........................	£425	
233		60c. green	50·00	£110
		a. Imperf (pair)........................	£475	
234		75c. yellow-brown	50·00	£110
		a. Imperf (pair)........................	£425	
		b. Imperf between (horiz or vert pair)...	£3250	
230/4 Set of 5			£150	£300

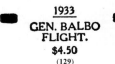

1933
GEN. BALBO
FLIGHT.
$4.50

(129)

(Surch by Robinson & Co, St. John's)

1933 (24 July). Air. Balbo Transatlantic Mass Formation Flight. No. **234** surch with T **129**. W **106**. P 14.

235		$4.50 on 75c. yellow-brown	£275	£325
		a. Surch inverted	£65000	
		b. Surch on 10c. (No. 231)........	£65000	

No. 235a. When this error was discovered the stamps were ordered to be officially destroyed but four copies which had been torn were recovered and skilfully repaired. In addition, four undamaged examples exist and the price quoted is for one of these (Price for repaired example, £20000, unused).

130 Sir Humphrey Gilbert   **131** Compton Castle, Devon   **132** Gilbert Coat of Arms

133 Eton College

134 Anchor token   **135** Gilbert commissioned by Elizabeth I

136 Fleet leaving Plymouth, 1583   **137** Arrival at St. John's

138 Annexation, 5th August, 1583   **139** Royal Arms

140 Gilbert in the *Squirrel*   **141** Map of Newfoundland, 1626

142 Queen Elizabeth   **143** Gilbert's statue at Truro

(Recess P.B.)

1933 (3 Aug). 350th Anniv of the Annexation by Sir Humphrey Gilbert. T **130/43**. W **106** (sideways* on vert designs). P 13½ (comb†).

236	**130**	1c. slate	1·00	1·50
		a. Imperf (pair)........................	50·00	
237	**131**	2c. green	1·75	70
		a. Imperf (pair)........................	50·00	
		b. Doubly printed	£375	
238	**132**	3c. chestnut	2·50	1·25
239	**133**	4c. carmine	80	50
		a. Imperf (pair)........................	50·00	
240	**134**	5c. violet	2·00	80
241	**135**	7c. greenish black	15·00	17·00
		a. Perf 14 (line)	13·00	45·00
242	**136**	8c. vermilion	8·00	15·00
		a. Brownish red	£350	
		b. Bisected (4c.) (on cover)	†	£400
243	**137**	9c. ultramarine	7·00	16·00
		a. Imperf (pair)........................	£225	

244	138	b. Perf 14 (line)		65·00	80·00
		10c. brown-lake		4·00	11·00
		a. Imperf (pair)		£275	
		b. Perf 14 (line)		80·00	90·00
245	139	14c. grey-black		16·00	30·00
		a. Perf 14 (line)		20·00	48·00
246	140	15c. claret		15·00	20·00
		w. Wmk top of shield to right		7·50	24·00
247	141	20c. grey-green		14·00	19·00
		a. Perf 14 (line)		25·00	42·00
		w. Wmk inverted		50·00	
248	142	24c. maroon		17·00	24·00
		a. Imperf (pair)		£110	
		b. Perf 14 (line)		29·00	45·00
		w. Wmk top of shield to right		38·00	
249	143	32c. olive-black		8·00	50·00
		a. Perf 14 (line)		22·00	70·00
		w. Wmk top of shield to right		20·00	55·00
236/49		Set of 14		90·00	£190

*The normal sideways watermark shows the top of the shield to left, as seen from the back of the stamp.

†Exact gauges for the two perforations are: 13½ comb = 13.4; 14 line = 13.8.

1935 (6 May). *Silver Jubilee. As Nos. 91/4 of Antigua, but ptd by B.W.* P 11×12.

250	133	4c. rosine		1·00	1·75
251		5c. bright violet		1·25	3·00
252		7c. blue		2·25	7·00
253		24c. olive-green		5·00	14·00
250/3		Set of 4		8·50	23·00
250s/3s		Perf "Specimen" Set of 4		£150	

1937 (12 May). *Coronation Issue. As Nos. 95/7 of Antigua, but name and value uncoloured on coloured background.* P 11×11½.

254	134	2c. green		1·00	3·00
255		4c. carmine		1·60	4·00
256		5c. purple		3·00	4·00
254/6		Set of 3		5·00	10·00
254s/6s		Perf "Specimen" Set of 3		95·00	

144 Atlantic Cod

145 Map of Newfoundland

146 Caribou

147 Corner Brook Paper Mills

148 Atlantic Salmon

149 Newfoundland Dog

150 Harp Seal

151 Cape Race

152 Bell Island

153 Sealing Fleet

154 The Banks Fishing Fleet

Die I   Die II

No. 258. In Die II the shading of the King's face is heavier and dots have been added down the ridge of the nose. The top frame line is thicker and more uniform.

Fish-hook flaw (R. 1/7 or 3/3)   Re-entry to right of design (inscr oval, tree and value) (R. 4/8)   Extra chimney (R. 6/5)

(Recess P.B.)

1937 (12 May). *Additional Coronation Issue.* T **144/54**. W **106**. P 14 (line)*.

257	144	1c. grey		3·00	30
		a. Pair, with and without wmk		24·00	
		b. Fish-hook flaw		27·00	
		cw. Wmk inverted		50·00	
		d. Perf 13½ (line)		3·50	50
		da. Pair, with and without wmk		28·00	
		db. Fish-hook flaw		32·00	
		e. Perf 13 (comb)		28·00	50·00
		ea. Pair, with and without wmk			
		eb. Fish-hook flaw		£170	
258	145	3c. orange-brown (I)		15·00	4·00
		a. Pair, with and without wmk		80·00	
		b. Imperf between (horiz pair)			
		c. Perf 13½ (line)		14·00	6·00
		ca. Pair, with and without wmk			
		cb. Imperf between (vert pair)		£450	
		d. Perf 13 (comb)		6·50	4·00
		e. Die II (P 14, line)		7·00	4·25
		ea. Pair, with and without wmk		£120	
		ec. Perf 13½ (line)		7·50	4·75
		eca. Pair, with and without wmk		£140	
		ecb. Imperf between (vert pair)		£550	
		ed. Perf 13 (comb)		7·00	4·00
		eda. Pair, with and without wmk		£120	
259	146	7c. bright ultramarine		2·50	1·25
		a. Pair, with and without wmk			
		b. Re-entry at right		65·00	
		c. Perf 13½ (line)		3·00	1·75
		ca. Pair, with and without wmk			
		cb. Re-entry at right		70·00	
		d. Perf 13 (comb)		£400	£500
		db. Re-entry at right		£1600	
260	147	8c. scarlet		2·00	4·00
		a. Pair, with and without wmk		70·00	
		b. Imperf between (horiz pair)		£800	
		c. Imperf between (vert pair)		£800	
		d. Imperf (pair)		£400	
		e. Perf 13½ (line)		2·75	4·50
		ea. Pair, with and without wmk		75·00	
		eb. Imperf between (vert pair)			
		f. Perf 13 (comb)		7·50	14·00
261	148	10c. blackish brown		5·00	9·00
		a. Pair, with and without wmk		95·00	
		b. Perf 13½ (line)		5·00	11·00
		ba. Pair, with and without wmk		80·00	
		c. Perf 13 (comb)		3·25	13·00
		cw. Wmk inverted		75·00	
262	149	14c. black		1·40	3·00

		a. Pair, with and without wmk		70·00	
		b. Perf 13½ (line)		1·75	4·25
		ba. Pair, with and without wmk		70·00	
		c. Perf 13 (comb)		£15000	£8500
263	150	15c. claret		13·00	4·50
		a. Pair, with and without wmk		85·00	
		bw. Wmk inverted		85·00	
		c. Perf 13½ (line)		13·00	5·50
		ca. Pair, with and without wmk		80·00	
		cb. Imperf between (vert pair)		£700	
		d. Perf 13 (comb)		23·00	27·00
		da. Pair, with and without wmk		£140	
264	151	20c. green		3·50	11·00
		a. Pair, with and without wmk		60·00	
		c. Extra chimney		60·00	
		dw. Wmk inverted		95·00	
		e. Perf 13½ (line)		3·00	13·00
		ea. Pair, with and without wmk		£150	
		eb. Imperf between (vert pair)		£1000	
		ec. Extra chimney		60·00	
		f. Perf 13 (comb)		2·50	9·50
		fc. Extra chimney		55·00	
265	152	24c. light blue		2·50	3·00
		a. Pair, with and without wmk		£170	
		c. Perf 13½ (line)		2·50	3·00
		ca. Pair, with and without wmk		£170	
		cb. Imperf between (vert pair)		£1400	
		d. Perf 13 (comb)		29·00	29·00
266	153	25c. slate		2·75	2·75
		a. Pair, with and without wmk		£150	
		b. Perf 13½ (line)		2·75	3·75
		ba. Pair, with and without wmk		£150	
		c. Perf 13 (comb)		32·00	70·00
267	154	48c. slate-purple		8·50	6·50
		a. Pair, with and without wmk		£200	
		c. Perf 13½ (line)		9·00	8·00
		ca. Pair, with and without wmk		£200	
		cb. Imperf between (vert pair)		£1500	
		d. Perf 13 (comb)		40·00	42·00
257/67		Set of 11		42·00	42·00

The line perforations measure 14.1 (14) or 13.7 (13½). The comb perforation measures 13.3×13.2. One example of the 7c. has been reported perforated 13½×14.

The paper used had the watermarks spaced for smaller format stamps. In consequence, the individual watermarks are out of alignment so that stamps from the second vertical row were sometimes without watermark.

155 King George VI   **156** Queen Mother

157 Queen Elizabeth II as princess   **158** Queen Mary

(Recess P.B.)

1938 (12 May). *T* **155/8**. W **106** (sideways*). P 13½ (comb).

268	155	2c. green		2·50	1·25
		a. Pair, with and without wmk		£160	
		b. Imperf (pair)		£110	
		w. Wmk top of shield to right		75·00	
269	156	3c. carmine		1·00	1·00
		a. Perf 14 (line)		£475	£325
		b. Pair, with and without wmk		£225	
		c. Imperf (pair)		£110	
270	157	4c. light blue		2·25	60
		a. Pair, with and without wmk		£110	
		b. Imperf (pair)		95·00	
		w. Wmk top of shield to right		75·00	
271	158	7c. deep ultramarine		1·00	6·50
		a. Pair, with and without wmk		£160	
		b. Imperf (pair)		£150	
268/71		Set of 4		6·00	8·50

* The normal sideways watermark shows the top of the shield to left, as seen from the back of the stamp.

For similar designs, perf 12½, see Nos. 277/81.

159 King George VI and Queen Elizabeth

(Recess B.W.)

1939 (17 June). *Royal Visit. No wmk.* P 13½.

272	159	5c. deep ultramarine		3·25	1·00

2

CENTS

(160)

1939 (20 Nov). *No. 272 surch as T* **160**, *at St. John's.*
273	**159**	2c. on 5c. deep ultramarine (Br.).........	2·50	50
274		4c. on 5c. deep ultramarine (C.)..........	2·00	1·00

161 Grenfell on the *Strathcona* (after painting by Gribble)

162 Memorial University College

(Recess C.B.N.)

1941 (1 Dec). *50th Anniv of Sir Wilfred Grenfell's Labrador Mission.* P 12.
275	**161**	5c. blue..............	30	1·00

Damaged "A" (R. 5/9)

(Recess Waterlow)

1941–44. W **106** (sideways* on vert designs). P 12½ (line).
276	**107**	1c. grey	20	1·75
277	**155**	2c. green	30	75
		w. Wmk top of shield to right........	35·00	
278	**156**	3c. carmine...........................	30	30
		a. Pair, with and without wmk	90·00	
		b. Damaged "A".......................	55·00	35·00
		w. Wmk top of shield to right........	35·00	
279	**157**	4c. blue (As No. 270).................	2·25	40
		a. Pair, with and without wmk	£170	
		w. Wmk top of shield to right........	40·00	
280	**111**	5c. violet (Die I) (P 13½ comb)......	£130	
		a. Perf 12½ (line) (6.42)............	2·75	85
		ab. Pair, with and without wmk	£150	
		ac. Printed double....................	£450	
		ad. Imperf vert (horiz pair)..........	£450	
		b. Imperf (pair).....................	£160	
281	**158**	7c. deep ultramarine (As No. 271)..	6·00	17·00
		a. Pair, with and without wmk	£180	
282	**121**	8c. rose-red	2·25	3·50
		a. Pair, with and without wmk	£170	
283	**113**	10c. black-brown	1·75	2·25
284	**114**	14c. black.............................	6·50	8·00
285	**115**	15c. claret............................	6·00	8·50
286	**116**	20c. green.............................	6·00	7·00
287	**122**	24c. blue..............................	3·25	19·00
		w. Wmk inverted	60·00	
288	**117**	25c. slate.............................	8·50	14·00
289	**118**	48c. red-brown (1944).................	4·00	7·50
276/89		Set of 14	45·00	80·00

*The normal sideways watermark shows the top of the shield to left, *as seen from the back of the stamp.*

Nos. 276/89 are redrawn versions of previous designs with slightly larger dimensions; the 5c. for example, measures 21 mm in width as opposed to the 20.4 mm of the Perkins Bacon printings.

No. 280. For Die I see note relating to No. 225.

(Recess C.B.N.)

1943 (1 Jan). P 12.
290	**162**	30c. carmine.........................	1·00	3·25

163 St. John's

TWO CENTS

(**164**)

(Recess C.B.N.)

1943 (1 June). *Air.* P 12.
291	**163**	7c. ultramarine	50	1·00

1946 (21 Mar). *No. 290 surch locally with T* **164**.
292	**162**	2c. on 30c. carmine.................	30	1·00

165 Queen Elizabeth II when Princess

166 Cabot off Cape Bonavista

(Recess Waterlow)

1947 (21 Apr). *Princess Elizabeth's 21st Birthday.* W **106** (sideways). P 12½.
293	**165**	4c. light blue	30	1·00
		a. Imperf vert (horiz pair).........	£400	

(Recess Waterlow)

1947 (24 June). *450th Anniv of Cabot's Discovery of Newfoundland.* W **106** (sideways). P 12½.
294	**166**	5c. mauve............................	20	1·00
		a. Imperf between (horiz pair).......	£1600	

STAMP BOOKLETS

1926. *Black on pink cover with Ayre and Sons advertisement on front. Stapled.*
SB1	40c. booklet containing eight 1c. and sixteen 2c. (Nos. 149/50) in blocks of 8	£1500

B **1**

1932 (2 Jan). *Black on buff cover as Type B* **1**. *Stapled.*
SB2	40c. booklet containing four 1c., twelve 2c. and four 3c. (Nos. 209b, 210c, 211c) in blocks of 4.....	£425
	a. Contents as No. SB2, but containing Nos. 209b, 210 and 211c..............	£500
	b. Contents as No. SB2, but containing Nos. 222d, 223d and 211d...............	£475

B **2**

1932. *Black on cream cover as Type B* **2**. *Stapled.*
SB3	40c. booklet containing four 1c., twelve 2c. and four 3c. (Nos. 222, 223, 211) in blocks of 4	£425

POSTAGE DUE STAMPS

D **1**   D **6ac**

(Litho John Dickinson & Co, Ltd)

1939 (1 May)–49. P 10.
D1	D **1**	1c. green	2·25	12·00
		a. Perf 11 (1949)....................	3·25	14·00
D2		2c. vermilion	13·00	7·50
		a. Perf 11×9 (1946).................	14·00	21·00
D3		3c. ultramarine	5·00	25·00
		a. Perf 11×9 (1949).................	13·00	48·00
		b. Perf 9	£800	
D4		4c. orange	9·00	20·00
		a. Perf 11×9 (May 1948).............	12·00	60·00
D5		5c. brown	5·50	28·00
D6		10c. violet	7·00	20·00
		a. Perf 11 (W 106) (1949)..........	18·00	85·00
		ab. Ditto. Imperf between (vert pair)...............................	£950	
		ac. "POSTAGE LUE" (R. 3/3 or 3/8)...............................	£140	£375
D1/6		Set of 6	38·00	£100

Newfoundland joined the Dominion of Canada on 31 March 1949.

NOVA SCOTIA

Organised postal services in Nova Scotia date from April 1754 when the first of a series of Deputy Postmasters was appointed, under the authority of the British G.P.O. This arrangement continued until 6 July 1851 when the colony assumed responsibility for its postal affairs.

For illustrations of the handstamp types see BRITISH POST OFFICES ABROAD notes, following GREAT BRITAIN.

AMHERST

CROWNED-CIRCLE HANDSTAMPS

CC1	CC **1** AMHERST. N.S.(R) (25.2.1845)		
		Price on cover	£1000

ST. MARGARETS BAY

CROWNED-CIRCLE HANDSTAMPS

CC2	CC **1** ST. MARGARETS BAY. N.S.(R) (30.6.1845)		
		Price on cover	£9500

Nos. CC1/2 were later used during temporary shortages of stamps, struck in red or black.

PRICES FOR STAMPS ON COVER
No. 1	*from × 5*
Nos. 2/4	*from × 2*
Nos. 5/8	*from × 4*
Nos. 9/10	*from × 10*
Nos. 11/13	*from × 2*
Nos. 14/15	—
No. 16	*from × 4*

PRICES FOR STAMPS ON COVER
Nos. 17/19	*from × 10*
Nos. 20/5	*from × 2*
No. 26	*from × 50*
Nos. 27/8	*from × 4*
No. 29	*from × 10*

1   **2**

Crown and Heraldic Flowers of United Kingdom and Mayflower of Nova Scotia.

(Recess P.B.)

1851 (1 Sept)–60. *Bluish paper. Imperf.*
1	**1**	1d. red-brown (12.5.53).....................	£2250	£400
		a. Bisected (½d.) (on cover) (1857)	†	£50000
2	**2**	3d. deep blue...........................	£1100	£160
		a. Bisected (1½d.) (on cover)	†	£2500
3		3d. bright blue.........................	£950	£120
		a. Bisected (1½d.) (on cover)	†	£2500
4		3d. pale blue (1857)....................	£800	£140
		a. Bisected (1½d.) (on cover)	†	£2500
5		6d. yellow-green........................	£4500	£450
		a. Bisected (3d.) (on cover)	†	£3250
		b. Quartered (1½d.) (on cover) (1860)...	†	£60000
6		6d. deep green (1857)...................	£10000	£750
		a. Bisected (3d.) (on cover)	†	£5000
7		1s. cold violet	£24000	£5000
7c		1s. deep purple (1851).................	£17000	£3750
		d. Watermarked	£22000	£5000
8		1s. purple (1857)......................	£16000	£2750
		a. Bisected (6d.) (on cover) (1860)..	†	£38000
		b. Quartered (3d.) (on cover) (1858)..	†	£80000

The watermark on No. 7d consists of the whole or part of a letter from the name "T. H. SAUNDERS" (the papermakers).

The stamps formerly catalogued on almost white paper are probably some from which the bluish paper has been discharged.

Reprints of all four values were made in 1890 on thin, hard, white paper. The 1d. is brown, the 3d. blue, the 6d. deep green, and the 1s. violet-black.

The 3d. bisects, which were authorised on 19 October 1854, are usually found used to make up the 7½d. rate.

(New Currency. 100 cents = 1 dollar)

3   **4**   **5**

(Recess American Bank Note Co, New York)

1863. P 12.
		(a) Yellowish paper.		
9	**3**	1c. jet black	4·00	14·00
		a. Bisected (½c.) (on cover)	†	£8000
10		1c. grey-black	3·75	14·00
11		2c. grey-purple	11·00	16·00
11a		2c. purple	17·00	15·00
12		5c. blue	£425	19·00
13		5c. deep blue	£425	19·00
14	**4**	8½c. deep green	3·50	42·00
15		8½c. yellow-green	3·50	42·00
16		10c. scarlet	18·00	28·00
17	**5**	12½c. black	30·00	28·00
17a		12½c. greyish black	—	28·00
		(b) White paper.		
18	**3**	1c. black	3·75	16·00
		a. Imperf vert (horiz pair)............	£160	
19		1c. grey	3·75	16·00
20		2c. dull purple	4·50	14·00
21		2c. purple	4·50	14·00
22		2c. grey-purple	4·50	14·00
		a. Bisected (1c.) (on cover)	†	£3500
23		2c. slate-purple	4·50	12·00
24		5c. blue	£450	23·00
25		5c. deep blue	£450	23·00
26	**4**	8½c. deep green	19·00	42·00
27		10c. scarlet	7·00	27·00
28		10c. vermilion	4·25	27·00
		a. Bisected (5c.) (on cover)	†	£750
29	**5**	12½c. black	55·00	32·00

Nova Scotia joined the Dominion of Canada on 1 July 1867.

PRINCE EDWARD ISLAND

Prince Edward Island, previously administered as part of Nova Scotia, became a separate colony in 1769.

PRICES FOR STAMPS ON COVER
Nos. 1/4	*from × 3*
No. 5	—
No. 6	*from × 5*
Nos. 7/8	*from × 10*
Nos. 9/11	*from × 8*
Nos. 12/18	*from × 6*

1   2   3

4   5   6

Two Dies of 2d.:

Die I. Left-hand frame and circle merge at centre left (all stamps in the sheet of 60 (10×6) except R. 2/5).

Die II. Left-hand frame and circle separate at centre left (R. 2/5). There is also a break in the top frame line.

(Typo Charles Whiting, London)

1861 (1 Jan). *Yellowish toned paper.*

(a) P 9.

1	1	2d. rose (I)	£350	£150
		a. Imperf between (horiz pair)	£6500	
		b. Imperf horiz (vert pair)		
		c. Bisected (1d.) (on cover)	†	£4000
		d. Die II		
2		2d. rose-carmine (I)	£375	£160
3	2	3d. blue	£800	£300
		a. Bisected (1½d.) (on cover)	†	£3500
		b. Double print	£2000	
4	3	6d. yellow-green	£1200	£475

(b) Rouletted.

5	1	2d. rose (I)	†	£6000

The 2d. and 3d., perf 9, were authorised to be bisected and used for half their normal value.

1862–69. *Yellowish toned paper.*

(a) P 11 (1862) or 11¼ (1869).

6	4	1d. brown-orange	48·00	75·00
6a		1d. rose (1869)	†	£500
7	6	9d. bluish lilac (29.3.62)	95·00	75·00
8		9d. dull mauve	95·00	75·00

(b) P 11½–12 (1863–69).

9	4	1d. yellow-orange (1863)	35·00	45·00
		a. Bisected (½d.) (on cover)	†	£2500
		b. Imperf between (horiz pair)	£450	
10		1d. orange-buff	38·00	45·00
11		1d. yellow	42·00	45·00
12	1	2d. rose (I) (1863)	14·00	12·00
		a. Imperf vert (horiz pair)		
		b. Bisected (1d.) (on cover)	†	£2000
		c. Die II	90·00	90·00
13		2d. deep rose (I)	15·00	15·00
		a. Die II	95·00	£100
14	2	3d. blue (1863)	22·00	22·00
		a. Imperf horiz (vert pair)		
		b. Bisected (1½d.) (on cover)		
15		3d. deep blue	22·00	22·00
16	5	4d. black (1869)	22·00	28·00
		a. Imperf vert (horiz pair)	£325	
		b. Bisected (2d.) (on cover)	†	£1800
		c. Imperf between (horiz strip of 3)	£400	
17	3	6d. yellow-green (15.12.66)	£120	£100
		a. Bisected (3d.) (on cover)	†	£3500
18		6d. blue-green (1868)	£100	£100
19	6	9d. lilac (1863)	85·00	85·00
20		9d. reddish mauve (1863)	85·00	85·00
		a. Imperf vert (horiz pair)	£650	
		b. Bisected (4½d.) (on cover)	†	£3000

A new perforator, gauging exactly 11¼, was introduced in 1869. Apart from No. 6a, it was used in compound with the perf 11½–12 machine.

(c) Perf compound of 11 or 11¼ (1869) and 11½–12.

21	4	1d. yellow-orange	£200	85·00
22	1	2d. rose (I)	£180	70·00
		a. Die II		
23	2	3d. blue	£225	70·00
24	5	4d. black	£300	£250
25	3	6d. yellow-green	£275	£275
26	6	9d. reddish mauve	£325	£275

1870. *Coarse, wove bluish white paper.* P 11½–12.

27	1	2d. rose (I)	13·00	13·00
		a. Die II	90·00	90·00
28		2d. rose-pink (I)	7·50	10·00
		a. Die II	70·00	80·00
		b. "TWC" (R. 6/4)	75·00	85·00
		c. Imperf between (horiz pair)	£225	
		d. Imperf horiz (vert pair)	£225	
29	2	3d. pale blue	10·00	14·00
30		3d. blue	10·00	14·00
		a. Imperf between (horiz pair)	£350	
31	5	4d. black	5·00	28·00
		a. Imperf between (horiz pair)	£200	
		b. Bisected (2d.) (on cover)	†	£1800

(New Currency. 100 cents = 1 dollar)

7

(Recess British-American Bank Note Co., Montreal and Ottawa)

1870 (1 June). P 12.

32	7	4½d. (3d. stg), yellow-brown	48·00	60·00
33		4½d. (3d. stg), deep brown	50·00	65·00

8   9   10

11   12   13

(Typo Charles Whiting, London)

1872 (1 Jan).

(a) P 11½–12.

34	8	1c. orange	6·00	20·00
35		1c. yellow-orange	6·00	17·00
36		1c. brown-orange	6·00	20·00
37	10	3c. rose	18·00	27·00
		a. Stop between "PRINCE. EDWARD"	55·00	75·00
		b. Bisected (1½c.) (on cover)	£500	
		c. Imperf horiz (vert pair)		

(b) Perf 12 to 12¼ large holes.

38	9	2c. blue	20·00	42·00
		a. Bisected (1c.) (on cover)	†	£3000
39	11	4c. yellow-green	6·50	23·00
40		4c. deep green	7·00	20·00
		a. Bisected (2c.) (on cover)	†	£3000
41	12	6c. black	5·00	21·00
		a. Bisected (3c.) (on cover)	†	£1600
		b. Imperf between (horiz pair)	£275	
		c. Imperf vert (horiz pair)		
42	13	12c. reddish mauve	5·00	38·00

(c) P 12½–13, smaller holes.

43	8	1c. orange	15·00	
44		1c. brown-orange	6·50	21·00
45	10	3c. rose	18·00	32·00
		a. Stop between "PRINCE. EDWARD"	65·00	85·00
45b	12	6c. black		£250

(d) Perf compound of (a) and (c) 11½–12×12½–13.

46	8	1c. orange	42·00	48·00
47	10	3c. rose	48·00	50·00
		a. Stop between "PRINCE. EDWARD"	£200	£225

Prince Edward Island joined the Dominion of Canada on 1 July 1873.

DOMINION OF CANADA

On 1 July 1867, Canada, Nova Scotia and New Brunswick were united to form the Dominion of Canada.

The provinces of Manitoba (1870), British Columbia (1871), Prince Edward Island (1873), Alberta (1905), Saskatchewan (1905), and Newfoundland (1949) were subsequently added, as were the Northwest Territories (1870) and Yukon Territory (1898).

---

13   14   15

Large types

PRINTERS. Nos. 46/120 were recess-printed by the British American Bank Note Co at Ottawa or Montreal.

1868 (1 Apr)–**90.** As T **13/15** (*various frames*).

I. *Ottawa printings.* P 12.

(a) Thin rather transparent crisp paper.

46	13	½c. black (1.4.68)	80·00	75·00
47	14	1c. red-brown (1.4.68)	£400	60·00
48		2c. grass-green (1.4.68)	£450	50·00
49		3c. red-brown (1.4.68)	£850	27·00
50		6c. blackish brown (1.4.68)	£1200	£170
51		12½c. bright blue (1.4.68)	£850	£130
52		15c. deep reddish purple	£1000	£180

In these first printings the impression is generally blurred and the lines of the background are less clearly defined than in later printings.

(b) Medium to stout wove paper (1868–71).

53	13	½c. black	60·00	55·00
54		½c. grey-black	60·00	55·00
		a. Imperf between (pair)		
		b. Watermarked (pair)	£12000	£6000
55	14	1c. red-brown	£30	45·00
		a. Laid paper	£10000	£2500
		b. Watermarked (1868)	£2000	£250
56		1c. deep orange (Jan, 1869)	£900	90·00
56a		1c. orange-yellow (May (?), 1869)	£800	75·00
56b		1c. pale orange-yellow	£850	85·00
		ba. Imperf		
57		2c. deep green	£400	35·00
57a		2c. pale emerald-green (1871)	£500	55·00
		ab. Bisected (1c. with 2c. to make 3c. rate) on cover	†	£4500
		ac. Laid paper	†	£80000
57d		2c. bluish green	£425	35·00
		da. Watermarked (1868)	£1900	£250
58		3c. brown-red	£800	17·00
		a. Laid paper	£7000	£375
		b. Watermarked (1868)	£2500	£180
59		6c. blackish brown (to chocolate)	£850	48·00
		a. Watermarked (1868)	£3750	£750
59b		6c. yellow-brown (1868)	£850	42·00
		ba. Bisected (3c.), on cover	†	£2250
60		12½c. bright blue	£600	45·00
		a. Imperf horiz (vert pair)	†	£12000
		b. Watermarked (1868)	£2250	£250
60c		12½c. pale dull blue (milky)	£650	55·00
61		15c. deep reddish purple	£600	60·00
61a		15c. pale reddish purple	£500	60·00
		ab. Watermarked (1868)	—	£1200
61b		15c. dull violet-grey	£225	30·00
		ba. Watermarked (1868)	£3250	£550
61c		15c. dull grey-purple	£300	30·00

The official date of issue was 1 April 1868. Scattered examples of most values can be found used in the second half of March.

The watermark on the stout paper stamps consists of the words "E & G BOTHWELL CLUTHA MILLS," in large double-lined capitals which can be found upright, inverted or reversed. Portions of one or two letters only may be found on most stamps, which occur in the early printings of 1868.

The paper may, in most cases, be easily divided if the stamps are laid face downwards and carefully compared. The thin hard paper is more or less transparent and shows the design through the stamp; the thicker paper is softer to the feel and more opaque.

Of the 2c. laid paper No. 57ac two examples only are known.

II. *Montreal printings.* Medium to stout wove paper.

(a) P 11½×12 or 11¾×12.

62	13	½c. black (1873)	75·00	75·00
63	15	5c. olive-green (1.10.75)	£750	75·00
		a. Perf 12	£3500	£800
64	14	15c. dull grey-purple (1874)	£800	£170
65		15c. lilac-grey (3.77)	£900	£160
		a. Script watermark	£20000	£2250
		b. "BOTHWELL" watermark	†	£750
66		15c. slate	£900	£300

(b) P 12.

67	14	15c. clear deep violet (1879)	£3000	£600
68		15c. deep slate (1881)	£150	30·00
69		15c. slaty blue (1887)	£150	30·00
70		15c. slate-purple (shades) (7.88–92)	65·00	17·00

No. 63a gauges 12 or above on all four sides.

The watermark on No. 65a is part of "Alex.Pirie & Sons" which appeared as script letters once per sheet in a small batch of the paper used for the 1877 printing. For a description of the sheet watermark on No. 65b, see note after No. 61c.

Several used examples of the 12½c. have been reported perforated 11½×12 or 11¾×12.

The last printing of the 15c. slate-purple, No. 70, took place at Ottawa.

III. *Ottawa printings. Thinnish paper of poor quality, often toned grey or yellowish.* P 12.

71	14	15c. slate-violet (shades) (5.90)	65·00	20·00
		a. Imperf (pair). Brown-purple	£1200	

Examples of No. 71 are generally found with yellowish streaky gum.

21 Small type

Strand of hair

Straw in hair

1870–88. *As T 21 (various frames). Ottawa (1870–73) and Montreal printings.* P 12 (or slightly under).

Papers (*a*) *1870–80. Medium to stout wove.*
       (*b*) *1870–72. Thin, soft, very white.*
       (*c*) *1878–97. Thinner and poorer quality.*

72	21	1c. bright orange (*a, b*) (2.1870–73)	£150	25·00
		a. Thick soft paper (1871)	£425	£120
73		1c. orange-yellow (*a*) (1876–79)	60·00	3·00
74		1c. pale dull yellow (*a*) (1877–79)..	40·00	2·25
75		1c. bright yellow (*a, c*) (1878–97)..	28·00	1·00
		a. Imperf (pair) (*c*)	£400	
		b. Bisected (½c.) (on *Railway News*)	†	£3500
		c. Printed both sides	£1700	
		d. Strand of hair	£650	£200
76		1c. lemon-yellow (*c*) (1880)	90·00	16·00
77		2c. dp green (*a, b*) (1872–73 & 1876–78)	85·00	2·50
78		2c. grass-green (*c*) (1878–88)	50·00	1·00
		a. Imperf (pair)	£450	
		b. Bisected (1c. with 2c. to make 3c. rate) on cover	†	£1600
79		3c. Indian red (*a*) (1.70)	£900	50·00
		a. Perf 12½ (2.70)	£5500	£600
80		3c. pale rose-red (9.70)	£300	9·00
81		3c. deep rose-red (*a, b*) (1870–73)..	£325	9·00
		a. Thick soft paper (1.71)	—	£150
82		3c. dull red (*a, c*) (1876–88)	70·00	2·25
83		3c. orange-red (*shades*) (*a, c*) (1876–88)	50·00	1·75
84		3c. rose-carm (*c*) (10.88.–4.89)	£350	11·00
85		5c. olive-green (*a, c*) (2.76–88)	£275	9·00
		a. Straw in hair	£1200	£375
86		6c. yellowish brown (*a, b, c*) (1872–73 and 1876–90)	£225	13·00
		a. Bisected (3c.) on cover	†	£1000
		b. Perf 12×11½ (1873)	†	—
87		10c. pale lilac-magenta (*a*) (1876–?)	£500	50·00
88		10c. deep lilac-magenta (*a, c*) (3.76–88)	£500	60·00
89		10c. lilac-pink (3.88)	£275	32·00

Nos. 75 and 78 were printed in the same shades during the second Ottawa period. Nos. 75a and 78a date from *circa* 1894–95.

There are four variants of the Strand of Hair, with the strand in the same position but varying in length. R. 2/13 and R. 3/16 have been identified. The illustration shows the "Long Strand".

Examples of paper (*a*) can often be found showing traces of ribbing, especially on the 2c. value.

No. 79a was issued in New Brunswick and Nova Scotia.

One used copy of the 10c. perf 12½ has been reported.

1873–79. *Montreal printings. Medium to stout wove paper.* P 11½×12 or 11¾×12.

90	21	1c. bright orange	£200	42·00
91		1c. orange-yellow (1873–79)	£170	15·00
92		1c. pale dull yellow (1877–79)	£160	20·00
93		1c. lemon-yellow (1879)	£200	20·00
94		2c. deep green (1873–78)	£250	21·00
95		3c. dull red (1875–79)	£250	20·00
96		3c. orange-red (1873–79)	£250	20·00
97		5c. olive-green (1.2.76–79)	£450	29·00
98		6c. yellowish brown (1873–79)	£450	42·00
99		10c. very pale lilac magenta (1874)..	£1000	£250
100		10c. deep lilac-magenta (1876–79)..	£750	£200

27

5c. on 6c. re-entry (R. 3/4)

1882–97. *Montreal (to March 1889) and Ottawa printings. Thinnish paper of poor quality.* P 12.

101	27	½c. black (7.82–97)	13·00	8·00
102		½c. grey-black	13·00	8·00
		ab. Imperf (pair) (1891–93?)	£500	
		ac. Imperf between (horiz pair)	£750	

1889–97. *Ottawa printings. Thinnish paper of poor quality, often toned grey or yellowish.* P 12.

103	21	2c. dull sea-green	50·00	1·25
104		2c. blue-green (7.89–91)	40·00	2·00
105		3c. bright vermilion (4.89–97)	38·00	80
		a. Imperf (pair) (1891–93?)	£400	
106		5c. brownish grey (5.89)	70·00	1·75
		a. Imperf (pair) (1891–93)	£475	
107		6c. deep chestnut (10.90)	35·00	9·50
		a. "5c." re-entry*	£2750	£1400
		b. Imperf (pair) (1891–93?)	£500	
108		6c. pale chestnut	42·00	9·50
109		10c. salmon-pink	£275	£110
110		10c. carmine-pink (4.90)	£200	27·00
		a. Imperf (pair) (1891–93?)	£600	
111		10c. brownish red (1894?)	£200	26·00
		a. Imperf (pair)	£500	

On No. 107a the top portion of the 5c. design cuts across "CANADA POSTAGE", the white circle surrounding the head, and can be seen on the top of the head itself. Lesser re-entries are visible on R. 2/10 and R. 3/1 from another plate.

The 1c. showed no change in the Ottawa printings, so is not included. The 2c. reverted to its previous grass-green shade in 1891.

28   **29**

(Recess B.A.B.N.)

1893 (17 Feb). P 12.

115	28	20c. vermilion	£225	48·00
		a. Imperf (pair)	£1200	
116		50c. blue	£250	35·00
		a. Imperf (*Prussian blue*) (pair)	£1300	

1893 (1 Aug). P 12.

117	29	8c. pale bluish grey	£100	5·50
		a. Imperf (pair)	£600	
118		8c. bluish slate	£110	5·50
119		8c. slate-purple	£100	5·50
120		8c. blackish purple	85·00	5·50
		a. Imperf (pair)	£600	

PRINTERS. The following stamps to No. 287 were recess-printed by the American Bank Note Co, Ottawa, which in 1923 became the Canadian Bank Note Co.

30

(Des L. Pereira and F. Brownell)

1897 (19 June). *Jubilee issue.* P 12.

121	30	½c. black	50·00	50·00
122		1c. orange	10·00	4·50
123		1c. orange-yellow	10·00	4·50
		a. Bisected (½c.) (on *Railway News*)	†	£3250
124		2c. green	18·00	9·00
125		2c. deep green	18·00	9·00
126		3c. carmine	12·00	2·25
127		5c. slate-blue	40·00	14·00
128		5c. deep blue	40·00	14·00
129		6c. brown	90·00	90·00
130		8c. slate-violet	32·00	30·00
131		10c. purple	55·00	48·00
132		15c. slate	90·00	90·00
133		20c. vermilion	90·00	90·00
134		50c. pale ultramarine	£130	95·00
135		50c. bright ultramarine	£130	£100
136		$1 lake	£450	£450
137		$2 deep violet	£750	£350
138		$3 bistre	£900	£700
139		$4 violet	£850	£600
140		$5 olive-green	£850	£600
121/40		*Set of 16*	£4000	£2750
133s/40s		Handstamped "Specimen" *Set of 7*	£1900	

No. 123a was used on issues of the *Railway News* of 5, 6 and 8 November 1897 and must be on a large part of the original newspaper with New Glasgow postmark.

31   **32**

(From photograph by W. & D. Downey, London)

1897–98. P 12.

141	31	½c. grey-black (9.11.97)	6·50	4·75
142		½c. black	7·50	5·00
		a. Imperf (pair)	£400	
143		1c. blue-green (12.97)	18·00	90
		a. Imperf (pair)	£400	
144		2c. violet (12.97)	18·00	1·50
		a. Imperf (pair)	£400	
145		3c. carmine (1.98)	27·00	1·00
		a. Imperf (pair)	£750	
146		5c. deep blue/*bluish* (12.97)	65·00	2·75
		a. Imperf (pair)	£400	
147		6c. brown (12.97)	60·00	25·00
		a. Imperf (pair)	£750	
148		8c. orange (12.97)	80·00	7·00
		a. Imperf (pair)	£450	
149		10c. brownish purple (1.98)	£130	55·00
		a. Imperf (pair)	£475	
141/9		*Set of 8*	£350	85·00

BOOKLET PANES. Most definitive booklets issued from 1900 onwards had either the two horizontal sides or all three outer edges imperforate. Stamps from the panes show one side or two adjacent sides imperforate.

Two types of the 2c.

Die Ia. Frame consists of four fine lines.
Die Ib. Frame has one thick line between two fine lines.

The die was retouched in 1900 for Plates 11 and 12, producing weak vertical frame lines and then retouched again in 1902 for Plates 15 to 20 resulting in much thicker frame lines. No. 155b covers both states of the retouching.

1898–1902. P 12.

150	32	½c. black (9.98)	4·00	1·10
		a. Imperf (pair)	£400	
151		1c. blue-green (6.98)	25·00	50
152		1c. deep green/*toned paper*	26·00	1·25
		a. Imperf (pair)	£850	
153		2c. dull purple (Die Ia) (9.98)	25·00	30
		a. Thick paper (6.99)	90·00	10·00
154		2c. violet (Die Ia)	23·00	30
154a		2c. reddish purple (Die Ia)	45·00	1·25
155		2c. rose-carmine (Die Ia) (20.8.99).	35·00	30
		a. Imperf (pair)	£350	
155b		2c. rose-carmine (Die Ib) (1900)	48·00	65
		ba. Booklet pane of 6 (11.6.00)	£750	
156		3c. rose-carmine (6.98)	55·00	1·00
157		5c. slate-blue/*bluish*	£110	2·50
		a. Imperf (pair)	£900	
158		5c. Prussian blue/*bluish*	£120	2·50
159		6c. brown (9.98)	95·00	55·00
		a. Imperf (pair)	£800	
160		7c. greenish yellow (23.12.02)	65·00	16·00
161		8c. orange-yellow (10.98)	£120	29·00
162		8c. brownish orange	£110	29·00
		a. Imperf (pair)	£800	
163		10c. pale brownish purple (11.98)..	£170	14·00
164		10c. deep brownish purple	£170	14·00
		a. Imperf (pair)	£850	
165		20c. olive-green (29.12.00)	£300	50·00
150/65		*Set of 11*	£900	£150

The 7c. and 20c. also exist imperforate, but unlike the values listed in this condition, they have no gum. (*Price*, 7c. £400, 20c. £1800 *pair, un*).

33

(Des R. Weir Crouch, G. Hahn, A. H. Howard and R. Holmes. Eng C. Skinner. Design recess, colours added by typo)

1898 (7 Dec). *Imperial Penny Postage. Design in black. British possessions in red. Oceans in colours given.* P 12.

166	33	2c. lavender	29·00	5·50
		a. Imperf (pair)	£350	
167		2c. greenish blue	26·00	5·00
		a. Imperf (pair)	£375	
168		2c. blue	26·00	4·75
		a. Imperf (pair)	£375	

Forgeries of Type 33 are without horizontal lines across the continents and have a forged Montreal postmark of 24.12.98.

1899 (4 Jan). *Provisionals used at Port Hood, Nova Scotia. No. 156 divided vertically and handstamped.*

169	32	"1" in blue, on13of 3c.	—	£3500
170		"2" in violet, on23of 3c.	—	£3000

Nos. 169/70 were prepared by the local postmaster during a shortage of 2c. stamps caused by a change in postage rates.

2 CENTS

(34)

35 King Edward VII

1899. *Surch with T 34, by Public Printing Office.*

171	31	2c. on 3c. carmine (8 Aug)	15·00	8·00
		a. Surch inverted	£275	
172	32	2c. on 3c. rose-carmine (28 July)	17·00	4·25
		a. Surch inverted	£275	

(Des King George V when Prince of Wales and J. A. Tilleard)

1903 (1 July)–**12**. P 12.

173	35	1c. pale green	25·00	50
174		1c. deep green	23·00	50
175		1c. green	23·00	50
176		2c. rose-carmine	20·00	50
		a. Booklet pane of 6	£750	£950
177		2c. pale rose-carmine	20·00	50
		a. Imperf (pair) (18.7.09)	28·00	32·00
178		5c. blue/*bluish*	80·00	2·50
179		5c. indigo/*bluish*	80·00	2·75
180		7c. yellow-olive	65·00	2·75
181		7c. greenish bistre	75·00	2·75
181*a*		7c. straw (1.12)	£120	40·00
182		10c. brown-lilac	£130	14·00
183		10c. pale dull purple	£130	14·00
184		10c. dull purple	£130	14·00
185		20c. pale olive-green (27.9.04)	£225	23·00
186		20c. deep olive-green	£250	23·00
		s. Handstamped "Specimen"	80·00	
187		50c. deep violet (19.11.08)	£350	85·00
173/87		*Set of* 7	£800	£110

The 1c., 5c., 7c. and 10c. exist imperforate but are believed to be proofs. (Prices per pair, 1c. £425, 5c. £750, 7c. £500, 10c. £750).

IMPERFORATE AND PART-PERFORATED SHEETS.
Prior to 1946 many Canadian issues exist imperforate, or with other perforation varieties, in the colours of the issued stamps and, usually, with gum. In the years before 1927 such examples are believed to come from imprimatur sheets, removed from the Canadian Post Office archives. From 1927 until 1946 it is known that the printers involved in the production of the various issues submitted several imperforate plate proof sheets of each stamp to the Post Office authorities for approval. Some of these sheets or part sheets were retained for record purposes, but the remainder found their way on to the philatelic market.

Part-perforated sheets also occur from 1927–29 issues.

From 1908 until 1946 we now only list and price such varieties of this type which are known to be genuine errors, sold from post offices. Where other imperforate or similar varieties are known they are recorded in footnotes.

It is possible, and in some cases probable, that some imperforate varieties listed before 1908 may have also been removed from the archives as mentioned above, but it is far harder to be explicit over the status of this earlier material.

36 King George V and Queen Mary when Prince and Princess of Wales

37 Jacques Cartier and Samuel Champlain

Re-entry (R. 5/4)

38 King Edward VII and Queen Alexandra

39 Champlain's house in Quebec

40 Generals Montcalm and Wolfe

41 Quebec in 1700

42 Champlain's departure for the West

43 Cartier's arrival before Quebec

(Des Machado)

1908 (16 July). *Quebec Tercentenary. T* 36/43. P 12.

188	36	½c. sepia	3·50	3·50
		a Re-entry	40·00	40·00
189	37	1c. blue-green	14·00	2·75
190	38	2c. carmine	18·00	1·00
191	39	5c. indigo	45·00	25·00
192	40	7c. olive-green	65·00	48·00
193	41	10c. violet	70·00	55·00
194	42	15c. brown-orange	85·00	70·00
195	43	20c. dull brown	£120	£100
188/95		*Set of* 8	£375	£275

Some values exist on both toned and white papers.

Nos. 188/95 exist imperforate. (*Price* £425, *un, for each pair*).

WET AND DRY PRINTINGS. Until the end of December 1922 all Canadian stamps were produced by the "wet" method of recess-printing in which the paper was dampened before printing, dried and then gummed.

In late December 1922 the Canadian Bank Note Co. began to use the "dry" process in which the paper was gummed before printing. Late printings of the 3c. brown were the first stamps to be produced by this method, but the changeover was not completed until January 1926.

"Dry" printings have a sharper appearance and can often be found with a degree of embossing showing on the reverse. Stamps from "wet" printings shrink during drying and are narrower than "dry" examples. In many cases the difference can be as great as 0.5 mm. On some early booklet panes the difference is in the vertical, rather than the horizontal, measurement.

On Nos. 196/215 all values only exist from "wet" printings, except the 3c., 20c. and 50c. which come from both types of printing.

44

1911–22. P 12.

196	44	1c. yellow-green (22.12.11)	6·00	50
		a. With fine horiz lines across stamp	38·00	8·50
197		1c. bluish green	5·50	50
		a. Booklet pane of 6 (1.5.13)	50·00	
198		1c. deep bluish green	6·00	50
199		1c. deep yellow-green	6·00	65
		a. Booklet pane of 6	18·00	
200		2c. rose-red (15.12.11)	5·00	50
201		2c. deep rose-red	5·00	50
		a. Booklet pane of 6 (1.12)	32·00	
202		2c. pale rose-red	5·00	50
		a. With fine horiz lines across stamp	25·00	13·00
203		2c. carmine	6·00	50
204		3c. brown (6.8.18)	6·00	50
205		3c. deep brown	5·00	50
		a. Booklet pane of 4+2 labels (2.22)	50·00	
205*b*		5c. deep blue (17.1.12)	60·00	75
206		5c. indigo	90·00	4·50
206*a*		5c. grey-blue	85·00	2·75
206*b*		7c. straw (12.1.12)	75·00	13·00
207		7c. pale sage-green (1914)	£200	32·00
208		7c. olive-yellow (1915)	20·00	3·00
209		7c. yellow-ochre (1916)	20·00	3·00
210		10c. brownish purple (12.1.12)	90·00	2·75
211		10c. reddish purple	£100	4·50
212		20c. olive-green (23.1.12)	30·00	1·50
213		20c. olive	30·00	1·75
214		50c. grey-black (26.1.12)	£100	8·00
215		50c. sepia	48·00	3·75
196/215		*Set of* 8	£225	11·00

The 20c. and 50c. values exist imperforate (*Price* £1800 *un, for each pair*).

1912 (1 Nov)–**21**. *For use in coil-machines.*

(a) P 12×imperf.

216	44	1c. yellow-green (1914)	3·50	10·00
217		1c. blue-green	15·00	23·00
		a. Two large holes at top and bottom (vert pair) (7.18)	75·00	90·00
218		2c. deep rose-red (1914)	26·00	23·00
218*a*		3c. brown (1921)	3·50	6·00

No. 217a has two large holes about 3½ mm in diameter in the top and bottom margins. They were for experimental use in a vending machine at Toronto in July 1918 and were only in use for two days.

The 1c. and 2c. also exist with two small "V" shaped holes about 9.5 mm apart at top which are gripper marks due to modifications made in vending machines in 1917.

(b) Imperf×perf 8.

219	44	1c. yellow-green (9.12)	14·00	5·00
220		1c. blue-green	18·00	5·00
		a. With fine horiz lines across stamp	55·00	
221		2c. carmine (9.12)	11·00	1·50
222		2c. rose-red	12·00	2·25
223		2c. scarlet	32·00	5·00
224		3c. brown (8.18)	5·00	2·00

(c) P 8×imperf.

224a	44	1c. blue-green (15.2.13)	60·00	48·00
224b		2c. carmine (15.2.13)	60·00	48·00

The stamps imperf×perf 8 were sold in coils over the counter; those perf 8×imperf were on sale in automatic machines. Varieties showing perf 12 on 2 or 3 adjacent sides and 1 or 2 sides imperf are from booklets, or the margins of sheets.

(45)

46

47

1915 (12 Feb). *Optd with T* 45.

225	44	5c. blue	£110	£200
226		20c. olive-green	55·00	£100
227		50c. sepia (R.)	£110	£160
225/7		*Set of* 3	£250	£425

These stamps were intended for tax purposes, but owing to ambiguity in an official circular dated 16 April 1915, it was for a time believed that their use for postal purposes was authorised. The position was clarified by a further circular on 20 May 1916 which made clear that Nos. 225/7 were for fiscal use only.

1915. P 12.

228	46	1c. green (15.4.15)	8·00	50
229		2c. carmine-red (16.4.15)	15·00	1·00
230		2c. rose-carmine	17·00	3·25

Die I

Die II

In Die I there is a long horizontal coloured line under the foot of the "T", and a solid bar of colour runs upwards from the "1" to the "T".

In Die II this solid bar of colour is absent, and there is a short horizontal line under the left side of the "T", with two short vertical dashes and a number of dots under the right-hand side.

1916 (1 Jan). P 12.

231	47	2c.+1c. rose-red (Die I)	28·00	1·25
232		2c.+1c. bright carmine (Die I)	28·00	1·25
233		2c.+1c. scarlet (Die I)	24·00	1·25

1916 (Feb). *Imperf×perf 8 (coils).*

234	47	2c.+1c. rose-red (Die I)	55·00	12·00

1916 (July). P 12×8.

235	47	2c.+1c. carmine-red (Die I)	20·00	48·00
236		2c.+1c. bright rose-red (Die I)	20·00	48·00

1916 (Aug). P 12.

237	47	2c.+1c. carmine-red (Die II)	£100	20·00

1916 (Aug). *Colour changed.*

(a) P 12.

238	47	2c. + 1c. brown (Die I)	£200	20·00
239		2c. + 1c. yellow-brown (Die II)	4·00	50
		a. Imperf (pair)	£900	
240		2c. + 1c. deep brown (Die II)	11·00	50

(b) Imperf×perf 8.

241	47	2c. + 1c. brown (Die I)	£100	7·50
		a. Pair, 241 and 243	£350	
243		2c. + 1c. deep brown (Die II)	40·00	3·50

No. 239a, which is a genuine error, should not be confused with ungummed proofs of the Die I stamp, No. 238 (*Price per pair*, £140).

This value also exists p 12×imperf or imperf×p 12, but was not issued with these perforations (*Price, in either instance*, £300, *un, per pair*).

48 Quebec Conference, 1864, from painting "The Fathers of Confederation", by Robert Harris

1917 (15 Sept). *50th Anniv of Confederation.* P 12.

244	48	3c. bistre-brown	18·00	2·00
245		3c. deep brown	20·00	2·25

No. 244 exists imperforate, without gum (*Price per pair*, £350 *un*).

Die I (top). Space between top of "N" and oval frame line and space between "CENT" and lower frame line.

Die II (bottom). "ONE CENT" appears larger so that "N" touches oval and "CENT" almost touches frame line. There are other differences but this is the most obvious one.

Die I (top). The lowest of the three horizontal lines of shading below the medals does not touch the three heavy diagonal lines; three complete white spaces over both "E's" of "THREE"; long centre bar to figures "3". Vertical spandrel lines fine.

Die II (bottom). The lowest horizontal line of shading touches the first of the three diagonal lines; two and a half spaces over first "E" and spaces over second "E" partly filled by stem of maple leaf; short centre bar to figures "3". Vertical spandrel lines thick. There are numerous other minor differences.

WET AND DRY PRINTINGS. See notes above No. 196.

On Nos. 246/63 all listed items occur from both "wet" and "dry" printings except Nos. 246aa/ab, 248aa, 256, 259, 260 and 262 which come "wet" only, and Nos. 246a, 248/a, 252/4a, 256b and 263 which are "dry" only.

1922–31. As T **44**.

(a) P 12.

246	**44**	1c. chrome-yellow (Die I) (7.6.22) .	2·50	60
		aa. Booklet pane of 4+2 labels (7.22)	55·00	
		ab. Booklet pane of 6 (12.22)........	29·00	
		a. Die II (1925)	5·50	30
247		2c. deep green (6.6.22)	2·25	10
		aa. Booklet pane of 4+2 labels (7.22)	40·00	
		ab. Booklet pane of 6 (12.22)........	£275	
		b. Thin paper (9.24)	3·00	4·50
248		3c. carmine (Die I) (18.12.23)........	3·75	10
		aa. Booklet pane of 4+2 labels (12.23)	35·00	
		a. Die II (11.24)	22·00	80
249		4c. olive-yellow (7.7.22)	8·00	3·50
		a. Yellow-ochre	8·00	3·50
250		5c. violet (2.2.22)	5·00	1·75
		a. Thin paper (9.24)	5·00	8·00
		b. Reddish violet (1925)............	7·00	2·00
251		7c. red-brown (12.12.24).............	12·00	7·00
		a. Thin paper	£130	30·00
252		8c. blue (1.9.25).....................	19·00	10·00
253		10c. blue (20.2.22)..................	17·00	3·25
254		10c. bistre-brown (1.8.25)	18·00	3·00
		a. Yellow-brown	18·00	3·00
255		$1 brown-orange (22.7.23).........	55·00	8·00
246/55 *Set of 10*			£130	32·00

The $1 differs from T **44** in that the value tablets are oval.

Nos. 249/52 ond 254/5 exist imperforate (*Prices per un pair* 4c. *to* 8c. £1300 *each*, 10c. £1400, $1 £1600).

(b) Imperf×perf 8.

256	**44**	1c. chrome-yellow (Die I) (1922) ...	4·00	5·50
		a. Imperf horiz (vert pair) (1924)..	£160	
		b. Die II (1925)	4·50	7·00
		c. Do. Imperf horiz (vert pair) (1927)	8·00	27·00
257		2c. deep green (26.7.22)	7·00	2·25
		b. Imperf horiz (vert pair) (1927)..	9·00	27·00
258		3c. carmine (Die I) (9.4.24).........	65·00	10·00
		a. Imperf horiz (vert pair) (1924)..	£250	
		b. Die II (1925)	85·00	26·00
256/8 *Set of 3*			70·00	

Nos. 256a, 256c, 257b and 258a come from coil printings sold in sheet form. Those issued in 1924 were from "wet" printings and those in 1927 from "dry". A "wet" printing of No. 257b, issued in 1924, also exists (*Price* £160 *mint*), but cannot be identified from that issued in 1927 except by the differences between "wet" and "dry" stamps.

(c) Imperf (pairs).

259	**44**	1c. chrome-yellow (Die I) (6.10.24)	50·00	70·00
260		2c. deep green (6.10.24)	50·00	70·00
261		3c. carmine (Die I) (31.12.23)†.....	28·00	45·00

(d) P 12×imperf.

262	**44**	2c. deep green (9.24)	65·00	65·00

(e) P 12×8.

263	**44**	3c. carmine (Die II) (24.6.31)	2·50	3·25

†Earliest known postmark.

Nos. 259 to 261 were on sale only at the Philatelic Branch, P.O. Dept, Ottawa.

No. 263 was produced by adding horizontal perforations to unused sheet stock of No. 258b. The stamps were then issued in 1931 pending the delivery of No. 293.

2 CENTS (49)	**2 CENTS** (50)

1926. *No. 248 surch.*

(a) With T **49**, *by the Govt Printing Bureau.*

264	**44**	2c. on 3c. carmine (12.10.26)..........	42·00	50·00
		a. Pair, one without surch....	£350	
		b. On Die II	£375	

(b) With T **50**, *by the Canadian Bank Note Co.*

265	**44**	2c. on 3c. carmine (4.11.26).............	16·00	23·00
		a. Surch double (partly treble)................................	£200	

51 Sir J. A. Macdonald   **52** "The Fathers of Confederation"

53 Parliament Buildings, Ottawa   **54** Sir W. Laurier

55 Canada, Map 1867–1927

1927 (29 June). *60th Anniv of Confederation.* P 12.

I. *Commemorative Issue. Inscr* "1867–1927 CANADA CONFEDERATION".

266	**51**	1c. orange...........................	2·50	1·50
267	**52**	2c. green............................	2·25	30
268	**53**	3c. carmine.........................	7·00	5·00
269	**54**	5c. violet	3·75	3·50
270	**55**	12c. blue	24·00	5·00
266/70 *Set of 5*			35·00	14·00

Nos. 266/70 exist imperforate, imperf×perf or perf×imperf (*Prices from* £80, *un, per pair*).

56 Darcy McGee   **57** Sir W. Laurier and Sir J. A. Macdonald

58 R. Baldwin and L. H. Lafontaine

II. *Historical Issue.*

271	**56**	5c. violet	3·00	2·50
272	**57**	12c. green..........................	17·00	4·50
273	**58**	20c. carmine	17·00	12·00
271/3 *Set of 3*			32·00	17·00

Nos. 271/3 exist imperforate, imperf×perf or perf×imperf (*Prices from* £80, *un, per pair*).

59

(Des H. Schwartz)

1928 (21 Sept). *Air.* P 12.

274	**59**	5c. olive-brown	6·00	3·75

No. 274 exists imperforate, imperf×perf or perf×imperf (*Price per pair*, £160, *un*).

60 King George V   **61** Mt Hurd and Indian Totem Poles

62 Quebec Bridge   **63** Harvesting with Horses

1928–29.

(a) P 12.

275	**60**	1c. orange (25.10.28)......................	2·75	1·00
		a. Booklet pane of 6	18·00	
276		2c. green (16.10.28).................	1·25	20
		a. Booklet pane of 6	18·00	
277		3c. lake (12.12.28)..................	17·00	16·00
278		4c. olive-bistre (16.8.29)	13·00	7·00
279		5c. violet (12.12.28).................	6·50	3·75
		a. Booklet pane of 6 (6.1.29).....	95·00	
280		8c. blue (21.12.28)..................	7·50	5·00
281	**61**	10c. green (5.12.28).................	8·50	1·25
282	**62**	12c. grey-black (8.1.29)..............	22·00	11·00
283	**63**	20c. lake (8.1.29)....................	27·00	12·00
284	**64**	50c. blue (8.1.29)...................	£110	38·00
285	**65**	$1 olive-green (8.1.29)..............	£120	65·00
		a. Brown-olive	£225	£100
275/85 *Set of 11*			£300	£140

(b) Imperf× perf 8 (5.11.28).

286	**60**	1c. orange	13·00	22·00
287		2c. green	13·00	5·50

Slight differences in the size of many Canadian stamps, due to paper shrinkage, are to be found.

Nos. 275/85 exist imperforate, imperf×perf or perf×imperf (*Prices per unused pair*, 1c. to 8c., *from* £80, 10c. to 20c., *from* £140, 50c. and $1, *from* £450). *Tête-bêche* horizontal pairs of the 1c., 2c. and 5c. are also known from uncut booklet sheets (*Prices per pair*, £275, *un*).

PRINTERS. The following stamps to No. 334 were recess-printed by the British American Bank Note Co, Ottawa.

66   **67** Parliamentary Library, Ottawa

68 The Old Citadel, Quebec   **69** Harvesting with Tractor

70 Acadian Memorial Church and Statue of "Evangeline", Grand Pre, Nova Scotia   **71** Mt Edith Cavell, Canadian Rockies

Die I   1c.   Die II   Die I   2c.   Die II

1c. Die I. Three thick coloured lines and one thin between "P" and ornament, at right. Curved line in ball-ornament short.

Die II. Four thick lines. Curved line longer.

2c. Die I. Three thick coloured lines between "P" and ornament, at left. Short line in ball.

Die II. Four thick lines. Curved line longer.

1930–31.

(a) P 11.

288	**66**	1c. orange (I) (17.7.30)..................	1·75	1·00
289		1c. green (I) (6.12.30)...............	1·50	10
		b. Booklet pane of 6 (21.7.31)......	25·00	
		d. Die II (8.31).....................	1·75	10
		da. Imperf (pair)...................	£1500	
		db. Booklet pane of 4+2 labels (13.11.31)........................	80·00	
290		2c. green (I) (6.6.30).................	1·75	10
		a. Booklet pane of 6 (17.6.30).....	35·00	
291		2c. scarlet (I) (17.11.30).............	1·25	1·75
		a. Booklet pane of 6 (17.11.30).....	23·00	
		b. Die II	1·00	10
292		2c. deep brown (I) (4.7.31)...........	1·50	3·75
		a. Booklet pane of 6 (23.7.31).....	38·00	
		b. Die II (4.7.31)..................	1·25	10
		ba. Booklet pane of 4+2 labels (13.11.31)........................	£110	
293		3c. scarlet (13.7.31)..................	1·00	10
		a. Booklet pane of 4+2 labels........	35·00	
294		4c. yellow-bistre (5.11.30)............	6·50	4·50
295		5c. violet (18.6.30)...................	2·75	4·50
296		5c. deep slate-blue (13.11.30)........	5·50	20
		a. Dull blue	17·00	65
297		8c. blue (13.8.30)...................	11·00	16·00
298		8c. red-orange (5.11.30).............	7·50	5·50
299	**67**	10c. olive-green (15.9.30)............	16·00	1·00
		a. Imperf (pair)....................	£1300	
300	**68**	12c. grey-black (4.12.30).............	14·00	5·50
301	**69**	20c. red (4.12.30)...................	22·00	1·25
302	**70**	50c. blue (4.12.30)..................	80·00	17·00
303	**71**	$1 olive-green (4.12.30).............	95·00	25·00
288/303 *Set of 16*			£225	70·00

(b) Imperf×perf 8½.

304	**66**	1c. orange (I) (14.7.30)...............	11·00	15·00
305		1c. green (I) (4.2.31)...............	6·00	7·00
306		2c. green (I) (27.6.30)...............	4·00	5·00
307		2c. scarlet (I) (19.11.30).............	4·50	6·50
308		2c. deep brown (I) (4.7.31)..........	9·00	1·50
309		3c. scarlet (13.7.31).................	14·00	1·50
304/9 *Set of 6*			42·00	32·00

Nos. 300/3 exist imperforate (*Prices per unused pair*, 12c. £650, 20c. £650, 50c. £700, $1 £850).

Some low values in the above and subsequent issues have been printed by both Rotary and "Flat plate" processes. The former can be distinguished by the gum, which has a striped appearance.

For 13c. bright violet, T **68**, see No. 325.

72 Mercury and Western Hemisphere   **73** Sir Georges Etienne Cartier

(Des H. Schwartz)

1930 (4 Dec). *Air.* P 11.

310	**72**	5c. deep brown......................	19·00	18·00

1931 (30 Sept). P 11.
312   **73**   10c. olive-green .... 8·00   20

No. 312 exists imperforate (*Price per pair, £400, un*).

(74)   (75)

1932 (22 Feb). *Air. No. 274 surch with T* **74**.
313   **59**   6c. on 5c. olive-brown .... 3·00   2·50

Examples of this stamp with surcharge inverted, surcharge double, surcharge triple or surcharge omitted in pair with normal are not now believed to have been regularly issued. Such "errors" have also been forged and collectors are warned against forged examples, some of which bear unauthorized markings which purport to be the guarantee of Stanley Gibbons Ltd.

1932 (21 June). *Nos. 291/b surch with T* **75**.
314   **66**   3c. on 2c. scarlet (I) .... 3·00   2·50
        a. Die II .... 1·00   60

76 King George V   **77** Duke of Windsor when Prince of Wales

78 Allegory of British Empire

OTTAWA CONFERENCE 1932

(79)

1932 (12 July). *Ottawa Conference.* P 11.

(a) Postage stamps.
315   **76**   3c. scarlet 70   80
316   **77**   5c. blue .... 9·50   5·00
317   **78**   13c. green .... 9·50   6·00

(b) Air. No. 310 surch with T **79**.
318   **72**   6c. on 5c. deep brown (B.) .... 10·00   13·00
315/18 *Set of 4* .... 27·00   22·00

80 King George V   "3" level Die I   "3" raised Die II

1932 (1 Dec)–**33**.

(a) P 11.
319   **80**   1c. green 60   10
        a. Booklet pane of 6 (28.12.33) .... 15·00
        b. Booklet pane of 4+2 labels
          (19.9.33) .... 80·00
320   2c. sepia 70   10
        a. Booklet pane of 6 (7.9.33) ...... 15·00
        b. Booklet pane of 4+2 labels
          (19.9.33) .... 80·00
321   3c. scarlet (Die I) .... 1·00   10
        a. Booklet pane of 4+2 labels
          (22.8.33) .... 50·00
        b. Die II (29.11.32) 85   10
        ba. Booklet pane of 4+2 labels
          (19.9.33) .... 35·00
322   4c. yellow-brown .... 35·00   9·00
323   5c. blue .... 10·00   10
        a. Imperf vert (horiz pair) £1200
324   8c. red-orange .... 24·00   4·25
325   **68**   13c. bright violet .... 45·00   2·25
319/25 *Set of 7* .... £100   14·00

Nos. 319/25 exist imperforate (*Prices per unused pair*, 1c. to 8c. £190, 13c. £600).

(b) Imperf×perf 8½ (1933).
326   **80**   1c. green (3.11.33) .... 14·00   3·75
327   2c. sepia (15.8.33) .... 19·00   3·50
328   3c. scarlet (Die II) (16.8.33) .... 12·00   1·50
326/8 *Set of 3* .... 40·00   8·00

81 Parliament Buildings, Ottawa

1933 (18 May). *U.P.U. Congress Preliminary Meeting.* P 11.
329   **81**   5c. blue .... 6·50   3·00

No. 329 exists imperforate (*Price per pair £550, un*).

WORLD'S GRAIN EXHIBITION & CONFERENCE

REGINA 1933

(82)

1933 (24 July). *World's Grain Exhibition and Conference, Regina. No. 301 optd with T* **82** *in blue.*
330   **69**   20c. red .... 16·00   7·00

No. 330 exists imperforate (*Price per pair £550, un*).

83 S.S. *Royal William* (after S. Skillett)   **84** Jacques Cartier approaching Land

1933 (17 Aug). *Centenary of First Trans-Atlantic Steamboat Crossing.* P 11.
331   **83**   5c. blue .... 12·00   3·00

No. 331 exists imperforate (*Price per pair £550, un*).

1934 (1 July). *Fourth Centenary of Discovery of Canada.* P 11.
332   **84**   3c. blue .... 3·25   1·50

No. 332 exists imperforate (*Price per pair £550, un*).

85 U.E.L. Statue, Hamilton   **86** Seal of New Brunswick

1934 (1 July). *150th Anniv of Arrival of United Empire Loyalists.* P 11.
333   **85**   10c. olive-green .... 8·50   5·00

No. 333 exists imperforate (*Price per pair £950, un*).

1934 (16 Aug). *150th Anniv of Province of New Brunswick.* P 11.
334   **86**   2c. red-brown .... 1·50   2·25

No. 334 exists imperforate (*Price per pair £550, un*).

PRINTERS. The following stamps were recess-printed (except where otherwise stated) by the Canadian Bank Note Co, Ottawa, until No. 616.

87 Queen Elizabeth II when Princess   **88** King George VI when Duke of York

89 King George V and Queen Mary   **90** King Edward VIII when Prince of Wales

91 Windsor Castle   **92** Royal Yacht *Britannia*

1935 (4 May). *Silver Jubilee. T* **87/92**. P 12.
335   **87**   1c. green 55   80
336   **88**   2c. brown 60   80
337   **89**   3c. carmine-red .... 1·75   80
338   **90**   5c. blue .... 5·50   7·00
339   **91**   10c. green .... 4·00   5·00
340   **92**   13c. blue .... 6·50   7·00
335/40 *Set of 6* .... 17·00   19·00

Nos. 335/40 exist imperforate (*Price £225, un, for each pair*).

93 King George V   **94** Royal Canadian Mounted Policeman

95 Confederation conference, Charlottetown, 1864   **96** Niagara Falls

97 Parliament Buildings, Victoria, British Columbia   **98** Champlain Monument, Quebec

99 Daedalus

1935 (1 June–5 Nov). *T* **93/99**.

(a) Postage. (i) P 12.
341   **93**   1c. green .... 1·75   10
        a. Booklet pane of 6 (19.8.35) ...... 26·00
        b. Booklet pane of 4+2 labels
          (22.7.35) .... 55·00
342   2c. brown .... 1·75   10
        a. Booklet pane of 6 (16.11.35) .... 26·00
        b. Booklet pane of 4+2 labels
          (22.7.35) .... 55·00
343   3c. scarlet .... 1·75   10
        a. Booklet pane of 6 (16.11.35) .... 30·00
        b. Printed on the gummed side £250
344   4c. yellow .... 3·50   1·75
345   5c. blue .... 3·50   10
        a. Imperf vert (horiz pair) £200
346   8c. orange .... 4·25   3·75
347   **94**   10c. carmine .... 6·50   50
348   **95**   13c. purple .... 7·50   65
349   **96**   20c. olive-green .... 18·00   70
350   **97**   50c. deep violet .... 25·00   4·75
351   **98** $1 bright blue .... 40·00   11·00
341/51 *Set of 11* .... £100   20·00

(ii) Coil stamps. Imperf×perf 8.
352   **93**   1c. green (5.11.35) .... 13·00   7·00
353   2c. brown (14.10.35) .... 9·50   4·50
354   3c. scarlet (20.7.35) .... 9·00   1·75
352/4 *Set of 3* .... 28·00   12·00

(b) Air. P 12.
355   **99**   6c. red-brown .... 3·00   1·00
        a. Imperf vert (horiz pair) £6000

Nos. 341/51 (*Prices per pair*, 1c. to 8c. *each* £140, 10c. *to* 50c. *each* £250, $1 £300, *un*) and 355 (*Price per pair* £500, *un*) exist imperforate.

100 King George VI and Queen Elizabeth

1937 (10 May). *Coronation.* P 12.
356   **100**   3c. carmine .... 1·25   1·00

No. 356 exists imperforate (*Price per pair £600, un*).

101 King George VI   **102** Memorial Chamber, Parliament Buildings, Ottawa

103 Entrance to Halifax Harbour

104 Fort Garry Gate, Winnipeg

105 Entrance, Vancouver Harbour

106 Chateau de Ramezay, Montreal

107 Fairchild 45-80 Sekani Seaplane over *Distributor* on River Mackenzie

(T **101**. Photograph by Bertram Park)

1937–38. T **101/107**.

(a) Postage. (i) P 12.

357	**101**	1c. green (1.4.37)	1·50	10
		a. Booklet pane of 4+2 labels (14.4.37)	28·00	
		b. Booklet pane of 6 (18.5.37)	4·00	
358		2c. brown (1.4.37)	1·75	10
		a. Booklet pane of 4+2 labels (14.4.37)	55·00	
		b. Booklet pane of 6 (3.5.38)	11·00	
359		3c. scarlet (1.4.37)	1·75	10
		a. Booklet pane of 4+2 labels (14.4.37)	4·25	
360		4c. yellow (10.5.37)	4·50	1·75
361		5c. blue (10.5.37)	4·25	10
362		8c. orange (10.5.37)	4·00	2·50
363	**102**	10c. rose-carmine (15.6.38)	5·00	20
		a. Red	5·00	10
364	**103**	13c. blue (15.11.38)	18·00	1·50
365	**104**	20c. red-brown (15.6.38)	22·00	10
366	**105**	50c. green (15.6.38)	48·00	11·00
367	**106**	$1 violet (15.6.38)	60·00	11·00
		a. Imperf horiz (vert pair)	£3500	
357/67 *Set of 11*			£150	26·00

Nos. 357/67 exist imperforate (*Prices per pair* 1c. to 8c. *each* £250, 10c. to 50c. *each* £350, $1 *each* £450 *un*).

(ii) Coil stamps. Imperf×perf 8.

368	**101**	1c. green (15.6.37)	3·50	3·25
369		2c. brown (18.6.37)	3·50	4·00
370		3c. scarlet (15.4.37)	21·00	1·00
368/70 *Set of 3*			25·00	7·50

(b) Air. P 12.

371	**107**	6c. blue (15.6.38)	11·00	1·00

No. 371 exists imperforate (*Price per pair* £500, *un*).

108 Queen Elizabeth II when Princess and Princess Margaret

109 National War Memorial

110 King George VI and Queen Elizabeth

1939 (15 May). *Royal Visit.* P 12.

372	**108**	1c. black and green	1·75	10
373	**109**	2c. black and brown	1·50	90
374	**110**	3c. black and carmine	1·00	10
372/4 *Set of 3*			3·75	1·00

Nos. 372/4 exist imperforate (*Price* £425, *un*, for each pair).

111 King George VI in Naval uniform

112 King George VI in Military uniform

113 King George VI in Air Force uniform

114 Grain Elevator

115 Farm Scene

116 Parliament Buildings

117 Ram Tank

118 Launching of Corvette H.M.C.S. *La Malbaie*, Sorel

119 Munitions factory

120 H.M.S. *Cossack* (destroyer)

121 Air Training Camp

1942 (1 July)–**48**. *War Effort.* T **111/121** and similar designs.

(a) Postage. (i) P 12.

375	**111**	1c. green	1·50	10
		a. Booklet pane of 4+2 labels (12.9.42)	25·00	
		b. Booklet pane of 6 (24.11.42)	2·50	
376	**112**	2c. brown	1·75	10
		a. Booklet pane of 4+2 labels (12.9.42)	30·00	
		b. Booklet pane of 6 (6.10.42)	18·00	
377	**113**	3c. carmine-lake	1·25	60
		a. Booklet pane of 4+2 labels (20.8.42)	4·25	
378		3c. purple (30.6.43)	90	10
		a. Booklet pane of 4+2 labels (28.8.43)	6·00	
		b. Booklet pane of 6 (24.11.47)	13·00	
379	**114**	4c. slate	5·50	1·00
380	**112**	4c. carmine-lake (9.4.43)	70	10
		a. Booklet pane of 6 (3.5.43)	3·50	
381	**111**	5c. blue	3·00	10
382	**115**	8c. red-brown	5·50	75
383	**116**	10c. brown	8·00	10
384	**117**	13c. dull green	7·50	8·00
385		14c. dull green (16.4.43)	19·00	1·00
386	**118**	20c. chocolate	16·00	35
387	**119**	50c. violet	26·00	4·50
388	**120**	$1 blue	42·00	7·00
375/88 *Set of 14*			£130	21·00

Nos. 375/88 exist imperforate (*Prices per pair* 1c. to 8c. *each* £225, 10c. to 20c. *each* £350, 50c. and $1 *each* £425, *un*).

(ii) Coil stamps. Imperf×perf 8.

389	**111**	1c. green (9.2.43)	1·00	1·50
390	**112**	2c. brown (24.11.42)	2·25	2·00
391	**113**	3c. carmine-lake (23.9.42)	2·00	6·00
392		3c. purple (19.8.43)	9·00	9·00
393	**112**	4c. carmine-lake (13.5.43)	6·50	1·50
389/93 *Set of 5*			19·00	14·00

(iii) Booklet stamps. Imperf×perf 12 (1.9.43).

394	**111**	1c. green	3·25	1·25
		a. Booklet pane of 3	9·00	
395	**113**	3c. purple	3·25	1·50
		a. Booklet pane of 3	9·00	
396	**112**	4c. carmine-lake	3·25	1·75
		a. Booklet pane of 3	9·00	
394/6 *Set of 3*			9·00	4·00

Nos. 394/6 are from booklets in which the stamps are in strips of three, imperforate at top and bottom and right-hand end.

(iv) Coil stamps. Imperf×perf 9½.

397	**111**	1c. green (13.7.48)	3·00	4·00
397a	**112**	2c. brown (1.10.48)	7·50	19·00
398	**113**	3c. purple (2.7.48)	4·75	6·00
398a	**112**	4c. carmine-lake (22.7.48)	7·00	3·50
397/8a *Set of 4*			20·00	29·00

(b) Air. P 12.

399	**121**	6c. blue (1.7.42)	24·00	7·50
400		7c. blue (16.4.43)	3·50	10

Nos. 399/400 exist imperforate (*Price* £550, *un*, for each pair).

122 Ontario Farm Scene

123 Great Bear Lake

124 St. Maurice River Power Station

125 Combine harvester

126 Lumbering in British Columbia

127 *Abegweit* (train ferry), Prince Edward Is.

128 Canada geese in flight

129 Alexander Graham Bell and "Fame"

1946 (16 Sept)–47. *Peace Re-conversion.* T **122/128**. P 12.

(a) Postage.

401	**122**	8c. brown	1·25	2·50
402	**123**	10c. olive-green	1·75	10
403	**124**	14c. sepia	4·00	1·75
404	**125**	20c. slate	3·00	10
405	**126**	50c. green	16·00	3·75
406	**127**	$1 purple	25·00	3·75

(b) Air.

407	**128**	7c. blue	4·50	10
		a. Booklet pane of 4 (24.11.47)	9·00	
401/7 *Set of 7*			50·00	11·00

1947 (3 Mar). *Birth Centenary of Bell (inventor of telephone).* P 12.

408	**129**	4c. blue	15	20

130 "Canadian Citizenship"

131 Queen Elizabeth II when Princess

1947 (1 July). *Advent of Canadian Citizenship and Eightieth Anniv of Confederation.* P 12.

409	**130**	4c. blue	10	20

(From photograph by Dorothy Wilding)

1948 (16 Feb). *Princess Elizabeth's Marriage.* P 12.

410	**131**	4c. blue	10	10

132 Queen Victoria, Parliament Building, Ottawa, and King George VI

133 Cabot's Ship *Matthew*

1948 (1 Oct). *One Hundred Years of Responsible Government.* P 12.

411	**132**	4c. grey	10	10

1949 (1 Apr). *Entry of Newfoundland into Canadian Confederation.* P 12.

412	**133**	4c. green	30	10

134 "Founding of Halifax, 1749" (C. W. Jefferys)

1949 (21 June). *Bicentenary of Halifax, Nova Scotia.* P 12.

413	**134**	4c. violet	30	10

135

136

137

138 King George VI

139 King George VI

(From photographs by Dorothy Wilding)

1949 (15 Nov)–**51**.(i) P 12.

414	**135**	1c. green	10	10
415	**136**	2c. sepia	1·25	35
415a		2c. olive-green (25.7.51)	1·25	
416	**137**	3c. purple	30	10
		a. Booklet pane of 4+2 labels (12.4.50)	2·25	
417	**138**	4c. carmine-lake	20	10
		a. Booklet pane of 6 (5.5.50)	27·00	
417b		4c. vermilion (2.6.51)	50	10
		ba. Booklet pane of 6	6·00	
418	**139**	5c. blue	2·00	20
414/18 Set of 7			5·00	50

(ii) Imperf×perf 9½ (coil stamps).

419	**135**	1c. green (18.5.50)	2·25	1·00
420	**136**	2c. sepia (18.5.50)	7·50	6·00
420a		2c. olive-green (9.10.51)	1·75	3·00
421	**137**	3c. purple (18.5.50)	2·25	2·75
422	**138**	4c. carmine-lake (20.4.50)	14·00	9·00
422a		4c. vermilion (27.11.51)	2·75	2·75
419/22a Set of 6			27·00	22·00

(iii) Imperf×perf 12 (booklets).

422b	**135**	1c. green (18.5.50)	50	1·75
		ba. Booklet pane of 3	1·50	
423	**137**	3c. purple (18.5.50)	1·25	1·00
		a. Booklet pane of 3	3·75	
423b	**138**	4c. carmine-lake (18.5.50)	15·00	8·00
		ba. Booklet pane of 3	45·00	
423c		4c. vermilion (25.10.51)	7·50	7·00
		ca. Booklet pane of 3	22·00	
422b/3c Set of 4			22·00	16·00

These booklet panes are imperforate at top, bottom and right-hand end.

140 King George VI

141 Oil Wells in Alberta

(From photograph by Dorothy Wilding)

1950 (19 Jan). As T **135/9** but without "POSTES POSTAGE", as T **140**.

(i) P 12.

424		1c. green	30	65
425		2c. sepia	30	2·50
426		3c. purple	30	65
427		4c. carmine-lake	30	20
428		5c. blue	30	1·25
424/8 Set of 5			1·40	4·75

(ii) Imperf×perf 9½ (coil stamps).

429		1c. green	30	1·00
430		3c. purple	80	1·50

1950 (1 Mar). P 12.

431	**141**	50c. green	6·00	1·00

142 Drying Furs

143 Fisherman

1950 (2 Oct). P 12.

432	**142**	10c. brown-purple	2·75	10

1951 (1 Feb). P 12.

433	**143**	$1 ultramarine	38·00	5·00

144 Sir R. L. Borden

145 W. L. Mackenzie King

1951 (25 June). Prime Ministers (1st issue). P 12.

434	**144**	3c. blue-green	10	50
435	**145**	4c. rose-carmine	10	10

See also Nos. 444/5, 475/6 and 483/4.

146 Mail Trains, 1851 and 1951

147 SS. *City of Toronto* and SS. *Prince George*

148 Mail Coach and DC-4M North Star

149 Reproduction of 3d., 1851

1951 (24 Sept). Canadian Stamp Centenary. P 12.

436	**146**	4c. black	35	10
437	**147**	5c. violet	65	1·75
438	**148**	7c. blue	35	1·00
439	**149**	15c. scarlet	1·40	10
436/9 Set of 4			2·50	2·75

150 Queen Elizabeth II when Princess and Duke of Edinburgh

1951 (26 Oct). Royal Visit. P 12.

440	**150**	4c. violet	10	10

STAMP BOOKLETS

Booklet Nos. SB1/48 are stapled.

All booklets up to and including No. SB41 contain panes consisting of two rows of three (3×2).

B 1

1900 (11 June). Red on pink cover. Two panes of six 2c. (No. 155ba).
SB1   25c. booklet. Cover as Type B **1** with English text   £1800

1903 (1 July). Red on pink cover. Two panes of six 2c. (No. 176a).
SB2   25c. booklet. Cover as Type B **1** with English text   £1900

1912 (Jan)–**16**. Red on pink cover. Two panes of six 2c. (No. 201a).
SB3   25c. booklet. Cover as Type B **1** with English text   60·00
   a. Cover handstamped "NOTICE Change in Postal Rates For New Rates See Postmaster"   60·00
   b. French text (4.16)   £130
   ba. Cover handstamped "AVIS Changement des tarifs Postaux Pour les nouveaux tarifs consulter le maitre de poste"   £100

1913 (1 May)–**16**. Green on pale green cover. Four panes of six 1c. (No. 197a).
SB4   25c. booklet. Cover as Type B **1** with English text   £375
   a. Containing pane No. 199a   65·00
   ab. Cover handstamped "NOTICE Change in Postal Rates For New Rates See Postmaster".   65·00
   b. French text (28.4.16)   £550
   ba. Containing pane No. 199a   £150
   bb. Cover handstamped "AVIS Changement des tarifs Postaux Pour les nouveaux tarifs consulter le maitre de poste"   £450

1922 (Mar). Black on brown cover. Two panes of four 3c. and 2 labels (No. 205a).
SB5   25c. booklet. Cover as Type B **1** with English text   £300
   a. French text   £600

1922 (July–Dec). Black on blue cover. Panes of four 1c., 2c. and 3c. (Nos. 246aa, 247aa, 205a) and 2 labels.
SB6   25c. booklet. Cover as Type B **1** with English text   £300
   a. French text (Dec)   £500

1922 (Dec). Black on orange cover. Four panes of six 1c. (No. 246ab).
SB7   25c. booklet. Cover as Type B **1** with English text   £100
   a. French text   £130

1922 (Dec). Black on green cover. Two panes of six 2c. (No. 247ab).
SB8   25c. booklet. Cover as Type B **1** with English text   £600
   a. French text   £700

1923 (Dec). Black on blue cover. Panes of four 1c., 2c. and 3c. (Nos. 246aa, 247aa, 248aa) and 2 labels.
SB9   25c. booklet. Cover as Type B **1** with English text   £200
   a. French text   £425

1923 (Dec)–**24**. Black on brown cover. Two panes of four 3c. (No. 248aa) and 2 labels.
SB10   25c. booklet. Cover as Type B **1** with English text   £180
   a. French text (5.24)   £275

B 2

1928 (16 Oct). Black on green cover. Two panes of six 2c. (No. 276a).
SB11   25c. booklet. Cover as Type B **2** with English text   55·00
   a. French text   85·00

1928 (25 Oct). Black on orange cover. Four panes of six 1c. (No. 275a).
SB12   25c. booklet. Cover as Type B **2** with English text   £100
   a. French text   £190

1929 (6 Jan). Plain manilla cover. Three panes of six 1c., two panes of six 2c. and one pane of six 5c. (Nos. 275a, 276a, 279a).
SB13   72c. booklet. Plain cover   £300
   a. With "Philatelic Div., Fin. Br. P.O. Dept., Ottawa" circular cachet on front cover   £800
   b. With "1928" in the centre of the circular cachet   £1200

1930 (17 June). Black on green cover. Two panes of six 2c. (No. 290a).
SB14   25c. booklet. Cover as Type B **2** with English text   80·00
   a. French text   £130

1930 (17 Nov). Black on red cover. Two panes of six 2c. (No. 291a).
SB15   25c. booklet. Cover as Type B **2** with English text   55·00
   a. French text   £110

1931 (13 July). Black on red cover. Two panes of four 3c. (No. 293a) and 2 labels.
SB16   25c. booklet. Cover as Type B **2** with English text   80·00
   a. French text   £110

1931 (21 July). Black on green cover. Four panes of six 1c. (No. 289b).
SB17   25c. booklet. Cover as Type B **2** with English text   £120
   a. French text   £160

1931 (23 July). Black on brown cover. Two panes of six 2c. (No. 292a).
SB18   25c. booklet. Cover as Type B **2** with English text   90·00
   a. French text   £275

1931 (13 Nov). Black on blue cover. Panes of four 1c., 2c. and 3c. (Nos. 289db, 292ba, 293a) and 2 labels.
SB19   25c. booklet. Cover as Type B **2** with English text   £250
   a. French text   £350

1933 (22 Aug–13 Nov). Black on red cover. Two panes of four 3c. (No. 321a) and 2 labels.
SB20   25c. booklet. Cover as Type B **2** with English text (13 Nov)   85·00
   a. French text (22 Aug)   £160

1933 (7 Sept). Black on brown cover. Two panes of six 2c. (No. 320a).
SB21   25c. booklet. Cover as Type B **2** with English text   £150
   a. French text   £300

1933 (19 Sept–5 Dec). Black on blue cover. Panes of four 1c., 2c. and 3c. (Nos. 319b, 320b, 321ba) and 2 labels.
SB22   25c. booklet. Cover as Type B **2** with English text   £200
   a. French text (5 Dec)   £300

1933 (28 Dec)–**34**. Black on green cover. Four panes of six 1c. (No. 319a).
SB23   25c. booklet. Cover as Type B **2** with English text   £100
   a. French text (26.3.34)   £150

B 3

1935 (1 June–8 Aug). Red on white cover. Two panes of four 3c. (No. 343a) and 2 labels.
SB24   25c. booklet. Cover as Type B **3** with English text (8 Aug)   60·00
   a. French text (1 June)   95·00

1935 (22 July–1 Sept). Blue on white cover. Panes of four 1c., 2c. and 3c. (Nos. 341b, 342b, 343a) and 2 labels.
SB25   25c. booklet. Cover as Type B **3** with English text   £140
   a. French text (1 Sept)   £180

1935 (19 Aug–18 Oct). Green on white cover. Four panes of six 1c. (No. 341a).
SB26   25c. booklet. Cover as Type B **3** with English text   90·00
   a. French text (18 Oct)   £130

1935 (16–18 Mar). Brown on white cover. Two panes of six 2c. (No. 342a).
SB27   25c. booklet. Cover as Type B **3** with English text   70·00
   a. French text (18 Mar)   £120

B 4

1937 (14 Apr)–**38**. *Blue and white cover. Panes of four 1c., 2c. and 3c. (Nos. 357a, 358a, 359a) and 2 labels.*
SB28   25c. booklet. Cover as Type B **3** with English text   85·00   £130
    a. French text (4.1.38)
SB29   25c. booklet. Cover as Type B **4** with English text
    57 mm wide ....   70·00
    a. English text 63 mm wide £110
    b. French text 57 mm wide (4.1.38)......   90·00
    ba. French text 63 mm wide £170

1937 (23–27 Apr). *Red and white cover. Two panes of four 3c. (No. 359a) and 2 labels.*
SB30   25c. booklet. Cover as Type B **3** with English text
    (27 Apr) ....   24·00
    a. French text (23 Apr) ....   50·00
SB31   25c. booklet. Cover as Type B **4** with English text
    (27 Apr) ....   10·00
    a. English text 63 mm wide ....   48·00
    b. French text 57 mm wide (23 Apr)......   13·00
    ba. French text 63 mm wide £170

1937 (18 May)–**38**. *Green and white cover. Four panes of six 1c. (No. 357b).*
SB32   25c. booklet. Cover as Type B **3** with English text   40·00
    a. French text (14.10.38) ....   60·00
SB33   25c. booklet. Cover as Type B **4** with English text
    57 mm wide ....   22·00
    a. English text 63 mm wide ....   60·00
    b. French text 57 mm wide (14.10.38)...   18·00
    ba. French text 63 mm wide £150

1938 (3 May)–**39**. *Brown and white cover. Two panes of six 2c. (No. 358b).*
SB34   25c. booklet. Cover as Type B **3** with English text   55·00
    a. French text (3.3.39) ....   75·00
SB35   25c. booklet. Cover as Type B **4** with English text
    57 mm wide ....   23·00
    a. English text 63 mm wide ....   70·00
    b. French text 57 mm wide ....   42·00
    ba. French text 63 mm wide £100

1942 (20–29 Aug). *Red and white cover. Two panes of four 3c. (No. 377a) and 2 labels.*
SB36   25c. booklet. Cover as Type B **4** with English text   8·50
    a. French text (29 Aug) ....   12·00

1942 (12–14 Sept). *Violet and white cover. Panes of four 1c., 2c. and 3c. (Nos. 375a, 376a, 377a), each with 2 labels.*
SB37   25c. booklet. Cover as Type B **4** with English text
    (14 Sept) ....   48·00
    a. French text (12 Sept) ....   90·00

1942 (6 Oct)–**43**. *Brown and white cover. Two panes of six 2c. (No. 376b).*
SB38   25c. booklet. Cover as Type B **4** with English text   48·00
    a. French text (6.4.43) ....   70·00

1942 (24 Nov)–**46**. *Green and white cover. Four panes of six 1c. (No. 375b).*
SB39   25c. booklet. Cover as Type B **4** with English text   11·00
    a. French text (16.2.43) ....   17·00
    b. Bilingual text (8.1.46) ....   25·00

1943 (3 May)–**46**. *Orange and white cover. One pane of six 4c. (No. 380a).*
SB40   25c. booklet. Cover as Type B **4** with English text   4·00
    a. French text (12.5.43) ....   15·00
    b. Bilingual text (8.1.46) ....   18·00

1943 (28 Aug)–**46**. *Purple and white cover. Two panes of four 3c. (No. 378a) and 2 labels.*
SB41   25c. booklet. Cover as Type B **4** with English text   10·00
    a. French text (7.9.43) ....   28·00
    b. Bilingual text (8.1.46) ....   22·00

B 5

1943 (1 Sept)–**46**. *Black and white cover. Panes of three 1c., 3c. and 4c. (Nos. 394a, 395a, 396a) (3×1).*
SB42   25c. booklet. Cover as Type B **5** with English text   30·00
    a. French text (18.9.43) ....   40·00
    c. Bilingual text (23.1.46) ....   38·00

B 6

1947 (24 Nov). *Brown on orange cover. Panes of six 3c. and 4c. (3×2) and two panes of four 7c. (2×2) (Nos. 378b, 380a, 407a).*
SB43 $1 booklet. Cover as Type B **6** with English text   25·00
    a. French text ....   40·00

1950 (12 Apr–18 May). *Purple and white cover. Two panes of four 3c. (No. 416a) and 2 labels (3×2).*
SB44   25c. booklet. Cover as Type B **4** with English text   5·00
    a. Bilingual text (18 May) ....   5·00

1950 (5–10 May). *Orange and white cover. One pane of six 4c. (No. 417a) (3×2).*
SB45   25c. booklet, Cover as Type B **4** with English text   35·00
    a. Stitched ....   60·00
    b. Bilingual text (10 May) ....   40·00

1950 (18 May). *Black and white cover. Panes of three 1c., 3c. and 4c. (Nos. 422ba, 423a, 423ba) (3×1).*
SB46   25c. booklet. Cover as Type B **5** with English text   50·00
    a. Bilingual text ....   55·00

1951 (2 June). *Orange and white cover. One pane of six 4c. (No. 417ba) (3×2).*
SB47   25c. booklet. Cover as Type B **4** with English text   6·00
    a. Stitched ....   12·00
    b. Bilingual text ....   12·00

1951 (25 Oct)–**52**. *Black and white cover. Panes of three 1c., 3c. and 4c. (Nos. 422ba, 423a, 423ca) (3×1).*
SB48   25c. booklet. Cover as Type B **5** with English text   32·00
    a. Bilingual text (9.7.52) ....   38·00

REGISTRATION STAMPS

R 1

(Eng and recess-printed British-American Bank Note Co, Montreal and Ottawa)

1875 (15 Nov)–**92**. *White wove paper.*

    (a) P 12 (or slightly under).
R1   R **1**   2c. orange ....   60·00   1·00
R2   2c. orange-red (1889) ....   70·00   6·00
R3   2c. vermilion ....   75·00   7·50
    a. Imperf (pair) ....   †   £3000
R4   2c. rose-carmine (1888) ....   £150   55·00
R5   5c. yellow-green (1878) ....   £110   1·50
R6   5c. deep green ....   85·00   1·25
    a. Imperf (pair) £650
R7   5c. blue-green (1888) ....   90·00   1·50
R7a   5c. dull sea-green (1892) ....   £130   3·25
R8   8c. bright blue £325   £225
R9   8c. dull blue £300   £200

    (b) P 12×11½ or 12×11¾.
R10   R **1**   2c. orange ....   £300   60·00
R11   5c. green (shades) £800   £150

SPECIAL DELIVERY STAMPS

PRINTERS. The following Special Delivery and Postage Due Stamps were recess-printed by the American Bank Note Co (to 1928), the British American Bank Note Co (to 1934), and the Canadian Bank Note Co (1935 onwards).

S 1

1898–1920. P 12.
S1   S **1**   10c. blue-green (28.6.98) ....   80·00   9·00
S2   10c. deep green (12.13) ....   50·00   8·00
S3   10c. yellowish green (8.20) ....   60·00   8·00

The differences between Types I and II (figures "10" with and without shading) formerly illustrated were due to wear of the plate. There was only one die.

S 2

S 3 Mail-carrying, 1867 and 1927

1922 (21 Aug). P 12.
S4   S **2**   20c. carmine-red ....   35·00   6·50

No. S4 exists in two slightly different sizes due to the use of "wet" or "dry" printing processes. See note below No. 195.

1927 (29 June). *60th Anniversary of Confederation.* P 12.
S5   S **3**   20c. orange ....   11·00   10·00

No. S5 exists imperforate, imperf×perf or perf×imperf (*Price, in each instance, £150 per pair, un*).

S 4

1930 (2 Sept). P 11.
S6   S **4**   20c. brown-red ....   42·00   7·00

1932 (24 Dec). *Type as S* **4**, *but inscr* "CENTS" *in place of* "TWENTY CENTS". P 11.
S7   20c. brown-red ....   45·00   15·00

No. S7 exists imperforate (*Price per pair £450, un*).

S 5 Allegory of Progress

(Des A. Foringer)

1935 (1 June). P 12.
S8   S **5**   20c. scarlet ....   3·50   3·00

No. S8 exists imperforate (*Price per pair £500, un*).

S 6 Canadian Coat of Arms

1938–39. P 12.
S9   S **6**   10c. green (1.4.39) ....   21·00   4·00
S10   20c. scarlet (15.6.38) ....   40·00   28·00

Nos. S9/10 exist imperforate (*Price £500, un, for each pair*).

(S **7**)

1939 (1 Mar). *Surch with Type S* **7**.
S11   S **6**   10c. on 20c. scarlet ....   10·00   12·00

S 8 Coat of Arms and Flags

S 9 Lockheed L.18 Lodestar

1942 (1 July)–**43**. *War Effort.* P 12.

    (a) Postage.
S12   S **8**   10c. green ....   7·50   30

    (b) Air.
S13   S **9**   16c. ultramarine ....   6·00   45
S14   17c. ultramarine (1.4.43) ....   4·50   55

Nos. S12/14 exist imperforate (*Prices per un pair* 10c. £500, 16c. £550, 17c. £550).

S 10 Arms of Canada and Peace Symbols

S 11 Canadair DC-4M North Star

1946 (16 Sept–5 Dec). P 12.

(a) Postage.

S15 S 10 10c. green .... 3·75 30

(b) Air. (i) Circumflex accent in "EXPRÊS".

S16 S 11 17c. ultramarine .... 4·50 5·50

(ii) Grave accent in "EXPRÈS".

S17 S 11 17c. ultramarine (5.12.46) .... 6·50 5·50

POSTAGE DUE STAMPS

PRINTERS. See note under "Special Delivery Stamps".

D 1   D 2

1906 (1 July)–28. P 12.

D1 D 1 1c. dull violet.............................. 10·00 2·75
D2 1c. red-violet (1916)..................... 11·00 3·75
  a. Thin paper (10.24) .... 15·00 20·00
D3 dull violet............................... 22·00 1·00
D4 2c. red-violet (1917)..................... 23·00 1·25
  a. Thin paper (10.24) .... 30·00 20·00
D5 4c. violet (3.7.28)....................... 45·00 50·00
D6 5c. dull violet............................. 28·00 3·75
D7 5c. red-violet (1917)..................... 28·00 3·75
  a. Thin paper (10.24) .... 19·00 30·00
D8 10c. violet (3.7.28)....................... 32·00 20·00
D1/8 Set of 5................................ £110 70·00

The 1c., 2c. and 5c. values exist imperforate without gum (*Price £325 for each un pair*).

Printings up to October 1924 used the "wet" method, those from mid 1925 onwards the "dry". For details of the differences between these two methods, see above No. 196.

1930–32. P 11.

D9 D 2 1c. bright violet (14.7.30)............. 8·50 11·00
D10 2c. bright violet (21.8.30)............. 7·50 1·90
D11 4c. bright violet (14.10.30)........... 15·00 6·50
D12 5c. bright violet (12.12.31)........... 16·00 30·00
D13 10c. bright violet (24.8.32)........... 65·00 29·00
D9/13 Set of 5................................ £100 70·00

Nos. D9/11 and D13 exist imperforate, No. D13 also exists imperf×perf (*Price for vertical pair £700, un*).

D 3   D 4

1933–34. P 11.

D14 D 3 1c. violet (5.5.34)...................... 9·50 14·00
D15 2c. violet (20.12.33)................... 7·50 4·50
D16 4c. violet (12.12.33)................... 12·00 15·00
D17 10c. violet (20.12.33)................... 24·00 35·00
D14/17 Set of 4................................ 48·00 60·00

No. D14 exists imperforate (*Price per pair £350, un*).

1935–65. P 12.

D18 D 4 1c. violet (14.10.35).................... 80 10
D19 2c. violet (9.9.35)...................... 2·75 10
D20 3c. violet (4.65)........................ 6·00 5·00
D21 4c. violet (2.7.35)...................... 1·50 10
D22 5c. violet (12.48)....................... 4·50 2·75
D23 6c. violet (1957)........................ 2·00 10
D24 10c. violet (16.9.35)..................... 70 10
D18/24 Set of 7................................ 16·00 10·00

The 1c., 2c., 4c. and 10c. exist imperforate (*Price £180 for each un pair*).

OFFICIAL STAMPS

Stamps perforated "O H M S" were introduced in May 1923 for use by the Receiver General's department in Ottawa and by the Assistant Receiver Generals' offices in provincial cities. From 1 July 1939 this use was extended to all departments of the federal government and such stamps continued to be produced until replaced by the "O.H.M.S." overprinted issue of 1949.

The perforated initials can appear either upright, inverted or sideways on individual stamps. The prices quoted are for the cheapest version.

Stamps perforated with Type O 1 are only priced used. Only isolated examples are known mint and these are very rare.

A number of forged examples of the perforated "O.H.M.S." are known, in particular of Type O 1. Many of these forged perforated initials were applied to stamps which had already been used and this can aid their detection. Genuine examples, postmarked after the perforated initials were applied, often show the cancellation ink bleeding into the holes.

(O 1) (Five holes in vertical bars of "H")   (O 2) (Four holes in vertical bars of "H")

1923 (May). Nos. 196/215 punctured as Type O 1.

O1 44 1c. yellow-green .... — 22·00
O2 2c. carmine .... — 20·00
O3 3c. brown .... — 18·00
O4 5c. deep blue .... — 22·00

O5 7c. yellow-ochre .... — 35·00
O6 10c. reddish purple .... — 35·00
O7 20c. olive .... — 22·00
O8 50c. sepia .... — 38·00
O1/8 Set of 8 .... £190

1923 (May). 50th Anniv of Confederation. No. 244 punctured as Type O 1.

O9 48 3c. bistre-brown .... — £120

1923 (May)–31. Nos. 246/55 and 263 punctured as Type O 1.

(a) P 12.

O10 44 1c. chrome-yellow (Die I) .... — 20·00
  a. Die II (1925) .... — 20·00
O11 2c. deep green .... — 15·00
O12 3c. carmine (Die I) (12.23) .... — 15·00
  a. Die II (1924) .... — 18·00
O13 4c. olive-yellow .... — 20·00
O14 5c. violet .... — 20·00
  a. Thin paper (1924) .... — 22·00
O15 7c. red-brown (1924) .... — 27·00
O16 8c. blue (1925) .... — 32·00
O17 10c. blue .... — 22·00
O18 10c. bistre-brown (1925) .... — 15·00
O19 $1 brown-orange (7.23) .... — 55·00
O10/19 Set of 10 .... £200

(b) P 12×8.

O20 44 3c. carmine (Die II) (1931) .... — 45·00

1927 (29 June). 60th Anniv of Confederation. Nos. 266/73 punctured as Type O 1.

(a) Commemorative issue.

O21 51 1c. orange .... — 20·00
O22 52 2c. green .... — 27·00
O23 53 3c. carmine .... — 35·00
O24 54 5c. violet .... — 24·00
O25 55 12c. blue .... — £150
O21/5 Set of 5 .... £225

(b) Historical issue.

O26 56 5c. green .... — 20·00
O27 57 12c. green .... — £120
O28 58 20c. carmine .... — 70·00
O26/8 Set of 3 .... £190

1928 (21 Sept). Air. No. 274 punctured as Type O 1.

O29 59 5c. olive-brown .... — 95·00

1928–29. Nos. 275/85 punctured as Type O 1.

O30 60 1c. orange .... — 25·00
O31 2c. green .... — 17·00
O32 3c. lake .... — 40·00
O33 4c. olive-bistre .... — 50·00
O34 5c. violet .... — 18·00
O35 8c. blue .... — 48·00
O36 61 10c. green .... — 15·00
O37 62 12c. grey-black .... — £150
O38 63 20c. lake .... — 42·00
O39 64 50c. blue .... — £200
O40 65 $1 olive-green .... — £150
O30/40 Set of 11 .... £650

1930–31. Nos. 288/97 and 300/5 punctured as Type O 1.

O41 66 1c. orange (Die I) .... — 25·00
O42 1c. orange (Die I) .... — 15·00
  a. Die II .... — 13·00
O43 2c. green (Die I) .... — 42·00
O44 2c. scarlet (Die I) .... — 20·00
  a. Die II .... — 18·00
O45 2c. deep brown (Die I) .... — 22·00
  a. Die II .... — 20·00
O46 3c. scarlet .... — 15·00
O47 4c. yellow-bistre .... — 45·00
O48 5c. violet .... — 30·00
O49 5c. deep slate-blue .... — 25·00
O50 8c. blue .... — 55·00
O51 8c. red-orange .... — 40·00
O52 67 10c. olive-green .... — 20·00
O53 68 12c. grey-black .... — 85·00
O54 69 20c. red .... — 42·00
O55 70 50c. blue .... — 60·00
O56 71 $1 olive-green .... — £140
O41/56 Set of 15 .... £600

1930 (4 Dec). Air. No. 310 punctured as Type O 1.

O57 72 5c. deep brown .... — £150

1931 (30 Sept). No. 312 punctured as Type O 1.

O58 73 10c. olive-green .... — 20·00

1932 (22 Feb). Air. No. 313 punctured as Type O 1.

O59 59 6c. on 5c. olive-brown .... — £100

1932 (21 June). Nos. 314/a punctured as Type O 1.

O60 66 3c. on 2c. scarlet (Die I) .... — 30·00
  a. Die II .... — 25·00

1932 (12 July). Ottawa Conference. Nos. 315/18 punctured as Type O 1.

(a) Postage.

O61 76 3c. scarlet .... — 17·00
O62 77 5c. blue .... — 27·00
O63 78 13c. green .... — £170

(b) Air.

O64 72 6c. on 5c. deep brown .... — £130
O61/4 Set of 4 .... £300

1932–33. Nos. 319/25 punctured as Type O 1.

O65 80 1c. green .... — 15·00
O66 2c. sepia .... — 15·00
O67 3c. scarlet .... — 15·00
O68 4c. yellow-brown .... — 45·00
O69 5c. blue .... — 22·00
O70 8c. red-orange .... — 45·00
O71 68 13c. bright violet .... — 45·00
O65/71 Set of 7 .... — £180

1933 (18 May). U.P.U. Congress Preliminary Meeting. No. 329 punctured as Type O 1.

O72 81 5c. blue .... — 42·00

1933 (24 July). World's Grain Exhibition and Conference, Regina. No. 330 punctured as Type O 1.

O73 69 20c. red .... — 48·00

1933 (17 Aug). Centenary of First Trans-Atlantic Steamboat Crossing. No. 331 punctured as Type O 1.

O74 83 5c. blue .... — 42·00

1934 (1 July). Fourth Centenary of Discovery of Canada. No. 332 punctured as Type O 1.

O75 84 3c. blue .... — 48·00

1934 (1 July). 150th Anniv of Arrival of United Empire Loyalists. No. 333 punctured as Type O 1.

O76 85 10c. olive-green .... — 50·00

1934 (16 Aug). 150th Anniv of Province of New Brunswick. No. 334 punctured as Type O 1.

O77 86 2c. red-brown .... — 60·00

1935 (4 May). Silver Jubilee. Nos. 335/40 punctured as Type O 1.

O78 87 1c. green .... — 27·00
O79 88 2c. brown .... — 35·00
O80 89 3c. carmine-red .... — 45·00
O81 90 5c. blue .... — 42·00
O82 91 10c. green .... — £110
O83 92 13c. blue .... — £110
O78/83 Set of 6 .... £325

1935. Nos. 341/51 and 355 punctured as Type O 1.

(a) Postage.

O84 93 1c. green .... — 17·00
O85 2c. brown .... — 30·00
O86 3c. scarlet .... — 48·00
O87 4c. yellow .... — 48·00
O88 5c. blue .... — 27·00
O89 8c. orange .... — 48·00
O90 94 10c. carmine .... — 38·00
O91 95 13c. purple .... — 48·00
O92 96 20c. olive-green .... — 50·00
O93 97 50c. deep violet .... — 35·00
O94 98 $1 bright blue .... — £100

(b) Air.

O95 99 6c. red-brown .... — 80·00
O84/95 Set of 12 .... £500

1937 (10 May). Coronation. No. 356 punctured as Type O 1.

O96 100 3c. carmine .... — 42·00

1937–38. Nos. 357/67, 370 and 371 punctured as Type O 1.

(a) Postage.

O97 101 1c. green .... — 2·50
O98 2c. brown .... — 2·75
O99 3c. scarlet .... — 2·50
O100 4c. yellow .... — 9·00
O101 5c. blue .... — 6·50
O102 8c. orange .... — 15·00
O103 102 10c. rose-carmine .... — 20·00
  a. Red .... — 23·00
O104 103 13c. blue .... — 28·00
O105 104 20c. red-brown .... — 28·00
O106 105 50c. green .... — 65·00
O107 106 $1 violet .... — 95·00
O97/107 Set of 11 .... £250

(b) Coil stamp.

O108 101 3c. scarlet .... — 65·00

(c) Air.

O109 107 6c. blue .... — 30·00

1939 (15 May). Royal Visit. Nos. 372/4 punctured as Type O 1.

O110 108 1c. black and green .... — 42·00
O111 109 2c. black and brown .... — 50·00
O112 110 3c. black and carmine .... — 42·00
O110/12 Set of 3 .... £120

1939 (1 July). Air. No. 274 punctured as Type O 2.

O113 59 5c. olive-brown .... 22·00 15·00

1939 (1 July). Nos. 347/50 and 355 punctured as Type O 2.

(a) Postage.

O114 94 10c. carmine........................ 55·00 38·00
O115 95 13c. purple......................... 65·00 38·00
O116 96 20c. olive-green.................... 85·00 48·00
O117 97 50c. deep violet.................... 65·00 38·00

(b) Air.

O118 99 6c. red-brown...................... 50·00 42·00
O114/18 Set of 5 .... £275 £180

1939 (1 July). Coronation. No. 356 punctured as Type O 2.

O119 100 3c. carmine........................ 75·00 45·00

1939 (1 July). Nos. 357/67, 369/70 and 371 punctured as Type O 2.

(a) Postage.

O120 101 1c. green.......................... 1·50 10
O121 2c. brown.......................... 2·25 10
O122 3c. scarlet........................ 2·50 10
O123 4c. yellow......................... 5·00 2·25
O124 5c. blue........................... 3·50 30
O125 8c. orange......................... 13·00 4·25
O126 102 10c. rose-carmine................. 60·00 3·25
  a. Red............................ 9·50 30
O127 103 13c. blue.......................... 16·00 1·50
O128 104 20c. red-brown.................... 38·00 2·00
O129 105 50c. green......................... 55·00 8·00
O130 106 $1 violet........................ £120 30·00
O120/30 Set of 11 .... £225 42·00

(b) Coil stamps.

O131	**101**	2c. brown	75·00	48·00
O132		3c. scarlet	75·00	48·00

(c) Air.

O133	**107**	6c. blue	3·00	80

1939 (1 July). *Royal Visit. Nos. 372/4 punctured as Type* O **2**.

O134	**108**	1c. black and green	90·00	38·00
O135	**109**	2c. black and brown	90·00	38·00
O136	**110**	3c. black and carmine	90·00	38·00
O134/6 *Set of 3*			£250	£100

1942–43. *War Effort. Nos. 375/88 and 399/400 punctured as Type* O **2**.

(a) Postage.

O137	**111**	1c. green	50	10
O138	**112**	2c. brown	50	10
O139	**113**	3c. carmine-lake	1·40	50
O140		3c. purple	75	10
O141	**114**	4c. slate	4·50	1·00
O142	**112**	4c. carmine-lake	55	10
O143	**111**	5c. blue	1·25	20
O144	–	8c. red-brown	7·50	2·00
O145	**116**	10c. brown	4·50	20
O146	**117**	13c. dull green	8·50	7·00
O147		14c. dull green	9·50	85
O148	**118**	20c. chocolate	15·00	70
O149	**119**	50c. violet	38·00	5·50
O150	**120**	$1 blue	90·00	25·00

(b) Air.

O151	**121**	6c. blue	4·00	2·75
O152		7c. blue	3·50	25
O137/52 *Set of 16*			£160	40·00

1946. *Peace Re-conversion. Nos. 401/7 punctured as Type* O **2**.

(a) Postage.

O153	**122**	8c. brown	18·00	4·00
O154	**123**	10c. olive-green	3·25	15
O155	**124**	14c. sepia	6·00	1·00
O156	**125**	20c. slate	7·00	50
O157	**126**	50c. green	28·00	6·00
O158	**127**	$1 purple	60·00	15·00

(b) Air.

O159	**128**	7c. blue	3·00	70
O153/9 *Set of 7*			£110	24·00

1949. *Nos. 415 and 416 punctured as Type* O **2**.

O160	**136**	2c. sepia	1·75	1·75
O161	**137**	3c. purple	1·75	1·75

O.H.M.S.

(O **3**)

1949. *Nos. 375/6, 378, 380 and 402/7 optd as Type* O **3** *by typography.*

(a) Postage.

O162	**111**	1c. green	2·75	3·00
		a. Missing stop after "S"	£180	60·00
O163	**112**	2c. brown	12·00	12·00
		a. Missing stop after "S"	£160	90·00
O164	**113**	3c. purple	1·75	2·50
O165	**112**	4c. carmine-lake	2·75	2·25
O166	**123**	10c. olive-green	4·25	15
		a. Missing stop after "S"	90·00	38·00
O167	**124**	14c. sepia	5·00	3·75
		a. Missing stop after "S"	£120	60·00
O168	**125**	20c. slate	12·00	60
		a. Missing stop after "S"	£170	55·00
O169	**126**	50c. green	£160	£120
		a. Missing stop after "S"	£950	£600
O170	**127**	$1 purple	45·00	48·00
		a. Missing stop after "S"	£2000	

(b) Air.

O171	**128**	7c. blue	24·00	7·00
		a. Missing stop after "S"	£140	70·00
O162/71 *Set of 10*			£225	£140

Forgeries exist of this overprint. Genuine examples are 2.3×15 mm and show the tops of all letters aligned, as are the stops.

Only a few sheets of the $1 showed the variety, No. O170a.

MISSING STOP VARIETIES. These occur on R. 6/2 of the lower left pane (Nos. O162a, O163a and O176a) or R. 10/2 of the lower left pane (O166a, O167a, O168a, O169a, O170a and O171a). No. O176a also occurs on R. 8/8 of the upper left pane in addition to R. 6/2 of the lower left pane.

1949–50. *Nos. 414/15, 416/17, 418 and 431 optd as Type* O **3** *by typography.*

O172	**135**	1c. green	2·50	1·00
O173	**136**	2c. sepia	3·50	1·50
O174	**137**	3c. purple	2·75	1·00
O175	**138**	4c. carmine-lake	2·75	15
O176	**139**	5c. blue (1949)	5·00	2·00
		a. Missing stop after "S"	85·00	40·00
O177	**141**	50c. green (1950)	32·00	28·00
O172/7 *Set of 6*			45·00	30·00

G   G

(O **4**)   (O **5**)

Variations in thickness are known in Type O **4** these are due to wear and subsequent cleaning of the plate. All are produced by typography. Examples showing the "G" applied by lithography are forgeries.

1950 (2 Oct)–**52.** *Nos. 402/4, 406/7, 414/18 and 431 optd with Type* O **4** *(1 to 5c.) or* O **5** *(7c. to $1).*

(a) Postage.

O178	**135**	1c. green	1·50	10
O179	**136**	2c. sepia	3·00	3·50
O180		2c. olive-green (11.51)	1·75	10
O181	**137**	3c. purple	2·25	10

O182	**138**	4c. carmine-lake	2·50	1·00
O183		4c. vermilion (1.5.52)	3·00	60
O184	**139**	5c. blue	3·50	1·50
O185	**123**	10c. olive-green	3·00	10
O186	**124**	14c. sepia	17·00	7·00
O187	**125**	20c. slate	29·00	30
O188	**141**	50c. green	15·00	16·00
O189	**127**	$1 purple	75·00	75·00

(b) Air.

O190	–	7c. blue	24·00	15·00
O178/90 *Set of 13*			£160	£110

1950–51. *Nos. 432/3 optd with Type* O **5**.

O191	**142**	10c. brown-purple	4·00	20
		a. Opt omitted in pair with normal	£500	£400
O192	**143**	$1 ultramarine (1.2.51)	65·00	75·00

On a small number of sheets of 10c. the opt was omitted from R7/1.

OFFICIAL SPECIAL DELIVERY STAMPS

1923 (May). *Nos. S3/4 punctured as Type* O **1**.

OS1	S **1**	10c. yellowish green	—	£110
OS2	S **2**	20c. carmine-red		85·00

1927 (29 June). *60th Anniv of Confederation. No. S5 punctured as Type* O **1**.

OS3	S **3**	20c. orange	—	85·00

1930 (2 Sept). *Inscr "TWENTY CENTS" at foot. No. S6 punctured as Type* O **1**.

OS4	S **4**	20c. brown-red		70·00

1932 (24 Dec). *Inscr "CENTS" at foot. No. S7 punctured as Type* O **1**.

OS5	S **4**	20c. brown-red		70·00

1935 (1 June). *No. S8 punctured as Type* O **1**.

OS6	S **5**	20c. scarlet		70·00

1938–39. *Nos. S9/10 punctured as Type* O **1**.

OS7	S **6**	10c. green		45·00
OS8		20c. scarlet		70·00

1939 (1 Mar). *No. S11 punctured as Type* O **1**.

OS9	S **6**	10c. on 20c. scarlet		70·00

1939 (1 July). *Inscr "CENTS" at foot. No. S7 punctured as Type* O **2**.

OS10	S **4**	20c. brown-red	£180	90·00

1939 (1 July). *No. S8 punctured as Type* O **2**.

OS11	S **5**	20c. scarlet	95·00	45·00

1939 (1 July). *No. S9 punctured as Type* O **2**.

OS12	S **6**	10c. green	7·00	6·00

1939 (1 July). *No. S11 punctured as Type* O **2**.

OS13	S **6**	10c. on 20c. scarlet	£120	60·00

1942–43. *Nos. S12/14 punctured as Type* O **2**.

(a) Postage.

OS14	S **8**	10c. green	9·00	7·50

(b) Air.

OS15	S **9**	16c. ultramarine	17·00	15·00
OS16		17c. ultramarine	11·00	8·50

1946–47. *Nos. S15/17 punctured as Type* O **2**.

(a) Postage.

OS17	S **10**	10c. green	7·00	4·75

(b) Air.

OS18	S **11**	17c. ultramarine (circumflex accent)	38·00	24·00
OS19		17c. ultramarine (grave accent)	65·00	65·00

1950. *No. S15 optd as Type* O **3**, *but larger.*

OS20	S **10**	10c. green	17·00	25·00

1950 (2 Oct). *No. S15 optd as Type* O **4**, *but larger.*

OS21	S **10**	10c. green	26·00	30·00

The use of official stamps was discontinued on 31 December 1963.

Cape of Good Hope
see South Africa

Cayman Islands

The first post office was opened at Georgetown in April 1889. The stamps of Jamaica with the following cancellations were used until 19 February 1901. At some stage, probably around 1891, a supply of the Jamaica 1889 1d., No. 27, was overprinted "CAYMAN ISLANDS", but these stamps were never issued. Two surviving examples are known, one unused and the other cancelled at Richmond in Jamaica.

Types of Jamaica

2	3	4
8	11	13

PRICES OF NOS. Z1/27. These are for a single stamp showing a clear impression of the postmark. Nos. Z1, 2, 6/8, 11/13, 18, 22, Z25 and Z26 are known used on cover and these are worth considerably more.

GEORGETOWN, GRAND CAYMAN

Z **1**

Z **2**   Z **3**

Stamps of JAMAICA *cancelled with Type* Z **1** *in purple.*

1889–94.

Z1	**8**	½d. yellow-green (No. 16)	£500
Z2	**11**	1d. purple and mauve (No. 27)	£500
Z2a	**2**	2d. slate (No. 20a)	£4750
Z3	**11**	2d. green (No. 28)	£900
Z4		2½d. dull purple and blue (No. 29)	£1100
Z5	**4**	4d. red-orange (No. 22)	£2750

Stamps of JAMAICA *cancelled with Type* Z **2** *in purple or black.*

1895–98.

Z6	**8**	½d. yellow-green (No. 16)	£600
Z7	**11**	1d. purple and mauve (No. 27)	£475
Z8		2½d. dull purple and blue (No. 29)	£800
Z9	**3**	3d. sage-green (No 21)	£3750

Stamps of JAMAICA *cancelled with Type* Z **3**

1898–1901.

Z10	**8**	½d. yellow-green (No. 16)	£475
		a. Green (No. 16a)	£475
Z11	**11**	1d. purple and mauve (No. 27)	£475
Z12	**13**	1d. red (No. 31) (1900)	£500
Z13	**11**	2½d. dull purple and blue (No. 29)	£700

OFFICIAL STAMPS

Stamps of JAMAICA *cancelled with Type* Z **1** *in purple.*

1890–94.

Z14	**8**	½d. green (No. O1) (opt 17–17½ mm long) ..	£1200
Z15		½d. green (No. O3) (opt 16 mm long) (1893)	£2750
Z16	**11**	1d. rose (No. O4)	£1200
Z17		2d. grey (No. O5)	£3500

Stamps of JAMAICA *cancelled with Type* Z **2** *in purple or black.*

1895–98.

Z18	**8**	½d. green (No. O3)	£2250
Z19	**11**	1d. rose (No. O5)	£3750
Z20		2d. grey (No. O5)	£3750

STAKE BAY, CAYMAN BRAC

Z **4**

Z 5

Stamps of JAMAICA *cancelled with Type Z* **4**.

1898–1900.
Z21	**8**	½d. yellow-green (No. 16)....................		£3000
Z22	**11**	1d. purple and mauve (No. 27)............		£3250
Z23		2d. green (No. 28)............................		£4000
Z24		2½d. dull purple and blue (No. 29).......		£3250

Stamps of JAMAICA *cancelled with Type Z* **5**.

1900–01.
Z25	**8**	½d. yellow-green (No. 16)....................		£3250
Z26	**11**	1d. purple and mauve (No. 27)............		£3000
Z27	**13**	1d. red (No. 31)...............................		£3000
Z28	**11**	2½d. dull purple and blue (No. 29).......		£2500

PRICES FOR STAMPS ON COVER TO 1945
Nos. 1/2	*from* × 25
Nos. 3/12	*from* × 5
Nos. 13/16	*from* × 4
Nos. 17/19	*from* × 12
Nos. 25/34	*from* × 5
Nos. 35/52b	*from* × 4
Nos. 53/67	*from* × 5
Nos. 69/83	*from* × 4
Nos. 84/95	*from* × 6
Nos. 96/9	*from* × 5
Nos. 100/11	*from* × 4
Nos. 112/14	*from* × 4
Nos. 115/26	*from* × 2

DEPENDENCY OF JAMAICA

(T **1/3**, **8/9** and **12/13** typo D.L.R.)

1900 (1 Nov). Wmk Crown CA. P 14.
1	**1**	1½d. deep green............................	12·00	19·00
		a. Pale green..............................	6·00	15·00
2		1d. rose-carmine........................	6·00	2·25
		a. Pale carmine..........................	13·00	12·00
1s/2s Optd "Specimen" Set of 2............................			£130	

(Dented frame under "A" (R. 1/6 of left pane). (The variety is believed to have occurred at some point between 9 January and 9 April 1902 and is then present on all subsequent printings of the "POSTAGE POSTAGE" design)

1902 (1 Jan)–**03**. Wmk Crown CA. P 14.
3	**2**	½d. green (15.9.02)......................	4·50	25·00
		a. Dented frame..........................	£140	
4		1d. carmine (6.3.03)....................	10·00	9·00
		a. Dented frame..........................	£190	£225
5		2½d. bright blue...........................	10·00	12·00
		a. Dented frame..........................	£200	
6		6d. brown.................................	29·00	60·00
		a. Dented frame..........................	£375	
7	**3**	1s. orange................................	60·00	£110
		a. Dented frame..........................	£550	£850
3/7 Set of 5			£100	£190
3s/7s Optd "Specimen" Set of 5............................			£200	

1905 (Feb–Oct). Wmk Mult Crown CA. P 14.
8	**2**	½d. green.................................	7·00	9·00
		a. Dented frame..........................	£150	£200
9		1d. carmine (18 Oct)....................	14·00	17·00
		a. Dented frame..........................	£325	£400
10		2½d. bright blue...........................	7·00	3·25
		a. Dented frame..........................	£170	£190
11		6d. brown.................................	16·00	38·00
		a. Dented frame..........................	£300	£450
12	**3**	1s. orange................................	32·00	48·00
		a. Dented frame..........................	£450	
8/12 Set of 5			65·00	£100

1907 (13 Mar). Wmk Mult Crown CA. P 14.
13	**3**	4d. brown and blue......................	32·00	60·00
		a. Dented frame..........................	£375	£600
14	**2**	6d. olive and rose.......................	32·00	70·00
		a. Dented frame..........................	£375	£600
15	**3**	1s. violet and green.....................	55·00	80·00
		a. Dented frame..........................	£500	
16		5s. salmon and green...................	£180	£300
		a. Dented frame..........................	£2250	£2750
13/16 Set of 4			£275	£450
13s/16s Optd "Specimen" Set of 4.....................			£200	

One				
Halfpenny.	½**D**	**1D**		
(4)	(5)	(6)		

1907 (30 Aug). No. 9 surch at Govt Printing Office, Kingston, with T **4**.
17	**2**	½d. on 1d. carmine......................	45·00	75·00
		a. Dented frame..........................	£450	£700

1907 (Nov). No. 16 handstamped at Georgetown P.O. with T **5** or **6**.
18	**3**	½d. on 5s. salmon and green (26 Nov)	£250	£375
		a. Surch inverted.........................	£38000	
		b. Surch double...........................	£11000	£11000
		c. Surch double, one inverted.........		
		d. Surch omitted (in pair with normal)..................................	£55000	
		e. Dented frame..........................	£2250	
19		1d. on 5s. salmon and green (23 Nov)...............................	£250	£350
		a. Surch double...........................	£18000	
		b. Surch inverted.........................	£60000	
		c. Dented frame..........................	£2250	£2750

The ½d. on 5s. may be found with the figures "1" or "2" omitted, owing to defective handstamping.

8	**9**	2½**D**
		(10)

1907 (27 Dec)–**09**. *Chalk-surfaced paper (3d. to 10s.). P 14.*

(a) Wmk Mult Crown CA.
25	**8**	½d. green.................................	2·50	4·00
26		1d. carmine..............................	1·50	75
27		2½d. ultramarine (30.3.08).............	3·50	3·50
28	**9**	3d. purple/yellow (30.3.08)...........	3·25	6·50
29		4d. black and red/yellow (30.3.08) ..	50·00	70·00
30	**8**	6d. dull purple and violet purple (2.10.08)...............................	10·00	35·00
		a. Dull and bright purple..............	32·00	55·00
31	**9**	1s. black/green (5.4.09)...............	8·00	22·00
32		5s. green and red/yellow (30.3.08) ..	38·00	60·00

(b) Wmk Crown CA (30.3.08).
33	**9**	1s. black/green..........................	60·00	85·00
34	**8**	10s. green and red/green................	£160	£225
25/34 Set of 10			£300	£450
25s/30s, 32s/4s Optd "Specimen" Set of 9..............			£325	

1908 (12 Feb). No. 13 handstamped locally with T **10**.
35	**3**	2½d. on 4d. brown and blue..............	£1600	£2750
		a. Surch double...........................	£32000	£20000
		b. Dented frame..........................	£11000	

No. 35 should only be purchased when accompanied by an expert committee's certificate or similar form of guarantee.

MANUSCRIPT PROVISIONALS. During May and June 1908 supplies of ½d. and 1d. stamps became exhausted, and the payment of postage was indicated by the postmistress, Miss Gwendolyn Parsons, using a manuscript endorsement. Such endorsements were in use from 12 May to 1 June.

MP1	"(Postage Paid G.A.P.)" (12 May to 1 June)		£3500
MP1a	"(Postage Paid G.A.P.)" ½ (23 May to 1 June)		£5500

In October of the same year there was a further shortage of ¼d. stamps and the manuscript endorsements were again applied by either the new Postmaster, William Graham McCausland or by Miss Parsons who remained as his assistant.

MP2	"Pd ¼d/W.G. McC" (4 to 27 October).......................		£250
MP2a	"¼d Pd./W.G. McC" (14 October).........................		£1300
MP3	"Paid" (7 October).......................................		£7500
MP4	"Pd ¼d" (8 October)......................................		£6500
MP5	"Paid ¼d/ GAP. asst." (15 October)......................		£6500

No. MP2 exists in different inks and formats.

Manuscript endorsement for the 2½d. rate is also known, but this is thought to have been done by oversight.

A 1d. surcharge on 4d. (No. 29), issued in mid-May, was intended as a revenue stamp and was never authorised for postal use (*price* £225 *un.*). Used examples were either cancelled by favour or passed through the post in error. Exists with surcharge inverted (*price* £1700 *un.*), surcharge double (*price* £2500 *un.*) or surcharge double, both inverted (*price* £2500 *un.*).

11	**12**	**13**

1908 (30 June)–**09**. Wmk Mult Crown CA. *Litho.* P 14.
38	**11**	¼d. brown.................................	2·50	50
		a. Grey-brown (2.09)....................	3·75	1·00
		s. Optd "Specimen".....................	85·00	

1912 (24 Apr)–**20**. *Die I.* Wmk Mult Crown CA. *Chalk-surfaced paper (3d. to 10s.). P 14.*
40	**13**	¼d. brown (10.2.13).....................	1·00	40
41	**12**	½d. green.................................	2·75	5·00
		w. Wmk inverted.........................		£350
42		1d. red (25.2.13)........................	3·25	2·50
43	**13**	2d. pale grey.............................	1·00	10·00
44	**12**	2½d. bright blue...........................	7·00	11·00
		a. Deep bright blue (9.11.17).........	18·00	25·00
45	**13**	3d. purple/yellow (26.11.14)..........	15·00	40·00

---

		a. White back (19.11.13)...............	3·50	8·00
		b. On lemon (12.3.18)..................	2·50	18·00
		bs. Optd "Specimen"....................	65·00	
		c. On orange-buff (1920)...............	10·00	30·00
		d. On buff (1920)........................		
		e. On pale yellow (1920)...............	3·50	30·00
46		4d. black and red/yellow (25.2.13) ..	1·00	10·00
47	**12**	6d. dull and bright purple (25.2.13) ..	3·75	7·50
48	**13**	1s. black/green (15.5.16)...............	3·50	26·00
		as. Optd "Specimen".....................	65·00	
		b. White back (19.11.13)...............	3·50	8·00
49		2s. purple and bright blue/blue.........	12·00	50·00
50		3s. green and violet.....................	19·00	65·00
51		5s. green and red (26.8.14)............	75·00	£160
52	**12**	10s. deep green and red/green (26.11.14)...............................	£120	£200
		as. Optd "Specimen".....................	95·00	
		b. White back (19.11.13)...............	90·00	£150
		c. On blue-green, olive back (5.10.18)...............................	£100	£190
40/52b Set of 13			£200	£425
40s/4s, 45as, 46s/7s, 48bs, 49s/51s, 52bs Optd "Specimen" Set of 13...			£375	

WAR STAMP.	WAR STAMP.	1½d Straight serif (Left-hand pane R. 10/2)
1½d	1½d	
(14)	(15)	

1917 (26 Feb). T **12** surch with T **14** or **15** at Kingston, Jamaica.
53	**14**	1½d. on 2½d. deep blue..................	11·00	11·00
		a. No fraction bar.......................	£140	£170
		b. Missing stop after "STAMP" (R. 1/4).................	£425	
54	**15**	1½d. on 2½d. deep blue..................	1·75	6·00
		a. No fraction bar.......................	70·00	£120
		b. Straight serif.........................	80·00	£150

On No. 53 "WAR STAMP" and "1½d." were applied separately.

WAR STAMP	WAR STAMP	WAR STAMP
1½d	1½d	1½d.
(16)	(17)	(18)

1917 (4 Sept). T **12** surch with T **16** or **17** by D.L.R.
55	**16**	1½d. on 2½d. deep blue..................	£750	£1900
56	**17**	1½d. on 2½d. deep blue..................	30	60
		s. Optd "Specimen"........	£120	
		x. Wmk reversed.........	95·00	

De La Rue replaced surcharge Type **16** by Type **17** after only a few sheets as it did not adequately obliterate the original face value. A small quantity, said to be 3½ sheets, of Type **16** was included in the consignment in error.

1919–20. T **12** and **13** (2½d. special printing), optd only, or surch in addition at Kingston (No. 58) or by D.L.R. (others).
57	**16**	½d. green (4.2.19).......................	60	2·50
		a. Short opt (right pane R. 10/1)...............................	24·00	
58	**18**	1½d. on 2d. grey (10.3.20)..............	1·75	7·00
59	**17**	1½d. on 2½d. orange (4.12.19).........	80	1·25
57s, 59s Optd "Specimen" Set of 2.....................			£110	

The ½d. stamps on *buff* paper, and later consignments of the 2d. T **13** on *pinkish*, derived their colour from the paper in which they were packed for despatch from England.

No. 57a shows the overprint 2 mm high instead of 2½ mm.

A further surcharge as No. 58, but in red, was prepared in Jamaica during April 1920, but these were not issued.

19	**20** King William IV and King George V	

1921 (4 Apr)–**26**. P 14.

(a) Wmk Mult Crown CA.
60	**19**	3d. purple/orange-buff..................	1·50	8·00
		aw. Wmk inverted.........................	£140	£180
		ay. Wmk inverted and reversed........	90·00	£140
		b. purple/pale yellow....................	45·00	60·00
		bw. Wmk reversed........................		
62		4d. red/yellow (1.4.22).................	1·00	4·00
63		1s. black/green..........................	1·25	9·50
		x. Wmk reversed.........................	£300	
64		5s. yellow-green/pale yellow...........	16·00	70·00
		a. Deep green/pale yellow.............	85·00	£130
		b. blue-green/pale yellow..............	90·00	£150
		c. Deep green/orange-buff (19.11.21)...............................	£130	£200
67		10s. carmine/green (19.11.21).........	60·00	£110
60/7 Set of 5			70·00	£180
60s/7s Optd "Specimen" Set of 5.....................			£200	

(b) Wmk Mult Script CA.
69	**19**	¼d. yellow-brown (1.4.22)..............	50	1·50
		y. Wmk inverted and reversed........	£250	
70		½d. pale grey-green (1.4.22)...........	50	30
		w. Wmk inverted.........................		
		y. Wmk inverted and reversed........		
71		1d. deep carmine-red (1.4.22).........	1·40	85
72		1½d. orange-brown........................	1·75	30
73		2d. slate-grey (1.4.22).................	1·75	4·00
74		2½d. bright blue (1.4.22)................	50	50
		x. Wmk reversed.........................	£300	

75		3d. purple/*yellow* (29.6.23).............	1·25	4·00
		y. Wmk inverted and reversed......	£300	
76		4½d. sage-green (29.6.23).............	2·50	3·00
77		6d. claret (1.4.22).....................	5·50	32·00
		a. Deep claret.........................	19·00	40·00
79		1s. black/*green* (15.5.25)............	9·50	32·00
80		2s. violet/*blue* (1.4.22).............	14·00	24·00
81		3s. violet (1.4.22).....................	23·00	16·00
82		5s. green/*yellow* (15.2.25).........	24·00	45·00
83		10s. carmine/*green* (5.9.26).......	60·00	85·00
69/83 *Set of 14*..............................			£130	£225
69s/83s Optd "Specimen" *Set of 14*........			£350	

An example of the 4d, No. 62, is known with the 'C' missing from the watermark in the top sheet margin.

"A.S.R." PROVISIONAL. On the night of 9/10 November 1932 the Cayman Brac Post Office at Stake Bay, and its contents, was destroyed by a hurricane. Pending the arrival of replacement stamp stocks and cancellation the Postmaster, Mr A. S. Rutty, initialled covers to indicate that postage had been paid. Those destined for overseas addresses additionally received a "Postage Paid" machine postmark in red when they passed through Kingston, Jamaica.

MP6	Endorsed "A.S.R." in manuscript...............................	£6500	
MP7	Endorsed "A.S.R." in manuscript and "Postage Paid" machine postmark in red	£9000	

These emergency arrangements lasted until 19 December.

(Recess Waterlow)

1932 (5 Dec). *Centenary of the "Assembly of Justices and Vestry".* Wmk Mult Script CA. P 12½.

84	**20**	¼d. brown	1·50	1·00
		a. "A" of "CA" missing from wmk.........................	£1100	£1100
85		½d. green............................	2·75	8·00
		a. "A" of "CA" reversed in wmk..	£1400	
86		1d. scarlet	2·75	9·00
87		1½d. red-orange	2·75	2·75
		a. "A" of "CA" missing from wmk.........................		
88		2d. grey	2·75	3·50
89		2½d. ultramarine	2·75	1·50
90		3d. olive-green	3·25	5·00
91		6d. purple	9·50	23·00
92		1s. black and brown...............	17·00	32·00
93		2s. black and ultramarine	45·00	75·00
94		5s. black and green	85·00	£120
95		10s. black and scarlet	£275	£350
84/95 *Set of 12*			£400	£550
84s/95s Perf "Specimen" *Set of 12*........			£500	

The design of Nos. 92/5 differs slightly from Type **20**.

No. 85a shows one "A" of the watermark reversed so that its head points to right when seen from the back. It is believed that this stamp may also exist with "A" missing.

Examples of all values are known showing a forged George Town postmark dated "DE 31 1932".

21 Cayman Islands   **22** Cat Boat

23 Red-footed Booby   **24** Queen or Pink Conch Shells

25 Hawksbill Turtles

(Recess Waterlow)

1935 (1 May). *T* **21/5**. Wmk Mult Script CA. P 12½.

96	**21**	¼d. black and brown.......................	50	1·00
97	**22**	½d. ultramarine and yellow-green....	1·00	1·00
98	**23**	1d. ultramarine and scarlet............	4·00	2·25
99	**24**	1½d. black and orange...................	1·50	1·75
100	**22**	2d. ultramarine and purple............	3·75	1·10
101	**25**	2½d. blue and black......................	3·25	1·25
102	**21**	3d. black and olive-green..............	2·50	3·00
103	**25**	6d. bright purple and black...........	8·50	4·00
104	**22**	1s. ultramarine and orange...........	6·00	6·50
105	**23**	2s. ultramarine and black.............	45·00	35·00
106	**25**	5s. green and black.....................	50·00	50·00
107	**24**	10s. black and scarlet...................	75·00	90·00
96/107 *Set of 12*			£180	£180
96s/107s Perf "Specimen" *Set of 12*........			£275	

Examples of all values are known showing a forged George Town postmark dated "AU 23 1936".

1935 (6 May). *Silver Jubilee. As Nos. 91/4 of Antigua.*

108		½d. black and green......................	15	1·00
		f. Diagonal line by turret.........	38·00	
		h. Dot by turret (15.5.25)........	65·00	
		i. Dash by turret.....................	80·00	
109		2½d. brown and deep blue.............	1·50	1·00

110		6d. light blue and olive-green................	1·50	5·00
		h. Dot by flagstaff..................	£190	
		i. Dash by turret.....................	£190	
111		1s. slate and green...................	7·50	7·50
		h. Dot by flagstaff..................	£325	
		i. Dash by turret.....................	£350	
108/11 *Set of 4*			9·50	13·00
108s/11s Perf "Specimen" *Set of 4*.........			£130	

For illustrations of plate varieties see Omnibus section following Zanzibar.

1937 (13 May). *Coronation Issue. As Nos. 95/7 of Antigua.* P 11×11½.

112		½d. green	30	1·90
113		1d. carmine	50	20
114		2½d. blue	95	40
112/14 *Set of 3*		1·60	2·25
112s/14s Perf "Specimen" *Set of 3*........		£100	

26 Beach View   **27** Dolphin (fish) (*Coryphaena hippurus*)

28 Cayman Islands map   **29** Hawksbill Turtles

30 *Rembro* (schooner)

(Recess D.L.R. (½d., 2d., 6d., 1s., 10s.), Waterlow (others))

1938 (5 May)–**48**. *T* **26/30**. Wmk Mult Script CA (sideways on ¼d., 1d., 1½d., 2½d., 3d., 2s., 5s.). Various perfs.

115	**26**	¼d. red-orange (P 12½)..............	70	55
		a. Perf 13½×12½ (16.7.43)........	10	65
116	**27**	½d. green (P 13×11½)	1·00	55
		a. Perf 14 (16.7.43)...............	1·25	1·40
		ab. "A" of "CA" missing from wmk.........................	£1100	
117	**28**	1d. scarlet (P 12½).................	30	75
118	**26**	1½d. black (P 12½)..................	30	10
119	**29**	2d. violet (P 11½×13)	3·00	40
		a. Perf 14 (16.7.43)...............	60	30
120	**30**	2½d. bright blue (P 12½)	40	20
120a		2½d. orange (P 12½) (25.8.47)	2·50	50
121	**28**	3d. orange (P 12½)..................	40	15
121a		3d. bright blue (P 12½) (25.8.47)..	3·00	30
122	**29**	6d. olive-green (P 11½×13)	11·00	4·00
		a. Perf 14 (16.7.43)...............	3·00	1·25
		b. Brownish olive (P 11½× 13) (8.7.47)........................	3·00	1·50
123	**27**	1s. red-brown (P 13×11½)..........	6·50	1·50
		a. Perf 14 (16.7.43)...............	4·50	2·00
		ab. "A" of "CA" missing from wmk.........................	£1300	
124	**26**	2s. yellow-green (*shades*) (P 12½)..	50·00	14·00
		a. Deep green (16.7.43)...........	25·00	9·00
125	**30**	5s. carmine-lake (P 12½)...........	32·00	15·00
		a. Crimson (1948)..................	70·00	22·00
126	**29**	10s. chocolate (P 11½×13)	23·00	9·00
		a. Perf 14 (16.7.43)...............	23·00	9·00
		aw. Wmk inverted		
115/26a *Set of 14*			85·00	35·00
115s/26s Perf "Specimen" *Set of 14*........			£400	

Stop after "1946" (Plate B1 R. 2/1)

1946 (26 Aug). *Victory. As Nos. 110/11 of Antigua.*

127		1½d. black	20	10
128		3d. orange-yellow	20	10
		a. Stop after "1946"...........	22·00	
127s/8s Perf "Specimen" *Set of 2*		90·00	

1948 (29 Nov). *Royal Silver Wedding. As Nos. 112/13 of Antigua.*

129		½d. green	10	75
130		10s. violet-blue	16·00	20·00

1949 (10 Oct). *75th Anniv of Universal Postal Union. As Nos. 114/17 of Antigua.*

131		2½d. orange	30	1·00
132		3d. deep blue	1·50	2·25
133		6d. olive	60	2·25
134		1s. red-brown	60	75
131/4 *Set of 4*		2·75	5·50

31 Cat Boat   **32** Coconut Grove, Cayman Brac

33 Green Turtle   **34** Thatch Rope Industry

35 Cayman Seamen   **36** Map of Cayman Islands

37 Parrotfish   **38** Bluff, Cayman Brac

39 Georgetown Harbour   **40** Turtle in "crawl"

41 *Ziroma* (schooner)   **42** Boat-building

43 Government Offices, Grand Cayman

(Recess B.W.)

1950 (2 Oct). *T* **31/43**. Wmk Mult Script CA. P 11½×11.

135	**31**	¼d. bright blue and pale scarlet	15	60
136	**32**	½d. reddish violet and emerald-green..........................	15	1·25
137	**33**	1d. olive-green and deep blue........	60	75
138	**34**	1½d. green and brown	30	75
139	**35**	2d. reddish violet and rose-carmine	1·25	1·50
140	**36**	2½d. turquoise and black..............	1·25	60
141	**37**	3d. bright green and light blue	1·40	1·50
142	**38**	6d. red-brown and blue...............	2·00	1·25
143	**39**	9d. scarlet and grey-green............	9·00	2·00
144	**40**	1s. brown and orange	3·25	2·75
145	**41**	2s. violet and reddish purple........	9·00	11·00
146	**42**	5s. olive-green and violet............	15·00	7·00
147	**43**	10s. black and scarlet	18·00	15·00
135/47 *Set of 13*			55·00	42·00

Ceylon

PRICES FOR STAMPS ON COVER TO 1945

No. 1	*from* × 5
Nos. 2/12	*from* × 4
Nos. 16/17	*from* × 5
Nos. 18/59	*from* × 8
Nos. 60/2	*from* × 15
Nos. 63/72	*from* × 8
Nos. 121/38	*from* × 6
Nos. 139/41	†
Nos. 142/3	*from* × 10
Nos. 146/51	*from* × 6
Nos. 151a/2	
Nos. 153/93	*from* × 8
Nos. 195/201	*from* × 12
Nos. 202/43	*from* × 6
Nos. 245/9	*from* × 4
Nos. 250/5	*from* × 5
Nos. 256/64	*from* × 4
Nos. 265/76	*from* × 4
Nos. 277/88	*from* × 4
Nos. 289/300	*from* × 8
Nos. 301/18	*from* × 2
Nos. 319/23	
Nos. 330/7b	*from* × 4
Nos. 338/56	*from* × 2
Nos. 357/60	
Nos. 361/2	*from* × 5
Nos. 363/7	*from* × 3
Nos. 368/78	*from* × 2
Nos. 379/82	*from* × 4
Nos. 383/5	*from* × 3
Nos. 386/97	*from* × 2
Nos. 398/9	*from* × 8
Nos. O1/17	*from* × 30

CROWN COLONY

PRICES. The prices of the imperf stamps of Ceylon vary greatly according to condition. The following prices are for fine copies with four margins.

Poor to medium specimens can be supplied at much lower prices.

| 1 | 2 | 3 |

NOTE. Beware of stamps of Type **2** which are often offered with corners added.

(Recess P.B.)

1857 (1 Apr). *Blued paper.* Wmk Star W w **1**. Imperf.
| 1 | 1 | 6d. purple-brown | £7500 | £450 |

Collectors should beware of proofs with faked watermark, often offered as originals.

PERKINS BACON "CANCELLED". For notes on these handstamps, showing "CANCELLED" between horizontal bars forming an oval, see Catalogue Introduction.

1857 (2 July)–**59**. Wmk Star, W w **1**. *White paper.*

(a) Imperf.
2	1	1d. deep turquoise-blue (24.8.57)....	£650	32·00
		a. Blue	£750	50·00
		b. Blued paper	—	£200
3		2d. green (*shades*) (24.8.57)	£160	55·00
		a. Yellowish green	£500	90·00
4	2	4d. dull rose (23.4.59)	£55000	£4500
5	1	5d. chestnut	£1500	£150
6		6d. purple-brown (1859)	£2000	£140
		a. Brown	£6500	£475
		b. Deep brown	£8000	£1000
		c. Light brown	—	£1000
7	2	8d. brown (23.4.59)	£24000	£1500
8		9d. purple-brown (23.4.59)	£38000	£900
9	3	10d. dull vermilion	£800	£300
10		1s. slate-violet	£4750	£200
11	2	1s.9d. green (H/S "CANCELLED" in oval £9000)	£800	£800
		a. Yellow-green	£4000	£3000
12		2s. dull blue (23.4.59)	£5500	£1200

(b) Unofficial perf 7½ (1s.9d.) or roul (others).
13	1	1d. blue	£6000	
14		2d. green	£2750	£1300
15	2	1s.9d. green	£7500	

Nos. 13/15 were privately produced, probably by commercial firms for their own convenience.

The 10d. also exists with "CANCELLED" in oval, but no examples are believed to be in private hands.

4

(Typo D.L.R.)

1857 (Oct)–**64.** No wmk. *Glazed paper.*

(a) Imperf.
16	4	½d. reddish lilac (*blued paper*)	£3250	£500
17		½d. dull mauve (1858)	£170	£200
		a. Private roul	£5500	

(b) P 12½.
| 18 | 4 | ½d. dull mauve (1864) | £225 | £180 |

(Recess P.B.)

1861–64. Wmk Star, W w **1**.

(a) Clean-cut and intermediate perf 14 to 15½.
19	1	1d. light blue	£1100	£200
		a. Dull blue (H/S "CANCELLED" in oval £10000)	£160	12·00
20		2d. green (*shades*)	£180	28·00
		a. Imperf between (vert pair)	†	—
		b. Yellowish green (H/S "CANCELLED" in oval £11000)	£190	24·00
21	2	4d. dull rose (H/S "CANCELLED" in oval £11000)	£2000	£300
22	1	5d. chestnut (H/S "CANCELLED" in oval £8000)	85·00	8·00
23		6d. brown (H/S "CANCELLED" in oval £9000)	£2000	£120
		a. Bistre-brown	—	£180
24	2	8d. brown (H/S "CANCELLED" in oval £10000)	£1900	£500
25		9d. purple-brown	£6500	£225
26	3	1s. slate-violet (H/S "CANCELLED" in oval £10000)	£100	13·00
27	2	2s. dull blue	£2750	£650

(b) Rough perf 14 to 15½.
28	1	1d. dull blue	£130	7·50
		a. Blued paper	£550	20·00
29		2d. green	£400	80·00
30	2	4d. rose-red	£425	90·00
		a. Deep rose-red	£450	£100
31	1	6d. deep brown	£850	£100
		a. Light brown	£1400	£140
		b. Olive-sepia	£750	90·00
32	2	8d. brown	£1400	£550
		a. Yellow-brown	£1400	£350
33		9d. deep brown(H/S"CANCELLED" in oval £9000)	85·00	70·00
		a. Light brown	£850	£100
		b. Olive-sepia	£550	65·00
34	3	10d. dull vermilion	£225	22·00
		a. Imperf vert (horiz pair)	†	—
35		1s. slate-violet	£225	15·00
36	2	1s.9d. light green (*prepared for use, but not issued*)	£700	
37		2s. dull blue (H/S "CANCELLED" in oval £10000)	£600	£140
		a. Deep dull blue	£850	£170

(c) P 12½ by D.L.R.
| 38 | 3 | 10d. dull vermilion (9.64) | £225 | 16·00 |

The line machine used for Nos. 19/37 produced perforations of variable quality due to wear, poor cleaning and faulty servicing, but it is generally accepted that the clean-cut and intermediate versions occurred on stamps perforated up to March 1861 and the rough variety when the machine was used after that date.

(Recess D.L.R.)

1862. No wmk. *Smooth paper.*

(a) P 13.
39	1	1d. dull blue	£140	6·00
40		5d. lake-brown	£1600	£150
41		6d. brown	£180	26·00
		a. Deep brown	£160	24·00
42	2	9d. brown	£1200	95·00
43	3	1s. slate-purple	£1800	80·00

(b) P 11½, 12.
| 44 | 1 | 1d. dull blue | £1400 | £130 |
| | | a. Imperf between (horiz pair) | † | £12000 |

Nos. 39/44 were printed on paper showing a papermaker's watermark of "T H SAUNDERS 1862", parts of which can be found on individual stamps. Examples are rare and command a premium.

The 1s. is known imperforate, but was not issued in this condition.

5 (23 mm high. "CC" oval)   **6** (21½ mm high. "CC" round and smaller)

(Typo (½d.) or recess (others) D.L.R.)

1863–65. W **5**. *Paper medium thin and slightly soft.*

(a) P 11½, 12.
| 45 | 1 | 1d. deep blue | £2500 | £325 |
| | | x. Wmk reversed | £3250 | £450 |

(b) P 13.
46	1	6d. sepia	£1600	£180
		x. Wmk reversed	—	£160
		y. Wmk inverted and reversed	£2250	£400
47	2	9d. sepia	£4250	£750

(c) P 12½.
| 48 | 4 | ½d. dull mauve (1864) | 48·00 | 35·00 |
| | | aw. Wmk inverted | £200 | 65·00 |

---

		b. Reddish lilac	60·00	42·00
		c. Mauve	35·00	35·00
49	1	1d. deep blue	£130	6·00
		a. Imperf	†	38·00
		w. Wmk inverted	£140	6·00
		x. Wmk reversed	†	50·00
		y. Wmk inverted and reversed	†	—
50		2d. grey-green (1864)	75·00	12·00
		a. Imperf	†	—
		bw. Wmk inverted	£225	55·00
		by. Wmk inverted and reversed	†	£110
		c. Bottle-green	†	£3500
		d. Yellowish green	£7500	£400
		dx. Wmk reversed	†	£800
		e. Emerald (wmk reversed)	£150	£100
		ew. Wmk inverted	£450	£275
51		2d. ochre (*wmk reversed*) (1866)	£225	£225
		w. Wmk inverted	£550	£550
		y. Wmk inverted and reversed	£450	£425
52	2	4d. rose-carmine (1865)	£650	£160
		ax. Wmk reversed	£800	
		b. Rose	£425	90·00
		bx. Wmk reversed	£475	£120
53	1	5d. red-brown (*shades*) (1865)	£190	70·00
		w. Wmk inverted	†	£170
		x. Wmk reversed	£250	60·00
54		5d. grey-olive (1866)	£1800	£350
		ax. Wmk reversed	£1500	£300
		b. Yellow-olive	£750	£225
		bx. Wmk reversed	£750	£225
55		6d. sepia	£160	4·00
		aw. Wmk reversed	†	70·00
		ax. Wmk reversed		
		b. Reddish brown	£190	12·00
		c. Blackish brown	£160	10·00
		ca. Double print	†	£3000
		cw. Wmk inverted	†	55·00
		cx. Wmk reversed	£200	42·00
		cy. Wmk inverted and reversed	†	£120
56	2	8d. reddish brown (*shades*) (1864)..	£100	50·00
		x. Wmk reversed	£150	75·00
		y. Wmk inverted and reversed	£300	95·00
57		9d. sepia	£300	45·00
		x. Wmk reversed	£500	80·00
58	3	10d. vermilion (1866)	£1900	60·00
		a. Imperf	†	£150
		b. Orange-red	£4000	£425
		bx. Wmk reversed	†	£550
59	2	2s. steel-blue (*shades*) (1864)	£275	35·00
		x. Wmk reversed	†	95·00
		y. Wmk inverted and reversed	£550	£180

Watermarks as Type **5** were arranged in four panes, each of 60, with the words "CROWN COLONIES" between the panes. Parts of this marginal watermark often appear on the stamps.

De La Rue had considerable difficulty matching the standard Crown CC watermark to the plates received from Perkins Bacon with the result that the watermark W **5** is frequently found misplaced.

A further aid to identifying the two watermarks is the distance between the top of the cross and the foot of "CC", which measures 2 mm on W **5** and 6.5 mm on W **6**.

The ½d. dull mauve, 2d. ochre and 5d. grey-olive with this watermark also exist imperforate, but are not known used. The 6d. sepia and 2s. steel-blue also exist imperforate on wove paper without watermark.

One used example of the 2d. grey-green is known showing private roulettes added to an imperforate stamp (*Price £3000*).

| 7 | 8 |

(Typo D.L.R.)

1866–68. Wmk Crown CC.

(a) P 12½.
| 60 | 7 | 3d. rose | £190 | 85·00 |

(b) P 14.
61	8	1d. blue (*shades*) (1868)	21·00	9·00
		w. Wmk inverted	†	£120
62	7	3d. carmine-rose (1867)	75·00	42·00
		a. Bright rose	80·00	48·00

Nos. 60/1 exist imperforate.

(Recess D.L.R.)

1867–70. W **6**. *Specially produced hand-made paper.* P 12½.
63	1	1d. dull blue	£170	12·00
		aw. Wmk inverted	£400	90·00
		ax. Wmk reversed	£170	12·00
		ay. Wmk inverted and reversed	†	£150
		b. Deep blue	£160	9·50
		bw. Wmk inverted	—	95·00
		bx. Wmk reversed	£250	32·00
64		2d. ochre	£130	12·00
		aw. Wmk inverted		
		ax. Wmk reversed	—	35·00
		b. Bistre	60·00	8·00
		bw. Wmk inverted	£120	
		c. Olive-bistre	£150	20·00
		cw. Wmk inverted	£150	
		d. Yellow	95·00	5·50
		dx. Wmk reversed	65·00	20·00
65	2	4d. rose	£200	55·00
		b. Rose-carmine	60·00	17·00
		bw. Wmk inverted	†	85·00
		bx. Wmk reversed	70·00	17·00
		by. Wmk inverted and reversed	£400	£130
66	1	5d. yellow-olive	95·00	15·00
		ax. Wmk reversed	85·00	19·00
		ay. Wmk inverted and reversed		
		b. Olive-green	£110	15·00
		bx. Wmk reversed		
		c. Bronze-green	38·00	48·00
67		6d. deep brown (1869)	85·00	10·00
		a. Blackish brown	£110	8·50

		aw. Wmk inverted	†	£100
		ax. Wmk reversed	£150	17·00
		b. *Red-brown*	38·00	35·00
68	2	8d. chocolate	70·00	55·00
		ax. Wmk reversed	—	95·00
		b. *Lake-brown*	£130	75·00
		bx. Wmk reversed	£250	£100
69		9d. bistre-brown (12.68)	£450	32·00
		ax. Wmk reversed	£375	25·00
		b. *Blackish brown*	50·00	6·00
70	3	10d. dull vermilion (*wmk reversed*)...	£3000	£140
		ay. Wmk inverted and reversed....	†	£225
		b. *Red-orange*	55·00	14·00
		bx. Wmk reversed		£11·00
		by. Wmk inverted and reversed......	£450	
		c. *Orange*	90·00	11·00
71		1s. reddish lilac (1870)..................	£275	27·00
		ax. Wmk reversed	£400	55·00
		b. *Reddish violet*	95·00	8·00
		bw. Wmk inverted	†	£130
		bx. Wmk reversed	£250	48·00
72	2	2s. steel-blue	£225	18·00
		ax. Wmk reversed	†	45·00
		b. *Deep blue*	£130	12·00
		bx. Wmk reversed	£170	18·00

Watermarks as Type **6** were arranged in one pane of 240 (12×20) with the words "CROWN COLONIES" twice in each side margin.

Unused examples of the 1d. dull blue, 1d. deep blue, 5d. yellow-olive, 6d. deep brown, 9d. blackish brown and 10d. red orange with this watermark exist imperforate.

PRINTERS. All stamps from No. 121 to 367 were typographed by De La Rue & Co. Ltd, London.

A wide variety of shades may be found on stamps of this period. We only list the most significant.

(New Currency. 100 cents = 1 rupee)

9	10	11
12	13	14
15	16	17

18	19

1872–80. Wmk Crown CC.

(a) P 14.

121	9	2c. pale brown (*shades*)	20·00	3·00
		w. Wmk inverted	£100	50·00
122	10	4c. grey	40·00	1·50
		w. Wmk inverted	—	55·00
123		4c. rosy-mauve (1880)..................	60·00	1·50
		w. Wmk inverted	£200	£110
124	11	8c. orange-yellow	40·00	5·50
		a. *Yellow*	30·00	6·00
		w. Wmk inverted	†	£130
126	12	16c. pale violet	90·00	2·75
		w. Wmk inverted	†	£130
127	13	24c. green	60·00	2·00
		w. Wmk inverted	†	£130
128	14	32c. slate (1877)	£150	15·00
		w. Wmk inverted	£400	£130
129	15	36c. blue	£160	20·00
		x. Wmk reversed	£325	85·00
130	16	48c. rose	75·00	6·50
		w. Wmk inverted	—	48·00
131	17	64c. red-brown (1877)	£300	65·00
132	18	96c. drab	£225	26·00
		w. Wmk inverted	—	£160
121/32 *Set of 11*			£1100	£130

(b) P 14×12½.

133	9	2c. brown	£350	65·00
134	10	4c. grey	£1600	27·00
135	11	8c. orange-yellow	£375	48·00
		w. Wmk inverted	†	£200

(c) P 12½.

136	9	2c. brown	£2750	£180
137	10	4c. grey	£1600	£275

(d) P 12½×14.

138	19	2r.50 dull-rose (1879)	£550	£300

(e) Prepared for use and sent out to Ceylon, but not issued unsurcharged.

139	14	32c. slate (P 14×12½)..................		£1100
140	17	64c. red-brown (P 14×12½)...........		£1300
141	19	2r.50 dull rose (P 12½)		£1700

FORGERIES—Beware of forged overprint and surcharge varieties on Victorian issues.

SIXTEEN

16

CENTS

(20)

1882 (Oct). *Nos. 127 and 131 surch as T **20** by Govt Printer.*

142	13	16c. on 24c. green..................	26·00	6·50
		a. Surch inverted..................		
143	17	20c. on 64c. red-brown..................	11·00	6·00
		a. Surch double	†	£1200

1883–98. Wmk Crown CA.

(a) P 14.

146	9	2c. pale brown	60·00	2·00
147		2c. dull green (1884)	2·50	15
		s. Optd "Specimen"	£350	
		w. Wmk inverted	£150	60·00
148	10	4c. rosy mauve	3·25	30
		w. Wmk inverted	†	£150
149		4c. rose (1884)	4·25	11·00
		s. Optd "Specimen"	£350	
150	11	8c. orange-yellow	4·50	9·00
		a. *Yellow* (1898)	3·50	7·50
151	12	16c. pale violet	£1700	£160

(b) Trial perforation. P 12.

151a	9	2c. dull green		£4000
151b	10	4c. rose		£4000
151c	13	24c. brown-purple		£4250

(c) Prepared for use and sent out to Ceylon, but not issued unsurcharged. P 14.

152	13	24c. brown-purple		£1300
		s. Optd "Specimen"		£550

Although delivered in 1884 it is believed that the 4c. rose, No. 149, was not used until the early 1890s.

See also Nos. 246, 256 and 258 for the 2c. and 4c. in different colours.

Postage &

FIVE CENTS

TEN CENTS

Revenue (21)

(22)

Twenty Cents (23)

One Rupee Twelve Cents (24)

1885 (1 Jan–Mar). *T **10/19** surch locally as T **21/24**.*

I.Wmk Crown CC.

(a) P 14.

153	21	5c. on 16c. pale violet..................	†	£3000
154		5c. on 24c. green..................	£3000	£110
155		5c. on 32c. slate	65·00	15·00
		a. Surch inverted..................	†	£1700
		b. *Dark grey*	£170	42·00
156		5c. on 36c. blue..................	£300	12·00
		a. Surch inverted..................	†	£2250
		x. Wmk reversed		£100
157		5c. on 48c. rose	£1600	60·00
158		5c. on 64c. red-brown..................	£110	7·50
		a. Surch double	†	£1400
159		5c. on 96c. drab	£500	70·00
161	22	10c. on 16c. pale violet..................	£6000	£2250
162		10c. on 24c. green..................	£425	£110
163		10c. on 36c. blue..................	£375	£180
164		10c. on 64c. red-brown..................	£425	£170
165		20c. on 24c. green..................	60·00	18·00
166	23	20c. on 32c. slate	70·00	55·00
		a. *Dark grey*	80·00	45·00
		aw. Wmk inverted	£200	
167		25c. on 32c. slate	17·00	4·50
		a. *Dark grey*	28·00	8·00
168		28c. on 48c. rose	40·00	7·00
		a. Surch double	†	£1700
169	22	30c. on 36c. blue..................	16·00	11·00
		x. Wmk reversed	11·00	8·50
		xa. Surch inverted..................	£225	£110
170		56c. on 96c. drab	25·00	20·00

(b) P 14×12½.

172	21	5c. on 32c. slate	£750	50·00
173		5c. on 64c. red-brown..................	£700	45·00
174	22	10c. on 64c. red-brown..................	70·00	£120
		a. Imperf between (vert pair)	£3250	
175	24	1r.12 on 2r.50 dull rose (P 12½).........	£550	95·00
176		1r.12 on 2r.50 dull rose (P 12½×14)...	£110	45·00

II. Wmk Crown CA. P 14.

178	21	5c. on 4c. rose (3.85)..................	22·00	4·00
		a. Surch inverted..................	†	£300
179		5c. on 8c. orange-yellow..................	80·00	8·00

---

		a. Surch double	†	£1900
		b. Surch inverted	†	£2500
180		5c. on 16c. pale violet..................	£110	13·00
		a. Surch inverted	†	£225
182		5c. on 24c. brown-purple..................	—	£500
184	22	10c. on 16c. pale violet..................	£6000	£1400
185		10c. on 24c. brown-purple..................	15·00	7·00
186		15c. on 16c. pale violet..................	12·00	8·00

The 5c. on 4c. rosy mauve and 5c. on 24c. green, both watermarked Crown CA, previously catalogued are now known to be forgeries.

REVENUE AND POSTAGE

5 CENTS	10 CENTS	1 R. 12 C.
(25)	(26)	(27)

1885. *T **11/15**, **18** and **19** surch with T **25/7** by D.L.R. P 14.*

(a) Wmk Crown CA.

187	25	5c. on 8c. lilac	19·00	1·50
		w. Wmk inverted	†	80·00
		x. Wmk reversed	†	£180
188	26	10c. on 24c. brown-purple..................	11·00	8·00
189		15c. on 16c. orange-yellow..................	60·00	11·00
190		28c. on 32c. slate	25·00	2·50
191		30c. on 36c. olive-green..................	28·00	14·00
192		56c. on 96c. drab	50·00	15·00

(b) Wmk Crown CC (sideways).

193	27	1r.12 on 2r.50 dull rose	42·00	95·00
187/93 *Set of 7*			£200	£130
187s/93s Optd "Specimen" *Set of 7*			£850	

28	29

1886. Wmk Crown CA. P 14.

195	28	5c. dull purple	2·50	10
		w. Wmk inverted	£140	90·00
196	29	15c. sage-green	6·00	1·50
		w. Wmk inverted	†	£150
197		15c. olive-green	6·50	1·50
198		25c. yellow-brown	4·25	1·40
		a. Value in yellow	£110	70·00
199		28c. slate	21·00	1·40
195s, 197s/9s Optd "Specimen" *Set of 4*			£250	

Six plates were used for the 5c., No. 195, between 1885 and 1901, each being replaced by its successor as it became worn. Examples from the worn plates show thicker lines in the background and masses of solid colour under the chin, in front of the throat, at the back of the neck and at the base.

30

1887. Wmk Crown CC (sideways). *White or blued paper.* P 14.

201	30	1r.12 dull rose	25·00	22·00
		a. Wmk upright	48·00	60·00
		aw. Wmk inverted	†	£180
		s. Optd "Specimen"	£130	

TWO CENTS	Two	2 Cents
(31)	(32)	(33)

		Two Cents
		(34)

	2 Cents
	(35)

1888–90. *Nos. 148/9 surch with T **31/5**.*

202	31	2c. on 4c. rosy mauve..................	1·40	80
		a. Surch inverted..................	21·00	20·00
		b. Surch double, one inverted	—	£250
203		2c. on 4c. rose	2·25	30
		a. Surch inverted..................	14·00	15·00
		b. Surch double	—	£275
204	32	2(c). on 4c. rosy mauve..................	75	30
		a. Surch inverted..................	30·00	30·00
		b. Surch double	75·00	75·00
		c. Surch double, one inverted	65·00	60·00
205		2(c). on 4c. rose	6·50	20
		a. Surch inverted..................	£275	
		b. Surch double	80·00	85·00
		c. Surch double, one inverted	85·00	90·00
206	33	2c. on 4c. rosy mauve..................	70·00	30·00
		a. Surch inverted..................	£120	38·00
		b. Surch double, one inverted	£150	
207		2c. on 4c. rose	2·50	75
		a. Surch inverted..................	14·00	8·50
		b. Surch double	£150	£130

		c. Surch double, one inverted	8·00	11·00
		w. Wmk inverted	£120	
208	34	2c. on 4c. rosy mauve	50·00	22·00
		a. Surch inverted	£150	30·00
209		2c. on 4c. rose	2·50	1·10
		a. Surch inverted	14·00	5·50
		b. Surch double	£110	£100
		c. Surch double, one inverted	14·00	7·50
210	35	2c. on 4c. rosy mauve	50·00	28·00
		a. Surch inverted	75·00	40·00
		b. Surch double, one inverted	90·00	90·00
		c. Surch double	—	£275
		d. "s" of "Cents" inverted (R. 3/5)	—	£450
		e. As d. Whole surch inverted		
211		2c. on 4c. rose	11·00	1·00
		a. Surch inverted	18·00	5·50
		b. Surch double	95·00	95·00
		c. Surch double, one inverted	20·00	9·00
		d. "s" of "Cents" inverted (R. 3/5)	£325	£190
		x. Wmk reversed	†	£110
209s, 211s Optd "Specimen" *Set of 2*			65·00	

The 4c. rose and the 4c. rosy mauve are found surcharged "Postal Commission 3 (or "Three") Cents". They denote the extra commission charged by the Post Office on postal orders which had not been cashed within three months of the date of issue. For a short time the Post Office did not object to the use of these stamps on letters.

POSTAGE

Five Cents

REVENUE
(36)

FIFTEEN CENTS
(37)

1890. *No. 197 surch with T* **36**.

233		5c. on 15c. olive-green	3·00	2·00
		a. Surch inverted	50·00	55·00
		b. Surch double	£100	£120
		c. "Flve" for "Five" (R. 1/1)	£110	85·00
		d. Variety as c, inverted	—	£1200
		e. "REVENUE" omitted	£170	£150
		f. Inverted "s" in "Cents" (R. 10/2)	70·00	80·00
		g. Variety as f, and whole surch inverted	£1400	
		h. "REVENUE" omitted and inverted "s" in "Cents"	£1100	
		i. "POSTAGE" and "A" spaced between "T" and "A" (R. 1/5)	70·00	75·00
		j. Variety as i, and whole surch inverted	—	£1100
		s. Optd "Specimen"	30·00	

1891. *Nos. 198/9 surch with T* **37**.

239	29	15c. on 25c. yellow-brown	13·00	13·00
240		15c. on 28c. slate	15·00	8·50

3 Cents
(38)

39

1892. *Nos. 148/9 and 199 surch with T* **38**.

241	10	3c. on 4c. rosy mauve	1·00	3·25
242		3c. on 4c. rose	4·75	8·00
		s. Optd "Specimen"	38·00	
		w. Wmk inverted	£120	
		ws. Optd "Specimen"	85·00	
243	29	3c. on 28c. slate	4·50	4·00
		a. Surch double	£140	
241/3 *Set of 3*			9·25	14·00

1893–99. Wmk Crown CA. P 14.

245	39	3c. terracotta and blue-green	3·50	45
246	10	4c. carmine-rose (1898)	8·00	8·50
247	29	30c. bright mauve and chestnut	4·25	2·25
		a. Bright violet and chestnut	5·00	2·50
249	19	2r.50 purple/red (1899)	29·00	50·00
245/9 *Set of 4*			40·00	55·00
245s, 247s/9s Optd "Specimen" *Set of 3*			60·00	

Six Cents
(40)

2 R. 25 C.
(41)

1898 (Dec)**–99**.

(a) No. 196 surch with T **40**.

250	29	6c. on 15c. sage-green	1·00	75

(b) As No. 138, but colour changed and perf 14, surch as T **41** *(1899)*.

254	19	1r.50 on 2r.50 slate	20·00	45·00
		w. Wmk inverted	£140	£190
255		2r.25 on 2r.50 yellow	35·00	80·00
250s/5s Optd "Specimen" *Set of 3*			70·00	

43

1899–1900. Wmk Crown CA (1r.50, 2r.25 wmk Crown CC). P 14.

256	9	2c. pale orange-brown	3·00	30
257	39	3c. deep green	3·00	55
258	10	4c. yellow	3·00	2·75
259	29	6c. rose and black	1·50	45
260	39	12c. sage-green and rose (1900)	4·00	7·00
261	29	15c. blue	5·50	1·25
262	39	75c. black and red-brown	5·50	6·50
263	43	1r.50 blue	22·00	38·00
264		2r.25 dull blue	32·00	38·00
256/64 *Set of 9*			70·00	85·00
256s/64s Optd "Specimen" *Set of 9*			£180	

44

45

46

47

48

1903 (29 May)**–05**. Wmk Crown CA. P 14.

265	44	2c. red-brown (21.7.03)	2·00	20
266	45	3c. green (11.6.03)	2·00	1·00
267		4c. orange-yellow and blue	2·00	3·75
268	46	5c. dull purple (2.7.03)	1·50	60
269	47	6c. carmine (5.11.03)	9·50	1·50
		w. Wmk inverted	75·00	
270	45	12c. sage-green and rosine (13.8.03)	5·00	11·00
271	48	15c. blue (2.7.03)	6·50	3·00
272	45	25c. bistre (11.8.03)	4·00	8·00
273		30c. dull violet and green	3·25	4·00
274	45	75c. dull blue and orange (31.3.05)	3·00	19·00
275	48	1r.50 greyish slate (7.4.04)	65·00	55·00
276		2r.25 brown and green (12.4.04)	65·00	50·00
265/76 *Set of 12*			£150	£140
265s/76s Optd "Specimen" *Set of 12*			£150	

1904 (13 Sept)**–05**. Wmk Mult Crown CA. *Ordinary paper*. P 14.

277	44	2c. red-brown (17.11.04)	1·50	10
278	45	3c. green (17.11.04)	1·50	15
279		4c. orange and ultramarine	2·50	1·50
		w. Wmk inverted	†	£150
280	46	5c. dull purple (29.11.04)	2·50	1·25
		a. Chalk-surfaced paper (5.10.05)	4·50	70
281	47	6c. carmine (11.10.04)	2·50	15
282	45	12c. sage-green and rosine (29.9.04)	1·50	1·75
283	48	15c. blue (1.12.04)	2·50	60
284		25c. bistre (5.1.05)	6·00	3·75
285		30c. violet and green (7.9.05)	2·50	3·00
286	45	75c. dull blue and orange (25.5.05)	5·25	8·00
287	48	1r.50 grey (5.1.05)	27·00	10·00
288		2r.25 brown and green (22.12.04)	22·00	29·00
277/88 *Set of 12*			70·00	50·00

50

51

1908. Wmk Mult Crown CA. P 14.

289	50	5c. deep purple (26 May)	2·75	10
290		5c. dull purple	4·00	30
291	51	6c. carmine (6 June)	1·50	10
289s, 291s Optd "Specimen" *Set of 2*			65·00	

1910 (1 Aug)**–11**. Wmk Mult Crown CA. P 14.

292	44	2c. brown-orange (20.5.11)	1·50	50
293	48	3c. green (5.7.11)	1·00	75
294		10c. sage-green and maroon	2·50	2·25
295		25c. grey	2·50	1·50
296		50c. chocolate	4·00	7·50
297		1r. purple/yellow	7·50	10·00
298		2r. red/yellow	15·00	28·00
299		5r. black/green	38·00	65·00
300		10r. black/red	90·00	£180
292/300 *Set of 9*			£150	£275
292s/300s Optd "Specimen" *Set of 9*			£190	

Examples of Nos. 298/300 are known showing a forged Colombo registered postmark dated '27.1.10'.

52

53

(A)

(B)

Most values in Type **52** were produced by two printing operations, using "Key" and "Duty" plates. Differences in the two Dies of the Key plate are described in the introduction to this catalogue.

In the Ceylon series, however, the 1c. and 5c. values, together with later printings of the 3c. and 6c., were printed from special plates at one operation. These plates can be identified by the large "C" in the value tablet (see illustration A). Examples of these values from Key and Duty plates printing have value tablet as illustration B. The 3c. and 5c. stamps from the single plates *resemble* Die I, and the 1c. and 6c. Die II, although in the latter case the inner top corners of the side panels are square and not curved.

1912–25. Wmk Mult Crown CA. *Chalk-surfaced paper (30c. to 100r.)*. P 14.

(a) Printed from single plates. Value tablet as A.

301	52	1c. brown (1919)	1·00	10
		w. Wmk inverted	22·00	
302		3c. blue-green (1919)	3·00	45
		w. Wmk inverted	20·00	30·00
		y. Wmk inverted and reversed	26·00	45·00
303		5c. purple	8·00	2·75
		a. Wmk sideways (Crown to right of CA)	£475	
		x. Wmk reversed	†	£140
		y. Wmk inverted and reversed	90·00	
304		5c. bright magenta	1·00	60
		w. Wmk inverted		90·00
305		6c. pale scarlet (1919)	10·00	85
		a. Wmk sideways (Crown to left of CA)	42·00	85·00
		w. Wmk inverted	30·00	45·00
306		6c. carmine	17·00	1·25
		a. Wmk sideways (Crown to right of CA)	55·00	
		aw. Wmk sideways (Crown to left of CA)	85·00	
		w. Wmk inverted and reversed	32·00	

(b) Printed from Key and Duty plates. Die I. 3c. and 6c. have value tablet as B.

307	52	2c. brown-orange	40	30
		a. Deep orange-brown	30	20
308		3c. yellow-green	6·50	2·25
		a. Deep green (1917)	4·50	1·10
309		6c. scarlet (*shades*)	1·10	50
		a. Wmk sideways	†	
310		10c. sage-green	3·00	1·75
		a. Deep sage-green (1917)	5·00	2·50
		w. Wmk inverted	£120	
311		15c. deep bright blue	2·50	1·25
		a. Ultramarine (1918)	1·75	1·25
		aw. Wmk inverted	24·00	
312		25c. orange and blue	6·50	4·50
		a. Yellow and blue (1917)	1·75	1·75
		aw. Wmk inverted	£120	£120
313		30c. blue-green and violet	4·00	3·25
		a. Yellow-green and violet (1915)	7·00	4·00
		ab. Wmk sideways (Crown to right of CA)	30·00	
		abw. Wmk Crown to left of CA	32·00	
		aw. Wmk inverted	48·00	
314		50c. black and scarlet	1·50	1·75
		w. Wmk inverted	19·00	
315		1r. purple/yellow	4·00	3·50
		a. White back (1913)	4·00	4·75
		as. Optd "Specimen"	50·00	
		b. On lemon (1915)	4·25	8·00
		bs. Optd "Specimen"	45·00	
		c. On orange-buff (1918)	26·00	35·00
		cw. Wmk inverted	75·00	
		d. On pale yellow (1922)	4·50	10·00
		ds. Optd "Specimen"	42·00	
316		2r. black and/yellow	3·25	12·00
		a. White back (1913)	2·75	12·00
		as. Optd "Specimen"	50·00	
		b. On lemon (1915)	25·00	27·00
		bs. Optd "Specimen"	40·00	
		c. On orange-buff (1919)	40·00	42·00
		cw. Wmk inverted	65·00	
		d. On pale yellow (1921)	40·00	40·00
317		5r. black/green	17·00	29·00
		a. White back (1914)	20·00	32·00
		as. Optd "Specimen"	48·00	
		b. On blue-grn (olive back) (1917)	18·00	35·00
		bs. Optd "Specimen"	60·00	
		bw. Wmk inverted	75·00	90·00
		c. Die II. On emerald back (1923)	45·00	95·00
		cs. Optd "Specimen"	60·00	
318		10r. purple and black/red	65·00	85·00
		aw. Wmk inverted	£170	
		b. Die II (1923)	75·00	£130
		bw. Wmk inverted	£350	
319		20r. black and red/blue	£130	£140
320	53	50r. dull purple	£425	
		a. Break in scroll	£850	
		b. Broken crown and scroll	£850	
		f. Damaged leaf at bottom right	£850	
		s. Optd "Specimen"	£160	
321		100r. grey-black	£1600	
		a. Break in scroll	£3000	
		b. Broken crown and scroll	£3000	
		f. Damaged leaf at bottom right	£3000	
		s. Optd "Specimen"	£300	

322		w. Wmk inverted	£3750	
	500r.	dull green	£6000	
		a. Break in scroll	£9000	
		b. Broken crown and scroll	£9000	
		f. Damaged leaf at bottom right....		
		s. Optd "Specimen"	£500	
323	1000r.	purple/*red* (1925)	£21000	
		b. Broken crown and scroll	£27000	
		e. Break in lines below left scroll .		
		f. Damaged leaf at bottom right....	£900	
		s. Optd "Specimen"		
301/18		*Set of 14*	95·00	£120
301s/19s		Optd "Specimen" *Set of 15*	£400	

For illustrations of the varieties on Nos. 320/3 see above No. 51*b* of Bermuda.

The 2c. and 5c. exist in coils, constructed from normal sheets, used in stamp-affixing machines introduced in 1915.

Sideways watermark varieties are described as seen *from the back of the stamp.*

The "substituted crown" watermark variety is known on the sheet margin of the 1c., No. 301.

WAR STAMP (54)   **WAR STAMP ONE CENT** (55)

1918 (18 Nov)–**19.** (a) *Optd with T* **54** *by Govt Printer, Colombo.*

330	52	2c. brown-orange	20	40
		a. Opt inverted	40·00	45·00
		b. Opt double	30·00	35·00
		c. Opt omitted in pair with opt inverted	£450	
331		3c. blue-green (No. 302) (1919)......	2·25	40
332		3c. deep green (No. 308*a*)	20	50
		a. Opt double	70·00	75·00
333		5c. purple	50	30
		a. Opt double	38·00	42·00
		w. Wmk inverted	90·00	
334		5c. bright magenta	2·75	2·25
		a. Opt inverted	40·00	45·00
		b. Opt double	30·00	40·00

(b) *Surch with T* **55.**

335	52	1c. on 5c. purple	50	40
		w. Wmk inverted	£120	
		y. Wmk inverted and reversed	90·00	
336		1c. on 5c. bright magenta	1·60	20
330s, 332s/3s, 335s Optd "Specimen" *Set of 4*........			£110	

Collectors are warned against forgeries of the errors in the "WAR STAMP" overprints.

1918. *Surch as T* **55**, *but without* "WAR STAMP".

337	52	1c. on 5c. purple	15	25
		a. Surch double	£160	
		bs. Optd "Specimen"	38·00	
		y. Wmk inverted and reversed.	£120	
337*c*		1c. on 5c. bright magenta	2·50	3·00

1921–32. *Wmk Mult Script CA. Chalk-surfaced paper* (30c. to 100r.). P 14.

(a) *Printed from single plates. Value tablet as A.*

338	52	1c. brown (1927)	1·00	35
339		3c. green (5.5.22)	3·25	75
		w. Wmk inverted	19·00	32·00
340		3c. slate-grey (1923)	75	20
		a. Wmk sideways	£1300	
		w. Wmk inverted	25·00	
341		5c. purple (1927)	60	15
342		6c. carmine-red (3.8.21)	2·00	75
		w. Wmk inverted	20·00	32·00
		y. Wmk inverted and reversed ...	40·00	
343		6c. bright violet (1922)	1·25	15
		w. Wmk inverted	25·00	
		y. Wmk inverted and reversed ...	40·00	

(b) *Printed from Key and Duty plates.*

344	52	2c. brown-orange (Die II) (1927)....	70	25
345		9c. red/*pale yellow* (Die I) (1926)	1·00	30
346		10c. sage-green (Die I) (16.9.21)	1·40	40
		aw. Wmk inverted	28·00	
		ay. Wmk inverted and reversed ...	25·00	40·00
		b. Die II (1924)	1·75	60
		c. Vert gutter pair. Die I and Die II. Nos. 346 and 346b..............	£300	
347		12c. rose-scarlet (Die I) (1925)	4·75	5·50
		a. Die II	1·00	2·25
		as. Optd "Specimen"	90·00	
		b. Vert gutter pair. Die I and Die II. Nos. 347/a	£150	
348		15c. ultramarine (Die I) (30.5.22) ...	3·25	11·00
349		15c. green/*pale yellow* (Die I) (1923).................................	2·00	1·25
		a. Die II (1924)	2·00	1·00
		aw. Wmk inverted	25·00	
		b. Vert gutter pair. Die I and Die II. Nos. 349/a	£275	
350		20c. bright blue (Die I) (1922)	3·75	6·00
		aw. Wmk inverted	50·00	
		b. Die II (1924)	3·50	45
		c. Vert gutter pair. Die I and Die II. Nos. 350 and 350b..............	£275	
351		25c. orange-yellow and blue (Die I) (17.10.21)	1·75	1·90
		aw. Wmk inverted	70·00	
		b. Die II (1924)	3·50	1·25
		c. Vert gutter pair. Die I and Die II. Nos. 351/b	£170	
352		30c. yellow-green & vio (Die I) (15.3.22)	1·60	3·25
		a. Die II (1924)	4·00	1·25
		b. Vert gutter pair. Die I and Die II. Nos. 352/a	£500	
353		50c. black and scarlet (Die II) (1922).................................	1·60	80
		a. Die I (1932)	55·00	75·00

354		1r. purple/*pale yellow* (Die I) (1923)	15·00	27·00
		a. Die II (1925)	18·00	24·00
		b. Vert gutter pair. Die I and Die II. Nos. 354/a	£375	
355		2r. black & red/*pale yell* (Die II) (1923)	7·00	8·00
356		5r. black/*emerald* (Die II) (1924) ...	32·00	55·00
357		20r. black and red/*blue* (Die II) (1924)	£160	£200
358	53	50r. dull purple (1924)	£475	£850
		a. Break in scroll	£900	
		b. Broken crown and scroll	£900	
		e. Break in lines below left scroll .	£900	
		f. Damaged leaf at bottom right....	£900	
		g. Gash in fruit and leaf	£900	
		s. Optd "Specimen"	£180	
359		100r. brownish grey (1924)	£1700	
		a. Break in scroll	£3000	
		b. Broken crown and scroll	£3000	
		e. Break in lines below left scroll .	£3000	
		f. Damaged leaf at bottom right....	£3000	
		h. grey-black	£1700	
		ha. Break in scroll	£3000	
		hb. Broken crown and scroll	£3000	
		he. Break in lines below left scroll .	£3000	
		hf. Damaged leaf at bottom right....	£3000	
		s. Optd "Specimen"	£375	
360		100r. dull purple and blue (24.10.27).	£1400	
		a. Break in scroll	£2500	
		b. Broken crown and scroll	£2500	
		e. Break in lines below left scroll .	£2500	
		f. Damaged leaf at bottom right....	£2500	
		g. Gash in fruit and leaf	£2500	
		s. Optd "Specimen"	£375	
338/56		*Set of 19*	70·00	95·00
338s/57s		Optd "Specimen" *Set of 20*	£500	

The 2c. to 30c. and 1r. values produced from Key and Duty plates were printed in sheets of 240 using two plates one above the other. Nos. 346c, 347b, 349b, 350c, 351b, 353b and 354b come from printings in 1924 and 1925 which combined Key Plate 7 (Die I) with Key Plate 12 (Die II).

No. 353a, from Key Plate 23, was a mistake; the "retired" Die I being issued in error when it became necessary to replace Key Plate 21.

For illustrations of the varieties on Nos. 358/60 see above No. 51*b* of Bermuda.

2 Cents.

(56)   57

(Surch at Ceylon Govt Printing Works)

1926 (27 Nov). *Surch as T* **56.**

361	52	2c. on 3c. slate-grey	80	1·00
		a. Surch double	70·00	
		b. Bar omitted	75·00	85·00
362		5c. on 6c. bright violet	50	40
361s/2s		Optd "Specimen" *Set of 2*	60·00	

No. 361b comes from the bottom horizontal row of the sheet which was often partially obscured by the selvedge during surcharging.

1927 (27 Nov)–**29.** *Wmk Mult Script CA. Chalk-surfaced paper.* P 14.

363	57	1r. dull and bright purple (1928)	2·50	1·25
364		2r. green and carmine (1929)..........	3·75	2·75
365		5r. green and brown-orange (1928).....	14·00	20·00
366		10r. green and brown-orange	38·00	80·00
367		20r. dull purple and blue	£120	£200
363/7		*Set of 5*	£150	£275
363s/7s		Optd "Specimen" *Set of 5*	£150	

No. 364. Collectors are warned against faked 2r. stamps, showing what purports to be a double centre.

58 Tapping Rubber

59 Adam's Peak

60 Colombo Harbour

61 Plucking tea

64 Coconut Palms

62 Hill paddy (rice)

63 River scene

65 Temple of the Tooth, Kandy

66 Ancient irrigation tank

67 Wild elephants

68 Trincomalee

(Recess D.L.R. (2, 3, 20, 50c.), B.W. (others))

1935 (1 May)–**36.** *T* **58/68.** Wmk Mult Script CA (sideways on 10, 15, 25, 30c. and 1r.). Various perfs.

368	58	2c. black and carmine (P 12×13)	30	40
		a. Perf 14	9·00	40
369	59	3c. blk and ol-green (P 13×12) (1.10.35)	35	40
		a. Perf 14	27·00	35
370	60	6c. black and blue (P 11×11½) (1.1.36)	30	30
371	61	9c. green & orange (P 11×11½) (1.1.36)	1·00	65
372	62	10c. black & purple (P 11½×11) (1.6.35)	1·25	2·25
373	63	15c. red-brown and green (P 11½×11)	1·00	50
374	64	20c. black & grey-blue (P 12×13) (1.1.36)	1·75	2·50
375	65	25c. deep blue and chocolate (P 11½×11)	1·40	1·25
376	66	30c. carm and green (P 11½×11) (1.8.35)	2·25	2·75
377	67	50c. black and mauve (P 14) (1.1.36)	10·00	1·75
378	68	1r. vio-bl & chocolate (P 11½×11) (1.7.35)	20·00	16·00
368/78		*Set of 11*	35·00	26·00
368s/78s		Perf "Specimen" *Set of 11*......	£180	

1935 (6 May). *Silver Jubilee. As Nos. 91/4 of Antigua.* P 13½×14.

379		6c. ultramarine and grey	65	30
		f. Diagonal line by turret	65·00	32·00
		g. Dot to left of chapel	95·00	48·00
		h. Dot by flagstaff	95·00	48·00
		i. Dash by turret	£100	55·00
380		9c. green and indigo	70	1·75
		f. Diagonal line by turret	85·00	£120
		g. Dot to left of chapel	£130	£170
		h. Dot by flagstaff	£130	£170
381		20c. brown and deep blue	4·25	2·75
		f. Diagonal line by turret	£190	£130
		g. Dot to left of chapel	£325	£190
382		50c. slate and purple	5·25	10·00
		f. Diagonal line by turret	£300	£375
		h. Dot by flagstaff	£375	£425
379/82		*Set of 4*	9·75	13·00
379s/82s		Perf "Specimen" *Set of 4*	£120	

For illustrations of plate varieties, see Omnibus section following Zanzibar.

1937 (12 May). *Coronation. As Nos. 95/7 of Antigua.* P 11×11½.

383		6c. carmine	65	50
384		9c. green	2·50	4·00
385		20c. blue	3·50	3·50
383/5		*Set of 3*	6·00	7·25
383s/5s		Perf "Specimen" *Set of 3*	90·00	

69 Tapping Rubber

70 Sigiriya (Lion Rock)

71 Ancient Guard-stone, Anuradhapura

72 King George VI

Comma flaw (Pl A R. 5/6)

Apostrophe flaw (Frame Pl IA R. 6/6)
(ptg of 1 Jan 1943 only)

(Recess B.W. (6, 10, 15, 20, 25, 30c., 1r., 2r. (both)), D.L.R (others)
T **72** typo D.L.R.)

1938–49. T **69/72** and designs as 1935–36, but with portrait of
King George VI instead of King George V, "POSTAGE &
REVENUE" omitted and some redrawn. Wmk Mult Script CA
(sideways on 10, 15, 25, 30c. and 1r.). Chalk-surfaced paper
(5r.). P 11×11½ (6, 20c., 2r. (both)), 11½×11 (10, 15, 25, 30c.,
1r.), 11½×13 (2c.), 13×11½ (3, 50c.), 13½ (5c.) or 14 (5r.).

386	69	2c. black and carmine (25.4.38)	15·00	1·75
		aa. Comma flaw	£120	1·75
		a. Perf 13½×13 (1938)	£120	1·75
		ab. Comma flaw	2·00	10
		b. Perf 13½ (25.4.38)	2·00	10
		c. Perf 11×11½ (17.2.44)	80	85
		cw. Wmk inverted	—	£750
		d. Perf 12 (22.4.49)	2·00	3·50
387	60	3c. black and deep blue-green		
		(21.3.38)	10·00	1·25
		a. Perf 13×13½ (1938)	£250	10·00
		b. Perf 13½ (21.3.38)	4·00	10
		c. Perf 14 (line) (7.41)	£120	1·00
		d. Perf 11½×11 (14.5.42)	80	10
		da. "A" of "CA" missing from wmk	£900	£900
		dw. Wmk inverted	†	—
		e. Perf 12 (14.1.46)	65	85
387f	64	5c. sage-green & orange (1.1.43)	30	10
		fa. Apostrophe flaw	70·00	35·00
		g. Perf 12 (1947)	1·75	30
388	60	6c. black and blue (1.1.38)	30	10
389	70	10c. black and light blue (1.2.38)	2·75	10
		a. Wmk upright (1.6.44)	2·50	50
390	63	15c. green and red-brown (1.1.38)	2·00	10
		a. Wmk upright (23.7.45)	2·75	60
391	61	20c. black and grey-blue (15.1.38)	3·25	10
392	65	25c. deep blue and chocolate		
		(15.1.38)	5·00	30
		a. Wmk upright (1944)	4·25	30
393	66	30c. carmine and green (1.2.38)	12·00	2·50
		a. Wmk upright (16.4.45)	13·00	4·00
394	67	50c. black and mauve (25.4.38)	£160	45·00
		a. Perf 13×13½ (25.4.38)	£350	2·75
		b. Perf 13½ (25.4.38)	19·00	30
		c. Perf 14 (line) (4.42)	£100	27·00
		d. Perf 11½×11 (14.5.42)	4·25	3·75
		da. "A" of "CA" missing from wmk	£900	
		e. Perf 12 (14.1.46)	4·25	20
395	68	1r. blue-violet and chocolate		
		(1.2.38)	17·00	1·25
		a. Wmk upright (1944)	18·00	2·25
396	71	2r. black and carmine (1.2.38)	13·00	2·50
		a. "A" of "CA" missing from wmk		
396b		2r. black and violet (15.3.47)	2·25	2·00
397	72	5r. green and purple (1.7.38)	40·00	5·50
		a. Ordinary paper. Green and pale purple (19.2.43)	15·00	4·00
386/97a (cheapest) Set of 14			70·00	11·50
386s/97s Perf "Specimen" Set of 14			£375	

Printings of the 2c., 3c. and 50c. perforated 11×11½ or 11½×11 were
produced by Bradbury, Wilkinson after the De La Rue works had been
bombed in December 1940.

(73)   (74)

1940–41. Nos. 388 and 391 surch by Govt Ptg Office, Colombo.

398	73	3c. on 6c. black and blue (10.5.41)	50	10
399	74	3c. on 20c. black and grey-blue (5.11.40)	3·00	1·50

1946 (10 Dec). Victory. As Nos. 110/11 of Antigua.

400		6c. blue	15	25
401		15c. brown	15	1·25
400s/1s Perf "Specimen" Set of 2			70·00	

75 Parliament Building

76 Adam's Peak

77 Temple of the Tooth

78 Anuradhapura

(Des R. Tenison and M. S. V. Rodrigo. Recess B.W.)

1947 (25 Nov). Inauguration of New Constitution. T **75/8**. Wmk
Mult Script CA. P 11×12 (horiz) or 12×11 (vert).

402	75	6c. black and blue	15	15
403	76	10c. black, orange and carmine	20	25
404	77	15c. green and purple	20	80
405	78	25c. ochre and emerald-green	20	1·00
402/5 Set of 4			65	2·00
402s/5s Perf "Specimen" Set of 4			85·00	

DOMINION

79 Lion Flag of Dominion

80 D. S. Senanayake

81 Lotus Flowers and Sinhalese Letters "Sri"

(Recess (flag typo) B.W.)

1949 (4 Feb–5 Apr). First Anniv of Independence.

(a) Wmk Mult Script CA (sideways on 4c.). P 12½×12 (4c.) or
12×12½ (5c.).

406	79	4c. yellow, carmine and brown	20	20
407	80	5c. brown and green	10	10

(b) W **81** (sideways on 15c.). P 13×12½ (15c.) or 12×12½ (25c.) (5
April).

408	79	15c. yellow, carmine and vermilion	50	15
409	80	25c. brown and blue	15	65
406/9 Set of 4			80	1·00

The 15c. is larger, measuring 28×12 mm.

82 Globe and Forms of Transport

83

84

CEYLON

(Recess U.L.R.)

1949 (10 Oct). 75th Anniv of Universal Postal Union. W **81**. P 13
(25c.) or 12 (others).

410	82	5c. brown and bluish green	75	10
411	83	15c. black and carmine	1·10	2·75
412	84	25c. black and ultramarine	1·10	1·10
410/12 Set of 3			2·75	3·50

85 Kandyan Dancer

86 Kiri Vehera Polonnaruwa

87 Vesak Orchid

88 Sigiriya (Lion Rock)

89 Octagon Library, Temple of the Tooth

90 Ruins at Madirigiriya

(Recess B.W.)

1950 (4 Feb). T **85/90**. W **81**. P 11×11½ (75c.), 11½×11 (1r.),
12×12½ (others).

413	85	4c. purple and scarlet	10	10
414	86	5c. green	10	10
415	87	15c. blue-green and violet	2·25	40
416	88	30c. carmine and yellow	30	70
417	89	75c. ultramarine and orange	6·00	20
418	90	1r. deep blue and brown	1·75	30
413/18 Set of 6			9·50	1·50

These stamps were issued with redrawn inscriptions in 1958/9.

91 Sambars, Ruhuna National Park

92 Ancient Guard-stone, Anuradhapura

93 Harvesting rice

94 Coconut trees

95 Sigiriya fresco

96 Star Orchid

97 Rubber Plantation

98 Outrigger canoe

99 Tea Plantation

100 River Gal Dam

101 Bas-relief, Anuradhapura   **102** Harvesting rice

I. No. 424 II.   No. 424a (Dot added)

(Photo Courvoisier)

1951 (1 Aug)–**54**. *T* **91/102**. No wmk. P 11½.

419	**91**	2c. brown and blue-green (15.5.54)	10	1·25
420	**92**	3c. black and slate-violet (15.5.54).	10	1·00
421	**93**	6c. brown-black & yellow-green (15.5.54)	10	30
422	**94**	10c. green and blue-grey	1·00	65
423	**95**	25c. orange-brown & bright blue (15.5.54)	10	20
424	**96**	35c. red and deep green (I) (1.2.52)..	1·50	1·50
		a. Type II (1954)	6·00	60
425	**97**	40c. deep brown (15.5.54)	5·00	1·00
426	**98**	50c. indigo and slate-grey (15.3.54)..	30	10
427	**99**	85c. black and deep blue-green (15.5.54)	75	30
428	**100**	2r. blue and deep brown (15.5.54)..	6·50	1·25
429	**101**	5r. brown and orange (15.3.54)	4·75	1·40
430	**102**	10r. red-brown and buff (15.3.54)..	45·00	14·00
419/30		*Set of 12*	60·00	19·00

Nos. 413/30 (except 422) were reissued in 1958–62, redrawn with 'CEYLON' much smaller and other inscriptions in Sinhalese.

STAMP BOOKLETS

1905 (Oct). *Black on grey (No. SB1) or black on buff (No. SB1a) covers. Stapled.*

SB1	1r.21, booklet containing twenty-four 5c. (No. 280) in blocks of 12	
SB1*a*	1r.45, booklet containing twenty-four 6c. (No. 281) in blocks of 6	£4000

1908. *Black on grey cover. Advertisement on back cover. Stapled.*

SB2	1r.20, booklet containing twenty-four 5c. (No. 289) in blocks of 12	

1912. *Black on grey cover. Advertisement on back cover. Stapled.*

SB2*a*	1r.20, booklet containing twenty-four 5c. (No. 304) in blocks of 12	

1919. *Black on orange covers. Telegraph details on back cover. Stapled.*

SB3	1r.44, booklet containing twenty-four 6c. (No. 311) in blocks of 6	
	a. Black on grey cover. Advertisement on back cover	
SB4	1r.44, booklet containing twenty-four 3c. and twelve 6c. (Nos. 310/11) in blocks of 6	
	a. Advertisement on back cover	

1922. *Black on green covers. "Fiat" advertisement on back cover. Stapled.*

SB5	1r.44, booklet containing twenty-four 6c. (No. 343) in blocks of 6	
SB6	1r.46, booklet containing twenty-four 6c. (No. 343) in blocks of 6	£3000
SB6*a*	1r.46, booklet containing twenty-four 3c. and twelve 6c. (Nos. 340/3) in blocks of 6	
	b. Black on orange cover. "Colombo Jewelry Store" advertisement on back cover	

1926. *Black on green covers. Kennedy & Co. (No. SB7) or Fiat (No. SB8) advertisements on back cover. Stapled.*

SB7	2r.06, booklet containing twelve 3c., 5c. on 6c. and 9c. (Nos. 340, 362 and 345) in blocks of 6	£2750
SB8	2r.16, booklet containing twenty-four 9c. (No. 345) in blocks of 6	

1932. *Black on green covers. Stapled.*

SB9	1r.80, booklet containing thirty 6c. (No. 343) in blocks of 6 and pane of three airmail labels...	£1200
SB10	2r.70, booklet containing thirty 9c. (No. 345) in blocks of 6 and pane of three airmail labels...	£1600

1935 (May). *Silver Jubilee of King George V. Black on light blue (No. SB11) or light green (No. SB12) covers. Stapled.*

SB11	1r.80, booklet containing thirty 6c. (No. 379) in blocks of 6	£1300
SB12	2r.70, booklet containing thirty 9c. (No. 380) in blocks of 6	£1600

1935 (Dec)–**36**. *Black on blue (No. SB13) or green (No. SB14) covers. Stapled.*

SB13	1r.80, booklet containing thirty 6c. (No. 370) in blocks of 6 and pane of four airmail labels ...	£800
	a. Stamps in blocks of 10	£800
SB14	2r.70, booklet containing thirty 9c. (No. 371) in blocks of 6 and pane of four airmail labels ...	£900
	a. Stamps in blocks of 10 (1936)	£900

1937 (Apr–June). *Coronation of King George VI. Black on blue (No. SB15) or olive-green (No. SB16) covers. Stapled.*

SB15	1r.80, booklet containing thirty 6c. (No. 383) in blocks of 10 and pane of four airmail labels (June)	£950
SB16	2r.70, booklet containing thirty 9c. (No. 384) in blocks of 10 and pane of four airmail labels ..	£1000

1938. *Black on blue (No. SB17) or grey (No. SB18) covers. Stapled.*

SB17	1r.80, booklet containing thirty 6c. (No. 388) in blocks of 10 and pane of four airmail labels ..	£1200
SB18	3r. booklet containing fifteen 20c. (No. 391) in blocks of 5 or 10 and pane of four airmail labels	£1200

1941. *Black on pink cover, with contents amended in manuscript. Stapled.*

SB19	1r.80, booklet containing sixty 3c. on 6c. (No. 398) in blocks of 10	
	a. Black on blue cover	

1951 (5 Dec). *Black on buff cover. Stitched.*

SB20	1r. booklet containing twenty 5c. (No. 414) in blocks of four and pane of airmail labels	12·00
	a. Containing two blocks of ten 5c. stamps and no airmail labels	45·00

1952 (21 Jan). *Black on green cover. Stitched.*

SB21	6r. booklet containing eight 75c. (No. 417) in blocks of 4 and two panes of four airmail labels	18·00

OFFICIAL STAMPS

1869. Issues of 1867–68 overprinted "SERVICE" in block letters. Although these stamps were prepared for use and sent out to the colony, they were never issued.

Prices:

Narrow "SERVICE"		Wide "SERVICE"	
No. 64*d*, 2d	70·00	No. 61, 1d	70·00
No. 67, 6d	70·00	No. 62, 3d	£130
No. 68, 8d	70·00		
No. 71, 1s	£160		
No. 72*b*, 2s	£120		
No. 72*b*, 2s. *imp*	£900		

Until 1 October 1895 all Official mail was carried free. After that date postage was paid on Official letters to the general public, on certain interdepartmental mail and on all packets over 1lb in weight. Nos. O1/17 were provided for this purpose.

On Service
(O **3**)

1895. *Optd with Type O* **3** *by the Govt Printer, Colombo.*

O1	**9**	2c. green (No. 147)	10·00	45
		w. Wmk inverted	†	—
O2	**39**	3c. terracotta and blue-green (No. 245)	10·00	1·00
O3	**28**	5c. dull purple (No. 195)	3·75	30
O4	**29**	15c. sage-green (No. 196)	14·00	50
O5		25c. yellow-brown (No. 198)	11·00	1·75
O6		30c. bright mauve and chestnut (No. 247)	13·00	60
O7	**30**	1r.12 dull rose (*wmk sideways*) (No. 201)	80·00	55·00
		a. Opt double, one albino	£275	
		b. Wmk upright	95·00	70·00
O1/7		*Set of 7*	£130	55·00

1899 (June)–**1900**. *Nos. 256/7 and 261/2 optd with Type O* **3**.

O8	**9**	2c. pale orange-brown (3.00)	8·00	60
O9	**39**	3c. deep green (9.00)	9·00	3·00
O10	**29**	15c. blue (9.00)	19·00	60
O11	**39**	75c. black and red-brown (R.)	5·50	6·50
O8/11		*Set of 4*	38·00	9·50

1903 (26 Nov)–**04**. *Nos. 265/6, 268 and 271/3 optd with Type O* **3**.

O12	**44**	2c. red-brown (4.1.04)	15·00	1·00
O13	**45**	3c. green	9·00	2·00
O14	**46**	5c. dull purple	22·00	1·50
O15	**48**	15c. blue	30·00	2·50
O16		25c. bistre (15.7.04)	24·00	18·00
O17		30c. dull violet and green (14.3.04)	14·00	1·50
O12/17		*Set of 6*	£100	24·00

Stamps overprinted "On Service" were withdrawn on 1 October 1904.

POSTAL FISCAL

1952 (1 Dec). *As T* **72** *but inscr* "REVENUE" *at sides. Chalk-surfaced paper.*

F1	10r. dull green and yellow-orange	75·00	35·00

This revenue stamp was on sale for postal use from 1 December 1952 until 14 March 1954.

Used price for stamp with identifiable postal cancellation.

Cook Islands
see after New Zealand

Cyprus

Cyprus was part of the Turkish Ottoman Empire from 1571.

The first records of an organised postal service date from 1871 when a post office was opened at Nicosia (Lefkosa) under the jurisdiction of the Damascus Head Post Office. Various stamps of Turkey from the 1868 issue onwards are known used from this office, cancelled "KIBRIS", in Arabic, within a double-lined oblong. Manuscript cancellations have also been reported. The records report the opening of a further office at Larnaca (Tuzla) in 1873, but no cancellation for this office has been identified.

To provide an overseas postal service the Austrian Empire opened a post office in Larnaca during 1845. Stamps of the Austrian Post Offices in the Turkish Empire were placed on sale there from 1 June 1864 and were cancelled with an unframed straight-line mark or circular date stamp. This Austrian post office closed on 6 August 1878.

BRITISH ADMINISTRATION

Following the convention with Turkey, Great Britain assumed the administration of Cyprus on 11 July 1878 and the first post office, as part of the British G.P.O. system, was opened at Larnaca on 27 July 1878. Further offices at Famagusta, Kyrenia, Limassol, Nicosia and Paphos followed in September 1878.

The stamps of Great Britain were supplied to the various offices as they opened and continued to be used until the Cyprus Administration assumed responsibility for the postal service on 1 April 1880. With the exception of "969" (Nicosia) similar numeral cancellations had previously been used at offices in Great Britain.

Numeral postmarks for Headquarters Camp, Nicosia ("D48") and Polymedia (Polemidhia) Camp, Limassol ("D47") were supplied by the G.P.O. in London during January 1881. These cancellations had three bars above and three bars below the numeral. Similar marks, but with four bars above and below, had previously been used in London on newspapers and bulk mail.

Although both three bar cancellations subsequently occur on Cyprus issues only, isolated examples have been found on loose Great Britain stamps and there are no known covers or pieces which confirm such usage in Cyprus.

For illustrations of the postmark types see BRITISH POST OFFICES ABROAD notes, following GREAT BRITAIN.

FAMAGUSTA

Stamps of GREAT BRITAIN cancelled "982" as Type 9.

1878–80.

Z1	½d. rose-red (1870–79) (Plate Nos. 11, 13)..........	£700
Z2	1d. rose-red (1864–79)...............................	£475
	Plate Nos. 145, 174, 181, 193, 202, 204, 206, 215, 217.	
Z3	2d. blue (1858–69) (Plate Nos. 13, 14, 15)..........	£950
Z4	2½d. rosy mauve (1876) (Plate Nos. 13, 16).........	£1100
Z5	6d. grey (1874–80) (Plate No. 15)...................	
Z6	1s. green (1873–77) (Plate No. 12)..................	£2000

KYRENIA

Stamps of GREAT BRITAIN cancelled "974" as Type 9.

1878–80.

Z8	½d. rose-red (1870–79) (Plate No. 13)	
Z9	1d. rose-red (1864–79)............ From	£550
	Plate Nos. 168, 171, 193, 196, 206, 207, 209, 220.	
Z10	2d. blue (1858–69) (Plate Nos. 13, 15)....... From	£850
Z11	2½d. rosy mauve (1876–79)............ From	£1000
Z12	4d. sage-green (1877) (Plate No. 16)	
Z13	6d. grey (1874–80) (Plate No. 16)	

LARNACA

Stamps of GREAT BRITAIN cancelled "942" as Type 9.

1878–80.

Z14	½d. rose-red (1870–79)............ From	£250
	Plate Nos. 11, 12, 13, 14, 15, 19, 20.	
Z15	1d. rose-red (1864–79)............	£170
	Plate Nos. 129, 131, 146, 154, 170, 171, 174, 175, 176, 177, 178, 179, 181, 182, 183, 184, 187, 188, 190, 191, 192, 193, 194, 195, 196, 197, 198, 199, 200, 201, 202, 203, 204, 205, 206, 207, 208, 209, 210, 212, 213, 214, 215, 216, 217, 218, 220, 221, 222, 225.	
Z16	1½d. lake-red (1870) (Plate No. 3).................	£1800
Z17	2d. blue (1858–69) (Plate Nos. 9, 13, 14, 15)......	£225
Z18	2½d. rosy mauve (1876–79)............ From	65·00
	Plate Nos. 4, 5, 6, 8, 9, 10, 11, 12, 13, 14, 15, 16, 17.	
Z19	2½d. blue (1880) (Plate Nos. 17, 18)...............	£500
Z21	4d. sage-green (1877) (Plate Nos. 15, 16)	£550
Z22	6d. grey (1874–76) (Plate Nos. 15, 16, 17)	£500
Z23	6d. pale buff (1872–73) (Plate No. 11)	£2000
Z24	8d. orange (1876)..................................	£4750
Z25	1s. green (1873–77) (Plate Nos. 12, 13)	£950
Z27	5s. rose (1874) (Plate No. 2)......................	£4750

LIMASSOL

Stamps of GREAT BRITAIN cancelled "975" as Type 9.

1878–80.

Z28	½d. rose-red (1870–79) (Plate Nos. 11, 13, 15, 19)..........	£450
Z29	1d. rose-red (1864–79)............ From	£275
	Plate Nos. 159, 160, 171, 173, 174, 177, 179, 184, 187, 190, 193, 195, 196, 197, 198, 200, 202, 206, 207, 208, 209, 210, 213, 215, 216, 218, 220, 221, 222, 225.	
Z30	1½d. lake-red (1870–74) (Plate No. 3)	£1900
Z31	2d. blue (1858–69) (Plate Nos. 14, 15).............	£400
Z32	2½d. rosy-mauve (1876–80)............ From	£190
	Plate Nos. 11, 12, 13, 14, 15, 16.	
Z33	2½d. blue (1880) (Plate No. 17)....................	£1200
Z34	4d. sage-green (Plate No. 16)......................	£750

NICOSIA

Stamps of GREAT BRITAIN cancelled "969" as Type 9.

1878–80.

Z35	½d. rose-red (1870–79)......................	£450
	Plate Nos. 12, 13, 14, 15, 20.	
Z36	1d. rose-red (1864–79)............ From	£275
	Plate Nos. 170, 171, 174, 189, 190, 192, 193, 195, 196, 198, 200, 202, 203, 205, 206, 207, 210, 212, 214, 215, 218, 221, 222, 225.	
	1½d. lake-red (1870) (Plate No. 5).................	£2500
Z37	2d. blue (1858–69) (Plate Nos. 14, 15).............	£450
Z38	2½d. rosy mauve (1876–79)............ From	£190
	Plate Nos. 10, 11, 12, 13, 14, 15, 16.	
Z42	4d. sage-green (1877) (Plate No. 16)	£850
Z43	6d. grey (1873) (Plate No. 16)	£850

PAPHOS

Stamps of GREAT BRITAIN cancelled "981" as Type 9.

1878–80.

Z44	½d. rose-red (1870–79) (Plate Nos. 13, 15).........	
Z45	1d. rose-red (1864–79)............ From	£500
	Plate Nos. 196, 201, 202, 204, 206, 213, 217.	
Z46	2d. blue (1858–69) (Plate No. 15)..................	£850
Z47	2½d. rosy mauve (1876–79)............ From	£500
	Plate Nos. 13, 14, 15, 16.	

PRICES FOR STAMPS ON COVER TO 1945

No. 1	from × 10
No. 2	from × 50
No. 3	from × 100
No. 4	from × 8
Nos. 5/6	—
Nos. 7/10	from × 15
Nos. 11/15	from × 5
No. 16	—
Nos. 16a/24	from × 10
No. 25	from × 40
No. 26	—
No. 27	from × 10
No. 28	—
No. 29	from × 30
Nos. 31/5a	from × 10
Nos. 36/7	—
Nos. 40/9	from × 8
Nos. 50/71	from × 5
Nos. 74/99	from × 4
Nos. 100/2	—
Nos. 103/17	from × 4
No. 117a	—
Nos. 118/31	from × 5
No. 132	—
Nos. 133/43	from × 5
Nos. 144/7	from × 6
Nos. 148/63	from × 5

PERFORATION. Nos. 1/122 are perf 14.

Stamps of Great Britain overprinted

CYPRUS (1)   CYPRUS (2)

(Optd by D.L.R.)

1880 (1 April).

1	1	½d. rose	£110	£100
		a. Opt double (Plate 15)	†	£15000

Plate No.	Un.	Used.	Plate No.	Un.	Used.
12.	£180	£250	19	£5000	£700
15.	£110	£100			

2	2	1d. red	12·00	38·00
		a. Opt double (Plate 208)	£16000	
		aa. Opt double (Plate 218)	£4250	
		b. Vert pair, top stamp without opt (Plate 208)	£20000	

Plate No.	Un.	Used.	Plate No.	Un.	Used.
174.	£1200	£1200	208.	£100	55·00
181.	£400	£180	215.	12·00	50·00
184.	£12000	£2250	216.	16·00	38·00
193.	£750	†	217.	13·00	50·00
196.	£650	†	218.	19·00	55·00
201.	15·00	50·00	220.	£350	£375
205.	60·00	55·00			

3	2	2½d. rosy mauve	2·50	9·50
		a. Large thin "C" (Plate 14) (BK, JK).............	50·00	£200
		b. Large thin "C" (Plate 15) (BK, JK).............	90·00	£450
		w. Wmk inverted (Plate 15)	£375	

14.	2·50	9·50	15.	3·75	26·00

4	2	4d. sage-green (Plate 16)	£120	£200
5		6d. grey (Plate 16)	£500	£650
6		1s. green (Plate 13)	£700	£450

No. 3 has been reported from Plate 9.

HALF-PENNY (3) 18 mm   **HALF-PENNY** (4) 16 or 16½ mm

HALF-PENNY (5) 13 mm   **30 PARAS** (6)

(Optd by Govt Ptg Office, Nicosia)

1881 (Feb–June). No. 2 surch.

7	3	½d. on 1d. red (Feb)..........	70·00	85·00

	a. "HALFPENN" (BG, LG) (all plates)............ From	£2250 £2250

Plate No.	Un.	Used.	Plate No.	Un.	Used.
174.	£170	£325	215.	£700	£750
181.	£170	£180	216.	70·00	85·00
201.	95·00	£130	217.	£850	£750
205.	75·00	85·00	218.	£475	£550
208.	£180	£275	220.	£275	£350

8	4	½d. on 1d. red (Apr)	£120	£160
		a. Surch double (Plates 201 and 216)	£2750	£2500

Plate No.	Un.	Used.	Plate No.	Un.	Used.
201.	£120	£160	218.	—	£10000
216.	£350	£400			

9	5	½d. on 1d. red (1 June)	45·00	65·00
		aa. Surch double (Plate 205)	£700	
		ab. Surch double (Plate 215)	£450	£600
		b. Surch treble (Plate 205)..	£3750	
		ba. Surch treble (Plate 215)..	£700	
		bc. Surch treble (Plate 218)..	£3750	
		c. Surch quadruple (Plate 205)	£4750	
		ca. Surch quadruple (Plate 215)	£4750	

Plate No.	Un.	Used.	Plate No.	Un.	Used.
205.	£300		217.	£150	85·00
215.	45·00	65·00	218.	75·00	£100

The surcharge on No. 8 was handstamped; the others were applied by lithography.

(New Currency: 40 paras = 1 piastre, 180 piastres = £1)

1881 (June). No. 2 surch with T 6 by lithography.

10	6	30 paras on 1d. red	£110	80·00
		a. Surch double, one invtd (Plate 216)	£4000	
		aa. Surch double, one invtd (Plate 220)	£1300	£1000

Plate No.	Un.	Used.	Plate No.	Un.	Used.
201.	£130	95·00	217.	£180	£180
216.	£110	80·00	220.	£150	£160

7

"US" damaged at foot (R. 5/5 of both panes)

(Typo D.L.R)

1881 (1 July). Die I. Wmk Crown CC.

11	7	½pi. emerald-green	£180	45·00
		w. Wmk inverted	£600	£350
12		1pi. rose	£375	32·00
13		2pi. blue	£450	32·00
		w. Wmk inverted	—	£650
14		4pi. pale olive-green	£900	£275
15		6pi. olive-grey	£1700	£450

Stamps of Queen Victoria initialled "J.A.B." or overprinted "POSTAL SURCHARGE" with or without the same initials were employed for accounting purposes between the Chief Post Office and sub-offices, the initials are those of the then Postmaster, Mr. J. A. Bulmer.

1882 (May)–86. Die I*. Wmk Crown CA.

16	7	½pi. emerald-green (5.82)...........	£5000	£475
		a. Dull green (4.83)	18·00	1·75
		ab. Top left triangle detached........	—	£250
17		30pa. pale mauve (7.6.82)...........	60·00	22·00
		a. Top left triangle detached........	£950	£550
		b. Damaged "US"	£700	£350
18		1pi. rose (3.83)...........	95·00	2·50
		a. Top left triangle detached........	—	£275
19		2pi. blue (4.83)	£130	2·50
		a. Top left triangle detached........	—	£275
20		4pi. deep olive-green (10.83)...........	£500	35·00
		a. Pale olive-green	£350	27·00
		ab. Top left triangle detached........	—	£650
21		6pi. olive-grey (7.82)...........	55·00	17·00
		a. Top left triangle detached........	—	£475
22		12pi. orange-brown (1886)...........	£180	35·00
		s. Optd "Specimen"	£800	
16a/22		Set of 7	£800	95·00

*For description and illustrations of Dies I and II see Introduction. For illustration of "top left triangle detached" variety see above No. 21 of Antigua.

No. 21 with manuscript "Specimen" endorsement is known with "CYPRUS" and value double.

See also Nos. 31/7.

½ (8)   ½ (9)   30 PARAS   Spur on "1" (position 3 in setting)

(Surch litho by Govt Ptg Office, Nicosia)

1882. Surch with T 8/9.

(a) Wmk crown CC.

23		½ on ½pi. emerald-green (6.82)...........	£650	75·00
		c. Spur on "1"	£900	£120
		w. Wmk inverted		
24		30pa. on 1pi. rose (22.5.82)...........	£1500	£110

(b) Wmk Crown CA.

25	7	½ on ½pi. emerald-green (27.5.82)...........	£150	6·50
		a. Surch double	†	£2750
		b. "½" inserted by hand	†	
		c. Spur on "1"	£225	12·00

Nos. 23 and 25 were surcharged by a setting of 6 arranged as a horizontal row.

No. 25b shows an additional handstamped "½" applied to examples on which the surcharge was so misplaced as to almost omit one of the original "½"s.

(10)   11

Varieties of numerals:

1   **1**   **1**
Normal   Large   Small

2   **2**
Normal   Large

1886 (Apr). *Surch with T* **10** *(fractions approx 6 mm apart) in typography.*

(a) Wmk Crown CC.

26	**7**	½ on ½pi. emerald-green	£20000	

(b) Wmk Crown CA.

27	**7**	½ on ½pi. emerald-green	£250	70·00
		a. Large "2" at right	£2500	£750

1886 (May–June). *Surch with T* **10** *(fractions approx 8 mm apart) in typography.*

(a) Wmk Crown CC.

28	**7**	½ on ½pi. emerald-green	£8000	£425
		a. Large "1" at left	—	£1700
		b. Small "1" at right	£15000	£2250
		c. Large "2" at left	—	£2250
		d. Large "2" at right	†	£2250

(b) Wmk Crown CA.

29	**7**	½ on ½pi. emerald-green (June)	£400	10·00
		a. Large "1" at left	£2750	£225
		b. Small "1" at right	£3000	£275
		c. Large "2" at left	£3250	£325
		d. Large "2" at right	£3000	£225

Nos. 28/9 were surcharged in a setting of 60. The large "1" at left and large "2" at right both occur in the fourth vertical row, the large "2" at left in the fifth vertical row and the small "1" at right in the top horizontal row.

A third type of this surcharge is known with the fractions spaced approximately 10 mm apart on CA paper with postmarks from August 1886. This may be due to the shifting of type.

1892–94. *Die II. Wmk Crown CA.*

31	**7**	½pi. dull green	6·50	70
32		30pa. mauve	6·00	7·00
		a. Damaged "US"	£190	£190
33		1pi. carmine	13·00	3·00
34		2pi. ultramarine	14·00	1·75
35		4pi. olive-green	50·00	29·00
		a. Pale olive-green	18·00	25·00
36		6pi. olive-grey (1894)	£180	£550
37		12pi. orange brown (1893)	£140	£325
31/7 Set of 7			£350	£800

1894 (14 Aug)–**96.** *Colours changed and new values. Die II. Wmk Crown CA.*

40	**7**	½pi. green and carmine (1896)	4·00	1·25
		w. Wmk inverted		
41		30pa. bright mauve and green (1896)	2·00	1·50
		a. Damaged "US"	£140	£110
42		1pi. carmine and blue (1896)	6·50	1·25
43		2pi. blue and purple (1896)	8·50	1·25
44		4pi. sage-green and purple (1896)	17·00	7·00
45		6pi. sepia and green (1896)	14·00	20·00
46		9pi. brown and carmine	15·00	20·00
47		12pi. orange-brown and black (1896)	17·00	55·00
48		18pi. greyish slate and brown	50·00	50·00
49		45pi. grey-purple and blue	90·00	£140
40/9 Set of 10			£200	£275
40s/9s Optd "Specimen" Set of 10			£325	

LIMASSOL FLOOD HANDSTAMP. Following a flood on 14 November 1894, which destroyed the local stamp stocks, the postmaster of Limassol produced a temporary handstamp showing "½C.P." which was applied to local letters with the usual c.d.s.

(Typo D.L.R.)

1902–04. *Wmk Crown CA.*

50	**11**	½pi. green and carmine (12.02)	4·75	1·25
		w. Wmk inverted	85·00	55·00
51		30pa. violet and green (2.03)	10·00	3·25
		a. Mauve and green	16·00	6·50
		b. Damaged "US"	£250	£120
52		1pi. carmine and blue (9.03)	21·00	3·00
53		2pi. blue and purple (2.03)	65·00	12·00
54		4pi. olive-green and purple (9.03)	30·00	19·00
55		6pi. sepia and green (9.03)	40·00	£120
56		9pi. brown and carmine (5.04)	£100	£200
57		12pi. chestnut and black (4.03)	15·00	60·00
58		18pi. black and brown (5.04)	80·00	£150
59		45pi. dull purple and ultramarine (10.03)	£200	£500
50/9 Set of 10			£500	£950
50sw/9s Optd "Specimen" Set of 10			£450	

The ½pi "SPECIMEN" is only known with watermark inverted.

Broken top left triangle
(Left pane R. 7/5)

1904–10. *Wmk Mult Crown CA.*

60	**11**	5pa. bistre and black (14.1.08)	1·00	70
		a. Broken top left triangle	55·00	55·00
		w. Wmk inverted	£950	
61		10pa. orange and green (12.06)	3·25	50
		aw. Wmk inverted	—	90·00
		b. Yellow and green	38·00	5·50
		bw. Wmk inverted	—	£100
		c. Broken top left triangle	80·00	48·00
62		½pi. green and carmine (1.7.04)	5·50	20
		a. Broken top left triangle	£100	35·00
		w. Wmk inverted	£110	75·00
		y. Wmk inverted and reversed	†	£350
63		30pa. purple and green (1.7.04)	16·00	1·50
		a. Violet and green (1910)	18·00	2·50
		b. Broken top left triangle	£200	70·00
		c. Damaged "US"	£200	60·00
		w. Wmk inverted	†	£800
64		1pi. carmine and blue (11.04)	7·00	1·00
		a. Broken top left triangle	£120	60·00
65		2pi. blue and purple (11.04)	8·00	1·75
		a. Broken top left triangle	£160	80·00
66		4pi. olive-green and purple (2.05)	14·00	9·00
		a. Broken top left triangle	£225	£190
67		6pi. sepia and green (17.7.04)	18·00	15·00
		a. Broken top left triangle	£250	£250
68		9pi. brown and carmine (30.5.04)	38·00	8·50
		a. Yellow-brown and carmine	35·00	22·00
		aw. Wmk inverted	£150	90·00
		b. Broken top left triangle	£400	£225
69		12pi. chestnut and black (4.06)	27·00	42·00
		a. Broken top left triangle	£375	
70		18pi. black and brown (16.6.04)	35·00	11·00
		a. Broken top left triangle	£450	£275
71		45pi. dull purple & ultram (15.6.04)	85·00	£140
		a. Broken top left triangle	£800	
60/71 Set of 12			£225	£200
60s/1s Optd "Specimen" Set of 2			£130	

12   13

Broken bottom left triangle
(Right pane R. 10/6)

(Typo D.L.R.)

1912 (July)–**15.** *Wmk Mult Crown CA.*

74	**12**	10pa. orange and green (11.12)	3·50	2·50
		a. Wmk sideways	†	£2750
		b. Orange-yellow & brt green (8.15)	2·25	1·25
		ba. Broken bottom left triangle	80·00	50·00
75		½pi. green and carmine	1·75	20
		a. Yellow-green and carmine	7·50	1·90
		ab. Broken bottom left triangle	95·00	60·00
		w. Wmk inverted	†	£950
76		30pa. violet and green (3.13)	2·50	60
		a. Broken bottom left triangle	80·00	45·00
		w. Wmk inverted		
77		1pi. rose-red and blue (9.12)	4·25	1·75
		a. Broken bottom left triangle	£110	55·00
		b. Carmine and blue (1.15?)	13·00	4·25
		ba. Broken bottom left triangle	£160	75·00
78		2pi. blue and purple (7.13)	6·50	2·00
		a. Broken bottom left triangle	£130	60·00
79		4pi. olive-green and purple	4·25	4·75
		a. Broken bottom left triangle	£100	£110
80		6pi. sepia and green	3·50	8·50
		a. Broken bottom left triangle	£100	
81		9pi. brown and carmine (3.15)	26·00	26·00
		a. Yellow-brown and carmine	30·00	29·00
		b. Broken bottom left triangle	£350	
82		12pi. chestnut and black (7.13)	18·00	42·00
		b. Broken bottom left triangle	£225	
83		18pi. black and brown (3.15)	28·00	35·00
		a. Broken bottom left triangle	£325	
84		45pi. dull purple and ultramarine (3.15)	85·00	£130
		a. Broken bottom left triangle	£650	
74/84 Set of 11			£160	£225
74s/84s Optd "Specimen" Set of 11			£450	

1921–23.(a) Wmk Mult Script CA.

85	**12**	10pa. orange and green	8·00	9·00
		a. Broken bottom left triangle	£120	£130
86		10pa. grey and yellow (1923)	12·00	7·50
		a. Broken bottom left triangle	£160	£130

87		30pa. violet and green	2·50	60
		a. Broken bottom left triangle	85·00	42·00
		w. Wmk inverted	†	£850
		y. Wmk inverted and reversed		
88		30pa. green (1923)	7·00	60
		a. Broken bottom left triangle	£140	42·00
89		1pi. carmine and blue	19·00	30·00
		a. Broken bottom left triangle	£200	
90		1pi. violet and red (1922)	3·00	4·00
		a. Broken bottom left triangle	90·00	£100
91		1½pi. yellow and black (1922)	7·00	5·00
		a. Broken bottom left triangle	£120	£110
92		2pi. blue and purple	23·00	15·00
		a. Broken bottom left triangle	£275	£180
93		2pi. carmine and blue (1922)	11·00	22·00
		a. Broken bottom left triangle	£180	
94		2¾pi. blue and purple (1922)	7·00	9·00
		a. Broken bottom left triangle	£160	£170
95		4pi. olive-green and purple	14·00	19·00
		a. Broken bottom left triangle	£190	
		w. Wmk inverted	†	£850
96		6pi. sepia and green (1923)	20·00	70·00
		a. Broken bottom left triangle	£225	
97		9pi. brown and carmine (1922)	30·00	75·00
		a. Yellow-brown and carmine	90·00	£130
		b. Broken bottom left triangle	£375	
98		18pi. black and brown (1923)	60·00	£130
		a. Broken bottom left triangle	£475	
99		45pi. dull purple & ultramarine (1923)	£190	£250
		a. Broken bottom left triangle	£950	
85/99 Set of 15			£375	£600
85s/99s Optd "Specimen" Set of 15			£550	

(b) Wmk Mult Crown CA (1923).

100	**12**	10s. green and red/pale yellow	£375	£750
		a. Broken bottom left triangle	£2000	
101		£1 purple and black/red	£1100	£2000
		a. Broken bottom left triangle	£4250	£6500
100s/1s Optd "Specimen" Set of 2			£500	

Examples of Nos. 96/101 are known showing a forged Limassol postmark dated "14 MR 25".

1924–28. *Chalk-surfaced paper.*

(a) Wmk Mult Crown CA.

102	**13**	£1 purple and black/red	£300	£750

(b) Wmk Mult Script CA.

103	**13**	¼pi. grey and chestnut	1·00	25
		w. Wmk inverted	†	£950
104		½pi. black	3·00	10·00
105		¾pi. green	2·25	1·00
106		1pi. purple and chestnut	2·00	1·00
107		1½pi. orange and black	2·00	9·00
108		2pi. carmine and green	2·50	15·00
109		2¾pi. bright blue and purple	3·25	3·50
110		4pi. sage-green and purple	3·25	3·25
111		4½pi. black and orange/emerald	3·50	3·75
112		6pi. olive-brown and green	3·75	6·50
113		9pi. brown and purple	6·00	4·50
114		12pi. chestnut and black	9·00	55·00
115		18pi. black and orange	20·00	5·00
116		45pi. purple and blue	42·00	38·00
117		90pi. green and red/yellow	90·00	£180
117a		£5 black/yellow (1928)	£3000	£6500
		as. Optd "Specimen"	£950	

Examples of No. 102 are known showing a forged Limassol postmark dated "14 MR 25" and of No. 117a showing a forged Registered Nicosia postmark dated "6 MAY 35".

CROWN COLONY

1925. Wmk Mult Script CA. *Chalk-surfaced paper (½, ¾ and 2pi.).*

118	**13**	½pi. green	2·25	1·00
119		¾pi. brownish black	2·25	30
120		1½pi. scarlet	3·25	50
121		2pi. yellow and black	8·50	3·25
122		2½pi. bright blue	3·25	50
102/22 (ex £5) Set of 21			£450	£950
102s/22s (ex £5) Optd "Specimen" Set of 21			£700	

In the above set the fraction bar in the value is horizontal. In Nos. 91, 94, 107 and 109 it is diagonal.

14 Silver Coin of   **15** Zeno (philosopher)
Amathus, 6th-cent B.C.

16 Map of Cyprus   **17** Discovery of body of St. Barnabas

18 Cloister, Abbey of Bella Paise

19 Badge of Cyprus

20 Tekke of Umm Haram

21 Statue of Richard I, Westminster

22 St. Nicholas Cathedral, Famagusta (now Lala Mustafa Pasha Mosque)

23 King George V

(Recess B.W.)

1928 (1 Feb). *50th Anniv of British Rule.* T **14**/**23**. Wmk Mult Script CA. P 12.

123	14	¾pi. deep dull purple	2·75	1·00
124	15	1pi. black and greenish blue	3·00	1·50
125	16	1½pi. scarlet	4·50	2·00
126	17	2½pi. light blue	3·50	2·25
127	18	4pi. deep brown	6·00	7·00
128	19	6pi. blue	9·00	23·00
129	20	9pi. maroon	7·50	11·00
130	21	18pi. black and brown	20·00	20·00
131	22	45pi. violet and blue	40·00	48·00
132	23	£1 blue and bistre-brown	£225	£300
123/32 *Set of 10*			£275	£375
123s/32s Optd "Specimen" *Set of 10*			£600	

24 Ruins of Vouni Palace

25 Small Marble Forum, Salamis

26 Church of St. Barnabas and St. Hilarion, Pensterona

27 Roman theatre, Soli

28 Kyrenia Harbour

29 Kolossi Castle

30 St. Sophia Cathedral, Nicosia (now Selimiye Mosque)

31 Bayraktar Mosque, Nicosia

32 Queen's window, St. Hilarion Castle

33 Buyuk Khan, Nicosia

34 Forest scene, Troodos

(Recess Waterlow)

1934 (1 Dec). T **24**/**34**. Wmk Mult Script CA (sideways on ½pi., 1½pi., 2½pi., 4½pi., 6pi., 9pi. and 18pi.). P 12½.

133	24	¼pi. ultramarine and orange-brown	1·00	65
		a. Imperf between (vert pair)	£30000	£19000
134	25	½pi. green	1·50	1·00
		a. Imperf between (vert pair)	£15000	£16000
135	26	¾pi. black and violet	2·00	30
		a. Imperf between (vert pair)	£32000	
136	27	1pi. black and red-brown	1·50	1·00
		a. Imperf between (vert pair)	£16000	£16000
		b. Imperf between (horiz pair)	£14000	
137	28	1½pi. carmine	2·50	75
138	29	2½pi. ultramarine	3·00	1·75
139	30	4½pi. black and crimson	3·00	4·25
140	31	6pi. black and blue	9·00	14·00
141	32	9pi. sepia and violet	8·50	5·50
142	33	18pi. black and olive-green	42·00	32·00
143	34	45pi. green and black	75·00	60·00
133/43 *Set of 11*			£130	£110
133s/43s Perf "Specimen" *Set of 11*			£375	

1935 (6 May). *Silver Jubilee. As Nos.* 91/4 *of Antigua, but ptd by Waterlow & Sons.* P 11×12.

144		¾pi. ultramarine and grey	2·00	1·00
145		1½pi. deep blue and scarlet	4·25	2·50
		l. Kite and horizontal log	£275	£275
146		2½pi. brown and deep blue	3·75	1·50
147		9pi. slate and purple	16·00	18·00
144/7 *Set of 4*			23·00	21·00
144s/7s Perf "Specimen" *Set of 4*			£170	

For illustration of plate variety see Omnibus section following Zanzibar.

1937 (12 May). *Coronation. As Nos.* 95/7 *of Antigua.* P 11×11½.

148		¾pi. grey	80	60
149		1½pi. carmine	1·25	1·00
150		2½pi. blue	2·25	1·75
148/50 *Set of 3*			3·75	3·00
148s/50s Perf "Specimen" *Set of 3*			£140	

35 Vouni Palace

36 Map of Cyprus

37 Othello's Tower, Famagusta

38 King George VI

(Recess Waterlow)

1938 (12 May)–**51**. T **35** to **38** *and other designs as* 1934, *but with portrait of King George VI.* Wmk Mult Script CA. P 12½.

151	35	¼pi. ultramarine and orange-brown	40	30
152	25	½pi. green	75	20
152*a*		½pi. violet (2.7.51)	2·25	30
153	26	¾pi. black and violet	15·00	75
154	27	1pi. orange	1·00	20
		a. Perf 13½×12½ (5.44)	£475	27·00
155	28	1½pi. carmine	5·50	1·50
155*a*		1½pi. violet (15.3.43)	1·00	45
155*ab*		1½pi. green (2.7.51)	3·00	70
155*b*	26	2pi. black and carmine (2.2.42)	1·25	20
		c. Perf 12½×13½ (10.44)	2·75	8·50
156	29	2½pi. ultramarine	30·00	2·50
156*a*		3pi. ultramarine (2.7.51)	2·00	30
156*b*		4pi. ultramarine (2.7.51)	3·00	50
157	36	4½pi. grey	1·00	20
158	31	6pi. black and blue	1·50	1·00
159	37	9pi. black and purple	2·50	30
160	33	18pi. black and olive-green	9·00	1·00
		a. Black and sage-green (19.8.47)	10·00	1·50
161	34	45pi. green and black	26·00	3·00
162	38	90pi. mauve and black	25·00	5·50
163		£1 scarlet and indigo	50·00	24·00
151/63 *Set of 19*			£160	38·00
151s/63s Perf "Specimen" *Set of 16*			£450	

Dot between "1" and "½" in right-hand value tablet (Pl B1 R. 9/1)

1946 (21 Oct). *Victory. As Nos.* 110/11 *of Antigua.*

164		1½pi. deep violet	25	10
		a. Dot between "1" and "½"	28·00	
165		3pi. blue	25	30
164s/5s Perf "Specimen" *Set of 2*			£120	

Extra decoration (R. 3/5)

1948 (20 Dec). *Royal Silver Wedding. As Nos.* 112/13 *of Antigua.*

166		1½pi. violet	75	40
		a. Extra decoration	42·00	45·00
167		£1 indigo	45·00	60·00

1949 (10 Oct). *75th Anniv of Universal Postal Union. As Nos.* 114/17 *of Antigua but inscr* "CYPRUS" *(recess).*

168		1½pi. violet	60	70
169		2pi. carmine-red	1·50	1·50
170		3pi. deep blue	1·00	1·00
171		9pi. purple	1·00	2·50
168/71 *Set of 4*			3·50	5·25

Cyrenaica *see* British Occupation of Italian Colonies

Dominica

CROWN COLONY

A British packet agency was operating on Dominica from about 1778, the date of the earliest known use of a postal marking. This was replaced by a branch office of the British G.P.O. which opened at Roseau on 8 May 1858. The stamps of Great Britain were used from that date until 1 May 1860, after which the colonial authorities assumed responsibility for the postal service. Until the introduction of Nos. 1/3 in 1874 No. CC1 and later handstamps were utilised.

For illustrations of handstamp and postmark types see BRITISH POST OFFICES ABROAD notes, following GREAT BRITAIN.

ROSEAU
CROWNED/CIRCLE HANDSTAMPS

CC1   CC 1 DOMINICA (Black or R.) (17.5.1845)

          Price on cover   £550

No. CC1 is also known struck in black on various adhesive stamps as late as 1883.

Stamps of GREAT BRITAIN *cancelled* "A 07" *as Type* **2**.

1858–60.

Z1	1d. rose-red (1857), *perf* 14	£275	
Z2	2d. blue (1858) (Plate No. 7)	£750	
Z3	4d. rose (1857)	£325	
Z4	6d. lilac (1856)	£300	
Z5	1s. green	£1400	

PRICES FOR STAMPS ON COVER TO 1945		
Nos. 1/3	*from* × 25	
No. 4	*from* × 40	
No. 5	*from* × 100	
No. 6	*from* × 40	
Nos. 7/8	*from* × 100	
No. 9	*from* × 40	
Nos. 10/12	*from* × 15	
Nos. 13/15	*from* × 100	
No. 17	*from* × 50	
Nos. 18/a		
No. 19	*from* × 40	
Nos. 20/5	*from* × 30	
No. 26		
Nos. 27/90	*from* × 5	
No. 91		
Nos. 92/8	*from* × 10	
Nos. 99/109	*from* × 3	
No. R1/3	*from* × 15	
No. R4	*from* × 50	
No. R6	*from* × 3	

1   **(2)**   **(3)**   **(4)**

(Typo D.L.R.)

1874 (4 May). Wmk Crown CC. P 12½.

1	1	1d. lilac	£150	50·00
2		6d. green	£550	£100
3		1s. dull magenta	£325	70·00

N C E   N C E

Normal   Malformed "CE" (R. 10/6)

1877–79. Wmk Crown CC. P 14.

4	1	½d. olive-yellow (1879)	15·00	55·00
5		1d. lilac	7·00	2·25
		a. Bisected vert or diag (½d.) (on cover or card)	†	£1800
		w. Wmk inverted	80·00	
6		2½d. red-brown (1879)	£225	29·00
		w. Wmk inverted	†	£150
7		4d. blue (1879)	£110	3·00
		a. Malformed "CE" in "PENCE"	£1500	£170
8		6d. green	£150	20·00
9		1s. magenta	£120	50·00

1882 (25 Nov)–**83.** No. 5 bisected vertically and surch.

10	2	½d.(d.), in black, on half 1d.	£180	45·00
		a. Surch inverted	£1000	£800
		b. Surcharges tête-bêche (pair)	£1800	
11	3	½d.(d.), in red, on half 1d. (12.82)	30·00	19·00
		a. Surch inverted	£1000	£475
		b. Surch double	£1600	£650
12	4	½d. in black, on half 1d. (3.83)	65·00	23·00
		b. Surch double	£800	

Type **4** is found reading up or down.

1883–86. Wmk Crown CA. P 14.

13	1	½d. olive-yellow	4·00	10·00
14		1d. lilac (1886)	32·00	14·00
		a. Bisected (½d.) (on cover)	†	£1900
15		2½d. red-brown (1884)	£140	2·25
		w. Wmk inverted	£375	

Half   One
Penny   Penny

(5)   (6)

1886 (1 Mar). Nos. 8 and 9 surch locally.

17	5	½d. on 6d. green	5·00	4·25
18	6	1d. on 6d. green	£22000	£10000
		a. Thick bar (approx 1 mm)	†	£16000
19		1d. on 1s. magenta	15·00	18·00
		a. Surch double	£6000	£3250

It is believed that only two sheets of the 1d. on 6d. were surcharged. On one of these sheets the six stamps in the top row showed the thick bar variety, No. 18a.

1886–90. Wmk Crown CA. P 14.

20	1	½d. dull green	2·00	5·50
22		1d. rose (1887)	17·00	18·00
		a. Deep carmine (1889)	3·25	7·50
		b. Bisected (½d.) (on cover)	†	£1800
		w. Wmk inverted	£150	
23		2½d. ultramarine (1888)	3·75	5·00
24		4d. grey	4·50	6·00
		a. Malformed "CE" in "PENCE"	£160	£225
25		6d. orange (1888)	12·00	55·00
26		1s. dull magenta (1890)	£160	£300
	20/6 Set of 6		£170	£350
	20s/5s Optd "Specimen" Set of 5		£350	

The stamps of Dominica were superseded by the general issue for Leeward Islands on 31 October 1890, but the sets following were in concurrent use with the stamps inscribed "LEEWARD ISLANDS" until 31 December 1939, when the island came under the administration of the Windward Islands.

9 "Roseau from the Sea"   10
(Lt. Caddy)

(T 9 to 11 typo D.L.R.)

1903 (1 Sept)–**07.** Wmk Crown CC (sideways* on T 9). Ordinary paper. P 14.

27	9	½d. green and grey-green	4·00	2·50
		a. Chalk-surfaced paper (1906)	14·00	18·00
28		1d. grey and red	8·00	75
		a. Chalk-surfaced paper (1906)	29·00	6·00
29		2d. green and brown	2·50	4·50
		a. Chalk-surfaced paper (1906)	26·00	38·00
30		2½d. grey and bright blue	5·00	4·00
		a. Chalk-surfaced paper (3.9.07)	21·00	50·00
31		3d. dull purple and grey-black	8·00	3·25
		a. Chalk-surfaced paper (1906)	38·00	30·00
32		6d. grey and chestnut	5·00	18·00
33		1s. magenta and grey-green	27·00	42·00
		a. Chalk-surfaced paper (1906)	75·00	£150
34		2s. grey-black and purple	26·00	29·00
35		2s.6d. grey-green and maize	18·00	75·00
36	10	5s. black and brown	90·00	£140
	27/36 Set of 10		£170	£275
	27s/36s Optd "Specimen" Set of 10		£150	

*The normal sideways watermark shows Crown to right of CC, as seen from the back of the stamp.

1907–08. Wmk Mult Crown CA (sideways* on T 9). Chalk-surfaced paper. P 14.

37	9	½d. green	3·50	3·25

38		1d. grey and red	2·00	40
39		2d. green and brown	5·50	16·00
40		2½d. grey and bright blue	4·50	21·00
41		3d. dull purple and grey-black	4·00	14·00
42		6d. black and chestnut	50·00	85·00
43		1s. magenta and grey-green (1908)	3·75	55·00
44		2s. grey-black and purple (1908)	22·00	32·00
45		2s.6d. grey-green and maize (1908)	22·00	65·00
46	10	5s. black and brown (1908)	60·00	60·00
	37/46 Set of 10		£160	£300

*The normal sideways watermark shows Crown to right of CA, as seen from the back of the stamp.

Examples of Nos. 27/36 and 37/46 are known showing a forged Gen. Post Office Dominica postmark dated "JU 1 11".

11   (12)

WAR TAX

ONE HALFPENNY

1908–21. Wmk Mult Crown CA (sideways* on T 9). Chalk-surfaced paper (3d., 6d., 1s.). P 14.

47	9	½d. blue-green	3·25	3·75
		aw. Wmk Crown to left of CA	2·50	2·75
		ay. Wmk sideways inverted and reversed		
		b. Dp green (wmk Crown to left of CA)	3·50	2·25
48		1d. carmine-red	3·00	30
		aw. Wmk Crown to left of CA	3·50	40
		b. Scarlet (1916)	1·50	40
		bw. Wmk Crown to left of CA	1·00	50
49		2d. grey (1909)	4·00	12·00
		aw. Wmk Crown to left of CA	4·00	16·00
		b. Slate (wmk Crown to left of CA) (1918)	3·50	12·00
50		2½d. blue	8·50	9·00
		aw. Wmk Crown to left of CA	—	9·00
		b. Bright blue (1918)	5·00	9·00
		bw. Wmk Crown to left of CA	6·00	13·00
51		3d. purple/yellow (1909)	3·00	4·25
		a. Ordinary paper (wmk Crown to left of CA) (1912)	3·00	4·50
		ab. On pale yellow (1920)	8·50	9·00
52		6d. dull and bright purple (1909)	10·00	13·00
		a. Ordinary paper. Dull purple (wmk Crown to left of CA) (1915)	3·50	18·00
53		1s. black/green (1910)	3·00	2·75
		a. Ordinary paper (wmk Crown to left of CA) (1912)	3·00	4·00
		as. Optd "Specimen" in red	65·00	
53b		2s. purple and deep blue/blue (wmk Crown to left of CA) (1919)	25·00	85·00
53c		2s.6d. black and red/blue (wmk Crown to left of CA) (1921)	25·00	90·00
54	11	5s. red and green/yellow (1914)	55·00	80·00
	47/54 Set of 10		£110	£275
	48s/54s Optd "Specimen" (1s. optd in blk) Set of 9		£180	

The watermark orientation differs according to the printings. Unless otherwise stated the watermark shows the Crown to right of CA as seen from the back of the stamp.

1916 (Sept). No. 47b surch with T 12 by De La Rue.

55	9	½d. on ½d. deep green (R.)	1·50	75
		a. Small "O" in "ONE"	6·50	7·50

No. 55a occurs on ten stamps within each sheet of 60.

1918 (18 Mar). No. 47b optd with T 12 locally, from D.L.R. plate, but with "ONE HALF-PENNY" blanked out.

56	9	½d. deep green (Blk.)	3·00	6·00
		w. Wmk Crown to right of CA		

The blanking out of the surcharge was not completely successful so that it almost always appears as an albino to a greater or lesser extent.

WAR TAX

(14)

1918 (1 June)–**19.** Nos. 47b and 51a optd with T 14 by De La Rue.

57	9	½d. deep green	15	50
		w. Wmk Crown to right of CA	50·00	
		x. Wmk reversed		
58		3d. purple/yellow (R.) (1919)	2·00	4·00

WAR TAX
1½D.   **1½ D.**

(15)   Short Fraction Bar (R. 6/4)

1919. As No. 50aw, but colour changed, surch with T 15 by De La Rue.

59	9	1½d. on 2½d. orange (R.)	15	55
		a. Short fraction bar	8·00	35·00
		b. "C" and "A" missing from wmk		

No. 59b shows the "C" omitted from one impression with the "A" missing from the next one to the left (as seen from the back of the stamp). The "C" is badly distorted in the second watermark.

1920 (1 June). As No. 59, but without "WAR TAX".

60	9	1½d. on 2½d. orange (Blk.)	3·50	4·50
		a. Short fraction bar	55·00	70·00
		b. "A" of "CA" missing from wmk		
	55s/60s Optd "Specimen" Set of 6		£170	

1921–22. Wmk Mult Script CA (sideways*). Chalk-surfaced paper (6d.). P 14.

62	9	½d. blue-green	2·50	15·00
63		1d. carmine-red	2·00	3·75
		w. Wmk Crown to right of CA	—	15·00
64		1½d. orange	3·00	12·00
65		2d. grey	2·75	3·25
66		2½d. bright blue	2·00	8·50
67		6d. purple	2·50	38·00
69		2s. purple and blue/blue (1922)	32·00	90·00
70		2s.6d. black and red/blue	32·00	£100
	62/70 Set of 8		70·00	£225
	62s/70s Optd "Specimen" Set of 8		£140	

*The normal sideways watermark shows Crown to left of CA, as seen from the back of the stamp.

The 1½d. has figures of value, in the lower corner and no ornamentation below words of value.

16

(Typo D.L.R.)

1923 (1 Mar)–**33.** Chalk-surfaced paper. P 14.

(a) Wmk Mult Script CA (sideways).*

71	16	½d. black and green	1·75	60
72		1d. black and bright violet	3·00	1·75
73		1d. black and scarlet (1933)	11·00	1·00
74		1½d. black and scarlet	3·75	65
75		1½d. black and red-brown (1933)	11·00	70
76		2d. black and grey	2·25	50
77		2½d. black and orange-yellow	2·00	9·00
78		2½d. black and ultramarine (1927)	5·00	2·00
79		3d. black and ultramarine	2·00	12·00
80		3d. black and red/yellow (1927)	1·75	1·00
81		4d. black and brown	3·00	5·50
82		6d. black and bright magenta	3·50	7·00
83		1s. black/emerald	2·25	2·75
84		2s. black and blue/blue	10·00	21·00
85		2s.6d. black and red/blue	18·00	21·00
86		3s. black and purple/yellow (1927)	3·25	12·00
87		4s. black and red/emerald	12·00	24·00
88		5s. black and green/yellow (1927)	22·00	48·00

(b) Wmk Mult Crown CA (sideways).*

89	16	3s. black and purple/yellow	4·00	65·00
90		5s. black and green/yellow	9·00	50·00
91		£1 black and purple/red	£225	£350
	71/91 Set of 21		£325	£550
	71s/91s Optd or Perf (Nos. 73s, 75s) "Specimen" Set of 21		£350	

*The normal sideways watermark shows Crown to left of CA, as seen from the back of the stamp.

Examples of most values are known showing a forged G.P.O. Dominica postmark dated "MY 19 27".

1935 (6 May). Silver Jubilee. As Nos. 91/4 of Antigua.

92		1d. deep blue and carmine	1·00	30
		f. Diagonal line by turret	42·00	
		h. Dot by flagstaff	70·00	
93		1½d. ultramarine and grey	2·50	1·75
		f. Diagonal line by turret	65·00	
		h. Dot by flagstaff	90·00	
94		2½d. brown and deep blue	2·50	3·00
95		1s. slate and purple	2·50	5·00
		h. Dot by flagstaff	£160	
		i. Dash by turret	£160	
	92/5 Set of 4		7·75	9·00
	92s/5s Perf "Specimen" Set of 4		75·00	

For illustrations of plate varieties see Omnibus section following Zanzibar.

1937 (12 May). Coronation. As Nos. 95/7 of Antigua. P 11×11½.

96		1d. carmine	40	10
97		1½d. yellow-brown	40	10
98		2½d. blue	60	1·75
	96/8 Set of 3		1·25	1·75
	96s/8s Perf "Specimen" Set of 3		75·00	

17 Fresh Water Lake   18 Layou River

(Recess Waterlow)

1938 (15 Aug)–**47.** T 17/18 and similar horiz designs. Wmk Mult Script CA. P 12½.

99	17	½d. brown and green	10	15
100	18	1d. grey and scarlet	20	20
101	—	1½d. green and purple	30	70
102	—	2d. carmine and grey-black	50	1·50
103	—	2½d. purple and bright blue	4·00	1·75
		a. purple and bright ultramarine (8.42)	20	1·25
104	18	3d. olive-green and brown	30	50
104a	—	3½d. ultramarine and purple (15.10.47)	2·25	2·00
105	17	6d. emerald-green and purple	1·75	1·50
105a	—	7d. green and yellow-brown (15.10.47)	2·25	1·50
106	—	1s. violet and olive-green	3·75	1·50
106a	18	1s.6d. slate and purple (15.10.47)	6·50	8·00
107	17	2s.6d. black and vermilion	12·00	4·75
108	18	5s. light blue and sepia	7·50	8·00
108a	—	10s. black and brown-orange (15.10.47)	14·00	15·00
	99/108a Set of 14		45·00	42·00

Designs:—1½d., 2½d., 3½d. Picking limes; 2d., 1s., 10s. Boiling Lake.

21 King George VI

(Photo Harrison)

1940 (15 Apr)–**42**. Wmk Mult Script CA. *Chalk-surfaced paper.*
P 15×14.
109	**21**	¼d. chocolate	1·00	15
		a. Ordinary paper (1942)	10	10
99s/109s Perf "Specimen" Set of 15			£250	

1946 (14 Oct). *Victory. As Nos. 110/11 of Antigua.*
110		1d. carmine	20	10
111		3½d. blue	20	10
110s/11s Perf "Specimen" Set of 2			65·00	

1948 (1 Dec). *Royal Silver Wedding. As Nos. 112/13 of Antigua.*
112		1d. scarlet	15	10
113		10s. red-brown	14·00	23·00

(New Currency. 100 cents = 1 B.W.I., later East Caribbean dollar)

1949 (10 Oct). *75th Anniv of Universal Postal Union. As Nos. 114/17 of Antigua.*
114		5c. blue	20	15
115		6c. brown	1·25	2·50
116		12c. purple	45	1·50
		a. "A" of "CA" missing from wmk	—	£500
117		24c. olive	30	30
114/17 Set of 4			2·00	4·00

1951 (16 Feb). *Inauguration of B.W.I. University College. As Nos. 118/19 of Antigua.*
118		3c. yellow-green and reddish violet	50	1·25
119		12c. deep green and carmine	75	40

22 King George VI   **23** Drying Cocoa

(Photo Harrison (½c.). Recess B.W. (others))

1951 (1 July). *T* **22** *and designs as T* **23**. Wmk Mult Script CA. *Chalk-surfaced paper (½c.).* P 15×14 (½c.), 13½×13 ($2.40), 13×13½ (others).
120		½c. chocolate	10	30
121		1c. black and vermilion	10	30
		b. "A" of "CA" missing from wmk	£500	
		c. "JA" for "CA" in wmk	£500	
122		2c. red-brown and deep green	10	30
		a. "C" of "CA" missing from wmk	£600	
		b. "A" of "CA" missing from wmk	£600	
		c. "JA" for "CA" in wmk		£600
123		3c. green and reddish violet	25	2·25
		a. "C" of "CA" missing from wmk	£500	
		c. "JA" for "CA" in wmk	£500	
124		4c. brown-orange and sepia	70	2·25
		a. "C" of "CA" missing from wmk	£600	
		b. "A" of "CA" missing from wmk	£600	
125		5c. black and carmine	85	30
		a. "C" of "CA" missing from wmk	£800	
		b. "A" of "CA" missing from wmk	£800	
		c. "JA" for "CA" in wmk		
126		6c. olive and chestnut	1·00	30
		a. "C" of "CA" missing from wmk	£600	
		b. Before "CA" missing from wmk	£1000	
127		8c. blue-green and blue	1·25	70
		b. "A" of "CA" missing from wmk	£1200	
128		12c. black and bright green	70	1·25
		a. "A" of "CA" missing from wmk	£1200	
129		14c. blue and violet	1·25	2·25
		a. "A" of "CA" missing from wmk	£1200	
		b. "A" of "CA" missing from wmk	†	£750
		c. "JA" for "CA" in wmk	£1000	
130		24c. reddish violet and rose-carmine	75	30
		a. "C" of "CA" missing from wmk	£1200	£1000
131		48c. bright green and red-orange	3·75	9·00
		a. "A" of "CA" missing from wmk	£1200	
		b. "A" of "CA" missing from wmk	£1200	
		c. "JA" for "CA" in wmk		
132		60c. carmine and black	3·75	6·50
		c. "JA" for "CA" in wmk	£800	
133		$1.20, emerald and black	4·50	6·50
		a. "C" of "CA" missing from wmk	£1400	
		b. "A" of "CA" missing from wmk	£1400	
134		$2.40, orange and black	23·00	42·00
120/34 Set of 15			35·00	65·00

Designs: *Horiz*—2c., 60c. Making Carib baskets; 3c., 48c. Lime plantation; 4c. Picking oranges; 5c. Bananas; 6c. Botanical Gardens; 8c. Drying vanilla beans; 12c., $1.20, Fresh Water Lake; 14c. Layou River; 24c. Boiling Lake. *Vert*—$2.40, Picking oranges.

Examples of Nos. 121b, 122b, 124b, 125b, 126b, 129b, 131b and 133b show traces of the *left leg of the "A", the listed variety shows no trace of the letter.*

Nos. 121c, 122c, 123c, 125c, 129c, 131c and 132c may represent an attempt to repair the missing "C" variety.

NEW CONSTITUTION 1951
(34)

1951 (15 Oct). *New Constitution. Nos. 123, 125, 127 and 129 optd with T* **34** *by B.W.*
135		3c. green and reddish violet	15	70
		a. "C" of "CA" missing from wmk	£600	£650

136		5c. black and carmine	15	1·25
		a. "JA" for "CA" in wmk	£700	
137		8c. blue-green and blue (R.)	15	15
		a. "JA" for "CA" in wmk		
138		14c. blue and violet (R.)	1·00	20
		b. "A" of "CA" missing from wmk	£900	
135/8 Set of 4			1·25	2·10

POSTAL FISCALS

REVENUE (R 1)   **Revenue** (R 2)

1879–88. *Optd with Type R* **1** *by De La Rue.* P 14.
(a) Wmk Crown CC.
R1	**1**	1d. lilac	80·00	8·00
		a. Bisected vert (½d.) on cover	†	£2500
R2		6d. green	3·00	24·00
		w. Wmk inverted	£120	
R3		1s. magenta	9·00	16·00
111/3 Set of 3			85·00	42·00

(b) Wmk Crown CA.
R4	**1**	1d. lilac (1888)	5·00	4·50

1888. *Optd with Type R* **2** *locally.* Wmk Crown CA.
R6	**1**	1d. rose	£250	70·00

East Africa (G.E.A.) *see* Tanganyika

East Africa and Uganda Protectorates *see* Kenya, Uganda and Tanganyika

Egypt

TURKISH SUZERAINTY

In 1517 Sultan Selim I added Egypt to the Ottoman Empire, and it stayed more or less under Turkish rule until 1805, when Mohammed Ali became governor. He established a dynasty of governors owing nominal allegiance to the Sultan of Turkey until 1914.

Khedive Ismail
18 January 1863–26 June 1879

He obtained the honorific title of Khedive (viceroy) from the Sultan in 1867.

The operations of British Consular Post Offices in Egypt date from August 1839 when the first packet agency, at Alexandria, was opened. Further agencies at Suez (1 January 1847) and Cairo (1856) followed. Alexandria became a post office on 17 March 1858 with Cairo following on 23 February 1859 and Suez on 1 January 1861.

Great Britain stamps were issued to Alexandria in March 1858 and to the other two offices in August/September 1859. "B 01" cancellations as Type **2** were issued to both Alexandria and Cairo. Cancellations with this number as Types **8**, **12** and **15** were only used at Alexandria.

Before 1 July 1873 combination covers showing Great Britain stamps and the first issue of Egypt exist with the latter paying the internal postage to the British Post Office at Alexandria.

The Cairo office closed on 30 June 1873 and the other two on 30 March 1878. Suez continued to function as a transit office for a number of years.

Stamps issued after 1877 can be found with the Egyptian cancellation "Port Said", but these are on letters posted from British ships.

For cancellations used during the 1882 and 1885 campaigns, see BRITISH FORCES IN EGYPT at the end of the listing.

For illustrations of the handstamp and postmark types see BRITISH POST OFFICES ABROAD notes following GREAT BRITAIN.

ALEXANDRIA

CROWNED-CIRCLE HANDSTAMPS
CC1	CC **1b**	ALEXANDRIA (R.)		
		(13.5.1843)	*Price on cover*	£2750

Stamps of GREAT BRITAIN cancelled "B 01" as in Types **2** *(also used at Cairo),* **8**, **12** *or* **15**.

1858 (Mar)–**78**.
Z1		½d. rose-red (1870–79)	*From*	19·00
		Plate Nos. 5, 6, 8, 10, 13, 14, 15, 19, 20.		
Z2		1d. rose-red (1857)		7·00
Z3		1d. rose-red (1861) (Alph IV)		
Z4		1d. rose-red (1864–79)	*From*	9·50
		Plate Nos. 71, 72, 73, 74, 76, 78, 79, 80, 81, 82, 83, 84, 85, 86, 87, 88, 89, 90, 91, 92, 93, 94, 95, 96, 97, 98, 99, 101, 102, 103, 104, 106, 107, 108, 109, 110, 111, 112, 113, 114, 115, 117, 118, 119, 120, 121, 122, 123, 124, 125, 127, 129, 130, 131, 133, 134, 136, 137, 138, 139, 140, 142, 143, 144, 145, 146, 147, 148, 149, 150, 152, 154, 156, 157, 159, 160, 162, 163, 165, 168, 169, 170, 171, 172, 174, 175, 177, 179, 180, 181, 182, 183, 185, 188, 190, 199, 200, 203, 206, 210, 220.		
Z5		2d. blue (1858–69)	*From*	9·50
		Plate Nos. 7, 8, 9, 13, 14, 15.		
Z6		2½d. rosy mauve (1875) (blued *paper*)	*From*	60·00
		Plate Nos. 1, 2, 3.		

Z7		2½d. rosy mauve (1875–6) (Plate. 1, 2, 3)		35·00
Z8		2½d. rosy mauve (*Error of Lettering*)		£1300
Z9		2½d. rosy mauve (1876–79)	*From*	25·00
		Plate Nos. 3, 4, 5, 6, 7, 8, 9.		
Z10		3d. carmine-rose (1862)		£120
Z11		3d. rose (1865) (Plate No. 4)		60·00
Z12		3d. rose (1867–73)	*From*	
		Plate Nos. 4, 5, 6, 7, 8, 9.		
Z13		3d. rose (1873–76)	*From*	26·00
		Plate Nos. 11, 12, 14, 15, 16, 18. 19.		
Z15		4d. rose (1857)		42·00
Z16		4d. red (1862) (Plate Nos. 3, 4)		42·00
Z17		4d. vermilion (1865–73)	*From*	29·00
		Plate Nos. 7, 8, 9, 10, 11, 12, 13, 14.		
Z18		4d. vermilion (1876) (Plate No. 15)		£160
Z19		4d. sage-green (1877) (Plate No. 15)		£110
Z20		6d. lilac (1856)		48·00
Z21		6d. lilac (1862) (Plate Nos. 3, 4)		42·00
Z22		6d. lilac (1865–67) (Plate Nos. 5, 6)		32·00
Z23		6d. lilac (1867) (Plate No. 6)		42·00
Z24		6d. violet (1867–70) (Plate Nos. 6, 8, 9)	*From*	38·00
		a. Imperf (Plate No. 8)		£2500
Z25		6d. buff (1872–73) (Plate Nos. 11, 12)	*From*	55·00
Z26		6d. chestnut (1872) (Plate No. 11)		27·00
Z27		6d. grey (1873) (Plate No. 12)		80·00
Z28		6d. grey (1874–76) (Plate Nos. 13, 14, 15)	*From*	23·00
Z29		9d. straw (1862)		£150
Z30		9d. bistre (1862)		
Z31		9d. straw (1865)		
Z32		9d. straw (1867)		
Z33		10d. red-brown (1867)		£130
Z34		1s. green (1856)		£120
Z35		1s. green (1862)		75·00
Z36		1s. green (1862) ("K" *variety*)		
Z37		1s. green (1865) (Plate No. 4)		35·00
Z38		1s. green (1867–73) (Plate Nos. 4, 5, 6, 7)	*From*	15·00
Z39		1s. green (1873–77)	*From*	27·00
		Plate Nos. 8, 9, 10, 11, 12, 13.		
Z40		2s. blue (1867)		£100
Z41		5s. rose (1867–74) (Plate Nos. 1, 2)	*From*	£250

CAIRO

CROWNED-CIRCLE HANDSTAMPS
CC2	CC **6**	CAIRO (R. or Blk). (23.3.1859)	*Price on cover*	£3750

Cancellation "B 01" as Type **2** (also issued at Alexandria) was used to cancel mail franked with Great Britain stamps between April 1859 and June 1873.

SUEZ

CROWNED-CIRCLE HANDSTAMPS
CC3	CC **1**	SUEZ (B. or Black) (16.7.1847)	*Price on cover*	£4250

Stamps of GREAT BRITAIN cancelled "B 02" as in Types **2** *and* **8**, *or with circular date stamp as Type* **5**.

1859 (Aug)–**78**.
Z42		½d. rose-red (1870–79)		30·00
		Plate Nos. 6, 10, 11, 12, 13, 14.		
Z43		1d. rose-red (1857)		10·00
Z44		1d. rose-red (1864–79)	*From*	12·00
		Plate Nos. 73, 74, 78, 79, 80, 81, 83, 84, 86, 87, 90, 91, 93, 94, 96, 97, 100, 101, 106, 107, 108, 110, 113, 118, 119, 120, 121, 122, 123, 124, 125, 129, 130, 131, 134, 136, 137, 138, 140, 142, 143, 144, 145, 147, 148, 149, 150, 151, 152, 153, 154, 156, 158, 159, 160, 161, 162, 163, 164, 165, 166, 167, 168, 170, 174, 176, 177, 178, 179, 180, 181, 184, 185, 186, 187, 189, 190, 205.		
Z45		2d. blue (1858–69)		15·00
		Plate Nos. 8, 9, 13, 14, 15.		
Z46		2½d. rosy mauve (1875) (blued *paper*)	*From*	65·00
		Plate Nos. 1, 2, 3.		
Z47		2½d. rosy mauve (1875–76)	*From*	35·00
		Plate Nos. 1, 2, 3.		
Z48		2½d. rosy mauve (*Error of Lettering*)		£1500
Z49		2½d. rosy mauve (1876–79)	*From*	27·00
		Plate Nos. 3, 4, 5, 6, 7, 8, 9, 10.		
Z50		3d. carmine-rose (1862)		£140
Z51		3d. rose (1865) (Plate No. 4)		75·00
Z52		3d. rose (1867–73) (Plate Nos. 5, 6, 7, 8, 10.)		
Z53		3d. rose (1873–76) (Plate Nos. 12, 16)	*From*	26·00
Z54		4d. rose (1857)		55·00
Z55		4d. red (1862) (Plate Nos. 3, 4)		48·00
Z56		4d. vermilion (1865–73)	*From*	29·00
		Plate Nos. 7, 8, 9, 10, 11, 12, 13, 14.		
Z57		4d. vermilion (1876) (Plate No. 15)		
Z58		4d. sage-green (1877) (Plate No. 15)		£130
Z59		6d. lilac (1856)		55·00
Z60		6d. lilac (1862) (Plate Nos. 3, 4)	*From*	45·00
Z61		6d. lilac (1865–67) (Plate Nos. 5, 6)	*From*	38·00
Z62		6d. lilac (1867) (Plate No. 6)		48·00
Z63		6d. violet (1867–70) (Plate Nos. 6, 8, 9)	*From*	38·00
Z64		6d. buff (1872–73) (Plate Nos. 11, 12)	*From*	65·00
Z65		6d. pale chestnut (Plate No.12) (1872)		£2500
Z66		6d. chestnut (1872) (Plate No. 11)		32·00
Z67		6d. grey (1873) (Plate No. 12)		95·00
Z68		6d. grey (1874–76)	*From*	28·00
		Plate Nos. 13, 14, 15, 16.		
Z69		8d. orange (1876)		
Z70		9d. straw (1862)		£180
		a. Thick paper		
Z71		9d. bistre (1862)		
Z72		9d. straw (1867)		
Z73		10d. red-brown (1867)		£180
Z74		1s. green (1856)		£150
Z75		1s. green (1862)		85·00
Z76		1s. green (1862) ("K" *variety*)		
Z77		1s. green (1865) (Plate No. 4)		48·00
Z78		1s. green (1867–73) (Plate Nos. 4, 5, 6, 7)	*From*	20·00
Z79		1s. green (1873–77)	*From*	30·00
		Plate Nos. 8, 9, 10, 11, 12.		
Z80		2s. blue (1867)		£160
Z81		5s. rose (1867–74) (Plate Nos. 1, 2)	*From*	£300

PRICES FOR STAMPS ON COVER		
Nos. 1/41	*from* × 8	
Nos. 42/3	*from* × 30	

(Currency: 40 paras = 1 piastre)

(3)

(Typo (1pi) or litho (others) Pellas Brothers, Genoa. Inscr (T **3**) applied typo (1, 2pi.) or litho (others))

1866 (1 Jan). *Various designs as T* **1** *with black inscriptions as T* **3**. *The lowest group of characters indicates the value.* 1pi. no wmk, others W **2** (inverted). P 12½.

1		5pa. grey	45·00	28·00
	a.	Greenish grey	45·00	28·00
	b.	Imperf (pair)	£180	
	c.	Imperf between (pair)	£300	
	d.	Perf 12½×13 and compound	50·00	48·00
	e.	Perf 13	£250	£300
	w.	Wmk upright	£250	£200
2		10pa. brown	55·00	30·00
	a.	Imperf (pair)	£160	
	b.	Imperf between (pair)	£350	
	c.	Perf 12½×13 and compound	80·00	48·00
	d.	Perf 12½×15	£250	£275
	e.	Perf 13	£170	£190
	w.	Wmk upright	65·00	30·00
3		20pa. pale blue	70·00	32·00
	a.	Greenish blue	70·00	32·00
	b.	Imperf (pair)	£240	
	c.	Imperf between (pair)	£400	
	d.	Perf 12½×13 and compound	£100	80·00
	e.	Perf 13	£425	£250
	w.	Wmk upright	70·00	32·00
4		1pi. claret	60·00	5·00
	a.	Imperf (pair)	£100	
	b.	Imperf between (pair)	£400	
	c.	Perf 12½×13 and compound	90·00	20·00
	d.	Perf 13	£300	£190
	e.	Perf 12½×15	£300	
5		2pi. yellow	90·00	45·00
	a.	Orange-yellow	90·00	45·00
	b.	Imperf (pair)		
	c.	Imperf between (pair)	£350	£350
	d.	Bisected diag (1pi.) (on cover)	†	£2250
	e.	Perf 12½×13 and compound	£120	48·00
	f.	Perf 12½×15	£130	
	w.	Wmk upright	90·00	45·00
6		5pi. rose	£250	£170
	a.	Imperf (pair)		
	b.	Imperf between (pair)	£1000	
	c.	Perf 12½×13 and compound	£275	
	d.	Error. Inscr 10pi., perf 12½×15	£900	£750
	da.	Imperf	£500	
	e.	Perf 13	£400	
	w.	Wmk upright	£250	£170
7		10pi. slate	£275	£250
	a.	Imperf (pair)	£600	
	b.	Imperf between (pair)	£2000	
	c.	Perf 12½×13 and compound	£425	£425
	d.	Perf 13	£1600	
	w.	Wmk upright	£275	£250

The 2pi. bisected was authorised for use between 16 and 31 July 1867 at Alexandria or Cairo.

Stamps perforated 12½, 12½×13 and compound, and 13 occur in the same sheets with the 13 gauge usually used on the top, left-hand, right-hand or bottom rows. Each sheet of 200 contained one stamp perforated 13 all round, two 13 on three sides, one 13 on two adjacent sides, eighteen 13×12½, eight 12½×13, eight 12½ and eighteen 13 at top or bottom. So many sheets were received imperforate or part-perforated that some stock was passed to V. Penasson of Alexandria who applied the 12½×15 gauge.

The two halves of each background differ in minor details of the ornamentation. All values can be found with either half at the top.

Proofs of all values exist on smooth paper, without watermark. Beware of forgeries.

All values also exist with the watermark reversed (*same price as upright*) or inverted and reversed (*same price as inverted*).

4   5

6

(Des F. Hoff. Litho V. Penasson, Alexandria)

1867 (1 Aug)–**71**. W **6** (*impressed on reverse*). P 15×12½.

11	4	5pa. orange-yellow	30·00	8·00
	a.	Imperf (pair)		
	b.	Imperf between (horiz pair)	£170	
	x.	Wmk impressed on face		
12		10pa. dull lilac	75·00	9·50
	b.	Bright mauve (7.69)	55·00	9·00
	ba.	Bisected diag (5pa.) (on piece) (17.11.71)	†	£750
	w.	Wmk inverted	£300	£200
	x.	Wmk impressed on face		
13		20pa. deep blue-green	£100	13·00
	a.	Pale blue-green	£100	13·00
	b.	Yellowish green (7.69)	£110	12·00
	x.	Wmk impressed on face		
14	5	1pi. dull rose-red *to* rose	16·00	1·00
	a.	Lake	£120	32·00
	b.	Imperf (pair)	£100	
	c.	Imperf between (horiz pair)	£170	
	d.	Bisected diag (20pa.) (on piece)	†	£750
	e.	Rouletted	55·00	
	w.	Wmk inverted	50·00	30·00
	x.	Wmk impressed on face		
15		2pi. bright blue	£110	17·00
	a.	Pale blue	£110	17·00
	b.	Imperf (pair)		
	c.	Imperf between (pair)	£425	
	d.	Bisected diag (1pi.) (on cover)	†	—
	e.	Perf 12½	£225	
16		5pi. brown	£300	£180
	x.	Wmk impressed on face		

Each value was engraved four times, the resulting blocks being used to form sheets of 200. There are therefore four types showing minor variations for each value.

No. 12ba was used on newspapers from Alexandria between 17 November 1871 and 20 January 1872.

Stamps printed both sides, both imperf and perf, come from printer's waste. The 1pi. rose without watermark is a proof.

7   **8** (Side panels transposed and inverted)

8a (I)   **8a** (II)

WATERMARK 8a. There are two types of this watermark which, as they are not always easy to distinguish, we do not list separately. Type II is slightly wider and less deep and the crescent is flatter than in Type I. The width measurement for Type I is generally about 14 mm and for Type II about 15 mm, but there is some variation within the sheets for both types.

Nos. 26/43, 45/7a, 49/a, 50/1 and 57 come with Type I only. Nos. 44a, 48/a, 52, 54b, 73/7 and 78 exist with both types of watermark (but No. 83 and official overprints on these stamps still require research); our prices are generally for Type II. Other watermarked issues between 1888 and 1907 have Type II watermarks only.

1872 (1 Jan)–**75**. T **7** (*the so-called "Penasson" printing**). Thick opaque paper. W **8a**. P 12½×13½.

A. LITHOGRAPHED.

26	7	20pa. blue (*shades*)	£120	50·00
	a.	Imperf (pair)		
	b.	Imperf between (pair)	—	£2000
	c.	Perf 13½	£200	55·00
	w.	Wmk inverted	£200	75·00
27		1pi. red (*shades*)	£225	10·00
	a.	Perf 13½	£500	23·00
	w.	Wmk inverted	£600	30·00

B. TYPOGRAPHED.

28	7	5pa. brown (*shades*)	7·00	4·50
	a.	Perf 13½	24·00	9·50
	w.	Wmk inverted	£100	60·00
29		10pa. mauve	6·00	3·00
	a.	Perf 13½	6·00	3·25
	w.	Wmk inverted	40·00	25·00
30		20pa. blue (*shades*)	55·00	4·00
	a.	Perf 13½	80·00	20·00
	w.	Wmk inverted	50·00	30·00
31		1pi. rose-red	55·00	1·00
	a.	Bisected (20pa.) (on piece with No. 31) (7.75)	†	£600
	b.	Perf 13½	80·00	3·50
	w.	Wmk inverted	38·00	25·00
32		2pi. chrome-yellow	85·00	4·00
	a.	Bisected (1pi.) (on piece) (7.74)	†	£650
	b.	Perf 13½	18·00	4·00
	w.	Wmk inverted		
33		2½pi. violet	80·00	18·00
	a.	Perf 13½	£700	£190
	w.	Wmk inverted	90·00	£100
34		5pi. yellow-green	£180	35·00
	a.	Tête-bêche (pair)	£8000	
	b.	Perf 13½	£275	55·00
	w.	Wmk inverted	£200	90·00

*It is now accepted that stamps in both processes were printed by the Goverment Printing Works at Bûlâq, Cairo, although Penasson may have been involved in the production of the dies.

The lithographed and typographed stamps each show the characteristic differences between these two processes:—

The typographed stamps show the coloured lines of the design impressed into the paper and an accumulation of ink along the margins of the lines.

The lithographed stamps are essentially flat in appearance, without the heaping of the ink. Many of the 20pa. show evidence of retouching, particularly of the outer frame lines.

The 1p. bisected was used at Gedda, on 5 July 1875, or Scio, and the 2pi. vertically bisected at Gallipolli or Scio.

See also footnote below No. 41.

1874 (Nov)–**75**. *Typo from new stereos at Bûlâq, on thinner paper.* W **8a**. P 12½.

35	8	5pa. brown (3.75)	11·00	3·75
	a.	Tête-bêche (vert pair)	35·00	35·00
	b.	Tête-bêche (horiz pair)	£275	£300
	c.	Imperf (pair)	£100	£120
	d.	Imperf between (pair)	£300	
	ew.	Wmk inverted	11·00	3·75
	f.	Perf 13½×12½	16·00	3·75
	fa.	Tête-bêche (vert pair)	60·00	60·00
	fb.	Tête-bêche (horiz pair)	£325	£350
	fw.	Wmk inverted	16·00	3·75
36	7	10pa. grey-lilac (*shades*) (8.75)	11·00	2·75
	a.	Tête-bêche (vert pair)	£140	£160
	b.	Tête-bêche (horiz pair)		
	c.	Imperf (pair)		
	dw.	Wmk inverted	11·00	2·75
	e.	Perf 13½×12½	24·00	3·25
	ea.	Tête-bêche (vert pair)	£140	£160
	ew.	Wmk inverted	24·00	3·50
37		20pa. grey-blue (*shades*) (2.75)	90·00	3·00
	b.	Bisected diag (10pa.) (on cover)	†	—
	cw.	Wmk inverted	90·00	3·00
	d.	Perf 13½×12½	10·00	2·50
	da.	Imperf between (pair)	£300	
38		1pi. red (*shades*) (4.75)	9·00	65
	a.	Tête-bêche (vert pair)	90·00	90·00
	b.	Tête-bêche (horiz pair)	£300	£300
	c.	Imperf (pair)		
	d.	Imperf between (pair)	£400	£400
	ew.	Wmk inverted	11·00	1·50
	f.	Perf 13½×12½	70·00	1·25
	fa.	Tête-bêche (vert pair)	£350	£350
	fb.	Tête-bêche (horiz pair)		
	fw.	Wmk inverted	80·00	7·50
39		2pi. yellow (12.74)	75·00	3·25
	a.	Tête-bêche (pair)	£400	£400
	bw.	Wmk inverted	90·00	7·50
	c.	Perf 13½×12½	5·50	6·00
	ca.	Tête-bêche (pair)	£400	£400
	cb.	Bisected diag (1pi.) (on cover) (4.75)	†	£2500
	cw.	Wmk inverted	7·50	6·50
	d.	Perf 12½×13½	65·00	15·00
	da.	Tête-bêche (pair)	£850	
	dw.	Wmk inverted	80·00	18·00
40		2½pi. violet	8·50	5·00
	a.	Tête-bêche (pair)	£350	
	bw.	Wmk inverted	12·00	7·50
	c.	perf 12½×13½	60·00	19·00
	ca.	Tête-bêche (pair)	£1000	90·00
	cw.	Wmk inverted	50·00	25·00
41		5pi. green	55·00	19·00
	a.	Imperf (pair)	†	
	bw.	Wmk inverted	£100	50·00
	c.	Perf 12½×13½	£300	£275

The 2pi. bisected was used at Gedda and are all postmarked 13 April.

The 1872 printings have a thick line of colour in the top margin of the sheet and the other margins are all plain, an exception being the 5pa., which on the majority of the sheets has the line at the right-hand side of the sheet. The 1874–75 printings have a wide fancy border all round every sheet.

The 1872 printings are on thick opaque paper, with the impressions sharp and clear. The 1874–75 printings are on thinner paper, often semi-transparent and oily in appearance, and having the impressions very blurred and badly printed. These are only general distinctions and there are a number of exceptions.

The majority of the 1874–75 stamps have blind or defective perforations, while the 1872 printings have clean-cut perfs.

The two printings of the 5pa. to 1pi. values can be identified by their perforation gauges, which are always different; the 5pa. also differs in the side panels (Types **7** and **8**). Only the perf 12½×13½ varieties of the three higher values may need to be distinguished. As well as the general points noted above the following features are also helpful:

2pi. In the 1872 issue the left-hand Arabic character in the top inscription is one complete shape, resembling an inverted "V" with a horizontal line on top. In the 1874 issue the character has three separate components, a line with two dots below.

2½ pi. There is a distinct thinning of the frame line in the top right-hand corner of the 1872 issue. This sometimes takes the form of a short white line within the frame.

5pi. In the 1872 issue the top frame line is split for its entire length; in the 1874 issue the line is solid for all or most of its length. The 1872 printing always has a white dot above the "P" of "PIASTRE"; this dot appears on only a few positions of the 1874 printing.

There seem to be many different compositions of the sheets containing the tête-bêche varieties, settings being known with 1, 3, 9 and 10 inverted stamps in various sheets. Sheets of the 5pa. are known with 9 of the 20 horizontal rows inverted, giving vertical tête-bêche pairs; four stamps were inverted within their row giving four horizontal tête-bêche pairs.

Examples of some values exist without watermark due to the paper being misplaced on the press.

(9)

1878 (Dec). *No. 40 surch as T* **9** *at Bûlâq.* P 12½.

42	7	5pa. on 2½pi. violet	6·00	6·00
	a.	Surch inverted	70·00	70·00
	b.	Tête-bêche (pair)	£3500	
	c.	Imperf (pair)	£900	
	dw.	Wmk inverted	7·50	7·50
	e.	Perf 12½×13½	6·50	8·00
	ea.	Surch inverted	£140	£140
	eb.	Tête-bêche (pair)		

43		ew. Wmk inverted	8·00	10·00
		10pa. on 2½ pi. violet	11·00	10·00
		a. Surch inverted	75·00	75·00
		b. Tête-bêche (pair)	£1500	
		dw. Wmk inverted	15·00	15·00
		e. Perf 12½×13½	15·00	15·00
		ea. Surch inverted	£110	£110
		eb. Tête-bêche (pair)	£1500	
		ew. Wmk inverted	25·00	25·00

10   **11**   **12**

13   **14**   **15**

(Typo De La Rue)

1879 (1 Apr). *Ordinary paper.* W **8a** (*inverted on* 10pa.). P 14.

44	10	5pa. deep brown	2·75	40
		a. Pale brown	2·75	40
		w. Wmk inverted	£120	£100
45	11	10pa. reddish lilac	50·00	3·00
		w. Wmk upright	†	£100
46	12	20pa. pale blue	60·00	1·75
		w. Wmk inverted	90·00	15·00
47	13	1pi. rose	28·00	20
		a. Pale rose	28·00	20
		w. Wmk inverted	60·00	10·00
48	14	2pi. orange	32·00	50
		a. Orange-yellow	30·00	80
		w. Wmk inverted	35·00	2·00
49	15	5pi. green	55·00	11·00
		a. Blue-green	55·00	10·00
		w. Wmk inverted	50·00	11·00

See also Nos. 50/6.

Khedive Tewfik
26 June 1879–7 January 1892

British troops were landed in Egypt in 1882 to secure the Suez Canal against a nationalist movement led by Arab Pasha. Arabi was defeated at Tel-el-Kebir and British troops remained in Egypt until 1954. A British resident and consul-general advised the Khedive. Holders of this post were Sir Evelyn Baring (Lord Cromer), 1883–1907; Sir Eldon Gorst, 1907–11; and Lord Kitchener, 1911–14.

1881–1902. *Colours changed. Ordinary paper.* W **8a** (*inverted on No. 50*). P 14.

50	11	10pa. claret (1.81)	50·00	7·00
51		10pa. bluish grey (25.1.82)	11·00	1·75
		w. Wmk inverted	40·00	3·00
52		10pa. green (15.12.84)	2·00	1·25
		w. Wmk inverted	30·00	10·00
53	12	20pa. rose-carmine (15.12.84)	16·00	55
		a. Bright rose	16·00	50
		w. Wmk inverted	35·00	7·00
54	13	1pi. blue (15.12.84)	6·00	20
		a. Deep ultramarine	7·00	20
		b. Pale ultramarine	5·50	20
		cw. Wmk inverted	26·00	10·00
		d. Chalk-surfaced paper. *Ultramarine* (1902)	3·00	10
		da. *Blue*	3·00	10
		dw. Wmk inverted	75·00	40·00
55	14	2pi. orange-brown (1.8.93)	12·00	30
		aw. Wmk inverted	80·00	40·00
		b. Chalk-surfaced paper (1902)	12·00	30
		ba. *Orange*	23·00	1·00
		bw. Wmk inverted	—	30·00
56	15	5pi. pale grey (15.12.84)	13·00	50
		a. *Slate*	11·00	50
		bw. Wmk inverted	—	£100
		c. Chalk-surfaced paper. *Slate-grey* (1902)	16·00	15
		cw. Wmk inverted	—	£100

(17)

1884 (1 Feb). *Surch with T* **17** *at Bûlâq.*

57	15	20pa. on 5pi. green	7·00	1·25
		a. Surch inverted	65·00	60·00
		w. Wmk inverted	50·00	30·00

(New Currency: 1000 milliemes = 100 piastres = £1 Egyptian)

18   **19**   **20**

21   **22**

1888 (1 Jan)**–1909.** *Ordinary paper.* W **8a.** P 14.

58	18	1m. pale brown	2·50	10
		a. Deep brown	2·75	10
		bw. Wmk inverted	25·00	4·00
		c. Chalk-surfaced paper. *Pale brown* (1902)	2·75	10
		ca. *Deep brown*	2·75	10
		cw. Wmk inverted	40·00	5·00
59	19	2m. blue-green	1·75	10
		a. *Green*	1·25	10
		bw. Wmk inverted	40·00	5·00
		c. Chalk-surfaced paper. *Green* (1902)	1·00	10
		cw. Wmk inverted	40·00	5·00
60	20	3m. maroon (1.1.92)	3·50	1·00
61		3m. yellow (1.8.93)	5·00	50
		a. *Orange-yellow*	4·75	15
		bw. Wmk inverted	45·00	15·00
		c. Chalk-surfaced paper. *Orange-yellow* (1902)	2·75	10
		cw. Wmk inverted	75·00	30·00
62	21	4m. verm (*chalk-surfaced paper*) (1906)	3·75	10
		a. Bisected (2m.) (on cover) (11.09)	†	—
		w. Wmk inverted	—	60·00
63		5m. rose-carmine	3·75	10
		a. *Bright rose*	3·75	10
		b. *Aniline rose*	4·75	10
		cw. Wmk inverted	—	75·00
		d. Chalk-surfaced paper. *Rose* (1902)	2·75	10
		da. *Deep aniline rose*	4·50	20
64	22	10p. mauve (1.1.89)	15·00	80
		a. *Aniline mauve*	18·00	80
		bw. Wmk inverted	—	50·00
		c. Chalk-surfaced paper. *Mauve* (1902)	22·00	50

No. 62a was used at Gizira in conjunction with the 1m. value and the Official, No. O64.

No. 63d exists in coils constructed from normal sheets.

Kedive Abbas Hilmi
7 January 1892–19 December 1914

A set of three values, in a common design showing Cleopatra and a Nile boat, was prepared in 1895 for the Nile Winter Fête, but not issued. Examples survive from the De La Rue archives.

29 Nile Feluccas   **30** Cleopatra from Temple of Dendera   **31** Ras-el-Tin Palace, Alexandria

32 Pyramids of Giza   **33** Sphinx   **34** Colossi of Amenophis III at Thebes

35 Archway of Ptolemy III, Karnak   **37** Rock Temple of Abu Simbel

36 Citadel, Cairo   **38** Aswân Dam

(Typo D.L.R.)

1914 (8 Jan). W **8a.** P 13½×14 (1m. to 10m.) or 14 (20m. to 200m.).

73	29	1m. sepia	1·25	40
		w. Wmk inverted	—	75·00
74	30	2m. green	2·75	20
		w. Wmk inverted	—	40·00
75	31	3m. yellow-orange	2·25	35
		a. Double impression		
		w. Wmk inverted	—	40·00
76	32	4m. vermilion	3·25	65
		w. Wmk inverted	—	40·00
77	33	5m. lake	3·50	10
		a. Wmk sideways star to right* (booklets)	10·00	22·00
		aw. Wmk sideways star to left	10·00	22·00
		w. Wmk inverted	15·00	10·00
78	34	10m. dull blue	4·75	10
		w. Wmk inverted	25·00	25·00
79	35	20m. olive	6·50	30
		w. Wmk inverted	60·00	40·00
80	36	50m. purple	15·00	40
		w. Wmk inverted	—	50·00
81	37	100m. slate	15·00	60
82	38	200m. maroon	26·00	3·50
73/82		Set of 10	70·00	6·00

*The normal sideways watermark shows the star to the right of the crescent, *as seen from the back of the stamp.*

All the above exist imperforate, but imperforate stamps without watermark are proofs.

See also Nos. 84/95.

BRITISH PROTECTORATE

On 18 December 1914, after war with Turkey had begun, Egypt was declared to be a British protectorate. Abbas Hilmi was deposed, and his uncle, Hussein Kamil, was proclaimed Sultan of Egypt.

Sultan Hussain Kamil
19 December 1914–9 October 1917

(39)

1915 (15 Oct). No. 75 surch with T **39**, at Bûlâq.

83	31	2m. on 3m. yellow-orange	55	2·25
		a. Surch inverted	£200	£200
		b. Surch double, one albino	£120	
		w. Wmk inverted		4·00

Sultan Ahmed Fuad
9 October 1917–15 March 1922

40   (A)   (B)

41 Statue of Rameses II, Luxor   **42**

(Typo Harrison)

1921–22. As Nos. 73/82 *and new designs* (15m.). W **40.** P 14 (20, 50, 100m.) or 13½×14 (others).

84	29	1m. sepia (A)	1·50	2·25
		a. Two dots omitted (B) (R. 10/10)	35·00	45·00
		w. Wmk inverted	10·00	7·50
85	30	2m. green	4·50	3·75
		a. Imperf between (pair)		
		w. Wmk inverted	15·00	10·00
86		2m. vermilion (1922)	4·25	80
		w. Wmk inverted	15·00	10·00
87	31	3m. yellow-orange	5·00	2·25
		w. Wmk inverted	16·00	10·00
88	32	4m. green (1922)	5·50	6·50
		w. Wmk inverted	—	10·00
89	33	5m. lake (1.21)	4·50	30
		a. Imperf between (pair)		
		w. Wmk inverted	15·00	10·00
90		5m. pink (11.21)	5·00	20
		w. Wmk inverted	15·00	10·00
91	34	10m. dull blue	5·00	20
		w. Wmk inverted	—	10·00
92		10m. lake (9.22)	1·75	30
		w. Wmk inverted	—	10·00
93	41	15m. indigo (3.22)	5·00	15
		w. Wmk inverted	—	8·00
94	42	15m. indigo	25·00	3·25
		w. Wmk inverted	26·00	10·00
95	35	20m. olive	9·50	30
		w. Wmk inverted	20·00	10·00
96	36	50m. purple	10·00	1·25
		w. Wmk inverted	18·00	12·00
97	37	100m. slate (1922)	75·00	7·50
84/97		Set of 14	£140	26·00

Type **42** was printed first; but because the Arabic inscription at right was felt to be unsuitable the stamps were withheld and the corrected Type **41** printed and issued. Type **42** was released later.

STAMP BOOKLETS

1903 (1 Jan). *Black on pink cover inscr "Egyptian Post Office" in English and French. Stapled.*

SB1   121m. booklet containing twenty-four 5m. (No. 63c) in blocks of 6 .... £4000

1903 (1 July). *Black on blue cover inscr "Egyptian Post Office" in English and French. Stapled.*

SB2   73m. booklet containing twenty-four 3m. (No. 61ab) in blocks of 6 ....

1911 (1 July). *Black on pink cover inscr "Egyptian Post Office" in English and Arabic. Stapled.*
SB3   120m. Contents as No. SB1...................................... £3000

1914 (8 Jan). *Black on pink cover inscr "Egyptian Post Office" in English and Arabic. Stapled.*
SB4   125m. booklet containing twenty-four 5m. (No. 77a)
       in blocks of 6 ....

1919 (1 Jan). *Black on pink cover inscr "Egyptian Post Office" in English and Arabic. Stapled.*
SB5   120m. Contents as No. SB4...................................... £2000

1921 (12 June). *Deep blue on pink cover inscr "POST OFFICE" in English and Arabic. Stapled.*
SB6   120m. booklet containing twenty-four 5m. (No. 89) in
       blocks of 6 ....
       a. Stitched £1600

1921 (Nov). *Deep blue or pink cover inscr "POST OFFICE" in English and Arabic. Stapled.*
SB7   120m. booklet containing twenty-four 5m. (No. 90) in
       blocks of 6 .... £1200

POSTAGE DUE STAMPS

D 16   D 23   D 24

(Des L. Barkhausen. Litho V. Penasson, Alexandria)

1884 (1 Jan). W 6 (*impressed on reverse*). P 10½.
D57 D 16 10pa. red .... 45·00 9·00
           a. Imperf (Pair) £110
           b. Imperf between (pair) £110
           x. Wmk impressed on face ....
D58   20pa. red .... £110 28·00
           x. Wmk impressed on face ....
D59   1pi. red .... £130 45·00
           x. Wmk impressed on face ....
D60   2pi. red .... £225 10·00
           w. Wmk inverted £325
           x. Wmk impressed on face ....
D61   5pi. red .... 14·00 42·00
           x. Wmk impressed on face ....

1886 (1 Aug)–**87**. No wmk. P 10½.
D62 D 16 10pa. rose-red (1887)...................... 60·00 12·00
           a. Imperf between (pair) .... 90·00
D63   20pa. rose-red .... £250 42·00
           a. Imperf between (pair) ....
D64   1pi. rose-red .... 30·00 8·00
           a. Imperf between (pair) £120 £120
D65   2pi. rose-red .... 30·00 3·75
           a. Imperf between (pair) £120

Specialists distinguish four types of each value in both these issues.

(Litho V. Penasson, Alexandria)

1888 (1 Jan). No wmk. P 11½.
D66 D 23 2m. green................................ 15·00 22·00
           a. Imperf between (pair) £170 £170
           b. Imperf (pair)............................. £170
D67   5m. rose-carmine .... 35·00 22·00
           a. Imperf (pair).............................
D68   1pi. blue .... £130 35·00
           a. Imperf between (pair) £170
D69   2p. orange .... £150 12·00
D70   5p. grey £200 £180
           a. With stop after left-hand
              "PIASTRES" £275 £225

Specialists distinguish four types of each value. No. D70a occurs on all examples of one of these types in the sheet except that on R. 2/1. Beware of forgeries of the 5p.

(Typo De La Rue)

1889 (Apr)–**1907**. *Ordinary paper.* W 8a. P 14.
D71 D 24 2m. green..................................... 7·00 50
           a. Bisected (1m.) (on cover with
              unbisected 2m.) (2.98)...........   †   £250
           bw. Wmk inverted .... 8·00 3·00
           c. Chalk-surfaced paper (1906).. 14·00 50
D72   4m. maroon .... 2·25 50
           aw. Wmk inverted .... 4·00 1·00
           c. Chalk-surfaced paper (1906).. 2·75 50
D73   1p. ultramarine .... 5·50 50
           aw. Wmk inverted .... 8·50 3·00
           b. Chalk-surfaced paper (1906).. 6·50 50
D74   2p. orange .... 5·50 70
           bw. Wmk inverted .... 5·00 70
           c. Chalk-surfaced paper (1907).. 5·00 70

No. D71a was authorised for use on Egyptian Army letters from the Sudan campaign which were only charged 3m. postage due.
See also Nos. 84/6 for stamps with watermark sideways.

(D 26)   (D 27)

Type D 26

The Arabic figure at right is less than 2 mm from the next character, which consists of a straight stroke only.

Type D 27

The distance is 3 mm and the straight character has a comma-like character above it. There are other minor differences.

1898 (7 May)–**1907**. *No. D74 surch at Bûlâq. Ordinary paper.*

(a) With Type D 26.
D75 D 24 3m. on 2p. orange .... 1·25 4·50
           a. Surch inverted................. 60·00 75·00
           b. Pair, one without surch ....
           c. Arabic "2" for "3" ....
           d. Arabic "3" over "2" £100

No. D75c occurred in the first printing on positions 10, 20, 30, 40, 50 and 60 of the pane of 60 (the Arabic figure is the right-hand character of the second line—see illustration on page xvii). In the second printing the correct figure was printed on top to form No. D75d. The error was corrected in subsequent printings.

(b) With Type D 27 (11.04).
D76 D 24 3m. on 2p. orange .... 4·25 15·00
           a. Surch inverted................. 50·00 60·00
           b. Chalk-surfaced paper
              (1907) ....
           ba. Surch inverted ....
           bb. Surch double ....

1914–**15**. *As Nos. D71/3 but wmk sideways*.*
D84 D 24 2m. bright green (1915).............. 14·00 4·25
           w. Wmk star to left of crescent ... 20·00 14·00
D85   4m. maroon .... 14·00 16·00
           w. Wmk star to left of crescent ... 24·00
D86   1p. dull ultramarine.................... 23·00 11·00
           w. Wmk star to left of crescent ... 18·00 12·00

*The normal sideways watermark shows star to right of crescent, as seen from the back of the stamp.

D 43   D 44

(Typo Harrison)

1921 (Apr)–**22**. *Chalk-surfaced paper.* W 40 (*sideways**). P 14×13½.
D98 D 43 2m. green...................................... 2·75 4·25
           w. Wmk stars below crescents ... 9·00 4·25
D99   2m. scarlet (1922) .... 1·00 1·75
           w. Wmk stars below crescents ... 7·50 4·00
D100   4m. scarlet .... 5·00 14·00
D101   4m. green (1922) .... 4·75 4·00
           w. Wmk stars below crescents ... 12·00 5·00
D102 D 44 10m. deep slate-blue (11.21).......... 7·50 19·00
D103   10m. lake (1922) .... 5·50 5·00
           w. Wmk stars below crescents ... 10·00 4·00
D98/103 Set of 6 .... 24·00 38·00

*The normal sideways watermark shows the stars above the crescents.

OFFICIAL STAMPS

O 25   (O 28)   "O.H.H.S."
                              (O 29)

(Typo De La Rue)

1893 (1 Jan)–**1914**. *Ordinary paper.* W 8a. P 14.
O64 O 25 (—) chestnut .... 2·75 10
           a. Chalk-surfaced paper (1903). 4·00 50
           bw. Wmk inverted .... 9·00
           c. Wmk sideways star to right.
              Chalk-surfaced paper (1914).. 10·00 9·00
           cw. Wmk sideways star to left.....

From January 1907 No. O64 was used on most official mail to addresses within Egypt. In 1907 it was replaced by Nos. O73/8, but the use of No. O64 for unregistered official mail to Egyptian addresses was resumed on 1 January 1909.
After No. O64c was withdrawn in 1915 the remaining stock was surcharged 1p., 2p., 3p. or 5p. for fiscal use.

1907 (1 Feb–Aug). *Nos. 54da, 56c, 58c, 59c, 61c and 63d optd with Type O 28 by De La Rue.*
O73 18 1m. pale brown .... 1·75 30
O74 19 2m. green .... 4·00 10
         a. Opt double ....
O75 20 3m. orange-yellow .... 2·75 1·25
O76 21 5m. rose .... 5·00 10
O77 13 1p. blue .... 2·00 10
O78 15 5p. slate-grey (Aug) .... 16·00 3·50
O73/8 Set of 6 .... 28·00 4·75

Nos. O73/8 were used on all official mail from February 1907 until 1 January 1909 after which their use was restricted to registered items and those sent to addresses overseas.

1913 (Nov). *No. 63d optd at Bûlâq.*

(a) With Type O 29.
O79 21 5m. rose ....   —   £300
         a. Opt inverted £6000

(b) As Type O 29 but without inverted commas.
O80 21 5m. rose .... 8·50 60
         a. No stop after "S" (R. 11/10).... 55·00 16·00
         b. Opt inverted ....   75·00

O.H.H.S.   O.H.H.S.   O.H.H.S.
(O 38)   (O 39)   (O 43)

1914 (Dec)–**15**. *Stamps of 1902–6 and 1914 optd with Type O 38 at Bûlâq.*
O83 29 1m. sepia (1.15) .... 1·50 3·75
         a. No stop after "S" (R. 10/10).... 12·00 25·00

---

				†	—
O84	19	2m. green (3.15)........................		4·25	7·00
		a. No stop after "S"		14·00	23·00
		b. Opt inverted		35·00	35·00
		c. Opt double		£325	
O85	31	3m. yellow-orange (3.15)...........		2·25	4·00
		a. No stop after "S" (R. 10/10)..		14·00	25·00
O86	21	4m. vermilion (12.14)................		4·75	2·50
		a. Opt inverted		£190	£140
		b. Pair, one without opt............			
O87	33	5m. lake (1.15)		4·00	1·25
		a. No stop after "S" (R. 10/10)..		15·00	22·00
O83/7 Set of 5				15·00	17·00

No. O84a occurs on three positions from the first printing and on two different positions from the second. Nos. O83a, O85a and O87a usually show a faint trace of the stop.

1915 (Oct). *Nos. 59ab, 62 and 77 optd lithographically with Type O 39 at Bûlâq.*
O88 19 2m. green...................................... 2·50 4·25
         a. Opt inverted .... 20·00 20·00
         b. Opt double .... 25·00
O89 21 4m. vermilion .... 6·50 7·00
O90 33 5m. lake .... 7·50 1·25
         a. Pair, one without opt............ £275

1922. *Nos. 84, etc optd lithographically with Type O 43 at Bûlâq.*
O98 29 1m. sepia (28.6)........................... 3·50 11·00
         a. Two dots omitted (B)................ £200
         w. Wmk inverted ....
O99 30 2m. vermilion (16.6)..................... 8·00 17·00
O100 31 3m. yellow-orange (28.6).............. 65·00 £130
O101 33 5m. pink (13.3)............................ 4·25 4·25

Egypt was declared to be an independent kingdom on 15 March 1922, and Sultan Ahmed Fuad became king.
Later stamp issues will be found listed in Part 19 (*Middle East*) of this catalogue.

EGYPTIAN POST OFFICES ABROAD

From 1865 Egypt operated various post offices in foreign countries. No special stamps were issued for these offices and use in them of unoverprinted Egyptian stamps can only be identified by the cancellation. Stamps with such cancellations are worth more than the used prices quoted in the Egypt listings.
Such offices operated in the following countries. An * indicates that details will be found under that heading elsewhere in the catalogue.

ETHIOPIA

A   B

C   D

MASSAWA. *Open Nov 1867 to 5 Dec 1885. Postmark types A (also without* REGIE), B, C, D. *An Arabic seal type is also known on stampless covers.*
SENHIT (*near Keren). Open 1878 to April 1885. Only one cover, cancelled "Mouderie Senhit" in 1879, is known, together with one showing possible hand-drawn cancellation.*
A post office is also recorded at Harar in 1878, but no postal marking has so far been reported.

SOMALILAND

Unoverprinted stamps of Egypt used from 1876 until 1884.

SUDAN

Unoverprinted stamps of Egypt used from 1867 until 1897.

TURKISH EMPIRE

G   H

I   J

K   L

M   N

O

The offices are listed according to the spelling on the cancellation. The present-day name (if different) and country are given in brackets.

ALESSANDRETTA (Iskenderun, Turkey). *Open 14 July 1870 to Feb 1872. Postmark types E, I.*

BAIROUT (Beirut, Lebanon). *Open 14 July 1870 to Feb 1872. Postmark types E, J.*

CAVALA (Kavala, Greece). *Open 14 July 1870 to Feb 1872. Postmark type E.*

COSTANTINOPOLI (Istanbul, Turkey). *Open 13 June 1865 to 30 June 1881. Postmark types E, F, O.*

DARDANELLI (Canakkle, Turkey). *Open 10 June 1868 to 30 June 1881. Postmark types H, K.*

DJEDDAH, *see* GEDDA.

GALIPOLI (Gelibolu, Turkey). *Open 10 June 1868 to 30 June 1881. Postmark types E, L.*

GEDDA, DJEDDAH (Jeddah, Saudi Arabia). *Open 8 June 1865 to 30 June 1881. Postmark types F, G (also with year replacing solid half-circle), O (all spelt GEDDA), D (spelt DJEDDAH).*

JAFFA (Jaffa, Israel). *Open 14 July 1870 to Feb 1872. Postmark type E.*

LAGOS (Port Logo, Greece). *Open 14 July 1870 to Feb 1872. Postmark type E.*

LATAKIA (Syria). *Open 14 July 1870 to Feb 1872. Postmark type E.*

LEROS (Aegean Is.). *Open July 1873 to January 1874 and May to October 1874. Postmark type E.*

MERSINA (Mersin, Turkey). *Open 14 July 1870 to Feb 1872. Postmark type E.*

METELINO (Lesbos, Greece). *Open 14 July 1870 to 30 June 1881. Postmark types E, M.*

RODI (Rhodes, Greece). *Open 13 Aug 1872 to 30 June 1881. Postmark type E.*

SALONNICCHI (Thessaloniki, Greece). *Open 14 July 1870 to Feb 1872. Postmark type E.*

SCIO (Chios, Aegean Is.). *Open 14 July 1870 to 30 June 1881. Postmark types E, N.*

SMIRNE (Izmir, Turkey). *Open 14 Nov 1865 to 30 June 1881. Postmark types E (also without "V. R."), F.*

TENEDOS (Bozcaada, Turkey). *Open 14 July 1870 to March 1871. Postmark type E.*

TRIPOLI (Lebanon). *Open 14 July 1870 to Feb 1872. Postmark type E.*

VOLO (Volos, Greece). *Open 14 July 1870 to Feb 1872. Postmark type E.*

BRITISH FORCES IN EGYPT

Following the rise of a nationalist movement led by Arabi Pasha, and serious disturbances in Alexandria, British troops landed at Ismalia in August 1882 and defeated the nationalists at Tel-el-Kebir on 13 September. A British Army Post Office detachment landed at Alexandria on 21 August and provided a postal service for the troops, using Great Britain stamps, from various locations until it was withdrawn on 7 October.

During the Gordon Relief Expedition of 1884–85 a postal detachment was sent to Suakin on the Red Sea. This operated between 25 March and 30 May 1885 using Great Britain stamps.

ZA 1

Stamps of GREAT BRITAIN *cancelled with Type* ZA **1**.

1882 (Aug–Oct).
ZA1   ½d. rose-red (Plate No. 20) £300
ZA2   ½d. green (1880) ....
ZA3   1d. Venetian red (1880) £175
ZA4   1d. lilac (1881) ....
ZA5   2½d. blue (1881) (Plate Nos. 21, 22, 23) £100

1885. *Used at Suakin.*
ZA6   ½d. slate-blue (1884) £300
ZA7   1d. lilac (1881) £225
ZA8   2½d. lilac (1884) ....
ZA9   5d. dull green (1884) £500

From 1 November 1932 to 29 February 1936 members of the British Forces in Egypt and their families were allowed to send letters to the British Isles at reduced rates. Special seals, which were on sale in booklets at N.A.A.F.I. Institutes and Canteens, were used instead of Egyptian stamps. These seals were stuck on the back of the envelopes, letters bearing the seals being franked on the front with a hand-stamp inscribed "EGYPT POSTAGE PREPAID" in a double circle surmounted by a crown.

PRICES FOR STAMPS ON COVER	
Nos. A1/9	*from* × 5
No. A10	*from* × 1·5
No. A11	*from* × 5
No. A12	*from* × 75
No. A13	*from* × 20
No. A14	*from* × 75
No. A15	*from* × 20

A 1

A 2

(Des Lt-Col. C. Fraser. Typo Hanbury, Tomsett & Co. Ltd, London)

1932 (1 Nov)–33. P 11.
            (a) Inscr "POSTAL SEAL".
A1   A **1**   1p. deep blue and red...................... 95·00   3·50
            (b) Inscr "LETTER SEAL".
A2   A **1**   1p. deep blue and red (8.33)............ 32·00   85

(Des Sgt. W. F. Lait. Litho Walker & Co, Amalgamated Press, Cairo)

1932 (26 Nov)–35. *Christmas Seals.* P 11½.
A3   A **2**   3m. black/*azure* .... 50·00   70·00
A4   3m. brown-lake (13.11.33)............... 7·50   50·00
A5   3m. deep blue (17.11.34) .... 7·00   28·00
A6   3m. vermilion (23.11.35) .... 1·25   40·00
            a. Pale vermilion (19.12.35)......... 8·50   22·00

A 3

(Des Miss Waugh. Photo Harrison)

1934 (1 June)–35.
            (a) P 14½×14.
A7   A **3**   1p. carmine .... 40·00   85
A8   1p. green (5.12.34) .... 4·00   4·00
            (b) P 13½×14.
A9   A **3**   1p. carmine (24.4.35) .... 2·50   3·00

(A 4)

1935 (6 May). *Silver Jubilee. As No. A9, but colour changed and optd with Type A* **4**, *in red.*
A10   A **3**   1p. ultramarine £250   £180

Xmas 1935
3 Milliemes
(A 5)

1935 (16 Dec). *Provisional Christmas Seal. No. A9 surch with Type A* **5**.
A11   A **3**   3m. on 1p. carmine......................... 16·00   70·00

The seals and letter stamps were replaced by the following Army Post stamps issued by the Egyptian Postal Administration. No. A9 was accepted for postage until 15 March 1936.

A **6** King Fuad I   A **7** King Farouk

W **48** of Egypt

(Types A **6**/A **7**. Photo Survey Dept, Cairo)

1936. W **48** of Egypt. P 13½ × 14.
A12   A **6**   3m. green (1.12.36).......................... 1·00   1·25
A13   10m. carmine (1.3.36) .... 4·50   10
            w. Wmk inverted ....

1939 (16 Dec). W **48** of Egypt. P 13×13½.
A14   A **7**   3m. green... 3·75   6·00
A15   10m. carmine..................................... 5·50   10
            w. Wmk inverted ....

These stamps were withdrawn in April 1941 but the concession, without the use of special stamps, continued until October 1951 when the postal agreement was abrogated.

SUEZ CANAL COMPANY

PRICES FOR STAMPS ON COVER	
Nos. 1/4	*from* × 20

100 Centimes = 1 Franc

On 30 November 1855 a concession to construct the Suez Canal was granted to Ferdinand de Lesseps and the Compagnie Universelle du Canal Maritime de Suez was formed. Work began in April 1859 and the canal was opened on 17 November 1869. In November 1875 the Khedive sold his shares in the company to the British Government, which then became the largest shareholder.

The company transported mail free of charge between Port Said and Suez from 1859 to 1867, when it was decided that payment should be made for the service and postage stamps were introduced in July 1868. Letters for destinations beyond Port Said or Suez required additional franking with Egyptian or French stamps.

The imposition of charges for the service was not welcomed by the public and in August the Egyptian Government agreed to take it over.

1

(Litho Chezaud, Aine & Tavernier, Paris)

1868 (8 July). *Imperf.*
1   **1**   1c. black £250   £1000
2   5c. green.. 85·00   £500
3   20c. blue... 75·00   £500
4   40c. pink £130   £750

Shades of all values exist.

Stamps can be found showing parts of the papermaker's watermark "LA+-F" (La Croix Frères).

These stamps were withdrawn from sale on 16 August 1868 and demonetised on 31 August.

Many forgeries exist, unused and cancelled. The vast majority of these forgeries show vertical lines, instead of cross-hatching, between "POSTES" and the central oval. It is believed that other forgeries, which do show cross-hatching, originate from the plate of the 40c. value which is missing from the company's archives. These are, however, on thin, brittle paper with smooth shiny gum.

JUBILEE COMMEMORATION 1935

Falkland Islands

PRICES FOR STAMPS ON COVER TO 1945	
No. 1	from × 100
No. 2	from × 50
Nos. 3/4	from × 10
No. 5	—
Nos. 6/10	from × 30
Nos. 11/12	from × 15
Nos. 13/17	from × 10
Nos. 17b/c	from × 100
Nos. 18/21	from × 10
Nos. 22/b	from × 30
Nos. 23/4	from × 100
Nos. 25/6	from × 30
No. 27	from × 20
No. 28	from × 40
No. 29	from × 5
No. 30/b	from × 50
No. 30c	from × 15
No. 31	from × 5
No. 32/b	from × 15
Nos. 41/2	—
Nos. 43/8	from × 12
Nos. 49/50	—
Nos. 60/5	from × 10
Nos. 66/9	—
Nos. 70/1	from × 10
No. 72/b	—
Nos. 73/9	from × 4
No. 80	—
No. 115	from × 2
Nos. 116/19	from × 20
Nos. 120/2	from × 6
Nos. 123/6	—
Nos. 127/34	from × 5
Nos. 135/8	—
Nos. 139/45	from × 50
Nos. 146/63	from × 5

CROWN COLONY

1   2

1869–76. *The Franks.*
FR1 **1** In black, *on cover* £9000
FR2 **2** In red, *on cover* (1876) £16000

On *piece*, No. FR1 on white or coloured paper £110; No. FR2 on white £180.

The first recorded use of No. FR1 is on a cover to London datestamped 4 January 1869. The use of these franks ceased when the first stamps were issued.

½d.
(4)

In the ½d., 2d., 2½d. and 9d. the figures of value in the lower corners are replaced by small rosettes and the words of value are in colour.

NOTE. Nos. 1, 2, 3, 4, 8, 10, 11 and 12 exist with one or two sides imperf from the margin of the sheets.

(Recess B.W.)

1878–79. No wmk. P 14, 14½.
1	3	1d. claret (19.6.78)	£750	£400
2		4d. grey-black (Sept 1879)	£1200	£150
		a. On wmkd paper	£2750	£500
3		6d. blue-green (19.6.78)	85·00	70·00
4		1s. bistre-brown (1878)	70·00	65·00

No. 2a shows portions of the papermaker's watermark—"R. TURNER, CHAFFORD MILLS"—in ornate double-lined capitals.

NOTES. The dates shown for Nos. 5/12 and 15/38 are those on which the printer delivered the various printings to the Crown Agents. Several months could elapse before the stamps went on sale in the Colony, depending on the availability of shipping.

The plates used for these stamps did not fit the paper so that the watermark appears in all sorts of positions on the stamp. Well centred examples are scarce. Examples can also be found showing parts of the marginal watermarks, either CROWN AGENTS horizontally in letters 12 mm high or "CROWN AGENTS FOR THE COLONIES" vertically in 7 mm letters. Both are in double-lined capitals.

1882 (22 Nov). Wmk Crown CA (upright). P 14, 14½.
5	3	1d. dull claret	£325	£160
		a. Imperf vert (horiz pair)	£55000	
		x. Wmk reversed	£850	
		y. Wmk inverted and reversed........	£550	£350
6		4d. grey-black	£400	85·00
		w. Wmk inverted	£650	£250

1885 (23 Mar)–91. Wmk Crown CA (sideways*). P 14, 14½.
7	3	1d. pale claret	75·00	50·00

---

		w. Wmk Crown to right of CA	90·00	70·00
		x. Wmk sideways reversed	£250	£120
		y. Wmk Crown to right of CA and reversed.................................	£190	£130
8		1d. brownish claret (3.10.87).......	£100	50·00
		a. Bisected (on cover) (1.1891).....	†	£2750
		w. Wmk Crown to right of CA	£120	50·00
		x. Wmk sideways reversed	£200	£100
		y. Wmk Crown to right of CA and reversed.................................	£200	£150
9		4d. pale grey-black	£650	70·00
		w. Wmk Crown to right of CA	£650	85·00
		x. Wmk sideways reversed	£700	£180
		y. Wmk Crown to right of CA and reversed.................................	£650	£140
10		4d. grey-black (3.10.87)	£400	48·00
		w. Wmk Crown to right of CA	£400	48·00
		x. Wmk sideways reversed	£800	£120
		y. Wmk Crown to right of CA and reversed.................................	£650	80·00

*The normal sideways watermark shows Crown to left of CA, *as seen from the back of the stamp.*
For No. 8a see note below No. 14.

1889 (26 Sept)–91. Wmk Crown CA (upright). P 14, 14½.
11	3	1d. red-brown (21.5.91)	£190	85·00
		a. Bisected (on cover) (7.91)	†	£3000
		x. Wmk reversed	£450	£300
12		4d. olive grey-black	£150	55·00
		w. Wmk inverted	£650	£350
		x. Wmk reversed	£425	£170

For No. 11a see note below No. 14.

1891 (Jan–11 July). *Nos. 8 and 11 bisected diagonally and each half handstamped with T* **4**.
13	3	½d. on half of 1d. brownish claret (No. 8)	£600	£300
		a. Unsevered pair	£3000	£1000
		b. Unsevered pair se-tenant with unsurcharged whole stamp	£22000	
		c. Bisect se-tenant with unsurcharged whole stamp	†	£1700
14		½d. on half of 1d. red-brown (No. 11) (11 July)	£700	£275
		a. Unsevered pair	£3750	£1500
		b. Bisect se-tenant with unsurcharged whole stamp	†	£1600

1891 PROVISIONALS. In 1891 the postage to the United Kingdom and Colonies was reduced from 4d. to 2½d. per half ounce. As no ½d. or 2½d. stamps were available the bisection of the 1d. was authorised from 1 January 1891. This authorisation was withdrawn on 11 January 1892, although bisects were accepted for postage until July of that year. The ½d. and 2½d. stamps were placed on sale from 10 September 1891.

Cork Cancel used in 1891

The Type **4** surcharge was not used regularly; unsurcharged bisects being employed far more frequently. Genuine bisects should be cancelled with the cork cancel illustrated above. The use of any other postmark, including a different cork cancel or an "F.I." obliterator, requires date evidence linked to known mail ship sailings to prove authenticity.

After 10 September 1891 the post office supplied "posthumous" examples of the surcharged bisects to collectors. These were without postal validity and differ from Type **4** by showing a large full stop, long fraction bar or curly tail to "2". Some of the posthumous surcharges were applied to No. 18 which was not used for the original bisects. Examples are also known showing the surcharge double, inverted or sideways.

1891 (10 Sept)–1902. Wmk Crown CA (upright). P 14, 14½.
15	3	½d. blue-green (10 Sept–Nov 1891)	22·00	26·00
		x. Wmk reversed	£350	£325
		y. Wmk inverted and reversed.......	£375	£375
16		½d. green (20.5.92)	16·00	15·00
		ax. Wmk reversed	£160	£160
		ay. Wmk inverted and reversed.......	£325	£325
		b. Deep green (15.4.96)	40·00	30·00
17		½d. deep yellow-green (1894–95)	17·00	21·00
		ay. Wmk inverted and reversed.......	£160	£160
		b. Yellow-green (19.6.99)	2·00	3·00
		c. Dull yellowish green (13.1.1902)	5·50	4·50
		cx. Wmk reversed	£350	£350
18		1d. orange red-brown (14.10.91)....	85·00	70·00
		a. Brown	£120	70·00
		w. Wmk inverted	£850	£375
		x. Wmk reversed	£200	£200
19		1d. reddish chestnut (20.4.92)	42·00	42·00
20		1d. orange-brn (wmk reversed) (18.1.94)	55·00	50·00
21		1d. claret (23.7.94)	£100	80·00
		x. Wmk reversed	75·00	50·00
22		1d. Venetian red (pale to deep) (1895–96)	19·00	17·00
		ax. Wmk reversed	10·00	12·00
		b. Venetian claret (1898?)	30·00	14·00
23		1d. pale red (19.6.99)	7·00	2·50
		x. Wmk reversed	£325	£300
24		1d. orange-red (13.1.1902)	13·00	4·00
25		2d. purple (pale to deep) (1895–98)	6·50	12·00
		x. Wmk reversed	£400	£425
26		2d. reddish purple (15.4.96)	5·00	11·00
27		2½d. pale chalky ultramarine (10.9.91)	£160	48·00
28		2½d. dull blue (19.11.91)	£160	25·00
		x. Wmk reversed	£325	£250
29		2½d. Prussian blue (18.1.94)	£225	£130

30		2½d. ultramarine (1894–96)	30·00	11·00
		ax. Wmk reversed......................	60·00	14·00
		ay. Wmk inverted and reversed.......	£650	
		b. Pale ultramarine (10.6.98)	35·00	15·00
		bx. Wmk reversed	£110	75·00
		c. Deep ultramarine (18.9.1901)..	38·00	35·00
		cx. Wmk reversed	£300	£300
31		4d. brownish black (wmk reversed) (18.1.94)	£750	£350
32		4d. olive-black (11.5.95)	11·00	21·00
33		6d. orange-yellow (19.11.91)	£180	£150
		x. Wmk reversed	65·00	48·00
34		6d. yellow (15.4.96)	40·00	48·00
35		9d. pale reddish orange (15.11.95)...	42·00	55·00
		x. Wmk reversed	£325	£375
		y. Wmk inverted and reversed........	£475	£475
36		9d. salmon (15.4.96)	48·00	55·00
		x. Wmk reversed	£325	£375
37		1s. grey-brown (15.11.95)	55·00	55·00
		x. Wmk reversed	£160	£170
38		1s. yellow-brown (15.4.96)	55·00	48·00
		x. Wmk reversed	£160	£170
17b/38		*Set of 8*	£170	£180
		15s, 26s, 28s, 33s, 35s Optd "Specimen" *Set of 5*....	£600	

The ½d. and 2½d. were first placed on sale in the Falkland Islands on 10 September 1891. Such stamps came from the August 1891 printing. The stock of the May printings sent to the Falkland Islands was lost on sea.

The 2½d. ultramarine printing can sometimes be found in a violet shade, but the reason for this is unknown.

5   6

(Recess B.W.)

1898 (5 Oct). Wmk Crown CC. P 14, 14½.
41	5	2s.6d. deep blue............	£250	£250
42	6	5s. red	£200	£225
		41s/2s Optd "Specimen" *Set of 2*	£475	

7   8

(Recess D.L.R.)

1904 (16 July)–12. Wmk Mult Crown CA. P 14.
43	7	½d. yellow-green	4·25	1·50
		aw. Wmk inverted	£300	£190
		ax. Wmk reversed	£750	
		b. Pale yellow-green (on thick paper) (6.08)	16·00	7·50
		bw. Wmk inverted		
		c. Deep yellow-green (7.11)	11·00	3·00
44		1d. vermilion	12·00	1·50
		aw. Wmk inverted	£300	£190
		ax. Wmk reversed	£400	£350
		b. Wmk sideways (7.06)	1·00	2·50
		c. Thick paper (1908)	19·00	1·75
		cw. Wmk inverted	£400	£350
		cx. Wmk reversed	£475	£350
		d. Dull coppery red (on thick paper) (3.08)	£200	35·00
		dx. Wmk reversed	£750	£400
		e. Orange-vermilion (7.11)	19·00	2·75
		ex. Wmk reversed	£400	£400
45		2d. purple (27.12.04)	17·00	23·00
		ax. Wmk reversed	£140	£140
		b. Reddish purple (13.1.12)	£225	£275
46		2½d. ultramarine (shades)	29·00	7·50
		aw. Wmk inverted	£275	£190
		ay. Wmk inverted and reversed.......	—	£650
		b. Deep blue (13.1.12)	£250	£150
47		6d. orange (27.12.04)	40·00	48·00
48		1s. brown (27.12.04)	40·00	32·00
		x. Wmk reversed	£160	£150
49	8	3s. green	£1700	£1300
		aw. Wmk inverted	£140	£120
		b. Deep green (4.07)	£1700	£1200
50		5s. red (27.12.04)	£200	£150
43/50		*Set of 8*	£425	£350
		43s/50s Optd "Specimen" *Set of 8*	£600	

Examples of Nos. 41/50 and earlier issues are known with a forged Falkland Islands postmark dated "OCT 15 10".

> For details of South Georgia underprint, South Georgia provisional handstamps and Port Foster handstamp see under FALKLAND ISLANDS DEPENDENCIES.

9   10

(Des B. MacKennal. Eng J. A. C. Harrison. Recess D.L.R.)

1912 (3 July)–**20**. Wmk Mult Crown CA. P 13¾×14 (comb) (½d. to 1s.) or 14 (line) (3s. to £1).

60	**9**	½d. yellow-green	2·75	3·50
		a. Perf 14 (line). *Deep yellow-green* (1914)	18·00	35·00
		b. Perf 14 (line). *Deep olive* (1918)	24·00	£120
		c. *Deep olive* (4.19)	3·50	38·00
		ca. *Printed both sides*	†	£6000
		d. *Dull yellowish green* (on thick greyish paper) (1920)	4·50	35·00
61		1d. orange-red	5·00	2·50
		a. Perf 14 (line). *Orange-vermilion* (1914, 1916)	28·00	2·50
		b. Perf 14 (line). *Vermilion* (1918)	†	£800
		c. *Orange-vermilion* (4.19)	3·75	3·00
		d. *Orange-vermilion* (on thick greyish paper) (1920)	7·00	2·00
		dx. Wmk reversed	£180	
62		2d. maroon	26·00	23·00
		a. Perf 14 (line). *Deep reddish purple* (1914)	£160	£110
		b. Perf 14 (line). *Maroon* (4.18)	£170	£120
		c. *Deep reddish purple* (4.19)	7·50	16·00
63		2½d. deep bright blue	19·00	24·00
		a. Perf 14 (line). *Deep bright blue* (1914)	29·00	35·00
		b. Perf 14 (line). *Deep blue* (1916, 4.18)	32·00	45·00
		c. *Deep blue* (4.19)	7·00	17·00
64		6d. yellow-orange (6.7.12)	14·00	20·00
		aw. Wmk inverted	£475	£425
		b. *Brown-orange* (4.19)	15·00	42·00
65		1s. light bistre-brown (6.7.12)	32·00	30·00
		a. *Pale bistre-brown* (4.19)	65·00	£110
		b. *Brown* (on thick greyish paper) (1920)	32·00	£140
66	**10**	3s. slate-green	85·00	80·00
67		5s. deep rose-red	£100	£100
		a. *Reddish maroon* (1914)	£225	£225
		b. *Maroon* (1916)	90·00	£110
		bx. Wmk reversed	£3250	£1900
68		10s. red/*green* (11.2.14)	£160	£250
69		£1 black/*red* (11.2.14)	£450	£500
60/9 *(inc 67b)* Set of 11			£850	£1000
60s/9s *(inc both 67s and 67as)* Optd "Specimen" Set of 11			£1500	

The exact measurement of the comb perforation used for Type **9** is 13.7×13.9. The line perforation, used for the 1914, 1916 and 1918 printings and for all the high values in Type **10**, measured 14.1×14.1.

It was previously believed that all examples of the 1d. in vermilion with the line perforation were overprinted to form No. 71, but it has now been established that some unoverprinted sheets of No. 61b were used during 1919.

Many of the sheets showed stamps from the left-hand side in a lighter shade than those from the right. It is believed that this was due to the weight of the impression. Such differences are particularly noticeable on the 2½d. 1916 and 1918 printings where the lighter shades, approaching milky blue in appearance, are scarce.

All 1919 printings show weak impressions of the background either side of the head caused by the poor plate quality.

Examples of all values are known with forged postmarks, including one of Falkland Islands dated "5 SP 19" and another of South Shetlands dated "20 MR 27".

WAR STAMP (11) **2½D** (12)

1918 (22 Oct*)–**20**. Optd by Govt Printing Press, Stanley, with T **11**.

70	**9**	½d. deep olive (line perf) (No. 60b)	1·00	11·00
		a. *Yellow-green* (No. 60) (4.19)	20·00	£500
		ab. *Albino opt*	£1700	
		b. *Deep olive* (comb perf) (No. 60c) (4.19)	50	6·50
		c. *Dull yellowish green* (on thick greyish paper) (No. 60d) (5.20)	8·00	70·00
		cx. Wmk reversed	£275	
71		1d. vermilion (line perf) (No. 61b)	2·00	18·00
		a. *Opt double, one albino*	£400	
		b. *Orange-verm* (line perf) (No. 61a) (4.19)	20·00	†
		c. *Orange-verm* (comb perf) (No. 61c) (4.19)	50	3·75
		ca. *Opt double*	£2250	
		cx. Wmk reversed	£475	
		d. *Orange-vermilion* (on thick greyish paper) (No. 61d) (5.20)	£110	£200
72		1s. light bistre-brown (No. 65)	35·00	80·00
		a. *Pale bistre-brown* (No. 65a) (4.19)	4·00	48·00
		ab. *Opt double, one albino*	£1600	
		ac. *Opt omitted* (in pair with normal)	£9000	
		b. *Brown* (on thick greyish paper) (No. 65b) (5.20)	5·50	45·00
		ba. *Opt double, one albino*	£1700	
		bw. Wmk inverted	£225	£325
		bx. Wmk reversed	£1100	

*Earliest known postal use. Cancellations dated 8 October were applied much later.

There were five printings of the "WAR STAMP" overprint, but all, except that in May 1920, used the same setting. Composition of the five printings was as follows:

October 1918. Nos. 70, 71 and 72.
January 1919. Nos. 70, 71 and 72.
April 1919. Nos. 70/b, 71b/c and 72a.
October 1919. Nos. 70b, 71c and 72a.
May 1920. Nos. 70c, 71d and 72b.

It is believed that the entire stock of No. 70a was sold to stamp dealers. Only a handful of used examples are known which may have subsequently been returned to the colony for cancellation.

No. 71ca exists in a block of 12 (6×2) from the bottom of a sheet on which the first stamp in the bottom row shows a single overprint, but the remainder have overprint double.

Examples of Nos. 70/2 are known with a forged Falkland Islands postmark dated "5 SP 19".

1921–28. Wmk Mult Script CA. P 14.

73	**9**	½d. yellowish green	3·00	4·00
		a. *Green* (1925)	3·00	4·00
74		1d. dull vermilion (1924)	5·00	1·25
		aw. Wmk inverted	†	£1800
		ay. Wmk inverted and reversed	£375	
		b. *Orange-vermilion* (shades) (1925)	5·50	1·25
75		2d. deep brown-purple (8.23)	17·00	7·00
		ax. Wmk reversed	—	£1600
		aw. Wmk inverted	£1700	
		b. *Purple-brown* (1927)	23·00	25·00
		c. *Reddish maroon* (1.28)	8·00	24·00
		cy. Wmk inverted and reversed		
76		2½d. deep blue	22·00	16·00
		a. *Indigo* (28.4.27)	16·00	20·00
		b. *Deep steel-blue* (1.28)	7·00	16·00
77		2½d. deep purple/*pale yellow* (8.23)	4·50	38·00
		a. *Pale purple/pale yellow* (1925)	4·50	38·00
		ay. Wmk inverted and reversed	£425	
78		6d. yellow-orange (1925)	8·00	38·00
		w. Wmk inverted	£275	
		x. Wmk reversed	£1500	
79		1s. deep ochre	17·00	48·00
80	**10**	3s. slate-green (8.23)	85·00	£160
73/80 Set of 8			£120	£275
73s/80s *(inc both 76s and 76as)* Optd "Specimen" Set of 9			£750	

Dates quoted above are those of despatch from Great Britain.

1928 (7 Feb). No. 75b surch with T **12**.

115	**9**	2½d. on 2d. purple-brown	£950	£1000
		a. *Surch double*	£35000	

No. 115 was produced on South Georgia during a shortage of 2½d. stamps. The provisional was withdrawn on 22 February 1928.

13 Fin Whale and Gentoo Penguins **14**

(Recess P.B.)

1929 (2 Sept)–**36**. P 14 (comb).

(a) Wmk Mult Script CA.

116	**13**	½d. green	1·25	3·00
		a. Line perf (1936)	4·00	8·00
117		1d. scarlet	3·75	80
		a. Line perf. *Deep red* (1936)	7·00	14·00
118		2d. grey	2·75	2·75
119		2½d. blue	2·75	2·25
120	**14**	4d. orange (*line perf*) (18.2.32)	16·00	13·00
		a. *Deep orange* (1936)	42·00	48·00
121	**13**	6d. purple	16·00	13·00
		a. Line perf. *Reddish purple* (1936)	45·00	25·00
122		1s. black/*emerald*	23·00	35·00
		a. Line perf. *On bright emerald* (1936)	23·00	27·00
123		2s.6d. carmine/*blue*	55·00	55·00
124		5s. green/*yellow*	85·00	£100
125		10s. carmine/*emerald*	£160	£190

(b) Wmk Mult Crown CA.

126	**13**	£1 black/*red*	£300	£375
116/26 Set of 11			£600	£700
116s/26s "Specimen" Set of 11			£1000	

Two kinds of perforation exist:

A. Comb perf 13.9:—original values of 1929.

B. Line perf 13.9, 14.2 or compound (small holes)—4d. and 1936 printings of ½d., 1d., 6d. and 1s. On some sheets the last vertical row of perforations shows larger holes.

Examples of most values are known with forged postmarks, including one of Port Stanley dated "14 JY 31" and another of South Georgia dated "AU 30 31".

15 Romney Marsh Ram **16** Iceberg

17 Whale-catcher *Bransfield* **18** Port Louis

19 Map of Falkland Islands **20** South Georgia

21 Fin Whale **22** Government House, Stanley

23 Battle Memorial **24** King Penguin

25 Coat of Arms

26 King George V Thick serif to "1" at left (R. 1/3, first printing only)

(Des (except 6d.) by G. Roberts. Eng and recess B.W.)

1933 (2 Jan–Apr). *Centenary of British Administration.* T **15/26**. Wmk Mult Script CA. P 12.

127	**15**	½d. black and green	1·75	7·00
128	**16**	1d. black and scarlet	3·50	2·25
		a. *Thick serif to 1 at left*	£170	£120
129	**17**	1½d. black and blue	16·00	17·00
130	**18**	2d. black and brown	10·00	22·00
131	**19**	3d. black and violet	17·00	22·00
132	**20**	4d. black and orange	17·00	17·00
133	**21**	6d. black and slate	50·00	70·00
134	**22**	1s. black and olive-green	48·00	75·00
135	**23**	2s.6d. black and violet	£170	£225
136	**24**	5s. black and yellow	£600	£850
		a. *Black and yellow-orange* (Apr)	£1700	£2000
137	**25**	10s. black and chestnut	£600	£950
138	**26**	£1 black and carmine	£1700	£2250
127/38 Set of 12			£3000	£4000
127s/38s Perf "Specimen" Set of 12			£2500	

Examples of all values are known with forged Port Stanley postmarks dated "6 JA 33". Some values have also been seen with part strikes of the forged Falkland Islands postmark mentioned below Nos. 60/9 and 70/2.

(Des H. Fleury. Recess B.W.)

1935 (7 May). *Silver Jubilee.* As Nos. 91/4 of Antigua, but printed by B.W. P 11×12.

139		1d. deep blue and scarlet	3·25	40
		b. *Short extra flagstaff*	£550	£425
		d. *Flagstaff on right-hand turret*	£350	£250
		e. *Double flagstaff*	£350	£225
140		2½d. brown and deep blue	12·00	1·75
		b. *Short extra flagstaff*	£1400	£900
		d. *Flagstaff on right-hand turret*	£350	£250
		e. *Double flagstaff*	£500	£350
		l. *Re-entry on value tablet* (R. 8/1)	£200	£110
141		4d. green and indigo	11·00	4·50
		b. *Short extra flagstaff*	£750	£475
		d. *Flagstaff on right-hand turret*	£475	£350
		e. *Double flagstaff*	£550	£400
142		1s. slate and purple	8·50	9·00
		a. *Extra flagstaff*	£3500	£2500
		b. *Short extra flagstaff*	£750	£400
		c. *Lightning conductor*	£2250	£1100
		d. *Flagstaff on right-hand turret*	£800	£450
		e. *Double flagstaff*	£850	£475
139/42 Set of 4			32·00	9·00
139s/42s Perf "Specimen" Set of 4			£475	

For illustrations of plate varieties see Omnibus section following Zanzibar

1937 (12 May). *Coronation.* As Nos. 95/7 of Antigua. P 11×11½.

143		½d. green	30	10
144		1d. carmine	1·00	50
145		2½d. blue	1·50	1·40
143/5 Set of 3			2·50	1·75
143s/5s Perf "Specimen" Set of 3			£300	

27 Whale's Jawbones

28 Black-necked Swan

29 Battle Memorial

30 Flock of sheep

31 Magellan Goose

32 *Discovery II* (polar supply vessel)

33 *William Scoresby* (supply ship)

34 Mount Sugar Top

34a Turkey Vultures

35 Gentoo Penguins

36 Southern Sealion

37 Deception Island

38 Arms of the Falkland Islands

(Des G. Roberts (Nos. 146, 148/9, 158 and 160/3), K. Lellman (No. 159). Recess B.W.)

1938 (3 Jan)–50. *T 27/38*. Wmk Mult Script CA. P 12.

146	27	½d. black and green (*shades*)	30	75
147	28	1d. black and carmine	32·00	80
		a. *Black and vermilion*	3·75	85
148	29	1d. black and violet (14.7.41)	2·50	1·75
		a. *Black and purple-violet*	7·50	2·00
149		2d. black and deep violet	1·25	50
150	28	2d. black and carmine-red (14.7.41)	1·50	2·25
		a. *Black and red*	2·75	1·00
151	30	2½d. black and bright blue	1·25	30
152	31	2½d. black and blue (15.6.49)	6·50	7·00
153	30	3d. black and blue (14.7.41)	6·50	2·75
		a. *Black and deep blue*	11·00	2·75
154	31	4d. black and purple	3·25	1·00
155	32	6d. slate-black and deep brown	10·00	2·50
		a. *Black and sepia (shades)*	2·50	1·50
156		6d. black (15.6.49)	6·50	4·25
157	33	9d. black and grey-blue	23·00	2·25
158	34	1s. light dull blue	75·00	18·00
		a. *Dull greenish blue*	45·00	3·25
		b. *Dull blue (greyish paper)*	23·00	—
		c. *Deep dull blue (thin paper)*	75·00	—
159	34a	1s.3d. black and carmine-red (11.12.46)	2·50	1·40
160	35	2s.6d. slate	55·00	15·00
161	36	5s. blue and chestnut	£140	70·00
		b. *Indigo and pale yellow-brown*	£850	90·00
		c. *Dull blue and yellow brown (greyish paper)*	£120	£300
		d. *Steel blue and buff-brown (thin paper) (9.50)*	£190	£300
162	37	10s. black and orange-brown	£130	42·00
		a. *Black and orange (1942?)*	£275	35·00
		b. *Black and red-orange (1949)*	75·00	£250
		c. *Black and deep reddish orange (1950)*	£350	£300
163	38	£1 *Black and violet*	£130	55·00
146/63 Set of 18			£425	£180
146/51s, 153/5s, 157/63s Perf "Specimen" Set of 16			£1600	

The 'thin paper' referred to will aid identification of Nos. 158c, 161d and 162c. It is more transparent than previous papers and has white gum.

Examples of values issued before 1946 are known with forged Port Stanley postmarks dated "14 JY 41" and "28 JY 43".

Crown flaw and re-entry (Pl 1, R. 8/5)

1946 (7 Oct). *Victory. As Nos. 110/11 of Antigua.* P 13½–14.

164		1d. dull violet	30	50
165		3d. blue	45	50
		a. Crown flaw and re-entry	50·00	50·00
164s/5s Perf "Specimen" Set of 2			£250	

1948 (1 Nov). *Royal Silver Wedding. As Nos. 112/13 of Antigua.*

166		2½d. ultramarine	2·00	1·00
167		£1 mauve	90·00	60·00

1949 (10 Oct). *75th Anniv of Universal Postal Union. As Nos. 114/17 of Antigua.*

168		1d. violet	1·50	1·00
169		3d. deep blue	5·00	2·25
170		1s.3d. deep blue-green	3·00	2·25
171		2s. blue	3·00	8·00
168/71 Set of 4			11·00	12·00

39 Sheep

40 *Fitzroy* (supply ship)

41 Magellan Goose

42 Map of Falkland Islands

43 Arms of the Colony

44 Auster Autocrat Aircraft

45 *John Biscoe* (research ship)

46 View of the Two Sisters

47 Gentoo Penguins

48 Kelp Goose and Gander

49 Sheep shearing

50 Battle Memorial

51 Southern Sealion and South American Fur Seal

52 Hulk of *Great Britain*

(Des from sketches by V. Spencer. Recess Waterlow)

1952 (2 Jan). *T 39/52*. Wmk Mult Script CA. P 13×13½ (vert) or 13½×13 (horiz).

172	39	½d. green	1·00	70
173	40	1d. scarlet	2·50	40
174	41	2d. violet	4·50	2·50
175	42	2½d. black and light ultramarine	1·25	50
176	43	3d. deep ultramarine	2·25	1·00
177	44	4d. reddish purple	9·00	1·50
178	45	6d. bistre-brown	12·00	1·00
179	46	9d. orange-yellow	9·00	2·00
180	47	1s. black	24·00	80
181	48	1s.3d. orange	15·00	5·00
182	49	2s.6d. olive-green	20·00	11·00
183	50	5s. purple	15·00	9·00
184	51	10s. grey	26·00	11·00
185	52	£1 black	29·00	18·00
172/185 Set of 14			£150	55·00

FALKLAND ISLANDS DEPENDENCIES

PRICES FOR STAMPS ON COVER TO 1945	
Nos. A1/D8	*from* × 20

A. GRAHAM LAND

For use at Port Lockroy (established 1 February 1944) and Hope Bay (established 12 February 1945) bases.

Falkland Islands definitive stamps with face values of 1s.3d. and above were also valid for use from Graham Land in conjunction with Nos. A1/8 and subsequently Nos. G1/16.

Stamps of FALKLAND ISLANDS *cancelled at Port Lockroy or Hope Bay with Graham Land circular datestamps between* 12 February 1944 *and* 31 January 1954.

1938–50. *King George VI (Nos. 159/63).*

Z1	1s.3d. black and carmine-red	£120
Z2	2s.6d. slate	55·00
Z3	5s. indigo and yellow-brown	£160
Z4	10s. black and orange	70·00
Z5	£1 black and violet	90·00

1952. *King George VI (Nos. 181/5).*

Z6	1s.3d. orange	£100
Z7	2s.6d. olive-green	£110
Z8	5s. purple	£130
Z9	10s. grey	£140
Z10	£1 black	£150

GRAHAM LAND

DEPENDENCY OF
(A 1)

1944 (12 Feb)–45. *Falkland Islands Nos. 146, 148, 150, 153/5, 157 and 158a optd with Type A 1, in red, by B.W.*

A1		½d. black and green	30	1·75
		a. *Blue-black and green*	£950	£500
A2		1d. black and violet	30	1·00
A3		2d. black and carmine-red	50	1·00
A4		3d. black and blue	50	1·00
A5		4d. black and purple	2·00	1·75
A6		6d. black and brown	16·00	2·25
		a. *Blue-black and brown (24.9.45)*	16·00	
A7		9d. black and grey-blue	1·00	1·25
A8		1s. deep blue	1·00	1·25
A1/8 Set of 8			19·00	10·00
A1s/8s Perf "Specimen" Set of 8			£475	

B. SOUTH GEORGIA

The stamps of Falkland Islands were used at the Grytviken whaling station on South Georgia from 3 December 1909.

Mr. J. Innes Wilson, the Stipendary Magistrate whose duties included those of postmaster, was issued with a stock of stamps, values ½d. to 5s., together with an example of the current "FALKLAND ISLANDS" circular datestamp. This was used to cancel the stamps, but, as it gave no indication that mail had originated at South Georgia, a straight-line handstamp inscribed "SOUTH GEORGIA", or subsequently "South Georgia", was also supplied. It was intended that this should be struck directly on to each letter or card below the stamp, but it can sometimes be found struck across the stamp instead.

The use of the "South Georgia" handstamp continued after the introduction of the "SOUTH GEORGIA" circular datestamp in June 1910 apparently for philatelic purposes, but no example has been reported used after June 1912.

SOUTH GEORGIA.
Z 1

South Georgia.
Z 2

			On piece	On cover/card
ZU1	Example of Type Z 1 used in conjunction with "FALKLAND ISLANDS" postmark (22 Dec 1909 to 30 March 1910) ..... *Price from*		£1500	£5500
ZU2	Example of Type Z 2 used in conjunction with "FALKLAND ISLANDS" postmark (May 1910) ..... *Price from*		£1000	£4000
ZU3	Example of Type Z 2 used in conjunction with "SOUTH GEORGIA" postmark (June 1910 to June 1912) ..... *Price from*		£275	£900

Stamps of FALKLAND ISLANDS *cancelled at Grytviken with South Georgia circular datestamps between* June 1910 *and* 31 January 1954.

1891–1902. *Queen Victoria (Nos. 32, 36 and 38).*

Z6	½d. green	
Z11	4d. olive-black	£250
Z12	9d. salmon	£250
Z13	1s. yellow-brown	£250

1904–12. *King Edward VII (Nos. 43/50)*.

Z14	½d. green		19·00
Z15	1d. vermilion		19·00
	d. Dull coppery red (on thick paper)		50·00
Z16	2d. purple		75·00
	b. Reddish purple		£325
Z17	2½d. ultramarine		26·00
	b. Deep blue		£200
Z18	6d. orange		£150
Z19	1s. brown		£150
Z20	3s. green		£325
Z21	5s. red		£375

SOUTH GEORGIA PROVISIONAL HANDSTAMPS

During October 1911 the arrival of the German South Polar Expedition at Grytviken, South Georgia, resulted in the local supply of stamps becoming exhausted. The Acting Magistrate, Mr. E. B. Binnie, who was also responsible for the postal facilities, produced a handstamp reading "Paid at (or At) SOUTH GEORGIA" which, together with a manuscript indication of the postage paid and his signature, was used on mail from 18 October 1911 to January 1912. Further examples, signed by John Innes Wilson, are known from February 1912.

PH1	"Paid 1 at SOUTH GEORGIA EBB"		
		Price on cover	£4500
PH1a	"Paid 1 At SOUTH GEORGIA EBB"		
	(16 Dec)	Price on cover	£4750
PH2	"Paid 2½ at SOUTH GEORGIA EBB"		
		Price on cover	£5000
PH2a	"Paid 2½ At SOUTH GEORGIA EBB"		
	(16 Dec)	Price on cover	£5500
PH3	"Paid 1 At SOUTH GEORGIA JIW"		
		Price on cover	£7000
PH4	"Paid 2½ At SOUTH GEORGIA JIW"		
		Price on cover	£7000

1912–23. *King George V. Wmk Mult Crown CA (Nos. 60/9)*.

Z22	½d. green		19·00
	a. Perf 14 (line). Deep yellow-green		38·00
	d. Dull yellowish green (on thick greyish paper)		45·00
Z23	1d. orange-red		13·00
	a. Perf 14 (line). Orange-vermilion		13·00
	d. Orange-vermilion		13·00
Z24	2d. maroon		50·00
Z25	2½d. deep bright blue		38·00
	c. Deep blue		35·00
Z26	6d. yellow-orange		65·00
	b. Brown-orange		70·00
	ba. Bisected (diag) (3d.) (on cover) (3.23)		£14000
Z27	1s. light bistre-brown		£120
	a. Pale bistre-brown		£150
	b. Brown (on thick greyish paper)		£180
Z28	3s. slate-green		£200
Z29	5s. deep rose-red		£250
	a. Reddish maroon		£350
	b. Maroon		£325
Z30	10s. red/green		£425
Z31	£1 black/red		£650

1918–20. *"WAR STAMP" ovpts (Nos. 70/2)*.

Z32	½d. deep olive		21·00
Z33	1d. vermilion		21·00
Z34	1s. light bistre-brown		£110

1921–28. *King George V. Wmk Mult Script CA (Nos. 73/80)*.

Z35	½d. yellowish green		6·50
Z36	1d. dull vermilion		5·50
Z37	2d. deep brown-purple		29·00
Z38	2½d. deep blue		26·00
	a. Bisected (diag) (1d.) (on cover) (3.23)		£9000
Z39	2½d. deep purple/pale yellow		55·00
Z40	6d. yellow-orange		55·00
Z41	1s. deep ochre		65·00
Z42	3s. slate-green		£225

1928 PROVISIONAL. For listing of the 2½d. on 2d. surcharge issued at Grytviken on 7 February 1928 see No. 115 of Falkland Islands.

1929–36. *King George V. Whale and Penguins design (Nos. 116/26)*.

Z43	½d. green		7·00
Z44	1d. scarlet		5·50
Z45	2d. grey		14·00
Z46	2½d. blue		6·00
Z47	4d. orange		27·00
Z48	6d. purple		38·00
Z49	1s. black/emerald		48·00
Z50	2s.6d. carmine/blue		£100
Z51	5s. green/yellow		£160
Z52	10s. carmine/emerald		£325
Z53	£1 black/red		£600

Examples of most values are known with forged postmarks dated "Au 30" in 1928, 1930 and 1931.

1933. *Centenary of British Administration (Nos. 127/38)*.

Z54	½d. black and green		9·50
Z55	1d. black and scarlet		5·00
Z56	1½d. black and blue		24·00
Z57	2d. black and brown		28·00
Z58	3d. black and violet		27·00
Z59	4d. black and orange		23·00
Z60	6d. black and slate		85·00
Z61	1s. black and olive-green		95·00
Z62	2s.6d. black and violet		£300
Z63	5s. black and yellow		£950
	a. Black and yellow-orange		£2250
Z64	10s. black and chestnut		£1200
Z65	£1 black and carmine		£2750

1935. *Silver Jubilee (Nos. 139/42)*.

Z66	1d. deep blue and scarlet		5·00
Z67	2½d. brown and deep blue		6·00
Z68	4d. green and indigo		7·00
Z69	1s. slate and purple		7·00

1937. *Coronation (Nos. 143/5)*.

Z70	½d. green		3·00
Z71	1d. carmine		3·00
Z72	2½d. blue		3·00

1938–50. *King George VI (Nos. 146/63)*.

Z73	½d. black and green		5·00
Z74	1d. black and carmine		7·50
	a. Black and scarlet		4·00
Z75	1d. black and violet		8·00
Z76	2d. black and deep violet		9·00
Z77	2d. black and carmine-red		11·00
Z78	2½d. black and bright blue (No. 151)		4·00
Z79	3d. black and blue		12·00
Z80	4d. black and purple		9·00
Z81	6d. black and brown		11·00
Z82	9d. black and grey-blue		15·00
Z83	1s. light dull blue		40·00
	a. Dull greenish blue		40·00
Z84	1s.3d. black and carmine-red		55·00
Z85	2s.6d. slate		38·00
Z86	5s. blue and chestnut		£150
	a. Indigo and yellow-brown		£140
	b. Steel blue and buff-brown		£350
Z87	10s. black and orange-brown		75·00
	a. Black and orange		65·00
Z88	£1 black and violet		85·00

Falkland Islands definitive stamps with values of 1s.3d. and above continued to be valid from South Georgia after the introduction of Nos. B1 and subsequently Nos. G1/16. Forged South Georgia postmarks exist dated "30 MR 49".

1952. *King George VI (Nos. 181/5)*.

Z89	1s.3d. orange		55·00
Z90	2s.6d. olive-green		£100
Z91	5s. purple		£110
Z92	10s. grey		£130
Z93	£1 black		£140

1944 (24 Feb)–45. *Falkland Islands Nos. 146, 148, 150, 153/5, 157 and 158a optd "SOUTH GEORGIA/DEPENDENCY OF", in red, as Type A 1 of Graham Land*.

B1	½d. black and green		30	1·75
	a. Wmk sideways		£3500	
B2	1d. black and violet		30	1·00
B3	2d. black and carmine-red		50	1·00
B4	3d. black and blue		50	1·00
B5	4d. black and purple		2·00	1·75
B6	6d. black and brown		16·00	2·25
	a. Blue-black and brown (24.9.45)		16·00	
B7	9d. black and grey-blue		1·00	1·25
B8	1s. deep blue		1·00	1·25
B1/8	Set of 8		19·00	10·00
B1s/8s Perf "Specimen" Set of 8			£475	

C. SOUTH ORKNEYS

Used from the *Fitzroy* in February 1944 and at Laurie Island (established January 1946).

Falkland Islands definitive stamps with face values of 1s.3d. and above were valid for use from the South Orkneys in conjunction with Nos. C1/8 and subsequently Nos. G1/16.

Stamps of FALKLAND ISLANDS *cancelled on the Fitzroy, at Laurie Island or at Signy Island with South Orkneys circular datestamps between* 21 February 1944 *and* 31 January 1954.

1938–50. *King George VI (Nos. 160/3)*.

Z95	2s.6d. slate		55·00
Z96	5s. indigo and yellow-brown		£160
Z97	10s. black and orange		70·00
Z98	£1 black and violet		90·00

1952. *King George VI (Nos. 181/5)*.

Z99	1s.3d. orange		£100
Z100	2s.6d. olive-green		£110
Z101	5s. purple		£130
Z102	10s. grey		£140
Z103	£1 black		£150

1944 (21 Feb)–45. *Falkland Islands Nos. 146, 148, 150, 153/5, 157 and 158a optd "SOUTH ORKNEYS/DEPENDENCY OF", in red, as Type A 1 of Graham Land*.

C1	½d. black and green		30	1·75
C2	1d. black and violet		30	1·00
	w. Wmk inverted		£4250	
C3	2d. black and carmine-red		50	1·00
C4	3d. black and blue		50	1·00
C5	4d. black and purple		2·00	1·75
C6	6d. black and brown		16·00	2·25
	a. Blue-black and brown (24.9.45)		16·00	
C7	9d. black and grey-blue		1·00	1·25
C8	1s. deep blue		1·00	1·25
C1/8 Set of 8			19·00	10·00
C1s/8s Perf "Specimen" Set of 8			£475	

D. SOUTH SHETLANDS

Postal facilities were first provided at the Port Foster whaling station on Deception Island for the 1912–13 whaling season and were available each year between November and the following April until March 1931.

No postmark was provided for the 1912–13 season and the local postmaster was instructed to cancel stamps on cover with a straight-line "PORT FOSTER" handstamp. Most letters so cancelled subsequently received a "FALKLAND ISLANDS" circular postmark dated between 19 and 28 March 1913. It is known that only low value stamps were available at Port Foster. Higher values, often with other "FALKLAND ISLANDS" postmark dates, were, it is believed, subsequently "made to order".

Stamps of FALKLAND ISLANDS *cancelled at Port Foster, Deception Island with part of "PORT FOSTER" straightline handstamp*.

1904–12. *King Edward VII (Nos. 43c, 44e)*.

Z104	½d. deep yellow-green		£1400
Z105	1d. orange-vermilion		£1400

1912. *King George V. Wmk Mult Crown CA (Nos. 60/1)*.

Z106	½d. yellow-green		£1400
Z107	1d. orange-red		£1400

Stamps of FALKLAND ISLANDS *cancelled at Port Foster with part of oval "DECEPTION ISLAND SOUTH SHETLANDS" postmark in black or violet between 1914 and 1927.*

1904–12. *King Edward VII (No. 43c)*.

Z108	½d. deep yellow-green		£350

1912–20. *King George V. Wmk Mult Crown CA (Nos. 60/9)*.

Z110	½d. yellow-green		£110
Z111	1d. orange-red		£110
Z112	2d. maroon		£140
Z113	2½d. deep bright blue		£140
Z114	6d. yellow-orange		£180
Z115	1s. light bistre-brown		£200
Z116	3s. slate-green		£450
Z117	5s. deep rose-red		£500
Z118	10s. red/green		£700
Z119	£1 black/red		£900

1918–20. *"WAR STAMP" ovpts (Nos. 70/2)*.

Z120	½d. deep olive		£140
Z121	1d. vermilion		£140
Z122	1s. light bistre-brown		£325

1921–28. *King George V. Wmk Mult Script CA (Nos. 73/80)*.

Z123	½d. yellowish green		£140
Z126	2½d. deep blue		£170
Z129	1s. deep ochre		£200

Stamps of FALKLAND ISLANDS *cancelled at Port Foster with "SOUTH SHETLANDS" circular datestamp between 1923 and March 1931.*

1912–20. *King George V. Wmk Mult Crown CA (Nos. 60/9)*.

Z129a	½d. dull yellowish green (on thick greyish paper)		90·00
Z130	1d. orange-vermilion		75·00
Z131	2d. deep reddish purple		85·00
Z132	2½d. deep bright blue		
	c. Deep blue		£120
Z133	6d. brown-orange		
Z134	1s. bistre-brown		
Z135	3s. slate-green		£275
Z136	5s. maroon		£325
Z137	10s. red/green		£475
Z138	£1 black/red		£850

Examples of all values are known with forged postmarks dated "20 MR 27".

1918–20. *"WAR STAMP" ovpts (Nos. 70/2)*.

Z139	1d. vermilion		£110
Z140	1s. light bistre-brown		

1921–28. *King George V. Wmk Mult Script CA (Nos. 73/80)*.

Z141	½d. yellowish green		45·00
Z142	1d. dull vermilion		45·00
Z143	2d. deep brown-purple		70·00
Z144	2½d. deep blue		60·00
Z145	2½d. deep purple/pale yellow		85·00
Z146	6d. yellow-orange		85·00
Z147	1s. deep ochre		85·00
Z148	3s. slate-green		£300

1929. *King George V. Whale and Penguins design (Nos. 116/26)*.

Z149	½d. green		75·00
Z150	1d. scarlet		75·00
Z151	2d. grey		95·00
Z152	2½d. blue		85·00
Z153	6d. purple		£110
Z154	1s. black/emerald		£110
Z155	2s.6d. carmine/blue		£180
Z156	5s. green/yellow		£200
Z157	10s. carmine/emerald		£425
Z158	£1 black/red		£750

The whaling station at Port Foster was abandoned at the end of the 1930–31 season.

It was reoccupied as a Falkland Islands Dependencies Survey base on 3 February 1944.

Falkland Islands definitive stamps with face values of 1s.3d. and above were valid for use from the South Shetlands in conjunction with Nos. D1/8 and subsequently Nos. G1/16.

Stamps of FALKLAND ISLANDS *cancelled at Port Foster or Admiralty Bay with South Shetlands circular datestamps between 5 February 1944 and 31 January 1954.*

1938–50. *King George VI (Nos. 160/3)*.

Z159	2s.6d. slate		55·00
Z160	5s. indigo and yellow-brown		£160
Z161	10s. black and orange		70·00
Z162	£1 black and violet		90·00

1952. *King George VI (Nos. 181/5)*.

Z163	1s.3d. orange		£100
Z164	2s.6d. olive-green		£110
Z165	5s. purple		£130
Z166	10s. grey		£140
Z167	£1 black		£150

1944 (5 Feb)–45. *Falkland Islands Nos. 146, 148, 150, 153/5, 157 and 158a optd "SOUTH SHETLANDS/DEPENDENCY OF", in red, as Type A 1 of Graham Land*.

D1	½d. black and green		30	1·75
D2	1d. black and violet		30	1·00
D3	2d. black and carmine-red		50	1·00
D4	3d. black and blue		50	1·00
D5	4d. black and purple		2·00	1·75
D6	6d. black and brown		16·00	2·25
	a. Blue-black and brown (24.9.45)		16·00	
D7	9d. black and grey-blue		1·00	1·25
D8	1s. deep blue		1·00	1·25
D1/8 Set of 8			19·00	10·00
D1s/8s Perf "Specimen" Set of 8			£475	

From 12 July 1946 to 16 July 1963, Graham Land, South Georgia, South Orkneys and South Shetlands used FALKLAND ISLANDS DEPENDENCIES stamps.

E. FALKLAND ISLANDS DEPENDENCIES

For use at the following bases:
Admiralty Bay (South Shetlands) (*opened* January 1948, *closed* January 1961)
Argentine Islands (Graham Land) (*opened* 1947)
Deception Island (South Shetlands)
Grytviken (South Georgia)
Hope Bay (Graham Land) (*closed* 4 February 1949, *opened* February 1952)
Laurie Island (South Orkneys) (*closed* 1947)
Port Lockroy (Graham Land) (*closed* 16 January 1962)
Signy Island (South Orkneys) (*opened* 1946)
Stonington Island (Graham Land) (*opened* 1946, *closed* 1950, *opened* 1958, *closed* 1959, *opened* 1960)

G 1

Gap in 80th parallel (R. 1/4, 1/9, 3/4, 3/9, 5/4 and 5/9)

Extra island (Plate 1 R. 3/9)

"SOUTH POKE" flaw (Plate 2 R. 6/8)

Missing "I" in "S. Shetland Is." (Plate 1 R. 1/2)

Extra dot by oval (Plate 1 R. 4/6)

Nos. G1/8

Dot in "T" of "SOUTH"
(R. 5/2, 5/4, 5/6, 5/8 and 5/10)

(Map litho, frame recess D.L.R.)

1946 (12 July*)–**49.** Wmk Mult Script CA (sideways). P 12.

(a) Map thick and coarse.

G1	G 1	½d. black and green	1·00	3·50
		a. Gap in 80th parallel	3·00	6·50
		aa. Extra island	£110	£140
		b. Missing "I"	£110	£140
		c. "SOUTH POKE"	£120	£150
		d. Extra dot by oval	£110	£140
G2		1d. black and violet	1·25	1·75
		a. Gap in 80th parallel	3·50	4·50
		aa. Extra island	£100	£120
		b. Missing "I"	£100	£120
		d. Extra dot by oval	£100	£120
G3		2d. black and carmine	1·25	2·50
		a. Gap in 80th parallel	3·50	5·50
		aa. Extra island	£120	£140
		b. Missing "I"	£120	£140
		d. Extra dot by oval	£120	£140
G4		3d. black and blue	1·25	2·50
		a. Gap in 80th parallel	3·50	8·50
		aa. Extra island	£120	£160
		b. Missing "I"	£120	£160
		d. Extra dot by oval	£120	£160
G5		4d. black and claret	2·25	4·75
		a. Gap in 80th parallel	6·00	9·50
		c. "SOUTH POKE"	£150	£180
G6		6d. black and orange	3·25	4·75
		a. Gap in 80th parallel	7·00	9·50
		aa. Extra island	£160	£190
		b. Missing "I"	£160	£190
		c. "SOUTH POKE"	£160	£190
		d. Extra dot by oval	£160	£190
		e. *Black and ochre*	50·00	95·00
		ea. Gap in 80th parallel	85·00	£150
		eaa. Extra island	£400	
		eb. Missing "I"	£400	
		ec. "SOUTH POKE"	£400	
		ed. Extra dot by oval	£400	
G7		9d. black and brown	2·00	3·75
		a. Gap in 80th parallel	5·50	8·50
		c. "SOUTH POKE"	£140	£170
G8		1s. black and purple	2·00	4·25
		a. Gap in 80th parallel	5·50	9·00
		c. "SOUTH POKE"	£140	£180
G1/8 *Set of 8*			13·00	27·00
G1s/8s Perf "Specimen" *Set of 8*			£700	

*This is the date of issue for South Georgia. Nos. G1/8 were released in London on 11 February.
The gap in the 80th parallel occurs six times in each sheet of all values in positions R. 1/4, 1/9, 3/4, 3/9, 5/4 and 5/9.

(b) Map thin and clear (16.2.48).

G9	G 1	½d. black and green	2·25	12·00
		a. Recess frame printed double, one albino and inverted	£1400	
		b. Dot in "T"	5·50	30·00
G10		1d. black and violet	1·50	15·00
		a. Dot in "T"	3·75	35·00
G11		2d. black and carmine	2·75	22·00
		a. Dot in "T"	6·50	48·00
G11a		2½d. black and deep blue (6.3.49)	6·50	5·00
G12		3d. black and blue	2·75	4·50
		a. Dot in "T"	6·50	10·00
G13		4d. black and claret	17·00	24·00
		a. Dot in "T"	35·00	50·00
G14		6d. black and orange	24·00	8·00
		a. Dot in "T"	50·00	18·00
G15		9d. black and brown	24·00	8·00
		a. Dot in "T"	50·00	18·00
G16		1s. black and purple	24·00	8·00
		a. Dot in "T"	50·00	18·00
G9/16 *Set of 9*			95·00	95·00

1946 (4 Oct*). Victory. As Nos. 110/11 *of Antigua.*

G17		1d. deep violet	50	50
G18		3d. blue	75	50
G17s/18s Perf "Specimen" *Set of 2*			£180	

*This is the date of issue for South Georgia. The stamps were placed on sale from the South Orkneys on 17 January 1947, from the South Shetlands on 30 January 1947 and from Graham Land on 10 February 1947.

1948 (6 Dec). Royal Silver Wedding. As Nos. 112/13 *of Antigua, but 1s. in recess.*

G19		2½d. ultramarine	1·75	2·50
G20		1s. violet-blue	1·75	2·50

1949 (10 Oct). 75th Anniv of U.P.U. As Nos. 114/17 *of Antigua.*

G21		1d. violet	1·00	2·25
G22		2d. carmine-red	5·00	3·50
G23		3d. deep blue	3·25	1·25
G24		6d. red-orange	4·00	3·00
G21/4 *Set of 4*			12·00	9·00

Nos. G9/16

On Nos. G9 to G16 the map is redrawn; the "o°" meridian does not pass through the "S" of "COATS", the "n" of "Alexander" is not joined to the "L" of "Land" below, and the loops of letters "s" and "t" are generally more open.

Fiji

King Cakobau 1852–Oct 1874

Christian missionaries reached Fiji in 1835 and early letters are known to and from their mission stations, sent via Sydney, Hobart or Auckland.

In 1852 Cakobau, the chief of the island of Bau, declared himself King of Fiji and converted to Christianity two years later. Internal problems and difficulties with the American government led the king to offer to cede Fiji to Great Britain. The offer was refused, but resulted in the appointment of a British Consul in 1858. A Consular Post Office operated from September 1858 until 1872 and franked mail with New South Wales stamps from 1863.

The destruction of plantations in the Confederacy during the American Civil War led to an increased demand for Fijian cotton and this upsurge in commercial activity encouraged *The Fiji Times* newspaper on Levuka to establish a postal service on 1 November 1870.

1

(Type-set and printed at the office of *The Fiji Times*, Levuka, Ovalau, Fiji)

1870 (1 Nov)–**71.** Rouletted in the printing.

(a) Quadrillé paper.

1	1	1d. black/rose	£3250	£3500
2		3d. black/rose	£3500	£3500
		a. Comma after "EXPRESS" (R. 4/4)	£4500	£4500
3		6d. black/rose	£2000	£2000
4		1s. black/rose	£1500	£1800

(b) Laid bâtonné paper (1871).

5	1	1d. black/rose	£900	£1800
		a. Vert strip of 4. Nos. 5, 7/9	£35000	
6		3d. black/rose	£1500	£2750
7		6d. black/rose	£1100	£1800
8		9d. black/rose	£2250	£3000
		a. Comma after "EXPRESS" (R. 4/4)	£3000	
9		1s. black/rose	£1200	£1400

Nos. 1/4 were printed *se-tenant* as a sheet of 24 (6×4) with the 6d. stamps in the first horizontal row, the 1s. in the second, the 1d. in the third and the 3d. in the fourth. Nos. 5/9 were produced from the same plate on which three of the 3d. impressions had been replaced with three 9d. values.

The issued stamps showed the vertical frame lines continuous from top to bottom of the sheet with the horizontal rules broken and not touching the verticals. Used examples are cancelled in manuscript, by an Australian arrival mark or by the star cancellation used at Bua.

There are no reprints of these stamps, but the 1d., 3d., 6d. and 1s. are known in the correct type on *yellow wove* paper and are believed to be proofs.

There are also three different sets of imitations made by the proprietors of *The Fiji Times* to meet the demands of collectors:—

The first was produced in 1876 on *white wove* paper, surfaced to simulate the appearance of vertically ribbed when viewed with light reflecting off its surface. Rouletted on dotted lines and arranged in sheets of 40 (5 rows of 8) comprising 1d., 3d., 6d., 9d. and 1s.; the horizontal frame lines are continuous and the vertical ones broken.

The second was produced before 1888 on *thick rosy mauve wove* paper, rouletted on dotted lines and arranged in sheets of 30 (5 rows of 6) comprising 1s., 9d., 6d., 3d. and 1d.; the vertical frame lines are continuous and the horizontal ones broken.

The third only came to light in the 1960s and is rare, only one complete sheet being recorded, which has since been destroyed. The sheet arrangement is the same as Nos. 1/4, which suggests that this was the first imitation to be produced. It is on *off-white wove* paper, rouletted on closely dotted or solid lines, with vertical frame lines continuous and the horizontal ones broken, as in the originals. These differ from the proofs mentioned above in that the lettering is slightly larger and the figures also differ.

King Cakobau established a formal government in June 1871 and stamps for the royal post office were ordered from Sydney. These arrived in October 1871 and the postal service was placed on a firm basis by the First Postal Act in December of that year. Under its terms *The Fiji Times* service closed on 17 January 1872 and the British Consular Post Office followed six months later.

Two

Cents

2	3	(4)

(Eng and electrotyped by A. L. Jackson. Typo Govt Printing Office, Sydney.)

1871 (Oct). *Wove paper.* Wmk impressed "FIJI POSTAGE" in small sans serif capitals across the middle row of stamps in the sheet. P 12½.

10	**2**	1d. blue	50·00	£120
11		3d. pale yellow-green	£110	£350
12	**3**	6d. rose	£140	£300

The 3d. differs from T **2** in having a white circle containing square dots surrounding the centre.

All three values are known *imperf*, but were not issued in that condition.

See notes after No. 33b.

1872 (13 Jan). *Surch as T* **4**, *in local currency, by Govt Ptg Office, Sydney.*

13	**2**	2c. on 1d. pale blue	50·00	65·00
		a. Deep blue	38·00	50·00
14		6c. on 3d. yellow-green	70·00	70·00
15	**3**	12c. on 6d. carmine-rose	£100	80·00

CROWN COLONY

King Cakobau renewed his offer to cede Fiji to Great Britain and this took place on 12 October 1874.

V.R.   V.R.   2d.
(5)   (6)   (7)

(Enlarged) Cross pattée stop Inverted "A"

Cross pattée stop after "R" (R. 3/6).
Round raised stop after "V" (R. 3/8).
Round raised stops after "V" and "R" (R. 3/9).
Inverted "A" for "V" (R. 3/10).
No stop after "R" (R. 2/3 on T **5**, R. 5/3 on T **6**).
Large stop after "R" (R. 5/10).

(Optd at *Polynesian Gazette* Office, Levuka)

1874 (21 Oct). *Nos.* 13/15 *optd.*

(a) With T **5**.

16	**2**	2c. on 1d. blue	£900	£250
		a. No stop after "R"	£2250	£1000
		b. Cross pattée stop after "R"	£2250	£1000
		c. Round raised stop after "V"	£2250	£1000
		d. Round raised stops after "V" and "R"	£2250	£1000
		e. Inverted "A" for "V"	£2250	£1000
		f. Vert pair. Nos. 16 and 19.	£6000	
17		6c. on 3d. green	£1500	£650
		a. No stop after "R"	£3750	£1600
		b. Cross pattée stop after "R"	£3750	£1600
		c. Round raised stop after "V"	£3750	£1600
		d. Round raised stops after "V" and "R"	£3750	£1600
		e. Inverted "A" for "V"	£3750	£1600
		f. Vert pair. Nos. 17 and 20.	£8000	
18	**3**	12c. on 6d. rose	£650	£200
		a. No stop after "R"	£2000	£1000
		b. Cross pattée stop after "R"	£2000	£1000
		c. Round raised stop after "V"	£2000	£1000
		d. Round raised stops after "V" and "R"	£2000	£1000
		e. Inverted "A" for "V"	£2000	£1000
		f. Opt inverted		£4500
		g. Vert pair. Nos. 18 and 21.	£4500	

(b) With T **6**.

19	**2**	2c. on 1d. blue	£1000	£275
		a. No stop after "R"	£2250	£1000
		f. Large stop after "R"	—	£1000
20		6c. on 3d. green	£1900	£900
		a. No stop after "R"	£3750	£1600
21	**3**	12c. on 6d. rose	£800	£225
		a. No stop after "R"	£2000	£1000
		b. Opt inverted	£5000	

Nos. 16/21 were produced in sheets of 50 (10×5) of which the top three rows were overprinted with Type **5** and the lower two with Type **6**.

1875. *Stamps of 1874 surch at Polynesian Gazette Office, Levuka, with T* **7**.

(a) In red (April).

22	**2**	2d. on 6c. on 3d. green (No. 17)	£550	£180
		a. No stop after "R"	£1600	£650
		b. Cross pattée stop after "R"	£1600	£650
		c. Round raised stop after "V"	£1600	£650
		d. Round raised stops after "V" and "R"	£1600	£650
		e. Inverted "A" for "V"	£1600	£650
		f. No stop after "2d" (R. 1/2)	£1600	£650
		g. Vert pair. Nos. 22/3	£3500	
23		2d. on 6c. on 3d. green (No. 20)	£700	£275
		a. No stop after "R"	£1600	£650
		b. Stop between "2" and "d" (R. 5/7)	£1600	£650

(b) In black (30 Sept).

24	**2**	2d. on 6c. on 3d. green (No. 17)	£1500	£500
		a. No stop after "R"	£3250	£1300
		b. Cross pattée stop after "R"	£3250	£1300
		c. Round raised stop after "V"	£3250	£1300
		d. Round raised stops after "V" and "R"	£3250	£1300

		e. Inverted "A" for "V"	£3250	£1300
		f. No stop after "2d" (R. 1/2)	£3250	£1300
		g. "V.R." double	£3250	£1300
		h. Vert pair. Nos. 24/5	£7500	
25		2d. on 6c. on 3d. green (No. 20)	£1900	£700
		a. No stop after "R"	£3250	£1300
		b. Stop between "2" and "d" (R. 5/7)	£3250	£1300
		c. "V.R." double	£3750	£3500

1875 (20 Nov). *No.* 15 *surch at Polynesian Gazette Office, Levuka, with T* **7** *and* "*V.R.*" *at one operation.*

(a) "*V.R.*" *T* **5**.

26	**3**	2d. on 12c. on 6d. rose	£2000	£850
		a. No stop after "R"	—	£2250
		b. Round raised stop after "R"	—	£1400
		c. Inverted "A" for "V" (R. 1/3, 2/8, 4/4)	£2750	£1200
		d. Do. and round raised stop after "V" (R. 3/3, 3/6, 3/8, 3/10)	£2500	£1000
		e. As "c" and round raised stops after "R" and "V" (R. 3/2, 3/9)	£3000	£1300
		f. Surch double	—	£4000
		g. Vert pair. Nos. 26/7	£8000	

(b) "*V.R.*" *T* **6**.

27	**3**	2d. on 12c. on 6d. rose	£2250	£900
		a. Surch double	—	£4250

The setting used for Nos. 26/7 was similar to that of Nos. 16/21, but the fourth stamp in the fourth row had a Type **5** "V.R." instead of a Type **6**.

The position of No. 26b is not known.

(8)   (9)

Two Pence

Void corner (R. 2/1)

(Typo Govt Printing Office, Sydney, from plates of 1871)

1876–77. *On paper previously lithographed* "*VR*" *as T* **8**, *the 3d. surch with T* **9**. *P* 12½.

(a) Wove paper (31.1.76).

28	**2**	1d. grey-blue	50·00	50·00
		a. Dull blue	50·00	50·00
		b. Doubly printed	£550	
		c. Void corner	£550	£325
		d. Imperf vert (horiz pair)	£850	
29		2d. on 3d. green	55·00	55·00
		a. Deep green	50·00	55·00
30	**3**	6d. pale rose	65·00	65·00
		a. Dull rose	50·00	55·00
		b. Carmine-rose	55·00	55·00
		c. Doubly printed	£2500	

(b) Laid paper (5.1.77).

31	**2**	1d. blue	20·00	32·00
		a. Deep blue	21·00	32·00
		b. Void corner	£300	£250
		c. Imperf vert (horiz pair)	£700	
32		2d. on 3d. yellow-green	60·00	70·00
		a. Deep yellow-green	60·00	70·00
		b. Imperf between (pair)	£850	
		c. Perf 10	£350	
		ca. Imperf vert (horiz pair)	£950	
		d. Perf 11	£300	
33	**3**	6d. rose	50·00	29·00
		a. Carmine-rose	50·00	35·00
		b. Imperf vert (horiz pair)	£700	

The extent of the void area on Nos. 28c and 31b varies.

The 3d. *green* is known without the surcharge T **9** on wove paper and also without the surcharge and the monogram. In this latter condition it can only be distinguished from No. 11 by its colour, which is a fuller, deeper yellow-green.

Stamps on both wove and laid paper *imperf* are from printer's trial or waste sheets and were not issued.

All values are known on laid paper without the monogram "VR" and the 3d. stamp also without the surcharge but these are also believed to be from printer's trial sheets which were never issued for postal purposes. Being on laid paper they are easily distinguishable from Nos. 10/12.

1877 (12 Oct). *Optd with T* **8** *and surch as T* **9**. *Laid paper. P* 12½.

34	**2**	4d. on 3d. mauve	85·00	25·00
		a. Imperf vert (horiz pair)	£850	

10   11

A   **Four Pence**
B   **Four Pence**

Type A: Length 12½ mm
Type B: Length 14 mm

Note also the different shape of the two "e"s.

(Typo from new plates made from original dies of 1871 with "CR" altered to "VR" at Govt Printing Office, Sydney. 2d. and 4d. made from old 3d. die.)

1878–99. *Surcharges as T* **9** *or as Types A or B for 4d. value. Wove paper with paper-maker's name* "*T. H. SAUNDERS*" *or* "*SANDERSON*" *in double-lined capitals extending over seven stamps in each full sheet.*

(a) P 12½ (1878–80).

35	**10**	1d. pale ultramarine (19.2.79)	9·50	9·50
		a. Ultramarine	13·00	9·50
36		2d. on 3d. green (17.10.78)	7·00	23·00
37		2d. yellow-green (1.9.79)	19·00	11·00
		a. Blue-green	32·00	15·00
		b. Error. Ultramarine	£25000	
38	**11**	6d. rose (30.7.80)	£100	23·00

(b) P 10 (1881–90).

39	**10**	1d. dull blue (11.5.82)	55·00	3·00
		a. Ultramarine	19·00	3·00
		b. Cambridge blue (12.7.83)	50·00	4·25
40		2d. yellow-green (20.10.81)	17·00	1·00
		a. Blue-green	27·00	5·50
41		4d. on 1d. mauve (29.1.90)	48·00	35·00
42		4d. on 2d. pale mauve (A) (23.5.83)	75·00	12·00
		a. Dull purple	75·00	12·00
43		4d. on 2d. dull purple (B) (7.11.88)..		£140
44		4d. mauve (13.9.90)	60·00	
		a. Deep purple	60·00	60·00
45	**11**	6d. pale rose (11.3.85)	70·00	20·00
		a. Bright rose	19·00	19·00

(c) P 10×12½ (1881–82).

46	**10**	1d. ultramarine (11.5.82)	£100	35·00
47		2d. green (20.10.81)	£160	60·00
48	**11**	6d. rose (20.10.81)	£350	55·00
		a. Pale rose	£350	55·00

(d) P 12½×10 (1888–90).

49	**10**	1d. ultramarine (1890)	—	£300
49a		2d. green (1888)		
49b		4d. on 2d. dull purple (A)		†

(e) P 10×11¾ (3.9.86).

50	**10**	1d. dull blue	70·00	14·00
		a. Ultramarine		
51		2d. yellow-green	65·00	8·50

(f) P 11¾×10 (1886–88).

51a	**10**	1d. dull blue (7.11.88)	£225	45·00
		ab. Ultramarine		
51b		2d. yellow-green (3.9.86)	—	£500
52	**11**	6d. rose (1887)	†	£750

(g) P 11×10 (1892–93).

53	**10**	1d. ultramarine (18.8.92)	16·00	13·00
54		2d. pale mauve (18.8.92)	13·00	14·00
55	**11**	6d. pale rose (14.2.93)	9·50	21·00
		a. Rose	15·00	24·00

(h) P 11 (1897–99).

56	**10**	4d. mauve (14.7.96)	14·00	9·50
57	**11**	6d. dull rose (14.7.96)	28·00	48·00
		a. Printed both sides (12.99)	£1200	£900
		b. Bright rose	45·00	55·00

(i) P 11×11¾ (1896)*.

58	**10**	4d. deep purple (14.7.96)	35·00	
		a. Bright purple	10·00	6·50
59	**11**	6d. rose (23.7.96)	32·00	
		a. Bright rose	9·50	3·75

(j) Imperf (pairs) (1882–90).

60	**10**	1d. ultramarine		
61		2d. yellow-green		
62		4d. on 2d. pale mauve		
63	**11**	6d. rose	—	£1300

*Under this heading are included stamps from several perforating machines with a gauge varying between 11.6 and 12.

No. 37b was printed in the colour of the 1d. in error. Only four examples have been reported, one of which was subsequently destroyed.

In the absence of detailed information on dates of issue printing dates are quoted for Nos. 35/63 and 76/103.

12   13

(Eng A. L. Jackson. Typo Govt Printing Office, Sydney)

1881–99. *Paper-maker's name wmkd as previous issue.*

(a) P 10 (19.10.81).

64	**12**	1s. pale brown	85·00	20·00
		a. Deep brown	85·00	22·00

(b) P 11×10 (1894).

65	**12**	1s. pale brown	48·00	48·00

(c) P 11 (1897).

66	**12**	1s. pale brown	45·00	14·00

		(d) P 11×11¾ (5.99).		
67	**12**	1s. pale brown	40·00	10·00
		a. Brown	40·00	10·00
		b. Deep brown	45·00	45·00
		(e) P 11¾×11 (3.97).		
68	**12**	1s. brown	55·00	50·00

Dates given of earliest known use.
Forgeries exist.

(Centre typo, frame litho Govt Printing Office, Sydney)

1882 (23 May). Toned paper wmkd with paper-maker's name "Cowan" in old English outline type once in each sheet. P 10.

69	**13**	5s. dull red and black	55·00	28·00

An unknown quantity of the 1s. and 264 sheets (13,200 stamps) of the 5s., both perf 10 and imperf, were cancelled by the Fiji Post Office and sold as remainders. A number of different "SUVA" remainder cancellations have been recorded between "15 DEC 00" and "21 DE 1902".

An electrotyped plate was also produced for the frame of the 5s. This printing was not used for postal purposes but examples were included among the remainders, all cancelled "15 DEC 00". The electrotyped printing, in dull orange and black, is on paper watermarked "NEW SOUTH WALES GOVERNMENT" in double-line capitals and, apart from the colour of the medallion, differs in a number of respects from the original, most notably in the circular frame surrounding the Queen's head, which is notably thicker than the litho printing. Examples are rare.

2½d.   2½d.
(14)   (15)

Types **14** (fraction bar 1 mm from "2") and **15** (fraction bar 2 mm from "2") are from the same setting of 50 (10×5) with Type **15** occurring on R. 1/2, 2/2, 3/2 and 4/2.

(Stamps typo in Sydney and surch at Govt Printing Office, Suva)

1891 (1 Jan). *T* **10** surch. P 10.

70	**14**	2½d. on 2d. green	48·00	50·00
71	**15**	2½d. on 2d. green	£130	£140

½d.   5ᵈ
(16)   (17)

FIVE PENCE   **FIVE PENCE**
(18) 2 mm spacing   (19) 3 mm spacing

1892 (1 Mar)–**93**. P 10.

(a) Surch on *T* **10**.

72	**16**	½d. on 1d. dull blue	50·00	75·00
		a. Ultramarine	50·00	70·00
73	**17**	5d. on 4d. deep purple (25.7.92)	50·00	70·00
		a. Dull purple	50·00	70·00

(b) Surch on *T* **11**.

74	**18**	5d. on 6d. brownish rose (30.11.92)	55·00	65·00
		a. Bright rose	55·00	60·00
		b. Perf 10×12½		
75	**19**	5d. on 6d. rose (4.1.93)	70·00	80·00
		a. Deep rose	60·00	70·00
		b. Brownish rose	60·00	

20   **21** Native Canoe   **22**

(Typo in Sydney)

1891–1902. Wmk in sheet, either "SANDERSON" or "NEW SOUTH WALES GOVERNMENT" in outline capitals.

(a) P 10 (1891–94).

76	**20**	½d. slate-grey (26.4.92)	4·50	4·75
77	**21**	1d. black (19.9.94)	13·00	4·25
78		2d. pale green (19.9.94)	95·00	13·00
79	**22**	2½d. chocolate (8.6.91)	42·00	18·00
80	**21**	5d. ultramarine (14.2.93)	80·00	55·00

(b) P 11×10 (1892–93).

81	**20**	½d. slate-grey (20.10.93)	7·00	18·00
82	**21**	1d. black (14.2.93)	8·00	4·25
83		2d. green (14.2.93)	15·00	6·00
84	**22**	2½d. chocolate (17.8.92)	20·00	26·00
		a. Brown	10·00	10·00
		b. Yellowish brown		
85	**21**	5d. ultramarine (14.2.93)	13·00	7·50

(c) P 11 (1893–96).

86	**20**	½d. slate-grey (2.6.96)	3·00	6·00
		a. Greenish slate	2·50	6·00
87	**21**	1d. black (31.10.95)	6·00	6·00
88		1d. pale mauve (2.6.96)	7·00	1·00
		a. Rosy mauve	8·00	1·00
89		2d. dull green (17.3.94)	7·00	80
		a. Emerald-green	7·50	2·00
90	**22**	2½d. brown (31.10.95)	25·00	10·00
		a. Yellowish brown	16·00	20·00
91	**21**	5d. ultramarine (14.2.93)	£150	

(d) P 10×11¾ (1893–94).

92	**20**	½d. greenish slate	£1000	
93	**21**	1d. black (20.7.93)	19·00	5·50
94		2d. dull green (19.9.94)	£600	£375

		(e) P 11¾×10 (19.9.94).		
94a	**20**	½d. greenish slate	—	£1000
		(f) P 11¾ (1894–98).		
95	**20**	½d. greenish slate (19.9.94)	2·75	10·00
		a. Grey	35·00	
96	**21**	1d. black (19.9.94)	£200	38·00
97		1d. rosy mauve (4.5.98)	6·00	7·50
98		2d. dull green (19.9.94)	90·00	42·00
		(g) P 11×11¾ (1895–97).		
99	**20**	½d. greenish slate (8.10.97)	1·00	3·75
100	**21**	1d. black (31.10.95)	£3000	£1500
101		1d. rosy mauve (14.7.96)	6·50	1·00
		a. Pale rosy mauve	4·50	2·00
102		2d. dull green (26.7.97)	38·00	4·00
103	**22**	2½d. brown (26.7.97)	11·00	17·00
		a. Yellow-brown	5·00	5·00
		(h) P 11¾×11 (1897–98).		
103b	**20**	½d. greenish slate (8.10.97)	4·50	9·00
103c	**21**	1d. rosy mauve (10.2.97)	13·00	5·00
103d		1d. black (4.5.98)	£200	£100

The 2½d. brown is known doubly printed, but only occurs in the remainders and with the special obliteration (*Price £120 cancelled-to-order*). It was never issued for postal use.

23   **24**

(Typo D.L.R.)

1903 (1 Feb). Wmk Crown CA. P 14.

104	**23**	½d. green and pale green	2·25	2·00
105		1d. dull purple and black/*red*	13·00	55
106	**24**	2d. dull purple and orange	3·75	1·25
107	**23**	2½d. dull purple and blue/*blue*	14·00	2·75
108		3d. dull purple and purple	1·50	3·25
109	**24**	4d. dull purple and black	1·50	2·50
110	**23**	5d. dull purple and green	1·50	2·50
111		6d. dull purple and carmine	1·50	1·75
112	**23**	1s. green and carmine	11·00	65·00
113	**24**	5s. green and black	65·00	£140
114		£1 grey-black and ultramarine	£325	£400
104/14 *Set of 11*			£400	£550
104s/14s Optd "Specimen" *Set of 11*			£300	

1904–09. Wmk Mult Crown CA. *Chalk-surfaced paper (1s.).* P 14.

115	**23**	½d. green and pale green	15·00	3·00
116		1d. purple and black/*red*	27·00	10
117		1s. green and carmine (1909)	28·00	40·00
115/17 *Set of 3*			60·00	40·00

1906–12. *Colours changed.* Wmk Mult Crown CA. *Chalk surfaced paper (6d. to £1).* P 14.

118	**23**	½d. green (1908)	11·00	3·25
119		1d. red (1906)	11·00	10
		w. Wmk inverted	†	—
120		2½d. bright blue (1910)	6·50	7·50
121	**24**	6d. dull purple (1910)	15·00	30·00
122	**23**	1s. black/*green* (1911)	4·75	10·00
123	**24**	5s. green and red/*yellow* (1911)	60·00	70·00
124	**23**	£1 purple and black/*red* (1912)	£300	£275
118/24 *Set of 7*			£350	£350
119s/24s Optd "Specimen" *Set of 6*			£325	

Nos. 112/14, 117 and 120/4 are known with a forged registered postmark of Suva dated "10 DEC 1909".

25   **26**   **WAR STAMP**
(27)

(Typo D.L.R.)

1912 (Oct)–**23**. Die I. Wmk Mult Crown CA. *Chalk-surfaced paper (5d. to £1).* P 14.

125	**26**	¼d. brown (1.4.16)	2·50	30
		a. Deep brown (1917)	1·50	40
		y. Wmk inverted and reversed		
126	**25**	½d. green	1·50	1·00
		a. Yellow-green (1916)	8·50	8·50
		b. Blue-green (1917)	1·25	50
		w. Wmk inverted	£110	
		y. Wmk inverted and reversed	£110	
127		1d. carmine	2·00	10
		a. Bright scarlet (1916)	2·00	75
		ax. Wmk reversed	†	
		b. Deep rose (1916)	9·50	2·00
		bw. Wmk inverted	†	
128	**26**	2d. greyish slate (5.14)	1·75	10
		a. Wmk sideways		
		b. "C" of "CA" missing from wmk.	†	
		w. Wmk inverted	—	£225
129	**25**	2½d. bright blue (5.14)	3·00	3·50
130		3d. purple/*yellow* (5.14)	4·25	5·50
		a. Wmk sideways	£350	£450
		b. On lemon (1915)	2·00	8·50
		c. On pale yellow (1921)	1·75	14·00
		ca. "A" of "CA" missing from wmk.		
		cw. Wmk inverted		
		d. Die II. *On pale yellow* (1922)	2·50	24·00
131	**26**	4d. black and red/*yellow* (5.14)	23·00	20·00
		a. On lemon	3·00	16·00
		b. On orange-buff (1920)	50·00	65·00
		c. On pale yellow (1921)	6·50	14·00
		cw. Wmk inverted	£400	
		d. Die II. *On pale yellow* (1922)	3·00	26·00

132	**25**	*ds.* Optd "Specimen"	40·00	
		5d. dull purple and olive-green (5.14)	4·75	11·00
133	**26**	6d. dull and bright purple (5.14)	2·00	5·50
134	**25**	1s. black/*green* (10.13)	1·25	14·00
		a. White back (4.14)	1·00	11·00
		b. On blue-green, olive back (1916)	3·00	10·00
		c. On emerald back (1921)	4·50	42·00
		cs. Optd Specimen"	45·00	
		d. Die II *On emerald back* (1922)	3·00	
135	**26**	2s.6d. black and red/*blue* (19.1.16)	32·00	30·00
136		5s. green and red/*yellow*	32·00	40·00
137	**25**	£1 purple and black/*red* (5.14)	£275	£275
		a. Die II (1923)	£250	£275
125/37 *Set of 13*			£300	£350
125s/37s Optd "Specimen" *Set of 13*			£425	

Bold "TA"(left pane, R. 5/4)

1915 (1 Dec)–**19**. Optd with *T* **27** by Govt Printer, Suva.

138	**25**	½d. green		
		a. Yellow-green (1916)	1·00	5·00
		b. Blue-green (1917)	75	2·75
		c. Opt inverted	£600	
		d. Opt double		
		e. Bold "TA"		
139		1d. carmine	27·00	23·00
		a. Bright scarlet	1·75	75
		ab. Horiz pair, one without opt	£5500	
		c. Opt inverted	£700	
		d. Deep rose (1919)	3·25	2·25
		e. Bold "TA"		
138s/9s H/S "Specimen" *Set of 2*			£120	

No. 139ab occurred on one pane of 120 only, the overprint being so misplaced that all the stamps of the last vertical row escaped it entirely.

The bold "TA" variety only occurs on later printings of Nos. 138/9.

Nos. 140/227 are no longer used.

1922–29. Die II. Wmk Mult Script CA. *Chalk-surfaced paper (1s. to 5s.).* P 14.

228	**26**	¼d. deep brown (1923)	2·50	24·00
229	**25**	½d. green (1923)	75	1·50
		w. Wmk inverted		
230		1d. carmine-red	2·50	75
231		1d. violet (6.1.27)	1·25	10
232	**26**	1½d. scarlet (6.1.27)	4·00	1·00
233		2d. grey	1·25	10
		a. Face value omitted	£20000	
234	**25**	3d. bright blue (1924)	2·75	1·00
235	**26**	4d. black and red/*lemon* (1924)	5·50	7·00
		a. On pale yellow (1929)	50·00	24·00
236	**25**	5d. dull purple and sage-green (1927)	1·50	1·50
237	**26**	6d. dull and bright purple	2·00	1·25
238	**25**	1s. black/*emerald* (1924)	6·00	5·00
		w. Wmk inverted		
239	**26**	2s. purple and blue/*blue* (6.1.27)	25·00	60·00
240		2s.6d. black and red/*blue* (1925)	11·00	32·00
241		5s. green and red/*pale yellow* (1926)	32·00	65·00
228/41 *Set of 14*			90·00	£180
228s/41s Optd "Specimen" *Set of 14*			£180	

The 2d. imperforate with watermark Type **10** of Ireland came from a trial printing and was not issued.

Only one example of No. 233a is known. It was caused by an obstruction during the printing of the duty plate.

1935 (6 May). *Silver Jubilee. As Nos. 91/4 of Antigua.*

242		1½d. deep blue and carmine	1·00	8·00
		a. Deep blue and aniline red	9·00	23·00
		b. Frame printed double, one albino	£1000	
		f. Diagonal line by turret	60·00	
		h. Dot by flagstaff	£130	
		i. Dash by turret	£130	
243		2d. ultramarine and grey	1·50	35
		f. Diagonal line by turret	80·00	
		g. Dot to left of chapel	£170	
244		3d. brown and deep blue	2·50	3·50
		f. Diagonal line by turret	£120	
		h. Dot by flagstaff	£225	
		i. Dash by turret	£225	
245		1s. slate and purple	5·50	8·00
		a. Frame printed double, one albino	£1500	
		f. Diagonal line by turret	£180	
		h. Dot by flagstaff	£325	
242/5 *Set of 4*			9·50	18·00
242s/5s Perf "Specimen" *Set of 4*			£110	

For illustrations of plate varieties see Omnibus section following Zanzibar.

1937 (12 May). *Coronation. As Nos. 95/7 of Antigua.* P 11×11½.

246		1d. purple	60	1·25
247		2d. grey-black	60	2·00
248		3d. Prussian blue	60	2·00
246/8 *Set of 3*			1·60	4·75
246s/8s Perf "Specimen" *Set of 3*			80·00	

28 Native sailing Canoe   **29** Native Village

30 Camakua (canoe)

31 Map of Fiji Islands

Two Dies of Type **30**:

Die I Empty   Die II Native in Canoe
Canoe

Two Dies of Type **31**:

Die I Without "180°"   Die II With "180°"

32 Government Offices

33 Canoe and arms of Fiji

34 Sugar cane

35 Arms of Fiji

36 Spearing fish by torchlight

37 Suva Harbour

38 River scene

39 Chief's hut

40 Paw-paw tree

41 Police bugler

Extra palm frond (R. 5/8)

Extra line (R. 10/2)

Scratch through value (R. 5/1)

Extra island (R. 10/5)

Spur on arms medallion (Pl 2 R. 4/2) (ptg of 26 Nov 1945)

(Des V. E. Ousey (½d., 1s., 2s.6d.), Miss C. D. Lovejoy (1d., 1½d., 5d.), Miss I. Stinson (3d., 5s.) and A. V. Guy (2d. (Nos. 253/4), 2½d., 6d., 2s.). Recess De La Rue (½d., 1½d., 2d., (Nos. 253/5a), 2½d., 6d., 8d., 1s.5d., 1s.6d.), Waterlow (others))

1938 (5 Apr)–**55**. *T* **28/41**. Wmk Mult Script CA. Various perfs.

249	**28**	½d. green (P 13½)	20	75
		a. Perf 14 (5.41)	20·00	3·50
		b. Perf 12 (8.48)	1·00	3·00
		ba. Extra palm frond	65·00	
250	**29**	1d. brown and blue (P 12½)	50	20
251	**30**	1½d. carmine (Die I) (P 13½)	15·00	35
252		1½d. carmine (Die II) (P 13½) (1.10.40)	1·40	3·00
		a. Deep carmine (10.42)	4·00	1·25
		b. Perf 14 (6.42)	20·00	19·00
		c. Perf 12 (21.7.49)	1·00	1·25
253	**31**	2d. brown and green (Die I) (P 13½)	40·00	40
		a. Extra line	£375	70·00
		b. Scratch through value	£375	
254		2d. brown and green (Die II) (P 13½) (1.10.40)	16·00	16·00
255	**32**	2d. green & mag (P 13½) (19.5.42)	40	60
		a. Perf 12 (27.5.46)	55	70
256	**31**	2½d. brown & grn (Die II) (P 14) (6.1.42)	1·00	1·00
		a. Extra island	40·00	
		b. Perf 13½ (6.1.42)	1·00	80
		ba. Extra island	40·00	
		c. Perf 12 (19.1.48)	1·00	50
		ca. Extra island	40·00	
257	**33**	3d. blue (P 12½)	1·00	30
		a. Spur on arms medallion	£250	£130
258	**34**	5d. blue and scarlet (P 12½)	42·00	10·00
259		5d. yell-green & scar (P 12½) (1.10.40)	20	30
260	**31**	6d. black (Die I) (P 13×12)	60·00	12·00
261		6d. black (Die II) (P 13½) (1.10.40)	3·00	2·25
		a. Violet-black (1.44)	25·00	28·00
		b. Perf 12. *Black* (5.6.47)	1·50	1·50
261c	**35**	8d. carmine (P 14) (15.11.48)	1·00	2·25
		d. Perf 13 (7.6.50)	70	2·75
262	**36**	1s. black and yellow (P 12½)	1·00	70
263	**35**	1s.5d. black & carm (P 14) (13.6.40)	20	10
263a		1s.6d. ultramarine (P 14) (1.8.50)	3·50	2·75
		b. Perf 13 (16.2.55)	1·25	15·00
264	**37**	2s. violet and orange (P 12½)	2·50	40
265	**38**	2s.6d. green and brown (P 12½)	2·75	1·50
266	**39**	5s. green and purple (P 12½)	2·75	1·75
266a	**40**	10s. orange & emer (P 12½) (13.3.50)	35·00	40·00
266b	**41**	£1 ultram & carm (P 12½) (13.3.50)	48·00	50·00
249/66b Set of 22			£250	£120
249s/66s (excl 8d. and 1s.6d.) Perf "Specimen" Set of 18			£475	

2½d.

(42)

1941 (10 Feb). No. 254 surch with T **42** by Govt Printer, Suva.
267	**31**	2½d. on 2d. brown and green	2·00	30

1946 (17 Aug). Victory. As Nos. 110/11 of Antigua.
268		2½d. green	10	1·25
		a. Printed double, one albino	£350	
269		3d. blue	10	10
268s/9s Perf "Specimen" Set of 2			80·00	

1948 (17 Dec). Royal Silver Wedding. As Nos. 112/13 of Antigua.
270		2½d. green	40	1·75
271		5s. violet-blue	14·00	8·00

1949 (10 Oct). 75th Anniv of U.P.U. As Nos. 114/17 of Antigua.
272		2d. bright reddish purple	30	75
273		3d. deep blue	2·00	3·00
274		6d. carmine-red	30	3·25
275		1s.6d. blue	35	1·25
272/5 Set of 4			2·75	7·50

43 Children Bathing

44 Rugby Football

(Recess B.W.)

1951 (17 Sept). Health Stamps. Wmk Mult Script CA. P 13½.
276	**43**	1d.+1d. brown	10	1·00
277	**44**	2d.+1d. green	30	1·00

STAMP BOOKLETS

1909. Black and red cover. Stapled.
SB1   2s. booklet containing eleven ½d. (No. 118) in blocks of 5 and 6, and eighteen 1d. (No. 119) in blocks of 6 .... £2750

1914. Black on red cover. Stapled.
SB2   2s. booklet containing eleven ½d. (No. 126) in blocks of 5 and 6, and eighteen 1d. (No. 127) in blocks of 6 .... £2500

1939 (10 Mar)–**40**. Black on deep green covers. No advertising pages. Stapled.
SB3   3s. booklet containing eight ½d. and eight 1d. (Nos. 249/50) in blocks of 8 and twelve 2d. (No. 253) in blocks of 6 .... £1100
   a. Including four advertising pages (black on pale greenish buff cover) (1940) £900
SB4   5s.9d. booklet containing ten ½d. and ten 1d. (Nos. 249/50) in blocks of 10 and twenty-seven 2d. (No. 253) in blocks of 9 .... £3750
   a. Including four advertising pages (black on pink cover) (1940) £3250

Nos. SB3/4 were produced locally and Nos. SB3a/4a by De La Rue.

POSTAGE DUE STAMPS

(Typo Govt Printer, Suva)

1917 (1 Jan). Thick yellowish white laid paper. No gum. P 11.
D1	D **1**	½d. black	£800	£425
		a. Se-tenant strip of 8: 1d.(×3)+½d.+4d.+3d.(×3)	£13000	
D2		1d. black	£375	£120
D3		2d. black	£300	75·00
D4		3d. black	£375	95·00
D5		4d. black	£850	£475

Nos. D1/2 and D4/5 were printed, se-tenant, in sheets of 96 (8×12) with each horizontal row containing three 1d., one ½d., one 4d. and three 3d. in that order. Only thirty-one such sheets were issued. The 2d. was printed separately in sheets of 84 (7×12). On all these sheets marginal copies were imperforate on the outer edge.

1917 (21 April)–**18**. Narrower setting, value in ½d. as Type D **2**.
D5a		½d. black	£475	£300
D5b		1d. black	£275	£130
D5c		2d. black (5.4.18)	£900	£600

1d. and 2d. stamps must have wide margins (3½ to 4mm) on the vertical sides to be Nos. D2 or D3. Stamps with narrow margins of approximately the same width on all four sides are Nos. D5b or D5c.

Nos. D5a/c were printed in separate sheets of 84 (7×12). The marginal copies are perforated on all sides.

FIJI

D 3   D 4

(Typo D.L.R.)

1918 (1 June). Wmk Mult Crown CA. P 14.

D6	D 3	½d. black	3·00	22·00
D7		1d. black	3·50	5·00
D8		2d. black	3·25	7·50
D9		3d. black	3·25	48·00
D10		4d. black	6·00	27·00
D6/10 Set of 5			17·00	£100
D6s/10s Optd "Specimen" Set of 5				£150

D9 exists with watermark sideways (Crown to right of CA *as seen from the back of the stamp*) and overprinted "SPECIMEN". (*Price,* £500).

No postage due stamps were in use between 31 August 1931 and 3 July 1940.

(Typo Waterlow)

1940 (3 July). Wmk Mult Script CA. P 12½.

D11	D 4	1d. emerald-green	7·00	70·00
D12		2d. emerald-green	10·00	70·00
D13		3d. emerald-green	13·00	75·00
D14		4d. emerald-green	15·00	80·00
D15		5d. emerald-green	17·00	85·00
D16		6d. emerald-green	19·00	85·00
D17		1s. carmine-lake	22·00	£110
D18		1s.6d. carmine-lake	23·00	£160
D11/18 Set of 8			£110	£650
D11s/18s Perf "Specimen" Set of 8				£180

All values are known with forged postmarks, including one of Levuka dated "8 APR 41" and others of Suva dated "12 AUG 42", "14 AU 42" or "20 MR 45".

The use of postage due stamps was discontinued on 30 April 1946.

Gambia

WEST AFRICAN SETTLEMENT

British traders were active in the River Gambia area from the beginning of the 17th century, but it was not until 1808 that it was officially recognised as a Settlement. Administration passed from the merchants to the Governor of Freetown (Sierra Leone) in 1821 and in 1843 Gambia became a separate colony with a Protectorate declared over the banks of the river for 300 miles inland in 1857. A period of colonial retrenchment in 1865 saw a return to Settlement status under Sierra Leone, but Gambia once again became a Crown Colony in 1888.

There was no government postal service before 1858.

PRICES. The prices of Nos. 1 to 8 are for fine copies, with good margins and embossing. Brilliant or poor copies can be supplied at prices consistent with their condition.

DOUBLE EMBOSSING. The majority of the stamps of T **1** with so-called "double embossing" are merely specimens in which the printing and embossing do not register accurately and have no special value. We no longer list "twice embossed" or "twice embossed, once inverted" varieties as they are considered to be outside the scope of this catalogue.

1

(Typo and embossed by D.L.R.)

1869 (18 Mar)–**72.** No wmk. Imperf.
1	1	4d. brown	£500	£190
2		4d. pale brown (1871)	£450	£200
3		6d. deep blue	£475	£200
3a		6d. blue	£550	£170
4		6d. pale blue (17.2.72)	£2500	£1000

Our prices for the 6d. pale blue, No. 4, are for stamps which are pale by comparison with specimens of the "deep blue" and "blue" colour groups listed under Nos. 3 and 3a. The date given is the earliest known postmark. An exceptionally pale shade is recognized by specialists and this is rare.

1874 (Aug). Wmk Crown CC. Imperf.
5	1	4d. brown	£375	£190
		w. Wmk inverted	£550	£300
		x. Wmk reversed	£550	£300
		y. Wmk inverted and reversed	£650	£350
6		4d. pale brown	£400	£200
7		6d. deep blue	£325	£200
		w. Wmk inverted	£450	£300
		x. Wmk reversed	£500	£325
		y. Wmk inverted and reversed	£500	£325
8		6d. blue	£325	£190
		a. Sloping label	£650	£375
		b. Wmk sideways	†	
		w. Wmk inverted	£450	£300

SLOPING LABEL VARIETY. Traces of this flaw first occur in the 6d. imperforate on R. 1/1 and R. 1/5. In the perforated printings the variety on R. 1/5 is much more pronounced and appears as illustrated above. Our listings are these examples from R. 1/5, less noticeable varieties of this type from R. 1/1, which slope from right to left, being worth less. These varieties continued to appear until the introduction of a new 6d. plate in 1893, used for No. 34.

1880–81. Wmk Crown CC. P 14*.

A. Wmk sideways†.
10A	1	½d. orange	£300	£250
		w. Wmk Crown to left of CC		
12A		1d. maroon	£450	£375
		w. Wmk Crown to left of CC		
		y. Wmk sideways inverted and reversed		
13A		2d. rose	£140	70·00
		w. Wmk Crown to left of CC		
14A		3d. bright ultramarine	£450	£400
		w. Wmk Crown to left of CC		
15A		4d. brown	£450	65·00
		w. Wmk Crown to left of CC	£425	60·00
16A		4d. pale brown	£425	60·00
		w. Wmk Crown to left of CC	£400	55·00

17A		6d. deep blue	£190	90·00
		c. Sloping label	£475	£250
18A		6d. blue	£180	90·00
		c. Sloping label	£475	£250
		w. Wmk Crown to left of CC		
19A		1s. green	£400	£275
20A		1s. deep green	£400	£275
		w. Wmk Crown to left of CC	£550	

10A/20A Set of 7	£2000	£1400

B. Wmk upright.
10B	1	½d. orange	9·50	16·00
11B		½d. dull orange	9·50	16·00
		w. Wmk inverted	65·00	
		x. Wmk reversed	55·00	
12B		1d. maroon	4·75	6·00
		w. Wmk inverted	£110	£110
13B		2d. rose	27·00	11·00
		w. Wmk inverted	†	£275
14B		3d. bright ultramarine	70·00	35·00
14cB		3d. pale dull ultramarine	55·00	28·00
		w. Wmk inverted	70·00	42·00
15B		4d. brown	£200	15·00
		w. Wmk inverted	†	£180
16B		4d. pale brown	£200	16·00
17B		6d. deep blue	90·00	45·00
		c. Sloping label	£250	£150
18B		6d. blue	90·00	45·00
		c. Sloping label	£250	£150
19B		1s. green	£250	£140
		w. Wmk inverted	†	£400
20B		1s. deep green	£250	£140

10B/20B Set of 7	£550	£225

*There were three different printings of these stamps. The original supply, sent in June 1880 and covering all seven values, had watermark sideways and was perforated by a line machine. In October of the same year a further printing of the lowest five values had the watermark changed to upright, but was still with line perforation. The final printing, sent May 1881 and containing all values, also had watermark upright, but was perforated on a comb machine.

†The normal sideways watermark shows Crown to right of CC, *as seen from the back of the stamp.*

1886–93. Wmk Crown CA (sideways*). P 14.
21	1	½d. myrtle-green (1887)	3·50	2·25
		w. Wmk Crown to right of CA	40·00	
		x. Wmk sideways reversed	60·00	
22		½d. grey-green	3·75	3·25
22b		1d. maroon	†	£15000
23		1d. crimson (1887)	7·00	8·50
23a		1d. aniline crimson	7·00	9·50
23b		1d. pale carmine	6·00	9·50
24		2d. orange (1887)	11·00	5·00
25		2d. deep orange	2·00	8·00
26		2½d. ultramarine (1887)	4·75	2·00
27		2½d. deep bright blue	4·00	1·25
		w. Wmk Crown to right of CA	£120	
28		3d. slate-grey (1886)	7·50	14·00
29		3d. grey	6·00	15·00
30		4d. brown (1887)	8·00	2·00
31		4d. deep brown	8·00	2·00
		a. Wmk upright	†	£1700
		w. Wmk Crown to right of CA	85·00	85·00
32		6d. yellowish olive-green (1886)	75·00	30·00
		a. Sloping label	£190	80·00
		bw. Wmk Crown to right of CA	£180	
32d		6d. olive-green (1887)	60·00	55·00
		da. Sloping label	£170	£140
33		6d. bronze-green (1889)	29·00	55·00
		a. Sloping label	65·00	£100
		bw. Wmk Crown to right of CA	£180	
33c		6d. deep bronze-green (1889)	30·00	55·00
		ca. Sloping label	65·00	£100
34		6d. slate-green (1893)	13·00	48·00
35		1s. violet (1887)	3·25	17·00
36		1s. deep violet	6·00	20·00
36b		1s. aniline violet	£1100	

21/36 Set of 8	42·00	70·00
21s/4s, 32s Optd "Specimen" Set of 4	£400	

*The normal sideways watermark shows Crown to left of CA, *as seen from the back of the stamp.*

The above were printed in panes of 15 on paper intended for larger panes. Hence the watermark is sometimes misplaced or omitted and letters from "CROWN AGENTS FOR THE COLONIES" from the margin may appear on the stamps.

The ½d., 2d., 3d., 4d. (No. 32) and 1s. with watermark Crown CA are known imperforate (*price from £1100, unused*).

Only three examples, all used, are recorded of the 1d. maroon, No. 22b.

The previously listed 3d. "pearl-grey" shade has been deleted as it is impossible to distinguish from other 3d. shades when it occurs on a single stamp. Sheets from this late printing can be identified by three coloured dots in the left sheet margin and one in the right, this being the reverse of the normal arrangement.

Only three used examples are known of the 4d. with upright watermark, No. 31a.

CROWN COLONY

2

Normal   Malformed   Repaired "S"
              "S"

The Malformed "S" occurs on R. 7/3 of the left pane from Key Plate 2. This was used to print the initial supply of all values. Printings of the ½d., 1d. and 2½d. despatched on 24 September 1898 had the "S" repaired as shown above. Subsequent printings of the ½d., 1d. and 3d. were from Key Plate 3.

(Typo D.L.R.)

1898 (2 May)–**1902.** Wmk Crown CA. P 14.
37	2	½d. dull green (*shades*)	2·75	1·75
		a. Malformed "S"	£300	
		b. Repaired "S"	£325	£275
38		1d. carmine (*shades*)	2·25	75
		a. Malformed "S"	£300	
		b. Repaired "S"	£325	£325
39		2d. orange and mauve	6·00	3·50
		a. Malformed "S"	£350	£350
40		2½d. ultramarine	1·75	2·50
		a. Malformed "S"	£300	
		b. Repaired "S"	£350	
41		3d. reddish purple and blue	27·00	12·00
		a. Malformed "S"	£425	
		b. *Deep purple and ultramarine* (1902)	90·00	£100
42		4d. brown and blue	10·00	30·00
		a. Malformed "S"	£375	
43		6d. olive-green and carmine	10·00	29·00
		a. Malformed "S"	£400	
44		1s. violet and green	30·00	65·00
		a. Malformed "S"	£550	

37/44 Set of 8	80·00	£130
37s/44s Optd "Specimen" Set of 8	£160	

3   **4**

Dented frame (R. 1/6 of left pane)

1902 (13 Mar)–**05.** Wmk Crown CA. P 14.
45	3	½d. green (19.4.02)	3·25	2·50
		a. Dented frame	95·00	95·00
46		1d. carmine	5·00	1·00
		a. Dented frame	£120	80·00
47		2d. orange and mauve (14.6.02)	3·25	2·00
		a. Dented frame	£140	£130
48		2½d. ultramarine (14.6.02)	30·00	18·00
		a. Dented frame	£350	£250
49		3d. purple and ultramarine (19.4.02)	12·00	3·50
		a. Dented frame	£250	£160
50		4d. brown and ultramarine (14.6.02)	3·25	25·00
		a. Dented frame	£180	
51		6d. pale sage-green & carmine (14.6.02)	6·00	12·00
		a. Dented frame	£200	
52		1s. violet and green (14.6.02)	42·00	80·00
		a. Dented frame	£425	
53	4	1s.6d. green and carmine/*yellow* (6.4.05)	7·00	18·00
		a. Dented frame	£250	
54		2s. deep slate and orange (14.6.02)	48·00	60·00
		a. Dented frame	£450	
55		2s.6d. purple and brown/*yellow* (6.4.05)	15·00	60·00
		a. Dented frame	£325	
56		3s. carmine and green/*yellow* (6.4.05)	20·00	60·00
		a. Dented frame	£350	

45/56 Set of 12	£170	£300
45s/56s Optd "Specimen" Set of 12	£190	

1904 (Aug)–**06.** Wmk Mult Crown CA. P 14.
57	3	½d. green (9.05)	4·50	30
		a. Dented frame	£120	80·00
58		1d. carmine	4·50	15
		a. Dented frame	£130	65·00
59		2d. orange and mauve (23.2.06)	12·00	2·25
		a. Dented frame	£225	£130
60		2½d. bright blue (8.05)	7·00	4·75
		a. *Bright blue and ultramarine*	15·00	25·00
		b. Dented frame	£170	£150
61		3d. purple and ultramarine (9.05) ..	8·00	2·00
		a. Dented frame	£180	£130
62		4d. brown and ultramarine (23.2.06)	18·00	40·00
		a. Dented frame	£300	
63	4	5d. grey and black (6.4.05)	14·00	20·00

64	3	6d. Dented frame	£275	
		6d. olive-green and carmine (23.2.06)	18·00	60·00
		a. Dented frame	£300	
65	4	7½d. green and carmine (6.4.05)	11·00	42·00
		a. Dented frame	£200	
66		10d. olive and carmine (6.4.05)	21·00	35·00
		a. Dented frame	£325	
67	3	1s. violet and green (9.05)	24·00	48·00
		a. Dented frame	£325	
68	4	2s. deep slate and orange (7.05)	70·00	90·00
		a. Dented frame	£475	
57/68 Set of 12			£190	£300
63s, 65s/6s Optd "Specimen" Set of 3			70·00	

See also Nos. 72/85.

HALF PENNY

ONE PENNY

(5)   (6)

1906 (10 Apr). *Nos. 55 and 56 surch with T 5 or 6 by Govt Printer.*

69		½d. on 2s.6d. purple and brown/*yellow*	50·00	60·00
		a. Dented frame	£500	
70		1d. on 3s. carmine and green/*yellow*	55·00	30·00
		a. Surch double	£1800	£5000
		b. Dented frame	£600	

No. 69 was surcharged in a setting of 30 (6×5), the spacing between the words and the bars being 5 mm on rows 1, 2 and 5; and 4 mm on rows 3 and 4. Constant varieties occur on R. 2/1 (broken "E") and R. 5/1 (dropped "Y") of the setting.

No. 70 was surcharged in a setting of 60 (6×10) and a similar dropped "Y" variety occurs on R. 6/3 and R. 8/4, the latter in conjunction with a dropped "E".

Both values were withdrawn on 24 April when fresh supplies of ½d. and 1d. definitives were received from London.

1909 (1 Oct). *Colours changed. Wmk Mult Crown CA. P 14.*

72	3	½d. blue-green	6·00	3·50
		a. Dented frame	£120	£110
73		1d. red	9·00	15
		a. Dented frame	£160	80·00
74		2d. greyish slate	1·75	11·00
		a. Dented frame	£140	
75		3d. purple/*yellow*	3·75	1·00
		a. *Purple/lemon-yellow*	5·50	1·75
		b. Dented frame	£150	£110
76		4d. black and red/*yellow*	1·50	65
		a. Dented frame	£150	£110
77	4	5d. orange and purple	1·50	1·25
		a. Dented frame	£160	£160
78	3	6d. dull and bright purple	2·25	2·25
		a. Dented frame	£170	£180
79	4	7½d. brown and blue	2·50	2·50
		a. Dented frame	£170	£180
80		10d. pale sage-green and carmine	2·75	7·00
		a. Dented frame	£180	
81	3	1s. black/*green*	3·25	17·00
		a. Dented frame	£180	
82	4	1s.6d. violet and green	17·00	60·00
		a. Dented frame	£275	
83		2s. purple and bright blue/*blue*	14·00	20·00
		a. Dented frame	£275	
84		2s.6d. black and red/*blue*	21·00	20·00
		a. Dented frame	£325	
85		3s. yellow and green	25·00	48·00
		a. Dented frame	£350	
72/85 Set of 14			£100	£170
73s/85s Optd "Specimen" Set of 13			£250	

Most values between Nos. 45 and 85 are known with forged postmarks. These include circular types of Bathurst, dated "JA 2 97", and Macarthy Island, dated "FE 17 10", and an oval registered Gambia postmark dated "22 JU 10".

7   8

Split "A" (R. 8/3 of left pane) (ptgs to 1918)

(Type D.L.R)

1912 (1 Sept)–**22.** *Wmk Mult Crown CA. Chalk-surfaced paper (5s.) P 14.*

86	7	½d. deep green	1·75	1·50
		a. Green	2·50	1·50
		b. Pale green (1916)	3·50	3·25
		c. Split "A"	85·00	
87		1d. red	2·50	80
		a. Rose-red	2·75	30
		b. Scarlet (1916)	4·50	90
		c. Split "A"	£100	
88	8	1½d. olive-green and blue-green	50	30
		a. Split "A"	95·00	
89	7	2d. greyish slate	50	2·75
		a. Split "A"	95·00	
90		2½d. deep bright blue	4·00	3·00
		a. Bright blue	4·50	2·50
		b. Split "A"	£160	
91		3d. purple/*yellow*	50	30
		a. On lemon (1917)	14·00	18·00
		b. On orange-buff (1920)	10·00	8·50
		c. On pale yellow	1·25	1·00
		d. Split "A"	£130	
92		4d. black and red/*yellow*	1·00	10·00
		a. On lemon (1917)	2·50	7·50
		b. On orange-buff (1920)	8·00	11·00
		c. On pale yellow	1·50	8·50

---

		d. Split "A"	£140	
		w. Wmk inverted	£130	
93	8	5d. orange and purple	1·00	2·00
		a. Split "A"	£150	
94	7	6d. dull and bright purple	1·00	2·50
		a. Split "A"	£150	
95	8	7½d. brown and blue	1·50	6·50
		a. Split "A"	£200	
96		10d. pale sage-green and carmine	2·25	17·00
		a. Deep sage-green and carmine	2·50	15·00
		b. Split "A"	£250	
97	7	1s. black/*green*	2·00	1·00
		a. On emerald back (1921)	1·00	20·00
		b. Split "A"	£170	
98	8	1s.6d. violet and green	11·00	10·00
		a. Split "A"	£425	
99		2s. purple and blue/*blue*	3·50	6·00
		a. Split "A"	£400	
100		2s.6d. black and red/*blue*	3·25	14·00
		a. Split "A"	£400	
101		3s. yellow and green	8·50	29·00
		a. Split "A"	£550	
102		5s. green and red/*pale yellow* (1922)	90·00	£150
86/102 Set of 17			£120	£225
86s/102s Optd "Specimen" Set of 17			£350	

1921–22. *Wmk Mult Script CA. Chalk-surfaced paper (4s.). P 14.*

108	7	½d. dull green	30	18·00
		x. Wmk reversed	£110	
109		1d. carmine-red	1·00	6·50
		x. Wmk reversed	£100	£100
110	8	1½d. olive-green and blue-green	1·25	13·00
		x. Wmk reversed	£110	
111	7	2d. grey	1·00	2·25
		x. Wmk reversed	90·00	
112		2½d. bright blue	50	7·00
113	8	5d. orange and purple	1·75	16·00
		x. Wmk reversed	48·00	
114	7	6d. dull and bright purple	1·75	17·00
		x. Wmk reversed	24·00	
115	8	7½d. brown and blue	2·00	32·00
		x. Wmk reversed	24·00	
116		10d. pale sage-green and carmine	7·00	16·00
		x. Wmk reversed	60·00	
117		4s. black and red (1922)	85·00	£150
		w. Wmk inverted	80·00	£170
108/17 Set of 10			90·00	£250
108s/17s Optd "Specimen" Set of 10			£200	

Forged postmarks of the types mentioned below No. 85 have also been seen on various values between No. 86 and 117. Collectors should beware of partial strikes which do not show the year date.

9   10

(Recess D.L.R.)

1922 (1 Sept)–**29.** *Portrait and shield in black. P 14*.*

(a) Wmk Mult Crown CA.

118	9	4d. red/*yellow* (a)	2·75	3·75
119		7½d. purple/*yellow* (a)	4·00	6·50
120	10	1s. purple/*yellow* (a)	12·00	26·00
		w. Wmk inverted	£100	£140
121		5s. purple/*yellow* (c)	42·00	£130
		w. Wmk inverted		
118/21 Set of 4			55·00	£150
118s/21s Optd or H/S (5s.) "Specimen" Set of 4			£140	

(b) Wmk Mult Script CA.

122	9	½d. green (abd)	55	55
123		½d. deep green (bd) (1925)	4·75	1·50
124		1d. brown (abd)	80	20
125		1½d. bright rose-scarlet (abd)	1·00	20
		w. Wmk inverted	†	£350
126		2d. grey (ab)	1·00	3·50
127		2½d. orange-yellow (b)	1·00	11·00
		w. Wmk inverted		£100
128		3d. bright blue (abd)	1·00	20
129		4d. red/*yellow* (bd) (1.3.27)	7·50	20·00
130		5d. sage-green (a)	2·00	10·00
131		6d. claret (ad)	1·25	30
132		7½d. purple/*yellow* (ab) (1927)	8·50	65·00
133		10d. blue (a)	4·50	18·00
134	10	1s. purple/*yellow* (aef) (9.24)	2·50	1·50
		a. Blackish purple/*yell-buff* (c) (1929)	45·00	45·00
135		1s.6d. purple/*yellow* (af)	11·00	14·00
136		2s. purple/*blue* (ac)	5·00	4·50
137		2s.6d. deep green (a)	5·50	9·50
138		3s. bright aniline violet (a)	14·00	55·00
139		3s. slate-purple (c) (1928)	£190	£375
140		4s. brown (ace)	7·50	16·00
141		5s. green/*yellow* (acf) (9.26)	14·00	42·00
142		10s. sage-green (ce)	70·00	£100
122/42 Set of 19			£140	£325
122s/42s Optd "Specimen" Set of 19				

Perforations. A number of different perforating machines were used for the various printings of these stamps and the following varieties are known: (*a*) the original 14 line perforation; (*b*) 14×13.8 comb perforation used for Type 9; (*c*) 13.8×13.7 comb perforation used for Type 10; (*d*) 13.7 line perforation used for Type 9; (*e*) 14×13.8 compound line perforation used for Type 10; (*f*) 13.8×14 compound line perforation used for Type 10. The occurrence of these perforations on the individual values is indicated by the letters shown after the colour descriptions above.

No. 139 has been faked, but note that this stamp is comb perf 13.8×13.7 whereas No. 138 is line perf 14 exactly. There are also shades of the slate-purple.

Most values of the above issue are known with a forged oval registered Gambia postmark dated "22 JU 10", often with the year date not shown. Collectors should exercise particular caution in buying used examples of No. 139.

1935 (6 May). *Silver Jubilee. As Nos. 91/4 of Antigua, but printed by B.W. P 11×12.*

143		1½d. deep blue and scarlet	60	1·00
		a. Extra flagstaff	£275	
		b. Short extra flagstaff	£200	
		c. Lightning conductor	£375	
		d. Flagstaff on right-hand turret	£275	
		e. Double flagstaff	£275	
144		3d. brown and deep blue	80	1·00
		a. Extra flagstaff	£180	
		b. Short extra flagstaff	£170	
		c. Lightning conductor	£180	
145		6d. light blue and olive-green	1·25	4·00
		a. Extra flagstaff	£160	
		b. Short extra flagstaff	£225	
		c. Lightning conductor	£190	
		d. Flagstaff on right-hand turret	£425	
146		1s. slate and purple	6·00	8·50
		a. Extra flagstaff	£225	
		b. Short extra flagstaff	£300	
		c. Lightning conductor	£275	
		d. Flagstaff on right-hand turret	£500	
143/6 Set of 4			7·75	13·00
143s/6s Perf "Specimen" Set of 4				

For illustrations of plate varieties see Omnibus section following Zanzibar.

Sheets from the second printing of the 6d. and 1s. in November 1935 had the extra flagstaff partially erased with a sharp point.

1937 (12 May). *Coronation. As Nos. 95/7 of Antigua. P 11×11½.*

147		1d. yellow-brown	30	1·25
148		1½d. carmine	30	60
149		3d. blue	55	1·50
147/9 Set of 3			1·00	3·00
147s/9s Perf "Specimen" Set of 3			80·00	

11 Elephant (from Colony Badge)

(Recess B.W.)

1938 (1 Apr)–**46.** *Wmk Mult Script CA. P 12.*

150	11	½d. black and emerald-green	15	70
151		1d. purple and brown	30	50
152		1½d. brown-lake and bright carmine	£150	12·00
		a. Brown-lake and scarlet	3·50	2·50
		b. Brown-lake and vermilion	30	2·00
152c		1½d. blue and black (2.1.45)	30	1·50
153		2d. blue and black	8·00	3·25
153a		2d. lake and scarlet (1.10.43)	60	2·25
154		3d. light blue and grey-blue	30	10
154a		5d. sage-green & purple-brn (13.3.41)	50	50
155		6d. olive-green and claret	1·50	35
156		1s. slate-blue and violet	2·50	10
156a		1s.3d. chocolate & lt blue (28.11.46)	3·25	2·50
157		2s. carmine and blue	5·00	3·25
158		2s.6d. sepia and dull green	12·00	2·50
159		4s. vermilion and purple	22·00	2·50
160		5s. blue and vermilion	22·00	4·00
161		10s. orange and black	22·00	7·00
150/61 Set of 16			90·00	28·00
150s/61s Perf "Specimen" Set of 16			£350	

1946 (6 Aug). *Victory. As Nos. 110/11 of Antigua.*

162		1½d. black	10	25
163		3d. blue	10	40
162s/3s Perf "Specimen" Set of 2			70·00	

1948 (24 Dec). *Royal Silver Wedding. As Nos.112/13 of Antigua.*

164		1½d. black	25	10
165		£1 mauve	15·00	16·00

1949 (10 Oct). *75th Anniv of Universal Postal Union. As Nos. 114/17 of Antigua.*

166		1½d. blue-black	30	1·50
167		3d. deep blue	1·25	2·00
168		6d. magenta	50	1·75
169		1s. violet	35	60
166/9 Set of 4			2·25	5·25

Gibraltar

CROWN COLONY

Early details of postal arrangements in Gibraltar are hard to establish, although it is known that postal facilities were provided by the Civil Secretary's Office from 1749. Gibraltar became a packet port in July 1806, although the Civil Secretary's office continued to be responsible for other mail. The two services were amalgamated on 1 January 1857 as a Branch Office of the British G.P.O., the control of the postal services not reverting to Gibraltar until 1 January 1886.

Spanish stamps could be used at Gibraltar from their introduction in 1850 and, indeed, such franking was required on letters weighing over ½ oz. sent to Spain after 1 July 1854. From 1 July 1856 until 1 January 1876 all mail to Spain required postage to be prepaid by Spanish stamps and these issues were supplied by the Gibraltar postal authorities, acting as a Spanish Postal Agent. The mail forwarded under this system was cancelled at San Roque with a horizontal barred oval, later replaced by a cartwheel type mark showing numeral 63. From 1857 combination covers showing the 2d. ship mail fee paid in British stamps and the inland postage by Spanish issues exist.

Stamps of Great Britain were issued for use in Gibraltar from 3 September 1857 (earliest recorded cover is dated 7 September 1857) to the end of 1885.

The initial supply contained 1d., 4d. and 6d. values. No supplies of the 2d. or 1s. were sent until the consignment of October 1857. No other values were supplied until early 1862.

For illustrations of the postmark types see BRITISH POST OFFICES ABROAD notes following GREAT BRITAIN.

Stamps of GREAT BRITAIN cancelled "G" as Type 1 (3 Sept 1857 to 19 Feb 1859)

Z1	1d. red-brown (1854) Die I, *wmk* Small Crown, *perf* 16	£375
Z2	1d. red-brown (1855) Die II, *wmk* Small Crown, *perf* 16	£650
Z3	1d. red-brown (1855), Die II, *wmk* Small Crown *perf* 14	£325
Z4	1d. red-brown (1855), Die II, *wmk* Large Crown, *perf* 14	85·00
Z5	1d. rose-red (1857), Die II, *wmk* Large Crown, *perf* 14	22·00
Z6	2d. blue (1855), *wmk* Small Crown, *perf* 14	£425
Z7	2d. blue (1855–58), *wmk* Large Crown, *perf* 16	£350
Z8	2d. blue (1855), *wmk* Large Crown, *perf* 14 (Plate Nos. 5, 6) .... *From*	65·00
Z9	2d. blue (1858) (Plate No. 7)	£300
Z10	4d. rose (1857)	55·00
Z11	a. Thick glazed paper	40·00
Z12	6d. lilac (1856)	£800
Z13	6d. lilac (1856) (blued *paper*)	£110
Z14	1s. green (1856)	
	a. Thick paper	
	1s. green (1856) (blued *paper*)	£1400

Stamps of GREAT BRITAIN cancelled "A 26" as in Types 2, 5, 11 or 14 (20 Feb 1859 to 31 Dec 1885).

Z15	½d. rose-red (1870–79) .... *From*	32·00
	Plate Nos. 4, 5, 6, 8, 10, 11, 12, 13, 14, 15, 19, 20.	
Z16	1d. red-brown (1841), *imperf*	£1500
Z17	1d. red-brown (1855), *wmk* Large Crown, *perf* 14	£180
Z18	1d. rose-red (1857), *wmk* Large Crown, *perf* 14	13·00
Z19	1d. rose-red (1864–79) .... *From*	22·00
	Plate Nos. 71, 72, 73, 74 ,76, 78, 79, 80, 81, 82, 83, 84, 85, 86, 87, 88, 89, 90, 91, 92, 93, 94, 95, 96, 97, 98, 99, 100, 101, 102, 103, 104, 105, 106, 107, 108, 109, 110, 111, 112, 113, 114, 115, 116, 117, 118, 119, 120, 121, 122, 123, 124, 125, 127, 129, 130, 131, 132, 133, 134, 135, 136, 137, 138, 139, 140, 141, 142, 143, 144, 145, 146, 147, 148, 149, 150, 151, 152, 153, 154, 155, 156, 157, 158, 159, 160, 161, 162, 163, 164, 165, 166, 167, 168, 169, 170, 171, 172, 173, 174, 175, 176, 177, 178, 179, 180, 181, 182, 183, 184, 185, 186, 187, 188, 189, 190, 191, 192, 193, 194, 195, 196, 197, 198, 199, 200, 201, 202, 203, 204, 205, 206, 207, 208, 209, 210, 211, 212, 213, 214, 215, 216, 217, 218, 219, 220, 221, 222, 223, 224, 225.	
Z20	1½d. lake-red (1870) (Plate No. 3)	£500
Z21	2d. blue (1855), *wmk* Large Crown, *perf* 14 Plate No. 6.	£140
Z22	2d. blue (1858–69) .... *From*	22·00
	Plate Nos. 7, 8, 9, 12, 13, 14, 15.	
Z23	2½d. rosy mauve (1875) (blued *paper*) .... *From*	£100
	Plate Nos. 1, 2, 3.	
Z24	2½d. rosy mauve (1875–76) .... *From*	28·00
	Plate Nos. 1, 2, 3.	
Z25	2½d. rosy mauve (*Error of Lettering*)	£2000
Z26	2½d. rosy mauve (1876–79) .... *From*	21·00
	Plate Nos. 3, 4, 5, 6, 7, 8, 9, 10, 11, 12, 13, 14, 15, 16, 17.	
Z27	2½d. blue (1880–81) .... *From*	13·00
	Plate Nos. 17, 18, 19, 20.	
Z28	2½d. blue (1881) (Plate Nos. 21, 22, 23) .... *From*	10·00
Z29	3d. carmine-rose (1862)	£200
Z30	3d. rose (1865) (Plate No. 4)	65·00
Z31	3d. rose (1867–73) .... *From*	45·00
	Plate Nos. 4, 5, 6, 7, 8, 9, 10.	
Z32	3d. rose (1873–76) .... *From*	55·00
	Plate Nos. 11, 12, 14, 15, 16, 17, 18, 19, 20.	
Z33	3d. rose (1881) (Plate Nos. 20, 21)	£150
Z34	3d. lilac (1883) (3d. *on* 3d.)	£150
Z35	4d. rose (1857)	70·00
Z36	4d. red (1862) (Plate No. 3, 4) .... *From*	48·00
Z37	4d. vermilion (1865–73) .... *From*	30·00
	Plate Nos. 7, 8, 9, 10, 11, 12, 13, 14.	
Z38	4d. vermilion (1876) (Plate No. 15)	£275
Z39	4d. sage-green (1877) (Plate Nos. 15, 16)	£120
Z40	4d. grey-green (1880) *wmk* Large Garter	£250
	Plate No. 17.	
Z41	4d. grey-brown (1880) *wmk* Crown .... *From*	55·00
	Plate Nos. 17, 18.	
Z42	6d. lilac (1856)	42·00
Z43	6d. lilac (1862) (Plate Nos. 3, 4) .... *From*	38·00
Z44	6d. lilac (1865–67) (Plate Nos. 5, 6) .... *From*	32·00
Z45	6d. lilac (1867) (Plate No. 6)	45·00
Z46	6d. violet (1867–70) (Plate Nos. 6, 8, 9) .... *From*	32·00
Z47	6d. buff (1872–73) (Plate Nos. 11, 12) .... *From*	£150
Z48	6d. chestnut (1872) (Plate No. 11)	35·00
Z49	6d. grey (1873) (Plate No. 12)	95·00
Z50	6d. grey (1874–80) .... *From*	32·00
	Plate Nos. 13, 14, 15, 16, 17.	
Z51	6d. grey (1881) (Plate Nos. 17, 18)	£225
Z52	6d. lilac (1883) (6d. *on* 6d.)	£100
Z53	8d. orange (1876)	£475
Z54	9d. bistre (1862)	£300
Z55	9d. straw (1862)	£650
Z56	9d. straw (1865)	£600
Z57	9d. straw (1867)	£200
Z58	10d. red-brown (1867)	£150
Z59	1s. green (1856)	£100
Z60	1s. green (1862)	70·00
Z61	1s. green (1862) ("K" *variety*)	£2000
Z62	1s. green (1865) (Plate No. 4)	60·00
Z63	1s. green (1873–77) (Plate Nos. 4, 5, 6, 7) .... *From*	28·00
Z64	1s. green (1873–77) .... *From*	65·00
	Plate Nos. 8, 9, 10, 11, 12, 13.	
Z65	1s. orange-brown (1880) (Plate No. 13)	£325
Z66	1s. orange-brown (1881) .... *From*	£100
	Plate Nos. 13, 14.	
Z67	2s. blue (1867)	£225
Z68	5s. rose (1867) (Plate No. 1)	£800

1880.

Z69	½d. deep green	26·00
Z70	½d. pale green	26·00
Z71	1d. Venetian red	25·00
Z72	1½d. Venetian red	£250
Z73	2d. pale rose	70·00
Z74	2d. deep rose	70·00
Z75	5d. indigo	£130

1881.

Z76	1d. lilac (14 *dots*)	30·00
Z77	1d. lilac (16 *dots*)	10·00

1884.

Z78	½d. slate-blue	24·00
Z79	2d. lilac	90·00
Z80	2½d. lilac	17·00
Z81	3d. lilac	
Z82	4d. dull green	£170
Z83	6d. dull green	

POSTAL FISCALS

Z83a	1d. purple (Die 4) (1878) *wmk* Small Anchor	£700
Z84	1d. purple (1881), *wmk* Orb	£1100

PRICES FOR STAMPS ON COVER TO 1945	
Nos. 1/2	*from* × 25
No. 3	*from* × 10
No. 4	*from* × 25
Nos. 5/6	*from* × 8
Nos. 7/33	*from* × 6
Nos. 39/45	*from* × 5
Nos. 46/109	*from* × 3
Nos. 110/13	*from* × 4
Nos. 114/17	*from* × 3
Nos. 118/20	*from* × 5
Nos. 121/31	*from* × 3

GIBRALTAR
(1)

1886 (1 Jan). *Contemporary types of Bermuda optd with T **1** by D.L.R. Wmk Crown CA. P 14.*

1	9	½d. dull green	14·00	8·00
2		1d. rose-red	60·00	4·25
3	2	2d. purple-brown	£110	75·00
		w. Wmk inverted		
4	11	2½d. ultramarine	£150	3·25
		a. Optd in blue-black	£500	£150
		w. Wmk inverted	—	£425
5	10	4d. orange-brown	£150	90·00
6	4	6d. deep lilac	£250	£190
7	5	1s. yellow-brown	£425	£350
		1/7 Set of 7	£1000	£650
		1s/3s, 4as/7s Optd "Specimen" Set of 7	£3250	

PRINTER. All Gibraltar stamps to No. 109 were typographed by De La Rue & Co, Ltd.

2   3
4   5

1886 (Nov)–87. Wmk Crown CA. P 14.

8	2	½d. dull green (1.87)	10·00	3·75
9	3	1d. rose (2.87)	42·00	4·25
10	4	2d. brown-purple (12.86)	30·00	22·00
		w. Wmk inverted	£475	
11	5	2½d. blue	80·00	2·75
		w. Wmk inverted	£250	70·00
12	4	4d. orange-brown (16.4.87)	75·00	75·00
13		6d. lilac (16.4.87)	£110	£110
14		1s. bistre (2.87)	£225	£190
		8/14 Set of 7	£500	£350
		8s/14s Optd "Specimen" Set of 7	£500	

Examples of Nos. 3, 6/7 and 14 are known showing a forged Gibraltar postmark dated "JU-13 87".

See also Nos. 39/45.

5 CENTIMOS   5
(6)

"5" with short foot (all stamps in 1st, 5th and 6th vertical columns (5c. on ½d.) or all stamps in 2nd vertical column (25c. on 2d., 25c. on 2½d., 50c. on 6d. and 75c. on 1s.)

1889 (1 Aug). *Surch as T **6***.

15	2	5c. on ½d. green	6·50	22·00
		a. "5" with short foot	6·50	22·00
16	3	10c. on 1d. rose	12·00	11·00
17	4	25c. on 2d. brown-purple	4·75	8·00
		a. "5" with short foot	10·00	15·00
		ab. Small "I" (R. 6/2)	£100	£160
		b. Broken "N" (R. 10/5)	£100	£160

18	5	25c. on 2½d. bright blue	20·00	2·25
		a. "5" with short foot	35·00	5·00
		ab. Small "I" (R. 6/2)	£325	£100
		b. Broken "N" (R. 10/5)	£325	£100
19	4	40c. on 4d. orange-brown	50·00	70·00
20		50c. on 6d. bright lilac	55·00	70·00
		a. "5" with short foot	£100	£120
21		75c. on 1s. bistre	55·00	65·00
		a. "5" with short foot	£100	£120
		15/21 Set of 7	£180	£225
		15s/21s Optd "Specimen" Set of 7	£350	

10c., 40c. and 50c. values from this issue and that of 1889–96 are known bisected and used for half their value from various post offices in Morocco (*price on cover from* £500). These bisects were never authorised by the Gibraltar Post Office.

Broken "M" (Pls 1 and 2 R. 4/5)

7   Flat top to "C" (Pl 2 R. 4/4)

1889 (8 Oct*)–96. *Issue in Spanish currency. Wmk Crown CA. P 14.*

22	7	5c. green	4·50	80
		a. Broken "M"	£140	70·00
		w. Wmk inverted	£250	£180
23		10c. carmine	4·50	50
		b. Value omitted	£5500	
24		20c. olive-green and brown (2.1.96)	42·00	18·00
		w. Wmk inverted	—	£350
25		20c. olive-green (8.7.96)	13·00	70·00
		a. Flat top to "C"	£200	
26		25c. ultramarine	20·00	70
		a. Deep ultramarine	32·00	80
27		40c. orange-brown	3·75	2·75
28		50c. bright lilac (1890)	3·25	2·00
29		75c. olive-green (1890)	32·00	32·00
30		1p. bistre (11.89)	75·00	20·00
31		1p. bistre and ultramarine (6.95)	4·75	6·00
32		2p. black and carmine (2.1.96)	11·00	30·00
33		5p. slate-grey (12.89)	42·00	£100
		22/33 Set of 12	£225	£250
		22s/4s, 26s/33s Optd "Specimen" Set of 11	£400	

*Earliest recorded postmark date.

1898 (1 Oct). *Reissue in Sterling currency. Wmk Crown CA. P 14.*

39	2	½d. grey-green	7·50	1·75
		w. Wmk inverted		
40	3	1d. carmine	7·50	50
		w. Wmk inverted	†	£1200
41	4	2d. brown-purple and ultramarine	22·00	1·75
42	5	2½d. bright ultramarine	32·00	50
		w. Wmk inverted	£225	75·00
43	4	4d. orange-brown and green	18·00	5·50
		a. "FOUR PENCE" trimmed at top (Pl 2 R. 8/4)	£450	
44		6d. violet and red	42·00	22·00
45		1s. bistre and carmine	38·00	16·00
		w. Wmk inverted		
		39/45 Set of 7	£150	42·00
		39s/45s Optd "Specimen" Set of 7	£275	

No. 39 is greyer than No. 8, No. 40 brighter than No. 9 and No. 42 much brighter than No. 11.

8   9

½   ½
Normal   Large "2"
2½d.

This occurs on R. 10/1 in each pane of 60. The diagonal stroke is also longer.

1903 (1 May). Wmk Crown CA. P 14.

46	8	½d. grey-green and green	10·00	9·50
47		1d. dull red/*red*	30·00	60
48		2d. grey-green and carmine	19·00	26·00
49		2½d. dull purple and black/*blue*	5·50	60
		a. Large "2" in "½"	£275	£130
50		6d. dull purple and violet	18·00	21·00
51		1s. black and carmine	28·00	35·00
52	9	2s. green and blue	£150	£200
53		4s. dull purple and green	95·00	£160
54		8s. dull purple and black/*blue*	£130	£160
55		£1 dull purple and black/*red*	£500	£600
		46/55 Set of 10	£900	£1100
		46s/55s Optd "Specimen" Set of 10	£500	

1904–08. Wmk Mult Crown CA. *Ordinary paper (½d. to 2d. and 6d. to 2s.) or chalk-surfaced paper (others). P 14.*

56	8	½d. dull and bright green (4.4.04*)	13·00	2·50
		a. Chalk-surfaced paper (10.05)	12·00	7·00

57		1d. dull purple/*red* (6.9.04*)...........	13·00	50
		a. Bisected (½d.) (on card)...........	†	£1400
		bw. Wmk inverted		
		c. Chalk-surfaced paper (16.9.05) .	5·00	85
58		2d. grey-green and carmine (9.1.05)........................	16·00	6·50
		a. Chalk-surfaced paper (2.07)	8·50	7·00
59		2½d. purple and black/*blue* (4.5.07)..	35·00	90·00
		a. Large "2" in "½"	£600	£900
60		6d. dull purple and violet (19.4.06).	42·00	24·00
		a. Chalk-surfaced paper (4.08)	30·00	13·00
61		1s. black and carmine (13.10.05) ..	55·00	15·00
		a. Chalk-surfaced paper (4.06)	50·00	15·00
62	**9**	2s. green and blue (2.2.05).........	85·00	£110
		a. Chalk-surfaced paper (10.07)	85·00	95·00
63		4s. deep green and green (6.08)....	£250	£325
64		£1 deep purple and black/*red* (15.3.08)......................	£500	£600
56/64 *Set of 9*			£900	£1000

*Earliest known date of use.

1906 (Oct)–**12**. *Colours changed.* Wmk Mult Crown CA. *Chalk-surfaced paper (6d. to 8s.).* P 14.

66	**8**	½d. blue-green (1907)...................	5·00	1·75
		x. Wmk reversed	†	£1200
67		1d. carmine	5·50	60
		a. Wmk sideways	£3500	£3500
		w. Wmk inverted	†	£500
68		2d. greyish slate (5.10)	8·00	11·00
69		2½d. ultramarine (6.07)	5·50	1·60
		a. Large "2" in "½"	£250	£120
70		6d. dull and bright purple (18.3.12)	£140	£375
71		1s. black/*green* (1910)...............	23·00	21·00
72	**9**	2s. purple and bright blue/*blue* (4.10).............................	50·00	48·00
73		4s. black and carmine (4.10)........	£120	£150
		x. Wmk reversed	£1600	£1700
74		8s. purple and green (1911)	£200	£225
66/74 *Set of 9*			£500	£750
67s/74s Optd "Specimen" *Set of 8*			£600	

Examples of Nos. 55, 64 and 73/4 are known showing a forged oval registered postmark dated "6 OC 10".

10	**11**

"HALEPENNY" (Pl 1 R. 7/3.
Occurs on ptgs from 1917)

1912 (17 July)–**24**. Wmk Mult Crown CA. *Ordinary paper (½d. to 2½d.) or chalk-surfaced paper (others).* P 14.

76	**10**	½d. blue-green	3·25	70
		a. Yellow-green (4.17).................	5·00	1·75
		b. "HALEPENNY"	£160	£120
		w. Wmk inverted	†	£950
		x. Wmk reversed	†	£1300
77		1d. carmine-red	3·50	75
		a. Scarlet (6.16)	3·50	1·25
		ay. Wmk inverted and reversed.......		
78		2d. greyish slate	9·50	1·50
79		2½d. deep bright blue	7·50	2·00
		a. Large "2" in "½"	£225	£130
		b. Pale ultramarine (1917)..........	7·00	2·00
		ba. Large "2" in "½"	£275	£130
80		6d. dull purple and mauve	9·00	17·00
81		1s. black/*green*	9·00	3·25
		a. Ordinary paper (8.18)..............	£550	
		b. On blue-green, olive back (1919)	15·00	26·00
		c. On emerald surface (12.23).......	27·00	65·00
		d. On emerald back (3.24)............	19·00	90·00
		ds. Optd "Specimen"	75·00	
82	**11**	2s. dull purple and blue/*blue*	26·00	3·50
83		4s. black and carmine	32·00	55·00
84		8s. dull purple and green	80·00	95·00
85		£1 dull purple and black/*red*......	£140	£225
76/85 *Set of 10*			£275	£350
76s/85s Optd "Specimen" *Set of 10*			£500	

WAR TAX

(12)

1918 (15 Apr). *Optd with* T **12** *by Beanland, Malin & Co, Gibraltar.*

86	**10**	½d. green	1·00	1·75
		a. Opt double	£850	
		b. "HALEPENNY"	£100	£150
		w. Wmk inverted	£475	
		y. Wmk inverted and reversed.......	£450	

Two printings of this overprint exist, the second being in slightly heavier type on a deeper shade of green.

3 PENCE		**THREE PENCE**
(I)		(II)

1921–**27**. Wmk Mult Script CA. *Chalk-surfaced paper (6d. to 8s.).* P 14.

89	**10**	½d. green (25.4.27)	1·50	1·50
90		1d. carmine-red (2.21).................	1·75	1·00

91		1½d. chestnut (1.12.22)	1·75	55
		a. Pale chestnut (7.24)................	1·75	30
		w. Wmk inverted	†	£750
93		2d. grey (17.2.21)	1·25	1·25
94		2½d. bright blue (2.21)	20·00	40·00
		a. Large "2" in "½"	£475	£600
95		3d. bright blue (I) (1.1.22)...........	3·00	4·25
		a. Ultramarine	2·50	1·50
97		6d. dull purple and mauve (1.23)	6·00	3·75
		a. Bright purple and magenta (22.7.26).............................	1·60	3·50
98		1s. black/*emerald* (20.6.24)	10·00	19·00
99	**11**	2s. grey-purple and blue/*blue* (20.6.24).............................	19·00	70·00
		a. Reddish purple and blue/*blue* (1925)	7·00	42·00
100		4s. black and carmine (20.6.24)......	65·00	£110
101		8s. dull purple and green (20.6.24).	£225	£400
89/101 *Set of 11*			£300	£550
89s/101s Optd "Specimen" *Set of 11*			£600	

The ½d. exists in coils, constructed from normal sheets, first issued in 1937.

1925 (15 Oct)–**32**. *New values and colours changed.* Wmk Mult Script CA. *Chalk-surfaced paper.* P 14.

102	**10**	1s. sage-green and black (8.1.29)....	14·00	24·00
		a. Olive and black (1932)	14·00	13·00
103	**11**	2s. red-brown and black (8.1.29) ...	9·50	30·00
104		2s.6d. green and black	9·50	19·00
105		5s. carmine and black	15·00	50·00
106		10s. deep ultramarine and black.....	32·00	70·00
107		£1 red-orange and black (16.11.27)	£150	£200
108		£5 violet and black	£1300	£4500
		s. Optd "Specimen"	£700	
102/7 *Set of 6*			£200	£350
102s/7s Optd or Perf (1s., 2s.) "Specimen" *Set of 6*			£425	

Examples of Nos. 83/5, 99/101 and 102/8 are known showing forged oval registered postmarks dated "24 JA 25" or "6 MY 35".

1930 (11 Apr). T **10** *inscribed "THREE PENCE".* Wmk Mult Script CA. P 14.

109		3d. ultramarine (II)......................	7·50	2·00
		s. Perf "Specimen"	70·00	

13 The Rock of Gibraltar

(Des Capt. H. St. C. Garrood. Recess D.L.R.)

1931–**33**. Wmk Mult Script CA. P 14.

110	**13**	1d. scarlet (1.7.31)	2·50	2·50
		a. Perf 13½×14	16·00	6·00
111		1½d. red-brown (1.7.31).................	1·75	2·25
		a. Perf 13½×14	13·00	4·00
112		2d. pale grey (1.11.32)	6·50	1·75
		a. Perf 13½×14	16·00	3·00
113		3d. blue (1.6.33).........................	5·50	3·00
		a. Perf 13½×14	24·00	38·00
110/13 *Set of 4*			15·00	8·50
110a/13a *Set of 4*			60·00	45·00
110s/13s Perf "Specimen" *Set of 4*			£170	

Figures of value take the place of both corner ornaments at the base of the 2d. and 3d.

1935 (6 May). *Silver Jubilee. As Nos. 91/4 of Antigua but ptd by B.W.* P 11×12.

114		2d. ultramarine and grey-black	1·60	2·50
		a. Extra flagstaff........................	65·00	90·00
		b. Short extra flagstaff................	£130	£150
		c. Lightning conductor................	80·00	£100
		d. Flagstaff on right-hand turret	£190	£200
		e. Double flagstaff......................	£190	£200
115		3d. brown and deep blue	3·25	3·50
		a. Extra flagstaff........................	£325	£350
		b. Short extra flagstaff................	£275	£300
		c. Lightning conductor................	£325	£350
116		6d. green and indigo	9·50	12·00
		a. Extra flagstaff........................	£250	£300
		b. Short extra flagstaff................	£425	£425
		c. Lightning conductor................	£250	£300
117		1s. slate and purple.....................	11·00	13·00
		a. Extra flagstaff........................	£225	£250
		b. Short extra flagstaff................	£400	£400
		c. Lightning conductor................	£250	£275
114/17 *Set of 4*			23·00	28·00
114s/17s Perf "Specimen" *Set of 4*			£200	

For illustrations of plate varieties see Omnibus section following Zanzibar.

1937 (12 May). *Coronation. As Nos. 95/7 of Antigua.* P 11×11½.

118		½d. green	25	50
119		2d. grey-black	1·50	3·25
120		3d. blue	2·75	6·25
118/20 *Set of 3*			4·00	6·25
118s/20s Perf "Specimen" *Set of 3*			£130	

14 King George VI	**15** Rock of Gibraltar

16 The Rock (North Side)   Ape on rock (R. 1/5)

Bird on memorial (R. 9/3)

Broken second "R" in "GIBRALTAR" (Frame Pl 2 R. 9/4)

(Des Captain H. St. C. Garrood. Recess D.L.R.)

1938 (25 Feb)–**51**. *Designs as T* **14/16**. Mult Script CA.

121		½d. deep green (P 13½×14)	10	40
122		1d. yellow-brown (P 14)...............	26·00	2·25
		a. Perf 13½ (1940)......................	27·00	2·25
		ab. Perf 13½. Wmk sideways (1940)........	6·50	7·00
		b. Perf 13. Wmk sideways. *Red-brown* (1942)...............................	50	60
		c. Perf 13. Wmk sideways. *Deep brown* (1944)	1·75	3·50
		d. Perf 13. *Red-brown* (1949)	3·00	1·50
123		1½d. carmine (P 14)	35·00	95
		a. Perf 13½	£250	30·00
123*b*		1½d. slate-violet (P 13) (1.1.43)	50	1·50
124		2d. grey (P 14)	28·00	40
		aa. Ape on rock	£300	48·00
		a. Perf 13½ (1940)......................	3·00	35
		ab. Perf 13½. Wmk sideways (1940)........	£650	42·00
		b. Perf 13. Wmk sideways (1943)........	1·00	1·25
		ba. "A" of "CA" missing from wmk ...	£1200	
124*c*		2d. carm (P 13) (*wmk sideways*) (15.7.44)	50	60
125		3d. light blue (P 13½)	24·00	1·00
		a. Perf 14	£130	5·00
		b. Perf 13 (1942)........................	50	30
		ba. Greenish blue (2.51)	3·50	2·00
125*c*		5d. red-orange (P 13) (1.10.47).......	1·25	1·25
126		6d. carm & grey-violet (P 13½) (16.3.38).	48·00	3·00
		a. Perf 14	£120	1·25
		b. Perf 13 (1942)........................	5·00	1·75
		c. Perf 13. *Scarlet and grey-violet* (1945)	6·00	3·75
127		1s. black and green (P 14) (16.3.38)..	42·00	23·00
		a. Perf 13½	70·00	6·00
		b. Perf 13 (1942)........................	3·25	4·25
		ba. Broken "R"	£275	
128		2s. black and brown (P 14) (16.3.38).	65·00	22·00
		a. Perf 13½	£120	32·00
		b. Perf 13 (1942)........................	5·00	6·50
		ba. Broken "R"	£325	
		bb. Bird on memorial	£250	
129		5s. black and carmine (P 14) (16.3.38).	95·00	£160
		a. Perf 13½	40·00	14·00
		b. Perf 13 (1944)........................	19·00	17·00
		ba. Broken "R"	£450	
130		10s. black and blue (P 14) (16.3.38).	65·00	£120
		a. Perf 13 (1943)........................	38·00	25·00
		ab. Broken "R"	£600	
131		£1 orange (P 13½×14) (16.3.38).....	38·00	45·00
121/31 *Set of 14*			£130	85·00
121s/31s Perf "Specimen" *Set of 14*			£700	

Designs:—½d., £1, Type **14**. *Horiz as T* **15/16**—1d., 1½d. (*both*), Type **15**; 2d. (*both*), Type **16**; 3d., 5d. Europa Point; 6d. Moorish Castle; 1s. Southport Gate; 2s. Eliott Memorial; 5s. Government House; 10s. Catalan Bay.

The ½d., 1d. and both colours of the 2d. exist in coils constructed from normal sheets. These were originally joined vertically, but, because of technical problems, the 1d. and 2d. grey were subsequently issued in horizontal coils. The 2d. carmine only exists in the horizontal version.

Examples of Nos. 129/31 are known showing forged oval registered postmarks dated "6 OC 43", "18 OC 43", "3 MR 44" and "4 AU 44".

1946 (12 Oct). *Victory. As Nos. 110/11 of Antigua.*

132		½d. green	10	1·25
133		3d. ultramarine	50	1·25
132s/3s Perf "Specimen" *Set of 2*			95·00	

1948 (1 Dec). *Royal Silver Wedding. As Nos. 112/13 of Antigua.*

134		½d. green	1·25	2·00
135		£1 brown-orange	55·00	70·00

1949 (10 Oct). *75th Anniv of Universal Postal Union. As Nos. 114/17 of Antigua.*

136		2d. carmine	1·00	1·25
137		3d. deep blue	2·00	1·50
138		6d. purple	1·25	2·00
139		1s. blue-green	1·00	3·25
136/9 *Set of 4*			4·75	7·25

NEW CONSTITUTION 1950
(23)

1950 (1 Aug). *Inauguration of Legislative Council. Nos.* 124c, 125ba, 126b *and* 127b *optd as T* **23**.

140	**16**	2d. carmine	30	1·50
141	–	3d. greenish blue	65	1·00
142	–	6d. carmine and grey-violet	75	2·00
		a. Opt double	£900	£1000
143	–	1s. black and green (R.)	75	2·00
		a. Broken "R"	75·00	
140/3	*Set of 4*		2·25	6·00

On stamps from the lower part of the sheet of No. 142a the two impressions are almost coincident.

STAMP BOOKLETS

1906 (Oct). *Black on red cover. Stapled.*
SB1 2s.½d. booklet containing twenty-four ½d. and twelve 1d. (Nos. 56a, 67) in blocks of 6 ....

1912 (17 July). *Black on red cover with Edwardian cypher. Stapled.*
SB2 2s.½d. booklet containing twenty-four ½d. and twelve 1d. (Nos. 76/7) in blocks of 6 ....

SB2 2s.½d. booklet containing twenty-four ½d. and twelve 1d. (Nos. 76/7) in blocks of 6 ....

Gilbert and Ellice Islands

No organised postal service existed in the Gilbert and Ellice Islands before the introduction of stamp issues in January 1911. A New Zealand Postal Agency was, however, provided on Fanning Island, one of the Line Islands, primarily for the use of the staff of the Pacific Cable Board cable station which was established in 1902. The agency opened on 29 November 1902 and continued to operate until replaced by a Protectorate post office on 14 February 1939. The cable station closed on 16 January 1964. Fanning Island is now known as Tabuaeran.

Z 1

The following NEW ZEALAND *stamps are known postmarked on Fanning Island with Type Z* **1** *(in use from November 1902 until November 1936. The earliest known cover is postmarked 20 December 1902.*

1882–1900 Q.V. (P 11) ½d., 1d., 2d. (Nos. 236/8)
1898 Pictorials (*no wmk*) 1d., 2d. (Nos. 247/8)
1900 Pictorials (*W* **38**) ½d. 1½d., 2d. (Nos. 273, 275b, 276)
1901 1d. "Universal" (*W* **38**) (No. 278)
1902 1d. "Universal" (*no wmk*) (No. 295)
1902 ½d. Pictorial (*W* **43**) (No. 302b)
1902–09 Pictorials (*W* **43**) 2d., 2½d., 3d., 6d., 8d., 9d., 1s., 2s., 5s. (Nos. 309, 312/13, 315, 319/20, 326, 328/9)
1907–08 Pictorials (*W* **43**) 4d. (No. 379)
1908 1d. "Universal" (*De La Rue paper*) 1d. (No. 386)
1909–12 King Edward VII (*typo*) ½d. (No. 387)
1909–16 King Edward VII (*recess*) 2d., 3d., 4d., 5d., 6d., 8d., 1s. (Nos. 388/91, 393/6, 398)
1909–26 1d. "Universal" (*W* **43**) 1d. (Nos. 405, 410)
1915–30 King George V (*recess*) 1½d., 2d. bright violet, 2½d., 3d., 4d. bright violet, 4½d., 6d., 7½d., 9d., 1s. (Nos. 416/17, 419/20, 422/3, 425/6, 429/30)
1915–34 King George V (*typo*) ½d., 1½d. (all 3), 2d., 3d. (Nos. 435/40, 446, 448, 449)
1915 "WAR STAMP" opt ½d. (No. 452)
1920 Victory 1d., 1½d. (Nos. 454/5)
1922 2d. on ½d. (No. 459)
1923–25 Penny Postage 1d. (No. 460)
1926–34 Admiral design 1d. (No. 468)
1935–36 Pictorials ½d., 2d., 4d., 8d., 1s. (Nos. 556, 559, 562, 565, 567)
1935 Silver Jubilee ½d., 1d., 6d. (Nos. 573/5)
1936 Anzac 1d. + 1d. (No. 592)

Z 2

The following NEW ZEALAND *stamps are known postmarked on Fanning Island with Type Z* **2** *(in use from 7 December 1936 to 13 February 1939):*

1935–36 Pictorials (*W* 43) 1d. (No. 557)
1936–39 Pictorials (*W* 98) ½d., 1d., 1½d. (Nos. 577/9)
1936 Chambers of Commerce Congress ½d. (No. 593)
1936 Health 1d.+1d. (No. 598)
1937 Coronation 1d., 2½d., 6d. (Nos. 599/601)
1938–39 King George VI ½d., 1d., 1½d. (Nos. 603, 605, 607)

The schooner which carried the mail from Fanning Island also called at Washington Island, another of the Line group. Problems arose, however, as the authorities insisted that mail from Washington must first pass through the Fanning Island Postal Agency before being forwarded which resulted in considerable delays. Matters were resolved by the opening of a New Zealand Postal Agency on Washington Island which operated from 1 February 1921 until the copra plantations were closed in early 1923. The postal agency was re-established on 15 May 1924, but finally closed on 30 March 1934. Covers from this second period occur with incorrectly dated postmarks. Manuscript markings on New Zealand Nos. 578, 599/600 and 692 are unofficial and were applied during the resettlement of the island between 1937 and 1948. Washington Island is now known as Teraina.

Z 3

The following NEW ZEALAND stamps are known postmarked on Washington Island with Type Z 3:

1909–16 King Edward VII 5d., 8d. (Nos. 402, 404b)
1915–30 King George V (*recess*) 6d., 7½d., 8d., 9d., 1s. (Nos. 425/7, 429/30)
1915–34 King George V (*typo*) ½d., 1½d., 2d., 3d. (Nos. 435, 438/9, 449)
1915 "WAR STAMP" opt ½d. (No. 452)
1920 Victory 1d., 1½d., 6d. (Nos. 454/5, 457)
1922 2d. on ½d. (No. 459)
1926–34 Admiral design 1d. (No. 468/a)

The above information is based on a special survey undertaken by members of the Kiribati & Tuvalu Philatelic Society and the Pacific Islands Study Circle, co-ordinated by Mr. Michael Shaw.

PRICES FOR STAMPS ON COVER TO 1945

Nos. 1/7	from × 5
Nos. 8/11	from × 10
Nos. 12/23	from × 6
No. 24	
No. 26	from × 15
Nos. 27/30	from × 6
No. 35	
Nos. 36/9	from × 4
Nos. 40/2	from × 12
Nos. 43/54	from × 4
Nos. D1/8	from × 5

BRITISH PROTECTORATE

GILBERT & ELLICE

PROTECTORATE

(1)

2 Pandanus Pine

1911 (1 Jan). *Stamps of Fiji optd with T* **1**. *Wmk Mult Crown CA. Chalk-surfaced paper (5d. to 1s.).*

1	**23**	½d. green	4·75	45·00
2		1d. red	45·00	28·00
3	**24**	2d. grey	9·00	15·00
4	**23**	2½d. ultramarine	12·00	32·00
5		5d. purple and olive-green	48·00	80·00
6	**24**	6d. dull and bright purple	20·00	45·00
7	**23**	1s. black/*green* (R.)	20·00	60·00
1/7	*Set of 7*		£140	£275
1s/7s	*Optd "Specimen" Set of 7*		£275	

The 2d. to 6d. are on special printings which were not issued without overprint.

Examples of Nos. 1/7 are known showing a forged Ocean Island postmark dated "JY 15 11".

(Recess D.L.R.)

1911 (Mar). *Wmk Mult Crown CA. P* 14.

8	**2**	½d. green	4·75	15·00
9		1d. carmine	2·00	7·00
		w. Wmk inverted	£375	
10		2d. grey	1·50	7·00
11		2½d. blue	5·00	11·00
8/11	*Set of 4*		11·50	35·00
8s/11s	*Optd "Specimen" Set of 4*		£140	

WAR TAX

3   (5)

(Typo D.L.R.)

1912 (May)–**24**. *Die I (½d. to 5s.) or Die II (£1). Wmk Mult Crown CA. Chalk-surfaced paper (3d. to £1). P* 14.

12	**3**	½d. green (7.12)	50	4·50
13		a. Yellow-green (1914)	4·50	11·00
		1d. carmine (12.12)	2·25	6·00
		a. Scarlet (1915)	3·75	11·00
14		2d. greyish slate (1.16)	15·00	26·00
15		2½d. bright blue (1.16)	1·75	11·00
16		3d. purple/*yellow* (1918)	2·50	8·50
17		4d. black and red/*yellow* (10.12)	75	7·00
18		5d. dull purple and sage-green	1·75	7·00
19		6d. dull and bright purple	1·25	7·50
20		1s. black/*green*	1·25	5·50
21		2s. purple and blue/*blue* (10.12)	14·00	30·00
22		2s.6d. black and red/*blue* (10.12)	16·00	25·00
23		5s. green and red/*yellow* (10.12)	32·00	60·00
24		£1 purple and black/*red* (Die II) (3.24)	£550	£1400
12/24	*Set of 13*		£600	£1400
12s/24s	*Optd "Specimen" Set of 13*		£600	

CROWN COLONY

1918 (June). *Optd with T* **5**.

26	**3**	1d. red	50	6·50
		s. Optd "Specimen"	65·00	

1922–27. *Die II. Wmk Mult Script CA. Chalk-surfaced paper (10s.). P* 14.

27	**3**	½d. green (1923)	3·25	3·25
28		1d. violet (1927)	4·50	5·00
29		1½d. scarlet (1924)	4·50	2·00
30		2d. slate-grey	7·00	27·00
35		10s. green and red/*emerald* (3.24)	£150	£350
27s/35s	*Optd "Specimen" Set of 5*		£275	

Examples of most values between Nos. 12 and 35 are known showing part strikes of the forged postmark mentioned below Nos. 1/7. Collectors should exercise particular caution when buying used examples of Nos. 24 and 35.

1935 (6 May). *Silver Jubilee. As Nos.* 91/4 *of Antigua, but ptd by B.W. P* 11×12.

36		1d. ultramarine and grey-black	2·25	9·00
		d. Flagstaff on right-hand turret	£200	
		e. Double flagstaff	£300	
37		1½d. deep blue and scarlet	1·75	3·75
		d. Flagstaff on right-hand turret	£200	
		e. Double flagstaff	£300	
38		3d. brown and deep blue	5·50	12·00
		d. Flagstaff on right-hand turret	£325	
		e. Double flagstaff	£375	
39		1s. slate and purple	20·00	20·00
		d. Flagstaff on right-hand turret	£450	
		e. Double flagstaff	£500	£550
36/9	*Set of 4*		26·00	40·00
36s/9s	*Perf "Specimen" Set of 4*		£140	

For illustrations of plate varieties see Omnibus section following Zanzibar.

1937 (12 May). *Coronation. As Nos.* 95/7 *of Antigua, but ptd by D.L.R. P* 14.

40		1d. violet	35	65
41		1½d. scarlet	35	65
42		3d. bright blue	40	70
40/2	*Set of 3*		1·00	1·75
40s/2s	*Perf "Specimen" Set of 3*		£100	

6 Great Frigate Bird   **7** Pandanus Pine

8 Canoe crossing Reef

(Recess B.W. (½d., 2d., 2s.6d.), Waterlow (1d., 5d., 6d., 2s., 5s.), D.L.R. (1½d., 2½d., 3d., 1s.).)

1939 (14 Jan)–**55**. *T* **6/8** *and similar horiz designs. Wmk Mult Script CA (sideways on ½d., 2d. and 2s.6d.). P* 11½×11 (½d., 2d., 2s.6d.), 12½ (1d., 5d., 6d., 2s., 5s.) *or* 13½ (1½d., 2½d., 3d., 1s.).

43		½d. indigo and deep bluish green	60	1·00
		a. "A" of "CA" missing from wmk		
44		1d. emerald and plum	30	1·50
45		1½d. brownish black and bright carmine	30	1·25
46		2d. red-brown and grey-black	75	1·00
47		2½d. brownish black and deep olive	40	70
		a. Brownish black and olive-green (12.5.43)	4·25	4·50
48		3d. brownish black and ultramarine	45	1·00
		a. Perf 12. Black and bright blue (24.8.55)	50	2·25
49		5d. deep ultramarine and sepia	4·25	1·50
		a. Ultramarine and sepia (12.5.43)	5·00	7·00
		b. Ultramarine and blackish brown (20.10.44)	4·25	5·00
50		6d. olive-green and deep violet	50	60
51		1s. brownish black and turquoise-green	15·00	2·25
		a. Brownish black and turquoise-blue (12.5.43)	7·00	3·25
		ab. Perf 12 (8.5.51)	2·75	16·00
52		2s. deep ultramarine and orange-red	10·00	10·00
53		2s.6d. deep blue and emerald	10·00	11·00
54		5s. deep rose-red and royal blue	13·00	14·00
43/54	*Set of 12*		38·00	40·00
43s/54s	*Perf "Specimen" Set of 12*		£325	

Designs: *As T* **6**—2d. Canoe and boat-house; 2s.6d. Gilbert Islands canoe. *As T* **7**—5d. Ellice Islands canoe; 2s. H.M.C.S. *Nimanoa*; 5s. Coat of arms. *As T* **8**—2½d. Native house; 3d. Seascape; 1s. Cantilever jetty, Ocean Island.

1946 (16 Dec). *Victory. As Nos.* 110/11 *of Antigua.*
55	1d. violet	15	50
56	3d. blue	15	50
55s/6s Perf "Specimen" *Set of* 2		80·00	

1949 (29 Aug). *Royal Silver Wedding. As Nos.* 112/13 *of Antigua.*
57	1d. violet	50	60
58	£1 scarlet	13·00	21·00

1949 (10 Oct). *75th Anniv of U.P.U. As Nos.* 114/17 *of Antigua.*
59	1d. purple	40	1·25
60	2d. grey-black	2·00	2·75
61	3d. deep blue	50	2·50
62	1s. blue	50	2·00
59/62 *Set of* 4		3·00	7·75

POSTAGE DUE STAMPS

D **1**

(Typo B.W.)

1940 (Aug). Wmk Mult Script CA. P 12.
D1	D **1**	1d. emerald-green	9·00	24·00
D2		2d. scarlet	9·50	24·00
D3		3d. brown	14·00	25·00
D4		4d. blue	16·00	32·00
D5		5d. grey-green	21·00	32·00
D6		6d. purple	21·00	32·00
D7		1s. violet	23·00	45·00
D8		1s.6d. turquoise-green	45·00	85·00
D1/8 *Set of* 8			£140	£275
D1s/8s Perf "Specimen" *Set of* 8			£180	

Examples of all values are known showing a forged Post Office Ocean Island postmark dated "16 DE 46".

Gold Coast

Gold Coast originally consisted of coastal forts, owned by the Royal African Company, trading with the interior. In 1821, due to raids by the Ashanti king, the British Government took over the forts, together with some of the hinterland, and the Gold Coast was placed under the Governor of Sierra Leone.

The administration was handed back to a merchantile company in 1828, but the forts returned to British Government rule in 1843. The colony was reconstituted by Royal Charter on 24 July 1874, and at that time also included the settlement at Lagos which became a separate colony in January 1886.

Following the end of the final Ashanti War the whole of the territory was annexed in September 1901.

A postal service was established at Cape Coast Castle in 1853. There is no record of British stamps being officially issued in the Colony before 1875, apart from those used on board the ships of the West African Squadron, but examples do, however, exist cancelled by Gold Coast postmarks.

CROWN COLONY

PRICES FOR STAMPS ON COVER TO 1945	
Nos. 1/3	*from* × 100
Nos. 4/8	*from* × 30
Nos. 9/10	*from* × 10
Nos. 11/20	*from* × 25
Nos. 22/5	
Nos. 26/34	*from* × 10
Nos. 35/6	*from* × 20
Nos. 38/69	*from* × 6
Nos. 70/98	*from* × 3
Nos. 100/2	—
Nos. 103/12	*from* × 5
Nos. 113/16	*from* × 6
Nos. 117/19	*from* × 4
Nos. 120/32	*from* × 3
No. D1	*from* × 6
No. D2	*from* × 20
Nos. D3/4	*from* × 12

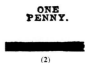
ONE
PENNY.

1 (2)

(Typo D.L.R.)

1875 (1 July). Wmk Crown CC. P 12½.
1	**1**	1d. blue	£475	80·00
2		4d. magenta	£450	£120
3		6d. orange	£700	65·00

1876–84. Wmk Crown CC. P 14.
4	**1**	½d. olive-yellow (1879)	75·00	26·00
		w. Wmk inverted	£190	
5		1d. blue	24·00	6·50

---

	a. Bisected (½d.) (on cover) (1884)	†	£3250
	w. Wmk inverted	£325	£140
6	2d. green (1879)	90·00	9·00
	a. Bisected (1d.) (on cover) (1884)	†	£2750
	b. Quartered (½d.) (on cover) (1884)	†	£5000
7	4d. magenta	£200	6·00
	a. Bisected (2d.) (on cover) (1884)	†	£6000
	b. Quartered (1d.) (on cover) (1884)	†	£8000
	w. Wmk inverted	£550	
8	6d. orange	£160	18·00
	a. Bisected (3d.) (1884)	†	£7500
	b. Sixth (1d.) (on cover) (1884)	†	£9000

During 1884 some values were in short supply and the use of bisects and other divided stamps is known as follows:

No. 5a. Used as part of 2½d. rate from Accra and Quittah.
No. 6a. Used as 1d. rate from Addah, Cape Coast Castle, Quittah, Salt Pond, Secondee and Winnebah.
No. 6b. Used as part of 2½d. rate from Cape Coast Castle.
No. 7a. Used as 2d. or as part of 2½d. rate from Quittah.
No. 7b. Used as 1d. rate from Appam, Axim, Cape Coast Castle and Winnebah.
No. 8a. Used as 3d. rate from Secondee.
No. 8b. Used as 1d. rate from Cape Coast Castle and Winnebah.

Examples of bisects used on piece are worth about 15% of the price quoted for those on cover.

The 4d., No. 7, is known surcharged "1 d". This was previously listed as No. 8c, but there are now serious doubts as to its authenticity. The three examples reported of this stamp all show *different* surcharges!

1883. Wmk Crown CA. P 14.
9	**1**	½d. olive-yellow (January)	£180	65·00
10		1d. blue (May)	£850	70·00

PENNY

Short "P" and distorted "E" (Pl 1 R. 5/6)
("P" repaired for Pl 2)

1884 (Aug)–**91.** Wmk Crown CA. P 14.
11	**1**	½d. green	3·50	1·25
		a. Dull green	3·50	1·00
		w. Wmk inverted	£150	£150
		x. Wmk reversed		
12		1d. rose-carmine	4·00	50
		a. Carmine	4·00	50
		b. Bisected (½d.) (on cover)	†	£3750
		c. Short "P" and distorted "E"	£140	
		w. Wmk inverted	†	£180
13		2d. grey	15·00	3·75
		aw. Wmk inverted	£200	£200
		b. Slate	5·00	50
		c. Bisected (1d.) (on cover)	†	£4250
		d. Quartered (½d.) (on cover)	†	—
14		2½d. ultramarine and orange (13.3.91)	5·00	70
		w. Wmk inverted		£190
15		3d. olive-yellow (9.89)	12·00	4·75
		a. Olive	12·00	4·75
16		4d. deep mauve (3.85)	12·00	2·00
		a. Rosy mauve	14·00	3·25
17		6d. orange (1.89)	12·00	5·00
		a. Orange-brown	12·00	5·00
		b. Bisected (3d.) (on cover)	†	£8000
18		1s. violet (1888)	32·00	12·00
		a. Bright mauve	7·00	1·25
19		2s. yellow-brown (1888)	80·00	35·00
		a. Deep brown	48·00	15·00
11/19a *Set of* 9			95·00	27·00
14s/15s, 18s/19s Optd "Specimen" *Set of* 4			£150	

During 1884 to 1886 and in 1889 some values were in short supply and the use of bisects and other divided stamps is known as follows:

No. 12b. Used as part of 2½d. rate from Cape Coast Castle.
No. 13c. Used as 1d. or as part of 2d. rate from Cape Coast Castle, Chamah, Dixcove and Elmina.
No. 13d. Used as part of 2½d. rate from Cape Coast Castle.
No. 17b. Used as 3d. from Appam.

1889 (Mar). *No.* 17 *surch with T* **2**.
20	**1**	1d. on 6d. orange	£120	48·00
		a. Surch double	†	£3500

In some sheets examples may be found with the bar and "PENNY" spaced 8 mm, the normal spacing being 7 mm.

USED HIGH VALUES. Until the introduction of airmail in 1929 there was no postal use for values over 10s. Post Offices did, however, apply postal cancellations to high value stamps required for telegram fees.

3 **4**

1889 (Sept)–**94.** Wmk Crown CA. P 14.
22	**3**	5s. dull mauve and blue	65·00	16·00
23		10s. dull mauve and red	80·00	15·00
		a. Dull mauve and carmine	£700	£250
24		20s. green and red	£3250	
25		20s. dull mauve and black/*red* (4.94)	£160	35·00
		w. Wmk inverted	£300	95·00
22a/5s Optd "Specimen" *Set of* 4			£400	

No. 24 was withdrawn from sale in April 1893 when a large part of the stock was stolen. No 20s. stamps were available until the arrival of the replacement printing a year later.

1898 (May)–**1902.** Wmk Crown CA. P 14.
26	**3**	½d. dull mauve and green	3·00	1·00
27		1d. dull mauve and rose	3·25	50
		w. Wmk inverted	—	£120
27b	**4**	2d. dull mauve and orange-red (1902)	50·00	£150
28	**3**	2½d. dull mauve and ultramarine	6·00	5·50
29	**4**	3d. dull mauve and orange	5·50	1·75
30		6d. dull mauve and violet	6·00	1·75
31	**3**	1s. green and black (1899)	10·00	18·00
32		2s. green and carmine	15·00	22·00
33		5s. green and mauve (1900)	55·00	50·00
34		10s. green and brown (1900)	£150	50·00
26/34 *Set of* 10			£275	£250
26s/34s Optd "Specimen" *Set of* 10			£180	

1901 (6 Oct). *Nos.* 28 *and* 30 *surch with T* **2**.
35		1d. on 2½d. dull mauve and ultramarine	4·00	4·25
		a. "ONE" omitted	£1000	
36		1d. on 6d. dull mauve and violet	4·00	3·50
		a. "ONE" omitted	£275	£550

6 **7** **8**

1902. Wmk Crown CA. P 14.
38	**6**	½d. dull purple and green (Aug)	1·50	40
39		1d. dull purple and carmine (May)	1·50	15
		w. Wmk inverted	£120	90·00
40	**7**	2d. dull purple and orange-red (Apr)	22·00	7·00
		w. Wmk inverted		
41	**6**	2½d. dull purple and ultramarine (Aug)	4·50	9·00
42	**7**	3d. dull purple and orange (Aug)	3·00	1·50
43		6d. dull purple and violet (Aug)	3·75	5·50
		w. Wmk inverted	—	£110
44	**6**	1s. green and black (Aug)	14·00	3·00
45		2s. green and carmine (Aug)	15·00	20·00
46		5s. green and mauve (Aug)	45·00	90·00
47		10s. green and brown (Aug)	60·00	£130
48		20s. purple and black/*red* (Aug)	£140	£180
38/48 *Set of* 11			£275	£400
38s/48s Optd "Specimen" *Set of* 11			£200	

Examples of Nos. 45/8 are known showing a forged Accra postmark dated "25 MAR 1902".

1904–06. Wmk Mult Crown CA. *Ordinary paper (½d. to 6d.) or chalk-surfaced paper (2s.6d.).*
49	**6**	½d. dull purple and green (3.06)	2·50	7·00
50		1d. dull purple and carmine (10.04)	9·50	30
		a. Chalk-surfaced paper (5.06)	10·00	2·00
		w. Wmk inverted		
51	**7**	2d. dull purple and orange-red (11.04)	5·50	50
		a. Chalk-surfaced paper (8.06)	27·00	2·25
52	**6**	2½d. dull purple and ultramarine (6.06)	48·00	48·00
53	**7**	3d. dull purple and orange (8.05)	60·00	6·00
		a. Chalk-surfaced paper (4.06)	16·00	60
54		6d. dull purple and violet (9.06)	70·00	3·00
		a. Chalk-surfaced paper (9.06)	40·00	1·75
57		2s.6d. green and yellow (3.06)	28·00	£110
		s. Optd Specimen"	45·00	
49/57 *Set of* 7			£130	£150

1907–13. Wmk Mult Crown CA. *Ordinary paper (½d. to 2½d. and 2s.) or chalk-surfaced paper (3d. to 1s., 2s.6d., 5s.).* P 14.
59	**6**	½d. dull green (5.07)	5·00	30
		a. Blue-green (1909)	9·50	2·00
60		1d. red (2.07)	9·00	40
61	**7**	2d. greyish slate (4.09)	2·25	40
62	**6**	2½d. blue (4.07)	9·50	2·00
		w. Wmk inverted	†	£275
63	**7**	3d. purple/*yellow* (16.4.09)	8·00	55
64		6d. dull and deep purple (12.08)	17·00	55
		a. Dull and bright purple (1911)	3·75	3·50
65	**6**	1s. black/*green* (10.09)	14·00	50
66		2s. purple and blue/*blue* (1910)	8·00	8·00
		a. Chalk-surfaced paper (1912)	18·00	16·00
67	**7**	2s.6d. black and red/*blue* (1911)	29·00	90·00
68		5s. green and red/*yellow* (1913)	55·00	£190
59/68 *Set of* 10			£130	£275
59s/68s Optd "Specimen" *Set of* 10			£250	

A 10s. green and red on green, and a 20s. purple and black on red, both Type **6**, were prepared for use but not issued. Both exist overprinted "SPECIMEN" (*Price for* 10s. *in this condition,* £275). An example of the 10s. exists without "SPECIMEN" overprint.

(Typo D.L.R.)

1908 (Nov). Wmk Mult Crown CA. P 14.
69	**8**	1d. red	4·00	10
		a. Wmk sideways	†	£1800
		s. Optd "Specimen"	45·00	

9 **10** **11**

(Typo D.L.R.)

1913–21. *Die I.* Wmk Mult Crown CA. *Chalk-surfaced paper (3d. to 20s.).* P 14.

70	9	½d. green	2·50	1·00
		a. Yellow-green (1916)	2·75	1·25
72	10	1d. red	1·25	10
		a. Scarlet (1917)	1·50	50
74	11	2d. grey	4·25	2·50
		a. Slate-grey (1920)	9·00	9·00
		w. Wmk inverted	†	£200
76	9	2½d. bright blue	7·00	1·00
		a. "A" of "CA" missing from wmk	£450	
		x. Wmk reversed	†	£200
77	11	3d. purple/yellow (8.15)	2·25	80
		as. Optd "Specimen"	35·00	
		aw. Wmk inverted	—	£110
		b. White back (9.13)	1·50	40
		c. On orange-buff (1919)	7·50	7·50
		cw. Wmk inverted		
		d. On buff (1920)		
		e. Die II. On pale yellow (1921)	45·00	5·00
		ew. Wmk inverted	†	£275
78		6d. dull and bright purple	3·75	2·25
79	9	1s. black/green	3·25	1·25
		a. Wmk sideways	†	£1100
		bw. Wmk inverted		
		c. On blue-green, olive back (1916)	7·50	75
		cs. Optd "Specimen"	48·00	
		cw. Wmk inverted	—	£160
		d. On emerald back (1920)	2·00	2·00
		ds. Optd "Specimen"	42·00	
		e. Die II. On emerald back (1921)	1·50	50
		es. Optd "Specimen"	48·00	
		ew. Wmk inverted		
80		2s. purple and blue/blue	8·50	3·00
		aw. Wmk inverted		£225
		b. Die II (1921)	£150	65·00
81	11	2s.6d. black and red/blue	6·00	13·00
		a. Die II (1921)	23·00	42·00
82	9	5s. green and red/yellow (1916)	16·00	55·00
		as. Optd "Specimen"	50·00	
		b. White back (10.13)	12·00	55·00
		c. On orange-buff (1919)	75·00	80·00
		d. On buff (1920)		
		e. On pale yellow (1921)	£100	£130
		f. Die II. On pale yellow (1921)	30·00	£130
		fw. Wmk inverted	£225	
83		10s. green and red/green	48·00	85·00
		a. On blue-green, olive back (1916)	19·00	65·00
		aw. Wmk inverted	£750	
		b. On emerald back (1921)	32·00	£140
84		20s. purple and black/red	£130	85·00
70/84		Set of 12	£180	£200
70s/6s, 77bs, 78s/81s, 82bs/4s Optd "Specimen" Set of 12				£275

The 10s. and 20s. were withdrawn locally from September 1920 and, in common with other Gold Coast stamps, were not available to stamp dealers from the Crown Agents in London.

WAR TAX

ONE PENNY

(12)

13 King George V and Christiansborg Castle

1918 (17 June). Surch with T **12**.

85	10	1d. on 1d. red	2·25	60
		s. Optd "Specimen"	50·00	

1921–24. *Die I (15s., £2) or Die II (others).* Wmk Mult Script CA. *Chalk-surfaced paper (6d. to £2).* P 14.

86	9	½d. green	80	50
87	10	1d. chocolate-brown (1922)	70	10
88	11	1½d. red (1922)	1·75	10
89		2d. grey	1·75	30
90	9	2½d. yellow-orange (1922)	1·00	9·00
91	11	3d. bright blue (1922)	1·75	60
94		6d. dull and bright purple	2·25	3·00
95	9	1s. black/emerald (1924)	3·25	3·25
96		2s. purple and blue/blue (1923)	3·25	3·25
97	11	2s.6d. black and red/blue (1924)	7·00	27·00
98	9	5s. green and red/pale yellow (1924)	13·00	60·00
100	11	15s. dull purple and green (Die I)	£140	£375
		a. Die II (1924)	£120	£375
		as. Optd "Specimen"	£100	
102		£2 green and orange (Die I)	£400	£1000
86/100a		Set of 12	£140	£450
86s/102s Optd "Specimen" Set of 13				£425

The Duty plate for the 1½d., 15s. and £2 has the words "GOLD COAST" in distinctly larger letters.

Examples of Nos. 100/a and 102 are known showing parts of forged Accra postmarks. These are dated "3 MAY 44" and "8 MAY 44", but are invariably positioned so that the year date is not shown.

(Des W. Palmer. Photo Harrison)

1928 (1 Aug). Wmk Mult Script CA. P 13½×15.

103	13	½d. blue-green	85	40
104		1d. red-brown	85	10
105		1½d. scarlet	1·50	1·50
106		2d. slate	1·50	20
107		2½d. orange-yellow	1·75	3·50
108		3d. bright blue	1·50	40
109		6d. black and purple	1·50	40
110		1s. black and red-orange	3·25	75
111		2s. black and bright violet	24·00	4·75
112		5s. carmine and sage-green	60·00	45·00
103/12		Set of 10	85·00	50·00
103s/12s Optd "Specimen" Set of 10				£200

1935 (6 May). Silver Jubilee. As Nos. 91/4 of Antigua, but printed by B.W. P 11×12.

113		1d. ultramarine and grey-black	60	50

		a. Extra flagstaff	£130	£100
		b. Short extra flagstaff	£170	
		c. Lightning conductor	£130	
		d. Flagstaff on right-hand turret	£225	
114		3d. brown and deep blue	3·00	6·00
		a. Extra flagstaff	£130	£150
		c. Lightning conductor	£170	
115		6d. green and indigo	9·00	15·00
		a. Extra flagstaff	£160	£190
		b. Short extra flagstaff	£325	
		c. Lightning conductor	£200	
		d. Flagstaff on right-hand turret	£400	
116		1s. slate and purple	5·00	23·00
		a. Extra flagstaff	£180	£275
		b. Short extra flagstaff	£275	
		c. Lightning conductor	£225	
113/16		Set of 4	16·00	40·00
113s/16s Perf "Specimen" Set of 4				£110

For illustrations of plate varieties see Omnibus section following Zanzibar.

1937 (12 May). Coronation. As Nos. 95/7 of Antigua. P 11×11½.

117		1d. buff	1·75	2·50
118		2d. slate	1·75	4·50
119		3d. blue	2·00	2·75
117/19		Set of 3	5·00	8·75
117s/19s Perf "Specimen" Set of 3				75·00

14

15 King George VI and Christiansborg Castle, Accra

(Recess B.W.)

1938 (1 Apr)–**44.** Wmk Mult Script CA. P 11½×12 (comb) (1s.3d., 10s.) or 12 (line) (others).

120	14	½d. green	4·75	1·75
		a. Perf 12×11½ (1940)	40	50
121		1d. red-brown	6·50	30
		a. Perf 12×11½ (1939)	40	10
122		1½d. scarlet	8·00	3·25
		a. Perf 12×11½ (1940)	40	50
123		2d. slate	8·00	1·50
		a. Perf 12×11½ (1940)	40	10
124		3d. blue	5·50	1·00
		a. Perf 12×11½ (1940)	40	35
125		4d. magenta	6·50	3·00
		a. Perf 12×11½ (1942)	80	1·25
126		6d. purple	9·50	50
		a. Perf 12×11½ (1939)	80	20
127		9d. orange	6·00	1·75
		a. Perf 12×11½ (1944)	1·25	55
128	15	1s. black and olive-green	13·00	2·25
		a. Perf 11½×12 (1940)	1·50	65
129		1s.3d. brown & turquoise-bl (12.4.41)	2·00	50
		a. Perf 11½×12 (1940)	5·00	50
130		2s. blue and violet	32·00	19·00
		a. Perf 11½×12 (1940)	5·00	50
131		5s. olive-green & carmine	60·00	23·00
		a. Perf 11½×12 (1940)	10·00	17·00
132		10s. black and violet (7.40)	7·00	25·00
120a/32		Set of 13	27·00	55·00
120s/32s Perf "Specimen" Set of 13				£250

The exact measurement of the comb perforated stamps is 12×11.8 (vertical designs) or 11.8×12 (horizontal designs).

The ½d. and 1d. values exist in coils constructed from normal sheets.

1946 (14 Oct). Victory. As Nos. 110/11 of Antigua. P 13½×14.

133		2d. slate-violet	16·00	2·75
		a. Perf 13½	10	10
134		4d. claret	2·50	3·75
		a. Perf 13½	1·50	3·25
133s/4as Perf "Specimen" Set of 2				75·00

16 Northern Territories Mounted Constabulary

17 Christiansborg Castle

(Des B. A. Johnston (1½d.), M. Ziorkley and B. A. Abban (2d.), P.O. draughtsman (2½d.), C. Gomez (1s.), M. Ziorkley (10s.); others from photographs. Recess B.W.)

1948 (1 July). T **16/17** and similar designs. Wmk Mult Script CA. P 12×11½ (vert) or 11½×12 (horiz).

135		½d. emerald-green	20	30
136		1d. blue	15	15
137		1½d. scarlet	1·25	80
138		2d. purple-brown	55	10
139		2½d. yellow-brown and scarlet	2·00	4·25
140		3d. light blue	4·00	50
141		4d. magenta	3·50	2·75
142		6d. black and orange	30	30
143		1s. black and vermilion	75	30
144		2s. sage-green and magenta	3·25	2·50
145		5s. purple and black	26·00	7·00
146		10s. black and sage-green	8·50	7·00
135/46		Set of 12	45·00	23·00
135s/46s Perf "Specimen" Set of 12				£250

Designs: Horiz—1½d. Emblem of Joint Provincial Council;

2½d. Map showing position of Gold Coast; 3d. Nsuta manganese mine; 4d. Lake Bosumtwi; 1s. Breaking cocoa pods; 2s. Gold Coast Regt Trooping the Colour; 5s. Surfboats. Vert—2d. Talking drums; 10s. Forest. Nos. 135/6 exist in coils constructed from normal sheets.

1948 (20 Dec). Royal Silver Wedding. As Nos. 112/13 of Antigua.

147		1½d. scarlet	30	50
148		10s. grey-olive	19·00	26·00

1949 (10 Oct). 75th Anniv of U.P.U. As Nos. 114/17 of Antigua.

149		2d. red-brown	25	20
		a. "A" of "CA" missing from wmk		
150		2½d. orange	1·50	4·00
151		3d. deep blue	35	1·75
152		1s. blue-green	35	35
149/52		Set of 4	2·25	5·50

As on other examples of this variety No. 149a shows traces of the left leg of the "A".

POSTAGE DUE STAMPS

D 1

(Typo D.L.R.)

1923 (6 Mar). Yellowish toned paper. Wmk Mult Script CA. P 14.

D1	D 1	½d. black	15·00	£120
D2		1d. red-brown	75	1·25
D3		2d. black	13·00	3·75
D4		3d. black	22·00	2·25
D1/4		Set of 4	45·00	£120
D1s/4s Optd "Specimen" Set of 4				75·00

A bottom marginal strip of six of No. D2 is known showing the "A" of "CA" omitted from the watermark in the margin below the third vertical column.

Normal	Lower serif at left of "3" missing (R. 9/1)

Column 4 (No. D8)	Column 5 (No. D8c)

The degree of inclination of the stroke on the 1s. value varies for each column of the sheet: Column 1, 2 and 6 104°, Column 3 108°, Column 4 107° and Column 5 (No. D8c) 100°.

1951–52. Wmk Mult Script CA. Chalk-surfaced paper. P 14.

D5	D 1	2d. black (13.12.51)	3·75	24·00
		a. Error. Crown missing, W 9a	£850	
		b. Error. St. Edward's Crown, W 9b	£425	
		c. Large "d" (R. 9/6, 10/6)	28·00	
		d. Serif on "d" (R. 1/6)	50·00	
D6		3d. black (13.12.51)	3·00	22·00
		a. Error. Crown missing, W 9a	£800	
		b. Error. St. Edward's Crown, W 9b	£400	
		c. Missing serif	42·00	
D7		6d. black (1.10.52)	1·75	8·00
		a. Error. Crown missing, W 9a	£1100	
		b. Error. St. Edward's Crown, W 9b	£750	
D8		1s. black (1.10.52)	1·75	65·00
		b. Error. St. Edward's Crown, W 9b	£900	
		c. Upright stroke	12·00	
D5/8		Set of 4	9·25	£110

For illustration of Nos. D5c/d see Nos. D4/6 of Bechuanaland.

Grenada

The earliest recorded postmark of the British administration of Grenada dates from 1784, and, although details of the early period are somewhat sparse, it would appear that the island's postal service was operated at a branch of the British G.P.O. In addition to a Packet Agency at St. George's, the capital, there was a further agency at Carriacou, in the Grenadines, which operated for a few years from 15 September 1847.

Stamps of Great Britain were supplied to the St. George's office from April 1858 until the colony assumed responsibility for the postal service on 1 May 1860. Following the take-over the crowned-circle handstamp, No. CC2, was again used until the Grenada adhesives were issued in 1861.

There was no internal postal service before 1861.

For illustrations of the handstamp and postmark types see BRITISH POST OFFICES ABROAD notes, following GREAT BRITAIN.

CARRIACOU

CROWNED-CIRCLE HANDSTAMPS

A crowned-circle handstamp for Carriacou is recorded in the G.P.O. proof book but no example has been reported used from Grenada.

ST. GEORGE'S

CROWNED-CIRCLE HANDSTAMPS

CC2 CC **1** GRENADA (R.) (24.10.1850) ...*Price on cover* £2000

Stamps of GREAT BRITAIN cancelled "A 15" as Type **2**.

1858–60.
Z1	1d. rose-red (1857), *perf* 14	£425	
Z2	2d. blue (1858) (Plate No. 7)	£1100	
Z3	4d. rose (1857)	£275	
Z4	6d. lilac (1856)	£120	
Z5	1s. green (1856)	£1200	

PRICES FOR STAMPS ON COVER TO 1945	
Nos. 1/19	*from* × 15
Nos. 20/3	*from* × 20
Nos. 24/6	*from* × 10
No. 27	*from* × 15
No. 28	—
No. 29	*from* × 10
Nos. 30/6	*from* × 20
Nos. 37/9	*from* × 10
No. 40	*from* × 30
Nos. 41/7	*from* × 10
Nos. 48/101	*from* × 4
Nos. 109/11	*from* × 8
Nos. 112/48	*from* × 4
Nos. 149/51	*from* × 10
No. 152/63	*from* × 4
Nos. D1/3	*from* × 25
Nos. D4/7	*from* × 12
Nos. D8/14	*from* × 20

CROWN COLONY

PRINTERS. Types **1** and **5** recess-printed by Perkins, Bacon and Co.

PERKINS BACON "CANCELLED". For notes on these handstamps, showing "CANCELLED" between horizontal bars forming an oval, see Catalogue Introduction.

1

2 Small Star

(Eng C. Jeens)

1861 (3 June)–62. No wmk. *Wove paper.*

(a) Rough perf 14 to 16.
1	**1**	1d. bluish green	£4500	£300
2		1d. green (5.62)	50·00	45·00
		a. Imperf between (horiz pair)		
3		6d. rose (*shades*) (H/S "CANCELLED" in oval £10000)	£900	90·00

(b) Perf 11 to 12½.
3a	**1**	6d. lake-red (6.62)		£750

The 1d. bluish green also exists handstamped "CANCELLED" in oval, but the only known example is in the Royal Collection.

No. 3a is only known unused, and may be the result of perforating machine trials undertaken by Perkins, Bacon. It has also been seen on horizontally laid paper (*Price* £1200).

SIDEWAYS WATERMARK. W **2/3** when sideways show two points of star downwards.

1863–71. W **2** (Small Star). Rough perf 14 to 16.
4	**1**	1d. green (3.64)	85·00	12·00
		a. Wmk sideways	—	24·00
5		1d. yellowish green	£110	26·00
6		6d. rose (*shades*) (5.63)	£600	13·00
		a. Wmk sideways		60·00
7		6d. orange-red (*shades*) (5.66)	£650	12·00
8		6d. dull rose-red (*wmk sideways*)	£3500	£225
9		6d. vermilion (5.71)	£750	12·00
		a. Double impression		£2000

1873 (Jan). W **2** (Small Star, sideways). Clean-cut perf 15.
10	**1**	1d. deep green	£100	42·00
		a. Bisected diag (on cover)	†	£9000
		b. Imperf between (pair)		£7000

No. 10a, and later bisected 1d. values, were authorised until 1881 to pay the island newspaper rate (½d.) or the newspaper rate to Great Britain (1½d.). Examples also exist on covers to France.

3 Large Star

4 Broad-pointed Star

1873 (Sept)–74. W **3** (Large Star). Intermediate perf 15.
11	**1**	1d. blue-green (*wmk sideways*) (2.74)	90·00	19·00
		a. Double impression		
		b. Bisected diag (on cover)	†	£9000
12		6d. orange-vermilion	£700	26·00

5

POSTAGE

ONE SHILLING

(6)

NOTE. The early ½d., 2½d., 4d. and 1s. postage stamps were made by surcharging the undenominated Type **5** design.

The surcharges were from two founts of type—one about 1½ mm high, the other 2 mm high—so there are short and tall letters on the same stamp; also the spacing varies considerably, so that the length of the words varies.

Examples of Type **5** with surcharges, but without the "POSTAGE" inscription, are revenue stamps.

1875 (July). *Surch with T* **6**. W **3**. P 14.
13	**5**	1s. deep mauve (B.)	£700	12·00
		a. "SHLLIING"	†	£700
		b. "NE SHILLING"	†	£2500
		c. Inverted "S" in "POSTAGE"	£3750	£500
		d. "OSTAGE"	£5500	£2000

1875 (Dec). W **3** (Large Star, upright).
14	**1**	1d. green to yellow-green (P 14)	80·00	8·00
		a. Bisected diag (on cover)	†	£9000
15		1d. green (P 15)	£8500	£2250

No. 14 was perforated at Somerset House. 40 sheets of No. 15 were perforated by Perkins, Bacon to replace spoilages and to complete the order.

1878 (Aug). W **2** (Small Star, sideways). Intermediate perf 15.
16	**1**	1d. green	£250	42·00
		b. Bisected diag (on cover)	†	£9000
17		6d. deep vermilion	£850	38·00
		a. Double impression	—	£2000

1879 (Dec). W **2** (Small Star, upright). Rough perf 15.
18	**1**	1d. pale green (*thin paper*)	£300	27·00
		a. Double impression		
		b. Bisected diag (on cover)	†	—

1881 (Apr). W **2** (Small Star, sideways). Rough perf 14½.
19	**1**	1d. green	£160	9·00
		a. Bisected diag (on cover)	†	£9000

POSTAGE **POSTAGE** **POSTAGE**

HALF-PENNY **TWO PENCE HALF-PENNY.** **FOUR PENCE**

(7) **(8)** **(9)**

1881 (Apr). *Surch with T* **7/9**. P 14½.

(a) W **3** *(Large Star, sideways on ½d.)*
20	**5**	½d. pale mauve	32·00	10·00
21		½d. deep mauve	13·00	5·50
		a. Imperf (pair)	£300	
		ab. Ditto. "OSTAGE" (R. 9/4)	£4500	
		b. Surch double	£300	
		c. "OSTAGE" (R. 9/4)	£190	£130
		d. No hyphen	£190	£130
		e. "ALF-PENNY"	£3500	
		f. Wmk upright	£300	£140
		g. Ditto. "OSTAGE" (R. 9/4)	£1700	£750
22		2½d. rose-lake	60·00	7·50
		a. Imperf (pair)	£600	
		b. Imperf between (horiz pair)	£4250	
		c. No stop	£250	75·00
		d. "PENCF" (R. 8/12)	£450	£180
23		4d. blue	£100	8·00
		a. Wmk sideways	†	£500
		b. Inverted "S" in "POSTAGE"		

(b) W **4** *(Broad-pointed Star).*
24	**5**	2½d. rose-lake	£160	50·00
		a. No stop	£550	£200
		b. "PENCF" (R. 8/12)	£750	£275
25		2½d. claret	£425	£120
		a. No stop	£1100	£500
		b. "PENCF" (R. 8/12)	£1600	£700
25c		2½d. deep claret	£625	£225
		a. No stop	£2250	£900
		b. "PENCF" (R. 8/12)	£2750	£1100
26		4d. blue	£250	£180

Examples of the "F" for "E" error on the 2½d. value should not be confused with a somewhat similar broken "E" variety. The latter is always without the stop and shows other damage to the "E". The authentic error always occurs with the full stop shown.

The "no stop" variety occurs on R. 3/4, R. 6/2, R. 8/3 and R. 9/7.

ONE PENNY **POSTAGE.**

(10) **(11)** **(12)**

1883 (Jan). *Revenue stamps (T* **5** *with green surcharge as in T* **10**) *optd for postage.* W **2** (Small Star). P 14½.

(a) Optd horizontally with T **11**.
27	**5**	1d. orange	£350	60·00
		a. "POSTAGE" inverted	£3000	£2250
		b. "POSTAGE" double	£1400	£1100
		c. Inverted "S" in "POSTAGE"	£1000	£600
		d. Bisected diag (on cover)	†	£3000

(b) Optd diagonally with T **11** *twice on each stamp, the stamp being cut and each half used as* ½d.
28	**5**	Half of 1d. orange	£650	£225
		a. Unsevered pair	£4500	£1200
		b. "POSTAGE" inverted	—	£1200

(c) Optd with T **12**, *the stamps divided diagonally and each half used as* ½d.
29	**5**	Half of 1d. orange	£275	£110
		a. Unsevered pair	£1500	£450

Nos. 27/9 exist with wmk either upright or sideways.

1d. Revenue stamps with "POSTAGE" added in black manuscript were used at Gouyave during February and March 1883 (*Price* £4000, *used*). Similar manuscript overprints, in red were also used at Grenville in June 1883 and in black or red at Sauteurs in September 1886 (*Price from* £6000, *used*).

d.
1
POSTAGE.

13 **(14)** **15**

(Typo D.L.R.)

1883. Wmk Crown CA. P 14.
30	**13**	½d. dull green (February)	1·25	1·00
		a. Tête-bêche (vert pair)	4·50	16·00
31		1d. carmine (February)	70·00	3·25
		a. Tête-bêche (vert pair)	£225	£250
32		2½d. ultramarine (May)	7·00	1·00
		a. Tête-bêche (vert pair)	26·00	50·00
33		4d. greyish slate (May)	7·00	1·75
		a. Tête-bêche (vert pair)	19·00	55·00
34		6d. mauve (May)	3·25	4·00
		a. Tête-bêche (vert pair)	18·00	55·00
35		8d. grey-brown (February)	10·00	12·00
		a. Tête-bêche (vert pair)	35·00	75·00
36		1s. pale violet (April)	£120	55·00
		a. Tête-bêche (vert pair)	£1500	£1800
30/36 *Set of 7*			£190	70·00

Types **13** and **15** were printed in rows tête-bêche in the sheets, so that 50% of the stamps have inverted watermarks.

1886 (1 Oct–Dec). *Revenue stamps (T* **5** *with green surch as T* **10**), *surch with T* **14**. P 14.

(a) Wmk Large Star, T **3**.
37	**5**	1d. on 1½d. orange	45·00	30·00
		a. Surch inverted	£300	£300
		b. Surch double	£500	£300
		c. "THRFE"	£250	£225
		d. "PFNCE"	£250	£225
		e. "HALH"	£250	£225
		f. Bisected diag (on cover)	†	£2250
38		1d. on 1s. orange (December)	40·00	30·00
		a. "POSTAGE" (no stop)	£425	
		b. "SHILLNG"	£450	£375
		c. Wide space (3½ mm) between "ONE" and "SHILLING"	£325	£250
		d. Bisected diag (on cover)	†	£2250

(b) Wmk Small Star, T **2**.
39	**5**	1d. on 4d. orange (November)	£160	90·00

1887 (Jan). Wmk Crown CA. P 14.
40	**15**	1d. carmine	2·25	1·75
		a. Tête-bêche (vert pair)	4·50	20·00
		s. Optd "Specimen"	50·00	

Due to the sheet formation 50% of the stamps have inverted watermarks.

4d. **HALF**
POSTAGE **PENNY**
  POSTAGE

(16) **(17)**

1888 (31 Mar)–91. *Revenue stamps (T* **5** *with green surch as T* **10**) *further surcharged.* W **2**. P 14½, *and* No. 35.

I. Surch with T **16**.

(a) 4 mm between value and "POSTAGE".
41	**5**	4d. on 2s. orange	40·00	19·00
		a. Upright "d" (R. 5/6)	£750	£450
		b. Wide space (2¼ mm) between "TWO" and "SHILLINGS"	£275	£150
		c. First "S" in "SHILLINGS" inverted	£475	£325
		d. Imperf between (horiz pair)	£6000	

(b) 5 mm between value and "POSTAGE".
42	**5**	4d. on 2s. orange	70·00	32·00
		a. Wide space	£350	£225
		b. "S" inverted	£650	£550

II. Surch as T **17** *(December 1889).*
43	**5**	½d. on 2s. orange	12·00	21·00
		a. Surch double	£300	£325
		b. Wide space	£110	£130
		c. "S" inverted	£275	£300

POSTAGE
d.
AND
REVENUE
(18)

POSTAGE
AND
1
REVENUE
1d.
(19)

2½d.
(20)

III. *Surch with T 18 (December 1890).*

44	5	1d. on 2s. orange	80·00	75·00
		a. Surch inverted		£750
		b. Wide space	£325	£325
		c. "S" inverted	£700	£650

IV. *Surch with T 19 (January 1891).*

45	5	1d. on 2s. orange	60·00	55·00
		a. No stop after "1d" (R. 3/8)	£375	
		b. Wide space	£250	£250
		c. "S" inverted	£500	£500
46	13	1d. on 8d. grey-brown	11·00	14·00
		a. Tête-bêche (vert pair)	40·00	60·00
		b. Surch inverted	£325	£275
		c. No stop after "1d" (R. 6/5)	£250	£250

V. *Surch with T 20 (December 1891).*

47	13	2½d. on 8d. grey-brown	8·00	11·00
		a. Tête-bêche (vert pair)	40·00	60·00
		b. Surch inverted		
		c. Surch double	£850	£800
		d. Surch double, one inverted	£550	£500
		e. Surch treble	—	£900
		f. Surch treble, two inverted	—	£1000
		s. Optd "Specimen"	£120	

The surcharges, Types **16/19**, were applied to half sheets as a setting of 60 (12×5).

The wide space between "TWO" and "SHILLINGS" occurs on R. 1/4 and 10/3 of the original 2s. Revenue stamp which was printed in sheets of 120 (12×10).

Type **18** was a two-step surcharge comprising "1d./Revenue", followed by "POSTAGE/AND". An example of No. 44 is known with the "POSTAGE" omitted due to faulty registration and the word applied by hand in a slightly different type style.

There are two varieties of fraction in Type **20**, which each occur 30 times in the setting; in one the "1" has horizontal serif and the "2" commences in a ball; in the other the "I" has sloping serif and the "2" is without ball.

See also D4/7.

21 **22** **23** Flagship of
Columbus. (Columbus
named Grenada "La
Concepcion")

(Typo D.L.R.)

1895 (6 Sept)–**99**. Wmk Crown CA. P 14.

48	22	½d. mauve and green (9.99)	2·50	1·75
49	21	1d. mauve and carmine (5.96)	4·50	75
50		2d. mauve and brown (9.99)	40·00	32·00
		x. Wmk reversed	—	£225
51		2½d. mauve and ultramarine	6·00	1·50
52	22	3d. mauve and orange	6·50	16·00
53	21	6d. mauve and green	13·00	38·00
54	22	8d. mauve and black	12·00	45·00
55		1s. green and orange	20·00	45·00
48/55 Set of 8			95·00	£160
48s/55s Optd "Specimen" Set of 8			£150	

(Recess D.L.R.)

1898 (15 Aug). *400th Anniv of Discovery of Grenada by Columbus.* Wmk Crown CC. P 14.

56	23	2½d. ultramarine	14·00	6·00
		a. Bluish paper	32·00	40·00
		s. Optd "Specimen"	85·00	

24 **25**

(Typo D.L.R.)

1902. Wmk Crown CA. P 14.

57	24	½d. dull purple and green	3·25	1·25
58	25	1d. dull purple and carmine	4·50	30
59		2d. dull purple and brown	3·00	10·00
60		2½d. dull purple and ultramarine	3·50	2·75
61	24	3d. dull purple and orange	3·75	9·00
62	25	6d. dull purple and green	2·50	17·00
63	24	1s. green and orange	4·75	28·00
64		2s. green and ultramarine	23·00	55·00
65	25	5s. green and carmine	42·00	65·00
66	24	10s. green and purple	£120	£375
57/66 Set of 10			£180	£375
57s/66s Optd "Specimen" Set of 10			£190	

1904–06. Wmk Mult Crown CA. *Ordinary paper.* P 14.

67	24	½d. purple and green (1905)	17·00	28·00
68	25	1d. purple and carmine	11·00	2·50
69		2d. purple and brown (1905)	55·00	£110
70		2½d. purple and ultramarine (1905)	55·00	65·00
71	24	3d. purple and orange (1905)	2·75	7·00

72	25	a. Chalk-surfaced paper	2·75	8·50
72	25	6d. purple and green (1906)	6·00	17·00
		a. Chalk-surfaced paper	8·50	24·00
73	24	1s. green and orange (1905)	6·00	28·00
74		2s. green and ultramarine (1906)	50·00	75·00
		a. Chalk-surfaced paper	30·00	75·00
75	25	5s. green and carmine (1906)	65·00	95·00
76	24	10s. green and purple (1906)	£150	£250
67/76 Set of 10			£350	£600

Examples of most values between Nos. 57 and 76 are known showing a forged G.P.O. Grenada B.W.I. postmark dated "OC 6 09".

26 Badge of the
Colony

27 Badge of the
Colony

(Recess D.L.R.)

1906. Wmk Mult Crown CA. P 14.

77	26	½d. green	4·50	30
78		1d. carmine	6·50	10
		y. Wmk inverted and reversed		
79		2d. orange	3·00	3·00
80		2½d. blue	6·00	1·75
		a. Ultramarine	9·00	3·50

(Typo D.L.R.)

1908. Wmk Crown CA. *Chalk-surfaced paper.* P 14.

82	27	1s. black/green	29·00	60·00
83		10s. green and red/green	£100	£200

1908–11. Wmk Mult Crown CA. *Chalk-surfaced paper.* P 14.

84	27	3d. dull purple/yellow	4·75	1·75
85		6d. dull purple and purple	20·00	23·00
86		1s. black/green (1911)	7·00	4·50
87		2s. blue and purple/blue	21·00	12·00
88		5s. green and red/yellow	60·00	70·00
77/88 Set of 11			£225	£325
77s/80s, 82s/5s, 87s/8s Optd "Specimen" Set of 10			£200	

Examples of Nos. 82/8 are known showing a forged G.P.O. Grenada B.W.I. postmark dated "OC 6 09".

WAR TAX **WAR TAX**

28 **29** **30**
(29) **(30)**

(Typo D.L.R.)

1913 (3 Jan)–**22**. Wmk Mult Crown CA. *Chalk-surfaced paper (3d. to 10s.).* P 14.

89	28	½d. yellow-green	1·00	1·60
90		½d. green	1·00	1·00
91		1d. red	2·25	30
92		1d. scarlet (1916)	5·00	10·00
		w. Wmk inverted		
93		2d. orange	1·75	30
94		2½d. bright blue	1·75	3·50
95		2½d. dull blue (1920)	4·75	5·50
96		3d. purple/yellow	65	85
		a. White back (3.14)	65	1·50
		as. Optd "Specimen"	32·00	
		b. On lemon (1917)	4·00	9·00
		c. On pale yellow (1921)	6·00	28·00
97		6d. dull and bright purple	1·50	9·00
98		1s. black/green	1·00	10·00
		a. White back (3.14)	1·25	7·50
		as. Optd "Specimen"	35·00	
		b. On blue-green, olive back (1917)	38·00	80·00
		c. On emerald surface	1·50	16·00
		d. On emerald back (6.22)	1·00	15·00
		ds. Optd "Specimen"	35·00	
		dw. Wmk inverted	90·00	
99		2s. purple and blue/blue	6·50	12·00
100		5s. green and red/yellow	17·00	60·00
		a. On pale yellow (1921)	25·00	75·00
		as. Optd "Specimen"	48·00	
101		10s. green and red/green	55·00	95·00
		a. On emerald back (6.22)	55·00	£160
		as. Optd "Specimen"	60·00	
89/101 Set of 10			80·00	£170
89s/101s Optd "Specimen" (1s. optd in red)			£180	
Set of 10			£180	
98sa 1s. optd in black			35·00	

1916 (1 June). *Optd with T 29 by Gout Press, St. George's.*

109	28	1d. red (shades)	2·25	1·75
		a. Opt inverted	£275	
		b. Triangle for "A" in "TAX"	55·00	70·00
		s. Handstamped "Specimen"	50·00	

A small "A" in "WAR", 2 mm high is found on Nos. 29, 38 and 48 of the setting of 60 and a very small "A" in "TAX", 1½ mm high, on No. 11. Value about twice normal. The normal "A" is 2¼ mm high.

No. 109b is on No. 56 of the setting.

1916 (1 Sept)–**18**. *Optd with T 30 in London.*

111	28	1d. scarlet	30	20
		a. Carmine-red/bluish (5.18)	3·75	1·50
		s. Optd "Specimen"	40·00	
		w. Wmk inverted	£130	

1921–32. Wmk Mult Script CA. *Chalk-surfaced paper (3d. (No. 122) to 10s.)* P 14.

112	28	½d. green	1·25	30
113		1d. carmine-red	80	75
114		1d. brown (1923)	1·50	30
115		1½d. rose-red (6.22)	1·50	1·50
116		2d. orange	1·25	30

117		2d. grey (1926)	2·50	2·75
117a		2½d. dull blue	4·50	3·50
118		2½d. grey (6.22)	1·00	9·00
119		2½d. bright blue (1926)	4·50	3·75
120		2½d. ultramarine (1931)	4·50	8·50
120a		2½d. chalky blue and blue (1932)	50·00	50·00
121		3d. bright blue (6.22)	1·25	11·00
122		3d. purple/yellow (1926)	3·00	5·00
123		4d. black and red/yellow (1926)	1·00	3·75
124		5d. dull purple & sage-green (27.12.22)	1·50	4·25
125		6d. dull and bright purple	1·25	21·00
126		6d. black and carmine (1926)	2·25	2·50
127		9d. dull purple and black (27.12.22)	2·25	9·50
128		1s. black/emerald (1923)	2·50	48·00
		y. Wmk inverted and reversed	£150	
129		1s. chestnut (1926)	3·00	10·00
130		2s. purple and blue/black (1922)	6·00	17·00
131		2s.6d. black and carmine/blue (1929)	7·00	22·00
132		3s. green and violet (27.12.22)	7·00	27·00
133		5s. green and red/pale yellow (1923)	12·00	35·00
134		10s. green and red/emerald (1923)	50·00	£130
112/19, 121/34 Set of 22			£110	£325
112s/34s Optd or Perf (2s.6d.) "Specimen" Set of 23			£375	

Some values of Nos. 89/101 and 112/34 have been seen with part strikes of the forged postmark mentioned after Nos. 67/76 and 77/88.

31 Grand Anse Beach   **32** Badge of the Colony

33 Grand Etang   **34** St. George's

(Recess Waterlow)

1934 (23 Oct)–**36**. Wmk Mult Script CA (sideways on T **32**). P 12½.

135	31	½d. green	15	1·25
		a. Perf 12½×13½ (1936)	4·75	48·00
136	32	1d. black and sepia	1·00	3·00
		a. Perf 13½×12½ (1936)	60	35
137	33	1½d. black and scarlet	4·75	3·25
		a. Perf 12½×13½ (1936)	1·25	40
138	32	2d. black and orange	1·00	75
139	34	2½d. blue	50	50
140	32	3d. black and olive-green	1·00	2·75
141		6d. black and purple	1·00	6·50
142		1s. black and brown	2·00	4·00
143		2s.6d. black and ultramarine	8·00	28·00
144		5s. black and violet	38·00	50·00
135/44 Set of 10			50·00	80·00
135s/44s Perf "Specimen" Set of 10			£160	

1935 (6 May). *Silver Jubilee. As Nos. 91/4 of Antigua but ptd by Waterlow.* P 11×12.

145		½d. black and green	80	1·25
		k. Kite and vertical log	50·00	
		l. Kite and horizontal log	70·00	
146		1d. ultramarine and grey	1·00	1·75
		l. Kite and horizontal log	80·00	
147		1½d. deep blue and scarlet	1·00	3·00
		l. Kite and horizontal log	£100	
148		1s. slate and purple	7·00	22·00
		l. Kite and horizontal log	£225	
145/8 Set of 4			9·00	25·00
145s/8s Perf "Specimen" Set of 4			90·00	

For illustrations of plate varieties see Omnibus section following Zanzibar.

1937 (12 May). *Coronation. As Nos. 95/7 of Antigua.* P 11×11½.

149		1d. violet	40	1·25
150		1½d. carmine	40	50
151		2½d. blue	80	1·25
149/51 Set of 3			1·40	2·75
149s/51s Perf "Specimen" Set of 3			75·00	

35 King George VI

(Photo Harrison)

1937 (12 July)–**50**. Wmk Mult Script CA. *Chalk-surfaced paper.* P 15×14.

152	35	¼d. brown	1·40	20
		a. Ordinary paper (11.42)	30	1·00
		b. Ordinary paper. Chocolate (1.45)	20	1·00
		c. Chalk-surfaced paper. Chocolate (8.50)	50	3·25

The ordinary paper is thick, smooth and opaque.

36 Grand Anse Beach

40 Badge of the Colony

Line on sail (Centre Pl 3 R. 1/1. Later partially retouched).

Colon flaw (R. 5/6. Corrected on ptg of Nov 1950)

(Recess D.L.R. (10s.), Waterlow (others))

1938 (16 Mar)–**50**. *As T* **31/4** (*but portrait of King George VI as in T* **36**) *and T* **40**. Wmk Mult Script CA (sideways on T **32**). P 12½ or 12×13 (10s.).

153	36	½d. yellow-green........................	6·50	1·25
		a. *Blue-green* (10.9.43)............	60	1·25
		b. Perf 12½×13½ (1938).............	6·00	80
		ba. *Blue-green*........................	6·50	5·00
154	32	1d. black and sepia....................	1·00	20
		a. Perf 13½×12½ (1938).............	50	50
		ab. Line on sail.......................	80·00	
155	33	1½d. black and scarlet................	50	85
		a. Perf 12½×13½ (1938).............	2·25	30
156	32	2d. black and orange..................	30	50
		a. Perf 12½×13½ (1938).............	2·50	85
		ab. Line on sail.......................	95·00	
157	34	2½d. bright blue........................	30	30
		a. Perf 12½×13½ (?March 1950)..	£6000	£180
158	32	3d. black and olive-green...........	14·00	1·40
		a. Perf 13½×12½ (16.3.38)........	6·00	1·00
		ab. *Black and brown-olive* (1942)...	30	80
		ac. Line on sail.......................	75·00	
		b. Perf 12½. *Black and brown-olive* (16.8.50)........................	30	1·90
		ba. Colon flaw.........................	75·00	
159		6d. black and purple..................	1·50	40
		a. Perf 13½×12½ (1942).............	2·25	50
160		1s. black and brown..................	2·25	40
		a. Perf 13½×12½ (1941).............	4·00	1·75
161		2s. black and ultramarine..........	22·00	1·75
		a. Perf 13½×12½ (1941).............	25·00	1·50
162		5s. black and violet..................	3·75	2·75
		a. Perf 13½×12½ (1947).............	2·75	5·50
163	40	10s. steel blue and carmine (*narrow*) (P 12×13).....................	55·00	9·00
		a. Perf 14. *Steel blue and bright carmine* (*narrow*)..................	£180	45·00
		b. Perf 14. *Slate-blue and bright carmine* (*narrow*) (1943)...........	£190	£110
		c. Perf 12. *Slate-blue and bright carmine* (*narrow*) (1943)...........	£600	£1500
		d. Perf 14. *Slate-blue and carmine lake* (*wide*) (1944).................	£100	8·00
		e. Perf 14. *Blue-black and carmine* (*narrow*) (1943).................	32·00	9·00
		ea. Frame printed double, one albino................................	£3500	
		f. Perf 14. *Blue-black and bright carmine* (*wide*) (1947)...........	25·00	25·00
152/63e *Set of 12*...........................			50·00	14·00
152s/63s Perf "Specimen" *Set of 12*.........			£225	

In the earlier printings of the 10s. the paper was dampened before printing and the subsequent shrinkage produced narrow frames 23½ to 23¾ mm wide. Later printings were made on dry paper producing wide frames 24¼ mm wide.

No. 163a is one of the earlier printings, line perf 13.8×14.1. Later printings of the 10s. are line perf 14.1.

Nos. 163b/c show a blurred centre caused by the use of a worn plate.

Nos. 163a and 163b may be found with gum more or less yellow due to local climatic conditions.

Examples of No. 163c are known showing forged St. George's postmarks dated "21 AU 42", "21 AU 43" or "2 OC 43".

1946 (25 Sept). *Victory. As Nos.* 110/11 *of Antigua.*

164		1½d. carmine........................	10	50
165		3½d. blue............................	10	1·00
164s/5s Perf "Specimen" *Set of 2*............			70·00	

1948 (27 Oct). *Royal Silver Wedding. As Nos.* 112/13 *of Antigua.*

166		1½d. scarlet........................	15	10
167		10s. slate-green....................	13·00	17·00

(New Currency. 100 cents = 1 West Indian, later Eastern Caribbean, dollar)

1949 (10 Oct). *75th Anniv of Universal Postal Union. As Nos.* 114/17 *of Antigua.*

168		5c. ultramarine....................	15	10
169		6c. olive............................	1·50	2·50
170		12c. magenta.......................	15	30
171		24c. red-brown.....................	15	40
168/71 *Set of 4*..............................			1·75	3·00

41 King George VI

42 Badge of the Colony

43 Badge of the Colony

(Recess B.W. (T **41**), D.L.R. (others))

1951 (8 Jan). Wmk Mult Script CA. P 11½ (T **41**), 11½×12½ (T **42**), and 11½×13 (T **43**).

172	41	½c. black and red-brown..................	15	1·60
173		1c. black and emerald-green..............	15	25
174		2c. black and brown......................	15	50
175		3c. black and rose-carmine...............	15	10
176		4c. black and orange.....................	35	40
177		5c. black and violet.....................	20	10
178		6c. black and olive......................	30	10
179		7c. black and light blue.................	1·75	10
180		12c. black and purple....................	2·25	30
181	42	25c. black and sepia.....................	2·25	80
182		50c. black and blue......................	6·50	40
183		$1.50, black and yellow-orange..........	7·50	7·00
184	43	$2.50, slate-blue and carmine...........	5·50	5·50
172/184 *Set of 13*...............................			24·00	15·00

1951 (16 Feb). *Inauguration of B.W.I. University College. As Nos.* 118/19 *of Antigua.*

185		3c. black and carmine...................	45	1·25
186		6c. black and olive.....................	45	50

NEW CONSTITUTION

1951
(44)

1951 (21 Sept). *New Constitution. Nos.* 175/7 *and* 180 *optd with T* **44** *by B.W.*

187	41	3c. black and rose-carmine.............	20	60
188		4c. black and orange...................	20	60
189		5c. black and violet (R.)..............	20	80
190		12c. black and purple..................	20	1·00
187/90 *Set of 4*..............................			70	2·75

POSTAGE DUE STAMPS

D 1

1d.
SURCHARGE
POSTAGE
(D 2)

(Typo D.L.R.)

1892 (18 Apr).

(a) Type D **1**. *Wmk Crown CA. P 14.*

D1	D 1	1d. blue-black.......................	25·00	1·50
D2		2d. blue-black.......................	£170	1·50
D3		3d. blue-black.......................	£180	2·50
D1/3 *Set of 3*...............................			£350	5·00

(b) Nos. 34 *and* 35 *surch locally as Type D* **2**.

D4	13	1d. on 6d. mauve (10.92)..............	90·00	1·25
		a. *Tête-bêche* (vert pair).........	£1600	£1100
		b. Surch double......................	—	£160
D5		1d. on 8d. grey-brown (8.92)..........	£1000	3·25
		a. *Tête-bêche* (vert pair).........	£4500	£1800
D6		2d. on 6d. mauve (10.92)..............	£170	2·50
		a. *Tête-bêche* (vert pair).........	£2250	£1400
D7		2d. on 8d. grey-brown (8.92)..........	£2000	10·00
		a. *Tête-bêche* (vert pair).........	£6500	£3500

Nos. D4/7 were in use from August to November 1892. As supplies of Nos. D1/3 were available from April or May of that year it would not appear that they were intended for postage due purposes. There was a shortage of 1d. postage stamps in July and August, but this was alleviated by Nos. 44/5 which were still available. The provisionals *may* have been intended for postal purposes, but the vast majority appear to have been used philatelically.

1906 (July)–**11**. Wmk Mult Crown CA. P 14.

D8	D 1	1d. blue-black (1911)..................	3·50	7·50
D9		2d. blue-black........................	11·00	1·75
D10		3d. blue-black (9.06).................	13·00	6·00
D8/10 *Set of 3*..............................			25·00	13·50

1921 (Dec)–**22**. *As Type D* **1**, *but inscr* "POSTAGE DUE". Wmk Mult Script CA. P 14.

D11		1d. black.............................	1·25	1·00
D12		1½d. black (15.12.22).................	8·50	21·00
D13		2d. black.............................	2·00	1·75
D14		3d. black.............................	2·00	4·50
D11/14 *Set of 4*.............................			12·00	25·00
D11s/14s Optd "Specimen" *Set of 4*..........			80·00	

1952 (1 Mar). *As Type D* **1**, *but inscr* "POSTAGE DUE". *Value in cents. Wmk Mult Script CA. Chalk-surfaced paper.* P 14.

D15		2c. black.............................	30	7·00
		a. Error. Crown missing. W **9**a........	£140	
		b. Error. St. Edward Crown. W **9**b.....	50·00	
D16		4c. black.............................	30	13·00
		a. Error. Crown missing. W **9**a........	£130	
		b. Error. St. Edward Crown. W **9**b.....	50·00	
D17		6c. black.............................	45	12·00
		a. Error. Crown missing. W **9**a........	£200	
		b. Error. St. Edward Crown. W **9**b.....	95·00	
D18		8c. black.............................	75	12·00
		a. Error. Crown missing. W **9**a........	£375	
		b. Error. St. Edward Crown. W **9**b.....	£180	
D15/18 *Set of 4*.............................			1·60	40·00

Griqualand West
see South Africa

Heligoland

Stamps of HAMBURG (see Part 7 (*Germany*) of this catalogue) were used in Heligoland until 16 April 1867. The Free City of Hamburg ran the Heligoland postal service between 1796 and 1 June 1866. Its stamps continued in use on the island until replaced by Heligoland issues.

PRICES FOR STAMPS ON COVER	
Nos. 1/19	*from* × 3

PRINTERS. All the stamps of Heligoland were typographed at the Imperial Printing Works, Berlin.

REPRINTS. Many of the stamps of Heligoland were subsequently reprinted at Berlin (between 1875 and 1885), Leipzig (1888) and Hamburg (1892 and 1895). Of these only the Berlin productions are difficult to distinguish from the originals so separate notes are provided for the individual values. Leipzig reprints can be identified by their highly surfaced paper and those from Hamburg by their 14 perforation. All of these reprints are worth much less than the original stamps priced below.

There was, in addition, a small reprinting of Nos. 13/19, made by the German government in 1890 for exchange purposes, but examples of this printing are far scarcer than the original stamps.

Forgeries, printed by lithography instead of typography, also exist for Nos. 1/4, 6 and 8 perforated 12½ or 13. Forged cancellations can also be found on originals and, on occasion, genuine postmarks on reprints.

1

(Currency. 16 schillings = 1 mark)

Three Dies of Embossed Head for Types **1** and **2**:

Die I   Die II

Die III

Die I.   Blob instead of curl beneath the chignon. Outline of two jewels at top of diadem.
Die II. Curl under chignon. One jewel at top of diadem.
Die III. Shorter curl under chignon. Two jewels at top of diadem.

(Des Wedding. Die eng E. Schilling)

1867 (Mar)–**68**. *Head Die I embossed in colourless relief. Roul.*

1	1	½sch. blue-green and rose..............	£300	£800
		a. Head Die II (7.68).................	£700	£1100
2		1sch. rose and blue-green (21.3.67)...	£160	£180
3		2sch. rose and grass-green (21.3.67)..	13·00	55·00
4		6sch. green and rose (21.3.67)........	15·00	£250

For Nos. 1/4 the second colour given is that of the spandrels on the ½ and 1sch., and of the spandrels and central background for the 2 and 6sch.

All four values exist from the Berlin, Leipzig and Hamburg reprintings. The following points are helpful in identifying originals from Berlin reprints; for Leipzig and Hamburg reprints see general note above:

½sch.   Reprints are all in yellowish green and show Head Die II
1sch.   All reprints are Head Die III
2sch.   Berlin reprints are in dull rose with a deeper blue-green
6sch.   Originals show white specks in green.

Berlin reprints have a more solid bluish green

1869 (Apr)–**73**. *Head embossed in colourless relief.* P 13½×14½.

5	1	¼sch. rose and green (background) (I) (quadrillé paper) (8.73)............	28.00	£1500
		a. Error. Green and rose (background) (9.73)	£120	£3000
		b. Deep rose and pale green (background) (11.73)	85.00	£1500
6		½sch. blue-green and rose (II)	£190	£200
		a. Yellow green and rose (7.71) ...	£140	£190
		b. Quadrille paper (6.73)	95.00	£150
7		¾sch. green and pale green (I) (quadrillé paper) (12.73)	32.00	£1100
8		1sch. rose and yellow-green (III) (7.71)	£140	£180
		a. Quadrillé paper. *Rose and pale blue-green* (6.73)	£120	£180
9		1½sch. green and green (I) (quadrillé paper) (9.73)	65.00	£250

For Nos. 5/9 the second colour given is that of the spandrels on the ½ and 1sch., of the central background on the ¼ and 1½sch., and of the central background, side labels and side marginal lines of the ¾sch.

No. 5a was a printing of the ¼sch. made in the colour combination of the 1½sch. by mistake.

A further printing of the ½sch. (head die I) in deep rose-red and yellowish green (background), on non-*quadrillé* paper, was made in December 1874, but not issued (*Price* £15, unused).

All five values exist from the Berlin, Leipzig and Hamburg reprintings. The following points are helpful in identifying originals from Berlin reprints; for Leipzig and Hamburg reprints see general note above:

¼sch. – All Berlin and some Hamburg reprints are Head Die II
½sch. – Berlin reprints on thinner paper with solid colour in the spandrels
¾sch. – Berlin reprints on thinner, non-quadrille paper
1sch. – Berlin reprints are on thinner paper or show many breaks in the rose line beneath "SCHILLING" at the top of the design or in the line above it at the foot
1½sch. – All Berlin and some Hamburg reprints are Head Die II

Berlin, Leipzig and Hamburg reprints also exist of the 2 and 6sch., but these values do not come as perforated originals.

(New Currency. 100 pfennig = 1 mark)

2   3   4

5

(Des H. Gätke. Die eng E. Schilling (T **2**), A. Schiffner (others))

1875 (Feb)–**90**. *Head Die II on T 2 embossed in colourless relief.* P 13½×14½.

10	2	1pf. (¼d.) deep green and rose	13.00	£500
11		2pf. (¼d.) deep rose and deep green	13.00	£600
12	3	3pf. (58d.) pale green, red and yellow (6.76)	£225	£1100
		a. Green, red and orange (6.77)....	£160	£850
13	2	5pf. (¾d.) deep yellow-green and rose	13.00	19.00
		a. Deep green and rose (6.90).......	17.00	42.00
14		10pf. (1½d.) deep rose and deep green	32.00	22.00
		a. Scarlet and pale blue-green (5.87)	12.00	22.00
15	3	20pf. (2½d.) rose, green and yellow (6.76)	£200	£120
		a. Rose-carmine, deep green and orange (4.80)	£150	50.00
		b. Dull red, pale green and lemon (7.88)	15.00	29.00
		c. Aniline verm., brt grn and lemon (6.90)	13.00	50.00
16	2	25pf. (3d.) deep green and rose	15.00	28.00
17		50pf. (6d.) rose and green	20.00	35.00
18	4	1m. (1s.) deep green, scarlet and black (8.79)	£140	£200
		a. Perf 11½	£1100	
		b. Deep green, aniline rose and black (5.89)	£140	£200
19	5	5m. (5s.) deep green, aniline rose, black and yellow (8.79)	£170	£950
		a. Perf 11½	£1100	
		ab. Imperf between (horiz pair)	£4250	

For stamps as Type **2** the first colour is that of the central background and the second that of the frame. On the 3pf. the first colour is that of the frame and the top band of the shield, the second is the centre band and the third the shield border. The 20pf. is similar, but has the centre band in the same colour as the frame and the upper band on the shield in the second colour.

The 1, 2 and 3pf. exist from the Berlin, Leipzig and Hamburg reprintings. There were no such reprints for the other values. The following points are helpful in identifying originals from Berlin reprints; for Leipzig and Hamburg reprints see general note above:

1pf. – Berlin printings show a peculiar shade of pink
2pf. – All reprints are much lighter in shade than the deep rose and deep green of the originals
3pf. – Berlin reprints either show the band around the shield in brownish orange, or have this feature in deep yellow with the other two colours lighter

Heligoland was ceded to Germany on 9 August 1890.

Hong Kong

CROWN COLONY

Hong Kong island was formally ceded to Great Britain on 26 January 1841. The Hong Kong Post Office was established in October 1841, when much of the business previously transacted through the Macao postal agency was transferred to the island. The first cancellation is known from April 1842, but local control of the posts was short-lived as the Hong Kong Office became a branch of the British G.P.O. on 15 April 1843.

The colonial authorities resumed control of the postal service on 1 May 1860 although the previously established postal agencies in the Chinese Treaty Ports remained part of the British G.P.O. system until 1 May 1868.

For illustrations of the handstamp types see BRITISH POST OFFICES ABROAD notes following GREAT BRITAIN.

CROWNED-CIRCLE HANDSTAMPS

CC1	CC **1b** HONG KONG (R.) (17.10.1843)	*Price on cover*	£750
CC2	CC **1** HONG KONG (R.) (21.8.1844)	*Price on cover*	£1000
CC3	CC **3** HONG KONG (R.) (16.6.1852)	*Price on cover*	£475

We no longer list the Great Britain stamps with obliteration "B 62" within oval. The Government notification dated 29 November 1862 stated that only the Hong Kong stamps to be issued on 8 December would be available for postage and the stamps formerly listed were all issued in Great Britain later than the date of the notice.

(Currency. 100 cents = 1 Hong Kong dollar)

PRICES FOR STAMPS ON COVER TO 1945

Nos. 1/7	*from* × 6
Nos. 8/12	*from* × 15
Nos. 13	*from* × 6
Nos. 14/17	*from* × 15
No. 18	*from* × 50
No. 19	*from* × 15
Nos. 20/27	*from* × 10
Nos. 28/36	*from* × 8
Nos. 37/9	*from* × 10
Nos. 40/4	*from* × 8
Nos. 45/50	*from* × 10
No. 51	*from* × 20
No. 52	*from* × 10
Nos. 53/4	—
No. 55	*from* × 10
Nos. 56/61	*from* × 10
Nos. 62/99	*from* × 4
Nos. 100/32	*from* × 3
Nos. 133/6	*from* × 2
Nos. 137/9	*from* × 4
Nos. 140/68	*from* × 2
Nos. D1/12	*from* × 10
Nos. F1/11	*from* × 20
No. F12	*from* × 4
Nos. P1/3	*from* × 2

PRINTERS. All definitive issues up to 1962 were typographed by De La Rue and Co., *except for some printings between 1941 and 1945.*

1   2   3

1862 (8 Dec)–**63**. No wmk. P 14.

1	1	2c. brown	£425	95.00
		a. Deep brown (1863)..................	£550	£120
2		8c. yellow-buff	£700	70.00
3		12c. pale greenish blue	£600	60.00
4	3	18c. lilac	£600	55.00
5		24c. green	£1000	£100
6		48c. rose	£2750	£350
7		96c. brownish grey	£3750	£450

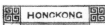

"GKON" of "HONGKONG" damaged at foot (Pl 1 lower right pane R. 9/5)

1863 (Aug)–**71**. Wmk Crown CC. P 14.

8	1	2c. deep brown (11.64)..................	£275	28.00
		a. Brown	£130	7.00
		b. Pale yellowish brown	£160	12.00
		w. Wmk inverted	£550	80.00
		y. Wmk inverted and reversed	†	£700
		x. Wmk reversed	—	£140
9	2	4c. grey	£140	15.00
		ay. Wmk inverted and reversed	†	£700
		b. Slate	£120	7.00
		bw. Wmk inverted	£425	80.00
		c. Deep slate	£160	13.00
		d. Greenish grey	£325	50.00
		dw. Wmk inverted	†	£375
		e. Bluish slate	£475	22.00
		ew. Wmk inverted	£1100	£150
		f. Perf 12½. Slate (8.70)	£12000	£275
		fw. Wmk inverted	—	£750
10		6c. lilac	£425	14.00

		a. Mauve............	£550	15.00
		w. Wmk inverted	£1100	80.00
		x. Wmk reversed	£1400	£100
11	1	8c. pale dull orange (10.64)............	£500	9.50
		a. Brownish orange............	£475	11.00
		b. Bright orange............	£425	11.00
		w. Wmk inverted	£1100	95.00
		x. Wmk reversed	£1200	£140
12		12c. pale greenish blue (4.65)............	£950	32.00
		a. Pale blue............	30.00	3.50
		b. Deep blue............	£250	12.00
		w. Wmk inverted	—	85.00
		x. Wmk reversed	—	90.00
13	3	18c. lilac (1866)	£7000	£300
		w. Wmk inverted	£10000	£900
		x. Wmk reversed	£18000	£1300
		y. Wmk inverted and reversed......	†	£2000
14		24c. green (10.64)	£500	8.50
		a. Pale green............	£600	15.00
		b. Deep green............	£900	28.00
		w. Wmk inverted	£2250	95.00
		x. Wmk reversed	£2000	£130
15	2	30c. vermilion............	£900	14.00
		a. Orange-vermilion............	£800	15.00
		b. "GKON" of "HONGKONG" damaged at foot	—	£1000
		w. Wmk inverted	£2250	£110
		x. Wmk reversed	—	£140
16		30c. mauve (14.8.71)	£250	5.50
		a. "GKON" of "HONGKONG" damaged at foot	—	£425
		w. Wmk inverted	£1000	90.00
		x. Wmk reversed	—	£140
17		48c. pale rose (1.65)	£1100	50.00
		a. Rose-carmine............	£850	27.00
		w. Wmk inverted	£2000	£130
		x. Wmk reversed	—	£180
18		96c. olive-bistre (1.65)	£50000	£700
		w. Wmk inverted	†	£2250
19		96c. brownish grey (1865)	£1400	60.00
		a. Brownish black............	£1600	50.00
		w. Wmk inverted	£2000	£180
		y. Wmk inverted and reversed......	†	£1600

There is a wide range of shades in this issue, of which we can only indicate the main groups.

No. 12 is the same shade as No. 3 without wmk, the impression having a waxy appearance.

A single used example of the 48c. in a bright claret shade is known. No other stamps in this shade, either mint or used, have been discovered. See also Nos. 22 and 28/31.

16 cents. (4)	**28** cents. (5)	**5** cents. (6)	**10** cents. (7)

ts.

No. 20b

1876 (Aug)–**77**. *Nos.* 13 *and* 16 *surch with T* **4** *or* 5 *by Noronha and Sons, Hong Kong.*

20	3	16c. on 18c. lilac (1.4.77)	£2250	£150
		a. Space between "n" and "t"	£7500	£900
		b. Space between "s" and stop	£7500	£900
		w. Wmk inverted	£5500	£900
21	2	28c. on 30c. mauve	£1400	50.00
		a. "GKON" of "HONGKONG" damaged at foot	—	£750

1877 (Aug). *New value. Wmk Crown CC. P 14.*

22	3	16c. yellow............	£1900	65.00
		w. Wmk inverted	£3750	£350

1880 (1 Mar–Sept). *Surch with T* **6** *or* 7 *by Noronha and Sons.*

23	1	5c. on 8c. brt orange (No. 11b) (Sept)	£1000	£100
		a. Surch inverted	†	£17000
		b. Surch double	†	£18000
24	3	5c. on 18c. lilac (No. 13)	£950	60.00
		x. Wmk reversed	£2000	£1000
		y. Wmk inverted and reversed	†	£3000
25	1	10c. on 12c. pale blue (No. 12a)	£1000	55.00
		a. Blue............	£1500	95.00
26	3	10c. on 16c. yellow (No. 22) (May)	£4250	£150
		a. Surch inverted	†	£75000
		b. Surch double	†	£75000
		w. Wmk inverted	—	£1600
27		10c. on 24c. green (No. 14) (June)	£1400	85.00
		w. Wmk inverted	—	£500

Two examples of No. 26b are known, both used in Shanghai.

1880 (Mar–Dec). *Colours changed and new values. Wmk Crown CC. P 14.*

28	1	2c. dull rose	£160	25.00
		a. Rose............	£170	26.00
		w. Wmk inverted	†	£300
29	2	5c. blue (Dec)	£475	48.00
		w. Wmk inverted	—	£200
30		10c. mauve (Nov)	£600	15.00
		w. Wmk inverted	—	£170
31	3	48c. brown	£1300	95.00

1882 (May)–**96**. Wmk Crown CA. P 14.

32	1	2c. rose-lake (7.82)	£180	28.00
		a. Rose-pink............	£200	29.00
		ab. Perf 12............	£70000	£70000
		w. Wmk inverted	—	£130
		x. Wmk reversed	—	£400
33		2c. carmine (1884)	40.00	1.75
		a. Aniline carmine............	—	£100
		w. Wmk inverted	—	£100
34	2	4c. slate-grey (1.4.96)	15.00	1.50

35		w. Wmk inverted		—	£100
		5c. pale blue		28·00	85
		a. Blue		29·00	85
		aw. Wmk inverted		£325	80·00
		x. Wmk reversed		—	£200
36		10c. dull mauve (8.82)		£700	15·00
		a. Green (2.84)		£140	1·25
37		10c. deep blue-green (1884)		£1800	38·00
		aw. Wmk inverted		†	£550
38		10c. purple/red (1.1.91)		27·00	1·25
		a. Grey-green		£425	80·00
		x. Wmk reversed		£750	£110
		y. Wmk inverted and reversed		—	—
39		30c. yellowish green (1.1.91)		£130	38·00
		a. Grey-green		85·00	23·00

38s, 39as Optd "Specimen" Set of 2 £400

Examples of No. 39 should not be confused with washed or faded stamps from the grey-green shade which tend to turn to a very yellow-green when dampened.

For other stamps with this watermark, but in colours changed to the U.P.U. scheme see Nos. 56/61.

20 CENTS (8) **50 CENTS** (9) **1 DOLLAR** (10)

1885 (Sept). As Nos. 15, 19 and 31, but wmkd Crown CA, surch with T **8** to **10** by De La Rue.

40	2	20c. on 30c. orange-red		£120	5·50
		a. Surch double		—	—
		w. Wmk inverted		£900	£300
41	3	50c. on 48c. yellowish brown		£400	35·00
		w. Wmk inverted		—	£250
42		$1 on 96c. grey-olive		£750	75·00

40s/2s Optd "Specimen" Set of 3 £1300

7 cents. (11) **14 cents.** (12)

弌 (13) (20c.) 五十 (14) (50c.) 壹員 (15) ($1)

1891 (1 Jan–Mar).

(a) Nos. 16 and 37 surch with T **11** or **12** by Noronha and Sons, Hong Kong.

43	2	7c. on 10c. green		75·00	8·00
		a. Antique "t" in "cents" (R. 1/1)		£600	£150
		b. Surch double		£6000	£1300
44		14c. on 30c. mauve (Feb)		£180	70·00
		a. Antique "t" in "cents" (R. 1/1)		£2750	£900
		b. "GKON" of "HONGKONG" damaged at foot		—	£1400

(b) As Nos. 40/2 (surch with T **8** to **10** by De La Rue), but colours changed.

45	2	20c. on 30c. yellowish green (No. 39)		£170	£160
46		a. Grey-green (No. 39a)		£110	£150
46	3	50c. on 48c. dull purple		£275	£300
47		$1 on 96c. purple/red		£800	£350

45as/7s Optd "Specimen" Set of 3 £850

(c) Nos. 45/7 with further surch, T **13/15**, in Chinese characters, handstamped locally (Mar).

48	2	20c. on 30c. yellowish green		55·00	9·00
		a. Grey-green		38·00	7·50
		b. Surch double		£25000	—
49	3	50c. on 48c. dull purple		80·00	5·50
50		$1 on 96c. purple/red		£450	22·00
		w. Wmk inverted		—	—

The true antique "t" variety (Nos. 43a and 44a) should not be confused with a small "t" showing a short foot. In the antique "t" the crossbar is accurately bisected by the vertical stroke, which is thicker at the top. The lower curve bends towards the right and does not turn upwards to the same extent as on the normal.

The handstamped surcharges on Nos. 48/50 were applied over the original Chinese face values. The single character for "2" was intended to convert "30c." to "20c.". There were six slightly different versions of the "2" handstamp and three for the "50c.".

The errors of the Chinese surcharges previously listed on the above issue and also on Nos. 52 and 55 are now omitted as being outside the scope of the catalogue. While some without doubt possess philatelic merit, it is impossible to distinguish between the genuine errors and the clandestine copies made to order with the original chops. No. 55c is retained as this represents a distinctly different chop which was used for the last part of the printing.

1841 Hong Kong (16) **JUBILEE 1891** (16) **10 CENTS** (17) 拾 (18) 拾 (19)

1891 (22 Jan). 50th Anniversary of Colony. Optd with T **16** by Noronha and Sons, Hong Kong.

51	1	2c. carmine (No. 33)		£450	£120
		a. Short "J" in "JUBILEE" (R. 1/6)		£700	£180
		b. Short "U" in "JUBILEE" (R. 1/5)		£700	£180
		c. Broken "1" in "1891" (R. 2/1)		£850	£275
		d. Tall narrow "K" in "Kong" (R. 1/3)		£1200	£450
		e. Opt double		£16000	£12000

---

		f. Space between "O" and "N" of "Hong" (R. 1/5)		£1600	£700

Most of the supply of No. 51, which was only on sale for three days, was overprinted from a setting of 12 (6×2) applied five times to complete each sheet. There were six printings from this setting, but a second setting, possibly of 30 or 60, was used for the seventh. Positions quoted are from the setting of twelve. Most varieties only occur in some printings and many less marked overprint flaws also exist.

The prices quoted for No. 51e are for examples on which the two impressions are distinctly separated. Examples on which the two impressions are almost coincidental are worth considerably less.

1898 (1 Apr). Wmk Crown CA. P 14.

(a) Surch with T **10** by D.L.R. and handstamped Chinese characters as T **15**.

52	3	$1 on 96c. black		£180	27·00
		a. Grey-black		£170	27·00

(b) Surch with T **10** only.

53	3	$1 on 96c. black		£3250	£4000
		a. Grey-black		£2750	£3750
		as. Optd "Specimen"		£600	—

1898 (1 Apr). *(a)* Surch with T **17** by Noronha and Sons, Hong Kong.

54	2	10c. on 30c. grey-green (No. 39a)		£550	£1000
		a. Figures "10" widely spaced (1½ mm)		£3750	—
		b. Surch double		—	—

Type **17** was applied in a horizontal setting of 12, No. 54a appearing on position 12 for the early printings only.

(b) As No. 54, but with handstamped Chinese characters, T **18**, in addition.

55	2	10c. on 30c. grey-green (No. 39a)		50·00	75·00
		a. Yellowish green		80·00	£110
		b. Figures "10" widely spaced (1½ mm)		£700	£900
		c. Chinese character large (Type **19**)		£900	£1000
		ca. Ditto. Figures "10" widely spaced		£6500	—
		d. Surch Type **17** double		—	—
		s. Handstamped "Specimen"		£140	—

1900 (Aug)–**01**. Wmk Crown CA. P 14.

56	1	2c. dull green		27·00	85
		w. Wmk inverted		£170	80·00
57	2	4c. carmine (1901)		19·00	85
		w. Wmk inverted		—	†
58		5c. yellow		22·00	6·50
		w. Wmk inverted		—	£375
59		10c. ultramarine		50·00	1·75
		w. Wmk inverted		—	£100
60	1	12c. blue (1901)		48·00	55·00
61	2	30c. brown (1901)		48·00	22·00

56/61 Set of 6 £190 80·00
56s/9s, 61s Optd "Specimen" Set of 5 £550

20

21

22

23

1903 (Jan–July). Wmk Crown CA. P 14.

62	20	1c. dull purple and brown		2·00	50
63		2c. dull green (July)		12·00	1·50
		w. Wmk inverted		—	—
64	21	4c. purple/red (July)		15·00	40
65		5c. dull green and brown-orange (July)		13·00	9·00
66		8c. slate and violet (12 Feb)		11·00	1·25
67	20	10c. purple and blue/blue (July)		42·00	1·50
68	23	12c. green and purple/yellow (12 Feb)		9·00	4·25
69		20c. slate and chestnut (June)		50·00	3·25
70	22	30c. dull green and black (21 May)		50·00	20·00
71	23	50c. dull green and magenta (June)		42·00	42·00
72	20	$1 purple and sage-green (June)		90·00	22·00
73	23	$2 slate and scarlet (July)		£300	£275
74	22	$3 slate and dull blue (July)		£350	£350
75	23	$5 purple and blue-green (June)		£500	£500
76	22	$10 slate and orange/blue (July)		£1200	£425
		w. Wmk inverted		†	—

62/76 Set of 15 £2250 £1500
62s/76s Optd "Specimen" Set of 15 £1700

No. 63w is known used at Shanghai.

1904 (4 Oct)–**06**. Wmk Mult Crown CA. Chalk-surfaced paper (8, 12c., $3, $5) or ordinary paper (others). P 14.

77	20	2c. dull green		10·00	1·50
		a. Chalk-surfaced paper (1906)		13·00	3·75
		aw. Wmk inverted		†	£850
78	21	4c. purple/red		23·00	40
		a. Chalk-surfaced paper (1906)		11·00	75
79		5c. dull green and brown-orange		35·00	9·50
		a. Chalk-surfaced paper (1906)		17·00	5·00
		aw. Wmk inverted		—	—
80		8c. slate and violet (1906)		13·00	2·00
81	20	10c. dull purple and blue (3.05)		22·00	1·25
82	23	12c. green and purple/yellow (1906)		15·00	5·50
83		20c. slate and chestnut		42·00	2·25

---

		a. Chalk-surfaced paper (1906)		35·00	2·25
		aw. Wmk inverted		†	£500
84	22	30c. dull green and black		45·00	23·00
		a. Chalk-surfaced paper (1906)		50·00	18·00
85	23	50c. green and magenta		80·00	9·00
		a. Chalk-surfaced paper (1906)		80·00	12·00
86	20	$1 purple and sage-green		£130	27·00
		a. Chalk-surfaced paper (1906)		£130	27·00
87	23	$2 slate and scarlet		£300	£130
88	22	$3 slate and dull blue (1905)		£250	£110
89	23	$5 purple and blue-green (1905)		£450	£375
90	22	$10 slate and orange/blue (5.05)		£1800	£1300
		aw. Wmk inverted		†	—
		b. Chalk-surfaced paper (1906)		£2000	£1100

77/90 Set of 14 £2750 £1700

No. 77aw is known used at Shanghai in October 1908 and 83aw at Hoihow in March 1908.

1907–11. Colours changed and new value. Wmk Mult Crown CA. Chalk-surfaced paper (6c. and 20c. to $2). P 14.

91	20	1c. brown (9.10)		4·75	1·00
		x. Wmk reversed		†	£1200
92		2c. deep green		26·00	1·75
		a. Green		26·00	1·50
		w. Wmk inverted		£1300	£800
93	21	4c. carmine-red		10·00	40
94	22	6c. orange-vermilion and purple (10.07)		26·00	5·00
95	20	10c. bright ultramarine		29·00	40
96	23	20c. purple and sage-green (3.11)		45·00	42·00
97	22	30c. purple and orange-yellow (3.11)		55·00	27·00
98	23	50c. black/green (3.11)		40·00	15·00
99		$2 carmine-red and black (1910)		£325	£325

91/9 Set of 9 £500 £375
91s, 93s/9s Optd "Specimen" Set of 8 £950

No. 91x was used at Canton during December 1912 and January 1913 and No. 92w at Shanghai during 1908.

24

25

26

27

28

(A) (B)

In Type A of the 25c. the upper Chinese character in the left-hand label has a short vertical stroke crossing it at the foot. In Type B this stroke is absent.

Crown broken at right (R9/2)

Broken flower at top right (Upper left pane R. 1/3)

1912 (9 Nov)–**21**. Wmk Mult Crown CA. Chalk-surfaced paper (12c. to $10). P 14.

100	24	1c. brown		3·00	55
		a. Black-brown		4·25	2·25
		b. Crown broken at right		£225	£160
101		2c. deep green		9·00	30
		a. Green		9·00	30
		w. Wmk inverted		†	—
		y. Wmk inverted and reversed		†	—
102	25	4c. carmine-red		4·50	30
		a. Scarlet (1914)		20·00	1·75
103	26	6c. yellow-orange		4·50	1·25
		a. Brown-orange		6·00	2·00
		w. Wmk inverted		£750	£750
104	25	8c. grey		24·00	5·50
		a. Slate (1914)		38·00	5·50
105	24	10c. ultramarine		35·00	30
		a. Deep bright ultramarine		24·00	30
106	27	12c. purple/yellow		6·00	8·00
		a. White back (1914)		7·00	14·00
		as. Optd "Specimen"		£110	—
107		20c. purple and sage-green		7·50	1·00
108	25	25c. purple & magenta (Type A) (1.14)		22·00	25·00
109		25c. purple and magenta (Type B) (8.19)		£170	65·00
		a. Broken flower		£2750	—
110	26	30c. purple and orange yellow		35·00	8·00
		a. Purple and orange		23·00	6·50
		w. Wmk inverted		—	—
111	27	50c. black/blue-green		21·00	1·50
		a. White back (5.14)		16·00	4·25
		as. Optd "Specimen"		£150	—
		b. On blue-green, olive back (1917)		£1300	30·00
		c. On emerald surface (9.19)		26·00	8·00
		d. On emerald back (7.12.21)		24·00	6·50
		ds. Optd "Specimen"		£160	—
		w. Wmk inverted		£2500	—
112	24	$1 purple and blue/blue		48·00	4·00
		w. Wmk inverted		£160	£110
113	27	$2 carmine-red and grey-black		£150	£150
114	26	$3 green and purple		£225	90·00
115	27	$5 green and red/green		£650	£400

153

		a. White back (5.14).....................	£600	£300
		as. Optd "Specimen"...................	£350	
		b. On blue-green, olive back		
		(1917).............................	£1100	£350
		bs. Optd "Specimen"...................	£375	
		bw. Wmk inverted.....................	£3500	
116	26	$10 purple and black/red...............	£600	85·00
100/16 Set of 17			£1800	£600
100s/16s Optd "Specimen" Set of 17			£1900	

No. 100b occurred in 1916 on R. 9/2 of the lower right pane before being retouched.

1921 (Jan)–**37.** Wmk Mult Script CA. Chalk-surfaced paper (12c. to $5). P 14.

117	24	1c. brown	1·00	40
118		2c. blue-green	2·75	50
		a. Yellow-green (1932)...............	9·50	1·50
		bw. Wmk inverted.....................	75·00	
118c		2c. grey (14.4.37)......................	20·00	7·50
119	26	3c. grey (8.10.31)......................	8·00	1·00
120		4c. carmine-rose	4·00	70
		a. Carmine-red (1932)...............	3·75	30
		b. Top of lower Chinese		
		characters at right broken off		
		(R. 9/4)............................	95·00	75·00
121		5c. violet (16.10.31)...................	11·00	1·00
122		8c. grey	15·00	38·00
123		8c. orange (7.12.21)..................	4·00	1·50
		w. Wmk inverted.....................	£950	
124	24	10c. bright ultramarine	5·00	30
		aw. Wmk inverted....................	£180	
124b	27	12c. purple/yellow (3.4.33)...........	15·00	2·50
125		20c. purple and sage-green (7.12.21)	6·50	30
126	28	25c. purple and magenta (B)		
		(7.12.21)...........................	5·50	70
		a. Broken flower	40·00	48·00
		w. Wmk inverted.....................	†	£300
127	26	30c. purple & chrome-yellow		
		(7.12.21)...........................	11·00	1·50
		a. Purple and orange-yellow.......	27·00	7·00
		w. Wmk inverted.....................	£200	
128	27	50c. black/emerald (1924)............	16·00	30
129	24	$1 purple and blue/blue (7.12.21)..	38·00	50
130	27	$2 carmine-red & grey-black		
		(7.12.21)...........................	£120	6·00
131	26	$3 green and dull purple (1926).....	£170	60·00
132	27	$5 green and red/emerald (1925)...	£475	70·00
117/32 Set of 18			£800	£170
117s/32s Optd or Perf (2c. grey, 3c., 5c., 12c.)				
"Specimen" Set of 18..............................			£1800	

No. 120b occurs on R. 9/4 of the lower left pane.

1935 (6 May). Silver Jubilee. As Nos. 91/4 of Antigua, but ptd by B.W. P 11×12.

133		3c. ultramarine and grey-black............	4·00	3·50
		c. Lightning conductor..................	£375	£225
134		5c. green and indigo	8·50	3·50
		a. Extra flagstaff.......................	£325	£275
		b. Short extra flagstaff................	£400	
		c. Lightning conductor.................	£350	£275
		d. Flagstaff on right-hand turret.....	£425	£275
		e. Double flagstaff.....................	£500	
135		10c. brown and deep blue................	20·00	1·75
136		20c. slate and purple....................	38·00	8·00
		b. Short extra flagstaff................	£800	£350
		d. Flagstaff on right-hand turret.....	£850	£375
		e. Double flagstaff.....................	£850	£375
133/6 Set of 4			60·00	15·00
133s/6s Perf "Specimen" Set of 4			£425	

For illustrations of plate varieties see Omnibus section following Zanzibar.

1937 (12 May). Coronation. As Nos. 95/7 of Antigua. P 11×11½.

137		4c. green	4·50	4·50
138		15c. carmine..............................	10·00	3·25
139		25c. blue..................................	13·00	3·25
137/9 Set of 3			25·00	10·00
137s/9s Perf "Specimen" Set of 3			£225	

King George VI

Short right leg to "R" (Right pane R. 7/3, Left pane R. 3/1)

1938–52. Wmk Mult Script CA. Chalk-surfaced paper (80c., $1 (No. 155), $2 (No. 157), $5 (No. 159), $10 (No. 161)). P 14.

140	29	1c. brown (24.5.38)	1·75	2·75
		a. Pale brown (4.2.52).................	2·25	6·50
141		2c. grey (5.4.38).........................	2·00	30
		a. Perf 14½×14 (28.9.45)..........	1·75	5·00
142		4c. orange (5.4.38)......................	4·50	2·00
		a. Perf 14½×14 (28.9.45)..........	4·50	3·25
143		5c. green (24.5.38)......................	1·25	20
		a. Perf 14½×14 (28.9.45)..........	2·50	5·00
144		8c. red-brown (1.11.41).................	1·75	2·50
		a. Imperf (pair)..........................	£25000	
145		10c. bright violet (13.4.38)............	50·00	75
		a. Perf 14½×14. Dull violet		
		(28.9.45)..........................	9·50	20
		b. Dull reddish violet (8.4.46).......	7·00	70
		c. Reddish lilac (9.4.47)...............	16·00	20
146		15c. scarlet (13.4.38)..................	2·00	30
147		20c. black (1.2.46)......................	1·25	30
148		20c. scarlet-vermilion (1.4.48)........	7·00	40
		a. Rose-red (25.4.51).................	17·00	5·50
149		25c. bright blue (5.4.38)................	29·00	2·25
150		25c. pale yellow-olive (24.9.46).......	4·75	2·00
151		30c. yellow-olive (13.4.38).............	£150	2·50
		a. Perf 14½×14. Yellowish olive		
		(28.9.45)..........................	24·00	8·50
152		30c. blue (27.12.46)....................	7·00	20
153		50c. purple (13.4.38)...................	55·00	70
		a. Perf 14½×14. Dp mag (28.9.45)	30·00	1·10
		ab. Printed both sides, inverted on		
		reverse.............................	£1200	

		b. Reddish purple (9.4.46)............	17·00	2·00
		c. Chalk-surfaced paper. Brt		
		purple (9.4.47).....................	9·00	20
154		80c. carmine (2.2.48)...................	5·00	1·00
155		$1 dull lilac and blue (chalk-		
		surfaced paper) (27.4.38).........	8·00	3·25
		a. Short right leg to "R"............	£120	
		b. Ordinary paper. Pale reddish		
		lilac and blue (28.9.45)............	13·00	11·00
		ba. Short right leg to "R"..........	£160	
156		$1 red-orange and green (8.4.46)...	18·00	30
		a. Short right leg to "R"............	£180	
		b. Chalk-surfaced paper (21.6.48).	48·00	1·75
		ba. Short right leg to "R"..........	£300	
		c. Chalk-surfaced paper. Yellow		
		orange and green (6.11.52).......	80·00	15·00
		ca. Short right leg to "R"..........	£475	
157		$2 red-orange and green (24.5.38).	75·00	18·00
158		$2 reddish violet and scarlet		
		(8.4.46).............................	32·00	4·00
		a. Chalk-surfaced paper (9.4.47)...	35·00	1·00
159		$5 dull lilac and scarlet (2.6.38).....	60·00	50·00
160		$5 green and violet (8.4.46).........	80·00	9·50
		a. Yellowish green and violet		
		(8.4.46).............................	£200	22·00
		ab. Chalk-surfaced paper (9.4.47)..	£110	3·50
161		$10 green and violet (2.6.38).........	£500	£100
162		$10 bright lilac and blue (8.4.46).....	£140	32·00
		a. Chalk-surfaced paper. Reddish		
		violet and blue (9.4.47)...........	£180	18·00
140/62 Set of 23			£900	£190
140s/62s Perf "Specimen" Set of 23			£2250	

Following bomb damage to the De La Rue works on the night of 29 December 1940 various emergency arrangements were made to complete current requisitions for Hong Kong stamps: ·

Nos. 141a, 143a, 145a, 151a and 153a (all printings perforated 14½×14 except the 4c.) were printed and perforated by Bradbury, Wilkinson & Co. Ltd. using De La Rue plates. These stamps are on rough-surfaced paper.

Nos. 142a and 144 were printed by Harrison & Sons in sheets of 120 (12×10) instead of the normal 120 two panes (6×10).

Printings of the $1 and $2 values were made by Williams, Lea & Co. using De La Rue plates.

With the exception of the 8c. it is believed that none of these printings were issued in Hong Kong before its occupation by the Japanese on 25 December 1941, although examples could be obtained in London from late 1941. The issue dates quoted are those on which the stamps were eventually released in Hong Kong following liberation in 1945.

Nos. 160/a were separate printings released in Hong Kong on the same day.

No. 144a. One imperforate sheet was found and most of the stamps were sold singly to the public at a branch P.O. and used for postage.

30 Street Scene

31 Empress of Japan (liner) and Junk

32 The University

32 The Harbour

34 The Hong Kong Bank

35 Falcon (clipper) and Short S.23 Empire 'C' class flying boat

(Des W. E. Jones. Recess B.W.)

1941 (26 Feb). Centenary of British Occupation. T 30/35. Wmk Mult Script CA (sideways on horiz designs). P 13½×13 (2c. and 25c.) or 13×13½ (others).

163		2c. orange and chocolate	5·50	2·00
164		4c. bright purple and carmine............	6·00	3·50
165		5c. black and green......................	3·00	50
166		15c. black and scarlet....................	6·00	1·75
167		25c. chocolate and blue.................	14·00	6·00
168		$1 blue and orange.....................	48·00	8·50
163/8 Set of 6			75·00	20·00
163s/8s Perf "Specimen" Set of 6			£425	

Hong Kong was under Japanese occupation from 25 December 1941 until 30 August 1945. The Japanese post offices in the colony were closed from 31 August and mail was carried free, marked with cachets reading "HONG KONG/1945/POSTAGE PAID". Military administration lasted until 1 May 1946. Hong Kong stamps were re-introduced on 28 September 1945.

36 King George VI and Phoenix

Extra stroke (R. 1/2)

(Des W. E. Jones. Recess D.L.R.)

1946 (29 Aug). Victory. Wmk Mult Script CA. P 13.

169	36	30c. blue and red (shades)................	2·75	1·75
		a. Extra stroke.........................	70·00	60·00
170		$1 brown and red	3·75	75
		a. Extra stroke.........................	95·00	50·00
169s/70s Perf "Specimen" Set of 2			£190	

Spur on "N" of "KONG" (R. 2/9)

1948 (22 Dec). Royal Silver Wedding. As Nos. 112/13 of Antigua.

171		10c. violet	3·00	1·00
		a. Spur on "N"........................	65·00	50·00
172		$10 carmine.............................	£300	95·00

1949 (10 Oct). 75th Anniv of Universal Postal Union. As Nos. 114/17 of Antigua.

173		10c. violet	4·50	1·00
174		20c. carmine-red	17·00	3·00
175		30c. deep blue	15·00	3·00
176		80c. bright reddish purple	35·00	9·50
173/6 Set of 4			65·00	15·00

STAMP BOOKLETS

BOOKLET CONTENTS. In Nos. SB1/4 and SB6/7 the 1c. and 2c. were normally each in blocks of 12 or two blocks of 6 and the 4c. in blocks of 12 and 4 or two blocks of 8, all having been taken from normal sheets. No. SB5 had both the 2c. and 4c. in blocks of 12 and 4 or as two blocks of 8. Other content formats exist.

1904 (1 Jan). Black on white cover showing contents and postage rates with "K & W LD" imprint on front. Stapled.

SB1 $1 booket containing twelve 1c. (No. 62), twelve 2c. (No. 56) and sixteen 4c. (No. 57) ....
a. 4c. No. 64 (King Edward VII) instead of No. 57 (Q.V.)...................................... £6500

1905–06. Black on white cover showing contents and postage rates with "Hongkong Printing Press" imprint on front. Metal fastener.

SB2 $1 booklet containing twelve 1c., twelve 2c. and sixteen 4c. (Nos. 62/4)................ £5500
a. 2c. and 4c. (Nos. 77/8) (MCA ordinary paper) instead of Nos. 63/4 (CA) (1906) £7500
b. 2c. and 4c. (Nos. 77a/8a) (MCA chalk-surfaced paper) instead of Nos. 77/8 (MCA ordinary paper) (1906)....................

Some examples of No. SB2 show the reference to Australia on the front cover deleted in manuscript. No. SB2a has the rate information reset to omit "EXCEPT AUSTRALIA".

1907 (Dec). Black on white cover showing contents and postage rates for both Hong Kong and Agencies in China with "Hongkong Printing Press" imprint. Metal fastener.

SB3 $1 booklet containing twelve 1c. (No. 62), twelve 2c. (No. 92) and sixteen 4c. (No. 93)..
a. Stapled... £3750

1910 (May)–**11.** Black on white cover showing contents, but no postage rates, with "Hongkong Printing Press" imprint on front. Stapled.

SB4 $1 booklet containing twelve 1c. (No. 62), twelve 2c. (No. 92) and sixteen 4c. (No. 93) ....
a. 1c. No. 91 (MCA) instead of No. 62 (CA) (9.11)... £3750

1912 (Apr). Black on cream cover showing contents, but no postage rates, with "Hongkong Printing Press" imprint on front. Stapled.

SB5 $1 booklet containing four 1c., sixteen 2c. and sixteen 4c. (Nos. 91/3)..................... £4500

1913 (Feb). Black on cream cover showing contents, but no postage rates, with "Hongkong Printing Press" imprint on front. Stapled.

SB6 $1 booklet containing twelve 1c., twelve 2c. and sixteen 4c. (Nos. 100/2) (MCA wmk)....... £3500

1922–24. Black on cream cover showing contents, but no postage rates, with "Hongkong Printing Press" imprint on front. Stapled.

SB7	$1 booklet containing twelve 1c., twelve 2c. and sixteen 4c. (Nos. 117/18, 120) (Script wmk).	£3750
	a. With Ye Olde Printers Ltd imprint (1924)	

POSTAGE DUE STAMPS

PRINTERS. Nos. D1/12 were typographed by De La Rue & Co.

D 1 Post-office Scales

1923 (Dec)–56. Wmk Mult Script CA. Ordinary paper. P 14.

D1	D 1	1c. brown	2·50	65
		a. Wmk sideways (1931)	1·50	3·25
		ab. Chalk-surfaced paper (21.3.56).	30	1·00
D2		2c. green	25·00	7·00
		a. Wmk sideways (1928)	11·00	5·00
D3		4c. scarlet	42·00	7·00
		a. Wmk sideways (1928)	28·00	6·00
D4		6c. yellow	28·00	13·00
		a. Wmk sideways (1931)	75·00	35·00
D5		10c. bright ultramarine	25·00	8·50
		a. Chalk-surfaced paper (1934)	£100	16·00
D1/5	*Set of 5*		£110	
D1a/5a	*Set of 5*		£190	55·00
D1s/5s	Optd "Specimen" *Set of 5*		£325	

1938 (Feb)–63. Wmk Mult Script CA (sideways). Ordinary paper. P 14.

D6	D 1	2c. grey	14·00	9·00
		a. Chalk-surfaced paper (21.3.56).	1·10	10·00
D7		4c. orange	19·00	6·50
		a. Chalk-surfaced paper. *Orange-yellow* (23.5.61)	2·50	10·00
D8		6c. scarlet	9·50	5·50
D9		8c. chestnut (26.2.46)	5·50	32·00
D10		10c. violet	35·00	50
		a. Chalk-surfaced paper (17.9.63).	16·00	14·00
D11		20c. black (26.2.46)	13·00	3·00
D12		50c. blue (7.47)	55·00	15·00
D6a/12	*Set of 7*		90·00	65·00
D6s/12s	Perf "Specimen" *Set of 7*		£375	

POSTCARD STAMPS

Stamps specially surcharged for use on Postcards.

PRICES. Those in the left-hand column are for unused examples on complete postcards; those on the right for used examples off card. Examples used on postcards are worth much more.

3 CENTS (P 1)   **THREE** (P 2)

1879 (1 Apr). Nos. 22 and 13 surch as Type P 1 by Noronha & Sons.

P1	3	3c. on 16c. yellow (No. 22)	£350	£425
P2		5c. on 18c. lilac (No. 13)	£350	£450

1879 (Nov). No. P 2 handstamped with Type P 2.

| P3 | 3 | 3c. on 5c. on 18c. lilac | £7000 | £7500 |

POSTAL FISCAL STAMPS

I. Stamps inscribed "STAMP DUTY"

NOTE. The dated circular "HONG KONG" cancellation with "PAID ALL" in lower segment was used for fiscal purposes, in black, from 1877. Previously it appears in red on mail to the U.S.A., but is usually not used as a cancellation.

F 1   F 2

F 3

1874–1902. Wmk Crown CC.

(a) P 15½×15.

F1	F 1	$2 olive-green	£350	60·00
F2	F 2	$3 dull violet	£325	42·00
		b. Bluish paper		
F3	F 3	$10 rose-carmine	£8000	£700

(b) P 14.

F4	F 1	$2 dull bluish green (10.97)	£400	£250
F5	F 2	$3 dull mauve (3.02)	£550	£475

---

	a. Bluish paper	£2000	
F6	F 3	$10 grey-green	£12000	£11000
F4s/5s	Optd "Specimen" *Set of 2*		£450

Nos. F1/3 and F7 exist on various papers, ranging from thin-thick. All three of the values perforated 15½×15 were authorised for postal use in 1874. The $10 rose-carmine was withdrawn from such use in 1880, the $2 in September 1897 and the $3 in 1902.

The $2 and $3 perforated 14 were available for postal purposes until July 1903. The $10 in grey-green was issued for fiscal purposes in 1884 and is known with postal cancellations.

12 CENTS. (F 4)   (F 5)

1880. No. F 3 surch with type F 4 by Noronha and Sons, Hong Kong.

F7	F 3	12c. on $10 rose-carmine	£850	£300

1890 (24 Dec). Wmk Crown CA. P 14.

F8	F 5	2c. dull purple	£110	26·00
		w. Wmk inverted		

No. F8 was authorised for postal use between 24 and 31 December 1890.

5 DOLLARS (F 6)   **ONE DOLLAR** (F 7)   (F 8)

1891 (1 Jan). Surch with Type F 6 by D.L.R. Wmk Crown CA. P 14.

F9	F 3	$5 on $10 purple/*red*	£325	£100
		s. Optd "Specimen"	£200	

No. F9 was in use for postal purposes until June 1903.

1897 (Sept). Surch with Type F 7 by Noronha and Sons, Hong Kong, and with the value in Chinese characters subsequently applied twice by handstamp as T 15.

F10	F 1	$1 on $2 olive-green (No. F 1)	£225	£120
		a. Both Chinese handstamps omitted	£3750	£2750
F11		$1 on $2 dull bluish green (No. F 4)	£250	£140
		a. Both Chinese handstamps omitted	£1900	£1600
		b. Diagonal Chinese handstamp omitted	£13000	
		c. Vertical Chinese handstamp omitted		
		s. Handstamped "Specimen"	£140	

1938 (11 Jan). Wmk Mult script CA. P 14.

F12	F 8	5c. green	75·00	13·00

No. F12 was authorised for postal use between 11 and 20 January 1938 due to a shortage of 5c., No 121.

Forged cancellations are known on this stamp inscribed "VICTORIA 9.AM 11 JA 38 HONG KONG" without side bars between the rings.

II. Stamps overprinted "S.O." (Stamp Office) or "S.D." (Stamp Duty)

S. O.   **S. D.**

邨厘   邨厘
(S 1)   (S 2)

1891 (1 Jan). Optd with Types S 1 or S 2.

S1	S 1	2c. carmine (No. 33)	£900	£375
S2	S 2	2c. carmine (No. 33)	£400	£190
		a. Opt inverted	†	£5500
S3	S 3	10c. purple/*red* (No. 38)	£1600	£425

Examples of No. S1 exist the "O" amended to "D" in manuscript.
Other fiscal stamps are found apparently postally used, but there is no evidence that this use was authorised.

JAPANESE OCCUPATION OF HONG KONG

Hong Kong surrendered to the Japanese on 25 December 1941. The postal service was not resumed until 22 January 1942 when the G.P.O. and Kowloon Central Office re-opened.

Japanese postmarks used in Hong Kong can be identified by the unique combination of horizontal lines in the central circle and three stars in the lower segment of the outer circle. Dates shown on such postmarks are in the sequence Year/Month/Day with the first shown as a Japanese regnal year number so that Showa 17 = 1942 and so on.

Initially six current Japanese definitives, 1, 2, 3, 4, 10 and 30s. (Nos. 297, 315/17, 322 and 327) were on sale, but the range gradually expanded to cover all values between ½s. and 10y. with Nos. 313/14, 318, 325, 328/31, 391, 395/6, 398/9 and 405 of Japan also available from Hong Kong post offices during the occupation. Philatelic covers exist showing other Japanese stamps, but these were not available from the local post offices. Supply of these Japanese stamps was interrupted and, during the period between 28 July 1942 and 21 April 1943, circular "Postage Paid" handstamps were sometimes used. A

---

substantial increase in postage rates on 16 April 1945 led to the issue of the local surcharges, Nos. J1/3.

PRICES FOR STAMPS ON COVER	
Nos. J1/3	*from* × 7

壹圓五拾錢 暫定 部督總港香
(1)

叁圓 暫定 部督總港香
(2)

1945 (16 Apr). Stamps of Japan surch with T 1 (No. J1) or as T 2.

J1	1.50 yen on 1s. brown	30·00	28·00
J2	3 yen on 2s. scarlet	12·00	22·00
J3	5 yen on 5s. claret	£900	£150

Designs (18½×22 mm):—1s. Girl Worker; 2s. Gen. Nogi; 5s. Admiral Togo.

No. J3 has four characters of value similarly arranged but differing from T 2.

BRITISH POST OFFICES IN CHINA

Under the terms of the 1842 Treaty of Nanking China granted Great Britain and its citizens commercial privileges in five Treaty Ports, Amoy, Canton, Foochow, Ningpo and Shanghai. British Consuls were appointed to each Port and their offices, as was usual during this period, collected and distributed mail for the British community. This system was formally recognised by a Hong Kong Government notice published on 16 April 1844. Mail from the consular offices was postmarked when it passed through Hong Kong.

The number of Chinese Treaty Ports was increased to sixteen by the ratification of the Treaty of Peking in 1860 with British postal facilities being eventually extended to the Ports of Chefoo, Hankow, Kiungchow (Hoihow), Swatow, Tainan (Anping) and Tientsin.

As postal business expanded the consular agencies were converted into packet agencies or post offices which passed under the direct control of the Hong Kong postal authorities on 1 May 1868.

In May 1898 the British Government leased the territory of Wei Hai Wei from China for use as a naval station to counter the Russian presence at Port Arthur.

The opening of the Trans-Siberia Railway and the extension of Imperial Penny Postage to the Treaty Port agencies resulted in them becoming a financial burden on the colonial post office. Control of the agencies reverted to the G.P.O., London, on 1 January 1911.

The pre-adhesive postal markings of the various agencies are a fascinating, but complex, subject. Full details can be found in *Hong Kong & the Treaty Ports of China & Japan* by F. W. Webb (reprinted edition J. Bendon, Limassol, 1992) and in various publications of the Hong Kong Study Circle.

From 15 October 1864 the use of Hong Kong stamps on mail from the Treaty Ports became compulsory, although such stamps were, initially, not cancelled (with the exception of Amoy) until they reached Hong Kong where the "B62" killer was applied. Cancellation of mail at the actual Ports commenced during 1866 and spreading to all the agencies during the next ten years. Shanghai had previously used a c.d.s. on adhesives during 1863 and again in 1865–66.

The main types of cancellation used between 1866 and 1930 are illustrated below. The illustrations show the style of each postmark and no attempt has been made to cover differences in type letters or figures, arrangement, diameter or colour.

Until 1885 the vertical and horizontal killers were used to obliterate the actual stamps with an impression of one of the circular date stamps shown elsewhere on the cover. Many of the early postmarks were also used as backstamps or transit marks and, in the notes which follow, references to use are for the first appearance of the mark, not necessarily its first use as an obliterator.

Illustrations in this section are taken from *Hong Kong & the Treaty Ports of China & Japan* by F. W. Webb and are reproduced with the permission of the Royal Philatelic Society, London.

Details of the stamps known used from each post office are taken, with permission, from *British Post Offices in the Far East* by Edward B. Proud, published by Proud-Bailey Co. Ltd.

Postmark Types

Type A Vertical killer   Type B Horizontal killer

Type C Name horizontal   Type D Name curved

Type **E** Double circle Name at top

Type **F** Double circle Name at foot

Type **G** Single circle Name at top

PRICES. The prices quoted in this section are for fine used stamps which show a clear impression of a substantial part of the cancellation.

AMOY

One of the five original Treaty Ports, opened to British trade by the Treaty of Nanking in 1842. A consular postal agency was established in 1844 which expanded in 1876 into two separate offices, one on the off-shore island of Ku Lang Seu and the other in Amoy itself.

Amoy "PAID" (*supplied* 1858) *used* 1859–67
Type **A** ("A1") (*supplied* 1866) *used at Ku Lang Seu* 1869–82
Type **D** (*supplied* 1866) *used* 1867–1922
Type **B** ("D27") (*supplied* 1876) *used at Amoy* 1876–84
Type **C** *used* 1876–94
Type **F** (*supplied* 1913) *used* 1916–22

Stamps of HONG KONG *cancelled at Amoy between* 1864 *and* 1916 *with postmarks detailed above.*

1862. No wmk (Nos. 1/7).
Z1	2c. brown	£200
Z2	8c. yellow-buff	£190
Z3	12c. pale greenish blue	£170
Z4	18c. lilac	£130
Z5	24c. green	£200
Z6	48c. rose	£1100
Z7	96c. brownish grey	£850

1863–71. Wmk Crown CC (Nos. 8/19).
Z8	2c. brown	35·00
Z9	4c. grey	40·00
	a. Perf 12½	
Z10	6c. lilac	65·00
Z11	8c. orange	45·00
Z12	12c. blue	20·00
Z13	18c. lilac	£900
Z14	24c. green	55·00
Z15	30c. vermilion	£100
Z16	30c. mauve	16·00
Z17	48c. rose	60·00
Z18	96c. olive-bistre	£1800
Z19	96c. brownish grey	£275

1876–77. (Nos. 20/1).
Z20	16c. on 18c. lilac	£350
Z21	28c. on 30c. mauve	£150

1877. Wmk Crown CC (No. 22).
Z22	16c. yellow	£130

1880. (Nos. 23/7).
Z23	5c. on 8c. orange	£140
Z24	5c. on 18c. lilac	£100
Z25	10c. on 12c. blue	£100
Z26	10c. on 16c. yellow	£225
Z27	10c. on 24c. green	£130

1880. Wmk Crown CC (Nos. 28/31).
Z28	2c. rose	48·00
Z29	5c. blue	75·00
Z30	10c. mauve	65·00
Z31	48c. brown	£190

1882–96. Wmk Crown CA (Nos. 32/9).
Z31a	2c. rose-lake	
Z32	2c. carmine	4·25
Z33	4c. slate-grey	11·00
Z34	5c. blue	4·25
Z35	10c. dull mauve	35·00
Z36	10c. green	4·75
Z37	10c. purple/*red*	4·75
Z38	30c. green	32·00

1885. (Nos. 40/2).
Z39	20c. on 30c. orange-red	14·00
Z40	50c. on 48c. yellowish brown	65·00
Z41	$1 on 96c. grey-olive	£100

1891. (Nos. 43/50).
Z42	7c. on 10c. green	22·00
Z43	14c. on 30c. mauve	£100
Z44	20c. on 30c. green (No. 48)	15·00
Z45	50c. on 48c. dull purple (No. 49)	16·00
Z46	$1 on 96c. purple/*red* (No. 50)	45·00

1891. *50th Anniv of Colony* (No. 51).
Z47	2c. carmine	£950

1898. (No. 52).
Z48	$1 on 96c. black	60·00

1898. (No. 55).
Z49	10c. on 30c. green	£225

1900–01. Wmk Crown CA (Nos. 56/61).
Z50	2c. dull green	4·25
Z51	4c. carmine	3·00
Z52	5c. yellow	17·00
Z53	10c. ultramarine	4·75
Z54	12c. blue	£140
Z55	30c. brown	65·00

1903. Wmk Crown CA (Nos. 62/76).
Z56	1c. dull purple and brown	4·50
Z57	2c. dull green	4·25
Z58	4c. purple/*red*	2·75
Z59	5c. dull green and brown-orange	19·00
Z60	8c. slate and violet	7·00
Z61	10c. purple and blue/*blue*	4·00
Z62	12c. green and purple/*yellow*	13·00
Z63	20c. slate and chestnut	9·50
Z64	30c. dull green and black	48·00
Z65	50c. dull green and magenta	75·00
Z67	$2 slate and scarlet	£400
Z68	$3 slate and dull blue	£600

1904–06. Wmk Mult Crown CA (Nos. 77/90).
Z71	2c. dull green	4·00
Z72	4c. purple/*red*	2·75
Z73	5c. dull green and brown-orange	15·00
Z74	8c. slate and violet	9·50
Z75	10c. purple and blue/*blue*	4·00
Z76	12c. green and purple/*yellow*	17·00
Z77	20c. slate and chestnut	9·00
Z78	30c. dull green and black	32·00
Z79	50c. green and magenta	29·00
Z80	$1 purple and sage-green	80·00
Z81	$2 slate and scarlet	£325
Z83	$5 purple and blue-green	£500

1907–11. Wmk Mult Crown CA (Nos. 91/9).
Z85	1c. brown	4·50
Z86	2c. green	4·00
Z87	4c. carmine-red	2·75
Z88	6c. orange-vermilion and purple	15·00
Z89	10c. bright ultramarine	3·75
Z90	20c. purple and sage-green	65·00
Z91	30c. purple and orange-yellow	60·00
Z92	50c. black/*green*	

1912–15. Wmk Crown CA (Nos. 100/16).
Z93	1c. brown	5·50
Z94	2c. green	5·00
Z95	4c. red	2·75
Z96	6c. orange	4·50
Z97	8c. grey	20·00
Z98	10c. ultramarine	4·00
Z99	12c. purple/*yellow*	22·00
Z100	20c. purple and sage-green	7·00
Z102	30c. purple and orange-yellow	18·00
Z103	50c. black/*green*	12·00
Z104	$1 purple and blue/*blue*	24·00
Z105	$3 green and purple	£150

POSTCARD STAMPS

1879. (Nos. P1/2).
ZP106	3c. on 16c. yellow	£650
ZP107	5c. on 18c. lilac	£700

POSTAL FISCAL STAMPS

1874–1902. Wmk Crown CC. P 15½×15 (Nos. F1/3).
ZF109	$2 olive-green	£160
ZF110	$3 dull violet	£160

1891. (No. F9).
ZF116	$5 on $10 purple/*red*	£300

1897. (No. F10).
ZF118	$1 on $2 olive-green	£300

ANPING

Anping is the port for Tainan, on the island of Formosa, opened to British trade in 1860. A British Vice-consulate operated in the port and mail is known postmarked there between 1889 and 1895. Formosa passed under Japanese control in 1895 and British Treaty Port rights then lapsed.

Type **D** *used* 1889–95

Stamps of HONG KONG *cancelled at Anping between* 1889 *and* 1895 *with postmark detailed above.*

1882–91. Wmk Crown CA (Nos. 32/9).
Z120	2c. carmine	£900
Z121	5c. blue	£750
Z123	10c. green	£850
Z124	10c. purple/*red*	£1000

1885. (Nos. 40/2).
Z126	20c. on 30c. orange-red	£950
Z127	50c. on 48c. yellowish brown	£1400

CANTON

A British postal service was organised in Canton from 1834, but was closed when the foreign communities were evacuated in August 1839. The city was one of the original Treaty Ports and a consular agency was opened there in 1844. The consulate closed during the riots of December 1856, being replaced by a temporary postal agency at Whampoa, further down the river. When British forces reached Canton a further temporary agency was set up on 23 March 1859, but both closed in July 1863 when the consulate was re-established.

Type **A** ("C1") (*supplied* 1866) *used* 1875–84
Type **C** (*supplied* 1866) *used* 1870–1901
Type **D** *used* 1890–1922

Stamps of HONG KONG *cancelled at Canton between* 1870 *and* 1916 *with postmarks detailed above.*

1862. No wmk (Nos. 1/7).
Z135	18c. lilac	£140

1863–71. Wmk Crown CC (Nos. 8/19).
Z136	2c. brown	40·00
Z137	4c. grey	42·00
Z138	6c. lilac	55·00
Z139	8c. orange	45·00
Z140	12c. blue	21·00
Z142	24c. green	65·00
Z143	30c. vermilion	
Z144	30c. mauve	20·00
Z145	48c. rose	90·00
Z147	96c. brownish grey	£225

1876–77. (Nos. 20/1).
Z148	16c. on 18c. lilac	£300
Z149	28c. on 30c. mauve	£120

1877. Wmk Crown CC (No. 22).
Z150	16c. yellow	£160

1880. (Nos. 23/7).
Z151	5c. on 8c. orange	£170
Z152	5c. on 18c. lilac	£130
Z153	10c. on 12c. blue	£120
Z154	10c. on 16c. yellow	£275
Z155	10c. on 24c. green	£160

1880. Wmk Crown CC (Nos. 28/31).
Z156	2c. rose	42·00
Z157	5c. blue	60·00
Z158	10c. mauve	50·00

1882–96. Wmk Crown CA (Nos. 32/9).
Z159	2c. rose-lake	38·00
Z160	2c. carmine	3·00
Z161	4c. slate-grey	12·00
Z162	5c. blue	4·75
Z163	10c. dull mauve	26·00
Z164	10c. green	9·00
Z165	10c. purple/*red*	4·50
Z166	30c. green	35·00

1886. (Nos. 40/2).
Z167	20c. on 30c. orange-red	13·00
Z168	50c. on 48c. yellowish brown	65·00
Z169	$1 on 96c. grey-olive	£110

1891. (Nos. 43/50).
Z170	7c. on 10c. green	22·00
Z171	14c. on 30c. mauve	£110
Z171a	20c. on 30c. green (No. 45)	£275
Z172	20c. on 30c. green (No. 48)	18·00
Z173	50c. on 48c. dull purple (No. 49)	20·00
Z174	$1 on 96c. purple/*red* (No. 50)	60·00

1891. *50th Anniv of Colony* (No. 51).
Z175	2c. carmine	£900

1898. (No. 52).
Z176	$1 on 96c. black	£130

1898. (No. 55).
Z177	10c. on 30c. grey-green	£170

1900–01. Wmk Crown CA (Nos. 56/61).
Z178	2c. dull green	4·00
Z179	4c. carmine	3·75
Z180	5c. yellow	27·00
Z181	10c. ultramarine	3·75
Z182	12c. blue	95·00
Z183	30c. brown	60·00

1903. Wmk Crown CA (Nos. 62/76).
Z184	1c. dull purple and brown	4·25
Z185	2c. dull Green Green	4·25
Z186	4c. purple/*red*	3·00
Z187	5c. dull green and brown-orange	19·00
Z188	8c. slate and violet	8·50
Z189	10c. purple and blue/*blue*	4·25
Z190	12c. green and purple/*yellow*	14·00
Z191	20c. slate and chestnut	8·00
Z192	30c. dull green and black	45·00

1904–06. Wmk Mult Crown CA (Nos. 77/90).
Z199	2c. dull green	4·00
Z200	4c. purple/*red*	3·00
Z201	5c. dull green and brown-orange	18·00
Z202	8c. slate and violet	13·00
Z203	10c. purple and blue/*blue*	4·00
Z204	12c. green and purple/*yellow*	21·00
Z205	20c. slate and chestnut	11·00
Z206	30c. dull green and black	32·00
Z207	50c. green and magenta	35·00
Z208	$1 purple and sage-green	60·00
Z209	$2 slate and scarlet	£450
Z210	$3 slate and dull blue	£550
Z212	$10 slate and orange/*blue*	£1500

1907–11. Wmk Mult Crown CA (Nos. 91/9).

Z213	1c. brown	4·25
Z214	2c. green	4·25
Z215	4c. carmine-red	3·00
Z216	6c. orange-vermilion and purple	16·00
Z217	10c. bright ultramarine	3·75
Z218	20c. purple and sage-green	70·00
Z219	30c. purple and orange-yellow	50·00
Z220	50c. black/green	42·00
Z221	$2 carmine-red and black	£400

1912–15. Wmk Mult Crown CA (Nos. 100/16).

Z222	1c. brown	4·25
Z223	2c. green	3·50
Z224	4c. red	2·50
Z225	6c. orange	4·25
Z226	8c. grey	18·00
Z227	10c. ultramarine	4·00
Z228	12c. purple/yellow	17·00
Z229	20c. purple and sage-green	6·00
Z230	25c. purple and magenta (type A)	65·00
Z231	30c. purple and orange-yellow	18·00
Z232	50c. black/green	6·50
Z233	$1 purple and blue/blue	32·00
Z234	$2 carmine red and grey-black	90·00
Z235	$3 green and purple	£160

POSTCARD STAMPS

1879. (Nos. P1/2).

ZP236	3c. on 16c. yellow	£600
ZP237	5c. on 18c. lilac	£700

POSTAL FISCAL STAMPS

1874–1902. Wmk Crown CC. P 15½×15 (Nos. F1/3).

ZF238	$2 olive-green	£180

1891. (No. F9).

ZF246	$5 on $10 purple/red	£375

1897. (No. F10).

ZF247	$1 on $2 olive-green	£375

CHEFOO

Chefoo was opened to British trade in 1860. Although a consulate was established in 1863 no organised postal agency was provided until 1 January 1903 when one was opened at the premises of Curtis Brothers, a commercial firm.

Type **E** (supplied 1902) used 1903–20
Type **D** (supplied 1907) used 1907–13
Type **F** used 1916–22

Stamps of HONG KONG *cancelled at Chefoo between* 1903 *and* 1916 *with postmarks detailed above.*

1882–96. Wmk Crown CA (Nos. 32/9).

Z249	5c. blue	32·00

1891. (Nos. 43/50).

Z250	20c. on 30c. grey-green (No. 48a)	48·00

1898. (No. 52).

Z251	$1 on 96c. black	95·00

1900–01. Wmk Crown CA (Nos. 56/61).

Z252	2c. dull green	27·00
Z253	4c. carmine	26·00
Z254	5c. yellow	60·00
Z255	10c. ultramarine	27·00
Z257	30c. brown	£120

1903. Wmk Crown CA (Nos. 62/76).

Z258	1c. dull purple and brown	10·00
Z259	2c. dull green	9·00
Z260	4c. purple/red	8·50
Z261	5c. dull green and brown-orange	22·00
Z262	8c. slate and violet	18·00
Z263	10c. purple and blue/blue	10·00
Z264	12c. green and purple/yellow	28·00
Z268	$1 purple and sage-green	

1904–06. Wmk Mult Crown CA (Nos. 77/90).

Z273	2c. dull green	9·00
Z274	4c. purple/red	7·50
Z275	5c. dull green and brown-orange	16·00
Z276	8c. slate and violet	17·00
Z277	10c. purple and blue/blue	9·00
Z278	12c. green and purple/yellow	25·00
Z279	20c. slate and chestnut	20·00
Z280	30c. dull green and black	50·00
Z281	50c. purple and magenta	50·00
Z282	$1 purple and sage-green	90·00
Z283	$2 slate and scarlet	£225
Z284	$3 slate and dull blue	£425
Z285	$5 purple and blue-green	

1907–11. Wmk Mult Crown CA (Nos. 91/9).

Z287	1c. brown	10·00
Z288	2c. green	9·50
Z289	4c. carmine-red	8·50
Z290	6c. orange-vermilion and purple	25·00
Z291	10c. bright ultramarine	9·00
Z292	20c. purple and sage-green	75·00
Z293	30c. purple and orange-yellow	55·00
Z295	$2 carmine-red and black	

1912–15. Wmk Mult Crown CA (Nos. 100/16).

Z296	1c. brown	8·00
Z297	2c. green	7·50
Z298	4c. red	6·00
Z299	6c. orange	13·00
Z300	8c. grey	28·00
Z301	10c. ultramarine	7·50
Z302	12c. purple/yellow	28·00
Z303	20c. purple and sage-green	11·00

Z305	30c. purple and orange-yellow	16·00
Z306	50c. black/green	10·00
Z307	$1 purple and blue/blue	14·00
Z308	$2 carmine-red and grey-black	85·00
Z309	$3 green and purple	£130
Z310	$5 green and red/green	£475
Z311	$10 purple and black/red	£300

FOOCHOW

Foochow, originally known as Foochowfoo, was one of the original Treaty Ports opened to British trade in 1842. A British consulate and postal agency was established in June 1844.

Type **A** ("F1") (supplied 1866) used 1873–84
Type **D** (inscr "FOOCHOWFOO") (supplied 1866) used 1867–1905
Type **D** (inscr "FOOCHOW") (supplied 1894) used 1894-1917
Type **E** (inscr "B.P.O.") used 1906–10
Type **F** used 1915–22

Stamps of HONG KONG *cancelled at Foochow between* 1867 *and* 1916 *with postmarks detailed above.*

1882. No wmk (Nos. 1/7).

Z312	18c. lilac	£160

1863–71. Wmk Crown CC (Nos. 8/19).

Z313	2c. brown	35·00
Z314	4c. grey	35·00
Z315	6c. lilac	45·00
Z316	8c. orange	50·00
Z317	12c. blue	18·00
Z318	18c. lilac	£850
Z319	24c. green	75·00
Z320	30c. vermilion	£160
Z321	30c. mauve	15·00
Z322	48c. rose	95·00
Z324	96c. brownish grey	£350

1876–77. (Nos. 20/1).

Z325	16c. on 18c. lilac	£325
Z326	28c. on 30c. mauve	£150

1877. Wmk Crown CC (No. 22).

Z327	16c. yellow	£140

1880. (Nos. 23/7).

Z328	5c. on 8c. orange	£350
Z329	5c. on 18c. lilac	£130
Z330	10c. on 12c. blue	£130
Z331	10c. on 16c. yellow	
Z332	10c. on 24c. green	£170

1880. Wmk Crown CC (Nos. 28/31).

Z333	2c. rose	38·00
Z334	5c. blue	70·00
Z335	10c. mauve	45·00
Z336	48c. brown	£190

1882–96. Wmk Crown CA (Nos. 32/9).

Z336a	2c. rose-lake	35·00
Z337	2c. carmine	2·50
Z338	4c. slate-grey	7·50
Z339	5c. blue	3·25
Z340	10c. dull mauve	30·00
Z341	10c. green	11·00
Z342	10c. purple/red	4·00
Z343	30c. green	38·00

1885. (Nos. 40/2).

Z344	20c. on 30c. orange-red	15·00
Z345	50c. on 48c. yellowish brown	55·00
Z346	$1 on 96c. grey-olive	95·00

1891. (Nos. 43/50).

Z347	7c. on 10c. green	
Z348	14c. on 30c. green	95·00
Z348a	20c. on 30c. green (No. 45)	£250
Z349	20c. on 30c. green (No. 48)	21·00
Z350	50c. on 48c. dull purple (No. 49)	25·00
Z351	$1 on 96c. purple/red (No. 50)	60·00

1898. (No. 52).

Z353	$1 on 96c. black	80·00

1898. (No. 55).

Z354	10c. on 30c. green	£225

1900–01. Wmk Crown CA (Nos. 56/61).

Z355	2c. dull green	3·75
Z356	4c. carmine	4·25
Z357	5c. yellow	18·00
Z358	10c. ultramarine	3·75
Z360	30c. brown	70·00

1903. Wmk Crown CA (Nos. 62/76).

Z361	1c. dull purple and brown	4·50
Z362	2c. dull green	4·00
Z363	4c. purple/red	2·75
Z364	5c. dull green and brown-orange	19·00
Z365	8c. slate and violet	10·00
Z366	10c. purple and blue/blue	4·25
Z367	12c. green and purple/yellow	16·00
Z368	20c. slate and chestnut	10·00
Z369	30c. dull green and black	40·00
Z370	50c. purple and magenta	60·00

1904–06. Wmk Mult Crown CA (Nos. 77/90).

Z376	2c. dull green	4·00
Z377	4c. purple/red	2·75
Z378	5c. dull green and brown-orange	13·00
Z379	8c. slate and violet	9·00
Z380	10c. purple and blue/blue	4·25
Z381	12c. green and purple/yellow	19·00
Z382	20c. slate and chestnut	9·00

Z383	30c. dull green and black	35·00
Z384	50c. green and magenta	32·00
Z385	$1 purple and sage-green	55·00

1907–11. Wmk Mult Crown CA (Nos. 91/9).

Z390	1c. brown	3·75
Z391	2c. green	3·75
Z392	4c. carmine-red	2·75
Z393	6c. orange-vermilion and purple	15·00
Z394	10c. bright ultramarine	3·50
Z395	20c. purple and sage-green	70·00
Z396	30c. purple and orange-yellow	50·00
Z397	50c. black/green	38·00

1912–15. Wmk Mult Crown CA (Nos. 100/16).

Z399	1c. brown	4·50
Z400	2c. green	4·00
Z401	4c. red	2·75
Z402	6c. orange	9·50
Z403	8c. grey	20·00
Z404	10c. ultramarine	4·00
Z406	20c. purple and sage-green	6·00
Z407	25c. purple and magenta (Type A)	
Z408	30c. purple and orange-yellow	14·00

POSTCARD STAMPS

1874–1902. (Nos. P1/2).

ZP413	3c. on 16c. yellow	£700

POSTAL FISCAL STAMPS

1874–1902. Wmk Crown CC. P 15½×15 (Nos. F1/3).

ZF415	$2 olive-green	£150
ZF416	$3 dull violet	£130

HANKOW

Hankow, on the Yangtse River 600 miles from the sea, became a Treaty Port in 1860. A British consulate opened the following year, but no organised British postal agency was established until 1872.

Type **D** (supplied 1874) used 1874–1916
Type **B** ("D29") (supplied 1876) used 1878–83
Type **F** used 1916–22

Stamps of HONG KONG *cancelled at Hankow between* 1874 *and* 1916 *with postmarks detailed above.*

1862. No wmk (Nos. 1/7).

Z426	18c. lilac	£225

1863–71. Wmk Crown CC (Nos. 8/19).

Z427	2c. brown	90·00
Z428	4c. grey	90·00
Z429	6c. lilac	£110
Z430	8c. orange	£100
Z431	12c. blue	35·00
Z432	18c. lilac	£900
Z433	24c. green	£150
Z435	30c. mauve	£100
Z436	48c. rose	£200
Z438	96c. brownish grey	

1876–77. (Nos. 20/1).

Z439	16c. on 18c. lilac	£400
Z440	28c. on 30c. mauve	£225

1877. Wmk Crown CC (No. 22).

Z441	16c. yellow	£500

1880. (Nos. 23/7).

Z442	5c. on 8c. orange	£200
Z443	5c. on 18c. lilac	£170
Z444	10c. on 12c. blue	£180
Z445	10c. on 16c. yellow	£375
Z446	10c. on 24c. green	£200

1880. Wmk Crown CC (Nos. 28/31).

Z447	2c. rose	70·00
Z448	5c. blue	80·00
Z449	10c. mauve	85·00
Z450	48c. brown	£300

1882–96. Wmk Crown CA (Nos. 32/9).

Z451	2c. carmine	7·50
Z452	4c. slate-grey	16·00
Z453	5c. blue	8·00
Z454	10c. dull mauve	70·00
Z455	10c. green	9·50
Z456	10c. purple/red	8·50
Z457	30c. green	48·00

1885. (Nos. 40/2).

Z458	20c. on 30c. orange-red	29·00
Z459	50c. on 48c. yellowish brown	70·00
Z460	$1 on 96c. grey-olive	£130

1891. (Nos. 43/50).

Z461	7c. on 10c. green	28·00
Z462	14c. on 30c. mauve	£120
Z463	20c. on 30c. green (No. 48)	21·00
Z464	50c. on 48c. dull purple (No. 49)	21·00
Z465	$1 on 96c. purple/red (No. 50)	60·00

1898. (No. 52).

Z467	$1 on 96c. black	80·00

1898. (No. 55).

Z468	10c. on 30c. green	£225

1900–01. Wmk Crown CA (Nos. 56/61).

Z469	2c. dull green	4·75
Z470	4c. carmine	5·00
Z471	5c. yellow	23·00
Z472	10c. ultramarine	6·50

Z473	12c. blue	£120
Z474	30c. brown	70·00

1903. Wmk Crown CA (Nos. 62/76).
Z475	1c. dull purple and brown	5·00
Z476	2c. dull green	4·75
Z477	4c. purple/*red*	4·00
Z478	5c. dull green and brown-orange	19·00
Z479	8c. slate and violet	15·00
Z480	10c. purple and blue/*blue*	4·50
Z481	12c. green and purple/*yellow*	18·00
Z482	20c. slate and chestnut	13·00
Z483	30c. dull green and black	40·00
Z484	50c. dull green and magenta	70·00
Z485	$1 purple and sage-green	55·00

1904–06. Wmk Mult Crown CA (Nos. 77/90).
Z490	2c. dull green	4·50
Z491	4c. purple/*red*	4·00
Z492	5c. dull green and brown-orange	17·00
Z493	8c. slate and violet	9·00
Z494	10c. purple and blue/*blue*	4·50
Z495	12c. green and purple/*yellow*	19·00
Z496	20c. slate and chestnut	15·00
Z497	30c. dull green and black	35·00
Z498	50c. green and magenta	27·00
Z499	$1 purple and sage-green	55·00
Z500	$2 slate and scarlet	£350
Z502	$5 purple and blue-green	£650
Z503	$10 slate and orange/*blue*	£1700

1907–11. Wmk Mult Crown CA (Nos. 91/9).
Z504	1c. brown	4·75
Z505	2c. green	4·25
Z506	4c. carmine-red	3·00
Z507	6c. orange-vermilion and purple	19·00
Z508	10c. bright ultramarine	4·50
Z509	20c. purple and sage-green	75·00
Z510	30c. purple and orange-yellow	60·00

1912–15. Wmk Mult Crown CA (Nos. 100/16).
Z513	1c. brown	5·50
Z514	2c. green	4·75
Z515	4c. red	3·75
Z516	6c. orange	9·50
Z518	10c. ultramarine	4·25
Z520	20c. purple and sage-green	11·00
Z522	30c. purple and orange-yellow	20·00
Z523	50c. black/*green*	13·00
Z524	$1 purple and blue/*blue*	50·00
Z527	$5 green and red/*green*	£500

POSTCARD STAMPS

1879. (Nos. P1/2).
ZP528	3c. on 16c. yellow	£900

POSTAL FISCAL STAMPS

1874–1902. Wmk Crown CC.

(a) P 15½×15 (Nos. F1/3).
ZF529	$2 olive-green	£190

(b) P 14 (Nos. F4/6).
ZF532	$2 dull bluish green	£400

1897. (No. F11).
ZF533	$1 on $2 dull bluish green	£500

KIUNGCHOW (HOIHOW)

Kiungchow, a city on the island of Hainan, and its port of Hoihow was added to the Treaty Port system in 1860. A consular postal agency was opened at Kiungchow in 1876, being transferred to Hoihow in 1878. A second agency was opened at Kiungchow in 1879.

Type **B** ("D28") (*supplied* 1876) *used* 1879–83
Type **D** (inscr "KIUNG-CHOW") (*supplied* 1878) *used* 1879–81

"REGISTERED KIUNG-CHOW" with "REGISTERED" removed
(*originally supplied* 1876) *used* 1883–85
Type **D** (inscr "HOIHOW") *used* 1885–1922

Stamps of HONG KONG *cancelled at Kiungchow (Hoihow) between* 1879 *and* 1916 *with postmarks detailed above.*

1863–71. Wmk Crown CC (Nos. 8/19).
Z540	2c. brown	£750
Z541	4c. grey	£550
Z542	6c. lilac	£1100
Z543	8c. orange	£1100
Z544	12c. blue	£550
Z546	24c. green	£1100
Z547	30c. vermilion	
Z548	30c. mauve	£300
Z549	48c. rose	£1500
Z551	96c. brownish grey	£1700

1876–77. (Nos. 20/1).
Z552	16c. on 18c. lilac	£1300
Z553	28c. on 30c. mauve	£1100

1877. (No. 22).
Z554	16c. yellow	£2250

1880. (Nos. 23/7).
Z555	5c. on 8c. orange	£800
Z556	5c. on 18c. lilac	£700
Z557	10c. on 12c. blue	£700
Z558	10c. on 16c. yellow	£1400
Z559	10c. on 24c. green	

1880. Wmk Crown CC (Nos. 28/31).
Z561	5c. blue	£600
Z562	10c. mauve	£750

1882–96. Wmk Crown CA (Nos. 32/9).
Z564	2c. carmine	48·00
Z565	4c. slate-grey	65·00
Z566	5c. blue	48·00
Z567	10c. dull mauve	£550
Z568	10c. green	60·00
Z569	10c. purple/*red*	48·00
Z570	30c. green	95·00

1886. (Nos. 40/2).
Z571	20c. on 30c. orange-red	£100
Z572	50c. on 48c. yellowish brown	£110
Z573	$1 on 96c. grey-olive	£190

1891. (Nos. 43/50).
Z574	7c. on 10c. green	£150
Z576	20c. on 30c. green (No. 48)	48·00
Z577	50c. on 48c. dull purple (No. 49)	65·00
Z578	$1 on 96c. purple/*red* (No. 50)	£130

1891. *50th Anniv of Colony* (No. 51).
Z579	2c. carmine	£2750

1898. (No. 52).
Z580	$1 on 96c. black	£250

1898. (No. 55).
Z581	10c. on 30c. green	£450

1900–01. Wmk Crown CA (Nos. 56/61).
Z582	2c. dull green	70·00
Z583	4c. carmine	32·00
Z584	5c. yellow	75·00
Z585	10c. ultramarine	38·00
Z587	30c. brown	£160

1903. Wmk Crown CA (Nos. 62/76).
Z588	1c. dull purple and brown	23·00
Z589	2c. dull green	23·00
Z590	4c. purple/*red*	18·00
Z591	5c. dull green and brown-orange	42·00
Z592	8c. slate and violet	40·00
Z593	10c. purple and blue/*blue*	21·00
Z594	12c. green and purple/*yellow*	48·00
Z597	50c. dull green & magenta	£160
Z598	$1 purple and sage-green	£225
Z599	$2 slate and scarlet	£750

1904. Wmk Mult Crown CA (Nos. 77/90).
Z603	2c. dull green	22·00
Z604	4c. purple/*red*	18·00
Z605	5c. dull green and brown-orange	42·00
Z606	8c. slate and violet	27·00
Z607	10c. purple and blue/*blue*	20·00
Z608	12c. green and purple/*yellow*	45·00
Z609	20c. slate and chestnut	55·00
Z610	30c. dull green and black	75·00
Z612	$1 purple and sage-green	£375

1907–11. Wmk Mult Crown CA (Nos. 91/9).
Z617	1c. brown	22·00
Z618	2c. green	21·00
Z619	4c. carmine-red	18·00
Z620	6c. orange-vermilion and purple	45·00
Z621	10c. bright ultramarine	20·00
Z622	20c. purple and sage-green	80·00

1912–15. Wmk Mult Crown CA (Nos. 100/16).
Z625	1c. brown	20·00
Z626	2c. green	19·00
Z627	4c. red	18·00
Z628	6c. orange	27·00
Z629	8c. grey	
Z630	10c. ultramarine	18·00
Z631	12c. purple/*yellow*	45·00
Z632	20c. purple and sage-green	38·00
Z633	25c. purple and magenta (Type A)	80·00
Z634	30c. purple and orange-yellow	
Z635	50c. black/*green*	55·00
Z636	$1 purple and blue/*blue*	60·00

POSTAL FISCAL STAMPS

1874–1902. Wmk Crown CC.

(a) P 15½×15 (Nos. F1/3).
ZF641	$2 olive-green	£325

(b) P 14 (Nos. F4/6).
ZF644	$2 dull bluish green	£450

1897. (Nos. F10/11).
ZF650	$1 on $2 olive-green	£400

NINGPO

Ningpo was one of the 1842 Treaty Ports and a consular postal agency was established there in 1844.

Type **A** ("N1") (*supplied* 1866) *used* 1870–82
Type **C** (*supplied* 1866) *used* 1870–99
Type **D** *used* 1899–1922

Stamps of HONG KONG *cancelled at Ningpo between* 1866 *and* 1916 *with postmarks detailed above.*

1862. No wmk (Nos. 1/7).
Z652	18c. lilac	£750

1863–71. Wmk Crown CC (Nos. 8/19).
Z653	2c. brown	£275
Z654	4c. grey	£275
	a. Perf 12½	
Z655	6c. lilac	£325
Z656	8c. orange	£275
Z657	12c. blue	£130
Z658	18c. lilac	
Z659	24c. green	£300
Z660	30c. vermilion	£350
Z661	30c. mauve	£110
Z662	48c. rose	£500
Z663	96c. olive-bistre	
Z664	96c. brownish grey	£650

1876–77. (Nos. 20/1).
Z665	16c. on 18c. lilac	£550
Z666	28c. on 30c. mauve	£325

1877. Wmk Crown CC (No. 22).
Z667	16c. yellow	£400

1880. (Nos. 23/7).
Z668	5c. on 8c. orange	£375
Z669	5c. on 18c. lilac	£300
Z670	10c. on 12c. blue	£325
Z672	10c. on 24c. green	£375

1880. Wmk Crown CC (Nos. 28/31).
Z674	5c. blue	£160
Z675	10c. mauve	£160
Z676	48c. brown	£650

1882–96. Wmk Crown CA (Nos. 32/9).
Z677	2c. carmine	45·00
Z678	4c. slate-grey	70·00
Z679	5c. blue	45·00
Z680	10c. dull mauve	£160
Z681	10c. green	50·00
Z682	10c. purple/*red*	50·00
Z683	30c. green	95·00

1885. (Nos. 40/2).
Z685	50c. on 48c. yellowish brown	£120

1891. (Nos. 43/50).
Z686	7c. on 10c. green	55·00
Z687	14c. on 30c. mauve	
Z688	20c. on 30c. green (No. 48)	40·00
Z689	50c. on 48c. dull purple (No. 49)	65·00
Z690	$1 on 96c. purple/*red* (No. 50)	£120

1898. (No. 52).
Z692	$1 on 96c. black	£140

1898. (No. 55).
Z693	10c. on 30c. green	£300

1900–01. Wmk Crown CA (Nos. 56/61).
Z694	2c. dull green	25·00
Z695	4c. carmine	22·00
Z697	10c. ultramarine	25·00

1903. Wmk Crown CA (Nos. 62/76).
Z700	1c. dull purple and brown	23·00
Z701	2c. dull green	23·00
Z702	4c. purple/*red*	17·00
Z703	5c. dull green and brown-orange	45·00
Z704	8c. slate and violet	26·00
Z705	10c. purple and blue/*blue*	19·00
Z706	12c. green and purple/*yellow*	55·00
Z709	50c. dull green and magenta	90·00

1904–06. Wmk Mult Crown CA (Nos. 77/90).
Z715	2c. dull green	21·00
Z716	4c. purple/*red*	19·00
Z718	8c. slate and violet	40·00
Z720	12c. green and purple/*yellow*	50·00
Z721	20c. slate and chestnut	50·00
Z722	30c. dull green and black	70·00
Z723	50c. green and magenta	65·00
Z724	$1 purple and sage-green	90·00

1907–11. Wmk Mult Crown CA (Nos. 91/9).
Z729	1c. brown	18·00
Z730	2c. green	18·00
Z731	4c. carmine-red	16·00
Z733	10c. bright ultramarine	18·00
Z734	20c. purple and sage-green	90·00
Z735	30c. purple and orange-yellow	80·00

1912–15. Wmk Mult Crown CA (Nos. 100/16).
Z738	1c. brown	19·00
Z739	2c. green	18·00
Z740	4c. red	17·00
Z742	8c. grey	50·00
Z743	10c. ultramarine	18·00
Z745	20c. purple and sage-green	
Z747	30c. purple and orange-yellow	
Z749	$1 purple and blue/*blue*	55·00

POSTCARD STAMPS

1879. (Nos. P1/2).
ZP751	3c. on 16c. yellow	£1100

POSTAL FISCAL STAMPS

1874–1902. Wmk Crown CC. P 15½×15 (Nos. F1/3).
ZF754	$2 olive-green	£300

1881. (No. F7).
ZF760	12c. on $10 rose-carmine	

1897. (No. F10).
ZF763	$1 on $2 olive-green	

SHANGHAI

Shanghai was one of the original Treaty Ports of 1842 and a packet agency was opened at the British consulate in April 1844. It moved to a separate premises in 1861 and was upgraded to a Post Office in September 1867.

British military post offices operated in Shanghai from 1927 until 1940.

Type **D** (inscr "SHANGHAE" (*supplied* 1861) *used* 1861–99

Sunburst *used* 1864–65
Type **A** ("S1") (*supplied* 1866) *used* 1866-85
Type **D** (inscr "SHANGHAI") (*supplied* 1885) *used* 1886-1906
Type **G** (inscr "B.R.O." at foot) (*supplied* 1904) *used*1904–21
Type **G** (inscr "Br.P.O." at foot) (*supplied* 1907) *used*1907–22
Type **E** (figures "I" to "VIII" at foot) *used* 1912–22

Stamps of HONG KONG *cancelled at Shanghai between* 1863 *and* 1916 *with postmarks detailed above.*

1862. No wmk (Nos. 1/7).
Z765	2c. brown	£100
Z766	8c. yellow-buff	£120
Z767	12c. pale greenish blue	90·00
Z768	18c. lilac	80·00
Z769	24c. green	£150
Z770	48c. rose	£450
Z771	96c. brownish grey	£550

1863–71. Wmk Crown CC (Nos. 8/19).
Z772	2c. brown	9·00
Z773	4c. grey	8·00
	a. Perf 12½	£275
Z774	6c. lilac	17·00
Z775	8c. orange	14·00
Z776	12c. blue	7·50
Z777	18c. lilac	£350
Z778	24c. green	12·00
Z779	30c. vermilion	19·00
Z780	30c. mauve	6·50
Z781	48c. rose	32·00
Z782	96c. olive-bistre	£900
Z783	96c. brownish grey	50·00

1876–77. (Nos. 20/1).
Z784	16c. on 18c. lilac	£170
Z785	28c. on 30c. mauve	55·00

1877. Wmk Crown CC (No. 22).
Z786	16c. yellow	70·00

1880. (Nos. 23/7).
Z787	5c. on 8c. orange	£100
Z788	5c. on 18c. lilac	60·00
Z789	10c. on 12c. blue	55·00
Z790	10c. on 16c. yellow	£170
Z791	10c. on 24c. green	85·00

1880. Wmk Crown CC (Nos. 28/31).
Z792	2c. rose	25·00
Z793	5c. blue	48·00
Z794	10c. mauve	18·00
Z795	48c. brown	£110

1882–96. Wmk Crown CA (Nos. 32/9).
Z795a	2c. rose-lake	30·00
Z796	2c. carmine	1·75
Z797	4c. slate-grey	2·50
Z798	5c. blue	1·10
Z799	10c. dull mauve	17·00
Z800	10c. green	1·50
Z801	10c. purple/*red*	1·40
Z802	30c. green	25·00

1885. (Nos. 40/2).
Z803	20c. on 30c. orange-red	7·00
Z804	50c. on 48c. yellowish brown	42·00
Z805	$1 on 96c. grey-olive	85·00

1891. (Nos. 43/50).
Z806	7c. on 10c. green	12·00
Z807	14c. on 30c. mauve	75·00
Z807a	20c. on 30c. green (No. 45)	£325
Z807b	50c. on 48c. dull purple (No. 46)	£400
Z807c	$1 on 96c. purple/*red* (No. 47)	8·00
Z808	20c. on 30c. green (No. 48)	7·00
Z809	50c. on 48c. dull purple (No. 49)	26·00
Z810	$1 on 96c. purple/*red* (No. 50)	

1898. (No. 52).
Z812	$1 on 96c. black	35·00

1898. (No. 55).
Z813	10c. on 30c. green	90·00

1900–01. Wmk Crown CA (Nos. 56/61).
Z814	2c. dull green	1·10
Z815	4c. carmine	1·10
Z816	5c. yellow	7·50
Z817	10c. ultramarine	4·25
Z818	12c. blue	70·00
Z819	30c. brown	29·00

1903. Wmk Crown CA (Nos. 62/76).
Z820	1c. dull purple and brown	75

Z821	2c. dull green	1·75
Z822	4c. purple/*red*	60
Z823	5c. dull green and brown-orange	11·00
Z824	8c. slate and violet	2·25
Z825	10c. purple and blue/*blue*	1·75
Z826	12c. green and purple/*yellow*	6·00
Z827	20c. slate and chestnut	4·25
Z828	30c. dull green and black	28·00
Z829	50c. dull green and magenta	48·00
Z830	$1 purple and sage-green	29·00
Z831	$2 slate and scarlet	£325
Z832	$3 slate and dull blue	£450
Z833	$5 purple and blue-green	£550
Z834	$10 slate and orange/*blue*	£600

1904–06. Wmk Mult Crown CA (Nos. 77/90).
Z835	2c. dull green	1·75
Z836	4c. purple/*red*	60
Z837	5c. dull green and brown-orange	7·50
Z838	8c. slate and violet	2·75
Z839	10c. purple and blue/*blue*	1·75
Z840	12c. green and purple/*yellow*	8·00
Z841	20c. slate and chestnut	2·75
Z842	30c. dull green and black	25·00
Z843	50c. green and magenta	12·00
Z844	$1 purple and sage-green	30·00
Z845	$2 slate and scarlet	£130
Z846	$3 slate and dull blue	£300
Z847	$5 purple and blue-green	£450
Z848	$10 slate and orange/*blue*	£1200

1907–11. Wmk Mult Crown CA (Nos. 91/9).
Z849	1c. brown	1·50
Z850	2c. green	1·90
Z851	4c. carmine-red	60
Z852	6c. orange-vermilion and purple	6·00
Z853	10c. bright ultramarine	60
Z854	20c. purple and sage-green	48·00
Z855	30c. purple and orange-yellow	30·00
Z856	50c. black/*green*	20·00
Z857	$2 carmine-red and black	£375

1912–15. Wmk Mult Crown CA (Nos. 100/16).
Z858	1c. brown	1·00
Z859	2c. green	60
Z860	4c. red	45
Z861	6c. orange	1·50
Z862	8c. grey	9·00
Z863	10c. ultramarine	50
Z864	12c. purple/*yellow*	9·00
Z865	20c. purple and sage-green	1·40
Z867	30c. purple and orange-yellow	9·00
Z868	50c. black/*green*	3·50
Z869	$1 purple and blue/*blue*	5·00

POSTCARD STAMPS

1879. (Nos. P1/2).
ZP871	3c. on 16c. yellow	£450
ZP872	5c. on 18c. lilac	£475

POSTAL FISCAL STAMPS

1874–1902. Wmk Crown CC.

(a) P 15½×15 (Nos. F1/5).
ZF874	$2 olive-green	65·00
ZF875	$3 dull violet	45·00
ZF876	$10 rose-carmine	£700

(b) P 14.
ZF877	$2 dull bluish green	£275
ZF878	$3 dull mauve	£500

1881. (No. F7).
ZF880	12c. on $10 rose-carmine	£300

1891. (No. F9).
ZF882	$5 on $10 purple/*red*	£140

1897. (No. F10/11).
ZF883	$1 on $2 olive-green	£170
ZF884	$1 on $2 dull bluish green	£250

SWATOW

Swatow became a Treaty Port in 1860 and a consular packet agency was opened in the area made available for foreign firms during the following year. In 1867 the original agency was transferred to the Chinese city on the other side of the Han river, but a second agency was subsequently opened in the foreign concession during 1883.

Type **A** ("S2") (*supplied* 1866) *used* 1875–85
Type **C** (*supplied* 1866) *used* 1866–90
Type **D** (*supplied* 1883) *used* 1884–1922
Type **F** *used* 1916–22

Stamps of HONG KONG *cancelled at Swatow between* 1866 *and* 1916 *with postmarks detailed above.*

1862. No wmk (Nos. 1/7).
Z885	18c. lilac	£275

1863–71. Wmk Crown CC (Nos. 8/19).
Z886	2c. brown	£120
Z887	4c. grey	£120
	a. Perf 12½	£425
Z888	6c. lilac	£425
Z889	8c. orange	£120
Z890	12c. blue	45·00
Z891	18c. lilac	£900
Z892	24c. green	£140
Z893	30c. vermilion	
Z894	30c. mauve	45·00
Z895	48c. rose	£170
Z897	96c. brownish grey	£700

1876–77. (Nos. 20/1).
Z898	16c. on 18c. lilac	£475
Z899	28c. on 30c. mauve	£250

1877. Wmk Crown CC (No. 22).
Z900	16c. yellow	£500

1880. (Nos. 23/7).
Z901	5c. on 8c. orange	£250
Z902	5c. on 18c. lilac	£200
Z903	10c. on 12c. blue	£225
Z904	10c. on 16c. yellow	£450
Z905	10c. on 24c. green	£300

1880. Wmk Crown CC (Nos. 28/31).
Z906	2c. rose	£100
Z907	5c. blue	£110
Z908	10c. mauve	£120

1882–96. Wmk Crown CA (Nos. 32/9).
Z910	2c. carmine	6·50
Z911	4c. slate-grey	21·00
Z912	5c. blue	7·00
Z913	10c. dull mauve	85·00
Z914	10c. green	9·00
Z915	10c. purple/*red*	6·50
Z916	30c. green	45·00

1885. (Nos. 40/2).
Z917	20c. on 30c. orange-red	15·00

1891. (Nos. 43/50).
Z919	7c. on 10c. green	27·00
Z920	14c. on 30c. mauve	£110
Z920a	50c. on 48c. dull purple (No. 46)	£375
Z921	$1 on 96c. purple/*red* (No. 47)	£550
Z922	20c. on 30c. green (No. 48)	23·00
Z923	50c. on 48c. dull purple (No. 49)	24·00
Z924	$1 on 96c. purple/*red* (No. 50)	48·00

1891. *50th Anniv of Colony* (No. 51).
Z925	2c. carmine	£950

1898. (No. 52).
Z926	$1 on 96c. black	75·00

1898. (No. 55).
Z927	10c. on 30c. green	£225

1900–01. Wmk Crown CA (Nos. 56/61).
Z928	2c. dull green	6·50
Z929	4c. carmine	5·00
Z930	5c. yellow	20·00
Z931	10c. ultramarine	5·50
Z933	30c. brown	48·00

1903. Wmk Crown CA (Nos. 62/76).
Z934	1c. dull purple and brown	5·50
Z935	2c. dull green	5·50
Z936	4c. purple/*red*	4·00
Z937	5c. dull green and brown-orange	17·00
Z938	8c. slate and violet	10·00
Z939	10c. purple and blue/*blue*	5·50
Z940	12c. green and purple/*yellow*	15·00
Z941	20c. slate and chestnut	8·50
Z942	30c. dull green and black	40·00
Z944	$1 purple and sage-green	65·00

1904–06. Wmk Mult Crown CA (Nos. 77/90).
Z949	2c. dull green	5·50
Z950	4c. purple/*red*	4·25
Z951	5c. dull green and brown-orange	17·00
Z952	8c. slate and violet	9·50
Z953	10c. purple and blue/*blue*	5·00
Z954	12c. green and purple/*yellow*	15·00
Z955	20c. slate and chestnut	9·50
Z956	30c. dull green and black	38·00
Z957	50c. green and magenta	60·00
Z958	$1 purple and sage-green	60·00
Z959	$2 slate and scarlet	£200
Z962	$10 slate and orange/*blue*	£1400

1907–11. Wmk Mult Crown CA (Nos. 91/9).
Z963	1c. brown	6·50
Z964	2c. green	6·50
Z965	4c. carmine-red	4·25
Z966	6c. orange-vermilion and purple	13·00
Z967	10c. bright ultramarine	4·75
Z969	30c. purple and orange-yellow	50·00
Z970	50c. black/*green*	35·00

1912–15. Wmk Mult Crown CA (Nos. 100/16).
Z972	1c. brown	4·75
Z973	2c. green	4·25
Z974	4c. red	3·75
Z975	6c. orange	6·50
Z976	8c. grey	20·00
Z977	10c. ultramarine	3·75
Z978	12c. purple/*yellow*	14·00
Z979	20c. purple and sage-green	5·00
Z980	25c. purple and magenta (Type A)	42·00
Z981	30c. purple and orange-yellow	19·00
Z982	50c. black/*green*	10·00
Z983	$1 purple and blue/*blue*	18·00

POSTCARD STAMPS

1879. (Nos. P1/2).
ZP986	3c. on 16c. yellow	£950

POSTAL FISCAL STAMPS

1874–1902. Wmk Crown CC.

(a) P 15½×15 (Nos. F1/3).
ZF988	$2 olive-green	£120
ZF989	$3 dull violet	£100

(b) P 14.
ZF991	$2 dull bluish green	£400

TIENTSIN

Tientsin became a Treaty Port in 1860. A British consulate was established in 1861, but no formal postal agency was organised there until 1882. It was not, however, very successful and was closed during 1890. The British Post Office reopened on 1 October 1906 under the management of the Chinese Engineering and Mining Company.

British military post offices operated in Tientsin from 1927 until 1940.

Type **E** used 1906–13
Type **G** (supplied 1907) used 1907–22

Stamps of HONG KONG cancelled at Tientsin between 1906 and 1916 with postmarks detailed above.

1903. Wmk Crown CA (Nos. 62/76).
Z998	1c. dull purple and brown	12·00
Z999	5c. dull green and brown-orange	27·00
Z1000	8c. slate and violet	11·00
Z1000a	12c. green and purple/yellow	32·00

1904–06. Wmk Mult Crown CA (Nos. 77/90).
Z1001	2c. dull green	5·00
Z1002	4c. purple/red	4·00
Z1003	5c. dull green and brown-orange	15·00
Z1004	8c. slate and violet	12·00
Z1005	10c. purple and blue/blue	4·75
Z1006	12c. green and purple/yellow	18·00
Z1007	20c. slate and chestnut	12·00
Z1008	30c. dull green and black	35·00
Z1009	50c. green and magenta	27·00
Z1010	$1 purple and sage-green	48·00
Z1011	$2 slate and scarlet	£190
Z1012	$3 slate and dull blue	£500
Z1013	$5 purple and blue-green	£650
Z1014	$10 slate and orange/blue	£1800

1907–11. Wmk Mult Crown CA (Nos. 91/9).
Z1015	1c. brown	5·50
Z1016	2c. green	4·25
Z1017	4c. carmine-red	3·50
Z1018	6c. orange-vermilion and purple	17·00
Z1019	10c. bright ultramarine	4·25
Z1020	20c. purple and sage-green	75·00
Z1021	30c. purple and orange-yellow	60·00
Z1022	50c. black/green	45·00
Z1023	$2 carmine-red and black	£475

1912–15. Wmk Mult Crown CA (Nos. 100/16).
Z1024	1c. brown	4·75
Z1025	2c. green	4·25
Z1026	4c. red	3·25
Z1027	6c. orange	6·50
Z1028	8c. grey	26·00
Z1029	10c. ultramarine	4·75
Z1030	12c. purple/yellow	26·00
Z1031	20c. purple and sage-green	8·00
Z1033	30c. purple and orange-yellow	15·00
Z1034	50c. black/green	9·00
Z1035	$1 purple and blue/blue	12·00
Z1037	$3 green and purple	£150
Z1038	$5 green and red/green	£500

WEI HAI WEI

The territory of Wei Hai Wei was leased from the Chinese occupied by the Japanese. At that time there were no organised postal services from the area, although a private local post did operate between the port and Chefoo from 8 December 1898 until 15 March 1899. A Chinese Imperial post office opened in March 1899 to be followed by a British postal agency on the offshore island of Liu Kung Tau on 1 September 1899. A second British agency opened at Port Edward on 1 April 1904.

Liu Kung Tau oval used 1899–1901
Type **D** (inscr "LIU KUNG TAU") (supplied 1899) used 1901–30

Stamps of HONG KONG cancelled at Liu Kung Tau between 1899 and 1916 with postmarks detailed above.

1863–71. Wmk Crown CC (Nos. 8/19).
Z1039	12c. pale blue	

1882–96. Wmk Crown CA (Nos. 32/9).
Z1040	2c. carmine	55·00
Z1041	4c. slate-grey	70·00
Z1042	5c. blue	55·00
Z1043	10c. purple/red	38·00
Z1044	30c. green	65·00

1891. (Nos. 48/50).
Z1045	20c. on 30c. green	45·00
Z1046	50c. on 48c. dull purple	45·00

1898. (No. 52).
Z1047	$1 on 96c. black	85·00

1900–01. Wmk Crown CA (Nos. 56/61).
Z1049	2c. dull green	7·50
Z1050	4c. purple/red	7·50
Z1051	5c. yellow	24·00
Z1052	10c. ultramarine	8·00
Z1053	12c. blue	£110
Z1054	30c. brown	70·00

1903. Wmk Crown CA (Nos. 62/76).
Z1055	1c. dull purple and brown	6·50
Z1056	2c. dull green	6·00
Z1057	4c. purple/red	5·00
Z1058	5c. dull green and brown-orange	18·00
Z1059	8c. slate and violet	14·00
Z1060	10c. purple and blue/blue	8·50
Z1061	12c. green and purple/yellow	26·00
Z1062	20c. slate and chestnut	14·00
Z1063	30c. dull green and black	45·00
Z1064	50c. dull green and magenta	80·00
Z1065	$1 purple and sage-green	65·00

1904–06. Wmk Mult Crown CA (Nos. 77/90).
Z1070	2c. dull green	6·50
Z1071	4c. purple/red	6·00
Z1073	8c. slate and violet	12·00
Z1076	20c. slate and chestnut	25·00
Z1077	30c. dull green and black	75·00
Z1078	50c. green and magenta	55·00

1907–11. Wmk Mult Crown CA (Nos. 91/9).
Z1084	1c. brown	7·00
Z1085	2c. green	7·00
Z1086	4c. carmine-red	5·00
Z1088	10c. bright ultramarine	6·00
Z1089	20c. purple and sage-green	80·00
Z1090	30c. purple and orange-yellow	65·00
Z1091	50c. black/green	55·00

1912–15. Wmk Mult Crown CA (Nos. 100/16).
Z1093	1c. brown	8·00
Z1094	2c. green	6·00
Z1095	4c. red	5·00
Z1096	6c. orange	10·00
Z1097	8c. grey	27·00
Z1098	10c. ultramarine	6·00
Z1104	$1 purple and blue/blue	26·00

POSTAL FISCAL STAMPS

1874–1902. Wmk Crown CC. P 14 (Nos. F4/6).
Z1106	$2 dull bluish green	£850

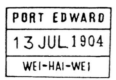

Port Edward rectangle used 1904–08
Type **D** (inscr "WEI-HAI-WEI" at top and "PORT EDWARD" at foot) (supplied 1907) used 1907–30

Stamps of HONG KONG cancelled at Port Edward between 1904 and 1916 with postmarks detailed above.

1900–01. Wmk Crown CA (Nos. 56/61).
Z1109	2c. dull green	65·00
Z1110	10c. ultramarine	80·00

1903. Wmk Crown CA (Nos. 62/76).
Z1111	1c. dull purple and brown	24·00
Z1112	2c. dull green	24·00
Z1113	4c. purple/red	22·00
Z1114	5c. dull green and brown-orange	32·00
Z1115	8c. slate and violet	32·00
Z1116	10c. purple and blue/blue	25·00
Z1117	12c. green and purple/yellow	45·00
Z1118	20c. slate and chestnut	65·00
Z1119	30c. dull green and black	65·00
Z1120	50c. dull green and magenta	75·00
Z1121	$1 purple and sage-green	70·00

1904–06. Wmk Mult Crown CA (Nos. 77/90).
Z1126	2c. dull green	14·00
Z1127	4c. purple/red	12·00
Z1128	5c. dull green and brown-orange	20·00
Z1129	8c. slate and violet	15·00
Z1132	20c. slate and chestnut	60·00
Z1133	30c. dull green and black	55·00
Z1134	50c. green and magenta	60·00

1907–11. Wmk Mult Crown CA (Nos. 91/9).
Z1140	1c. brown	13·00
Z1141	2c. green	13·00
Z1142	4c. carmine-red	8·50
Z1143	6c. orange-vermilion and purple	25·00
Z1144	10c. bright ultramarine	9·50
Z1148	50c. black/green	40·00

1912–15. Wmk Mult Crown CA (Nos. 100/16).
Z1151	1c. brown	11·00
Z1152	2c. green	8·00
Z1153	4c. red	4·75
Z1155	8c. grey	24·00
Z1156	10c. ultramarine	5·50
Z1158	20c. purple and sage-green	15·00
Z1161	50c. black/green	18·00
Z1162	$1 purple and blue/blue	20·00

PRICES FOR STAMPS ON COVER
Nos. 1/14	from × 50
Nos. 15/17	—
Nos. 18/28	from × 30

The overprinted stamps Nos. 1/17 were introduced on 1 January 1917 to prevent currency speculation in the Treaty Ports. They were used in the then-existing agencies of Amoy, Canton, Chefoo, Foochow, Hankow, Hoihow, Ningpo, Shanghai, Swatow, Tientsin and were also supplied to the British naval base of Wei Hai Wei.

CHINA
(1)

1917 (1 Jan)–**21.** Stamps of Hong Kong, 1912–21 (wmk Mult Crown CA), optd with T **1**, at Somerset House.
1	1c. brown	5·00	1·50
	a. Black-brown	4·50	2·50
	b. Crown broken at right	£350	£400
	c. Wmk sideways	†	£2750
	w. Wmk inverted	†	£1200
2	2c. green	8·00	30
3	4c. carmine-red	6·00	30
4	6c. orange	6·00	60
5	8c. slate	13·00	1·25
6	10c. ultramarine	13·00	30
	y. Wmk inverted and reversed	†	£500
7	12c. purple/yellow	13·00	5·00
8	20c. purple and sage-green	13·00	60
9	25c. purple and magenta (A)	8·00	15·00
11	30c. purple and orange-yellow	38·00	5·50
12	50c. black/blue-green (olive back)	70·00	1·50
	a. Emerald surface (1917?)	48·00	8·50
	b. On emerald back (1919)	38·00	5·50
	c. On white back (1920)	£500	£100
13	$1 reddish purple and bright blue/blue	70·00	2·50
	a. Grey-purple and blue/blue (1921)	70·00	7·00
14	$2 carmine-red and grey-black	£225	60·00
15	$3 green and purple	£600	£180
16	$5 green and red/blue-green (olive back)	£350	£250
17	$10 purple and black/red	£900	£500
1/17	Set of 16	£2000	£900
	12s/17s H/S "Specimen" Set of 6	£2250	

1922 (Mar)–**27.** As last, but wmk Mult Script CA.
18	1c. brown	2·50	3·75
19	2c. green	4·00	2·25
	w. Wmk inverted	£225	
20	4c. carmine-rose	7·00	2·25
	a. Lower Chinese character at right broken at top	£225	£200
21	6c. orange-yellow	4·75	4·25
22	8c. grey	9·00	16·00
23	10c. bright ultramarine	10·00	3·75
	w. Wmk inverted	£160	
24	20c. purple and sage-green	15·00	5·00
25	25c. purple and magenta (B)	24·00	70·00
	a. Broken flower	£500	
26	50c. black/emerald (1927)	60·00	£180
	s. Handstamped "Specimen"	£275	
27	$1 purple and blue/blue	80·00	65·00
28	$2 carmine-red and grey-black	£200	£250
18/28	Set of 11	£375	£550

STAMP BOOKLETS

1917. Black on red cover inscribed "BRITISH POST OFFICE AGENCIES IN CHINA". Stapled.
SB1	$1 booklet containing eight 2c., six 4c. and six 10c. (Nos. 2/3, 6)	£5000

1922. Cover as No. SB1. Stapled.
SB2	$1 booklet containing eight 2c., six 4c., and six 10c. (Nos. 19/20, 23)	£4750

The British P.O.'s in the Treaty Ports closed by agreement with the Chinese on 30 November 1922, but the above over printed issues continued in use at the Wei Hai Wei offices until they in turn closed on 30 September 1930. Under the terms of the Convention signed with China the Royal Navy continued to use the base at Wei Hai Wei until the mid-1930s.

BRITISH POST OFFICES IN JAPAN

Under the terms of the Anglo-Japanese Treaty of Yedo, signed on 26 August 1858, five Japanese ports were opened to British trade. British consulates were established at Decima (Nagasaki), Kanagawa (Yokohama), Hiogo (Kobe) and Hakodadi (Hakodate). The postage stamps of Hong Kong became available at the Yokohama and Nagasaki consulates during October 1864 and at Hiogo in 1869, although cancellation of mail did not commence until 1866 at Yokohama and Nagasaki or 1876 at Hiogo. Japan became a member of the U.P.U. on 1 June 1877 and all of the British Postal Agencies were closed by the end of 1879.

For illustrations of postmark types see BRITISH POST OFFICES IN CHINA.

HAKODATE

A British consular office existed at Hakodate, but it was never issued with a c.d.s. obliterator or Hong Kong stamps. No British covers are recorded from this consulate prior to opening of the Japanese Post Office.

HIOGO

The Port of Hiogo (Kobe) was first opened to foreigners on 1 January 1868. The British Consular mail service at Hiogo commenced during 1869 to serve the foreigners at Hiogo, Kobe and Osaka. The cities of Hiogo and Kobe later merged to become the single city of Kobe. The consular office at Hiogo closed on 30 November 1879.

Type **B** ("D30") (supplied 1876) used 1876–79
Type **D** (supplied 1876) used 1876–79

Stamps of HONG KONG cancelled at Hiogo between 1876 and 1879 with postmarks detailed above.

1863–71. Wmk Crown CC (Nos. 8/19).
Z1	2c. brown	£4750
Z2	4c. grey	£3500
Z3	6c. lilac	£4250
Z4	8c. orange	£4000
Z5	12c. blue	£4750
Z6	18c. lilac	
Z7	24c. green	£3500
Z8	30c. vermilion	
Z9	30c. mauve	£4750
Z10	48c. rose	£6500
Z12	96c. brownish grey	£6500

1877. (Nos. 20/1).
Z13	16c. on 18c. lilac	

1877. Wmk Crown CC (No. 22).
Z15   16c. yellow..   £5500

NAGASAKI

The British Consulate opened in Nagasaki on 14 June 1859, but, with few British residents at the port, the consular staff found it inconvenient to carry out postal duties so that few Nagasaki c.d.s. or "N2" cancellations exist. The postal service was terminated on 30 September 1879.

Type **A** ("N2") (*supplied* 1866) *used* 1876–79
Type **D** (*supplied* 1866) *used* 1876–79

Stamps of HONG KONG *cancelled at Nagasaki between* 1876 *and* 1879 *with postmarks detailed above.*

1862. No wmk (Nos. 1/8).
Z15*a*   18c. lilac..   £2500

1863–71. Wmk Crown CC (Nos. 8/19).
Z16   2c. brown..   £1900
Z17   4c. grey..   £1700
Z18   6c. lilac...   £1600
Z19   8c. orange...   £1700
Z20   12c. blue..   £1800
Z21   18c. lilac..   £3250
Z22   24c. green..   £2750
Z24   30c. mauve..   £2250
Z25   48c. rose...   £3000
Z27   96c. brownish grey ....

1876–77. (Nos. 20/1).
Z28   16c. on 18c. lilac................................   £2500
Z29   28c. on 30c. mauve...........................   £1800

1877. Wmk Crown CC (No. 22).
Z30   16c. yellow..   £2500

YOKOHAMA

The British Consulate opened in Kanagawa on 21 July 1859, but was relocated to Yokohama where it provided postal services from 1 July 1860 until a separate Post Office was established in July 1867. The British Post Office in Yokohama closed on 31 December 1879.

Type **A** ("Yl") (*supplied* 1866) *used* 1867–79
Type **D** (*supplied* 1866) *used* 1866–79

Stamps of HONG KONG *cancelled at Yokohama between* 1866 *and* 1879 *with postmarks detailed above.*

1862. No wmk (Nos. 1/8).
Z30*a*   8c. yellow-buff...................................   £250
Z31   18c. lilac..   £100

1863–71. Wmk Crown CC (Nos. 8/19).
Z32   2c. brown..   19·00
Z33   4c. grey..   20·00
        a. Perf 12½....................................   £550
Z34   6c. lilac...   25·00
Z35   8c. orange...   25·00
Z36   12c. blue..   19·00
Z37   18c. lilac..   £650
Z38   24c. green..   21·00
Z39   30c. vermilion......................................   55·00
Z40   30c. mauve..   19·00
Z41   48c. rose...   50·00
Z42   96c. olive-bistre £3750
Z43   96c. brownish grey ....   65·00

1876–77. (Nos. 20/1).
Z44   16c. on 18c. lilac................................   £300
Z45   28c. on 30c. mauve...........................   80·00

1877. Wmk Crown CC (No. 22).
Z46   16c. yellow..   £120

POSTAL FISCAL STAMPS

1874. Wmk Crown CC. P 15½×15 (Nos. F1/3).
ZF47 $2 olive-green......................................   £120
ZF48 $3 dull violet.......................................   £110
ZF49 $10 rose-carmine.................................   £1400

India

(Currency. 12 pies = 1 anna; 16 annas = 1 rupee)

ISSUE FOR SIND PROVINCE

1

1852 (1 July). "Scinde Dawk." *Embossed.*

S1	**1**	½a. white	£4750	£850
S2		½a. blue	£13000	£3750
S3		½a. scarlet	£70000	£9000

These stamps were issued under the authority of Sir Bartle Frere, Commissioner in Sind.

No. S3 is on sealing wax (usually cracked). Perfect copies are very rare.

It is believed that examples in red were issued first followed, in turn, by those in white and blue. The latter, which shows an extra ring round the circumference, may have been produced by De La Rue. The Scinde Dawks were withdrawn in October 1854.

EAST INDIA COMPANY ADMINISTRATION

2 (*Much reduced*)

3

The ½a., 1a. and 4a. were lithographed in Calcutta at the office of the Surveyor-General. The die was engraved by Mr. Maniruddin (spelling uncertain). *Ungummed* paper watermarked as T **2** (the "No. 4" paper) with the Arms of the East India Co in the sheet. The watermark is sideways on the ½a. and 1a., and upright on the 4a. where the paper was trimmed so that only the central portion showing the oval and the arms was used. Imperforate.

1854 (1 April).

1	**3**	½a. vermilion		£850
		a. Deep vermilion		£1400

This stamp, with 9½ arches in the side border, was prepared for use and a supply was sent to Bombay, but was not officially issued.

The vermilion shade is normally found on toned paper and the deep vermilion on white.

ILLUSTRATIONS. Types **4/8** are shown twice actual size.

4

1854 (1 Oct)–**55**. *Die I.*

2	**4**	½a. blue	65·00	16·00
		a. Printed on both sides	†	£9000
		b. Printed double	†	£7000
3		½a. pale blue	90·00	23·00
4		½a. deep blue	75·00	20·00
5		½a. indigo	£250	65·00

We give the official date of validity. Stamps were on sale to the public from mid September. Actual usage at Toungoo, Burma, is known from mid August.

These stamps were printed between 5 May and 29 July 1854 (Printing 30 millions).

4a

Die II.

6	**4a**	½a. blue	55·00	75·00
7		½a. indigo	65·00	85·00

The bulk were printed between 1 and 12 August 1854, with some extra sheets on or before 2 November (Printing about 2 millions).

5

Die III (1855).

8	**5**	½a. pale blue	£850	38·00
8a		½a. blue	£800	35·00
9		½a. greenish blue	£1500	£160
10		½a. deep blue	£1000	70·00

These stamps were printed between 3 July and 25 August 1855 (Printing about 4¾ millions).

THE THREE DIES OF THE ½ ANNA

DIE I. *Chignon shading* mostly solid blobs of colour. *Corner ornaments*, solid blue stars with long points, always conspicuous. *Band below diadem* always heavily shaded. *Diadem and jewels*. The middle and right-hand jewels usually show a clearly defined cross. *Outer frame lines*. Stamps with white or faintly shaded chignons and weak frame lines are usually Die I (worn state).

DIE II. *Chignon* normally shows much less shading. A strong line of colour separates hair and chignon. *Corner ornaments*. The right blue star is characteristic (see illustration) but tends to disappear. It never obliterates the white cross. *Band below diadem*. As Die I but heavier, sometimes solid. *Diadem and jewels*. As Die I but usually fainter. *Outer frame lines*. Always strong and conspicuous.

DIE III. *Chignon shading* shows numerous fine lines, often blurred. *Corner ornaments* have a small hollow blue star with short points, which tends to disappear as in Die II. *Band below diadem*, shows light shading or hardly any shading. *Diadem and jewels*. Jewels usually marked with a solid squat star. The ornaments between the stars appear in the shape of a characteristic white "w". *Frame lines* variable

The above notes give the general characteristics of the three Dies, but there are a few exceptions due to retouching, etc.

---

6 (*See note below No. 14*)

Die I.

11	**6**	1a. deep red	£425	50·00
12		1a. red	£275	35·00

Printing of these stamps commenced on 26 July 1854, and continued into August (Printing, see note below No. 14).

7

Die II: With more lines in the chignon than in Die I, and with white curved line where chignon joins head*.

13	**7**	1a. deep red	£160	50·00
14		1a. dull red	50·00	38·00

*Very worn printings of Die II may be found with chignon nearly as white as in Die I.

In stamps of Die I, however, the small blob of red projecting from the hair into the chignon is always visible.

These stamps were printed in August and September 1854 (Total printing, Dies I and II together, about 7¾ millions).

8

Die III. With pointed bust (1855).

15	**8**	1a. red	£1000	£130
16		1a. dull red	£1600	£180

These stamps were printed between 7 July and 25 August 1855 (Printing, about 1½ millions).

9

NOTE. Our catalogue prices for Four Annas stamps are for cut-square specimens, with clear margins and in good condition. Cut-to-shape copies are worth from 3% to 20% of these prices according to condition.

Four Dies of the Head:—

I   II

DIE I. Band of diadem and chignon strongly shaded.
DIE II. Lines in band of diadem worn. Few lines in the upper part of the chignon, which, however, shows a strong drawn comma-like mark.

IIIA   III

DIE IIIA. Upper part of chignon partly redrawn, showing two short, curved vertical lines in the NE corner. "Comma" has disappeared.
DIE III. Upper part of chignon completely redrawn, but band of diadem shows only a few short lines.

Two Dies of the Frame:—

Die I. Outer frame lines weak. Very small dots of colour, or none at all, in the "R" and "A's". The white lines to the right of "INDIA" are separated, by a line of colour, from the inner white circle.

Die II. Outer frame lines strengthened. Dots in the "R" and "A's" strong. White lines to right of "INDIA" break into inner white circle.

(Des Capt. H. Thuillier)

1854 (15 Oct)–**55**. W 2 upright, central portion only. Imperf.

1st Printing. Head Die I. Frame Die I. Stamps widely spaced and separated by blue wavy line.

			Un	Used	Us pr
17	9	4a. indigo and red....	£4500	£500	£1900
18		4a. blue and pale red	£4500	£425	£1700
		a. Head inverted.....	†	£32000/£110000	†

This printing was made between 13 and 28 Oct 1854 (Printing, 206,040).

Twenty-seven confirmed examples of No. 18a are now known, only three of which are cut-square. The range of prices quoted reflects the difference in value between a sound cut-to-shape stamp and the finest example known.

2nd Printing. Head Die II. Frame Die I. Stamps widely spaced and separated by blue wavy line.

19	9	4a. blue and red	£4250	£275	£1100
		a. Blue (head) printed double..	†	£6500	†
20		4a. indigo and deep red	£4250	£325	£1300

This printing was made between 1 and 13 Dec 1854 (Printing, 393,960). No. 19a is only known used cut-to-shape.

3rd Printing. Head Dies II, IIIA and III. Frame Dies I and II. Stamps, often in bright shades, widely spaced and separated by wavy line (1855).

21	9	4a. blue and red (shades) (Head III, Frame I)	£10000	£1100	£3500
		a. Head II, Frame I	—	£1600	£5000
		b. Head IIIA, Frame I	—	£1600	£5000
		c. Head III, Frame II..............	—	—	£10000

This printing was made between 10 March and 2 April 1855 (Printing, 138,960).

4th Printing. Head Die III. Frame Die II. Stamps closely spaced 2 to 2½ mm without separating line (1855).

22	9	4a. deep blue and red................	£2750	£275	£900
23		4a. blue and red	£2750	£225	£800
		a. Blue (head) printed double..	†	£5000	†
24		4a. pale blue and pale red.........	£2750	£300	£950

This printing was made between 3 April and 9 May 1855 (Printing, 540,960).

No. 23a is only known used cut-to-shape.

5th Printing. Head Die III. Frame Die II. Stamps spaced 4 to 6 mm without separating line (1855).

25	9	4a. blue and rose-red	£4750	£400	£1700
26		4a. deep blue and red................	£4750	£400	£1700

This printing was made between 4 Oct and 3 Nov 1855 (Printing, 380,064).

Serrated perf about 18, or pin-perf.

27		½a. blue (Die I).........................		†	£4000
28		1a. red (Die I)		†	£2250
29		1a. red (Die II).........................		†	£2000
30		4a. blue and red (Die II)		†	£9500

This is believed to be an unofficial perforation. Most of the known specimens bear Madras circle postmarks (C122 to C126), but some are known with Bombay postmarks. Beware of fakes.

BISECTS. The bisected stamps for issues between 1854 and 1860 were used exclusively in the Straits Settlements during shortages of certain values. Prices quoted are for those with Singapore "B 172" cancellations. Penang marks are considerably rarer.

10   11

(Plate made at Mint, Calcutta. Typo Stamp Office)

1854 (4 Oct). Sheet wmk sideways, as W 2 but with "No. 3" at top left. Imperf.

31	10	2a. green (shades)	90·00	24·00
		a. Bisected (1a.) (1857) (on cover)...............................	†	£130000
34		2a. emerald-green	£1000	

The 2a. was also printed on paper with a sideways sheet watermark incorporating the words "STAMP OFFICE. One Ana" in double-ring circle, etc. (Price £475 unused, £375 used).

Apart from the rare emerald shade, there is a range of shades of No. 31 varying from bluish to yellowish green.

Many stamps show traces of lines external to the design shown in our illustration. Stamps with this frame on all four sides are scarce.

Many reprints of the ½, 1, 2, and 4a. exist.

PRINTERS. All Indian stamps from No. 35 to 200 were typographed by De La Rue & Co.

1855 (1 Oct). Blue glazed paper. No wmk. P 14.

35	11	4a. black	£500	17·00
		a. Imperf (pair)......................	£3500	£3500
		b. Bisected (2a.) (1859) (on cover)...............................	†	£7500
36		8a. carmine (Die I)...................	£450	15·00
		a. Imperf (pair)......................	£1900	
		b. Bisected (4a.) (1859) (on cover)...............................	†	£55000

The first supply of the 4a. was on white paper, but it is difficult to distinguish it from No. 45.

In the 8a. the paper varies from deep blue to almost white.

For difference between Die I and Die II in the 8a., see illustrations above No. 73.

1856–64. Paper yellowish to white. No wmk. P 14.

37	11	½a. blue (Die I)........................	70·00	3·75
		a. Imperf (pair)......................	£350	£1100
38		½a. pale blue (Die I).................	65·00	1·75
39		1a. brown................................	50·00	2·75
		a. Imperf between (vert pair)........		
		b. Imperf (pair)......................	£750	£1400
		c. Bisected (½a.) (1859) (on cover)...............................	†	£60000
40		1a. deep brown........................	80·00	3·75
41		2a. dull pink (1860)	£500	30·00
		a. Imperf (pair)......................	£1800	
42		2a. yellow-buff (1859)...............	£275	30·00
		a. Imperf (pair)......................	£1100	£2000
43		2a. yellow (1863)......................	£375	32·00
44		2a. orange (1858)......................	£475	35·00
		a. Imperf (pair)......................		
45		4a. black	£300	9·50
		a. Bisected diagonally (2a.) (1859) (on cover)...................	†	£22000
		b. Imperf (pair)......................	£1900	£1900
46		4a. grey-black	£250	4·75
47		4a. green (1864)........................	£1100	38·00
48		8a. carmine (Die I)....................	£350	22·00
49		8a. pale carmine (Die I)	£400	22·00
		a. Bisected (4a.) (1859) (on cover)...............................	†	£55000

Prepared for use, but not officially issued.

50	11	2a. yellow-green	£800	£900
		a. Imperf (pair)......................	£1900	

This stamp is known with trial obliterations, and a few are known postally used. It also exists imperf, but is not known used thus.

For difference between Die I and Die II in the ½a., see illustrations above No. 73.

CROWN COLONY

On the 1 November 1858, Her Majesty Queen Victoria assumed the government of the territories in India "heretofore administered in trust by the Honourable East India Company".

12   13

1860 (9 May). No wmk. P 14.

51	12	8p. purple/bluish	£200	85·00
52		8p. purple/white.......................	42·00	5·00
53		a. Bisected diagonally (4p.) (1862) (on cover)...................	†	£60000
		b. Imperf (pair)......................	£2500	£3500
53		8p. mauve................................	65·00	7·50

1865. Paper yellowish to white. W 13. P 14.

54	11	½a. blue (Die I).........................	13·00	75
		a. Imperf.................................	†	£800
		w. Wmk inverted	—	21·00
55		½a. pale blue (Die I)...................	13·00	75
56	12	8p. purple/bluish	8·50	10·00
		w. Wmk inverted	30·00	
57		8p. mauve................................	11·00	10·00
58	11	1a. pale brown	7·00	90
59		1a. deep brown.........................	6·00	80
		w. Wmk inverted	55·00	26·00
60		1a. chocolate............................	10·00	1·00
61		2a. yellow................................	£100	5·50
62		2a. orange	50·00	2·25
		a. Imperf (pair)......................	†	£3000
63		2a. brown-orange	23·00	2·00
		w. Wmk inverted	65·00	35·00
64		4a. green..................................	£350	23·00
		w. Wmk inverted	†	£100
65		8a. carmine (Die I)....................	£1200	75·00
		w. Wmk inverted	£1800	£180

The 8p. mauve, No. 57, is found variously surcharged "NINE" or "NINE PIE" by local postmasters, to indicate that it was being sold for 9 pies, as was the case during 1874. Such surcharges were made without Government sanction. (Price, from £450 unused).

The stamps of India, wmk Elephant's Head, surcharged with a crown and value in "cents", were used in the Straits Settlements.

14   (15)   (16)

1866 (28 June). Fiscal stamps as T 14 optd. Wmk Crown over "INDIA". P 14 (at sides only).

(a) As T 15.

66		6a. purple (G.).........................	£650	£110
		a. Overprint inverted................	†	£9000

There are 20 different types of this overprint.

(b) With T 16.

68		6a. purple (G.).........................	£1200	£140

17   18

Die I   Die II

Two Dies of 4a.:—
Die I.—Mouth closed, line from corner of mouth downwards only. Pointed chin.
Die II.—Mouth slightly open; lips, chin, and throat defined by line of colour. Rounded chin.

1866 (1 Aug)–**78**. W 13. P 14.

69	17	4a. green (Die I)	75·00	3·75
70		4a. deep green (Die I)................	75·00	3·75
71		4a. blue-green (Die II) (1878)	22·00	2·75
72	18	6a.8p. slate (4.67)	45·00	22·00
		a. Imperf (pair)......................	£1800	

Die I (8a.) Die I (½a.)

Die II (8a.) Die II (½a.)

1868 (1 Jan). *Die II. Profile redrawn and different diadem.* W **13**.
P **14**.
73	**11**	8a. rose (Die II)	32·00	6·00
		w. Wmk inverted	50·00	
74		8a. pale rose (Die II)	32·00	6·00

1873. *Die II. Features, especially the mouth, more firmly drawn.*
W **13**. P **14**.
75	**11**	½a. deep blue (Die II)	5·00	60
76		½a. blue (Die II)	5·00	60
		w. Wmk inverted	48·00	
		y. Wmk inverted and reversed	†	80·00

19 20

1874 (18 July–1 Sept). W **13**. P **14**.
77	**19**	9p. bright mauve (18.7.74)	15·00	14·00
78		9p. pale mauve	15·00	14·00
79	**20**	1r. slate (1.9.74)	45·00	25·00

21 22

1876 (19 Aug). W **13**. P **14**.
80	**21**	6a. olive-bistre	7·50	2·50
		w. Wmk inverted	70·00	
81		6a. pale brown	6·50	1·50
82	**22**	12a. Venetian red	9·00	22·00

EMPIRE

Queen Victoria assumed the title of Empress of India in 1877, and
the inscription on the stamps was altered from "EAST INDIA" to
"INDIA".

23 24 25

26 27 28

29 30 31

32 33 34

1882 (1 Jan)–**90**. W **34**. P **14**.
84	**23**	½a. deep blue-green (1883)	4·00	10
		w. Wmk inverted		
85		½a. blue-green	4·00	10
		a. Double impression	£450	£600
		w. Wmk inverted	—	75·00
86	**24**	9p. rose (1883)	1·00	2·25
87		9p. aniline carmine	1·00	2·25

		w. Wmk inverted	—	75·00
88	**25**	1a. brown-purple (1883)	4·50	30
89		1a. plum	4·50	30
		w. Wmk inverted	—	75·00
90	**26**	1a.6p. sepia	1·00	1·25
91	**27**	2a. pale blue (1883)	4·00	30
92		2a. blue	4·00	30
		a. Double impression	£900	£1200
93	**28**	3a. orange	15·00	6·00
94		3a. brown-orange (1890)	9·00	1·50
		w. Wmk inverted	—	85·00
95	**29**	4a. olive-green (6.85)	14·00	1·25
96		4a. slate-green	14·00	1·25
		w. Wmk inverted	—	65·00
97	**30**	4a.6p. yellow-green (1.5.86)	21·00	5·00
98	**31**	8a. dull mauve (1883)	25·00	2·00
99		8a. magenta	24·00	2·00
100	**32**	12a. purple/*red* (1.4.88)	7·50	3·25
		w. Wmk inverted	—	85·00
101	**33**	1r. slate (1883)	18·00	5·00
		w. Wmk inverted	—	75·00
84/101 *Set of 11*			95·00	20·00
97s, 100s Handstamped "Specimen" *Set of 2*			75·00	

No. 92a is from a sheet of 2a. stamps with a very marked double
impression issued in Karachi in early 1898.

2½ As.
(35) 36 37

1891 (1 Jan). *No. 97 surch with T* **35** *by Govt Press, Calcutta.*
| 102 | **30** | 2½a. on 4½a. yellow-green | 3·50 | 60 |
| | | a. Surch double, one albino | | |

There are several varieties in this surcharge due to variations in the
relative positions of the letters and figures.

1892 (Jan)–**97**. W **34**. P **14**.
103	**36**	2a.6p. yellow-green	3·00	40
104		2a.6p. pale blue-green (1897)	3·50	80
105	**37**	1r. green and rose	25·00	6·00
106		1r. green and aniline carmine	12·00	2·00

38 (39) 40
¼ ¼
Slanting
serif
(Lower
pane
R. 1/1)

USED HIGH VALUES. It is necessary to emphasise that used prices
quoted for the following and all later high value stamps are for postally
used copies.

(Head of Queen from portrait by von Angeli)

1895 (1 Sept). W **34**. P **14**.
107	**38**	2r. carmine and yellow-brown	40·00	11·00
107a		2r. carmine and brown	45·00	13·00
108		3r. brown and green	30·00	10·00
109		5r. ultramarine and violet	42·00	28·00
107/9 *Set of 3*			£100	45·00

1898 (1 Oct). *No. 85 surch with T* **39** *by Govt Press, Calcutta.*
110	**23**	¼a. on ½a. blue-green	10	50
		a. Surch double	£200	
		b. Double impression of stamp	£225	
		c. Slanting serif on "1"	22·00	

1899. W **34**. P **14**.
| 111 | **40** | 3p. aniline carmine | 40 | 10 |

1900 (1 Oct)–**02**. W **34**. P **14**.
112	**40**	3p. grey	75	1·25
113	**23**	½a. pale yellow-green	1·60	50
114		½a. yellow-green	2·50	50
115	**25**	1a. carmine	2·00	20
116	**27**	2a. pale violet	4·00	2·25
117		2a. mauve (1902)	8·00	3·00
118	**36**	2a.6p. ultramarine	3·25	4·00
112/18 *Set of 5*			10·50	7·50

41 42 43

44 45 46

47 48 49

50 51 52

1902 (9 Aug)–**11**. W **34**. P **14**.
119	**41**	3p. grey	1·00	10
120		3p. slate-grey (1904)	1·00	10
121	**42**	½a. yellow-green	1·50	20
122		½a. green	1·50	20
123	**43**	1a. carmine	1·50	10
124	**44**	2a. violet (13.5.03)	4·00	40
125		2a. mauve	3·75	10
126	**45**	2a.6p. ultramarine (1902)	4·75	60
		w. Wmk inverted	†	£170
127	**46**	3a. orange-brown (1902)	4·75	60
128	**47**	4a. olive (20.4.03)	3·00	60
129		4a. pale olive	4·00	60
130		4a. olive-brown	9·00	3·00
131	**48**	6a. olive-bistre (6.8.03)	12·00	4·75
132		6a. maize	10·00	4·50
133	**49**	8a. purple (*shades*) (8.5.03)	8·50	1·00
134		8a. claret (1910)	14·00	1·00
135	**50**	12a. purple/*red* (1903)	8·50	2·00
136	**51**	1r. green and carmine (1903)	6·50	70
137		1r. green and scarlet (1911)	40·00	3·00
138	**52**	2r. rose-red and yellow-brown (1903)	42·00	4·00
139		2r. carmine and yellow-brown	42·00	4·00
		w. Wmk inverted	†	£200
140		3r. brown and green (1904)	29·00	20·00
141		3r. red-brown and green (1911)	40·00	22·00
142		5r. ultramarine and violet (1904)	65·00	35·00
143		5r. ultramarine and deep lilac (1911)	£110	48·00
144		10r. green and carmine (1909)	£120	28·00
146		15r. blue and olive-brown (1909)	£150	42·00
147		25r. brownish orange and blue (1909)	£850	£850
119/47 *Set of 17*			£1200	£900

No. 147 can often be found with telegraph cancellation; these can be
supplied at one third of the price given above.

1905 (2 Feb). *No. 122 surch with T* **39**.
| 148 | **42** | ¼ on ½a. green | 55 | 10 |
| | | a. Surch inverted | — | £850 |

It is doubtful if No. 148a exists unused with genuine surcharge.

53 54

1906 (6 Dec)–**07**. W **34**. P **14**.
| 149 | **53** | ½a. green | 3·00 | 10 |
| 150 | **54** | 1a. carmine (7.1.07) | 1·75 | 10 |

55 56 57

58 * 59 60

61 62 63

64 65 66

67 — "Rs" flaw in right value tablet (R. 1/4)

69　　**70**　　**71**

*T **58**. Two types of the 1½a.; (A) As illustrated. (B) Inscribed "1½ As". "ONE AND A HALF ANNAS".

1911 (1 Dec)–**22**. W **34**. P 14.

151	55	3p. grey (1912)	1·40	20
		w. Wmk inverted		
152		3p. pale grey	1·50	20
153		3p. bluish grey (1922)	2·00	50
		w. Wmk inverted	13·00	
154		3p. slate	1·50	20
		a. "Rs" flaw	15·00	20·00
154b		3p. violet-grey	2·50	50
155	56	½a. light green (1912)	1·60	15
		w. Wmk inverted	40·00	
156		½a. emerald	2·25	15
		w. Wmk inverted	†	38·00
157		½a. bright green	2·25	15
159	57	1a. rose-carmine	2·50	20
160		1a. carmine	2·50	20
161		1a. aniline carmine	2·25	15
162		1a. pale rose-carmine (chalk-surfaced paper) (1918)	3·00	40
163	58	1½a. chocolate (Type A) (1919)	3·00	30
164		1½a. grey-brown (Type A)	7·50	2·50
165		1½a. chocolate (Type B) (1921)	3·25	4·50
		w. Wmk inverted	9·00	
166	59	2a. purple	3·25	40
167		2a. reddish purple	6·00	30
168		2a. deep mauve	5·00	40
		w. Wmk inverted	22·00	
169		2a. bright reddish violet	6·50	50
170	60	2a.6p. ultramarine (1912)	2·75	3·00
171	61	2a.6p. ultramarine (1913)	2·75	20
172	62	3a. orange	4·00	20
173		3a. dull orange	8·00	45
174	63	4a. deep olive (1912)	6·00	50
175		4a. olive-green	6·00	50
		w. Wmk inverted	22·00	
177	64	6a. yellow-bistre (1912)	4·00	1·25
178		6a. brown-ochre	4·00	1·00
179	65	8a. deep magenta (1912)	6·00	1·75
180		8a. deep mauve	13·00	1·10
		w. Wmk inverted	60·00	
181		8a. bright mauve	35·00	7·00
182		8a. purple	16·00	1·75
183	66	12a. carmine-lake (1912)	6·00	2·25
184		12a. claret	17·00	2·50
185	67	1r. red-brown and deep blue-green (1913)	18·00	2·00
		w. Wmk inverted	48·00	
186		1r. brown and green (shades)	22·00	1·50
186a		1r. orange-brown and deep turquoise-green	38·00	3·75
187		2r. carmine and brown (1913)	21·00	1·75
		w. Wmk inverted	70·00	
188		5r. ultramarine and violet (1913)	50·00	6·50
189		10r. green and scarlet (1913)	75·00	12·00
190		15r. blue and olive (1913)	£100	24·00
191		25r. orange and blue (1913)	£180	85·00
151/91 Set of 19			£450	85·00

Examples of the ½a. printed double are now believed to be forgeries.

FORGERIES.—Collectors are warned against forgeries of all the later surcharges of India, and particularly the errors.

NINE

PIES

(**68**)

1921 (10 June). T **57** surch with T **68**.

192		9p. on 1a. rose-carmine	85	30
		a. Error. "NINE NINE"	75·00	£130
		b. Error. "PIES PIES"	75·00	£130
		c. Surch double	£160	£190
		w. Wmk inverted	†	65·00
193		9p. on 1a. carmine-pink	1·75	60
194		9p. on 1a. aniline carmine	9·00	3·50

In the initial setting of the surcharge No. 192a occurred on R. 2/13-16 of the fourth pane and No. 192b on R. 4/13-16 of the third. For the second setting No. 192a was corrected. Examples of No. 192b still occur but on R. 2/13-16 of the third pane. Later printings showed this corrected also.

1922. T **56** surch with T **39**.

195		¼a. on ½a. bright green	50	35
		a. Surch inverted	9·00	
		b. Surch omitted (in horiz pair with normal)	£200	
		c. Slanting serif on "1"	30·00	
		w. Wmk inverted		
196		¼a. on ½a. emerald	2·50	1·00
		w. Wmk inverted		

1922–26. W **34**. P 14.

197	57	1a. chocolate	1·00	10
		w. Wmk inverted	22·00	
198	58	1½a. rose-carmine (Type B) (1926)	3·00	30
199	61	2a.6p. orange (1926)	5·00	2·50
200	62	3a. ultramarine (1923)	12·00	60
197/200 Set of 4			19·00	3·25

PRINTERS. The following issues of postage and contemporary official stamps were all printed by the Security Printing Press, Nasik, unless otherwise stated.

1926–33. Typo. W **69**. P 14.

201	55	3p. slate	30	10
		w. Wmk inverted	1·40	30
202	56	½a. green	1·25	10
		w. Wmk inverted	2·50	30
203	57	1a. chocolate	50	10
		a. Tête-bêche (pair) (1932)	1·25	10·00
		w. Wmk inverted	50	10
204	58	1½a. rose-carmine (Type B) (1929)	2·75	10
		w. Wmk inverted	3·00	30
205	59	2a. bright purple	8·00	9·00
		a. Stop under "s" in right value tablet (R. 4/16)	£100	
		w. Wmk inverted	†	40·00
206	70	2a. purple	1·75	10
		a. Tête-bêche (pair) (1933)	9·00	40·00
		w. Wmk inverted	1·75	30
207	61	2a.6p. orange (1929)	2·25	10
208	62	3a. ultramarine	2·25	40
		3a. ultramarine	9·50	1·00
209		3a. blue (1928)	9·50	10
		w. Wmk inverted	9·50	75
210	63	4a. pale sage-green	1·50	10
		w. Wmk inverted	—	8·00
211	71	4a. sage-green	6·00	10
		w. Wmk inverted	14·00	50
212	65	8a. reddish purple	4·00	10
			6·00	40
213	66	12a. claret	5·00	30
			7·00	80
214	67	1r. chocolate and green	5·00	45
		a. Chocolate (head) omitted	£5000	
		w. Wmk inverted	9·00	75
215		2r. carmine and orange	14·00	80
		w. Wmk inverted	14·00	1·50
216		5r. ultramarine and purple	27·00	1·25
		w. Wmk inverted	45·00	2·00
217		10r. green and scarlet (1927)	55·00	3·00
		w. Wmk inverted	£100	5·00
218		15r. blue and olive (1928)	45·00	30·00
		w. Wmk inverted	25·00	30·00
219		25r. orange and blue (1928)	£100	35·00
		w. Wmk inverted	£140	50·00
201/19 Set of 18			£250	70·00

Examples of the ½a. printed double are believed to be forgeries.

72 De Havilland D.H. 66 Hercules

Missing tree-top (R. 11/6 of 8a.)　　Reversed serif on second "I" of "INDIA"

(Des R. Grant. Litho)

1929 (22 Oct). Air. W **69** (sideways*). P 14.

220	72	2a. deep blue-green	3·50	65
		w. Wmk stars pointing left	1·75	75
221		3a. blue	1·00	2·00
		a. "Q" for "O" in "POSTAGE" (R.11/4)	£100	75·00
		w. Wmk stars pointing left	2·50	2·25
222		4a. olive-green	2·75	1·25
		w. Wmk stars pointing left	3·50	1·25
223		6a. bistre	2·25	1·00
		w. Wmk stars pointing left	2·50	1·00
224		8a. purple	3·00	1·00
		a. Missing tree-top	£130	75·00
		b. Reversed serif	£250	£130
		w. Wmk stars pointing left	3·50	1·00
225		12a. rose-red	14·00	6·00
		w. Wmk stars pointing left	13·00	6·00
220/5 Set of 6			21·00	10·50

*The normal sideways watermark shows the stars pointing right, as seen from the back of the stamp.

73 Purana Qila

---

74 War Memorial Arch

75 Council House

76 The Viceroy's House

77 Government of India Secretariat

78 Dominion Columns and the Secretariat

(Des H. W. Barr. Litho)

1931 (9 Feb). Inauguration of New Delhi. T **73/78**. W **69** (sideways*). P 13½×14.

226	73	¼a. olive-green and orange-brown	2·00	3·50
		a. "F" for "P" in "PURANA"	£110	£120
		w. Wmk stars pointing left	1·75	3·50
227	74	½a. violet and green	1·25	40
		w. Wmk stars pointing left	2·00	40
228	75	1a. mauve and chocolate	1·25	20
		w. Wmk stars pointing left	2·50	25
229	76	2a. green and blue	1·50	3·25
		w. Wmk stars pointing left	2·00	1·25
230	77	3a. chocolate and carmine	3·75	2·50
		w. Wmk stars pointing left	2·50	2·50
231	78	1r. violet and green	11·00	28·00
		w. Wmk stars pointing left	9·00	28·00
226/31 Set of 6			15·00	32·00

*The normal sideways watermark shows the stars pointing to the right, as seen from the back of the stamp.

79　　**80**　　**81**

82　　**83**

9p. litho. Heavier and longer lines on face. King's nose often shows 6 horizontal lines and always has lowest line long and thin

9p. typo. Lines lighter and shorter. Always 5 lines on King's nose with the lowest short and thick

(T **82/3** des T. I. Archer. 9p. litho or typo; 1a.3p, 3a.6p. litho; others typo)

1932–36. W **69**. P 14.

232	79	½a. green (1934)	5·00	10
		w. Wmk inverted	—	1·25
233	80	9p. deep green (litho) (22.4.32)	2·50	10
		aw. Wmk inverted	3·50	1·25
233b		9p. deep green (typo) (27.8.34)	2·75	10
234	81	1a. chocolate (1934)	4·50	10
		w. Wmk inverted	10·00	1·25

235	82	1a.3p. mauve (22.4.32)..........................	75	10
		w. Wmk inverted	1·00	30
236	70	2a. vermilion	11·00	4·00
		aw. Wmk inverted	15·00	7·50
236b	59	2a. vermilion (1934)	3·75	50
		bw. Wmk inverted	—	17·00
236c		2a. vermilion (small die) (1936)......	5·00	30
		cw. Wmk inverted	—	7·50
237	62	3a. carmine	8·00	10
		w. Wmk inverted	—	1·75
238	83	3a.6p. ultramarine (22.4.32)	4·75	20
		w. Wmk inverted	4·75	30
239	64	6a. bistre (1935)	7·50	1·50
		w. Wmk inverted	—	15·00
232/9 Set of 9			42·00	5·50

No. 236b measures 19×22.6 mm and No. 236c 18.4×21.8 mm.

84 Gateway of India, Bombay

85 Victoria Memorial, Calcutta

86 Rameswaram Temple, Madras

87 Jain Temple, Calcutta

88 Taj Mahal, Agra

89 Golden Temple, Amritsar

90 Pagoda in Mandalay

"Bird" flaw (R. 9/3)

1935 (6 May). *Silver Jubilee. T* **84/90.** *Litho.* W **69** (sideways*).
P 13½×14.

240		½a. black and yellow-green	1·10	20
		w. Wmk stars pointing left	1·00	15
241		9p. black and grey-green	1·00	20
		w. Wmk stars pointing left	75	30
242		1a. black and brown	2·00	20
		w. Wmk stars pointing left	1·25	10
243		1¼a. black and bright violet	65	10
		w. Wmk stars pointing left	1·00	15
244		2½a. black and orange	2·75	1·60
		w. Wmk stars pointing left	1·75	1·60
245		3½a. black and dull ultramarine	3·75	4·00
		a. "Bird" flaw	£150	£100
		w. Wmk stars pointing left	4·25	4·00
246		8a. black and purple	3·50	3·25
		w. Wmk stars pointing left	5·50	3·75
240/6 Set of 7			11·50	8·00

*The normal sideways watermark shows the stars pointing to the
right, *as seen from the back of the stamp.*

91 King George
VI

92 Dak Runner

93 Dak bullock cart

94 Dak tonga

95 Dak camel

96 Mail train

97 *Strathnaver* (liner)

98 Post truck

99 Armstrong Whitworth A.W.27
Ensign I mail plane (small head)

100 King George VI

1937 (23 Aug)–**40.** *T* **91/100.** *Typo.* W **69.** P 13½×14 or 14×13½
(*T* **93**).

247	91	3p. slate (15.12.37)	1·00	10
248		½a. red-brown (15.12.37)	5·00	10
		w. Wmk inverted		
249		9p. green	8·00	30
		w. Wmk inverted		
250		1a. carmine	1·25	10
		a. Tête-bêche (vert pair) (1940).....	2·75	1·75
		w. Wmk inverted (from booklets)..	1·75	1·50
251	92	2a. vermilion (15.12.37)	6·00	30
		w. Wmk inverted		
252	93	2a.6p. bright violet (15.12.37)............	1·50	20
		w. Wmk inverted	—	22·00
253	94	3a. yellow-green (15.12.37)............	7·00	30
		w. Wmk inverted	—	22·00
254	95	3a.6p. bright blue (15.12.37)............	3·50	50
255	96	4a. brown (15.12.37).......................	13·00	20
		w. Wmk inverted	—	22·00
256	97	6a. turquoise-green (15.12.37)........	14·00	80
257	98	8a. slate-violet (15.12.37)...............	7·50	50
		w. Wmk inverted		
258	99	12a. lake (15.12.37)	18·00	1·10
		w. Wmk inverted		
259	100	1r. grey and red-brown (15.12.37)..	1·25	15
		w. Wmk inverted		
260		2r. purple and brown (15.12.37).....	5·00	30
		w. Wmk inverted	29·00	
261		5r. green and blue (15.12.37).......	25·00	50
		w. Wmk inverted	50·00	
262		10r. purple and claret (15.12.37)	19·00	80
		w. Wmk inverted	†	60·00
263		15r. brown and green (15.12.37).....	75·00	60·00
		w. Wmk inverted	£130	£110
264		25r. slate-violet and purple (15.12.37).	20·00	14·00
		w. Wmk inverted	—	£120
247/64 Set of 18			£275	75·00

No. 250a comes from surplus booklet sheets issued as normal stock
following the rise in postal rates.

100a King
George VI

101 King
George VI

102 King
George VI

103 Armstrong Whitworth A.W.27
Ensign I mail plane (large head)

(T **100a/102** des T. I. Archer. Typo (1½a. on 3a. litho also))

1940–43. W **69.** P 13½×14.

265	100a	3p. slate	30	10
		w. Wmk inverted	10·00	
266		½a. purple (1.10.42)	1·00	10
		w. Wmk inverted	—	12·00
267		9p. green	1·00	10
		w. Wmk inverted	—	15·00
268		1a. carmine (1.4.43)	1·25	10
		w. Wmk inverted		
269	101	1a.3p. yellow-brown	1·00	10
		aw. Wmk inverted		
269b		1½a. dull violet (9.42)	1·25	10
		bw. Wmk inverted		
270		2a. vermilion	1·50	10
		w. Wmk inverted		
271		3a. bright violet (1942)	3·25	10
		w. Wmk inverted	—	10·00
272		3½a. bright blue	1·25	75
		w. Wmk inverted		
273	102	4a. brown	1·25	10
		w. Wmk inverted		
274		6a. turquoise-green	3·75	10
		w. Wmk inverted	†	35·00
275		8a. slate-violet	1·50	30
		w. Wmk inverted		
276		12a. lake	5·00	1·00
277	103	14a. purple (15.10.40)	18·00	2·00
265/77 Set of 14			38·00	3·75

The 1½a. and 3a. at first printed by lithography and were of
finer execution and without Jubilee lines in the sheet margins. The two
values exist with watermark inverted from both processes.

105 "Victory" and King George
VI

3 PIES
(**106**)

1946 (2 Jan). *Victory. Litho.* W **69.** P 13.

278	105	9p. yellow-green (8.2.46).................	50	1·50
279		1½a. dull violet	30	30
		w. Wmk inverted	—	24·00
280		3½a. bright blue..............................	85	1·25
281		12a. claret (8.2.46)	1·50	1·25
278/81 Set of 4			2·75	3·75

1946 (8 Aug). *Surch with T* **106.**

282	101	3p. on 1a.3p. yellow-brown	10	15

DOMINION

301 Asokan Capital
(Inscr reads "Long
Live India")

302 Indian National Flag

303 Douglas DC-4

(Des T. I. Archer. Litho)

1947 (21 Nov–15 Dec). *Independence.* W **69.** P 14×13½ (1½a.) or
13½×14 (others).

301	301	1½a. grey-green (15 Dec)	15	10
302	302	3½a. orange-red, blue and green	1·00	2·25
		w. Wmk inverted	11·00	11·00
303	303	12a. ultramarine (15 Dec)................	1·50	2·75
301/3 Set of 3			2·40	4·50

304 Lockheed Constellation

(Des T. I. Archer. Litho)

1948 (29 May). *Air. Inauguration of India—U.K. Air Service.* W **69.**
P 13½×14.

304	304	12a. black and ultramarine	1·25	3·00

305 Mahatma Gandhi   **306** Mahatma Gandhi

(Photo Courvoisier)

1948 (15 Aug). *First Anniv of Independence.* P 11½.

305	**305**	1½a. brown	2·75	60
306		3½a. violet	4·25	2·50
307		12a. grey-green	6·00	1·75
308	**306**	10r. purple-brown and lake	45·00	40·00
305/8 *Set of 4*			50·00	42·00

307 Ajanta Panel   **308** Konarak Horse   **309** Trimurti

310 Bodhisattva   **311** Nataraja   **312** Sanchi Stupa, East Gate

313 Bodh Gaya Temple   **314** Bhuvanesvara   **315** Gol Gumbad, Bijapur

316 Kandarya Mahadeva Temple   **317** Golden Temple, Amritsar

318 Victory Tower, Chittorgarh   **319** Red Fort, Delhi

320 Taj Mahal, Agra   **321** Qutb Minar, Delhi

322 Satrunjaya Temple, Palitana

(Des T. I. Archer and I. M. Das. Typo (low values), litho (rupee values))

1949 (15 Aug). W **69** (sideways* on 6p., 1r. and 10r.). P 14 (3p. to 2a.), 13½ (3a. to 12a.), 14×13½ (1r. and 10r.), 13½×14 (2r. and 5r.), 13 (15r.).

309	**307**	3p. slate-violet	15	10
		w. Wmk inverted		
310	**308**	6p. purple-brown	25	10
		w. Wmk star pointing right	2·00	1·00
311	**309**	9p. yellow-green	40	10
		w. Wmk inverted	†	55·00
312	**310**	1a. turquoise	60	10
		w. Wmk inverted		
313	**311**	2a. carmine	80	10
		w. Wmk inverted	18·00	1·25
314	**312**	3a. brown-orange	1·50	10
		w. Wmk inverted	†	75·00
315	**313**	3½a. bright blue	1·50	3·75
316	**314**	4a. lake	4·00	30
		w. Wmk inverted	22·00	
317	**315**	6a. violet	1·50	30
		w. Wmk inverted	3·25	1·00
318	**316**	8a. turquoise-green	1·50	10
		w. Wmk inverted	—	55·00
319	**317**	12a. dull blue	1·50	30
		w. Wmk inverted	13·00	
320	**318**	1r. dull violet and green	9·00	10
		w. Wmk star pointing left	26·00	1·25
321	**319**	2r. claret and violet	11·00	20
		w. Wmk inverted	50·00	2·00
322	**320**	5r. blue-green and red-brown	28·00	1·50
		w. Wmk inverted	70·00	3·00
323	**321**	10r. purple-brown and deep blue	55·00	8·50
		a. Purple-brown and blue	95·00	4·75
		aw. Wmk star pointing left	£150	60·00
324	**322**	15r. brown and claret	16·00	21·00
309/24 *Set of 16*			£120	29·00

*The normal sideways watermark has the star pointing to the left on the 6p. value and to the right on the 1r. and 10r. (323*a*) when seen from the back of the stamp.

For T **310** with statue reversed see No. 333.

323 Globe and Asokan Capital

1949 (10 Oct). *75th Anniv of U.P.U.* Litho. W **69**. P 13.

325	**323**	9p. green	1·00	3·00
326		2a. rose	1·00	2·50
327		3½a. bright blue	1·50	2·50
328		12a. brown-purple	2·00	2·50
325/8 *Set of 4*			5·00	9·50

REPUBLIC

324 Rejoicing Crowds

325 Quill, ink-well and verse

326 Ear of corn and plough

327 Spinning-wheel and cloth

(Des D. J. Keymer & Co. Litho)

1950 (26 Jan). *Inauguration of Republic.* T **324/7**. W **69** (sideways on 3½a.). P 13.

329		2a. scarlet	1·25	50
		w. Wmk inverted	23·00	2·75
330		3½a. ultramarine	1·75	3·75
331		4a. violet	1·75	1·25

332		12a. maroon	3·50	2·25
		w. Wmk inverted	24·00	7·00
329/32 *Set of 4*			7·50	7·00

328 As T **310**, but statue reversed

1950 (15 July)–**51**. *Typo.* W **69**. P 14 (1a.), 13½ (others).

333	**328**	1a. turquoise	4·00	10
		aw. Wmk inverted		
333*b*	**313**	2½a. lake (30.4.51)	3·00	3·25
333*c*	**314**	4a. bright blue (30.4.51)	6·00	10
333/*c Set of 3*			11·50	3·25

329 Stegodon ganesa   **330** Torch

1951 (13 Jan). *Centenary of Geological Survey of India.* Litho. W **69**. P 13.

334	**329**	2a. black and claret	2·00	1·25

1951 (4 Mar). *First Asian Games, New Delhi.* Litho. W **69** (sideways). P 14.

335	**330**	2a. reddish purple & brn-orge	1·00	1·00
336		12a. chocolate and light blue	4·00	2·25

STAMP BOOKLETS

1904. *Black on green (No. SB1) or black on pink (No. SB2) covers. Stapled.*

SB1	12¼a. booklet containing twenty-four ½a. (No. 121) in blocks of 6	£1000
SB2	12¼a. booklet containing twelve 1a. (No. 123) in blocks of 6	£1000

1906–11. *Black on green (No. SB3), black on pink (No. SB4) or black on green and pink (No. SB5) match book type covers inscr "Post Office of India" and royal cypher of King Edward VII. Stapled.*

SB3	1r. booklet containing thirty-two ½a. (No. 149) in blocks of 4	£550
	a. Without "Post Office of India" inscr	£500
	b. Ditto and showing royal cypher of King George V (1911)	£450
SB4	1r. booklet containing sixteen 1a. (No. 150) in blocks of 4 (1907)	£500
	a. Without "Post Office of India" inscr	£450
	b. Ditto and showing royal cypher of King George V (1911)	£475
SB5	1r. booklet containing sixteen ½a. and eight 1a. (Nos. 149/50) in blocks of 4 (1907)	£1100
	a. Without "Post Office of India" inscr	£950
	b. Ditto and showing royal cypher of King George V (1911)	£900

1912–22. *Black on green (Nos. SB6/7, SB12), black on pink (No. SB8), black on green and pink (No. SB9), black on purple (No. SB10) or black on blue (No. SB11) match book type covers with foreign postage rates on back. Stapled.*

SB6	1r. booklet containing sixty-four 3p. (No. 152) in blocks of 4 (blank back cover)	£600
SB7	1r. booklet containing thirty-two ½a. (No. 155) in blocks of 4	£225
	a. Blank back cover	£225
	b. Advertisement contractor's notice on back cover	£325
	c. Advertisement on back (1922)	£300
SB8	1r. booklet containing sixteen 1a. (No. 159) in blocks of 4	£170
	a. Blank back cover	£170
	b. Advertisements on front flap and back cover (1922)	£200
SB9	1r. booklet containing sixteen ½a. and eight 1a. (Nos. 155, 159) in blocks of 4 (blank back cover)	£160
	a. Advertisement on back	£190
	b. Foreign postage rates on back	£170
SB10	1r.8a. booklet containing sixteen 1½a. (No. 163) in blocks of 4 (1919)	£375
	a. Blank back cover (1921)	£350
SB11	2r. booklet containing sixteen 2a. (No. 169) in blocks of 4 (blank back cover) (1921)	£500
	a. Black on purple cover with postage rates on back (1922)	£500
SB12	2r. booklet containing sixteen 2a. (No. 166) in blocks of 4 (1922)	£500
	a. Black on purple cover	£500

1921. *Black on buff match book type cover. Stapled.*

SB13	1r.2a. booklet containing twenty-four 9p. on 1a. (No. 192) in blocks of 4	£110

1922. *Black on brown (No. SB14) or black on green and pink (No. SB15) match book type covers with foreign postage rates on back. Stapled.*

SB14	1r. booklet containing sixteen 1a. (No. 197) in blocks of 4	£225

	a. Advertisement on back	£275
	b. Advertisements on front flap and back cover .	
	c. Black on lilac cover with blank back...........	£250
	ca. Advertisements on front flap and back cover .	£350
	d. Black on pink cover with blank back	£300
SB15	1r. booklet containing sixteen ½a. and eight 1a. (Nos. 155, 197) in blocks of 4 (blank back cover)	£500

1926–28. *Black on brown (No. SB16) or black on purple (No. SB17) match book type covers with foreign postage rates on back. Stapled.*

SB16	1r. booklet containing sixteen 1a. (No. 203) in blocks of 4	£110
SB17	2r. booklet containing sixteen 2a. (No. 205) in blocks of 4	£325
	a. Containing No. 206 (1928)	£400

1929. *Black on brown (No. SB18) or black on purple (No. SB19) separate leaf covers. Stitched.*

SB18	1r. booklet containing sixteen 1a. (No. 203) in blocks of 4 (blank back cover)	£110
	a. Advertisement contractor's notice on back cover	£100
	b. Advertisements on front flap and back cover .	£130
	c. Advertisement on back cover	£130
SB19	2r. booklet containing sixteen 2a. (No. 205) in blocks of 4 (foreign postage rates on back cover)	£350
	a. Advertisement contractor's notice on back cover	£350
	b. Containing No. 206 (foreign postage rates on back cover)	£425
	ba. Advertisement contractor's notice on back cover	£425

1932. *Black on brown cover. Stitched.*

SB20	1r.4a. booklet containing sixteen 1¼a. (No. 235) in blocks of 4	£350

1934. *Black on buff cover. Stitched.*

SB21	1r. booklet containing sixteen 1a. (No. 234) in blocks of 4	£190

1937. *Black on red cover. Stamps with wmk upright or inverted. Stitched.*

SB22	1r. booklet containing sixteen 1a. (No. 250) in blocks of 4	£250

OFFICIAL STAMPS

Stamps overprinted "POSTAL SERVICE" or "I.P.N." were not used as postage stamps, and are therefore omitted.

Service.
(O **1**)

(Optd by the Military Orphanage Press, Calcutta)

1866 (1 Aug)–**72.** *Optd with Type O* **1**. *P* 14.

(a) No wmk.

O1	11	½a. blue............................	—	£275
O2		½a. pale blue........................	£1200	£130
		a. Opt inverted		
O3		1a. brown........................	—	£170
O4		1a. deep brown....................		£130
O5		8a. carmine........................	23·00	55·00

(b) Wmk Elephant's Head, T13.

O6	11	½a. blue............................	£275	22·00
		w. Wmk inverted	†	£150
O7		½a. pale blue........................	£250	12·00
		a. Opt inverted		
		b. No dot on "i" (No. 50 on pane) ..	—	£300
		c. No stop (No. 77 on pane)........		£250
O8	12	8p. purple (1.72)	22·00	50·00
		a. No dot on "i"	£275	£350
		b. No stop	£275	
O9	11	1a. brown........................	£225	16·00
O10		1a. deep brown....................	£250	38·00
		a. No dot on "i"	—	£475
		b. No stop		£400
O11		2a. orange........................	£180	85·00
O12		2a. yellow........................	£180	90·00
		a. Opt inverted		
		b. Imperf		
		c. Raised dot between "c" and "e"	†	£1600
		w. Wmk inverted	£250	
		y. Wmk inverted and reversed......	†	£350
O13		4a. green........................	£200	85·00
		a. Opt inverted		
O14	17	4a. green (Die 1)	£1000	£250

A variety with wide and more open capital "S" occurs six times in sheets of all values except No. O8. Price four times the normal.

Reprints exist of Nos. O6, O9 and O14; the latter is Die II instead of Die I.

Reprints of the overprint have also been made, in different setting, on the 8 pies, purple, no watermark.

O 2	O 6

O 3	O 4

(No. O15 surch at Calcutta, others optd at Madras)

1866 (Oct). *Fiscal stamps, Nos. O15/18 with top and bottom inscrs removed, surch or optd. Wmk Crown over "INDIA".*

(a) Surch as in Type O **2**. *Thick blue glazed paper. Imperf×perf* 14.

O15	O **2**	2a. purple	£275	£225

(b) Optd "SERVICE POSTAGE" in two lines as in Types O3/4 and similar type. Imperf×perf 14.

O16	O **3**	2a. purple (G.)........................	£800	£400
O17	O **4**	4a. purple (G.)........................	£3500	£1100
O18	—	8a. purple (G.)........................	£3750	£3750
		a. Optd on complete stamp (inscr "FOREIGN BILL")................	†	£11000

(c) Optd "SERVICE POSTAGE" in semi-circle. Wmk Large Crown. P 15½×15.

O19	O **6**	½a. mauve/lilac (G.)......................	£400	85·00
		a. Opt double	£2750	

So-called reprints of Nos. O15 to O18 are known, but in these the surcharge differs entirely in the spacing, etc., of the words; they are more properly described as Government imitations. The imitations of No. O15 have surcharge in *black* or in *green*. No. O19 exists with reprinted overprint which has a full stop after "POSTAGE".

PRINTERS. The following stamps up to No. O108 were overprinted by De La Rue and thereafter Official stamps were printed or overprinted by the Security Printing Press at Nasik.

On   **On**

Service.   **H. S.**   **H. S.**
         M.   **M.**

(O **7**)   (O **8**)   (O **9**)

1867–73. *Optd with Type O7. Wmk Elephant's Head, T* 13. P 14.

O20	11	½a. blue (Die I)	42·00	50
		w. Wmk inverted	†	90·00
O21		½a. pale blue (Die I)	50·00	2·25
O22		½a. blue (Die II) (1873)	£150	70·00
O23		1a. brown........................	45·00	50
		w. Wmk inverted	†	£110
O24		1a. deep brown....................	48·00	2·25
O25		1a. chocolate......................	50·00	2·25
O26		2a. yellow........................	26·00	2·50
O27		2a. orange........................	6·00	2·25
O28	17	4a. pale green (Die I)	18·00	2·00
O29		4a. green (Die I)	3·25	1·50
O30	11	8a. rose (Die II) (1868)	3·25	1·50
O30a		8a. pale rose (Die II)................	3·75	1·50
		aw. Wmk inverted	40·00	25·00

Prepared for use, but not issued.

O30b	18	6a.8p. slate......................	£300	

1874–82. *Optd with Type O 8.*

(a) In black.

O31	11	½a. blue (Die II)	13·00	20
O32		1a. brown........................	18·00	20
O33		2a. yellow........................	60·00	38·00
O33a		2a. orange........................	50·00	24·00
O34	17	4a. green (Die I)	19·00	3·00
O35	11	8a. rose (Die II)	8·50	6·00

(b) Optd in blue-black.

O36	11	½a. blue (Die II) (1877)	£325	45·00
O37		1a. brown (1882)	£550	£120

1883–99. *Wmk Star, T* 34. *Optd with Type O* **9**. *P* 14.

O37a	40	3p. aniline carmine (1899)............	20	10
O38	23	½a. deep blue-green................	2·50	10
		a. Opt double	†	£1300
		b. Opt inverted	†	£1000
O39		½a. blue-green....................	2·25	10
O40	25	1a. brown-purple..................	3·50	50
		a. Opt inverted	£350	£450
		aw. Wmk inverted	†	£550
		b. Opt double	†	£1400
		c. Opt omitted (in horiz pair with normal)........................	£1700	
O41		1a. plum........................	1·00	10
O42	27	2a. pale blue......................	7·50	60
O43		2a. blue........................	8·50	60
O44	29	4a. olive-green....................	22·00	50
O44a		4a. slate-green....................	22·00	50
O45	31	8a. dull mauve....................	22·00	1·25
O46		8a. magenta......................	10·00	50
O47	37	1r. green and rose (1892)............	48·00	4·50
O48		1r. green and carmine (1892)........	18·00	40
O37a/48 Set of 7			55·00	2·00

1900. *Colours changed. Optd with Type O* **9**.

O49	23	½a. pale yellow-green................	2·50	90
O49a		½a. yellow-green..................	4·00	50
		ab. Opt double	£1000	
O50	25	1a. carmine......................	3·50	10
		a. Opt inverted	†	£1500

O51	27	b. Opt double	†	£1600
		2a. pale violet....................	40·00	1·50
O52		2a. mauve........................	48·00	50
O49/52 Set of 3			42·00	1·00

1902–09. *Stamps of King Edward VII optd with Type O* **9**.

O54	41	3p. grey (1903)......................	2·50	1·00
O55		3p. slate-grey (1905)................	2·50	1·00
		a. No stop after "M" (R. 6/10)....	£200	£140
O56	42	½a. green........................	1·25	30
O57	43	1a. carmine......................	1·00	30
O58	44	2a. violet........................	4·50	40
O59		2a. mauve........................	3·25	40
O60	47	4a. olive........................	12·00	30
O61		4a. pale olive......................	12·00	30
O62	48	6a. olive-bistre (1909)	1·50	15
O63	49	8a. purple (*shades*)................	6·00	1·00
O64		8a. claret........................	8·00	85
O65	51	1r. green and carmine (1905)........	4·00	80
O54/65 Set of 8			28·00	3·00

1906. *New types. Optd with Type O* **9**.

O66	53	½a. green........................	1·25	10
		a. No stop after "M" (R. 6/10)....	£130	60·00
O67	54	1a. carmine......................	2·00	10
		a. No stop after "M" (R. 6/10)....	£190	90·00
		b. Opt albino (in pair with normal)........................	£1200	

On

H. S.

M.
(O **9a**)

1909. *Optd with Type O* **9a**.

O68	52	2r. carmine and yellow-brown........	9·50	1·50
O68a		2r. rose-red and yellow-brown........	9·50	1·50
O69		5r. ultramarine and violet............	14·00	1·50
O70		10r. green and carmine	30·00	17·00
O70a		10r. green and scarlet	75·00	7·00
O71		15r. blue and olive-brown	70·00	40·00
O72		25r. brownish orange and blue........	£150	60·00
O68/72 Set of 5			£250	£100

NINE

SERVICE	**SERVICE**	**PIES**
(O **10**) (14 mm)	(O **11**) (21½ mm)	(O **12**)

1912–13. *Stamps of King George V (wmk Single Star, T* 34) *optd with Type O* **10** *or O* **11** (*rupee values*).

O73	55	3p. grey........................	40	10
O73a		3p. pale grey......................	30	10
O74		3p. bluish grey....................	1·25	10
		a. Opt omitted (in pair with normal)........................		
O75		3p. slate........................	75	30
		a. "Rs" Flaw		
O75b		3p. violet-grey....................	3·25	30
O76	56	½a. light green....................	50	10
O77		½a. emerald......................	50	15
O78		½a. bright-green..................	50	15
		a. Opt double	£100	
O80	57	1a. rose-carmine..................	1·00	10
O81		1a. carmine......................	1·60	10
O82		1a. aniline carmine................	1·60	10
		a. Opt double	†	£900
O83	59	2a. purple........................	75	30
O83a		2a. reddish purple..................	75	25
O84		2a. deep mauve....................	75	30
O84a		2a. bright reddish violet............	3·00	40
O85	63	4a. deep olive......................	1·00	10
O86		4a. olive-green....................	1·00	10
O87	64	6a. yellow-bistre..................	1·50	2·50
O88		6a. brown-ochre..................	4·00	4·25
O89	65	8a. deep magenta..................	2·75	1·25
O89a		8a. deep mauve....................	3·00	1·25
O90		8a. bright mauve..................	22·00	3·75
O91	67	1r. red-brown and deep blue-grn (1913)........................	3·50	1·75
O91a		1r. brown and green	2·75	1·40
O92		2r. rose-carmine & brown (1913)...	4·25	7·00
O93		5r. ultramarine and violet (1913).....	18·00	25·00
O94		10r. green and scarlet (1913).........	55·00	50·00
O95		15r. blue and olive (1913)............	£100	£110
O96		25r. orange and blue (1913).........	£225	£170
O73/96 Set of 13			£350	£325

1921. *No. O80 surch with Type O* **12**.

O97	57	9p. on 1a. rose-carmine..............	1·25	75

1922. *No. 197 optd with Type O* **10**.

O98	57	1a. chocolate......................	2·25	10

(O 13)   (O 14)

1925. *Official stamps surcharged.*

(a) Issue of 1909, as Type O **13**.

O 99	52	1r. on 15r. blue and olive	4·25	4·00
O100		1r. on 25r. chestnut and blue	20·00	70·00
O101		2r. on 10r. green and scarlet	3·75	4·25
O101a		2r. on 10r. green and carmine	£225	55·00

(b) Issue of 1912 with Type O **14**.

O102	67	1r. on 15r. blue and olive	19·00	75·00
O103		1r. on 25r. orange and blue	5·50	11·00
		a. Surch inverted	£800	

(c) Issue of 1912, as Type O **13**.

O104	67	2r. on 10r. green and scarlet	£900	

Examples of the above showing other surcharge errors are believed to be of clandestine origin.

(O 15)   (O 16)

1926. *No. O62 surch with Type O* **15**.

O105	48	1a. on 6a. olive-bistre	30	30

1926. *Postage stamps of 1911–22 (wmk Single Star), surch as Type O* **16**.

O106	58	1a. on 1½a. chocolate (A)	20	10
O107		1a. on 1½a. chocolate (B)	3·50	4·50
		a. Error. On 1a. chocolate (197)	£180	
O108	61	1a. on 2a.6p. ultramarine	60	80

The surcharge on No. O108 has no bars at top.
Examples of Nos. O106/7 with inverted or double surcharges are believed to be of clandestine origin.

SERVICE
(O 17) (13½ mm)

SERVICE
(O 18) (19½ mm)

1926–31. *Stamps of King George V (wmk Multiple Star, T* **69***) optd with Types O* **17** *or O* **18** *(rupee values).*

O109	55	3p. slate (1.10.29)	40	10
		w. Wmk inverted	2·50	75
O110	56	½a. green (1931)	8·50	60
		w. Wmk inverted	—	1·75
O111	57	1a. chocolate	15	10
		w. Wmk inverted	2·50	60
O112	70	2a. purple	30	10
		w. Wmk inverted	2·25	50
O113	71	4a. sage-green	50	20
		w. Wmk inverted	2·50	1·25
O115	65	8a. reddish purple	2·00	10
		w. Wmk inverted	80	30
O116	66	12a. claret (1927)	70	2·50
		w. Wmk inverted	—	4·25
O117	67	1r. chocolate and green (1930)	4·50	1·00
		w. Wmk inverted	4·25	2·75
O118		2r. carmine and orange (1930)	9·00	9·00
		w. Wmk inverted	—	17·00
O120		10r. green and scarlet (1931)	80·00	90·00
O109/20 Set of 10			90·00	55·00

1930. *As No. O111, but optd as Type O* **10** *(14 mm).*

O125	57	1a. chocolate	—	5·50
		w. Wmk inverted	£100	6·50

1932–36. *Stamps of King George V (wmk Mult Star, T* **69***) optd with Type O* **17**.

O126	79	½a. green (1935)	1·50	10
O127	80	9p. deep green (litho)	30	15
		aw. Wmk inverted	—	5·50
O127b		9p. deep green (typo)	2·00	15
O127c	81	1a. chocolate (1936)	2·50	10
		cw. Wmk inverted	4·50	70
O128	82	1a.3p. mauve	30	10
		w. Wmk inverted	60	40
O129	70	2a. vermilion	1·50	2·50
		w. Wmk inverted	—	
O130	59	2a. vermilion (1935)	3·25	1·25
		aw. Wmk inverted	—	10·00
O130b		2a. verm (small die) (1936)	1·25	10
		bw. Wmk inverted	—	
O131	61	2a.6p. orange (22.4.32)	50	10
		w. Wmk inverted	2·25	1·00
O132	63	4a. sage-green (1935)	1·75	10
		w. Wmk inverted	—	
O133	64	6a. bistre (1936)	21·00	10·00
O126/33 Set of 9			28·00	11·00

1937–39. *Stamps of King George VI optd as Types O* **17** *or O* **18** *(rupee values).*

O135	91	½a. red-brown (1938)	17·00	1·00
O136		9p. green (1937)	19·00	1·00
O137		1a. carmine (1938)	3·50	10
O138	100	1r. grey and red-brown (5.38)	50	50
O139		2r. purple and brown (5.38)	1·75	2·50

O140		w. Wmk inverted	—	28·00
		5r. green and blue (10.38)	5·00	6·50
		w. Wmk inverted		
O141		10r. purple and claret (1939)	14·00	8·00
		w. Wmk inverted	80·00	
O135/41 Set of 7			55·00	18·00

SERVICE
1A
(O 19)   O 20

1939 (May). *Stamp of King George V, surch with Type O* **19**.

O142	82	1a. on 1¼a. mauve	12·00	20
		w. Wmk inverted	—	5·00

(Des T. I. Archer)

1939 (1 June)–42. *Typo. W* **69***. P* 14.

O143	O **20**	3p. slate	60	10
O144		½a. red-brown	6·50	10
O144a		½a. purple (1942)	30	10
O145		9p. green	30	10
O146		1a. carmine	30	10
O146a		1a.3p. yellow-brown (1941)	3·50	70
		aw. Wmk inverted		
O146b		1½a. dull violet (1942)	65	10
		bw. Wmk inverted		
O147		2a. vermilion	60	10
		w. Wmk inverted		
O148		2½a. bright violet	60	1·25
O149		4a. brown	60	10
O150		8a. slate-violet	90	30
O143/50 Set of 11			13·00	2·00

1948 (15 Aug). *First Anniv of Independence. Nos. 305/8 optd as Type O* **17**.

O150a	305	1½a. brown	42·00	35·00
O150b		3½a. violet	£850	£550
O150c		12a. grey-green	£2500	£1900
O150d	306	10r. purple-brown and lake	£13000	

Nos. O150a/d were only issued to the Governor-General's Secretariat.

O 21 Asokan Capital   O 22

(Des T.I. Archer)

1950 (2 Jan)–51. *Typo (O* **21***) or litho (O* **22***). W* **69***. P* 14.

O151	O **21**	3p. slate-violet (1.7.50)	15	10
O152		6p. purple-brown (1.7.50)	30	10
O153		9p. green (1.7.50)	1·25	10
O154		1a. turquoise (1.7.50)	1·25	10
O155		2a. carmine (1.7.50)	1·75	10
		w. Wmk inverted		
O156		3a. red-orange (1.7.50)	4·25	2·50
O157		4a. lake (1.7.50)	6·00	20
O158		4a. ultramarine (1.10.51)	50	10
O159		6a. bright violet (1.7.50)	4·00	1·50
O160		8a. red-brown (1.7.50)	2·00	10
		w. Wmk inverted	15·00	
O161	O **22**	1r. violet	3·00	10
		w. Wmk inverted		
O162		2r. rose-carmine	1·00	70
O163		5r. bluish green	2·00	2·00
O164		10r. reddish brown	3·00	22·00
O151/64 Set of 14			27·00	26·00

INDIA USED ABROAD

In the years following 1858 the influence of the Indian Empire, political, military and economic, extended beyond its borders into neighbouring states, the Arabian Gulf, East Africa and the Far East. Such influence often led to the establishment of Indian civil post offices in the countries concerned where unoverprinted stamps of India were used.

Such offices operated in the following countries. An * indicates that details will be found under that heading elsewhere in the catalogue.

ADEN*

Unoverprinted stamps of India used from 1854 until 1937.

BAHRAIN*

Unoverprinted stamps of India used from 1884 until 1933.

BRITISH EAST AFRICA
(KENYA, UGANDA AND TANGANYIKA)*

Unoverprinted stamps of India used during August and September 1890.

FRENCH INDIAN SETTLEMENTS

The first Indian post office, at Chandernagore, was open in 1784 to be followed by offices in the other four Settlements. By an agreement with the French, dating from 1814, these offices handled mail destined for British India, Great Britain, the British Empire and most other foreign destinations except France and the French colonies. In later years the system was expanded by a number of sub-offices and it continued to operate until the French territories were absorbed into India on 2 May 1950 (Chandernagore) or 1 November 1954.

Chandernagore.	Opened 1784.	Used numeral cancellations "B86" or "86".
Sub-offices:		
Gondalpara	(opened 1906)	
Lakhiganj	(opened 1909)	
Temata	(opened 1891)	
Karikal.	Opened 1794.	Used numeral cancellations in "C147", "147" or "6/M-21".
Sub-offices:		
Ambagarattur	(opened 1904)	
Kottuchari	(opened 1901)	
Nedungaon	(opened 1903)	
Puraiyar Road	(opened 1901)	
Settur	(opened 1905)	
Tirumalrayapatnam	(opened 1875)	– used numeral cancellation "6/M-21/1"
Tiramilur	(opened 1898)	
Mahe.	Opened 1795.	Used numeral cancellations "C192" or "9/M-14".
Pondicherry.	Opened 1787.	Used numeral cancellations "C111", "111" (also used elsewhere),"6/M-19" (also used elsewhere) or "6/M-20".
Sub-offices:		
Ariyankuppam	(opened 1904)	
Bahoor	(opened 1885)	
Mudaliarpet	(opened 1897)	
Muthialpet	(opened 1885)	
Pondicherry Bazaar	(opened 1902)	
Pondicherry Railway Station	(opened 1895)	
Olugarai	(opened 1907)	
Vallinur	(opened 1875)	used numeral cancellation "M-19/1"
Yanam.	Opened 1876.	Used numeral cancellation "5/M-4".

IRAN

The British East India Company was active in the Arabian Gulf from the early years of the 17th century with their first factory (trading centre) being established at Jask in 1619. After 1853 this commercial presence was converted into a political arm of the Indian Government culminating in the appointment of a Political Resident to Bushire in 1862.

The first Indian post office in Iran (Persia) opened at Bushire on 1 May 1864 with monthly mail services operating to the Resident there and to the British Legation at Tehran. Further offices in the other Gulf ports followed, but, unless otherwise stated below, all were closed on 1 April 1923.

Abadan.	Opened 1917.	
Ahwaz.	Opened March 1915.	
Bandar Abbas.	Opened 1 April 1867.	Used numeral cancellations "258", "22" or "I/K-5".
Bushire.	Opened I May 1864.	Used numeral cancellations "308", "26" (also used elsewhere) or "K-5".
Chabbar.	Opened 20 August 1913.	
Duzdab.	Opened 1922. Closed 1927?	
Henjam.	Opened 21 June 1913.	
Jask.	Opened 1 September 1880.	
Kuh-Malik-Siah-Ziarat.	Opened January 1906. Closed 1924.	
Linga.	Opened 1 April 1867.	Used numeral cancellations "21" or "2/K-5".
Maidan-i-Naphtan.	Opened 1917.	
Mirjawa.	Opened January 1921. Closed 1930.	
Mohammera.	Opened 19 July 1892.	

IRAQ*

Unoverprinted stamps of India used from 1868 until 1918.

KUWAIT*

Unoverprinted stamps of India used from 1904 until 1923.

MALAYA (STRAITS SETTLEMENTS)*

Unoverprinted stamps of India used from 1854 until 1867.

MUSCAT*

Unoverprinted stamps of India used from 1864 until 1947.

NEPAL

A post office was opened in the British Residency at Kathmandu in 1816 following the end of the Gurkha War. Stamps of India were used from 1854, initially with "B137", "137" or "C-37" numeral cancellations. The Residency Post Office continued to provide the overseas mail service after Nepal introduced its own issues in 1881.

In 1920 the Residency Post Office became the British Legation Post Office. On the independence of India in 1947 the service was transferred to the Indian Embassy and continued to function until 1965.

PORTUGUESE INDIA

A British post office was open in Damaun by 1823 and Indian stamps were used there until November 1883, some with "13" and "3/B-19" numeral cancellations.

No other British post offices were opened in the Portuguese territories, but from 1854 Indian stamps were sold by the local post offices. Between 1871 and 1877 mail intended for, or passing through, British India required combined franking of India and Portuguese India issues. After 1877 the two postal administrations accepted the validity of each other's stamps.

SOMALILAND PROTECTORATE*

Unoverprinted stamps of India used from 1887 until 1903.

TIBET

The first Indian post office in Tibet accompanied the Tibetan Frontier Commission in 1903. The Younghusband Military Expedition to Lhasa in the following year operated a number of Field Post Offices which were replaced by civil post offices at Gartok (opened 23 September 1906), Gyantse (opened March 1905), Pharijong (opened 1905) and Yatung (opened 1905). All Indian post offices in Tibet closed on 1 April 1955 except Gartok which, it is believed, did not operate after 1943. A temporary post office, C-622, operated at Gyantse between July 1954 and August 1955 following a flood disaster.

TRUCIAL STATES

Unoverprinted stamps of India used at Dubai from 19 August 1909 until 1947.

ZANZIBAR*

Unoverprinted stamps of India used from 1875 until 1895.

CHINA EXPEDITIONARY FORCE

Following the outbreak of the Boxer Rising in North China the Peking Legations were besieged by the rebels in June 1900. An international force, including an Indian division, was assembled for their relief. The Legations were relieved on 14 August 1900, but operations against the Boxers continued in North China with Allied garrisons at key cities and along the Peking–Tientsin–Shanhaikwan railway. The last Indian Army battalion, and accompanying Field Post Offices, did not leave North China until 1 November 1923.

Field Post Offices accompanied the Indian troops and commenced operations on 23 July 1900 using unoverprinted Indian postage and official stamps. The unoverprinted postage issues were replaced in mid-August by stamps overprinted "C.E.F." to prevent currency speculation. The use of unoverprinted official stamps continued as they were not valid for public postage.

PRICES FOR STAMPS ON COVER	
Nos. C1/10	*from* × 15
No. C10*c*	†
Nos. C11/22	*from* × 8
No. C23	*from* × 10
Nos. C24/5	*from* × 20
Nos. C26/8	*from* × 4
Nos. C29/34	*from* × 3

C. E. F.
(C 1)

Stamps of India overprinted with Type C 1, in black

1900 (16 Aug). *Stamps of Queen Victoria.*

C1	40	3p. carmine	40	1·25
		a. No stop after "C" (R. 1/2)		
		b. No stop after "F"	£160	
		c. Opt double, one albino		
C2	23	½a. blue-green	75	30
		a. Opt double		
		b. No stop after "F"	£160	
C3	25	1a. plum	4·25	1·50
		a. No stop after "F"	£225	
C4	27	2a. pale blue	3·00	9·00
		a. No stop after "F"	£225	
C5	36	2a.6p. green	2·75	13·00
		a. No stop after "F"	£325	
C6	28	3a. orange	2·75	16·00
		a. Opt double, one albino	£120	
		b. No stop after "F"	£325	
C7	29	4a. olive-green	2·75	7·50
		a. Opt double, one albino	£120	
		b. No stop after "F"	£325	
C8	31	8a. magenta	2·75	19·00
		a. No stop after "F"	£375	
		b. Opt double, one albino	£120	
C9	32	12a. purple/*red*	17·00	16·00
		a. Opt double, one albino	£160	
		b. No stop after "F"	£450	
C10	37	1r. green and carmine	24·00	26·00
		a. No stop after "F"	£450	£450
		b. Opt double, one albino	£180	
C1/10 *Set of 10*			55·00	£100

Prepared, but not issued.

C10*c*	26	1a.6p. sepia		£225

The missing stop after "F" variety occurs in the ninth row of the upper pane.

1904 (27 Feb).

C11	25	1a. carmine	35·00	8·00

1905 (16 Sept)–**11**. *Stamps of King Edward VII.*

C12	41	3p. grey (4.11)	6·50	7·50

---

		a. Opt double, one albino	£120	
		b. Opt triple, one albino	£375	
		c. Slate-grey	6·50	7·50
C13	43	1a. carmine	7·50	70
		a. Opt double, one albino	£100	
C14	44	2a. mauve (11.3.11)	14·00	2·50
		a. Opt double, one albino	£130	
C15	45	2a.6p. ultramarine (11.3.11)	3·25	5·00
C16	46	3a. orange-brown (11.3.11)	3·75	4·00
C17	47	4a. olive-green (11.3.11)	8·50	15·00
C18	49	8a. claret (11.3.11)	8·00	7·50
		a. Purple	60·00	55·00
C19	50	12a. purple/*red* (1909)	11·00	19·00
		a. No stop after "E"	£500	
C20	51	1r. green and carmine (11.3.11)	16·00	28·00
C12/20 *Set of 9*			70·00	80·00

1908 (Dec)–**09**. "POSTAGE & REVENUE".

C21	53	½a. green (No. 149) (29.9.09)	1·75	1·50
		a. Opt double, one albino	£110	
C22	54	1a. carmine (No. 150)	2·75	30
		a. Opt double, one albino	£150	

1914 (5 May)–**22**. *Stamps of King George V.* Wmk Star.

C23	55	3p. grey (7.10.14)	7·00	29·00
		a. Opt double, one albino	£300	
C24	56	½a. light green	4·00	6·00
		a. Emerald		35·00
C25	57	1a. aniline carmine	5·00	4·00
C26	58	1½a. chocolate (Type A) (9.3.21)	27·00	85·00
		a. Opt double, one albino	£180	
C27	59	2a. purple (11.19)	19·00	75·00
		a. Deep mauve	24·00	85·00
		ab. Opt triple	£425	
C28	61	2a.6p. bright blue (2.19)	15·00	28·00
C29	62	3a. orange (5.22)	29·00	£250
C30	63	4a. olive-green (5.22)	26·00	£180
		a. Opt double, one albino	£350	
C32	65	8a. deep mauve (12.21)	25·00	£375
C33	66	12a. carmine-lake (8.20)	26·00	£130
C34	67	1r. brown and green (10.21)	65·00	£350
C23/34 *Set of 11*			£225	£1300

Most dates quoted for Nos. C23/34 are those of the earliest recorded postmarks.

On No. C27a two of the overprints are only lightly inked.

BRITISH RAILWAY ADMINISTRATION

As a vital communications link the North China Railway (Peking–Tientsin–Shanhaikwan) was captured by Russian forces during operations against the Boxers. Control of the line was subsequently, in February 1901, assigned to the China Expeditionary Force and a British Railway Administration was set up to run it. By international agreement the line was to provide postal services for the other national contingents and also, to a lesser extent, for the civilian population. Travelling post offices were introduced and, on 20 April 1901, a late letter service for which an additional fee of 5c. was charged.

Type 32 of China

B.R.A.
5
Five Cents
(BR 35)

1901 (20 Apr). *No.* 108 *of China surch with Type* BR 35.

BR133	32	5c. on ½c. brown (Bk.)	£325	£100
		a. Surch inverted	£8000	£2500
		b. Surch in green	£275	£140
		ba. Imperf between (horiz pair)	†	£16000

No. BR133 was used for the collection of the 5c. late letter fee and was affixed to correspondence by a postal official at the railway station. It was cancelled with a violet circular postmark showing "RAILWAY POST OFFICE" at top and the name of the station (PEKING, TIENTSIN, TONGKU, TONGSHAN or SHANHAIKWAN) at foot. With the exception of official mail it could only be used in combination with Indian stamps overprinted "C.E.F.", stamps from the other allied contingents or of the Chinese Imperial Post (*Price used on cover:* No. BR133 *from* £275. No. BR133b *from* £325).

It is suggested that stamps overprinted in black were used at Tientsin and Tongku with those in green being available at Peking, Tongshan and Shanhaikwan.

The late fee charge was abolished on 20 May 1901 and No. BR133 was then withdrawn. The British Railway Administration continued to run the line, and its travelling post offices, until it was returned to its private owners in September 1902.

INDIAN EXPEDITIONARY FORCES
1914–21

Nos. E1/13 were for use of Indian forces sent overseas during the First World War and its aftermath. Examples were first used in France during September 1914. Other areas where the stamps were used included East Africa, Mesopotamia and Turkey. "I.E.F." overprints ceased to be valid for postage on 15 October 1921.

PRICES FOR STAMPS ON COVER	
Nos. E1/13	*from* × 10

I. E. F.
(E 1)

1914 (Sept). *Stamps of India (King George V) optd with Type* E 1.

E1	55	3p. grey	15	30
		a. No stop after "F"	23·00	28·00
		b. No stop after "E"	£110	£110
		c. Opt double	42·00	35·00
E2	56	½a. light green	50	30
		a. No stop after "F"	75·00	75·00
		b. Opt double	£140	£275
E3	57	1a. aniline carmine	1·25	30

---

		a. No stop after "F"	32·00	38·00
E4		1a. carmine	4·25	4·25
E5	59	2a. purple	1·25	30
		a. No stop after "F"	55·00	70·00
		b. No stop after "E"	£250	£275
E6	61	2a.6p. ultramarine	1·50	3·50
		a. No stop after "F"	£170	£180
E7	62	3a. orange	1·00	1·50
		a. No stop after "F"	£160	£170
E8	63	4a. olive-green	1·00	1·50
		a. No stop after "F"	£250	£275
E9	65	8a. deep magenta	1·25	2·50
		a. No stop after "F"	£250	£275
E10		8a. deep mauve	11·00	15·00
E11	66	12a. carmine-lake	2·25	6·00
		a. No stop after "F"	£300	£300
		b. Opt double, one albino	55·00	
E12		12a. claret		
E13	67	1r. red-brown and deep blue-green	2·50	4·00
		a. No stop after "F"	£100	
		b. Brown and green	3·50	5·00
E1/13 *Set of 10*			11·50	18·00

The "no stop after F" variety occurred on R. 4/12 of the upper pane, in one printing.

INDIAN NATIONAL ARMY

The following were prepared for use in the Japanese occupied areas of India during the drive on Imphal.

Genuine examples are inscribed "PROVISIONAL GOVERNMENT OF FREE INDIA". Forgeries also exist inscribed "PROVISIONAL GOVT. OF FREE INDIA".

Typo in Rangoon. No gum. Perf 11½ or imperf. 1p. violet, 1p. maroon, 1a. green. *Price from* £60 *each unused.*

Ten stamps, sharing six different designs, inscribed "AZAD HIND", were produced in Germany during the Second World War, but did no postal duty.

JAPANESE OCCUPATION OF THE ANDAMAN AND NICOBAR ISLANDS

The Andaman Islands in the Bay of Bengal were occupied on the 23 March 1942 and the Nicobar Islands in July 1942. Civil administration was resumed in October 1945.

The following Indian stamps were surcharged with large figures preceded by a decimal point:

Postage stamps—.3 on ½a. (No. 248), .5 on 1a. (No. 250), .10 on 2a. (No. 236b), .30 on 6a. (No. 274).

Official stamps—.10 on 1a.3p. (No. O146a), .20 on 3p. (No. O143), .20 in red on 3p. (No. O143).

Prices from £400 *each unused.*

INDIAN CONVENTION STATES

The following issues resulted from a series of postal conventions agreed between the Imperial Government and the state administrations of Patiala (1 October 1884), Gwalior, Jind and Nabha (1 July 1885), and Chamba and Faridkot (1 January 1887).

Under the terms of these conventions the British Indian Post Office supplied overprinted British India issues to the state administrations which, in turn, had to conform to a number of conditions covering the issue of stamps, rates of postage and the exchange of mail.

Such overprinted issues were valid for postage within the state of issue, to other "Convention States" and to destinations in British India.

Stamps of Chamba, Gwalior, Jind, Nabha and Patiala ceased to be valid for postage on 1 January 1951, when they were replaced by those of the Republic of India, valid from 1 April 1950.

RULERS OF INDIAN CONVENTION AND FEUDATORY STATES. Details of the rulers of the various states during the period when stamps were issued are now provided in a somewhat simplified form which omits reference to minor titles. Dates quoted are of the various reigns, extended to 1971 when the titles of the surviving rulers of the former princely states were abolished by the Indian Government.

During the absorption of the Convention and Feudatory States there was often an interim period during which the administration was handed over. In some instances it is only possible to quote the end of this interim period as the point of transfer.

STAMPS OF INDIA OVERPRINTED

In the Queen Victoria issues we omit varieties due to broken type, including the numerous small "A" varieties which may have come about through damaged type. We do, however, list the small "G", small "R" and tall "R" in "GWALIOR" as these were definitely the result of the use of type of the wrong size.

Variations in the length of the words due to unequal spacing when setting are also omitted.

CHAMBA

PRICES FOR STAMPS ON COVER	
Nos. 1/27	*from* × 20
Nos. 28/120	*from* × 12
Nos. O1/86	*from* × 25

Raja Sham Singh, 1873–1904

CHAMBA STATE (1)   **CHAMBA** (2)

1887 (1 Jan)–**95**. *Queen Victoria. Optd with T* 1.

1	23	½a. blue-green	60	75
		a. "CHMABA"	£375	£500

		b. "8TATE"	£700	
		c. Opt double	£600	
2	25	1a. brown-purple	1·75	2·00
		a. "CHMABA"	£475	£550
		b. "8TATE"	£1300	
3		1a. plum	2·50	2·00
4	26	1a.6p. sepia (1895)	2·00	12·00
5	27	2a. dull blue	2·00	2·50
		b. "CHMABA"	£1800	£2500
		c. "8TATE"	£1800	
6		2a. ultramarine	1·25	1·75
7	36	2a.6p. green (1895)	30·00	90·00
8	28	3a. orange (1887)	8·50	20·00
9		3a. brown-orange (1891)	2·00	5·00
		a. "CHMABA"	£4500	£6500
		b. Opt inverted		
10	29	4a. olive-green	4·50	8·50
		a. "CHMABA"	£1400	£2250
		b. "8TATE"	£3750	
11		4a. slate-green	4·25	6·50
		a. Opt double, one albino	75·00	
12	21	6a. olive-bistre (1890)	4·25	18·00
		a. Opt treble, two albino	95·00	
13		6a. bistre-brown	15·00	18·00
14	31	8a. dull mauve (1887)	8·00	10·00
		a. "CHMABA"	£4000	£4000
15		8a. magenta (1895)	6·00	18·00
16	32	12a. purple/red (1890)	5·50	14·00
		a. "CHMABA"	£7500	
		b. First "T" in "STATE" inverted..	£7500	
		c. Opt double, one albino	45·00	
17	33	1r. slate (1887)	42·00	£130
		a. "CHMABA"	£12000	
18	37	1r. green and carmine (1895)	8·50	15·00
		a. Opt double one albino	60·00	
19	38	2r. carmine and yellow-brown (1895)	90·00	£350
20		3r. brown and green (1895)	£100	£300
21		5r. ultramarine and violet (1895)....	£110	£475
		a. Opt double, one albino	£180	
1/21 Set of 15			£375	£1300

1900–04. *Colours changed.*

22	40	3p. carmine	40	60
		a. Opt double, one albino	42·00	
23		3p. grey (1904)	40	1·75
		a. Opt inverted	80·00	
24	23	½a. pale yellow-green (1902)	1·75	3·25
25		½a. yellow-green (1903)	50	1·25
26	25	1a. carmine (1902)	50	30
27	27	2a. pale violet (1903)	9·00	28·00
22/7 Set of 5			9·75	29·00

Raja Bhuri Singh, 1904–1919

1903–05. *King Edward VII. Optd with T 1.*

28	41	3p. pale grey	15	1·25
29		3p. slate-grey (1905)	30	1·25
30	42	½a. green	60	40
31	43	1a. carmine	1·25	60
32	44	2a. pale violet (1904)	1·75	3·25
33		2a. mauve	1·60	3·00
34	46	3a. orange-brown (1905)	3·75	4·75
		a. Opt double, one albino	42·00	
35	47	4a. olive (1904)	5·50	18·00
36	48	6a. olive-bistre (1905)	4·00	20·00
		a. Opt double, one albino	42·00	
37	49	8a. purple (shades) (1904)	5·00	20·00
38		8a. claret	10·00	25·00
39	50	12a. purple/red (1905)	6·50	27·00
		a. Opt double, one albino	42·00	
40	51	1r. green and carmine (1904)	7·00	22·00
		a. Opt double, one albino	55·00	
28/40 Set of 10			30·00	£100

1907. *Nos. 149/50 of India optd with T 1.*

41	53	½a. green	1·75	3·50
		a. Opt double, one albino	35·00	
42	54	1a. carmine	1·75	3·50

1913. *King George V optd with T 1.*

43	55	3p. grey	20	80
		a. Pale grey	1·00	
		b. Bluish grey	1·00	
44	56	½a. light green	70	90
		a. Emerald	1·00	1·25
		b. Bright green	1·00	
		w. Wmk inverted		
45	57	1a. rose-carmine	7·50	9·00
		a. Aniline carmine	1·50	3·25
		ab. Opt double, one albino	40·00	
47	59	2a. purple	3·25	9·50
		a. Reddish purple	3·75	9·50
		b. Deep mauve	5·00	
		c. Bright reddish violet	7·00	
48	62	3a. orange	3·50	7·50
		a. Dull orange	—	7·00
49	63	4a. olive	3·25	4·50
50	64	6a. yellow-bistre	3·50	5·50
		a. Brown-ochre	4·25	5·00
51	65	8a. deep magenta	4·50	13·00
		a. Deep mauve	5·00	12·00
		b. Bright mauve	8·50	
		c. Purple	8·50	
52	66	12a. carmine-lake	4·25	11·00
		a. Claret	8·50	13·00
53	67	1r. red-brown and deep blue-green	15·00	26·00
		a. Opt double, one albino	38·00	
		b. Brown and green	15·00	25·00
		c. Orange-brown and deep turquoise-green	20·00	
43/53 Set of 10			35·00	70·00

Raja Ram Singh, 1919–1935

1921. *No. 192 of India optd with T 2.*

54	57	9p. on 1a. rose-carmine	1·00	17·00

1923–27. *Optd with T 1. New values, etc.*

55	57	1a. chocolate	2·50	4·50
56	58	1½a. chocolate (Type A)	23·00	£110

57		1½a. chocolate (Type B) (1924)	1·75	5·50
58		1½a. rose-carmine (Type B) (1927)	75	20·00
59	61	2a.6p. ultramarine	60	3·50
60		2a.6p. orange (1927)	2·00	18·00
61	62	3a. ultramarine (1924)	3·00	20·00
		a. Opt double, one albino	50·00	
55/61 Set of 7			30·00	£160

Nos. 58 and 60 with inverted overprint are of clandestine origin.

CHAMBA STATE

1927–37. *King George V (Nasik printing, wmk Mult Star). Optd at Nasik with T 3 or 4 (1r.).*

62	55	3p. slate (1928)	10	1·40
		w. Wmk inverted	3·75	
63	56	½a. green (1928)	20	2·00
		w. Wmk inverted	2·00	
64	80	9p. deep green (litho) (1932)	3·75	16·00
64a		9p. deep green (typo) (1932)	8·50	18·00
65	57	1a. chocolate	1·75	1·00
		w. Wmk inverted	4·00	1·50
66	82	1a.3p. mauve (1932)	1·10	5·50
		w. Wmk inverted	4·00	5·50
67	58	1½a. rose-carmine (B) (1932)	5·50	6·50
		w. Wmk inverted	6·00	6·50
68	70	2a. purple (1928)	1·75	3·25
69	61	2a.6p. orange (1932)	2·25	16·00
		w. Wmk inverted	2·25	17·00
70	62	3a. bright blue (1928)	1·00	18·00
71	71	4a. sage-green (1928)	1·00	5·50
72	64	6a. bistre (wmk inverted) (1937)	26·00	£150
73	65	8a. reddish purple (1928)	1·40	10·00
		w. Wmk inverted	1·25	8·50
74	66	12a. claret (1928)	1·40	13·00
75	67	1r. chocolate and green (1928)	8·50	26·00
		w. Wmk inverted	11·00	26·00
62/75 Set of 14			50·00	£250

Raja Lakshman Singh, 1935–1971

1935–36. *New types and colours. Optd with T 3.*

76	79	½a. green	1·10	9·00
77	81	1a. chocolate	2·00	1·00
78	59	2a. vermilion (No. 236b)	1·10	23·00
79		2a. vermilion (small die, No. 236c)	£110	£130
80	62	3a. carmine	2·00	10·00
81	63	4a. sage-green (1936)	4·25	15·00
76/81 Set of 6			£110	£170

1938. *King George VI. Nos. 247/64 optd with T 3 (3p. to 1a.), T 5 (2a. to 12a.) or T 4 (rupee values).*

82	91	3p. slate	9·00	17·00
83		½a. red-brown	1·25	10·00
84		9p. green	9·00	30·00
85		1a. carmine	1·25	3·00
86	92	2a. vermilion	6·50	12·00
87	93	2a.6p. bright violet	7·00	27·00
88	94	3a. yellow-green	7·50	25·00
89	95	3a.6p. bright blue	7·50	26·00
90	96	4a. brown	20·00	24·00
91	97	6a. turquoise-green	21·00	60·00
92	98	8a. slate-violet	20·00	55·00
93	99	12a. lake	14·00	55·00
94	100	1r. grey and red-brown	30·00	65·00
95		2r. purple and brown	50·00	£300
96		5r. green and blue	85·00	£425
97		10r. purple and claret	£130	£650
98		15r. brown and green	£160	£900
99		25r. slate-violet and purple	£225	£950
82/99 Set of 18			£700	£3250

1942–47. *Optd with T 6 (to 12a.), "CHAMBA" only, as in T 5 (14a.) or T 7 (rupee values).*

(a) Stamps of 1937. W 69 (inverted on 15r.).

100	91	½a. red-brown	42·00	35·00
101		1a. carmine	55·00	48·00
102	100	1r. grey and red-brown	20·00	60·00
103		2r. purple and brown	24·00	£250
104		5r. green and blue	45·00	£275
105		10r. purple and claret	70·00	£450
106		15r. brown and green	£150	£750
		w. Wmk upright	—	£950
107		25r. slate-violet and purple	£140	£750
100/7 Set of 8			£500	£2250

(b) Stamps of 1940–43.

108	100a	3p. slate	70	4·50
109		½a. purple (1943)	70	5·00
110		9p. green	1·10	15·00
111		1a. carmine (1943)	1·25	4·25
112	101	1½a. dull violet (1943)	1·25	11·00
113		2a. vermilion (1943)	6·50	13·00
114		3a. bright violet	17·00	38·00
115		3½a. bright blue	9·50	40·00
116	102	4a. brown	12·00	12·00
117		6a. turquoise-green	15·00	40·00
118		8a. slate-violet	15·00	48·00
119		12a. lake	21·00	60·00
120	103	14a. purple (1947)	12·00	3·00
108/120 Set of 13			£100	£275

The 3a. exists printed by lithography or typography.

OFFICIAL STAMPS

1887 (1 Jan)**–98.** *Queen Victoria. Optd with Type O 1.*

O1	23	½a. blue-green	50	10

---

		a. "CHMABA"	£190	£180
		b. "SERV CE"		
		c. "8TATE"	£700	
		d. Thin seriffed "I" in "SERVICE"	£150	
O2	25	1a. brown-purple	2·00	1·00
		a. "CHMABA"	£375	£350
		b. "SERV CE"	£3000	
		c. "8TATE"	£1700	
		d. "SERVICE" double	£1700	£1000
		e. "SERVICE" double, one albino	55·00	
O3		1a. plum	1·75	10
		a. Thin seriffed "I" in "SERVICE"	£180	
O4	27	2a. dull blue	2·50	1·00
		a. "CHMABA"	£1000	£1000
O5		2a. ultramarine (1887)	2·00	2·00
		a. Thin seriffed "I" in "SERVICE"	£300	
O6	28	3a. orange (1890)		
O7		3a. brown-orange (1891)	2·25	11·00
		a. "CHMABA"	£2750	£3000
		b. Thin seriffed "I" in "SERVICE"		
		c. Opt double, one albino		
O8	29	4a. olive-green	3·00	6·00
		a. "CHMABA"	£1000	£1800
		b. "SERV CE"	£3250	
		c. "8TATE"	£3250	
O9		4a. slate-green	1·75	8·50
		a. Thin seriffed "I" in "SERVICE"		
O10	21	6a. olive-bistre (1890)	4·50	12·00
		a. "SERVICE" double, one albino	55·00	
O11		6a. bistre-brown		
O12	31	8a. dull mauve (1887)	4·00	7·00
		a. "CHMABA"	£6500	£6500
O13		8a. magenta (1895)	2·75	2·25
		a. Thin seriffed "I" in "SERVICE"	£550	
O14	32	12a. purple/red (1890)	8·50	42·00
		a. "CHMABA"	£6500	
		b. First "T" in "STATE" inverted..	£7000	
		c. Thin seriffed "I" in "SERVICE"		
		d. "SERVICE" double, one albino	55·00	
		e. "CHAMBA STATE" double, one albino	55·00	
O15	33	1r. slate (1890)	13·00	£130
		a. "CHMABA"	£5000	
O16	37	1r. green and carmine (1898)	6·00	38·00
		a. Thin seriffed "I" in "SERVICE"		
O1/16 Set of 10			38·00	£200

Printings up to and including that of December 1895 had the "SERVICE" overprint applied to sheets of stamps already overprinted with Type 1. From the printing of September 1898 onwards both "SERVICE" and "CHAMBA STATE" were overprinted at the same time. Nos. O6, O8 and O12 only exist using the first method, and No. O16 was only printed using the second.

The thin seriffed "I" in "SERVICE" variety occurred on R. 19/12 of the September 1898 printing only.

1902–04. *Colours changed. Optd as Type O 1.*

O17	40	3p. grey (1904)	45	60
O18	23	½a. pale yellow-green	75	3·50
O19		½a. yellow-green	4·00	2·00
O20	25	1a. carmine	1·00	40
O21	27	2a. pale violet (1903)	10·00	30·00
O17/21 Set of 4			11·00	30·00

1903–05. *King Edward VII. Stamps of India optd as Type O 1.*

O22	41	3p. pale grey	30	15
		a. Opt double, one albino	38·00	
O23		3p. slate-grey (1905)	30	65
O24	42	½a. yellow-green	25	10
O25	43	1a. carmine	1·00	30
O26	44	2a. pale violet (1904)	2·50	1·50
O27		2a. mauve	1·25	1·00
O28	47	4a. olive (1905)	3·50	18·00
O29	49	8a. purple (1905)	6·50	17·00
O30		8a. claret	8·50	23·00
		a. Opt double, one albino	42·00	
O31	51	1r. green and carmine (1905)	1·75	12·00
O22/31 Set of 7			13·00	45·00

The 2a. mauve King Edward VII, overprinted "On H.M.S.", was discovered in Calcutta, but was not sent to Chamba, and is an unissued variety (*Price un.* £38).

1907. *Nos. 149/50 of India, optd with Type O 1.*

O32	53	½a. green	40	75
		a. Opt inverted	£4000	£4500
		b. Opt double, one albino	38·00	
O33	54	1a. carmine	2·25	2·00

The inverted overprint, No. O32a, was due to an inverted cliché on R. 20/1 which was corrected after a few sheets had been printed.

1913–23. *King George V Official stamps (wmk Single Star) optd with T 1.*

O34	55	3p. grey	20	40
		a. Pale grey	50	75
		b. Bluish grey	50	75
		c. Slate	40	1·00
O36	56	½a. light green	10	40
		a. Emerald	1·75	40
		b. Bright green	20	30
O38	57	1a. aniline carmine	10	10
		a. Rose-carmine	4·50	50
O40	59	2a. purple (1914)	1·10	13·00
		a. Reddish purple		
		b. Bright reddish violet (1923)	7·50	13·00
O41	63	4a. olive	1·10	17·00
O42	65	8a. deep magenta	1·75	18·00
		a. Deep mauve	4·00	18·00
O43	67	1r. red-brown and deep blue-green (1914)	4·75	28·00
		a. Opt double, one albino	40·00	
		b. Brown and green	6·00	29·00
O34/43 Set of 7			8·25	70·00

No. O36 with inverted overprint and No. O38*a* with double or inverted overprint (on gummed side) are of clandestine origin.

1914. *King George V. Optd with Type* O **1**.

O44	59	2a. purple	15·00	
O45	63	4a. olive	13·00	

1921. *No.* O97 *of India optd with T* **2** *at top.*

| O46 | 57 | 9p. on 1a. rose-carmine | 15 | 7·00 |

1925. *As 1913–14. New colour.*

| O47 | 57 | 1a. chocolate | 3·25 | 50 |

CHAMBA STATE SERVICE (O 2) / SERVICE (O 3)

1927–39. *King George V (Nasik printing, wmk Mult Star), optd at Nasik with Type* O **2** *or* O **3** *(rupee values).*

O48	55	3p. slate (1928)	50	35
O49	56	w. Wmk inverted	—	1·25
O49	56	½a. green (1928)	35	15
O50	80	9p. deep green (1932)	3·00	9·50
O51	57	1a. chocolate	20	10
		w. Wmk inverted	1·50	30
O52	82	1a.3p. mauve (1932)	5·00	70
O53	70	2a. purple (1928)	1·75	60
O54	71	4a. sage-green (1928)	1·25	2·25
O55	65	8a. reddish purple (1930)	6·00	9·50
		w. Wmk inverted	7·50	
O56	66	12a. claret (1928)	3·50	22·00
		w. Wmk inverted	12·00	
O57	67	1r. chocolate and green (1930)	13·00	40·00
O58		2r. carmine and orange (1939)	21·00	£200
O59		5r. ultramarine and purple (1939)	42·00	£250
O60		10r. green and scarlet (1939)	60·00	£250
O48/60 *Set of 13*			£140	£700

1935–39. *New types and colours. Optd with Type* O **2**.

O61	79	½a. green	4·50	50
O62	81	1a. chocolate	2·50	45
O63	59	2a. vermilion	4·25	1·00
O64		2a. vermilion (*small die*) (1939)	6·50	17·00
O65	63	4a. sage-green (1936)	6·50	6·50
O61/5 *Set of 5*			22·00	23·00

1938–40. *King George VI. Optd with Type* O **2** *or* O **3** *(rupee values).*

O66	91	9p. green	20·00	55·00
O67		1a. carmine	20·00	4·25
O68	100	1r. grey and red-brown (1940?)	£250	£700
O69		2r. purple and brown (1939)	42·00	£350
O70		5r. purple and blue (1939)	60·00	£400
O71		10r. purple and claret (1939)	85·00	£700
O66/71 *Set of 6*			£425	£2000

CHAMBA SERVICE (O 4)

1940–43.

(a) Official stamps optd with T **6**.

O72	O 20	3p. slate	70	1·00
O73		½a. red-brown	22·00	3·00
O74		½a. purple (1943)	70	3·00
O75		9p. green	6·00	9·00
		w. Wmk inverted	18·00	14·00
O76		1a. carmine (1941)	70	2·50
O77		1a.3p. yellow-brown (1941)	70·00	18·00
O78		1½a. dull violet (1943)	6·50	7·50
O79		2a. vermilion	6·50	7·50
O80		2½a. bright violet (1941)	3·25	21·00
O81		4a. brown	6·50	14·00
O82		8a. slate-violet	15·00	60·00
		w. Wmk inverted	14·00	60·00

(b) Postage stamps optd with Type O **4**.

O83	100	1r. grey and red-brown (1942)	20·00	£190
O84		2r. purple and brown (1942)	35·00	£250
O85		5r. green and blue (1942)	65·00	£375
O86		10r. purple and claret (1942)	75·00	£650
O72/86 *Set of 15*			£300	£1400

Chamba became part of Himachal Pradesh on 15 April 1948.

FARIDKOT

For earlier issues, see under INDIAN FEUDATORY STATES

PRICES FOR STAMPS ON COVER	
Nos. 1/17	*from* × 30
Nos. O1/15	*from* × 40

Raja Bikram Singh, 1874–1898

FARIDKOT STATE (1)

1887 (1 Jan)**–1900.** *Queen Victoria. Optd with T* **1**.

1	23	½a. deep green	2·00	1·40
		a. "ARIDKOT"		
		b. "FAR DKOT"	—	£1700
		c. Opt double, one albino	48·00	
2	25	1a. brown-purple	1·50	2·25
3		1a. plum	2·00	2·00
4	27	2a. blue	3·00	6·00
5		2a. deep blue	3·75	7·00
6	28	3a. orange	7·00	11·00
7		3a. brown-orange (1893)	3·50	5·00

8	29	4a. olive-green	8·00	16·00
		a. "ARIDKOT"	£130	
9		4a. slate-green	8·00	22·00
10	21	6a. olive-bistre	32·00	60·00
		a. "ARIDKOT"	£1700	
		b. Opt double, one albino	50·00	
11		6a. bistre-brown	2·00	16·00
12	31	8a. dull mauve	13·00	40·00
		a. "ARIDKOT"	£2500	
13		8a. magenta	19·00	£130
		a. Opt double, one albino	40·00	
14	32	12a. purple/red (1900)	40·00	£400
15	33	1r. slate	42·00	£375
		a. "ARIDKOT"	£3000	
16	37	1r. green and carmine (1893)	35·00	£100
		a. Opt double, one albino	60·00	
1/16 *Set of 10*			£140	£850

The ½a., 1a., 2a., 3a., 4a., 8a. and 1r. (No. 16) are known with broken "O" (looking like a "C") in "FARIDKOT".

Raja Balbir Singh, 1898–1906

1900. *Optd with T* **1**.

| 17 | 40 | 3p. carmine | 1·50 | 40·00 |

OFFICIAL STAMPS

SERVICE

FARIDKOT STATE (O 1)

1887 (1 Jan)**–98.** *Queen Victoria. Optd with Type* O **1**.

O1	23	½a. deep green	50	60
		a. "SERV CE"	£1700	
		b. "FAR DKOT"	£2500	
		c. Thin seriffed "I" in "SERVICE"	£200	
		d. "FARIDKOT STATE" double, one albino	42·00	
O2	25	1a. brown-purple	1·00	1·75
		a. Thin seriffed "I" in "SERVICE"	£225	
		b. Opt double, one albino	50·00	
O3		1a. plum	1·25	1·50
		a. "SERV CE"	£3000	
O4	27	2a. dull blue	2·00	9·50
		a. "SERV CE"	£3000	
O5		2a. deep blue	2·50	14·00
O6	28	3a. orange	6·50	9·50
		a. "SERVICE" double, one albino		
O7		3a. brown-orange (12.98)	3·00	32·00
		a. Thin seriffed "I" in "SERVICE"	£550	
O8	29	4a. olive-green	4·75	25·00
		a. "SERV CE"	£2750	
		b. "ARIDKOT"		
		c. "SERVICE" treble, two albino	85·00	
O9		4a. slate-green	12·00	42·00
		a. "SERVICE" double, one albino	40·00	
O10	21	6a. olive-bistre	32·00	95·00
		a. "ARIDKOT"	£1300	
		b. "SERVIC"	£2750	
		c. "SERVICE" double, one albino	55·00	
		d. "FARIDKOT STATE" double, one albino	55·00	
O11		6a. bistre-brown	22·00	26·00
O12	31	8a. dull mauve	8·00	27·00
		a. "SERV CE"	£2750	
O13		8a. magenta	17·00	£130
O14	33	1r. slate	50·00	£225
		a. "SERVICE" double, one albino	85·00	
O15	37	1r. green and carmine (12.98)	85·00	£600
		a. Thin seriffed "I" in "SERVICE"		
O1/15 *Set of 9*			£160	£850

The ½a., 1a., 2a., 3a., 4a., 8a. and 1r. (No. O15) are known with the broken "O".

Printings up to and including that of November 1895 had the "SERVICE" overprint applied to sheets already overprinted with Type **1**. From December 1898 onwards "SERVICE" and "FARIDKOT STATE" were overprinted at one operation to provide fresh supplies of Nos. O1/3, O7 and O15.

The thin seriffed "I" variety occurs on the December 1898 overprinting only.

This State ceased to use overprinted stamps after 31 March 1901.

GWALIOR

PRICES FOR STAMPS ON COVER	
Nos. 1/3	*from* × 10
Nos. 4/11	
Nos. 12/66	*from* × 5
Nos. 67/128	*from* × 4
Nos. 129/37	*from* × 3
Nos. O1/94	*from* × 12

OVERPRINTS. From 1885 to 1926 these were applied by the Government of India Central Printing Press, Calcutta, and from 1927 at the Security Press, Nasik, *unless otherwise stated.*

Maharaja Jayaji Rao Sindhia, 1843–1886

गवालियर

GWALIOR | गवालियर
(1) | (2)

GWALIOR / GWALIOR
Small "G" | Small "R"

GWALIOR / GWALIOR
Tall "R" (original state) | Tall "R" (damaged state)

OVERPRINT VARIETIES OF TYPE 2.

Small "G" — Occurs on R. 7/11 from June 1900 printing of ½, 1, 2, 3, 4a. and 3p. (No. 38), and on R. 3/1 of a left pane from May 1901 printing of 2, 3 and 5r.

Small "R" — Occurs on R. 9/3 from June 1900 printing of 3p. to 4a. and on R. 2/3 from May 1901 printing of 2, 3 and 5r.

Tall "R" Occurs on R. 20/2 from printings between June 1900 and May 1907. The top of the letter is damaged on printings from February 1903 onwards.

1885 (1 July)**–97.** *Queen Victoria.* I. *Optd with T* **1**.

(a) Space between two lines of overprint 13 mm. Hindi inscription 13 to 14 mm long (May 1885).

1	23	½a. blue-green	£130	27·00
2	25	1a. brown-purple	85·00	29·00
3	27	2a. dull blue	70·00	15·00
1/3 *Set of 3*			£250	65·00

A variety exists of the ½a. in which the space between the two lines of overprint is only 9½ mm but this is probably from a proof sheet.

(b) Space between two lines of overprint 15 mm on 4a. and 6a. and 16 to 17 mm on other values (June 1885). Hindi inscription 13 to 14 mm long.

4	23	½a. blue-green	50·00	
		a. Opt double, one albino	70·00	
		b. Hindi inscr 15 to 15½ mm long	£110	
		ba. Opt double, one albino	£170	
		c. Pair. Nos. 4/4b	£650	
5	25	1a. brown-purple	60·00	
		a. Opt double, one albino	70·00	
		b. Hindi inscr 15 to 15½ mm long	£120	
		ba. Opt double, one albino	£140	
		c. Pair. Nos. 5/5b	£650	
6	26	1a.6p. sepia	80·00	
		b. Hindi inscr 15 to 15½ mm long	£190	
		c. Pair. Nos. 6/6b	£750	
7	27	2a. dull blue	60·00	
		b. Hindi inscr 15 to 15½ mm long	£110	
		c. Pair. Nos. 7/7b	£425	
8	17	4a. green	85·00	
		b. Hindi inscr 15 to 15½ mm long	£160	
		c. Pair. Nos. 8/8b	£800	
9	21	6a. olive-bistre	85·00	
		a. Opt double, one albino	95·00	
		b. Hindi inscr 15 to 15½ mm long	£200	
		ba. Opt double, one albino	£225	
		c. Pair. Nos. 9/9b	£800	
10	31	8a. dull mauve	75·00	
		b. Hindi inscr 15 to 15½ mm long	£160	
		c. Pair. Nos. 10/10b	£800	
11	33	1r. slate	70·00	
		b. Hindi inscr 15 to 15½ mm long	£160	
		c. Pair. Nos. 11/11b	£800	
4/11 *Set of 8*			£500	
4b/11b *Set of 8*			£1100	

The two types of overprint on these stamps occur in the same settings, with about a quarter of the stamps in each sheet showing the long inscription. Nos. 4/7 and 10/11 were overprinted in sheets of 240 and Nos. 8/9 in half-sheets of 160.

II. *Optd with T* **2**. *Hindi inscription 13 to 14 mm long.*

(a) In red (Sept 1885).

12	23	½a. blue-green	1·25	20
		b. Hindi inscr 15 to 15½ mm long	2·00	70
		c. Pair. Nos. 12/12b	14·00	16·00
13	27	2a. dull blue	18·00	16·00
		b. Hindi inscr 15 to 15½ mm long	38·00	38·00
		c. Pair. Nos. 13/13b	£400	£425
14	17	4a. green	24·00	14·00
		b. Hindi inscr 15 to 15½ mm long	£200	£100
		c. Pair. Nos. 14/14b	£700	
15	33	1r. slate	8·00	22·00
		aw. Wmk inverted	16·00	30·00
		b. Hindi inscr 15 to 15½ mm long	38·00	75·00
		bw. Wmk inverted	48·00	95·00
		c. Pair. Nos. 15/15b	75·00	£130
		cw. Wmk inverted	90·00	
12/15 *Set of 4*			45·00	48·00
12b/15b *Set of 4*			£250	£190

No. 14 was overprinted in half-sheets of 160, about 40 stamps having the Hindi inscription 15 to 15½ mm long. The remaining three values were from a setting of 240 containing 166 13 to 14 mm long and 74 15 to 15½ mm long.

Reprints have been made of Nos. 12 to 15, but the majority of the specimens have the word "REPRINT" overprinted upon them.

(b) In black (1885–97).

16	23	½a. blue-green (1889)	1·75	1·75
		a. Opt double		
		b. Opt double, one albino	21·00	
		c. Hindi inscr 15 to 15½ mm long	40	10
		ca. Opt double	†	£750
		cb. Opt double, one albino	75·00	
		cc. "GWALICR"	85·00	£100
		cd. Small "G"	65·00	48·00
		ce. Small "R"	80·00	
		cf. Tall "R"	85·00	85·00
		d. Pair. Nos. 16/16c	55·00	60·00
17	24	9p. carmine (1891)	32·00	55·00
		a. Opt double, one albino		
		c. Hindi inscr 15 to 15½ mm long	60·00	80·00
		ca. Opt double, one albino	85·00	
		d. Pair. Nos. 17/17c	£275	
18	25	1a. brown-purple	1·50	20
		c. Hindi inscr 15 to 15½ mm long	3·00	35
		d. Pair. Nos. 18/18c	16·00	17·00
19		1a. plum (*Hindi inscr 15 to 15½ mm long*)	3·00	10
		a. Small "G"	75·00	55·00
		b. Small "R"	85·00	
		c. Tall "R"	£110	

20	**26**	1a.6p. sepia	1·25	1·40
		c. Hindi inscr 15 to 15½ mm long	1·75	60
		d. Pair. Nos. 20/20c	16·00	19·00
21	**27**	2a. dull blue	7·00	80
		c. Hindi inscr 15 to 15½ mm long	2·00	10
		ca. "R" omitted	£475	£475
		d. Pair. Nos. 21/21c	£150	£160
22		2a. deep blue	10·00	2·25
		c. Hindi inscr 15 to 15½ mm long	3·00	50
		ca. Small "G"	£150	£150
		cb. Small "R"	£225	
		cc. Tall "R"	£225	£225
		d. Pair. Nos. 22/22c	£180	
23	**36**	2a.6p. yellow-green (*Hindi inscr 15 to 15½ mm long*) (1896)	7·00	18·00
		a. "GWALICR"	£650	
24	**28**	3a. orange	7·00	13·00
		c. Opt double, one albino	55·00	
		c. Hindi inscr 15 to 15½ mm long	60·00	42·00
		ca. Opt double, one albino		
		d. Pair. Nos. 24/24c	£300	
25		3a. brown-orange	30·00	5·50
		c. Hindi inscr 15 to 15½ mm long	3·00	15
		ca. Opt double, one albino	40·00	
		cb. Small "R"	£250	£250
		cc. Small "R"	£700	
		cd. Tall "R"	£200	£200
		d. Pair. Nos. 25/25c	£225	
26	**29**	4a. olive-green (1889)	8·00	1·25
		c. Hindi inscr 15 to 15½ mm long	12·00	3·50
		d. Pair. Nos. 26/26c	£120	
27		4a. slate-green	9·00	1·75
		c. Hindi inscr 15 to 15½ mm long	4·00	1·00
		ca. Opt double, one albino	65·00	
		cb. Small "G"	£500	£325
		cc. Small "R"	£500	
		cd. Tall "R"	£350	£350
		d. Pair. Nos. 27/27c	40·00	
28	**21**	6a. olive-bistre	8·00	16·00
		c. Hindi inscr 15 to 15½ mm long	4·00	16·00
		ca. Opt double, one albino	40·00	
		d. Pair. Nos. 28/28c	65·00	
29		6a. bistre-brown	2·75	7·50
		c. Hindi inscr 15 to 15½ mm long	3·75	11·00
		d. Pair. Nos. 29/29c	26·00	
30	**31**	8a. dull mauve	12·00	38·00
		c. Hindi inscr 15 to 15½ mm long	4·25	1·00
		d. Pair. Nos. 30/30c	£350	
31		8a. magenta (*Hindi inscr 15 to 15½ mm long*) (1897)	7·00	8·00
32	**32**	12a. purple/red (1891)	3·75	8·00
		c. Hindi inscr 15 to 15½ mm long	3·00	65
		ca. Pair, one without opt	£3500	
		cb. Tall "R"	£1100	£800
		d. Pair. Nos. 32/32c	80·00	
33	**33**	1r. slate (1889)	£100	£400
		c. Hindi inscr 15 to 15½ mm long	3·25	1·75
		d. Pair. Nos. 33/33c	£500	
34	**37**	1r. green and carmine (*Hindi inscr 15 to 15½ mm long*) (1896)	5·00	4·50
		a. Opt double, one albino	85·00	
		b. "GWALICR"	£850	£1200
35	**38**	2r. carmine and yellow-brown (*Hindi inscr 15 to 15½ mm long*) (1896)	5·50	3·00
		a. Small "G"	£325	£180
		b. Small "R"	£350	£200
		c. Opt double, one albino	80·00	
36		3r. brown and green (*Hindi inscr 15 to 15½ mm long*) (1896)	7·50	3·50
		a. Small "G"	£375	£190
		b. Small "R"	£400	£225
37		5r. ultramarine and violet (*Hindi inscr 15 to 15½ mm long*) (1896)	14·00	6·50
		a. Small "G"	£375	£225
		b. Small "R"	£425	£250
16/37	*Set of 16*		90·00	90·00

Printings to 1891 continued to use the setting showing both types, but subsequently a new setting containing the larger overprint only was used.

The ½a., 1a., 2a. and 3a. exist with space between "I" and "O" of "GWALIOR".

The "GWALICR" error occurs on R. 1/5 in the May 1896 printing only.

Maharaja Madhav Rao Sindhia, 1886–1925

1899–1911.

(a) Optd with T 2 (B).

38	**40**	3p. carmine	40	20
		a. Opt inverted	£900	£475
		b. Small "G"	55·00	55·00
		d. Small "R"	65·00	
		e. Tall "R"	50·00	
		f. Opt double, one albino	42·00	
39		3p. grey (1904)	7·00	60·00
		e. Tall "R"	£250	
		f. Opt double, one albino	55·00	
40	**23**	½a. pale yellow-green (1901)	1·00	1·25
		e. Tall "R"	90·00	
		f. Opt double, one albino	23·00	
40g		½a. yellow-green (1903)	3·25	1·50
		ge. Tall "R"	£130	
41	**25**	1a. carmine (1901)	1·10	35
		e. Tall "R"	95·00	
		f. Opt double, one albino	48·00	
42	**27**	2a. pale violet (1903)	2·00	5·00
		e. Tall "R"	£140	
43	**36**	2a.6p. ultramarine (1903)	1·10	5·50
		e. Tall "R"	£200	
38/43	*Set of 6*		11·00	65·00

(b) Optd as T 2, but "GWALIOR" 13 mm long. Opt spaced 2¾ mm.

44	**38**	3r. brown and green (1911)	£200	£200
45		5r. ultramarine and violet (1910)	60·00	55·00
		a. Opt double, one albino	£100	

1903–11. *King Edward VII. Optd as T 2.*

A. "GWALIOR" 14 mm long. Overprint spaced 1¾ mm (1903–06).

46A	**41**	3p. pale grey	1·00	20

		e. Tall "R"	35·00	42·00
		f. Slate-grey (1905)	1·25	30
		fe. Tall "R"	40·00	48·00
48A	**42**	½a. green	20	10
		e. Tall "R"	35·00	42·00
49A	**43**	1a. carmine	40·00	48·00
		e. Tall "R"	40·00	
		f. Opt double, one albino	40·00	
50A	**44**	2a. pale violet (1904)	1·60	70
		e. Tall "R"	95·00	
		f. Mauve	2·50	20
		fe. Tall "R"	£130	£110
52A	**45**	2a.6p. ultramarine (1904)	22·00	75·00
		e. Tall "R"	£950	
53A	**46**	3a. orange-brown (1904)	1·50	35
		e. Tall "R"	£130	£130
54A	**47**	4a. olive	2·00	40
		e. Tall "R"	£200	£170
		f. Pale olive	10·00	2·50
		fe. Tall "R"	£350	
56A	**48**	6a. olive-bistre (1904)	2·75	3·00
		e. Tall "R"	£950	
57A	**49**	8a. purple (*shades*) (1905)	4·00	1·40
		e. Tall "R"	£375	£275
59A	**50**	12a. purple/red (1905)	3·00	18·00
		e. Tall "R"	£950	
60A	**51**	1r. green and carmine (1905)	2·50	1·75
		e. Tall "R"	£750	£750
61A	**52**	2r. carmine and yellow-brown (1906)	32·00	42·00
		a. Opt double, one albino	55·00	
46A/61A	*Set of 12*		65·00	£130

B. "GWALIOR" 13 mm long. Overprint spaced 2¾ mm (1908–11).

46B	**41**	3p. pale grey	2·50	10
		f. Slate-grey	2·75	40
49B	**43**	1a. carmine	4·00	1·00
50fB		2a. mauve	3·00	15
52B	**45**	2a.6p. ultramarine	1·25	7·50
53B	**46**	3a. orange-brown	3·50	20
54fB		4a. pale olive	3·75	60
56B	**48**	6a. olive-bistre	5·00	1·25
57B	**49**	8a. purple (*shades*)	8·00	1·50
		f. Claret	19·00	2·25
		fa. Opt double, one albino	55·00	
59B	**50**	12a. purple/red	3·75	3·25
		f. Opt double, one albino	70·00	
60B	**51**	1r. green and carmine	6·00	1·10
61B	**52**	2r. carmine and yellow-brown	9·00	11·00
		a. Opt double, one albino	55·00	
62B		3r. brown and green (1910)	26·00	45·00
		a. Red-brown and green	60·00	70·00
63B		5r. ultramarine and violet (1911)	19·00	27·00
46B/63B	*Set of 13*		85·00	90·00

1907–08. *Nos. 149 and 150 of India optd as T 2.*

(a) "GWALIOR" 14 mm long. Overprint spaced 1¾ mm.

64	**53**	½a. green	10	70
		e. Tall "R"	50·00	80·00

(b) "GWALIOR" 13 mm long. Overprint spaced 2¾ mm (1908).

65	**53**	½a. green	1·10	20
66	**54**	1a. carmine	1·50	20

1912–14. *King George V. Optd as T 2.*

67	**55**	3p. grey	10	10
		a. Opt double	†	£950
		b. Pale grey	50	10
		c. Bluish grey	—	50
		d. Slate	60	30
		da. "Rs" flaw	32·00	38·00
68	**56**	½a. light green	20	10
		a. Emerald	1·00	35
		b. Bright green	60	10
		ba. Opt inverted	†	£375
69	**57**	1a. aniline carmine	25	10
		a. Opt double	25·00	
70	**59**	2a. purple	60	10
		a. Reddish purple	70	10
		aw. Wmk inverted	†	85·00
		b. Deep mauve	1·75	50
		c. Bright reddish violet	1·75	40
71	**62**	3a. orange	60	15
		a. Dull orange	70	25
72	**63**	4a. olive (1913)	60	60
73	**64**	6a. yellow-bistre	1·25	1·60
		a. Brown-ochre	1·00	1·10
74	**65**	8a. deep magenta (1913)	1·50	70
		a. Deep mauve	3·00	30
		b. Bright mauve	7·50	1·25
75	**66**	12a. carmine-lake (1914)	1·25	3·25
		a. Claret	—	4·25
76	**67**	1r. red-brown and deep blue-green (1913)	8·00	70
		a. Opt double, one albino	20·00	
		b. Brown and green	7·00	40
		ba. Opt double	£650	
		c. Orange-brown and deep turquoise-green	15·00	2·50
77		2r. carmine-rose and brown (1913)	4·50	4·50
		a. Opt double, one albino	50·00	
78		5r. ultramarine and violet (1913)	21·00	6·50
		a. Opt double, one albino	70·00	
67/78	*Set of 12*		35·00	15·50

GWALIOR
(3)

1921. *No. 192 of India optd with T 3.*

79	**57**	9p. on 1a. rose-carmine	10	50

No. 79 with inverted overprint is of clandestine origin.

1923–27. *Optd as T 2. New colours and values.*

80	**57**	1a. chocolate	1·00	10
		a. Opt double, one albino	42·00	
81	**58**	1½a. chocolate (B) (1925)	1·75	50
82		1½a. rose-carmine (B) (1927)	20	20
83	**61**	2a. ultramarine (1925)	2·00	1·75
84		2a.6p. orange (1927)	35	50
85	**62**	3a. ultramarine (1924)	2·00	60

80/5	*Set of 6*		6·50	3·25

No. 82 with inverted overprint is of clandestine origin.

Maharaja George Jivaji Rao Sindhia, 1925–1961

GWALIOR
गवालियर
(4)

GWALIOR
गवालियर
(5)

1928–36. *King George V (Nasik printing, wmk Mult Star), optd at Nasik with T 4 or 5 (rupee values).*

86	**55**	3p. slate (1932)	75	15
		w. Wmk inverted	1·00	1·00
87	**56**	½a. green (1930)	1·50	10
		w. Wmk inverted		
88	**80**	9p. deep green (*litho*) (1932)	2·50	20
		aw. Wmk inverted	2·75	80
88b		9p. deep green (*typo*)	3·00	50
89	**57**	1a. chocolate	85	10
		w. Wmk inverted	—	1·25
90	**82**	1a.3p. mauve (1936)	50	15
91	**70**	2a. purple	75	30
		w. Wmk inverted	75	30
92	**62**	3a. bright blue	1·00	40
93	**71**	4a. sage-green	1·25	1·00
		w. Wmk inverted	1·75	2·25
94	**65**	8a. reddish purple (*wmk inverted*)	1·25	1·10
95	**66**	12a. claret	1·75	3·00
96	**67**	1r. chocolate and green	2·50	3·50
		w. Wmk inverted	5·00	3·25
97		2r. carmine and orange	10·00	5·50
		w. Wmk inverted	8·00	4·50
98		5r. ultramarine and purple (*wmk inverted*) (1929)	18·00	24·00
99		10r. green and scarlet (1930)	55·00	40·00
100		15r. blue & olive (*wmk inverted*) (1930)	90·00	60·00
101		25r. orange and blue (1930)	£190	£140
86/101	*Set of 16*		£325	£250

1935–36. *New types and colours. Optd with T 4.*

102	**79**	½a. green (1936)	50	20
		w. Wmk inverted	4·50	3·00
103	**81**	1a. chocolate	20	10
104	**59**	2a. vermilion (1936)	2·50	3·00
102/4	*Set of 3*		2·75	3·00

1938–48. *King George VI. Nos. 247/50, 253, 255/6 and 259/64 optd with T 4 or 5 (rupee values).*

105	**91**	3p. slate	8·00	10
106		½a. red-brown	8·00	10
107		9p. green (1939)	42·00	3·50
108		1a. carmine	7·50	15
109	**94**	½a. yellow-green (1939)	22·00	4·25
110	**96**	4a. brown	42·00	2·75
111	**97**	6a. turquoise-green (1939)	3·25	9·50
112	**100**	1r. grey and red-brown (1942)	10·00	1·50
113		2r. purple and brown (1948)	45·00	9·00
114		5r. green and blue (1948)	30·00	35·00
115		10r. purple and claret (1948)	30·00	40·00
116		15r. brown and green (1948)	90·00	£160
117		25r. slate-violet and purple (1948)	80·00	£120
105/117	*Set of 13*		£375	£325

1942–45. *King George VI. Optd with T 4.*

118	**100a**	3p. slate	45	10
		w. Wmk inverted	—	17·00
119		½a. purple (1943)	75	10
120		9p. green	45	10
121		1a. carmine (Jivaji) (1943)	75	10
		a. Opt double		£160
122	**101**	1½a. dull violet	6·50	20
123		2a. vermilion	1·00	20
124		3a. bright violet	15·00	1·50
		a. Opt double		£170
125	**102**	4a. brown	2·50	20
126		6a. turquoise-green (1945)	14·00	24·00
127		8a. slate-violet (1944)	3·25	2·75
128		12a. lake (1943)	4·50	21·00
118/28	*Set of 11*		45·00	45·00

The 1½a. and 3a. exist printed by lithography or typography.

GWALIOR
गवालियर
(6)

1949 (Apr). *King George VI. Optd with T 6 at the Alizah Printing Press, Gwalior.*

129	**100a**	3p. slate	1·50	50
130		½a. purple	1·00	50
131		1a. carmine	1·00	60
132	**101**	2a. vermilion	22·00	2·00
133		3a. bright violet	55·00	27·00
134	**102**	4a. brown	5·50	2·75
135		6a. turquoise-green	48·00	55·00
136		8a. slate-violet	£100	50·00
137		12a. lake	£375	£130
129/37	*Set of 9*		£550	£225

OFFICIAL STAMPS

गवालियर

गवालियर

सरविस
(O 1)

सरविस
(O 2)

1895–96. *Queen Victoria. Optd with Type* O **1.**

O1	23	½a. blue-green	50	10
		a. Hindi characters transposed	26·00	28·00
		b. 4th Hindi character omitted	£475	40·00
		c. Opt double	†	£950
O2	25	1a. brown-purple	10·00	1·25
O3		1a. plum	1·50	10
		a. Hindi characters transposed	40·00	42·00
		b. 4th Hindi character omitted		65·00
O4	27	2a. dull blue	2·50	40
O5		2a. deep blue	1·50	40
		a. Hindi characters transposed	65·00	80·00
		b. 4th Hindi character omitted	80·00	£100
O6	29	4a. olive-green	2·75	1·00
		a. Hindi characters transposed	£550	£600
		b. 4th Hindi character omitted	£2750	£1400
O7		4a. slate-green	2·25	1·10
		a. Hindi characters transposed	£300	£350
O8	31	8a. dull mauve	3·50	2·50
		a. Opt double, one albino	40·00	
O9		8a. magenta	3·00	2·00
		a. Hindi characters transposed	£1300	£1500
		b. 4th Hindi character omitted		
O10	37	1r. green and carmine (1896)	7·00	3·00
		a. Hindi characters transposed	£2750	
O1/10 Set of 6			14·00	6·00

In the errors listed above it is the last two Hindi characters that are transposed, so that the word reads "Sersiv". The error occurs on R. 19/1 in the sheet from the early printings up to May 1896.

1901–04. *Colours changed.*

O23	40	3p. carmine (1902)	85	25
O24		3p. grey (1904)	2·00	2·75
O25	23	½a. pale yellow-green	4·50	15
O26		½a. yellow-green	75	10
O27	25	1a. carmine	5·00	10
O28	27	2a. pale violet (1903)	1·25	1·50
O23/8 Set of 5			9·00	4·00

1903–08. *King Edward VII. Optd as Type* O **1.**

(a) Overprint spaced 10 mm (1903–5).

O29	41	3p. pale grey	70	10
		a. Slate-grey (1905)	70	10
O31	42	½a. green	3·00	10
O32	43	1a. carmine	1·10	10
O33	44	2a. pale violet (1905)	2·25	50
		a. Mauve	1·50	30
O35	47	4a. olive (1905)	15·00	1·25
		a. Opt double, one albino	55·00	
O36	49	8a. purple (1905)	6·00	70
		a. Claret	17·00	4·50
		ab. Opt double, one albino	45·00	
O38	51	1r. green and carmine (1905)	2·75	1·75
		a. Opt double, one albino	75·00	
O29/38 Set of 7			27·00	3·75

(b) Overprint spaced 8 mm (1907–8).

O39	41	3p. pale grey	5·00	15
		a. Slate-grey (1908)	8·00	1·25
O41	42	½a. green	3·25	15
O42	43	1a. carmine	1·50	10
O43	44	2a. mauve	15·00	75
O44	47	4a. olive	4·00	1·00
O45	49	8a. purple	3·75	3·75
O46	51	1r. green and carmine (1908)	38·00	13·00
O39/46 Set of 7			65·00	17·00

1907–08. *Nos. 149 and 150 of India optd as Type* O **1.**

(a) Overprint spaced 10 mm (1908).

O47	53	½a. green	7·50	10
O48	54	1a. carmine	6·00	15
		a. Opt double, one albino	38·00	

(b) Overprint spaced 8 mm (1907).

O49	53	½a. green	1·75	15
O50	54	1a. carmine	60·00	3·00

1913–23. *King George V. Optd with Type* O **1.**

O51	55	3p. grey	25	10
		a. Pair, one without opt.	£1500	
		b. Pale grey	25	10
		ba. Opt double	—	30
		c. Bluish grey	25	10
		d. Slate	75·00	
		e. The "Rs" flaw		
O52	56	½a. light green	20	10
		b. Emerald		10
		ba. Opt double	£110	£160
		c. Bright green	20	10
O53	57	1a. rose-carmine	10·00	50
		a. Aniline carmine	30	10
		ab. Opt double	65·00	
O54		1a. chocolate (1923)	3·25	15
O55	59	2a. purple	80	50
		a. Reddish purple	1·50	20
		b. Deep mauve	2·50	
		c. Bright reddish violet	1·60	30
O56	63	4a. olive	60	1·00
O57	65	8a. deep magenta	1·00	2·00
		a. Deep mauve	1·25	1·00
		b. Bright mauve	2·75	
O58	67	1r. red-brown and deep blue-green	26·00	22·00
		a. Opt double, one albino	70·00	
		b. Brown and green	22·00	20·00
		c. Orange-brown and deep turquoise-green	27·00	22·00
O51/8 Set of 8			26·00	21·00

1921. *No. O97 of India optd with T* **3.**

O59	57	9p. on 1a. rose-carmine	10	30

1927–35. *King George V (Nasik printing, wmk Mult Star), optd at Nasik as Type* O **1** *(but top line measures 13 mm instead of 14 mm) or with Type* O **2** *(rupee values).*

O61	55	3p. slate	30	10
		w. Wmk inverted	10	50
O62	56	½a. green	10	15
		w. Wmk inverted	2·75	
O63	80	9p. deep green (1932)	10	15
O64	57	1a. chocolate	10	10

O65	82	1a.3p. mauve (1933)	50	15
		w. Wmk inverted	3·50	
O66	70	2a. purple	20	15
		w. Wmk inverted	3·00	
O67	71	4a. sage-green	75	30
		w. Wmk inverted		1·75
O68	65	8a. reddish purple (1928)	60	1·10
		w. Wmk inverted	2·50	1·75
O69	67	1r. chocolate and green	1·00	1·75
		w. Wmk inverted	1·90	3·00
O70		2r. carmine and orange (1935)	14·00	15·00
O71		5r. ultramarine and purple (1932)	19·00	£160
O72		10r. green and scarlet (1932)	£140	£400
O61/72 Set of 12			£180	£550

1936–37. *New types. Optd as Type* O **1** *(13 mm).*

O73	79	½a. green	15	15
		w. Wmk inverted	—	3·75
O74	81	1a. chocolate	15	15
O75	59	2a. vermilion	20	40
O76		2a. vermilion (*small die*)	2·50	1·10
O77	63	4a. sage-green (1937)	60	75
O73/7 Set of 5			3·25	2·25

1938. *King George VI. Optd as Type* O **1** *(13 mm).*

O78	91	½a. red-brown	6·50	30
O79		1a. carmine	1·10	20

गवालियर (O 3)

1A——1A (O 4)

1940–42. *Official stamps optd with Type* O **3.**

O80	O20	3p. slate	50	10
O81		½a. red-brown	3·75	25
O82		½a. purple (1942)	50	10
O83		9p. green (1942)	70	60
O84		1a. carmine	2·25	10
O85		1a.3p. yellow-brown (1942)	42·00	1·75
		w. Wmk inverted	—	20·00
O86		1½a. dull violet (1942)	1·00	30
O87		2a. vermilion	1·00	30
O88		4a. brown (1942)	1·25	2·75
O89		8a. slate-violet (1942)	4·00	8·50
O80/9 Set of 10			50·00	12·50

1941. *Stamp of 1932 (King George V) optd with Type* O **1** *and surch with Type* O **4.**

O90	82	1a. on 1a.3p. mauve	24·00	2·75
		w. Wmk inverted	35·00	7·50

1942–47. *King George VI. Optd with Type* O **2.**

O91	100	1r. grey and red-brown	10·00	18·00
O92		2r. purple and brown	18·00	85·00
O93		5r. green and blue (1943)	30·00	£500
O94		10r. purple and claret (1947)	80·00	£1000
O91/4 Set of 4			£120	£1500

Gwalior became part of Madhya Bharat by 1 July 1948.

JIND

For earlier issues, see under INDIAN FEUDATORY STATES

PRICES FOR STAMPS ON COVER	
Nos. 1/4	*from* × 20
Nos. 5/16	—
Nos. 17/40	*from* × 15
Nos. 41/149	*from* × 8
Nos. O1/86	*from* × 15

Raja Raghubir Singh, 1864–1887

JHIND (1) STATE (2) JEEND STATE (2) JHIND STATE (3)

1885 (1 July). *Queen Victoria. Optd with T* **1.**

1	23	½a. blue-green	4·00	4·50
		a. Opt inverted	85·00	£100
2	25	1a. brown-purple	35·00	48·00
		a. Opt inverted	£850	£900
3	27	2a. dull blue	16·00	18·00
		a. Opt inverted	£600	£650
4	17	4a. green	60·00	80·00
5	31	8a. dull mauve	£425	
		a. Opt inverted	£10000	
6	33	1r. slate	£475	
		a. Opt inverted	£12000	
1/6 Set of 6			£900	

The overprint inverted errors occurred on R. 10/8 in the setting of 120, although it is believed that one pane of the ½a. had the overprint inverted on the entire pane. Examples of inverted overprints on the ½a., 1a. and 2a. with the lines much less curved are thought to come from a trial printing.

All six values exist with reprinted overprint. This has the words "JHIND" and "STATE" 8 and 9 mm in length respectively, whereas in the originals the words are 9 and 9½ mm.

1885. *Optd with T* **3.**

7	23	½a. blue-green (R.)		£120
8	25	1a. brown-purple		£120
9	27	2a. dull blue (R.)		£120
10	17	4a. green (R.)		£160
		a. Opt double, one albino		£200
11	31	8a. dull mauve		£170
12	33	1r. slate (R.)		£180
7/12 Set of 6				£800

1886. *Optd with T* **3,** *in red.*

13	23	½a. blue-green	30·00	
		a. "JEIND" for "JHIND"	£1000	
14	27	2a. dull blue	32·00	
		a. "JEIND" for "JHIND"	£1200	
		b. Opt double, one albino	70·00	
15	17	4a. green	55·00	
		a. Opt double, one albino	60·00	
		b. Opt treble, two albino	90·00	
16	33	1r. slate	55·00	
		a. "JEIND" for "JHIND"	£1800	
13/16 Set of 4			£150	

Examples of No. 14a usually show an additional albino "SERVICE" overprint as Type O **16.**

1886–99. *Optd with T* **3.**

17	23	½a. blue-green	80	10
		a. Opt inverted	£200	
18	25	1a. brown-purple	1·75	20
		a. "JEIND" for "JHIND"	£500	
		b. Opt double, one albino	42·00	
19		1a. plum (1899)	3·50	85
20	26	1a.6p. sepia (1896)	2·00	3·25
		a. Opt double, one albino	48·00	
21	27	2a. dull blue	2·25	40
22		2a. ultramarine	2·00	60
		a. Opt double, one albino	48·00	
23	28	3a. brown-orange (1891)	2·50	60
24	29	4a. olive-green	3·50	2·00
25		4a. slate-green	4·50	3·25
26	21	6a. olive-bistre (1891)	7·50	19·00
		a. Opt double, one albino	40·00	
27		6a. bistre-brown	3·00	12·00
28	31	8a. dull mauve	6·50	17·00
		a. "JEIND" for "JHIND"	£1600	
29		8a. magenta (1897)	9·00	26·00
		a. Opt double, one albino	42·00	
30	32	12a. purple/*red* (1896)	6·00	23·00
		a. Opt double, one albino	42·00	
31	33	1r. slate	12·00	48·00
32	37	1r. green and carmine (1897)	10·00	50·00
33	38	2r. carmine and yellow-brown (1896)	£300	£850
34		3r. brown and green (1896)	£475	£800
35		5r. ultramarine and violet (1896)	£500	£800
17/35 Set of 14			£1200	£2250

Varieties exist in which the word "JHIND" measures 10½ mm and 9¾ mm instead of 10 mm. Such varieties are to be found on Nos. 17, 18, 21, 24, 28 and 31.

Raja (Maharaja from 1911) Ranbir Singh, 1887–1959

1900–04. *Colours changed.*

36	40	3p. carmine	1·10	1·25
37		3p. grey (1904)	40	3·50
38	23	½a. pale yellow-green (1902)	4·00	6·00
39		½a. yellow-green (1903)	9·00	12·00
40	25	1a. carmine (1902)	75	6·00
		a. Opt double, one albino	38·00	
36/40 Set of 4			5·50	15·00

1903–09. *King Edward VII. Optd with T* **3.**

41	41	3p. pale grey	25	10
		a. Opt double, one albino	18·00	
42		3p. slate-grey (1905)	40	60
43	42	½a. green	1·50	1·60
44	43	1a. carmine	2·25	1·50
45	44	2a. pale violet	2·75	2·25
46		2a. mauve (1906)	2·25	80
		a. Opt double, one albino	38·00	
47	45	2a.6p. ultramarine (1909)	75	6·00
		a. Opt double, one albino	26·00	
48	46	3a. orange-brown	1·75	40
		a. Opt double	£110	£200
49	47	4a. olive	7·50	9·50
		a. Opt double, one albino	45·00	
50		4a. pale olive	8·00	9·50
51	48	6a. bistre (1905)	6·50	20·00
		a. Opt double, one albino	42·00	
52	49	8a. purple (*shades*)	15·00	20·00
53		8a. claret	15·00	30·00
54	50	12a. purple/*red* (1905)	2·75	12·00
55	51	1r. green and carmine (1905)	3·00	18·00
		a. Opt double, one albino	55·00	
41/55 Set of 11			28·00	80·00

1907–09. *Nos. 149/50 of India optd with T* **3.**

56	53	½a. green	30	20
57	54	1a. carmine (1909)	1·00	70

1913. *King George V. Optd with T* **3.**

58	55	3p. grey	10	2·00
59	56	½a. light green	10	75
60	57	1a. aniline carmine	10	45
61	59	2a. purple	15	4·00
62	62	3a. orange	1·50	12·00
63	64	6a. yellow-bistre	7·00	26·00
58/63 Set of 6			8·25	40·00

JIND STATE (4) JIND STATE (5) JIND STATE (6)

1914–27. *King George V. Optd with T* **4.**

64	55	3p. grey	1·00	50
		a. Pale grey	1·00	20
		b. Bluish grey	2·00	30
		c. Slate	2·00	
65	56	½a. light green	2·25	15
		a. Emerald		75
		b. Bright green	2·50	30
66	57	1a. aniline carmine	1·60	15
67	58	1½a. chocolate (Type A) (1922)	2·75	5·00
68		1½a. chocolate (Type B) (1924)	50	1·50
69	59	2a. purple	3·50	75
		a. Reddish purple	7·00	75
		b. Bright reddish violet (1922)	7·00	75
70	61	2a.6p. ultramarine (1922)	35	4·25
71	62	3a. orange	50	3·50
72	63	4a. olive	1·75	8·50

73	64	6a. yellow-bistre	3·50	16·00
		a. Brown-ochre	3·25	14·00
74	65	8a. deep magenta	4·50	13·00
		a. Deep mauve (1925)	8·50	12·00
		b. Bright mauve (1918)	—	20·00
75	66	12a. carmine-lake	4·00	17·00
76	67	1r. red-brown and deep blue-green.	10·00	20·00
		a. Opt double, one albino	35·00	
		b. Brown and green	15·00	
77		2r. carmine and yellow-brown (1927)	6·00	£130
78		5r. ultramarine and violet (1927)....	42·00	£250
64/78		Set of 15	75·00	£425

No. 71 with inverted overprint is of clandestine origin.

1922. No. 192 of India optd "JIND" in block capitals.

79	57	9p. on 1a. rose-carmine	1·25	13·00

1924–27. Optd with T 4. New colours.

80	57	1a. chocolate	5·00	2·50
81	58	1½a. rose-carmine (Type B) (1927)	20	1·50
82	61	2a.6p. orange (1927)	75	7·00
83	62	3a. bright blue (1925)	1·75	4·25
80/3		Set of 4	7·00	14·00

Nos. 81/2 with inverted overprint are of clandestine origin.

1927–37. King George V (Nasik printing, wmk Mult Star), optd at Nasik with T 5 or 6 (rupee values).

84	55	3p. slate	10	10
		w. Wmk inverted	2·50	
85	56	½a. green (1929)	10	35
86	80	9p. deep green (1932)	2·25	40
87	57	1a. chocolate (1928)	15	10
		w. Wmk inverted	—	1·75
88	82	1a.3p. mauve (1932)	25	30
89	58	1½a. rose-carmine (Type B) (1930)	60	3·00
		w. Wmk inverted	1·25	3·00
90	70	2a. purple (1928)	2·75	40
		w. Wmk inverted	2·75	40
91	61	2a.6p. orange (1930)	1·25	
		w. Wmk inverted	1·10	9·50
92	62	3a. bright blue (1930)	5·50	15·00
		w. Wmk inverted	11·00	
93	83	3a.6p. ultramarine (1937)	3·50	22·00
		w. Wmk inverted	60	18·00
94	71	4a. sage-green (1928)	4·75	3·00
		w. Wmk inverted	1·50	3·00
95	64	6a. bistre (1937)	65	19·00
		w. Wmk inverted	5·50	
96	65	8a. reddish purple (1930)	5·00	2·00
		w. Wmk inverted	5·00	
97	66	12a. claret (1930)	5·00	
		w. Wmk inverted	7·00	20·00
98	67	1r. chocolate and green (1930)	4·25	5·00
99		2r. carmine and orange (1930)	38·00	£140
		w. Wmk inverted	23·00	
100		5r. ultramarine and purple (1928)	13·00	40·00
		w. Wmk inverted	45·00	
101		10r. green and carmine (1928)	15·00	18·00
102		15r. blue & olive (wmk inverted) (1929)	85·00	£600
103		25r. orange and blue (1929)	£130	£750
84/103		Set of 20	£275	£1500

1934. New types and colours. Optd with T 5.

104	79	½a. green	30	25
105	81	1a. chocolate	2·00	30
		w. Wmk inverted	—	3·75
106	59	2a. vermilion	2·75	60
107	62	3a. carmine	3·25	40
108	63	4a. sage-green	3·25	1·50
104/8		Set of 5	10·50	2·75

1937–38. King George VI. Nos. 247/64 optd with T 5 or T 6 (rupee values).

109	91	3p. slate	12·00	2·00
110		½a. red-brown	75	4·00
111		9p. green (1937)	75	3·50
112		1a. carmine (1937)	75	60
113	92	2a. vermilion	1·75	17·00
114	93	2a.6p. bright violet	1·25	20·00
115	94	3a. yellow-green	6·50	17·00
116	95	3a.6p. bright blue	3·25	20·00
117	96	4a. brown	9·50	17·00
118	97	6a. turquoise-green	6·00	25·00
119	98	8a. slate-violet	5·00	21·00
120	99	12a. lake	2·75	27·00
121	100	1r. grey and red-brown	12·00	38·00
122		2r. purple and brown	15·00	£110
123		5r. green and blue	25·00	80·00
124		10r. purple and claret	45·00	75·00
125		15r. brown and green	£100	£750
126		25r. slate-violet and purple	£475	£850
109/26		Set of 18	£650	£1800

JIND

(7)

1941–43. King George VI. Optd with T 7.

(a) Stamps of 1937. W 69 (inverted on 15r.).

127	91	3p. slate	14·00	20·00
128		½a. red-brown	1·00	2·00
129		9p. green	13·00	17·00
130		1a. carmine	1·00	5·00
131	100	1r. grey and red-brown	9·00	24·00
132		2r. purple and brown	18·00	30·00
133		5r. green and blue	40·00	90·00
134		10r. purple and claret	55·00	85·00
135		15r. brown and green	£130	£160
136		25r. slate-violet and purple	60·00	£350
127/36		Set of 10	£300	£700

(b) Stamps of 1940–43.

137	100a	3p. slate (1942)	50	1·00
138		½a. purple (1943)	50	1·75
139		9p. green (1942)	75	3·75
140		1a. carmine (1942)	65	1·50
141	101	1a.3p. yellow-green (1942)	1·00	4·50
142		1½a. dull violet (1942)	8·00	1·50

143		2a. vermilion	1·75	4·25
144		3a. bright violet (1942)	25·00	5·00
145		3½a. bright blue	9·00	10·00
146	102	4a. brown	5·00	5·00
147		6a. turquoise-green	5·50	15·00
148		8a. slate-violet	3·25	13·00
149		12a. lake	14·00	16·00
137/149		Set of 13	70·00	75·00

The 1½a. and 3a. exist printed by lithography or typography.

OFFICIAL STAMPS

SERVICE

SERVICE	SERVICE	JHIND STATE
(O 14)	(O 15)	(O 16)

1885 (1 July). Queen Victoria. Nos. 1/3 of Jind optd with Type O 14.

O1	23	½a. blue green	1·50	30
		a. Opt Type 1 inverted	95·00	60·00
O2	25	1a. brown-purple	70	10
		a. Opt Type 1 inverted	12·00	7·50
O3	27	2a. dull blue	35·00	42·00
		a. Opt Type 1 inverted	£1000	

The three values have had the overprint reprinted in the same way as the ordinary stamps of 1885. See note after No. 6.

1885. Nos. 7/9 of Jind optd with Type O 15.

O7	23	½a. blue-green (R.)	95·00	
		a. "JEEND STATE" double, one albino	£150	
O8	25	1a. brown-purple	75·00	
O9	27	2a. dull blue (R.)	85·00	
O7/9		Set of 3	£225	

1886. Optd with Type O 16, in red.

O10	23	½a. blue-green	20·00	
		a. "ERVICE"	£3500	
		b. "JEIND"	£700	
		c. "JHIND STATE" double, one albino	65·00	
O11	27	2a. dull blue	28·00	
		a. "ERVICE"	£2000	
		b. "JEIND"	£1100	
		c. "SERVICE" double, one albino	50·00	
		d. "JHIND STATE" double, one albino	50·00	

1886–1902. Optd with Type O 16.

O12	23	½a. blue-green	1·50	10
		a. "JHIND STATE" double, one albino	42·00	
O13	25	1a. brown-purple	24·00	
		a. "ERVICE"		
		b. "JEIND"	£500	
		c. "SERVICE" double, one albino	27·00	
O14		1a. plum (1902)	11·00	1·00
O15	27	2a. dull blue	3·00	80
		a. "SERVICE" double, one albino	48·00	
		b. "SERVICE" treble, two albino..	48·00	
O16		2a. ultramarine	1·50	30
		a. "JHIND STATE" double, one albino	48·00	
O17	29	4a. olive-green (1892)	3·00	1·50
		a. "JHIND STATE" double, one albino	40·00	
O18		4a. slate-green	2·75	2·25
O19	31	8a. dull mauve (1892)	5·00	3·75
O20		8a. magenta (1897)	4·75	7·50
		a. "JHIND STATE" double, one albino	42·00	
O21	37	1r. green and carmine (1896)	6·00	42·00
		a. "SERVICE" double, one albino	55·00	
		b. "JHIND STATE" treble, two albino	65·00	
O12/21		Set of 6	25·00	45·00

Varieties mentioned in note after No. 35 exist on Nos. O12, O15, O17 and O20.

Printings up to and including that of October 1897 had the "SERVICE" overprint. Type O 15, applied to sheets already overprinted with Type 3. From the printing of December 1899 onwards "SERVICE" and "JHIND STATE" were overprinted at one operation, as Type O 16, to provide fresh supplies of Nos. O12, O14 and O21.

1902. Colour changed. Optd with Type O 16.

O22	23	½a. yellow-green	2·25	30
		a. "V" of "SERVICE" omitted	£130	70·00

No. O22a normally shows a tiny trace of the "V" remaining. Examples showing the letter completely missing are worth much more.

1903–06. King Edward VII stamps of India optd with Type O 16.

O23	41	3p. pale grey	75	10
O24		3p. slate-grey (1906)	75	10
O25	42	½a. green	30	10
		a. "HIND"	£2500	£275
		b. Opt double, one albino	32·00	
		c. "SERV CE"	†	£250
O26	43	1a. carmine	2·50	10
		a. "HIND"	£2750	£250
		b. Opt double, one albino	35·00	
O27	44	2a. pale violet	2·25	75
O28		2a. mauve	1·50	10
O29	47	4a. olive	1·25	45
		a. Opt double, one albino	45·00	
O30	49	8a. purple (shades)	8·50	5·00
O31		8a. claret	5·00	1·50
O32	51	1r. green and carmine (1906)	2·50	2·25
O23/32		Set of 7	20·00	4·00

The "HIND" error Nos. O25a and O26a occurred on one position in the bottom row of the sheet.

1907. Nos. 149/50 of India optd with Type O 16.

O33	53	½a. green	75	10
O34	54	1a. carmine	1·25	10

1914–27. King George V. Official stamps of India optd with T 4.

O35	55	3p. grey	10	10
		a. "JIND STATE" double, one albino	42·00	
		b. Pale grey	10	10
		c. Bluish grey	—	30
O36	56	½a. light green	10	10
		a. Emerald	1·50	40
		b. Bright green	35	10
O37	57	1a. aniline carmine	75	10
		a. Pale rose-carmine	2·00	10
O39	59	2a. purple	25	30
		a. Reddish purple	—	15
		b. Deep mauve	1·75	30
O40	63	4a. olive	1·00	20
O41	64	6a. brown-ochre (1926)	1·75	2·25
O42	65	8a. deep magenta	70	1·00
		a. Deep mauve	1·75	1·50
O43	67	1r. red-brown and deep blue-green.	2·00	1·75
		a. "JIND STATE" double, one albino	42·00	
		b. Brown and green	7·00	
O44		2r. carmine and yellow-brown (1927)	15·00	75·00
O45		5r. ultramarine and violet (1927)....	21·00	£200
O35/45		Set of 10	38·00	£250

No. O40 with double overprint is of clandestine origin.

1924. As 1914–27. New colour.

O46	57	1a. chocolate	60	10

JIND STATE SERVICE	JIND STATE SERVICE	JIND SERVICE
(O 17)	(O 18)	(O 19)

1927–37. King George V (Nasik printing, wmk Mult Star), optd with Types O 17 or O 18 (rupee values).

O47	55	3p. slate (1928)	10	20
O48	56	½a. green (1929)	10	90
O49	80	9p. deep green (litho) (1932)	60	15
O49a		9p. deep green (typo)	—	75
O50	57	1a. chocolate	10	10
		w. Wmk inverted	85	
O51	82	1a.3p. mauve (1932)	40	15
		w. Wmk inverted	1·60	80
O52	70	2a. purple (1929)	25	15
O53	61	2a.6p. orange (1937)	1·00	20·00
O54	71	4a. sage-green (1929)	35	25
		w. Wmk inverted	1·75	1·25
O55	64	6a. bistre (1937)	2·75	
		w. Wmk inverted	3·75	15·00
O56	65	8a. reddish purple (1929)	—	1·75
		w. Wmk inverted	60	1·75
O57	66	12a. claret (1928)	2·00	16·00
O58	67	1r. chocolate and green (1928)	4·25	4·50
O59		2r. carmine and orange (1930)	45·00	38·00
		w. Wmk inverted	35·00	
O60		5r. ultramarine and purple (1929)	13·00	£225
O61		10r. green and carmine (1928)	35·00	£130
		w. Wmk inverted	48·00	
O47/61		Set of 15	85·00	£400

1934. Optd with Type O 17.

O62	79	½a. green	20	15
O63	81	1a. chocolate	20	15
O64	59	2a. vermilion	30	15
		w. Wmk inverted	1·00	2·00
O65	63	4a. sage-green	5·50	30
O62/5		Set of 4	5·75	65

1937–40. King George VI. Optd with Types O 17 or O 18 (rupee values).

O66	91	½a. red-brown (1938)	55·00	30
O67		9p. green	1·25	12·00
O68		1a. carmine	75	30
O69	100	1r. grey and red-brown (1940)	30·00	48·00
O70		2r. purple and brown (1940)	42·00	£200
O71		5r. green and blue (1940)	75·00	£350
O72		10r. purple and claret (1940)	£300	£950
O66/72		Set of 7	£450	£1400

1939–43.

(a) Official stamps optd with T 7.

O73	O 20	3p. slate	60	1·50
O74		½a. red-brown	1·50	80
O75		½a. purple (1943)	60	30
O76		9p. green	3·00	11·00
O77		1a. carmine	3·75	15
O78		1½a. dull violet (1942)	9·00	1·75
O79		2a. vermilion	6·50	30
		w. Wmk inverted	11·00	3·25
O80		2½a. bright violet	5·00	9·00
O81		4a. brown	8·50	3·75
O82		8a. slate-violet	7·50	6·50

(b) Postage stamps optd with Type O 19.

O83	100	1r. grey and red-brown (1942)	18·00	48·00
O84		2r. purple and brown (1942)	35·00	£150
O85		5r. green and blue (1942)	70·00	£375
O86		10r. purple and claret (1942)	£130	£475
O73/86		Set of 14	£275	£1000

Jind was absorbed into the Patiala and East Punjab States Union by 20 August 1948.

NABHA

PRICES FOR STAMPS ON COVER	
Nos. 1/3	from × 15
Nos. 4/6	—
Nos. 10/36	from × 12
Nos. 37/117	from × 7
Nos. O1/68	from × 15

Raja Hira Singh, 1871–1911.

(1)   NABHA STATE (2)

1885 (1 July). *Queen Victoria. Optd with T* **1**.
1	23	½a. blue-green	3·75	5·00
2	25	1a. brown-purple	48·00	£170
3	27	2a. dull blue	20·00	55·00
4	17	4a. green	80·00	£200
5	31	8a. dull mauve	£325	
6	33	1r. slate	£350	
1/6 *Set of 6*			£750	

All six values have had the overprint reprinted. On the reprints the words "NABHA" and "STATE" both measure 9¼ mm in length, whereas on the originals these words measure 11 and 10 mm respectively. The varieties with overprint double come from the reprints.

1885 (Nov)–**1900**. *Optd with T* **2**.
(a) In red.
10	23	½a. blue-green	70	70
11	27	2a. dull blue	2·50	2·00
		a. Opt double, one albino	55·00	
12	17	4a. green	38·00	£190
13	33	1r. slate	£120	£275
		a. Opt double, one albino	£160	
10/13 *Set of 4*			£140	£425

(b) In black (Nov 1885–97).
14	23	½a. blue-green (1888)	50	10
15	24	9p. carmine (1892)	1·75	3·25
16	25	1a. brown-purple	2·50	90
17		1a. plum	2·25	90
18	26	1a.6p. sepia (1891)	1·50	3·50
		a. "ABHA" for "NABHA"	£300	
19	27	2a. dull blue (1888)	2·50	1·75
20		2a. ultramarine (1888)	2·50	1·75
21	28	3a. orange (1889)	8·50	21·00
		a. Opt double, one albino	35·00	
22		3a. brown-orange	3·50	2·00
23	29	4a. olive-green (1888)	5·00	2·75
24		4a. slate-green	5·50	2·25
25	21	6a. olive-bistre (1889)	7·00	14·00
26		6a. bistre-brown	3·25	3·50
27	31	8a. dull mauve (1889)	3·00	2·50
		a. Opt double, one albino	42·00	
28	32	12a. purple/*red* (1889)	4·00	
		a. Opt double, one albino	38·00	
29	33	1r. slate (1888)	13·00	50·00
30	37	1r. green and carmine (1893)	12·00	5·50
		a. "N BHA" for "NABHA"		
		b. Opt double, one albino	55·00	
31	38	2r. carmine and yellow-brown (1897)	£130	£275
		a. Opt double, one albino	£225	
32		3r. brown and green (1897)	£130	£350
33		5r. ultramarine and violet (1897)	£130	£475
14/33 *Set of 15*			£400	£1100

(c) New value. In black (Nov 1900).
36	40	3p. carmine	30	20

1903–09. *King Edward VII. Optd with T* **2**.
37	41	3p. pale grey	75	15
		a. "NAB STA" for "NABHA STATE"	£850	
		b. Opt double, one albino	25·00	
37c		3p. slate-grey (1906)	75	15
38	42	½a. green	1·10	60
		a. "NABH" for "NABHA"	£1000	
39	43	1a. carmine	1·60	1·00
40	44	2a. pale violet	2·00	3·00
40a		2a. mauve	3·00	35
40b	45	2a.6p. ultramarine (1909)	19·00	90·00
		ba. Opt double, one albino	32·00	
41	46	3a. orange-brown	1·25	40
		a. Opt double, one albino	42·00	
42	47	4a. olive	3·75	1·75
43	48	6a. olive-bistre	3·25	17·00
		a. Opt double, one albino	29·00	
44	49	8a. purple	9·50	23·00
44a		8a. claret	13·00	24·00
45	50	12a. purple/*red*	4·00	24·00
46	51	1r. green and carmine	9·00	16·00
37/46 *Set of 11*			50·00	£160

1907. *Nos. 149/50 of India optd with T* **2**.
47	53	½a. green	1·50	1·25
48	54	1a. carmine	1·25	70

Maharaja Ripudaman (Gurcharan) Singh, 1911–1928.

1913. *King George V. Optd with T* **2**.
49	55	3p. grey	35	40
		a. Pale grey	25	20
		b. Bluish grey	1·25	30
		c. Slate	1·00	
50	56	½a. light green	40	20
		a. Emerald	1·75	50
		b. Bright green	50	20
51	57	1a. aniline carmine	1·10	10
52	59	2a. purple	80	80
		a. Reddish purple	1·25	60
		b. Deep mauve	1·50	60
53	62	3a. orange	50	35
		a. Dull orange	1·00	50
54	63	4a. olive	65	1·60
55	64	6a. yellow-bistre	1·00	5·50
		a. Brown-ochre	1·00	6·00
56	65	8a. deep magenta	5·00	5·50
		a. Deep mauve	4·50	4·75
		b. Bright mauve	6·00	
57	66	12a. carmine-lake	2·25	22·00
58	67	1r. red-brown and deep blue-green.	9·00	6·00
		a. Opt double, one albino	42·00	
		b. Brown and green	15·00	5·00
		c. Orange-brown and deep turquoise-green	17·00	
49/58 *Set of 10*			18·00	35·00

1924. *As 1913. New colour.*
59	57	1a. chocolate	5·50	3·00

No. 59 with inverted or double overprint is of clandestine origin.

NABHA STATE (3)   NABHA STATE (4)

1927–36. *King George V (Nasik printing, wmk Mult Star), optd as T* **3** *or* **4** *(rupee values).*
60	55	3p. slate (1932)	1·75	15
		w. Wmk inverted	3·25	1·50
61	56	½a. green (1928)	80	20
61a	80	9p. deep green (*litho*) (1934)	11·00	11·00
61b		9p. deep green (*typo*)	2·25	1·10
62	57	1a. chocolate	1·50	15
		w. Wmk inverted		
63	82	1a.3p. mauve (1936)	2·25	6·50
		w. Wmk inverted		75
64	70	2a. purple (1932)	2·50	35
65	61	2a.6p. orange (1932)	1·00	8·50
66	62	3a. bright blue (1930)	2·75	1·40
67	71	4a. sage-green (1932)	3·75	2·00
71	67	2r. carmine and orange (1932)	28·00	£110
72		5r. ultramarine and purple (*wmk inverted*) (1932)	70·00	£325
60/72 *Set of 11*			£100	£400

Maharaja Partab Singh, 1928–1971

1936–37. *New types and colours. Optd as T* **3**.
73	79	½a. green	50	40
74	81	1a. chocolate	50	30
75	62	3a. carmine (1937)	4·00	15·00
76	63	4a. sage-green (1937)	5·00	4·25
73/6 *Set of 4*			9·00	18·00

NABHA STATE (5)   NABHA (6)

1938. *King George VI. Nos. 247/64 optd as T* **3** *(3p. to 1a.), T* **5** *(2a. to 12a.) or T* **4** *(rupee values). W* **69** *(inverted on 15r.)*
77	91	3p. slate	7·50	1·00
78		½a. red-brown	7·00	1·25
79		9p. green	20·00	4·50
80		1a. carmine	3·00	80
81	92	2a. vermilion	1·25	7·00
82	93	2a.6p. bright violet	1·25	10·00
83	94	3a. yellow-green	1·40	6·00
84	95	3a.6p. bright blue	1·40	22·00
85	96	4a. brown	7·00	7·00
86	97	6a. turquoise-green	3·00	23·00
87	98	8a. slate-violet	2·25	22·00
88	99	12a. lake	2·50	22·00
89	100	1r. grey and red-brown	11·00	28·00
90		2r. purple and brown	28·00	£100
91		5r. green and blue	38·00	£180
92		10r. purple and claret	55·00	£400
93		15r. brown and green	£170	£750
94		25r. slate-violet and purple	£140	£750
		w. Wmk inverted	£250	£850
77/94 *Set of 18*			£425	£2000

1941–45. *King George VI. Optd with T* **6**.
(a) Stamps of 1937.
95	91	3p. slate (1942)	35·00	4·50
96		½a. red-brown (1942)	80·00	6·00
97		9p. green (1942)	11·00	14·00
98		1a. carmine (1942)	11·00	3·50
95/8 *Set of 4*			£120	25·00

(b) Stamps of 1940–43.
105	100	3p. slate (1942)	1·25	1·00
106		½a. purple (1943)	3·00	1·40
107		9p. green (1942)	2·50	1·40
108		1a. carmine (1945)	1·00	3·75
109	101	1a.3p. yellow-brown	1·00	3·25
110		1½a. dull violet (1942)	2·50	2·50
111		2a. vermilion (1943)	1·10	4·25
112		3a. bright violet (1943)	6·50	4·50
113		3½a. bright blue (1944)	17·00	55·00
114	102	4a. brown	1·75	1·00
115		6a. turquoise-green (1943)	12·00	50·00
116		8a. slate-violet (1943)	11·00	38·00
117		12a. lake (1943)	9·00	55·00
105/17 *Set of 13*			60·00	£200

The 1½a. exists printed by lithography or typography.

OFFICIAL STAMPS

SERVICE

NABHA STATE SERVICE (O 8)   NABHA STATE (O 9)

1885 (1 July). *Nos. 1/3 of Nabha optd with Type* O **8**.
O1	23	½a. blue-green	4·00	1·10
O2	25	1a. brown-purple	70	20
		a. Opt Type O **8** double	†	£1600
O3	27	2a. dull blue	75·00	£150
O1/3 *Set of 3*			75·00	£150

The three values have had the overprint reprinted in the same way as the ordinary stamps of 1885.

1885 (Nov)–**97**. *Optd with Type* O **9**.
(a) In red.
O4	23	½a. blue-green	7·00	4·75
O5	27	2a. deep blue	1·60	55

(b) In black (Nov 1885–97).
O6	23	½a. blue-green (1888)	40	10
		a. "SERVICE." with stop	£120	2·25
		b. "S ATE" for "STATE"		
		c. "SERVICE" double, one albino	38·00	
O7	25	1a. brown-purple	1·50	60
O8		1a. plum	1·50	25
		a. "SERVICE." with stop	8·00	75
		ab. "SERVICE." with stop, and "NABHA STATE" double	£1600	£250
O9	27	2a. dull blue (1888)	2·75	1·25
O10		2a. ultramarine	3·25	1·60
O11	28	3a. orange (1889)	25·00	85·00
O12		3a. brown-orange	26·00	85·00
		a. "NABHA STATE" double, one albino	55·00	
O13	29	4a. olive-green (1888)	3·25	1·25
O14		4a. slate-green	3·50	1·25
O15	21	6a. olive-bistre (1889)	20·00	30·00
		a. "SERVICE" double, one albino	42·00	
O16		6a. bistre-brown	£650	
O17	31	8a. dull mauve (1889)	2·75	1·25
O18	32	12a. purple/*red* (1889)	6·50	20·00
		a. SERVICE" double, one albino	42·00	
		b. "NABHA STATE" double, one albino	38·00	
O19	33	1r. slate (1889)	38·00	£300
O20	37	1r. green and carmine (1.97)	30·00	80·00
O6/20 *Set of 10*			£120	£475

Printings up to and including that of August 1895 had the "SERVICE" overprint applied to sheets of stamps already overprinted with Type 2. From the printing of January 1897 onwards the two parts of the overprint were applied at one operation. This method was only used for printings of the ½a., 1a. and 1r. (O20).

1903–06. *King Edward VII stamps of India optd with Type* O **9**.
O24	41	3p. pale grey (1906)	5·00	22·00
O25		3p. slate-grey (1906)	2·00	16·00
		a. Opt double, one albino	35·00	
O26	42	½a. green	80	35
O27	43	1a. carmine	80	10
O28	44	2a. pale violet	2·75	1·25
O29		2a. mauve	2·25	40
		a. Opt double, one albino	42·00	
O30	47	4a. olive	1·60	50
O32	49	8a. purple (*shades*)	1·60	1·50
		a. Opt double, one albino	32·00	
O33		8a. claret	10·00	4·50
O34	51	1r. green and carmine	1·60	2·50
O24/34 *Set of 7*			9·50	19·00

1907. *Nos. 149/50 of India optd with Type* O **9**.
O35	53	½a. green	1·25	50
		a. Opt double, one albino	20·00	
O36	54	1a. carmine	75	30
		a. Opt double, one albino	35·00	

1913. *King George V. Optd with Type* O **9**.
O37	63	4a. olive	10·00	60·00
O38	67	1r. red-brown and deep blue-green.	55·00	£450
		a. Opt double, one albino	£110	

1913. *Official stamps of India optd with T* **2**.
O39	55	3p. grey	1·00	11·00
		a. Pale grey	1·00	9·00
		b. Bluish grey	1·00	9·00
		c. Slate	75	9·00
O40	56	½a. light green	70	20
		a. Emerald	1·00	10
		b. Bright green	60	15
O41	57	1a. aniline carmine	50	10
O42	59	2a. purple	75	60
		a. Reddish purple	1·75	30
		b. Deep mauve	1·50	20
		c. Bright reddish violet		
O43	63	4a. olive	75	50
O44	65	8a. deep magenta	1·50	2·00
		a. Deep mauve	2·75	
		b. Bright mauve	3·50	
O46	67	1r. red-brown & deep blue-green.	5·00	3·50
		a. Brown and green	7·00	3·50
O39/46 *Set of 7*			9·00	14·00

NABHA STATE SERVICE (O 10)   NABHA SERVICE (O 11)

1932–42. *King George V (Nasik printing, wmk Mult Star), optd at Nasik with Type* O **10**.
O47	55	3p. slate	10	15
O48	81	1a. chocolate (1935)	15	15
O49	63	4a. sage-green (1942?)	21·00	2·50
O50	65	8a. reddish purple (1937)	1·00	2·25
O47/50 *Set of 4*			21·00	4·50

1938. *King George VI. Optd as Type* O **10**.
O53	91	9p. green	4·25	4·00
O54		1a. carmine	18·00	1·10

1940–43.
(a) Official stamps optd with T **6**.
O55	O **20**	3p. slate (1942)	1·25	1·50
O56		½a. red-brown (1942)	1·10	30
O57		½a. purple (1943)	4·00	1·00
O58		9p. green (1942)	1·25	30
O59		1a. carmine (1942)	60	20
O61		1½a. dull violet (1942)	70	40
O62		2a. vermilion (1942)	2·25	1·50

		w. Wmk inverted	4·25	2·00
O64		4a. brown (1942)	3·50	3·25
O65		8a. slate-violet (1942)	5·50	18·00

(b) Postage stamps optd with Type O 11.

O66	**100**	1r. grey and red-brown (1942)........	8·50	38·00
O67		2r. purple and brown (1942)	28·00	£170
O68		5r. green and blue (1942)	£170	£500
O55/68 Set of 12			£200	£650

Nabha was absorbed into the Patiala and East Punjab States Union by 20 August 1948.

PATIALA

PRICES FOR STAMPS ON COVER
Nos. 1/6	*from* × 10
Nos. 7/34	*from* × 6
Nos. 35/45	*from* × 8
Nos. 46/115	*from* × 4
Nos. O1/84	*from* × 15

Maharaja Rajindra Singh, 1876–1900

	PUTTIALLA		PATIALA	
	STATE		STATE	
(1)	(2)		(3)	

1884 (1 Oct). *Queen Victoria. Optd with T* **1**, *in red.*

1	**23**	½a. blue-green	3·75	4·25
		a. Opt double, one sideways.....	£2750	£700
		b. Opt double, one albino	75·00	
2	**25**	1a. brown-purple.......................	48·00	65·00
		a. Opt double..........................		
		b. Optd in red and in black...........	£650	
3	**27**	2a. dull blue	13·00	14·00
4	**17**	4a. green	80·00	90·00
5	**31**	8a. dull mauve	£400	£950
		a. Opt inverted	£9000	
		b. Optd in red and in black	£110	£400
		ba. Ditto. Opts inverted	£6000	
		c. Opt double, one albino	£450	
6	**33**	1r. slate	£130	£550
1/6 Set of 6			£600	£1500

Nos. 5a and 5ba each occur once in the setting of 120. The 8a. value also exists with a trial overprint (showing the words more curved) reading downwards (*Price £550 unused*), which should not be confused with No. 5a.

1885. *Optd with T* **2**.

(a) In red.

7	**23**	½a. blue-green	2·25	30
		a. "AUTTIALLA"	15·00	28·00
		b. "STATE" only		
		c. Wide spacing between lines	6·50	7·00
8	**27**	2a. dull blue	5·00	1·75
		a. "AUTTIALLA"	38·00	
		b. Wide spacing between lines	25·00	25·00
		ba. Ditto "AUTTIALLA"	£700	
9	**17**	4a. green	3·25	3·50
		a. Optd in red and in black	£225	
		b. Wide spacing between lines	£400	
		c. Opt double, one albino	45·00	
10	**33**	1r. slate	13·00	75·00
		a. "AUTTIALLA"	£450	
		b. Wide spacing between lines	£400	

(b) In black.

11	**25**	1a. brown-purple.......................	60	30
		a. Optd in red and in black	10·00	80·00
		b. "AUTTIALLA"	70·00	
		ba. Ditto. Optd in red and in black .	£1500	
		c. Opt double	£225	£250
		d. Wide spacing between lines	£275	
12	**31**	8a. dull mauve	20·00	45·00
		a. "AUTTIALLA"	£350	
		b. Opt double, one albino	80·00	
		c. Wide spacing between lines	£400	
7/12 Set of 6			40·00	£110

The ½, 2 and 4a. (T **29**), and 1r. (all overprinted in black), are proofs.

All six values exist with reprinted overprints, and the error "AUTTIALLA STATE" has been reprinted in complete sheets on all values and in addition in black on the ½, 2, 4a. and 1r. Nearly all these however, are found with the word "REPRINT" overprinted upon them. On the genuine "AUTTIALLA" errors, which occur on R. 9/12 in the setting of 120, the word "STATE" is 8½ mm long; on the reprints only 7¾ mm.

Nos. 7c, 8b, 9b, 10b, 11d and 12c show 1¼ mm spacing between the two lines of overprint. The normal spacing is ¾ mm.

Nos. 7/8 and 10/12 exist with error "PUTTILLA", but their status is uncertain (*Price, from £600, unused*).

1891–96. *Optd with T* **3**.

13	**23**	½a. blue-green (1892).....................	40	10
14	**24**	9p. carmine.............................	1·00	2·25
15	**25**	1a. brown-purple.......................	1·40	30
16		1a. plum................................	1·75	80
		a. "PATIALA" omitted	£180	£375
		b. "PA" omitted.......................		
		c. "PATIA" omitted...................		
		d. "PATIAL" omitted.................		
17	**26**	1a.6p. sepia............................	1·25	1·50
18	**27**	2a. dull blue (1896)...................	1·25	30
19		2a. ultramarine	1·75	1·00
20	**28**	3a. brown-orange.....................	2·25	60
21	**29**	4a. olive-green (1896)	2·25	60
		a. "PATIALA" omitted	£450	£225
22		4a. slate-green	2·50	60
23	**21**	6a. bistre-brown......................	2·50	13·00
24		6a. olive-bistre	3·75	19·00
		a. Opt double, one albino	55·00	
25	**31**	8a. dull mauve		

26		8a. magenta (1896).....................	2·75	13·00
27	**32**	12a. magenta/*red*	2·50	14·00
28	**37**	1r. green and carmine (1896)........	4·25	48·00
29	**38**	2r. carmine and yellow-brown (1895)	£120	£750
30		3r. brown and green (1895)	£170	£800
		a. Opt double, one albino	£225	
		b. Opt treble, two albino	£170	
31		5r. ultramarine and violet (1895)....	£200	£850
13/31 Set of 14			£450	£2250

The errors on the 1a. plum and 4a. olive-green occur on R. 19/1 in the December 1898 printing. Nos. 16b/d are early stages of the error before the entire word was omitted.

1899–1902. *Colours changed and new value. Optd with T* **3**.

32	**40**	3p. carmine (1899).....................	30	15
		a. Pair, one without opt..............	£3500	
		b. Opt double, one albino	42·00	
33	**23**	½a. pale yellow-green.................	1·00	40
34	**25**	1a. carmine.............................	2·50	1·25
32/4 Set of 3			3·50	1·60

Maharaja Bhupindra Singh, 1900–1938

1903–06. *King Edward VII. Optd with T* **3**.

35	**41**	3p. pale grey	40	10
		a. Additional albino opt of Jind Type 3	£225	
		b. "S" in "STATE" sideways (R. 20/1)	£900	£900
36		3p. slate-grey (1906)	60	10
37	**42**	½a. green..............................	1·10	15
38	**43**	1a. carmine............................	90	10
		a. Horiz pair, one without opt	£900	
39	**44**	2a. pale violet	1·40	65
		a. Mauve..............................	9·00	1·00
40	**46**	2a. orange-brown	1·60	35
41	**47**	4a. olive (1905)	2·75	1·25
42	**48**	6a. olive-bistre (1905)	3·25	8·50
43	**49**	8a. purple (1906)	3·75	2·25
44	**50**	12a. purple/*red* (1906)	7·00	23·00
45	**51**	1r. green and carmine (1905).......	4·00	5·00
35/45 Set of 10			24·00	38·00

1912. *Nos. 149/50 of India optd with T* **3**.

46	**53**	½a. green..............................	40	25
47	**54**	1a. carmine............................	1·75	1·00

1912–26. *King George V. Optd with T* **3**.

48	**55**	3p. grey	25	10
		a. Pale grey	1·00	15
		b. Bluish grey	1·75	
		c. Slate	1·75	30
		ca. "Rs" flaw.........................	30·00	
49	**56**	½a. light green	70	20
		a. Emerald	1·40	30
		b. Bright green	1·00	35
50	**57**	1a. aniline carmine...................	1·60	20
51	**58**	1½a. chocolate (Type A) (1922)	30	55
52	**59**	2a. purple	1·25	1·00
		a. Reddish purple	2·00	
		b. Deep mauve	2·00	
		c. Bright reddish violet	2·00	
53	**62**	3a. orange.............................	2·50	1·25
54	**63**	3a. olive	3·50	3·00
55	**64**	6a. yellow-bistre	1·75	3·75
		a. Brown-ochre (1921)	3·75	5·00
56	**65**	8a. deep magenta	3·00	2·25
		a. Purple (1921)	5·00	2·75
57	**66**	12a. carmine-lake......................	3·75	8·50
58	**67**	1r. red-brown and deep blue-green.	7·50	13·00
		a. Opt double, one albino	38·00	
		b. Brown and green (1924)..........	10·00	
59		2r. carmine & yell-brn (1926).......	14·00	£140
60		5r. ultramarine and violet (1926)....	30·00	£170

1923–26. *As 1912–26. New colours.*

61	**57**	1a. chocolate	2·75	40
62	**62**	3a. ultramarine (1926)................	3·25	8·00
48/62 Set of 15			70·00	£325

	PATIALA STATE	
PATIALA STATE	(5)	
(4)		

1928–34. *King George V (Nasik printing, wmk Mult Star) optd at Nasik with T* **4** *or* **5** *(rupee values).*

63	**55**	3p. slate (1932)	2·00	10
		w. Wmk inverted	3·25	1·25
64	**56**	½a. green..............................	25	10
		w. Wmk inverted	2·50	1·25
65	**80**	9p. deep green (*litho*) (1934).......	2·25	1·00
65a		9p. deep green (*typo*)	2·25	35
66	**57**	1a. chocolate	75	25
		w. Wmk inverted	3·25	1·10
67	**82**	1a.3p. mauve (1932)	3·00	15
		w. Wmk inverted	3·75	1·40
68	**70**	2a. purple	1·75	40
		w. Wmk inverted	3·25	
69	**61**	2a.6p. orange (1934).................	4·50	2·25
		w. Wmk inverted	3·00	
70	**62**	3a. bright blue (1929)................	3·00	2·25
71	**71**	4a. sage-green	4·50	1·50
		w. Wmk inverted	7·00	
72	**65**	8a. reddish purple (1933)............	6·00	3·25
73	**67**	1r. chocolate and green (1929)	7·00	9·00
		w. Wmk inverted	21·00	13·00
74		2r. carmine and orange..............	25·00	
		w. Wmk inverted	11·00	50·00
63/74w Set of 12			40·00	60·00

1935–37. *Optd with T* **4**.

75	**79**	½a. blue-green (1937).................	85	30
76	**81**	1a. chocolate (1936)	1·10	20
77	**59**	2a. vermilion (No. 236b) (1936)	40	1·50
78	**62**	3a. carmine............................	9·00	6·00
		w. Wmk inverted	5·50	8·00
79	**63**	4a. sage-green	1·75	2·50
75/9 Set of 5			8·50	9·50

PATIALA STATE	PATIALA	PATIALA
(6)	(7)	(8)

1937–38. *King George VI. Nos. 247/64 optd with T* **4** *(3p. to 1a.),* *T* **6** *(2a. to 12a.), or T* **5** *(rupee values).*

80	**91**	3p. slate	25·00	35
81		½a. red-brown	10·00	50
82		9p. green (1937)......................	5·00	1·00
83		1a. carmine (1937)...................	2·75	20
84	**92**	2a. vermilion..........................	1·50	8·50
85	**93**	2a.6p. bright violet...................	4·50	18·00
86	**94**	3a. yellow-green	4·50	18·00
87	**95**	3a.6p. bright blue	6·00	22·00
88	**96**	4a. brown	23·00	15·00
89	**97**	6a. turquoise-green	22·00	50·00
90	**98**	8a. slate-violet	24·00	38·00
91	**99**	12a. lake	23·00	60·00
92	**100**	1r. grey and red-brown...............	22·00	40·00
93		2r. purple and brown	26·00	95·00
94		5r. green and blue	32·00	£200
95		10r. purple and claret	45·00	£350
96		15r. brown and green	£100	£550
97		25r. slate-violet and purple	£130	£550
80/97 Set of 18			£450	£1800

Maharaja Yadavindra Singh, 1938–1971

1941–46. *King George VI. Optd with T* **7** *or* **8** *(rupee value).*

(a) Stamps of 1937.

98	**91**	3p. slate	10·00	2·25
99		½a. red-brown	6·50	1·75
100		9p. green..............................	£250	6·50
		w. Wmk inverted		
101		1a. carmine...........................	23·00	2·00
102	**100**	1r. grey and red-brown (1946).......	13·00	80·00
98/102 Set of 5			£275	85·00

(b) Stamps of 1940–43.

103	**100a**	3p. slate (1942)	4·00	15
104		½a. purple (1943)	4·00	15
		a. Pair, one without opt.............	£6000	
105		9p. green (1942)	1·50	15
		a. Vert pair, one without opt........	£3250	
106		1a. carmine (1944)...................	1·00	10
107	**101**	1a.3p. yellow-brown	1·60	3·25
108		1½a. violet (1942)	12·00	3·25
109		2a. vermilion (1944).................	9·00	50
110		3a. bright violet (1944)..............	8·00	2·50
111		3½a. bright blue (1944)..............	19·00	35·00
112	**102**	4a. brown (1944)	8·00	3·50
113		6a. turquoise-green (1944)..........	3·25	16·00
114		8a. slate-violet (1944)...............	3·00	13·00
115		12a. lake (1945)	18·00	75·00
103/15 Set of 13			85·00	£140

The 1½a. exists printed by lithography or typography.

OFFICIAL STAMPS

SERVICE	SERVICE
(O 2)	(O 3)

1884 (1 Oct). *Nos. 1/3 of Patiala optd with Type O* **2**, *in black.*

O1	**23**	½a. blue-green	15·00	30
O2	**25**	1a. brown-purple.......................	1·00	10
		a. Opt Type **1** inverted	£1800	£275
		b. Opt Type **1** double...............	†	£120
		c. "SERVICE" double.................	£1800	£600
		d. "SERVICE" inverted	†	£1600
		w. Wmk inverted	†	£325
O3	**27**	2a. dull blue	£4500	£170

Essays of No. O3 exist on which "STATE" measures 10 mm long (normal 9 mm) and the words of the Type **1** overprint are more curved. These are rare (*Price £950 unused*).

1885–90.

(a) No. 7 of Patiala optd with Type O **2**, *in black.*

O4	**23**	½a. blue-green	1·00	25
		a. "SERVICE" double.................	†	£600
		b. "AUTTIALLA"	60·00	16·00
		ba. "AUTTIALLA", and "SERVICE" double...............................	†	£4750

(b) No. 11 of Patiala optd with Type O **2**, *in black.*

O5	**25**	1a. brown purple	1·00	10
		a. "SERVICE" double.................	£1800	
		b. "SERVICE" double, one inverted	†	£550
		c. "AUTTIALLA"	£600	45·00
		d. "PUTTIALLA STATE" double .	†	£1400

(c) As No. 7 of Patiala, but optd in black, and No. 8, optd with Type O **3**.

O6	**23**	½a. blue-green (Bk.) (1890)	1·50	10
O7	**27**	2a. dull blue (R.)	75	30
		a. "SERVICE" double, one inverted	30·00	£180

Stamps as Nos. O4/5, but with Type O **3** (in red on the ½a.), were prepared for use but not issued, although some were erroneously overprinted "REPRINT". No. O7 with overprint in black is a proof. The ½a "AUTTIALLA" has been reprinted in complete sheets, and can be found with "AUTTIALLA" double.

No. O7 exists with error "PUTTILLA", but its status is uncertain.

SERVICE

PATIALA STATE	PATIALA STATE SERVICE	PATIALA STATE SERVICE
(O 4)	(O 5)	(O 6)

1891 (Nov)–**1900**. *Optd with Type O* **4**, *in black.*

O8	**23**	½a. blue-green (9.95).................	40	10
		a. "SERVICE" inverted	55·00	
		b. "SERV CE"	£1000	
		c. "STA E"	£600	£500
O9	**25**	1a. plum (10.1900)	5·00	10
		a. "SERVICE" inverted	60·00	

O10	27	2a. dull blue (12.98)	4·50	2·00
		a. Deep blue	3·25	2·00
		b. "SERVICE" inverted	60·00	£180
		ba. "SERV CE" inverted	£2000	
		c. Thin seriffed "I" in "SERVICE"	£200	
O12	28	3a. brown-orange	1·50	2·75
		a. "SERV CE"	£2500	
O13	29	4a. olive-green	1·40	70
		a. Slate-green (9.95)	1·40	30
		b. "SERV CE"	£1200	
O15	21	6a. bistre-brown	1·60	35
		a. Olive-bistre	£1200	
		dull mauve	2·75	1·25
O16	31	8a. dull mauve	2·75	1·25
		a. Magenta (12.98)	2·75	1·60
		b. "SERV CE"	£3750	
		c. Thin seriffed "I" in "SERVICE"	£425	
O18	32	12a. purple/red	1·50	60
		a. "SERV CE"	£5000	
O19	33	1r. slate	2·00	65
		a. "SERV CE"	£5000	
O8/19		Set of 9	17·50	7·25

Stamps from the first printing of November 1891 (Nos. O12/13, O15/16, O18/19) had the "SERVICE" overprint, as Type O 3, applied to sheets already overprinted with Type 3. Subsequent printings of Nos. O8/10a, O13a and O16a had both overprints applied at one operation as shown on Type O 4.

The errors with "SERVICE" inverted occur from a trial printing, in two operations, during 1894, which was probably not issued. Some of the "SERV CE" varieties may also come from the same trial printing.

1902 (Jan)–03. Optd with Type O 4.

O20	25	1a. carmine	75	10
O21	37	1r. green and carmine (5.03)	6·00	9·50

1903–10. King Edward VII stamps of India optd with Type O 4.

O22	41	3p. pale grey	40	10
		a. Slate-grey (1909)	50	15
O24	42	½a. green	75	10
O25	43	1a. carmine	60	10
O26	44	2a. pale violet (1905)	80	25
		a. Mauve	80	10
O28	46	3a. orange-brown	3·50	3·00
O29	47	4a. olive (1905)	2·00	20
		a. Opt double, one albino	50·00	
O30	49	8a. purple (shades)	1·75	75
		a. Claret (1910)	4·50	2·25
O32	51	1r. green and carmine (1906)	1·75	80
O22/32		Set of 8	10·50	4·75

1907. Nos. 149/50 of India optd with Type O 4.

O33	53	½a. green	50	20
O34	54	1a. carmine	50	10

1913–26. King George V. Official stamps of India optd with T 3.

O35	55	3p. grey	10	20
		a. Pale grey	30	30
		b. Slate (1926)	30	30
O36	56	½a. light green	10	10
		a. Emerald	2·00	50
		b. Bright green	75	40
O37	57	1a. aniline carmine	10	10
O38		1a. chocolate (1925)	7·50	1·00
O39	59	2a. purple	90	60
		a. Reddish purple		1·25
		b. Deep mauve	1·25	35
O40	63	4a. olive	50	35
O41	64	6a. brown-ochre (1926)	1·75	2·50
O42	65	8a. deep magenta	55	70
O43	67	1r. red-brown and deep blue-green	1·40	1·40
O44		2r. carmine and yellow-brown (1926)	18·00	50·00
		a. Opt double, one albino	60·00	
O45		5r. ultramarine and violet (1926)	10·00	20·00
O35/45		Set of 11	38·00	70·00

1927–36. King George V (Nasik printing, wmk Mult Star), optd at Nasik with Type O 5 or Type O 6 (rupee values).

O47	55	3p. slate	10	10
		a. Blue opt	1·75	1·50
		w. Wmk inverted	3·00	1·25
O48	56	½a. green (1932)	1·00	55
		w. Wmk inverted	—	3·25
O49	57	1a. chocolate	15	10
		w. Wmk inverted	1·50	50
O50	82	1a.3p. mauve (1932)	40	10
		w. Wmk inverted	3·75	20
O51	70	2a. purple	20	30
		w. Wmk inverted		
O52		2a. vermilion (1933)	30	35
O53	61	2a.6p. orange (1933)	2·75	35
		w. Wmk inverted	80	80
O54	71	4a. sage-green (1935)	50	30
		w. Wmk inverted	3·00	1·50
O55	65	8a. reddish purple (1929)	1·00	65
		w. Wmk inverted	1·00	80
O56	67	1r. chocolate and green (1929)	4·75	3·00
		w. Wmk inverted	2·75	3·00
O57		2r. carmine and orange (1936)	12·00	38·00
O47/57		Set of 11	17·00	40·00

1935–39. New types. Optd with Type O 5.

O58	79	½a. green (1936)	10	10
O59	81	1a. chocolate (1936)	35	30
O60	59	2a. vermilion	15	30
O61		2a. vermilion (small die) (1939)	17·00	4·00
O62	63	4a. sage-green (1936)	2·25	1·25
O58/62		Set of 5	18·00	5·50

1937–39. King George VI. Optd with Type O 5 or O 6 (rupee values).

O63	91	½a. red-brown (1938)	75	20
O64		9p. green (1938)	13·00	55·00
O65		1a. carmine	75	40
O66	100	1r. grey and red-brown (1939)	1·00	6·50
O67		2r. purple and brown (1939)	5·00	5·00
O68		5r. green and blue (1939)	15·00	55·00
O63/8		Set of 6	32·00	£110

1A_____1A 1A SERVICE 1A PATIALA SERVICE
(O 7)   (O 8)   (O 9)

1939–40. Stamp of 1932 (King George V).

(a) Optd with Types O 5 and O 7.

O69	82	1a. on 1a.3p. mauve	11·00	2·75
		w. Wmk inverted	11·00	3·25

(b) Optd with T 4 and O 8.

O70	82	1a. on 1a.3p. mauve (1940)	9·00	2·75
		w. Wmk inverted	8·50	3·25

"SERVICE" measures 9¼ mm on No. O69 but only 8¾ mm on O70.

1939–44.

(a) Official stamps optd with T 7.

O71	O 20	3p. slate (1940)	1·75	10
O72		½a. red-brown	5·00	10
		w. Wmk inverted	—	14·00
O73		½a. purple (1942)	75	10
O74		9p. green	75	40
		w. Wmk inverted		
O75		1a. carmine	3·25	10
O76		1a.3p. yellow-brown (1941)	1·00	25
O77		1½a. dull violet (1944)	6·50	1·00
O78		2a. vermilion (1940)	10·00	35
		w. Wmk inverted	15·00	
O79		2½a. bright violet (1940)	3·50	75
O80		4a. brown (1943)	1·75	2·50
O81		8a. slate-violet (1944)	4·00	6·00

(b) Postage stamps optd with Type O 9.

O82	100	1r. grey and red-brown (1943)	5·00	10·00
O83		2r. purple and brown (1944)	12·00	60·00
O84		5r. green and blue (1944)	20·00	80·00
O71/84		Set of 14	65·00	£140

Patiala became part of the Patiala and East Punjab States Union by 20 August 1948.

INDIAN FEUDATORY STATES

These stamps were only valid for use within their respective states, *unless otherwise indicated.*

Postage stamps of the Indian States, current at that date, were replaced by those of the Republic of India on 1 April 1950.

Unless otherwise stated, all became obsolete on 1 May 1950 (with the exception of the "Anchal" stamps of Travancore-Cochin which remained current until 1 July 1951 or Sept 1951 for the Official issues).

ALWAR

PRICES FOR STAMPS ON COVER	
Nos. 1/2	from × 25
No. 3	from × 50
No. 4	
No. 5	from × 50

Maharao Raja (Maharaja from 1889) Mangal Singh, 1874–1892.

1 (¼a.).

1877. Litho. Rouletted.

1	1	¼a. steel blue	15·00	7·50
		a. Bright greenish blue	8·50	7·00
		b. Ultramarine	4·25	1·10
		c. Grey-blue (shades)	4·00	1·10
2		1a. pale yellowish brown	9·00	25
		a. Brown (shades)	3·25	1·25
		b. Chocolate	10·00	8·00
		c. Pale reddish brown	2·75	1·50

Maharaja Jai Singh, 1892–1937.

1899–1901. Redrawn. P 12.

(a) Wide margins between stamps.

3	1	¼a. slate-blue	7·50	3·00
		a. Imperf between (horiz pair)	£350	£450
		b. Imperf between (vert pair)	£700	£750
4		¼a. emerald-green	£550	

(b) Narrower margins (1901).

5	1	¼a. emerald-green	4·50	2·50
		a. Imperf between (horiz pair)	£250	£300
		b. Imperf between (vert pair)	£250	£300
		c. Imperf horiz (vert pair)	£275	
		d. Imperf (pair)	£325	
		e. Pale yellow-green	6·50	2·75
		ea. Imperf (pair)	£550	
		eb. Imperf between (horiz pair)	†	£550

In the redrawn type only the bottom outer frameline is thick, whereas in the original 1877 issue the left-hand frameline is also thick, as shown in Type 1.

The stamps of Alwar became obsolete on 1 July 1902.

BAHAWALPUR

See after PAKISTAN

BAMRA

PRICES FOR STAMPS ON COVER	
Nos. 1/6	
Nos. 8/40	from × 25

Raja Sudhal Deo, 1869–1903

GUM. The stamps of Bamra were issued without gum.

BAMRA postage ଶ୍ରୀଶ୍ ५७୫୦। 1 (¼a.)	BAMRA postage ଶ୍ରୀଶ୍ 1a	BAMRA postage ଶ୍ରୀଶ୍ 2 (½a.)
BAMRA postage ଶ୍ରୀଶ୍ ५୦। 3 (1a.)	BAMRA postage ଶ୍ରୀଶ୍ 4 (2a.)	BAMRA postage ଶ୍ରୀଶ୍ 5 (4a.)
	BAMRA postage ଶ୍ରୀଶ୍ 6 (8a.)	

(illustrations actual size)

(Typo Jagannata Ballabh Press, Deogarh)

1888. Imperf.

1	1	¼a. black/yellow	£450	
		a. "g" inverted (R. 5/1)	£4250	
		b. Last native character inverted	£4250	
		c. Last native character as Type 1a	£4250	
2	2	½a. black/rose	80·00	
		a. "g" inverted (R. 5/1)	£1500	
3	3	1a. black/blue	55·00	
		a. "g" inverted (R. 5/1)	£1300	
		b. Scroll inverted (R. 8/4)	£1100	
4	4	2a. black/green	80·00	£325
		a. "a" omitted (R. 8/3)	£1500	
		b. Scroll inverted (R. 8/4)	£1300	
5	5	4a. black/yellow	70·00	£325
		a. "a" omitted (R. 8/3)	£1400	
		b. Scroll inverted (R. 8/4)	£1200	
6	6	8a. black/rose	42·00	
		a. "a" omitted (R. 8/3)	£1200	
		b. Horiz pair, one printed on back	£700	
		c. Scroll inverted (R. 8/4)	£1000	

These stamps were all printed from the same plate of 96 stamps, 12×8, but for some values only part of the plate was used. There are 96 varieties of the ½, 4 and 8a., 72 of the 1a., 80 of the 2a. and not less than 88 of the ¼a.

The scroll ornament can be found pointing to either the right or the left.

There are two forms of the third native character. In the first five horizontal rows it is as in T 1 and in the last three rows as in T 4.

These stamps have been reprinted: the ¼a. and ½a. in blocks of 8 varieties (all showing scroll pointing to right), and all the values in blocks of 20 varieties (all showing scroll pointing to left). On the reprints the fourth character is of a quite different shape.

8

1890 (July)–93. Black on coloured paper. Nos. 24/5 and 39/40 show face value as "One Rupee".

(a) "Postage" with capital "P".

8	8	¼a. on rose-lilac	4·25	5·50
		a. "Eeudatory" (R. 2/4)	20·00	32·00
		b. "Quatrer" (R. 1/3)	20·00	32·00
		c. Inverted "e" in "Postage" (R. 2/3)	20·00	32·00
9		¼a. on bright rose	2·00	3·00
10		¼a. on reddish purple	2·00	2·75
		a. First "a" in "anna" inverted (R. 3/3)	45·00	50·00
		b. "AMRA" inverted (R. 4/4)	65·00	65·00
		c. "M" and second "A" in "BAMRA" inverted (R. 4/4)	85·00	85·00
11		½a. on dull green	3·00	3·00
		a. "Eeudatory" (R. 2/4)	55·00	70·00
12		½a. on blue-green	4·75	4·25
13		1a. on bistre-yellow	4·50	3·25
		a. "Eeudatory" (R. 2/4)	£120	£140
14		1a. on orange-yellow	42·00	42·00
		a. "annas" for "anna"	£180	£190
15		2a. on rose-lilac	18·00	32·00
		a. "Eeudatory" (R. 2/4)	£170	£350
16		2a. on bright rose	4·25	4·75
17		2a. on dull rose	12·00	7·50
18		4a. on rose-lilac	£600	£850
		a. "Eeudatory" (R. 2/4)	£4000	
19		4a. on dull rose	9·50	6·50
		a. "Eeudatory" (R. 2/4)	£1000	£1100
		b. "BAMBA" (R. 2/1)	£1000	£1100
20		4a. on reddish purple	6·50	8·50
20a		4a. on deep pink	16·00	13·00
21		8a. on rose-lilac	24·00	60·00
		a. "Foudatory" and "Postagc" (R. 1/2)	£200	£325
		b. "BAMBA" (R. 2/1)	£200	£325
22		8a. on bright rose	14·00	18·00
23		8a. on dull rose	26·00	16·00
24		1r. on rose-lilac	55·00	90·00

	a. "Eeudatory" (R. 2/4)..................	£475	£600
	b. "BAMBA" (R. 2/1)..................	£400	£475
	c. "Postagc" (R. 1/2)..................	£400	£475
25	1r. on *bright rose*.....................	19·00	21·00
	a. Small "r" in "rupee"	£190	£190

(b) "postage" with small "p" (1891–93).

26	8	¼a. on *bright rose*.....................	2·00	3·00
27		¼a. on *reddish purple*...................	2·00	2·75
28		½a. on *dull green*......................	4·00	4·00
		a. First "a" in "anna" inverted (R. 3/3)...................	35·00	38·00
29		½a. on *blue-green*......................	4·75	4·25
		a. First "a" in "anna" inverted (R. 3/3)...................	38·00	38·00
30		1a. on *bistre-yellow*..................	4·00	3·25
31		1a. on *orange-yellow*.................	42·00	42·00
32		2a. on *bright rose*....................	4·75	4·75
33		2a. on *dull rose*......................	11·00	8·00
34		4a. on *dull rose*......................	12·00	6·50
35		4a. on *dull rose*......................	7·50	9·50
35a		4a. on *deep pink*.....................	18·00	15·00
36		8a. on *rose-lilac*....................	50·00	95·00
37		8a. on *dull rose*......................	17·00	20·00
38		8a. on *dull rose*......................	26·00	16·00
39		1r. on *rose-lilac*....................	80·00	£140
40		1r. on *bright rose*...................	23·00	23·00
		a. Small "r" in "rupee"	£225	£225
		b. Small "r" in "rupee" and native characters in the order 2, 3, 1, 4, 5 (R. 4/4)...................	£1500	£1500

There are 10 settings of Type **8**. The first setting (of 20 (4×5)) has capital "P" throughout. The remaining settings (of 16 (4×4)) have capital "P" and small "p" mixed.

For the first setting the 8a. and 1r. values were printed within the same block, the ten left-hand stamps being 8a. values and the ten right-hand stamps 1r.

The various stamps were distributed between the settings as follows:

Setting I—Nos. 8/c, 11/a, 13/a, 15/a, 18/19a, 21, 24/a
Setting II—Nos. 19, 19b, 21/b, 24, 24b/c, 34, 36, 39
Setting III—Nos. 9, 11, 13, 16, 26, 28, 30, 34
Setting IV—Nos. 20, 22, 25, 35, 37, 40
Setting V—Nos. 10, 10b/c, 20a, 27, 35a
Setting VI—Nos. 11, 12, 28, 28a, 29/a
Setting VII—Nos. 10/a, 12, 17, 19, 23, 25a, 27, 29, 33/4, 38, 40a/b
Setting VIII—Nos.17, 33
Setting IX—Nos. 10/a, 12, 14/a, 17, 19, 23, 27, 29, 31, 33/4, 38
Setting X—Nos. 19, 34

There are 4 sizes of the central ornament, which represents an elephant's trunk holding a stick:—(*a*) 4 mm long; (*b*) 5 mm; (*c*) 6½ mm; (*d*) 11 mm. These ornaments are found pointing to right or left, either upright or inverted.

Ornaments (*a*) are found in all settings; (*b*) in all settings from Settings III to X; (*c*) in Settings I and II; and (*d*) only in Setting I.

The stamps of Bamra have been obsolete since 1 January 1895.

BARWANI

PROCESS. All Barwani stamps are typographed from clichés, and are in sheets of 4, *unless otherwise indicated.*

Issues to about 1930 were printed by the Barwani State Printing Press, and subsequently by the *Times of India* Press, Bombay.

GUM. Nos. 1/31 were issued without gum.

BOOKLET PANES. Those stamps which were printed in sheets of 4 were issued in stamp booklets, binding holes appearing in the side margin.

Rana Ranjit Singh, 1894–1930

| | 1 | 2 | 3 |

1921 (Mar ?). *Clear impression. Medium wove paper.* P 7 all round.

1	1	¼a. blue-green (*dull to deep*)	£140	£375
2		½a. dull blue	£275	£550
		a. Imperf (pair)......................	—	£1800

No. 1 also exists perforated on two sides only.

1921 (June). *Blurred impression. Soft wove paper.* P 7 on two or three sides.

3	1	¼a. green (*shades*).....................	22·00	£110
4		½a. ultramarine (*dull to pale*)..........	17·00	£160

NOTE. As the small sheets of Barwani stamps were often not perforated all round, many of the earlier stamps are perforated on two or three sides only. Owing to the elementary method of printing, the colours vary greatly in depth, even within a single sheet.

1921. *Clear impression. Vertically laid bâtonné paper. Imperf.*

5	1	¼a. green (*shades*)........................	20·00	75·00
6		½a. blue-green	5·00	
		a. Perf 11 at top or bottom only	4·00	

It is suggested that No. 5 may be an error due to printing from the wrong plate.

1922? *Clear impression. Thickish glazed wove paper.* P 7 on two or three sides.

7	1	¼a. dull blue	95·00	

1922. *Smooth, soft medium wove paper.* P 7 on two or three sides.

(a) Clear impression.

8	1	¼a. deep grey-blue	55·00	£120

(b) Poor impression.

9	1	¼a. steel blue	17·00	

Examples of No. 9 exist with perforations on all four sides.

1922. P 11 on two or three sides.

(a) Thick, glazed white wove paper.

10	2	1a. vermilion (*shades*)	2·25	20·00
		a. Imperf between (vert pair)........	£275	
		b. Doubly printed	£900	
11		2a. purple (*to violet*)...................	2·25	24·00
		a. Doubly printed	£275	
		b. Imperf between (horiz pair).......	£225	£375
		c. Imperf between (vert pair)........	£180	

(b) Thick, toned wove paper.

12	2	2a. purple	17·00	50·00

1922. *Poor impression. Thin, poor wove paper.* Pin-perf 8½ on two or three sides.

13	1	¼a. grey (*to grey-blue*)	1·60	42·00
		a. Imperf (pair)....................	£400	
		b. Imperf between (vert pair)........	£150	

1923. *Thin, smooth, unglazed wove paper.* P 11 on two or three sides.

14	1	½a. green (*pale to deep*)...............	1·25	20·00
		a. Imperf between (vert pair)........	£550	
15	2	1a. brown-red	£2750	£3500

1923. *Poor impression. Thick, soft wove paper.* P 7.

16	1	½a. green (*pale to deep*)	25·00	

No. 16 also exists perforated on two or three sides.

1923 (Mar?). *Poor quality wove paper.* P 7 on two or three sides.

17	1	¼a. black	75·00	£325
		a. Imperf between (horiz pair).......	£2000	

1923 (May?). *Horizontally laid bâtonné paper.* P 12.

18	1	¼a. rose (*shades*).....................	2·00	13·00
		a. Imperf between (vert pair)........	£450	
		ab. Imperf between (horiz pair).......	£900	
		b. Pin perf 6	£150	75·00
		c. Perf compound of 12 and 6.......	48·00	70·00
		d. Perf 7	£800	£900
		da. On wove paper.....................	£3250	

No. 18 was issued in sheets of 12 (3 panes of 4) and was printed on paper showing a sheet watermark of Britannia and a double-lined inscription. No. 18d was only issued in booklet panes of 4.

1925. *Vertically laid bâtonné paper.* P 11.

19	1	¼a. blue (*pale to deep*)	1·25	11·00
		a. Tête-bêche (horiz pair)...............	£2500	

No. 19 was issued in sheets of 8 and was printed on paper with a sheet watermark of a shell and an inscription "SHELL" in double-lined capitals.

1927. *Very poor impression. Thin, brittle wove paper.* P 7.

20	1	¼a. milky blue (*shades*)	9·00	32·00
21		½a. yellow-green (*shades*).............	10·00	65·00
		a. Imperf between (horiz pair)......	£1000	
22	3	4a. orange-brown	85·00	£400
		a. Imperf between (horiz pair)......	£1600	
20/2 Set of 3			95·00	£450

1927. *Thick wove paper.* Sewing machine perf 6-10.

23	3	4a. yellow-brown	£100	
		a. Imperf between (horiz pair).......	£2500	
		b. Perf 7	20·00	£225
		c. *Orange-brown*.....................	£130	£425

1928–32? *Thick glazed paper.*

(a) P 7.

24	1	¼a. deep bright blue	11·00	
25		½a. bright yellow-green	24·00	

(b) P 10½ (rough) (Nov 1928).

26	1	¼a. ultramarine	5·50	
		a. Tête-bêche (horiz pair)............	11·00	
		b. Horiz pair, one stamp printed on reverse	£1800	
27		½a. apple-green	4·75	
		a. Tête-bêche (vert pair).............	9·00	

(c) P 11 (clean-cut) (1929–32?).

28	1	¼a. bright blue	2·25	13·00
		a. *Indigo*............................	1·75	13·00
		ab. Imperf between (horiz pair).......	80·00	
		ac. Imperf between (horiz strip of 4).............................	£400	
		b. *Deep dull blue*......................	1·50	13·00
		ba. Imperf between (vert pair).........	£300	
		c. *Ultramarine*	2·00	14·00
29		½a. myrtle-green	2·75	14·00
		a. Imperf between (horiz pair).......	£250	
		b. *Turquoise-green*	3·50	16·00
		ba. Imperf between (vert pair)........	£500	£600
30	2	1a. rose-carmine (1931)	14·00	£2000
		a. Imperf between (horiz pair).......	†	
31	3	4a. salmon (*to orange*) (1931)	70·00	£180
		a. Imperf between (horiz pair).......	£2250	
28/31 Set of 4			80·00	£225

No. 26 was printed in sheets of 8 (4×2) with the two centre pairs *tête-bêche* while No. 27, in similar sheets, had the two horizontal rows *tête-bêche*. Both sheets are always found with one long side imperforate.

Nos. 28/31 were printed in sheets of 8, the two lower values existing either 4×2 or 2×4 and the two higher values 4×2 only. No *tête-bêche* pairs were included in these printings. It is believed that a small printing of No. 31 was produced in sheets of 4, but details are uncertain.

Rana Devi Singh, 1930–1971

| **4** Rana Devi Singh | **5** Rana Devi Singh |

1932 (Oct)–47. *Medium to thick wove paper.*

A. Close setting (2½–4½ mm). P 11, 12 or compound (1932–41).

32A	4	¼a. slate	2·00	21·00
33A		½a. blue-green	3·50	21·00
34A		1a. brown	3·50	20·00
		a. Imperf between (horiz pair)......	£1400	
35A	5	2a. purple (*shades*)	3·75	38·00
36A		4a. olive-green	6·00	38·00
32A/6A Set of 5			17·00	£130

B. Wide setting (6–7 mm). P 11 (1945–47).

32B	4	¼a. slate	4·25	28·00
33B		½a. blue-green	4·50	21·00
34B		1a. brown	11·00	21·00
		b. *Chocolate. Perf 8½* (1947).......	14·00	48·00
35aB		2a. rose-carmine	£275	£550
36B		4a. olive-green	23·00	42·00

The measurements given in the heading indicate the vertical spacing between impressions. There are eight settings of this interesting issue: four "Close" where the overall stamp dimensions from centre to centre of perfs vary in width from 21½ to 23 mm and in height from 25 to 27½ mm; three "Wide", width 23–23½ mm and height 29–30 mm and one "Medium" (26½×31 mm) (No. 34Bb only).

1933–47. P 11.

A. Close setting (3–4½ mm). Thick, cream-surfaced wove paper (1933 and 1941 (No. 38Aa)).

37A	1	¼a. black	4·25	65·00
38A		½a. blue-green	10·00	29·00
		a. *Yellowish green* (1941)	9·00	26·00
39A	2	1a. brown (*shades*)	19·00	27·00
42A	3	4a. sage-green	35·00	90·00

B. Wide setting (7–10 mm). Medium to thick wove paper (1939–47).

37B	1	¼a. black (1945)	4·50	32·00
38aB		½a. yellowish green (1945).............	4·50	35·00
39B	2	1a. brown (*shades*)	13·00	26·00
		a. *Perf 8½* (5 mm) (1947)	12·00	45·00
40B		2a. bright purple	90·00	£275
41B		2a. rose-carmine (1945)	26·00	£110
42B	3	4a. sage-green (1941)	30·00	65·00
		a. *Pale sage-green* (1939)	13·00	42·00

There were two "Close" settings (over-all stamp size 25×29 mm) and five "Wide" settings with over-all sizes 26½–31½ × 31–36½ mm. There was also one "Medium" setting (26½×31 mm) but this was confined to the 1a. perf 8½, No. 39a.

1938. P 11.

43	5	1a. brown	35·00	65·00

Stamps printed in red with designs similar to Types **3** and **5** were intended for fiscal use.

STAMP BOOKLETS

Nos. 1/17, 18d/da and 20/5 are believed to have been issued in sewn or stapled booklets, usually containing thirty-two examples of one value in blocks of 4. All these early booklets had plain covers, often in shades of brown. Few complete booklets have survived from this period.

Nos. 32/47, produced by the *Times of India* Press in a series of nine printings between 1932 and 1947, were only issued in booklet form. Booklets from the 1932, 1933, 1937 and 1939 printings had plain card or paper covers in various colours, usually containing eight blocks of 4, except for the 1933 printing, which contained twenty blocks of 4. Booklets from the 1945 printing had plain white tissue covers from the same stock as the interleaving. All these booklets were stapled at left.

The following booklets, from a printing in 1941, and a series of three printings in 1947, had printed covers, produced by a handstamp in the case of Nos. SB14/15.

1941. *Buff, green (No. SB3) or blue (No. SB7) card covers inscribed "BARWANI STATE POSTAGE STAMPS", booklet value in brackets and number and value of stamps thus "(Rs 4) 32 2 Annas". Panes of 4 with margin at left only. Stapled.*

(a) Booklets 59×55 mm.

SB1	8a. booklet containing thirty-two ¼a. (No. 32A)	£900
SB2	1r. booklet containing thirty-two ½a. (No. 33A)	£1000
SB3	2r. booklet containing thirty-two 1a. (No. 34A) ..	£1100
SB4	4r. booklet containing thirty-two 2a. (No. 35A) ..	£450
SB5	8r. booklet containing thirty-two 4a. (No. 36A) ..	£650

(b) Booklets 63×60 mm (No. SB6) or 73×72 mm (No. SB7).

SB6	1r. booklet containing thirty-two ½a. (No. 38Aa)	£1000
SB7	8r. booklet containing thirty-two 4a. (No. 42B)...	£1300

1947. *Grey tissue covers inscribed "32 STAMPS VALUE ....." Panes of 4 with margins all round. Stapled at left.*

(a) Booklets 70×95 mm.

SB8	1r. booklet containing thirty-two ½a. (No. 33B)..	£650
SB9	2r. booklet containing thirty-two 1a. (No. 34B)..	£1100
SB10	8r. booklet containing thirty-two 4a. (No. 36B)...	£1100

(b) Booklets 76×95 mm.

SB11	8a. booklet containing thirty-two ¼a. (No. 37B)..	£950
SB12	2r. booklet containing thirty-two 1a. (No. 41B)..	£1000
SB13	8r. booklet containing thirty-two 4a. (No. 42Ba)..	£550

1947. *Buff paper covers with violet handstamp inscribed "32 STAMPS VALUE Rs 2/-". Panes of 4 with margins all round, Sewn with twine at left.*

SB14	2r. booklets (71×69 mm) containing thirty-two 1a. (No. 34Ba)	£550
SB15	2r. booklet (71×73 mm) containing thirty-two 1a. (No. 39Ba)	£450

1947. Grey tissue covers inscribed "32 STAMPS VALUE As 8". Panes of 4 with margins all round. Stapled at left.

SB16	8a. booklet (70×75 mm) containing thirty-two ¼a. (No. 32B)	£250
SB17	8a. booklet (85×75 mm) containing thirty-two ¼a. (No. 37B)	£325

Barwani became part of Madhya Bharat by 1 July 1948.

BHOPAL

PRICES FOR STAMPS ON COVER	
Nos. 1/100	*from* × 10
Nos. O301/57	*from* × 15

The correct English inscription on these stamps is "H.H. NAWAB SHAH JAHAN BEGAM". In the case of Nos. 22 and 23 the normal stamps are spelt "BEGAN" and specimens with "BEGAM" are "errors".

As the stamps were printed from lithographic stones on which each unit was drawn separately by hand, numerous errors of spelling occurred. These are constant on all sheets and are listed. Some of our illustrations inadvertently include errors of spelling.

ILLUSTRATIONS. Types 1/3a and 6/12a are shown actual size.

EMBOSSING. Nos. 1/99 were only valid for postage when embossed with the device, in Urdu, of the ruling Begam. On T 1/3 and 6 to 12a. this was intended to fill the central part of the design. Almost all varieties can be found with the embossing inverted or sideways, as well as upright.

Shah Jahan   Sultan Johan

(actual size)

The various basic types were often in concurrent use but for greater convenience the following list is arranged according to types instead of being in strict chronological order.

GUM. Nos. 1/99 were issued without gum.

Nawab Shah Jahan Begam, 16 November 1868–15 June 1901

1 (½a.)

1872. Litho.

(a) Double frame. Sheets of 20 (5×4).

1	1	¼a. black	£550	£425
		a. "BFGAM" (R. 3/1)	£1600	£1400
		b. "BEGAN" (R. 2/2, R. 4/4)	£900	£800
		c. "EGAM" (R. 4/5)	£1600	£1400
2		½a. red	19·00	42·00
		a. "BFGAM" (R. 3/1)	70·00	£150
		b. "BEGAN" (R. 2/2, R. 4/4)	45·00	95·00
		c. "EGAM" (R. 4/5)	70·00	£150

2 (½a.)

(b) Single frame. Sheets of 20 (4×5).

3	2	¼a. black	†	£5000
4		½a. red	35·00	65·00
		a. "NWAB" (R. 2/2)	£160	£275

3 (¼a.)   3a (¼a.)

1878 (1 Jan). All lettered "EEGAM" for "BEGAM". Sheets of 20 (4×5).

(a) Plate 1. Frame lines extend horiz and vert between stamps throughout sheet.

5	3	¼a. black	8·00	14·00

(b) Plate 2. Frame lines normal.

5a	3	¼a. black	8·00	16·00

Apart from the frame line difference between Types 3 and 3a the stamps can also be distinguished by the differences in the value tablets, notably the thin vertical line in the centre in Type 3a compared with the slightly diagonal and heavier line in Type 3.

4 (¼a.)   5 (½a.)

1878 (June?)*–79.* Value in parenthesis (Nos. 6/7). Sheets of 32 (4×8). Imperf.

6	4	¼a. green (1879)	14·00	24·00
7		¼a. green (perf) (1879)	10·00	16·00
8	5	½a. red	7·00	14·00
		a. "JAHN" (R. 5/2)	32·00	
		b. "NWAB" (R. 3/2, R. 4/2)	20·00	
		c. "EEGAM" (R. 1/3)	32·00	
9		½a. brown	26·00	42·00
		a. "JAHN" (R. 5/2)	£150	£190
		b. "NWAB" (R. 3/2, R. 4/2)	90·00	£130
		c. "EEGAM" (R. 1/3)	£150	£190

The ¼a. shows the "N" of "NAWAB" reversed on R. 6/4 and the "N" of "JAHAN" reversed on R. 1/2–4 and R. 2/2-4.

1880. T 5 redrawn; value not in parenthesis. Sheets of 32 (4×8).

(a) Imperf.

10		¼a. blue-green		8·50
		a. "NAWA" (R. 2/2–4)		26·00
		b. "CHAH" (R. 8/3)		75·00
11		½a. brown-red	18·00	22·00

(b) Perf.

12		¼a. blue-green		10·00
		a. "NAWA" (R. 2/2–4)		40·00
		b. "CHAH" (R. 8/3)		£100
13		½a. brown-red		18·00

The ¼a. shows the "N" of "NAWAB" reversed on R. 8/4. Nos. 12/13 sometimes come with gum.

1884. T 5 again redrawn. Sheets of 32 (4×8), some with value in parenthesis, others not. Perf.

14		¼a. greenish blue	5·50	14·00
		a. "ANAWAB" (R. 8/1–4)	14·00	

In this plate there is a slanting dash under and to left of the letters "JA" of "JAHAN," instead of a character like a large comma, as on all previous varieties of this design. With the exception of R. 1/1 all stamps in the sheet show "N" of "JAHAN" reversed.

1895. T 5 again redrawn. Sheets of 8 (2×4). Laid paper.

15		¼a. red (imperf)	7·00	3·25
16		¼a. red (perf)	—	£750

In these cases where the same design has been redrawn several times, and each time in a number of varieties of type, it is not easy to distinguish the various issues. Nos. 6 and 7 may be distinguished from Nos. 10 and 12 by the presence or absence of the parenthesis marks (); 8, 9 and 11 differ principally in colour; 8 and 15 are very much alike, but differ in the value as well as in paper.

6 (1a.)

1881. Sheets of 24 (4×6). Imperf.

17	6	¼a. black	6·00	20·00
		a. "NWAB" (R. 6/2–4)	15·00	
18		½a. red	5·00	14·00
		a. "NWAB" (R. 6/2–4)	12·00	
19		1a. brown	4·50	16·00
		a. "NWAB" (R. 6/2–4)	9·50	
20		2a. blue	3·25	16·00
		a. "NWAB" (R. 6/2–4)	6·50	
21		4a. buff	17·00	60·00
		a. "NWAB" (R. 6/2–4)	48·00	
17/21		Set of 5	32·00	£110

In this issue all values were produced from the same drawing, and therefore show exactly the same varieties of type. The value at foot in this and all the following issues is given in only one form.

7 (½a.)

1886. Similar to T 6 but normally lettered (incorrectly) "BEGAN"; larger lettering. Sheets of 32 (4×8).

(a) Imperf.

22	7	½a. pale red	2·75	10·00
		a. "BEGAM" (R. 2/1)	12·00	30·00
		b. "NWAB" (R. 3/4)	12·00	

(b) Perf.

23	7	½a. pale red		£650
		a. "BEGAM" (R. 2/1)		£1100
		b. "NWAB" (R. 3/4)		£1100

8 (4a.)

1886. T 8. T 6 redrawn. Sheets of 24 (4×6). The "M" of "BEGAM" is an inverted "W". The width of the stamps is rather greater than the height.

(a) Wove paper. Imperf.

24	8	4a. yellow		£900
		a. "EEGAM" (R. 2/3–4, R. 3/3–4, R. 4/2, R. 4/4, R. 6/1)		£1100

(b) Laid paper.

25	8	4a. yellow (imperf)	10·00	32·00
		a. "EEGAM" (R. 2/3–4, R. 3/3–4, R. 4/2, R. 4/4, R. 6/1)	15·00	
26		4a. yellow (perf)	4·25	18·00
		a. "EEGAM" (R. 2/3–4, R. 3/3–1, R. 4/2, R. 4/4, R. 6/1)	6·50	26·00

1889. T 6 again redrawn. Sheets of 32 (4×8) lettered "BEGAN".

27		¼a. black (perf)	1·75	4·75
		a. "EEGAN" (R. 7/3)	14·00	28·00
		b. Imperf between (horiz pair)	£225	
28		¼a. black (imperf)	1·75	4·50
		a. "EEGAN" (R. 7/3)	16·00	28·00

9 (¼a.)

1889–90. T 9. T 6 again redrawn. Sheets of 24 (4×6), all with "M" like an inverted "W". Wove paper.

(a) Imperf.

29	9	¼a. black	2·25	2·00
30		1a. brown	2·25	4·75
		a. "EEGAM" (R. 2/3)	14·00	26·00
		b. "BBGAM" (R. 3/1)	14·00	26·00
31		2a. blue	2·00	2·25
		a. "BBGAM" (R. 1/2)	8·50	14·00
		b. "NAWAH" (R. 4/2)	8·50	14·00
32		4a. orange-yellow	2·50	3·75
29/32		Set of 4	8·00	11·50

(b) Perf.

33	9	¼a. black	2·75	3·75
		a. Imperf between (horiz pair)	£275	
34		1a. brown	4·50	6·50
		a. "EEGAM" (R. 2/3)	25·00	35·00
		b. "BBGAM" (R. 3/1)	25·00	35·00
35		2a. blue	2·25	3·00
		a. "BBGAM" (R. 1/2)	9·00	17·00
		b. "NAWAH" (R. 4/2)	9·00	17·00
36		4a. orange-yellow	3·00	7·00
33/6		Set of 4	11·00	18·00

Nos. 32 and 36 are nearly square, in many cases rather larger in height than in width.

1891. As last, but sheets of 32 (4×8).

37	9	½a. red (imperf)	2·00	3·75
38		½a. red (perf)	1·75	4·75

1894–98. T 6 again redrawn.

(a) Sheets of 24 (4×6), almost all showing a character inside the octagon below, as in T 9. Wove paper.

39		1a. deep brown (imperf)	7·50	4·25
		a. Red-brown	35·00	
		b. Printed both sides	—	£500
41		1a. deep brown (perf)	7·00	4·25

10 (1a.)

(b) As Nos. 39/41, but printed from a new stone showing the lines blurred and shaky. Wove paper. Imperf (1898).

42	10	1a. purple-brown......................	3·25	4·25
		a. "NAWAH" (R. 4/1).............	17·00	23·00
43		1a. purple-brown/buff	3·25	4·25
		a. "NAWAH" (R. 4/1).............	17·00	23·00
		b. Printed on both sides		

The above are known without embossing.

11 (¼a.)

1895. Sheets of 8 (2×4), lettered "EEGAM". White laid paper.

44	11	¼a. black (imperf)...................	3·50	3·00
		a. "A" inserted (R. 4/2)	8·50	7·00
45		¼a. black (perf).....................	90·00	40·00
		a. "NAW B" (R. 4/2)	£300	£150

On the perf stamp the second "A" in "NAWAB" was missing on R. 4/2 in the setting. This letter was later inserted for the imperf printing varying progressively from small to large.

12 (½a.)

1895. Narrow label at bottom. Sheets of 8 (2×4), lettered "W W" for "H H". Laid paper.

| 46 | 12 | ½a. black (imperf)............................. | 1·50 | 1·75 |

12a

1896. Sheets of 8 (2×4). Laid paper.

| 47 | 12 | ½a. red (imperf)........................... | 2·25 | 2·25 |

No. 47 is a combination of Types 1 and 6, having the double outer frame to the octagon and the value in one form only.

13 (¼a.) 14 (¼a.)

1884. Sheets of 32 (4×8). Perf.

48	13	¼a. blue-green........................	£140	£170
		a. "JAN" (R. 2/1–2, R. 3/1, R. 3/3–4, R. 4/1–3, R. 5/1–3).............	£140	£170
		b. "BEGM" (R. 2/3–4).............	£350	£400
		c. "NWAB" and "JAN" (R. 3/2) ...	£600	
		ca. "NWAB" and "JN" (R. 5/4)	£600	
		d. "SHAHAN" (R. 4/4).............	£600	
		e. "JAHA" (R. 6/2–4).............	£275	

1896. T 14, double-lined frame round each stamp. Sheets of 6 (2×3), lettered "JAN". Laid paper.

| 49 | 14 | ¼a. bright green (imperf)................. | 5·50 | 14·00 |

15 (½a.) 16 (¼a.)

1884. Sheets of 32 (4×8). Laid paper.

50	15	¼a. blue-green (imperf)	£140	£160
		a. "NWAB" (R. 1/1).............	£375	
		b. "SAH" (R. 1/4).............	£375	
		c. "NAWA" and "JANAN" (R. 3/2).............	£375	
51		¼a. blue-green (perf).............	1·00	4·00
		a. "NWAB" (R. 1/1).............	3·75	
		b. "SAH" (R. 1/4).............	3·75	
		c. "NAWA" and "JANAN" (R. 3/2).............	3·75	
		d. Imperf between (vert pair)........	£275	
52		½a. black (imperf).............	2·25	2·50
		a. "NWAB" (R. 1/1).............	9·50	11·00
		b. "SAH" (R. 1/4).............	9·50	11·00

---

		c. "NAWA" and "JANAN" (R. 3/2).............	9·50	11·00
53		½a. black (perf).............	90	3·25
		a. "NWAB" (R. 1/1).............	3·50	8·00
		b. "SAH" (R. 1/4).............	3·50	8·00
		c. "NAWA" and "JANAN" (R. 3/2).............	3·50	8·00

The ¼a. of this issue is in blue-green, or greenish blue. Both values were printed from the same stone, the value alone being altered. There are therefore the same varieties of each. These are the only stamps of this design on laid paper.

Both values show the "N" of "NAWAB" reversed on R. 1/1–4, R. 2/1–4, R. 3/1–4 and the "N" of "JAHAN" reversed on R. 1/1–4, R. 2/1–7, R. 3/4.

1886. T 15 redrawn. Sheets of 32 (4×8). Wove paper.

54		¼a. green (imperf)	55	3·25
		a. "NAWA" (R. 6/3–4)	1·75	6·50
		b. "NWAB" (R. 1/1).............	2·75	8·50
		c. "NWABA" (R. 7/4).............	2·75	8·50
		d. "NAWAA" (R. 6/2).............	2·75	8·50
		e. "BEGAAM" and "NWABA" (R. 7/3).............	2·75	8·50
55		¼a. green (perf).............	2·50	4·00
		a. "NAWA" (R. 6/3–4).............	8·00	
		b. "NWAB" (R. 1/1).............	12·00	
		c. "NWABA" (R. 7/4).............	12·00	
		d. "NAWAA" (R. 6/2).............	12·00	
		e. "BEGAAM" and "NWABA" (R. 7/3).............	12·00	
		f. Imperf between (horiz pair)........	£150	
56		½a. red (imperf).............	65	1·75
		a. "SAH" (R. 1/4).............	3·75	6·00
		b. "NAWABA" (R. 6/3–4).............	3·00	4·75

The ¼a. varies from yellow-green to deep green.
All examples of the ¼a. value show the "N" of "NAWAB" reversed. On the same value the "N" of "JAHAN" is reversed on all positions except R. 3/2, R. 4/1, R. 4/3. On the ½a. both "N"s are always reversed.

1888. T 15 again redrawn. Sheets of 32 (4×8), letters in upper angles smaller. "N" of "NAWAB" correct. Wove paper.

57		¼a. deep green (imperf)................	1·00	2·00
		a. "SAH" (R. 6/2).............	4·50	7·00
		b. "NAWA" (R. 4/4).............	4·50	7·00
58		¼a. deep green (perf).............	2·00	2·75
		a. "SAH" (R. 6/2).............	7·00	8·50
		b. "NAWA" (R. 4/4).............	7·00	8·50
		c. Imperf between (vert pair)........	£200	

Nos. 50 to 58 have the dash under the letter "JA" as in No. 14.

1891. T 15 again redrawn. Sheets of 32 (4×8), lettered "NWAB." Wove paper.

(a) Imperf.

| 59 | | ½a. red .... | 2·00 | 1·50 |
| | | a. "SAH" (R. 2/4) .... | 6·00 | |

(b) P 3 to 4½, or about 7.

| 60 | | ½a. red .... | 80 | 2·00 |
| | | a. "SAH" (R. 2/4) .... | 5·00 | |

Nos. 59 and 60 have the comma under "JA". The "N" of "JAHAN" is reversed on R. 1/1–3, R. 2/1–2.

1894. T 15 again redrawn; letters in corners larger than in 1888, value in very small characters. Sheets of 32 (4×8), all with "G" in left-hand lower corner. Wove paper.

61		¼a. green (imperf)	1·50	1·50
		a. "NAWAH" (R. 4/4).............	7·00	7·50
		b. Value in brackets (R. 1/1)........	7·00	7·50
62		¼a. green (perf).............	3·00	2·25
		a. "NAWAH" (R. 4/4).............	12·00	10·00
		b. Value in brackets (R. 1/1)........	12·00	10·00

Nos. 61 and 62 have neither the dash nor the comma under "JA".

1898. T 16; oval narrower, stops after "H.H.", space after "NAWAB". The line down the centre is under the first "H" of "SHAH" or between "HA" instead of being under the second "H" or between "AH". Sheets of 32 (4×8). Wove paper. Imperf.

63	16	¼a. bright green................	75	80
		a. "SHAN" (R. 1/1).............	3·50	3·50
64		¼a. pale green.............	80	70
		a. "SHAN" (R. 1/1).............	3·50	3·50
65		¼a. black.............	50	50
		a. "SHAN" (R. 1/1).............	3·25	3·50

1899. T 15 redrawn. Sheets of 32 (4×8), the first "A" of "NAWAB" always absent. Numerous defective and malformed letters. Wove paper. Imperf.

66		½a. black................	4·50	5·50
		a. "NWASBAHJANNI" (R. 2/4)...........	21·00	25·00
		b. "SBAH" (R. 3/3, R. 4/3–4, R.5/1–2, R. 6/4).............	9·50	13·00
		c. "SBAN" (R. 8/2).............	21·00	25·00
		d. "NWIB" (R. 3/2).............	21·00	25·00
		e. "BEIAM" (R. 4/4).............	21·00	25·00
		f. "SHH" (R. 6/3).............	21·00	25·00
		g. "SBAH" and "BBGAM" (R. 3/4).........	21·00	25·00
		h. "BBGAM" (R. 1/3).............	21·00	25·00

17 (8a.) 18 (¼a.)

1890. T 17. Sheets of 10 (2×5). Single-line frame to each stamp.

(a) Wove paper.

67	17	8a. slate-green (imperf)	50·00	90·00
		a. "HAH" (R. 3/1, R. 4/1, R. 5/1).......	65·00	£110
		b. "JABAN" (R. 2/2).............	70·00	
68		8a. slate-green (perf).............	50·00	90·00
		a. "HAH" (R. 3/1, R. 4/1, R. 5/1).......	65·00	
		b. "JABAN" (R. 2/2).............	70·00	

(b) Thin laid paper.

69	17	8a. green-black (imperf)	65·00	£130
		a. "HAH" (R. 3/1, R. 4/1, R. 5/1).	75·00	
		b. "JABAN" (R. 2/2).............	80·00	
70		8a. green-black (perf).............	65·00	£130
		a. "HAH" (R. 3/1, R. 4/1, R. 5/1).	80·00	£150
		b. "JABAN" (R. 2/2).............	85·00	

The "N" of "NAWAB" is reversed on R. 5/2 and the "N" of "JAHAN" on R. 1/1–2, R. 2/2, R. 3/2, R. 4/2 and R. 5/2.

1893. T 17 redrawn. No frame to each stamp, but a frame to the sheet. Sheets of 10 (2×5).

(a) Wove paper.

| 71 | | 8a. green-black (imperf)................ | 22·00 | 22·00 |
| 72 | | 8a. green-black (perf)............. | 28·00 | 38·00 |

(b) Thin laid paper. Imperf.

| 73 | | 8a. green-black.................... | £180 | £225 |

1898. Printed from a new stone. Lettering irregular. Sheets of 10 (2×5). Wove paper. Imperf.

74		8a. green-black................	42·00	55·00
		a. Reversed "E" in "BEGAM" (R. 1/2, R. 3/2).............	85·00	95·00
75		8a. black.............	40·00	55·00
		a. Reversed "E" in "BEGAM" (R. 1/2, R. 3/2).............	85·00	95·00

1896–1901. Sheets of 32 (4×8).

(a) Wove paper. Imperf.

| 76 | 18 | ¼a. black................ | 1·40 | 1·40 |

(b) Printed from a new stone, lines shaky (1899).

| 77 | 18 | ¼a. black............. | 2·75 | 2·75 |

(c) The same, on thick wove paper (1901).

| 78 | 18 | ¼a. black............. | £500 | £550 |

Nawab Sultan Jahan Begam, 16 June 1901–17 May 1926

19 (¼a.) 20

1902. T 19. With the octagonal embossed device of the previous issues. Sheets of 16 (4×4) ¼a. or 8 (2×4) others. Thin, yellowish wove paper. Imperf.

79	19	¼a. rose................	4·75	8·00
80		¼a. rose-red.............	3·25	5·00
81		½a. black.............	3·50	6·00
		a. Printed both sides..................	£650	£650
82		1a. brown.............	6·00	15·00
83		1a. red-brown.............	5·00	13·00
84		2a. blue.............	7·50	13·00
85		4a. orange.............	60·00	90·00
86		4a. yellow.............	38·00	75·00
87		8a. lilac.............	95·00	£170
88		1r. rose.............	£225	£350
79/88 Set of 7			£350	£550

1903. With a circular embossed device. Sheets of 16 (4×4) ¼a. (two plates) or 8 (2×4) (others). Wove paper.

89	19	¼a. rose-red.............	1·50	4·50
		a. Laid paper.............	1·00	7·00
90		¼a. red.............	1·25	4·25
		a. Laid paper.............	30	5·00
91		½a. black.............	1·25	5·00
		a. Laid paper.............	1·00	7·50
92		1a. brown.............	2·50	6·50
		a. Laid paper.............	95·00	
93		1a. red-brown.............	6·50	
		a. Laid paper.............		
94		2a. blue.............	6·00	22·00
		a. Laid paper.............	£170	£190
95		4a. orange (laid paper).............	£275	£275
96		4a. yellow.............	18·00	48·00
		a. Laid paper.............	£130	£120
97		8a. lilac.............	48·00	£130
		a. Laid paper.............	£1500	
98		1r. rose.............	75·00	£170
		a. Laid paper.............	£1200	
89/98 Set of 7			£140	£350

1903. No. 71 optd with initial of the new Begam, either 6 or 11 mm long, in red.

| 99 | | 8a. green-black.................... | £120 | £120 |
| | | a. Opt inverted............. | £325 | £325 |

Some of the previous stamps remained on sale (and probably in use) after the issue of the series of 1902, and some of these were afterwards put on sale with the new form of embossing; fresh plates were made of some of the old designs, in imitation of the earlier issues, and impressions from these were also sold with the new embossed device. We no longer list these doubtful items.

(Recess Perkins, Bacon & Co)

1908. P 13½.

100	20	1a. green....................	3·75	4·25
		a. Printed both sides..................	£110	
		b. Imperf (pair).............		

The ordinary postage stamps of Bhopal became obsolete on 1 July 1908.

OFFICIAL STAMPS

SERVICE SERVICE
(O 1) (O 2)

(Recess and optd Perkins, Bacon)

1908–11. As T 20, *but inscribed "H.H. BEGUM'S SERVICE" at left.* No wmk. P 13 to 14. Overprinted.

(a) With Type O1.

O301	½a. yellow-green	2·25	10
	a. Imperf (pair)	£140	
	b. Pair, one without overprint	£550	
	c. Opt double, one inverted	£110	
	ca. Ditto. Imperf (pair)	£160	
	d. Opt inverted	£160	£140
	e. Imperf between (horiz pair)	£700	
O302	1a. carmine-red	4·25	40
	a. Opt inverted	£100	90·00
	b. Imperf (pair)	£120	
	c. Red	5·50	10
O303	2a. ultramarine	24·00	10
	a. Imperf (pair)	55·00	
O304	4a. brown (1911)	13·00	55
O301/4 Set of 4		38·00	75

(b) With Type O2.

O305	½a. yellow-green	6·50	80
O306	1a. carmine-red	9·00	90
O307	2a. ultramarine	3·75	60
	a. Opt inverted	25·00	
O308	4a. brown (1911)	80·00	1·50
	a. Opt inverted	20·00	70·00
	b. Opt double	£110	
	c. Imperf (pair)	85·00	
	d. Imperf (pair) and opt inverted	90·00	
O305/8 Set of 4		90·00	3·50

The two overprints differ in the shape of the letters, noticeably in the "R".

Nawab Mohammad Hamidullah. Khan

17 May 1928 to transfer of administration to India, 1 June 1949

SERVICE

(O 3)   (O 4)

(Des T. I. Archer. Litho Indian Govt Ptg Wks, Nasik)

1930 (1 July)–**31**. Type O4 (25½×30½ mm) optd with Type O 3. P 14.

O309	O 4 ½a. sage-green (1931)	11·00	1·75
O310	1a. carmine-red	11·00	15
O311	2a. ultramarine	9·50	45
O312	4a. chocolate	10·00	90
O309/12 Set of 4		38·00	3·00

The ½a., 2a. and 4a. are inscribed "POSTAGE" at left.

(Litho Perkins, Bacon)

1932–34. As Type O 4 (21×25 mm), but inscr "POSTAGE" at left. Optd with Type O 1.

(a) "BHOPAL STATE" at right. P 13.

O313	¼a. orange	2·50	50
	a. Perf 11½ (1933)	6·50	20
	b. Perf 14 (1934)	11·00	30
	c. Perf 13½ (1934)	12·00	30
	ca. Vert pair, one without opt	£120	

(b) "BHOPAL GOVT" at right. P 13½.

O314	½a. yellow-green	6·00	10
O315	1a. carmine-red	10·00	15
	a. Vert pair, one without opt	£200	
O316	2a. ultramarine	9·50	45
O317	4a. chocolate	9·00	1·00
	a. Perf 14 (1934)	15·00	40
O313/17 Set of 5		32·00	1·10

No. O317 is comb-perforated and No. O317a line-perforated.

¼A	THREE PIES	ONE ANNA
(O 5)	(O 6)	(O 7)

1935–36. Nos. O314, O316 and O317 surch as Types O 5 to O 7.

O318	O 5 ¼a. on ½a. yellow-green (R.)	28·00	14·00
	a. Surch inverted	£180	80·00
	b. Vert pair. Nos. O318/19	45·00	23·00
	ba. Ditto. Surch inverted	£400	£170
O319	O 6 3p. on ½a. yellow-green (R.)	3·50	3·50
	a. "THEEE PIES" (R. 7/10)	70·00	50·00
	b. "THRFE" for "THREE" (R. 10/6)	70·00	50·00
	c. Surch inverted	80·00	40·00
O320	O 5 ¼a. on 2a. ultramarine (R.)	27·00	19·00
	a. Surch inverted	£180	70·00
	b. Vert pair. Nos. O320/1	42·00	28·00
	ba. Ditto. Surch inverted	£400	£160
O321	O 6 3p. on 2a. ultramarine (R.)	4·50	4·25
	a. Surch inverted	80·00	40·00
	b. "THEEE PIES" (R. 7/10)	75·00	48·00
	ba. Ditto. Surch inverted	£600	£475
	c. "THRFE" for "THREE" (R. 10/6)	75·00	48·00
	ca. Ditto. Surch inverted	£600	£475
O322	O 5 ¼a. on 4a. chocolate (R.)	£900	£325
	a. Vert pair. Nos. O322 and O324	£1400	£500
O323	¼a. on 4a. chocolate (No. O317a) (Blk.) (25.5.36)	75·00	25·00
	a. Vert pair. Nos. O323 and O325	£110	50·00
O324	O 6 3p. on 4a. chocolate (R.)	£120	60·00
	a. "THEEE PIES" (R. 7/10)	£600	£450

	c. "THRFE" for "THREE" (R. 10/6)	£600	£450
O325	3p. on 4a. chocolate (No. O317a) (Blk.) (25.5.36)	2·50	3·25
	a. "THRER" for "THREE" (R. 8/2)	£375	£225
	b. "FHREE" for "THREE" (R. 3/10, R. 10/1)	£400	£300
	c. "PISE" for "PIES" (R. 10/10)	£600	£425
	d. "PIFS" for "PIES" (R. 7/9)	£350	£225
O326	O 7 1a. on ½a. yellow-green (V.)	4·25	1·50
	a. Surch inverted	65·00	42·00
	b. First "N" in "ANNA" inverted (R. 4/5)	85·00	55·00
	ba. Ditto. Surch inverted	£600	£450
O327	1a. on 2a. ultramarine (R.)	2·25	1·75
	a. Surch inverted	80·00	38·00
	b. First "N" in "ANNA" inverted (R. 4/5)	75·00	50·00
	ba. Ditto. Surch inverted	£600	£450
O327d	1a. on 2a. ultramarine (V.)	48·00	48·00
	da. Surch inverted	90·00	90·00
	db. First "N" in "ANNA" inverted (R. 4/5)	£550	£550
	dc. Ditto. Surch inverted	£900	£900
O328	1a. on 2a. ultram (Blk.) (25.5.36)	70	2·00
	a. "ANNO"	£1800	
O329	1a. on 4a. chocolate (B.)	5·50	5·00
	a. First "N" in "ANNA" inverted (R. 4/5)	95·00	80·00
	b. Perf 14	11·00	5·50
	ba. Ditto. First "N" in "ANNA" inverted (R. 4/5)	£200	95·00

Nos. O318 to O325 are arranged in composite sheets of 100 (10×10). The two upper horizontal rows of each value are surcharged as Type O 5 and the next five rows as Type O 6. The remaining three rows are also surcharged as Type O 6 but in a slightly narrower setting.

The surcharge on No. O323 differs from Type O 5 in the shape of the figures and letter.

O 8

(Des T. I. Archer. Litho Indian Govt Ptg Wks, Nasik (No. O330). Typo Bhopal Govt Ptg Wks (others))

1935–39. As Type O 8.

(a) Litho. Inscr "BHOPAL GOVT POSTAGE". Optd "SERVICE" (13½ mm). P 13½.

O330	1a.3p. blue and claret	3·50	1·00

(b) Typo. Inscr "BHOPAL STATE POSTAGE". Optd "SERVICE" (11 mm). P 12.

O331	1a.6p. blue and claret (1937)	2·50	85
	a. Imperf between (pair)	£180	£190
	b. Opt omitted	£160	£120
	c. Opt double, one inverted	£425	£425
	d. Imperf (pair)	†	£160
	e. Blue printing double	†	£150
O332	1a.6p. claret (1939)	6·00	1·75
	a. Imperf between (pair)	£180	£190
	b. Opt omitted	—	£375
	c. Opt double, one inverted	—	£375
	d. Opt double	—	£375

PRINTERS. From No. O333 all issues were printed by the Bhopal Govt Ptg Wks in typography.

O 9	O 10 Taj Mahal and Be-Nazir Palaces

1936 (July)–**38**. Optd "SERVICE". P 12.

O333	O 9 ¼a. orange (Br.)	90	60
	a. Imperf between (vert pair)	£160	
	ab. Imperf between (horiz pair)	†	£325
	b. Opt inverted	£375	£275
	c. Black opt	8·50	75
	ca. Opt inverted	†	£350
	cb. Opt double	†	£300
O334	¼a. yellow (Br.) (1938)	3·75	1·25
O335	1a. scarlet	1·50	10
	a. Imperf between (horiz pair)	£140	£130
	b. Imperf between (vert pair)	†	£275
	c. Imperf between (block of four)	£375	£375
	d. Imperf vert (horiz pair)	†	£150

1936–49. As Type O 10 (various palaces). P 12.

(a) Optd "SERVICE" (13½ mm).

O336	½a. purple-brown and yellow-green	70	80
	a. Imperf between (horiz pair)	†	£190
	ab. Imperf between (horiz pair)	†	£190
	b. Opt double	£275	
	c. Frame double	£120	15·00
	d. Purple-brown and green (1938)	70	40

(b) Optd "SERVICE" (11 mm).

O337	2a. brown and blue (1937)	2·00	90
	a. Imperf between (vert pair)	†	£300
	ab. Imperf between (horiz pair)	†	£200
	b. Opt inverted	£300	£350
	c. Opt omitted		£375
	d. Pair, one without opt		£550
	e. As d. but opt inverted		£850

O338	2a. green and violet (1938)	10·00	30
	a. Imperf between (vert pair)	†	£225
	b. Imperf between (vert strip of 3)	£140	£160
	c. Frame double	†	£250
	d. Centre double	†	£275
O339	4a. blue and brown (1937)	3·75	50
	a. Imperf between (horiz pair)	†	£600
	b. Opt omitted	†	£275
	c. Opt double	†	£140
	d. Centre double	†	£350
	e. Blue and reddish brown (1938)	3·25	55
	ea. Frame double	†	£250
O340	8a. bright purple and blue (1938)	5·00	2·25
	a. Imperf between (vert pair)	†	£375
	b. Opt omitted	†	£150
	c. Opt double	†	£140
	d. Imperf vert (horiz pair) and opt omitted	†	£275
	e. Imperf (pair) and opt omitted	†	£275
O341	1r. blue and reddish purple (Br.) (1938)	22·00	8·00
	a. Imperf horiz (vert pair)	†	£1300
	b. Opt in black (1942)	16·00	4·50
	ba. Light blue and bright purple	38·00	28·00
	bb. Laid paper	£650	£700
O336/41b Set of 6		32·00	8·00

(c) Optd "SERVICE" (11½ mm) with serifs.

O342	1r. dull blue and bright purple (Blk.) (1949)	45·00	80·00
	a. "SREVICE" for "SERVICE" (R. 6/6)	£130	£200
	b. "SERVICE" omitted	£800	

(d) Optd "SERVICE" (13½ mm) with serifs.

O343	8a. bright purple and blue (1949)	80·00	£110
	a. "SERAICE" for "SERVICE" (R. 6/5)	£400	£500
	b. Fig "1" for "I" in "SERVICE" (R. 7/1)	£400	£500

The ½a. is inscr "BHOPAL GOVT" below the arms, other values have "BHOPAL STATE".

Designs:—(37½×22½ mm) ½a. The Moti Mahal; 2a. The Moti Masjid. (39×24 mm)—8a. Ahmadabad Palace. (45½×27½ mm)—1r. Rait Ghat.

O 11 Tiger	O 13 The Moti Mahal

1940. As Type O 11 (animals). P 12.

O344	¼a. bright blue	4·25	1·75
O345	1a. bright purple (Spotted Deer)	23·00	2·50

1941. As Type O 8 but coloured centre inscr "SERVICE"; bottom frame inscr "BHOPAL STATE POSTAGE". P 12.

O346	1a.3p. emerald-green	1·50	1·75
	a. Imperf between (pair)	£450	£475

1944–47. As Type O 13 (various palaces). P 12.

O347	½a. green	90	1·00
	a. Imperf (pair)	†	90·00
	b. Imperf between (vert pair)	†	£170
	c. Doubly printed	†	£140
O348	2a. violet	9·00	3·75
	a. Imperf (pair)	†	90·00
	c. Bright purple (1945)	2·50	3·75
	d. Mauve (1947)	11·00	15·00
	e. Error. Chocolate (imperf)	£200	£200
O349	4a. chocolate	6·00	2·25
	a. Imperf (pair)	†	£110
	b. Imperf vert (horiz pair)	†	£225
	c. Doubly printed	†	£160
O347/9 Set of 3		8·50	6·25

Design inscr "BHOPAL STATE":—2a. The Moti Masjid; 4a. Be-Nazir Palaces.

O 14 Arms of Bhopal	2 As. (O 15)	2 As. (O 16)

1944–49. P 12.

O350	O 14 3p. bright blue	75	85
	a. Imperf between (vert pair)	£120	£130
	b. Imperf between (horiz pair)	†	£250
	c. Stamp doubly printed	48·00	
O351	9p. chestnut (shades) (1945)	8·50	3·50
	a. Imperf (pair)	†	£180
	b. Orange-brown	2·00	3·75
O352	1a. purple (1945)	4·25	1·75
	a. Imperf horiz (vert pair)	†	£375
	b. Violet (1946)	8·00	3·25
O353	1½a. claret (1945)	1·25	1·25
	a. Imperf between (horiz pair)	†	£350
	b. Imperf between (vert pair)	†	£375
O354	3a. yellow	11·00	13·00
	a. Imperf between (horiz pair)	†	£180
	b. Imperf horiz (vert pair)	†	£225
	d. Orange-brown (1949)	£100	£100
O355	6a. carmine (1945)	16·00	45·00
	a. Imperf (pair)	†	£225
	b. Imperf horiz (vert pair)	†	£275
	c. Imperf vert (horiz pair)	†	£275
O350/5 Set of 6		32·00	60·00

1949 (July). Surch with Type O15. P 12.

O356	O 14 2a. on 1½a. claret	2·50	7·50

	a. Stop omitted		12·00	28·00
	b. Imperf (pair)		£225	£275
	ba. Stop omitted (pair)		£550	£650
	c. "2" omitted (in pair with normal)			£850

The "stop omitted" variety occurs on positions 60 and 69 in the sheet of 81.

1949. *Surch with Type* O**16.** *Imperf.*

O357	O **14**	2a. on 1½a. claret	£850	£850
		a. Perf 12	£900	£900

Three different types of "2" occur in the setting of Type O **16**.

BHOR

PRICES FOR STAMPS ON COVER	
Nos. 1/2	*from* × 40
No. 3	*from* × 6

GUM. The stamps of Bhor were issued without gum.

Pandit Shankar Rao, 1871–1922

| | 1 | | 2 | |

1879. *Handstamped. Very thick to thin native paper.* Imperf.

1	**1**	½a. carmine (*shades*)	3·25	4·75
		a. *Tête-bêche* (pair)	£700	
2	**2**	1a. carmine (*shades*)	5·50	7·50

3

1901. *Typo. Wove paper.* Imperf.

3	**3**	½a. red	14·00	40·00

BIJAWAR

PRICES FOR STAMPS ON COVER
The stamps of Bijawar are very rare used on cover.

Maharaja Sarwant Singh, 1899–1941

| | 1 | | 2 | |

(Typo Lakshmi Art Ptg Works, Bombay)

1935 (1 July)–**36.**

(a) P 11.

1	**1**	3p. brown	6·50	4·75
		a. Imperf (pair)	8·00	
		b. Imperf between (vert pair)	85·00	
		c. Imperf horiz (vert pair)	50·00	
2		6p. carmine	5·50	5·00
		a. Imperf (pair)	85·00	
		b. Imperf between (vert pair)	80·00	
		c. Imperf between (horiz pair)	85·00	£130
		d. Imperf horiz (vert pair)	90·00	
3		9p. violet	7·50	4·25
		a. Imperf (pair)	£140	
		b. Imperf between (vert pair)	95·00	
		c. Imperf between (horiz pair)	80·00	
		d. Imperf horiz (vert pair)	90·00	
4		1a. blue	8·00	5·00
		a. Imperf (pair)	85·00	
		b. Imperf between (vert pair)	90·00	
		c. Imperf between (horiz pair)	£150	
		d. Imperf horiz (vert pair)	95·00	
		e. Imperf vert (horiz strip of 3)	£170	
5		2a. deep green	8·00	4·75
		a. Imperf (pair)	£100	
		b. Imperf horiz (vert pair)	11·00	
		c. Imperf between (vert pair)	35·00	
		d. Imperf between (horiz pair)	50·00	85·00
1/5		*Set of* 5	32·00	21·00

(b) Roul 7 (1936).

6	**1**	3p. brown	5·00	4·75
		a. Printed on gummed side	£500	
7		6p. carmine	6·00	21·00
8		9p. violet	5·50	90·00
9		1a. blue	9·00	£100
10		2a. deep green	11·00	£110
6/10		*Set of* 5	32·00	£300

1937 (May). *Typo.* P 9.

11	**2**	4a. orange	13·00	70·00
		a. Imperf between (vert pair)	£140	

	b. Imperf (pair)		£200	
12	6a. lemon		13·00	70·00
	a. Imperf between (vert pair)		£150	
	b. Imperf (pair)		£200	
13	8a. emerald-green		14·00	95·00
	a. Imperf (pair)		£225	
14	12a. greenish blue		14·00	95·00
	a. Imperf (pair)		£250	
15	1r. bright violet		38·00	£150
	a. "1 Rs" for "1 R" (R. 1/2)		50·00	£300
	b. Imperf (pair)		£300	
	ba. "1 Rs" for "1 R" (R. 1/2)		£850	
11/15	*Set of* 5		85·00	£450

The stamps of Bijawar were withdrawn in 1941.

BUNDI

PRICES FOR STAMPS ON COVER	
No. 1	*from* × 2
No. 2	*from* × 4
Nos. 3/53	*from* × 10
Nos. 54/63	*from* × 5
Nos. 64/78	*from* × 2
Nos. 79/92	*from* × 10
Nos. O1/52	*from* × 15
Nos. O53/9	*from* × 20

GUM. Nos. 1/17 were issued without gum.

ILLUSTRATIONS. Types **1/10** and the tablet inscriptions for Type **11** are shown actual size.

In Nos. 1 to 17 characters denoting the value are below the dagger, except in Nos. 2a, 11 and 17.

All Bundi stamps until 1914 are lithographed and imperforate.

Maharao Raja Raghubir Singh, 1889–1927

1

1894 (May). *Each stamp with a distinct frame and the stamps not connected by the framing lines. Three vertical lines on dagger. Laid or wove paper.*

1	**1**	½a. slate-grey	£11000	£1900
		a. Last two letters of value below the rest	†	£5500

2 (Block of four stamps)

1894 (Dec). *Stamps joined together, with no space between them. Two vertical lines on dagger. Thin wove paper.*

2	**2**	½a. slate-grey	40·00	45·00
		a. Value at top, name below	£225	£275
		b. Right upper ornament omitted	£2000	£2000
		c. Last two letters of value below the rest	£1400	£1400
		d. Left lower ornament omitted	£2000	£2000

No. 2 was printed in sheets of 294, comprising two panes (10×14 and 11×14) side by side, in *tête-bêche* format. In the 10×14 pane No. 2a occurs on R1/1-10, No.2b on R11/7 and No. 2d on R2/9. In the 11×14 pane No. 2c occurs on R2/11, 8/3 and 10/1.

3

1896 (Nov). *Dagger shorter, lines thicker. Stamps separate. Laid paper.*

3	**3**	½a. slate-grey	5·00	9·50
		a. Last two letters of value below the rest	£375	£475

No. 3 was printed in sheets of 168, comprising two panes (7×12) side by side.

| 4 (1 anna) | 5 (2 annas) |

6 (2 annas)

1897–98. *No shading in centre of blade of dagger. The stamps have spaces between them, but are connected by the framing lines, both vertically and horizontally. Laid paper.*

I. *Blade of dagger comparatively narrow, and either triangular, as in T* **4** *and* **6***, or with the left-hand corner not touching the bar behind it, as in T* **5** *(1897–98).*

4	**4**	1a. Indian red	12·00	24·00
5		1a. red	10·00	15·00
6	**5**	2a. green	15·00	21·00
7	**6**	2a. yellow-green	12·00	15·00
8	**5**	4a. green	60·00	85·00
9		8a. Indian red	95·00	£225
10		1r. yellow/*blue*	£275	£475
4/10		*Set of* 5	£400	£750

7

II. *Blade varying in shape, but as a rule not touching the bar; value above and name below the dagger, instead of the reverse* (Jan 1898).

11	**7**	4a. emerald-green	38·00	
		a. Yellow-green	25·00	60·00

| 8 (½ anna) | 9 (1 anna) |

III. *Blade wider and (except on the ½ a.) almost diamond shaped; it nearly always touches the bar* (1898–1900).

12	**8**	½a. slate-grey (5.2.98)	4·25	4·25
13	**9**	1a. Indian red (7.98)	3·25	3·25
14		2a. pale green (9.11.98)	11·00	15·00
		a. First two characters of value (= two) omitted	£1800	£1800
15		8a. Indian red (7.98)	11·00	15·00
16		1r. yellow/*blue* (7.98)	28·00	48·00
		a. On wove paper	14·00	23·00
12/16a		*Set of* 5	40·00	55·00

10

IV. *Inscriptions as on No.* **11***; point of dagger to left* (9.11.98).

17	**10**	4a. green	28·00	32·00
		a. Yellow-green	15·00	21·00

All the above stamps are lithographed in large sheets, containing as many varieties of type as there are stamps in the sheets.

11 Raja protecting
Sacred Cows

Type **11** was produced from separate clichés printed as a block of four. The same clichés were used for all values, but not necessarily in the same order within the block. The Devanagri inscriptions, "RAJ BUNDI" at top and the face value at bottom, were inserted into the basic clichés as required so that various differences exist within the 58 settings which have been identified.

The denominations may be identified from the following illustrations. The ½a., 3a. and rupee values can be easily distinguished by their colours.

Bottom tablets:—

¼a.	1a.
2a.	2½a.
4a.	6a.
8a.	10a.
12a.	1r.

The nine versions of the inscriptions are as follows:

A	B

Top tablet

Type A. Top tablet has inscription in two separate words with a curved line over the first character in the second. The second word has three characters. Bottom tablet has short line above the first character in the second word.

Type B. Top tablet as Type A, but without the curved line over the first character in the second word. Bottom tablet as Type A.

C

Type C. Top tablet as Type B, but with large loop beneath the first character in the second word. This loop is usually joined to the main character, but is sometimes detached as in the illustration. Bottom tablet as Type A.

D	E
Top tablet	Bottom tablet

Type D. Top tablet in thinner lettering with the inscription shown as one word of six characters. The fourth character has a curved line above it, as in Type A, and a loop beneath, as in Type C. Bottom tablet as Type A, but thinner letters.

Type E. Top tablet as Type C. Bottom tablet shows a redrawn first character to the second word. This has the line at top extending over the entire character.

F

Bottom tablet

Type F. Top tablet as Type B. Bottom tablet as Type E, but first character in second word differs.

G	H

Type G. Top tablet as Type C, but without dot over first character in second word. There are now four characters in the second word. Bottom tablet as Type E.

Type H. Top tablet as Type G, but with characters larger and bolder. Bottom tablet as Type E, but with characters larger and bolder.

I

Type I. Top tablet as Type H. Bottom tablet as Type E.

Some settings contained more than one inscription type within the block of four so that se-tenant examples are known of Type B with Type C (¼, 1, 2, 4, 8, 10 and 12a.), Type C with Type E (¼, ½ and 4a.) and Type E with Type F (½ and 4a.). Type F only exists from this mixed setting.

1914 (Oct)–**41**. T **11**. Typo. Ungummed paper except for Nos. 73/8.

I. Rouletted in colour.

(a) Inscriptions as Type A. Thin wove paper (1916–23).

18		½a. black	2·50	10·00
19		1a. vermilion	5·00	21·00
20		2a. emerald	5·00	38·00
	a.	Deep green (coarse ptg on medium wove paper) (1923)	4·00	9·00
21		2½a. chrome-yellow (shades) (1917)	9·00	35·00
	a.	Printed both sides	£1200	
22		3a. chestnut (1917)	23·00	38·00
23		4a. yellow-green	20·00	
24		6a. cobalt (1917)	21·00	95·00
25		1r. reddish violet (1917)	25·00	£100

A special printing of the 1a. took place in late 1917 in connection with the "OUR DAY" Red Cross Society Fund. This had the "RAJ BUNDI" inscription in the bottom tablet with the face value below it. The top tablet carried four Devanagri characters for "OUR DAY". No evidence has been found to suggest that this 1a. stamp was used for postal purposes (Price, £190 unused).

(b) Inscriptions as Type B. Thin wove or pelure paper (1914–23).

25a		¼a. cobalt (1916)	3·75	21·00
	ab.	Stamp doubly printed	£425	
26		¼a. ultramarine (shades) (1917)	1·90	4·25
	a.	Indigo (1923)	4·00	8·00
	b.	Error. Black (1923)		
27		½a. black	2·75	6·00
28		1a. vermilion (1915)	3·25	11·00
	a.	Carmine (1923)	9·50	11·00
	b.	Red (shades) (1923)	5·50	11·00
29		2a. emerald (shades) (1915)	6·50	20·00
30		2½a. olive-yellow (1917)	6·50	25·00
31		3a. chestnut (1917)	7·50	40·00
32		4a. apple-green (1915)	3·50	38·00
32a		4a. olive-yellow (1917)	£140	£170
33		6a. pale ultramarine (shades) (1917)	13·00	90·00
	a.	Deep ultramarine (1917)	7·00	£100
34		8a. orange (1915)	7·50	95·00
35		10a. olive-sepia (1917)	£225	£500
	a.	Yellow-brown	£300	
36		12a. sage-green (1917)	£600	
36a		1r. lilac (shades) (1915)	25·00	

(c) Inscriptions as Type C. Thin to medium wove paper (1917–41).

37		¼a. ultramarine (shades) (1923)	7·50	8·50
	a.	Indigo (1923)	6·50	10·00
	b.	Error. Black (1923)		
	c.	Cobalt (medium wove paper) (1937)	21·00	19·00
38		½a. black	1·50	4·50
39		1a. orange-red	18·00	60·00
	a.	Carmine (1923)	19·00	24·00
	b.	Deep red (medium wove paper) (1936)	21·00	21·00
40		2a. emerald	11·00	25·00
	a.	Sage-green	8·50	25·00
41		4a. yellow-green (shades)	55·00	£110
	a.	Olive-yellow	£110	£160
	b.	Bright apple-green (medium wove paper) (1936)	£475	£250
42		8a. reddish orange	9·00	60·00
43		10a. brown-olive	16·00	90·00
	a.	Olive-sepia	40·00	£130
	b.	Yellow-brown	75·00	
44		12a. sage-green	13·00	90·00
45		1r. lilac	25·00	£140
46		2r. red-brown and black	75·00	£225
	a.	Chocolate and black (medium wove paper) (1936)	65·00	£275
47		3r. blue and red-brown	£110	£275
	a.	Grey-blue and chocolate (medium wove paper) (1941)	£110	
	ab.	Chocolate (inscriptions) inverted	£12000	
48		4r. emerald and scarlet	£225	£350
49		5r. scarlet and emerald	£250	£375

(d) Inscriptions as Type D. Thin wove paper (1918?).

50		2½a. buff (shades)	13·00	48·00
51		3a. red-brown	23·00	27·00
	a.	Semi-circle and dot omitted from 4th character	38·00	42·00
52		10a. bistre	32·00	£100
	a.	4th character turned to left instead of downwards	48·00	
53		12a. grey-olive	40·00	£100
	a.	4th character turned to left instead of downwards	65·00	
	b.	Blackish green	65·00	

---

	ba.	4th character turned to left instead of downwards	95·00	

(e) Inscriptions as Type E.

(i) Medium wove paper (1930–37).

54		¼a. deep slate	18·00	24·00
54a		¼a. indigo (thin wove paper) (1935)	20·00	24·00
	b.	Cobalt (1937)	21·00	17·00
55		½a. black	15·00	14·00
56		1a. carmine-red	23·00	30·00
57		3a. chocolate (shades) (1936)	11·00	35·00
58		4a. yellow-olive (1935)	£600	£200
	a.	Bright apple-green (1936)	£550	£200
	ab.	No tail to 4th character	£850	£350
59		¼a. indigo (1932)	23·00	28·00
60		½a. black	85·00	90·00
61		1a. bright scarlet (1931)	20·00	24·00
	a.	Carmine-red	75·00	85·00

(ii) Very thick wove paper (1930–32).

(See entries 59–61 above)

(iii) Thin horizontally laid paper (1935).

62		¼a. indigo	4·50	21·00
63		½a. scarlet-vermilion	9·50	27·00

Nos. 62 and 63 exist in tête-bêche blocks of four on the same or opposite sides of the paper.

(f) Inscriptions as Type F. Medium wove paper (1935).

63a		½a. black	90·00	
63b		4a. yellow-olive	£1000	£600

(g) Inscriptions as Type G.

(i) Horizontally laid paper (1935).

64		½a. black	85·00	85·00
	a.	Vert laid paper	80·00	80·00
65		1a. scarlet	70·00	50·00
66		4a. bright green	20·00	40·00

(ii) Medium wove paper (1936).

66a		½a. black	4·00	25·00
66b		4a. yellow-green	£1000	£500

(h) Inscriptions as Type H. Medium wove paper (1935–41).

67		¼a. ultramarine	1·75	7·00
68		½a. black (1938)	75·00	75·00
69		1a. deep red	8·00	35·00
	a.	Rosine (1938)	17·00	38·00
70		4a. emerald (1938)	18·00	27·00
71		4r. yellow-green and vermilion (1941)	£190	
72		5r. vermilion and yellow-green (1941)	£250	

No. 70 shows the currency spelt as "ANE" with the last letter missing and an accent over the Devanagri "N".

II. P 11.

(a) Inscriptions as Type H. Medium wove paper with gum (1939–41).

73		¼a. ultramarine	25·00	38·00
	a.	Greenish blue (1941)	1·75	48·00
74		½a. black	32·00	32·00
75		1a. scarlet-vermilion (1940)	£120	60·00
	a.	Rose (1940)	12·00	50·00
76		4a. yellow-green (1941)	16·00	75·00

(b) Inscriptions as Type I. Medium wove paper with gum (1940).

77		½a. black	£150	£100
78		2a. bright apple-green	50·00	50·00

FISCAL USE. Collectors are warned that the low values of the later settings of Type 11 were extensively used for fiscal purposes. Stamps which have been fraudulently cleaned of pen-cancels, regummed or provided with forged postmarks are frequently met with. Particular care should be exercised with examples of Nos. 58/a, 64/5, 68/70, 74/5a and 77.

Maharao Raja Ishwari Singh, 1927–1945

20

1941–44. Typo. P 11.

79	**20**	3p. bright blue	2·00	4·00
80		6p. deep blue	4·00	7·00
81		1a. orange-red	5·50	8·50
82		2a. chestnut	7·50	17·00
	a.	Deep brown (no gum) (1944)	15·00	19·00
83		4a. bright green	13·00	48·00
84		8a. dull green	17·00	£170
85		1r. deep blue	40·00	£250
79/85 Set of 7			£100	£450

The first printing only of Nos. 79/85 is usually with gum; all further printings, including No. 82a, are without gum.

Maharao Raja Bahadur Singh, 1945–1971

21 Maharao Raja
Bahadur Singh

22 Bundi

(Typo Times of India Press, Bombay)

1947. P 11.

86	**21**	¼a. blue-green	2·25	35·00
87		½a. violet	2·00	30·00
88		1a. yellow-green	2·00	30·00
89	—	2a. vermilion	1·90	60·00

90	–	4a. orange.................................	1·90	85·00
91	**22**	8a. ultramarine...........................	3·00	
92		1r. chocolate.............................	15·00	
86/92		Set of 7....................................	25·00	

On the 2 and 4a. the Maharao is in Indian dress.

OFFICIAL STAMPS

PRICES. Prices for Nos. O1/52 are for unused examples. Used stamps are generally worth a small premium over the prices quoted.

बूंदी	**BUNDI**

सरविस	**SERVICE**
(O 1)	(O 2)

BUNDI

SERVICE
(O 3)

1915–41. T **11** handstamped as Types O 1/3. Ungummed paper except Nos. O47/52.

A. Optd with Type O 1. B. Optd with Type O 2. C. Optd with Type O 3.

I. Rouletted in colour

(a) Inscriptions as Type A. Thin wove paper.

		A	B	C
O1	½a. black..................................	£325	†	†
	a. Red opt.............................	£325	†	†
O1b	2a. emerald.............................	3·50	£275	†
	ba. Deep green (coarse ptg on medium wove paper).............	6·50	15·00	£275
	bb. Red opt............................	15·00	17·00	†
O2	2½a. chrome-yellow (shades)......	3·25	18·00	£275
	a. Red opt.............................	£225	£250	†
O3	3a. chestnut............................	3·00	23·00	†
	a. Green opt..........................	£180	†	†
	b. Red opt.............................	£250	£250	†
O4	6a. cobalt...............................	25·00	28·00	£325
	a. Red opt.............................	£300	£325	£350
O5	1r. reddish violet....................	50·00	48·00	†
	a. Red opt.............................	£375	£400	†

(b) Inscriptions as Type B. Thin wove or pelure paper.

O6	¼a. ultramarine (shades)...........	1·60	1·75	7·50
		1·25	4·00	£190
O7	½a. black...............................	8·50	6·00	32·00
	a. Red opt.............................	4·50	11·00	£190
O8	1a. vermilion..........................	4·00	†	†
	a. Red opt.............................	—	†	†
	b. Carmine...........................	27·00	14·00	80·00
	c. Red (shades).....................		7·00	†
O9	2a. emerald (shades)................	32·00	42·00	†
	a. Red opt.............................	—	£140	†
O9b	3a. chestnut (R.).....................	—	†	†
O10	4a. apple-green.......................	12·00	75·00	£275
	a. Red opt.............................	£325	†	†
O10b	4a. olive-yellow.......................	£275	£300	†
	ba. Red opt............................			£550
O11	6a. pale ultramarine (shades).....	14·00	£275	†
	a. Red opt.............................	£400	£400	†
	b. Deep ultramarine...............	60·00	80·00	†
	ba. Red opt............................	£200	£180	†
O12	8a. orange..............................	48·00	65·00	£400
	a. Red opt.............................	£350	†	†
O13	10a. olive-sepia........................	£190	£250	£600
	a. Red opt.............................	£700	£750	£900
O14	12a. sage-green........................	£140	£475	£650
	a. Red opt.............................	†	†	£900
O14b	1r. lilac.................................	£325	†	†

(c) Inscriptions as Type C. Thin to medium wove paper.

O15	¼a. ultramarine (shades)..........	3·75	4·00	19·00
	a. Red opt.............................	1·00	5·50	£300
	b. Green opt..........................	4·25	48·00	†
	c. Cobalt (medium wove paper)...............................	55·00	55·00	£350
	ca. Red opt............................	40·00	17·00	£120
O16	½a. black...............................	9·00	3·00	12·00
	a. Red opt.............................	75	8·00	£200
	b. Green opt..........................	3·00	†	†
O17	1a. orange-red........................	1·25	—	†
	a. Carmine...........................	25·00	9·00	21·00
	b. Deep red (medium wove paper)...............................	35·00	48·00	85·00
	ba. Red opt............................	†	£160	†
O18	2a. emerald............................	5·00	17·00	75·00
	a. Red opt.............................	†	£120	†
	b. Sage-green........................	11·00	13·00	85·00
O19	4a. yellow-green (shades).........	10·00	70·00	†
	b. Red opt.............................	†	†	†
	c. Olive-yellow......................	£130	£120	†
	ca. Red opt............................	£400	£400	†
O20	8a. reddish orange..................	15·00	29·00	£275
	a. Red opt.............................	£300	£425	†
O21	10a. brown-olive......................	55·00	85·00	£450
	a. Red opt.............................	£450	£450	£500
O22	12a. sage-green........................	45·00	£100	£500
	a. Red opt.............................	£550	†	£600
O23	1r. lilac.................................	£130	†	†
	a. Red opt.............................	£400	†	†
O24	2r. red-brown and black...........	£400	£190	†
		†	£1000	†
	b. Green opt..........................	£1000	†	†
	c. Chocolate and black (medium wove paper)............	£750	£750	†
O25	3r. blue and red-brown............	£350	£225	†
	a. Red opt.............................	£950	†	†
	b. Grey-blue & chocolate (medium wove paper)............	£1000	£1000	†
	ba. Red opt............................	£1100	†	†

O26	4r. emerald and scarlet............	£300	£300	†
O27	5r. scarlet and emerald............	£325	£325	†

(d) Inscriptions as Type D. Thin wove paper.

O28	2½a. buff (shades).....................	15·00	18·00	†
	b. Red opt.............................	£250	—	†
O29	3a. red-brown.........................	35·00	26·00	†
	a. Variety as No. 51a..............	55·00	48·00	†
	b. Red opt.............................	†	£450	†
O30	10a. bistre..............................	48·00	90·00	£500
	a. Variety as No. 52a..............	80·00	£150	£750
	b. Red opt.............................	£425	£550	†
	ba. Variety as No. 52a..............	£550	†	†
O31	12a. grey-olive........................	65·00	95·00	£500
	a. Variety as No. 53a..............	95·00	£160	£750
	b. Red opt.............................	£475	£550	†
	ba. Variety as No. 53a..............	£650	†	†

(e) Inscriptions as Type E.

(i) Medium wove paper.

O32	¼a. deep slate........................	32·00	16·00	†
	a. Red opt.............................	27·00	42·00	†
O32b	¼a. indigo (thin wove paper).....	38·00	42·00	†
	ba. Red opt............................	40·00	45·00	†
	bb. Green opt.........................	95·00	£120	†
	c. Cobalt..............................	60·00	60·00	£400
	ca. Red opt............................	38·00	30·00	£120
O33	½a. black...............................	42·00	12·00	†
	a. Red opt.............................	23·00	10·00	†
	b. Green opt..........................	£300	£225	†
O34	1a. carmine-red......................	38·00	38·00	£375
O35	3a. chocolate (shades).............	£180	£120	£250
	a. Red opt.............................	£500	£500	†
O35b	4a. yellow-olive......................	†	£1200	†
	ba. Bright apple-green.............	£1400	†	†

(ii) Very thick wove paper.

O36	¼a. indigo..............................	9·50	12·00	†
	a. Red opt.............................	25·00	50·00	†
	b. Green opt..........................	90·00	†	†
O37	½a. black...............................	£130	£140	†
O38	1a. bright scarlet....................	14·00	18·00	£300
	a. Carmine-red......................	£110	80·00	†

(iii) Thin horizontally laid paper.

O39	¼a. indigo..............................	75·00	90·00	†
	a. Red opt.............................	5·00	8·00	£225
O40	1a. scarlet-vermilion...............	42·00	26·00	†
	a. Red opt.............................	£350	£375	†

Nos. O39/40a exist in *tête-bêche* blocks of four on the same or opposite sides of the paper.

(f) Inscriptions as Type F. Medium wove paper.

O40b	½a. black...............................	—	£450	†
	ba. Red opt............................	£400	£450	†
O40c	4a. yellow-olive......................	†	£1500	†

(g) Inscriptions as Type G.

(i) Horizontally laid paper.

O41	½a. black...............................	£450	†	†
	a. Red opt.............................	£130	£130	†
	b. Vert laid paper...................	£150	£160	†
O42	4a. bright green......................	£200	£200	£425
	a. Red opt.............................	£275	£375	†

(ii) Medium wove paper.

O42b	½a. black...............................	£275	£275	†
	ba. Red opt............................	£350	£350	†

(h) Inscriptions as Type H. Medium wove paper.

O43	¼a. ultramarine......................	25·00	75·00	†
	a. Red opt.............................	£190	£400	†
O44	½a. black...............................	75·00	£120	†
	a. Red opt.............................	60·00	†	£500
O45	1a. rosine..............................	£200	£180	£475
O46	4a. emerald............................	£170	£225	£500
	a. Red opt.............................	£475	†	£500

II. P 11.

(a) Inscriptions as Type H. Medium wove paper with gum.

O47	¼a. ultramarine......................	45·00	60·00	£130
	a. Red opt.............................	80·00	90·00	†
	b. Greenish blue....................	70·00	70·00	£180
	c. Ditto. Red opt....................	£200	†	†
O48	½a. black...............................	48·00	65·00	£400
	a. Red opt.............................	95·00	£350	£225
O49	1a. scarlet-vermilion...............	£225	£250	£475
	a. Stamp doubly printed.........	†	†	£1000
	b. Rose................................	£150	£130	£350
O50	2a. yellow-green.....................	£475	£225	£400

(b) Inscriptions as Type I. Medium wove paper with gum.

O51	½a. black...............................	£140	£300	£500
	a. Red opt.............................	£425	£500	†
O52	2a. bright apple-green..............	£475	£475	£900

Until 1941 it was the general practice to carry official mail free but some of the above undoubtedly exist postally used.

1941. Nos. 79 to 85 optd "SERVICE".

O53	**20**	3p. bright blue (R.).................	5·50	14·00
O54		6p. deep blue (R.)..................	14·00	14·00
O55		1a. orange-red.......................	14·00	9·50
O56		2a. brown.............................	14·00	11·00
O57		4a. bright green.....................	40·00	90·00
O58		8a. dull green........................	£160	£475
O59		1r. deep blue (R.)..................	£200	£550
O53/9		Set of 7................................	£400	£1000

Two different types of "R" occur in the "SERVICE" overprint. On five positions in the sheet of 12 the "R" shows a larger loop and a pointed diagonal leg.

Bundi became part of the Rajasthan Union by 15 April 1948.

BUSSAHIR (BASHAHR)

PRICES FOR STAMPS ON COVER	
Nos. 1/21	*from* × 8
Nos. 22/23	*from* × 2
Nos. 24/43	*from* × 8

Raja Shamsher Singh, 1850–1914

The initials are those of the Tika Raghunath Singh, son of the then Raja, who was the organiser and former director of the State Post Office.

(Litho at the Bussahir Press by Maulvi Karam Bakhsh, Rampur)

1895 (20 June). Laid paper. Optd with T **9** in pale greenish blue (B.), rose (R.), mauve (M.) or lake (L.). With or without gum.

(a) Imperf.

1	**1**	¼a. pink (M.) (1.9.95)..............	£2000	
		a. Monogram in rose..............	£2750	
2	**2**	½a. grey (R.).........................	£450	£600
		a. Monogram in mauve...........		
3	**3**	1a. vermilion (M.)..................	£180	
4	**4**	2a. orange-yellow (M.)............	65·00	£180
		a. Monogram in rose..............	£120	£190
		b. Monogram in lake..............	85·00	
		c. Monogram in blue..............	£200	
5	**5**	4a. slate-violet (M.)...............	£110	
		a. Monogram in rose..............	£150	
		b. Monogram in lake..............	£160	
		c. Without monogram..............	£325	
		d. Thick paper......................	£200	
6	**6**	8a. red-brown (M.)..................	£120	£200
		a. Monogram in blue..............	£150	
		b. Monogram in rose..............	£180	
		c. Monogram in lake..............	£250	
		e. Thick paper......................	£130	
7	**7**	12a. green (L.).........................	£275	
		a. Monogram in mauve...........		
8	**8**	1r. ultramarine (R.)...............	£110	
		a. Monogram in mauve...........	£180	
		b. Monogram in lake..............	£150	
		c. Without monogram..............	£325	

(b) Perf with a sewing machine; gauge and size of holes varying between 7 and 11½.

9	**1**	¼a. pink (B.).........................	60·00	90·00
		a. Monogram in mauve...........	—	£160
		b. Without monogram..............	£325	£130
10	**2**	½a. grey (R.).........................	22·00	£120
		a. Without monogram..............	£700	
11	**3**	1a. vermilion (M.)..................	23·00	85·00
12	**4**	2a. orange-yellow (B.)............	32·00	90·00
		a. Monogram in rose..............		
		b. Monogram in mauve...........	£110	
		c. Without monogram..............	—	£200
13	**5**	4a. slate-violet (B.)...............	23·00	90·00
		a. Monogram in rose..............	32·00	£120
		b. Monogram in mauve...........	48·00	
		c. Without monogram..............	42·00	
14	**6**	8a. red-brown (M.)..................	23·00	£100
		a. Monogram in blue..............	60·00	£160
		b. Monogram in rose..............	90·00	
		c. Without monogram..............	£120	£325
15	**7**	12a. green (R.).........................	70·00	£120
		a. Monogram in mauve...........	£140	
		b. Monogram in lake..............	£130	
		c. Without monogram..............	£190	
16	**8**	1r. ultramarine (R.)...............	40·00	£110
		a. Monogram in mauve...........	£110	
		b. Without monogram..............	£275	£375
9/16		Set of 8................................	£250	£700

1899. As 1895, but pin-perf or rouletted.

17	**3**	1a. vermilion (M.)..................	£180	£200
18	**4**	2a. orange-yellow (M.)............	55·00	£150
		a. Monogram in lake..............	65·00	
		b. Monogram in rose..............	90·00	
		c. Monogram in blue..............	£150	
		d. Without monogram..............	£150	
19	**5**	4a. slate-violet (L.)...............	£275	
		a. Monogram in blue..............		
		b. Monogram in rose..............	£350	
		c. Monogram in mauve...........	£350	
20	**7**	12a. green (R.).........................	£450	£550
21	**8**	1r. ultramarine (R.)...............	£450	

Nos. 1 to 21 were in sheets of 24. They seem to have been overprinted and perforated as required. Those first issued for use were perforated, but they were subsequently supplied imperf, both to collectors and for use. Nos. 17 to 21 were some of the last supplies. No rule seems to have been observed as to the colour of the overprinted monogram; pale blue, rose and mauve were used from the first. The pale blue varies to greenish blue or blue-green, and appears quite green on the yellow stamps. The lake is possibly a mixture of the mauve and the rose—it is a quite distinct colour and apparently later than the others. Specimens without overprint are either remainders left in the Treasury or copies that have escaped accidentally; they have been found sticking to the backs of others that bore the overprint.

Varieties may also be found doubly overprinted, in two different colours.

| 10 | 11 | 12 |

T **11**. Lines of shading above and at bottom left and right of shield.
T **12**. White dots above shield and ornaments in bottom corners.

| 13 | 14 |
| 15 | 16 |

(Printed at the Bussahir Press by Maulvi Karam Bakhsh)

1896–97. *Wove paper. Optd with monogram "R.S.", T 9, in rose. Recess singly from line-engraved dies. With or without gum. Various perfs.*
22	10	¼a. deep violet (1897)	—	£900
23	11	½a. grey-blue	£700	£250
23a		½a. deep blue (1897)		£375

No. 23 exists sewing-machine perf about 10 and also perf 14½–16. Nos. 22 and 23a are pin-perf.

1896–1900. *As Nos. 22/3, but lithographed in sheets of various sizes. No gum.*

(a) Imperf.
24	10	¼a. slate-violet (R.)	7·00	
		a. Monogram in mauve	9·00	
		b. Monogram in blue	12·00	
		c. Monogram in lake	20·00	
25	11	½a. blue (*shades*) (R.)	8·50	17·00
		a. Monogram in mauve	8·50	17·00
		b. Monogram in lake	9·50	
		c. Without monogram		
		d. Laid paper (B.)	£130	
		da. Monogram in mauve		
26	13	1a. olive (*shades*) (R.)	16·00	38·00
		a. Monogram in mauve	40·00	
		b. Monogram in blue	40·00	

(b) Pin-perf or rouletted.
27	10	¼a. slate-violet (R.)	19·00	17·00
		a. Monogram in lake	23·00	20·00
		b. Monogram in mauve	—	30·00
28	11	½a. blue (*shades*) (R.)	13·00	29·00
		a. Monogram in mauve	17·00	30·00
		b. Monogram in lake	32·00	42·00
		c. Monogram in blue	£130	
		d. Laid paper (M.)		
29	13	1a. olive (*shades*) (R.)	24·00	
		a. Monogram in mauve	50·00	50·00
		b. Monogram in lake	50·00	50·00
30	14	2a. orange-yellow (B.)	£700	£750

Originally printings of the ¼a. and ½a. were in sheets of 8 (stone I), but this was subsequently increased to 24 (4×6). The 1a. and 2a. were always in sheets of 4.

Nos. 25d/da were printed from stone I and care is needed to distinguish this laid paper printing from some of the reprints on similar paper. Stamps from stone I are without marginal lines and are very clear impressions; reprints from stone IV have thick marginal lines and, in those shades similar to No. 25, show indistinct impressions.

1900–01. *¼a., 1a, colours changed; ½a. redrawn type; 2a. with dash before "STATE" and characters in lower left label; 4a. new value. No gum.*

(a) Imperf.
31	10	¼a. vermilion (M.)	4·50	9·50
		a. Monogram in blue	4·75	9·50
		b. Without monogram		
31c	12	½a. blue (M.)	10·00	24·00
		ca. Monogram in rose	30·00	
		cb. Without monogram	50·00	
32	13	1a. vermilion (M.)	4·50	14·00
		a. Monogram in blue	7·00	9·50
		b. Monogram in lake		
		c. Without monogram	45·00	
33	15	2a. ochre (M.) (9.00)	42·00	85·00
34		2a. yellow (M.) (11.00)	45·00	
		a. Monogram in blue	45·00	90·00
		b. Without monogram	75·00	
35		2a. orange (B.) (1.01)	50·00	85·00
		a. Monogram in mauve	50·00	80·00
		b. Without monogram	60·00	
36	16	4a. claret (R.)	48·00	£100

---

		a. Monogram in mauve	65·00	£120
		b. Monogram in blue	85·00	£140
		c. Without monogram	32·00	

(b) Pin-perf or rouletted.
37	10	¼a. vermilion (M.)	4·00	9·50
		a. Monogram in blue	4·75	
		b. Without monogram		
37c	12	½a. blue (M.)	45·00	65·00
38	13	1a. vermilion (M.)	6·00	14·00
		a. Monogram in blue	9·00	11·00
39		1a. brown-red (M.) (3.01)	—	£200
40	15	2a. ochre (M.) (9.00)	55·00	
		a. Monogram in blue		
41		2a. yellow (M.) (11.00)	40·00	70·00
		a. Monogram in rose	65·00	90·00
		b. Monogram in blue	75·00	£100
42		2a. orange (M.) (1.01)	55·00	65·00
		a. Monogram in blue	80·00	80·00
		b. Without monogram	—	£225
43	16	4a. claret (R.)	60·00	
		a. Monogram in blue	70·00	£150
		b. Monogram in mauve	95·00	

The ¼a., ½a. and 1a. are in sheets of 24; the 2a. in sheets of 50 differing throughout in the dash and the characters added at lower left; the 4a. in sheets of 28.

(17)

The stamps formerly catalogued with large overprint "R.N.S." (T **17**) are now believed never to have been issued for use.

Remainders are also found with overprint "P.S.", the initials of Padam Singh who succeeded Raghunath Singh in the direction of the Post Office, and with the original monogram "R.S." in a damaged state, giving it the appearance of a double-lined "R".

The stamps of Bussahir have been obsolete since 1 April 1901. Numerous remainders were sold after this date, and all values were later reprinted in the colours of the originals, or in fancy colours, from the original stones, or from new ones. Printings were also made from new types, similar to those of the second issue of the 8a., 12a. and 1r. values, in sheets of 8.

Reprints are frequently found on laid paper.

Collectors are warned against obliterated copies bearing the Rampur postmark with date "19 MA 1900." Many thousand remainders and reprints were thus obliterated for export after the closing of the State Post Office.

CHARKHARI

PRICES FOR STAMPS ON COVER	
Nos. 1/4	*from × 2*
Nos. 5/26	*from × 20*
Nos. 27/44	*from × 3*
Nos. 45/53	*from × 100*
Nos. 54/5	*from × 5*
No. 56	*from × 2*

Maharaja Malkhan Singh, 1880–1908

1

¼ ½ 1 2 4
¼ ½ 1 2 4

The top row shows the figures of value used in the stamps of 1894–97, and the bottom row those for the 1904 issue. In the 4a. the figure slopes slightly to the right in the first issue, and to the left in the second.

1894. *Typo from a single die. No gum. Imperf.*
1	1	¼ anna, rose	£1200	£700
2		1 annas, dull green	£1800	£2250
3		2 annas, dull green	£2250	
4		4 annas, dull green	£1300	

Nos. 1/2 are known pin-perforated.

1897. *Inscr "ANNA". No gum. Imperf.*
5	1	¼a. magenta	60·00	75·00
		a. Purple	3·75	3·75
		b. Violet	3·25	3·25
6		½a. purple	3·25	4·25
		a. Violet	2·50	3·00
7		1a. blue-green	5·00	8·50
		a. Turquoise-blue	4·50	5·50
		b. Indigo	13·00	21·00
		c. Figure of value inverted	£1300	
8		2a. blue-green	9·00	16·00
		a. Turquoise-blue	7·00	8·00
		b. Indigo	17·00	25·00
9		4a. blue-green	11·00	18·00
		a. Turquoise-blue	6·50	12·00
		b. Indigo	27·00	42·00
		ba. Figure of value sideways	£1300	
5/9 Set of 5			21·00	28·00

Minor varieties may be found with the first "A" in "ANNA" not printed.

All values are known on various coloured papers, but these are proofs or trial impressions.

1902–04. *Numerals changed as illustrated above. No gum.*
10	1	¼a. violet	1·75	2·50
11		½a. violet	4·00	3·50
12		1a. green	5·00	15·00
13		2a. green	30·00	30·00

| 14 | | 4a. green | 20·00 | 32·00 |
| 10/14 *Set of 5* | | | 55·00 | 75·00 |

Stamps of this issue can be found showing part of the papermaker's watermark. "Mercantile Script Extra Strong John Haddon & Co.".

Maharaja Jujhar Singh, 1908–1914

2 (Right-hand sword over left)

Type I

Type II

Type I. "P" of "POSTAGE" in same size as other letters. "E" small with long upper and lower arms. White dot often appears on one or both of the sword hilts.

Type II. "P" larger than the other letters. "E" large with short upper and lower arms. No dots occur on the hilts.

1909–19. *Litho in Calcutta. Wove paper. P 11.*

(a) Type I.
15	2	1p. chestnut	42·00	45·00
		a. Pale chestnut	4·25	38·00
		b. Orange-brown	4·25	38·00
		c. "CHARKHAPI"	32·00	
16		1p. turquoise-blue	60	45
		a. Imperf between (horiz pair)	£160	
		b. Greenish blue (1911)	90	1·00
		c. Pale turquoise-green	1·50	70
17		½a. vermilion	2·00	1·00
		a. Imperf (pair)	£850	
		b. Deep rose-red	90	1·25
18		1a. sage-green	2·75	2·25
		a. Yellow-olive	2·00	1·60
19		2a. grey-blue	3·00	3·25
		a. Dull violet-blue	3·00	3·50
20		4a. deep green	4·00	5·00
21		8a. brown-red	7·50	18·00
22		1r. pale chestnut	13·00	38·00
15a/22 *Set of 8*			32·00	95·00

(b) Type II.
24	2	1p. turquoise-blue	4·25	4·25
25		½a. vermilion	2·00	1·60
		b. Deep rose-red	5·50	5·50
26		1a. yellow-olive (1919)	3·25	9·00
		a. Sage-green	2·25	1·60
24/6 *Set of 3*			7·50	6·75

No. 15, from the original printing, shows an upstroke to the "1", not present on other brown printings of this value.

See also Nos. 31/44.

3 "I" below Swords. Right sword overlaps left. Double framelines. | 4 "JI" below Swords. Left sword overlaps right. Single frameline.

1912–17. *Handstamped. Wove paper. No gum. Imperf.*
27	3	1p. violet	£600	80·00
		a. Dull purple	—	90·00
28	4	1p. violet (1917)	7·00	5·00
		a. Dull purple	16·00	5·50
		b. Tête-bêche (pair)	75·00	75·00
		c. Laid paper		£475
		d. Pair, one stamp sideways	—	£130

Maharaja Ganga Singh, 1914–1920
Maharaja Arimardan Singh, 1920–1942

5 (actual size 63×25 mm) | 6 (Left-hand sword over right)

1921. *Handstamped. No gum.*

(a) Wove paper. Imperf.
| 29 | 5 | 1a. violet | 70·00 | 80·00 |
| | | a. Dull purple | 90·00 | 95·00 |

(b) Laid paper. P 11.
| 30 | 5 | 1a. violet | 65·00 | £120 |
| | | a. Imperf | £160 | £170 |

(Typo State Ptg Press, Charkhari)

1930–45. *Wove paper. No gum. Imperf.*
| 31 | 6 | 1p. deep violet | 35 | 14·00 |
| | | a. Vert pair, top ptd inverted on back, bottom normal upright | 13·00 | |

		b. *Tête-bêche* (vert pair)...............	£325	
		c. Perf 11×imperf (horiz pair)		
		(1939)...........................	65·00	65·00
		d. *Bluish slate*.....................	22·00	
		e. Laid paper (1944).............	—	£350
32		1p. dull *to* light green (*pelure*)		
		(1943)...........................	60·00	£190
33		1p. violet (1943).....................	19·00	£140
		a. *Tête-bêche* (vert pair).......	55·00	
34		½a. deep olive................	2·00	14·00
35		½a. red-brown (1940)...........	6·00	24·00
		a. *Tête-bêche* (vert pair).......	£450	
36		½a. black (*pelure*) (1943)......	60·00	£170
37		½a. red (*shades*) (1943)........	20·00	38·00
		a. *Tête-bêche* (vert pair).......	42·00	
		b. Laid paper (1944)...........	—	£300
38		½a. grey-brown (1943)...........	65·00	80·00
39		1a. green...........................	1·50	15·00
		a. *Emerald* (1938).............	45·00	70·00
40		1a. chocolate (1940)...........	10·00	24·00
		a. *Tête-bêche* (vert pair).......	75·00	
		b. *Lake-brown*.................	—	55·00
41		1a. red (1940).....................	£110	60·00
		a. *Carmine*........................	—	60·00
		b. Laid paper (1944)...........	—	£325
42		2a. light blue...................	1·25	17·00
		a. *Tête-bêche* (vert pair).......	9·50	
43		2a. greenish grey (1941?)......	50·00	70·00
		a. *Tête-bêche* (vert pair).......	£100	
		b. Laid paper (1944)...........	—	£350
		c. *Greyish green*..............	80·00	£170
43d		2a. yellow-green (1945)........	—	£850
44		4a. carmine.........................	3·00	20·00
		a. *Tête-bêche* (vert pair).......		14·00

There are two different versions of No. 37a, one with the stamps *tête-bêche* base to base and the other showing them top to top.

7 Goverdhan Temple   ½ As. (8)

(Typo Batliboi Litho Works, Bombay)

1931 (25 June). *T* **7** *and similar designs.* P 11, 11½, 12 or compound.

45		½a. blue-green...................	1·75	10
		a. Imperf between (horiz pair)..............	35·00	11·00
		b. Imperf between (vert pair)...............	35·00	35·00
		c. Imperf horiz (vert pair)................	35·00	
46		1a. blackish brown..............	1·60	10
		a. Imperf between (horiz pair)..............	11·00	8·00
		b. Imperf between (vert pair)...............	12·00	8·00
		c. Imperf horiz (vert pair)................	12·00	
47		2a. violet.........................	1·25	10
		a. Imperf between (horiz pair)..............	30·00	25·00
		b. Imperf between (vert pair)...............	30·00	25·00
		c. Imperf horiz (vert pair)................	22·00	
		d. Doubly printed..................	9·50	
48		4a. olive-green...................	1·25	15
		a. Imperf between (vert pair)...............	60·00	60·00
49		8a. magenta.......................	1·75	10
		a. Imperf between (horiz pair)..............	40·00	25·00
		b. Imperf between (vert pair)...............	40·00	40·00
		c. Imperf horiz (vert pair)................	40·00	13·00
50		1r. green and rose..............	2·50	20
		a. Imperf between (vert pair)...............	£100	£100
		b. Green (centre) omitted........	—	£150
		c. Imperf horiz (vert pair)................	£120	
51		2r. red and brown..............	3·50	25
		a. Imperf horiz (vert pair)................	£100	15·00
52		3r. chocolate and blue-green..	13·00	40
		a. Imperf between (horiz pair)..............		£170
		b. *Tête-bêche* (pair)...........	£225	20·00
		c. Chocolate (centre) omitted...	21·00	
53		5r. turquoise and purple......	9·00	50
		a. Imperf between (horiz pair)..............	£170	
		b. Centre inverted................	70·00	30·00
		c. Centre doubly printed........	—	90·00
45/53		Set of 9..........................	32·00	1·60

Designs:—½a. The Lake; 1a. Imlia Palace; 2a. Industrial School; 4a. Bird's-eye view of City; 8a. The Fort; 1r. Guest House. 2r. Palace Gate; 3r. Temples at Rainpur.

This issue was the subject of speculative manipulation, large stocks being thrown on the market cancelled-to-order at very low prices and unused at less than face value. The issue was an authorized one but was eventually withdrawn by the State authorities.

1939 (1 Dec)–**40.** *Nos. 21/2 surch as T* **8**.

54	**2**	½a. on 8a. brown-red (1940).......	32·00	£120
		a. No space between		
		"½" and "As".................	32·00	£120
		b. Surch inverted............	£275	£375
		c. "1" of "½" inverted ...	£275	
55		1a. on 1r. chestnut (1940).......	£100	£375
		a. Surch inverted............	£300	
56		"1 ANNA" on 1r. chestnut.........	£900	£900

Maharaja Jaiendra Singh, 1942–1971

Charkhari became part of Vindhya Pradesh by 1 May 1948.

COCHIN

(6 puttans = 5 annas. 12 pies = 1 anna; 16 annas = 1 rupee)

Stamps of Cochin were also valid on mail posted to Travancore.

PRICES FOR STAMPS ON COVER	
Nos. 1/3	*from* × 30
Nos. 4/5	*from* × 10
Nos. 6/6b	*from* × 3
Nos. 7/9	*from* × 20
Nos. 11/22	*from* × 15
Nos. 26/128	*from* × 8
Nos. O1/105	*from* × 15

Raja Kerala Varma I, 1888–1895

1   **2**

(Dies eng P. Orr & Sons, Madras; typo Cochin Govt, Ernakulam)

1892 (13 Apr). *No wmk, or wmk large Umbrella in the sheet.* P 12.

1	**1**	½ put. buff.........................	2·50	3·00
		a. *Orange-buff*................	2·75	2·75
		b. *Yellow*.........................	2·75	3·25
		c. Imperf (pair)...............		2·25
2		1 put. purple......................	2·75	2·25
		a. Imperf between (vert pair)........	†	£2250
3	**2**	2 put. deep violet...............	2·00	2·25
1/3		Set of 3.........................	6·50	6·50

1893. *Laid paper.* P 12.

4		1 ½ put. orange-buff..............	£475	£130
		a. *Orange*........................	—	£130
		b. *Yellow*.........................	—	£130

WATERMARKS. Prior to the 1911–23 issue, printed by Perkins, Bacon & Co, little attention was paid to the position of the watermark. Inverted and sideways watermarks are frequently found in the 1898 and 1902–03 issues.

1894. *Wmk small Umbrella on each stamp.* P 12.

5	**1**	½ put. buff.........................	5·50	3·75
		a. *Orange*	2·00	1·50
		ab. Imperf (pair)...............		
		b. *Yellow*.........................	3·75	1·00
6		1 put. purple.....................	6·00	6·00
7	**2**	2 put. deep violet..............	3·75	4·25
		a. Imperf (pair)...............		
		b. Doubly printed..............	†	£1300
		c. Printed both sides..........	£1600	
		d. *Tête-bêche* (pair)..........	£3500	
5/7		Set of 3.........................	10·00	10·00

The paper watermarked with a small umbrella is more transparent than that of the previous issue. The wmk is not easy to distinguish.
The 1 put. in deep violet was a special printing for fiscal use only.

Raja Rama Varma I, 1895–1914

1896 (End). *Similar to T* **1**, *but* 28×33 *mm.* P 12.

(a) Wmk Arms and inscription in sheet.

8		1 put. violet	85·00	85·00

(b) Wmk Conch Shell to each stamp.

9		1 put. deep violet...............	19·00	32·00

Nos. 8/9 were intended for fiscal use, but are also known used for postal purposes.

3   **4**

5   **6**

1898. *Thin yellowish paper. Wmk small Umbrella on each stamp. With or without gum.* P 12.

11	**3**	3 pies, blue......................	1·40	1·10
		a. Imperf between (horiz pair).......	£500	
		b. Imperf between (vert pair)........	£600	
		c. Doubly printed..................	£600	
12	**4**	½ put. green.......................	1·50	1·10
		a. Imperf between (horiz pair).......	£1000	£1000
		b. Stamp sideways (in pair)...	†	£2500
13	**5**	1 put. pink........................	3·50	1·75
		a. *Tête-bêche* (pair)..........	£3000	£2000
		b. Laid paper..................	†	£1600
		ba. Laid paper. *Tête-bêche* (pair)...	†	£7000
		c. *Red*............................	3·50	1·75
		d. *Carmine-red*................	3·75	1·90
14	**6**	2 put. deep violet...............	3·00	2·00
		a. Imperf between (vert pair)........	£500	
		b. Imperf between (vert strip of 3)	£650	
11/14		Set of 4.........................	8·00	5·00

1902–03. *Thick white paper. Wmk small Umbrella on each stamp. With or without gum.* P 12.

16	**3**	3 pies, blue......................	1·10	10
		a. Doubly printed..................	—	£275
		b. Imperf between (horiz pair).......	†	£750
17	**4**	½ put. green.......................	1·25	40
		a. Stamp sideways (in pair)........	£750	£750
		b. Doubly printed..................	—	£275
		c. Imperf between (horiz pair).......	†	£1000
18	**5**	1 put. pink (1903)...............	1·75	10
		a. *Tête-bêche* (pair)..........	†	£3250
19	**6**	2 put. deep violet...............	2·50	50
		a. Doubly printed..................	£850	£300
16/19		Set of 4.........................	6·00	1·00

(7)   (7a)   (7b)

1909. *T* **3** *(Paper and perf of 1903), surch with T* **7**. *Wmk is always sideways. No gum.*

22	**3**	2 on 3 pies, rosy mauve..........	15	50
		a. Surch Type 7 inverted.......	90·00	90·00
		b. Surch Type 7a................	£700	£400
		c. Surch Type 7b................	£150	
		d. Stamps *tête-bêche*........	£150	£170
		e. Stamps and surchs *tête-bêche*	£190	£225

Varieties a, d and e were caused by the inversion of one stamp (No. 7) in the plate and the consequent inversion of the corresponding surcharge to correct the error.

Types 7a and 7b were applied by handstamp to correct the omission of the surcharge on R. 3/2 in different settings. Other sheets show a handstamped version of Type 7.

8 Raja Rama Varma I   **8a**

(Recess Perkins, Bacon & Co)

1911–13. *Currency in pies and annas.* W **8a**. P 14.

26	**8**	2p. brown	30	10
		a. Imperf (pair)...............		
27		3p. blue...........................	1·10	10
		a. Perf 14×12½................	27·00	2·50
		w. Wmk inverted................	—	75·00
28		4p. green..........................	1·50	10
		aw. Wmk inverted................	—	£130
28b		4p. apple-green...................	2·50	40
		bw. Wmk inverted................		
29		9p. carmine.......................	1·10	10
		a. Wmk sideways...............		
30		1a. brown-orange.................	2·75	10
31		1½a. grey (1913).................	6·00	45
32		2a. grey (1913)..................	7·50	40
33		3a. vermilion (1913)............	35·00	35·00
26/33		Set of 8.........................	50·00	35·00

No. 27a is line perforated. Nos. 27 and 33 exist perforated 14 either from comb or line machines. The other values only come from the comb machine.

Raja (Maharaja from 1921) Rama Varma II, 1914–1932

9 Raja Rama Varma II   **10** Raja Rama Varma II

I   (2p.)   II

I   (1a.)   II

(Recess Perkins, Bacon & Co)

1916–30. W **8a**. P 13½ to 14.

35	**10**	2p. brown (Die I) (*a*) (*b*) (*c*)..	6·50	10
		a. Imperf (pair)...............	£550	
		b. Die II (*b*) (*c*) (1930)..	1·60	10
36		4p. green (*a*) (*b*)...........	1·00	10
37		6p. red-brown (*a*) (*b*) (*c*) (1922)...	2·50	10
		w. Wmk inverted................	—	£100
38		8p. sepia (*b*) (1923)..........	1·50	10
39		9p. carmine (*a*)...............	17·00	25
40		10p. blue (*b*) (1923)..........	4·50	10
41	**9**	1a. orange (Die I) (*a*)........	15·00	2·25
		a. Die II (*a*) (*b*) (1922)...	9·50	30
42	**10**	1½a. purple (*b*) (1923).........	2·75	20
43		2a. grey (*a*) (*b*) (*d*).......	4·25	10
44		2¼a. yellow-green (*a*) (*d*) (1922)..	5·50	3·25
45		3a. vermilion (*a*) (*b*)........	11·00	35
35/45		Set of 11.........................	55·00	4·50

Four different perforating heads were used for this issue: (*a*) comb 13.9; (*b*) comb 13.6; (*c*) line 13.8; (*d*) line 14.2. Values on which each perforation occur are shown above. Stamps with perforation (*a*) are on hand-made paper, while the other perforations are on softer machine-made paper with a horizontal mesh.

Two pies   Two pies   Two pies
(11)   (12)   (13)

2   2

Two Pies (14)   Two Pies (15)

1922–29. *T* **8** *(P 14), surch with T* **11/15.**

46	**11**	2p. on 3p. blue..................................	40	30
		a. Surch double	£325	£325
47	**12**	2p. on 3p. blue..................................	2·75	1·00
		a. Surch double	£650	
		b. "Pies" for "pies" (R. 4/8) ...	45·00	21·00
		ba. Surch double	£650	
		c. Perf 12½ at foot		
48	**13**	2p. on 3p. blue (6.24).....................	5·50	35
		a. "Pies" for "pies" (R. 4/8) ...	55·00	16·00
		b. Perf 14×12½	14·00	18·00
		ba. Ditto. "Pies" for "pies" (R. 4/8)	£225	£275
49	**14**	2p. on 3p. blue (1929).....................	9·00	9·00
		a. Surch double	£325	
		b. Surch with Type **15**..........	65·00	£110
		ba. Ditto. Surch double	£1600	

There are four settings of these overprints. The first (July 1922) consisted of 39 stamps with Type **11**, and 9 with Type **12**, and in Type **11** the centre of the "2" is above the "o" of "Two". In the second setting (May 1924) there were 36 of Type **11** and 12 of Type **12**, and the centre of the figure is above the space between "Two" and "Pies". The third setting (June 1924) consists of stamps with Type **13** only.

The fourth setting (1929) was also in sheets of 48. No. 49b being the first stamp in the first row.

No. 47c is from the bottom row of a sheet and was re-perforated 12½ line at foot as the bottom line of 14 perforations were too far from the design.

ONE ANNA ഒരു അണ (16)   Three Pies ൩ 3 (17)

ANCHAL & REVENUE (16)   മൂന്ന പൈ (17)

1928. *Surch with T* **16.**

50	**10**	1a. on 2¼a. yellow-green (a).............	5·00	12·00
		a. "REVENUF" for "REVENUE"	50·00	80·00
		b. Surch double		

1932–33. *Surch as T* **17.** W **8a.** P 13½.

51	**10**	3p. on 4p. green (b).......................	1·10	1·25
		a. "r" in "Three" inverted...	†	£350
52		3p. on 8p. sepia (b)	2·00	2·75
53		9p. on 10p. blue (b).....................	1·50	3·25
51/3 *Set of 3*			4·25	6·50

Maharaja Rama Varma III, 1932–1941

18 Maharaja Rama Varma III

(Recess Perkins, Bacon & Co)

1933–38. *T* **18** *(but frame and inscription of 1a. as T* **9**). W **8a.** P 13×13½.

54	**18**	2p. brown (1936)	70	50
55		4p. green......................................	60	10
56		6p. red-brown...............................	70	10
57	—	1a. brown-orange	70	20
58	**18**	1a.8p. carmine	3·00	5·50
59		2a. grey (1938)	5·00	1·40
60		2¼a. yellow-green	1·50	30
61		3a. vermilion (1938)	5·00	1·40
62		3a.4p. violet.................................	1·75	1·40
63		6a.8p. sepia.................................	1·75	13·00
64		10a. blue....................................	3·00	15·00
54/64 *Set of 11*			21·00	35·00

For stamps in this design, but lithographed, see Nos. 67/71.

1934. *Surcharged as T* **14.** W **8a.** P 13½.

65	**10**	6p. on 8p. sepia (R.) (b)....................	75	60
66		6p. on 10p. blue (R.) (b)...................	1·75	2·00

"DOUBLE PRINTS". The errors previously listed under this description are now identified as blanket offsets, a type of variety outside the scope of this catalogue. Examples occur on issues from 1938 onwards.

SPACING OF OVERPRINTS AND SURCHARGES. The typeset overprints and surcharges issued from 1939 onwards show considerable differences in spacing. Except for specialists, however, these differences have little significance as they occur within the same settings and do not represent separate printings.

(Litho The Associated Printers, Madras)

1938. W **8a.** P 11.

67	**18**	2p. brown	1·00	40
		aw. Wmk inverted	£150	75·00
		b. Perf 13×13½	5·50	70
68		4p. green......................................	1·00	35
		aw. Wmk inverted		
		b. Perf 13×13½	8·00	18·00
69		6p. red-brown...............................	2·25	10
		aw. Wmk inverted	†	
		b. Perf 13×13½	†	£3000
70		1a. brown-orange	65·00	85·00
		aw. Wmk inverted		
		b. Perf 13×13½	90·00	£120
71		2¼a. sage-green	6·00	25
		a. Perf 13×13½	15·00	6·50
67/71 *Set of 5*			70·00	85·00

Most examples of Nos. 70/b were used fiscally. Collectors are warned against examples which have been cleaned and regummed or provided with forged postmarks.

ANCHAL (19)   ANCHAL (19a)   THREE PIES (20)

SURCHARGED   ANCHAL

ONE ANNA THREE PIES (21)   NINE PIES (22)

ANCHAL   ANCHAL

NINE PIES (23)   SURCHARGED NINE PIES (24)

1939 *(Jan). Nos.* 57 *and* 70 *optd with T* **19a.**

72	**18**	1a. brown-orange (recess) (T **19**)....	4·00	1·50
		w. Wmk inverted	†	£130
73		1a. brown-orange (litho) (T **19**)	£300	1·50
		aw. Wmk inverted	†	
		b. Perf 13×13½	—	£300
74		1a. brown-orange (litho) (T **19a**)	75	1·60
		a. Perf 13×13½	12·00	50

In 1939 it was decided that there would be separate 1a. stamps for revenue and postal purposes. The "ANCHAL" overprints were applied to stamps intended for postal purposes.

1942–44. *T* **18** *variously optd or surch.*

I. Recess-printed stamp. No. 58.

75		3p. on 1a.8p. carmine (T **20**)	£200	90·00
76		3p. on 1a.8p. carmine (T **21**)	4·75	9·50
77		6p. on 1a.8p. carmine (T **20**)	3·25	20·00
78		1a.3p. on 1a.8p. carmine (T **21**)	1·00	40

II. Lithographed stamps. Nos. 68, 70 *and* 70b.

79		3p. on 4p. (T **21**)	6·00	4·00
		a. Perf 13×13½	15·00	4·00
80		6p. on 1a. (T **22**)	£425	£225
		a. "SIX PIES" double	†	£1000
81		6p. on 1a. (T **23**)	£250	£180
		a. Perf 13×13½	£140	60·00
82		9p. on 1a. (T **22**)	£130	£120
83		9p. on 1a. (T **23**) (P 13×13½)	£325	40·00
84		9p. on 1a. (T **24**) (P 13×13½)	21·00	6·50

Maharaja Kerala Varma II, 1941–1943

26 Maharaja Kerala Varma II

27 (The actual measurement of this wmk is 6¼ × 358in.)

(Litho The Associated Printers, Madras)

1943. *Frame of 1a. inscr* "ANCHAL & REVENUE". P 13×13½.

(a) W **8a.**

85	**26**	2p. grey-brown...............................	2·75	3·75
		a. Perf 11	†	£1900
85b		4p. green......................................	£750	£325
85c		1a. brown-orange	90·00	£110
85/c *Set of 3*			£800	£400

(b) W **27.**

86	**26**	2p. grey-brown...............................	27·00	3·25
		a. Perf 11	†	£2750
87		4p. green......................................	7·00	22·00
		a. Perf 11	3·00	4·75
88		6p. red-brown...............................	2·50	10
		a. Perf 11	8·00	1·60
89		9p. ultramarine (P 11)	38·00	1·00
		a. Imperf between (horiz pair).......	£1800	
90		1a. brown-orange	£200	£180
		a. Perf 11	22·00	50·00
91		2¼a. yellow-green	25·00	2·50
		a. Perf 11	28·00	8·50

Part of W **27** appears on many stamps in each sheet, while others are entirely without wmk.

Although inscribed "ANCHAL (= Postage) & REVENUE" most examples of Nos. 85c and 90/a were used fiscally. Collectors are warned against examples which have been cleaned and regummed or provided with forged postmarks.

Maharaja Ravi Varma, 1943–1946

1943. *T* **26** *variously optd or surch.* P 13×13½.

(a) W **8a.**

92		3p. on 4p. (T **21**)	80·00	19·00
92a		9p. on 1a. (T **23**)	5·50	3·50
92b		9p. on 1a. (T **24**)	6·50	2·75
92c		1a.3p. on 1a. (T **21**)	†	£3500

(b) W **27.**

93		2p. on 6p. (T **20**)	75	3·75
		a. Perf 11	85	2·75
94		3p. on 4p. (T **20**) (P 11)	4·00	10
95		3p. on 4p. (T **21**)	4·75	10
96		3p. on 6p. (T **20**)	85	20
		a. Perf 11	85	85
97		4p. on 6p. (T **20**)	4·00	10·00

No. 92c is believed to be an error; a sheet of No. 85b, having been included in a stock of No. O52 intended to become No. O66.

28 Maharaja Ravi Varma   **29** Maharaja Ravi Varma

I   II

(Litho The Associated Printers, Madras)

1944–48. W **27** *No gum.*

(a) Type I. P 11.

98	**28**	9p. ultramarine (1944)	14·00	3·00

(b) Type II. P 13.

98a	**28**	9p. ultramarine (1946)	12·00	17·00
		ab. Imperf between (horiz pair)	42·00	3·25
99		1a.3p. magenta (1948)	7·00	8·50
		a. Perf 13×13½	£250	50·00
100		1a.9p. ultramarine (shades) (1948).......	8·50	14·00
98a/100 *Set of 3*			25·00	23·00

Nos. 98a/100 are line-perforated, Nos. 98ab and 99a comb-perforated.

Maharaja Kerala Varma III, 1946–48

(Litho The Associated Printers, Madras)

1946–48. *Frame of 1a. inscr* "ANCHAL & REVENUE". W **27.** *No gum (except for stamps perf 11).* P 13.

101	**29**	2p. chocolate	2·00	20
		a. Imperf horiz (vert pair)	£2000	£2000
		c. Perf 11	8·00	60
		d. Perf 11×13	£375	£140
102		3p. carmine	50	30
103		4p. grey-green	£2250	80·00
104		6p. red-brown (1947)	21·00	4·75
		a. Perf 11	£160	4·75
105		9p. ultramarine	50	10
		a. Imperf between (horiz pair).......	†	£1800
106		1a. orange (1948)	7·50	29·00
		a. Perf 11	£500	
107		2a. black......................................	£120	8·00
		a. Perf 11	£140	6·50
108		3a. vermilion	75·00	1·00
101/8 *Set of 8*			£2250	£110

Although inscribed "ANCHAL (=Postage) & REVENUE" most examples of No. 106 were used fiscally.

The 1a.3p. magenta, 1a.9p. ultramarine and 2¼a. yellow-green in Type **29** subsequently appeared surcharged or overprinted for official use. Examples of the 1a.3p. magenta exist without overprint, but may have not been issued in this state (*Price £250 unused*).

30 Maharaja Kerala
Varma III

Die I   Die II

Two dies of 2p.:
Die I. Back of headdress almost touches value tablet. Narrow strip of tunic visible below collar.
Die II. Back of headdress further away from tablet. Wider strip of tunic visible below collar.

Die I   Die II

Two dies of 3a.4p.
Die I. Frame around head broken by value tablets. Two white lines below value inscription.
Die II. Continuous frame around head. Single white line below value inscription.

Tail to turban flaw (R. 1/7)

(Litho The Associated Printers, Madras)

1948–50. W **27** (upright or inverted). P 11.
109	**30**	2p. grey-brown (I)...............................	1·75	15
		a. Imperf vert (horiz pair).............	†	£1800
		b. Die II...................................	£150	1·50
110		3p. carmine.....................................	75	15
		a. Imperf between (vert pair)........	—	£1500
111		4p. green..	16·00	2·75
		a. Imperf vert (horiz pair).............	£275	£325
112		6p. chestnut....................................	16·00	25
		a. Imperf vert (horiz pair).............	£800	
113		9p. ultramarine...............................	2·50	35
114		2a. black..	55·00	2·00
115		3a. orange-red................................	70·00	1·00
		a. Imperf vert (horiz pair).............	£2000	
116		3a.4p. violet (1950).........................	70·00	£350
		a. Tail to turban flaw..................	£250	£650
		b. Die II...................................	£180	
109/16 *Set of 8*...			£200	£350

Maharaja Rama Varma IV, 1948–1964

31 Chinese Nets   **32** Dutch Palace

(Litho The Associated Printers, Madras)

1949. W **27**. P 11.
117	**31**	2a. black...................................	4·25	7·50
		a. Imperf vert (horiz pair).............	£425	
118	**32**	2¼a. green..................................	2·75	8·00
		a. Imperf vert (horiz pair).............	£425	

A used example of a 2¼a. value in a slightly different design exists showing a larger portrait of the ruler, the conch shell at upper right pointing to the right and with shading below "DUTCH PALACE". This may have come from a proof sheet subsequently used for postal purposes.

SIX PIES

ആറു പൈ
(33)

പൈ
Normal

പൈ
Error

Due to similarities between two Malayalam characters some values of the 1948 provisional issue exist with an error in the second word of the Malayalam surcharge. On Nos. 119, 122 and O103 this occurs twice in the setting of 48. No. 125 shows four examples and No. O104b one. Most instances are as illustrated above, but in two instances on the setting for No. 125 the error occurs on the second character.

1949. Surch as T **33**.
(i) On 1944–48 issue. P 13.
119	**28**	6p. on 1a.3p. magenta.................	4·75	4·00
		a. Incorrect character	35·00	30·00
120		1a. on 1a.9p. ultramarine (R.).............	1·50	1·40

(ii) On 1946–48 issue.
121	**29**	3p. on 9p. ultramarine	9·00	21·00
122		6p. on 1a.3p. magenta	15·00	13·00
		a. Surch double	†	£500
		b. Incorrect character	90·00	85·00
123		1a. on 1a.9p. ultramarine (R.).............	3·00	2·25
		a. Surch in black	†	£2500
		b. Black surch with smaller native characters 7½ mm instead of 10 mm long	†	£3500

(iii) On 1948–50 issue.
124	**30**	3p. on 9p. ultramarine	2·00	1·75
		a. Larger native characters 20 mm instead of 16½ mm long	2·50	50
		ab. Imperf between (vert pair)..	†	£1600
		b. Surch double	£475	
		c. Surch both sides..................	£375	
125		3p. on 9p. ultramarine (R.)...............	4·50	2·75
		a. Incorrect character	27·00	22·00
126		6p. on 9p. ultramarine (R.).................	1·75	40
119/26 *Set of 8*..			38·00	42·00

The 9p. ultramarine (T **29**) with 6p. surcharge (T **33**) in red was prepared for use but not issued (*Price £200 unused*)

1949. Surch as T **20**. W **27**. P 13.
127	**29**	6p. on 1a. orange...................	60·00	£140
128		9p. on 1a. orange...................	90·00	£140

OFFICIAL STAMPS

On   ON   ON

C   G   C   G   C   G

S   S   S

(O **1**)   (O **2** Small "ON")   (O **3** "G" without serif)

1913. Optd with Type O **1** (3p.) or O **2** (others).
O1	**8**	3p. blue (R.).............................	£120	10
		a. Black opt...........................	†	£1100
		b. Inverted "S".......................	—	50·00
		c. Opt double.........................	†	£550
O2		4p. green (*wmk sideways*).............	8·50	10
		a. Opt inverted.......................	—	£275
O3		9p. carmine.............................	£110	10
		a. Wmk sideways.....................	15·00	10
		w. Wmk inverted.....................	†	95·00
O4		1½a. purple..............................	42·00	10
		a. Opt double.........................	—	£600
O5		2a. grey..................................	13·00	10
O6		3a. vermilion...........................	50·00	35
O7		6a. violet................................	50·00	2·00
O8		12a. ultramarine.......................	40·00	6·50
O9		1½r. deep green.......................	35·00	70·00
O1/9 *Set of 9*...			£325	75·00

1919–33. Optd as Type O **3**.
O10	**10**	4p. green (a) (b)........................	3·75	10
		a. Opt double.........................	—	£450
O11		6p. red-brown (a) (b) (1922).........	9·50	10
		a. Opt double.........................	—	£400
		w. Wmk inverted.....................	†	—
O12		8p. sepia (b) (1923)...................	11·00	10
O13		9p. carmine (a) (b).....................	55·00	10
O14		10p. blue (b) (1923)....................	12·00	10
		a. Opt double.........................	†	£600
O15		1½a. purple (a) (b) (1921)............	5·50	10
		a. Opt double.........................	†	£600

O16		2a. grey (b) (1923)....................	40·00	20
O17		2¼a. yellow-green (a) (b) (1922)......	12·00	10
		a. Opt double.........................	†	£375
O18		3a. vermilion (a) (b) (c)...............	17·00	25
		a. Opt inverted.......................	†	£400
O19		6a. violet (a) (b) (1924)..............	38·00	50
O19a		12a. ultramarine (a) (b) (1929)........	15·00	4·50
O19b		1½r. deep green (a) (b) (1933)........	23·00	£110
O10/19b *Set of 12*..			£200	£110

All values exist showing a straight-backed "C" variety on R. 4/1.

8

ON   ON

C   G   C   G

Eight pies   S   S
(O **4** 27½ mm high)   (O **5** Straight back to "C")   (O **6** Circular "O"; "N" without serifs)

1923 (Jan)–**24**. T **8** and **10** surch with Type O **4**.
O20		8p. on 9p. carmine (No. O3)...........	£350	1·60
		a. "Pies" for "pies" (R. 4/8)........	£1000	55·00
		b. Wmk sideways.....................	£130	20
		ba. "Pies" for "pies" (R. 4/8)........	£375	18·00
		c. Surch double.......................	†	£350
O21		8p. on 9p. carm (a) (b) (No. O13) (11.24)..	70·00	10
		a. "Pies" for "pies" (R. 4/8)........	£190	12·00
		b. Surch double.......................	—	£275
		c. Opt Type O **3** double.............	†	£300

Varieties with smaller "i" or "t" in "Eight" and small "i" in "Pies" are also known from a number of positions in the setting.

1925 (Apr). T **10** surch as Type O **4**.
O22		10p. on 9p. carmine (b) (No. O13)....	80·00	80
		b. Surch double.......................	†	£300
		c. Surch 25 mm high (a)..............	£200	1·00
		ca. Surch double.......................	†	£325

1929. T **8** surch as Type O **4**.
O23		10p. on 9p. carmine (No. O3a)........	£1000	13·00
		a. Surch double.......................	†	£475
		b. Wmk upright........................	—	60·00

1929–31. Optd with Type O **5**.
O24	**10**	4p. green (b) (1931)...................	22·00	1·40
		a. Inverted "S".......................	£170	14·00
O25		6p. red-brown (b) (c) (d) (1930).....	13·00	10
		a. Inverted "S".......................	95·00	10
O26		8p. sepia (b) (1930)..................	7·00	10
		a. Inverted "S".......................	60·00	4·75
O27		10p. blue (b)...........................	6·00	10
		a. Inverted "S".......................	55·00	5·00
O28		2a. grey (b) (1930)...................	35·00	15
		a. Inverted "S".......................	£200	7·50
O29		3a. vermilion (b) (1930)..............	8·00	15
		a. Inverted "S".......................	90·00	8·00
O30		6a. violet (b) (d) (1930).............	90·00	5·00
		a. Inverted "S".......................	£550	90·00
O24/30 *Set of 7*...			£160	4·25

1933. Nos. O26/7 surch as T **14**, in red.
O32	**10**	6p. on 8p. sepia (b)..................	2·25	10
		a. Inverted "S".......................	20·00	4·25
O33		6p. on 10p. blue (b)...................	4·00	10
		a. Inverted "S".......................	40·00	3·75

The inverted "S" varieties occur on R. 2/1 of one setting of this overprint only.

1933–38. Recess-printed stamps of 1933–38 optd.
*(a) With Type O **5**.*
O34	**18**	4p. green..............................	3·25	10
O35		6p. red-brown (1934).................	3·00	10
O36		1a. brown-orange....................	15·00	10
O37		1a.8p. carmine........................	1·50	30
O38		2a. grey................................	15·00	10
O39		2¼a. yellow-green....................	4·50	10
O40		3a. vermilion..........................	42·00	10
O41		3a.4p. violet..........................	1·50	15
O42		6a.8p. sepia..........................	1·50	20
O43		10a. blue..............................	1·50	70
O34/43 *Set of 10*......................................			80·00	1·75

*(b) With Type O **6** (typo).*
O44	**18**	1a. brown-orange (1937).............	38·00	60
O45		2a. grey-black (1938)................	21·00	2·00
O46		3a. vermilion (1938).................	11·00	2·25
O44/6 *Set of 3*...			65·00	4·25

ON   ON

C   G   C   G

S   S

(O **7** Curved back to "c")   (O **8**)

ON   ON   ON

C   G   C   G   C   G

S   S   S

(O **9** Circular "O";   (O **10** Oval "O")   (O **11**
N with serifs)

1938–44. *Lithographed stamps of 1938.* W **8a**, optd.

(a) With Type O 7 or O 8 (1a). P 11.

O47	18	4p. green	28·00	2·50
		a. Inverted "S"	35·00	2·50
		b. Perf 13×13½	21·00	2·75
O48		6p. red-brown	25·00	40
		a. Inverted "S"	30·00	50
O49		1a. brown-orange	£275	2·50
O50		2a. grey-black	18·00	90
		a. Inverted "S"	19·00	1·00

(b) With Type O 9 (litho) or O 10 (6p.).

O51	18	6p. red-brown (P 13×13½)	11·00	3·75
O52		1a. brown-orange	1·00	10
O53		3a. vermilion	3·00	1·25

(c) With Type O 11.

O53a	18	6p. red-brown	£850	£400

The inverted "S" varieties, Nos. O47a, O48a and O50a, occur 21 times in the setting of 48.

1942–43. *Unissued stamps optd with Type O 10. Litho.* W **27**. P 11.

O54	18	4p. green	65·00	16·00
		a. Perf 13×13½	2·25	70
O55		6p. red-brown	£130	11·00
		a. Perf 13×13½	20·00	70
		ab. Optd both sides	†	£150
O56		1a. brown-orange	12·00	5·00
		a. Perf 13×13½	1·60	4·25
		ab. Optd both sides	†	£150
O56b		2a. grey-black (1943)	60·00	80
		ba. Opt omitted	†	£1200
O56c		2¼a. sage-green (1943)	£1400	6·50
O56d		3a. vermilion (1943)	18·00	6·00

1943. *Official stamps variously surch with T 20 or 21.*

(i) On 1½a. purple of 1919–33.

O57	10	3p. on 1½a. (b) (T 20)	£550	24·00

(ii) On recess printed 1a.8p. carmine of 1933–44 (Type O 5 opt).

O58		3p. on 1a.8p. (T 21)	5·50	2·50
O59		9p. on 1a.8p. (T 20)	£120	27·00
O60		1a.9p. on 1a.8p. (T 20)	2·50	2·25
O61		1a.9p. on 1a.8p. (T 21)	80	30

(iii) On lithographed stamps of 1938–44. P 11. (a) W 8a.

O62	18	3p. on 4p. (Types O 7 and 20) (P 13×13½)	25·00	9·00
		a. Surch double	£375	£160
O63		3p. on 4p. (Types O 7 and 21) (P 13×13½)	£140	55·00
O64		3p. on 1a. (Types O 9 and 20)	2·00	3·50
O65		9p. on 1a. (Types O 9 and 20)	£250	50·00
O66		1a.3p. on 1a. (Types O 9 and 21)	£300	95·00

(b) W 27.

O67	18	3p. on 4p. (Types O 10 and 20) (P 13×13½)	90·00	50·00
O67a		3p. on 4p. (Types O 10 and 21) (P 13×13½)	£750	
O67b		3p. on 1a. (Types O 10 and 20)	£140	75·00
		ba. Perf 13×13½	95·00	75·00

1944. *Optd with Type O 10. W 27. P 13×13½.*

O68	26	4p. green	32·00	5·50
		a. Perf 11	£130	5·50
		b. Perf 13	£400	65·00
O69		6p. red-brown	2·25	10
		a. Opt double	—	70·00
		b. Perf 11	70	70·00
		ba. Opt double	—	70·00
		c. Perf 13	7·00	2·50
O70		1a. brown-orange	£2500	50·00
O71		2a. black	5·50	60
O72		2¼a. yellow-green	3·25	1·00
		a. Optd both sides	†	£130
O73		3a. vermilion	8·50	1·25
		a. Perf 11	8·50	40

Stamps perforated 13×13½ are from a comb machine; those perforated 13 from a line perforator.

1944. *Optd with Type O 10 and variously surch as Types 20 and 21.* W **27**.

O74	26	3p. on 4p. (T 20)	2·75	10
		a. Perf 11	7·50	60
		ab. Optd Type O 10 on both sides	†	£140
O75		3p. on 4p. (T 21)	4·50	30
		a. Perf 11	£375	£170
O76		3p. on 1a. (T 20)	22·00	5·50
O77		9p. on 6p. (T 20)	9·00	2·75
		a. Stamp printed both sides	†	£425
O78		9p. on 6p. (T 21)	3·50	30
O79		1a.3p. on 1a. (T 20)	9·50	2·25
O80		1a.3p. on 1a. (T 21)	3·25	10
O74/80 Set of 7			50·00	10·00

1946–47. *Stamps of 1944–48 (Head Type II) optd with Type O 10. P 13.*

O81	28	9p. ultramarine	2·75	10
		a. Stamp printed both sides	†	£500
		b. Perf 13×13½	4·50	10
O82		1a.3p. magenta (1947)	1·60	20
		a. Optd both sides	19·00	12·00
		b. Optd on both sides	†	
		ba. Optd both sides, opt double and inverted on reverse	50·00	
O83		1a.9p. ultramarine (1947)	40	1·00
		a. Opt double		
		b. Pair, one without opt	†	£1500
O81/3 Set of 3			4·25	1·10

1946–48. *Stamps of 1946–48 and unissued values optd with Type O 2. P 13.*

O84	29	3p. carmine	1·00	10
		a. Stamp printed both sides	†	£550
O85		4p. grey-green	28·00	6·00
O86		6p. red-brown	10·00	1·00
O87		9p. ultramarine	75	10
O88		1a.3p. magenta	3·00	1·00
O89		1a.9p. ultramarine	3·75	40
O90		2a. black	13·00	3·00

O91		2¼a. yellow-green	22·00	4·00
O84/91 Set of 8			75·00	14·00

1948–49. *Stamps of 1948–50 and unissued values optd with Type O 7.*

O92	30	3p. carmine	1·25	15
		a. "C" for "G" in opt	14·00	3·25
O93		4p. green	1·25	30
		a. Imperf between (horiz pair)	†	£1400
		b. Imperf between (vert pair)	†	£1400
		c. Optd on both sides	75·00	75·00
		d. "C" for "G" in opt	15·00	5·00
O94		6p. chestnut	2·50	30
		a. Imperf between (vert pair)	†	£1600
		b. "C" for "G" in opt	24·00	4·00
O95		9p. ultramarine	2·75	10
		a. "C" for "G" in opt	25·00	3·75
O96		2a. black	2·75	15
		a. "C" for "G" in opt	26·00	4·25
O97		2¼a. yellow-green	3·00	6·00
		a. "C" for "G" in opt	28·00	48·00
O98		3a. orange-red	1·10	70
		a. "C" for "G" in opt	18·00	9·50
O99		3a.4p. violet (I)	42·00	40·00
		a. "C" for "G" in opt	£275	£300
		b. Tail to turban flaw	£275	
		c. Die II	70·00	60·00
O92/9 Set of 8			50·00	15·00

The "C" for "G" variety occurs on R. 1/4. Nos. O92/9, O103/4 and O104b also exist with a flat back to "G" which occurs twice in each sheet on R. 1/5 and R. 2/8.

No. O93 exists with watermark sideways, but can usually only be identified when in multiples.

1949. *Official stamps surch as T 33.*

(i) On 1944 issue.

O100	28	1a. on 1a.9p. ultramarine (R.)	60	60

(ii) On 1948 issue.

O101	29	1a. on 1a.9p. ultramarine (R.)	22·00	15·00

(iii) On 1949 issue.

O103	30	6p. on 3p. carmine	1·00	60
		a. Imperf between (vert pair)	†	£1000
		b. Surch double	†	£300
		c. "C" for "G" in opt	13·00	10·00
		d. Incorrect character	13·00	10·00
O104	30	9p. on 4p. green (18 mm long)	75	2·75
		a. Imperf between (horiz pair)	£650	£750
		b. Larger native characters, 22 mm long	1·10	1·00
		ba. Ditto. Imperf between (horiz pair)	£650	£650
		bb. Incorrect character	18·00	15·00
		c. "C" for "G" in opt	16·00	26·00
		ca. Ditto. Larger native characters, 22 mm long	20·00	16·00
O100/4 Set of 4			22·00	15·50

No. O104 exists with watermark sideways, but can usually only be identified when in multiples.

1949. *No. 124a, but with lines of surch 17½ mm apart, optd "SERVICE".*

O105	30	3p.on 9p. ultramarine	60	70
		a. Imperf between (horiz pair)	†	£1700

From 1 July 1949 Cochin formed part of the new state of Travancore-Cochin. Existing stocks of Cochin issues continued to be used in conjunction with stamps of Travancore surcharged in Indian currency.

DHAR

PRICES FOR STAMPS ON COVER	
Nos. 1/4	*from × 50*
No. 5	*from × 30*
No. 6	
Nos. 7/9	*from × 50*
No. 10	

Raja (Maharaja from 1877) Anand Rao Puar III, 1857–1898

1   2

अर्धा बलड.   अधॉ लिबड.   आधॉ डबल.

No. 1c   No. 1d   No. 2

1897–1900. *Type-set. Colour-fugitive paper. With oval hand-stamp in black. No gum. Imperf.*

1	1	½p. black/red (three characters at bottom left)	2·75	3·00
		a. Handstamp omitted	£275	
		b. Line below upper inscription (R. 2/2)	65·00	65·00
		c. Character transposed (R. 2/3)	25·00	25·00
		d. Character transposed (R. 2/5)	65·00	
2		½p. black/red (four characters at bottom left)	2·75	3·50
		a. Handstamp omitted	£190	
3		¼a. black/orange	3·00	4·25
		a. Handstamp omitted	£225	
4		½a. black/magenta	4·25	5·00
		a. Handstamp omitted	£250	£200
		b. Line below upper inscription (R. 2/2)	£100	£120
5		1a. black/green	8·50	15·00
		a. Handstamp omitted	£425	
		b. Printed both sides	£750	

		c. Line below upper inscription (R. 2/2)	£200	£225
6		2a. black/yellow	28·00	48·00
		e. Top right corner ornament transposed with one from top of frame (R. 2/5)	£110	£150
1/6 Set of 6			45·00	70·00

Nos. 1/6 were each issued in sheets of 10 (5×2), but may, on the evidence of a single sheet of the ½ price value, have been printed in sheets of 20 containing two of the issued sheets *tête-bêche*.

Research has identified individual characteristics for stamps printed from each position in the sheet.

The same research suggests that the type remained assembled during the entire period of production, being amended as necessary to provide the different values. Seven main settings have been identified with changes sometimes occurring during their use which form subsettings.

The distribution of stamps between the main settings was as follows:

Setting I—½p.
Setting II—½a., 1a.
Setting III—1a.
Setting IV—½p., ½a., 1a.
Setting V—½p.
Setting VI—½p. (No. 2). ¼a.
Setting VII—2a.

The listed constant errors all occurred during Setting IV.

In No. 1c the three characters forming the second word in the lower inscription are transposed to the order (2) (3) (1) and in No. 1d to the order (3) (2) (1).

On Nos. 1b, 4b and 5c the line which normally appears above the upper inscription is transposed so that it appears below the characters.

All values show many other constant varieties including mistakes in the corner and border ornaments, and also both constant and non-constant missing lines, dots and characters.

Examples of complete forgeries and faked varieties on genuine stamps exist.

Raja (Maharaja from 1918) Udaji Rao Puar II, 1898–1926

(Typo at Bombay)

1898–1900. P 11 to 12.

7	2	½a. carmine	4·25	6·50
		a. Imperf (pair)	40·00	
		b. Deep rose	3·75	6·00
8		1a. claret	3·75	8·00
9		1a. reddish violet	4·25	15·00
		a. Imperf between (horiz pair)	£425	
		b. Imperf (pair)	£110	
10		2a. deep green	7·00	24·00
7/10 Set of 4			17·00	48·00

The stamps of Dhar have been obsolete since 31 March 1901.

DUNGARPUR

PRICES FOR STAMPS ON COVER	
Nos. 1/15	*from × 2*

Maharawal Lakshman Singh, 1918–1971

1 State Arms

(Litho Shri Lakshman Bijaya Printing Press, Dungarpur)

1933–47. P 11.

1	1	¼a. bistre-yellow	—	£190
2		¼a. rose (1935)	—	£600
3		¼a. red-brown (1937)	—	£375
4		1a. pale turquoise-blue	—	£160
5		1a. rose (1938)	—	£2000
6		1a.3p. deep reddish violet (1935)	—	£250
7		2a. deep dull green (1947)	£1500	£350
8		4a. rose-red (1934)	—	£600

Nos. 2 and 5 are known in a *se-tenant* strip of 3, the centre stamp being the 1a. value.

2   3   4

Maharawal Lakshman Singh

Three dies of ½a. (*shown actual size*):

Die I. Size 21×25½ mm. Large portrait (head 5 mm and turban 7½ mm wide), correctly aligned (sheets of 12 and left-hand stamps in subsequent blocks of four *se-tenant* horizontally with Die II)

Die II. Size 20×24½ mm. Large portrait (head 4¾ mm and turban 7 mm wide), but with less detail at foot and with distinct tilt to left (right-hand stamps in sheets of four horizontally *se-tenant* with Die I)

Die III. Size 21×25½ mm. Small portrait (head 4½ mm and turban 6½ mm wide) (sheets of 4)

(Typo L. V. Indap & Co, Bombay)

1939–46. T **2** *(various frames)* and **3/4**. Various perfs.

9	2	¼a. orange (P 12, 11, 10½ or 10)	£950	80·00
10		½a. verm (Die I) (P 12, 11 or 10½)	£300	60·00
		a. Die II (P 10½) (1944).............	£300	75·00
		ab. Horiz pair. Die I and Die II.......	£650	£190
		b. Die III (P 10) (1945)............	£400	60·00
		c. Imperf between (vert pair)..........	†	£3000
11		1a. deep blue (P 12, 11, 10½ or 10)	£300	55·00
12	3	1a.3p. brt mauve (P 10½ or 10)		
		(1944)	£950	£225
13	4	1½a. deep violet (P 10) (1946)..........	£1000	£225
14		2a. brt green (P 12, pin perf 11½)		
		(1943)	£1300	£450
15		4a. brown (P 12, 10½ or 10)		
		(1940)	£950	£190

Stamps perforated 12, 11 and 10½ were printed in sheets of 12 (4×3) which were imperforate along the top, bottom and, sometimes, at right so that examples exist with one or two adjacent sides imperforate. Stamps perforated 10 were printed in sheets of 4 either imperforate at top, bottom and right-hand side or fully perforated.

Dungarpur became part of Rajasthan by 15 April 1948.

DUTTIA (DATIA)

PRICES FOR STAMPS ON COVER	
Nos. 1/7	—
Nos. 8/11	*from* × 5
Nos. 12/15	—
Nos. 16/40	*from* × 20

All the stamps of Duttia were impressed with a circular handstamp (as a rule in *blue*) before issue.

This handstamp shows the figure of Ganesh in the centre, surrounded by an inscription in Devanagari reading "DATIYA STET POSTAJ 1893". Stamps could not be used for postage without this control mark.

PROCESS. Nos. 1/15 were type-set and printed singly. Nos. 16/40 were typo from plates comprising 8 or more clichés.

GUM. The stamps of Duttia (*except* No. 25c) were issued without gum.

Maharaja Bhawani Singh, 1857–1907

Rectangular labels each showing a double hand-drawn frame (in black for the 1a. and in red for the others), face value in black and the Ganesh handstamp are known on thin cream (½a.), rose (1a.), orange (2a.) or pale yellow (4a.) paper. These are considered by some specialists to be the first stamps of Duttia, possibly issued during 1893, but the evidence for this is inconclusive.

1 (2a.)   **2** (½a.) Ganesh   **3** (4a.)

1894?. *Rosettes in lower corners. Control handstamp in blue.* Imperf.

1	1	½a. black/*green*	£15000	
2		2a. grey-blue/*yellow*......................	£3000	
		a. Handstamp in black	£3250	
		b. Handstamp in red....................	†	£20000

Only three examples of No. 1 have been reported. In each instance the Devanagari inscription was originally 8a., but was amended in manuscript to ½a.

1896. *Control handstamp in blue.* Imperf.

3	2	1a. red	£3000	£3750
		a. Handstamp in black	£3000	£3750
		b. Handstamp in brown..................	£3500	

1896. *Control handstamp in blue.* Imperf.

4	3	¼a. black/*orange*	£3500	
		a. Without handstamp	£2500	

5		½a. black/*blue-green*......................	£7500	
		a. Without handstamp	£2500	
6		2a. black/*yellow*	£2250	
		a. Without handstamp	£11000	
7		4a. black/*rose*	£1300	
		a. Without handstamp	£14000	

Two types of centre:

I   II

Type I.	Small Ganesh. Height 13 mm. Width of statue 11 mm. Width of pedestal 8 mm.
Type II.	Large Ganesh. Height 13½ mm. Width of statue 11½ mm. Width of pedestal 11½ mm. "Flag" in god's right hand; "angle" above left. All stamps also show dot at top right corner.

1897–98. Imperf.

8	2	½a. black/*green* (I) (value in one		
		group)................................	60·00	£400
		a. *Tête-bêche* (horiz pair)..............	£1100	
		b. Value in two groups.................	22·00	£250
		ba. *Tête-bêche* (vert pair).............	£1100	
		bb. Doubly printed......................	£2750	
		bc. Type II (1898)....................	26·00	
9		1a. black/*white*	90·00	£300
		a. *Tête-bêche* (horiz pair)..............	£1100	
		b. Laid paper	20·00	
		ba. *Tête-bêche* (vert pair).............	£900	
		c. Type II (1898).....................	£100	
		ca. Laid paper	26·00	
10		2a. black/*yellow* (I)	28·00	£275
		a. On lemon	40·00	
		b. Type II (1898)....................	38·00	£325
11		4a. black/*rose* (I)........................	24·00	£225
		a. *Tête-bêche* (horiz pair)..............	£275	
		b. *Tête-bêche* (vert pair).............	£150	£500
		c. Doubly printed.....................	£2750	
		d. Type II (1898)....................	28·00	

A used example of the 4a. is known showing black roulettes at foot.

4 (½a.)   **5** (2a.)

1897. *Name spelt "DATIA."* Imperf.

12	4	½a. black/*green*	90·00	£500
13		1a. black/*white*	£170	
14		2a. black/*yellow*	£110	£500
		a. *Tête-bêche* (vert pair).............	£4250	
15		4a. black/*rose*	£100	£500
		a. *Tête-bêche* (vert pair).............	£4250	
12/15 Set of 4				£425

1899–1906.

(a) Rouletted in colour or in black, horizontally and at end of rows.

16	5	¼a. vermilion	3·25	
		a. Rose-red	2·75	
		b. Pale rose	2·50	
		c. Lake	3·75	19·00
		d. Carmine	3·75	
		e. Brownish red	8·50	
		ea. *Tête-bêche* (pair)...................	£3000	
17		½a. black/*blue-green*......................	2·75	19·00
		a. On deep green	5·50	
		b. On yellow-green (pelure)............	4·75	20·00
		c. On dull green (1906)................	3·00	
18		1a. black/*white*	3·00	19·00
19		2a. black/*lemon-yellow*	8·50	
		a. On orange-yellow	11·00	
		b. On buff-yellow	3·00	21·00
		ba. Handstamp in black	12·00	
		bb. Without handstamp..................	£350	
		c. On pale yellow (1906)	2·75	21·00
20		4a. black/*deep rose*	3·25	20·00
		a. *Tête-bêche* (pair)...................		
		b. Handstamp in black	17·00	
		c. Without handstamp	£250	

(b) Rouletted in colour between horizontal rows, but imperf at top and bottom and at ends of rows.

20d	5	¼a. brownish red	40·00	
21		1a. black/*white*	14·00	45·00
		a. Without handstamp	£550	

One setting of 16 (8×2) of the ¼a. value (No. 16e) showed an inverted cliché at R. 1/2.

1904–05. *Without rouletting.*

22	5	¼a. red	3·75	28·00
		a. Without handstamp	£400	
23		½a. black/*green*...........................	16·00	
24		1a. black (1905).........................	13·00	35·00

Maharaja Govind Singh, 1907–1955

1911. P 13½. *Stamps very wide apart.*

25	5	¼a. carmine	6·50	45·00
		a. Imperf horiz (vert pair)............	£250	
		b. Imperf between (horiz pair)......	£275	
		c. Stamps closer together (with		
		gum)	8·00	35·00
		d. As c. Imperf vert (horiz pair)	£120	
25e		1a. black		£850

No. 25e was mainly used for fiscal purposes (*Price on piece,* £80), but one example has been seen used on a registered postcard.

1912?. *Printed close together.*

(a) Coloured roulette× imperf.

26	5	½a. black/*green*	7·50	35·00

(b) Printed wide apart. P 13½× coloured roulette (¼a.) or 13½×imperf (½a.).

27	5	¼a. carmine	5·50	38·00
		a. Without handstamp	£275	
28		½a. black/*dull green*	12·00	42·00

1916. *Colours changed. Control handstamp in blue (Nos. 29/33) or black (No. 34).* Imperf.

29	5	¼a. deep blue	5·50	24·00
30		½a. green.................................	5·50	25·00
		a. Without handstamp	†	£850
31		1a. purple	6·50	26·00
		a. *Tête-bêche* (vert pair).............	24·00	
		ab. Without handstamp..................	£850	
32		2a. brown	15·00	30·00
33		2a. lilac	6·00	27·00
		a. Handstamp in black	29·00	
		b. Without handstamp	£225	
34		4a. Venetian red (date?)................	75·00	
		a. Without handstamp	£650	

1918. *Colours changed.*

(a) Imperf.

35	5	½a. blue..................................	3·50	16·00
36		1a. pink	3·50	18·00
		a. Handstamp in black	8·50	
		b. Without handstamp	£200	

(b) P 11½.

37	5	¼a. black	5·00	23·00

1920. *Rouletted.*

38	5	¼a. blue..................................	2·75	12·00
		a. Roul×perf 7	35·00	35·00
		b. Imperf between (vert pair).........	£500	
		c. Without handstamp	£140	
		d. Handstamp in black	8·50	
39		½a. pink	3·50	16·00
		a. Roul×perf 7	£190	
		b. Without handstamp	£190	
		c. Handstamp in black		

1920. Rough perf about 7.

40	5	½a. dull red	15·00	38·00
		a. Handstamp in black	42·00	
		b. Without handstamp	£225	

The stamps of Duttia have been obsolete since 1 April 1921.

FARIDKOT

PRICES FOR STAMPS ON COVER	
Nos. N1/4	*from* × 10
Nos. N5/6	*from* × 50
Nos. N7/8	—

GUM. The stamps of Faridkot (Nos. N1/8) were issued without gum.

Raja Bikram Singh, 1874–1898

N **1** (1 folus=	N **2** (1 paisa=	N **3**
¼a.)	¼a.)	

1879–86. *Rough, handstamped impression.* Imperf.

(a) Native thick laid paper.

N1	N 1	1f. ultramarine	40·00	42·00
N2	N 2	1p. ultramarine	£130	£130

(b) Ordinary laid paper.

N3	N 1	1f. ultramarine	14·00	16·00
N4	N 2	1p. ultramarine	75·00	90·00

(c) Wove paper, thick to thinnish.

N5	N 1	1f. ultramarine	2·50	4·00
		a. *Tête-bêche* (pair)...................	£275	
N6	N 2	1p. ultramarine	4·00	9·50
		a. Pair, one stamp sideways..........	£1300	

(d) Thin wove whity brown paper.

N7	N 2	1p. ultramarine	30·00	32·00

Faridkot signed a postal convention with the Imperial Government which led to the provision of India issues overprinted "FARIDKOT STATE" from 1 January 1887. These are listed in the Convention States section.

Although the previous issues were no longer valid for postal purposes the state authorities continued to sell them to collectors for many years after 1887. Initially remaining stocks of Nos. N1/7 were on offer, but these were soon supplemented by Type N **1** handstamped in other colours, examples of a ½a., handstamped in various colours, which had originally been prepared in 1877 and by a replacement 1p, as Type N **3**, (*Price* £1.50 *unused, tête-bêche pair,* £225, *unused*) which had not done postal duty before the convention came into force. The sale of such items was clearly an important source of revenue as the 1f. as Type N **1**, yet another version of the 1p. and the ½a. subsequently appeared printed in sheets by lithography for sale to stamp collectors.

HYDERABAD

PRICES FOR STAMPS ON COVER	
Nos. 1/3	*from* × 10
Nos. 4/12	—
Nos. 13/60	*from* × 5
Nos. O1/53	*from* × 10

The official title of the State in English was The Dominions of the Nizam and in Urdu "Sarkar-i-Asafia" (State of the successors of Asaf). This Urdu inscription appears in many of the designs.

Nawab Mir Mahbub Ali Khan Asaf Jah VI, 1869–1911

1   2

(Eng Mr. Rapkin. Plates by Nissen & Parker, London. Recess Mint, Hyderabad)

1869 (8 Sept). P 11½.
1	**1**	1a. olive-green	17·00	7·50
		a. Imperf between (horiz pair)	£150	
		b. Imperf horiz (vert pair)	£500	£110
		c. Imperf (pair)	£400	£400
		d. Imperf vert (horiz pair)	†	£350

Reprints in the colour of the issue, and also in fancy colours, were made in 1880 on white wove paper, perforated 12½. Fakes of No. 1c are known created by the removal of the outer perforations from examples of Nos. 1a/b.

1870 (16 May). *Locally engraved; 240 varieties of each value; wove paper. Recess.* P 11½.
2	**2**	½a. brown	4·00	4·25
3		2a. sage-green	50·00	45·00

Stamps exist showing traces of lines in the paper, but they do not appear to be printed on true laid paper.

Reprints of both values were made in 1880 on white wove paper, perforated 12½: the ½a. in grey-brown, yellow-brown, sea-green, dull blue and carmine and the 2a. in bright green and in blue-green.

3

A Normal   2a.   B Variety

In A the coloured lines surrounding each of the four labels join a coloured circle round their inner edge, in B this circle is missing.

C   3a.   D

C. Normal. D. Character ^ omitted

Left side of central inscription omitted (Pl 4 R. 2/11)

Dot at top of central inscription omitted

Second dot in bottom label omitted

Centre dot in bottom label omitted

(Plates by Bradbury, Wilkinson & Co. Recess Mint, Hyderabad)

1871–1909.

(a) No wmk.

(i) Rough perf 11½.
4	**3**	½a. red-brown	18·00	20·00
		a. Dot at top of central inscription omitted	£160	
5		1a. purple-brown	£120	£130
		a. Imperf horiz (vert pair)	†	£1700
		b. Dot at top of central inscription omitted	£800	£800
6		2a. green (A)	£1100	
7		3a. ochre-brown	38·00	48·00
8		4a. slate	£150	£150
9		8a. deep brown		
10		12a. dull blue	£325	

(ii) Pin perf 8-9.
11	**3**	½a. red-brown	—	£450
12		1a. drab	£350	£170

(iii) P 12½.
13	**3**	½a. orange-brown	2·25	10
		a. Imperf vert (horiz pair)	†	85·00
		ab. Imperf horiz (vert pair)	†	£700
		b. Orange	2·25	10
		c. Red-brown	2·25	10
		d. Brick-red	2·25	10
		da. Imperf vert (horiz pair)	†	85·00
		db. Doubly printed	£450	£160
		e. Rose-red	2·25	20
		ea. Doubly printed	†	£225
		f. Error. Magenta	48·00	8·00
		g. Left side of central inscription omitted	£275	75·00
		h. Dot at top of central inscription omitted	55·00	2·50
14		1a. purple-brown	6·50	6·50
		a. Doubly printed	£450	
		b. Drab	1·00	15
		ba. Imperf (pair)	—	£325
		bb. Doubly printed	£200	
		c. Grey-black	1·75	10
		ca. Imperf (pair)	†	£850
		d. Black (1909)	1·75	10
		da. Doubly printed	£450	£250
		db. Imperf vert (horiz pair)	†	£800
		dc. Imperf horiz (vert pair)	†	£800
		e. Dot at top of central inscription omitted		£140
		f. Second dot in bottom label omitted	£100	40·00
15		2a. green (A)	3·25	15
		a. Deep green (A)	3·50	40
		b. Blue-green (A)	3·25	40
		ba. Blue-green (B)	£200	65·00
		c. Pale green (A)	3·25	15
		ca. Pale green (B)	£200	75·00
		d. Sage-green (A) (1909)	3·25	35
		da. Sage-green (B)	£150	48·00
		e. Dot at top of central inscription omitted	£325	£100
		f. Centre dot in bottom panel omitted	£140	45·00
16		3a. ochre-brown (C)	2·50	1·40
		a. Character omitted (D)	£190	75·00
		b. Chestnut (C)	2·25	1·25
		ba. Character omitted (D)	£140	60·00
17		4a. slate	6·50	3·00
		a. Imperf horiz (vert pair)	£800	£800
		b. Greenish grey	4·50	2·75
		ba. Imperf vert (horiz pair)	£1300	
		c. Olive-green	5·00	2·00

18		8a. deep brown	2·50	3·50
		a. Imperf vert (horiz pair)	£800	
19		12a. pale ultramarine	3·75	7·00
		a. Grey-green	4·00	4·00
13/19 Set of 7			17·50	10·00

(b) W **7**. P 12½.
19b	**3**	1a. black (1909)	£120	14·00
19c		2a. sage-green (A) (1909)	£375	£100
19d		12a. bluish grey (1909)	£1000	

(4)   5

1898. *Surch with T* **4**. P 12½.
20	**3**	¼a. on ½a. orange-brown	50	85
		a. Surch inverted	35·00	23·00
		b. Pair, one without surcharge	£500	
		c. Left side of central inscription omitted	£160	

(Des Khusrat Ullah. Recess Mint, Hyderabad)

1900 (20 Sept). P 12½.
21	**5**	¼a. deep blue	5·00	3·25
		a. Pale blue	5·00	3·25

6   7

(Plates by Allan G. Wyon, London. Recess Mint, Hyderabad)

1905 (7 Aug). W **7**. P 12½.
22	**6**	¼a. dull blue	1·75	60
		a. Imperf (pair)	32·00	£100
		b. Dull ultramarine	5·00	80
		ba. Perf 11×12½	30·00	24·00
		c. Pale blue-green	22·00	2·75
23		½a. orange	5·00	35
		a. Perf 11		
		b. Vermilion	3·25	25
		ba. Imperf (pair)	30·00	£100
		c. Yellow	80·00	17·00

1908–11. W **7**. P 12½.
24	**6**	¼a. grey	75	10
		a. Imperf between (horiz pair)	£325	£325
		b. Imperf between (vert pair)	†	£325
		c. Perf 11½, 12	2·00	35
		d. Perf 11	65·00	20·00
25		½a. green	3·75	10
		a. Imperf between (vert pair)	£300	
		b. Perf 11½, 12	5·00	10
		c. Perf 13½	£110	35·00
		d. Pale green	3·75	20
		da. Perf 11½, 12	5·00	10
		e. Blue-green	6·00	10
26		1a. carmine	2·50	10
		a. Perf 11½, 12	6·00	1·00
		b. Perf 11	28·00	8·50
		c. Double impression (P 12½×11).		
27		2a. lilac	2·00	40
		a. Perf 11½, 12	3·50	1·10
		b. Perf 11	2·50	55
		c. Perf 13½	1·60	15
		ca. Imperf between (horiz pair)	†	£450
		cb. Rose-lilac	1·40	10
28		3a. brown-orange (1909)	2·00	75
		a. Perf 11½, 12	8·00	2·00
		b. Perf 11	1·25	60
		c. Perf 13½	2·00	30
29		4a. olive-green (1909)	2·00	75
		a. Perf 11½, 12	6·50	4·50
		b. Perf 11	30·00	11·00
		ba. Imperf between (pair)	£650	£650
		c. Perf 13½	1·10	30
30		8a. purple (1911)	3·50	5·00
		a. Perf 11½, 12		
		b. Perf 11	1·75	4·00
		c. Perf 13½	1·25	70
31		12a. blue-green (1911)	£110	70·00
		a. Perf 11½, 12	16·00	22·00
		b. Perf 11		
		c. Perf 13½	5·50	3·00
24/31c Set of 8			16·00	4·25

The above perforations also exist compound.

Nawab Mir Osman Ali Khan Asaf Jah VII, 1911–1967

1912. *New plates engraved by Bradbury, Wilkinson & Co.* W **7**. P 12½.
32	**6**	¼a. grey-black	1·40	10
		a. Imperf horiz (vert pair)	†	£300
		b. Perf 11½, 12	80	35
		c. Perf 11	90	15
		ca. Imperf between (horiz pair)	†	£300
		cb. Imperf between (vert pair)	†	£300
		d. Perf 13½	60	10
33		¼a. brown-purple (*shades*) (P 13½)	1·25	10
		a. Imperf horiz (vert pair)	†	£300
34		½a. deep green	1·25	10
		a. Imperf between (pair)	†	£325
		b. Imperf (pair). Laid paper	£100	80·00

c. Perf 11½, 12	7·50	55
d. Perf 11	8·50	10
e. Perf 13½		

The above perforations also exist compound.

In Wyon's ¼a. stamp the fraction of value is closer to the end of the label than in the B.W. issue. In the Wyon ¼a. and ½a. the value in English and the label below are further apart than in the B.W.

Wyon's ¼a. measures 19½×20 mm and the ½a. 19½×20½ mm; both stamps from the Bradbury plates measure 19¾×21½ mm.

8 Symbols

9

1915. *Inscr "Post & Receipt".* W **7**. P 13½.

35	**8**	½a. green	1·00	
		a. Imperf between (pair)	75·00	
		b. *Emerald-green*	3·25	
		c. Perf 12½	6·50	
		ca. Imperf between (pair)		
		d. Perf 11	60	
		da. Imperf between (pair)	†	
		db. Imperf vert (horiz pair)	†	
		e. Imperf (pair)	£160	
36		1a. carmine	2·00	
		a. Imperf between (pair)	£250	
		b. *Scarlet*	1·50	
		ba. Imperf between (horiz pair)	†	
		bb. Imperf between (vert pair)	†	
		bc. Imperf vert (horiz pair)	†	
		c. Perf 12½	17·00	
		ca. Imperf between (pair)		
		cc. *Scarlet*		
		d. Perf 11	1·25	
		da. Scarlet		
		e. Imperf (pair)	£200	

The above perforations also exist compound.

For ½a. claret, see No. 58.

1927 (1 Feb). As W **7**, but larger and sideways. P 13½.

37	**9**	1r. yellow	9·00	

10 (4 pies)

11 (8 pies)

1930 (6 May). *Surch as T* **10** *and* **11**. W **7**. P 13½.

38	**6**	4p. on ¼a. grey-black (R.)	75·00	20·00
		a. Perf 11	†	£200
		b. Perf 12½	†	80·00
		c. Perf 11½, 12	†	£450
39		4p. on ¼a. brown-purple (R.)	30	10·00
		a. Imperf between (pair)	£500	£500
		b. Surch double	†	£200
		c. Perf 11	†	£450
		d. Black surch	£450	£450
40	**8**	8p.on ½a. green (R.)	30	10·00
		a. Imperf between (horiz pair)	†	£250
		b. Perf 11	£275	£140
		c. Perf 12½	†	£275

12 Symbols

13 The Char Minar

14 High Court of Justice   15 Osman Sagar Reservoir

16 Entrance to Ajanta Caves   17 Bidar College

---

18 Victory Tower, Daulatabad

(Plates by De La Rue. Recess Stamps Office, Hyderabad)

1931 (12 Nov)–**47**. *T* **12/18**. W **7**. Wove paper. P 13½.

41	**12**	4p. black	30	10
		a. Laid paper (1947)	2·50	5·50
		b. Imperf (pair)	50·00	90·00
42		8p. green	50	10
		a. Imperf between (vert pair)	—	£650
		b. Imperf (pair)	60·00	£110
		c. Laid paper (1947)	3·00	4·50
43	**13**	1a. brown (*shades*)	50	10
		a. Imperf between (horiz pair)	—	£650
		b. Perf 11	†	£800
44	**14**	2a. violet (*shades*)	3·00	10
		a. Imperf (pair)	£130	£225
45	**15**	4a. ultramarine	1·60	70
		a. Imperf (pair)	£140	£300
46	**16**	8a. orange	6·00	4·00
		a. *Yellow-orange* (1944)	70·00	32·00
47	**17**	12a. scarlet	6·50	12·00
48	**18**	1r. yellow	4·00	4·75
41/8 *Set of 8*			21·00	20·00

10 Nos. 41a and 42c have a large sheet watermark "THE NIZAM's GOVERNMENT HYDERABAD DECCAN" and arms within a circle, but this does not appear on all stamps.

19 Unani General Hospital

20 Osmania General Hospital

21 Osmania University   22 Osmania Jubilee Hall

(Litho Indian Security Printing Press, Nasik)

1937 (13 Feb). *T* **19/22**, *inscr* "H.E.H. THE NIZAM'S SILVER JUBILEE". P 14.

49	**19**	4p. slate and violet	60	1·75
50	**20**	8p. slate and brown	1·00	1·75
51	**21**	1a. slate and orange-yellow	1·40	1·40
52	**22**	2a. slate and green	1·75	4·50
49/52 *Set of 4*			4·25	8·50

23 Family Reunion

(Des T. I. Archer. Typo)

1945 (6 Dec). *Victory.* W **7** (*very faint*). *Wove paper.* P 13½.

53	**23**	1a. blue	10	10
		a. Imperf between (vert pair)	£600	
		b. Laid paper	70	70

No. 53b shows the sheet watermark described beneath Nos. 41/8.

24 Town Hall

(Des. T. I. Archer. Litho Government Press)

1947 (17 Feb). *Reformed Legislature.* P 13½.

54	**24**	1a. black	1·60	1·90
		a. Imperf between (pair)	—	£850

---

25 Power House, Hyderabad

26 Kaktyai Arch, Warangal Fort

27 Golkunda Fort

(Des T. I. Archer. Typo)

1947–49. *As T* **25/27** (*inscr* "H. E. H. THE NIZAM'S GOVT. POSTAGE*"*). W **7**. P 13½.

55	**25**	1a.4p. green	1·25	1·90
56	**26**	3a. greenish blue	2·00	3·75
		a. *Bluish green*	2·75	4·00
57	**27**	6a. sepia	4·50	16·00
		a. *Red-brown* (1949)	18·00	30·00
		ab. Imperf (pair)	£130	
55/7 *Set of 3*			7·00	19·00

1947. As 1915 issue but colour changed. P 13½.

58	**8**	½a. claret	2·25	75
		a. Imperf between (horizontal pair)	—	£325
		b. Imperf between (vert pair)	—	£600

An Independence commemorative set of four, 4p., 8p., 1a. and 2a., was prepared in 1948, but not issued.

1948. As T **12** ("POSTAGE" at foot). Recess. W **7**. P 13½.

59		6p. claret	8·50	7·50

Following intervention by the forces of the Dominion of India during September 1948 the Hyderabad postal system was taken over by the Dominion authorities, operating as an agency of the India Post Office.

1949. *T* **12** ("POSTAGE" at top). Litho. W **7**. P 13½.

60	**12**	2p. bistre-brown	1·75	2·50
		a. Imperf between (horizontal pair)	†	£800
		b. Imperf (pair)	£150	£475

No. 60 was produced from a transfer taken from a plate of the 4p., No. 41, with each impression amended appropriately.

OFFICIAL STAMPS

Official stamps became valid for postage within India from 1910.

(O 1)   (O 1a)   (O 2)

1873.

I. Handstamped as Type O **1** *in red.*

O1	**1**	1a. olive-green	85·00	25·00
		a. Black opt	—	£300
O2	**2**	½a. brown		£650
		a. Black opt		£550
O3		2a. sage-green		£550
		a. Black opt		£180

At least ten different handstamps as Type O 1 were used to produce Nos. O1/17. These differ in the size, shape and spacing of the characters. The prices quoted are for the cheapest versions where more than one is known to exist on a particular stamp.

Imitations of these overprints on genuine stamps and on reprints are found horizontally or vertically in various shades of red, in magenta and in black.

II. T **3** *handstamped as Type O* **1** *in red.*

(a) Rough perf 11½.

O4		½a. red-brown		
		a. Black opt	—	£750
O5		1a. purple-brown		£1000
		a. Black opt	£130	£160
O6		2a. green (A)		
		a. Black opt	—	£950
O7		4a. slate		
		a. Black opt	—	£1200
O8		8a. deep brown		
		a. Black opt	£1200	£950
O8b		12a. dull blue	—	£1200

(b) Pin perf 8–9.

O8c		1a. drab (*black opt*)	7·50	90·00
		ca. Second dot in bottom label omitted	£160	

(c) P 12½.

O9		½a. red-brown	15·00	4·50
		a. Black opt	9·50	3·25
		ab. Left side of central inscription omitted		£180
		ac. Dot at top of central inscription omitted		55·00
O11		1a. purple-brown	£110	75·00
		a. Black opt		30·00
O12		1a. drab	19·00	20·00
		a. Black opt	2·25	2·00
		ab. Second dot in bottom label omitted	£100	95·00
O13		2a. green (*to deep*) (A)	38·00	32·00
		a. Black opt	4·00	5·00
		ab. Inner circle missing (B)	£275	
		ac. Centre dot in bottom label omitted	£140	£140
O14		3a. ochre-brown	£140	£140
		a. Black opt	35·00	28·00
O15		4a. slate	65·00	40·00

	a. Black opt	17·00	16·00
O16	8a. deep brown	70·00	£120
	a. Imperf vert (horiz pair)	£700	
	b. Black opt	45·00	38·00
O17	12a. blue	£110	£140
	a. Black opt	50·00	80·00

The use of Official Stamps (Sarkari) was discontinued in 1878, but was resumed in 1909, when the current stamps were over-printed from a new die.

1909–11. *Optd with Type O 1a.*

(a) On Type 3. P 12½.

O18	½a. orange-brown	£100	4·75
	a. Opt inverted	†	£475
O19	1a. black	85·00	40
	a. Second dot in bottom label omitted ..	—	6·50
O20	2a. sage-green (A)	90·00	60
	a. Optd on No. 15da (B)	—	10·00
	b. Stamp doubly printed	†	£160
	c. Centre dot in bottom label omitted ...	—	9·00
	d. Opt double	†	£225
O20e	2a. ochre-brown	5·50	2·25
	ea. Character omitted (D)		£400
O20f	4a. olive-green	£375	5·00
	fa. Perf 11½, 12		£325
O20g	8a. deep brown	—	38·00
O20h	12a. grey-green	—	80·00

(b) On Type 6 (Wyon ptgs). P 12½.

O21	½a. orange	—	2·50
	a. Vermilion	£120	15
	ab. Opt inverted	†	£400
	ac. Imperf horiz (vert pair)	†	£400
O22	½a. green	19·00	10
	a. Pale green	19·00	10
	b. Opt inverted	†	75·00
	d. Imperf between (vert pair)	†	£300
	e. Imperf between (horiz pair)	†	£275
	e. Stamp doubly printed	†	£140
	f. Perf 11½, 12	17·00	30
	fa. Pale green	17·00	30
	fb. Opt inverted	†	75·00
	g. Perf 11	†	
	ga. Pale green		
	h. Perf 13½	—	80·00
O23	1a. carmine	55·00	15
	a. Opt double	£200	
	b. Perf 11½, 12	70·00	30
	ba. Stamp doubly printed	—	£140
	c. Perf 11	—	5·50
O24	2a. lilac	55·00	50
	a. Perf 11½, 12	£100	5·00
	b. Perf 11	£400	
O25	3a. brown-orange	£140	13·00
	b. Perf 11½, 12	£225	26·00
	ba. Opt inverted	†	£190
	c. Perf 11	£400	45·00
	d. Perf 13½	—	85·00
O26	4a. olive-green (1911)	26·00	70
	a. Perf 11½, 12	£100	3·25
	b. Perf 11	—	18·00
O27	8a. purple (1911)	13·00	2·75
	a. Perf 11½, 12	£110	8·00
	b. Perf 11	£400	£120
O28	12a. blue-green (1911)	9·00	2·50
	a. Imperf between (horiz pair)	£950	
	b. Perf 11½, 12	28·00	3·75
	c. Perf 11	†	£400

(c) On Type 6 (Bradbury Wilkinson ptgs). P 11.

O28d	6 ½a. deep green	£475	

1911–12. *Optd with Type O 2.*

(a) Type 6 (Wyon printings). P 13½ (8a, 12a.) or 12½ (others).

O29	¼a. grey	55·00	1·00
	a. Perf 11½, 12	24·00	50
	ab. Imperf between (vert pair)	†	£350
	b. Perf 11	90·00	38·00
	c. Perf 13½		
O30	½a. pale green	42·00	2·00
	a. Perf 11½, 12	—	30
	ab. Imperf between (vert pair)	†	£375
	b. Perf 13½		
O31	1a. carmine	1·50	15
	a. Opt inverted	—	40·00
	b. Imperf horiz (vert pair)	†	£350
	c. Perf 11½, 12	5·50	15
	d. Perf 11	1·25	15
	e. Perf 13½		
O32	2a. lilac	7·50	1·60
	a. Perf 11½, 12	22·00	3·25
	b. Perf 11	1·50	75
	c. Perf 13½	6·50	10
	ca. Imperf between (horiz pair)	†	£450
	cb. Rose-lilac	1·75	10
O33	3a. brown-orange	21·00	3·75
	a. Opt inverted	†	80·00
	b. Perf 11½, 12	14·00	3·00
	ba. Opt inverted	†	85·00
	c. Perf 11	30·00	3·75
	ca. Opt inverted	†	80·00
	d. Perf 13½	20·00	60
	da. Opt inverted	—	70·00
O34	4a. olive-green	16·00	2·50
	a. Opt inverted	—	80·00
	b. Perf 11½, 12	4·50	3·25
	ba. Opt inverted	—	85·00
	c. Perf 11	3·75	1·50
	d. Perf 13½	3·75	15
	da. Opt inverted	†	80·00
O35	8a. purple	5·50	20
	a. Perf 11½, 12		
	b. Perf 11	£375	48·00
	c. Perf 12½	—	£375
O36	12a. blue-green	20·00	1·75
	a. Perf 11½, 12		
	b. Perf 11		
	c. Perf 12½		

(b) Type 6 (Bradbury, Wilkinson printings). P 12½.

O37	¼a. grey-black	3·75	60

	a. Opt inverted	†	65·00
	b. Pair, one without opt		
	c. Imperf between (vert pair)	†	£275
	d. Perf 11½, 12	8·50	1·50
	da. Opt inverted	†	65·00
	db. Pair, one without opt		
	e. Perf 11	1·75	40
	ea. Opt sideways	†	65·00
	f. Perf 13½	3·75	10
	fa. Opt inverted	†	70·00
	fb. Pair, one without opt	†	£140
	fc. Imperf between (horiz pair)	†	£250
O38	¼a. brown-purple (*shades*) (P 13½)	3·00	10
	a. Imperf horiz (vert pair)	†	£275
	b. Imperf between (horiz pair)	†	£300
O39	½a. deep green	3·75	25
	a. Opt inverted	—	25·00
	b. Perf 11½, 12	9·50	1·75
	ba. Pair, one without opt	†	£140
	c. Perf 11	3·25	15
	ca. Opt inverted	—	28·00
	cb. Imperf between (vert pair)	†	£300
	d. Perf 13½	2·75	10
	da. Imperf between (horiz pair)	†	£225
	db. Imperf between (vert pair)	†	£300
	dc. Yellow-green		70

1917–20. *T 8 optd with Type O 2. P 13½.*

O40	½a. green	2·75	10
	a. Opt inverted	†	22·00
	b. Pair, one without opt	†	£100
	c. Imperf between (horiz pair)	†	£160
	ca. Imperf vert (horiz pair)	†	£170
	d. Imperf between (vert pair)	†	£250
	e. Emerald-green	3·75	40
	f. Perf 12½	—	4·00
	g. Perf 11	8·00	30
	ga. Opt inverted	†	24·00
	gb. Pair, one without opt		
O41	1a. carmine	4·00	10
	a. Opt inverted	†	27·00
	b. Opt double	†	85·00
	c. Imperf horiz (vert pair)	†	£250
	d. Stamp printed double		
	e. Scarlet (1920)	2·00	10
	ea. Stamp printed double	†	£170
	eb. Imperf between (horiz pair)	†	£300
	ec. Imperf between (vert pair)	†	£200
	ed. Imperf between (vert pair)	†	£250
	ee. Opt inverted	†	£100
	f. Perf 12½	—	3·50
	g. Perf 11	12·00	15
	ga. Opt inverted	†	18·00
	gb. Scarlet (1920)		24·00

1930–34. *T 6 and 8 optd as Type O 2 and surch at top of stamp, in red, as T 10 or 11.*

O42	4p. on ¼a. grey-black (O37f) (1934)	£375	17·00
O43	4p. on ¼a. brown-purple (O38)	1·75	10
	b. Imperf between (horiz pair)	†	£250
	c. Imperf between (vert pair)	†	£225
	d. Imperf horiz (vert pair)	†	£225
	e. Red surch double	†	95·00
	f. Black opt double	†	£200
	g. Perf 11	†	£475
	h. Stamp doubly printed	†	£180
O44	8p. on ½a. green (O40)	1·25	10
	c. Imperf between (horiz pair)	†	£200
	ca. Imperf between (vert pair)	†	£250
	d. Red surch double	†	95·00
	e. Stamp doubly printed	†	£180
	f. Black opt double	†	£200
O45	8p. on ½a. yellow-green (O39db)	35·00	45·00

For Nos. O42/5 the red surcharge was intended to appear on the upper part of the stamp, above the official overprint, Type O 2, but surcharge and overprint are not infrequently found superimposed on one another.

1934–44. *Nos. 41/8 optd with Type O 2.*

O46	4p. black	2·00	10
	a. Imperf (pair)	75·00	
	b. Imperf between (vert pair)	£650	£600
	c. Imperf between (horiz pair)	—	£600
O47	8p. green	1·00	10
	a. Opt inverted	†	£160
	b. Imperf between (horiz pair)	—	£600
	c. Opt double	†	£120
	d. Imperf (pair)	£150	£180
O48	1a. brown	1·50	10
	a. Imperf between (vert pair)	£500	£475
	b. Imperf between (horiz pair)		£475
	c. Imperf (pair)	£140	£180
	d. Opt double		£170
O49	2a. violet	6·50	10
	a. Imperf vert (horiz pair)	†	£1100
O50	4a. ultramarine	3·00	25
	a. Opt double	†	£450
	b. Imperf between (vert pair)	†	£1300
O51	8a. orange (1935)	12·00	60
	a. Yellow-orange (1944)	—	40·00
O52	12a. scarlet (1935)	10·00	1·75
O53	1r. yellow (1935)	17·00	2·50
O46/53 Set of 8		48·00	5·00

1947. *No. 58 optd with Type O 2.*

O54	8 ½a. claret	6·00	7·00

1949. *No. 60 optd with Type O 2.*

O55	12 2p. bistre-brown	6·00	9·00

1950. *No. 59 optd with Type O 2.*

O56	6p. claret	7·00	21·00

IDAR

PRICES FOR STAMPS ON COVER	
Nos. 1/2b	from × 2
Nos. 3/6	from × 3
Nos. F1/5	from × 2

Maharaja Himmat Singh, 1931–1960

1 Maharaja HimmatSingh   2 Maharaja HimmatSingh

(Typo M. N. Kothari & Sons, Bombay)

1932 (1 Oct)–43. P 11.

(a) White panels.

1	1	½a. light green	—	38·00
		a. Pale yellow-green (thick paper) (1939)	20·00	23·00
		b. Emerald (1941)	18·00	23·00
		ba. Imperf between (pair)	£1600	
		c. Yellow-green (1943)	15·00	22·00
		ca. Imperf between (horiz pair)	£1500	

(b) Coloured panels.

2	1	½a. pale yellow-green (thick paper) (1939)	35·00	28·00
		a. Emerald (1941)	23·00	26·00
		b. Yellow-green (1943)	14·00	24·00

In No. 2 the whole design is composed of half-tone dots. In No. 1 the dots are confined to the oval portrait.

(Typo P. G. Mehta & Co, Hitmatnagar)

1944 (21 Oct). P 12.

3	2	½a. blue-green	3·25	70·00
		a. Imperf between (vert pair)	£250	
		b. Yellow-green	3·25	70·00
		ba. Imperf between (vert pair)	12·00	
4		1a. violet	3·25	60·00
		a. Imperf (pair)	£200	
		b. Imperf vert (horiz pair)	£225	
5		2a. blue	3·50	95·00
		a. Imperf between (vert pair)	75·00	
		b. Imperf between (horiz pair)	£200	
6		4a. vermilion	3·75	£100
		a. Doubly printed	£800	
3/6 Set of 4			12·00	£300

Nos. 1 to 6 are from booklet panes of 4 stamps, producing single stamps with one or two adjacent sides imperf.
The 4a. violet is believed to be a colour trial (*Price £350, unused*).

POSTAL FISCAL STAMPS

F 1   F 2

1936 (?). *Typo. P 11½ on two or three sides.*

F1	F 1	1a. reddish lilac and bright green	—	£550

1940 (?)–45. *Typo. P 12 on two or three sides.*

F2	—	1a. violet	—	£150
		a. Perf 11	£130	£150
F3	F 2	1a. violet (1943)	£100	£150
F4		1¼a. on 1a. violet	£140	£325
F5		1¼a. yellow-green (1945)	18·00	
		a. Imperf between (vert pair)	40·00	
		b. Blue-green (1945)	75·00	£140

No. F2 shows the portrait as Type 1. Used prices are for examples with postal cancellations. No. F4 shows a handstamped surcharge in Gujerati.

Idar became part of Bombay Province on 10 June 1948.

INDORE
(HOLKAR STATE)

PRICES FOR STAMPS ON COVER	
Nos. 1/15	from × 20
Nos. 16/43	from × 6
Nos. S1/7	from × 40

Maharaja Tukoji Rao Holkar II, 1843–1886

1 Maharaja Tukoji Rao Holkar II

(Litho Waterlow & Sons)

1886 (6 Jan). P 15.

(a) Thick white paper.

1	1	½a. bright mauve	12·00	11·00

(b) Thin white or yellowish paper.

2	1	½a. pale mauve	3·25	2·00
		a. Dull mauve	3·50	2·50

Maharaja Shivaji Rao Holkar, 1886–1903

2 Type I   2a Type II

TYPES 2 AND 2a. In addition to the difference in the topline character (marked by arrow), the two Types can be distinguished by the difference in the angles of the 6-pointed stars and the appearance of the lettering. In Type I the top characters are smaller and more cramped than the bottom; in Type II both are in the same style and similarly spaced.

1889 (Sept). *Handstamped. No gum. Imperf.*

3	2	½a. black/*pink*	40·00	38·00
4	2a	½a. black/*pink*	3·25	3·75
		a. Tête-bêche (pair)	£225	

3 Maharaja Shivaji Rao Holkar   4 Maharaja Tukoji Holkar III   5 Maharaja Tukoji Holkar III

(Recess Waterlow)

1889–92. *Medium wove paper.* P 14 to 15.

5	3	¼a. orange (9.2.92)	1·25	80
		a. Imperf between (horiz pair)	†	£600
		b. Very thick wove paper	2·00	1·25
		c. Yellow	2·00	1·25
6		½a. dull violet	2·25	75
		a. Brown-purple	2·00	15
		b. Imperf between (vert pair)	£550	
7		1a. green (7.2.92)	2·25	1·00
		a. Imperf between (vert pair)	£900	
		b. Very thick wove paper	75·00	
8		2a. vermilion (7.2.92)	5·50	1·75
		a. Very thick wove paper	7·00	3·50
5/8 Set of 4			10·00	3·25

Maharaja Tukoji Rao Holkar III, 1903–1926

(Recess Perkins, Bacon & Co)

1904–20. P 13½, 14.

9	4	¼a. orange	50	10
10	5	½a. lake (1909)	8·50	10
		a. Brown-lake (shades)	11·00	15
		b. Imperf (pair)	21·00	
11		1a. green	2·00	10
		a. Imperf (pair)	£120	
		b. Perf 12½ (1920)	†	£120
12		2a. brown	13·00	75
		a. Imperf (pair)	75·00	
13		3a. violet	21·00	7·00
14		4a. ultramarine	16·00	3·25
		a. Dull blue	5·00	1·40
9/14a Set of 6			45·00	8·50

पाव आना.
(6)

7 Maharaja YeshwantRao Holkar II

1905 (June). *No. 6a surch "QUARTER ANNA" in Devanagari, as T 6.*

15	3	¼a. on ½a. brown-purple	5·00	20·00

On 1 March 1908 the Indore State postal service was amalgamated with the Indian Imperial system. Under the terms of the agreement stamps showing the Maharaja would still be used for official mail sent to addresses within the state. Initially Nos. 9/14 were used for this purpose, the "SERVICE" overprints, Nos. S1/7, being withdrawn.

Maharaja Yeshwant Rao Holkar II, 1926–1961

(Recess Perkins, Bacon & Co)

1927–37. P 13 to 14.

16	7	¼a. orange (a) (d) (e)	50	20
17		½a. claret (a) (d) (e)	1·75	10
18		1a. green (a) (d) (e)	2·25	10
19		1¼a. green (c) (d) (1933)	3·00	60
20		2a. sepia (a)	6·50	2·00
21		2a. bluish green (d) (1936)	13·00	1·75
		a. Imperf (pair)	25·00	£160
22		3a. deep violet (a)	1·75	9·50
23		3a. Prussian blue (d) (1935?)	17·00	
		a. Imperf (pair)	30·00	£400
24		3½a. violet (d) (1934)	7·00	10·00

		a. Imperf (pair)	55·00	£400
25		4a. ultramarine (a)	5·50	4·25
26		4a. yellow-brown (d) (1937)	30·00	1·75
		a. Imperf (pair)	30·00	£275
27		8a. slate-grey (a)	5·50	4·50
28		8a. red-orange (1937)	24·00	21·00
29		12a. carmine (d) (1934)	5·00	10·00
30	–	1r. black and light blue (b)	8·00	14·00
31	–	2r. black and carmine (b)	48·00	50·00
32	–	5r. black & brown-orange (b)	80·00	85·00

Nos. 30/32 are as Type **7**, but larger, size 23×28 mm.

Five different perforating heads were used for this issue: (*a*) comb 13.6; (*b*) comb 13.9; (*c*) line 13.2; (*d*) line 13.8; (*e*) line 14.2. Values on which each perforation occur are indicated above.

Nos. 21a, 23a, 24a and 26a were specifically ordered by the state government in 1933 and are known used for postage *circa* 1938–42. A plate proof of the 1r. in green and carmine is also known postally used (*Price of pair £38 unused, £400 used*).

Nos. 16/19 and 28/32 also exist as imperforate plate proofs, but these were never sent to India.

QUARTER ANNA
(8)

9

1940 (1 Aug). *Surch in words as T 8 by Times of India Press, Bombay.*

33	7	¼a. on 5r. black and brown-orange (b)	13·00	1·75
		a. Surch double (Blk.+G.)	†	£425
34		½a. on 2r. black and carmine (b)	22·00	3·00
35		1a. on 1¼a. green (c) (d) (e)	21·00	80
		b. Surch inverted (d)	90·00	
		c. Surch double (c)	£400	
33/5 Set of 3			50·00	5·00

(Typo "Times of India" Press, Bombay)

1940–46. P 11.

36	9	¼a. red-orange	2·00	10
37		½a. claret (1941)	3·00	10
38		1a. green (1941)	9·00	10
39		1¼a. yellow-green (1941)	16·00	1·75
		a. Imperf (pair)	£225	
40		2a. turquoise-blue (1941)	11·00	1·00
41		4a. yellow-brown (1946)	14·00	12·00

Larger size (23× 28 mm).

42		2r. black and carmine (1943)	12·00	£160
43		5r. black and yellow-orange (1943)	12·00	£200
36/43 Set of 8			70·00	£350

OFFICIAL STAMPS

SERVICE   SERVICE
(S 1)   (S 2)

1904–06.

(a) Optd with Type S 1.

S1	4	¼a. orange (1906)	40	1·00
S2	5	½a. lake	25	10
		a. Opt inverted	21·00	38·00
		b. Opt double	21·00	
		c. Imperf (pair)	65·00	
		d. Brown-lake	25	10
		da. Opt inverted	18·00	
		e. Pair, one without opt	£500	
S3		1a. green	15	20
S4		2a. brown (1905)	30	30
		a. Vert pair, one without opt	£800	
S5		3a. violet (1906)	2·00	3·25
		a. Imperf (pair)	£325	
S6		4a. ultramarine (1905)	4·50	1·50

(b) Optd with Type S 2.

S7	5	½a. lake	10	1·00
		a. Opt double	£450	
S1/7 Set of 7			7·00	6·50

Types S **1** and S **2** differ chiefly in the shape of the letter "R".

Indore became part of Madhya Bharat by 1 July 1948.

JAIPUR

PRICES FOR STAMPS ON COVER

No. 1	*from* × 3
No. 2	*from* × 2
Nos. 3/5	*from* × 10
Nos. 6/70	*from* × 4
Nos. 71/80	*from* × 6
Nos. O1/34	*from* × 8

Maharaja Sawai Madho Singh II, 1880–1922

1   1a   2

Chariot of the Sun God, Surya

Type 1–Value at sides in small letters and characters. "HALF ANNA", shown as one word except for R. 1/1 and 1/3, measuring between 13½ and 15 mm. Sheets of 12 (4×3) with stamps 2 to 2½ mm apart.

Type 1a–Value in large letters and characters. "HALF ANNA", always with a gap between the two words, measuring between 14½ and 15½ mm. Sheets of 24 (4×6) with stamps 3 to 4 mm apart.

Type 2–Value in large letters and characters. "HALF ANNA" measuring 16 to 17 mm. Both side inscriptions start below the inner frame line. Sheets of 24 (4×6) with stamps 1½ to 2 mm apart.

(Litho Durbar Press, Jaipur)

1904 (14 July). Roughly perf 14.

1	1	½a. pale blue	£120	£160
		a. Ultramarine (a)	£170	£200
		b. Imperf, ultramarine	£375	
2	1a	½a. grey-blue	£1800	£200
		a. Imperf	£350	£200
		b. Ultramarine	—	£325
3	2	½a. pale blue	2·75	6·00
		a. Deep blue	3·00	6·00
		b. Ultramarine	3·25	6·00
		c. Imperf	£350	£350
4	1	1a. dull red	4·50	13·00
		a. Scarlet	4·50	13·00
5		2a. pale green	4·75	13·00
		a. Emerald-green	5·00	

Nos. 1b, 2a and 3c are on gummed paper. Imperforate plate proofs also exist for Nos. 1/5, but these are ungummed.

3 Chariot of the Sun God, Surya

(Recess Perkins, Bacon & Co)

1904. P 12.

6	3	½a. blue	5·50	8·00
		a. Perf 12½	25·00	18·00
		b. Perf comp of 12 and 12½	15·00	18·00
7		1a. brown-red	55·00	55·00
		a. Perf 12½	£140	£140
		b. Perf comp of 12 and 12½	£120	£120
		c. Carmine	2·25	4·50
		ca. Imperf between (vert pair)	£550	£750
		cb. Perf comp of 12 and 12½	10·00	17·00
8		2a. deep green	7·50	14·00
		a. Perf 12½	£170	£120
		b. Perf comp of 12 and 12½	26·00	38·00

Nos. 6b, 7b, 7cb and 8b occur on the bottom two rows of sheets otherwise perforated 12.

1905–08. Wmk "JAs WRIGLEY & SON Ld. 219" "SPECIAL POSTAGE PAPER LONDON" or "PERKINS BACON & Co Ld LONDON" in sheet. P 13½

9	3	¼a. olive-yellow (1906)	75	1·00
10		½a. blue (1906)	3·00	2·75
		a. Indigo	1·25	50
11		1a. brown-red (1906)	6·50	4·25
		a. Bright red (1908)	3·00	50
12		2a. deep green (1906)	2·50	1·00
13		4a. chestnut	6·00	2·00
14		8a. bright violet	3·00	2·75
15		1r. orange-yellow	20·00	18·00
		a. Yellow	22·00	16·00
		b. Yellow-ochre	23·00	27·00
9/15 Set of 7			32·00	21·00

३ आना
(5)

4 Chariot of the Sun God, Surya

(Typo Jaipur State Press)

1911. *Thin wove paper. No gum. Imperf.*

16	4	¼a. green	2·25	3·00
		a. Printed double	7·00	
		ab. Ditto, one inverted		
		b. "¼" inverted in right upper corner (R. 1/2)	5·50	
		c. No stop after "STATE" (R. 3/1)	5·50	
17		¼a. greenish yellow	30	70
		a. Printed double		
		b. "¼" inverted in right upper corner (R. 1/2)	1·50	
		c. No stop after "STATE" (R. 3/1)	1·50	
18		½a. ultramarine	30	70
		a. Printed double	2·00	
		b. No stop after "STATE" (R. 3/1)	75	
		c. Large "J" in "JAIPUR" (R. 1/2)	75	
		d. "13" for "½" at lower left (R. 3/1)		
		e. "1½a." at lower right (R. 3/2)	1·50	
19		½a. grey-blue	2·75	2·50
		a. No stop after "STATE" (R. 3/1)	3·75	
		b. Large "J" in "JAIPUR" (R. 1/2)	3·75	
		c. "13" for "½" at lower left (R. 3/1)	4·25	
		d. "1½a." at lower right (R. 3/2)	4·75	
20		1a. rose-red	50	90
		a. Printed double	£200	
21		2a. greyish green	2·75	5·50
		a. Deep green	2·00	6·00
		ab. Printed double	£225	

Issued in sheets of 6 (2×3). There are three recognised settings. Nos. 18d/e and 19c/d come from Setting B, and Nos. 16b/c, 17b/c, 18b/c and 19a/b from Setting C.

One sheet of the ¼a. is known in blue.

(Typo Jaipur State Press)

1912–22. Paper-maker's wmk "DORLING & CO. LONDON" in sheet. P 11.

22	3	¼a. pale olive-yellow	50	1·25
		a. Imperf horiz (vert pair)	£200	£200
		b. Imperf vert (horiz pair)	—	£160
23		¼a. olive	60	1·50
		a. Imperf between (horiz pair)	£190	
		b. Imperf vert (horiz pair)	£200	
		c. Imperf horiz (vert pair)	£200	
		d. Tête-bêche (pair)	£450	
24		¼a. bistre	30	1·50
		a. Imperf between (horiz pair)	£200	
		b. Imperf between (vert pair)	†	£325
		c. Imperf horiz (vert pair)	†	£325
		d. Doubly printed	†	£650
25		½a. pale ultramarine	1·25	1·00
		a. Imperf vert (horiz pair)	†	£500
		b. Blue	1·25	75
		ba. Imperf between (horiz pair)	£375	
26		1a. carmine (1918)	4·75	4·75
		a. Imperf vert (horiz pair)	†	£750
		b. Imperf horiz (vert pair)	†	£750
27		1a. rose-red	4·25	9·50
		a. Imperf between (vert pair)	£750	
28		1a. scarlet (1922)	3·25	3·00
		a. Imperf between (vert pair)	£800	£800
29		2a. green (1918)	3·50	4·25
30		4a. chocolate	5·50	8·50
31		4a. pale brown	6·00	9·50
		a. Imperf vert (horiz pair)	£500	
22/31		Set of 5	12·50	16·00

Maharaja Sawai Man Singh II 1922–1970

1926. Surch with T **5**.

32	3	3a. on 8a. bright violet (R.)	1·50	3·00
		a. Surch inverted	£170	£140
33		3a. on 1r. yellow (R.)	2·25	5·50
		a. Surch inverted	£475	£170
		c. Yellow-ochre	9·00	11·00

1928. As 1913–18 issue. Wmk "DORLING & CO. LONDON" (½a., 1a., 2a.) or "OVERLAND BANK" (all values) in sheet. No gum. P 12.

34	3	½a. ultramarine	3·00	4·00
		a. Perf comp of 12 and 11	15·00	8·50
35		1a. rose-red	25·00	17·00
		a. Imperf between (vert pair)	£500	
36		1a. scarlet	40·00	12·00
		a. Perf comp of 12 and 11	55·00	25·00
37		2a. green	85·00	28·00
		a. Perf comp of 12 and 11	£225	60·00
38		8a. bright violet		£350 £475
39		1r. orange-vermilion		

The "OVERLAND BANK" paper has a coarser texture. The ½a. and 2a. values also exist on this paper perforated 11, but such stamps are difficult to distinguish from examples of Nos. 25 and 29.

6 Chariot of the Sun God, Surya

7 Maharaja Sawai Man Singh II

8 Elephant and State Banner

9 Sowar in Armour

10 Common Peafowl

11 Bullock carriage

12 Elephant carriage

13 Albert Museum

14 Sireh Deorhi Gate

15 Chandra Mahal

16 Amber Palace

17 Maharajas Jai Singh and Man Singh

(Des T. I. Archer. Litho Indian Security Printing Press, Nasik)

1931 (14 Mar). Investiture of Maharaja. T **6/17**. No wmk. P 14.

40	6	¼a. black and deep lake	2·50	2·50
41	7	½a. black and violet	40	20
42	8	1a. black and blue	8·00	8·50
43	9	2a. black and buff	8·00	8·50
44	10	2½a. black and carmine	30·00	55·00
45	11	3a. black and myrtle	16·00	42·00
46	12	4a. black and olive-green	16·00	55·00
47	13	6a. black and deep blue	6·00	55·00
48	14	8a. black and chocolate	16·00	80·00
49	15	1r. black and pale olive	35·00	£275
50	16	2r. black and yellow-green	35·00	£325
51	17	5r. black and purple	48·00	£350
40/51		Set of 12	£200	£1100

Eighteen of these sets were issued for presentation purposes with a special overprint "INVESTITURE-MARCH 14,1931" in red (Price for set of 12 £3500 unused, £4500 used).

18 Maharaja Sawai Man Singh II

One Rupee
(19)

(Des T. I. Archer. Litho Indian Security Printing Press, Nasik)

1932–46. P 14.

(a) Inscr "POSTAGE & REVENUE".

52	18	1a. black and blue	2·50	1·25
53		2a. black and buff	3·50	2·25
54		4a. black and grey-green	4·50	10·00
55		8a. black and chocolate	6·00	13·00
56		1r. black and yellow-bistre	24·00	£100
57		2r. black and yellow-green	85·00	£425
52/7		Set of 6	£110	£500

(b) Inscr "POSTAGE".

58	7	¼a. black and brown-lake	40	30
59		¾a. black and brown-red (1943?)	7·00	3·75
60		1a. black and blue (1943?)	8·50	3·50
61		2a. black and buff (1943?)	8·50	4·25
62		2½a. black and carmine	3·50	2·75
63		3a. black and green	3·25	70
64		4a. black and grey-green (1943?)	40·00	£140
65		6a. black and deep blue	4·75	27·00
		a. Black and pale blue (1946)	8·50	70·00
66		8a. black and chocolate (1946)	24·00	£110
67		1r. black and yellow-bistre (1946)	20·00	£160
58/67		Set of 10	£110	£400

1936. Nos. 57 and 51 surch with T **19**.

68	10	1r. on 2r. black and yellow-green (R.)	8·50	95·00
69	—	1r. on 5r. black and purple	8·50	75·00

पाव आना
(20)

21 Palace Gate

22 Maharaja and Amber Palace

23 Map of Jaipur

24 Observatory

25 Wind Palace

26 Coat of Arms

27 Amber Fort Gate

28 Chariot of the Sun

29 Maharaja's portrait between State flags

1938 (Dec). No. 41 surch "QUARTER ANNA" in Devanagari, T **20**.

70		7	¼a. on ½a. black and violet (R.)	12·00	16·00

(Recess D.L.R.)

1947 (Dec)–**48.** Silver Jubilee of Maharajas Accession to Throne. T **21/9.** P 13½×14.

71	21	¼a. red-brown and green (5.48)	1·25	4·00
72	22	½a. green and violet	50	3·75
73	23	¾a. black and lake (5.48)	1·25	4·75
74	24	1a. red-brown and ultramarine	75	4·00
75	25	2a. violet and scarlet	1·00	4·25
76	26	3a. green and black (5.48)	1·40	5·50
77	27	4a. ultramarine and brown	75	4·25
78	28	8a. vermilion and brown	75	5·00
79	29	1r. purple and green (5.48)	2·50	38·00
71/9		Set of 9	9·00	65·00

3 PIES
= =
(30)

1947 (1 Dec). No. 41 surch with T **30**.

80	7	3p. on ½a. black and violet (R.)	15·00	25·00
		a. "PIE" for "PIES"	45·00	95·00
		b. Bars at left vertical	65·00	£100
		c. Surch inverted	45·00	38·00
		d. Surch inverted and "PIE" for "PIES"	£200	£190
		e. Surch double, one inverted	70·00	55·00
		f. As variety e, but inverted surch showing "PIE" for "PIES"	£425	£400

There were three settings of Type **14**, each applied to quarter sheets of 30 (6×5). No. 80a occurs in two of these settings on R. 5/5 and one of these settings also shows No. 80b on R. 6/1.

OFFICIAL STAMPS

SERVICE (O 1)   **SERVICE** (O 2)

1928 (13 Nov)–**31.** T **3** typographed. No gum (except for Nos. O 6/a). P 11, 12, or compound. Wmk "DORLING & CO. LONDON" (4a.) or "OVERLAND BANK" (others).

(a) Optd with Type O **1**.

O1		¼a. olive	1·75	2·25
		a. Bistre	1·75	1·75
O2		½a. pale ultramarine (Blk.)	85	20
		a. Imperf between (horiz pair)	£350	£350
		b. Imperf between (vert pair)	†	£700
		c. Opt inverted	†	£400
		d. Opt double (R. and Blk.)	†	£475
O3		½a. pale ultramarine (R.) (13.10.30)	2·50	30
		a. Imperf horiz (vert pair)	£700	
		b. Stamp doubly printed	†	£475
O3c		1a. rose-red	1·00	30
		d. Imperf between (horiz pair)	†	£700
O4		1a. scarlet	1·25	50
		a. Opt inverted	£800	£800
		b. Imperf between (horiz pair)	†	£750
O5		2a. green	1·00	40
		a. Imperf between (vert pair)	†	£850
		b. Imperf between (horiz pair)	£850	£850
O6		4a. pale brown (with gum)	4·75	1·75
		a. Chocolate (with gum)	2·00	1·75
O7		8a. bright violet (R.) (13.10.30)	17·00	55·00
O8		1r. orange-vermilion	35·00	£325

(b) Optd with Type O **2**.

O9		½a. ultramarine (Blk.) (11.2.31)	£180	15
		a. Imperf vert (horiz pair)	†	£800
O10		½a. ultramarine (R.) (15.10.30)	£200	15
		a. Imperf between (vert pair)	†	£800
O11		8a. bright violet (11.2.31)	£425	£190
O12		1r. orange-vermilion (11.2.31)	£450	£275

SERVICE (O 3)   आध आना (O 4)

1931–37. Nos. 41/3 and 46 optd at Nasik with Type O **3**, in red.

O13	7	½a. black and violet	30	10
O14	—	1a. black and blue	£250	2·50
O15	8	2a. black and buff (1936)	3·50	5·50
O16	—	4a. black and olive-green (1937)	42·00	35·00
O13/16		Set of 4	£275	40·00

1932. No. O5 surch with Type O **4**.

O17	3	½a. on 2a. green	£150	1·50

1932–37. Nos. 52/6 optd at Nasik with Type O **3**, in red.

O18	10	1a. black and blue	3·75	15
O19		2a. black and buff	4·50	15
O20		4a. black and grey-green (1937)	£325	9·50
O21		8a. black and chocolate	9·50	1·10
O22		1r. black and yellow-bistre	25·00	23·00
O18/22		Set of 5	£350	30·00

1936–46. *Stamps of 1932–46, inscr* "POSTAGE".

(a) Optd at Nasik with Type O 3, in red.

O23	7	¼a. black and brown-lake (1936).....	40	10
O24		¾a. black and brown-red (1944)......	1·50	50
O25		1a. black and blue (1941?)......	4·00	30
O26		2a. black and buff (date?).............	4·00	2·75
O27		2½a. black and carmine (1946)......	10·00	£100
O28		4a. black and grey-green (1942)......	4·50	6·00
O29		8a. black and chocolate (1943).......	4·00	7·50
O30		1r. black and yellow-bistre (date?) .	40·00	
O23/9 *Set of 7*.........			26·00	£110

(b) Optd locally as Type O 2 (16 mm long), in black.

O31	7	¼a. black and red-brown (1936)......	85·00	65·00

9 PIES

(O 5)

1947. *No. O25 surch with Type O 5, in red.*

O32	7	9p. on 1a. black and blue..................	3·75	3·25

1947 (Dec). *No. O13 surch as T 14, but "3 PIES" placed higher.*

O33	7	3p. on ½a. black and violet (R.)........	5·00	12·00
		a. Surch double, one inverted	45·00	45·00
		ab. "PIE" for "PIES" in inverted surcharge............	£275	£300
		c. Surch inverted	—	£1400

1948 (Dec). *No. O13 surch "THREE-QUARTER ANNA" in Devanagari, as T 12, but with two bars on each side.*

O34	7	¾a. on ½a. black and violet (R.)........	17·00	18·00
		a. Surch double	£1300	£1300

There are three different types of surcharge in the setting of 30, which vary in one or other of the Devanagari characters.

Jaipur became part of Rajasthan by 7 April 1949.

JAMMU AND KASHMIR

PRICES FOR STAMPS ON COVER

Nos. 1/73	*from* × 3
Nos. 74/84	*from* × 2
No. 85	—
Nos. 86/9	*from* × 2
Nos. 90/101	*from* × 10
Nos. 101b/23	*from* × 5
Nos. 124/36	*from* × 10
Nos. 138/9	*from* × 100
Nos. 140/61a	*from* × 15
Nos. 162/8	*from* × 5
No. O1	*from* × 2
Nos. O2/4	*from* × 4
No. O5	—
Nos. O6/14	*from* × 30
Nos. O15/18	—

ILLUSTRATIONS. Designs of Jammu and Kashmir are illustrated actual size.

Maharaja Ranhir Singh, 1857–1885

1 (½a.)

2 (1a.)

3 (4a.)

Characters denoting the value (on the circular stamps only) are approximately as shown in the central circles of the stamps illustrated above.

These characters were taken from Punjabi merchants' notation and were not familiar to most of the inhabitants of the state. Type 1 was certainly the ½ anna value, but there has long been controversy over the correct face values of Types 2 and 3.

The study of surviving material suggests that, to some extent, this confusion involved contemporary post office officials. Although covers posted at Jammu, where the stamps were in use for twelve years, show Type 2 used as the 1a. value and Type 3 as the 4a., those originating from Srinagar (Kashmir) during 1866–68 show both Types 2 and 3 used as 1a. stamps.

In the following listing we have followed contemporary usage at Jammu and this reflects the prevailing opinion amongst modern authorities.

GUM. The stamps of Jammu and Kashmir were issued without gum.

PRICES. Prices for the circular stamps, Nos. 1/49, are for cut-square examples. Cut-to-shape examples are worth from 10% to 20% of these prices, according to condition.

A. Handstamped in watercolours

1866 (23 Mar). *Native paper, thick to thin, usually having the appearance of laid paper and tinted grey or brown. For Jammu and Kashmir.*

1	1	½a. grey-black	£225	95·00
2		½a. ultramarine	£2750	£2750
3	2	1a. royal blue	—	£500
3a		1a. ultramarine	£550	£110
4		1a. grey-black	£1500	£1300
5	3	4a. royal blue	—	£500
5a		4a. ultramarine	£800	£400

No. 4 may be an error of colour. It is only known used in Kashmir.

1867–76. *Reissued for use in Jammu only.*

6	3	4a. grey-black	£2000	
7		4a. indigo	£2250	£1300
8		4a. red (1869)	95·00	£130
9		4a. orange-red (1872)	£200	£300
10		4a. orange (1872)	£200	
11		4a. carmine-red (1876)	£1100	

1874–76. *Special Printings.*

12	1	½a. red	95·00	£325
12a		½a. orange-red	£650	£700
13	2	1a. red	£180	£300
13a		1a. orange-red	£650	£700
13b		1a. orange	£850	
14	1	½a. deep black	24·00	£170
		a. *Tête-bêche* (pair)	£550	
15	2	1a. deep black		£300
16	3	4a. deep black		£275
17	1	½a. bright blue (1876)	£350	£425
18	2	1a. bright blue (1876)	£120	£350
19	3	4a. bright blue (1876)	£200	
20	1	½a. emerald-green	£110	£275
21	2	1a. emerald-green	£120	£275
22	3	4a. emerald-green	£275	£450
23	1	½a. yellow	£700	£900
24	2	1a. yellow	£900	
25	3	4a. yellow	£550	
25a		4a. deep blue-black (1876)	£1500	£850

These special printings were available for use, but little used.

B. Handstamped in oil colours. Heavy blurred prints

1877 (June)–78.

(a) Native paper.

26	1	½a. red	38·00	60·00
27	2	1a. red	45·00	£180
28	3	4a. red	£300	£500
29	1	½a. black	35·00	60·00
32		½a. slate-blue	£150	£250
34	2	1a. slate-blue	35·00	£275
35	1	½a. sage-green	£130	
36	2	1a. sage-green	£140	
37	3	4a. sage-green	£140	

(b) European laid paper, medium to thick.

38	1	½a. red	—	£1100
39	3	4a. red	£425	£475
41	1	½a. black	30·00	60·00
		a. Printed both sides...........	£850	
		b. *Tête-bêche* (pair)	£450	
44		½a. slate-blue	50·00	£275
45	2	1a. slate-blue	60·00	£375
46	3	4a. slate-blue	£850	£850
47		4a. sage-green	£1400	£1600
48	1	½a. yellow	£150	

(c) Thick yellowish wove paper.

49	1	½a. red (1878)	—	£900

Forgeries exist of the ½a. and 1a. in types which were at one time supposed to be authentic.

Reprints and imitations (of which some of each were found in the official remainder stock) exist in a great variety of fancy colours, both on native paper, usually thinner and smoother than that of the originals, and on various thin European *wove* papers, on which the originals were never printed.

The imitations, which do not agree in type with the above illustrations, are also to be found on *laid* paper.

All the reprints, etc. are in oil colours or printer's ink. The originals in oil colour are usually blurred, particularly when on native paper. The reprints, etc. are usually clear.

FOR USE IN JAMMU

½a.   ½a.

1a.   ½a.

4

T 4 to 11 have a star at the top of the oval band; the characters denoting the value are in the upper part of the inner oval. All are dated 1923, corresponding with A.D. 1866.

T 4. Printed in blocks of four, three varieties of ½ anna and one of 1 anna.

1867 (Sept). *In watercolour on native paper.*

52		½a. grey-black	£1100	£400
53		1a. grey-black	£2750	£1600
54		½a. indigo	£400	£300
55		1a. indigo	£850	£400
56		½a. deep ultramarine	£300	£180
57		1a. deep ultramarine	£750	£400
58		½a. deep violet-blue	£200	£175
59		1a. deep violet-blue	£800	£400

1868 (May)–**72**. *In watercolour on native paper.*

60		½a. red (*shades*)	8·00	4·00
61		1a. red (*shades*)	18·00	12·00
62		½a. orange-red	£225	75·00
63		1a. orange-red	£800	£325
64		½a. orange (1872)	£120	£130
65		1a. orange (1872)	£2750	£1600

1874–76. *Special printings; in watercolour on native paper.*

66		½a. bright blue (1876)	£1500	£350
67		1a. bright blue (1876)	£450	£375
68		½a. emerald-green	£2250	£1200
69		1a. emerald-green	£3250	£1900
69a		½a. jet-black	£150	£180
69b		1a. jet-black	£2250	£1700

1877 (June)–**78**. *In oil colour.*

(a) Native paper.

70		½a. red	11·00	8·00
71		1a. red	35·00	25·00
72		½a. brown-red (1878)	—	42·00
73		1a. brown-red (1878)	—	£140
74		½a. black	†	£1100
75		1a. black	†	£2500
76		½a. deep blue-black	†	£1700
77		1a. deep blue-black	†	£4250

(b) Laid paper (medium or thick).

78		½a. red	—	£1000

(c) Thick wove paper.

79		½a. red	†	£450
80		1a. red		

(d) Thin laid, bâtonné paper.

84		½a. red	†	£1600
85		1a. red	£4250	

The circular and rectangular stamps listed under the heading "Special Printings" did not supersede those in *red*, which was the normal colour for Jammu down to 1878. It is not known for what reason other colours were used during that period, but these stamps were printed in 1874 or 1875 and were certainly put into use. The rectangular stamps were again printed in *black* (jet-black, as against the greyish black of the 1867 printings) at that time, and impressions of the two periods can also be distinguished by the obliterations, which until 1868 were in *magenta* and after that in *black*.

There are reprints of these, in *oil* colour, *brown-red* and *bright blue*, on native paper; they are very clearly printed, which is not the case with the originals in *oil* colour.

4a

1877 (Sept). *Provisional. Seal obliterator of Jammu handstamped in red watercolour on pieces of native paper, and used as a ½ anna stamp.*

86	4	(½a.) rose-red	—	£1200

FOR USE IN KASHMIR

5

1866 (Sept(?)). *Printed from a single die. Native laid paper.*

87	5	½a. black	£3250	£425

Forgeries of this stamp are commonly found, copied from an illustration in *Le Timbre-Poste*.

6 (½a.)

7 (1a.)

1867 (Apr). *Native laid paper.*

88	6	½a. black	£1400	£190
89	7	1a. black	£2500	£475

Printed in sheets of 25 (5×5), the four top rows being ½a. and the bottom row 1a.

8 (¼a.)   9 (2a.)

10 (4a.)   11 (8a.)

1867–77. *Native laid paper.*

90	8	¼a. black	4·00	4·50
91	6	½a. ultramarine (6.67)	4·50	1·50
		a. Bisected (¼a.) (on cover) (1877)	†	£8500
92		½a. violet-blue (1870)	8·00	4·25
93	7	1a. ultramarine (6.67)	£4000	£1600
94		1a. orange (7.67)	14·00	11·00
95		1a. brown-orange (1868)	14·00	11·00
96		1a. orange-vermilion (1876)	18·00	12·00
97	9	2a. yellow	18·00	20·00
98		2a. buff	27·00	22·00
99	10	4a. emerald-green	45·00	45·00
		a. Tête-bêche (pair)	£1100	
100		4a. sage-green	£325	£160
100a		4a. myrtle-green	£800	£800
101	11	4a. red (1868)	48·00	45·00
		a. Tête-bêche (pair)	£3750	

Of the above, the ½a. and 1a. were printed from the same plate of 25 as Nos. 88/9, the ¼a. and 2a. from a new plate of 10 (5×2), the top row being ¼a. and the lower 2a., and the 4a. and 8a. from single dies. Varieties at one time catalogued upon European papers were apparently never put into circulation, though some of them were printed while these stamps were still in use.

Nos. 86 to 101 are in watercolour.

No. 91a was used at Srinagar, in conjunction with an India ½a., and was cancelled "KASHMIR 5/L-6".

FOR USE IN JAMMU AND KASHMIR

In the following issues there are 15 varieties on the sheets of the18a., ¼a. and ½a.; 20 varieties of the 1a. and 2a. and 8 varieties of the 4a. and 8a. The value is in the lower part of the central oval.

12 (¼a.)   13 (½a.)

14 (1a.)   15 (2a.)

16 (4a.)   17 (8a.)

1878 (May)–79. *Provisional printings.*

I. *Ordinary white laid paper, of varying thickness.*

(a) Rough perf 10 to 12 (i) or 13 to 16 (ii).

101b	12	¼a. red (i)		
102	13	½a. red (i)	14·00	16·00
103	14	1a. red (i)	£1200	
104	13	½a. slate-violet (i)	75·00	75·00
104a	14	1a. violet (ii)		
104b	15	2a. violet (i)	£1700	

(b) Imperf.

105	13	½a. slate-violet (*shades*)	17·00	15·00
106	14	1a. slate-purple	26·00	27·00
107		1a. mauve	42·00	40·00
108	15	2a. violet	27·00	27·00

109		2a. bright mauve	40·00	35·00
110		2a. slate-mauve	60·00	60·00
111		2a. dull blue	£110	£110
112	12	2a. red	22·00	20·00
113	13	½a. red	9·00	10·00
114	14	1a. red	8·50	11·00
115	15	2a. red	85·00	85·00
116	16	4a. red	£200	£180

II. *Medium wove paper.*

(a) Rough perf 10 to 12.

117	13	½a. red	—	£300

(b) Imperf.

117b	12	¼a. red		
118	13	½a. red	17·00	9·00
119	14	1a. red	15·00	11·00
120	15	2a. red	70·00	

III. *Thick wove paper.* Imperf.

121	13	½a. red	29·00	55·00
122	14	1a. red	48·00	23·00
123	15	2a. red	21·00	24·00

Of the above stamps those in red were intended for use in Jammu and those in shades of violet and blue for use in Kashmir.

1879. *Definitive issue. Thin wove paper, fine to coarse.*

(a) Rough perf 10 to 12.

124	13	½a. red	£350	£250

(b) Imperf.

125	12	¼a. red	3·25	4·25
126	13	½a. red	85	85
		a. Bisected (¼a.) on postcard	†	£5500
127	14	1a. red	2·50	3·25
128	15	2a. red	3·25	4·50
129	16	4a. red	10·00	10·00
130	17	8a. red	11·00	12·00

The plates were transferred from Jammu to Srinagar in early 1881 when further printings in red and all orange stamps were produced.

1880 (Mar). *Provisional printing in watercolour on thin bâtonné paper.* Imperf.

130a	12	¼a. ultramarine	£850	£550

1881–83. *As Nos. 124 to 130. Colour changed.*

(a) Rough perf 10 to 12.

130b	13	½a. orange		

(b) Imperf.

131	12	¼a. orange	10·00	14·00
132	13	½a. orange	23·00	16·00
133	14	1a. orange	23·00	13·00
		a. Bisected (½a.) (on cover)	†	£8500
134	15	2a. orange	17·00	13·00
135	16	4a. orange	40·00	50·00
136	17	8a. orange	70·00	75·00

Nos. 126a and 133a were used at Leh between April and July 1883.

Nos. 125/30 and 132/6 were re-issued between 1890 and 1894 and used concurrently with the stamps which follow. Such re-issues can be identified by the "three circle" cancellations, introduced in December 1890.

18 (¹/₈a.)

1883–94. *New colours. Thin wove papers, toned, coarse to fine, or fine white (1889).* Imperf.

138	18	¹/₈a. yellow-brown	1·25	1·75
139		¹/₈a. yellow	1·25	1·75
140	12	¼a. sepia	1·10	75
141		¼a. brown	1·10	75
		a. Double impression	£1200	
142		¼a. pale brown	1·10	75
		a. Error. Green	70·00	
143	13	½a. dull blue	7·00	
144		½a. bright blue	50·00	
145		½a. vermilion	1·25	70
146		½a. rose	1·40	1·00
147		½a. orange-red	1·10	70
148	14	1a. greenish grey	85	85
149		1a. bright green	1·25	1·25
		a. Double impression		
150		1a. dull green	85	85
151		1a. blue-green	1·75	
152	15	2a. red/yellow	2·50	1·25
153		2a. red/yellow-green	3·50	3·75
154		2a. red/deep green	17·00	17·00
155	16	4a. deep green	3·75	4·50
156		4a. green	4·00	3·75
157		4a. pale green	4·00	3·25
158		4a. sage-green	4·25	
159	17	8a. pale blue	8·00	9·50
159a		8a. deep blue	12·00	14·00
160		8a. bright blue	11·00	13·00
161		8a. indigo-blue	15·00	15·00
161a		8a. slate-lilac	10·00	20·00

Well-executed forgeries of the ¼a. to 8a. have come from India, mostly postmarked; they may be detected by the type, which does not agree with any variety on the genuine sheets, and also, in the low values, by the margins being filled in with colour, all but a thin white frame round the stamp. The forgeries of the 8a. are in sheets of eight like the originals.

Other forgeries of nearly all values also exist, showing all varieties of type. All values are on thin, coarse wove paper.

In February 1890, a forgery, in watercolour, of the ½a. orange on thin wove or on thin laid paper appeared, and many have been found genuinely used during 1890 and 1891 (*Price* £4).

Nos. 143 and 144 were never issued.

Examples of the ½a. brown, ½a. orange-red and 1a. green on wove paper exist with clean-cut perf 12.

There is a reference in the Jammu and Kashmir State Administration Report covering 1890–91 to the re-introduction of perforating and the machine-gumming of paper at the Jammu printing works.

The few known examples, the ½a. being only recorded used, the others unused or used, would appear to date from this period, but there is, as yet, no direct confirmation as to their status.

Maharaja Partap Singh, 1885–1925

1887–94. *Thin creamy laid paper.* Imperf.

162	18	¹/₈a. yellow	55·00	65·00
163	12	¼a. brown	9·00	6·50
164	13	½a. brown-red (March 1887)	—	75·00
165		½a. orange-red	9·50	6·00
166	14	1a. grey-green	£100	£100
168	17	8a. blue (*Printed in watercolour*)	£150	£150
		a. On wove paper	£100	£100

19

T 19 represents a ¼a. stamp, which exists in sheets of twelve varieties, in *red* and *black* on thin wove and laid papers, also in *red* on native paper, but which does not appear ever to have been issued for use. It was first seen in 1886.

The ¼a. *brown* and the 4a. *green* both exist on ordinary white laid paper and the ½a. *red* on native paper. None of these are known to have been in use.

OFFICIAL STAMPS

1878.

I. *White laid paper.*

(a) Rough perf 10 to 12.

O1	13	½a. black	—	£1800

(b) Imperf.

O2	13	½a. black	95·00	90·00
O3	14	1a. black	65·00	65·00
O4	15	2a. black	55·00	55·00

II. *Medium wove paper.* Imperf.

O5	14	1a. black	£325	

1880–94. *Thin wove papers, toned, coarse to fine, or fine white (1889).* Imperf.

O6	12	¼a. black	1·50	1·75
		a. Double print	£200	
O7	13	½a. black	15	60
		a. Printed both sides	£425	
O8	14	1a. black	20	90
O9	15	2a. black	30	45
O10	16	4a. black	1·00	1·50
O11	17	8a. black	2·25	1·10

1887–94. *Thin creamy laid paper.* Imperf.

O12	12	¼a. black	7·50	8·00
O13	13	½a. black	4·25	4·50
O14	14	1a. black	2·50	3·25
O15	15	2a. black	14·00	
O16	16	4a. black	50·00	60·00
O17	17	8a. black	28·00	50·00

1889. *Stout white wove paper.* Imperf.

O18	12	¼a. black	£225	£150

The stamps of Jammu and Kashmir have been obsolete since 1 November 1894.

JASDAN

PRICES FOR STAMPS ON COVER	
Nos. 1/2	*from* × 2
No. 3	*from* × 3
Nos. 4/6	*from* × 4

Darbar Ala Khachar, 1919–1971

1 Sun

(Typo L. V. Indap & Co, Bombay)

1942 (15 Mar)–47. *Stamps from booklet panes. Various perfs.*

1	1a. deep myrtle-green (P 10½)	£1200	£800
2	1a. light green (P 12)	£600	£600
3	1a. light green (P 10½) (1943)	£150	£180
4	1a. pale yellow-green (P 8½–9) (1946)	18·00	£150

5		1a. dull yellow-green (P 10) (1945)........	27·00	£170
6		1a. bluish green (P 8½–9) (1947)............	22·00	£150

Nos. 1/4 were issued in panes of four with the stamps imperforate on one or two sides; Nos. 5/6 were in panes of eight perforated all round. A 1a. rose with the arms of Jasdan in the centre is a fiscal stamp.

Jasdan was merged with the United State of Kathiawar (later Saurashtra) by 15 April 1948.

JHALAWAR

PRICES FOR STAMPS ON COVER	
Nos. 1/2	*from* × 30

Maharaj Rana Zalim Singh, 1875–1896

1 (1 paisa)   **2** (¼ anna)

(Figure of an Apsara, "RHEMBA", a dancing nymph of the Hindu Paradise)

1886–90. *Typo in horizontal strips of 12. Laid paper. No gum.*

1	1	1p. yellow-green	4·75	13·00
		a. Blue-green	£110	50·00
2	2	¼a. green (*shades*)	1·25	2·50

The stamps formerly listed as on wove paper are from sheets on laid paper, with the laid paper lines almost invisible.

The Maharaj Rana was deposed in 1896 and much of the state's territory transferred to Kotah on 1 January 1899.

Raj (Maharaj from 1918) Rana Rhawani Singh, 1899–1929

The stamps of Jhalawar have been obsolete since 1 November 1900.

JIND

PRICES FOR STAMPS ON COVER	
The stamps of Jind are very rare used on cover.	

ILLUSTRATIONS. Designs of Jind are illustrated actual size.

Raja Raghubir Singh, 1864–1887

J 1 (½a.)   **J 2** (1a.)

J 3 (2a.)   **J 4** (4a.)

J 5 (8a.)

(Litho Jind State Rajah's Press, Sungroor)

1874. *Thin yellowish paper. Imperf.*

J1	J 1	½a. blue......................................	6·50	3·75
		a. No frame to value. (Retouched all over) (R. 4/7)	£350	£180
J2	J 2	1a. rosy mauve..........................	7·00	6·50
J3	J 3	2a. yellow..................................	1·00	4·00
J4		2a. brown-buff	£200	£120
J5	J 4	4a. green...................................	22·00	6·00
J6	J 5	8a. dull purple	£600	£160
J6a		8a. bluish violet........................	£200	90·00
J7		8a. slate-blue	£170	80·00

Nos. J1/7 were produced from two sets of stones. Those from the first set had rather blurred impressions, but those from the second are clearer with a conspicuous white frame around the value. Nos. J4 and J6a/13 were only printed from the second set.

1876. *Bluish laid card-paper. No gum. Imperf.*

J8	J 1	½a. blue......................................	75	4·25
J9	J 2	1a. purple..................................	2·00	9·50
J10	J 3	2a. brown..................................	3·50	13·00
J11	J 4	4a. green...................................	3·00	13·00
J11a	J 5	8a. bluish violet........................	8·50	22·00
J12		8a. slate-blue	7·00	11·00
J13		8a. steel-blue	9·00	16·00

Stocks of the ½a. (No. J8) and 2a. (No. J4) were perforated 12 in 1885 for use as fiscal stamps.

J 6 (¼a.)   **J 7** (½a.)

J 8 (1a.)   **J 9** (2a.)

J 10 (4a.)   **J 11** (8a.)

(Litho Jind State Rajah's Press, Sungroor)

1882–85. *Types* **J 6** *to* **J 11**. *No gum.*

A. Imperf *(1882–4).*

(a) Thin yellowish wove paper.

J15	¼a. buff (*shades*)	30	1·50
J16	¼a. red-brown	30	1·50
	a. Doubly printed	45·00	
J17	½a. lemon	1·75	1·75
J18	½a. buff...	1·90	1·50
J19	½a. brown-buff	80	60
J20	1a. brown (*shades*)	1·75	3·25
J21	2a. blue...	1·75	8·50
J22	2a. deep blue	2·50	1·00
J23	4a. sage-green	1·50	1·00
J24	4a. blue-green	1·75	3·00
J25	8a. red	6·00	4·50

(b) Various thick laid papers.

J26	¼a. brown-buff	1·25	
J27	½a. lemon	1·25	
J28	½a. brown-buff		
J29	1a. brown	1·25	2·50
J30	2a. blue...	18·00	21·00
J31	8a. red	2·50	10·00

(c) Thick white wove paper.

J32	¼a. brown-buff	16·00	
J33	½a. brown-buff	32·00	
J34	1a. brown	5·00	
J35	8a. red	4·75	10·00

B. Perf 12 *(1885).*

(a) Thin yellowish wove paper.

J36	¼a. buff (*shades*)	75	2·75
	a. Doubly printed	90·00	
J37	¼a. red-brown	3·50	
J38	½a. lemon	£150	£150
J39	½a. buff...	60	3·75
J40	½a. brown-buff	3·00	5·00
J41	1a. brown (*shades*)	2·50	5·00
J42	2a. blue...	3·50	9·50
J43	2a. deep blue	2·75	6·00
J44	4a. sage-green	5·00	10·00
J45	4a. blue-green	2·00	
	a. Imperf vert (horiz pair)	£550	
J46	8a. red	11·00	

(b) Various thick laid papers.

J47	¼a. brown-buff	7·50	
J48	½a. lemon	£120	24·00
J49	1a. brown	1·50	
J50	2a. blue...	22·00	26·00
J51	8a. red	2·50	9·50

(c) Thick white wove paper.

J52	1a. brown		
J53	8a. red		9·50

The perforated stamps ceased to be used for postal purposes in July 1885, but were used as fiscals to at least the mid-1920s. Other varieties exist, but they must either be fiscals or reprints, and it is not quite certain that all those listed above were issued as early as 1885.

Jind became a Convention State and from 1 July 1885 used overprinted Indian stamps.

KISHANGARH

PRICES FOR STAMPS ON COVER	
Nos. 1/3	—
Nos. 4/91	*from* × 8
Nos. O1/32	*from* × 30

GUM. The stamps of Kishangarh were issued without gum, *except for* Nos. 42/50 and O17/24.

Maharaja Sardul Singh, 1879–1900

1

1899–1900. *Medium wove paper. Typo from a plate of 8 (4× 2).*

1	1	1a. green (*imperf*)	22·00	55·00
2		1a. green (*pin-perf*) (1900)	70·00	

1900. *Thin white wove paper. Printed from a single die. Imperf.*

3	1	1a. blue...	£400	

ILLUSTRATIONS. Types **2** to **10a** are shown actual size.

2 (¼a.)   **3** (½a.)

4 (1a.)   **5** (2a.)Maharaja Sardul Singh

6 (4a.)   **7** (1r.)

8 (2r.)   **9** (5r.)

1899 (Sept)**–1901**. *Thin white wove paper.*

(a) Imperf.

4	2	¼a. green (1900)	£550	£800
5		¼a. carmine....................................	7·50	
		a. *Rose-pink*.................................	1·00	2·50
6		¼a. magenta....................................	5·00	5·00
		a. Doubly printed	95·00	
7	3	½a. lilac (1900)	£140	£275
8		½a. red (1899)	£2250	£1200
9		½a. green (1899)	32·00	38·00
10		½a. pale yellow-olive	45·00	45·00
11		½a. slate-blue (1900)	40·00	40·00
		b. *Deep blue*.................................	6·50	7·50
		c. *Light blue*	1·60	1·75
		ca. Pair, one stamp sideways..........	£1200	
12	4	1a. slate	4·50	5·00
		a. Laid paper	50·00	
12b		1a. pink..	70·00	£190
13		1a. mauve.......................................	6·50	5·50
		a. Laid paper	38·00	
14		1a. brown-lilac	1·10	1·00
		a. Laid paper	30·00	
15	5	2a. dull orange	4·50	4·50
		a. Laid paper	£550	£475
16	6	4a. chocolate	6·00	
		a. *Lake-brown*	6·00	9·50
		b. *Chestnut*	6·00	9·50
		c. *Light green* (*shades*)	80·00	80·00
17	7	1r. dull green	21·00	32·00
18		1r. brown-lilac	25·00	25·00
19	8	2r. brown-red	80·00	£120
		a. Laid paper	60·00	
20	9	5r. mauve	75·00	95·00
		a. Laid paper	75·00	

(b) Pin-perf 12½ or 14 (from Nov 1899).

21	2	¼a. green	£250	£450
		a. Imperf between (pair)	£1200	
22		¼a. carmine....................................	5·00	6·00
		a. *Rose-pink*.................................	25	40
		ab. *Tête-bêche* (horiz pair).............	£1000	

		ac. Doubly printed	£100	
		b. Rose		
23		¼a. magenta	5·00	7·00
		a. Bright purple		
		ab. Doubly printed		
24	**3**	½a. green	18·00	24·00
		a. Imperf between (pair)	£170	
25		½a. pale yellow-olive	13·00	16·00
		a. Imperf vert (horiz pair)	£170	
		b. Imperf between (horiz pair)	†	£400
26		½a. deep blue	1·90	3·25
		a. Light blue	85	50
		ab. Doubly printed	£130	£130
27	**4**	1a. slate	4·75	3·25
		a. Laid paper	45·00	21·00
27b		1a. pink	80·00	£225
28		1a. mauve	1·00	1·75
		a. Laid paper	38·00	13·00
29		1a. brown-lilac	75	1·00
		a. Laid paper	35·00	13·00
30	**5**	2a. dull orange	4·00	5·00
		a. Laid paper	£700	
31	**6**	4a. chocolate	2·00	5·50
		a. Lake-brown	2·50	5·50
		b. Chestnut	3·50	6·00
		c. Laid paper (shades)	65·00	60·00
32	**7**	1r. dull green	10·00	15·00
		a. Laid paper	85·00	
33		1r. pale olive-yellow	£800	
34	**8**	2r. brown-red	35·00	50·00
		a. Laid paper	42·00	
35	**9**	5r. mauve	35·00	50·00
		a. Laid paper	70·00	

All the above, both imperf and pin-perf, were printed singly, sometimes on paper with spaces marked in pencil. They exist in vertical *tête-bêche* pairs imperf between from the centre of the sheet. *Prices from 3×normal, unused.* No. 22ab is an error.

FISCAL STAMPS. Many of the following issues were produced in different colours for fiscal purposes. Such usage is indicated by the initials "M.C.", punched hole or violet Stamp Office handstamp.

Maharaja Madan Singh, 1900–1926

10 (¼a.)   **10a** (1r.)

1901. *Toned wove paper.* Pin-perf.

36	**10**	¼a. dull pink	8·00	6·00
37	**4**	1a. violet	42·00	27·00
38	**10a**	1r. dull green	14·00	16·00
36/8 *Set of 3*			55·00	45·00

Nos. 36/8 were printed in sheets of 24. Sheets of the 1r. were always torn to remove R. 5/4 where the cliché is believed to have been defective.

The 1a. (No. 37) differs from T **4** in having an inscription in native characters below the words "ONE ANNA".

11 (½a.)   **12** Maharaja Sardul Singh

1903. *Litho. Thick white wove glazed paper.* Imperf.

39	**11**	½a. pink	12·00	3·00
		a. Printed both sides	†	£1300
40	**12**	2a. dull yellow	3·00	6·00

12a (8a.)

1904. *Printed singly. Thin paper.* Pin-perf.

41	**12a**	8a. grey	5·00	7·50
		a. Tête-bêche (vert pair)	26·00	
		b. Doubly printed	£130	

13 Maharaja Madan Singh   **14** Maharaja Madan Singh

(Recess Perkins, Bacon & Co)

1904–10. *With gum.* P 12½.

42	**13**	¼a. carmine	45	75
		a. Perf 13½ (1910)	1·00	55

---

		b. Perf 12×12½	£110	
43		½a. chestnut	2·00	1·00
		a. Perf 13½ (1906)	1·10	30
44		1a. blue	4·75	2·75
		a. Perf 13½ (1906)	2·00	2·25
45		2a. orange-yellow	15·00	7·00
		a. Perf 13½ (1907)	20·00	17·00
46		4a. brown	19·00	19·00
		a. Perf 13½ (1907)	15·00	17·00
		b. Perf 12	70·00	50·00
47		8a. violet (1905)	10·00	22·00
48		1r. green	26·00	40·00
49		2r. olive-yellow	26·00	£160
50		5r. purple-brown	24·00	£190
42/50 *Set of 9*			£110	£400

Stamps in other colours, all perforated 13½, were produced by Perkins Bacon as business samples.

1912. *Printed from half-tone blocks. No ornaments to left and right of value in English; large ornaments on either side of value in Hindi. Small stop after "STATE".*

(a) Thin wove paper. Rouletted.

51	**14**	2a. deep violet ("TWO ANNA")	4·50	8·00
		a. Tête-bêche (vert pair)	10·00	35·00
		b. Imperf (pair)		£450

No. 51 is printed in four rows, each inverted in respect to that above and below it.

(b) Thick white chalk-surfaced paper. Imperf.

52	**14**	2a. lilac ("TWO ANNA")	£1600	£750

(c) Thick white chalk-surfaced paper. Rouletted in colour (Medallion only in half-tone).

53	**14**	¼a. ultramarine	16·00	16·00

1913. *No ornaments on either side of value in English. Small ornaments in bottom label. With stop after "STATE". Thick white chalk-surfaced paper. Rouletted.*

54	**14**	2a. purple ("TWO ANNAS")	2·50	5·00

15

पाव अना

No. 59e. This occurs on R. 3/3 on one setting only

2 **TWO ANNAS** 2	2 **TWO ANNAS** 2
No. 60. Small figures	No. 60b. Large figures

(Typo Diamond Soap Works, Kishangarh)

1913 (Aug). *Thick surfaced paper. Half-tone centre. Type-set inscriptions. Rouletted. Inscr "KISHANGARH".*

59	**15**	¼a. pale blue	30	90
		a. Imperf (pair)	7·00	
		b. Roul×imperf (horiz pair)	25·00	
		ba. Imperf between (horiz pair)	42·00	
		c. "QUARTER" (R. 4/4)	5·00	7·00
		ca. As last, imperf (pair)	28·00	
		cb. As last, roul×imperf	55·00	
		d. "KISHANGAHR" (R. 2/3)	5·00	7·00
		da. As last, imperf (pair)	28·00	
		db. As last, roul×imperf	55·00	
		dc. As last, imperf between (horiz pair)	85·00	
		e. Character omitted	7·00	7·00
		ea. As last, imperf (pair)	32·00	
60		2a. purple	7·00	18·00
		a. "KISHANGAHR" (R. 2/3)	50·00	90·00
		b. Large figures "2"	32·00	55·00

1913–16. *Stamps printed far apart, horizontally and vertically, otherwise as No. 54, except as noted below.*

63	**14**	¼a. blue	20	45
64		½a. green (1915)	20	1·00
		a. Printed both sides	£225	
		b. Imperf (pair)	£150	£150
		c. Emerald-green (1916)	1·75	4·00
65		1a. red	1·00	2·50
		a. Without stop*	1·40	5·50
		ab. Imperf (pair)	£190	
66		2a. purple ("TWO ANNAS") (1915)	6·00	8·00
67		4a. bright blue	6·00	8·00
68		8a. brown	7·00	40·00
69		1r. mauve	16·00	£120
		a. Imperf (pair)	£300	
70		2r. deep green	95·00	£325
71		5r. brown	40·00	£425
63/71 *Set of 9*			£150	£850

*For this issue, ornaments were added on either side of the English value (except in the ¼a.) and the inscription in the right label was without stop, except in the case of No. 65.

In Nos. 70 and 71 the value is expressed as "RUPIES" instead of "RUPEES".

Initial printings of the ¼a., 1a. and 4a. values were in sheets of 20 containing two panes of 10 separated by a central gutter margin. Stamps from these sheets measure 20×25½ mm and have heavier screening dots on the perforation margins than on the designs. Subsequent printings of these stamps, and of other values in the set, were from single pane sheets of 20 on which the designs measured 19½×23¾ mm and with the screening dots uniform across the sheet.

Maharaja Yagyanarayan Singh, 1926–1939

16 Maharaja Yagyanarayan Singh   **17** Maharaja Yagyanarayan Singh

1928–36. *Thick surfaced paper.* Typo. Pin-perf.

72	**16**	¼a. light blue	80	2·00
73		½a. yellow-green	3·25	2·00
		a. Deep green	3·00	3·00
		ab. Imperf (pair)	£100	£100
		ac. Imperf between (vert or horiz pair)	£130	£130
74	**17**	1a. carmine	75	1·50
		a. Imperf (pair)	£190	£120
75		2a. purple	3·00	8·50
75a		2a. magenta (1936)	7·00	12·00
		a. Imperf (pair)	£325	
76	**16**	4a. chestnut	1·50	1·75
		a. Imperf (pair)	£120	
77		8a. violet	4·00	27·00
78		1r. light green	17·00	60·00
79		2r. lemon-yellow (1929)	28·00	£200
80		5r. claret (1929)	40·00	£250
		a. Imperf (pair)	£120	
72/80 *Set of 9*			90·00	£500

The 4a. to 5r. are slightly larger than, but otherwise similar to, the ¼a. and ½a. The 8a. has a dotted background covering the whole design.

Maharaja Samar Singh, 1939–1971

1943–47. *As last, but thick, soft, unsurfaced paper. Poor impression.* Typo. Pin-perf.

81	**16**	¼a. pale dull blue (1945)	4·50	11·00
		a. Imperf (pair)	35·00	
82		¼a. greenish blue (1947)	2·50	9·00
		a. Imperf (pair)	28·00	
83		½a. deep green (1944)	1·25	2·50
		a. Imperf (pair)	25·00	25·00
		b. Imperf between (vert or horiz pair)	50·00	
84		½a. yellow-green (1946)	6·50	9·00
		a. Imperf (pair)	35·00	35·00
		b. Imperf between (vert or horiz pair)	50·00	
85	**17**	1a. carmine-red (1944)	7·50	3·50
		a. Double print	£300	
		b. Imperf (pair)	35·00	35·00
		c. Imperf between (vert or horiz pair)	50·00	
		d. Red-orange (1947)	80·00	32·00
		da. Imperf (pair)	£140	£100
86		2a. bright magenta	11·00	13·00
		a. Imperf (pair)	75·00	80·00
87		2a. maroon (1947)	90·00	16·00
		a. Imperf (pair)	48·00	50·00
		b. Imperf between (vert or horiz pair)	£130	
88	**16**	4a. brown (1944)	26·00	18·00
		a. Imperf (pair)	£150	
89		8a. violet (1945)	48·00	£150
90		1r. green (1945)	60·00	£160
		a. Imperf (pair)	£200	£350
90b		2r. yellow (date?)		
		ba. Imperf (pair)	£550	
91		5r. claret (1945)	£650	£700
		a. Imperf (pair)	£375	

OFFICIAL STAMPS

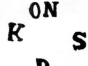

(O 1)

1918. *Handstamped with Type O* **1**.

(a) Stamps of 1899–1901.

(i) Imperf.

O1	**2**	¼a. green	—	£160
O2		¼a. rose-pink	—	7·00
		a. Pair, one without opt	—	80·00
O3	**4**	1a. mauve	—	60·00
O3a		1a. brown-lilac	50·00	5·50
		a. Pair, one without opt	£200	80·00
O4	**6**	4a. chocolate	—	£120

(ii) Pin-perf.

O5	**2**	¼a. green	—	£120
O6		¼a. rose-pink	2·25	60
		a. Pair, one without opt	90·00	42·00
		b. Stamp doubly printed	95·00	65·00
O7	**3**	½a. light blue	£400	42·00
O8	**4**	1a. mauve	48·00	1·50
		a. Pair, one without opt	†	£110
O9		1a. brown-lilac	45·00	1·50
O10	**5**	2a. dull orange	—	£140
O11	**6**	4a. chocolate	60·00	16·00
		a. Pair, one without opt	—	90·00
O12	**7**	1r. dull green	£170	£120
O13	**8**	2r. brown-red	—	£900
O14	**9**	5r. mauve	—	£1800

(b) Stamp of 1901.

O14a	**10**	1r. dull green	—	£850

(c) Stamps of 1903 and 1904.

O15	12	2a. dull yellow	80·00	5·00
		Stamp printed both sides	†	£850
		a. Red opt	£425	£250
O16	12a	8a. grey	85·00	22·00
		a. Red opt		£250

(d) Stamps of 1904–5. P 13½ (¼a. to 4a.) or 12½ (others).

O17	13	¼a. carmine	—	£300
O18		½a. chestnut	75	35
		a. Pair, one without opt	—	55·00
O19		1a. blue	9·00	4·00
		a. Red opt	24·00	7·00
		b. Pair, one without opt	—	75·00
O20		2a. orange-yellow	—	£950
O21		4a. brown	60·00	18·00
		a. Red opt	80·00	38·00
O22		8a. violet	£375	£225
		a. Red opt		£250
O23		1r. green	£750	£700
		a. Red opt		£650
O24		5r. purple-brown		

(e) Stamps of 1913.

O25	15	¼a. pale blue		6·00
		a. Imperf (pair)		85·00
		b. Roul×imperf (horiz pair)		£160
		c. "QUARTER"		22·00
		ca. As last, imperf (pair)		£140
		d. "KISHNGAHR"		22·00
		da. As last, imperf (pair)		£140
		e. Character omitted		22·00
		ea. As last, imperf (pair)		£140
O26	14	2a. purple (No. 54)	—	95·00
		a. Red opt	£150	20·00
O27	15	2a. purple	£500	£550
		"KISHANGAHR"	£950	
		b. Large figures "2"	£700	£750

(f) Stamps of 1913–16.

O28	14	¼a. blue	60	50
		a. Red opt	2·00	1·75
O29		½a. green	90	75
		a. Pair, one without opt	—	75·00
		b. Red opt	3·75	1·60
		ba. Pair, one without opt	—	£150
O30		1a. red	14·00	7·00
		a. Without stop (No. 65a)	1·00	1·00
		ab. Pair, one without opt	—	£140
		ac. Red opt	£130	80·00
O31		2a. purple	7·50	4·00
		a. Red opt	£130	65·00
		b. Pair, one without opt	—	80·00
O32		4a. bright blue	24·00	15·00
		a. Red opt	—	32·00
O33		8a. brown	£120	15·00
		a. Red opt	—	90·00
O34		1r. mauve	£350	£325
O35		2r. deep green		
O36		5r. brown	£1700	

This overprint is found inverted as often as it is upright; and many other "errors" exist.

Kishangarh became part of Rajasthan by 15 April 1948.

LAS BELA

PRICES FOR STAMPS ON COVER	
Nos. 1/12	*from* × 8

Mir Kamal Khan, 1896–1926

1   **2**

(Litho Thacker & Co, Bombay)

1897–98. *Thick paper.* P 11½.

1	1	½a. black on *white*	24·00	16·00

1898–1900. P 11½.

2	1	½a. black on *greyish blue* (1898)	16·00	9·00
3		½a. black on *greenish grey* (1899)	14·00	8·00
		a. "BFLA" for "BELA"	£170	
		b. Imperf between (horiz strip of 3)		
4		½a. black on *thin white surfaced paper* (1899)	26·00	42·00
5		½a. black on *slate* (1900)	27·00	42·00
		a. Imperf between (horiz pair)	£900	

1901–02. P 11½.

6	1	½a. black on *pale grey*	13·00	9·00
		a. "BFLA" for "BELA"	£140	£180
7		½a. black on *pale green* (1902)	21·00	23·00
8	2	1a. black on *orange*	19·00	21·00

There are at least 14 settings of the above ½a. stamps, the sheets varying from 16 to 30 stamps.

No. 6a occurred on R. 3/2 of the July 1901 printing in sheets of 16 (4×4).

1904 (Feb–Nov). *Stamps printed wider apart.* P 11½.

11	1	½a. black on *pale blue*	13·00	7·50
		a. Imperf between (pair)	£750	
		b. Imperf between (horiz strip of 3)	£1000	
		c. Perf 12½ (Nov)	18·00	11·00
12		½a. black on *pale green*	13·00	7·50
		c. Perf 12½ (Nov)	18·00	11·00

There are five plates of the above two stamps, each consisting of 18 (3×6) varieties.

All the coloured papers of the ½a. show coloured fibres, similar to those in granite paper.

The stamps of Las Bela have been obsolete since 1 April 1907.

MORVI

PRICES FOR STAMPS ON COVER	
Nos. 1/17	*from* × 6
Nos. 18/19	*from* × 3

Thakur (Maharaja from 1926) Lakhdirji, 1922–48

1 Maharaja   **2** Maharaja   **3** Maharaja
Lakhdirji   Lakhdirji   Lakhdirji

1931 (1 April). Typo. P 12.

(a) Printed in blocks of four. Stamps 10 mm apart (Nos. 1/2) or 6½ mm apart (No. 3). Perf on two or three sides.

1	1	3p. deep red	3·00	15·00
2		½a. blue	26·00	40·00
3		2a. yellow-brown	95·00	
1/3 Set of 3			£110	

(b) Printed in two blocks of four. Stamps 5½ mm apart. Perf on four sides.

4	1	3p. bright scarlet	6·00	22·00
		a. Error. Dull blue	4·25	22·00
		b. Ditto. Double print	£600	
		c. Ditto. Printed on gummed side.	£600	
5		½a. dull blue	3·25	15·00
		a. Chalk-surfaced paper	3·00	15·00
6		1a. brown-red	3·25	15·00
7		2a. yellow-brown	4·00	35·00
4/7 Set of 4			14·50	90·00

Nos. 1/3 were supplied to post offices in panes of four sewn into bundles with interleaving.

1932–33. *Horizontal background lines wider apart and portrait smaller than in T 1.* Typo. P 11.

8	2	3p. carmine-rose (*shades*)	4·25	12·00
9		6p. green	6·50	15·00
		a. Imperf between (horiz pair)	£1800	
		b. Emerald-green	5·00	12·00
10		1a. ultramarine (*to deep*)	3·75	12·00
		a. Imperf between (vert pair)	£1400	
11		2a. bright violet (1933)	10·00	35·00
		a. Imperf between (vert pair)	£1400	
8/11 Set of 4			21·00	65·00

1934. Typo. London ptg. P 14.

12	3	3p. carmine	2·50	3·00
13		6p. emerald-green	1·25	6·00
14		1a. purple-brown	1·40	12·00
		a. Imperf between (horiz pair)	†	£1300
15		2a. bright violet	2·50	23·00
12/15 Set of 4			7·00	40·00

1935–48. Typo. *Morvi Press ptg. Rough perf 11.*

16	3	3p. scarlet (*shades*)	1·50	3·75
		a. Imperf between (horiz pair)	£1300	
17		6p. grey-green	1·25	3·00
		a. Emerald-green	7·50	27·00
		b. Yellow-green	8·00	
18		1a. brown	12·00	15·00
		a. Pale yellow-brown	16·00	26·00
		b. Chocolate	23·00	32·00
19		2a. dull violet (*to deep*)	2·50	17·00
16/19 Set of 4			10·00	35·00

Nos. 17a, 18a and 18b were issued between 1944 and 1948.

Maharaja Mahendra Singh, 1948–1957

Morvi was merged with the United State of Kathiawar (later Saurashtra) by 15 April 1948.

NANDGAON

PRICES FOR STAMPS ON COVER
The stamps of Nandgaon are very rare used on cover.

GUM. The stamps of Nandgaon were issued without gum.

Raja Mahant Balram Das, 1883–1897

1   **2** (½a.)

(Litho at Poona)

1891. Imperf.

1	1	½a. blue	6·00	£170
		a. Dull blue	6·50	
2		2a. rose	24·00	£500

The few covers in existence franked with Nos. 1/2 have undated manuscript cancellations, but other forms are known on loose examples.

The state was under Imperial administration from January 1888 to November 1891 and it is possible that Nos. 1/2 may have appeared in late 1887.

Last character in top line omitted

(Typo Balram Press, Raj-Nandgaon)

1893 (1 Jan)–**94.** *Printed in sheets of 16 (4×4). Imperf.*

(a) Stamps printed wide apart (8 to 10 mm) without wavy lines between them. Thin, toned wove paper.

3	2	½a. dull *to* deep green	12·00	85·00
4		2a. red	11·00	85·00
		b. Dull rose	11·00	85·00

(b) Stamps printed closer together (4 to 7 mm) with wavy lines between them. Thin, white wove paper (1894).

5	2	½a. green	24·00	65·00
		a. Last character in top line omitted (R. 4/3)	90·00	
6		1a. rose	55·00	£120
		ba. Laid paper	£225	

There were three settings of Type **2** with a number of separate printings made from the third:

Setting I - Nos. 3, 4, 4a, 4b, O2
Setting II - Nos. 5, 5b, 6, 6a, 6b
Setting III - Nos. 5, 6ba, O3, O3a, O4, O4a, O5 and subsequent reprints.

The same clichés were used for all values with the face value inscriptions changed. These exist in two different sizes with both occurring on the ½a., the small on the 1a. and the large on the 2a. except for No. O5 which has the small type.

The ordinary postage stamps of Nandgaon became obsolete on 1 July 1894.

OFFICIAL STAMPS

(O **1**) ("M.B.D." = Mahant Balram Das)

1893. *Handstamped with ruler's initials in oval. Type* O **1**, *in purple.*

O1	1	½a. blue	£350	
O2		2a. rose	£850	

1894. *Handstamped with Type* O **1** *in purple.*

(a) Stamps printed wide apart (8 to 10 mm) without wavy lines between them. Thin, toned wove paper.

O2a	2	½a. dull green	£500	
O3		2a. red	25·00	£140

(b) Stamps printed closer together (4 to 7 mm) with wavy lines between them. Thin, white wove paper.

O4	2	½a. yellow-green	6·00	11·00
		a. Sage-green	7·50	
O5		1a. rose (*shades*)	10·00	35·00
		a. Thin laid paper	11·00	80·00
O6		2a. rose (*shades*)	9·00	23·00

Further printings took place in 1895 after the Official stamps were withdrawn from postal use on 31 December 1894. These were all on thin, white wove paper with the ½a. and 2a. in slightly different shades and the 1a. in brown or ultramarine.

There is a forgery of the handstamp, Type O **1**, which shows 8 mm between the two ornaments below the initials instead of the normal 4 mm.

NAWANAGAR

PRICES FOR STAMPS ON COVER	
No. 1	*from* × 20
No. 2	*from* × 8
Nos. 3/4	*from* × 2
No. 5	—
Nos. 6/12	—
Nos. 13/15	*from* × 100
Nos. 16/18	—

GUM. The stamps of Nawanagar were issued without gum.

Jam Vibhaji 1882–1895

1 (1 docra)   **2** (2 docra)   **3** (3 docra)

1877. *Typo in sheets of 32 (4×8 or 8×4). Laid paper.*

(a) Imperf.

1	**1**	1doc. blue (*shades*)	75	25·00
		a. *Tête-bêche* (pair)	£1200	
		b. Doubly printed	£100	

(b) Perf 12½ (line).

2	**1**	1doc. slate-blue	80·00	£140
		a. Perf 11 (harrow)	90·00	
		ab. *Tête-bêche* (pair)	£1500	

The inverted clichés which cause the *tête-bêche* pairs come from different settings and occur on R. 3/2 (No. 1a) or R. 4/4 (No. 2ab) of sheets of 32 (4×8).

1877. T **2** and **3**. *Type-set in black. Wove paper. Thick horizontal and vertical frame lines. Stamp 19 mm wide.*

3		1doc. *deep mauve*	£3500	£200
		a. Stamp 14½-15 mm wide	†	£375
		b. Stamp 16 mm wide	†	£300
4		2doc. *green*	£3500	£1700
5		3doc. *yellow*	£3500	£1700

1880. *As last, but thin frame lines, as illustrated. Stamp 15 to 18 mm wide.*

6		1doc. *deep mauve*	3·50	9·50
		a. *On rose*	3·50	
		ab. Stamp 14 mm wide	3·50	7·50
7		1doc. *magenta* (stamp 14 mm wide)	3·50	
8		2doc. *yellow-green*	4·50	13·00
		a. *On blue-green*	8·00	
		b. *Error. Yellow*	£350	
		c. Stamp 14 mm wide	4·25	10·00
		ca. *On blue-green*	9·50	
9		3doc. *orange-yellow*	11·00	
		a. *On yellow*	5·00	18·00
		ab. On laid paper	£100	
		b. Stamp 14 mm wide. *On yellow*	6·00	12·00
		ba. On laid paper	45·00	

There are several different settings of each value of this series.

No. 8b occurs in the sheet of the 3 doc. value from one setting only.

4 (1 docra)

1893. *Typo in sheets of 36. P 12.*

(a) Thick paper.

10	**4**	1doc. black	3·50	
		a. Imperf (pair)	£550	
11		3doc. orange	3·75	

(b) Thick laid paper.

12	**4**	1doc. black	£650	

(c) Thin wove paper.

13	**4**	1doc. black to grey	1·75	6·00
		a. Imperf between (pair)	£475	
		b. Imperf (pair)	£450	
		c. Imperf horiz (vert pair)	£650	
		d. Imperf between (horiz strip of 6)	£1300	
14		2doc. green	1·75	6·50
		a. Imperf (pair)	£550	
		b. Imperf between (vert pair)	£600	
15		3doc. orange-yellow	2·00	11·00
		a. Imperf between (pair)	£600	
		b. *Orange*	1·75	10·00
		ba. Imperf (pair)	£500	
		bb. Imperf vert (horiz pair)	£550	
		bc. Imperf between (horiz pair)	£550	

(d) Thin, soft wove paper.

16	**4**	1doc. black		
17		2doc. deep green	3·50	
18		3doc. brown-orange	4·50	

Cancellations for postal purposes were intaglio seals, applied in black. Other forms of cancellation were only used on remainders.

The stamps of Nawanagar became obsolete on 1 January 1895.

NEPAL

Nepal being an independent state, its stamps will be found listed in Part 21 (*South-East Asia*) of this catalogue.

ORCHHA

A set of four stamps, ½a. red, 1a. violet, 2a. yellow and 4a. deep blue-green, in a design similar to T **2**, was prepared in 1897 with State authority but not put into use. These exist both imperforate and pin-perforated. (*Price for set of 4, £16 unused or c.t.o.*)

Maharaja Partab Singh, 1874–1930

1   **2**

(T **1/2** litho Shri Pratap Prabhakar)

1913. *Background to arms unshaded, Very blurred impression. Wove paper. No gum. Imperf.*

1	**1**	½a. green	35·00	£100
2		1a. red	20·00	£180

1914–35. *Background shaded with short horizontal lines. Clearer impression. Wove paper. No gum. Imperf.*

3	**2**	¼a. bright ultramarine	2·00	4·50
		a. *Grey-blue*	40	4·25
		b. *Deep blue*	1·60	3·75
		ba. Laid paper	£600	
4		½a. green (*shades*)	55	5·50
		a. *Dull green*	1·50	6·00
		b. *Apple-green*	2·25	5·00
5		1a. carmine	2·50	7·00
		a. Laid paper	—	£450
		b. *Indian red*	1·75	12·00
		c. *Carmine*	2·50	6·50
		ca. Laid paper (1935)	£200	£250
6		2a. red-brown (1916)	4·50	24·00
		a. *Light brown*	11·00	25·00
		b. *Chestnut*	19·00	26·00
7		4a. ochre (1917)	11·00	35·00
		a. *Yellow-orange*	8·00	35·00
		b. *Yellow*	10·00	35·00
3/7 Set of 5			13·50	65·00

There are two sizes of T **2** in the setting of 8 (4×2). In each value stamps from the upper row are slightly taller than those from the lower.

Maharaja Vir Singh II, 1930–1956

3 Maharaja Vir   **4** Maharaja Vir
Singh II   Singh II

(Typo Lakshmi Art Ptg Wks, Bombay)

1935 (1 Apr). *Thick, chalk-surfaced wove paper. P 9½, 10, 10×9½, 11, 11×9½, 11½, 11½×11, 11½×12, 12 or 12×11.*

8	**3**	¼a. purple and slate	1·75	3·50
		a. Imperf between (vert pair)		
		b. *Ordinary paper*	50	3·00
		ba. Imperf between (vert pair)	11·00	
		bb. Imperf vert (horiz pair)	65·00	
		bc. Imperf horiz (vert pair)	65·00	
9		½a. olive-grey and emerald	50	2·25
		a. Imperf (pair)	75·00	
10		¾a. magenta and deep myrtle-green	50	2·25
		a. Imperf (pair)	75·00	
11		1a. myrtle-green and purple-brown	50	2·25
		a. Imperf (pair)	65·00	85·00
		b. Imperf horiz (vert pair)		
		c. Imperf vert (horiz pair)		
12		1¼a. slate and mauve	50	2·25
		a. Imperf (pair)	75·00	£275
		b. Imperf between (horiz pair)	75·00	
		c. Frame doubly printed	75·00	
13		1½a. brown and scarlet	50	2·25
		a. Imperf between (vert pair)	75·00	
		b. Imperf between (horiz pair)	75·00	
14		2a. blue and red-orange	50	2·25
		a. Imperf (pair)	13·00	
		b. Imperf between (horiz pair)	75·00	
15		2½a. olive-brown and dull orange	65	2·50
		a. Imperf (pair)	13·00	
		b. Imperf between (horiz pair)	75·00	
16		3a. bright blue and magenta	65	2·50
		a. Imperf between (horiz pair)	75·00	£120
		b. Imperf (pair)	75·00	
17		4a. deep reddish purple and sage-green	65	4·50
		a. Imperf (pair)	9·00	
		b. Imperf between (vert pair)	75·00	
		c. Imperf vert (horiz pair)	75·00	
18		6a. black and pale ochre	70	4·50
		a. Imperf (pair)	9·00	
19		8a. brown and purple	2·25	5·50
		a. Imperf (pair)	9·00	
		b. Imperf between (horiz pair)	85·00	
20		12a. bright emerald and bright purple	1·00	5·50
		a. Imperf (pair)	9·00	
		b. Imperf between (vert pair)	85·00	
21		12a. pale greenish blue and bright purple	28·00	80·00
22		1r. chocolate and myrtle-green	80	6·50
		a. Imperf (pair)	9·50	
		b. Imperf between (horiz pair)	75·00	
23	**4**	1r. chocolate and myrtle-green	10·00	24·00
		a. Imperf (pair)	85·00	
		b. Imperf between (horiz pair)	£100	
24	**3**	2r. purple-brown and bistre-yellow	3·00	17·00
		a. Imperf (pair)	9·50	
25		3r. black and greenish blue	1·50	17·00
		a. Imperf (pair)	9·50	
26		4r. black and brown	3·00	19·00
		a. Imperf (pair)	9·50	
27		5r. bright blue and plum	3·00	20·00
		a. Imperf (pair)	9·50	
28		10r. bronze-green and cerise	7·00	27·00
		a. Imperf (pair)	13·00	
		b. Imperf between (horiz pair)	95·00	
29		15r. black and bronze-green	12·00	65·00
		a. Imperf (pair)	13·00	
30		25r. red-orange and blue	16·00	75·00
		a. Imperf (pair)	16·00	
8/20, 22/30 Set of 22			60·00	£275

Values to 5r. except the 1a., are inscribed "POSTAGE", and the remaining values inscribed "POSTAGE & REVENUE".

The central portrait of Type **3** is taken from a half-tone block and consists of large square dots. The portrait of Type **4** has a background of lines.

Owing to a lack of proper State control considerable quantities of these stamps circulated at below face value and the issue was subsequently withdrawn, supplies being exchanged for the 1939–42 issue. We are, however, now satisfied that the lower values at least did genuine postal duty until 1939.

Used prices are for stamps cancelled-to-order, postally used examples being worth considerably more.

5 Maharaja   **6** Maharaja VirSingh II
VirSingh II

(Litho Indian Security Printing Press, Nasik)

1939–42?. P 13½×14 (T **5**) or 14×13½ (T **6**).

31	**5**	¼a. chocolate	3·75	75·00
32		½a. yellow-green	3·75	60·00
33		¾a. bright blue	4·75	95·00
34		1a. scarlet	3·75	19·00
35		1¼a. blue	4·00	95·00
36		1½a. mauve	4·25	£120
37		2a. vermilion	3·75	75·00
38		2½a. turquoise-green	5·00	£200
39		3a. slate-violet	6·50	£110
40		4a. slate	7·50	27·00
41		8a. magenta	12·00	£200
42	**6**	1r. grey-green	20·00	
43		2r. bright violet	45·00	£550
44		5r. yellow-orange	£140	
45		10r. turquoise-green (1942)	£500	
46		15r. slate-lilac (date ?)	£11000	
47		25r. claret (date ?)	£7500	

Orchha became part of Vindhya Pradesh by 1 May 1948.

POONCH

Poonch was ruled by a junior branch of the Jammu and Kashmir princely family and by treaty, was subject to the "advice and consent" of the Maharaja of that state.

The Poonch postal service operated an office at Kahuta in the Punjab which acted as the office of exchange between the state post and that of British India.

GUM. The stamps of Poonch were issued without gum, except for some examples of Nos. 7/10.

The stamps of Poonch are all imperforate, and handstamped in watercolours.

ILLUSTRATIONS. Designs of Poonch are illustrated actual size.

Raja Moti Singh, 1852–1892

1   **2**

1876. T **1** (22×21 mm). *Central face value in circle and five rosettes in outer frame. Yellowish white, wove paper.*

1		6p. red	£11000	£150

1877. *As* T **1** (19×17 mm). *Central face value in oval and two rosettes in outer frame. Same paper.*

1a		½a. red	£13000	£4500

1879. T **2** (21×19 mm). *Central face value in oval and one rosette in outer frame. Same paper.*

2		½a. red	—	£4500

3 (½a.)   **4** (1a.)

5 (2a.) **6** (4a.)

1880. *Yellowish white, wove paper.*

3	3	½a. red	45·00	17·00
4	4	1a. red	£100	60·00
5	5	2a. red	£180	£120
6	6	4a. red	£200	£140

1884. *Toned wove bâtonné paper.*

7	3	½a. red	4·50	4·50
8	4	1a. red	21·00	
9	5	2a. red	19·00	22·00
10	6	4a. red	42·00	42·00

These are sometimes found gummed.

7 (1 pice)

1884–87. *Various papers.*

(a) White laid bâtonné or ribbed bâtonné.

11	7	1p. red	24·00	24·00
		a. Pair, one stamp sideways	£250	
12	3	½a. red	2·75	3·50
		a. Tête-bêche (pair)	£2750	
13	4	1a. red	4·00	
		a. Pair, one stamp sideways	£1300	
14	5	2a. red	9·50	11·00
15	6	4a. red	14·00	

(b) Thick white laid paper.

22	7	1p. red	£110	
23	3	½a. red	75·00	
24	4	1a. red	80·00	
25	5	2a. red	85·00	
26	6	4a. red	£100	

(c) Yellow wove bâtonné.

27	7	1p. red	3·75	3·75
		a. Pair, one stamp sideways	40·00	
28	3	½a. red	5·50	6·00
29	4	1a. red	48·00	
30	5	2a. red	9·00	11·00
31	6	4a. red	4·75	4·75

(d) Orange-buff wove bâtonné.

32	7	1p. red	3·25	3·50
		a. Pair, one stamp sideways	28·00	35·00
		b. Tête-bêche (pair)	42·00	
33	3	½a. red	26·00	
34	5	2a. red	90·00	
35	6	4a. red	23·00	

(e) Yellow laid paper.

36	7	1p. red	2·25	3·50
		a. Pair, one stamp sideways	19·00	
		b. Tête-bêche (pair)	28·00	
37	3	½a. red	4·00	
38	4	1a. red	50·00	
39	5	2a. red	55·00	60·00
40	6	4a. red	45·00	

(f) Yellow laid bâtonné.

41	7	1p. red	12·00	10·00

(g) Buff laid or ribbed bâtonné paper thicker than (d).

42	4	1a. red	70·00	
43	6	4a. red	75·00	

(h) Blue-green laid paper (1887).

44	3	½a. red	42·00	
45	4	1a. red	3·25	5·00
46	5	2a. red	40·00	
47	6	4a. red	65·00	

(i) Yellow-green laid paper.

48	3	½a. red	42·00	

(j) Blue-green wove bâtonné.

49	7	1p. red	45·00	42·00
49a	3	½a. red	£1200	
50	4	1a. red	2·50	3·75

(k) Lavender wove bâtonné.

51	4	1a. red	80·00	
52	5	2a. red	2·75	3·75
		a. Pair, one stamp sideways	£2750	

(l) Blue wove bâtonné.

53	7	1p. red	2·75	2·50
		a. Pair, one stamp sideways	28·00	38·00
		b. Tête-bêche (pair)	42·00	
54	4	1a. red	£375	£400

(m) Various coloured papers.

55	7	1p. red/grey-blue laid	8·50	5·50
		a. Tête-bêche (pair)	£300	
56		1p. red/lilac laid	50·00	55·00
		a. Pair, one stamp sideways	£350	£350
		b. Tête-bêche (pair)	£325	

1888. *Printed in aniline rose on various papers.*

57	7	1p. on *blue wove bâtonné*	5·50	
		a. Tête-bêche (pair)	80·00	
58		1p. on *buff laid*	15·00	
		a. Tête-bêche (pair)	£120	
59	3	½a. on *white laid*	23·00	
60	4	1a. on *green laid*	16·00	19·00
61		1a. on *green wove bâtonné*	9·00	9·50
62	5	2a. on *lavender wove bâtonné*	8·50	8·50
63	6	4a. on *yellow laid*	15·00	18·00
		a. Pair, one stamp sideways	£800	
		b. Tête-bêche (pair)	£800	

OFFICIAL STAMPS

Raja Baldeo Singh, 1892–1918

1887.

(a) White laid bâtonné paper.

O1	7	1p. black	2·50	2·75
		a. Pair, one stamp sideways	15·00	18·00
		b. Tête-bêche (pair)	18·00	
O2	3	½a. black	3·00	3·75
O3	4	1a. black	2·75	3·00
O4	5	2a. black	4·75	4·75
O5	6	4a. black	7·50	11·00

(b) White or toned wove bâtonné paper.

O6	7	1p. black	2·50	
		a. Pair, one stamp sideways	27·00	
		b. Tête-bêche (pair)	38·00	
O7	3	½a. black	3·00	3·50
		a. Pair, one stamp sideways	£1800	
O8	4	1a. black	15·00	14·00
O9	5	2a. black	6·50	6·50
O10	6	4a. black	10·00	

RAJASTHAN

Rajasthan was formed in 1948–49 from a number of States in Rajputana; these included Bundi, Jaipur and Kishangarh, whose posts continued to function more or less separately until ordered by the Indian Government to close on 1 April 1950.

PRICES FOR STAMPS ON COVER	
Nos. 1/7	*from* × 15
Nos. 8/10	
Nos. 11/12	*from* × 5
Nos. 13/14	
Nos. 15/25	*from* × 4
Nos. 26/42	*from* × 3
No. 43	*from* × 5
Nos. 44/60	*from* × 3
No. 61	*from* × 5
Nos. 62/5	—

BUNDI

(1)

1948–49. *Nos. 86/92 of Bundi. (a) Handstamped with T 1.*
A. In black. B. In violet. C. In blue.

			A	B	C
1		¼a. blue-green	5·50	6·00	30·00
		a. Pair, one without opt	£325	†	†
2		½a. violet	5·50	4·50	40·00
		a. Pair, one without opt	£350	£325	†
3		1a. yellow-green	4·75	13·00	42·00
		a. Pair, one without opt	†	£325	†
4		2a. vermilion	11·00	28·00	—
5		4a. orange	42·00	30·00	£110
6		8a. ultramarine	7·00	8·00	70·00
7		1r. chocolate	—	£225	85·00

The above prices are for unused, used stamps being worth about six times the unused prices. Most of these handstamps are known, sideways, inverted or double.

(b) Machine-printed as T 1 in black.

8		¼a. blue-green		
9		½a. violet		
10		1a. yellow-green		
11		2a. vermilion	7·50	70·00
		a. Opt inverted	£250	
12		4a. orange	3·50	70·00
		a. Opt double	£225	
13		8a. ultramarine	20·00	
		a. Opt inverted	£550	
		b. Opt double	£375	
14		1r. chocolate	7·50	

JAIPUR

राजस्थान

RAJASTHAN

(2)

1950 (26 Jan). *T 7 of Jaipur optd with T 2.*

15		¼a. black and brown-lake (No. 58) (B.)	6·50	19·00
16		½a. black and violet (No. 41) (R.)	5·00	20·00
17		¾a. black and brown-red (No. 59) (Blue-blk.)	9·00	24·00

		a. Opt in pale blue	15·00	40·00
18		1a. black and blue (No. 60) (R.)	6·00	42·00
19		2a. black and buff (No. 61) (R.)	8·00	55·00
20		2½a. black and carmine (No. 62) (B.)	8·50	27·00
21		3a. black and green (No. 63) (R.)	10·00	65·00
22		4a. black and grey-green (No. 64) (R.)	9·00	75·00
23		6a. black and pale blue (No. 65a) (R.)	9·50	£100
24		8a. black and chocolate (No. 66) (R.)	16·00	£150
25		1r. black and yellow-bistre (No. 67) (R.)	20·00	£200
15/25		Set of 11	95·00	£700

KISHANGARH

1948 (Oct)–**49.** *Various stamps of Kishangarh handstamped with T 1 in red.*

(a) On stamps of 1899–1901.

26		¼a. rose-pink (No. 5a) (B.)		£225
26a		¼a. rose-pink (No. 22a)	—	£200
27		½a. deep blue (No. 26)		£450
29		1a. brown-lilac (No. 29)	14·00	40·00
		b. Imperf (pair)	40·00	90·00
		c. Violet handstamp	—	£350
		d. Black handstamp		£400
30		4a. chocolate (No. 31)	75·00	£100
		a. Violet handstamp	—	£475
31		1r. dull green (No. 32)	£275	£300
31a		2r. brown-red (No. 34)	£350	
32		5r. mauve (No. 35)	£325	£325

(b) On stamps of 1904–10.

33	13	½a. chestnut	—	£160
33a		1a. blue		£225
34		4a. brown	13·00	
		a. Blue handstamp		£225
35	12	8a. grey	£100	£160
36	13	8a. violet	11·00	
37		1r. green	12·00	
38		2r. olive-yellow	19·00	
39		5r. purple-brown	27·00	
		a. Blue handstamp		£425

(c) On stamps of 1912–16.

40	14	½a. green (No. 64)	£400	£200
41		1a. red		£200
42		2a. deep violet (No. 51)	£450	
43		2a. purple (No. 66)	3·00	8·00
		a. Pair, one without handstamp	£400	
44		4a. bright blue	—	£475
45		8a. brown	5·00	
		a. Pair, one without handstamp	£400	
46		1r. brown	10·00	
47		2r. deep green	10·00	
48		5r. brown	£400	

(d) On stamps of 1928–36.

49	16	½a. yellow-green	£150	
49a		2a. magenta		£400
50		4a. chestnut	£225	
51		8a. violet	6·00	55·00
		a. Pair, one without handstamp	£375	
52		1r. light green	21·00	
53		2r. lemon-yellow	16·00	
54		5r. claret	16·00	

(e) On stamps of 1943–47.

55	16	¼a. pale dull blue	95·00	95·00
56		¼a. greenish blue	48·00	48·00
		a. Imperf (pair)	£225	
57		½a. deep green	30·00	30·00
		a. Violet handstamp		£200
57b		½a. yellow-green	40·00	40·00
		ba. Imperf (pair)	£225	
		bb. Blue handstamp	—	£200
58	17	1a. carmine-red	60·00	60·00
		a. Violet handstamp		£225
58b		1a. orange-red (*imperf*)	£150	
		ba. Blue handstamp	£160	
59		2a. bright magenta	£170	£170
60		2a. maroon (*imperf*)	£200	
61	16	4a. brown	2·50	8·00
		a. Pair, one without handstamp	£275	
62		8a. violet	15·00	55·00
63		1r. green	6·50	
64		2r. yellow	95·00	
65		5r. claret	50·00	

A 1a. value in deep violet-blue was issued for revenue purposes, but is known postally used (*Price £80 used*).

RAJPIPLA

PRICES FOR STAMPS ON COVER	
No. 1	*from* × 50
Nos. 2/3	—

Maharana Ganbhir Singh, 1860–1897

The Rajpipla state post was opened to the public sometime in the late 1870s. Adhesive stamps were preceded by postal stationery lettersheets which were first reported in 1879.

1 (1 pice) **2** (2a.) **3** (4a.)

1880. *Litho. With or without gum (1p.) or no gum (others). P 11 (1p.) or 12½.*

1	1	1p. blue (1 June)	3·25	35·00
2	2	2a. green	28·00	£100
		a. Imperf between (pair)	£550	£550
3	3	4a. red	15·00	65·00
1/3		Set of 3	42·00	£180

No. 1 was produced in sheets of 64 (8×8) and the higher values in sheets of 20 (5×4).

These stamps became obsolete in 1886 when the Imperial postal service absorbed the Rajpipla state post.

SHAHPURA

PRICES FOR STAMPS ON COVER	
Nos. 1/4	*from* × 2
No. F1	*from* × 2

DATES. Those quoted are of first known use.

Rajadhiraj Nahar Singh, 1870–1932

RAJ SHAHPURA Postage 1 pice	RAJ SHAHPURA 1 pice
1	2

1914–17. *Typo.*
1	1	1p. carmine/*bluish grey* (P 11)........	—	£750
2		1p. carmine/*drab* (*imperf*) (1917)....	—	£1100

Some examples of No. 1 are imperforate on one side or on two adjacent sides.

1920–28. *Typo. Imperf.*
3	2	1p. carmine/*drab* (1928)..................	—	£1300
4		1a. black/*pink*...................................	—	£1500

POSTAL FISCAL
Rajadhiraj Umaid Singh, 1932–1947
Rajadhiraj Sudarshan Deo, 1947–1971

F 1

1932–47. *Typo.* P 11, 11½ or 12.
F1	F 1	1a. red (*shades*).............................	75·00	£250
		a. Pin-perf 7 (1947)		

Nos. F1/a were used for both fiscal and postal purposes. Manuscript cancellations must be assumed to be fiscal, unless on cover showing other evidence of postal use. The design was first issued for fiscal purposes in 1898.

Shahpura became part of Rajasthan by 15 April 1948.

SIRMOOR

PRICES FOR STAMPS ON COVER
The stamps of Sirmoor are very rare used on cover.

Raja Shamsher Parkash, 1886–1898

1 (1 pice)	2	3 Raja Shamsher Parkash

1878 (June)**–80.** *Litho.* P 11½.
1	1	1p. pale green................................	14·00	£275
2		1p. blue (on *laid* paper) (1880)	4·25	£160
		a. Imperf between (pair)................	£350	
		b. Imperf (pair).............................	£350	

(Litho at Calcutta)

1892. *Thick wove paper.* P 11½.
3	2	1p. yellow-green.............................	1·10	1·00
		a. Imperf between (vert pair)........	70·00	
		b. *Deep green*...............................	75	75
		ba. Imperf between (vert pair).........	70·00	70·00
4		1p. blue..	1·00	80
		a. Imperf between (vert pair)........	60·00	60·00
		b. Imperf between (horiz pair).......	60·00	60·00
		c. Imperf vert (horiz pair).............	60·00	
		d. Imperf (pair).............................	75·00	

These were originally made as reprints, about 1891, to supply collectors, but there being very little demand for them they were put into use. The design was copied (including the perforations) from an illustration in a dealer's catalogue.

A   B

C   D

There were seven printings of stamps as Type **3**, all in sheets of 70 (10×7) and made up from groups of transfers which can be traced through minor varieties.

Printings I to V and VII of the 3p. and 6p. are as Types A and C (both with large white dots evenly spaced between the ends of the upper and lower inscriptions).

Printing VI is as Type B (small white dots and less space) and Type D (large white dots unevenly positioned between the inscriptions).

(Litho Waterlow)

1885–96. P 14 to 15.
5	3	3p. chocolate (A)	65	30
		a. Brown (B) (1896)......................	30	35
6		3p. orange (A) (1888)	1·50	20
		a. Type B (1896)............................	30	20
		ab. Imperf (pair).............................	£550	
7		6p. blue-green (C)............................	4·25	3·50
		a. Green (C) (1888)	95	50
		b. Bright green (C) (1891).............	60·00	60·00
		c. Deep green (C) (1894)...............	60	35
		d. Yellowish green (D) (1896)........	40	1·50
8		1a. bright blue.................................	2·50	3·50
		a. Dull blue (1891)........................	8·00	4·50
		b. Steel-blue (1891)......................	85·00	85·00
		c. Grey-blue (1894).......................	2·25	1·00
		d. Slate-blue (1896)......................	50	2·50
9		2a. pink..	4·25	13·00
		a. Carmine (1894).........................	3·50	3·00
		b. Rose-red (1896)........................	3·25	4·00

Composition of the various printings was as follows:
Printing I — Nos. 5, 7, 8 and 9
Printing II — Nos. 6 and 7*a*
Printing III — Nos. 6, 7*b* and 8*a*
Printing IV — Nos. 5, 6, 7*a*, and 8*b*
Printing V — Nos. 6, 7*c*, 8*c* and 9
Printing VI — Nos. 5*a*, 6*a*, 7*d*, 8*d* and 9*b*
Printing VII — Only exists overprinted "On S. S. S." (Nos. 78/81).

4 Indian Elephant	5 Raja Shamsher Parkash

(Recess Waterlow & Sons)

1894–99. P 12 to 15 and compounds.
22	4	3p. orange-brown	3·00	30
23		6p. green.......................................	75	30
		a. Imperf between (vert pair)........	£2250	
24		1a. blue...	4·00	1·75
25		2a. rose..	2·75	1·25
26		3a. yellow-green..............................	21·00	40·00
27		4a. deep green................................	13·00	21·00
28		8a. deep blue...................................	16·00	26·00
29		1r. vermilion..................................	35·00	65·00
22/9 Set of 8			85·00	£140

Raja Surindra Bikram Parkash, 1898–1911

(Recess Waterlow & Sons)

1899. P 13 to 15.
30	5	3a. yellow-green..............................	3·25	22·00
31		4a. deep green................................	4·50	20·00
32		8a. deep blue...................................	6·50	16·00
33		1r. vermilion..................................	10·00	45·00
30/3 Set of 4			22·00	95·00

OFFICIAL STAMPS

NOTE. The varieties occurring in the machine-printed "On S.S.S." overprints may, of course, also be found in the inverted and double overprints, and many of them are known thus.

Roman figures denote printings of the basic stamps (Nos. 7/21). Where more than one printing was overprinted the prices quoted are for the commonest.

I. MACHINE-PRINTED

On
S. S.
S.
(11)

1890. Optd with T **11**.

(a) In black.
50	3	6p. green (C).................................	£1100	£1100
		a. Stop before first "S"	60·00	£170
51		2a. pink..	60·00	
		a. Stop before first "S"	£150	

(b) In red.
52	3	6p. green (C).................................	20·00	2·75
		a. Stop before first "S"	60·00	25·00
53		1a. bright blue.................................	50·00	15·00
		a. Stop before first "S"	£130	60·00
		b. Opt inverted	£1300	£700

(c) Doubly optd in red and in black.
53c	3	6p. green (C).................................	£1000	£1000
		ca. Stop before first "S"	£2250	£2250

Nos. 50, 52 and 53*c* are from Printing II and the remainder from Printing I.

On   On
S.   S.   S.   S.
S.   S.
(12)   (13)

1891. *Optd with T* **12**.

(a) In black.
54	3	3p. orange (A)	2·75	35·00
		a. Opt inverted	£475	
55		6p. green (C).................................	1·50	1·50
		a. Opt double	£170	
		b. No stop after lower "S"	22·00	22·00
		c. Raised stop before lower "S"....	£160	£120
56		1a. bright blue.................................	£375	£450
57		2a. pink..	16·00	65·00

(b) In red.
58	3	6p. green (C).................................	27·00	3·00
		a. Opt inverted	£225	£180
		b. Opt double	£225	£190
59		1a. bright blue.................................	24·00	30·00
		a. Opt inverted	†	£550
		b. Opt double	†	£550
		c. No stop after lower "S"............	£190	£200

(c) In black and red.
59d	3	6p. green (C).................................		£1200

Nos. 54/5, 58 and 59*d* are from Printing II and the others from Printing I.

1892–97. *Optd with T* **13**.

(a) In black.
60	3	3p. orange (A)	60	50
		a. Type B......................................	3·00	60
		b. Opt inverted	£225	
		c. First "S" inverted and stop raised	5·00	5·00
		d. No stop after lower "S"	5·00	5·00
		e. Raised stop after second "S"	35·00	16·00
		f. Vertical pair, Types **12** and **13**..	£150	
61		6p. green (C).................................	7·00	1·75
		a. Deep green (C)	1·60	50
		b. First "S" inverted and stop raised	38·00	16·00
		c. Raised stop after second "S"	38·00	14·00
		d. No stop after lower "S"	48·00	19·00
		e. Opt double	£600	
62		1a. steel-blue..................................		
		a. Grey-blue...................................	10·00	1·00
		b. Opt double	£375	
		c. First "S" inverted and stop raised	40·00	10·00
		d. No stop after lower "S"	£170	65·00
		e. Raised stop after second "S"	70·00	12·00
63		2a. pink..	13·00	19·00
		a. Carmine....................................	7·00	7·00
		b. Opt double	£850	£850
		c. First "S" inverted and stop raised	40·00	40·00
		d. No stop after lower "S"	40·00	40·00
		e. Raised stop after second "S".....	£160	£150

(b) In red.
64	3	6p. green (C).................................	4·50	50
		a. Bright green (C).........................	9·50	1·00
		b. Opt inverted	£130	£100
		c. First "S" inverted and stop raised	23·00	5·00
		d. Vertical pair, Types **12** and **13**...	£150	£150
65		1a. bright blue.................................	16·00	3·75
		a. Steel-blue..................................	11·00	1·00
		b. Opt inverted	£300	£200
		c. Opt double	£325	
		d. First "S" inverted and stop raised	38·00	8·00
		e. No stop after lower "S"	38·00	8·00

(c) Doubly overprinted in black and red.
65f	3	6p. bright green (C)	—	£1100
		fa. Green (C). Red opt inverted......	†	£1600

The printings used for this issue were as follows:
Printing I — Nos. 63 and 65
Printing II — Nos. 60, 64 and 65*fa*
Printing III — Nos. 60, 64*a* and 65*f*
Printing IV — Nos. 61, 62, 64 and 65*a*
Printing V — Nos. 60, 61*a*, 62*a* and 63*a*
Printing VI — No. 60*a*

There are seven settings of this overprint, the first of which was a composite setting of 20 (10×2), with examples of Type **12** in the upper row. The inverted "S" and the missing stop occur in the 3rd and 6th settings with the latter also including the raised stop after second "S".

On   On
S.   S.   S.   S.
S.   S.
(14)   (15)

1896–97. *Optd as T* **14**.
66	3	3p. orange (B) (1897)	12·00	1·25
		a. Comma after first "S"...............	50·00	30·00
		b. Opt inverted		
		c. Opt double	†	£650
67		6p. deep green (C)	5·50	60
		a. Yellowish green (D)	—	3·50

	b. Comma after first "S"...............	48·00	19·00
	c. Comma after lower "S"...............	£180	21·00
	d. "S" at right inverted...............	£180	45·00
68	1a. grey-blue...............	7·50	1·25
	a. Comma after first "S"...............	65·00	22·00
	b. Comma after lower "S"...............	£200	25·00
	c. "S" at right inverted...............	—	48·00
69	2a. carmine (1897)...............	17·00	14·00
	a. Comma after first "S"...............	£120	£120

Nos. 66 and 67a are from Printing VI and the remainder from Printing V.

There are four settings of this overprint, (1) 23 mm high, includes the comma after lower "S"; (2) and (3) 25 mm high, with variety, comma after first "S"; (4) 25 mm high, with variety, "S" at right inverted.

1898 (Nov). Optd with T **15**.

70	3	6p. deep green (C)...............	£200	9·50
		a. Yellowish green (D)...............	£190	7·50
		b. Small "S" at right...............	£350	25·00
		c. Comma after lower "S"...............	—	55·00
		d. Lower "S" inverted and stop raised...............	—	55·00
71		1a. grey-blue...............	£225	17·00
		a. Small "S" at right...............	£375	42·00
		b. Small "S" without stop...............	—	£190

No. 70a is from Printing VI and the others Printing V.

There are two settings of this overprint. Nos. 70b and 71a/b occur in the first setting, and Nos. 70c/d in the second setting.

(16)   (17)

1899 (July). Optd with T **16**.

72	3	3p. orange (B)...............	£300	7·50
73		6p. deep green (C)...............	—	23·00

No. 72 is from Printing VI and No. 73 from Printing V.

1899 (Dec)–**1900**. Optd as T **17**.

74	3	3p. orange (B)...............	—	8·00
		a. Raised stop after lower "S"...............	†	70·00
		b. Comma after first "S"...............	†	£250
		c. No stop after first "S"...............	†	£140
75		6p. deep green (C)...............	—	7·00
		a. Yellowish green (D)...............	†	8·00
		b. Raised stop after lower "S"...............	†	70·00
		c. Comma after first "S"...............	†	£225
		d. No stop after first "S"...............	†	£200
76		1a. bright blue...............	†	£170
		a. Grey-blue...............	†	10·00
		b. Slate-blue...............		13·00
		c. Raised stop after lower "S"...............	†	£100
		d. Comma after first "S"...............	†	£275
		e. No stop after first "S"...............	†	£150
77		2a. carmine...............		£130
		a. Raised stop after lower "S"...............	†	£500

There are two settings of this overprint: (1) 22 mm high, with raised stop variety; (2) 23 mm high, with "comma" and "no stop" varieties.

The printings used for this issue were as follows:
Printing   I   — No. 76
Printing   V   — Nos. 75, 76a and 77
Printing   VI   — Nos. 74, 75a and 76b

(18)   (19)

(Optd by Waterlow & Sons)

1900. Optd with T **18**.

78	3	3p. orange...............	3·00	7·50
79		6p. green...............	50	45
80		1a. blue...............	35	60
81		2a. carmine...............	3·25	60·00

Nos. 78/81 were from Printing VII which was not issued without the overprint.

II. HANDSTAMPED

The words "On" and each letter "S" struck separately (except for Type **22** which was applied at one operation).

1894. Handstamped with T **19**.

(a) In black.

82	3	3p. orange (A)...............	3·25	3·75
		a. "On" only...............	70·00	
83		6p. green (C)...............	5·00	6·00
		a. Deep green (C)...............	11·00	13·00
		b. "On" only...............	70·00	70·00
84		1a. bright blue...............	55·00	42·00
		a. Dull blue...............	18·00	19·00
		b. Steel-blue...............		
		c. Grey-blue...............	19·00	17·00
		d. "On" only...............	—	95·00
85		2a. carmine...............	18·00	18·00
		a. "On" only...............	£110	

(b) In red.

86	3	6p. green (C)...............	£130	£140
86a		1a. grey-blue...............	£425	£425

The printings used for this issue were as follows:

Printing   I   — No. 84
Printing   III   — No. 84a
Printing   IV   — Nos. 83, 84b and 86
Printing   V   — Nos. 82, 83a, 84c, 85 and 86a

1896. Handstamped with letters similar to those of T **13**, with stops, but irregular.

87	3	3p. orange (A)...............	90·00	70·00
		a. Type B		
88		6p. green (C)...............		
		a. Deep green (C)...............	80·00	65·00
		b. "On" omitted...............	£160	
88c		1a. grey-blue...............	£110	£110
89		2a. carmine...............	£200	

Printings used for this issue were as follows:

Printing   II   — No. 88
Printing   III   — No. 87
Printing   IV   — No. 88
Printing   V   — Nos. 87, 88a, 88c and 89
Printing   VI   — No. 87a

1897. Handstamped with letters similar to those of T **14**, with stops, but irregular.

90	3	3p. orange (B)...............	10·00	19·00
91		6p. deep green (C)...............	65·00	75·00
		a. "On" only...............	—	£110
92		1a. grey-blue...............	£325	£325
		a. "On" only...............	—	£110
93		2a. carmine...............	£130	£130

No. 90 was from Printing VI and the remainder from Printing V.

1897. Handstamped with letters similar to those of T **16**, with stops, but irregular.

93a	3	6p. deep green (C)...............	£170	£140

No. 93a is from Printing V.

(20)   (21)

1896.

*(a) Handstamped with T **20**.*

94	3	3p. orange (A)...............	65·00	70·00
95		2a. carmine...............	70·00	75·00

*(b) Handstamped with T **21**.*

96	3	3p. orange (A)...............	£170	£180
97		6p. bright green (C)...............		
98		1a. bright blue...............	£300	
		a. Dull blue...............		
98b		2a. carmine...............	£325	

No. 98 comes from Printing 1, No. 98a from Printing III, No. 97 possibly from Printing IV and the remainder from Printing V.

(22)   (23)

*(c) Handstamped with T **22**.*

99	3	3p. orange (B)...............	£120	
100		6p. deep green...............	£180	
101		1a. grey-blue...............	£225	
101a		2a. carmine...............	£375	

No. 99 is from Printing VI and the others from Printing V.

1899. Handstamped with T **23**.

102	3	3p. orange (A)...............	—	£180
		a. Type B...............	21·00	7·00
103		6p. green (C)...............		
		a. Deep green (C)...............	25·00	17·00
		b. Yellowish green (D)...............	15·00	16·00
104		1a. bright blue...............	—	£130
		a. Grey-blue...............	48·00	42·00
105		2a. pink...............		
		a. Carmine...............	55·00	27·00
		b. Rose-red...............	70·00	45·00
		c. "On" only...............	—	£140

Printings used for this issue were as follows:
Printing   I   — Nos. 104 and 105
Printing   IV   — Nos. 102 and 103
Printing   V   — Nos. 102, 103a, 104a and 105a
Printing   VI   — Nos. 102a, 103b and 105b

(24)

1901 (?). Handstamped with T **24**.

105d	3	6p. yellowish green (D)...............	—	£425

From Printing VI.

III. MIXED MACHINE-PRINTED AND HANDSTAMPED

1896.

*(i) Handstamped "On" as in T **19**, and machine-printed opt T **13** complete.*

106	3	6p. green (C)...............	—	£550

*(ii) Handstamped opt as T **14**, and machine-printed opt T **13** complete.*

107	3	6p. deep green (C)...............		

No.106 is from Printing IV and No. 107 from Printing V.

Various other types of these handstamps are known to exist, but in the absence of evidence of their authenticity we do not list them. It is stated that stamps of T **4** were never officially overprinted.

The stamps of Sirmoor have been obsolete since 1 April 1902.

SORUTH

PRICES FOR STAMPS ON COVER	
Nos. 1/2	from × 5
Nos. 4/4a	—
Nos. 5/8	from × 1
No. 8a	from × 3
No. 9	from × 1
Nos. 10/11	from × 5
No. 11e	from × 1
No. 12	from × 4
No. 13	from × 5
Nos. 14/15	from × 3
Nos. 16/24	from × 20
Nos. 33/6	from × 50
Nos. 37/8	from × 10
Nos. 40/1	from × 50
Nos. 42/57	from × 10
Nos. O1/13	from × 20
No. 58	from × 15
No. 59	from × 6
No. 60	from × 10
No. 61	from × 6
Nos. O14/22	from × 10

The name "Saurashtra", corrupted to "Sorath" or "Soruth", was originally used for all the territory later known as Kathiawar. Strictly speaking the name should have been applied only to a portion of Kathiawar including the state of Junagadh. As collectors have known these issues under the heading of "Soruth" for so long, we retain the name.

GUM. Nos. 1/47 of Soruth were issued without gum.

JUNAGADH

Nawab Mahabat Khan II, 1851–1882

(Currency 40 dokras or 16 annas = 1 koree)

1 (="Saurashtra Post 1864–65")

1864 (Nov). Handstamped in water-colour. Imperf.

1	1	(1a.) black/azure to grey (laid)............	£650	75·00
2		(1a.) black/azure to grey (wove)........	—	£160
4		(1a.) black/cream (laid)...............	†	£1500
4a		(1a.) black/cream (wove)...............	—	£850

ILLUSTRATIONS. Types **2** to **11** are shown actual size.

2 (1a.) (Devanagri numeral)   3 (1a.) (Gujarati numeral)

4 (4a.) (Devanagri numeral)   5 (4a.) (Gujarati numeral)

Differences in first character of bottom line on Nos. 8/a:

ऊ   क

Type A "u" (error)   Type B "ka" (correct)

(Typeset Nitiprakash Ptg Press, Junagadh)

1868 (June)–**75**. *Designs as T* **2** *to* **5**. *Imperf*.

A. Inscriptions in Gujarati characters. Wove paper.

5		1a. black/*yellowish*	†	£12000

B. Inscriptions in Devanagari characters (as in the illustrations).

I. Accents over first letters in top and bottom lines. Wove paper.

6		1a. red/*green*	†	£3000
7		1a. red/*blue*	†	£3000
7a		1a. red/*yellow*	†	£4500
8		1a. black/*pink* (first character in bottom line as Type A)	†	£1300
8a		1a. black/*pink* (first character in bottom line as Type B)	£950	£140
9		2a. black/*yellow* (1869)	†	£4750

II. Accents over second letters in top and bottom lines.

(a) Wove paper.

10	2	1a. black/*pink* (1869)	£500	70·00
		a. Printed both sides	†	—
		b. First two characters in last word of bottom line omitted (R. 4/1) .	—	£700

(b) Laid paper.

11	2	1a. black/*azure* (1870)	80·00	9·00
		a. Final character in both top and bottom lines omitted (R. 1/1)	—	£180
		b. First two characters in last word of bottom line omitted (R. 4/1) .	—	£140
		c. Doubly printed	†	£800
		d. *Se-tenant* pair. Nos. 11/12	£375	£140
11e		1a. black/*white*	†	£4000
12	3	1a. black/*azure* (1870)	£200	20·00
		a. Printed both sides	†	£900
		b. Final character in bottom line omitted (R. 1/1)	£550	£140
		c. Accent omitted from last word in bottom line (R. 5/2, 5/4)	—	£100
		d. Large numeral (R. 4/1)	£700	£180
		e. First character in middle line omitted (R. 2/4)	—	£350
		f. Central two characters in middle line omitted (R. 2/4)	—	£550
13		1a. red/*white* (1875)	20·00	22·00
		a. First two characters in bottom line omitted (R. 5/1)	95·00	£130
14	5	4a. black/*white*	£225	£400
		a. First two characters in last word of bottom line omitted (R. 4/1) .	£1000	
		b. Final character in bottom line omitted (R. 5/2)	£2250	
15	4	4a. black/*white*	£130	£200
		a. Final character in bottom line omitted (R. 1/1)	£500	

The settings of Nos. 5/7 are unknown.

Nos. 10/15, and probably Nos. 8/9, were printed in sheets of 20 (4×5). The same type was used throughout, but changes occurred as the loose type was amended.

1a.   Setting I (pink wove paper) (No. 8)
      Setting II (pink wove paper) (No. 8a)
      Setting III (pink wove paper) (No. 10)
      Setting IV (Devanagri numerals only) (pink wove paper) (Nos. 10/b)
      Setting IVA (Devanagri numerals only) (azure vertical laid paper) (Nos. 11, 11b)
      Setting IVB (Devanagri and Gujarati numerals mixed) (azure horizontal laid paper) (Nos. 11/a, 11d, 12)
      Setting IVC (Devanagri and Gujarati numerals mixed) (azure or white vertical laid paper) (Nos. 11, 11c/d, 11e, 12/b 12e/f)
      Setting IVD (Devanagri and Gujarati numerals mixed) (azure vertical laid paper) (Nos. 11, 11d, 12, 12d)
      Setting IVE (Gujarati numerals only) (white vertical laid paper) (Nos. 13/a)

2a.   Setting I (probably derived from 1a.
      Setting II) (yellow wove paper) (No. 9)

4a.   Setting IA (Gujarati numerals only) (white vertical laid paper) (Nos. 14/a)
      Setting IB (Devanagri numerals only) (white horizontal laid paper) (No. 15)
      Setting IC (Devanagri numerals only) (white vertical laid paper) (Nos. 15/a)
      Setting ID (only Gujarati numerals so far identified) (white vertical laid paper) (Nos. 14, 14b)

Settings IVA/D of the 1a. were subsequently adapted to form settings IA/D of the 4a.

The two known examples of No. 8 both come from the top row of the sheet. Marginal inscriptions indicate that No. 8a is from a separate setting.

Official imitations, consisting of 1a. carmine-red on white wove and white laid, 1a. black on blue wove, 4a. black on white wove, 4a. black on blue wove, 4a. red on white laid—all imperforate; 1a. carmine-red on white laid, 1a. black on blue wove, 1a. black on white laid and blue wove—all perforated 12, were made in 1890. Entire sheets of originals have 20 stamps (4×5), the imitations only 4 or 16.

6   7

(Typo Nitiprakash Ptg Press, Junagadh)

1878 (16 Jan)–**86**. *Laid paper with the lines wide apart. Imperf*

16	6	1a. green	90	40
		a. Printed both sides	£500	£550
		b. Laid lines close together (1886)	90	40
17	7	4a. vermilion	2·50	1·75
		a. Printed both sides	£650	
		b. *Scarlet/bluish*	3·50	3·00
18		4a. brown	13·00	

Nawab Bahadur Khan III, 1882–1892

1886. P 12. (a) *On toned laid paper with the lines close together.*

19	6	1a. green	40	15
		a. Imperf vert (horiz pair)	£130	
		b. Imperf between (vert pair)	†	£325
		c. Imperf horiz (vert pair)	†	£325
		d. Doubly printed	†	£450
		e. Error. Blue	£600	£600
		f. On bluish white laid paper	3·50	4·50
		fa. Imperf between (vert pair)	£190	£225
		fb. Imperf vert (horiz pair)	£190	
		g. Emerald-green	3·25	2·00
20	7	4a. red	2·00	1·00
		a. On bluish white laid paper	10·00	16·00
		ab. Printed both sides	£375	
		b. Carmine	3·75	3·00
21		4a. brown	10·00	

(b) Wove paper.

22	6	1a. green	2·75	1·25
		a. Imperf (pair)	75·00	95·00
		b. Error. Blue		£600
		c. Imperf horiz (vert pair)	£150	
23	7	4a. red	4·25	10·00
		a. Imperf (pair)	£190	£250
		b. Imperf between (horiz pair)	£350	
		c. Imperf vert (horiz pair)	£350	
24		4a. brown	16·00	

There is a very wide range of colours in both values. The laid paper, on which imperforate printings continued to appear until 1912, is found both vertical and horizontal.

The 1a. was originally issued in sheets of 15 (5×3), but later appeared in sheets of 20 (5×4) with marginal inscriptions. Stamps were sometimes printed in double sheets showing two impressions of the plate printed *tête-bêche* on the same or opposite sides of the paper.

The 4a. was in horizontal strips of 5. No. 20 exists as a sheet of 10 (5×2), with two impressions of the plate printed *tête-bêche*, and No. 23 in a similar sized sheet but with both impressions upright.

Nawab Rasul Khan 1892–1911
Nawab Mahabat Khan III, 1911–1959

(Indian currency)

        (8)
                           (9)

1913 (1 Jan). *Surch in Indian currency with T* **8** *or* **9**. P 12.

(a) On toned wove paper.

33	6	3p. on 1a. emerald-green	15	20
		a. Imperf (pair)	£350	
		b. Imperf between (horiz pair)	£325	
		c. Imperf vert (horiz pair)	£325	
		d. Doubly printed	£225	
34	7	1a. on 4a. red	2·25	6·00
		a. Imperf (pair)	£650	
		b. Capital "A" in "Anna"	6·00	
		c. Surch inverted	£700	
		d. Imperf between (horiz pair)		

(b) On white wove paper.

35	6	3p. on 1a. emerald-green	15	20
		a. Imperf between vert (pair)..	£500	
		b. Surch inverted	35·00	20·00
		c. Surch double	†	£400
36	7	1a. on 4a. carmine	2·00	6·00
		a. Imperf (pair)		
		b. Surch both sides	£750	
		c. Capital "A" in "Anna"	14·00	

(c) On white laid paper.

37	6	3p. on 1a. emerald-green	75·00	30·00
		a. Imperf (pair)	—	£450
		b. Larger English surch (21 mm long with capital "p" in "Pies") inverted	†	£1900
38	7	1a. on 4a. red	7·50	48·00
		a. Capital "A" in "Anna"	£350	
		b. Surch inverted	£700	
		c. Surch double	£700	
		d. Surch double, one inverted	£700	

The 1a. surcharge with capital "A" in "Anna" comes from a separate setting.

10   11

(Dies eng Thacker & Co, Bombay. Typo Junagadh State Press)

1914 (1 Sept). *New plates. T* **6/7** *redrawn as T* **10/11**. *Wove paper.* P 12.

40	10	3p. green	1·10	35
		a. Imperf (pair)	7·50	24·00
		b. Imperf vert (horiz pair)	90·00	
		c. Laid paper	3·00	1·50
		ca. Imperf (pair)	18·00	35·00
		d. Error. Red (imperf)	†	£2250
41	11	1a. red	1·50	2·00
		a. Imperf (pair)	20·00	85·00
		b. Imperf horiz (vert pair)	£475	
		c. Laid paper	£250	£110

---

12 Nawab Mahabat   13 Nawab Mahabat
    Khan III   Khan III

(Dies eng Popatlal Bhimji Pandya. Typo Junagadh State Press)

1923 (1 Sept). *Blurred impression. Laid paper.* Pin-perf 12.

42	12	1a. red	3·00	9·00

Sheets of 16 stamps (8×2).
This setting was later printed on wove paper, but single examples cannot readily be distinguished from No. 46b.

ત્રણ પાઇ   ત્રણ પાઇ
(14)   (14a)

1923 (1 Sept). *Surch with T* **14**.

43	12	3p. on 1a. red	4·25	7·00
		a. Surch with T **14a**	4·75	12·00

Four stamps in the setting have surch. T **14a**, i.e. with top of last character curved to right.

1923 (Oct). *Blurred impression. Wove paper.* Pin-perf 12, small holes.

44	13	3p. mauve	35	45

Sheets of 16 (4×4).

1924. *Clear impression. Wove paper.* P 12, large holes.

45	13	3p. mauve (1.24)	2·00	35
		a. Imperf (pair)	£300	
46	12	1a. red (4.24)	7·50	8·00
		a. Imperf (pair)	60·00	
		b. Pin perf	3·50	4·00

The first plate of the 3p., which printed No. 44, produced unsatisfactory impressions, so it was replaced by a second plate, producing two panes of 16 (4×4), from which No. 45 comes. Sheets printed from the first plate had very large margins.
The 1a. is also from a new plate, giving a clearer impression. Sheets of 16 stamps (4×4).

1929. *Clear impressions. Laid paper.* P 12, large holes.

47	13	3p. mauve	5·00	4·00
		a. Imperf (pair)	3·25	35·00
		b. Perf 11	12·00	8·50
		ba. Imperf between (horiz pair)	3·00	25·00

Sheets of two panes of 16 (4×4).
The laid paper shows several sheet watermarks.
No. 47ba was intentional to create a 6p. franking required by a rate change in October 1929.

15 Junagadh City   16 Gir Lion

17 Nawab Mahabat   18 Kathi Horse
   Khan III

(Des Amir Sheikh Mahamadbhai. Litho Indian Security Printing Press, Nasik)

1929 (1 Oct). *Inscr* "POSTAGE". P 14.

49	15	3p. black and blackish green	1·00	10
50	16	½a. black and deep blue	5·50	10
51	17	1a. black and carmine	5·00	1·00
52	18	2a. black and dull orange	13·00	2·00
		a. Grey and dull yellow	28·00	1·90
53	15	3a. black and carmine	5·50	10·00
54	16	4a. black and purple	13·00	25·00
55	18	8a. black and yellow-green	13·00	22·00
56	17	1r. black and pale blue	10·00	26·00
49/56 Set of 8			60·00	80·00

1935 (1 Jan). *As T* **17**, *but inscr* "POSTAGE AND REVENUE". P 14.

57	17	1a. black and carmine	7·50	1·00

OFFICIAL STAMPS
SARKARI
(O 1)

1929 (1 Oct). *Optd with Type* O **1**, *in vermilion, at Nasik.*

O1	15	3p. black and blackish green	1·75	15
		a. Red opt	1·50	10
O2	16	½a. black and deep blue	3·25	10
		a. Red opt	4·00	40
O3	17	1a. black and carmine (No. 51)	4·00	35
		a. Red opt	3·00	15
O4	18	2a. black and dull orange	2·50	1·25
		a. Grey and dull yellow	21·00	60

		b. Red opt..............................	25·00	2·75
O5	15	3a. black and carmine................	75	30
		a. Red opt..............................	17·00	1·50
O6	16	4a. black and purple.................	4·00	45
		a. Red opt..............................	21·00	2·75
O7	18	8a. black and yellow-green.........	3·75	2·75
O8	17	1r. black and pale blue..............	3·00	20·00
O1/8		Set of 8	20·00	22·00

SARKARI   SARKARI
(O 2)   (O 3)

1932 (Jan)–35. *Optd with Type O* 2, *in red, at Junagadh State Press.*

O9	15	3a. black and carmine................	22·00	18·00
		a. Optd with Type O 3 (1.35)......	95·00	7·00
O10	16	4a. black and purple.................	28·00	16·00
O11	18	8a. black and yellow-green.........	32·00	18·00
O12	17	1r. black and pale blue..............	30·00	90·00
		a. Optd with Type O 3 (1.35)......	£150	£120
O9/12		Set of 4	£100	£120

1938. *No. 57 optd with Type O* 1, *in vermilion.*

O13	17	1a. black and carmine................	16·00	2·25
		a. Brown-red opt.....................	13·00	1·50

The state was occupied by Indian troops on 9 November 1947 following the flight of the Nawab to Pakistan.

UNITED STATE OF SAURASHTRA

The administration of Junagadh state was assumed by the Government of India on 9 November 1947. An Executive Council took office on 1 June 1948.

Under the new Constitution of India the United State of Saurashtra was formed on 15 February 1948, comprising 221 former states and estates of Kathiawar, including Jasdan, Morvi, Nawanagar and Wadhwan, but excluding Junagadh. A referendum was held by the Executive Council of Junagadh which then joined the United State on 20 January 1949. It is believed that the following issues were only used in Junagadh.

The following issues were surcharged at the Junagadh State Press.

POSTAGE & REVENUE
ONE ANNA
(19)
Postage & Revenue
ONE ANNA
(20)

1949. *Stamps of 1929 surch.*

(a) With T **19** *in red.*

58	16	1a. on ½a. black and deep blue (5.49)	9·50	5·00
		a. Surch double	†	£500
		b. "AFNA" for "ANNA" and inverted "N" in "REVENUE"		£2500
		c. Larger first "A" in "ANNA" (R. 2/5)............	80·00	60·00

(b) With T **20** *in green.*

59	18	1a. on 2a. grey and dull yellow (2.49)......	15·00	24·00
		a. "evenue" omitted	—	£650

No. 58b may have occurred on R. 2/5 with No. 58c being caused by its correction.

A number of other varieties occur on No. 58, including: small "V" in "REVENUE" (R. 2/3); small "N" in "REVENUE" (R. 2/4, 3/4); small "E" in "POSTAGE" (R. 3/2); thick "A" in "POSTAGE" (R. 4/4); inverted "N" in "REVENUE" and small second "A" in "ANNA" (R. 4/5); small "O" in "ONE" (R. 5/1); small "V" and "U" in "REVENUE" (R. 6/3); small "N" in "ONE" (R. 7/2).

In No. 59 no stop after "ANNA" is known on R. 1/4, 4/2, 7/4 and 8/3 and small "N" in "ONE" on R. 2/4.

21

(Typo Waterlow)

1949 (Sept). *Court Fee stamps of Bhavnagar state optd "SAURASHTRA" and further optd "U.S.S. REVENUE & POSTAGE" as in T* **21**, *in black.* P 11.

60	21	1a. purple............................	10·00	9·50
		a. "POSTAGE" omitted (R. 1/2)...	£325	£225
		b. Opt double	£300	£350

The Court Fee stamps were in sheets of 80 (8×10) and were overprinted in a setting of 40 applied twice to each sheet.

Minor varieties include small "S" in "POSTAGE" (R. 2/1 of the setting); small "N" in "POSTAGE" (R. 2/7); small "U" in "REVENUE" (R. 3/2); small "V" in "REVENUE" (R. 3/8, 5/5); and small "O" in "POSTAGE" (R. 4/7).

Various missing stop varieties also occur.

POSTAGE & REVENUE
ONE ANNA
(22)

1950 (2 Mar). *Stamp of 1929 surch with T* **22**.

61	15	1a. on 3p. black and blackish green	40·00	55·00

---

		a. "P" of "POSTAGE" omitted (R. 8/1)..........................	£500	£600
		b. "O" of "ONE" omitted (R. 6/1)...........................		£750

Other minor varieties include small second "A" in "ANNA" (R. 1/2); small "S" in "POSTAGE" with small "V" in "REVENUE" (R. 3/4, 6/1) and small "V" in "REVENUE" (R. 2/3, 3/1).

OFFICIAL STAMPS

1948 (July–Dec). *Nos. O4/O7 surch "ONE ANNA" (2¼ mm high) by Junagadh State Press.*

O14	18	1a. on 2a. grey & dull yellow (B.)..	£10000	26·00
O15	15	1a. on 3a. black and carmine (Aug)..	£2750	65·00
		a. Surch double	†	£3000
O16	16	1a. on 4a. black and purple (Dec)......	£375	60·00
		a. "ANNE" for "ANNA" (R. 5/4).....................	£2750	£425
		b. "ANNN" for "ANNA" (R. 7/5).....................	£2750	£425
O17	18	1a. on 8a. black & yellow-green (Dec)........................	£350	45·00
		a. "ANNE" for "ANNA" (R. 5/4).....................	£2750	£325
		b. "ANNN" for "ANNA" (R. 7/5).....................	£2750	£325

Numerous minor varieties of fount occur in this surcharge.

1948 (Nov). *Handstamped "ONE ANNA" (4 mm high).*

O18	17	1a. on 1r. (No. O8).....................	£1800	42·00
O19		1a. on 1r. (No. O12)....................	£750	45·00
		a. Optd on No. O12a		75·00

A used copy of No. O12 is known surcharged in black as on Nos. O14/17. This may have come from a proof sheet.

1949 (Jan). *Postage stamps optd with Type O* 2, *in red.*

O20	15	3p. black and blackish green	£250	14·00
O21	16	½a. black and deep blue	£600	14·00
O22	18	1a. on 2a. grey and dull yellow (No. 59)........................	80·00	24·00

Various wrong fount letters occur in the above surcharges.

MANUSCRIPT OVERPRINTS. Nos. 49, 50, 57, 58, 59 and 60 are known with manuscript overprints reading "Service" or "SARKARI" (in English or Gujerati script), usually in red. Such provisionals were used at Gadhda and Una between June and December 1949 *(Price from £120 each, used on piece).*

The United State of Saurashtra postal service was incorporated into that of India on 30 March 1950.

TRAVANCORE

PRICES FOR STAMPS ON COVER	
Nos. 1/77	*from* × 10
Nos. O1/108	*from* × 15

(16 cash = 1 chuckram; 28 chuckrams = 1 rupee)

"Anchel" or "Anchal" = Post Office Department.

The stamps of Travancore were valid on mail posted to Cochin.

PRINTERS. All stamps of Travancore were printed by the Stamp Manufactory, Trivandrum, *unless otherwise stated.*

PRINTING METHODS. The dies were engraved on brass from which electrotypes were made and locked together in a forme for printing the stamps. As individual electrotypes became worn they were replaced by new ones and their positions in the forme were sometimes changed. This makes it difficult to plate the early issues. From 1901 plates were made which are characterised by a frame (or "Jubilee" line) round the margins of the sheets.

Up to the 6 cash of 1910 the dies were engraved by Dharmalingham Asari.

SHADES. We list only the main groups of shades but there are many others in view of the large number of printings and the use of fugitive inks. Sometimes shade variation is noticeable within the same sheet.

Maharaja Rama Varma X, 1885–1924

1 Conch or Chank Shell

1888 (16 Oct). *As T* **1**, *but each value differs slightly. Laid paper.* P 12.

1	1	1ch. ultramarine (*shades*)	4·50	4·00
2		2ch. red	5·00	11·00
3		4ch. green	19·00	16·00
1/3		Set of 3	26·00	28·00

The paper bears a large sheet watermark showing a large conch shell surmounted by "GOVERNMENT" in large outline letters, in an arch with "OF TRAVANCORE" at foot in a straight line. Many stamps in the sheet are without watermark.

These stamps on laid paper in abnormal colours are proofs.

2

Three forms of watermark Type **2**.(*as seen from the back of the stamp*)

WATERMARKS AND PAPERS.

Type A appeared upright on early printings of the 1, 2 and 4ch. values on odd-sized sheets which did not fit the number of shells. Later it was always sideways with 15 mm between the shells on standard-sized sheets of 84 (14×6) containing 60 shells (10×6). It therefore never appears centred on the stamps and it occurs on hand-made papers only.

Type B is similar in shape but can easily be distinguished as it is invariably upright, with 11 mm between the shells, and is well centred on the stamps. It also occurs only on handmade papers. It was introduced in 1904 and from 1914, when Type A was brought back into use, it was employed concurrently until 1924.

Type C is quite different in shape and occurs on machine-made papers. There are two versions. The first, in use from 1924 to 1939, has 84 shells 11 mm apart and is always upright and well centred. The second, introduced in 1929 and believed not to have been used after 1930, has 60 shells (12×5) 15 mm apart and is invariably badly centred so that some stamps in the sheet are without watermark. This second version is normally found upright, but a few sideways watermark varieties are known and listed as Nos. 35g, 37c, O31j and O32i. We do not distinguish between the two versions of Type C in the lists, but stamps known to exist in the second version are indicated in footnotes. The machine-made paper is generally smoother and of more even texture.

NO WATERMARK VARIETIES. Some of these were formerly listed but we have now decided to omit them as they do not occur in full sheets. They arise in the following circumstances: (*a*) on sheets with wmk A; (*b*) on sheets with the wide-spaced form of wmk C; and (*c*) on late printings of the pictorial issues of 1939–46. They are best collected in pairs, with and without watermark.

DATES OF ISSUE. In the absence of more definite information the dates voted usually refer to the first reported date of new printings on different watermarks but many were not noted at the time and the dates of these are indicated by a query. Dated postmarks on single stamps are difficult to find.

1889–1904. *Wove paper.* Wmk A (upright or sideways). P 12 (sometimes rough).

4	1	½ch. slate-lilac (1894)	2·25	50
		a. Doubly printed	†	£275
		b. Reddish lilac	60	25
		ba. Imperf between (vert pair)......	£275	£275
		bb. Doubly printed		£275
		c. Purple (1899)	1·25	25
		ca. Doubly printed	†	£275
		d. Dull purple (1904)	1·50	25
5	5	¾ch. black (14.3.01)	3·00	1·25
6	1	1ch. ultramarine	1·50	15
		a. Tête-bêche (pair)	£2500	£2250
		b. Doubly printed	†	£400
		c. Imperf vert (horiz pair)..........	†	£425
		d. Imperf between (vert pair)......	†	£425
		e. Pale ultramarine (1892)	2·75	20
		f. Violet-blue (1901)	3·50	40
7		2ch. salmon (1890)	4·00	1·00
		a. Rose (1891)	3·50	30
		ab. Imperf (pair)	†	£450
		b. Pale pink (1899)	3·00	35
		ba. Imperf between (vert pair)......	£170	
		bb. Doubly printed	£250	
		c. Red (1904)	3·00	15
		ca. Imperf between (horiz pair)....	£350	£350
8		4ch. green.............................	3·25	70
		a. Yellow-green (1901)..............	2·50	55
		b. Dull green (1904)	6·50	1·00
		ba. Doubly printed	†	£425

Nos. 6, 6d, 7 and 8 occur with the watermark upright and sideways. No. 7a is known only with the watermark upright. The remainder exist only with the watermark sideways.

The sheet sizes were as follows:

½ch. 56 (14×4) except No. 4d which was 84 (14×6), initially without border, later with border.

¾ch. 84 (14×6) with border.

1ch. No. 6, 80 (10×8) and later 84 (14×6) without border and then with border; No. 6d, 96 (16×6); No. 6e, 84 (14×6) with border.

2ch. No. 7, 80 (10×8); No. 7a, 70 (10×7); Nos. 7b, 7c, 60 (10×6).

4ch. No. 8, 60 (10×6); Nos. 8a/b, 84 (14×6) with border.

After 1904 all stamps in Types **3** to **8** were in standard-sized sheets of 84 (14×6) with border.

For later printings watermarked Type A, see Nos. 23/30.

1904–20. Wmk B, upright (centred). P 12, sometimes rough.

9	3	4ca. pink (11.08)	30	10
10	1	6ca. chestnut (2.10)	30	10
		a. Imperf between (horiz pair)	†	£250
11		½ch. reddish lilac	1·25	10
		a. Reddish violet (6.10)	1·25	10
		b. Lilac	1·25	10
		c. "CHUCRRAM" (R. 5/6)	6·00	3·50
		d. Imperf horiz (vert pair)	†	£180
12	4	10ca. pink (1920)	30·00	5·50
13	5	¾ch. black	1·50	25
14	1	1ch. bright blue		
		a. Blue	3·75	30
		b. Deep blue	3·75	30
		c. Indigo (8.10)	75	10
		d. Chalky blue (1912)	4·25	70
15		1¼ch. claret (shades) (10.14)	55	55
		a. Imperf between (horiz pair)	£300	£300
16		2ch. salmon	18·00	6·00
		a. Red (8.10)	60	10
17	6	3ch. violet (11.3.11)	2·75	20
		a. Imperf between (vert pair)	£250	£250
		b. Imperf between (vert strip of 3)	†	£325
18	1	4ch. dull green	13·00	4·50
		a. Slate-green	2·75	35
19	7	7ch. claret (1916)	2·00	50
		a. Error. Carmine-red	—	50·00
20	8	14ch. orange-yellow (1916)	2·75	2·25
		a. Imperf vert (horiz strip of 3)	£450	

(9) (10)

1906. Surch as T 9. Wmk B.

21	1	¼ on ½ch. reddish lilac	60	30
		a. Reddish violet	60	20
		b. Lilac	80	30
		c. "CHUCRRAM" (R. 5/6)	4·00	3·50
		d. Surch inverted	55·00	32·00
22		38 on ½ch. reddish lilac	40	35
		a. Reddish violet	40	35
		b. Lilac	50	35
		c. "CHUCRRAM" (R. 5/6)	3·75	3·75
		d. Surch inverted		48·00
		e. Surch double		
		f. "8" omitted	—	40·00

1914–22. Reversion to wmk A (sideways). P 12 (sometimes rough).

23	3	4ca. pink (1915)	8·00	60
24	4	5ca. olive-bistre (30.10.21)	80	55
		a. Imperf between (horiz pair)	48·00	55·00
		b. Imperf between (horiz strip of 3)	£100	£110
		c. "TRAVANCOPE"	—	8·00
25	1	6ca. orange-brown (2.15)	5·50	40
26		½ch. reddish violet (12.14)	3·00	40
		a. "CHUCRRAM" (R. 5/6)	11·00	4·00
		b. Imperf between (horiz pair)	£190	
27	4	10ca. pink (26.10.21)	40	10
28	1	1ch. grey-blue (5.22)	12·00	2·75
		a. Deep blue	12·00	2·75
29		1¼ch. claret (12.19)	13·00	35
		a. Imperf between (horiz pair)	†	£300
30	6	3ch. reddish lilac (8.22)	14·00	1·50

1921 (Mar). Surch as T 10. Wmk A (sideways).

31	3	1c. on 4ca. pink	15	20
		a. Surch inverted	23·00	10·00
		b. On wmk B (upright)		
32	1	5c. on 1ch. grey-blue (R.)	1·00	10
		a. Deep blue	1·00	10
		b. Stamp printed both sides		
		c. Imperf between (vert pair)	†	£250
		d. Surch inverted	13·00	8·50
		e. Surch double	60·00	42·00
		f. On wmk B (upright). Deep blue	25·00	20·00
		fa. Surch inverted	†	£170

ALBINO OVERPRINT VARIETIES. Stamps with overprint double, one albino are frequently found in the provisional and official issues of Travancore, and are only worth a small premium over the normal prices.

Maharaja Bala Rama Varma XI, 1924–1971

1924–39. Wmk C. Machine-made paper. P 12.

33	4	5ca. olive-bistre (18.6.25)	11·00	2·75
		a. Imperf between (horiz pair)	£170	
		b. "TRAVANCOPE"	—	13·00
34		5ca. chocolate (1930)	2·75	20
		a. Imperf between (horiz pair)	38·00	
		b. Imperf between (vert pair)	†	£170
35	1	6ca. brown-red (3.24)	4·25	10
		a. Imperf between (horiz pair)	25·00	27·00
		b. Imperf between (vert pair)	£120	120
		c. Printed both sides	50·00	
		d. Perf 12½	4·25	50
		e. Perf comp of 12 and 12½	6·00	4·00
		f. Perf 12½×11	—	£100
		g. Wmk sideways	—	21·00
36		½ch. reddish violet (date?)	4·25	4·25
		a. "CHUCRRAM" (R. 5/6)	32·00	
37	4	10ca. pink (8.24)	2·25	10
		a. Imperf between (horiz pair)	85·00	85·00
		b. Imperf between (vert pair)	25·00	28·00
		c. Wmk sideways (16.9.28)	—	8·00
38	5	¾ch. black (4.10.32)	9·00	50
39		¾ch. mauve (16.11.32)	35	10
		a. Imperf between (horiz pair)	†	£170
		b. Perf 12½ (8.37)	10·00	70
		ba. Imperf between (horiz pair)	£150	
		c. Perf comp of 12 and 12½	16·00	6·50
		ca. Imperf between (horiz pair)	£190	
40		¾ch. reddish violet (1939)	3·75	70

		a. Perf 12½	5·00	50
		b. Perf comp 12 and 12½	8·00	2·25
		c. Perf 11	—	£100
		d. Perf comp of 12 and 11	—	£100
41	1	1ch. slate-blue (8.26)	2·75	30
		a. Indigo	4·25	20
		b. Imperf between (horiz pair)	†	£250
		c. Imperf between (vert pair)	†	£250
		d. Perf 12½	10·00	1·10
42		1½ch. rose (1932)	2·75	10
		a. Imperf between (horiz strip of 3)	£200	
		b. Perf 12½	22·00	2·75
		c. Perf comp of 12 and 12½	—	38·00
43		2ch. carmine-red (4.6.29)	3·00	30
44	6	3ch. violet (4.25)	6·50	15
		a. Imperf between (vert pair)	90·00	90·00
		b. Perf 12½	11·00	
		c. Perf comp of 12 and 12½	—	35·00
45	1	4ch. grey-green (5.4.34)	5·00	45
46	7	7ch. claret (1925)	10·00	1·75
		a. Doubly printed	†	£425
		b. Carmine-red (date?)	65·00	55·00
		c. Brown-purple (1932)	16·00	4·50
		ca. Perf 12½	8·50	16·00
		cb. Perf comb of 12 and 12½	7·50	16·00
46d	8	14ch. orange-yellow (date?)	40·00	
		da. Perf 12½	£180	

It is believed that the 12½ perforation and the perf 12 and 12½ compound were introduced in 1937 and that the 11 perforation came later, probably in 1939.

The 5ca. chocolate, 6ca., 10ca. and 3ch. also exist on the widespaced watermark (60 shells to the sheet of 84).

11 Sri Padmanabha Shrine

12 State Chariot   **13** Maharaja Bala Rama Varma XI

(Des M. R. Madhawan Unnithan. Plates by Calcutta Chromotype Co. Typo Stamp Manufactory, Trivandrum)

1931 (6 Nov). Coronation. Cream or white paper. Wmk C. P 11½, 12.

47	11	6ca. black and green	1·60	1·60
		a. Imperf between (horiz pair)	£180	£200
48	12	10ca. black and ultramarine	1·25	70
		a. Imperf between (vert pair)	†	£450
49	13	3ch. black and purple	2·75	2·75
47/9 Set of 3			5·00	4·50

(14)   (15)   **16** Maharaja Bala Rama Varma XI and Subramania Shrine

1932 (14 Jan).(i) Surch as T 14.

(a) Wmk A (sideways).

50	1	1c. on 1¼ch. claret	15	50
		a. Imperf between (horiz pair)	£120	
		b. Surch inverted	4·25	7·50
		c. Surch double	30·00	30·00
		d. Pair, one without surch.	£110	£130
		e. "c" omitted	45·00	45·00
51		2c. on 1¼ch. claret	15	20
		a. Surch inverted	4·25	7·00
		b. Surch double	28·00	
		c. Surch double, one inverted	60·00	
		d. Surch treble	70·00	
		e. Surch treble, one inverted	70·00	70·00
		f. Pair, one without surch.	£110	£120
		g. "2" omitted	45·00	45·00
		h. "c" omitted	45·00	45·00
		i. Imperf between (horiz pair)	£120	
		j. Imperf between (vert pair)	£130	

(b) Wmk B (upright).

52	1	1c. on 1¼ch. claret	1·00	1·00
		a. Surch inverted	21·00	
		b. Surch double	38·00	
53		2c. on 1¼ch. claret	6·50	6·50
		a. Imperf between (horiz pair)	£140	

(c) Wmk C.

54	1	1c. on 1¼ch. claret	14·00	19·00
		a. Surch inverted	65·00	70·00
55		2c. on 1¼ch. claret	28·00	19·00

(ii) Surch as T 10. Wmk B.

56	1	2c. on 1¼ch. claret	4·00	15·00

1932 (5 Mar). Surch as T 15. Wmk C.

57	4	1c. on 5ca. chocolate	15	15
		a. Imperf between (horiz pair)	£130	
		b. Surch inverted	7·50	10·00
		c. Surch inverted on back only	75·00	
		d. Pair, one without surch.	£110	
		e. "1" omitted	38·00	
		f. "C" omitted	—	38·00
		g. "TRAVANCOPE"	8·50	
58		1c. on 5ca. slate-purple	1·25	20
		a. Surch inverted	†	£250
		b. "1" inverted	85·00	85·00
59		2c. on 10ca. pink	15	15
		a. Imperf between (horiz pair)	£130	
		b. Surch inverted	5·00	8·00
		c. Surch double	21·00	23·00
		d. Surch double, one inverted	75·00	75·00
		e. Surch double, both inverted	50·00	

No. 58 was not issued without the surcharge.

(Plates by Indian Security Printing Press, Nasik. Typo Stamp Manufactory, Trivandrum)

1937 (29 Mar). Temple Entry Proclamation. T 16 and similar horiz designs. Wmk C. P 12.

60		6ca. carmine	2·00	1·25
		a. Imperf between (horiz strip of 3)	£500	
		b. Perf 12½	2·00	1·60
		c. Compound perf	35·00	35·00
61		12ca. bright blue	3·00	40
		a. Perf 12½	3·50	70
		ab. Imperf between (vert pair)	£450	
		b. Compound perf	55·00	
62		1½ch. yellow-green	1·50	1·75
		a. Imperf between (vert pair)	£375	
		b. Perf 12½	25·00	6·50
		c. Compound perf		
63		3ch. violet	3·75	2·25
		a. Perf 12½	4·75	3·25
60/3 Set of 4			9·25	5·00

Designs:—Maharaja's portrait and temples—12ca. Sri Pad-manabha; 1½ ch. Mahadeva; 3ch. Kanyakumari.

COMPOUND PERFS. This term covers stamps perf compound of 12½ and 11, 12 and 11 or 12 and 12½, and where two or more combinations exist the prices are for the commonest. Such compounds can occur on values which do not exist, perf 12 all round.

17 Lake Ashtamudi   **18** Maharaja Bala Rama Varma XI

(Des Nilakantha Pellai. Plates by Indian Security Printing Press, Nasik. Typo Stamp Manufactory, Trivandrum)

1939 (9 Nov). Maharaja's 27th Birthday. T 17/18 and similar designs. Wmk C. P 12½.

64		1ch. yellow-green	5·00	10
		a. Imperf between (horiz pair)	22·00	
		b. Perf 11	10·00	10
		ba. Imperf between (vert pair)	38·00	50·00
		bb. Imperf between (vert strip of 3)	22·00	40·00
		c. Perf 12	21·00	1·75
		ca. Imperf between (horiz pair)	20·00	
		cb. Imperf between (vert pair)	45·00	
		d. Compound perf	25·00	2·75
		da. Imperf between (vert pair)	£140	
65		1½ch. scarlet	3·25	4·00
		a. Doubly printed	£325	
		b. Imperf between (horiz pair)	29·00	
		c. Imperf between (vert pair)	25·00	
		d. Perf 11	4·25	21·00
		e. Imperf horiz (vert pair)	8·00	
		e. Perf 12	32·00	4·50
		f. Perf 13½	16·00	60·00
		g. Compound perf	45·00	6·50
		h. Imperf (pair)	30·00	
66		2ch. orange	6·00	2·00
		a. Perf 11	18·00	75
		b. Perf 12	£100	4·50
		c. Compound perf	£100	6·50
67		3ch. brown	6·00	10
		a. Doubly printed	—	£160
		b. Imperf between (horiz pair)	42·00	65·00
		c. Perf 11	20·00	30
		ca. Doubly printed	42·00	60·00
		d. Perf 12	38·00	3·50
		da. Imperf between (vert pair)	£130	£150
		e. Compound perf	35·00	1·00
68		4ch. red	7·50	40
		a. Perf 11	35·00	50
		b. Perf 12	32·00	7·50
		c. Compound perf	£170	£120
69		7ch. pale blue	10·00	18·00
		a. Perf 11	90·00	30·00
		ab. Blue	85·00	29·00
		b. Compound perf	£100	38·00
70		14ch. turquoise-green	7·00	60·00
		a. Perf 12	12·00	£100
64/70 Set of 7			40·00	75·00

Designs: Vert as T 18—1½ch., 3ch. Portraits of Maharaja in different frames. Horiz as T 17—4ch. Sri Padmanabha Shrine; 7ch. Cape Comorin; 14ch. Pachipari Reservoir.

19 Maharaja and Aruvikara Falls

2 CASH
(20)

(Des Nilakantha Pellai. Plates by Indian Security Printing Press, Nasik. Typo Stamp Manufactory, Trivandrum)

1941 (20 Oct). *Maharaja's 29th Birthday. T* **19** *and similar horiz design.* Wmk C. P 12½.

71	6ca. blackish violet	7·50	10
	a. Perf 11	6·50	10
	ab. Imperf between (vert pair)	20·00	
	ac. Imperf horiz (vert pair)	45·00	65·00
	b. Perf 12	24·00	1·50
	ba. Imperf between (horiz pair)	24·00	
	bb. Imperf between (vert pair)	50·00	
	bc. Imperf between (vert strip of 3)	22·00	
	c. Compound perf	8·00	1·00
72	¾ch. brown	8·50	20
	a. Perf 11	10·00	20
	ab. Imperf between (horiz pair)	£170	
	ac. Imperf between (vert pair)	30·00	48·00
	ad. Imperf between (vert strip of 3)	28·00	
	ae. Block of four imperf between (horiz and vert)	£225	
	b. Perf 12	55·00	9·50
	c. Compound perf	13·00	1·10

Design:—¾ch. Maharaja and Marthanda Varma Bridge, Alwaye.

1943 (17 Sept). *Nos. 65, 71 (colour changed) and 72 surch as T* **20**. P 12½.

73	2ca. on 1½ch. scarlet	1·50	1·10
	a. Imperf between (vert pair)	45·00	
	b. "2" omitted	£300	£300
	c. "CA" omitted	£475	
	d. "ASH" omitted	£475	
	e. Perf 11	40	25
	ea. "CA" omitted	£475	
	f. Compound perf	60	1·10
	fa. Imperf between (vert pair)	£150	
	fb. "2" omitted	£325	
74	4ca. on ¾ch. brown	3·75	1·50
	a. Perf 11	4·50	30
	b. Perf 12	—	£140
	c. Compound perf	5·00	1·00
75	8ca. on 6ca. scarlet	4·75	10
	a. Perf 11	4·00	10
	ab. Imperf between (horiz pair)	40·00	
	b. Perf 12	—	80·00
	c. Compound perf	15·00	7·00
73/5 *Set of 3*		7·25	60

21 Maharaja Bala Rama Varma XI

SPECIAL
(22)

(Des Nilakantha Pellai. Plates by Indian Security Printing Press, Nasik. Typo Stamp Manufactory, Trivandrum)

1946 (24 Oct). *Maharaja's 34th Birthday.* Wmk C. P 12½.

76	**21** 8ca. carmine	26·00	3·75
	a. Perf 11	1·00	1·75
	b. Perf 12	38·00	2·50
	ba. Imperf between (horiz pair)	38·00	55·00
	bb. Imperf between (horiz strip of 3)	55·00	
	c. Compound perf		

1946. *No. O103 revalidated for ordinary postage with opt T* **22**, *in orange.* P 12½.

77	**19** 6ca. blackish violet	6·00	2·75
	a. Perf 11	38·00	6·00
	b. Compound perf	6·00	6·00

OFFICIAL STAMPS

GUM. Soon after 1911 the Official stamps were issued without gum. Thus only the initial printings of the 1, 2, 3 and 4ch. values were gummed. As Nos. O38/9, O41/2 and O95 were overprinted on stamps intended for normal postage these, also, have gum.

PRINTINGS. Sometimes special printings of postage stamps were made specifically for overprinting for Official use, thus accounting for Official stamps appearing with watermarks or in shades not listed in the postage issues.

SETTINGS. These are based on the study of complete sheets of 84, and the measurements given are those of the majority of stamps on the sheet. Examples are known showing different measurements as each overprint was set individually in loose type, but these are not included in the listings.

On **On**

S. **S** **S** **S**
(O 1) (O 2)

Rounded "O"

1911 (16 Aug)–30. *Contemporary stamps optd with Type* O **1** (*13 mm wide*). P 12, sometimes rough.

(a) Wmk B (upright) (*16.8.11-21*).

O1	**3** 4ca. pink (1916)	20	10

		a. Opt inverted	†	80·00
		b. Opt double	£110	85·00
		c. "S S" inverted	38·00	17·00
		d. Imperf (pair)	£275	£275
		e. Stamp doubly printed	†	£275
		f. Left "S" inverted		18·00
O2	1	6ca. chestnut (date ?)	35·00	35·00
O3		½ch. reddish lilac (R.) (1919)	1·25	35
		a. "CHUCRRAM" (R. 5/6)	11·00	4·75
O4	4	10ca. pink (1921)	20·00	3·50
		a. "O" inverted	55·00	10·00
		b. Left "S" inverted	55·00	10·00
		c. Right "S" inverted	55·00	10·00
		d. Opt inverted	†	£120
O5	1	1ch. chalky blue (R.)	65	10
		a. Imperf between (vert pair)	†	£180
		b. Opt inverted	7·00	4·25
		c. Opt double	60·00	50·00
		d. "nO" for "On"	75·00	75·00
		e. "O" inverted	7·50	2·25
		f. Left "S" inverted	8·00	2·25
		g. Right "S" inverted	8·50	2·50
		h. "S S" inverted	—	50·00
O6		2ch. red	35	10
		a. Opt inverted	8·00	8·00
		b. "O" inverted	8·50	1·25
		c. Left "S" inverted	8·50	1·25
		d. Right "S" inverted	9·50	2·25
O7		2ch. red (B.) (date ?)	—	£100
O8	6	3ch. violet	35	10
		a. Imperf between (vert pair)	£190	£190
		b. Imperf vert (horiz pair)	£160	
		c. Opt inverted	10·00	10·00
		d. Opt double	80·00	65·00
		e. "S" inverted	4·75	1·00
		f. Right "S" omitted	£120	£110
		g. Left "S" inverted	£120	£110
O9		3ch. violet (B.) (date ?)	£150	75·00
O10	1	4ch. slate-green	55	10
		a. Imperf between (horiz pair)	—	£275
		b. Opt inverted	50·00	13·00
		c. Opt double	£120	90·00
		d. "O" inverted	11·00	2·40
		e. Left "S" inverted	12·00	3·50
		f. Right "S" inverted	13·00	4·00
		g. Left "S" omitted	£120	£110
O11		4ch. slate-green (B.) (1921)	—	65·00
		a. "O" inverted	—	£150
		b. Left "S" inverted	—	£150
		c. Right "S" inverted		£150

(b) Wmk A (sideways) (*1919–25*).

O12	3	4ca. pink	4·00	15
		a. Imperf (pair)	£325	£325
		b. Opt inverted	70·00	17·00
		c. "O" inverted	38·00	8·50
		d. Left "S" inverted	42·00	11·00
		e. Right "S" inverted	42·00	12·00
O13		4ca. pink (B.) (1921)	50·00	75
		a. "O" inverted	—	23·00
O14	4	5ca. olive-bistre (1921)	75	10
		a. Opt inverted	13·00	9·00
		b. "O" inverted	5·50	1·50
		c. Left "S" inverted	6·50	1·50
		d. Right "S" inverted	6·50	1·50
O15	1	6ca. orange-brown (1921)	30	10
		a. Imperf between (vert pair)	†	£200
		b. Opt inverted	13·00	9·00
		c. Opt double	75·00	75·00
		d. "O" inverted	6·00	1·60
		e. Left "S" inverted	7·50	1·75
		f. Right "S" inverted	8·00	1·75
O16		6ca. orange-brown (B.) (1921)	12·00	1·50
		a. Opt inverted	£120	£110
		b. "O" inverted	50·00	14·00
		c. Left "S" inverted	50·00	14·00
		d. Right "S" inverted	50·00	14·00
O17		½ch. reddish violet (R.) (date?)	2·25	25
		a. Reddish lilac (date?)	2·25	25
		b. Imperf between (horiz pair)	£160	£150
		c. Imperf between (vert pair)	65·00	70·00
		d. Stamp doubly printed	50·00	
		e. Opt inverted	12·00	3·50
		f. Opt double, both inverted	£150	
		g. "CHUCRRAM" (R. 5/6)	11·00	3·75
		h. "On" omitted	—	£140
		i. Right "S" inverted	—	30·00
		j. Right "S" omitted	—	£140
O18	4	10ca. pink (3.21)	65	10
		a. Scarlet (1925?)	—	11·00
		b. Opt inverted	—	19·00
		c. Opt double	90·00	75·00
		d. "O" inverted	9·50	3·00
		e. Left "S" inverted	8·00	2·25
		f. Right "S" inverted	9·50	3·00
		g. Imperf between (horiz pair)	—	£150
O19		10ca. pink (B.) (date?)	75·00	21·00
		a. Opt inverted	—	80·00
		b. "O" inverted	—	60·00
O20	1	1ch. grey-blue (R.) (date?)	4·75	60
		a. Deep blue	4·75	80
		b. "O" inverted	40·00	8·00
		c. Left "S" inverted	42·00	10·00
		d. "On" omitted		
		e. Opt inverted	†	70·00
O21		1¼ch. claret (12.19)	40	10
		a. Stamp doubly printed	—	£300
		b. Opt inverted	9·00	8·00
		c. Opt double	45·00	
		d. "O" inverted	12·00	2·00
		e. Left "S" inverted	16·00	3·50
		f. Right "S" inverted	16·00	4·00
		g. Error. Carmine	50·00	
O22		1¼ch. claret (B.) (1921)	—	75·00
		a. "O" inverted	—	£160
		b. Left "S" inverted	—	£160
		c. Right "S" inverted	—	£160

(c) Wmk C (*1925–30*).

O23	4	5ca. olive-bistre (1926)	40	40
		a. Imperf between (horiz pair)	£200	£200
		b. Opt inverted	21·00	18·00
		c. "O" inverted (R. 1/7)	5·50	3·25
		d. Left "S" inverted (R. 6/1, 6/8)	4·75	2·75

		e. Right "S" inverted (R. 6/7)	5·50	3·25
O23f		5ca. chocolate (1930)	55·00	
		fa. Opt inverted		£120
O24		10ca. pink (1926)	4·00	15
		a. Imperf between (vert pair)	—	£190
		b. Opt inverted	70·00	70·00
		c. "O" inverted (R. 1/7)	27·00	4·00
		d. Left "S" inverted (R. 6/1, 6/8)	22·00	2·50
		e. Right "S" inverted (R. 6/7)	27·00	3·00
		f. Stamp doubly printed	†	£120
O25	1	1¼ch. claret (1926)	17·00	60
		a. "O" inverted (R. 1/7)	60·00	7·00
		b. Left "S" inverted (R. 6/1, 6/8)	50·00	7·00
		c. Right "S" inverted (R. 6/7)	60·00	7·00
		d. Opt double	†	£110
O26	7	7ch. claret	1·50	30
		a. "O" inverted (R. 1/7)	16·00	4·00
		b. Left "S" inverted (R. 6/1, 6/8)	14·00	3·50
		c. Right "S" inverted (R. 6/7)	16·00	4·00
		d. Error. Carmine-red	60·00	
O27	8	14ch. orange-yellow	2·25	40
		a. "O" inverted (R. 1/7)	16·00	4·00
		b. Left "S" inverted (R. 6/1, 6/8)	14·00	3·00
		c. Right "S" inverted (R. 6/7)	16·00	3·75

1926–30. *Contemporary stamps optd with Type* O **2** (*16½ mm wide*). Wmk C. P 12.

O28	4	5ca. olive-bistre	4·00	30
		a. Right "S" inverted	20·00	4·25
		b. Left "S" inverted	23·00	5·50
O29		5ca. chocolate (1930)	25	50
		a. Imperf between (vert pair)	†	£275
		b. Opt inverted	20·00	
		c. "O" inverted	4·00	5·00
		d. Left "S" inverted	4·00	5·00
O30	1	6ca. brown-red (date?)	4·75	1·00
		a. "O" inverted	22·00	7·00
		b. Left "S" inverted	25·00	8·50
		c. Opt double	†	£140
O31	4	10ca. pink	30	10
		a. Imperf between (horiz pair)	75·00	75·00
		b. Imperf between (vert pair)	60·00	60·00
		c. Imperf vert (horiz strip of 3)	†	£160
		d. Opt inverted	9·00	9·00
		e. "Ou" for "On"	45·00	45·00
		f. "O" inverted	4·75	1·75
		g. Left "S" inverted	4·25	1·60
		h. Right "S" inverted	4·00	1·75
		i. Left "S" omitted	42·00	42·00
		j. Wmk sideways	22·00	9·50
O32	1	1¼ch. claret (shades)	1·75	30
		a. Imperf between (horiz pair)	90·00	£100
		b. Imperf between (vert pair)	£110	£120
		c. Opt inverted	22·00	22·00
		d. "O" inverted	20·00	4·25
		e. Left "S" inverted	20·00	4·25
		f. Right "S" inverted	20·00	4·25
		g. Left "S" omitted	£130	£120
		h. Right "S" omitted	£130	£120
		i. Wmk sideways		10·00
		ia. Imperf between (vert pair)	£140	
O33	6	3ch. violet	10·00	80
		a. Opt inverted	†	£120
		b. "O" inverted	50·00	18·00
		c. "O" omitted	£100	85·00
		d. "Ou" for "On"	£140	£140
		e. Left "S" inverted	—	35·00
O34	7	7ch. claret (date?)	£110	3·00
O35	8	14ch. orange-yellow	42·00	85
		a. Imperf between (vert pair)	£475	
		b. "O" inverted	£100	£100

The 5ca. olive-bistre, 3ch. and 7ch. exist only with the normal watermark spaced 11 mm; the 5ca. chocolate and 14ch. exist only with the wide 15 mm spacing; the 6ca., 10ca. and 1¼ch. exist in both forms.

On **On** **On**

S **S** **S** **S** **S**
(O 3) (O 4) Italic (O 5)
"S S"

1930. Wmk C. P 12.

(a) Optd with Type O 3.

O36	4	10ca. pink	£200	£150
O37	1	1¼ch. carmine-rose	4·50	3·25

(b) Optd with Type O 4.

O38	5	¾ch. black (R.)	35	30
		a. Left "S" omitted	90·00	90·00
		b. Right "S" omitted	90·00	
		c. Large roman "S" at left	—	£100

(c) Optd with Type O 5.

O39	5	¾ch. black (R.)	35	15
		a. Opt inverted	†	£200
		b. "n" omitted	£100	£100
O40	1	4ch. slate-green (R.)	29·00	15·00

On **On**

On

S **S** **S** **S** **S** **S**
(O 6) (O 7) Oval "O" (O 8)

1930–39?. *Contemporary stamps overprinted.* P 12.

(a) With Type O 6 (16 mm high).

(i) Wmk A.

O41	3	4ca. pink	25·00	60·00

		a. Large right "S" as Type O 2 (R. 6/14)	£120	£200
O42	3	4ca. pink	20·00	60·00
		a. Large right "S" as Type O 2 (R. 6/14)	£110	£200

(iii) Wmk C.

O43	1	6ca. brown-red (1932)	35	10
		a. Opt inverted	20·00	
		b. Opt double	45·00	45·00
		c. "O" inverted (R. 5/11-12)	8·00	5·00
O44	4	10ca. pink	3·00	1·25
O45	5	¾ch. mauve (1933)	3·75	10
		a. Imperf between (horiz pair)	£100	75·00
		b. Imperf between (horiz strip of 3)	†	£140
		c. Imperf between (vert pair)	†	£120
		d. Stamp doubly printed	†	£180
		e. Perf 12½	7·00	40
		f. Perf comp of 12 and 12½	17·00	2·25
		g. Right "S" inverted		27·00
O46	1	1¼ch. carmine-rose	14·00	1·75
		a. Opt double	£110	85·00
		b. Large right "S" as Type O 2 (R. 6/14)	£120	55·00
O47		4ch. grey-green	1·75	5·50
O48		4ch. grey-green (R.) (27.10.30)	70	20
		a. Imperf between (horiz pair)	£140	£140
		b. Opt double	25·00	25·00
		c. "O" inverted	35·00	20·00
		d. Large right "S" as Type O 2 (R. 6/14)	48·00	30·00
		e. Imperf between (vert pair)	£140	
		f. "O" inverted (R. 5/11-12)	50·00	
O49	8	14ch. orange-yellow (1931)	9·00	1·75
		a. Imperf between (vert pair)	†	£170

For the 1½ch. and 3ch., and for Nos. O43 and O48/9 but perf 12½, see Nos. O66/70 (new setting combining Types O 6 and O 8).

(b) With Type O 7 (14 mm high). Wmk C.

O50	3	4ca. pink	12·00	38·00
		a. "O" inverted	50·00	95·00
O51	4	5ca. chocolate (1932)	22·00	9·00
		a. Opt inverted	65·00	65·00
O52	1	6ca. brown-red	20	10
		a. Imperf between (vert pair)	60·00	60·00
		b. Opt inverted	26·00	
		c. Opt double	†	65·00
		d. "nO" for "On"	£130	£130
		e. Right "S" inverted	25·00	18·00
		f. Left "S" omitted	—	80·00
		g. Large "n" as Type O 5 (R. 1/1, 1/14)	20·00	12·00
		h. Large italic left "S" as Type O 5	22·00	13·00
		i. Perf 12½		9·50
		j. Perf compound of 12 and 12½	—	24·00
O53		½ch. reddish violet (1932)	40	15
		a. "CHUCRRAM" (R. 5/6)	8·50	5·50
		b. "Ou" for "On"	65·00	65·00
		c. Left "S" omitted	—	£130
		d. "O" of "On" omitted	£180	
O54		½ch. reddish violet (R.) (1935)	20	10
		a. Imperf between (vert pair)	£120	£120
		b. "CHUCRRAM" (R. 5/6)	4·00	3·25
		c. Left "S" inverted	26·00	23·00
O55	4	10ca. pink (date ?)	4·00	2·75
		a. Imperf between (horiz pair)	12·00	22·00
		b. Imperf between (vert pair)	10·00	21·00
		c. "O" inverted	40·00	24·00
		d. Right "S" inverted	40·00	24·00
O56	5	¾ch. mauve (1933?)	30	15
		a. Imperf between (vert pair)	†	£150
		b. "Ou" for "On"	70·00	65·00
		c. "O" inverted	26·00	22·00
		d. Right "S" inverted		22·00
		e. Opt double	†	£130
		f. Perf comp of 12 and 12½	28·00	18·00
O57	1	1ch. deep blue (R.) (1935)	1·75	40
		a. Slate-blue	1·00	25
		b. Imperf between (horiz pair)	£130	£130
		c. Imperf between (vert pair)	27·00	40·00
		d. Perf 12½	8·50	4·00
		e. Perf comp of 12 and 12½	23·00	8·50
O58		1½ch. claret	1·40	1·60
O59		1½ch. rose (1933)	40	10
		a. Imperf between (vert pair)	†	£160
		b. Opt double	70·00	70·00
		c. "O" inverted	4·75	2·50
		e. Large "n" as Type O 5 (R. 1/1, 1/14)	50·00	23·00
		f. Large italic left "S" as Type O 5	55·00	23·00
		g. Left "S" inverted	—	26·00
		h. Perf 12½	—	11·00
		i. Perf comp of 12 and 12½	—	24·00
		ia. Stamp doubly printed	—	£200
O60	6	3ch. reddish violet (1933)	1·25	60
		a. "O" inverted	23·00	£100
		b. Opt double	†	£100
O61		3ch. violet (R.) (1934)	80	10
		a. Imperf between (horiz pair)	95·00	48·00
		b. Imperf between (vert pair)	70·00	42·00
		c. Opt inverted	†	50·00
		d. "O" inverted	22·00	13·00
		e. Perf 12½		2·75
		ea. Imperf between (vert pair)	†	£190
		f. Perf comp of 12 and 12½	—	12·00
		fa. Imperf between (horiz pair)	†	£190
		g. "Ou" for "On"	—	85·00
O63		4ch. grey-green (R.) (1935?)	1·25	20
		a. "Ou" for "On" (R. 1/1)	65·00	45·00
O64	7	7ch. claret (shades)	1·25	30
		a. Imperf between (vert pair)	30·00	40·00
		b. "O" inverted	45·00	20·00
		c. Left "S" inverted	50·00	25·00
		d. Perf 12½	—	9·00
		e. Perf comp of 12 and 12½	—	8·00
		ea. Imperf between (vert pair)	†	£120
		eb. Imperf between (vert strip of 3)	£160	£160
O65	8	14ch. orange (1933)	1·75	40
		a. Imperf between (horiz pair)	38·00	50·00

		b. Imperf between (vert pair)	£170	
		c. Opt inverted	£375	£350

(c) New setting combining Type O 8 (18 mm high) in top row with Type O 6 (16 mm high) for remainder. Wmk C (dates?).

A. Type O 8.

O66A	1	6ca. brown-red	7·50	4·00
		a. Perf 12½	8·00	4·00
O67A		1½ch. rose	45·00	6·50
		a. Perf 12½	70·00	8·50
O68A	6	3ch. violet (R.)	65·00	8·50
		a. Perf 12½	90·00	25·00
		b. Perf comp of 12 and 12½	£120	30·00
O69A	1	4ch. grey-green (R.)	50·00	24·00
		a. Perf 12½	65·00	24·00
O70A	8	14ch. orange-yellow	60·00	18·00
		a. Perf 12½	65·00	19·00

B. Type O 6.

O66Ba	1	6ca. brown-red (P 12½)	3·25	1·00
		ab. Imperf between (vert pair)	£120	£120
		ac. "O" inverted	17·00	8·50
		g. Perf comp of 12 and 12½	—	19·00
O67B		1½ch. rose	12·00	35
		a. Perf 12½	21·00	60
		b. "O" inverted	70·00	20·00
		c. Perf comp of 12 and 12½	—	25·00
O68B	6	3ch. violet (R.)	12·00	1·00
		a. Perf 12½	22·00	1·25
		b. Perf comp of 12 and 12½	32·00	7·50
O69Ba	1	4ch. grey-green (R.) (P 12½)	8·50	3·25
		ab. Imperf between (horiz pair)	†	£200
		ac. "O" inverted	85·00	38·00
O70Ba	8	14ch. orange-yellow (P 12½)	15·00	1·00

Nos. O66/70A/B in vertical se-tenant pairs are very scarce. As with the postage issues it is believed that the 12½ and compound perforations were issued between 1937 and 1939.

1 ch

8 c (O 9) **1 ch** Wrong fount "1c" (R. 6/7)

1932. *Official stamps surch as T 14 or with Type O 9. P 12.*

(a) With opt Type O 1.

(i) Wmk A (sideways).

O71	4	6c. on 5ca. olive-bistre	55·00	24·00
		a. "O" inverted	£180	80·00
		b. Left "S" inverted	£170	75·00
		c. Right "S" inverted	£180	80·00

(ii) Wmk C.

O72	4	6c. on 5ca. olive-bistre	29·00	11·00
		a. "O" inverted	75·00	25·00
		b. Left "S" inverted	70·00	23·00
		c. Right "S" inverted	75·00	25·00
O73		12c. on 10ca. pink	£150	

(b) With opt Type O 2. Wmk C.

O74	4	6c. on 5ca. olive-bistre	1·60	1·60
		a. Opt and surch inverted	50·00	
		b. Surch inverted	75·00	
		c. Left "S" inverted	15·00	7·50
		d. Right "S" inverted	15·00	7·50
		e. "6" omitted	—	85·00
O75		6c. on 5ca. chocolate	20	25
		a. Surch inverted	9·00	10·00
		b. Surch double	£100	
		c. Surch double, one inverted	95·00	
		d. "O" inverted	4·50	4·50
		e. Left "S" inverted	4·50	4·50
		f. Pair, one without surch	£275	
O76		12c. on 10ca. pink	1·75	1·25
		a. Opt inverted	15·00	16·00
		b. Surch inverted	7·00	7·00
		c. Opt and surch inverted	38·00	38·00
		d. Pair, one without surch	£250	
		e. "O" inverted	8·50	5·00
		f. Left "S" inverted	8·50	5·00
		g. "Ou" for "On"	95·00	95·00
		h. Right "S" inverted	8·50	5·00
		i. "c" omitted (R. 6/1)	60·00	60·00
O77	1	1ch.8c. on 1¼ch. claret	2·75	1·00
		a. Surch inverted	†	95·00
		b. "O" inverted	12·00	4·50
		c. Left "S" inverted	12·00	4·50
		d. Right "S" inverted	12·00	4·50
		e. Wrong fount "1 c"	30·00	19·00

(c) With opt Type O 3. Wmk C.

O78	4	12c. on 10ca. pink	†	£400
O79	1	1ch.8c. on 1¼ch. carmine-rose	55·00	38·00
		a. "n" omitted	£225	
		b. Wrong fount "1 c"	£200	£150

(d) With opt Type O 6. Wmk C.

O80	4	12c. on 10ca. pink	95·00	27·00
O81	1	1ch.8c. on 1¼ch. carmine-rose	£110	21·00
		a. Wrong fount "1 c"	£300	90·00
		b. "h" omitted	—	
		c. Brown-red	—	22·00

(e) With opt Type O 7. Wmk C.

O82	4	6c. on 5ca. chocolate	20	30
		a. Opt inverted	75·00	75·00
		b. Surch inverted	11·00	12·00
		c. Right "S" omitted	£120	£120
		d. Two quads for right "S"	£500	
		e. Right "S" inverted		28·00
O83		12c. on 10ca. pink	20	15

		a. Opt inverted	7·50	8·50
		b. Surch inverted	6·00	7·00
		c. Opt and surch inverted	35·00	35·00
		d. Opt double	†	90·00
		e. "O" inverted	18·00	18·00
		f. Right "S" inverted	19·00	19·00
		g. "On" omitted	—	£110
		h. "n" omitted	—	£110
		i. "c" omitted (R. 6/1)	35·00	35·00
		j. Surch double	†	£100
O84	1	1ch.8c. on 1¼ch. claret	35	25
		a. Imperf between (vert pair)	†	£325
		b. Surch inverted	14·00	15·00
		d. Surch double	65·00	
		e. "O" inverted	4·50	2·75
		f. Wrong fount "1 c"	19·00	15·00

SERVICE (O 10) 13 mm ("R" with curved tail) **SERVICE** (O 11) 13½ mm ("R" with straight tail) **SERVICE 8 CASH** (O 12)

1939-41. *Nos. 35 and 40 with type-set opt, Type O 10. P 12½.*

O85	1	6ca. brown-red (1941)	80	30
		a. Perf 11	1·40	75
		b. Perf 12	70	30
		c. Compound perf	70	1·10
O86	5	¾ch. reddish violet	£130	65·00
		a. Perf 12	27·00	1·40
		b. Compound perf	£120	65·00

1939 (9 Nov). *Maharaja's 27th Birthday. Nos. 64/70 with type-set opt, Type O 10. P 12½.*

O87		1ch. yellow-green	6·00	25
O88		1½ch. scarlet	6·50	1·00
		a. "SESVICE"	£100	27·00
		b. Perf 12	48·00	8·50
		ba. "SESVICE"	—	£160
		bb. Imperf between (horiz pair)	†	£225
		c. Compound perf	15·00	2·50
O89		2ch. orange	6·50	6·50
		a. "SESVICE"	£110	£130
		b. Compound perf	£110	£110
O90		3ch. brown	5·50	20
		a. "SESVICE"	85·00	21·00
		b. Perf 12	26·00	45
		ba. "SESVICE"	£250	48·00
		c. Compound perf	£110	4·00
O91		4ch. red	13·00	4·50
O92		7ch. pale blue	14·00	3·25
O93		14ch. turquoise-green	17·00	4·50
O87/93		Set of 7	60·00	18·00

1940 ((?))-45. *Nos. 40a and 42b optd with Type O 11 from stereos. P 12½.*

O94	5	¾ch. reddish violet	15·00	20
		a. Imperf between (horiz pair)	£140	£150
		b. Perf 11	60·00	1·10
		c. Perf 12	22·00	20
		d. Compound perf	45·00	75
O95	1	1½ch. rose (1945)	13·00	8·00
		a. Perf 11	4·50	1·00
		b. Compound perf	22·00	12·00

1941 (?)-42. *Nos. 64/70 optd with Type O 11 from stereos. P 12½.*

O96		1ch. yellow-green	1·10	10
		a. Imperf between (vert pair)	50·00	55·00
		b. Opt inverted	†	42·00
		c. Opt double	22·00	
		d. Perf 11	75	10
		da. Imperf between (vert pair)	38·00	
		db. Opt double	£130	£130
		e. Perf 12	3·00	50
		ea. Imperf between (vert pair)	95·00	95·00
		eb. Stamp doubly printed	£130	
		ec. Opt inverted	†	£130
		ed. Opt double	23·00	30·00
		f. Compound perf	8·00	1·00
		fa. Imperf between (vert pair)	†	£170
O97		1½ch. scarlet	4·25	10
		a. Imperf between (horiz pair)	65·00	
		b. Perf 11	2·25	15
		ba. Imperf between (vert pair)	£130	£130
		bb. Imperf between (vert strip of 3)	95·00	
		bc. Imperf between (horiz pair)	†	£140
		c. Perf 12	7·00	50
		ca. Imperf between (vert strip of 3)	£180	
		d. Compound perf	3·50	30
		e. Imperf (pair)	26·00	
O98		2ch. orange	2·25	30
		a. Perf 11	9·50	1·75
		ab. Imperf between (vert pair)	†	£550
		b. Perf 12	£100	£100
		ba. Imperf between (vert pair)	£550	£550
		c. Compound perf	£100	£100
O99		3ch. brown	1·60	20
		a. Imperf between (vert pair)	†	£550
		b. Perf 11	3·25	10
		c. Perf 12	6·00	2·00
		ca. Imperf between (vert pair)	£550	£550
		d. Compound perf	19·00	75
O100		4ch. red	3·50	85
		a. Perf 11	4·00	50
		b. Perf 12	19·00	4·75
		c. Compound perf	60·00	21·00
O101		7ch. pale blue	8·50	35
		a. Perf 11	6·00	4·75
		b. Perf 12	25·00	9·50
		c. Compound perf	20·00	4·50
		d. Blue (P 11)	13·00	6·50
		da. Perf 12	10·00	6·00
		db. Compound perf	28·00	18·00
O102		14ch. turquoise-green	15·00	70
		a. Perf 11	15·00	1·50
		b. Perf 12	10·00	2·40
		c. Compound perf	70·00	8·50
O96/102		Set of 7	24·00	1·90

1942. *Maharaja's 29th Birthday. Nos 71/2 optd with Type O* **11.** *P* 12½.

O103		6ca. blackish violet	40	50
		a. Perf 11	70	1·00
		b. Perf 12	70·00	7·50
		c. Compound perf	1·50	1·00
O104		¾ch. brown	5·50	10
		a. Imperf between (vert pair)	†	£400
		b. Perf 11	8·00	10
		c. Perf 12	70·00	2·75
		d. Compound perf	10·00	85

1943. *Surch with Type O* **12.** *P* 12½.

O105	**19**	8ca. on 6ca. scarlet	3·00	20
		a. Perf 11	1·25	10
		ab. Surch inverted	†	£1100
		b. Compound perf	8·00	1·25

1943–45. *Nos. 73/4 optd with Type O* **11.** *P* 12½.

O106		2ca. on 1½ca. scarlet	50	70
		a. Perf 11	50	15
		ab. Pair, one without surch	£300	
		b. Compound perf	70	1·00
		ba. "2" omitted	£400	£400
		c. Perf 12		
O107		4ca. on ¾ch. brown (1945)	3·75	30
		a. Perf 11	2·50	20
		b. Compound perf	2·25	1·25

1946. *Maharaja's 34th Birthday. Optd with Type O* **11.** *P* 11.

O108	**21**	8ca. carmine	2·25	70
		a. Imperf between (horiz pair)	42·00	
		ab. Imperf between (vert pair)	†	£200
		b. Opt double	†	£250
		c. Perf 12½	3·50	1·10
		ca. Stamp doubly printed	30·00	
		d. Perf 12	3·50	1·40
		da. Stamp doubly printed	45·00	

From 1 July 1949 Travancore formed part of the new State of Travancore-Cochin and stamps of Travancore surcharged in Indian currency were used.

TRAVANCORE-COCHIN

On 1 July 1949 the United State of Travancore and Cochin was formed ("U.S.T.C.") and the name was changed to State of Travancore-Cochin ("T.C.") by the new constitution of India on 26 January 1950.

PRICES FOR STAMPS ON COVER	
Nos. 1/13	*from × 8*
Nos. O1/17	*from × 15*

NO WATERMARK VARIETIES. These were formerly listed but we have now decided to omit them as they do not occur in full sheets. They are best collected in pairs, with and without watermarks.

COMPOUND PERFS. The notes above Type **17** of Travancore also apply here.

VALIDITY OF STAMPS. From 6 June 1950 the stamps of Travancore-Cochin were valid on mail from both Indian and state post offices to destinations in India and abroad.

ONE ANNA
ഒരണ
(1) 2p. on 6ca.

രണ്ട് പൈസ	രണ്ട് രപപസ
Normal	1st character of 2nd group as 1st character of 1st group (Rt pane R. 14/2)

1949 (1 July). *Stamps of Travancore surch in "PIES" or "ANNAS" as T* **1.** *P* 12½.

1	**19**	2p. on 6ca. blackish violet (R.)	3·25	1·50
		a. Surch inverted	42·00	
		b. Character error	£160	£100
		c. "O" inverted (Rt pane R. 13/1)	40·00	17·00
		d. Perf 11	2·00	30
		da. Imperf between (vert pair)	£190	£190
		db. Pair, one without surch	£110	
		dc. Character error	£150	90·00
		dd. "O" inverted (Rt pane R. 13/1)	40·00	19·00
		e. Perf 12	40	20
		ea. Imperf between (horiz pair)	70·00	
		eb. Imperf between (vert pair)	6·00	17·00
		ec. Surch inverted	£110	
		ed. Character error	£150	90·00
		ee. Imperf between (vert strip of 3)	35·00	
		ef. Block of four imperf between (horiz and vert)	65·00	
		eg. "O" inverted (Rt pane R. 13/1)	35·00	18·00
		eh. Imperf between (horiz strip of 3)	70·00	
		f. Perf 14	†	£500
		g. Imperf (pair)	8·50	
		ga. Character error	£250	
		h. Compound perf	—	35·00
2	**21**	4p. on 8ca. carmine	1·50	30
		a. Surch inverted	50·00	
		b. "S" inverted (Rt pane R. 3/7)	95·00	45·00
		c. Perf 11	2·50	30
		ca. Imperf between (vert pair)	£180	£180
		cb. Surch inverted	£110	
		cc. Pair, one without surch	£140	
		cd. "FOUP" for "FOUR"	£180	£100
		ce. "S" inverted (Rt pane R. 3/7)	95·00	45·00

---

		d. Perf 12	1·25	30
		da. Imperf between (vert pair)	20·00	
		db. Pair, one without surch	£130	
		dc. "FOUP" for "FOUR"	£130	85·00
		dd. "S" inverted (Rt pane R. 3/7)	£100	50·00
		de. Surch inverted	£140	
		e. Imperf (pair)	70·00	
		f. Compound perf	—	38·00
		g. Perf 13½	†	£600
3	**17**	½a. on 1ch. yellow-green	3·75	30
		a. "NANA" for "ANNA" (Lt paneR. 3/3)	£150	85·00
		b. Inverted "H" in "HALF"	—	£110
		c. Imperf between (vert pair)	†	£160
		d. Perf 11	3·00	30
		da. Imperf between (vert pair)	30·00	
		db. Surch inverted	†	£200
		dc. "NANA" for "ANNA" (Lt paneR. 3/3)	£190	£110
		dd. Inverted "H" in "HALF"	—	£100
		e. Perf 12	65	40
		ea. Imperf between (horiz pair)	60·00	65·00
		eb. Imperf between (vert pair)	6·00	14·00
		ec. Surch inverted	5·00	
		ed. "NANA" for "ANNA" (Lt paneR. 3/3)	£250	£120
		ee. Block of four imperf between (horiz and vert)	50·00	
		f. Perf 14	†	£425
		g. Imperf (pair)	9·00	20·00
		h. Compound perf	—	35·00
4	**18**	1a. on 2ch. orange	3·75	30
		a. Perf 11	55	30
		ab. Surch double	50·00	
		b. Perf 12	4·00	50
		ba. Imperf between (horiz pair)	8·00	
		bb. Imperf between (vert pair)	4·25	12·00
		bc. Block of four imperf between (horiz and vert)	50·00	
		c. Perf 13½	£170	2·00
		d. Imperf (pair)	8·50	
		e. Compound perf	40·00	23·00
5	—	2a. on 4ch. red (68)	3·75	60
		a. Surch inverted	†	£275
		b. "O" inverted	45·00	17·00
		c. Perf 11	3·75	60
		ca. "O" inverted	—	19·00
		d. Perf 12	3·00	55
		da. "O" inverted	50·00	19·00
		e. Compound perf	45·00	26·00
6	**18**	3a. on 7ch. pale blue (69)	13·00	5·50
		a. Perf 11	5·00	3·50
		ab. Blue	65·00	4·75
		ac. "3" omitted	†	£650
		b. Perf 12	12·00	3·00
		c. Compound perf	—	65·00
		ca. Blue	—	90·00
7	—	6a. on 14ch. turquoise-green (70)	17·00	30·00
		a. Accent omitted from native surch (Rt pane R. 13/4)	£300	£325
		b. Perf 11	16·00	26·00
		ba. Accent omitted from native surch (Rt pane R. 13/4)	£300	£325
		c. Perf 12	16·00	27·00
		ca. Accent omitted from native surch (Rt pane R. 13/4)	£325	£350
		d. Compound perf	38·00	42·00
		da. Accent omitted from native surch (Rt pane R. 13/4)	£425	
		e. Imperf (pair)		
1/7 Set of 7			24·00	28·00

There are two settings of the ½a. surcharge. In one the first native character is under the second downstroke of the "H" and in the other it is under the first downstroke of the "A" of "HALF". They occur on stamps perf 12½, 11 and 12 equally commonly and also on the Official stamps.

U. S. T. C.	T.-C.	SIX PIES
(2)	**(3)**	**(4)**

1949. *No.* 106 *of Cochin optd with T* **2.**

8	**29**	1a. orange	5·50	65·00
		a. No stop after "S" (R. 1/6)	75·00	
		b. Raised stop after "T" (R. 4/1)	75·00	

1950 (1 Apr). *No.* 106 *of Cochin optd with T* **3.**

9	**29**	1a. orange	7·00	60·00
		a. No stop after "T"	55·00	£250
		b. Opt inverted	£275	
		ba. No stop after "T"	£1600	

The no stop variety occurs on No. 5 in the sheet and again on No. 8 in conjunction with a short hyphen

1950 (1 Apr). *No.* 9 *surch as T* **4.**

10	**29**	6p. on 1a. orange	4·00	50·00
		a. No stop after "T" (R. 1/5)	21·00	
		b. Error. Surch on No. 8	15·00	
		ba. No stop after "S"	£200	
		bb. Raised stop after "T"	£200	
11		9p. on 1a. orange	4·00	45·00
		a. No stop after "T" (R. 1/5)	21·00	
		b. Error. Surch on No. 8	£160	
		ba. No stop after "S"	£650	
		bb. Raised stop after "T"	£650	

---

5 Conch or Chank Shell   **6** Palm Trees

(Litho Indian Security Printing Press, Nasik)

1950 (24 Oct). W **69** of India. P 14.

12	**5**	2p. rose-carmine	2·75	3·00
13	**6**	4p. ultramarine	3·50	15·00

The ordinary issues of Travancore-Cochin became obsolete on 1 July 1951.

OFFICIAL STAMPS

VALIDITY. Travancore-Cochin official stamps were valid for use throughout India from 30 September 1950.

SERVICE	SERVICE
(O 1)	(O 2)

1949 (1 July)–51. *Stamps of Travancore surch with value as T* **1** *and optd "SERVICE". No gum. P* 12½.

(a) With Type O **1.**

(i) Wmk C of Travancore.

O1	**19**	2p. on 6ca. blackish violet (R.)	1·75	70
		a. Imperf between (vert pair)	£180	£180
		b. Character error (Rt pane R. 14/2)	38·00	26·00
		c. "O" inverted	25·00	13·00
		d. Pair, one without surch	£160	
		e. Perf 11	1·00	20
		ea. Imperf between (vert pair)	£180	£180
		eb. Character error (Rt pane R. 14/2)	42·00	32·00
		ec. "O" inverted	25·00	12·00
		f. Perf 12	40	40
		fa. Imperf between (horiz pair)	8·50	20·00
		fb. Imperf between (vert pair)	6·00	
		fc. Character error (Rt pane R. 14/2)	38·00	28·00
		fd. "O" inverted	24·00	
		fe. Block of four imperf between (horiz and vert)	27·00	
		g. Imperf (pair)	8·50	21·00
		ga. Character error (Rt pane R. 14/2)	£250	
		h. Compound perf	60·00	
O2	**21**	4p. on 8ca. carmine	3·50	1·00
		a. "FOUB" for "FOUR" (Lt paneR. 2/3)	£190	£110
		b. Perf 11	3·50	30
		ba. "FOUB" for "FOUR" (Lt paneR. 2/3)	95·00	32·00
		c. Perf 12	3·50	55
		ca. "FOUB" for "FOUR" (Lt paneR. 2/3)	£110	55·00
		cb. "FOUR PIES" omitted (in pair with normal)	£750	
		d. Compound perf	19·00	17·00
O3	**17**	½a. on 1ch. yellow-green	60	25
		a. Pair, one without surch	90·00	
		b. Surch inverted	27·00	
		c. "NANA" for "ANNA" (Lt paneR. 3/3)	£250	80·00
		d. Perf 11	1·00	25
		da. Pair, one without surch	£160	
		db. Surch inverted	65·00	
		dc. "NANA" for "ANNA" (Lt paneR. 3/3)	£250	95·00
		e. Perf 12	11·00	2·00
		ea. "NANA" for "ANNA" (Lt paneR. 3/3)	£425	£170
		eb. Pair, one without surch	£110	
		ec. Surch inverted on back only	£300	
		f. Compound perf	—	23·00
O4	**18**	1a. on 2ch. orange	18·00	6·50
		a. Surch inverted	90·00	
		b. Pair, one without surch	£600	
		c. Perf 11	16·00	7·50
		ca. Pair, one without surch	£650	
O5	—	2a. on 4ch. red (68)	1·75	1·00
		a. Perf 11	6·00	60
		ba. Surch inverted	£800	
		bb. "O" inverted	—	42·00
		c. Perf 12	6·00	5·00
		ca. "O" inverted	—	80·00
		cb. Pair, one without surch	£300	
		d. Compound perf	—	32·00
		e. Imperf (pair)	12·00	
O6	—	3a. on 7ch. pale blue (69)	6·50	2·50
		a. Imperf between (vert pair)	20·00	
		b. Blue	45·00	8·00
		c. Perf 11	3·50	1·00
		ca. Blue	45·00	7·50
		d. Perf 12	4·00	5·00
		da. Imperf between (horiz pair)	19·00	
		db. Imperf between (vert pair)	8·50	
		dc. Block of four imperf between (horiz and vert)	40·00	
		dd. Blue	45·00	5·00

O7		e. Imperf (pair)................	11·00	
	–	6a. on 14ch. turquoise-green (70).	17·00	10·00
		a. Imperf between (vert pair)................	30·00	
		b. Perf 11	15·00	9·50
		c. Perf 12	48·00	10·00
		ca. Imperf between (horiz pair)................	27·00	
		cb. Imperf between (vert pair)................	32·00	
		cc. Block of four imperf between (horiz and vert)	60·00	
		d. Imperf (pair)...............	14·00	
O1/7 Set of 7			35·00	16·00

(ii) W 27 of Cochin.

O8	**19**	2p. on 6ca. blackish violet (R.)	30	1·50
		a. Type O 1 double	18·00	
		b. Perf 11	50	1·50
		c. Perf 12	1·00	1·50
O9	–	2a. on 4ch. red (68)....................	2·50	1·60
		a. Perf 11	70	65
		ab. Imperf between (vert pair)	£275	£275
		b. Compound perf	55·00	30·00

(b) With Type O 2.

(i) Wmk C of Travancore.

O10	**21**	4p. on 8ca. carmine.	75	20
		a. "FOUB" for "FOUR" (Lt pane R. 2/3)...............	£100	38·00
		b. 2nd "E" of "SERVICE" in wrong fount	£120	50·00
		c. "S" in "PIES" inverted ...	—	60·00
		d. Imperf between (vert pair)................	†	£160
		e. Perf 11	30	20
		ea. Imperf between (horiz pair)................	4·75	
		eb. Imperf between (vert pair)................	35·00	
		ec. "FOUB" for "FOUR" (Lt pane R. 2/3)...............	95·00	32·00
		ed. 2nd "E" of "SERVICE" in wrong fount	£120	60·00
		ee. "S" in "PIES" inverted ...	—	80·00
		ef. Block of four imperf between (horiz and vert).	35·00	
		f. Perf 12	30	20
		fa. Imperf between (horiz pair)................	6·50	
		fb. Imperf between (vert pair)................	2·00	
		fc. Block of four imperf between (horiz and vert).	15·00	26·00
		fd. "FOUB" for "FOUR" (Lt pane R. 2/3)...............	£110	40·00
		ff. 2nd "E" of "SERVICE" in wrong fount	£120	50·00
		fg. "FOUK" for "FOUR".....	†	£550
		fh. Imperf between (vert strip of 3)	50·00	
		fi. Imperf between (horiz strip of 3)	55·00	
		g. Perf 13½	4·25	1·25
		h. Compound perf	8·00	8·00
		i. Imperf (pair)..............	6·00	
		ia. 2nd "E" of "SERVICE" in wrong fount	£180	
O11	**17**	½a. on 1ch. yellow-green	80	20
		a. "AANA" for "ANNA" (Rt pane R. 13/1)	£190	60·00
		b. Perf 11	30	20
		ba. Imperf between (horiz pair)................	80·00	80·00
		bb. Imperf between (vert pair)................	10·00	
		bc. Block of four imperf between (horiz and vert).	60·00	
		bd. "AANA" for "ANNA" (Rt pane R. 13/1)	75·00	40·00
		c. Perf 12	1·00	15
		ca. Imperf between (horiz pair)................	3·50	
		cb. Imperf between (vert pair)................	3·50	11·00
		cc. "AANA" for "ANNA" (Rt pane R. 13/1)	£100	55·00
		cd. Block of four imperf between (horiz and vert).	25·00	
		d. Compound perf	23·00	16·00
		da. "AANA" for "ANNA" (Rt pane R. 13/1)	—	£200
		e. Imperf (pair).................	7·50	18·00
O12	**18**	1a. on 2ch. orange...........................	40	30
		a. Imperf between (vert pair)................	†	£170
		ab. Imperf between (horiz pair)................	†	£170
		b. Perf 11	3·50	50
		ba. Imperf between (horiz pair)................	8·00	20·00
		bb. Imperf between (vert pair)................	£100	£100
		c. Perf 12	40	20
		ca. Imperf between (horiz pair)................	7·00	
		cb. Imperf between (vert pair)................	3·75	14·00
		cc. Block of four imperf between (horiz and vert).	22·00	
		d. Compound perf	27·00	18·00
		e. Imperf (pair).................	15·00	
O13	–	2a. on 4ch. red (68)..........................	4·00	80
		a. "O" inverted (Lt pane R. 14/3)	90·00	40·00
		b. Perf 11	1·50	1·10
		ba. "O" inverted (Lt pane R. 14/3)	80·00	42·00
		c. Perf 12	9·50	1·10
		ca. Imperf between (vert pair)................	£130	£140

		cb. "O" inverted (Lt pane R. 14/3)	£140	40·00
		cc. Pair, one without surch ...	†	£850
		d. Compound perf..............	24·00	13·00
O14	–	3a. on 7ch. pale blue (69)............	8·00	1·10
		a. "S" inverted in "SERVICE"(Lt pane R. 6/3)............	75·00	32·00
		b. First "E" inverted (Lt pane R. 7/4)............	£170	£130
		c. "C" inverted (Lt pane R.4/1 and 5/1)	90·00	75·00
		d. Second "E" inverted (Lt pane R. 3/2)............	£160	£120
		e. Perf 11	1·50	1·10
		ea. "S" inverted in "SERVICE"(Lt pane R. 6/3)............	50·00	32·00
		f. Perf 12	3·75	1·60
		fa. "S" inverted in "SERVICE"(Lt pane R. 6/3)............	£130	80·00
		g. Compound perf..............	—	48·00
		h. Imperf (pair)...............	48·00	
O15	–	6a. on 14ch. turquoise-green (70)........	1·50	4·25
		a. Accent omitted from native surch	16·00	13·00
		b. "S" inverted in "SERVICE"(Lt pane R. 11/4)............	80·00	42·00
		c. Perf 11	13·00	3·75
		ca. Accent omitted from native surch	60·00	22·00
		cb. "S" inverted in "SERVICE"(Lt pane R. 11/4)............	£140	50·00
		d. Perf 12	42·00	4·75
		da. Accent omitted from native surch	£130	30·00
		db. "S" inverted in "SERVICE"(Lt pane R. 11/4)............	£275	65·00
		e. Compound perf..............	85·00	85·00
O10/15 Set of 6			5·00	5·50

(ii) W 27 of Cochin.

O16	**17**	½a. on 1ch. yellow-green	2·50	65
		a. Perf 11	40	40
		b. Perf 12	18·00	10·00
		c. Compound perf	11·00	3·00
O17	**18**	1a. on 2ch. orange............................	1·75	75
		a. Perf 11	50	40
		b. Perf 12	12·00	4·00
		c. Perf 13½	2·00	1·00
		d. Compound perf	5·00	3·00

Nos. O2, O10, O12 and O17 have the value at top in English and at bottom in native characters with "SERVICE" in between. All others have "SERVICE" below the surcharge.

Type O 2 was overprinted at one operation with the surcharges.

Nos. O10b, O10ed, O10ff and O10ia, show the second "E" of "SERVICE" with serifs matching those on the surcharge. The variety occurred on Right pane R. 10/6 and R. 11/6, but was soon corrected.

The "accent omitted" varieties on No. O15 occur on Left pane R. 5/1 and Right pane R. 1/4, 12/4, 14/1 and 13/4.

The Official stamps became obsolete in September 1951.

WADHWAN

PRICES FOR STAMPS ON COVER	
No. 1	*from* × 30
No. 2	—
Nos. 3/6	*from* × 30

Thakur Bal Singh, 1885–1910

1

(Litho Thacker & Co, Bombay)

1888–94.

(a) Thin toned wove paper.

1	**1**	½ pice, black (I, III) (P 12½ *large holes*)....................................	18·00	65·00
		a. Imperf between (vert pair) (I)................................		
		b. Pin-perf 6½ irregular (I)	£100	
		c. Compound of 12½ and pin-perf 6½ (I)....................	£180	
2		½ pice, black (II) (P 12½ *irregular small holes*)...................	45·00	

(b) Medium toned wove paper.

3	**1**	½ pice, black (III) (P 12½).............	12·00	48·00
4		½ pice, black (V) (P 12)............	9·50	13·00

(c) Thick off-white or toned wove paper.

5	**1**	½ pice, black (IV, VI) (P 12) (7.92).	8·00	9·00
		a. Perf compound of 12 and 11 (IV)............................	20·00	50·00
6		½ pice, black (VII) (*fine impression*) (P 12) (1894)............	8·00	22·00

Sheets from the Stone IV printing had at least one horizontal line of perforations gauging 11, normally between the bottom two rows of the sheet.

These stamps were lithographed from seven different stones taken from a single die. Brief details of the individual stones are as follows: Stone I–No. 1. Sheet size not known, but possibly 28 (4×7). Sheet margins imperforate Stone II–No. 2. Sheets of 42 (7×6) with imperforate margins Stone III–Nos. 1 (thin paper) and 3 (medium paper). Sheets of 40 (4×10) with imperforate margins Stone IV–Nos. 5/a. Sheets of 32 (4×8) with imperforate margins at top and right Stone V–No. 4. Sheets of 20 (4×5) with imperforate margins at top, right and bottom Stone VI–No. 5. Sheets of 30 (5×6) with all margins perforated Stone VII–No. 6. Sheets of 32 (4×8) with all margins perforated. Much finer impression than the other stones

Stamps from stones I and II come with or without the dot before "STATE". Those from the later stones always show the dot. The shading on the pennant above the shield can also be used in stone identification. Stamps from stones I to III show heavy shading on the pennant, but this is less evident on stone IV and reduced further to a short line or dot on stones V to VII. There is a ")" hairline after "HALF" on the majority of stamps from Stone III.

The stamps of Wadhwan became obsolete on 1 January 1895.

Ionian Islands

The British occupation of the Ionian Islands was completed in 1814 and the archipelago was placed under the protection of Great Britain by the Treaty of Paris of 9 November 1815. The United States of the Ionian Islands were given local self-government, which included responsibility for the postal services. Crowned-circle handstamps were, however, supplied in 1844, although it is believed these were intended for use on prepaid mail to foreign destinations.

Examples of the Great Britain 1855 1d. red-brown stamp are known used at Corfu, cancelled as No. CC2, but it is believed that these originate from mail sent by the British garrison.

For illustrations of the handstamp types see BRITISH POST OFFICES ABROAD notes, following GREAT BRITAIN.

CEPHALONIA

CROWNED-CIRCLE HANDSTAMPS

CC1   CC 1 CEPHALONIA (19.4.1844) ..... *Price on cover*   £1700

CORFU

CROWNED-CIRCLE HANDSTAMPS

CC2   CC 1 CORFU (19.4.1844) .... *Price on cover*   £550
CC3   CC 1 CORFU (G. or B.) (1844) .... *Price on cover*   —

ZANTE

CROWNED-CIRCLE HANDSTAMPS

CC4   CC 1 ZANTE (G. or B.) (19.4.1844) *Price on cover*   £1300

Nos. CC1/2 were later, circa 1860/1, struck in green (Cephalonia) or red (Corfu).

It is believed that examples of No. CC4 in black are from an unauthorised use of this handstamp which is now on display in the local museum. A similar handstamp, but without "PAID AT" was introduced in 1861.

PRICES FOR STAMPS ON COVER	
Nos. 1/3	*from × 10*

PERKINS BACON "CANCELLED". For notes on these handstamps, showing "CANCELLED" between horizontal bars forming an oval, see Catalogue Introduction.

1

(Eng C. Jeens. Recess Perkins, Bacon & Co)

1859 (15 June). Imperf.
1	1	(½d.) orange (no wmk) (H/S "CANCELLED" in oval £11000)	90·00	£500
2		(1d.) blue (wmk "2") (H/S "CANCELLED" in oval £11000)	23·00	£180
3		(2d.) carmine (wmk "1") (H/S "CANCELLED" in oval £11100)	17·00	£180

On 30 May 1864, the islands were ceded to Greece, and these stamps became obsolete.

Great care should be exercised in buying used stamps, on or off cover, as forged postmarks are plentiful.

Iraq

Indian post offices were opened at Baghdad and Basra, then part of the Turkish Empire, on 1 January 1868. Unoverprinted stamps of India were used, Baghdad being allocated numeral cancellations "356", "18" and "K-6", and Basra (also spelt Bussorah, Busreh, Busrah, Busra) "357", "19" and "1/K-6".

Both offices closed on 30 September 1914, but Basra re-opened in December 1914 when Indian stamps overprinted "I.E.F." were used.

(Currency. 16 annas = 1 rupee)

I. ISSUES FOR BAGHDAD

PRICES FOR STAMPS ON COVER	
Nos. 1/25	*from × 6*

BRITISH OCCUPATION

British and Indian troops occupied the port of Basra on 22 November 1914 to protect the oil pipeline. They then advanced up the rivers, and after a hard campaign, took Baghdad from the Turks on 11 March 1917.

BAGHDAD
IN BRITISH OCCUPATION
2 Ans
(1)

1917 (1 Sept). Stamps of Turkey, surch as *T* **1** *in three operations.*

(a) Pictorial designs of 1914. T **32**, *etc., and* **31**.
1	32	¼a. on 2pa. claret (Obelisk)	£140	£170
		a. "IN BRITISH" omitted	£7000	
2	34	¼a. on 5pa. dull purple (Leander's Tower)	£100	£110
		a. Value omitted	£6500	
3	36	½a. on 10pa. green (Lighthouse garden)..	£650	£800
4	31	½a. on 10pa. green (Mosque of Selim).....	£1100	£1300
5	37	1a. on 20pa. red (Castle)	£425	£475
		a. "BAGHDAD" double	£1400	
6	38	2a. on 1pi. bright blue (Mosque)..........	£170	£200

(b) As (a), but overprinted with small five-pointed Star.
7	37	1a. on 20pa. red (B.)	£250	£300
		a. "OCCUPATION" omitted............	£5500	
		b. "BAGHDAD" double	£1400	
8	38	2a. on 1pi. bright blue (R.)	£3500	£4000

(c) Postal Jubilee stamps (Old G.P.O.). P 12½.
9	60	½a. on 10pa. carmine	£450	£500
		a. Perf 13½	£900	£1000
10		1a. on 20pa. blue................................	£4250	
		a. Value omitted	£8000	
		b. Perf 13½	£950	£1200
11		2a. on 1pi. black and violet................	£225	£250
		a. "BAGHDAD" omitted........	£5500	
		b. Perf 13½	£100	£110
		ba. "IN BRITISH" twice	†	£7000

(d) T **30** *(G.P.O., Constantinople) with opt T* **26**.
12	30	2a. on 1pi. ultramarine	£425	£550
		a. "IN BRITISH" omitted..........	£7500	

No. 11ba shows "BAGHDAD" superimposed on a second impression of "IN BRITISH" at the top of the stamp. The only known example is on cover.

(e) Stamps optd with six-pointed Star and Arabic date "1331" within Crescent. T **53** *(except No. 16, which has five-pointed Star and Arabic "1332", T* **57**).
13	30	½a. on 10pa. green (R.)	£100	£110
14		1a. on 20pa. rose	£400	£450
		a. Value omitted	£4250	£4250
		b. Optd with T **26** (Arabic letter "B") also	£5000	£5000
15	23	1a. on 20pa. rose (No. 554a)...............	£450	£500
		a. Value omitted	£7500	
16	21	1a. on 20pa. carmine (No. 732)...........	£3750	£4500
17	30	2a. on 1pi. ultramarine (R.)..............	£110	£130
		a. "BAGHDAD" omitted........	†	£8000
18	21	2a. on 1pi. dull blue (No. 543) (R.)...	£180	£200
		a. "OCCUPATION" omitted.....	£7500	

(f) Stamps with similar opt, but date between Star and Crescent (Nos. 19 and 22, T **54**; *others T* **55** *five-pointed Star).*
19	23	½a. on 10pa. grey-green (No. 609a) (R.)..	£120	£140
		a. "OCCUPATION" omitted........	£6000	
20	60	½a. on 10pa. carmine (P 12½) (B.)......	£170	£190
		a. Perf 13½	£375	£425
21	30	1a. on 20pa. rose	£120	£140
22	28	1a. on 20pa. rose (Plate II) (No. 617)...	£425	£475
23	15	1a. on 20pa. claret (No. 630).............		
		on 20pa.	£190	£200
		a. "OCCUPATION" omitted........	£6500	£6500
24	30	2a. on 1pi. ultramarine (R.).............	£180	£200
		a. "OCCUPATION" omitted........	£6500	
		b. "BAGHDAD" omitted........	£6500	
25	28	2a. on 1pi. ultramarine (Pl. II) (No. 645)..	£1500	£1700

The last group *(f)* have the Crescent obliterated by hand in violet-black ink, as this included the inscription, "Tax for the relief of children of martyrs".

II. ISSUES FOR MOSUL

PRICES FOR STAMPS ON COVER	
Nos. 1/8	*from × 40*

BRITISH OCCUPATION

A British and Indian force occupied Mosul on 1 November 1918.

As the status of the vilayet was disputed stocks of "IRAQ IN BRITISH OCCUPATION" surcharges were withdrawn in early 1919 and replaced by Nos. 1/8.

POSTAGE

I.E.F. 'D'

1 Anna   4   4
(1)   I   II

Two types of tougra in central design:
(a) Large "tougra" or sign-manual of El Ghazi 7 mm high.
(b) Smaller "tougra" of Sultan Rechad 5½ mm high.

Two types of 4a. surcharge:
I. Normal "4". Apostrophes on D 3½ mm apart.
II. Small "4". Apostrophes on D 4½ mm apart.

1919 (1 Feb). Turkish Fiscal stamps surch as *T* **1** *by Govt Press, Baghdad.* P 11½ (½a.), 12 (1a.), or 12½ (others).
1		½a. on 1pi. green and red	2·25	1·90
2		1a. on 20pa. black/*red* (*a*)................	1·40	1·75

---

		a. Imperf between (horiz pair).........	£600		
		b. Surch double	£500		
		c. "A" of "Anna" omitted...............	£200		
3		1a. on 20pa. black/*red* (*b*).............	4·00	3·00	
		b. Surch double	£600		
4		2½a. on 1pi. mauve and yellow (*b*)............	1·50	1·50	
		a. No bar to fraction (R. 2/4).......	38·00	50·00	
		b. Surch double	£750		
5		3a. on 20pa. green (*a*).......................	1·60	4·00	
6		3a. on 20pa. green and orange (*b*)......	45·00	60·00	
7		4a. on 1pi. deep violet (*a*) (I)............	3·00	3·50	
		a. "4" omitted	£1500		
		c. Surch double	£900		
7d		4a. on 1pi. deep violet (*a*) (II)............	10·00	14·00	
		da. Surch double, one with "4" omitted	£2500		
8		8a. on 10pa. lake (*a*)	4·00	5·00	
		a. Surch inverted	£700	£800	
		b. Surch double	£600	£700	
		c. No apostrophe after "D" (R. 1/5)	32·00	42·00	
		d. Surch inverted. No apostrophe after "D"			
		e. "na" of "Anna" omitted..............	£250		
		f. Error. 8a. on 1pi. deep violet.......	£2000		

No. 4a occurs on some sheets only. No. 8c comes from the first setting only.

Nos. 1/8 were replaced by "IRAQ IN BRITISH OCCUPATION" surcharges during 1921.

In December 1925 the League of Nations awarded the vilayet of Mosul to Iraq.

III. ISSUES FOR IRAQ

PRICES FOR STAMPS ON COVER	
Nos. 1/18	*from × 4*
Nos. 41/154	*from × 2*
Nos. O19/171	*from × 2*

BRITISH OCCUPATION

IRAQ
IN BRITISH OCCUPATION
1 An.
(1)   A   B

1918 (1 Sept)–**21**. Turkish pictorial issue of 1914, surch as *T* **1** *by Bradbury Wilkinson.* P 12.

(a) No wmk. Tougra as A (1 Sept 1918–20).
1	34	¼a. on 5pa. dull purple	50	1·00
2	36	½a. on 10pa. green	70	20
3	37	1a. on 20pa. red	50	10
4	34	1½a. on 5pa. dull purple (1920)	5·00	50
5	38	2½a. on 1pi. bright blue	1·25	1·40
		a. Surch inverted	£4250	
6	39	3a. on 1½pi. grey and rose	1·25	25
		a. Surch double (Bk. + R.)	£2000	£2750
7	40	4a. on 1¾pi. red-brown and grey............	1·50	25
		a. Centre inverted	†	£18000
8	41	6a. on 2pi. black and green (32 mm surch)..	1·60	1·50
		a. Centre omitted	£11000	
		b. Surch 27 mm wide	75·00	1·75
9	42	8a. on 2½pi. green and orange (30 mm surch)..	1·25	70
		a. Surch inverted	†	£11000
		b. Surch 27 mm wide	11·00	70
10	43	12a. on 5pi. deep lilac	1·75	4·00
11	44	1r. on 10pi. red-brown	2·25	1·40
12	45	2r. on 25pi. yellow-green	7·50	2·50
13	46	5r. on 50pi. rose (32 mm surch)...........	20·00	22·00
		a. Surch 27 mm wide	32·00	27·00
14	47	10r. on 100pi. indigo	60·00	17·00
1/14		Set of 14	95·00	45·00
1s/14s		(ex 1½a. on 5pa.) Perf "Specimen" Set of 13	£325	

(b) No wmk. Tougra as B (one device instead of two) (1921).
15	44	1r. on 10pi. red-brown...................	£120	24·00

(c) Wmk Mult Script CA (sideways on ½a., 1½a.) (1921).
16	36	½a. on 10pa. green............................	1·50	2·00
17	34	1½a. on 5pa. dull purple	1·50	1·00
18	45	2r. on 25pi. yellow-green	13·00	11·00
16/18		Set of 3	14·50	12·50
16s/18s		Optd "Specimen" Set of 3	70·00	

Designs: *Horiz*—5pa. Leander's Tower; 10pa. Lighthouse-garden, Stamboul; 20pa. Castle of Europe; 1pi. Mosque of Sultan Ahmed; 1½ pi. Martyrs of Liberty Monument; 1¾pi. Fountains of Suleiman; 2pi. Cruiser *Hamidiye*; 2½ pi. Candilli, Bosphorus; 5pi. Former Ministry of War; 10pi. Sweet Waters of Europe; 25pi. Suleiman Mosque; 50pi. Bosphorus at Rumeli Hisar; 100pi. Sultan Ahmed's Fountain.

The original settings of Nos. 1/18 showed the surcharge 27 mm wide, except for the 2½a. (24 mm), 4a. (26½ mm), 6a. (32 mm), 8a. (30½ mm), 12a. (33 mm), 1r. (31½ mm), 2r. (30 mm) and 5r. (32 mm). The 6a., 8a. and 5r. came from a subsequent setting with the surcharge 27mm wide.

Nos. 2, 3, 5, 6 and 7/9 are known bisected and used on philatelic covers. All such covers have Makinah or F.P.O. 339 cancellations.

During January 1923 an outbreak of cholera in Baghdad led to the temporary use for postal purposes of the above issue overprinted "REVENUE".

LEAGUE OF NATIONS MANDATE

On 25 April 1920 the Supreme Council of the Allies assigned to the United Kingdom a mandate under the League of Nations to administer Iraq.

The Emir Faisal, King of Syria in 1920, was proclaimed King of Iraq on 23 August 1921.

King Faisal I
23 August 1921–8 September 1933

2 Sunni Mosque, Muadhdham

3 Winged Cherub

4 Allegory of Date Palm

(Des Miss Edith Cheesman (½a., 1a., 4a., 6a., 8a., 2r., 5r., 10r.), Mrs. C. Garbett (Miss M. Maynard) (others). Typo (1r.) or recess (others) Bradbury, Wilkinson)

1923 (1 June)–**25**. *T* **2/4** *and similar designs.* Wmk Mult Script CA (sideways on 2a., 3a., 4a., 8a., 5r.). P 12.

41	2	½a. olive-green	1·00	10
42	–	1a. brown	2·75	10
43	3	1½a. lake	1·00	10
44	–	2a. orange-buff	1·25	15
45	–	3a. grey-blue (1923)	1·25	15
46	–	4a. violet	3·00	30
		w. Wmk crown to left of CA	£200	£110
47	–	6a. greenish blue	1·25	30
48	–	8a. olive-bistre	3·00	30
49	4	1r. brown and blue-green	7·50	1·50
50	2	2r. black	14·00	7·00
51	–	2r. olive-bistre (1925)	45·00	3·25
52	–	5r. orange	28·00	13·00
53	–	10r. lake	32·00	20·00
41/53 *Set of 13*			£130	40·00
41s/53s Optd "Specimen" *Set of 13*			£300	

Designs: *Horiz (as T* **2**)—1a. Gufas on the Tigris. (30×24 *mm*)—2a. Bull From Babylonian wall-sculpture, 6a., 10r. Shiah Mosque, Kadhimain. (34×24 *mm*)—3a. Arch of Ctesiphon. *Vert (as T* **3**)—4a., 8a., 5r. Tribal Standard, Dulaim Camel Corps.

The normal sideways watermark on Nos. 44, 45, 46, 48 and 52 shows the crown to right of CA, *as seen from the back of the stamp.*

With the exception of Nos. 49 and 50, later printings of these stamps and of No. 78 are on a thinner paper.

10   **11** King Faisal I   **12**

(Recess Bradbury, Wilkinson)

1927 (1 Apr). Wmk Mult Script CA. P 12.

78	10	1r. red-brown	7·50	50
		s. Optd "Specimen"	38·00	

See note below No. 53.

(Recess Bradbury Wilkinson)

1931 (17 Feb). Wmk Mult Script CA (sideways on 1r. to 25r.). P 12.

80	11	½a. green	1·50	30
81	–	1a. red-brown	1·50	30
82	–	1½a. scarlet	1·50	50
83	–	2a. orange	1·25	10
84	–	3a. blue	1·25	20
85	–	4a. slate-purple	1·25	2·50
86	–	6a. greenish blue	1·50	50
87	–	8a. deep green	1·50	3·00
88	12	1r. chocolate	3·50	50
89	–	2r. yellow-brown	6·50	6·00
90	–	5r. orange	22·00	35·00
91	–	10r. scarlet	70·00	85·00
92	10	25r. violet	£600	£750
80/91 *Set of 12*			£100	£120
80s/92s Perf "Specimen" *Set of 13*			£550	

(New Currency. 1000 fils = 1 dinar)

(13)   **(14)**

Normal "SIN"   Error "SAD" (R. 8/16 of second setting)

(Surcharged at Govt Ptg Wks, Baghdad)

1932 (1–21 Apr). *Nos. 80/92 and 46 surch in "Fils" or "Dinar" as T* **13** *or* **14**.

106	11	2f. on ½a. green (R.)	50	10
		a. Wide space between "2" and "Fils"	20·00	20·00
107		3f. on ½a. green	50	10
		a. Surch double	£150	
		b. Surch inverted	£150	
		c. Arabic letter "SAD" instead of "SIN"	26·00	26·00
		d. Wide space between "3" and "Fils"	20·00	20·00
108		4f. on 1a. red-brown (21.4.32) (G.)	2·25	25
		a. Wide space between "4" and "Fils"	45·00	30·00
109		5f. on 1a. red-brown	75	10
		a. Inverted Arabic "5" (R. 8/11)	38·00	42·00
		b. Surch inverted	£275	
110		8f. on 1½a. scarlet	50	50
		a. Surch inverted	£150	
111		10f. on 2a. orange	50	10
		a. Inverted Arabic "1" (R. 8/13)	24·00	24·00
		b. No space between "10" and "Fils"	50	10
112		15f. on 3a. blue	1·50	1·00
113		20f. on 4a. slate-purple	1·75	1·75
		a. Surch inverted	£300	
114	–	25f. on 4a. violet (No. 46)	3·00	4·50
		a. "Flis" for "Fils" (R. 2/1, 10/8, 10/15)	£350	£425
		b. Inverted Arabic "5" (R. 10/7, 10/14)	£425	£550
		c. Vars a and b in se-tenant pair	£950	
		d. Error 20f. on 4a. violet (R. 10/1, 10/9)	£2250	
115	11	30f. on 6a. greenish blue	2·50	60
		a. Error 80f. on 6a. greenish blue	£2250	
116		40f. on 8a. deep green	2·50	4·25
117	12	75f. on 1r. chocolate	2·00	4·25
		a. Inverted Arabic "5"	40·00	60·00
118		100f. on 2r. yellow-brown	5·50	4·00
119		200f. on 5r. orange	17·00	26·00
120		½d. on 10r. scarlet	60·00	85·00
		a. No bar in English "½"	£800	£900
		b. Scarlet-vermilion	65·00	£100
121	10	1d. on 25r. violet	£120	£200
106/121 *Set of 16*			£200	£300

Nos. 106/13 and 115/16 were in sheets of 160 (16×10) No. 114 sheets of 150 (15×10) and Nos. 117/21 sheets of 100 (10×10). There were three settings of the surcharge for the 3f. and two settings for the 5, 10, 25, 40, 100 and 200f. Nos. 109a and 111a come from the first setting and Nos. 107c, 111b and 114a/b come from the second setting.

The "wide space" varieties, Nos. 106a, 107a and 108a, show a 2 mm space between the numeral and "Fils" instead of 1 mm. On No. 106a it occurs on R. 8/5 and R. 8/13, on 107d on R. 10/ 5 and R. 10/10 of the first setting and R. 6/6 of the second and on No. 108a on R. 7/1 and R. 7/9, although R. 7/9 is also known with normal spacing.

No. 109a occurs in the first setting and can be easily identified as it shows the point of the Arabic numeral at the foot of the surcharge.

All 10f. stamps from the second setting are as No. 111b except for R. 4/7–8 and 15–16 where the spacing is the same as for the first setting (Type **13**).

No. 114d shows "20" instead of "25". Many examples of this error were removed from the sheets before issue. The Arabic value "25" was unaltered.

No. 115a shows the error in the English face value only.

No. 117a occurs on R. 1/2, 1/7 and a third position in the first vertical row not yet identified.

No. 120a occurs on R. 1/2, r. 2/3 and R. 10/1.

No. 120b was a special printing of No. 91 which does not exist unsurcharged.

15

1932 (9 May–June). *T* **10** *to* **12**, *but with values altered to "FILS" or "DINAR" as in T* **15**. Wmk Mult Script CA (sideways on 50f. to 1d.). P 12.

138	11	2f. ultramarine (6.32)	50	20
139		3f. green	50	10
140		4f. brown-purple (6.32)	50	10
141		5f. grey-green	50	10
142		8f. scarlet	1·50	10
143		10f. yellow	1·50	10
144		15f. blue	1·50	10
145		20f. orange	1·75	50
146		25f. mauve	2·00	50
147		30f. bronze-green	2·25	15
148		40f. violet	1·50	1·00
149	12	50f. brown	1·50	20
150		75f. dull ultramarine	3·50	2·75
151		100f. deep green	5·50	70
152		200f. scarlet	13·00	3·25
153	10	½d. deep blue	45·00	45·00
154		1d. claret	95·00	95·00
138/54 *Set of 17*			£160	£130
138s/54s Perf "Specimen" *Set of 17*			£275	

OFFICIAL STAMPS

ON STATE SERVICE

(O 2)

1920 (16 May)–**23**. *As Nos. 1/18, but surch includes additional wording "ON STATE SERVICE" as Type* O **2** *in black.*

(a) No wmk. Tougra as A.

O19	36	½a. on 10pa. blue-green	8·00	1·75
O20	37	1a. on 20pa. red	3·00	60
O21	34	1½a. on 5pa. purple-brown	21·00	2·50
O22	38	2½a. on 1pi. brown	3·00	3·00
O23	39	3a. on 1½pi. black and rose	19·00	80
O24	40	4a. on 1¾pi. red-brown and grey-blue	22·00	3·25

O25	41	6a. on 2pi. black and green	20·00	5·50
	42	8a. on 2½pi. yellow-green and orange-brown	19·00	3·50
O27	43	12a. on 5pi. purple	13·00	9·00
O28	44	1r. on 10pi. red-brown	19·00	8·00
O29	45	2r. on 25pi. olive-green	23·00	12·00
O30	46	5r. on 50pi. rose-carmine	40·00	32·00
O31	47	10r. on 100pi. slate-blue	60·00	80·00
O19/31 *Set of 13*			£250	£140

(b) No wmk. Tougra as B (No. 15) (1922).

O32	44	1r. on 10pi. red-brown	27·00	7·00

(c) Wmk Mult Script CA (sideways on ½a. to 8a.) (1921–23).

O33	36	½a. on 10pa. green	1·00	1·00
O34	37	1a. on 20pa. red	4·50	1·00
O35	34	1½a. on 5pa. purple-brown	2·75	65
O36	40	4a. on 1¾pi. red-brown and grey-blue	2·00	2·00
O37	41	6a. on 2pi. black and green (10.3.23)	20·00	£110
O38	42	8a. on 2½pi. yellow-green and orange-brown	3·25	2·00
O39	43	12a. on 5pi. purple (10.3.23)	20·00	70·00
O40	45	2r. on 25pi. olive-green (10.3.23)	60·00	90·00
O33/40 *Set of 8*			£100	£250
O33s/40s Optd "Specimen" *Set of 8*			£160	

Nos. O25/6, O30 and O37/8 only exist from the setting with the surcharge 27½ mm wide.

ON STATE SERVICE   ON STATE SERVICE

(O 6)   (O 7)

1923. *Optd with Types* O **6** *(horiz designs) or* O **7** *(vert designs).*

O54	2	½a. olive-green	1·50	1·25
O55	–	1a. brown	1·75	20
O56	3	1½a. lake	1·75	2·25
O57	–	2a. orange-buff	2·00	40
O58	–	3a. grey-blue	2·50	1·25
O59	–	4a. violet	4·25	1·25
O60	–	6a. greenish blue	3·75	1·25
O61	–	8a. olive-bistre	4·00	2·75
O62	4	1r. brown and blue-green	8·50	2·50
O63	2	2r. black (R.)	21·00	9·00
O64	–	5r. orange	48·00	30·00
O65	–	10r. lake	85·00	48·00
O54/65 *Set of 12*			£170	90·00
O54s/65s Optd "Specimen" *Set of 12*			£275	

(O 8)   (O 9)

1924–25. *Optd with Types* O **8** *(horiz designs) or* O **9** *(vert designs).*

O66	2	½a. olive-green	1·25	10
O67	–	1a. brown	1·00	10
O68	3	1½a. lake	1·00	30
O69	–	2a. orange-buff	1·50	10
O70	–	3a. grey-blue	2·00	10
O71	–	4a. violet	4·00	30
O72	–	6a. greenish blue	1·75	20
O73	–	8a. olive-bistre	3·75	35
O74	4	1r. brown and blue-green	9·50	1·50
O75	2	2r. olive-bistre (1925)	35·00	3·75
O76	–	5r. orange	55·00	42·00
O77	–	10r. lake	85·00	42·00
O66/77 *Set of 12*			£180	80·00
O66s/77s Optd "Specimen" *Set of 12*			£275	

1927 (1 Apr). *Optd with Type* O **9**.

O79	10	1r. red-brown	6·50	1·75
		s. Optd "Specimen"	38·00	

ON STATE SERVICE

(O 12)   (O 13)

1931. *Optd.*

(a) As Type O **12**.

O93	11	½a. green	65	2·75
O94	–	1a. red-brown	80	10
O95	–	1½a. scarlet	4·50	22·00
O96	–	2a. orange	80	10
O97	–	3a. blue	85	1·25
O98	–	4a. slate-purple	1·00	1·50
O99	–	6a. greenish blue	4·50	21·00
O100	–	8a. deep green	4·75	21·00

(b) As Type O **13**, *horizontally.*

O101	12	1r. chocolate	14·00	20·00
O102	–	2r. yellow-brown	22·00	70·00
O103	–	5r. orange	42·00	£130
O104	–	10r. scarlet	90·00	£200

(c) As Type O **13**, *vertically upwards.*

O105	10	25r. violet	£650	£850
O93/104 *Set of 12*			£170	£425
O93s/105s Perf "Specimen" *Set of 13*			£500	

1932 (1 Apr). *Official issues of 1924–25 and 1931 surch in "FILS" or "DINAR", as T 13 or 14.*

O122	11	3f. on ½a. green	3·75	3·50
		a. Pair, one without surch	£350	
O123		4f. on 1a. red-brown (G.)	2·50	10
O124		5f. on 1a. red-brown	2·50	10
		a. Inverted Arabic "5" (R. 8/11)	55·00	35·00
O125	3	8f. on 1½a. lake (No. O68)	6·50	50
O126	11	10f. on 2a. orange	3·00	10
		a. Inverted Arabic "1" (R. 8/13)	45·00	32·00
		b. "10" omitted	†	£1700
		c. No space between "10" and "Fils"	3·00	10
O127		15f. on 3a. blue	4·25	3·00
O128		20f. on 4a. slate-purple	4·25	3·00
O129		25f. on 4a. slate-purple	4·50	2·00
O130	–	30f. on 6a. greenish blue (No. O72)	5·50	1·75
O131	11	40f. on 8a. deep green	4·00	3·50
		a. "Flis" for "Fils" (R. 7/5, 7/13)	£300	£375
O132	12	50f. on 1r. chocolate	7·00	3·50
		a. Inverted Arabic "5" (R. 1/2)	£100	£110
O133		75f. on 1r. chocolate	6·50	6·00
		a. Inverted Arabic "5"	60·00	65·00
O134	2	100f. on 2r. olive-bistre (surch at top)	21·00	3·50
		a. Surch at foot	23·00	13·00
O135	–	200f. on 5r. orange (No. O76)	23·00	23·00
O136	–	½d. on 10r. lake (No. O77)	70·00	90·00
		a. No bar in English "½" (R. 2/10)	£850	£1100
O137	10	1d. on 25r. violet	£140	£225
O122/37		Set of 16	£275	£325

Nos. O122/4, O126/9 and O131 were in sheets of 160 (16×10), Nos. O130, O134 and O136 150 (10×15), No. O135 150 (15×10) and Nos. O125, O132/3 and O137 in sheets of 100 (10×10). There was a second setting of the surcharge for the 3f. (equivalent to the third postage setting), 10f. to 25f., 40f. to 100f. and 1d. Nos. O126c, O131a and O134a come from the second setting.

All 10f. stamps from the second setting are as No. O134a.

For notes on other varieties see below No. 121.

1932 (9 May). *Optd.*

(a) As Type O 12.

O155	11	2f. ultramarine	1·50	10
O156		3f. green	1·50	10
O157		4f. brown-purple	1·50	10
O158		5f. grey-green	1·50	10
O159		8f. scarlet	1·50	10
O160		10f. yellow	2·25	10
O161		15f. blue	2·50	10
O162		20f. orange	2·50	15
O163		25f. mauve	2·50	15
O164		30f. bronze-green	3·50	20
O165		40f. violet	4·50	30

(b) As Type O 13, horizontally.

O166	12	50f. brown	3·25	20
O167		75f. dull ultramarine	2·50	1·00
O168		100f. deep green	11·00	2·00
O169		200f. scarlet	20·00	6·50

(c) As Type O 13, vertically upwards.

O170	10	½d. deep blue	12·00	26·00
O171		1d. claret	70·00	95·00
O155/71		Set of 17	£130	£120
O155s/71s		Perf "Specimen" Set of 17	£325	

The British Mandate was given up on 3 October 1932 and Iraq became an independent kingdom. Later issues will be found listed in Part 19 (*Middle East*) of this catalogue.

Ireland

All the issues of Ireland are listed together here, in this section of the Gibbons Catalogue, purely as a matter of convenience to collectors.

PRICES FOR STAMPS ON COVER TO 1945

Nos. 1/15	*from* × 5
Nos. 17/21	*from* × 3
Nos. 26/9a	*from* × 5
Nos. 30/43	*from* × 4
Nos. 44/6	—
Nos. 47/63	*from* × 5
Nos. 64/6	*from* × 3
Nos. 67/70	*from* × 6
Nos. 71/82	*from* × 2
Nos. 83/8	*from* × 3
Nos. 89/98	*from* × 2
Nos. 99/104	*from* × 3
Nos. 105/37	*from* × 2
Nos. D1/4	*from* × 7
Nos. D5/14	*from* × 6

PROVISIONAL GOVERNMENT

16 January—6 December 1922

Stamps of Great Britain overprinted.
T 104/8, W 100; T 109, W 110

RIALTAR
SEALADAC
NA
hÉIReANN
1922

(1)

RIALTAR
SEALADAC
NA
hÉIReANN
1922.

(2)

RIALTAR
SEALADAC
NA hÉIReANN
1922

(3)

("Provisional Government of Ireland, 1922")

1922 (17 Feb–July). *T 104 to 108 (W 100) and 109 of Great Britain overprinted in black.*

(a) With T 1, by Dollard Printing House Ltd. Optd in black.*

1	105	½d. green	1·75	40
		a. Opt inverted	£450	£600
		w. Wmk inverted		£400
2	104	1d. scarlet	1·75	40
		a. Opt inverted	£275	£325
		b. Opt double, both inverted, one albino	£350	
		c. Opt double	†	£1000
		w. Wmk inverted	—	£250
3		1d. carmine-red	4·25	1·00
4		2½d. bright blue	2·00	6·00
		a. Red opt (1 Apr)	1·50	3·75
5	106	3d. bluish violet	4·50	4·50
6		4d. grey-green	4·50	14·00
		a. Red opt (1 Apr)	8·50	15·00
		b. Carmine opt (July)	45·00	65·00
7	107	5d. yellow-brown	4·25	8·50
		x. Wmk reversed	—	£325
8	108	9d. agate	13·00	22·00
		a. Opt double, one albino	£300	
		b. Red opt (1 Apr)	15·00	18·00
		c. Carmine opt (July)	85·00	90·00
9		10d. turquoise-blue	8·50	45·00
1/9		Set of 8	35·00	85·00

*All values except 2½d. and 4d. are known with greyish black overprint, but these are difficult to distinguish.

The carmine overprints on the 4d. and 9d. may have been produced by Alex Thom & Co. Ltd. There was a further overprinting of the 2½d. at the same time, but this is difficult to distinguish.

The ½d. with red overprint is a trial or proof printing (*Price* £160).

Bogus inverted T 1 overprints exist on the 2d., 4d., 9d and 1s. values.

(b) With T 2, by Alex Thom & Co Ltd.

10	105	1½d. red-brown	2·25	1·25
		a. Error. ""PENCF"	£375	£300
		w. Wmk inverted	—	£225
		x. Wmk reversed	—	£225
12	106	2d. orange (Die I)	4·00	50
		a. Opt inverted	£190	£275
		w. Wmk inverted	—	£225
		x. Wmk reversed	£400	£225
13		2d. orange (Die II)	3·25	50
		a. Opt inverted	£325	£425
		w. Wmk inverted	—	£225
14	107	6d. reddish pur (*chalk-surfaced paper*)	15·00	16·00
15	108	1s. bistre-brown	13·00	9·50
10/15		Set of 5	35·00	25·00

Varieties occur throughout the T 2 overprint in the relative positions of the lines of the overprint, the "R" of "Rialtas" being over either the "Se" or "S" of "Sealadac" or intermediately.

(c) With T 3 by Dollard Printing House Ltd.

17	109	2s.6d. chocolate-brown	45·00	80·00
18		2s.6d. reddish brown	65·00	90·00
19		5s. rose-red	70·00	£150
21		10s. dull grey-blue	£140	£325
17/21		Set of 3	£225	£500

1922 (19 June–Aug). *Optd as T 2, in black, by Harrison & Sons, for use in horiz and vert coils.*

26	105	½d. green	2·50	14·00
27	104	1d. scarlet	3·25	6·50
28	105	1½d. red-brown (21.6)	4·00	38·00
29	106	2d. bright orange (Die I)	19·00	40·00
29a		2d. bright orange (Die II) (August)	20·00	30·00
		ay. Wmk inverted and reversed	—	£300
26/9a		Set of 5	45·00	£110

The Harrison overprint measures 15×17 mm (maximum) against the 14½×16 mm of T 2 (Thom printing) and is a much bolder black than the latter, while the individual letters are taller, the "i" of "Rialtas" being specially outstanding as it extends below the foot of the "R".

The "R" of "Rialtas" is always over the "Se" of "Sealadac".

1922. *Optd by Thom.*

(a) As T 2 but bolder, in dull to shiny blue-black or red (June–Nov).

30	105	½d. green	3·00	80
31	104	1d. scarlet	2·50	50
		a. "Q" for "O" (No. 357ab)	£1300	£1200
		b. Reversed "Q" for "O" (No. 357ac)	£350	£250
		w. Wmk inverted	†	£400
32	105	1½d. red-brown	3·50	3·50
33	106	2d. orange (Die I)	18·00	1·50
34		2d. orange (Die II)	3·25	50
		y. Wmk inverted and reversed	£150	£150
35	104	2½d. blue (R.)	6·00	22·00
36	106	3d. violet	3·25	2·00
		w. Wmk inverted and reversed	90·00	95·00
37		4d. grey-green (R.)	3·25	6·00
38	107	5d. yellow-brown	5·50	10·00
39		6d. reddish pur (*chalk-surfaced paper*)	8·50	3·25
		w. Wmk inverted	£130	85·00
40	108	9d. agate (R.)	14·00	17·00
41		9d. olive-green (R.)	5·50	38·00
42		10d. turquoise-blue	27·00	60·00
43		1s. bistre-brown	10·00	12·00
30/43		Set of 14	£100	£160

Both 2d. stamps exist with the overprint inverted but there remains some doubt as to whether they were issued.

These Thom printings are distinguishable from the Harrison printings by the size of the overprint, and from the previous Thom printings by the intensity and colour of the overprint, the latter being best seen when the stamp is looked through with a strong light behind it.

(b) As with T 3, but bolder, in shiny blue-black (Oct–Dec).

44	109	2s.6d. chocolate-brown	£200	£275
45		5s. rose-red	£225	£300
46		10s. dull grey-blue	£900	£1100
44/6		Set of 3	£1200	£1500

The above differ from Nos. 17/21 not only in the bolder impression and colour of the ink but also in the "h" and "e" of "heireann" which are closer together and horizontally aligned.

RIALTAR
SEALADAC
NA
hÉIReANN
1922.

(4)

SAORSTÁT
ÉIReANN
1922

(5 Wide date)
("Irish Free State 1922")

1922 (21 Nov–Dec). *Optd by Thom with T 4 (wider setting) in shiny blue-black.*

47	105	½d. green	1·00	1·75
		a. Opt in jet-black	£100	90·00
48	104	1d. scarlet	5·50	2·50
		w. Wmk inverted	†	£150
49	105	1½d. red-brown (4 December)	3·00	12·00
50	106	2d. orange (Die II)	9·00	7·00
51	108	1s. olive-bistre (4 December)	45·00	60·00
47/51		Set of 5	55·00	75·00

The overprint T 4 measures 15¾ × 16 mm (maximum).

IRISH FREE STATE

6 December 1922—29 December 1937

1922 (Dec)–**23.**

(a) Optd by Thom with T 5, in dull to shiny blue-black or red.

52	105	½d. green	1·50	30
		a. No accent in "Saorstat"	£1200	£1000
		b. Accent inserted by hand	95·00	£120
53	104	1d. scarlet	1·50	10
		aa. No accent in "Saorstat"	£11000	£8500
		a. No accent and final "t" missing	£10000	£7000
		b. Accent inserted by hand	£150	£180
		c. Accent and "t" inserted	£225	£275
		d. Accent and 'at' inserted	£225	£275
		e. Reversed "Q" for "O" (No. 357ac)	£325	£250
54	105	1½d. red-brown	3·50	8·50
55	106	2d. orange (Die II)	1·50	1·00
56	104	2½d. bright blue (R.) (6.1.23)	6·50	8·50
		a. No accent	£160	£280
57	106	3d. bluish violet (6.1.23)	4·25	11·00
		a. No accent	£325	£375
58		4d. grey-green (R.) (16.1.23)	3·50	9·00
		a. No accent	£170	£225
59	107	5d. yellow-brown	4·00	4·75
60		6d. reddish pur (*chalk-surfaced paper*)	2·00	2·00
		a. Accent inserted by hand	£800	£800
		y. Wmk inverted and reversed	75·00	42·00
61	108	9d. olive-green (R.)	4·00	5·50
		a. No accent	£275	£300
62		10d. turquoise-blue	18·00	60·00
63		1s. bistre-brown	7·00	11·00
		a. No accent	£8000	£9000
		b. Accent inserted by hand	£700	£750
64	109	2s.6d. chocolate-brown	40·00	55·00
		a. Major Re-entry (R. 1/2)	£1100	£1300
		b. No accent	£425	£475
		c. Accent reversed	£550	£650
65		5s. rose-red	75·00	£140
		a. No accent	£550	£700
		b. Accent reversed	£750	£850
66		10s. dull grey-blue	£170	£325
		a. No accent	£2750	£3500
		b. Accent reversed	£3750	£4500
52/66		Set of 15	£300	£550

The "no accent" and "accent inserted" varieties on the ½d. to 1s. values occur on R. 15/12. On the 2s.6d. to 10s. values the "no accent" varieties occur on R. 3/2 and R. 8/2, the "accent reversed" on R. 7/4.

The accents inserted by hand are in dull black. The reversed accents are grave (thus "à") instead of acute ("á"). A variety with "S" of "Saorstat" directly over "é" of "éireann", instead of to left, may be found in all values except the 2½d. and 4d. In the 2s. 6d., 5s. and 10s. it is very slightly to the left in the "S" over "é" variety, bringing the "á" of "Saorstat" directly above the last "n" of "éireann".

(b) Optd with T 5, in dull or shiny blue-black, by Harrison, for use in horiz or vert coils (7.3.23).

67		½d. green	1·75	11·00
		a. Long "1" in "1922"	20·00	50·00
		y. Wmk inverted and reversed	†	
68		1d. scarlet	4·00	11·00
		a. Long "1" in "1922"	75·00	£140
69		1½d. red-brown	6·50	45·00
		a. Long "1" in "1922"	85·00	£225
70		2d. orange (Die II)	8·00	12·00
		a. Long "1" in "1922"	32·00	50·00
		w. Wmk inverted	—	£180
67/70		Set of 4	18·00	70·00

In the Harrison overprint the characters are rather bolder than those of the Thom overprint, and the foot of the "1" of "1922" is usually rounded instead of square. The long "1" in "1922" has a serif at foot. The second "e" of "eireann" appears to be slightly raised.

PRINTERS. The following and all subsequent issues to No. 148 were printed at the Government Printing Works, Dublin, *unless otherwise stated.*

6 "Sword of Light" **7** Map of Ireland **8** Arms of Ireland

9 Celtic Cross **10**

(Des J. J. O'Reilly, *T* **6**; J. Ingram, *T* **7**; Miss M. Girling, *T* **8**; and Miss L. Williams, *T* **9**. Typo. Plates made by Royal Mint, London)

1922 (6 Dec)–**34**. W **10**. P 15×14.

71	6	½d. bright green (20.4.23)	2·00	90
		a. Imperf × perf 14, Wmk sideways (11.34)	20·00	45·00
		w. Wmk inverted	35·00	15·00
72	7	1d. carmine (23.2.23)	1·00	10
		aw. Wmk inverted	35·00	8·00
		b. Perf 15 × imperf (single perf) (1933)	90·00	£180
		bw. Ditto. Wmk inverted	£110	£180
		c. Perf 15 × imperf (7.34)	12·00	42·00
		d. Booklet pane. Three stamps plus three printed labels (21.8.31)	£300	
		dw. Wmk inverted	£300	
73		1½d. claret (2.2.23)	1·60	2·50
		w. Wmk inverted	£1200	
74		2d. grey-green (6.12.22)	1·50	10
		a. Imperf × perf 14, Wmk sideways (11.34)	38·00	70·00
		b. Perf 15 × imperf (1934)	£10000	£1500
		w. Wmk inverted	24·00	6·00
		y. Wmk inverted and reversed	35·00	15·00
75	8	2½d. red-brown (7.9.23)	4·00	4·25
		w. Wmk inverted	60·00	20·00
76	9	3d. ultramarine (16.3.23)	2·00	75
		w. Wmk inverted	75·00	25·00
77	8	4d. slate-blue (28.9.23)	2·00	3·25
		w. Wmk inverted	£110	40·00
78	6	5d. deep violet (11.5.23)	8·00	9·50
79		6d. claret (21.12.23)	4·50	3·50
		w. Wmk inverted	£150	50·00
80	8	9d. deep violet (26.10.23)	13·00	8·00
81	9	10d. brown (11.5.23)	9·00	18·00
82	6	1s light blue (15.6.23)	17·00	5·50
71/82 *Set of 12*			55·00	45·00

No. 72b is imperf vertically except for a single perf at each top corner. It was issued for use in automatic machines.

See also Nos. 111/22.

SAORSTÁT ÉIREANN 1922
(**11** Narrow Date)

12 Daniel O'Connell

1925 (Aug)–**28**. *T* **109** *of Great Britain* (Bradbury, Wilkinson printing) optd at the Government Printing Works, Dublin or by Harrison and Sons.

*(a) With T **11** in black or grey-black (25.8.25).*

83	2s.6d. chocolate-brown	40·00	90·00
	a. Wide and narrow date (pair) (1927)	£275	
84	5s. rose-red	60·00	£140
	a. Wide and narrow date (pair) (1927)	£450	
85	10s. dull grey-blue	£140	£325
	a. Wide and narrow date (pair) (1927)	£1200	
83/5 *Set of 3*		£225	£500

The varieties with wide and narrow date *se-tenant* are from what is known as the "composite setting," in which some stamps showed the wide date, as *T* **5**, while in others the figures were close together, as in *T* **11**.

Single specimens of this printing with wide date may be distinguished from Nos. 64 to 66 by the colour of the ink, which is black or grey-black in the composite setting and blue-black in the Thom printing.

The type of the "composite" overprint usually shows distinct signs of wear.

*(b) As T **5** (wide date) in black (1927–28).*

86	2s.6d. chocolate-brown (9.12.27)	48·00	55·00
	a. Circumflex accent over "a"	£275	£325
	b. No accent over "a"	£450	£475
	c. Flat accent on "a"	£400	£450
87	5s. rose-red (2.28)	75·00	95·00
	a. Circumflex accent over "a"	£425	£500
	c. Flat accent on "a"	£550	£650
88	10s. dull grey-blue (15.2.28)	£180	£200
	a. Circumflex accent over "a"	£1000	£1200
	c. Flat accent on "a"	£1200	£1400
86/8 *Set of 3*		£275	£325

This printing can be distinguished from the Thom overprints in dull black, by the clear, heavy impression (in deep black) which often shows in relief on the back of the stamp.

The variety showing a circumflex accent over the "a" occurred on R. 9/2. The overprint in this position finally deteriorated to such an extent that some examples of the 2s.6d. were without accent (No. 86b). A new cliché was then introduced with the accent virtually flat and which also showed damage to the "a" and the crossbar of the "t".

(Des L. Whelan. Typo)

1929 (22 June). *Catholic Emancipation Centenary.* W **10**. P 15×14.

89	12	2d. grey-green	50	45
90		3d. blue	4·00	8·50
91		9d. bright violet	4·00	4·00
89/91 *Set of 3*			7·50	11·50

13 Shannon Barrage **14** Reaper

(Des E. L. Lawrenson. Typo)

1930 (15 Oct). *Completion of Shannon Hydro-Electric Scheme.* W **10**. P 15×14.

92	13	2d. agate	1·00	55

(*T* **14** and **15** des G. Atkinson. Typo)

1931 (12 June). *Bicentenary of the Royal Dublin Society.* W **10**. P 15×14.

93	14	2d. blue	65	30

15 The Cross of Cong **16** Adoration of the Cross **17** Hurler

1932 (12 May). *International Eucharistic Congress.* W **10**. P 15×14.

94	15	2d. grey-green	1·50	30
		w. Wmk inverted	†	—
95		3d. blue	2·50	5·00

(*T* **16** to **19** des R. J. King. Typo)

1933 (18 Sept). *"Holy Year".* W **10**. P 15×14.

96	16	2d. grey-green	1·25	15
97		3d. blue	2·75	2·00

1934 (27 July). *Golden Jubilee of the Gaelic Athletic Association.* W **10**. P 15×14.

98	17	2d. green	1·25	55

1935 (Mar–July). *T* **109** *of Great Britain* (Waterlow printings) optd as *T* **5** (wide date), at the Government Printing Works, Dublin.

99	109	2s.6d. chocolate (No. 450)	45·00	60·00
		a. Flat accent on "a" (R. 9/2)	£300	£300
100		5s. bright rose-red (No. 451)	85·00	90·00
		a. Flat accent on "a" (R. 9/2)	£400	£400
101		10s. indigo (No. 452)	£300	£325
		a. Flat accent on "a" (R. 9/2)	£1100	£1100
99/101 *Set of 3*			£375	£425

18 St. Patrick **19** Ireland and New Constitution

1937 (8 Sept). W **10**. P 14×15.

102	18	2s.6d. emerald-green	£140	65·00
		w. Wmk inverted	£600	£225
103		5s. maroon	£180	£120
		w. Wmk inverted	£500	£225
104		10s. deep blue	£140	55·00
		w. Wmk inverted	£650	£200
102/4 *Set of 3*			£425	£200

See also Nos. 123/5.

EIRE

29 December 1937–17 April 1949

1937 (29 Dec). *Constitution Day.* W **10**. P 15×14.

105	19	2d. claret	1·75	20
		w. Wmk inverted	—	£200
106		3d. blue	4·25	3·75

For similar stamps see Nos. 176/7.

20 Father Mathew

(Des S. Keating. Typo)

1938 (1 July). *Centenary of Temperance Crusade.* W **10**. P 15×14.

107	20	2d. agate	2·00	50
		w. Wmk inverted	†	—
108		3d. blue	11·00	6·50

---

21 George Washington, American Eagle and Irish Harp **22**

(Des G. Atkinson. Typo)

1939 (1 Mar). *150th Anniv of U.S. Constitution and Installation of First U.S. President.* W **10**. P 15×14.

109	21	2d. scarlet	1·75	1·00
110		3d. blue	3·25	4·50

SIZE OF WATERMARK. *T* **22** can be found in various sizes from about 8 to 10 mm high. This is due to the use of two different dandy rolls supplied by different firms and to the effects of paper shrinkage and other factors such as pressure and machine speed.

White line above left value tablet joining horizontal line to ornament (R. 3/7)

1940–68. *Typo.* W **22**. P 15×14 or 14×15 (2s.6d. to 10s.).

111	6	½d. bright green (24.11.40)	2·00	40
		w. Wmk inverted	55·00	8·00
112	7	1d. carmine (26.10.40)	30	10
		aw. Wmk inverted	2·00	30
		b. From coils. Perf 14 × imperf (9.40)	60·00	65·00
		c. From coils. Perf 15 × imperf (20.3.46)	40·00	19·00
		cw. Wmk inverted	40·00	19·00
		d. Booklet pane. Three stamps plus three printed labels	£2000	
		dw. Wmk inverted	£2000	
113		1½d. claret (1.40)	15·00	30
		w. Wmk inverted	40·00	9·00
114		2d. grey-green (1.40)	30	10
		w Wmk inverted	2·50	1·25
115	8	2½d. red-brown (3.41)	9·50	15
		w. Wmk inverted	20·00	4·50
116	9	3d. blue(12.40)	70	10
		w. Wmk inverted	3·75	1·00
117	8	4d. slate-blue (12.40)	55	10
		w. Wmk inverted	16·00	3·25
118	6	5d. deep violet (7.40)	65	10
		w. Wmk inverted	30·00	10·00
119		6d. claret (3.42)	2·25	50
		aw. Wmk inverted	24·00	7·00
		b. Chalk-surfaced paper (1967)	1·25	20
		bw. Wmk inverted	13·00	2·50
119c		8d. scarlet (12.9.49)	80	80
		cw. Wmk inverted	40·00	14·00
120	8	9d. deep violet (7.40)	1·50	80
		w. Wmk inverted	10·00	2·25
121	9	10d. brown (7.40)	60	80
		aw. Wmk inverted	11·00	4·25
121b		11d. rose (12.9.49)	1·50	2·25
122	6	1s. light blue (6.40)	65·00	17·00
		w. Wmk inverted	£750	£170
123	18	2s.6d. emerald-green (10.2.43)	40·00	1·25
		aw. Wmk inverted	95·00	23·00
		b. Chalk-surfaced paper (1967)	1·50	2·00
		bw. Wmk inverted	32·00	4·25
124		5s. maroon (15.12.42)	40·00	3·00
		a. Line flaw	£200	40·00
		bw. Wmk inverted	£180	40·00
		c. Chalk-surfaced paper (1968?)	13·00	4·25
		ca. Purple	4·00	8·50
		cb. Line flaw	95·00	50·00
		cw. Wmk inverted	35·00	9·50
125		10s. deep blue (7.45)	60·00	7·00
		aw. Wmk inverted	£200	80·00
		b. Chalk-surfaced paper (1968)	19·00	12·00
		ba. Blue	5·00	16·00
		bw. Wmk inverted	£140	65·00
111/25 *Set of 17*			£100	30·00

There is a wide range of shades and also variation in paper used in this issue.

The 3d. and 5d. were issued with a similar design (17×21 mm), printed photo on chalk-surfaced paper in 1966 (5d.) and 1967 (3d.).

1941
I dCUIMNE AISÉIRĠE 1916
(**23** Trans "In memory of the rising of 1916")

24 Volunteer and G.P.O., Dublin

1941 (12 Apr). *25th Anniv of Easter Rising (1916). Provisional issue. T* **7** *and* **9** (2d. in new colour), optd with *T* **23**.

126	7	2d. orange (G.)	1·25	70
127	9	3d. blue (V.)	24·00	11·00

(Des V. Brown. Typo)

1941 (27 Oct). *25th Anniv of Easter Rising (1916). Definitive issue.* W **22**. P 15×14.

128	24	2½d. blue-black	2·25	80

25 Dr. Douglas
Hyde

26 Sir William
Rowan Hamilton

27 Bro. Michael
O'Clery

(Des S. O'Sullivan. Typo)

1943 (31 July). *50th Anniv of Founding of Gaelic League.* W **22**.
P 15×14.

129	**25**	½d. green	75	30
130		2½d. claret	1·60	10

(Des S. O'Sullivan from a bust by Hogan. Typo)

1943 (13 Nov). *Centenary of Announcement of Discovery of
Quaternions.* W **22**. P 15×14.

131	**26**	½d. green	40	60
132		2½d. brown	2·00	10

(Des R. J. King. Typo)

1944 (30 June). *Tercentenary of Death of Michael O'Clery.
(Commemorating the "Annals of the Four Masters".* W **22**
(sideways*). P 14×15.

133	**27**	½d. emerald-green	10	10
		w. Wmk facing right	55	20
134		1s. red-brown	1·00	10
		w. Wmk facing right	3·00	75

*The normal sideways watermark shows the top of the e facing left,
as seen from the back of the stamp.

Although issued as commemoratives these two stamps were kept in
use as part of the current issue, replacing Nos. 111 and 122.

28 Edmund
Ignatius Rice

29 "Youth Sowing
Seeds of Freedom"

(Des S. O'Sullivan. Typo)

1944 (29 Aug). *Death Centenary of Edmund Rice (founder of Irish
Christian Brothers).* W **22**. P 15×14.

135	**28**	2½d. slate	1·50	45
		w. Wmk inverted	†	£150

(Des R. J. King. Typo)

1945 (15 Sept). *Centenary of Death of Thomas Davis (founder of
Young Ireland Movement).* W **22**. P 15×14.

136	**29**	2½d. blue	1·00	50
		w. Wmk inverted	—	£150
137		6d. claret	6·00	4·75

30 "Country and Homestead"

(Des R. J. King. Typo)

1946 (16 Sept). *Birth Centenaries of Davitt and Parnell (land
reformers).* W **22**. P 15×14.

138	**30**	2½d. scarlet	2·00	25
139		3d. blue	3·00	3·75

31 Angel Victor over Rock of
Cashel

(Des R. J. King. Recess Waterlow (1d. to 1s.3d. until 1961), D. L.
R. (8d., 1s.3d. from 1961 and 1s.5d.))

1948 (7 Apr)–**65**. Air. T **31** and similar horiz designs. W **22**. P 15
(1s. 5d.) or 15×4 (others).

140	**31**	1d. chocolate (4.4.49)	1·75	4·00
141		3d. blue	3·00	2·50
142		6d. magenta	1·00	1·75
142b		8d. lake-brown (13.12.54)	6·50	8·50
143		1s. green (4.4.49)	1·00	1·75
143a		1s.3d. red-orange (13.12.54)	8·00	1·25
		aw. Wmk inverted	£600	£275
143b		1s.5d. deep ultramarine (1.4.65)	3·25	1·50
140/3b Set of 7			22·00	19·00

Design:—3d, 8d. Lough Derg; 6d. Croagh Patrick; 1s. Glendalough

35 Theobald Wolfe Tone

(Des K. Uhlemann. Typo)

1948 (19 Nov). *150th Anniv of Insurrection.* W **22**. P 15×14.

144	**35**	2½d. reddish purple	1·00	10
		w. Wmk inverted	†	
145		3d. violet	3·25	3·75

REPUBLIC OF IRELAND

18 April 1949

36 Leinster House and Arms of
Provinces

37 J. C. Mangan

(Des Muriel Brandt. Typo)

1949 (21 Nov). *International Recognition of Republic.* W **22**.
P 15×14.

146	**36**	2½d. reddish brown	1·50	10
		w. Wmk inverted	†	—
147		3d. bright blue	6·00	4·25

(Des R. J. King. Typo)

1949 (5 Dec). *Death Centenary of James Clarence Mangan (poet).*
W **22**. P 15×14.

148	**37**	1d. green	1·50	35
		w. Wmk inverted	†	

38 Statue of St.
Peter, Rome

(Recess Waterlow & Sons)

1950 (11 Sept). *Holy Year.* W **22**. P 12½.

149	**38**	2½d. violet	1·00	40
150		3d. blue	8·00	11·00
151		9d. brown	8·00	11·00
149/51 Set of 3			15·00	20·00

STAMP BOOKLETS

Nos. SB1 to SB24 are stitched. Subsequent booklets have their panes
attached by the selvedge, *unless otherwise stated.*

B 1 Harp and Monogram

B 2 Harp and "EIRE"

1931 (21 Aug)–**40**. *Black on red cover as Type B* **1**.

SB1	2s. booklet containing six ½d., six 2d. (Nos. 71, 74), each in block of 6, and nine 1d. (No. 72) in block of 6 and pane of 3 stamps and 3 labels (No. 72d or 72dw)	*From*	£2750

Edition Nos.:—31–1, 31–2, 32–3, 33–4, 33–5, 34–6, 34–
7, 35–8, 35–9, 36–10, 36–11, 37–12, 37–13, 37–14, 15–38,
16–38, 17–38

	a. Cover as Type B **2**	*From*	£3000

Edition Nos.:—18–39, 19–39, 20–39, 21–40, 22–40

1940. *Black on red cover as Type B* **2**.

SB2	2s. booklet containing six ½d., six 2d. (Nos. 71, 74), each in block of 6, and nine 1d. (No. 72) in block of 6 and pane of 3 stamps and 3 labels (No. 112d or 112dw)		£8500

Edition No.:—22–40

1940. *Black on red cover as Type B* **2**.

SB3	2s. booklet containing six ½d., six 2d. (Nos. 111, 114), each in block of 6, and nine 1d. (No. 112) in block of 6 and pane of 3 stamps and 3 labels (No. 112d or 112dw)		£8500

Edition No.:—23–40

1941–44. *Black on red cover as Type B* **2**.

SB4	2s. booklet containing twelve ½d., six 1d. and six 2d. (Nos. 111/12, 114) in blocks of 6	*From*	£1100

Edition Nos.:—24–41, 25–42, 26–44

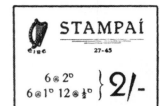

B 3

1945. *Black on red cover as Type B* **3**.

SB5	2s. booklet containing twelve ½d., six 1d. and six 2d. (Nos. 111/12, 114) in blocks of 6		£1000

Edition No.:—27–45

1946. *Black on buff cover as Type B* **2**.

SB6	2s. booklet containing twelve ½d., six 1d. and six 2d. (Nos. 111/12, 114) in blocks of 6		£750

Edition Nos.:—28–46

1946–47. *Black on buff cover as Type B* **2**.

SB7	2s. booklet containing twelve ½d., six 1d. and six 2d. (Nos. 133, 112, 114) in blocks of 6	*From*	£350

Edition Nos.:—29–46, 30–47

B 4 Harp only

1948–50. *Black on red cover as Type B* **4**.

SB8	2s.6d. booklet containing six ½d., twelve 1d. and six 2½d. (Nos. 133, 112, 115) in blocks of 6	*From*	£150

Edition Nos.:—31–48, 32–49, 33–50

1951–53. *Black on buff cover as Type B* **4**.

SB9	2s.6d. booklet containing six ½d., twelve 1d. and six 2½d. (Nos. 133, 112, 115) in blocks of 6	*From*	55·00

Edition Nos.:—34–51, 35–52, 36–53

POSTAGE DUE STAMPS

From 1922 to 1925 Great Britain postage due stamps in both script and
block watermarks were used without overprint.

D 1

(Des Ruby McConnell. Typo Govt Printing Works, Dublin)

1925 (20 Feb). W **10**. P 14×15.

D1	D **1**	½d. emerald-green	12·00	16·00
D2		1d. carmine	15·00	3·00
		a. Wmk sideways	£800	£400
		w. Wmk inverted	£350	75·00
		y. Wmk inverted and reversed	£150	£150
D3		2d. deep green	38·00	5·50
		a. Wmk sideways	50·00	17·00
		w. Wmk inverted	90·00	35·00
D4		6d. plum	6·50	7·50
D1/4 Set of 4			65·00	29·00

1940–70. W **22**. P 14×15.

D5	D **1**	½d. emerald-green (1942)	35·00	23·00
		w. Wmk inverted		£350
D6		1d. carmine (1941)	1·50	70
		w. Wmk inverted		
D7		1½d. vermilion (1953)	2·50	6·50
		w. Wmk inverted	17·00	24·00
D8		2d. deep green (1940)	2·75	70
		w. Wmk inverted	£250	75·00
D9		3d. blue (10.11.52)	2·50	3·00
		w. Wmk inverted	7·00	5·00
D10		5d. blue-violet (3.3.43)	4·50	3·00
		w. Wmk inverted	6·50	7·00
D11		6d. plum (21.3.60)	3·75	2·00
		a. Wmk sideways (1968)	6·00	7·00
D12		8d. orange (30.10.62)	8·50	9·50
		w. Wmk inverted	17·00	19·00
D13		10d. bright purple (27.1.65)	8·50	7·50
D14		1s. apple-green (10.2.69)	6·00	9·50
		a. Wmk sideways (1970)	75·00	80·00
D5/14 Set of 10			65·00	55·00

Jamaica

Records show that the first local Postmaster for Jamaica on a regular basis was appointed as early as 1671, although a reasonably organised service did not evolve until 1687–8. In the early years of the 18th century overseas mail was carried by the British packets, but between 1704 and 1711 this service was run on a commercial basis by Edmund Dummer. Following the collapse of the Dummer scheme Jamaica was virtually without a Post Office until 1720 and it was not until 1755 that overseas mail was again carried by British packets.

Stamps of Great Britain were used in Jamaica from 8 May 1858, initially on overseas mail only, but their use was extended to mail sent to Jamaican addresses from 1 February 1859. The island assumed responsibility for the postal service on 1 August 1860 and the use of Great Britain stamps then ceased.

KINGSTON

Z 1

Stamps of GREAT BRITAIN *cancelled* "A 01" *as Type Z* **1**.

1858–60.
Z1	1d. rose-red (1857), *perf 16*.........	£325
Z2	1d. rose-red (1857), *perf 14*.........	42·00
Z4	4d. rose-carmine *or* rose (1857).........	42·00
Z5	6d. lilac (1856).........	42·00
Z6	1s. green (1856).........	£160

Z 2

Stamps of GREAT BRITAIN *cancelled* "A 01" *as Type Z* **2**.

1859–60.
Z7	1d. rose-red (1857), *perf 14*.........	£190
Z9	4d. rose-carmine *or* rose (1857).........	48·00
Z10	6d. lilac (1856).........	48·00
Z11	1s. green (1856).........	£375

Z 3

Stamps of GREAT BRITAIN *cancelled* "A 01" *as Type Z* **3**.

1859–60.
Z12	1d. rose-red (1857), *perf 14*.........	£250
Z14	4d. rose-carmine *or* rose (1857).........	£150
	a. Thick *glazed* paper.........	£425
Z15	6d. lilac (1856).........	£150
Z16	1s. green (1856).........	

Cancellation "A 01" was later used by the London, Foreign Branch Office.

OTHER JAMAICA POST OFFICES

British stamps were issued to several District post offices between 8 May 1858 and 1 March 1859 (i.e. before the Obliterators A 27—A 78 were issued). These can only be distinguished (off the cover) when they have the Town's date-stamp on them. They are worth about three times the price of those with an obliteration number.

Stamps of GREAT BRITAIN *cancelled* "A 27" *to* "A 78" *as Type Z* **1**.

1859–60. "A 27". ALEXANDRIA
Z17	1d. rose-red (1857), *perf 14*.........	£500
Z17a	2d. blue (1855) Large Crown, *perf 14* (Plate 6) ...	£600
Z18	4d. rose (1857).........	£190
Z19	6d. lilac (1856).........	£450

"A 28". ANNOTTO BAY
Z20	1d. rose-red (1857), *perf 14*.........	£350
Z21	4d. rose (1857).........	90·00
Z22	6d. lilac (1856).........	£275

"A 29". BATH
Z23	1d. rose-red (1857), *perf 14*.........	£150
Z24	4d. rose (1857).........	£100
Z25	6d. lilac (1856).........	£450

"A 30". BLACK RIVER
Z26	1d. rose-red (1857), *perf 14*.........	£150
Z27	4d. rose (1857).........	70·00
Z28	6d. lilac (1856).........	£150

"A 31". BROWN'S TOWN
Z29	1d. rose-red (1857), *perf 14*.........	£190
Z30	4d. rose (1857).........	£190
Z31	6d. lilac (1856).........	£190

"A 32". BUFF BAY
Z32	1d. rose-red (1857), *perf 14*.........	£150
Z33	1d. rose (1857).........	£180
Z34	6d. lilac (1856).........	£150

"A 33". CHAPELTON
Z35	1d. rose-red (1857), *perf 14*.........	£190
Z36	4d. rose (1857).........	£130
Z37	6d. lilac (1856).........	£190

"A 34". CLAREMONT
Z38	1d. rose-red (1857), *perf 14*.........	£350
Z39	4d. rose (1857).........	£180
Z40	6d. lilac (1856).........	£350

"A 35". CLARENDON
Z41	1d. rose-red (1857), *perf 14*.........	£300
Z42	4d. rose (1857).........	£130
Z43	6d. lilac (1856).........	£190

"A 36". DRY HARBOUR
Z44	1d. rose-red (1857), *perf 14*.........	£450
Z45	4d. rose (1857).........	£375
Z46	6d. lilac (1856).........	£325

"A 37". DUNCANS
Z47	1d. rose-red (1857), *perf 14*.........	£450
Z48	4d. rose (1857).........	£450
Z49	6d. lilac (1856).........	£325

"A 38". EWARTON

A 38 was allocated to EWARTON but this office was closed towards the end of 1858 before the postmark arrived. A 38 was re-issued to Falmouth in 1862.

"A 39". FALMOUTH
Z53	1d. rose-red (1857), *perf 14*.........	£100
Z54	4d. rose (1857).........	60·00
Z55	6d. lilac (1856).........	75·00
Z56	1s. green (1856).........	£700

"A 40". FLINT RIVER
Z57	1d. rose-red (1857), *perf 14*.........	£180
Z58	4d. rose (1857).........	£130
Z59	6d. lilac (1856).........	£180
Z60	1s. green (1856).........	£700

"A 41". GAYLE
Z61	1d. rose-red (1857), *perf 14*.........	£500
Z62	4d. rose (1857).........	£150
Z63	6d. lilac (1856).........	£160
Z64	1s. green (1856).........	£375

"A 42". GOLDEN SPRING
Z65	1d. rose-red (1857), *perf 14*.........	£200
Z66	4d. rose (1857).........	£180
Z67	6d. lilac (1856).........	£450
Z68	1s. green (1856).........	£700

"A 43". GORDON TOWN
Z69	1d. rose-red (1857), *perf 14*.........	
Z70	4d. rose (1857).........	
Z71	6d. lilac (1856).........	£500

"A 44". GOSHEN
Z72	1d. rose-red (1857), *perf 14*.........	£150
Z73	4d. rose (1857).........	£140
Z74	6d. lilac (1856).........	70·00

"A 45". GRANGE HILL
Z75	1d. rose-red (1857), *perf 14*.........	£180
Z76	4d. rose (1857).........	60·00
Z77	6d. lilac (1856).........	75·00
Z77a	1s. green (1856).........	£600

"A 46". GREEN ISLAND
Z78	1d. rose-red (1857), *perf 14*.........	£350
Z79	4d. rose (1857).........	£180
Z80	6d. lilac (1856).........	£300
Z81	1s. green (1856).........	£700

"A 47". HIGHGATE
Z82	1d. rose-red (1857), *perf 14*.........	£200
Z83	4d. rose (1857).........	£140
Z84	6d. lilac (1856).........	£200

"A 48". HOPE BAY
Z85	1d. rose-red (1857), *perf 14*.........	£450
Z86	4d. rose (1857).........	£180
Z87	6d. lilac (1856).........	£450

"A 49". LILLIPUT
Z88	1d. rose-red (1857), *perf 14*.........	£180
Z89	4d. rose (1857).........	£180
Z90	6d. lilac (1856).........	90·00

"A 50". LITTLE RIVER

A 50 was allocated for use at LITTLE RIVER but this office was closed late in 1858, before the obliterator could be issued. Issued to Malvern in 1862.

"A 51". LUCEA
Z91	1d. rose-red (1857), *perf 14*.........	£275
Z92	4d. rose (1857).........	70·00
Z93	6d. lilac (1856).........	£180

"A 52". MANCHIONEAL
Z94	1d. rose-red (1857), *perf 14*.........	£350
Z95	4d. rose (1857).........	£190
Z96	6d. lilac (1856).........	

"A 53". MANDEVILLE
Z97	1d. rose-red (1857), *perf 14*.........	£190
Z98	4d. rose (1857).........	70·00
Z99	6d. lilac (1856).........	£170

"A 54". MAY HILL
Z100	1d. rose-red (1857), *perf 14*.........	£100
Z101	4d. rose (1857).........	95·00
Z102	6d. lilac (1856).........	70·00

"A 55". MILE GULLY
Z103	1d. rose-red (1857), *perf 14*.........	£300
Z104	4d. rose (1857).........	£180
Z105	6d. lilac (1856).........	£180

"A 56". MONEAGUE
Z106	1d. rose-red (1857), *perf 14*.........	£180
Z107	4d. rose (1857).........	£225
Z108	6d. lilac (1856).........	£450

"A 57". MONTEGO BAY
Z109	1d. rose-red (1857), *perf 14*.........	£190
Z110	4d. rose (1857).........	60·00
Z111	6d. lilac (1856).........	70·00
Z112	1s. green (1856).........	£700

"A 58". MONTPELIER
Z113	1d. rose-red (1857), *perf 14*.........	
Z114	4d. rose (1857).........	
Z115	6d. lilac (1856).........	£750

"A 59". MORANT BAY
Z116	1d. rose-red (1857), *perf 14*.........	£350
Z117	4d. rose (1857).........	70·00
Z118	6d. lilac (1856).........	75·00

"A 60". OCHO RIOS
Z119	1d. rose-red (1857), *perf 14*.........	
Z120	4d. rose (1857).........	95·00
Z121	6d. lilac (1856).........	£170

"A 61". OLD HARBOUR
Z122	1d. rose-red (1857), *perf 14*.........	£180
Z123	4d. rose (1857).........	£140
Z124	6d. lilac (1856).........	£140

"A 62". PLANTAIN GARDEN RIVER
Z125	1d. rose-red (1857), *perf 14*.........	£140
Z126	4d. rose (1857).........	95·00
Z127	6d. lilac (1856).........	£140

"A 63". PEAR TREE GROVE

No genuine specimen of A 63 has been found on a British stamp.

"A 64". PORT ANTONIO
Z131	1d. rose-red (1857), *perf 14*.........	£425
Z132	4d. rose (1857).........	£275
Z133	6d. lilac (1856).........	£275

"A 65". PORT MORANT
Z134	1d. rose-red (1857), *perf 14*.........	£275
Z135	4d. rose (1857).........	£100
Z136	6d. lilac (1856).........	£275

"A 66". PORT MARIA
Z137	1d. rose-red (1857), *perf 14*.........	£180
Z138	4d. rose (1857).........	75·00
Z139	6d. lilac (1856).........	£275

"A 67". PORT ROYAL
Z140	1d. rose-red (1857), *perf 14*.........	£350
Z140a	2d. blue (1858) (plate 9).........	£350
Z141	4d. rose (1857).........	£350
Z142	6d. lilac (1856).........	£350

"A 68". PORUS
Z143	1d. rose-red (1857), *perf 14*.........	£180
Z144	4d. rose (1857).........	90·00
Z145	6d. lilac (1856).........	£350

"A 69". RAMBLE
Z146	1d. rose-red (1857), *perf 14*.........	£180
Z147	4d. rose (1857).........	£180
	a. Thick glazed paper.........	£425
Z149	6d. lilac (1856).........	£275

"A 70". RIO BUENO
Z150	1d. rose-red (1857), *perf 14*.........	
Z151	4d. rose (1857).........	£170
Z152	6d. lilac (1856).........	£110

"A 71". RODNEY HALL
Z153	1d. rose-red (1857), *perf 14*.........	£150
Z154	4d. rose (1857).........	£100
Z155	6d. lilac (1856).........	£130

"A 72". ST. DAVID
Z156	1d. rose-red (1857), *perf 14*.........	£180
Z157	4d. rose (1857).........	£350
Z158	6d. lilac (1856).........	

"A 73". ST. ANN'S BAY
Z159	1d. rose-red (1857), *perf 14*.........	£180
Z160	4d. rose (1857).........	95·00
Z161	6d. lilac (1856).........	£180

"A 74". SALT GUT
Z162	1d. rose-red (1857), *perf 14*.........	£170
Z163	4d. rose (1857).........	
Z164	6d. lilac (1856).........	£180

"A 75". SAVANNAH-LA-MAR
Z165	1d. rose-red (1857), *perf 14*.........	£100
Z166	4d. rose (1857).........	65·00
Z167	6d. lilac (1856).........	£180
Z168	1s. green (1856).........	£600

"A 76". SPANISH TOWN
Z169	1d. rose-red (1857), *perf 14*.........	£110
Z170	4d. rose (1857).........	60·00
Z171	6d. lilac (1856).........	£100
Z172	1s. green (1856).........	£450

"A 77". STEWART TOWN
Z173	1d. rose-red (1857), *perf 14*.........	£450
Z174	4d. rose (1857).........	£300
Z175	6d. lilac (1856).........	£180

"A 78". VERE
Z176	1d. rose-red (1857), *perf 14*.........	£275
Z177	4d. rose (1857).........	90·00
Z178	6d. lilac (1856).........	65·00
Z179	1s. green (1856).........	£700

PRICES FOR STAMPS ON COVER

Nos. 1/6	*from* × 4
Nos. 7/15	*from* × 6
Nos. 16/26	*from* × 8
Nos. 27/9	*from* × 6
No. 30	*from* × 5
Nos. 31/2	*from* × 15
Nos. 33/6	*from* × 5
Nos. 37/56	*from* × 3
No. 57	*from* × 4
Nos. 58/67	*from* × 3
Nos. 68/77	*from* × 6
Nos. 78/89	*from* × 3
Nos. 90/103	*from* × 4
Nos. 104/7	*from* × 5
Nos. 108/17	*from* × 3
Nos. 118/20	*from* × 5
Nos. 121/33a	*from* × 4
Nos. 134/40	*from* × 8
Nos. F1/9	*from* × 3
Nos. O1/5	*from* × 3

CROWN COLONY

PRINTERS. Until 1923, all the stamps of Jamaica were typographed by De La Rue & Co, Ltd, London, *unless otherwise stated.*

The official dates of issue are given, where known, but where definite information is not available the dates are those of earliest known use, etc.

1   2   3

4   5   6

7   A

1860 (23 Nov)–**70**. W **7**. P 14.

1	1	1d. pale blue	60·00	15·00
		a. *Pale greenish blue*	80·00	19·00
		b. *Blue*	50·00	12·00
		c. *Deep blue* (1865)	£110	28·00
		d. *Bisected* (½d.) (20.11.61) (on cover)	†	£650
		w. Wmk inverted	£120	42·00
2	2	2d. rose	£190	50·00
		a. *Deep rose*	£130	50·00
		w. Wmk inverted	—	70·00
3	3	3d. green (10.9.63)	£130	25·00
		w. Wmk inverted	£160	40·00
4	4	4d. brown-orange	£200	48·00
		a. *Red-orange*	£200	22·00
		w. Wmk inverted		
5	5	6d. dull lilac	£180	22·00
		a. *Grey-purple*	£275	32·00
		b. *Deep purple* (1870)	£800	50·00
		w. Wmk inverted	—	80·00
6	6	1s. yellow-brown	£450	25·00
		a. *Purple-brown* (1862)	£550	23·00
		b. *Dull brown* (1868)	£180	27·00
		c. "$" for "S" in "SHILLING" (A)	£2250	£600
		w. Wmk inverted	—	55·00

The diagonal bisection of the 1d. was authorised by a P.O. notice dated 20 November 1861 to pay the ½d. rate for newspapers or book post. Specimens are only of value when on original envelope or wrapper. The authority was withdrawn as from 1 December 1872. Fakes are frequently met with. Other bisections were unauthorised.

The so-called "dollar variety" of the 1s. occurs once in each sheet of stamps in all shades and in later colours, etc, on the second stamp in the second row of the left upper pane. The prices quoted above are for the dull brown shade, the prices for the other shades being proportionate to their normal value.

All values except the 3d. are known imperf, mint only.

There are two types of watermark in the 3d. and 1s., one being short and squat and the other elongated.

8   9   10

1870–83. Wmk Crown CC.

(a) P 14.

7	8	½d. claret (29.10.72)	15·00	3·50
		a. *Deep claret* (1883)	17·00	5·50
		w. Wmk inverted	—	35·00
8	1	1d. blue (4.73)	65·00	75
		a. *Deep blue*	70·00	1·50
		w. Wmk inverted	£140	27·00
9	2	2d. rose (4.70)	70·00	70
		a. *Deep rose*	80·00	1·00
		w. Wmk inverted	95·00	27·00
10	3	3d. green (1.3.70)	95·00	8·50
		w. Wmk inverted	—	65·00
11	4	4d. brown-orange (1872)	£200	11·00
		a. *Red-orange* (1883)	£350	6·00
		w. Wmk inverted	—	55·00
12	5	6d. mauve (10.3.71)	70·00	5·50
		w. Wmk inverted	—	42·00
13	6	1s. dull brown (*to deep*) (23.2.73)	25·00	8·50
		a. "$" for "S" in "SHILLING" (A)	£1300	£600
		w. Wmk inverted	—	65·00

(b) P 12½.

14	9	2s. Venetian red (27.8.75)	40·00	19·00
		w. Wmk inverted	60·00	70·00
15	10	5s. lilac (27.8.75)	90·00	£140
		w. Wmk inverted	£120	£190
7/15		Set of 9	£600	£170

The ½d., 1d., 4d., 2s. and 5s. are known imperforate.

1883–97. Wmk Crown CA. P 14.

16	8	½d. yellow-green (2.85)	3·50	1·00
		a. *Green*	1·00	10
		w. Wmk inverted	—	27·00
		x. Wmk reversed	—	42·00
17	1	1d. blue (1884)	£325	4·50
18		1d. rose (*to deep*) (3.3.85)	65·00	85
		a. *Carmine* (1886)	40·00	60
		w. Wmk inverted	—	42·00
19	2	2d. rose (*to deep*) (17.3.84)	£200	4·00
		w. Wmk inverted	—	55·00
20		2d. grey (1885)	£110	4·00
		a. *Slate* (1886)	80·00	50
		w. Wmk inverted	—	28·00
21	3	3d. sage-green (11.86)	4·00	1·00
		a. *Pale olive-green*	2·50	1·25
22	4	4d. red-orange* (9.3.83)	£400	22·00
		aw. Wmk inverted		
		b. *Red-brown* (*shades*) (1885)	2·00	35
		bw. Wmk inverted	70·00	28·00
23	5	6d. deep yellow (4.10.90)	24·00	7·00
		a. *Orange-yellow*	4·00	3·50
24	6	1s. brown (*to deep*) (3.97)	5·00	6·00
		a. "$" for "S" in "SHILLING" (A)	£800	£500
		b. *Chocolate*	15·00	12·00
25	9	2s. Venetian red (2.97)	27·00	21·00
26	10	5s. lilac (2.97)	55·00	80·00
16/26		Set of 11	£650	£110
		16s, 18s, 20s/3s Optd "Specimen" Set of 6	£500	

*No. 22 is the same colour as No. 11a.

The 1d. carmine, 2d. slate, and 2s. are known imperf. All values to the 6d. inclusive are known perf 12. These are proofs.

TWO PENCE HALF-PENNY

11   (12)

1889 (8 Mar)–**91**. *Value tablet in second colour.* Wmk Crown CA. P 14.

27	11	1d. purple and mauve	4·25	20
		w. Wmk inverted	—	27·00
28		2d. green	20·00	3·50
		a. *Deep green* (*brown gum*)	7·50	6·00
		aw. Wmk inverted	—	70·00
29		2½d. dull purple and blue (25.2.91)	5·50	50
		w. Wmk inverted	—	75·00
27/9		Set of 3	16·00	3·75
		27s/9s Optd "Specimen" Set of 3	£110	

A very wide range of shades may be found in the 1d. The headplate was printed in many shades of purple, and the dutyplate in various shades of mauve and purple and also in carmine, etc. There are fewer shades for the other values and they are not so pronounced.

1890 (4 June)–**91**. *No. 22b surch with T* **12** *by C. Vendryes, Kingston.*

30	4	2½d. on 4d. red-brown	27·00	9·50
		a. Spacing between lines of surch 1½ mm (2.91)	32·00	17·00
		b. Surch double	£325	£225
		c. "PFNNY" for "PENNY"	75·00	65·00
		ca. Ditto and broken "K" for "Y"	£130	£110
		w. Wmk inverted	75·00	38·00

This provisional was issued pending receipt of No. 29 which is listed above for convenience of reference.

Three settings exist. (1) Ten varieties arranged in a single vertical row and repeated six times in the pane. (2) Twelve varieties, in two horizontal rows of six, repeated five times, alternate rows show 1 and 1½ mm spacing between lines of surcharge. (3) Three varieties, arranged horizontally and repeated twenty times. All these settings can be reconstructed by examination of the spacing and relative position of the words of the surcharge and of the broken letters, etc, which are numerous.

A variety reading "PFNNK", with the "K" unbroken, is a forgery. Surcharges misplaced either horizontally or vertically are met with, the normal position being central at the foot of the stamp with "HALF-PENNY" covering the old value.

13 Llandovery Falls, Jamaica (photo by Dr. J. Johnston)   **14** Arms of Jamaica

(Recess D.L.R.)

1900 (1 May)–**01**. Wmk Crown CC (sideways*). P 14.

31	13	1d. red	4·00	20
		w. Wmk Crown to left of CC	4·25	50
		x. Wmk reversed	—	42·00
		y. Wmk sideways inverted and reversed		
32		1d. slate-black and red (25.9.01)	3·50	20
		a. Blued paper	£110	£100
		b. Imperf between (vert pair)	£9000	
		w. Wmk Crown to left of CC	12·00	11·00
		x. Wmk reversed	—	42·00
		y. Wmk sideways inverted and reversed		
		31s/2s Optd "Specimen" Set of 2	£130	

*The normal sideways wmk shows Crown to right of CC, *as seen from the back of the stamp.*

Many shades exist of both centre and frame of the bi-coloured 1d. which was, of course, printed from two plates and the design shows minor differences from that of the 1d. red which was printed from a single plate.

(Typo D.L.R.)

1903 (16 Nov)–**04**. Wmk Crown CA. P 14.

33	14	½d. grey and dull green	1·50	30
		a. "SER.ET" for "SERVIET"	40·00	45·00
		w. Wmk inverted	30·00	30·00
34		1d. grey and carmine (24.2.04)	1·75	10
		a. "SER.ET" for "SERVIET"	32·00	35·00
35		2½d. grey and ultramarine	3·50	30
		a. "SER.ET" for "SERVIET"	60·00	75·00
36		5d. grey and yellow (1.3.04)	15·00	23·00
		a. "SER.ET" for "SERVIET"	£750	£950
		w. Wmk inverted	90·00	
33/6		Set of 4	20·00	23·00
		33s/6s Optd "Specimen" Set of 4	£130	

The "SER.ET" variety occurs on R. 4/2 of the left upper pane. It was corrected by De La Rue in July 1905.

The centres of the above and later bi-coloured stamps in the Arms type vary in colour from grey to grey-black.

15 Arms type redrawn   **16** Arms type redrawn

1905–11. Wmk Mult Crown CA. P 14.

(a) Arms types. Chalk-surfaced paper.

37	14	½d. grey and dull green (20.11.05)	4·50	20
		a. "SER.ET" for "SERVIET"	26·00	40·00
		w. Wmk inverted		
38	15	½d. yell-grn (*ordinary paper*) (8.11.06)	8·50	50
		aw. Wmk inverted	†	£110
		b. *Dull green*	3·75	20
		c. *Deep green*	4·50	20
39	14	1d. grey and carmine (20.11.05)	18·00	50
		w. Wmk inverted	—	90·00
40	16	1d. carmine (*ordinary paper*) (1.10.06)	1·50	10
		w. Wmk inverted	38·00	
41	14	2½d. grey and ultramarine (12.11.07)	3·00	4·25
42		2½d. pale ultramarine (*ordinary paper*) (21.9.10)	2·75	1·25
		a. *Deep ultramarine*	1·75	1·75
43		5d. grey and orange-yellow (24.4.07)	60·00	70·00
		a. "SER.ET" for "SERVIET"	£1000	£1200
44		6d. dull and bright purple (18.8.11)	13·00	12·00
45		5s. grey and violet (11.05)	45·00	40·00
37/45		Set of 9	£130	£110
		38s, 40s, 42s, 44s/5s Optd "Specimen" Set of 5	£160	

See note below No. 36 concerning grey centres.

(b) Queen Victoria types. Ordinary paper.

46	3	3d. olive-green (3.8.05)	6·00	3·75
		a. *Sage-green* (1907)	5·00	3·00
47		3d. purple/yellow (10.3.10)	4·50	3·50
		a. Chalk-surfaced paper. *Pale purple/yellow* (11.7.10)	2·00	1·50
		aw. Wmk inverted	45·00	48·00
48	4	4d. red-brown (6.6.08)	70·00	75·00
49		4d. black/yellow (chalk-surfaced paper) (21.9.10)	7·50	42·00
50		4d. red/yellow (3.10.11)	1·50	8·00
51	5	6d. dull orange (27.6.06)	15·00	25·00
		a. *Golden yellow* (9.09)	25·00	50·00

52		6d. lilac (19.11.09)............................	27·00	42·00
		a. Chalk-surfaced paper. *Purple* (7.10)..................................	10·00	19·00
53	**6**	1s. brown (11.06).................................	19·00	30·00
		a. *Deep brown*..................................	27·00	45·00
		b. "$" for "S" in "SHILLING" (A)...	£1300	£1400
54		1s. black/*green* (chalk-surfaced *paper*) (21.9.10).................	4·50	8·50
		a. "$" for "S" in "SHILLING" (A)...	£950	£1200
55	**9**	2s. Venetian red (11.08).................	£100	£150
56		2s. pur/*bl* (chalk-surfaced *paper*) (21.9.10).................................	6·50	3·50
46/56		Set of 11	£200	£325
47s, 49s, 50s, 52s, 54s/56s Optd "Specimen"				
		Set of 6		£190

No. 38 exists in coils constructed from normal sheets.

17   **18**

(T **17/18** typo D.L.R.)

1911 (3 Feb). Wmk Mult Crown CA. P 14.

57	**17**	2d. grey	3·25	13·00
		s. Optd "Specimen"	35·00	

1912–20. Wmk Mult Crown CA. *Chalk-surfaced paper (3d. to 5s.).* P 14.

58	**18**	1d. carmine-red (5.12.12)	1·50	10
		a. *Scarlet* (1916)	2·00	70
59		1½d. brown-orange (13.7.16)	1·00	60
		a. *Yellow-orange*	13·00	1·00
		b. Wmk sideways	†	£1500
60		2d. grey (2.8.12).............................	2·00	1·75
		a. *Slate-grey*	1·25	3·00
61		2½d. blue (13.2.13)............................	1·50	15
		a. *Deep bright blue*	65	1·00
62		3d. purple/*yellow* (6.3.12)...............	50	45
		a. *White back* (2.4.13)..................	55	40
		b. *On lemon* (25.9.16).................	3·75	1·50
		bs. Optd "Specimen"	32·00	
		w. Wmk inverted		
63		4d. black and red/*yellow* (4.4.13).....	50	3·50
		a. *White back* (7.5.14).................	75	4·00
		b. *On lemon* (1916).....................	23·00	19·00
		bs. Optd "Specimen"	32·00	
		c. *On pale yellow* (1919)	22·00	15·00
64		6d. dull and bright purple (14.11.12)	4·50	9·00
		a. *Dull purple and bright mauve* (1915)...	75	1·00
		b. *Dull purple & bright magenta* (1920)..	3·50	2·25
65		1s. black/*green* (2.8.12)...................	2·25	2·00
		a. *White back* (4.1.15)..................	1·00	4·75
		b. *On blue-green, olive back* (1920)...	2·25	5·50
66		2s. purple and bright blue/*blue* (10.1.19).....................................	13·00	25·00
67		5s. green and red/*yellow* (5.9.19)....	70·00	90·00
		a. *On pale yellow* (1920)	70·00	90·00
		b. *On orange-buff* (1920)..............	£130	£160
58/67		Set of 10	80·00	£110
58s/67s Optd "Specimen" Set of 10				£200

No. 58 exists in coils constructed from normal sheets.

The paper of No. 67 is a bright yellow and the gum rough and dull. No. 67*a* is on practically the normal creamy "pale yellow" paper, and the gum is smooth and shiny. The paper of No. 67*b* approaches the "coffee" colour of the true "orange-buff", and the colours of both head and frame are paler, the latter being of a carmine tone.

For the ½d. and 6d. with Script wmk see Nos. 89*a*/90.

RED CROSS LABELS. A voluntary organization, the Jamaica War Stamp League later the Jamaica Patriotic Stamp League, was founded in November 1915 by Mr. Lewis Ashenheim, a Kingston solicitor. The aims of the League were to support the British Red Cross, collect funds for the purchase of aircraft for the Royal Flying Corps and the relief of Polish Jews.

One fund-raising method used was the sale, from 1 December 1915, of ½d. charity labels. These labels, which were available from post offices, depicted a bi-plane above a cross and were printed in red by Dennison Manufacturing Company, Framingham, U.S.A., the stamps being perforated 12 except for those along the edges of the sheet which have one side imperforate.

From 22 December 1915 supplies of the labels were overprinted "JAMAICA" in red, the colour of this overprint being changed to black from 15 January 1916. Copies sold from 11 March 1916 carried an additional "Half-Penny" surcharge, also in black.

Such labels had no postal validity when used by the general public, but, by special order of the Governor, were accepted for the payment of postage on the League's official mail. To obtain this concession the envelopes had to be inscribed "Red Cross Business" or "Jamaica Patriotic Stamp League" and the labels used endorsed with Mr. Ashenheim's signature. Such covers are rare.

WAR	WAR	
WAR STAMP.	**STAMP.**	**STAMP.**
(19)	**(20)**	**(21)**

(T **19/21** optd Govt Printing Office, Kingston)

1916 (1 Apr–Sept). Optd with T **19**.

68	**15**	½d. yellow-green	10	35
		a. No stop after "STAMP" (R. 18/2)...	10·00	24·00
		b. Opt double	£110	£130
		c. Opt inverted	95·00	£120
		d. Space between "W" and "A" (R. 20/1)...	11·00	24·00
		e. *Blue-green*................................	10	60

---

		ea. No stop after "STAMP" (R. 3/11 or 11/1)...........................	11·00	24·00
		eb. Space between "W" and "A" (R. 20/1).....................................	15·00	30·00
		w. Wmk inverted		
69	**18**	3d. purple/*yellow* (white back)	15·00	29·00
		a. *On lemon* (6.16)..........................	1·00	17·00
		ab. No stop after "STAMP" (R. 8/6 or 9/6)...	24·00	80·00
		b. *On pale yellow* (9.16).................	10·00	26·00

Minor varieties: ½d. (i) Small "P"; (ii) "WARISTAMP" (raised quad between words); (iii) Two stops after "STAMP". 3d. "WARISTAMP". There were several settings of the overprint used for each value. Where two positions are quoted for a variety these did not occur on the same sheet.

NOTE. The above and succeeding stamps with "WAR STAMP" overprint were issued for payment of a special war tax on letters and postcards or on parcels. Ordinary unoverprinted stamps could also be used for this purpose.

1916 (Sept–Dec). Optd with T **20**.

70	**15**	½d. blue-green (*shades*) (2.10.16)....	10	30
		a. No stop after "STAMP" (R. 5/7)..	11·00	32·00
		b. Opt omitted (in pair with normal).......................................	£3750	£3500
		c. "R" inserted by hand (R. 1/10) .	£1200	£1000
		w. Wmk inverted	40·00	
71	**18**	1½d. orange (1.9.16)..........................	10	15
		aa. Wmk sideways	†	£1700
		a. No stop after "STAMP" (R. 4/12, 8/6, 10/10, 11/1, 18/12, 19/12).............................	5·00	7·50
		b. "S" in "STAMP" omitted (R. 6/12) (Dec)............................	£130	£140
		c. "S" inserted by hand..................	£350	
		d. "R" in "WAR" omitted (R. 1/10)..	£1800	£1700
		e. "R" inserted by hand	£950	£850
		f. Inverted "d" for "P"....................	£200	£160
		w. Wmk inverted	16·00	16·00
72		3d. purple/*lemon* (2.10.16)...............	2·00	1·00
		aa. Opt inverted	£300	
		a. No stop after "STAMP" (R. 5/7)..	32·00	55·00
		b. "S" in "STAMP" omitted (R. 6/12) (Dec)............................	£500	£500
		c. "S" inserted by hand..................	£200	£200
		e. *On yellow* (12.16).......................	7·50	9·00
		ea. "S" in "STAMP" omitted (R. 6/12)..	£700	£700
		eb. "S" inserted by hand.................	£425	£375

Nos. 70c, 71c, 71e, 72c and 72eb show the missing "R" or "S" inserted by handstamp. The 3d. is known with this "S" handstamp inverted or double.

Minor varieties, such as raised quads, small stop, double stop, spaced letters and letters of different sizes, also exist in this overprint. The setting was altered several times.

1917 (March). Optd with T **21**.

73	**15**	½d. blue-green (*shades*) (25.3.17)....	50	30
		a. No stop after "STAMP" (R. 2/5, 8/11, 8/12)	9·00	22·00
		b. Stop inserted and "P" impressed a second time (R. 7/6)..	£250	
		c. Optd on back only	£180	
		d. Opt inverted	15·00	38·00
74	**18**	1½d. orange (3.3.17)..........................	20	10
		aa. Wmk sideways	†	£1500
		a. No stop after "STAMP" (R. 2/5, 8/11, 8/12)	3·00	18·00
		b. Stop inserted and "P" impressed a second time (R. 7/6)..	£250	
		c. Opt double	80·00	85·00
		d. Opt inverted	80·00	75·00
		e. "WAP STAMP" (R. 6/2).............		
		w. Wmk inverted	16·00	21·00
75		3d. purple/*yellow* (3.3.17)...............	50	1·40
		a. No stop after "STAMP" (R. 2/5, 8/11, 8/12)	16·00	38·00
		b. Stop inserted and "P" impressed a second time (R. 7/6)..	£225	
		c. Opt inverted	£140	
		d. Opt sideways (reading up)........	£350	
		da. Opt omitted (in horiz pair with No. 75d)............................	£2750	

No. 75da shows the left-hand stamp as No. 75d and the right-hand stamp without overprint.

There are numerous minor varieties in this overprint with the setting being altered several times.

WAR STAMP
(22)

1919 (4 Oct)–**20**. Optd with T **22** in red by D.L.R.

76	**15**	½d. green..	20	15
77	**18**	3d. purple/*yellow*.............................	5·00	3·00
		a. *Pale purple/buff* (3.1.20)	3·50	1·25
		b. *Deep purple/buff* (1920)	8·00	6·00
76s/7s Optd "Specimen" Set of 2				70·00

We list the most distinct variations in the 3d. The buff tone of the paper varies considerably in depth.

23 Jamaica Exhibition, 1891   **24** Arawak Woman preparing Cassava

---

25 War Contingent embarking, 1915   **26** King's House, Spanish Town

Re-entry. Nos. 80a, 93a

The greater part of the design is re-entered, the hull showing in very solid colour and the people appear very blurred. There are also minor re-entries on stamps above (R. 7/4 and 6/4).

27 Return of War Contingent, 1919   A   B

28 Landing of Columbus, 1494   **29** Cathedral, Spanish Town

34

(Typo (½d., 1d.), recess (others) D.L.R.)

1919–21. T **23/29**, **34** and similar vert designs. Wmk Mult Crown CA (sideways* on 1d., 1½d. and 10s.). *Chalk-surfaced paper (½d., 1d.).* P 14.

78	**23**	½d. green and olive-green (12.11.20).................................	1·00	1·00
		w. Wmk inverted		
		x. Wmk reversed		
		y. Wmk inverted and reversed.......		
79	**24**	1d. carmine and orange (3.10.21)...	1·75	1·75
		w. Wmk Crown to left of CA........		
80	**25**	1½d. green (*shades*) (4.7.19).............	40	1·00
		a. Major re-entry (R. 8/4)	70·00	
		b. "C" of "CA" missing from wmk...	†	£250
		c. "A" of "CA" missing from wmk...	£375	
		w. Wmk Crown to left of CA........	21·00	
		y. Wmk sideways inverted and reversed......................................	—	40·00
81	**26**	2d. indigo and green (18.2.21)	1·00	4·00
		w. Wmk inverted	35·00	
		y. Wmk inverted and reversed.......	38·00	
82	**27**	2½d. deep blue and blue (A) (18.2.21).....................................	13·00	3·00
		a. *Blue-black and deep blue*	1·50	1·75
		b. "C" of "CA" missing from wmk...	£250	£200
		c. "A" of "CA" missing from wmk...	£200	
		w. Wmk inverted	32·00	
		x. Wmk reversed	32·00	
83	**28**	3d. myrtle-green and blue (8.4.21)..	1·50	2·50
		w. Wmk inverted	32·00	35·00
		x. Wmk reversed	†	£100
84	**29**	4d. brown and deep green (21.1.21)	2·50	9·00
		w. Wmk inverted		
		x. Wmk reversed		
85	**—**	1s. orange-yell & red-orge (10.12.20)...................................	3·75	5·50
		a. Frame inverted	£29000	£22000

	b. "C" of "CA" missing from wmk.		£450	
	c. "A" of "CA" missing from wmk.		£475	
	w. Wmk inverted		—	
	x. Wmk reversed		—	
86	—	2s. light blue and brown (10.12.20)	13·00	26·00
	"C" of "CA" missing from wmk.		£600	
	c. "A" of "CA" missing from wmk.			
	w. Wmk inverted		35·00	42·00
	x. Wmk reversed		—	
	y. Wmk inverted and reversed			
87	—	3s. violet-blue and orange (10.12.20)	20·00	90·00
88	—	5s. blue and yellow-orange (15.4.21)	55·00	80·00
	a. Blue and pale dull orange		48·00	75·00
	w. Wmk inverted		—	
	x. Wmk reversed		—	
89	—	10s. myrtle-green (6.5.20)	75·00	£150
78/89 Set of 12			£150	£325
78s/89s Optd "Specimen" Set of 12			£250	

Designs: Vert—1s. Statue of Queen Victoria, Kingston; 2s. Admiral Rodney Memorial Spanish Town; 3s. Sir Charles Metcalfe Statue, Kingston; 5s. Jamaican scenery.

*The normal sideways wmk on Nos. 79/80 shows Crown to right of CA, as seen from the back of the stamp.

The 2½d. of the above series showed the Union Jack at left, incorrectly, as indicated in illustration A. In the issue on paper with Script wmk the design was corrected (Illustration B).

An example of No. 80 has been reported with the "A" inverted to the left of and above its normal position.

The "C" omitted variety has been reported on an example of No. 88 overprinted "Specimen".

A 6d. stamp showing the reading of the Declaration of Freedom from Slavery in 1836 was prepared and sent out in April 1921, but for political reasons was not issued and the stock was destroyed. Copies overprinted "Specimen" are known on both the Mult CA and Script CA papers, and are worth £700 each. The Mult CA "Specimen" exists with watermark reversed (Price, £900). Price without "Specimen" on Script CA £27000.

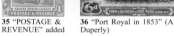

"Bow" flaw (R.18/12)

1921 (21 Oct)–**27.** Wmk Mult Script CA. Chalk-surfaced paper (6d.). P 14.

89a	18	½d. green (3.11.27)	1·75	10
	ab. Bow flaw	50·00	25·00
	as. Optd "Specimen"	45·00	
90		6d. dull purple and bright magenta	9·50	4·00
	s. Optd "Specimen"	40·00	

35 "POSTAGE & REVENUE" added   **36** "Port Royal in 1853" (A. Duperly)

(Printing as before; the 6d. recess-printed)

1921–29. As Nos. 78/89. Wmk Mult Script CA (sideways* on 1d. and 1½d.). Chalk-surfaced paper (½d., 1d.). P 14.

91	23	½d. green and olive-green (5.2.22)	50	50
	a. Green and deep olive-green	30	50
	w. Wmk inverted	30·00	30·00
92	35	1d. carmine and orange (5.12.21)	1·50	10
	w. Wmk Crown to right of CA	16·00	16·00
	x. Wmk reversed	—	45·00
93	25	1½d. green (shades) (2.2.21)	1·25	45
	a. Major re-entry (R. 8/4)	70·00	
	w. Wmk Crown to left of CA	—	22·00
	x. Wmk reversed	24·00	24·00
	y. Wmk sideways inverted and reversed	—	48·00
94	26	2d. indigo and green (4.11.21)	6·50	80
	a. Indigo and grey-green (1925)	9·00	1·00
	w. Wmk inverted	†	—
95	27	2½d. deep blue and blue (B) (4.11.21)	5·50	1·75
	a. Dull blue and blue (B)	6·00	60
	w. Wmk inverted	28·00	28·00
	x. Wmk reversed	—	
	y. Wmk inverted and reversed		
96	28	3d. myrtle-green and blue (6.3.22)	2·50	70
	a. Green and pale blue	1·25	15
	w. Wmk inverted	—	
	x. Wmk reversed	—	
97	29	4d. brown and deep green (5.12.21)	1·00	30
	a. Chocolate and dull green	1·00	30
	w. Wmk inverted	30·00	
	x. Wmk reversed	40·00	
98	36	6d. black and blue (5.12.22)	12·00	2·00
	a. Grey and dull blue	12·00	1·50
99	—	1s. orange and red-orange (4.11.21)	1·75	80
	a. Orange-yellow and brown-orange	1·75	65
	w. Wmk inverted	—	
	x. Wmk reversed	—	£120
100	—	2s. light blue and brown (5.2.22)	3·25	65
	w. Wmk inverted	30·00	30·00
101	—	3s. violet-blue and orange (23.8.21)	11·00	9·00
102	—	5s. blue and yellow-brown (8.11.23)	28·00	25·00

	a. Blue and pale dull orange	60·00	70·00
	b. Blue and yellow-orange (1927)	26·00	23·00
	c. Blue and pale bistre-brown (1929)	27·00	22·00
	w. Wmk inverted	—	£160
	x. Wmk reversed		
103	34	10s. myrtle-green (3.22)	50·00	70·00
91/103 Set of 13			£110	95·00
91s/103s Optd "Specimen" Set of 13			£250	

*The normal sideways wmk shows Crown to left of CA on No. 92 or Crown to right of CA on No. 93, both as seen from the back of the stamp.

The frame of No. 102a is the same colour as that of No. 88a.

The designs of all values of the pictorial series, with the exception of the 5s. and 10s. (which originated with the Governor, Sir Leslie Probyn), were selected by Mr. F. C. Cundall, F.S.A. The 1d. and 5s. were drawn by Miss Cundall, the 3d. by Mrs. Cundall, and the 10s. by De La Rue & Co. The 6d. is from a lithograph. The other designs are from photographs, the frames of all being the work of Miss Cundall and Miss Wood.

    37   **38**

    39

(Centres from photos by Miss V. F. Taylor. Frames des F. C. Cundall, F.S.A., and drawn by Miss Cundall. Recess B.W.)

1923 (1 Nov). Child Welfare. Wmk Mult Script CA. P 12.

104	37	½d.+½d. black and green	60	5·50
105	38	1d.+½d. black and scarlet	1·75	10·00
106	39	2½d.+½d. black and blue	8·50	18·00
104/6 Set of 3			9·50	30·00
104s/6s Optd "Specimen" Set of 3			£120	

Sold at a premium of ½d. for the Child Welfare League, these stamps were on sale annually from 1 November to 31 January, until 31 January 1927, when their sale ceased, the remainders being destroyed on 21 February 1927.

40   **41**   **42**

Die I   Die II

(Recess D.L.R.)

1929–32. Wmk Mult Script CA. P 14.

108	40	1d. scarlet (Die I) (15.3.29)	3·50	20
	a. Die II (1932)	6·00	10
109	41	1½d. chocolate (18.1.29)	2·50	15
110	42	9d. maroon (5.3.29)	3·75	1·00
108/10 Set of 3			8·75	1·10
108s/10s Optd "Specimen" Set of 3			80·00	

In Die I the shading below JAMAICA is formed of thickened parallel lines, and in Die II of diagonal cross-hatching.

43 Coco Palms at Don Christopher's Cove   **44** Wag Water River, St. Andrew

45 Priestman's River, Portland

(Dies eng and recess Waterlow)

1932. Wmk Mult Script CA (sideways on 2d. and 2½d.). P 12½.

111	43	2d. black and green (4.11.32)	18·00	2·75
	a. Imperf between (vert pair)	£6000	
112	44	2½d. turquoise-blue & ultram (5.3.32)	4·25	1·50

	a. Imperf between (vert pair)	£13000	£13000
113	45	6d. grey-black and purple (4.2.32)	17·00	2·00
111/13 Set of 3			35·00	5·50
111s/13s Perf "Specimen" Set of 3			85·00	

1935 (6 May). Silver Jubilee. As Nos. 91/4 of Antigua, but ptd by B.W. P 11×12.

114		1d. deep blue and scarlet	50	15
	b. Short extra flagstaff	£950	
	d. Flagstaff on right-hand turret	95·00	
	e. Double flagstaff	95·00	
115		1½d. ultramarine and grey-black	60	1·50
	a. Extra flagstaff	80·00	£110
	b. Short extra flagstaff	95·00	£120
	c. Lightning conductor	85·00	
116		6d. green and indigo	6·50	17·00
	a. Extra flagstaff	£180	£225
	b. Short extra flagstaff	£225	
	c. Lightning conductor	£170	
117		1s. slate and purple	5·00	9·50
	a. Extra flagstaff	£250	£300
	b. Short extra flagstaff	£325	
	c. Lightning conductor	£200	
114/17 Set of 4			11·50	25·00
114s/17s Perf "Specimen" Set of 4			95·00	

For illustrations of plate varieties see Omnibus section following Zanzibar.

1937 (12 May). Coronation. As Nos. 95/7 of Antigua, but printed by D.L.R. P 14.

118		1d. scarlet	30	15
119		1½d. grey-black	65	30
120		2½d. bright blue	1·00	70
118/20 Set of 3			1·75	1·00
118s/20s Perf "Specimen" Set of 3			75·00	

48 King George VI   **49** Coco Palms at Don Christopher's Cove

50 Bananas

51 Citrus Grove   **52** Kingston Harbour

53 Sugar Industry   **54** Bamboo Walk

55 King George VI   **56** Tobacco Growing and Cigar Making

Repaired chimney (Centre plate 1 R. 11/1)

(Recess D.L.R. (T **48**, 5s. and 10s.), Waterlow (others))

1938 (10 Oct)–**52.** T **48/56** and as Nos. 88, 112/13, but with inset portrait of King George VI, as in T **49**. Wmk Mult Script CA. P 13½×14 (½d., 1d., 1½d., 5s.), 14 (5s., 10s.) or 12½ (others).

121	48	½d. blue-green (10.10.38)	1·75	10
	a. Wmk sideways	†	£4500
121b		½d. orange (25.10.51)	1·00	30
122		1d. scarlet	1·25	10

122a		1d. blue-green (25.10.51)	1·50	10
123		1½d. brown	1·25	10
124	49	2d. grey and green (10.12.38)	1·25	80
		a. Perf 13×13½ (1939)	2·75	50
		ab. "C" of "CA" missing from wmk	£1100	
		b. Perf 12½×13 (1951)	1·25	10
125	44	2½d. greenish blue & ultram (10.12.38)	3·00	1·75
126	50	3d. ultramarine and green (10.12.38)	75	1·50
		a. "A" of "CA" missing from wmk	£1100	
126b		3d. greenish blue and ultram (15.8.49)	1·50	1·25
126c		3d. green and scarlet (1.7.52)	3·00	30
127	51	4d. brown and green (10.12.38)	50	10
128	45	6d. grey and purple (10.12.38)	5·00	30
		a. Perf 13½×13 (10.10.50)	2·25	10
129	52	9d. lake (10.12.38)	50	50
		a. "A" of "CA" missing from wmk		
130	53	1s. green and purple-brown (10.12.38)	6·00	20
		a. Repaired chimney	£500	£100
131	54	2s. blue and chocolate (10.12.38)	23·00	1·00
132	—	5s. slate-blue & yellow-orge (10.12.38)	14·00	3·75
		a. Perf 14, line (1941)	£4000	£190
		b. Perf 14 (24.10.49)	7·00	3·00
		ba. Blue and orange (10.10.50)	7·50	3·00
133	55	10s. myrtle-green (10.12.38)	11·00	9·00
		aa. Perf 13 (10.10.50)	11·00	7·00
133a	56	£1 chocolate and violet (15.8.49)	32·00	27·00
121/33a		Set of 18	90·00	40·00
121s/33s		Perf "Specimen" Set of 13	£275	

No. 130a occurred in conjunction with Frame plate 2 on printings between 1942 and 1951.

No. 132a shows the emergency use of a line perforation machine, giving an irregular gauge of 14–14.15, after the De La Rue works were damaged in December 1940. The normal comb measures 13.8×13.7.

Nos. 121 and 122 exist in coils constructed from normal sheets.

SELF-GOVERNMENT

57 Courthouse, Falmouth **58** King Charles II and King George VI

59 Institute of Jamaica

(Recess Waterlow)

1945 (20 Aug)–**46**. *New Constitution. T* **57/9** *and similar designs.* Wmk Mult Script CA. P 12½.

134	57	1½d. sepia	20	30
		a. Perf 12½×13 (1946)	5·00	50
135	58	2d. green	11·00	90
		a. Perf 12½×13 (1945)	30	50
136	59	3d. ultramarine	20	50
		a. Perf 13 (1946)	2·50	2·75
137	—	4½d. slate	30	30
		a. Perf 13 (1946)	2·50	2·50
138	—	2s. red-brown	30	50
139	—	5s. indigo	1·25	1·00
140	59	10s. green	1·00	2·25
134/40		Set of 7	3·25	4·75
134s/40s		Perf "Specimen" Set of 7	£150	

Designs: *Vert* (as *T* 57)—2s. "Labour and Learning". *Horiz* (as *T* 59)—4½d. House of Assembly; 5s. Scroll, flag and King George VI.

1946 (14 Oct). *Victory. As Nos.* 110/11 *of Antigua.* P 13½×14.

141		1½d. purple-brown	2·50	10
		a. Perf 13½	30	2·50
142		3d. blue	3·50	2·50
		a. Perf 13½	30	4·75
141s/2s		Perf "Specimen" Set of 2	65·00	

1948 (1 Dec). *Royal Silver Wedding. As Nos.* 112/13 *of Antigua.*

143		1½d. red-brown (P 14×15)	30	10
144		£1 scarlet (P 11½×11)	25·00	55·00

1949 (10 Oct). *75th Anniv of Universal Postal Union. As Nos.* 114/17 *of Antigua.*

145		1½d. red-brown (P 13½–14)	20	15
146		2d. deep blue-green (P 11×11½)	1·25	3·25
147		3d. deep blue (P 11×11½)	35	1·25
148		6d. purple (P 13½–14)	40	2·50
145/8		Set of 4	2·00	6·50

(Recess Waterlow)

1951 (16 Feb). *Inauguration of B.W.I. University College. As Nos.* 118/19 *of Antigua.* P 14×14½.

149		2d. black and red-brown	30	50
150		6d. grey-black and purple	35	30

---

69 Scout Badge and Map of Caribbean **70** Scout Badge and Map of Jamaica

(Litho B.W.)

1952 (5 Mar). *First Caribbean Scout Jamboree.* Wmk Mult Script CA. P 13½×13 (2d.) or 13×13½ (6d.).

151	69	2d. blue, apple-green and black	15	10
152	70	6d. yellow-green, carmine-red and black	40	50

STAMP BOOKLETS

1912. *Black on red covers. Stapled.*

SB1	2s. booklet containing twenty-four 1d. (No. 40) in blocks of 6 (9 Mar)	
SB2	2s. booklet containing twelve ½d. and eighteen 1d. (Nos. 38, 58), each in blocks of 6 (5 Dec)	£1300

1923 (Dec). *Black on red cover. Stapled.*

SB3	2s. booklet containing twelve ½d. (No. 91) in blocks of 4 and eighteen 1d. (No. 92) in blocks of 6	£850

1928. *Black on red cover. Stapled.*

SB4	2s. booklet containing twelve ½d. and eighteen 1d. (No. 89a, 92) in blocks of 6	£1500

1928 (5 Sept). *Black on red cover. Stapled.*

SB5	1s.6d. booklet containing twelve ½d. and 1d. (Nos. 89a, 92), each in blocks of 6	

1929 (July)–**32**. *Black on red cover. Stapled.*

SB6	2s. booklet containing six ½d., twelve 1d. and six 1½d. (Nos. 89a, 108/9) in blocks of 6	£1100
	a. With 1d. Die II (No. 108a) (1932)	

1930–33. *Black on red cover. Stapled.*

SB7	2s. booklet containing twelve ½d. and eighteen 1d. (Nos. 89a, 108), each in blocks of 6	£850
	a. With 1d. Die II (No. 108a) (1933)	£850
	b. Black on blue cover (1933)	£1500

1935. *Silver Jubilee. Black on pink cover. Stapled.*

SB8	2s. booklet containing twenty-four 1d. (No. 114) in blocks of 6	£1400
	a. In blocks of 4	£2000

1938–40. *Black on green cover inscr "JAMAICA POSTAGE STAMPS" in one line. Inland Postage Rates on interleaf. Stapled.*

SB9	2s. booklet containing twelve ½d. and eighteen 1d. (Nos. 121/2), each in blocks of 6 (inland letter rate 1d. per oz)	£425
	a. Inland letter rate 1½d. for first 2 oz (1940)	£500

1942–47. *Black on blue cover inscr "JAMAICA POSTAGE STAMPS" in three lines. Inland Postage Rates on inside front cover. Stapled.*

SB10	2s. booklet containing twelve ½d. and eighteen 1d. (Nos. 121/2), each in blocks of 6 (Inland letter rate 1½d. for first 2 oz)	£225
	a. Black on yellow cover (1947)	£110

1946. *New Constitution. Black on blue cover. Stapled.*

SB12	2s. booklet containing sixteen 1½d. (No. 134a) in blocks of 4	£225

1952. *Black on yellow cover. Stapled.*

SB13	2s. booklet containing twelve ½d and eighteen 1d. (Nos. 121b, 122a), each in blocks of 6	25·00

POSTAL FISCALS

Revenue stamps were authorised for postal use by Post Office notice of 12 October 1887.

F 1

(Typo D.L.R.)

1865–73. P 14.

(a) Wmk Pineapple (T **7**).

F1	F **1**	1d. rose (1865)	75·00	95·00
		a. Imperf (pair)	£500	

(b) Wmk Crown CC.

F2	F **1**	1d. rose (1871)	55·00	55·00

(c) Wmk CA over Crown (Type w **7** sideways, covering two stamps).

F 2 **F 3**

(Typo D.L.R.)

1855–74. *(Issued). Glazed paper.* P 14.

(a) No wmk.

F4	F **2**	1½d. blue/*blue* (1857)	55·00	48·00
		a. Imperf (1855)		
		b. *Blue on white*	60·00	60·00
F5		3d. purple/*blue* (1857)	55·00	55·00
		a. Imperf (1855)		
		b. *Purple on lilac* (1857)	55·00	55·00
		ba. Imperf (1855)		
		c. *Purple on white* (1857)	65·00	55·00

(b) Wmk Crown CC.

F6	F **2**	3d. purple/*lilac* (1874)	18·00	19·00

All the above stamps *imperf* are exceedingly rare postally used.

1858 (1 Jan). *(Issued).* Wmk P 15½×15.

F7	F **3**	1s. rose/*bluish*	80·00	85·00
F8		5s. lilac/*bluish*	£375	£425
F9		10s. green/*bluish*	£450	£500

Telegraph stamps were also used postally, but no authority was given for such use.

OFFICIAL STAMPS

OFFICIAL **OFFICIAL**
(O 1) (O 2)

1890 (1 Apr)–**91**. *No.* 16a *optd with Type* O **1** *by C. Vendryes, Kingston.*

(a) "OFFICIAL" 17 to 17½ mm long.

O1	8	½d. green	11·00	1·75
		a. "O" omitted	£600	
		b. One "I" omitted		
		c. Both "I"s omitted	£650	£650
		d. "L" omitted	£700	£700
		e. Opt inverted	80·00	85·00
		f. Opt double	80·00	85·00
		g. Opt double, one inverted	£400	£400
		h. Opt double, one vertical	£650	
		j. Pair, overprints tête-bêche		

(b) "OFFICIAL" 15 to 16 mm long.

O2	8	½d. green (3.91)	28·00	25·00
		a. Opt double	£600	

There were five settings of the locally-overprinted Officials. No. O1 occurred from settings I (2×10), II (3×6), IV and V (horizontal row of 6 each). No. O2 came from setting III (2×6). There were numerous minor varieties, due to broken type, etc. (*e.g.* a broken "E" used for "F").

Stamps with the 17–17½ mm opt were reissued in 1894 during a temporary shortage of No. O3.

1890 (1 Apr)–**91**. *Optd with Type* O **2** *by D.L.R.* Wmk Crown CA. P 14.

O3	8	½d. green (1891)	10·00	1·25
O4	11	1d. rose	5·50	1·25
O5		2d. grey	13·00	1·25
O3/5		Set of 3	26·00	3·50
O3s/5s		Optd "Specimen" Set of 3	£110	

Nos. O4/5 were not issued without overprint.

The use of Official stamps ceased from 1 January 1898.

Kenya, Uganda and Tanganyika

BRITISH EAST AFRICA

The area which became British East Africa had been part of the domain of the Zanzibari Sultans since 1794. In 1887 the administration of the province was granted to the British East Africa Association, incorporated as the Imperial British East Africa Company the following year.

Company post offices were established at Lamu and Mombasa in May 1890, British mails having previously been sent via the Indian post office on Zanzibar, opened in 1875.

A German postal agency opened at Lamu on 22 November 1888 and continued to operate until 31 March 1891, using German stamps. These can be identified by the "LAMU/OSTAFRIKA" cancellations and are listed under German East Africa in our Part 7 (*Germany*) catalogue.

PRICES FOR STAMPS ON COVER	
Nos. 1/3	*from* × 10
Nos. 4/19	*from* × 30
Nos. 20/6	*from* × 3
Nos. 27/8	*from* × 8
Nos. 29/30	*from* × 20
No. 31	*from* × 10
No. 32	—
Nos. 33/47	*from* × 10
No. 48	*from* × 15

(Currency. 16 annas = 1 rupee)

BRITISH EAST AFRICA COMPANY ADMINISTRATION

BRITISH EAST AFRICA COMPANY

BRITISH EAST AFRICA COMPANY

HALF ANNA
(1)

1 ANNA
(2)

(Surch D.L.R.)

1890 (23 May). *Stamps of Great Britain (Queen Victoria) surch as T* **1** *or T* **2** *(1a. and 4a.).*

1	½a. on 1d. deep purple (No. 173).........	£275	£200
2	1a. on 2d. grey-green and carmine (No. 200)	£475	£275
3	4a. on 5d. dull purple and blue (No. 207a)........	£500	£300

A copy of the ½a. with the short crossbar of "F" in "HALF" omitted exists in the Royal Collection but is the only known example.

The second stamp of each horizontal row of the 4a. on 5d. had the "BRITISH" shifted to the left, placing the "B" directly over the "S" of "EAST". In the normal overprint the "B" is over "ST" as shown in Type (**2**).

Following the exhaustion of stocks of Nos. 1/3, stamps of India were used at Mombasa (and occasionally at Lamu) from late July 1890 until the arrival of Nos. 4/19. The following listing is for stamps clearly cancelled with the MOMBASA 21 mm circular date stamp (code "C"). Examples with LAMU circular date stamp are worth much more. Indian stamps used after October 1890, including other values, came from ship mail.

Stamps of INDIA 1882–90 (Nos. 84/101) cancelled at Mombasa between July and October 1890.

Z1	½a. blue-green	£500
Z2	1a. brown-purple	£450
Z3	1a.6p. sepia	£750
Z4	2a. blue..	£850
Z5	3a. orange	£850
Z6	4a.6p. yellow-green	£275
Z7	8a. dull mauve	£450
Z8	1r. slate	£850

3

4

5 ANNAS.
(5)

(Litho B.W.)

1890 (14 Oct)–95. P 14.

4	3	½a. dull brown	3·75	7·00
		a. Imperf (pair)............................	£1400	£600
		b. Deep brown (21.10.93)............	70	5·50
		ba. Imperf (pair)...........................	£900	£375
		bb. Imperf between (horiz pair)......	£1600	£650
		bc. Imperf between (vert pair)........	£1000	£500
		c. Pale brown (16.1.95)................	1·00	10·00
5		1a. blue-green	5·50	7·00
		aa. "ANL" (broken "D") (R. 6/5) ...	£750	£750
		ab. Ditto. "ANL" (broken "D") (R. 6/5)...............................	£14000	
		b. Deep blue-green (16.1.95)........	75	
		ba. Imperf (pair)		
6		2a. vermilion.............................	2·75	4·25
		a. Imperf (pair)............................	£2000	£750
7		2½a. black/*yellow-buff* (9.91).......	95·00	26·00
		a. Imperf between (horiz pair).......	£4750	
		b. Black/*pale buff* (9.92).............	£100	5·00
		c. Black/*bright yellow* (21.10.93)..	4·50	5·00
		cb. Imperf (pair)...........................	£1000	£400
		cc. Imperf between (horiz pair).......	£1400	£450
		cd. Imperf between (vert pair)........	£1400	£600
8		3a. black/*dull red* (30.3.91).........	14·00	15·00
		a. Black/*bright red* (21.10.93)	2·00	7·50
		ab. Imperf (pair)..........................	£950	£400
		ac. Imperf between (horiz pair).......	£900	£425
		ad. Imperf between (vert pair)........	£700	£375
9		4a. yellow-brown	2·50	7·50
		a. Imperf (pair)............................	£2250	£1000
10		4a. grey (*imperf*)	£1200	£1400
11		4½a. dull violet (30.3.91).............	35·00	15·00
		a. Brown-purple (21.10.93)	2·50	17·00
		ab. Imperf (pair)..........................	£1600	£450
		ac. Imperf between (horiz pair).......	£1400	£950
		ad. Imperf between (vert pair)........	£1000	£500
12		8a. blue......................................	5·50	9·50
		a. Imperf (pair)............................	£4500	£900
13		8a. grey	£275	£225
14		1r. carmine	6·00	9·00
		a. Imperf (pair)............................	£12000	£1000
15		1r. grey-green	£225	£225
16	4	2r. brick-red..............................	14·00	32·00
17		3r. slate-purple	9·50	48·00
18		4r. ultramarine	12·00	48·00
19		5r. grey-green	30·00	70·00
4/9, 11/19	*Set of 15*	£500	£500

For the 5a. and 7½a. see Nos. 29/30.
The dates quoted for these stamps are of the earliest recorded use

---

of the various consignments based on known shipping movements. It is possible that the initial supply may have been placed on sale before 14 October 1890, as an example of the ½a. exists postmarked on 13 October, at Mombasa.

The paper of Nos. 7, 7b, 7c, 8 and 8a is coloured on the surface only.

Printings of 1890/92 are on thin paper having the outer margins of the sheets imperf and bearing sheet watermark "PURE LINEN WOVE BANK" and "W. C. S. & Co." in a monogram, the trademark of the makers, Messrs. William Collins, Sons & Co.

1893/94 printings are on thicker coarser paper with outer margins perforated through the selvedge and without watermark. Single specimens cannot always be distinguished by lack of watermark alone. Exceptions are the 1893 printings of the 2½a. and 3a. which were on Wiggins Teape paper showing a sheet watermark of "1011" in figures 1 centimetre high.

Nos. 7 (coloured through) and 16/19 on thick unwatermarked paper are from a special printing made for presentation purposes.

The printings of the 4a., 8a. and 1r. values in grey were intended for fiscal purposes, but in the event, were made available for postal use.

Forgeries of the 4a., 8a., 1r. grey and 2 to 5r. exist. The latter are common and can be distinguished by the scroll above "LIGHT" where there are five vertical lines of shading in the forgeries and seven in the genuine stamps. Forged cancellations exist on the commoner stamps. Beware of "imperf" stamps made by trimming margins of stamps from marginal rows.

1891. *Mombasa Provisionals.*

(a) New value handstamped in dull violet, with original face value obliterated and initials added in black manuscript.

20	3	"½ Anna" on 2a. verm ("A.D.") (January)	£5500	£850
		a. "½ Anna" double	†	£7000
		b. Original face value not obliterated	†	£2000
21		"1 Anna" on 4a. brn ("A.B.") (February).	£9500	£1900

(b) Manuscript value and initials in black.

22	3	"½ Anna" on 2a. verm ("A.D.") (original face value not obliterated) (January)...............................	†	£2500
		a. Error. "½ Annas" ("A. D.")................................		
23		"½ Anna" on 2a. vermilion ("A.B.") (February)	£5000	£850
		a. Error. "½ Annas" ("A. B.")....................................	†	£1000
24		"½ Anna" on 3a. black/*dull red* ("A.B.") (May).....................	£8000	£2000
25		"1 Anna" on 3a. black/*dull red* ("V.H.M.") (June)...................	£8000	£1200
26		"1 Anna" on 4a. brown ("A.B.") (March).	£4750	£1500

A.D. = Andrew Dick, Chief Accountant.
A.B. = Archibald Brown, Cashier of the Company.
V.H.M. = Victor H. Mackenzie, Bank Manager.

(Surch B.W.)

1894 (1 Nov). *Surch as T* **5**.

27	3	5a. on 8a. blue.........................	70·00	85·00
28		7½a. on 1r. carmine.............................	70·00	85·00
27s/8s	Handstamped "Specimen" *Set of 2*	90·00	

Forgeries exist.

1895 (16 Jan). No wmk. P 14.

29	3	5a. black/*grey-blue*.....................	1·25	10·00
30		7½a. black....................................	1·25	16·00
29s/30s	Handstamped "Specimen" *Set of 2*	75·00	

The date quoted is that of earliest known use of stamps from this consignment.

These two stamps have "LD" after "COMPANY" in the inscription. The paper of No. 29 is coloured on the surface only.

1895 (Feb). *No.* **8** *surch with manuscript value and initials ("T.E.C.R."). Original face value obliterated in manuscript.*

31	3	"½ anna" on 3a. black/*dull red* (19.2)........	£425	50·00
32		"1 anna" on 3a. black/*dull red* (22.2)	£5500	£2500

T.E.C.R. = T.E.C. Remington, Postmaster at Mombasa.
Similar manuscript surcharges on the black/*bright red* shade (No. 8a) are believed to be forgeries.

The Company experienced considerable financial problems during 1894 with the result that the British Government agreed to assume the administration of the territory, as a protectorate, on 1 July 1895.

IMPERIAL ADMINISTRATION

BRITISH EAST AFRICA
(6)

2½
(7)

(Handstamped at Mombasa)

1895 (9 July). *Handstamped with T* **6**.

33	3	½a. deep brown.......................	75·00	24·00
		a. Pale brown	£110	45·00
		b. Dull brown	†	£2250
		c. Double	£450	£425
		d. Inverted	£5000	
34		1a. blue-green	£150	£110
		a. Double	£475	£450
		b. "ANL" (broken "D") (R. 6/5) ...	£2500	
35		2a. vermilion.............................	£180	95·00
		a. Double	£650	£475
36		2½a. black/*bright yellow*	£180	55·00
		a. Double	£650	£425
37		3a. black/*dull red*	85·00	50·00
38		4a. yellow-brown	50·00	35·00
		a. Double	£475	£450
39		4½a. dull violet	£200	£100
		a. Double	£700	£550
		b. Brown-purple	£1200	£950
		ba. Double	£2750	£2000
40		5a. black/*grey-blue*	£225	£140
		a. Double	£900	£800
		b. Inverted	†	£3500

41		7½a. black..................................	£120	80·00
		a. Double	£650	£550
42		8a. blue....................................	95·00	75·00
		b. Inverted	£600	
		b. Inverted	£5500	
43		1r. carmine	55·00	50·00
		a. Double	£550	£550
44	4	2r. brick-red..............................	£450	£250
45		3r. slate-purple	£225	£120
		a. Double	£900	£900
		b. Inverted		
46		4r. ultramarine	£190	£160
		a. Double	£800	£800
47		5r. grey-green	£425	£250
		a. Double	£1300	£1300
33/47	*Set of 15*	£2250	£1400

Forgeries exist.
The ½a. stamps used for this issue were mainly from the 1893–94 printings on thicker paper, but two used examples are known on the 1890–92 thin paper printing with sheet watermark (No. **4**).

1895 (29 Sept). *No.* **39** *surch with T* **7** *by The Zanzibar Gazette.*

48	3	2½a. on 4½a. dull violet (R.).............	£180	75·00
		a. Opt (*T* 6) double	£1000	£850

British East Africa
(8)

British East Africa
(9)

SETTING OF TYPE 8. This consisted of 120 impressions in 10 horizontal rows of 12 stamps. This matched the size of the pane for all the Indian issues to 1r. with the exception of the 6a. The sheets of this value contained four panes, each 8×10, which meant that the outer vertical margins also received the overprint.

The setting of Type **9** is not known.

Although only the one setting was used for the low values it is known that some of the overprint errors occurred, or were corrected, during the course of the various printings.

(Overprinted at the offices of *The Zanzibar Gazette*)

1895 (27 Oct)–96. *Stamps of India (Queen Victoria) optd with T* **8** *or* **9** *(2r. to 5r.).* W **13** (Elephant Head) (6a.) or W **34** (Large Star) (others) of India.

49	3	½a. blue-green (No. 85) (8.11.95)........	7·00	5·50
		a. "Brltish" for "British".................	£6000	£5000
		b. "Br1tish" for "British" (R. 10/12)..	£400	
		c. "Afr1ca" for "Africa" (R. 1/11)	£450	
		d. Opt double, one albino	£225	
		e. "Brit" for "British"		
50		1a. plum (No. 89) (8.11.95)............	6·50	6·00
		a. "Brltish" for "British".................	£7000	£3750
		b. "Br1tish" for "British" (R. 10/12)..	£450	
		c. "Afr1ca" for "Africa" (R. 1/11)	£500	
		d. "Brit" for "British"		
51		1a. 6p. sepia (No. 90) (23.11.95)........	4·25	4·00
		a. "Br1tish" for "British" (R. 10/12)..	£500	£500
		b. "Afr1ca" for "Africa" (R. 1/11)	£550	
52		2a. blue (No. 92) (8.11.95)..............	6·50	3·00
		a. "Brltsh" for "British"	£7000	£7000
		b. "Br1tish" for "British" (R. 10/12)..	£400	£275
		c. "Afr1ca" for "Africa" (R. 1/11)	£450	£325
53		2a. 6p. yellow-green (No. 103)..........	7·50	2·50
		a. "Biitish" for "British"	£7500	
		b. "Bpitish" for "British"	£7500	
		c. "Brltish" for "British"	†	£4000
		d. "Eas" for "East" (R. 2/12)...........	£1100	£1400
		e. "Br1tish" for "British" (R. 10/12)..	£550	£300
		f. "Afr1ca" for "Africa" (R. 1/11)	£600	£325
		g. "Brit" for "British"		
54		3a. brown-orange (No. 94) (18.12.95)...	12·00	11·00
		a. "Br1tish" for "British" (R. 10/12)..	£550	£550
		b. "Afr1ca" for "Africa" (R. 1/11)	£650	
		c. Opt double, one albino	£750	
55		4a. olive-green (No. 95) (18.12.95)......	38·00	30·00
		a. Slate-green	28·00	24·00
		b. "Br1tish" for "British" (R. 10/12)..	£700	£550
		c. "Afr1ca" for "Africa" (R. 1/11)	£750	£600
56		6a. pale brown (No. 81) (18.12.95)......	40·00	50·00
		a. "Br1tish" for "British" (R. 10/8)..	£1300	
		b. "Afr1ca" for "Africa" (R. 1/7)	£1300	
		c. "E st" for "East"	†	
		d. Opt double, one albino	£550	
57		8a. dull mauve (No. 98) (18.12.95)......	90·00	70·00
		a. "Br1tish" for "British" (R. 10/12)..	£800	
		b. "Afr1ca" for "Africa" (R. 1/11)	£850	
		c. Magenta (1896)	28·00	50·00
		ca. "Br1tish" for "British" (R. 10/12)..	£800	£700
		cb. "Afr1ca" for "Africa" (R. 1/11)	£850	£750
		cc. Inverted "a" for "t" of "East" (R. 2/12)...........................	†	£14000
58		12a. purple/*red* (No. 100) (18.12.95).....	22·00	32·00
		a. "Br1tish" for "British" (R. 10/12)..	£750	£750
		b. "Afr1ca" for "Africa" (R. 1/11)	£800	
59		1r. slate (No. 101) (18.12.95)...........	95·00	65·00
		a. "Br1tish" for "British" (R. 10/12)..	£750	
		b. "Afr1ca" for "Africa" (R. 1/11)	£800	
60		1r. green & aniline carm (No. 106) (1896)................................	45·00	£130
		a. Inverted "a" for "t" of "East" (R. 2/12)............................	£9000	
		b. "Br1tish" for "British" (R. 10/12)..	£1300	
		c. "Afr1ca" for "Africa" (R. 1/11)	£1300	
		d. Opt double, one sideways..........	£425	£900
		e. Opt double, one albino	£600	
61		2r. carm & yellow-brn (No. 107) (18.12.95)............................	90·00	£150
		a. "B" handstamped	£6000	£6000
62		3r. brown and green (No. 108) (18.12.95)............................	£110	£160
		a. "B" handstamped	£6000	£6000
		b. Opt double	£1400	
63		5r. ultramarine & vio (No. 109) (18.12.95)............................	£130	£160
		a. Opt double	£2250	
		b. "B" handstamped	£5500	£5500

	c. Opt double, one albino		£1400
49/63	Set of 15	£550	£750

The relative horizontal positions of the three lines of the overprint vary considerably but the distance vertically between the lines of the overprint is constant.

In both the "Br1tish" and "Afr1ca" errors the figure one is in a smaller type size.

There are other varieties, such as inverted "s" in "British", wide and narrow "B", and inverted "V" for "A" in "Africa" (R.1/1 and R.6/7).

During the overprinting of Nos. 61/3 the "B" of "British" sometimes failed to print so that only traces of the letter appeared. It was replaced by a handstamped "B" which is often out of alignment with the rest of the overprint. The handstamp is known double.

The 2, 3 and 5r., normally overprinted in larger type than the lower values, are also known with a smaller overprint, for use as specimen stamps for the U.P.U. These were not issued for postal purposes (*Price £450 un per set*). The lower values were reprinted at the same time using similar type to the original overprint.

Forgeries exist.

2½
(10)   11

1895 (20 Dec). *No. 51 surch locally with T 10 in bright red.*

64	2½ on 1½a. sepia	95·00	45·00
	a. Inverted "1" in fraction (R. 5/7, 10/7)	£900	£600
	b. "Br1tish" for "British" (R. 10/12)	£1400	
	c. "Afr1ca" for "Africa" (R. 1/11)	£1400	

The setting of Type 10 was in 5 horizontal rows of 12 stamps, repeated twice for each pane.

No. 51 also exists surcharged with T 12, 13 and 14 in brown-red. These stamps were sent to the Postal Union authorities at Berne, but were never issued to the public (*Price unused: T 12 £85, T 13 £190, T 14 £140*).

(Recess D.L.R.)

1896 (26 May)–**1901**. Wmk Crown CA. P 14.

65	11	½a. yellow-green	2·75	80
		x. Wmk reversed	†	—
66		1a. carmine-rose	7·50	40
		a. Bright rose-red	6·50	40
		b. Rosine (1901)	22·00	4·00
		w. Wmk inverted	£140	£140
		x. Wmk reversed	£200	£170
67		2a. chocolate	6·00	4·50
		x. Wmk reversed	†	£200
68		2½a. deep blue	10·00	1·75
		a. Violet-blue	16·00	2·50
		b. Inverted "S" in "ANNAS" (R. 1/1)	£140	60·00
		x. Wmk reversed	£200	£170
69		3a. grey	4·75	8·50
		x. Wmk reversed	£140	£140
70		4a. deep green	6·00	3·50
71		4½a. orange-yellow	9·50	16·00
72		5a. yellow-bistre	7·50	4·50
73		7½a. mauve	6·00	22·00
74		8a. grey-olive	6·00	5·50
75		1r. pale dull blue	60·00	65·00
		a. Ultramarine	85·00	65·00
76		2r. orange	65·00	27·00
77		3r. deep violet	65·00	32·00
78		4r. carmine-lake	60·00	70·00
79		5r. sepia	55·00	40·00
		a. Thin "U" in "RUPEES" (R. 3/2)	£1400	£1300
		x. Wmk reversed	†	£425
65/79	Set of 15		£325	£225
65s/79s	Optd "Specimen" Set of 15		£275	

Examples of some values exist apparently without watermark due to the paper being misplaced on the press.

(Overprinted at the offices of *The Zanzibar Gazette*)

1897 (2 Jan). *Nos. 156/7, 159 and 165/7 of Zanzibar optd with T 8.* Wmk Single Rosette.

80		½a. yellow-green and red	55·00	45·00
81		1a. indigo and red	95·00	90·00
82		2a. red-brown and red	38·00	21·00
83		4½a. orange and red	50·00	30·00
		a. No right serif to left-hand "4"	£800	
		b. No fraction bar at right	£800	£500
		w. Wmk inverted		
84		5a. bistre and red	55·00	45·00
		a. "Bri" for "British"	£1600	£1600
85		7½a. mauve and red	50·00	35·00
		a. "Bri" for "British"	£1700	
		b. Optd on front and back		
80/5	Set of 6		£300	£225

Nos. 84a and 85a appear to have occurred when the type was obscured during part of the overprinting.

The above six stamps exist with an overprint similar to T 8 but normally showing a stop after "Africa". These overprints (in red on the 1a.) were made officially to supply the U.P.U. (*Price £300 un per set*). However, the stop does not always show. Pieces are known showing overprints with and without stop se-tenant (including the red overprint on the 1a.).

Stamps of Zanzibar, wmk "Multiple Rosettes" and overprinted with T 8 are forgeries.

2½   2½   2½
(12)   (13)   (14)

SETTING OF TYPES 12/14. The setting of 60 (6×10) contained 26 examples of Type **12**, 10 of Type **13** and 24 of Type **14**.

1897 (2 Jan). *Nos. 157 and 162 of Zanzibar optd with T 8 and further surch locally, in red.*

86	12	2½ on 1a. indigo and red	£110	65·00
		b. Opt Type 8 double	£6000	
87	13	2½ on 1a. indigo and red	£250	£110
88	14	2½ on 1a. indigo and red	£130	75·00
		a. Opt Type 8 double	£6500	
89	12	2½ on 3a. grey and red	£110	55·00
90	13	2½ on 3a. grey and red	£250	£100
91	14	2½ on 3a. grey and red	£130	60·00
86/91	Set of 6		£900	£400

Both the notes after No. 85 also apply here.

A special printing with the 2½ surcharge on the 1a. and 3a. stamps overprinted as T 8 but *with stop after "Africa"*. It also included a "2" over "1" error in T 14.

15

(Recess D.L.R.)

1897 (Nov)–**1903**. Wmk Crown CC. P 14.

92	15	1r. grey-blue	80·00	35·00
		a. Dull blue (1901)	70·00	35·00
		b. Bright ultramarine (1903)	£350	£250
93		2r. orange	90·00	90·00
94		3r. deep violet	£120	£140
95		4r. carmine	£350	£425
		x. Wmk reversed	£500	£500
		y. Wmk inverted and reversed	£900	
96		5r. deep sepia	£300	£375
97		10r. yellow-bistre	£325	£375
		s. Optd "Specimen"	65·00	
		x. Wmk reversed	£700	
98		20r. pale green	£750	£1600
		a. Optd "Specimen"	£125	
99		50r. mauve	£1600	
		s. Optd "Specimen"	£250	
		x. Wmk reversed	£1800	£6000
		xs. Optd "Specimen"	£275	
92s/6s	Optd "Specimen" Set of 5		£180	

On 1 April 1901 the postal administrations of British East Africa and Uganda were merged. Subsequent issues were inscribed "EAST AFRICA AND UGANDA PROTECTORATES".

EAST AFRICA AND UGANDA PROTECTORATES

For earlier issues see BRITISH EAST AFRICA and UGANDA.
For the issues of the Mandated Territory of Tanganyika and the wartime issues that preceded them, see TANGANYIKA.

PRICES FOR STAMPS ON COVER TO 1945	
Nos. 1/43	*from* × 3
Nos. 44/75	*from* × 2
Nos. 76/95	*from* × 3
Nos. 96/105	—
Nos. 110/23	*from* × 2
Nos. 124/7	*from* × 3
Nos. 128/34	*from* × 5
Nos. 131/54	*from* × 3
Nos. D1/12	*from* × 8

PRINTERS. All the stamps issued between 1903 and 1927 were typographed by De La Rue & Co. Ltd, London.

USED HIGH VALUES. Beware of cleaned fiscally cancelled copies with faked postmarks.

1   2

1903 (24 July)–**04**. P 14.

(a) Wmk Crown CA.

1	1	½a. green (16.2.04)	4·00	12·00
2		1a. grey and red	1·75	1·00
3		2a. dull and bright purple (24.7.03)	8·50	2·50
		w. Wmk inverted	£140	£140
4		2½a. blue	12·00	48·00
5		3a. brown-purple and green	17·00	55·00
6		4a. grey-green and black	11·00	22·00
7		5a. grey and orange-brown	18·00	48·00
8		8a. grey and pale blue	21·00	40·00

(b) Wmk Crown CC. Ordinary paper.

9	2	1r. green	16·00	55·00
		a. Chalk-surfaced paper	50·00	90·00
10		2r. dull and bright purple	70·00	80·00
11		3r. grey-green and black	90·00	£170
12		4r. grey and emerald-green	95·00	£170
13		5r. grey and red	£100	£170
14		10r. grey and ultramarine	£200	£350
		a. Chalk-surfaced paper	£300	£375
		w. Wmk inverted	£475	

15		20r. grey and stone	£550	£1200
		s. Optd "Specimen"	£120	
16		50r. grey and red-brown	£1500	£2750
		s. Optd "Specimen"	£275	
		w. Wmk inverted	£2750	
1/13	Set of 13		£425	£800
1s/14s	Optd "Specimen" Set of 14		£300	

1904–07. Wmk Mult Crown CA. *Ordinary paper* (½a. to 8a.) *or chalk-surfaced paper* (1r. to 50r.).

17	1	½a. grey-green	8·50	3·00
		a. Chalk-surfaced paper	8·50	3·25
18		1a. grey and red	3·75	80
		a. Chalk-surfaced paper	9·00	1·75
19		2a. dull and bright purple	3·25	2·75
		a. Chalk-surfaced paper	2·75	2·75
20		2½a. blue	8·00	30·00
21		2½a. ultramarine and blue	7·50	17·00
22		3a. brown-purple and green	3·75	32·00
		a. Chalk-surfaced paper	3·75	28·00
23		4a. grey-green and black	7·50	18·00
		a. Chalk-surfaced paper	7·50	18·00
24		5a. grey and orange-brown	8·00	15·00
		a. Chalk-surfaced paper	6·50	28·00
25		8a. grey and pale blue	7·00	8·50
		a. Chalk-surfaced paper	7·00	19·00
26	2	1r. green (1907)	27·00	60·00
		w. Wmk inverted	†	£375
27		2r. dull and bright purple (1906)	38·00	55·00
28		3r. grey-green and black (1907)	55·00	£100
29		4r. grey and emerald-green (1907)	80·00	£140
		w. Wmk inverted	£350	
30		5r. grey and red (1907)	90·00	£110
31		10r. grey and ultramarine (1907)	£180	£225
		w. Wmk inverted	£450	£500
32		20r. grey and stone (1907)	£550	£950
33		50r. grey and red-brown (1907)	£1600	£2750
17/30	Set of 13		£300	£500

(New Currency. 100 cents = 1 rupee)

1907–08. Wmk Mult Crown CA. *Chalk-surfaced paper* (10, 12, 25, 50, 75c.). P 14.

34	1	1c. brown	2·50	15
35		3c. grey-green	14·00	70
		a. Blue-green	16·00	2·75
36		6c. red	2·75	10
37		10c. lilac and pale olive	9·00	8·50
38		12c. dull and bright purple	10·00	2·75
39		15c. bright blue	24·00	8·50
40		25c. grey-green and black	10·00	7·00
41		50c. grey-green and orange-brown	12·00	12·00
42		75c. grey and pale blue (1908)	4·50	32·00
34/42	Set of 9		80·00	65·00
34s/42s	Optd "Specimen" Set of 9		£180	

Original   Redrawn

1910. T **1** *redrawn. Printed from a single plate.* Wmk Mult Crown CA. P 14.

43		6c. red	14·00	30

In the redrawn type a fine white line has been cut around the value tablets and above the name tablet separating the latter from the leaves above, EAST AFRICA AND UGANDA is in shorter and thicker letters and PROTECTORATES in taller letters than in No. 36

3   4   **4 cents**
(5)

1912–21. Wmk Mult Crown CA. *Chalk-surfaced paper* (25c. to 500r.). P 14.

44	3	1c. black	30	1·75
45		3c. green	2·00	60
		a. Deep blue-green (1917)	4·50	1·50
		w. Wmk inverted	†	—
46		6c. red	1·00	60
		a. Scarlet (1917)	15·00	2·50
47		10c. yellow-orange	2·00	50
		a. Orange (1921)	10·00	3·00
48		12c. slate-grey	2·75	50
49		15c. bright blue	2·75	80
		w. Wmk inverted		
50		25c. black and red/yellow	50	1·25
		a. White back (5.14)	50	4·50
		as. Optd "Specimen"	35·00	
		b. On lemon (1916)	11·00	11·00
		bs. Optd "Specimen"	35·00	
		c. On orange-buff (1921)	45·00	17·00
		d. On pale yellow (1921)	10·00	5·00
51		50c. black and lilac	1·50	1·25
52		75c. black/green	1·50	17·00
		a. White back (5.14)	1·00	16·00
		as. Optd "Specimen"	35·00	
		b. On blue-green, olive back	6·00	7·50
		bs. Optd "Specimen"	35·00	
		c. On emerald, olive back (1919)	42·00	£150
		d. On emerald back (1921)	11·00	55·00
53	4	1r. black/green	1·75	4·25
		a. On emerald back (1919)	5·00	50·00
54		2r. red and black/blue	20·00	38·00
		w. Wmk inverted	£200	
55		3r. violet and green	20·00	90·00
56		4r. red and green/yellow	45·00	£100
		a. On pale yellow	£100	£170
57		5r. blue and dull purple	48·00	£140

58		10r. red and green/*green*	£130	£200
59		20r. black and purple/*red*	£325	£325
60		20r. purple and blue/*blue* (1918)	£400	£450
61		50r. dull rose-red and dull greyish green	£600	£650
		a. Carmine and green	£750	£800
		s. Optd "Specimen"	£150	
62		100r. purple and black/*red*	£5500	£2500
		s. Optd "Specimen"	£325	
63		500r. green and red/*green*	£21000	
		s. Optd "Specimen"	£650	
44/58	*Set of 15*		£250	£550
44s/60s	Optd "Specimen" *Set of 17*		£600	

For values in this series overprinted "G.E.A." (German East Africa) see Tanganyika Nos. 45/62.

1919 (7 Apr). *No. 46a surch with T **5** by the Swift Press, Nairobi.*

64	**3**	4c. on 6c. scarlet (*shades*)	1·25	15
		a. Bars omitted	40·00	70·00
		b. Surch double	£120	£200
		c. Surch inverted	£275	£375
		d. Pair, one without surch	£1600	£1800
		e. Surch on back	£400	
		s. Handstamped "Specimen"	60·00	

1921–22. *Wmk Mult Script CA. Chalk-surfaced paper (50c. to 50r.).* P 14.

65	**3**	1c. black	70	1·75
		w. Wmk inverted	£275	£275
66		3c. green	6·00	7·00
		a. Blue-green	15·00	10·00
67		6c. carmine-red	6·00	10·00
68		10c. orange (12.21)	8·50	1·25
69		12c. slate-grey	6·50	£110
70		15c. bright blue	10·00	17·00
71		50c. black and dull purple	14·00	£110
72	**4**	2r. red and black/*blue*	70·00	£180
73		3r. violet and green	£120	£275
74		5r. blue and dull purple	£150	£250
75		50r. carmine and green	£2000	£4500
		s. Optd "Specimen"	£350	
65/74	*Set of 10*		£350	£850
65s/74s	Optd "Specimen" *Set of 10*		£300	

For values in this series overprinted "G.E.A." see Tanganyika Nos. 63/73.

KENYA AND UGANDA
(New Currency. 100 cents = 1 East Africa shilling)

On 23 July 1920, Kenya became a Crown Colony with the exception of the coastal strip, previously part of the Sultan of Zanzibar's territories, which remained a protectorate.

The northern province of Jubaland was ceded to Italy on 29 June 1925 and later incorporated into Italian Somaliland.

6   7

1922 (1 Nov)**–27**. *Wmk Mult Script CA.* P 14.

(a) Wmk upright. Ordinary paper.

76	**6**	1c. pale brown	1·00	3·00
		a. Deep brown (1923)	1·50	3·50
		ax. Wmk reversed	£160	
77		5c. dull violet	3·75	75
		a. Bright violet	7·00	1·50
78		5c. green (1927)	2·00	50
79		10c. green	1·50	30
		w. Wmk inverted		
80		10c. black (5.27)	4·00	20
81		12c. jet-black	8·00	35·00
		a. Grey-black	4·75	26·00
82		15c. rose-carmine	1·25	10
83		20c. dull orange-yellow	3·25	10
		a. Bright orange	4·25	10
84		30c. ultramarine	2·00	50
85		50c. grey	2·50	10
86		75c. olive	5·00	9·00

(b) Wmk sideways*. Chalk-surfaced paper.

87	**7**	1s. green	4·25	2·50
88		2s. dull purple	8·00	10·00
		w. Wmk Crown to right of CA	£100	
89		2s.50, brown (1.10.25)	18·00	80·00
90		3s. brownish grey	17·00	6·50
		a. Jet-black	45·00	32·00
91		4s. grey (1.10.25)	23·00	85·00
		w. Wmk Crown to right of CA	48·00	£130
92		5s. carmine-red	22·00	22·00
93		7s.50, orange-yellow (1.10.25)	75·00	£160
94		10s. bright blue	48·00	48·00
		w. Wmk Crown to right of CA		
95		£1 black and orange	£160	£250
96		£2 green and purple (1.10.25)	£700	£1100
		s. Optd "Specimen"	£160	
97		£3 purple and yellow (1.10.25)	£950	
		s. Optd "Specimen"	£160	
98		£4 black and magenta (1.10.25)	£1800	
		s. Optd "Specimen"	£200	
99		£5 black and blue	£2000	
		s. Optd "Specimen"	£250	
		w. Wmk Crown to right of CA	£2500	
100		£10 black and brown	£8500	
		s. Optd "Specimen"	£325	
		w. Wmk Crown to right of CA	£13000	
101		£20 red and green (1.10.25)	£18000	
		s. Optd "Specimen"	£500	
102		£25 black and red	£22000	
		s. Optd "Specimen"	£500	
		w. Wmk Crown to right of CA	£26000	
103		£50 black and brown	£29000	
		s. Optd "Specimen"	£600	
104		£75 purple and grey (1.10.25)	£75000	
		s. Optd "Specimen"	£800	
105		£100 red and black (1.10.25)	£85000	
		s. Optd "Specimen"	£950	
76/95	*Set of 20*		£350	£600
76s/95s	Optd "Specimen" *Set of 20*		£475	

Nos. 87/94 were printed in two operations sometimes causing shade differences between the head and the frame.

*The normal sideways watermark shows Crown to left of CA, *as seen from the back of the stamp.*

KENYA, UGANDA AND TANGANYIKA

The postal administrations of Kenya, Tanganyika and Uganda were amalgamated on 1 January 1933. On the independence of the three territories the combined administration became the East African Posts and Telecommunications Corporation.

8 South African Crowned Cranes   **9** Dhow on Lake Victoria

10 Lion   **11** Kilimanjaro

12 Nile Railway Bridge, Ripon Falls   **13** Mt. Kenya

14 Lake Naivasha   I   II

(Des 1c., 20c., 10s., R. C. Luck, 10c., £1, A. Ross, 15c., 2s., G. Gill Holmes, 30c., 5s., R. N. Ambasana, 65c., L. R. Cutts. T **10** typo, remainder recess D.L.R.)

1935 (1 May)**–37**. *Wmk Mult Script CA. Chalk-surfaced paper (10c., £1).* P 12×13 (**10**), 14 (**9** and **14**) and 13 (remainder).

110	**8**	1c. black and red-brown	1·00	1·50
111	**9**	5c. black and green (I)	1·75	40
		a. Rope joined to sail (II) (1937)	20·00	4·75
		b. Perf 13×12 (I) (1936)	£4500	£600
		ba. Rope joined to sail (II) (1937)	£650	£190
112	**10**	10c. black and yellow	3·75	60
113	**11**	15c. black and scarlet	2·50	10
		a. Frame double, one albino	†	—
114	**8**	20c. black and orange	3·50	20
115	**12**	30c. black and blue	2·50	1·00
116	**9**	50c. bright purple and black (I)	2·00	10
117	**13**	65c. black and brown	3·25	2·00
118	**14**	1s. black and green	1·75	75
		a. Perf 13×12 (1936)	£1300	£120
119	**11**	2s. lake and purple	5·50	4·00
120	**14**	3s. blue and black	8·00	15·00
		a. Perf 13×12 (1936)	£2000	
121	**12**	5s. black and carmine	17·00	27·00
122	**8**	10s. purple and blue	65·00	85·00
123	**10**	£1 black and red	£170	£200
110/23	*Set of 14*		£250	£300
110s/23s	Perf "Specimen" *Set of 14*		£325	

Line through "0" of 1910 (R. 4/2)

1935 (6 May). *Silver Jubilee. As Nos. 91/4 of Antigua.* P 13½×14.

124		20c. light blue and olive-green	1·25	10
		f. Diagonal line by turret	80·00	45·00
		g. Dot to left of chapel	£140	75·00
		h. Dot by flagstaff	£140	75·00
		i. Dash by turret	£160	75·00
125		30c. brown and deep blue	2·50	3·50
		f. Diagonal line by turret	£140	£160
		g. Dot to left of chapel	£250	
		h. Dot by flagstaff	£250	
		i. Dash by turret	£250	
126		65c. green and indigo	1·75	2·75
		f. Diagonal line by turret	£150	
		g. Dot to left of chapel	£225	
127		1s. slate and purple	2·00	2·50
		f. Diagonal line by turret	£150	
		g. Dot to left of chapel	£275	
		h. Dot by flagstaff	£275	
		i. Line through "0" of 1910	£120	£140

124/7	*Set of 4*		6·75	8·00
124s/7s	Perf "Specimen" *Set of 4*		£140	

For illustrations of the other plate varieties see Omnibus section following Zanzibar.

Broken leaf (R. 6/1)

1937 (12 May). *Coronation. As Nos, 95/7 of Antigua, but printed by D.L.R.*

128		5c. green	20	10
129		20c. orange	40	30
		a. Broken leaf	45·00	
130		30c. bright blue	60	1·75
128/30	*Set of 3*		1·10	1·90
128s/30s	Perf "Specimen" *Set of 3*		85·00	

15 Dhow on Lake Victoria

Damaged left-hand value tablet (Frame Pl 2–2, with Centre Pl 4A or 4B, R. 9/6)   Retouched value tablet (Frame Pl 2–2, with Centre Pls 4B, 5, 6 or 7, R. 9/6)

Break in bird's breast (Frame Pl 2–2, with Centre Pls 4A or 4B, R. 2/5)

Sky retouch (Pl 7A R. 10/6)

Damage on mountain (Pl 7B R. 6/7. August 1948 ptg. Retouched in June 1949 for 10c. and 1s.)   Mountain retouch (Pl 7B, R. 5/10 and 6/7. Ptgs from June 1949 onwards)

With dot   Dot removed

In the 50c. printing of 14 June 1950 using Frame-plate 3, the dot was removed by retouching on all but five stamps (R. 5/2, 6/1, 7/2, 7/4 and 9/1). In addition, other stamps show traces of the dot where the retouching was not completely effective.

PERFORATIONS. In this issue, to aid identification, the perforations are indicated to the nearest quarter.

(*T* **10** typo, others recess D.L.R.)

1938 (11 Apr)–**54**. *As T* **8** *to* **14** *(but with portrait of King George VI in place of King George V, as in T* **15**). *Wmk Mult Script CA. Chalk-surfaced paper (£1).*

131	8	1c. black & red-brown (P 13¼)		
		(2.5.38)	2·00	85
		a. Perf 13¼×13¾. *Black & chocolate-brown* (1942)	30	50
		ab. "A" of "CA" missing from wmk.	£400	
		ac. Damaged value tablet	90·00	
		ad. Retouched value tablet	45·00	65·00
		ae. Break in bird's breast	85·00	
		af. Black & dp chocolate-brn (10.6.46)	2·25	2·25
		ag. Ditto. Retouched tablet	50·00	70·00
		ah. Black and red-brown (26.9.51)	3·50	3·00
132	15	5c. black and green (II) (P 13×11¾)	4·25	50
133		5c. reddish brown & orange (P 13¼×11¾) (1.6.49)	50	3·50
		a. Perf 13×12½ (14.6.50)	1·75	3·00
134	14	10c. red-brn & orge (P 13×11¾) (2.5.38)	2·25	10
		aw. Wmk inverted	£120	6·50
		b. Perf 14 (22.4.41)		
135		10c. black and green (P 13×11¾) (1.6.49)	30	1·25
		a. Mountain retouch	75·00	75·00
		b. Sky retouch		
		c. Perf 13×12½ (14.6.50)	2·00	10
136		10c. brown and grey (P 13×12½) (1.4.52)	1·25	55
137	11	15c. black and rose-red (2.5.38)	22·00	55
		a. Perf 13¾×13¼ (2.43)	5·50	3·75
		ab. "A" of "CA" missing from wmk.		
138		15c. black & green (P 13¼ × 13¼) (1.4.52)	2·00	4·50
139	8	20c. black and orange (2.5.38)	38·00	30
		a. Perf 14 (19.5.41)	55·00	1·75
		b. Perf 13¼×13¾ (25.2.42)	7·00	10
		ba. Deep black and deep orange (21.6.51)	17·00	1·50
		bw. Wmk inverted	†	—
140	15	25c. blk & carm-red (P 13×12½) (1.4.52)	1·25	2·25
141	12	30c. black & dull vio-bl (P 13¼) (2.5.38)	50·00	40
		a. Perf 14 (3.7.41)	£140	11·00
		b. Perf 13¼×13¾ (10.5.42)	2·75	10
142		30c. dull purple and brown (P 13¼ × 13¾) (1.4.52)	1·50	40
143	8	40c. black & blue (P 13¼×13¾) (1.4.52)	1·75	3·25
144	15	50c. purple & blk (II) (P 13×11¾) (2.5.38)	17·00	1·00
		a. Rope not joined to sail (I) (R. 2/5).	£225	£225
		b. Dull claret and black (29.7.47)	65·00	7·00
		c. Brown purple and black (4.48)	70·00	6·50
		d. Reddish purple and black (28.4.49)	38·00	4·50
		e. Ditto. Perf 13×12½ (10.49)	6·00	55
		ea. Dot removed (14.6.50)	20·00	55
		eb. Ditto. In pair with normal	£375	£130
		ew. Wmk inverted	†	£3500
145	14	1s. black & yellowish brn (P 13×11¾) (2.5.38)	22·00	30
		a. Black and brown (9.42)	11·00	30
		ab. Damage on mountain	—	£400
		ac. Mountain retouch	£1000	£1800
		aw. Wmk inverted	†	£2500
		b. Perf 13×12½ (10.49)	11·00	60
		ba. Deep black and brown (clearer impression) (14.6.50)	23·00	2·25
146	11	2s. lake-brn & brn-pur (P 13¼) (2.5.38)	£110	2·00
		a. Perf 14 (1941)	70·00	11·00
		b. Perf 13¾×13¼ (24.2.44)	23·00	30
147	14	3s. dull ultramarine & blk (P 13×11¾) (2.5.38)	38·00	4·00
		a. Deep violet-blue and black (29.4.47)	50·00	9·00
		ab. Damage on mountain	£1800	
		ac. Perf 13×12½ (14.6.50)	28·00	4·00
148	12	5s. black and carmine (P 13¼) (2.5.38)	£130	16·00
		a. Perf 14 (1941)	40·00	2·25
		b. Perf 13¾×13¼ (24.2.44)	28·00	1·25
149	8	10s. purple and blue (P 13¼) (2.5.38)	£120	21·00
		a. Perf 14. *Reddish purple & bl* (1941)	32·00	19·00
		b. Perf 13¼×13¾ (24.2.44)	42·00	3·75
150	10	£1 black and red (P 11¾ × 13) (12.10.38)	£300	£120
		a. Perf 14 (1941)	24·00	17·00
		ab. Ordinary paper (24.2.44)	25·00	18·00
		b. Perf 12½ (21.1.54)	13·00	30·00
131/50a (*cheapest*)		Set of 20	£160	
131s/50s		Perf "Specimen" Set of 13	£550	

No. 131ab occurs once in some sheets, always in the sixth vertical row.

The first printing of the 50c. utilised the King George V centre plate on which each impression had been individually corrected to show the rope joined to sail. R. 2/5 was missed, however, and this continued to show Type I until replaced by a further printing from a new plate in September 1938.

Stamps perf 14, together with Nos. 131a, 137a, 139b, 141b, 146b, 148b and 149b, are the result of air raid damage to the De La Rue works which destroyed the normal perforators. Dates quoted for these stamps represent earliest known postmarks.

10ᶜ
KENYA
TANGANYIKA
UGANDA
(16)

A screw head in the surcharging forme appears as a crescent moon (R. 20/4)

1941 (1 July)–**42**. *Pictorial Stamps of South Africa variously surch as T* **16** *by Government Printer, Pretoria. Inscr alternately in English and Afrikaans.*

			Unused pair	Used pair	Used single
151		5c. on 1d. grey & carmine (No. 56)	1·25	1·75	15
152		10c. on 3d. ultramarine (No. 59)	4·00	9·00	30
153		20c. on 6d. green & verm (No. 61a)	3·50	3·50	20
154		70c. on 1s. brown and chalky blue (No. 62) (20.4.42)	17·00	5·00	45
		a. Crescent moon flaw	65·00		
151/4		Set of 4	23·00	17·00	1·00
151s/4s		Handstamped "Specimen" Set of 4	£225		

1946 (11 Nov). *Victory. As Nos. 110/11 of Antigua.*

155		20c. red-orange	30	10
156		30c. blue	30	75
155s/6s		Perf "Specimen" Set of 2	70·00	

Examples of Nos. 155/6 were prereleased at Lindi on 15 October 1946.

1948 (1 Dec). *Royal Silver Wedding. As Nos. 112/13 of Antigua.*

157		20c. orange	15	10
158		£1 scarlet	38·00	60·00

1949 (10 Oct). *75th Anniv of Universal Postal Union. As Nos. 114/17 of Antigua.*

159		20c. red-orange	15	10
160		30c. deep blue	1·75	1·75
161		50c. grey	45	20
162		1s. red-brown	50	40
159/62		Set of 4	2·50	2·25

17 Lake Naivasha

(Recess D.L.R.)

1952 (1 Feb). *Visit of Princess Elizabeth and Duke of Edinburgh. Wmk Mult Script CA. P 13×12½.*

163	17	10c. black and green	20	1·50
164		1s. black and brown	50	2·00

STAMP BOOKLETS

1912–17. *Black on pink cover. Letter rate given as 6 cents per oz. Stapled.*

SB1	1r.80, booklet containing twelve 3c. and twenty four 6c. (Nos. 45/6), each in blocks of 6	£1300	
	a. Letter rate 6 cents per ½oz. Contains Nos. 45a/6a		
SB2	2r. booklet containing six 3c. and thirty 6c. (Nos. 45/6), each in blocks of 6	£1300	

1938. *Black on pink cover. Stapled.*

SB3	3s.40, booklet containing twelve 15c. and eight 20c. (Nos. 137, 139), each in blocks of 4	£200	

1950–52. *Blue on yellow cover. Stapled.*

SB4	1s. booklet containing four 5c. and eight 10c. (Nos. 133a, 135c), each in blocks of 4	£140	
	a. Contents as SB4, but 10c. changed to No. 136. Stitched (1952)	38·00	

POSTAGE DUE STAMPS

D **1**   D **2**

(Typo Waterlow)

1928 (Sept)–**33**. Wmk Mult Script CA. P 15×14.

D1	D **1**	5c. violet	2·50	50
D2		10c. vermilion	2·50	15
D3		20c. yellow-green	2·50	3·00
D4		30c. brown (1931)	17·00	14·00
D5		40c. dull blue	6·50	14·00
D6		1s. grey-green (1933)	70·00	£130
D1/6		Set of 6	90·00	£150
D1s/6s		Optd or Perf (30c., 1s.) "Specimen" Set of 6	£190	

(Typo D.L.R.)

1935 (1 May)–**60**. Wmk Mult Script CA. P 14.

D7	D **2**	5c. violet	2·75	1·75
D8		10c. scarlet	30	50
D9		20c. green	40	50
D10		30c. brown	1·25	50
		a. Bistre-brown (19.7.60)	3·00	8·50
D11		40c. ultramarine	1·50	3·00
D12		1s. grey	19·00	19·00
D7/12		Set of 6	22·00	23·00
D7s/12s		Perf "Specimen" Set of 6	£140	

Kuwait

Kuwait, an independent Arab shaikhdom since 1756, placed itself under British protection in 1899 to counter the spread of Ottoman influence in the Arabian Gulf.

The first, somewhat limited, postal service, via Bushire, commenced with the appointment of a Political Agent to Kuwait in August 1904. Because of diplomatic problems this system continued until 21 January 1915 when a regular Indian post office was established.

Limited supplies of Indian stamps were used by the Political Agency postal service, but these became available to the general public from 21 January 1915. Stamps seen postally used from Kuwait before 1923 are usually ½a., 1a., 1r. or 5r. values, with the occasional Official issue. Much more common are values to 15r., both postage and Official, used telegraphically.

Before 1910 the name of the shaikhdom was spelt "KOWEIT" and this spelling appears on various circular postmarks used between 1915 and 1923. The more modern version of the name was first used for a postal cancellation in 1923.

1915 "KOWEIT"

1923 "KUWAIT"

On 1 August 1921 responsibility for the Kuwait postal service passed to the Iraq Post Office.

PRICES FOR STAMPS ON COVER TO 1945	
Nos. 1/15	*from* × 5
Nos. 16/29	*from* × 3
Nos. 31/51	*from* × 2
Nos. 52/63	*from* × 4
Nos. O1/27	*from* × 10

USED HIGH VALUES. It is necessary to emphasize that used prices quoted for high value stamps are for postally used examples.

(Currency. 16 annas = 1 rupee)

KUWAIT   **KUWAIT**
(1)   (2)

1923 (1 Apr)–**24**. *Stamps of India (King George V), optd with T* **1** *or* **2** *(rupee values, 15½ mm) by Indian Govt Ptg Wks. W* **34** *(Large Star) of India. P 14.*

1		½a. emerald (No. 156)	3·50	7·00
		a. Opt double	£225	
		b. Vert pair, one without opt	£550	
		c. Light green		
2		1a. chocolate (No. 197)	3·00	3·50
		a. Opt double	£325	
		b. Opt omitted (lower stamp of vert pair)	£900	
3		1½a. chocolate (A) ("ANNA") (No. 163)	2·50	4·50
4		2a. bright reddish violet (No. 169)	3·75	5·00
		a. Reddish purple	6·00	

5	2a. 6p. ultramarine (No. 171)	2·75	8·00
6	3a. dull orange (No. 173)	4·25	20·00
7	3a. ultramarine (No. 200) (1924)	9·00	2·75
8	4a. deep olive (No. 174)	8·00	24·00
	a. Olive-green	10·00	
9	6a. brown-ochre (No. 178)	8·50	13·00
10	8a. purple (No. 182)	8·00	32·00
11	12a. carmine-lake (No. 183)	14·00	42·00
	a. Claret	14·00	42·00
12	1r. brown and green (No. 186)	22·00	38·00
	a. Orange-brown & deep turquoise-green	25·00	40·00
13	2r. carmine and brown (No. 187)	42·00	95·00
14	5r. ultramarine and violet (No. 188)	85·00	£225
15	10r. green and scarlet (No. 189)	£150	£475
1/15	Set of 15	£325	£850

Essays of the overprint using the obsolete spelling "KOWEIT" were prepared in 1923 and can be found on the original 14 values of the postage stamps and on the 13 stamps of the Official series. (*Price per set of 27 unused £22000*).

Nos. 1/4 and 6/7 are all known with inverted overprint and the overprint is also known on examples of India No. 165 ("ANNAS"). It is doubtful if such errors were actually sold at the Kuwait Post Office, although some are known on registered or ordinary covers.

KUWAIT (3)   **KUWAIT** (4)

1929–37. *Stamps of India (King George V, Nasik printing), optd with T 3 or 4 (rupee values).* W **69** (Mult Stars) of India. P 14.

16	½a. green (No. 202)	3·25	1·40
	aw. Wmk inverted	3·25	2·50
16b	½a. green (No. 232) (1934)	4·50	1·40
	bw. Wmk inverted		12·00
17	1a. chocolate (No. 203)	7·00	2·00
	aw. Wmk inverted	15·00	5·50
17b	1a. chocolate (No. 234) (1934)	6·00	1·25
18	2a. purple (No. 206)	3·25	1·25
19	2a. vermilion (No. 236)	20·00	85·00
	aw. Wmk inverted	20·00	90·00
19b	2a. vermilion (No. 236b) (1934)	16·00	6·50
19c	2a. vermilion (*small die*) (No. 236c) (1937)	4·50	2·50
20	3a. blue (No. 209)	2·75	2·00
21	3a. carmine (No. 237)	5·50	4·25
22	4a. sage-green (*wmk inverted*) (No. 211w)	25·00	80·00
	w. Wmk upright	45·00	
22a	4a. pale sage-green (No. 210) (1934)	6·50	14·00
22b	6a. bistre (No. 239) (1937)	22·00	55·00
23	8a. reddish purple (No. 212)	20·00	13·00
	w. Wmk inverted	9·00	22·00
24	12a. claret (*wmk inverted*) (No. 213w) (1933)	22·00	40·00
	w. Wmk upright	—	60·00
25	1r. chocolate and green (No. 214)	45·00	27·00
	a. Extended "T"	£375	
	w. Wmk inverted	13·00	
26	2r. carm & orge (*wmk inverted*) (No. 215w)	13·00	65·00
	a. Extended "T"	£375	£750
	w. Wmk upright	£150	150
27	5r. ultramarine and purple (No. 216) (1937)	85·00	£250
	a. Extended "T"	£600	
28	10r. green and scarlet (No. 217) (1934)	£180	£425
	a. Extended "T"	£1100	
29	15r. bl & ol (*wmk inverted*) (No. 218w) (1937)	£600	£850
	a. Extended "T"	£2000	
16/29	Set of 20	£950	£1700

The "T" of "KUWAIT" shows a ¾ mm downward extension on R. 3/2, lower left pane.

Nos. 16, 17, 18/19 and 22 are inscribed "INDIA POSTAGE & REVENUE". The remainder are inscribed "INDIA POSTAGE".

No. 19b measures 19×22.6 mm and No. 19c 18.4×21.8 mm.

Examples of most values are known showing a forged Kuwait postmark dated "11 NOV 37".

1933 (1 Feb)–**34.** *Air. Nos. 220/3 of India optd as T 2 (16½ mm).*

31	2a. deep blue-green	14·00	27·00
	w. Wmk stars to right	14·00	27·00
32	3a. blue	3·00	2·50
	w. Wmk stars to right	3·00	3·25
33	4a. olive-green	£100	£180
34	6a. bistre (2.34)	4·25	4·50
	w. Wmk stars to right	4·25	4·50
31/4	Set of 4	£110	£190

The normal sideways watermark on Nos. 31/4 shows stars pointing to left, *as seen from the back of the stamp*.

The 3a. value exists with a most pronounced lithography double print. *Price £850 un., £650 used.* Examples of this and other stamps with slight double prints are of little additional value.

1939. *Nos. 248, 250/1, 253, 255/63 of India (King George VI) optd with T 3 or 4 (rupee values).*

36	½a. red-brown	7·00	1·75
38	1a. carmine	7·00	1·75
39	2a. vermilion	7·00	2·75
41	3a. yellow-green	7·50	2·00
43	4a. brown	38·00	19·00
44	6a. turquoise-green	25·00	10·00
45	8a. slate-violet	28·00	32·00
46	12a. lake	20·00	65·00
47	1r. grey and red-brown	16·00	4·00
	a. Extended "T"	£375	£300
	b. Opt triple, one inverted		
48	2r. purple and brown	4·50	16·00
	a. Extended "T"	£350	£400
49	5r. green and blue	15·00	20·00
	a. Extended "T"	£500	
50	10r. purple and claret	60·00	75·00
	a. Opt double	£400	
	b. Extended "T"	£750	
51	15r. brown and green	£180	£250
	a. Extended "T"	£1000	
	w. Wmk inverted	90·00	£170
36/51w	Set of 13	£300	£375

On later printings the extended "T" variety was corrected in two stages.

Examples of most values are known showing a forged Kuwait postmark dated "17 NOV 39".

> Following the rebellion in Iraq, control of the Kuwait postal service was assumed by the Indian authorities on 24 May 1941. Unoverprinted stamps of INDIA were used in Kuwait between 1941 and 1945.

1945. *Nos. 265/8 and 269a of India (King George VI, on white background) optd with T 3.*

52	3p. slate	2·50	4·50
53	½a. purple	1·75	3·50
54	9p. green	3·75	10·00
55	1a. carmine	1·75	2·25
56	1½a. dull violet	4·25	8·50
57	2a. vermilion	4·25	4·25
58	3a. bright violet	5·50	7·00
59	3½a. bright blue	4·25	9·00
60	4a. brown	5·50	3·25
60a	6a. turquoise-green	14·00	11·00
61	8a. slate-violet	7·00	5·50
62	12a. lake	8·50	4·75
63	14a. purple	15·00	18·00
52/63	Set of 13	70·00	80·00

Following a short period of Pakistani control, from August 1947 the Kuwait postal service passed to British administration on 1 April 1948.

KUWAIT **1 ANNA** (5)   **KUWAIT** **5 RUPEES** (6)

NOTE. From 1948 onwards, for stamps with similar surcharges, but without name of country, see British Postal Agencies in Eastern Arabia.

1948 (1 Apr)–**49.** *Nos. 470, 475 476a/7 478a and 485/90 of Great Britain (King George VI), surch as T 5 or 6 (rupee values).*

64	½a. on ½d. pale green	1·75	1·75
65	1a. on 1d. pale scarlet	1·75	1·75
66	1½a. on 1½d. pale red-brown	2·00	1·75
67	2a. on 2d. pale orange	1·75	1·75
68	2½a. on 2½d. light ultramarine	2·00	1·00
69	3a. on 3d. pale violet	1·50	80
	a. Pair, one surch albino		
70	6a. on 6d. purple	1·50	75
71	1r. on 1s. bistre-brown	3·50	2·00
72	2r. on 2s. 6d. yellow-green	3·75	4·50
73	5r. on 5s. red	5·50	4·50
73a	10r. on 10s. ultramarine (4.7.49)	38·00	7·00
64/73a	Set of 11	55·00	25·00

KUWAIT 2½ ANNAS (7)   **KUWAIT 15 RUPEES** (8)

1948 (1 May). *Royal Silver Wedding. Nos. 493/4 of Great Britain surch with T 7 or 8.*

74	2½a. on 2½d. ultramarine	2·00	2·25
75	15r. on £1 blue	32·00	35·00
	a. Short bars (R. 3/4)	£140	£160

No. 75a has the bars cancelling the original face value 3 mm long instead of the 3½ mm of the normal surcharge.

1948 (29 July). *Olympic Games. Nos. 495/8 of Great Britain surch as T 7, but in one line (6a.) or two lines (others).*

76	2½a. on 2½d. ultramarine	1·00	2·75
77	3a. on 3d. violet	1·00	2·75
78	6a. on 6d. bright purple	1·25	2·75
79	1r. on 1s. brown	1·25	2·75
76/9	Set of 4	4·00	10·00

1949 (10 Oct). *75th Anniv of U.P.U. Nos. 499/502 of Great Britain surch "KUWAIT" and new values.*

80	2½a. on 2½d. ultramarine	1·00	2·75
	a. Lake in India	55·00	
81	3a. on 3d. violet	1·00	3·50
82	6a. on 6d. bright purple	1·00	3·50
83	1r. on 1s. brown	1·00	1·25
80/3	Set of 4	3·50	10·00

KUWAIT   **KUWAIT**

2 RUPEES Type I   **2 RUPEES** Type II

(8a)

KUWAIT 10 RUPEES

KUWAIT 10 RUPEES

(8b)

2r. Type I Type-set surcharge. "2" level with "RUPEES". Surcharge sharp.

Type II. Plate-printed surcharge. "2" raised. Surcharge worn.

10r. Type I. Type-set surcharge. "1" and "0" spaced. Surcharge sharp and clean.

Type II. Plate-printed surcharge. "1" and "0" closer together. Surcharge appears heavy and worn, see especially "A", "R" and "P".

KUWAIT Extra bar in centre (R. 7/2)   **KUWAIT** Extra bar at top (R. 2/2)

1950 (2 Oct)–**54.** *Nos. 503/11 of Great Britain (King George VI) surch us T5 or 8a/b (rupee values).*

84	½a. on ½d. pale orange (3.5.51)	2·00	1·50
85	1a. on 1d. light ultramarine (3.5.51)	2·00	1·60
86	1½a. on 1½d. pale green (3.5.51)	2·00	2·25
87	2a. on 2d. pale red-brown (3.5.51)	2·00	1·50
88	2½a. on 2½d. pale scarlet (3.5.51)	2·00	2·75
89	3a. on 3d. light ultramarine	2·50	1·50
90	2r. on 2s. 6d. yellow-green (I) (3.5.51)	15·00	4·75
	a. Extra bar in centre	£600	£400
	b. Type II surch (1954)	£200	50·00
91	5r. on 5s. red (3.5.51)	23·00	5·00
	a. Extra bar at top	£425	£300
92	10r. on 10s. ultramarine (I) (3.5.51)	32·00	8·00
	a. Type II surch (1952)	£250	55·00
84/92	Set of 9	75·00	26·00

No. 92a is known with surch spaced 10 mm apart instead of 9 mm.

OFFICIAL STAMPS

KUWAIT SERVICE (O 1)   **KUWAIT SERVICE** (O 2)

1923–24. *Stamps of India (King George V), optd with Type O 1 or O 2 (rupee values, 15½–16 mm).* W **34** (Large Star) of India. P 14.

O1	½a. light green (No. 155)	2·50	28·00
	a. Opt double, one albino	85·00	
O2	1a. chocolate (No. 197)	3·00	17·00
	a. Opt double, one albino	80·00	
O3	1½a. chocolate (No. 163)	3·50	42·00
O4	2a. bright reddish violet (No. 169)	6·00	29·00
	a. Reddish purple	8·00	
O5	2a. 6p. ultramarine (No. 171)	4·50	70·00
O6	3a. dull orange (No. 173)	3·50	70·00
O7	3a. ultramarine (No. 200) (1924)	5·00	60·00
O8	4a. olive-green (No. 175)	3·50	65·00
O9	8a. purple (No. 182)	6·00	£100
O10	1r. brown and green (No. 186)	20·00	£160
	a. Orange-brown & deep turquoise-green	24·00	
	b. Opt double, one albino	£110	
O11	2r. carmine and brown (No. 187)	20·00	£225
O12	5r. ultramarine and violet (No. 188)	80·00	£425
	a. Opt double, one albino	£150	
O13	10r. green and scarlet (No. 189)	£140	£375
O14	15r. blue and olive (No. 190)	£200	£550
O1/14	Set of 14	£450	£2000

1929–33. *Nos. 203, 206, 209 and 211/18w of India (King George V, Nasik printing) optd as Types O 1 (spaced 10 mm) or O 2 (14½ mm × 19–20 mm wide).* W **69** (Mult Stars) of India. P 14.

O16	1a. chocolate		
	w. Wmk inverted	4·25	27·00
O17	2a. purple	55·00	£180
O19	3a. blue	4·50	40·00
O20	4a. sage-green	4·25	75·00
	w. Wmk inverted		
O21	8a. reddish purple	5·00	95·00
	w. Wmk inverted	7·50	
O22	12a. claret	27·00	£180
	w. Wmk inverted	45·00	
O23	1r. chocolate and green	5·50	£190
O24	2r. carmine and orange (*wmk inverted*)	8·50	£300
O25	5r. ultramarine & purple (*wmk inverted*)	28·00	£425
O26	10r. green and scarlet	55·00	£650
O27	15r. blue and olive (*wmk inverted*)	£140	£1200
O16w/27	Set of 11	£300	£3000

Labuan *see* North Borneo

Lagos *see* Nigeria

Leeward Islands

The Federal Colony of the Leeward Islands was constituted in 1871 formalising links between Antigua, British Virgin Islands, Dominica, Montserrat and St. Kitts-Nevis which stretched back to the 1670s. Issues for the individual islands were superseded by those inscribed "LEEWARD ISLANDS", but were in concurrent use with them from 1903. Dominica was transferred to the Windward Islands on 31 December 1939.

PRICES FOR STAMPS ON COVER TO 1945	
Nos. 1/8	*from* × 10
Nos. 9/16	*from* × 12
Nos. 17/19	*from* × 8
Nos. 20/8	*from* × 5
Nos. 29/35	*from* × 4
Nos. 36/45	*from* × 5
Nos. 46/57	*from* × 4
Nos. 58/87	*from* × 5
Nos. 88/91	*from* × 6
Nos. 92/4	*from* × 10
Nos. 95/114	*from* × 5

PRINTERS. All the stamps of Leeward Islands were typographed by De La Rue & Co, Ltd, London, *except where otherwise stated.*

(1)

(2)

1890 (31 Oct). *Name and value in second colour. Wmk Crown CA.* P 14.

1	1	½d. dull mauve and green	3·50	1·25
2		1d. dull mauve and rose	4·25	20
3		2½d. dull mauve and blue	5·50	20
		w. Wmk inverted	£300	£180
4		4d. dull mauve and orange	5·00	8·50
5		6d. dull mauve and brown	11·00	13·00
6		7d. dull mauve and slate	5·50	12·00
7	2	1s. green and carmine	21·00	50·00
8		5s. green and blue	£120	£250
1/8 *Set of 8*			£160	£300
1s/8s Optd "Specimen" *Set of 8*			£200	

The colours of this issue are fugitive.

(3)

One Penny

(4)

One Penny

(5)

1897 (22 July). *Queen Victoria's Diamond Jubilee. Handstamped with T 3.*

9	1	½d. dull mauve and green	4·50	15·00
		a. Opt double	£1400	
10		1d. dull mauve and rose	5·00	15·00
		a. Opt double	£1000	
		b. Opt triple	£3250	
11		2½d. dull mauve and blue	5·50	15·00
		a. Opt double	£1200	
12		4d. dull mauve and orange	40·00	70·00
		a. Opt double	£1200	
13		6d. dull mauve and brown	50·00	90·00
		a. Opt double	£1500	
14		7d. dull mauve and slate	50·00	95·00
		a. Opt double	£1500	
15	2	1s. green and carmine	£120	£190
		a. Opt double	£2000	
16		5s. green and blue	£450	£750
		a. Opt double	£5500	
9/16 *Set of 8*			£600	£1100

Beware of forgeries.

1902 (11 Aug). *Nos. 4/6 surch locally.*

17	4	1d. on 4d. dull mauve and orange	3·75	6·00
		a. Pair, one with tall narrow "O" in "One"	35·00	70·00
		b. Surch double		
18		1d. on 6d. dull mauve and brown	4·75	11·00
		a. Pair, one with tall narrow "O" in "One"	50·00	£120
19	5	1d. on 7d. dull mauve and slate	4·25	8·00
17/19 *Set of 3*			11·50	23·00

The tall narrow "O" variety occurred on R. 1/1, 5/3, 5/5 and 7/4.

6

7

8

LEEWARD ISLANDS

Wide "A" (R. 6/1 of both panes. Replaced in 1912)

LEEWARD ISLANDS

Dropped "R" (R.1/1 of both panes from Pl 2 (1st ptg only))

1902 (1 Sept–Oct). Wmk Crown CA. P 14.

20	6	½d. dull purple and green	5·50	1·00
21		1d. dull purple and carmine	7·00	20
22	7	2d. dull purple and ochre (Oct)	2·75	4·25
23	6	2½d. dull purple and ultramarine	5·50	2·25
		a. Wide "A" in "LEEWARD"	£225	£150
24	7	3d. dull purple and black (Oct)	5·00	7·50
25	6	6d. dull purple and brown	2·50	8·00
26	8	1s. green and carmine	3·75	19·00
		a. Dropped "R" in "LEEWARD"	£350	£550
27	7	2s.6d. green and black (Oct)	27·00	70·00
28		5s. green and blue	48·00	75·00
20/8 *Set of 9*			95·00	£170
20s/8s Optd "Specimen" *Set of 9*			£140	

1905 (Apr)–08. Wmk Mult Crown CA. *Ordinary paper (½d., 3d.) or chalk-surfaced paper (others).*

29	6	½d. dull purple and green (2.06)	3·50	2·00
		a. Chalk-surfaced paper (25.7.08)	22·00	13·00
30		1d. dull purple and carmine (29.8.06)	8·50	80
31	7	2d. dull purple and ochre (25.7.08)	6·00	16·00
32	6	2½d. dull purple and ultramarine (23.7.06)	60·00	38·00
		a. Wide "A" in "LEEWARD"	£550	£375
33	7	3d. dull purple and black	14·00	45·00
		a. Chalk-surfaced paper (18.4.08)	45·00	75·00
34	6	6d. dull purple and brown (15.7.08)	42·00	70·00
35	8	1s. green and carmine (15.7.08)	42·00	£100
29/35 *Set of 7*			£160	£225

1907 (14 Apr)–11. Wmk Mult Crown CA. *Chalk-surfaced paper (3d. to 5s.).* P 14.

36	7	¼d. brown (7.8.09)	2·75	1·75
37	6	½d. dull green	3·50	1·25
38		1d. bright red (7.07)	10·00	80
		a. Rose-carmine (1910)	38·00	3·50
39	7	2d. grey (3.8.11)	3·50	7·50
40	6	2½d. bright blue (5.07)	7·00	4·25
		a. Wide "A" in "LEEWARD"	£225	£180
41	7	3d. purple/*yellow* (28.10.10)	3·50	7·50
42	6	6d. dull and bright purple (3.8.11)	8·50	7·00
43	8	1s. black/*green* (3.8.11)	5·50	21·00
44	7	2s.6d. black and red/*blue* (15.9.11)	40·00	48·00
45	8	5s. green and red/*yellow* (21.11.10)	42·00	65·00
36/45 *Set of 10*			£110	£150
36s/45s Optd "Specimen" *Set of 10*			£200	

10

11

12

13

1912 (23 Oct)–22. *Die I (¼d. to 3d., 6d., 1s., 2s.6d. 5s.) or Die II (4d., 2s.). Wmk Mult Crown CA. Chalk-surfaced paper (3d. to 5s.).* P 14.

46	10	¼d. brown	1·75	1·00
		a. Pale brown	3·50	2·00
47	11	½d. yellow-green (12.12)	5·50	2·00
		a. Deep green (1916)	5·50	1·50
48		1d. red	5·00	1·00
		a. Bright scarlet (8.15)	7·50	1·00
49	10	2d. slate-grey (9.1.13)	4·00	5·50
50	11	2½d. bright blue	3·25	7·00
		a. Deep bright blue (1914)	3·75	4·00
51	10	3d. purple/*yellow* (9.1.13)	1·75	12·00
		a. White back (11.13)	70·00	£140
		as. Optd "Specimen"	45·00	
		b. On lemon (11.14)	5·50	16·00
		c. On buff (1920)	35·00	50·00
		cs. Optd "Specimen"	45·00	
		d. On orange-buff (1920)	4·25	15·00
		dw. Wmk inverted	£275	
52		4d. blk & red/*pale yell* (Die II) (12.5.22)	4·00	22·00
53	11	6d. dull and bright purple (9.1.13)	3·00	8·00
54	12	1s. black/*green* (9.1.13)	3·00	8·00
		a. White back (11.13)	55·00	38·00

		as. Optd "Specimen"	48·00	
		b. On blue-green, olive back (1917)	9·50	8·00
		bs. Optd "Specimen"	50·00	
55	10	2s. purple & blue/*blue* (Die II) (12.5.22)	9·50	55·00
56		2s.6d. black and red (11.13)	14·00	42·00
57	12	5s. green and red/*yellow* (9.14)	50·00	95·00
		a. White back (11.13)	42·00	80·00
		as. Optd "Specimen"	55·00	
		b. On lemon (1915)	29·00	£100
		c. On orange-buff (1920)	£110	£190
46/57b *Set of 12*			75·00	£200
46s/57s Optd "Specimen" *Set of 12*			£275	

Nos. 51a, 54a and 57 were only on sale from Montserrat.

WARD ISLA

"D I" shaved at foot 1d. R. 7/3 of left pane (all ptgs between Sept 1947 and July 1949. 1s. R. 9/6 of right pane (all ptgs between 1932 and 1938).

1921 (Oct)–32. Wmk Mult Script CA or Mult Crown CA (£1). *Chalk-surfaced paper (3d. to £1).* P 14.

(a) Die II (1921–29).

58	10	¼d. brown (1.4.22)	2·25	1·00
59	11	½d. blue-green	1·00	75
60		1d. carmine-red	2·25	55
61		1d. bright violet (21.8.22)	2·25	1·00
62		1d. bright scarlet (1929)	9·00	2·25
63	10	1½d. carmine-red (10.9.26)	3·25	2·00
64		1½d. red-brown (1929)	1·25	10
65		2d. slate-grey (6.22)	2·00	80
		w Wmk inverted		†
		x. Wmk reversed		£170
66	11	2½d. orange-yellow (22.9.23)	6·50	50·00
67		2½d. bright blue (1.3.27)	3·50	1·25
68	10	3d. light ultramarine (22.9.23)	6·50	26·00
		a. Deep ultramarine (1925)	50·00	50·00
69		3d. purple/*yellow* (1.7.27)	1·50	6·50
70		4d. black and red/*pale yellow* (2.24)	3·00	21·00
71		5d. dull purple and olive-green (12.5.22)	2·50	4·25
72	11	6d. dull and bright purple (17.7.23)	10·00	28·00
73	12	1s. black/*emerald* (17.7.23)	6·50	16·00
74	10	2s. purple and blue/*blue* (12.5.22)	16·00	42·00
		a. Red-purple and blue/*blue* (1926)	7·50	48·00
		aw. Wmk inverted	£250	
75		2s.6d. black and red/*blue* (17.7.23)	6·50	23·00
76		3s. bright green and violet (12.5.22)	12·00	£100
77		4s. black and red (12.5.22)	12·00	42·00
78	12	5s. green and red/*pale yellow* (17.7.23)	40·00	70·00
79	13	10s. green and red/*green* (1928)	65·00	95·00
		a. Break in scroll	£225	
		b. Broken crown and scroll	£225	
		e. Break in lines below left scroll	£225	
		f. Damaged leaf at bottom right	£225	
80		£1 purple and black/*red* (1928)	£225	£250
		a. Break in scroll	£425	
		b. Broken crown and scroll	£425	
		e. Break in lines below left scroll	£425	
		f. Damaged leaf at bottom right	£425	
58/80 *Set of 22*			£375	£650
58s/80s Optd or Perf (1d. bright scarlet, 1½d. red-brown, 10s., £1) "Specimen" *Set of 23*			£550	

(b) Reversion to Die I (Plate 23) (1931–32).

81	10	¼d. brown	7·00	16·00
82	11	½d. blue-green	27·00	35·00
83		1d. bright scarlet	29·00	75
84	10	1½d. red-brown	4·25	1·00
85	11	2½d. bright blue	7·00	3·50
86		6d. dull and bright purple	22·00	85·00
87	12	1s. black/*emerald*	55·00	75·00
		a. "D I" flaw	£475	
		b. "A" of "CA" missing from wmk	—	£2000
81/7 *Set of 7*			£140	£200

No. 60 may not have been used locally before January 1923.

No. 68a was issued in St. Kitts-Nevis.

Nos. 59, 62 and 82/3 exist in coils, constructed from normal sheets. No. 82 was only issued in this form.

For illustrations of varieties on Nos. 79/80 see above No. 51b of Burmuda.

Nos. 81/7 result from the use, in error, of Die I which had previously been "retired" in late 1920, to produce Plate 23.

1935 (6 May). *Silver Jubilee. As Nos. 91/4 of Antigua, but printed by Waterlow.* P 11×12.

88		1d. deep blue and scarlet	1·60	1·50
89		1½d. ultramarine and grey	2·25	70
90		2½d. brown and deep blue	2·25	3·50
91		1s. slate and purple	12·00	20·00
		k. Kite and vertical log	£325	
		l. Kite and horizontal log	£350	
88/91 *Set of 4*			16·00	23·00
88s/91s Perf "Specimen" *Set of 4*			£100	

For illustrations of plate varieties see Omnibus section following Zanzibar.

1937 (12 May). *Coronation. As Nos. 95/7 of Antigua, but printed by D.L.R.*

92		1d. scarlet	70	30
93		1½d. buff	70	1·00
94		2½d. bright blue	80	1·25
92/4 *Set of 3*			2·00	2·25
92s/4s Perf "Specimen". *Set of 3*			80·00	

14	15

(Die A) (Die B)

In Die B the figure "1" has a broader top and more projecting serif.

"ISLANDS" flaw (R. 1/2 of right pane) (Pl. 2 ptgs from November 1942 until corrected in July 1949)

Broken second "E" in "LEEWARD" (R. 4/1 of right pane) (Pl. 3 ptgs from August 1942 until corrected in June 1949) (A similar variety occurs on 5s.)

Broken top right scroll (R. 5/11) (1942 ptg of 10s. only. Corrected on £1 value from same period)

Broken lower right scroll (R. 5/12. 1942 ptgs only)

Missing pearl (R. 5/1. 1944 ptgs only)

Gash in chin (R. 2/5. 1942 ptgs only)

1938 (25 Nov)–**51**. *T 14 (and similar type, but shaded value tablet, ½d., 1d., 2½d., 6d.) and 15 (10s., £1). Chalk-surfaced paper (3d. to £1). P 14.*

(a) Wmk Mult Script CA.

95	¼d. brown	60	1·50
	a. Chalk-surfaced paper. *Dp brn* (13.6.49)	30	1·75
96	½d. emerald	70	70
	a. "ISLANDS" flaw	75·00	
97	½d. slate-grey (*chalk-surfaced paper*) (1.7.49)	1·00	1·50
98	1d. scarlet (Die A)	9·50	2·50
99	1d. scarlet (*shades*) (Die B) (1940)	2·25	1·75
	a. "D I" flaw (9.47)	£200	
	b. Carmine (9.42)	1·50	7·00
	c. Red (13.9.48)	6·00	3·50
	ca. "D I" flaw	£200	
100	1d. bl-grn (*chalk-surfaced paper*) (1.7.49)	55	15
	a. "D I" flaw	£180	
101	1½d. chestnut	1·00	50
102	1½d. yellow-orange and black (*chalk-surfaced paper*) (1.7.49)	85	40
103	2d. olive-grey	3·00	1·25
	a. Slate-grey (11.42)	5·50	3·00
104	2d. scarlet (*chalk-surfaced paper*) (1.7.49)	1·40	1·25
105	2½d. bright blue	17·00	2·50
	a. Light bright blue (11.42)	80	1·25
106	2½d. black and purple (*chalk-surfaced paper*) (1.7.49)	55	1·25
107	3d. orange	35·00	2·75
	a. Ordinary paper. *Pale orange* (11.42)	50	85
108	3d. bright blue (1.7.49)	65	15
109	6d. deep dull purple and bright purple	23·00	5·50
	a. Ordinary paper (8.42)	6·50	2·25
	ab. Broken "E"	£350	
	b. Purple and deep magenta (29.9.47)	8·50	3·50
	ba. Broken "E"	£425	£350
110	1s. black/*emerald*	16·00	2·00
	a. "D I" flaw	£475	
	b. Ordinary paper (3.42)	4·25	1·00
	ba. Grey and black/*emerald* (8.42)	18·00	4·00
	bb. Black and grey/*emerald* (11.42)	£130	13·00

111	2s. reddish purple and blue/*blue*	21·00	2·75
	a. Ordinary paper (3.42)	10·00	2·00
	ab. *Deep purple and blue/blue* (29.9.47)	11·00	2·50
112	5s. green and red/*yellow*	48·00	17·00
	a. Broken "E" (R. 3/4 of left pane)	£800	£600
	b. Ordinary paper (12.43)	32·00	15·00
	ba. Broken "E" (R. 3/4 of left pane)	£700	
	c. *Bright green and red/yellow* (24.10.51)	55·00	50·00
113	10s. bluish green and deep red/*green*	£200	£130
	a. Ordinary paper. *Pale green and dull red/green* (26.6.44*)	£550	£300
	ad. Broken top right scroll	£3250	
	ae. Broken lower right scroll	£3250	£3250
	af. Gash in chin	£3250	£3250
	b. Ordinary paper. *Green and red/green* (22.2.45*)	£150	70·00
	c. Ordinary paper. *Deep green and deep vermilion/green* (15.10.47*)	£120	75·00
	ca. Missing pearl	£1300	

(b) Wmk Mult Crown CA

114	£1 brown-purple and black/*red*	£325	£275
	a. Purple and black/carmine (21.9.42*)	85·00	45·00
	ae. Broken lower right scroll	£1200	£700
	af. Gash in chin	£1200	£700
	b. *Brown-purple & black/salmon* (5.2.45*)	35·00	24·00
	ba. Missing pearl	£1100	£800
	c. Perf 13. *Violet & black/scarlet* (4.1.52*)	32·00	38·00
	ca. Wmk sideways	£4000	
	cw. Wmk inverted	£4000	
95/114b	Set of 19	£190	£110
95/114s	Perf "Specimen" Set of 13	£500	

*Dates quoted for Nos. 113a/14c are earliest known postmark dates. Nos. 113a and 114a were despatched to the Leeward Islands in March 1942, Nos. 113b and 114b in December 1943, No. 113c in June 1944 and No. 114c on 13 December 1951.

Nos. 96, 98/9 and 99b exist in coils constructed from normal sheets.

Printings of the 10s. in March 1942 (No. 113a) and of the £1 in February and October 1942 (No. 114a) were made by Williams Lea & Co. Ltd. following bomb damage to the De La Rue works in 1940.

For illustrations of Nos. 99a, 99ca, 100a and 110a see above No. 58.

1946 (1 Nov). *Victory. As Nos. 110/11 of Antigua.*

115	1½d. brown	15	75
116	3d. red-orange	15	75
115s/16s	Perf "Specimen" Set of 2	75·00	

1949 (2 Jan). *Royal Silver Wedding. As Nos. 112/13 of Antigua.*

117	2½d. ultramarine	10	10
118	5s. green	4·25	4·00

1949 (10 Oct). *75th Anniv of Universal Postal Union. As Nos. 114/17 of Antigua.*

119	2½d. blue-black	15	2·00
120	3d. deep blue	2·00	2·00
121	6d. magenta	15	2·00
122	1s. blue-green	15	2·00
119/22	Set of 4	2·25	7·25

(New Currency. 100 cents = 1 B.W.I. dollar)

1951 (16 Feb). *Inauguration of B.W.I. University College. As Nos. 118/19 of Antigua.*

123	3c. orange and black	30	1·25
124	12c. rose-carmine and reddish violet	70	1·25

Long Island

PRICES FOR STAMPS ON COVER
Most covers from Long Island are philatelic, but these are worth from × 2 (Nos. 1/3) or from × 5 (Nos. 4/36).

The Turkish island of Chustan (or Keustan) in the Gulf of Smyrna was occupied by the Royal Navy during April 1916 and renamed Long Island.

The following stamps were provided by the Civil Administrator, Lieut-Cmdr H. Pirie-Gordon, for the postal service inaugurated on 7 May 1916.

USED STAMPS. Stamps of Long Island were cancelled by hand-drawn circular date stamps in blue crayon for the Northend post office ("N") or in red crayon for Nikola post office ("S").

QUANTITIES ISSUED. The figures quoted do not include the remainders subsequently recorded as having been destroyed.

(1)	2

1916 (7 May). *Turkish fiscal stamps surch by typewriter as in T 1. No wmk. P 12.*

1	½d. on 20pa. green and buff (new value in red, remainder of surch in black)	£3000	£4750
2	1d. on 10pa. carmine and buff	£3500	£4750
3	2½d. on 1pi. violet and buff (R.)	£3000	£4750

Quantities issued: ½d. 25; 1d.20; 2½d. 25.

1916 (7 May). *Typewritten as T 2 in various colours of ribbon and carbon. Each stamp initialled by the Civil Administrator. No gum. Imperf.*

(a) On pale green paper with horizontal grey lines. No wmk. Sheets of 12 (4×3) or 16 (4×4) with stamps initialled in red ink.

4	½d. black	£1400	£1100
	a. "GRI" double	£2500	
	b. "7" for "&"	£3750	
5	½d. blue	£1100	
	a. "G.R.I." double	£2500	
	b. "7" for "&"	£3750	
6	½d. mauve	£475	£600
	a. "G.R.I." double	£1300	
	b. "7" for "&"	£3000	

Quantity issued: 140 in all.

(b) On thin horiz laid paper with sheet wmk of "Silver Linen" in double-lined letters. Sheets of 20 (4×5) or 16 (some ptgs of 1s.) with stamps initialled in red ink.

7	½d. black	£500	£700
	a. "postage" for "Postage"	£2750	
	b. "7" for "&"	£2750	
8	½d. blue	£800	£850
	b. "7" for "&"	£2750	
9	½d. mauve	£275	£350
	a. "postage" for "Postage"	£1300	
	b. "7" for "&"	£1600	
10	1d. black	£190	£375
	a. "7" for "&"	£1500	
	b. "Rvevue" for "Revenue"	£1500	
	c. "Postagg" for "Postage"	£2500	
11	1d. blue	£300	£450
	a. "7" for "&"	£2500	
	c. "postage" for "Postage"	£2500	
	e. "G.R?I?" for "G.R.I."	£2500	
	f. "ONR" for "ONE"	£1300	
12	1d. mauve	£150	£300
	a. "7" for "&"	£1700	
	b. "Rvevue" for "Revenue"	£2500	
	c. "postage" for "Postage"	£2500	
	e. "G.R?I?" for "G.R.I."	†	£2500
	f. "ONR" for "ONE"	£1000	£1300
	g. "Postagg" for "Postage"	£1600	
13	1d. red	£180	£325
	a. "7" for "&"	£1600	
	c. "postage" for "Postage"	£2500	
	f. "ONR" for "ONE"	£1300	£1400
14	2½d. black	£1100	
15	2½d. blue	£1100	£1400
16	2½d. mauve	£2500	£1500
17	6d. black (inscr "SIX PENCE")	£1500	£2500
	a. "SIXPENCE" (one word)	£3000	
	b. Without red ink initials	†	£2500
19	6d. mauve (inscr "SIX PENCE")	£600	£1100
	a. "SIXPENCE" (one word)	£2250	
20	1s. black	£150	£400
	a. "ISLANA" for "ISLAND"	£2500	
	b. "Postge" for "Postage"	£1300	£1800
	c. "Rebenue" for "Revenue"	£2500	
21	1s. blue	£1400	
22	1s. mauve	£140	£475
	a. "ISLANA" for "ISLAND"	£1700	
	b. "Postge" for "Postage"	£2500	
	c. "Rebenue" for "Revenue"	£2500	

Quantities issued (all colours); ½d. 237; 1d. 881; 2½d. 80; 6d. 89; 1s. 383.

(c) On thin wove paper. No wmk. Sheets of 24 with stamps initialled in indelible pencil.

23	½d. black	£400	£500
25	½d. mauve	£850	
26	1d. black	£475	£600
27	1d. red	£6500	£1200
30	2d. black	£225	£550
	b. Error. 1d. and 2d. se-tenant	£5500	
	c. Initialled in red ink	£1200	£1300
31	2d. mauve	£225	£375
	a. Error. 1d. and 2d. se-tenant	£5550	
32	2½d. black	£475	£650
33	2½d. blue	£1500	
34	2½d. mauve	£1300	£1300
35	6d. black	£250	£550
	a. "Rvenne &" for "Revenue"	£2500	
	b. Error. 2d. and 6d. se-tenant, also "ISLND" for "ISLAND"	£5500	£5500
	c. "PENCC"	£2000	
36	6d. blue	£1000	
	a. "Rvenne &" for "Revenue"	£3000	
	b. Error. 2d. and 6d. se-tenant, also "ISLND" for "ISLAND"	£6000	
	c. "PENCC"	£2500	

Quantities issued (all colours); ½d. 114; 1d. 120; 2d. 249; 2½d. 115; 6d.200.

TOP SHEETS AND CARBONS. It is believed that the production sequence of the typewritten stamps was as follows:

½d. on pale green (Nos. 4/6)

Two black sheets of 12 (4×3) and one of 16 (4×4)

Two blue carbon sheets of 12 (4×3) and one of 16 (4×4)

Five mauve carbon sheets of 12, two from one top sheet and three from the other

Varieties: "7" for "&" occurs on an unknown position from one of the sheets of 12 and "G.R.I." double occurs on R. 3/2-4 of the other

½d. on laid paper (Nos. 7/9) in sheets of 20 (4×5)

Three black top sheets

Three blue carbon sheets

Eight mauve carbon sheets, two or three from each top sheet

Varieties: "postage" occurs on R. 3/2 of one top sheet and "7" for "&" on R. 4/2 of another d. on laid paper (Nos. 10/13) in sheets of 20 (4×5)

Eleven red top sheets

Fifteen black carbon sheets, three each from five of the top sheets

Six blue carbon sheets, one each from six of the top sheets

Twenty-two mauve carbon sheets, probably two from each top sheet

Varieties: "7" for "&" on R. 3/3, "postage" on R. 3/3, "Rvevue" on R. 1/3 and "Postagg" on R. 2/4, all from different top sheets. The position of "G.R?I?" is not known. "ONR" occurs from three different top sheets on R. 5/1, R. 5/2 & 4 or R. 4/1 and 5/2

2½d. on laid paper (Nos. 14/16) in sheets of 20 (4×5)

One black top sheet

One blue carbon sheet

Two mauve carbon sheets

6d. on laid paper (Nos. 17/19) in sheets of 20 (4×5)

One black top sheet

One blue carbon sheet*

Three mauve carbon sheets

Variety: "SIXPENCE" occurs on R. 1/2-3

1s. on laid paper (Nos. 20/2)

Five black top sheets, four of 20 (4×5) and one of 16 (4×4)

Nine black carbon sheets three each from two of the top sheets of 20 and three from the top sheet of 16

Two blue carbon sheets, one each from two of the top sheets of 20

Twelve mauve carbon sheets, nine from various top sheets of 20 and three from the top sheet of 16

Varieties: "ISLANA" occurs on R. 1/2 of one of the sheets of 20 and "Postge" on R. 1/3 of the sheet of 16. "Rebenue" comes from one of the other sheets of 20

½d. on wove paper (Nos. 23/5) in sheets of 24 (4×6)

One black top sheet

Three black carbon sheets

One blue carbon sheet*

One mauve carbon sheet

1d. on wove paper (Nos. 26/7) in sheets of 24 (4×6)

One red top sheet

Three black carbon sheets

One blue carbon sheet*

One mauve carbon sheet*

2d. on wove paper (Nos. 30/1) in sheets of 24 (4×6)

Two black top sheets

Six black carbon sheets, three from each top sheet. One initialled in red ink

Four mauve carbon sheets, two from each top sheet

Variety: the "1d." error occurs on R. 5/2 from one top sheet

2½d. on wove paper (Nos. 32/4) in sheets of 24 (4×6)

One black top sheet

Three black carbon sheets

One blue carbon sheet

One mauve carbon sheet

6d. on wove paper (Nos. 35/6) in sheets of 24 (4×6)

Two black top sheets

Six black carbon sheets, three from each top sheet

Two blue carbon sheets, one from each top sheet

Varieties: the "2d." error occurs on R. 5/3 from one top sheet which also showed "PENCC" on R. 3/2, and "Rvenne &" on R. 4/1 of the other

*These carbons are described in written records, but their existence has yet to be confirmed by actual examples.

Madagascar

PRICES FOR STAMPS ON COVER

Nos. 1/47	—
Nos. 50/6	from × 75
Nos. 57/62	from × 30

BRITISH CONSULAR MAIL

After May 1883 mail from the British community at Antananarivo, the capital, was sent by runner to the British Consulate at Tamatave for forwarding via the French Post Office.

In March of the following year the British Vice-Consul at Antananarivo, Mr. W. C. Pickersgill, reorganised this service and issued stamps for use on both local and overseas mail. Such stamps were only gummed at one of the top corners. This was to facilitate their removal from overseas mail where they were replaced by Mauritius stamps (at Port Louis) or by French issues (at the Vice-Consulate) for transmission via Tamatave and Reunion. Local mail usually had the stamps removed also, being marked with a "PAID" or a Vice-Consular handstamp, although a few covers have survived intact.

CONDITION. Due to the type of paper used, stamps of the British Consular Mail are usually found with slight faults, especially thins. Our prices are for average examples, really fine stamps being worth a premium.

USED STAMPS. Postmarks are not usually found on these issues. Cancellations usually take the form of a manuscript line or cross in crayon, ink or pencil or as five parallel horizontal bars in black, red or violet, approximately 15 mm long. Examples of Nos. 1/3, 5/8 and 11 showing a red diagonal line are believed to be cancelled-to-order.

1

2

1884 (Mar). *Typo locally. Rouletted vertically in colour. No gum, except on one upper corner. With circular consular handstamp reading* "BRITISH VICE-CONSULATE ANTANANARIVO" *around Royal arms in black.*

(a) Inscr "LETTER".

1	1	6d. (½ oz) magenta	£400	£425
		a. Violet handstamp	£2000	
2		1s. (1 oz) magenta	£375	£400
3		1s.6d. (1½oz) magenta	£425	
4		2s. (2 oz) magenta	£600	£650

(b) Inscr "POSTAL PACKET".

5	1	1d. (½ oz) magenta	£450	£375
		a. Without handstamp	£5500	£5500
6		2d. (2 oz) magenta	£275	£275
7		3d. (3 oz) magenta	£300	£275
8		4d. (1 oz amended in ms to "4 oz") magenta	£700	£600
		a. Without manuscript amendment	£3750	£3750
		ab. Without handstamp	£1200	
		ac. Without handstamp	£4500	£4500

Nos. 1/8 were printed in horizontal strips of four, each strip containing two impressions of the setting. Each strip usually contained two stamps with normal stops after "B.C.M." and two with a hollow stop after "B" (1d., 2d., 3d., 4d., 6d. and 2s.) or after "M" (1s. and 1s.6d.), although the 2d. and 3d. have also been seen with a hollow stop after "M" and the 6d. with hollow stops after both "B" and "C".

Several values are known with the handstamp either inverted or double.

1886. *Manuscript provisionals.*

(a) No. 2 with "SHILLING" *erased and* "PENNY" *written above in red ink.*

9	1	1d. on 1s. (1 oz) magenta	......

(b) No. 2 surch "4½d." *and* "W.C.P." *in red ink with a line through the original value.*

10	1	4½d. on 1s. (1 oz) magenta	......

1886. *As No. 1, but colour changed. Handstamped with circular* "BRITISH VICE-CONSULATE ANTANANARIVO" *in black.*

11	1	6d. (½ oz) rose-red	£750	£650

1886. *As No. 8a, but handstamped* "BRITISH CONSULAR MAIL ANTANANARIVO" *in black.*

12	1	4d. (1 oz) magenta	£1600	
		a. Violet handstamp	£4750	

1886. *Typo locally.* "POSTAGE" *and value in words printed in black. Rouletted vertically in colour. No gum, except on one upper corner.*

I. "POSTAGE" *29½ mm long. Stops after* "POSTAGE" *and value.*

(a) Handstamped "BRITISH VICE-CONSULATE ANTANANARIVO" *in black.*

14	2	1d. rose	£100	£130
		a. Violet handstamp	£275	
15		1½d. rose	£1500	£1000
		a. Violet handstamp	£900	£750
16		2d. rose	£150	
		a. Violet handstamp	£275	
17		3d. rose	£1500	£950
		a. Violet handstamp	£375	£325
18		4½d. rose	£950	£500
		a. Violet handstamp	£500	£300
19		8d. rose	£2750	£2500
		a. Violet handstamp	£1300	£1300
20		9d. rose	£2750	£2500
		a. Violet handstamp	£950	

(b) Handstamped "BRITISH CONSULAR MAIL ANTANANARIVO" *in black.*

21	2	1d. rose	80·00	
22		1½d. rose	85·00	
23		2d. rose	£100	
24		3d. rose	£100	£150
		a. Handstamp in red	†	£10000
25		4½d. rose	£110	£140
		a. Handstamp in red	†	£6000
26		8d. rose	£130	
		a. Handstamp in violet	£1300	
27		9d. rose	£140	£180
		a. Without handstamp	£3500	
		b. Handstamp in violet	£275	

II. "POSTAGE" *29½ mm long. No stops after* "POSTAGE" *or value.*

(a) Handstamped "BRITISH VICE-CONSULATE ANTANANARIVO" *in violet.*

28	2	1d. rose		£900
29		1½d. rose		£1800
30		3d. rose		£1100
31		4½d. rose		£1500
32		6d. rose		£1200

(b) Handstamped "BRITISH CONSULAR MAIL ANTANANARIVO" *in black.*

33	2	1d. rose	80·00	£130
		a. Without handstamp	£2500	
		b. Violet handstamp	£100	
34		1½d. rose	80·00	£120
		a. Without handstamp	£2500	
		b. Violet handstamp	£170	
35		2d. rose	80·00	£120
		b. Violet handstamp	£170	
36		3d. rose	£850	£130
		a. Without handstamp	£3750	
		b. Violet handstamp	£150	
37		4½d. rose	85·00	£130
		a. Without handstamp	£4000	
		b. Violet handstamp	£150	
38		6d. rose	90·00	£130
		a. Without handstamp	£4000	
		b. Violet handstamp	£350	

III. "POSTAGE" *24½ mm long. No stop after* "POSTAGE", *but stop after value.*

(a) Handstamped "BRITISH VICE-CONSULATE ANTANANARIVO" *in violet.*

39	2	4d. rose		£400
40		8d. rose		£550
40a		1s. rose		£10000
41		1s.6d. rose		£4750
42		2s. rose		£2500
		a. Handstamp in black		£9000

(b) Handstamped "BRITISH CONSULAR MAIL ANTANANARIVO" *in black.*

43		4d. rose		£200
		a. Without handstamp		£3000
		b. Violet handstamp		£425
44		8d. rose		£950
		a. Without handstamp		£3250
		b. Violet handstamp		£600
45		1s. rose		£450
		a. Without handstamp		£3750
		b. Violet handstamp		£1200
46		1s.6d. rose		£550
		a. Without handstamp		£3500
		b. Violet handstamp		£1300
47		2s. rose		£600
		a. Without handstamp		£3750
		b. Violet handstamp		£1500

The above were also printed in horizontal strips of four.

The stamps of the British Consular Mail were suppressed in 1887, but the postal service continued with the charges paid in cash.

BRITISH INLAND MAIL

In January 1895 the Malagasy government agreed that a syndicate of British merchants at Antananarivo, including the Vice-Consul, should operate an inland postal service during the war with France. Mail was sent by runner to the port of Vatomandry and forwarded via Durban where Natal stamps were added.

Nos. 50/62 were cancelled with dated circular postmarks inscribed "BRITISH MAIL".

4	5 Malagasy Runners

(Typeset London Missionary Society Press, Antananarivo)

1895 (1 Jan). *Rouletted in black.*

(a) Thick laid paper.

50	4	4d. black	30·00	14·00
		a. "FUOR" for "FOUR" (R. 3/2)	—	£900

(b) In black on coloured wove paper.

51	4	1d. blue-grey	30·00	13·00
52		6d. pale yellow	30·00	13·00
53		8d. salmon	30·00	13·00
54		1s. fawn	40·00	13·00
55		2s. bright rose	60·00	22·00
		a. Italic "2" at left (R. 1/2)	£140	60·00
56		4s. grey	65·00	13·00
50/6 Set of 7			£250	90·00

There are six types of each value, printed in blocks of 6 (2×3) separated by gutters, four times on each sheet; the upper and lower blocks being *tête-bêche*.

(Typo John Haddon & Co, London)

1895 (Mar). *The inscription in the lower label varies for each value.* P 12.

57	5	2d. blue	7·00	50·00
		a. Imperf between (horiz pair)	£400	
58		4d. rose	7·50	50·00
		a. Imperf between (horiz pair)	£250	
		b. Imperf between (vert pair)	£275	
		c. Imperf vert (horiz pair)	£275	
59		6d. green	7·50	50·00
		a. Imperf between (horiz pair)	£650	
60		1s. slate-blue	7·50	70·00
		a. Imperf between (horiz pair)	£425	
61		2s. chocolate	17·00	90·00
		a. Imperf between (horiz pair)	£475	
62		4s. bright purple	30·00	£130
		a. Imperf between (horiz pair)	£1700	
57/62 Set of 6			70·00	£400

This post was suppressed when the French entered Antananarivo on 30 September 1895.

Malaya

The Federation of Malaya was formed on 1 February 1948 by the former Straits Settlements of Malacca and Penang, the four Federated Malay States and the five Unfederated States. It did not, however, issue any stamps until it became an independent member of the Commonwealth in 1957.

The philatelic history of the component parts of the federation is most complex.

The method adopted is to show the general issues for the area first, before dealing with the issues for the individual States. The section is divided as follows:

I. STRAITS SETTLEMENTS
II. FEDERATED MALAY STATES
III. MALAYAN POSTAL UNION
IV. MALAYA (BRITISH MILITARY ADMINISTRATION)
V. MALAYAN STATES—Johore, Kedah, Kelantan, Malacca, Negri Sembilan (with Sungei Ujong), Pahang, Penang, Perak, Perlis, Selangor, Trengganu
VI. SIAMESE POSTS IN NORTHERN MALAYA 1887–1909
VII. JAPANESE OCCUPATION OF MALAYA 1942–45
VIII. THAI OCCUPATION OF MALAYA 1943–45

I. STRAITS SETTLEMENTS

The three original Settlements, Malacca, Penang (with Province Wellesley) and Singapore (with Christmas Island), were formed into a Crown Colony on 1 April 1867. The Cocos (Keeling) Islands were transferred to Straits Settlements on 7 February 1886. Labuan was attached to the Colony in 1896, becoming the fourth Settlement in 1906, but was transferred to North Borneo in 1946.

The first known prestamp cover with postal markings from Penang (Prince of Wales Island) is dated March 1806 and from Malacca, under British civil administration, February 1841. The civil post office at Singapore opened on 1 February 1823.

The stamps of India were used at all three post offices from late in 1854 until the Straits Settlements became a separate colony on 1 September 1867.

The Indian stamps were initially cancelled by dumb obliterators and their use in the Straits Settlements can only be identified from complete covers. In 1856 cancellations of the standard Indian octagonal type were issued, numbered "B 109" for Malacca, "B 147" for Penang and "B 172" for Singapore.

CURRENCY. Before 1867 official accounts of the East India Company administration for the Straits Settlements were kept in rupees, although the vast majority of commercial transactions used Spanish American

233

silver dollars, supplies of which reached Malaya via the Philippines.

This confusing situation was rapidly amended when the Straits Settlements became a Crown Colony on 1 April 1867 and Spanish American dollars were declared to be the only legal currency. In 1874 American trade dollars and Japanese yen were also accepted, but in 1890 recognition of the Spanish American dollars was restricted to those from the Mexican mints. A shortage of silver coinage led to the introduction of silver British trade dollars in 1895 which also circulated in Hong Kong and Labuan.

Dollar banknotes first appeared in 1899, but Mexican dollars were not finally replaced until the issue of silver Straits Settlements dollars in 1903, the gold value of which was set at 2s.4d. in January 1906.

A   B

C

The Penang and Singapore octagonals were replaced by a duplex type, consisting of a double-ringed datestamp and a diamond-shaped obliterator containing the office number, in 1863 and 1865 respectively.

D

E

PRICES. Catalogue prices in this section are for stamps with clearly legible, if partial, examples of the postmarks.

EAST INDIA COMPANY ADMINISTRATION
MALACCA

Stamps of INDIA cancelled with Type A.

1854. *(Nos. 2/34).*
Z1	½a. blue (Die I)	£1300
Z2	1a. red (Die I)	£1000
Z3	1a. dull red (Die II)	£1100
Z4	2a. green	£1500
Z4a	4a. blue *and* pale red (Head Die I) (cut-to-shape)	£1600
Z5	4a. blue and red (Head Die II) (cut-to-shape)	£1600
Z5a	4a. blue and red (Head Die III) (cut-to-shape)	£1600

1855. *(Nos. 35/6).*
Z6	8a. carmine *(Die I)*/blue glazed	£450

1856–64. *(Nos. 37/49).*
Z7	½a. pale blue (Die I)	£300
Z8	1a. brown	£200
Z8a	2a. dull pink	£325
Z9	2a. yellow-buff	£225
Z10	2a. yellow	£250
Z11	4a. green	£425
Z12	8a. carmine (Die I)	£300

1860. *(Nos. 51/3).*
Z13	8p. purple/bluish	£750
Z14	8p. purple/white	£375

1865. *(Nos. 54/65).*
Z15	4a. green	£425

PENANG

Stamps of INDIA cancelled with Type B.

1854. *(Nos. 2/34).*
Z20	½a. blue (Die I)	£425
Z21	1a. red (Die I)	£170
Z22	2a. green	£275
Z23	4a. blue *and* pale red (Head Die I)	£1600
Z24	4a. blue and red (Head Die II)	£1600
Z25	4a. blue and red (Head Die III)	£1100

1855. *(Nos. 35/6).*
Z26	4a. black/blue glazed	90·00

Z27	8a. carmine (Die I)/blue glazed	80·00
	a. Bisected (4a.) (1860) (on cover)	£60000

1856–64. *(Nos. 37/49).*
Z28	½a. pale blue (Die I)	85·00
Z29	1a. brown	50·00
Z30	2a. dull pink	75·00
Z31	2a. yellow-buff	70·00
Z32	2a. yellow	70·00
Z33	2a. orange	70·00
Z34	4a. black	50·00
Z35	8a. carmine (Die I)	65·00

1860. *(Nos. 51/3).*
Z36	8p. purple/white	£150

Stamps of INDIA cancelled with Type D.

1854. *(Nos. 2/34).*
Z38	1a. red (Die I)	£2750

1856–64. *(Nos. 37/49).*
Z39	½a. pale blue (Die I)	£190
Z40	1a. brown	55·00
Z41	2a. yellow	65·00
Z42	4a. black	55·00
Z43	4a. green	£160
Z44	8a. carmine (Die I)	60·00

1860. *(Nos. 51/3).*
Z45	8p. purple/white	90·00
Z46	8p. mauve	90·00

1865. *(Nos. 54/65).*
Z47	8p. purple/white	
Z48	1a. deep brown	55·00
Z49	2a. yellow	65·00
Z50	4a. green	£170
Z51	8a. carmine (Die I)	

1866–67. *(Nos. 69/72).*
Z52	4a. green *(Die I)*	£180

OFFICIAL STAMPS

1866–67. *(No. O2)*
Z54	½a. pale blue	

SINGAPORE

Stamps of INDIA cancelled with Type C.

1854. *(Nos. 2/34).*
Z60	½a. blue (Die I)	£170
Z61	1a. red (Die I)	£110
Z62	1a. dull red (Die II)	£140
Z63	1a. red (Die III)	£1300
Z64	2a. green	80·00
	a. Bisected (1a.) (1857) (on cover)	£130000
Z65	4a. blue *and* pale red (Head Die I)	£1200
Z66	4a. blue and red (Head Die II)	£1300
Z67	4a. blue and red (Head Die III)	£800

1855. *(Nos. 35/6).*
Z68	4a. black/blue glazed	40·00
	a. Bisected *(2a.)* (1859) (on cover)	£7500
Z69	8a. carmine/blue glazed	40·00
	a. Bisected (4a.) (1859) (on cover)	£55000

1856–66. *(Nos. 37/49).*
Z70	½a. pale blue (Die I)	42·00
Z71	1a. brown	24·00
	a. Bisected (½a.) (1859) (on cover)	£60000
Z72	2a. dull pink	42·00
Z73	2a. yellow-buff	35·00
Z74	2a. yellow	38·00
Z75	2a. orange	42·00
Z76	4a. black	24·00
	a. Bisected *(2a.)* (1859) (on cover)	£21000
Z77	4a. green	£120
Z78	8a. carmine (Die I)	32·00
	a. Bisected (4a.) (1866) (on cover)	£55000

1860–61. *(Nos. 51/3).*
Z79	8p. purple/bluish	£500
Z80	8p. purple/white	65·00
	a. Bisected diagonally (4p.) (1861) (on cover)	£55000
Z81	8p. mauve	70·00

1865. *(Nos. 54/65).*
Z82	½a. blue (Die I)	50·00
Z83	8p. purple	£130
Z84	1a. deep brown	40·00
Z85	2a. yellow	42·00
Z86	2a. orange	42·00
Z87	4a. green	£110
Z88	8a. carmine (Die I)	£275

1866–67. *(Nos. 69/72).*
Z89	4a. green *(Die I)*	£140
Z90	6a.8p. slate	£300

OFFICIAL STAMPS

1866–67. *(Nos. O6/14).*
Z91	½a. pale blue	£400
Z92	2a. yellow	£550

Stamps of INDIA cancelled with Type E.

1856–64. *(Nos. 37/49).*
Z100	1a. brown	£275
Z101	2a. yellow	£350
Z102	4a. black	£350
Z103	8a. carmine (Die I)	£350

1860. *(Nos. 51/3).*
Z104	8p. purple/white	£375

1865. *(Nos. 54/65).*
Z105	2a. yellow	£325
Z106	2a. orange	£325
Z107	4a. green	£400

PRICES FOR STAMPS ON COVER		
Nos.1/9	*from* × 15	
No. 10		
Nos.11/19	*from* × 8	
Nos.20/1	*from* × 20	
Nos.22/39	*from* × 10	
Nos.41/6	*from* × 20	
No. 47		
Nos.48/9	*from* × 20	
Nos.50/62	*from* × 20	
Nos.63/71	*from* × 15	
No. 72		
Nos.73/8	*from* × 20	
No. 80	*from* × 30	
Nos.82/5	*from* × 10	
Nos.86/7	*from* × 20	
Nos.88/94	*from* × 15	
Nos.95/105	*from* × 8	
Nos.106/9	*from* × 20	
Nos.110/21	*from* × 6	
No. 122		
Nos.123/6	*from* × 5	
Nos.127/38	*from* × 4	
Nos.139/40		
Nos.141/51	*from* × 4	
Nos.152/67	*from* × 4	
Nos.168/9		
Nos.193/212	*from* × 3	
Nos.213/15		
Nos.216/17	*from* × 10	
Nos.218/40a	*from* × 3	
Nos.240b/d		
Nos.241/55	*from* × 15	
Nos.256/9	*from* × 4	
Nos.260/98	*from* × 3	
Nos.D1/6	*from* × 20	

PRINTERS. All Straits Settlements issues were printed in typography by De La Rue & Co, Ltd, London, *unless otherwise stated.*

USED PRICES. The prices quoted for Nos. 1/9 are for fine used examples. Those showing parts of commercial "chops" are worth less.

CROWN COLONY
(Currency. 100 cents = 1 Spanish American dollar)

THREE HALF CENTS   **32 CENTS**
(1)   (2)

1867 (1 Sept). *Nos. 54, 59, 61, 69 and 73 of India surch as T* **1** *or* **2** *(24c., 32c.) by De La Rue.* W **13** (Elephant's head) *of India.* P 14.
1	1½c. on ½a. blue (Die I) (R.)	90·00	£200
2	2c. on 1a. deep brown (R.)	£130	80·00
3	3c. on 1a. deep brown (B.)	£130	85·00
4	4c. on 1a. deep brown (Bk.)	£250	£250
5	6c. on 2a. yellow (P.)	£550	£225
6	8c. on 2a. yellow (G.)	£190	42·00
7	12c. on 4a. green (R.)	£950	£300
	a. Surch double	£2250	
8	24c. on 8a. rose (Die II) (B.)	£425	80·00
9	32c. on 2a. yellow (Bk.)	£350	90·00

The 32c. was re-issued for postal use in 1884.
No. 7a. is only known unused.

1869. (?) *No. 1 with "THREE HALF" deleted and "2" written above, in black manuscript.*
10	2 on 1½c. on ½a. blue	£12000	£5000

This stamp has been known from very early days and was apparently used at Penang, but nothing is known of its history.

5   6   7

8   9

1867 (Dec)–**72.** *Ornaments in corners differ for each value.* Wmk Crown CC. P 14.
11	**5**	2c. brown (6.68)	30·00	4·50
		a. Yellow-brown	32·00	4·50
		b. Deep brown	85·00	12·00
		w. Wmk inverted	†	£150
12		4c. rose (7.68)	55·00	8·00
		a. Deep rose	65·00	11·00
		w. Wmk inverted		£150
13		6c. dull lilac (1.68)	90·00	16·00
		a. *Bright lilac*	95·00	16·00
		w. Wmk inverted	†	£180
14	**6**	8c. orange-yellow (1.68)	£150	11·00
		a. *Orange*	£150	11·00
		w. Wmk inverted	£325	£110

15		12c. blue	£120	6·50
		a. Ultramarine	£130	9·00
		w. Wmk inverted	£350	
16	7	24c. blue-green	£120	5·00
		a. Yellow-green	£250	21·00
17	8	30c. claret (12.72)	£225	11·00
			†	£325
18	9	32c. pale red	£475	65·00
		w. Wmk inverted	†	£250
19		96c. grey	£300	48·00
		a. Perf 12½ (6.71)	£2250	£225

Five Cents. **Seven Cents.**
(10) (11)

1879 (May). *Nos. 14a and 18 surch with T* **10** *and* **11**.

20	6	5c. on 8c. orange	£100	£150
		a. No stop after "Cents"	£800	£850
		b. "F i" spaced	£850	£900
21	9	7c. on 32c. pale red	£130	£160
		a. No stop after "Cents"	£1200	£1300

The no stop error occured once in the setting.

10 cents.
(12)

10 **10** **10** **10**
(a) (b) (c) (d)

10 **10** **10** **10**
(e) (f) (g) (h)

10 **10** **10** **10** **10**
(i) (j) (jj) (k) (l)

(a) "1" thin curved serif and thin foot; "0" narrow.
(b) "1" thick curved serif and thick foot: "0" broad. Both numerals heavy.
(c) "1" as (a); "0" as (b).
(d) "1" as (a) but thicker; "0" as (a).
(e) As (a) but sides of "0" thicker.
(f) "1" as (d); "0" as (e).
(g) As (a) but "0" narrower.
(h) "1" thin, curved serif and thick foot; "0" as (g).
(i) "1" as (b); "0" as (a).
(j) "1" as (d); "0" as (g) but raised.
(jj) "1" as (a) but shorter, and with shorter serif and thicker foot; "0" as (g) but level with "1".
(k) "1" as (jj); "0" as (a).
(l) "1" straight serif; "0" as (g).

1880 (Mar). *No. 17 surch with T* **12** *(showing numerals (a) to (jj))*.

22		10c. on 30c. claret (a)	£400	80·00
23		10c. on 30c. claret (b)	£375	75·00
24		10c. on 30c. claret (c)	£6000	£750
25		10c. on 30c. claret (d)	£2500	£250
26		10c. on 30c. claret (e)	£10000	£1500
27		10c. on 30c. claret (f)	£10000	£1500
28		10c. on 30c. claret (h)	£3750	£475
29		10c. on 30c. claret (h)	£10000	£1500
30		10c. on 30c. claret (i)	£10000	£1500
31		10c. on 30c. claret (j)	£10000	£1500
32		10c. on 30c. claret (jj)	£10000	£1500

Nos. 22/32 come from the same setting of 60 (6×10) containing twenty examples of No. 22 (R. 1/1-2, 1/4, 1/6, 2/1-6, 3/1, 3/3, 3/5, 4/1, 4/3-4, 10/1, 10/3-5), twenty-two of No. 23 (R. 4/6, 5/1-6, 6/1-6, 7/1, 8/2-4, 9/1-5), six of No. 25 (R. 1/5, 3/2, 3/4, 4/2, 4/5, 10/2), four of No. 28 (R. 7/2-5), two of No. 24 (R. 9/6, 10/6) and one each of Nos. 26 (R. 3/6), 27 (R. 1/3), 29 (R. 7/6), 30 (R. 8/1), 31 (R. 8/6) and 32 (R. 8/5).

No. 23 is known with large stop after "cents" and also with stop low.

1880 (Apr). *No. 17 surch as T* **12**, *but without "cents.", showing numerals (a) to (c), (g) to (i), (k) and (l)*.

33		10 on 30c. claret (a)	£180	50·00
		w. Wmk inverted	†	£170
34		10 on 30c. claret (b)	£190	50·00
		w. Wmk inverted	†	£170
35		10 on 30c. claret (c)	£600	£110
		w. Wmk inverted	†	£375
36		10 on 30c. claret (g)	£1500	£325
		aw. Wmk inverted	†	£750
36b		10 on 30c. claret (h)	†	
37		10 on 30c. claret (i)	£4250	£850
38		10 on 30c. claret (k)	£4250	£850
39		10 on 30c. claret (l)	£4250	£850

Nos. 33/9 were surcharged from an amended setting of 60 (6×10) of which 59 positions have been identified. Of those known No. 33 occurs on twenty-four (R. 6/1-2, 7/1-6, 8/1-6, 9/1-2, 9/6, 10/1-3). No. 34 on twenty-one (R. 1/2-6, 2/1-6, 3/1-6, 4/3-5, 5/6), No. 35 on eight (R. 1/1, 4/2, 4/6, 5/1-5), No. 36 on three (R. 9/3-5) and Nos. 37 (R. 10/6), 38 (R. 10/4) and 39 (R. 10/5) on one each. R. 4/1 remains unidentified.

The existence of No. 36b, known as a single example from the 6th vertical column, and a stamp in the Royal Collection with "1" as (b) and "0" as (g) suggests that there may have been another setting.

5 **5** **5**
cents. cents. cents.
(13) (14) (15)

1880 (Aug). *No. 14a surch with T* **13** *to* **15**.

41	13	5c. on 8c. orange	£140	£170
42	14	5c. on 8c. orange	£130	£160
43	15	5c. on 8c. orange	£500	£600

Surcharged in a setting of 60 (6×10) with *T* **13** on rows one to four, *T* **14** on rows five to nine and *T* **15** on row ten.

10 cents. **5 cents.**
(16) (17)

1880–81. *Nos. 13, 15/a and 17 surch with T* **16**.

44		10c. on 6c. lilac (11.81)	60·00	6·00
		a. Surch double	—	£2500
45		10c. on 12c. ultramarine (1.81)	70·00	16·00
		a. Blue	50·00	9·00
46		10c. on 30c. claret (12.80)	£400	90·00

A second printing of the 10c. on 6c. has the surcharge heavier and the "10" usually more to the left or right of "cents".

1882 (Jan). *No. 12 surch with T* **17**.

47		5c. on 4c. rose	£275	£300

18   19

1882 (Jan). *Wmk Crown CC. P* 14.

48	18	5c. purple-brown	90·00	£100
49	19	10c. slate	£425	65·00
		s. Optd "Specimen"	£425	

1882. *Wmk Crown CA. P* 14.

50	5	2c. brown (Aug)	£275	40·00
51		4c. red (April)	£120	6·50
52	6	8c. orange (Sept)	3·00	1·00
		w. Wmk inverted		
53	19	10c. slate (Oct)	6·00	1·25
		w. Wmk inverted		

For the 4c. in deep carmine see No. 98.

TWO CENTS **TWO CENTS** **TWO CENTS**
20a "S" wide   20b "E" and "S" wide   20c "N" wide

TWO CENTS **TWO CENTS** **TWO CENTS**
20d All letters narrow   20e "EN" and "S" wide   20f "E" wide

1883 (Apr). *Nos. 52 and 18 surch with T* **20a/f**.

54	20a	2c. on 8c. orange	£225	£110
55	20b	2c. on 8c. orange	£225	£110
56	20c	2c. on 8c. orange	£225	£110
57	20d	2c. on 8c. orange	£130	80·00
		a. Surch double	£2750	£1000
58	20e	2c. on 8c. orange	£1300	£550
59	20a	2c. on 32c. pale red	£750	£200
60	20f	2c. on 32c. pale red	£900	£250
		a. Surch double		

The 8c. was surcharged using one of two triplet settings, either 54 + 55 + 56 or 57 + 57 + 57, applied to rows 2 to 10. A single handstamp, either No. 57 or No. 58, was then used to complete row 1. The 32c. was surcharged in the same way with a triplet of 59 + 60 + 59 and a single handstamp as No. 60.

2 Cents. **4 Cents** **8 Cents**
(21) (22) (23)

1883 (June–July). *Nos. 51 and 15 surch with T* **21**.

61	2c. on 4c. rose	75·00	85·00
	a. "s" of "Cents" inverted	£1200	£1300
62	2c. on 12c. blue (July)	£300	£150
	a. "s" of "Cents" inverted	£4500	£2500

The inverted "S" error occurred once in the setting of 60.

Broken oval above "O" of "POSTAGE" (Lower right pane R. 10/5)

1883 (July)–91. *Wmk Crown CA. P* 14.

63	5	2c. pale rose	35·00	3·50
		a. Bright rose (1889)	8·00	85
64		4c. pale brown	28·00	1·75
		a. Broken oval	£275	60·00
		b. Deep brown	40·00	3·25
		ba. Broken oval	£400	90·00
		w. Wmk inverted	£130	80·00
65	18	5c. blue (8.83)	14·00	1·00
		w. Wmk inverted	†	£225
66	5	6c. lilac (11.84)	25·00	10·00
		a. Violet	2·00	4·50
		w. Wmk inverted	—	£150
67	6	8c. brown-purple	65·00	13·00
68	7	24c. yellow-green (2.84)	75·00	7·00
		a. Blue-green	5·00	3·75
		w. Wmk inverted	†	£200
69	8	30c. claret (9.91)	11·00	12·00
		w. Wmk inverted	90·00	75·00
70	9	32c. orange-vermilion (1.87)	7·50	2·75
		w. Wmk inverted	60·00	60·00
71		96c. olive-grey (7.88)	75·00	50·00
63a/71		*Set of 9*	£200	75·00
63s/5s, 67s		*Optd "Specimen" Set of 4*	£950	

Most examples of the 4c. in shades of olive-bistre are thought to be colour changelings.

For the 4c. in deep carmine and 12c. in claret see Nos. 98 and 102.

1884 (Feb–Aug). *Nos. 65, 15 and 67 surch with T* **22** *or* **23**.

72	18	4c. on 5c. blue (Aug)	£3250	£4000
73		4c. on 5c. blue (R.) (Aug)	£120	£100
74	6	8c. on 12c. blue	£500	£150
		w. Wmk inverted	†	£475
75		8c. on 12c. brown-purple (Aug)	£375	£140
		a. Inverted "8"	†	
		b. "s" of "Cents" low (R. 5/1)	£3500	£1300

1884 (Aug). *No. 65 surch with T* **20d/f**.

76	20d	2c. on 5c. blue	£130	£140
77	20e	2c. on 5c. blue	£130	£140
		a. Pair, with and without surch..		
		b. Surch double		
78	20f	2c. on 5c. blue	£130	£140

Surcharged as a triplet, 77 + 76 + 78. On No. 76 "TS" are dropped below the line.

8 **3** **THREE CENTS**
CENTS CENTS
(24) (25) (26)

1884 (Sept). *No. 75 additionally surch with large numeral as T* **24** *in red*.

80	6	8 on 8c. on 12c. dull purple	£275	£300
		a. Surch T **24** double	£5000	
		b. Surch T **23** in blue	£8000	
		c. "s" of "Cents" low	£2250	£2500

Examples as No. 75, but with Type **23** in blue, were further surcharged in error.

A similar "4" surcharge in red on No. 73 exists from a trial printing of which seven examples are known, all used on an official's correspondence (*Price £25000 used*).

1885. *No. 65 and T* **9** *in new colour, wmk Crown CA, surch with T* **25** *or* **26**.

82	25	3c. on 5c. blue (Sept)	£130	£225
		a. Surch double	£2500	
83	26	3c. on 5c. pale magenta (Dec)	3·00	3·75
		a. Deep magenta	1·25	1·00
		s. Optd "Specimen"	£225	

The surcharge on No. 82 was applied locally by a triplet setting. No. 83 was surcharged by De La Rue in complete panes.

3 cents **2 Cents**
(27) (28)

1886 (Apr). *No. 48 surch with T* **27**.

84	18	3c. on 5c. purple-brown	£200	£225

The surcharge on No. 84 was applied by a triplet setting.

1887 (July). *No. 65 surch with T* **28**.

85	18	2c. on 5c. blue	25·00	70·00
		a. "C" of "Cents" omitted	—	£3000
		b. Surch double	£1200	£1100

The surcharge on No. 85 was applied by a triplet setting.

10 CENTS **THIRTY CENTS**
(29) (30)

1891 (Nov). *Nos. 68 and 70 surch with T* **29** *and* **30**.

86	7	10c. on 24c. yellow-green	3·50	1·25
		a. Narrow "0" in "10" (R. 4/6)	28·00	30·00
		w. Wmk inverted	60·00	65·00
87	9	30c. on 32c. orange-vermilion	8·50	3·50
		w. Wmk inverted		

The "R" of "THIRTY" and "N" of "CENTS" are found wide or narrow and in all possible combinations.

ONE CENT **ONE CENT**
(31) (32)

1892. *Stamps of 1882–91 (wmk Crown CA) surch with T* **31**.
88	1c. on 2c. bright rose (Mar)		2·00	3·75
89	1c. on 4c. brown (Apr)		5·00	5·50
	a. Surch double		£1500	
	b. Broken oval		£120	£130
	w. Wmk inverted		£160	
90	1c. on 6c. lilac (Feb)		1·40	6·00
	a. Surch double, one inverted		£1600	£1500
	w. Wmk inverted		£160	
91	1c. on 8c. orange (Jan)		1·00	1·25
92	1c. on 12c. brown-purple (Mar)		5·00	9·00
88/92	*Set of* 5		13·00	23·00

The three settings used for Nos. 88/92 contained various combinations of the following varieties: "ON" of "ONE" and "N" of "CENT" wide; "O" wide, "N" of "ONE" narrow and "N" of "CENT" wide; "O" narrow and both letters "N" wide; "ON" narrow and "N" of "CENT" wide; "O" wide and both letters "N" wide; "O" wide and "N" of "CENT" narrow; "ON" and "N" of "CENT" narrow; "O" narrow, "N" of "ONE" wide and "N" of "CENT" narrow. Antique "N" and "E" letters also occur.

1892–94. *Colours changed. Wmk Crown CA. P* 14. *Surch with T* **32** *and* **26** *by De La Rue.*
93	**6**	1c. on 8c. green (3.92)	1·00	1·50
94	**9**	3c. on 32c. carmine-rose (6.94)	2·25	70
		a. Surch omitted	£4000	
93s/4s		Optd "Specimen" *Set of* 2	£130	

No. 94a comes from a sheet found at Singapore on which all stamps in the upper left pane had the surcharge omitted. Five vertical inter-panneau pairs still exist with the surcharge omitted on the upper stamps (*Price* £30000 *unused*). The only used example of the error is on cover.

4 cents.

33	34	(35)

1892 (Mar)**–99.** *Wmk Crown CA. P* 14.
95	**33**	1c. green (9.92)	4·50	70
		a. Malformed "S"	£375	£140
		b. Repaired "S"	£350	£130
96		3c. carmine-rose (2.95)	11·00	40
		a. Malformed "S"	£475	£150
97		3c. brown (3.99)	7·00	60
		a. Repaired "S"	£425	£150
		b. *Yellow-brown*	6·00	60
98	**5**	4c. deep carmine (7.99)	6·00	1·25
		a. Broken oval	£150	80·00
99	**18**	5c. brown (6.94)	7·00	1·00
100		5c. magenta (7.99)	2·25	2·00
101	**6**	8c. ultramarine (6.94)	4·50	50
		a. *Bright blue*	7·00	80
102		12c. claret (3.94)	14·00	8·50
103	**33**	25c. purple-brown and green	26·00	6·50
		a. Malformed "S"	£800	£375
		b. Repaired "S"	£750	£350
		c. *Dull purple and green*	26·00	6·00
104		50c. olive-green and carmine	20·00	2·50
		a. Repaired "S"	£800	£325
105	**34**	$5 orange and carmine (10.98)	£325	£250
		a. Repaired "S"	£3250	£3250
95/105		*Set of* 11	£375	£250
95s/101s, 103s/5s		Optd "Specimen" *Set of* 10	£500	

For illustrations of 95a/b, 96a, 97a, 103a/b, 104a and 105a see above Gambia No. 37.

1898 (26 Dec)**.** *T* **18** *and* **6** *surch with T* **35** *at Singapore.*
106	4c. on 5c. brown (No. 99)		2·75	4·75
107	4c. on 5c. blue (No. 65)		4·50	14·00
	a. Surch double		—	£1500
108	4c. on 8c. ultramarine (No. 101)		1·60	2·75
	a. Surch double		£1200	£1100
	b. *Bright blue* (No. 101a)		1·00	1·00
106/8b	*Set of* 3		7·25	18·00

Nos. 107 and 108b exist with stop spaced 1½ mm from the "S" (R. 10/6).

FOUR CENTS

(36)	37	38

1899 (Mar)**.** *T* **18** *(wmk Crown CA. P* 14*), surch with T* **36** *by De La Rue.*
109	4c. on 5c. carmine		1·00	30
	a. Surch omitted		£28000	
	s. Optd "Specimen"		48·00	
	x. Wmk reversed		80·00	

No. 109a is only known unused.

1902 (Apr)**–03.** *Wmk Crown CA. P* 14.
110	**37**	1c. grey-green (7.02)	2·75	3·00
		a. *Pale green*	4·50	3·25
111		3c. dull purple and orange	3·50	20
		w. Wmk inverted	—	£250
112		4c. purple/*red* (9.02)	4·75	30
113	**38**	5c. dull purple (8.02)	5·50	85
114		8c. purple/*blue*	4·25	20
115		10c. purple and black/*yellow* (9.02)	25·00	1·50
116	**37**	25c. dull purple and green (8.02)	14·00	6·00
117	**38**	30c. grey and carmine (7.02)	18·00	8·00
118	**37**	50c. deep green and carmine (9.02)	20·00	20·00
		a. *Dull green and carmine*	23·00	23·00
119	**38**	$1 dull green and black (9.02)	23·00	70·00
120	**37**	$2 dull green and black (9.02)	75·00	75·00
121	**38**	$5 dull green & brown-orange (10.02)	£200	£170
122	**37**	$100 purple and green/*yellow* (3.03)	£12000	
		s. Optd "Specimen"	£500	
110/21		*Set of* 12	£350	£325
110s/21s		Optd "Specimen" *Set of* 12	£375	

(Currency 100 cents = 1 Straits, later Malayan, dollar)

39	40

41	42

(Des N. Trotter and W. Egerton)

1903 (Dec)**–04.** *Wmk Crown CA. P* 14.
123	**39**	1c. grey-green	2·25	8·00
124	**40**	3c. dull purple (1.04)	11·00	4·50
125	**41**	4c. purple/*red* (4.04)	6·50	30
		w. Wmk inverted	†	£250
126	**42**	8c. purple/*blue* (7.04)	50·00	1·25
123/6		*Set of* 4	65·00	12·50
123s/6s		Optd "Specimen" *Set of* 4	£160	

1904 (Aug)**–10.** *Wmk Multiple Crown CA. Ordinary paper(1c. to $1 and $5)or chalk-surfaced paper($2, $25, $100). P* 14.
127	**39**	1c. deep green (9.04)	3·50	10
		a. Chalk-surfaced paper (12.05)	11·00	1·50
		aw. Wmk inverted	£100	65·00
128	**40**	3c. dull purple	2·50	30
		a. Chalk-surfaced paper (8.06)	11·00	1·50
		aw. Wmk inverted	£110	75·00
		b. *Plum* (2.08)	8·00	1·75
129	**41**	4c. purple/*red* (11.04)	13·00	75
		a. Chalk-surfaced paper (10.05)	13·00	1·25
		aw. Wmk inverted	75·00	60·00
130	**38**	5c. dull purple (12.06)	13·00	2·25
		a. Chalk-surfaced paper (12.06)	16·00	8·50
		ay. Wmk inverted and reversed	†	£300
131	**42**	8c. purple/*blue* (8.05)	32·00	1·50
		a. Chalk-surfaced paper (12.05)	27·00	2·75
132	**38**	10c. purple and black/*yellow* (8.05)	8·00	80
		a. Chalk-surfaced paper (11.05)	12·00	3·00
133	**37**	25c. dull purple and green (1.05)	38·00	25·00
		a. Chalk-surfaced paper (11.05)	45·00	25·00
134	**38**	30c. grey and carmine (3.05)	48·00	2·50
		a. Chalk-surfaced paper (3.06)	55·00	2·75
135	**37**	50c. dull green and carmine (10.05)	60·00	15·00
		a. Chalk-surfaced paper (11.06)	30·00	15·00
136	**38**	$1 dull green and black (3.05)	55·00	24·00
		a. Chalk-surfaced paper (3.06)	48·00	18·00
137	**37**	$2 dull green and black (10.05)	£110	90·00
138	**38**	$5 dull green & brown-orange (10.05)	£225	£170
		a. Chalk-surfaced paper (1.08)	£200	£150
139	**37**	$25 grey-green and black (7.06)	£1800	£1800
		s. Optd "Specimen"	£250	
140		$100 purple and green/*yellow* (6.10)	£13000	
127/38	*Set of* 12		£500	£275

STRAITS SETTLEMENTS.
(43)

Straits Settlements
(44)

STRAITS SETTLEMENTS.

FOUR CENTS.

(45)

1906 (20 Dec)**–07.** *T* **18** *of Labuan (Nos. 117 etc.) optd with T* **43** *or* **44** *(10c.) or additionally surch with T* **45***, in black (No. 145), claret (No. 151) or brown-red (others) at Singapore. P* 13½–14.
141		1c. black and purple (P 14½–15)	70·00	£180
		a. Perf 14	£325	£450
		b. Line through "B"	£650	
142		2c. black and green	£350	£425
		a. Perf 14½–15	£180	£325
		b. Perf 13½–14 comp 12–13	£1200	£1200
		c. Line through "B"	£1100	
143		3c. black and sepia (1.07)	20·00	85·00
		a. Line through "B"	£350	
144		4c. on 12c. black and yellow	2·75	6·50
		a. No stop after "CENTS" (R. 1/8, 6/8)	£400	
		b. Line through "B"	£180	£275
145		4c. on 16c. green and brown (Blk.)	5·50	8·00
		a. "STRAITS SETTLEMENTS" in both brown-red and black	£650	£700
		b. Ditto. In vert pair with normal	£5000	
		c. Line through "B"	£190	£300
146		4c. on 18c. black and pale brown	2·75	7·00
		a. No stop after "CENTS" (R. 1/8, 6/8)	£325	
		b. "FOUR CENTS" and bar double	£8000	
		c. "FOUR CENTS" and bar 1½ mm below normal position (pair with normal)	£1600	
		d. Line through "B"	£180	£275
147		8c. black and vermilion	3·75	8·00
		a. Line through "B"	£180	£300
148		10c. brown and slate	8·50	8·50
		a. No stop after "Settlements" (R. 1/4, 6/4)	£375	
		b. Line through "B"	£250	£275
149		25c. green and greenish blue (1.07)	19·00	42·00

---

		a. Perf 14½–15	£100	£150
		b. Perf 13½–14 comp 14½–15	£400	
		c. Line through "B"	£350	
150		50c. dull purple and lilac (1.07)	18·00	70·00
		a. Line through "B"	£400	
151		$1 claret and orange (Claret) (1.07)	48·00	£120
		a. Perf 14½–15	£700	
		b. Line through "B"	£650	£1000
141/51	*Set of* 11		£350	£750

Nos. 141/51 were overprinted by a setting of 50 (10×5) applied twice to the sheets of 100. The "FOUR CENTS" surcharges were applied separately by a similar setting.

No. 145a shows impressions of Type **43** in both brown-red and black. It is known from one complete sheet and the top half of another.

No. 146b occurred on row 5 from one sheet only. No. 146c occurred on R. 4/10 and 9/10 of the first printing.

The line through "B" flaw occurs on R. 5/10 of the basic stamp. For illustration see Labuan.

46	47

1906 (Sept)**–12.** *Wmk Mult Crown CA. Ordinary paper(1c. to 10c.)or chalk-surfaced paper(21c. to $500). P* 14.
152	**39**	1c. blue-green (3.10)	23·00	1·10
153	**40**	3c. red (6.08)	4·25	10
154	**41**	4c. red (7.07)	6·50	2·50
155		4c. dull purple (2.08)	6·00	10
		a. Chalk-surfaced paper (1.12)	11·00	2·50
		as. Optd "Specimen"	90·00	
156		4c. claret (9.11)	2·50	80
157	**38**	5c. orange (4.09)	2·75	2·50
158	**42**	8c. blue	3·75	80
159	**38**	10c. purple/*yellow* (7.08)	9·00	1·00
		a. Chalk-surfaced paper (5.12)	17·00	9·00
160	**46**	21c. dull purple and claret (11.10)	6·50	38·00
161	**37**	25c. dull and bright purple (7.09)	16·00	8·00
162	**38**	30c. purple and orange-yellow (11.09)	45·00	4·25
163	**46**	45c. black/*green* (11.10)	2·50	4·00
164	**37**	50c. black/*green* (4.10)	5·00	5·00
165	**38**	$1 black and red/*blue* (10.10)	15·00	5·50
166	**37**	$2 green and red/*yellow* (12.09)	24·00	24·00
167	**38**	$5 green and red/*green* (11.09)	£130	75·00
		w. Wmk inverted	£950	
168	**47**	$25 purple and blue/*blue* (5.11)	£1700	£1300
		s. Optd "Specimen"	£350	
169		$500 purple and orange (5.10)	£110000	
		s. Optd "Specimen"	£1500	
152/67	*Set of* 16		£275	£160
153s/67s	Optd "Specimen" *Set of* 15		£750	

Beware of dangerous forgeries of No. 169.

48	49	50

51	52	53

54

1912–23. *$25, $100 and $500 as T* **47**, *but with head of King George V. Die I (5, 10, 25, 30, 50c., $1, $2, $5). Wmk Mult Crown CA. Ordinary paper(Nos. 193/6, 198/201, 203) or chalk-surfaced paper (others). P* 14.
193	**48**	1c. green (3.13)	7·00	1·25
		a. *Pale green* (1.14)	7·50	1·25
		b. *Blue-green* (1917)	7·50	1·75
		bw. Wmk inverted	†	£275
194		1c. black (2.19)	2·00	1·00
		w. Wmk inverted	†	£275
195	**52**	2c. green (10.19)	1·50	50
196	**49**	2c. red (2.13)	3·25	1·25
		a. *Scarlet* (2.17)	2·50	10
		y. Wmk inverted and reversed	£275	
197	**50**	4c. dull purple (3.13)	2·00	60
		a. Wmk sideways	†	£1700
		w. Wmk inverted	†	£275
198		4c. rose-scarlet (2.19)	2·25	15
		b. *Carmine*	1·75	20
199	**51**	5c. orange (8.12)	2·00	50
		a. *Yellow-orange*	3·25	1·00
200	**52**	6c. dull claret (3.20)	2·00	50
		a. *Deep claret*	6·50	2·75
		aw. Wmk inverted	£275	£275
201		8c. ultramarine (3.13)	2·75	80
		w. Wmk inverted	†	£275
202	**51**	10c. purple/*yellow* (9.12)	1·50	1·00
		aw. Wmk inverted	†	£300

		b. *White back* (1913)......................	1·50	1·10
		bs. Optd "Specimen".....................	50·00	
		c. *On lemon* (1916)......................	17·00	1·25
		cs. Optd "Specimen".....................	75·00	
		d. Wmk sideways.....................	†	£3250
203		10c. deep bright blue (1918)......	6·50	40
		a. *Bright blue* (1919)...............	4·00	50
204	53	21c. dull and bright purple (11.13) ...	7·00	9·50
205	54	25c. dull and mauve (7.14)........	14·00	11·00
		aw. Wmk inverted...................	£130	£150
		b. *Dull purple and violet* (1919)...	70·00	13·00
207	51	30c. dull purple and orange (12.14)..	8·00	2·75
208	53	45c. black/*green* (*white back*) (12.14)	6·50	18·00
		a. *On blue-green, olive back* (7.18).....................	3·75	20·00
		as. Optd "Specimen"...............	60·00	
		b. *On emerald back* (6.22).....	3·25	13·00
209	54	50c. black/*green* (7.14)............	5·50	3·50
		a. *On blue-green, olive back* (1918).....................	18·00	7·50
		b. *On emerald back* (1921).....	12·00	9·50
		c. Die II. *On emerald back* (1922)	3·00	4·00
		cs. Optd "Specimen"...............	60·00	
210	51	$1 black and red/*blue* (10.14)...	10·00	9·50
		w. Wmk inverted...................	£150	£160
211	54	$2 grn & red/*yell, white back* (1914).....................	12·00	45·00
		a. *Green and red/yellow* (1915).....	11·00	45·00
		as. Optd "Specimen"...............	60·00	
		b. *On orange-buff* (1921)........	60·00	75·00
		c. *On pale yellow* (1921)........	65·00	85·00
212	51	$5 grn & red/*grn, white back* (11.13).....................	90·00	45·00
		a. *Green and red/green* (1915)......	90·00	70·00
		as. Optd "Specimen"...............	80·00	
		b. *On blue-green, olive back* (1918).....................	£160	95·00
		bw. Wmk inverted...................		
		c. *On emerald back* (1920)......	£190	£110
		d. Die II. *On emerald back* (1923)	£110	75·00
		ds. Optd "Specimen"...............	95·00	
213	—	$25 purple and blue/*blue*.........	£1500	£450
		a. Break in scroll................	£2500	
		b. Broken crown and scroll.......	£2500	
		e. Break in lines below scroll.....	£2500	
		f. Damaged leaf at bottom right....	£2500	
		s. Optd "Specimen"...............	£300	
214	—	$100 black and carmine/*blue* (8.12)...	£6500	
		a. Break in scroll................	£9500	
		b. Broken crown and scroll.......	£9500	
		e. Break in lines below scroll........		
		f. Damaged leaf at bottom right....		
		s. Optd "Specimen"...............	£650	
215	—	$500 purple and orange-brown (8.12)	£65000	
		a. Break in scroll................	£80000	
		b. Broken crown and scroll.......	£80000	
		f. Damaged leaf at bottom right....		
		s. Optd "Specimen"...............	£1700	
193/212 *Set of 19*			£160	£130
193s/212s Optd "Specimen" *Set of 19*			£750	

The 6c. is similar to *T* **52**, but the head is in a beaded oval as in *T* **53**. The 2c., 6c. (and 12c. below) have figures of value on a circular ground while in the 8c. this is of oval shape.

For illustrations of the varieties on Nos. 213/15 see above No. 51*b* of Bermuda.

RED CROSS

MALAYA-BORNEO
2c. EXHIBITION.
(55) (56)

1917 (1 May). *Surch with T* **55**.

216	49	2c. on 3c. scarlet......................	2·75	28·00
		a. No stop (R. 2/3)...............	£400	£750
217	50	2c. on 4c. dull purple..............	3·75	28·00
		a. No stop (R. 2/3)...............	£450	£750

Nos. 216a and 217a occur in the first setting only.

Type I	Type II
25c	**25c**

The duty plate for the 25c. value was replaced in 1926. In Type II the solid shading forming the back of the figure 2 extends to the top of the curve; the upturned end of the foot of the 2 is short; two background lines above figure 5; c close to 5; STRAITS SETTLEMENTS in taller letters.

1921–33. Wmk Mult Script CA. *Ordinary paper* (1c. to 6c., 10c. (No. 230), 12c.) or chalk-surfaced paper (others). P 14.

218	48	1c. black (3.22)............................	50	10
219	52	2c. green (5.21)..........................	50	10
		w. Wmk inverted...................	35·00	
		x. Wmk reversed...................	†	—
		y. Wmk inverted and reversed.......		
220		2c. brown (3.25)..........................	7·00	2·50
221	49	3c. green (9.23)..........................	1·50	80
		w. Wmk inverted...................	35·00	
222	50	4c. carmine-red (9.21)	2·00	4·50
223		4c. bright violet (8.24)...............	60	10
		w. Wmk inverted...................	35·00	
224		4c. orange (8.29).......................	1·00	10
225	51	5c. orange (Die I) (5.21)............	1·50	15
		a. Wmk sideways...................	†	£2750
		bw. Wmk inverted...................	35·00	
		bx. Wmk reversed...................	†	—
		c. Die II (1922).....................	2·25	1·25
226		5c. brown (Die II) (1932)...........	2·75	10
		a. Die I (1933).......................	5·00	10
		b. Face value omitted................	£20000	
227	52	6c. dull claret (10.22)...............	2·00	15

228		w. Wmk inverted......................	35·00	42·00
229		6c. rose-pink (2.25)...................	22·00	9·50
230		6c. scarlet (1.27)......................	2·50	10
	51	10c. bright blue (Die I) (1921)........	1·75	3·25
231		w. Wmk inverted......................	35·00	
		10c. purple/*pale yellow* (Die I) (1923).....................	2·50	8·50
		a. Die II (11.26).....................	2·25	30
		b. *Purple/brt yellow* (Die II) (1932).....................	13·00	2·50
		ba. Die I (1933).....................	7·00	10
232	52	12c. bright blue (1.22).................	1·25	20
		w. Wmk inverted......................	35·00	
233	53	21c. dull and bright purple (2.23)...	6·00	50·00
234	54	25c. dull purple and mauve (Die I, Type I) (1921)...............	28·00	75·00
		a. Die II, Type I (1923).........	15·00	3·75
		b. Die II, Type II (1927)........	5·00	1·75
235	51	30c. dull purple & orange (Die I) (1921).....................	23·00	42·00
		a. Die II (1922).....................	2·00	1·25
236	53	35c. dull purple & orange-yellow (8.22).....................	12·00	6·00
		a. *Dull purple and orange*............	3·50	5·50
237		35c. scarlet and purple (4.31).....	10·00	7·00
238	54	50c. black/*emerald* (9.25)........	1·75	40
239	51	$1 black and red/*blue* (Die II) (1921).....................	6·00	65
240	54	$2 grn & red/*pale yell* (Die II) (1923).....................	10·00	8·00
240a	51	$5 green and red/*green* (Die II) (1926).....................	90·00	32·00
240b	—	$25 purple and blue/*blue* (5.23)	£750	£130
		ba. Break in scroll................	£1500	
		bb. Broken crown and scroll.........	£1500	
		be. Break through lines below left scroll.....................		
		bf. Damaged leaf at bottom right....		
		bs. Optd "Specimen"...............	£225	
240c	—	$100 black and carmine/*blue* (5.23)...	£5500	£1800
		ca. Break in scroll................	£8000	
		cb. Broken crown and scroll.........	£8000	
		ce. Break through lines below left scroll.....................		
		cf. Damaged leaf at bottom right....		
		cs. Optd "Specimen"...............	£550	
240d	—	$500 purple and orange-brown (4.23)	£45000	
		da. Break in scroll................	£55000	
		db. Broken crown and scroll.........	£60000	
		de. Break through lines below left scroll.....................		
		df. Damaged leaf at bottom right....		
		ds. Optd "Specimen"...............	£1500	
218/40a *Set of 24*			£160	£110
218s/40as (*ex* 6c. rose-pink) Optd or Perf (Nos. 224s, 226s, 237s) "Specimen" *Set of 23*			£650	

Nos. 240*b/d* are as Type **47**, but with portrait of George V.

No. 226b was caused by a progressive inking failure, resulting in the value being completely omitted on R. 10/10 of a single sheet.

The 2c. green was reissued in 1927, and exists with "Specimen" overprint 15.5×1.75 mm instead of the 14.5×2.5 mm of the original issue (*Price*, £65).

An 8c. carmine was prepared but not issued (Optd "Specimen" £425).

The paper of Nos. 231b/ba is the normal *pale yellow* at the back, but with a bright yellow surface.

In 1926 new Key and Duty plates were made of 100 (10×10) instead of the usual 60 (6×10).

For illustrations of the varieties on Nos. 240*b/d* see above No. 51*b* of Bermuda.

SETTINGS OF TYPE 56. Nos. 241/55 were produced using a typeset block of 12 (6×2) overprints from which ten stereos were taken to provide a forme for the complete sheet of 120. Two such formes were prepared of which the second was only used for a limited number of Straits Settlements sheets in addition to the Kedah and Trengganu issues.

Several constant varieties occur on the original typeset block of 12 and so appear ten times on sheets printed from both Settings I and II. These include:

Oval last "O" in "BORNEO" (R. 1/3 of typeset block of 12)

Raised stop after "EXHIBITION" (R. 2/2 of typeset block of 12)

Small second "A" in "MALAYA" (R. 2/6 of typeset block of 12).

The two formes also produced constant varieties in each setting which include:

Setting I
No hyphen (Left pane. R. 7/1 or 9/2)

No stop (Left and right panes. Either on R. 10/4 (right pane) or, for some sheets, on other stamps from even numbered horizontal rows in the 4th vertical column (both panes))

Third "I" in "EXHIBITION" omitted (R. 8/5, 10/5 (left pane)). This must have occurred very late in the use of this setting and is only found on the 5c. and 10c.

Setting II
No stop (Left pane. R. 1/5)

"EXH.BITION" (Left pane. Stamps from even numbered horizontal rows in the 3rd vertical column)

1922 (31 Mar). Malaya-Borneo Exhibition, Singapore. Optd with *T* **56**.

(a) Wmk Mult Crown CA (Nos. 195, 198/9, 201, 205, 208a, 210, 211b and 212b).

241	52	2c. green............................	28·00	75·00
		b. Oval last "O" in "BORNEO"....	55·00	£120
		c. Raised stop after "EXHIBITION"..................	55·00	£120
		d. Small second "A" in "MALAYA"........................	55·00	£120
		e. No hyphen......................	£170	
		f. No stop.........................	65·00	£130
242	50	4c. rose-scarlet....................	8·00	23·00
		b. Oval last "O" in "BORNEO"....	16·00	42·00
		c. Raised stop after "EXHIBITION"..................	16·00	42·00
		d. Small second "A" in "MALAYA"........................	16·00	42·00
		e. No hyphen......................	60·00	
		f. No stop.........................	20·00	48·00
		h. "EXH.BITION".................	60·00	

243	51	5c. orange...........................	6·00	19·00
		b. Oval last "O" in "BORNEO"....	12·00	35·00
		c. Raised stop after "EXHIBITION"..................	12·00	35·00
		d. Small second "A" in "MALAYA"........................	12·00	35·00
		e. No hyphen......................	42·00	
		f. No stop.........................	14·00	40·00
		h. "EXH.BITION".................	42·00	
244	52	8c. ultramarine.....................	1·75	8·50
		b. Oval last "O" in "BORNEO"....	4·75	16·00
		c. Raised stop after "EXHIBITION"..................	4·75	16·00
		d. Small second "A" in "MALAYA"........................	4·75	16·00
		e. No hyphen......................	28·00	
		f. No stop.........................	5·50	18·00
		h. "EXH.BITION".................	28·00	
245	54	25c. dull purple and mauve.........	3·25	38·00
		b. Oval last "O" in "BORNEO"....	8·50	65·00
		c. Raised stop after "EXHIBITION"..................	8·50	65·00
		d. Small second "A" in "MALAYA"........................	8·50	65·00
		e. No hyphen......................	38·00	
		f. No stop.........................	9·50	75·00
		h. "EXH.BITION".................	38·00	
246	53	45c. black/*blue-green* (olive back)	3·00	32·00
		b. Oval last "O" in "BORNEO"....	8·00	55·00
		c. Raised stop after "EXHIBITION"..................	8·00	55·00
		d. Small second "A" in "MALAYA"........................	8·00	55·00
		e. No hyphen......................	35·00	
		f. No stop.........................	9·00	65·00
247	51	$1 black and red/*blue*..............	£275	£900
		b. Oval last "O" in "BORNEO"....	£425	
		c. Raised stop after "EXHIBITION"..................	£425	
		d. Small second "A" in "MALAYA"........................	£425	
		e. No hyphen......................	£475	
248	54	$2 green and red/*orange-buff*......	26·00	£120
		a. *On pale yellow* (No. 211c).....	65·00	£160
		b. Oval last "O" in "BORNEO"....	48·00	£200
		c. Raised stop after "EXHIBITION"..................	48·00	£200
		d. Small second "A" in "MALAYA"........................	48·00	£200
		e. No hyphen......................	£170	
		f. No stop.........................	55·00	£225
		h. "EXH.BITION".................		
249	51	$5 green & red/*blue-green* (olive-back)....................	£250	£450
		b. Oval last "O" in "BORNEO"....	£375	
		c. Raised stop after "EXHIBITION"..................	£375	
		d. Small second "A" in "MALAYA"........................	£375	
		e. No hyphen......................	£1300	
		f. No stop.........................	£400	

(b) Wmk Mult Script CA (Nos. 218/19, 222, 225b, 230 and 239).

250	48	1c. black...........................	3·00	15·00
		b. Oval last "O" in "BORNEO"....	7·00	23·00
		c. Raised stop after "EXHIBITION"..................	7·00	23·00
		d. Small second "A" in "MALAYA"........................	7·00	23·00
		e. No hyphen......................	35·00	
		f. No stop.........................	8·50	26·00
		h. "EXH.BITION".................	35·00	
251	52	2c. green...........................	2·50	15·00
		b. Oval last "O" in "BORNEO"....	5·50	24·00
		c. Raised stop after "EXHIBITION"..................	5·50	24·00
		d. Small second "A" in "MALAYA"........................	5·50	24·00
		e. No hyphen......................	28·00	
		f. No stop.........................	6·50	26·00
		h. "EXH.BITION".................	28·00	
252	50	4c. carmine-red....................	3·50	32·00
		b. Oval last "O" in "BORNEO"....	8·00	60·00
		c. Raised stop after "EXHIBITION"..................	8·00	60·00
		d. Small second "A" in "MALAYA"........................	8·00	60·00
		e. No hyphen......................	35·00	
		f. No stop.........................	9·00	65·00
253	51	5c. orange (Die II)................	2·75	45·00
		b. Oval last "O" in "BORNEO"....	7·00	75·00
		c. Raised stop after "EXHIBITION"..................	7·00	75·00
		d. Small second "A" in "MALAYA"........................	7·00	75·00
		e. No hyphen......................	35·00	
		f. No stop.........................	8·50	85·00
		g. Third "I" in "EXHIBITION" omitted.....................	£1500	
254		10c. bright blue....................	2·25	26·00
		b. Oval last "O" in "BORNEO"....	6·00	48·00
		c. Raised stop after "EXHIBITION"..................	6·00	48·00
		d. Small second "A" in "MALAYA"........................	6·00	48·00
		e. No hyphen......................	28·00	
		f. No stop.........................	7·00	55·00
		g. Third "I" in "EXHIBITION" omitted.....................	£800	
255		$1 black and red/*blue* (Die II)........	20·00	£130
		b. Oval last "O" in "BORNEO"....	42·00	£225
		c. Raised stop after "EXHIBITION"..................	42·00	£225
		d. Small second "A" in "MALAYA"........................	42·00	£225
		f. No stop.........................	48·00	£250
		h. "EXH.BITION".................		
242/55 *Set of 11*			£300	£800

Examples of most values are known with part strikes of a forged Singapore postmark dated "AU 1 1910".

1935 (6 May). *Silver Jubilee. As Nos. 91/4 of Antigua. but ptd by Waterlow & Sons.* P 11×12.

256	5c. ultramarine and grey	3·00	30
257	8c. green and indigo	3·00	3·25
258	12c. brown and deep blue	3·00	5·00
	j. Damaged turret	£400	
259	25c. slate and purple	3·25	6·00
256/9 *Set of 4*		11·00	13·00
256s/9s Perf "Specimen" *Set of 4*		£180	

For illustration of plate variety see Omnibus section following Zanzibar.

57   **58**

1936 (1 Jan)–**37**. *Chalk-surfaced paper.* Wmk Mult Script CA. P 14.

260	**57**	1c. black (1.1.37)	1·00	20
261		2c. green (1.2.36)	1·25	70
262		4c. orange (15.6.36)	2·25	70
263		5c. brown (1.8.36)	1·00	30
264		6c. scarlet (1.2.36)	1·25	1·10
265		8c. grey	2·25	70
266		10c. dull purple (1.7.36)	2·25	60
267		12c. bright ultramarine (1.9.36)	2·00	2·50
268		25c. purple and scarlet (1.2.36)	1·25	50
269		30c. dull purple and orange	1·25	3·25
270		40c. scarlet and dull purple	1·25	2·50
271		50c. black/*emerald* (1.9.36)	4·50	1·25
272		$1 black and red/*blue* (1.7.36)	19·00	1·75
273		$2 green and scarlet (1.4.36)	48·00	10·00
274		$5 green and red/*emerald* (1.1.37)	£110	10·00
260/74 *Set of 15*			£180	32·00
260s/74s Perf "Specimen" *Set of 15*			£350	

1937 (12 May). *Coronation. As Nos. 95/7 of Antigua, but printed by D.L.R.*

275	4c. orange	40	10
276	8c. grey-black	1·00	10
277	12c. bright blue	2·00	1·00
275/7 *Set of 3*		3·00	1·10
275s/7s Perf "Specimen" *Set of 3*		£120	

1937–41. *Chalk-surfaced paper.* Wmk Mult Script CA. P 14 or 15×14 (15c.).

(a) Die I (printed at two operations).

278	**58**	1c. black (1.1.38)	7·50	10
279		2c. green (6.12.37)	18·00	20
280		4c. orange (1.1.38)	19·00	20
281		5c. brown (19.11.37)	20·00	30
282		6c. scarlet (1.1.38)	11·00	50
283		8c. grey (26.1.38)	38·00	10
284		10c. dull purple (8.11.37)	8·00	10
285		12c. ultramarine (10.1.38)	8·00	50
286		25c. purple and scarlet (11.12.37)	42·00	1·10
287		30c. dull purple and orange (1.12.37)	20·00	2·00
288		40c. scarlet and dull purple (20.12.37)	13·00	2·25
289		50c. black/*emerald* (26.1.38)	11·00	10
290		$1 black and red/*blue* (26.1.38)	15·00	20
291		$2 green and scarlet (26.1.38)	32·00	7·00
292		$5 green and red/*emerald* (26.1.38)	25·00	3·75

(b) Die II (printed at one operation).

293	**58**	2c. green (28.12.38)	50·00	40
294		2c. green (6.10.41)	2·00	14·00
295		3c. green (*ordinary paper*) (5.9.41)	5·50	4·00
296		4c. orange (29.10.38)	80·00	10
297		5c. brown (18.2.39)	28·00	10
298		15c. ultramarine (*ordinary paper*) (6.10.41)	6·00	10·00
278/98 *Set of 18*			£275	42·00
278s/92s 294s/5s, 298s Perf "Specimen" *Set of 18*			£475	

Die I. Lines of background outside central oval touch the oval and the foliage of the palm tree is usually joined to the oval frame. The downward-pointing palm frond, opposite the King's eye, has two points.

Die II. Lines of background are separated from the oval by a white line and the foliage of the palm trees does not touch the outer frame. The palm frond has only one point.

Nos. 295 and 298 were printed by Harrison and Sons following bomb damage to the De La Rue works on 29 December 1940.

The 6c. grey, 8c. scarlet and $5 purple and orange were only issued with the BMA overprint, but the 8c. without overprint is known although in this state it was never issued (*Price* £14).

STAMP BOOKLETS

1914–19. *Black on blue (No. SB1) or grey (No. SB1b) covers, Stapled.*

SB1 $1 booklet containing twenty-five 4c. dull purple (No. 197) in two blocks of 12 and one single
    a. Containing 4c. rose-scarlet (No. 198) (1919).
SB1b $1 booklet containing four 1c., sixteen 3c. and twelve 4c. (Nos. 193, 196/7) in blocks of four.

1921. *Black on blue cover. Stapled.*

SB2 $1 booklet containing twenty-five 4c. (No. 222) in two blocks of 12 and one single

1922. *Black on red cover. Stapled.*

SB3 $1 booklet containing 5c. (No. 225) in block of 8 and 6c. (No. 227) in block of 10 .... £1700

1925–29. *Black on red cover. Stapled.*

SB4 $1.20 booklet containing thirty 4c. bright violet (No. 223) in blocks of 10 .... £3000
    a. Containing 4c. orange (No. 224) (1929) £3250

1927. *Black on grey (No. SB5), green (No. SB6) or blue (No. SB7) covers. Stapled.*

SB5 $1 booklet containing 4c. and 6c. (Nos. 223, 229) in blocks of 10 .... £2250
SB6 $1.20 booklet containing twenty 6c. (No. 229) in blocks of 10 .... £2500
SB7 $1.20 booklet containing 2c., 4c. and 6c. (Nos. 219, 223, 229) in blocks of 10 .... £3250

1933. *Black on buff cover. Stapled.*

SB8 $1 booklet containing twenty 5c. (No. 226a) in blocks of 10 ....

1936. *Stapled.*

SB9 $1 booklet containing twenty 5c. (No. 263) in blocks of 10 ....
SB10 $1.30 booklet containing 5c. and 8c. (Nos. 263, 265) in blocks of 10 ....

1938. *Black on buff (No. SB11) or black on green (No. SB12) covers. Stapled.*

SB11 $1 booklet containing twenty 5c. (No. 281) in blocks of 10 .... £2250
SB12 $1.30 booklet containing 5c. and 8c. (Nos. 281, 283) in blocks of 10 and pane of airmail labels £2500

POSTAGE DUE STAMPS

D 1

1924 (1 Jan)–**26**. Wmk Mult Script CA. P 14.

D1	D 1	1c. violet	5·00	6·50
D2		2c. black	3·25	1·25
D3		4c. green (5.26)	2·00	4·75
D4		8c. scarlet	4·50	55
D5		10c. orange	6·00	85
D6		12c. bright blue	7·00	65
D1/6 *Set of 6*			25·00	13·00
D1s/6s *Set of 6*			£250	

For later issues of Postage Due stamps, see MALAYAN POSTAL UNION.

POSTAL FISCAL STAMPS

1938. *T 47, but with head of King George VI and inscribed "REVENUE" at each side.* Wmk Mult Script CA. P 14.

F1	$25 purple and blue/*blue*	£400	£300

No. F1 was regularly used for postal purposes in 1941, although no specific authorisation for such use has been discovered.

The Straits Settlements were occupied by the Japanese in 1942.

After the Second World War the stamps of MALAYA (BRITISH MILITARY ADMINISTRATION) were used. In 1946 Singapore became a separate Crown Colony and Labuan was transferred to North Borneo. Separate stamps were issued for Malacca and Penang, which both joined the Malayan Federation on 1 February 1948.

II. FEDERATED MALAY STATES

On 1 July 1896, the States of Negri Sembilan, Pahang, Perak and Selangor were organised on a federal basis to be known as the Federated Malay States. For the time being each State continued with individual issues, but stamps for the use of the Federation replaced these in 1900.

PRICES FOR STAMPS ON COVER	
Nos. 1/13	*from* × 12
No. 14	—
Nos. 15/22	*from* × 10
Nos. 23/5	*from* × 3
No. 26	—
Nos. 27/50	*from* × 6
No. 51	—
Nos. 52/81	*from* × 5
No. 82	—
Nos. D1/6	*from* × 10

PRINTERS. All issues of the Federated Malay States were printed in typography by De La Rue & Co, Ltd, London, *unless otherwise stated.*

(1)   **(2)**

1900. Optd with T 1 (cent values) or 2 (dollar values).

(a) Stamps of Negri Sembilan (T 3).

1	1c. dull purple and green	3·00	7·50
2	2c. dull purple and brown	29·00	65·00
3	3c. dull purple and black	2·75	4·00
4	5c. dull purple and olive-yellow	70·00	£170
5	10c. dull purple and orange	9·00	29·00
6	20c. green and olive	85·00	£100
7	25c. green and carmine	£250	£350
8	50c. green and black	90·00	£130
1/8 *Set of 8*		£475	£750
1s/8s Optd "Specimen" *Set of 8*		£190	

(b) Stamps of Perak (T 44 and 45).

9	5c. dull purple and olive-yellow	18·00	55·00
10	10c. dull purple and orange	75·00	65·00
11	$1 green and pale green	£170	£225
	w. Wmk inverted	£850	
12	$2 green and carmine	£140	£225
13	$5 green and ultramarine	£400	£550
14	$25 green and orange	£8500	
	s. Optd "Specimen"	£375	
11s/13s Optd "Specimen" *Set of 3*		£150	

The Negri Sembilan 3c. dull purple and black does not exist without overprint Type **1**.

> The stamps of STRAITS SETTLEMENTS were used in Federated Malay States from 16 July 1900 until replaced by the 1900–1 issue.

3   **4**

1900–01. P 14.

(a) T 3. Wmk Crown CA, sideways (1901).

15	1c. black and green	8·00	7·50
	a. Grey and green	3·75	1·00
	b. Grey-brown and green	10·00	30
16	3c. black and brown	11·00	4·00
	a. Grey and brown	6·00	35
	b. Grey-brown and brown	5·50	20
17	4c. black and carmine	16·00	6·50
	a. Grey and carmine	7·50	4·50
	b. Grey-brown and carmine	24·00	2·25
18	5c. green and carmine/*yellow*	2·25	3·00
19	8c. black and ultramarine	42·00	18·00
	a. Grey and ultramarine	20·00	5·50
	b. Grey-brown and ultramarine	27·00	3·75
20	10c. black and claret	£100	40·00
	a. Grey and claret	75·00	8·50
	b. Black and purple	£130	35·00
	c. Grey and purple	80·00	12·00
	d. Grey-brown and purple	85·00	7·00
21	20c. mauve and black	17·00	10·00
22	50c. black and orange-brown	£150	£130
	a. Grey and orange-brown	£100	50·00
	b. Grey-brown and orange-brown	90·00	42·00
15/22b *Set of 8*		£200	60·00
15s/22s Optd "Specimen" *Set of 8*		£190	

Later printings in 1903–4 show the two upper lines of shading in the background at the corner nearest to the "S" of "STATE" blurred and running into one another, whereas in earlier printings these lines are distinct. Two plates were used for printing the central design of T **3**. In Plate 1 the lines of background are regular throughout, but in Plate 2 they are lighter around the head and back of the tiger. The 5c. was the only value with single wmk to be printed from Plate 2. Stamps with multiple wmk were printed for a short time from Plate 1, and show the two blurred lines of background near "S" of "STATE," but the majority of these stamps were printed from Plate 2 and later plates.

(b) T 4. Wmk Crown CC (1900).

23	$1 green and pale green	£110	£120
24	$2 green and carmine	£120	£130
25	$5 green and bright ultramarine	£275	£300
	a. Green and pale ultramarine	£275	£275
26	$25 green and orange	£2500	£1400
	s. Optd "Specimen"	£275	
23s/5s Optd "Specimen" *Set of 3*		£150	

Two dies for 1c. green and 4c. scarlet

Die I. "Head" and duty plates. Thick frame line below "MALAY" and in the 1c. the "c" is thin whilst in the 4c. it is thick.

Die II. Single working plate. Thin frame line below "MALAY" and in the 1c. the "c" is thicker whilst in the 4c. it is thinner.

1904 (Aug)–**22**. *T 3 and T 4 (dollar values).* Wmk Mult Crown CA (sideways* on T 3). *Ordinary paper (1c. to 50c.) or chalk-surfaced paper ($1 to $25).*

27	1c. grey and green (8.04)	70·00	8·50
	a. Grey-brown and green	35·00	70
28	1c. green (Die I) (8.7.06)	14·00	30
29	1c. green (Die II) (1908)	6·50	20
	a. Yellow-green	19·00	90
	aw. Wmk Crown to right of CA	48·00	9·00
	b. Blue-green	24·00	1·75
30	1c. deep brown (21.1.19)	2·25	90
	w. Wmk Crown to right of CA		
31	2c. green (18.2.19)	2·50	30
	w. Wmk Crown to right of CA	48·00	12·00
32	3c. grey and brown (10.04)	60·00	10·00
	a. Grey-brown and brown (12.05)	42·00	1·75
	ab. Chalk-surfaced paper	40·00	2·75
33	3c. brown (11.7.06)	8·00	15
34	3c. carmine (2.2.09)	3·25	10
	aw. Wmk Crown to right of CA	7·50	40
	b. Scarlet (1.17)	16·00	50
	bw. Wmk Crown to right of CA	25·00	4·25
35	3c. grey (29.10.18)	2·00	20
	w. Wmk Crown to right of CA	42·00	12·00
36	4c. grey and scarlet (8.04)	48·00	4·500
	a. Chalk-surfaced paper. Grey and rose	20·00	2·50
	b. Grey-brown and scarlet	40·00	3·25
	c. Black and scarlet	22·00	2·50

	d. Black and rose		6·00	80
	dw. Wmk Crown to right of CA		9·00	80
	e. Black and deep rose (aniline) (1909)		50·00	5·00
	f. Jet black and rose (1914)		25·00	2·25
37	4c. scarlet (Die I) (11.2.19)		3·50	4·75
38	4c. scarlet (Die II) (15.4.19)		1·75	15
	aw. Wmk Crown to right of CA		48·00	5·50
	b. Wmk upright (2.22)		£750	£375
39	5c. green and carmine/yellow (5.06)		10·00	2·25
	aw. Wmk Crown to right of CA		65·00	19·00
	b. Chalk-surfaced paper		29·00	5·00
	c. Deep green and carmine/yellow		13·00	2·75
	d. On orange-buff (1921)		16·00	8·00
	e. On pale yellow (4.22)		12·00	6·00
40	6c. orange (11.2.19)		2·75	3·00
41	8c. grey and ultramarine (2.05)		70·00	21·00
	aw. Wmk Crown to right of CA			
	b. Grey-brown and ultramarine (12.05)		19·00	4·25
	ba. Chalk-surfaced paper		65·00	13·00
	bb. Wmk upright (3.07)		9·00	4·75
42	8c. ultramarine (8.3.10)		13·00	1·00
	aw. Wmk Crown to right of CA		80·00	26·00
	b. Deep blue (1918)		16·00	1·25
43	10c. grey-brown and claret (5.04)		75·00	7·00
	a. Chalk-surfaced paper (1905)		95·00	10·00
	b. Black and claret		26·00	65
	bw. Wmk Crown to right of CA		40·00	1·50
	c. Grey-brown and purple (1905)		70·00	3·25
	d. Black and purple		26·00	2·75
	dy. Wmk Crown to right of CA and reversed		†	£250
	e. Jet-black and bright purple (1914)		85·00	5·00
44	10c. deep blue (3.6.19)		6·50	1·75
	a. Bright blue		6·50	1·00
	ab. Wmk inverted		†	—
	aw. Wmk Crown to right of CA		60·00	21·00
45	20c. mauve and black (3.05)		14·00	1·25
	a. Chalk-surfaced paper		13·00	3·00
	w. Wmk Crown to right of CA		75·00	21·00
46	35c. scarlet/pale yellow (25.8.22)		5·50	12·00
47	50c. grey and orange (3.05)		70·00	9·50
	aw. Wmk Crown to right of CA		£180	55·00
	b. Wmk inverted		†	—
	c. Grey-brown and orange-brown (1906)		48·00	9·00
	caw. Wmk Crown to right of CA		†	—
	cb. Chalk-surfaced paper. Grey-brown and orange-brown		50·00	7·50
	cbw. Wmk Crown to right of CA		†	75·00
	cc. Grey and orange-brown		60·00	9·00
	cd. Black and orange-brown		85·00	16·00
	ce. Jet-black and orange-brown (1914)		£110	20·00
48	$1 grey-green and green (11.07)		70·00	45·00
	a. Green and pale green		90·00	45·00
	aw. Wmk inverted			
49	$2 green and carmine (4.12.07)		80·00	£110
	a. Printed on the gummed side			
	y. Wmk inverted and reversed		†	—
50	$5 green and blue (1.08)		£180	£130
51	$25 green and orange (12.09)		£1200	£750
	27/50 Set of 22		£500	£300
	28s, 30s/1s, 33s/5s, 38s, 40s, 42s, 44s, 46s Optd "Specimen" Set of 11		£475	

*The normal sideways watermark shows Crown to left of CA, *as seen from the back of the stamp*.

Nos. 29/b, 30, 31, 33, 34/b and 35 were printed from single working plates and all the rest from double plates.

Most examples of No. 47b have fiscal cancellations, but at least one is known postally used.

1922–34. Wmk Mult Script CA(sideways* on *T 3*). *Ordinary paper (1c. to 10c. (No. 66), 12c., 20c. (No. 69a), 35c. (No. 72)) or chalk-surfaced paper (others).*

52	3	1c. deep blue (1.8.22)	1·50	3·25
		w. Wmk Crown to right of CA	48·00	48·00
53		1c. black (12.6.23)	75	20
54		2c. brown (5.8.25)	6·50	7·50
55		2c. green (15.6.26)	3·00	10
		a. Wmk upright	£275	
56		3c. grey (27.12.22)	1·75	7·50
		w. Wmk Crown to right of CA	60·00	60·00
57		3c. green (22.1.24)	1·25	1·50
58		3c. brown (31.5.27)	2·50	50
		a. Wmk upright	£275	
59		4c. carmine-red (Die II) (27.11.23)	3·50	50
		w. Wmk Crown to right of CA	40·00	18·00
60		4c. orange (9.11.26)	1·50	10
		a. No watermark	£300	£200
		b. Wmk upright	£275	
61		5c. mauve/pale yellow (17.3.22)	1·00	20
		w. Wmk Crown to right of CA	48·00	38·00
62		5c. brown (1.3.32)	3·50	10
63		6c. orange (2.5.22)	1·00	45
		w. Wmk Crown to right of CA	85·00	
64		6c. scarlet (9.11.26)	1·50	10
65		10c. bright blue (23.10.23)	1·25	8·00
		w. Wmk Crown to right of CA		
66		10c. black and blue (18.1.24†)	2·00	75
67		10c. purple/pale yellow (14.7.31)	3·75	40
68		12c. ultramarine (12.9.22)	1·25	10
		w. Wmk Crown to right of CA	60·00	32·00
		x. Wmk sideways reversed	£170	
69		20c. dull purple & black (chalk-surfaced paper) (3.4.23)	4·00	1·50
		a. Ordinary paper (29.12.26)	38·00	2·50
		b. Wmk inverted	†	£180
70		25c. purple and bright magenta (3.9.29)	2·75	1·50
71		30c. purple and orange-yellow (3.9.29)	3·25	3·50
72		35c. scarlet/pale yellow (6.11.28)	3·25	23·00
73		35c. scarlet and purple (29.9.31)	13·00	14·00
74		50c. black and orange (24.4.24)	13·00	10·00
		aw. Wmk Crown to right of CA	£130	
		b. Black and orange-brown	29·00	5·00
75		50c. black/green (16.6.31) (1909)	4·00	2·50
76	4	$1 pale green and claret (2.2.26)	22·00	90·00
		a. Grey-green and emerald (5.10.26)	18·00	48·00
77	3	$1 black and red/blue (10.3.31)	12·00	3·50
78	4	$2 green and carmine (17.8.26)	21·00	70·00

79	3	$2 green and red/yellow (6.2.34)	38·00	35·00
80	4	$5 green and blue (24.2.25)	£100	£180
		w. Wmk inverted		£800
81	3	$5 green and red/green (7.34)	£160	£160
82	4	$25 green and orange (14.2.28)	£900	£700
		s. Optd "Specimen"		£225
	52/81 Set of 30		£400	£500
	52s/81s Optd or Perf (No. 62s, 67s, 70s/1s, 73s, 77s, 79s, 81s) "Specimen" Set of 30		£1100	

*The normal sideways watermark shows Crown to left of CA, *as seen from the back of the stamp*.

†No. 66 was released in London by the Crown Agents some months earlier but this is the official date of issue in the States.

Nos. 52, 56 and 59 were printed from single working plates and the rest from double plates.

No. 55 exists in coils constructed from normal sheets.

The 5c. mauve on white Script paper is the result of soaking early printings of No. 61 in water.

STAMP BOOKLETS

1909. *Black on pink (Nos. SB1/2) or black on buff (No. SB3) covers. Stapled.*

SB1	25c. booklet containing twenty-four 1c. (No. 29) in blocks of 6	£2000	
	a. Black on green cover (1917)	£2000	
	b. Black on blue cover (1917)	£2000	
SB2	73c. booklet containing twenty-four 3c. (No. 34) in blocks of 6	£2000	
	a. Black on red cover (1917)	£2000	
	b. Black on blue cover (1917)	£2000	
SB3	97c. booklet containing twenty-four 4c. (No. 36d) in blocks of 6	£2250	

1919. *Black on green (No. SB4) or black on pink (No. SB5) covers. Stapled.*

SB4	49c. booklet containing twenty-four 2c. (No. 31) in blocks of 6	£5000
SB5	97c. booklet containing twenty-four 4c. (No. 37) in blocks of 6	£1800

1922. *Black on buff cover (No. SB7). Stapled.*

SB6	$1.21 booklet containing twenty-four 5c. (No. 61) in blocks of 6	£2750
SB7	$1.45 booklet containing twenty-four 6c. (No. 63) in blocks of 6	£2250

1926. *As Nos. SB4, SB3 and SB7, but sold at face value without premium. Black on green (No. SB8), black on pink (No. SB9) or black on buff (No. SB10) covers. Stapled.*

SB8	48c. booklet containing twenty-four 2c. (No. 55) in blocks of 6	
SB9	96c. booklet containing twenty-four 4c. (No. 60) in blocks of 6	£2250
SB10	$1.44 booklet containing twenty-four 6c. (No. 64) in blocks of 6	£2250

1926. *Black on grey cover. Stapled.*

SB11	$1 booklet containing 4c. and 6c. (Nos. 60, 64) each in block of 10	£2250

1927. *Black on bluish green cover. Stapled.*

SB12	$1.50 booklet containing 2c., 3c., 4c. and 6c. (Nos. 55, 58, 60, 64) each in block of 10	£2750

1927–30. *Black on red (No. SB13), black on green (No. SB14) or black on blue (No. SB15) covers. Stapled.*

SB13	$1.20 booklet containing thirty 4c. (No. 60) in blocks of 6	£2500
	a. Black on orange cover (1930)	
SB14	$1.20 booklet containing twenty 6c. (No. 64) in blocks of 10 (1928)	£3000
SB15	$1.20 booklet containing 2c., 4c. and 6c. (Nos. 55, 60, 64) each in block of 10 (1928)	£2250
	a. Black on white cover (1930)	

1934. *Black on buff cover. Stapled.*

SB16	$1 booklet containing twenty 5c. (No. 62) in blocks of 10	£2750

POSTAGE DUE STAMPS

D 1

(Typo Waterlow)

1924 (1 Dec)–**26.** Wmk Mult Script CA (sideways*). P 15×14.

D1	D 1	1c. violet	4·75	30·00
		w. Wmk Crown to left of CA (1926)	16·00	25·00
D2		2c. black	1·75	5·00
		w. Wmk Crown to left of CA (1926)	4·00	3·25
D3		4c. green (wmk Crown to left of CA) (27.4.26)	2·25	5·00
D4		8c. red	5·50	30·00
		w. Wmk Crown to left of CA (1926)	15·00	18·00
D5		10c. orange	9·00	17·00
		w. Wmk Crown to left of CA (1926)	24·00	19·00
D6		12c. blue	9·00	27·00
		w. Wmk Crown to left of CA (1926)	15·00	12·00
	D1/6 Set of 6		29·00	70·00
	D1s/6s Optd "Specimen" Set of 6		£180	

*The normal sideways watermark shows Crown to right of CA, *as seen from the back of the stamp*.

The issues of the Federated Malay States were replaced by stamps for the individual States from 1935 onwards.

III. MALAYAN POSTAL UNION

The Malayan Postal Union was organised in 1934 and, initially, covered the Straits Settlements and the Federated Malay States. Stamps of the Straits Settlements together with issues for the individual States continued to be used, but Malayan Postal Union postage due stamps were introduced in 1936.

Following the end of the Second World War the use of these postage dues spread throughout Malaya and to Singapore.

PRICES FOR STAMPS ON COVER TO 1945	
Nos. D1/6	from × 10
Nos. D7/13	from × 4

POSTAGE DUE STAMPS

D 1

(Typo Waterlow until 1961, then D.L.R.)

1936 (June)–**38.** Wmk Mult Script CA. P 15×14.

D1	D 1	1c. slate-purple (4.38)	7·50	70
D2		4c. green (9.36)	21·00	1·00
D3		8c. scarlet	11·00	3·50
D4		10c. yellow-orange	17·00	30
D5		12c. pale ultramarine (9.36)	17·00	14·00
D6		50c. black (1.38)	28·00	6·00
	D1/6 Set of 6		90·00	23·00
	D1s/6s Perf "Specimen" Set of 6		£225	

For use in Negri Sembilan, Pahang, Perak, Selangor and Straits Settlements including Singapore.

1945–49. *New values and colours.* Wmk Mult Script CA. P 15×14.

D7	D 1	1c. purple	3·25	2·00
D8		3c. green	6·00	5·00
D9		5c. scarlet	6·00	3·50
D10		8c. yellow-orange (1949)	13·00	14·00
		s. Perf "Specimen"	75·00	
D11		9c. yellow-orange	35·00	40·00
D12		15c. pale ultramarine	£110	28·00
D13		20c. blue (1948)	8·00	5·00
		s. Perf "Specimen"	75·00	
	D7/13 Set of 7		£160	90·00

1951 (8 Aug)–**63.** Wmk Mult Script CA. P 14.

D14	D 1	1c. violet (21.8.52)	70	1·60
D15		2c. deep slate-blue (16.11.53)	1·25	2·25
		a. Perf 12½ (15.11.60)	1·00	17·00
		ab. Chalk-surfaced paper (10.7.62)	1·00	9·00
		ac. Ditto. Imperf horiz (vert pair)	†	£11000
D16		3c. deep green (21.8.52)	24·00	12·00
D17		4c. sepia (16.11.53)	70	7·00
		a. Perf 12½ (15.11.60)	1·00	19·00
		ab. Chalk-surfaced paper. Bistre-brown (10.7.62)	80	16·00
D18		5c. vermilion	48·00	12·00
D19		8c. yellow-orange	2·25	4·50
D20		12c. bright purple (1.2.54)	1·25	6·00
		a. Perf 12½. Chalk-surfaced paper (10.7.62)	2·00	24·00
D21		20c. blue	5·50	6·50
		a. Perf 12½. Deep blue (10.12.57)	7·00	26·00
		ab. Chalk-surfaced paper (15.10.63)	4·00	38·00
	D14/21 Set of 8		70·00	45·00

Nos. D7 to D21ab were for use in the Federation and Singapore.

IV. MALAYA (BRITISH MILITARY ADMINISTRATION)

Following the Japanese surrender on 2 September 1945 British troops landed in Malaya which was placed under a British Military Administration. The Director of Posts was ashore at Singapore on 6 September and had reached Kuala Lumpur by 13 September. Postal services in Singapore and Johore resumed on 17 September and had spread to the remainder of the country by 5 October. No stamps were initially available so all mail up to 1 oz. was carried free until the first overprinted stamps appeared on 19 October.

De La Rue had overprinted available stocks of pre-war Straits Settlements stamps earlier in 1945 and initial supplies of these London overprints were placed on sale from 19 October (Nos. 1, 2a, 4, 6a, 7 and 8a) with the 15c. and 25c. (Nos. 11 and 13a) issued later. A second consignment contained dollar values including the $5 purple and orange. Duplicate plates were subsequently sent to the Government Printing Office at Kuala Lumpur, where the overprinting of surviving local stocks of the 1c., 5c., 10c., 15c. (overprinted in black) and $5 green and red on emerald took place, and to Australia for those shipments which had been diverted there in 1941.

The stamps were used throughout all Malay States and in Singapore. From 1948 this general issue was gradually replaced by individual issues for each state. The last usage was in Kelantan where B M A overprints were not withdrawn until 10 July 1951.

B M A
MALAYA
(1)

1945 (19 Oct)–**48.** *T **58** of Straits Settlements from Die I (double-plate printing) or Die II (single-plate printing) optd with T **1**.* Wmk Mult Script CA. *Chalk-surfaced paper.* P 14 or 15×14 (No. 11).

1		1c. black (I) (R.)	3·75	60
		a. Ordinary paper	10	30
2		2c. orange (II) (8.7.47)	5·00	60
		a. Ordinary paper (19.10.45)	20	10
		w. Wmk inverted	†	£1400
3		2c. orange (I) (ordinary paper) (9.46)	23·00	3·75
4		3c. yellow-green (II) (ordinary paper)	70	50
		a. Blue-green (27.1.47)	4·25	3·50

	b. Chalk-surfaced paper. *Blue-grn*			
	(8.7.47)		14·00	1·00
5	5c. brown (II) (24.10.45)		70	1·00
6	6c. grey (II) (22.3.48)		19·00	3·50
	a. Ordinary paper (19.10.45)		30	20
7	8c. scarlet (II) (*ordinary paper*)		30	10
8	10c. purple (I) (12.45)		4·75	80
	a. Ordinary paper (19.10.45)		50	10
	b. *Slate-purple* (12.45)		4·00	30
	c. *Magenta* (22.3.48)		7·50	70
9	10c. purple (II) (28.7.48)		19·00	3·25
10	12c. bright ultramarine (I) (11.45)		1·75	7·50
11	15c. brt ultram (II) (*ordinary paper*)			
	(11.45)		2·50	8·50
12	15c. bright ultramarine (II) (R.) (22.3.48)		30·00	1·00
	a. Ordinary paper (12.45)		75	20
	b. *Blue* (27.11.47)		60·00	85
	ba. *Blue* (8.7.47)		£120	14·00
13	25c. dull purple and scarlet (I) (22.3.48) ..		18·00	2·00
	a. Ordinary paper (12.45)		1·40	30
	ab. Opt double		£4750	
	ac. "A" of "CA" missing from watermark		†	—
14	50c. black/*emerald* (I) (R.) (12.45)		27·00	2·25
	a. Ordinary paper		75	10
15	$1 black and red (I) (*ordinary paper*) (12.45)		2·00	10
16	$2 green & scar (I) (*ordinary paper*) (12.45)		2·75	75
17	$5 green and red/*emerald* (I) (11.45)		85·00	£100
18	$5 pur & orge (I) (*ordinary paper*) (12.45)		3·75	3·00
	1/18 Set of 15		90·00	£100
	1s/11s, 13s/16s, 18s Perf "Specimen" Set of 14		£475	

The 8c. grey with "BMA" opt was prepared but not officially issued (*Price £375 unused*).

Nos. 3 and 9 do not exist without the overprint.

Initial printings on ordinary paper were produced by Harrison and Sons in 1941 following bomb damage to the De La Rue works on 29 December 1940.

No. 8 with reddish purple medallion and dull purple frame is from a 1947 printing with the head in fugitive ink which discolours with moisture.

Postal forgeries of the 50c. value exist made by dyeing examples of the 1c. and then altering the face value to 50c.

In 1946 8c. and 15c. stamps in the Crown Colony Victory design were prepared for the Malayan Union, but not issued. Examples of the 8c. carmine from this issue exist from unofficial leakages (*Price £375 unused*).

V. MALAYAN STATES

PRINTERS. All Malayan States stamps were printed in typography by De La Rue and Co. Ltd, London, *unless otherwise stated*.

JOHORE

A British adviser was appointed to Johore in 1914. The state joined the Federation of Malaya on 1 February 1948.

Until 1 January 1899 mail for addresses outside Malaya had the external postage paid by stamps of the STRAITS SETTLEMENTS.

PRICES FOR STAMPS ON COVER TO 1945

Nos. 1/2		
Nos. 3/5	*from × 15*	
No. 6	*from × 20*	
Nos. 7/8		
Nos. 9/15	*from × 25*	
No. 16		
Nos. 17/20	*from × 15*	
Nos. 21/31		
Nos. 32/8	*from × 15*	
Nos. 39/53	*from × 8*	
Nos. 54/60	*from × 6*	
Nos. 61/74	*from × 8*	
Nos. 75/7		
Nos. 78/87	*from × 8*	
No. 88	*from × 10*	
Nos. 89/102	*from × 6*	
Nos. 103/25	*from × 5*	
Nos. 126/8		
Nos. 129/30	*from × 6*	
Nos. D1/5	*from × 5*	

(1)

1876 (July). *No. 11 of Straits Settlements handstamped with T* **1**.
1   2c. brown £15000   £4750

No. 1 is known with the handstamp double.

From September 1878 to August 1884 no overprinted stamps were supplied by Singapore to Johore.

JOHORE
(2)

JOHORE   **JOHORE**   **JOHORE**
(3) ("H" and "E"   (4) ("H" wide,   (5) ("H" and "E"
wide. "J" raised.   "E" narrow. Opt   wide. Opt 16¾ mm
Opt 16 mm long)   16 mm long)   long)

JOHORE.   **JOHORE**   **JOHORE**
(6)   (7)   (8)

1884 (June)–**86**. *No. 63 of Straits Settlements optd with T* **2/8**.
2	**2**	2c. pale rose	£5500	
3	**3**	2c. pale rose (8.84)	£1600	£550
		a. Opt double	£3000	£1600

4	**4**	2c. pale rose (8.84)	£1900	£650
		a. Opt double	—	£1700
5	**5**	2c. pale rose (8.84)	£1600	£550
		a. Opt double	—	£1700
6	**6**	2c. pale rose (3.85)	£170	£180
		a. Opt double	£1000	
7	**7**	2c. pale rose (1885)	£2500	
8	**8**	2c. pale rose (4.86)	95·00	£100

Nos. 3 to 7 were from triplet settings, either 3+4+5 or three examples of the same overprint. Nos. 2 and 8 are probably single unit handstamps.

JOHOR   **JOHOR**   **JOHOR**
(9) (All letters   (10)   (11) ("H" wide)
narrow)

JOHOR   **JOHOR**   **JOHOR.**
(12)   (13)   (14)

JOHOR   **JOHOR**
(15)   (16)

JOHOR
Thin, narrow "J"

1884 (Aug)–**91**. *Nos. 63/a of Straits Settlements optd with T* **9/16**.
9	**9**	2c. pale rose	13·00	19·00
		a. Opt double	£750	
10	**10**	2c. pale rose (10.84)	13·00	9·00
		a. Thin, narrow "J" (R. 6/6)	£170	£130
		b. Opt double	£750	
		c. *Bright rose* (1890)	13·00	13·00
		ca. Thin, narrow "J" (R. 6/6)	£180	£190
		cb. Opt double	£800	
11	**11**	2c. pale rose (2.85)	90·00	90·00
12	**12**	2c. pale rose (1886)	55·00	55·00
		a. Opt double	£750	
13	**13**	2c. pale rose (1886)	45·00	48·00
14	**14**	2c. pale rose (1888)	£140	60·00
		a. Thin, narrow "J"	£700	£375
		b. Opt double	£750	
15	**15**	2c. bright rose (9.90)	16·00	16·00
16	**16**	2c. bright rose (1891)	£8000	

Settings:
No. 9– various triplets with the length of the overprint varying from 12 to 15 mm
No. 10– triplet or 60 (6×10)
No. 11– two types, length 13¼ mm and 14¼ mm, from separate printings, both triplets of 11+9+9
No. 12– triplet
No. 13– triplet
No. 14– 30 (3×10)
No. 15– No. 15–60 (6×10)
No. 16– not known. As no used examples are known it is possible that this stamp was not issued.

JOHOR   **JOHOR**
Two   *Two*
CENTS   CENTS
────   ────
(17)   (18)

JOHOR   **JOHOR**
Two   *Two*
CENTS   CENTS
(19)   (20)

1891 (May). *No. 68 of Straits Settlements surch as T* **17/20**.
17	**17**	2c. on 24c. green	27·00	40·00
		a. "CENST" (R. 5/4)	£900	£475
		b. Thin, narrow "J" (R. 5/6)	£400	£400
		w. Wmk inverted	£160	£160
18	**18**	2c. on 24c. green	£130	£140
		a. Thin, narrow "J" (R. 6/6)	£425	£425
		w. Wmk inverted	£425	
19	**19**	2c. on 24c. green	40·00	55·00
		w. Wmk inverted	£250	£250
20	**20**	2c. on 24c. green	£120	£130
		w. Wmk inverted	£425	

Nos. 17/20 come from the same setting of 60. Type **17** occurs on horizontal rows 1 to 5, Type **18** on row 6, Type **19** on rows 7, 8 and 9 and Type **20** on row 10.
The setting was altered to remove the "CENST" error and in doing so the thin, narrow "J" was moved from R. 5/6 to 6/6. Otherwise the two settings were the same.

     3 cents.

21 Sultan   (22)   **KEMAHKOTAAN**
Aboubakar   (23)

1891 (16 Nov)–**94**. *No wmk. P* 14.
21	**21**	1c. dull purple and mauve (7.94)	60	50
22		2c. dull purple and yellow	60	1·50
23		3c. dull purple and carmine (7.94)..	60	50
24		4c. dull purple and black	2·75	18·00
25		5c. dull purple and green	7·00	21·00
26		6c. dull purple and blue	8·00	21·00
27		$1 green and carmine	75·00	£160
		21/7 Set of 7	85·00	£200

1894 (Mar). *Surch with T* **22**.
28	**21**	3c. on 4c. dull purple and black	2·50	50
		a. No stop (R. 5/11)	90·00	70·00
29		3c. on 5c. dull purple and green	2·00	3·50
		a. No stop (R. 5/11)	£120	£150
		b. "3 cents." spaced 3½ mm from bar	£130	90·00
30		3c. on 6c. dull purple and blue	3·25	4·00
		a. No stop (R. 5/11)	£170	£190
31		3c. on $1 green and carmine	11·00	70·00
		a. No stop (R. 5/11)	£400	£700
		28/31 Set of 4	17·00	65·00

No. 29b shows the surcharge spaced 3½ mm from the bar instead of the normal 7½ mm. It appears to come from a separate setting as a cancelled-to-order block of eight is known.

1896 (Mar). *Coronation of Sultan Ibrahim. Optd with T* **23**.
32	**21**	1c. dull purple and mauve	50	1·00
		a. "KETAHKOTAAN"	3·75	5·00
33		2c. dull purple and yellow	50	1·00
		a. "KETAHKOTAAN"	4·50	7·00
34		3c. dull purple and carmine	55	1·00
		a. "KETAHKOTAAN"	8·50	10·00
35		4c. dull purple and black	80	2·25
		a. "KETAHKOTAAN"	2·75	11·00
36		5c. dull purple and green	3·50	7·50
		a. "KETAHKOTAAN"	3·50	7·50
37		6c. dull purple and blue	3·50	6·50
		a. "KETAHKOTAAN"	7·00	10·00
38		$1 green and carmine	50·00	£110
		a. "KETAHKOTAAN"	38·00	£160
		32/8 Set of 7	55·00	£120
		32a/8a Set of 7	60·00	£190

Stamps overprinted "KETAHKOTAAN" (= We mourn) come from the first overprinting. The overprint was subsequently changed to the intended "KEMAHKOTAAN" (= Coronation), but both were issued together some months after the Coronation of Sultan Ibrahim had taken place.

24 Sultan Ibrahim   25 Sultan Ibrahim

26   27

1896 (26 Aug)–**99**. W **27**. P 14.
39	**24**	1c. green	80	1·25
40		2c. green and blue	35	30
41		3c. green and purple	4·00	2·75
		a. *Green and dull claret*	4·00	2·50
42		4c. green and carmine	1·00	1·50
43		4c. yellow and red (1899)	1·50	1·00
44		5c. green and brown	2·00	2·00
45		6c. green and yellow	2·00	3·75
46	**25**	10c. green and black (1898)	7·00	48·00
47		25c. green and mauve (1898)	9·00	42·00
48		50c. green and carmine (1898)	16·00	45·00
49	**24**	$1 dull purple and green (1898).....	32·00	75·00
50	**26**	$2 dull purple and carmine (1898).	38·00	80·00
51		$3 dull purple and blue (1898).....	35·00	£110
52		$4 dull purple and brown (1898)..	35·00	85·00
53		$5 dull purple and yellow (1898)...	75·00	£130
		39/53 Set of 15	£225	£550

Nos. 42 and 43 were reissued in 1918 to meet a shortage of 4c. stamps.

3 cents.   **10 cents.**
(28)   (29)

1903 (Apr). *Surch with T* **28** *or* **29**.
54	**24**	3c. on 4c. yellow and red	60	1·10
		a. Original value uncancelled	3·75	20·00
55		10c. on 4c. green and carmine	2·50	9·00
		a. Tall "1" in "10" (R. 9/12)	75·00	£130
		b. Original value uncancelled	20·00	70·00
		ba. As b, with tall "1" in "10" (R. 9/12)	£950	£1300

The bars on these stamps were ruled by hand with pen and ink.

50 Cents.   **One Dollar**
(30)   (31)

1903 (Oct). *Surch with T* **30** *or* **31**.
56	**26**	50c. on $3 dull purple and blue	30·00	80·00
57		$1 on $2 dull purple and carmine	60·00	£110
		a. "e" of "One" inverted (R. 7/9) ..	£1500	

10 CENTS.
(32)

1904. *Surch as T* **32**.
58	**24**	10c. on 4c. yellow and red (Apr)	20·00	40·00
		a. Surcharge double	£6500	
59		10c. on 4c. green and carmine (Aug)	9·50	48·00
60	**26**	50c. on $5 dull purple and yellow (May)	70·00	£160
		58/60 Set of 3	90·00	£225

| 33 | 34 | 35 Sultan Sir Ibrahim |

1904 (Sept)–**10**. W **27**. *Ordinary paper*. P 14.

61	33	1c. dull purple and green	2·00	40
		a. Chalk-surfaced paper (10.09)	8·00	8·00
62		2c. dull purple and orange	3·00	3·75
		a. Chalk-surfaced paper (10.10)	9·00	13·00
63		3c. dull purple and olive-black	4·75	60
		a. Chalk-surfaced paper	—	£100
64		4c. dull purple and carmine	8·00	3·00
65		5c. dull purple and sage-green	2·50	3·00
66	35	8c. dull purple and blue	4·25	10·00
67	34	10c. dull purple and black	50·00	11·00
		a. Chalk-surfaced paper (1910)	90·00	80·00
68		25c. dull purple and green	8·50	40·00
69		50c. dull purple and red	45·00	17·00
70	33	$1 green and mauve	13·00	55·00
71	35	$2 green and carmine	24·00	50·00
72		$3 green and blue	28·00	75·00
73		$4 green and brown	28·00	£100
74		$5 green and orange	48·00	85·00
75	34	$10 green and black	70·00	£160
76		$50 green and ultramarine	£250	£350
77		$100 green and scarlet	£400	£600
61/75 Set of 15			£300	£550

1910–19. Wmk Mult Rosettes (vertical). *Chalk-surfaced paper*. P 14.

78	33	1c. dull purple and green (1912)	1·25	15
79		2c. dull purple and orange (1912)	6·00	1·00
80		3c. dull purple and olive-black (1912)	10·00	65
		a. Wmk horizontal (1910)	10·00	19·00
81		4c. dull purple and carmine (1912)	11·00	1·00
		a. Wmk horizontal (1910)	20·00	50·00
82		5c. dull purple and sage-green (1912)	6·00	2·75
83	35	8c. dull purple and blue (1912)	4·00	7·50
84	34	10c. dull purple and black (1912)	50·00	3·00
		a. Wmk horizontal (1911)	26·00	75·00
85		25c. dull purple and green (1912)	14·00	40·00
86		50c. dull purple and red (1919)	55·00	£120
87	33	$1 green and mauve (1918)	80·00	£110
78/87 Set of 10			£190	£250

3 CENTS.

(36)

37 Sultan Sir Ibrahim and Sultana

1912 (Mar). No. 66 surch with T **36**.

88		3c. on 8c. dull purple and blue	4·00	8·50
		a. "T" of "CENTS" omitted	£1200	
		b. Bars double		

No. 88b shows the bars printed twice with the upper pair partly erased.

1918–20. Wmk Mult Crown CA. *Chalk-surfaced paper*. P 14.

89	33	2c. dull purple and green (1919)	50	1·00
		w. Wmk inverted	†	£250
90		2c. purple and orange (1919)	1·00	4·25
91		4c. purple and red	1·75	70
92		5c. dull purple and sage-green (1920)	2·00	7·50
		w. Wmk inverted	£160	
		ws. Ditto, optd "Specimen"	60·00	
93	34	10c. dull purple and blue	2·00	1·40
94		21c. dull purple and orange (1919)	2·25	2·50
95		25c. dull purple and green (1920)	8·00	24·00
96		50c. dull purple and red (6.18)	24·00	55·00
97	33	$1 green and mauve	14·00	70·00
98	35	$2 green and carmine	23·00	50·00
99		$3 green and blue	50·00	£120
100		$4 green and brown	60·00	£150
101		$5 green and orange	£100	£180
102	34	$10 green and black	£250	£400
89/102 Set of 14			£500	£950
89s/102s Optd "Specimen" Set of 14			£475	

1922–40. Wmk Mult Script CA. *Chalk-surfaced paper*. P 14.

103	33	1c. dull purple and black	30	20
104		2c. purple and sepia (1924)	1·25	4·00
105		2c. green (1928)	50	40
106		3c. green (1925)	2·00	4·50
107		3c. purple and sepia (1928)	1·40	1·50
108		4c. purple and carmine (1924)	2·50	20
109		5c. dull purple and sage-green	50	30
		w. Wmk inverted		
110		6c. dull purple and claret	50	50
111	34	10c. dull purple and blue	16·00	32·00
		w. Wmk inverted	†	£250
112		10c. dull purple and yellow	50	25
113	33	12c. dull purple and blue	1·00	1·25
114		12c. ultramarine (1940)	45·00	3·25
115	34	21c. dull purple and orange (1928)	2·00	3·00
116		25c. dull purple and myrtle	3·75	40
117	35	30c. dull purple and orange (1936)	8·00	7·50
118		40c. dull purple and brown (1936)	8·00	8·50
119	34	50c. dull purple and red	3·75	1·25
120	33	$1 green and mauve	3·75	1·25
121	35	$2 green and carmine (1923)	7·50	4·00
122		$3 green and blue (1925)	60·00	90·00
123		$4 green and brown (1926)	90·00	£170
		w. Wmk inverted		
124		$5 green and orange	55·00	50·00

125	34	$10 green and black (1924)	£200	£350
126		$50 green and ultramarine	£800	
127		$100 green and scarlet	£1600	
		s. Optd "Specimen"	£275	
128	35	$500 blue and red (1926)	£20000	
		s. Optd "Specimen"	£750	
103/25 Set of 23			£450	£650
103s/25s Optd or Perf (12c. ultram, 30c., 40c.) "Specimen" Set of 23			£700	

Printings of the 1c., 2c., 6c., 10c., 50c., $1, $2, $5 and $10 were made in 1941 by Williams, Lea & Co. Ltd. following bomb damage to the De La Rue works on 29 December 1940.

(Recess Waterlow)

1935 (15 May). *50th Anniv of Treaty Relations with Great Britain.* Wmk Mult Script CA (sideways). P 12½.

129	37	8c. bright violet and slate	3·50	2·25
		s. Perf "Specimen"	60·00	

| 38 Sultan Sir Ibrahim | 39 Sultan Sir Ibrahim |

(Recess D.L.R.)

1940 (Feb). Wmk Mult Script CA. P 13½.

130	38	8c. black and pale blue	19·00	1·00
		s. Perf "Specimen"	60·00	

1948 (1 Dec). *Royal Silver Wedding. As Nos. 112/13 of Antigua.*

131		10c. violet	20	75
132		$5 green	25·00	40·00

1949 (2 May)–**55**. Wmk Mult Script CA. *Chalk-surfaced paper*. P 17½×18.

133	39	1c. black	50	10
134		2c. orange	20	20
		a. Orange-yellow (22.1.52)	1·25	1·75
135		3c. green	50	1·00
		a. Yellow-green (22.1.52)	17·00	3·25
136		4c. brown	75	10
136a		5c. bright purple (1.9.52)	30	30
137		6c. grey	60	20
		a. Pale grey (22.1.52)	60	50
		ac. Error. St. Edward's Crown W 9b	£1600	£1400
138		8c. scarlet	3·25	1·25
138a		8c. green (1.9.52)	4·25	2·25
139		10c. magenta	70	10
		aa. Imperf (pair)	£2500	
139a		12c. scarlet (1.9.52)	4·25	5·00
140		15c. ultramarine	3·00	10
141		20c. black and green	60	1·00
141a		20c. bright blue (1.9.52)	1·00	10
142		25c. purple and orange	2·00	10
142a		30c. scarlet and purple (4.9.55)	1·75	2·75
142b		35c. scarlet and purple (1.9.52)	4·75	1·25
143		40c. red and purple	4·50	11·00
144		50c. black and blue	2·75	10
145		$1 blue and purple	5·50	2·00
146		$2 green and scarlet	15·00	7·00
147		$5 green and brown	40·00	12·00
133/47 Set of 21			85·00	42·00

1949 (10 Oct). *75th Anniv of U.P.U. As Nos. 114/17 of Antigua.*

148		10c. purple	30	40
149		15c. deep blue	1·75	1·00
150		25c. orange	65	3·00
151		50c. blue-black	1·25	3·50
148/51 Set of 4			3·50	7·00

STAMP BOOKLETS

1928. *Black on white card. Interleaved with tissue. Stapled.*

SB1 $2 booklet containing ten 1c. and 2c. (Nos. 103, 105), twenty 4c. (No. 108), each in blocks of 10 and eighteen 5c. (No. 109) in blocks of 6 .... £2000

1929. *Black on pink cover. Stapled.*

SB2 $1 booklet containing 2c., 3c. and 5c. (Nos. 105, 107, 109) in blocks of 10 ....

1930. *Black on buff cover. Stapled.*

SB3 $1 booklet containing ten 1c. and 5c. (Nos. 103, 109) and twenty 2c. (Nos. 105) in blocks of 10 ....

POSTAGE DUE STAMPS

D 1

(Typo Waterlow)

1938 (1 Jan). Wmk Mult Script CA. P 12½.

D1	D 1	1c. carmine	15·00	40·00
D2		4c. green	40·00	40·00
D3		8c. scarlet	48·00	£140
D4		10c. brown	48·00	48·00
D5		12c. purple	55·00	£130
D1/5 Set of 5			£180	£350
D1s/5s Perf "Specimen" Set of 5			£150	

KEDAH

The Thai monarchy exercised suzerainty over Kedah and the other northern states of the Malay peninsula from the 16th century onwards. The extent of Thai involvement in its internal affairs was very variable, being dependent on the strength, or otherwise, of the Bangkok administration and the degree of co-operation of the local ruler. The Thai postal service, which had been inaugurated in 1883, gradually extended into the north of the Malay peninsula.

The first Post Office was established in Kedah in 1887.

Stamps of Thailand used in Kedah

Types of Thailand (Siam)

| 1 | 2 | 9 |

| (12) | (17) | (18) |

4 atts	4 atts
(24)	(25)

1 Atts.
(27)

ราคา๑อัฐ	2 Atts.	2
(27)	(28)	(33)

1 Att.
(34)

1 Att.
(36)

ราคา๑ อัฐ	ราคา๑อัฐ	1 Att.
(34)	(35)	(36)

| 2 Atts. | 10 Atts. |

ราคา ๒ อัฐ	2 Atts.	ราคา๑๐อัฐ
(37)	(38)	(39)

4 Atts.	4 Atts.
(40)	(41)

1 Att.
(42)

ราคา๑อัฐ	2 Atts.	3 Atts.	4 Atts.
(42)	(44)	(45)	(46)

2 Atts.
(48a)

1 Att.

49	50	๑ อัฐ
		(51)

๔ อัฐ

1att.
(56)

9 Atts
(59)

The following types of postmark were used on Siamese stamps from the Malay tributary states:

Type A. Single ring with date at foot (examples from 1900 show the year in manuscript)

Type B. Single ring with date in centre

Type C. Double ring. Bilingual

Type D. Double ring. English at top and ornament at foot

PRICES are for stamps showing a large part of the postmark with the inscription clearly visible.

Alor Star

The Siamese post office at Alor Star was opened during 1887 with the first known postmark being dated 27 October.

A straight-line obliteration showing "KEDAH" between short vertical dashes is not believed to be genuine.

Stamps of SIAM cancelled as Type A inscribed "KEDAH".

1883. (Nos. 1/5).
Z2	1	1att. rose-carmine	£225
Z3		1sio. red	£425
Z4	2	1sik. yellow	£425

1897–91 (Nos 11/18).
Z6	9	1a. green	80·00
Z7		2a. green and carmine	70·00
Z8		3a. green and blue	90·00
Z9		4a. green and brown	80·00
Z10		8a. green and yellow	80·00
Z11		12a. purple and carmine	70·00
Z12		24a. purple and blue	80·00
Z13		64a. purple and brown	£130

1889–91. Surch as T 12 (Nos. Z15, Z19), T 17 (No. Z21) or T 18 (No. Z22) (Nos. 20/30).
Z15	9	1a. on 2a. rose-carmine	90·00
Z19		1a. on 3a. red	£100
Z21		2a. on 3a. yellow	£130
Z22		2a. on 3a. green and blue	£160

1892. Surch as T 24/5 (with or without stop) and Siamese handstamp (Nos. 33/6).
Z28	9	4a. on 24a. purple and blue (Type 24)	90·00
Z29		4a. on 24a. purple and blue (Type 25)	£110
Z30		4a. on 24a. purple and blue (Type 24 with stop)	£110
Z31		4a. on 24a. purple and blue (Type 25 ith stop)	£110

1894. Surch as T 27 with variations of English figures as T 28 and 33 (Nos. 37/44).
Z34	9	2a. on 64a. purple and brown (Type 28)	90·00
Z39		2a. on 64a. purple and brown (Type 33)	90·00

1894. Surch with T 34 (No. 45).
Z41	9	1a. on 64a. purple and brown	£110

1894–95. Surch as T 35 with variations of English figures as T 36/9 (Nos. 46/50).
Z42	9	1a. on 64a. purple and brown (Type 35)	90·00
Z43		1a. on 64a. purple and brown (Type 36)	90·00
Z44		1a. on 64a. purple and brown (Type 37)	90·00
Z45		2a. on 64a. purple and brown (Type 38)	90·00
Z46		10a. on 24a. purple and blue (Type 39)	90·00

1896. Surch as T 39 (Siamese) and T 40 (English) (No. 51).
Z47	9	4a. on 12a. purple and carmine	90·00

1897. Surch as T 39 (Siamese) and T 41 (English) (No. 52).
Z48	9	4a. on 12a. purple and carmine	90·00

1898–99. Surch as T 42 with variations of English section as T 44/6 (Nos. 53/62).
Z49	9	1a. on 12a. purple and carmine (Type 42–11½ mm long)	£120
Z52		2a. on 64a. purple and brown (Type 44)	£100
Z53		3a. on 12a. purple and carmine (Type 45–13½ mm long)	90·00
Z54		3a. on 12a. purple and carmine (Type 45–11½ to 11¾ mm long)	90·00
Z55		4a. on 12a. purple & carm (Type 46–8 mm long)	90·00
Z56		4a. on 12a. purple and carmine (Type 46–8½ to 9 mm long)	90·00

1899. Surch in Siamese and English with T 48a (Nos. 63/6).
Z62	9	2a. on 64a. purple and brown	£100

1899–1904. (Nos. 67/81).
Z63	49	1a. olive-green (wide Siamese characters in face value)	90·00
Z64		2a. grass-green	70·00
Z65		3a. red and blue	75·00
Z66		4a. carmine	70·00
Z67		8a. deep green and orange	70·00
Z69		12a. brown-purple and carmine	£110
Z70		24a. brown-purple and blue	£160
Z71		64a. brown-purple and chestnut	£130

1899. (Nos. 82/6).
Z72	50	1a. green	£275
Z73		2a. green and red	£425

Stamps of SIAM cancelled as Type B inscr "KEDAH" (from March 1901).

1887–91. (Nos. 11/18).
Z74	9	12a. purple and carmine	70·00
Z75		24a. purple and brown	70·00

1898–99. Surch with T 42 with variations of English section as T 45/6 (Nos. 53/62).
Z76	9	1a. on 12a. pur & carm (Type 42–11½ mm long)	90·00
Z81		3a. on 12a. purple and carmine (Type 45–11½ to 11¾ mm long)	70·00
Z83		4a. on 12a. purple and carmine (Type 46–8½ to 9 mm long)	70·00
Z84		4a. on 24a. purple and blue (Type 46)	75·00

1899–1904. (Nos. 67/81).
Z86	49	1a. olive-green (wide Siamese characters in face value)	70·00
		a. Narrow Siamese characters in face value	65·00
Z87		2a. grass-green	55·00
Z88		2a. scarlet and pale blue	55·00
Z89		3a. red and blue	65·00
Z90		3a. deep green	65·00
Z91		4a. carmine	55·00
Z92		4a. chocolate and pink	60·00
Z93		8a. deep green and orange	55·00
Z94		10a. ultramarine	55·00
Z95		12a. brown-purple and carmine	65·00
Z96		24a. brown-purple and blue	£130
Z97		64a. brown-purple and chestnut	£120

1905–09. (Nos. 92/105).
Z102	53	1a. green and orange	55·00
Z103		2a. grey and deep violet	55·00
Z104		3a. green	65·00
Z105		4a. pale red and sepia	55·00
Z106		5a. carmine	65·00
Z107		8a. olive-bistre and dull black	55·00
Z108		12a. blue	65·00
Z109		24a. red-brown	£160
Z110		1t. bistre and deep blue	£160

Stamps of SIAM cancelled as Type C inscr "Kedah" at foot (from July 1907).

1887–91. (Nos. 11/18).
Z111	9	12a. purple and carmine	80·00

1899–1904. (Nos.67/81).
Z112	49	1a. olive-green (wide Siamese characters in face value)	65·00
		a. Narrow Siamese characters in face value	60·00
Z113		3a. red and blue	55·00
Z114		3a. red and blue	65·00
Z116		8a. deep green and orange	65·00
Z117		10a. ultramarine	60·00
Z118		12a. brown-purple and carmine	60·00

1905–09. (Nos. 95/105).
Z128	53	1a. green and orange	55·00
Z129		2a. grey and deep violet	55·00
Z130		3a. green	65·00
Z131		4a. pale red and sepia	55·00
Z132		4a. scarlet	65·00
Z133		5a. carmine	65·00
Z134		8a. olive-bistre and dull black	55·00
Z135		9a. blue	55·00
Z136		18a. red-brown	90·00
Z137		24a. red-brown	£160
Z138		1t. bistre and deep blue	£160

1907. Surch with T 56 (No. 109).
Z139	9	1a. on 24a. purple and blue	65·00

Kuala Muda

The earliest known postmark for Kuala Muda is dated 7 July 1907.

Stamps of SIAM cancelled as Type B inscr "KUALA MUDA" (from Oct 1907).

1887–91. (Nos. 11/18).
Z143	9	12a. purple and carmine	£325

1899–1904. (Nos. 67/81).
Z144	49	2a. scarlet and pale blue	£325
Z145		24a. brown-purple and blue	£325

1905–09. (Nos. 92/105).
Z146	53	1a. green and orange	£325
Z147		2a. grey and deep violet	£325
Z148		3a. green	£350
Z150		5a. carmine	£350
Z151		8a. olive-bistre and dull black	£325

Stamps of SIAM cancelled as Type C inscr "Kwala Muda" at foot (from 1907).

1887–91. (Nos. 11/18).
Z155	9	12a. purple and carmine	£150

1899–1904. (Nos. 67/81).
Z156	49	8a. deep green and orange	£180
Z157		10a. ultramarine	£180

1905–09. (Nos. 92/105).
Z158	53	1a. green and orange	£180
Z159		2a. grey and deep violet	£180
Z160		3a. green	£190
Z161		4a. pale red and sepia	£180
Z162		4a. scarlet	£180
Z163		5a. carmine	£200
Z164		8a. olive-bistre and dull black	£180
Z165		9a. blue	£150
Z166		24a. red-brown	£375

1907. Surch with T 56 (No. 109).
Z167	9	1a. on 24a. purple and blue	£150

Kulim

The earliest known postmark for Kulim is dated 7th July 1907.

Stamps of SIAM cancelled as Type D inscr "KULIM" (from July 1907).

1887–91. (Nos. 11/18).
Z173	9	12a. purple and carmine	£325

1899–1904. (Nos. 67/81).
Z174	49	8a. deep green and orange	£325

1905–09. (Nos. 92/105).
Z175	53	1a. green and orange	£350
Z176		2a. grey and deep violet	£350
Z177		3a. green	£375
Z178		4a. pale red and sepia	£325
Z179		4a. scarlet	£325
Z180		5a. carmine	£350
Z181		8a. olive-bistre and dull black	£325
Z182		9a. blue	£325

1907. Surch with T 56 (No. 109).
Z184	9	1a. on 24a. purple and blue	£325

Stamps of SIAM cancelled as Type C inscr "Kulim" at foot (from Feb 1908).

1887–91. (Nos. 11/18).
Z190	9	12a. purple and carmine	£130

1899–1904. (Nos. 67/81).
Z191	49	8a. deep green and orange	£130
Z192		10a. ultramarine	£140

1905–09. (Nos. 92/105).
Z196	53	4a. pale red and sepia	£130
Z197		4a. scarlet	£130
Z198		5a. carmine	£140
Z199		9a. blue	£140
Z200		24a. red-brown	£325
Z201		1t. bistre and deep blue	£325

1907. Surch with T 56 (No. 109).
Z202	9	1a. on 24a. purple and blue	£140

Langkawi

The earliest known postmark for Langkawi is dated 16 Feb 1908.

Stamps of SIAM cancelled as Type D inscr "LANGKAWI" (from Feb 1908).

1899–1904. (Nos. 67/81).
Z208	49	8a. deep green and orange	£325
Z209		10a. ultramarine	£325

1905–09. (Nos. 92/105).
Z212	53	3a. green	£350
Z213		4a. pale red and sepia	£325
Z215		8a. olive-bistre and dull black	£325

Stamps of SIAM cancelled as Type C inscr "Langkawi" at foot (from Nov 1908).

1887–91. (Nos. 11/18).
Z219	9	12a. purple and carmine	£140

1899–1904. *(Nos. 67/81).*
Z220	**49**	1a. olive-green (Type B)	£150
Z221		8a. green and orange	£140

1905–09. *(Nos. 92/105).*
Z222	**53**	2a. grey and deep violet	£140
Z223		3a. green	£190
Z224		4a. pale red and sepia	£140
Z225		4a. scarlet	£150
Z226		8a. olive-bistre and dull black	£140
Z228		24a. red-brown	£375
Z229		1t. bistre and deep blue	£375

1907. Surch with T **56** *(No. 109).*
Z230	**9**	1a. on 24a. purple and blue	£150

Suzerainty over Kedah was transferred by Thailand to Great Britain on 15 July 1909 and the following day stamps of the FEDERATED MALAY STATES were placed on sale in post offices in the state.

A Treaty of Friendship between Great Britain and Kedah was signed on 1 November 1923 and the state joined the Federation of Malaya on 1 February 1948.

Stamps of the Federated Malay States used in Kedah

Alor Star

Cancelled as Type C inscribed "Kedah"

1909–12. *(Nos. 29–49).*
Z231	**3**	1c. green (Die II)	30·00
Z232		3c. carmine	35·00
Z233		4c. black and rose	35·00
Z234		5c. green and carmine/*yellow*	85·00
Z235		8c. grey-brown and ultramarine	85·00
		a. Wmk upright	50·00
Z236		10c. black and purple	65·00
Z237		20c. mauve and black (chalk-surfaced paper)	70·00
Z238		50c. grey-brown and orange-brown (chalk-surfaced paper)	75·00

Type F

Cancelled as Type F

1909–12. *(No. 34)*
Z241	**3**	3c. carmine	55·00

Type G

Cancelled as Type G

1909–12. *(Nos. 34–47cc)*
Z242	**3**	1c. green (Die II)	45·00
Z243		3c. carmine	45·00
Z244		4c. balck and rose	70·00
Z245		8c. grey-brown and ultramarine	70·00
		a. Wmk upright	70·00
Z246		10c. black and purple	70·00
Z247		50c. grey-brown and orange-brown (chalk-surfaced paper)	80·00

Kulim

Type H

Cancelled as Type H

1909–12. *(Nos. 34–45a)*
Z248	**3**	1c. green (Die II)	50·00
Z249		3c. carmine	45·00
Z250		4c. black and rose	50·00
Z251		5c. green and carmine/*yellow*	75·00

Z252		10c. black and purple	75·00
Z253		20c. mauve and black (chalk-surfaced paper)	65·00

Type I

Cancelled as Type I

1909–12. *(Nos. 34–36d)*
Z254		3c. carmine	45·00
Z255		4c. black and rose	55·00

Langkawi

Cancelled as Type H inscribed "LANGKAWI"

1909–12. *(Nos. 34–41bb)*
Z256	**3**	3c. carmine	75·00
Z257		8c. grey-brown and ultramarine (wmk upright)	75·00
Z258		$1 grey-green and green	£150
Z259		$2 green and carmine	£250

Cancelled as Type I inscribed "LANGKAWI"

1909–12. *(Nos. 29–43d)*
Z260	**3**	1c. green (Die II)	75·00
Z261		3c. carmine	40·00
Z262		10c. black and purple	75·00

Kuala Muda

Cancelled as Type B inscribed "KUALA MUDA"

1909–12. *(Nos. 29–41bb)*
Z263	**3**	1c. green (Die II)	60·00
Z264		3c. carmine	40·00
Z265		4c. black and rose	70·00
Z266		5c. green and carmine/*yellow*	70·00
Z267		8c. grey-brown and ultramarine (wmk upright)	70·00

Jitra

The post office in Jitra was opened in 1910.

Type J

Cancelled as Type J

1910–12. *(No. 34)*
Z268	**3**	3c. carmine	60·00

Cancelled as Type I inscribed "JITRA"

1910–12. *(Nos. 29–34)*
Z269	**3**	1c. green (Die II)	40·00
Z270		3c. carmine	35·00

Lunas

The post office in Lunas was opened in 1910.

Type K

Cancelled as Type K

1910–12. *(No. 34)*
Z271	**3**	3c. carmine	80·00

Cancelled as Type I inscribed "LUNAS"

1910–12. *(Nos. 29–36d)*
Z272	**3**	1c. green (Die II)	50·00
Z273		3c. carmine	50·00
Z274		4c. black and rose	75·00

Semiling

The post office in Semiling was opened in 1910.

Cancelled as Type I inscribed "SEMILING"

1910–12. *(Nos. 29–41b)*
Z275	**3**	1c. green (Die II)	40·00
Z276		3c. carmine	70·00
Z277		4c. black and rose	70·00
Z278		8c. grey-brown and ultramarine (wmk upright)	70·00

Sungei Patani

The post office in Sungei Patani was opened in 1911.

Cancelled as Type I inscribed "SUNGEI PATANI"

1911–12. *(Nos. 29–34)*
Z279	**3**	1c. green (Die II)	85·00
Z280		3c. carmine	85·00

Yen

The post office in Yen was opened in 1910.

Cancelled as Type I inscribed "YEN"

1910–12. *(No. 34)*
Z281	**3**	1c. green (Die II)	90·00
Z282		3c. carmine	90·00

PRICES FOR STAMPS ON COVER TO 1945		
Nos. 1/14	*from* × 15	
Nos. 15/23	*from* × 10	
Nos. 24/40	*from* × 8	
Nos. 41/8	*from* × 12	
Nos. 49/51	—	
Nos. 52/9	from × 4	
Nos. 60/8	*from* × 3	
Nos. 68a/9	from × 4	

1 Sheaf of Rice   **2** Malay ploughing

3 Council Chamber, Alor Star

(Recess D.L.R.)

1912 (16 June). Wmk Mult Crown CA (sideways* on 10c. to $5). P 14.
1	**1**	1c. black and green	60	25
		y. Wmk inverted and reversed	†	£275
2		3c. black and red	4·50	30
3		4c. rose and grey	10·00	25
4		5c. green and chestnut	2·25	3·00
5		8c. black and ultramarine	3·75	3·50
6	**2**	10c. blue and sepia	2·25	1·00
		w. Wmk Crown to left of CA	†	—
		y. Wmk Crown to left of CA and reversed	†	£250
7		20c. black and green	4·75	4·00
		x. Wmk reversed	£170	
8		30c. black and rose	3·00	11·00
9		40c. black and purple	3·50	14·00
10		50c. brown and blue	9·00	13·00
11	**3**	$1 black and red/*yellow*	16·00	22·00
		w. Wmk Crown to left of CA	48·00	
		x. Wmk reversed	£275	
		y. Wmk Crown to left of CA and reversed		
12		$2 green and brown	22·00	85·00
13		$3 black and blue/*blue*	80·00	£170
		a. "A" of "CA" missing from wmk	£1500	
14		$5 black and red	85·00	£170
1/14	*Set of* 14		£225	£450
1s/14s	*Optd* "Specimen" *Set of* 14		£300	

*The normal sideways watermark shows the Crown to right of CA, *as seen from the back of the stamp.*

Due to an increase in postal rates 1c. and 4c. stamps of STRAITS SETTLEMENTS were used in Kedah for some months from March 1919.

Short sheaf (R. 10/1)

(i)   (ii)

DOUBLE AND SINGLE PLATES. (i) Printed from separate plates for frame and centre, with dotted shading extending close to the central sheaf. Soft impression of centre with little clear detail.

(ii) Printed from single plate, with white space around sheaf. Centre more deeply etched with sharp image.

1919 (June)–**21**. *New colours and values.* Wmk Mult Crown CA (sideways* on 21c., 25c.). P 14.

15	**1**	1c. brown (i) (18.8.19)	55	50
		w. Wmk inverted	£100	£130
		y. Wmk inverted and reversed	†	£250
18		2c. green (ii)	50	30
19		3c. deep purple (i) (1920)	65	1·25
		x. Wmk reversed	£300	
		y. Wmk inverted and reversed	80·00	£120
20		4c. rose (i)	4·00	30
21		4c. red (ii) (18.8.19)	3·25	1·00
		a. Short sheaf	£120	60·00
		w. Wmk inverted		
22	**2**	21c. mauve and purple (18.8.19)	5·50	60·00
		a. "A" of "CA" missing from wmk	—	£600
		w. Wmk Crown to left of CA	£130	£160
		x. Wmk reversed	£275	
		y. Wmk Crown to left of CA and reversed	£250	
23		25c. blue and purple (1921)	1·75	26·00
		a. "A" of "CA" missing from wmk	£500	
15/23 *Set of 6*			10·50	75·00
15s/23s Optd "Specimen" *Set of 6*			£150	

*The normal sideways watermark shows Crown to right of CA, *as seen from the back of the stamp.*

(4)   (5)

(Surch by Ribeiro & Co, Penang)

1919 (Mar). *Surch as T* **4**.

24	**3**	50c. on $2 green and brown	70·00	75·00
		a. "C" of "CENTS" inserted by handstamp (R. 6/4)	£1200	£1300
25		$1 on $3 black and blue/*blue*	20·00	90·00

Nos. 24/5 were surcharged from settings of 30 (5×6).

Two types of centre plate for Type **2** wmkd Mult Script CA:

Type I (Plate 1) (produced by electrotyping)

Type II (Plate 2) (produced by transfer die)

A new common centre plate, 2, was prepared from the original die in 1926. Stamps from Plate 2, produced using a transfer die, show considerably more detail of the ground and have the oxen, ploughman's hat and his clothing much more deeply cut as illustrated in Type II above.

1921–**32**. Wmk Mult Script CA (sideways* on 10c. to $5). P 14.

26	**1**	1c. brown (ii)	70	20
		w. Wmk inverted	†	£250
		y. Wmk inverted and reversed	†	£250
27		2c. dull green (ii) (Type I)	1·50	20
28		3c. deep purple (ii)	80	70
		w. Wmk inverted	£275	
29		4c. deep carmine (ii)	5·00	20
		a. Short sheaf	£160	32·00
30	**2**	10c. blue and sepia (I)	2·75	75
		ax. Wmk reversed	£300	

		ay. Wmk Crown to left of CA and reversed	£100	
		b. Type II (wmk Crown to left of CA) (1927)	48·00	3·25
		by. Wmk Crown to right of CA and reversed	£350	£225
31		20c. black and yellow-green (I)	4·00	2·00
32		21c. mauve and purple (I)	2·25	13·00
33		25c. blue and purple (I)	2·25	9·00
		a. Type II (wmk Crown to left of CA) (1932)	80·00	4·00
34		30c. black and rose (I) (1922)	3·00	11·00
		a. Type II (wmk Crown to left of CA) (1927)	45·00	3·00
35		40c. black and purple (I)	4·25	50·00
		aw. Wmk Crown to left of CA (1924)	38·00	48·00
		b. Type II (wmk Crown to left of CA) (1932)	85·00	26·00
36		50c. brown and grey-blue (I)	2·75	16·00
		aw. Wmk Crown to left of CA (1924)	32·00	18·00
		b. Type II (wmk Crown to left of CA) (1932)	90·00	8·50
37	**3**	$1 black and red/*yellow* (1924)	60·00	65·00
		w. Wmk Crown to left of CA	6·50	9·50
38		$2 myrtle and brown	13·00	95·00
		w. Wmk Crown to left of CA (1924)	32·00	85·00
39		$3 black and blue/*blue*	70·00	95·00
		w. Wmk Crown to left of CA (1924)	90·00	80·00
40		$5 black and deep carmine	80·00	£150
		w. Wmk Crown to left of CA (1926)	£100	£150
26/40 *Set of 15*			£180	£350
26s/40s Optd "Specimen" *Set of 15*			£300	

*The normal sideways watermark shows Crown to right of CA, *as seen from the back of the stamp.*

Nos. 26/40 were produced by De La Rue using the "wet" method of recess-printing during which the stamps contracted when they were dried before gumming. From 1933 the firm adopted the "dry" method, using pre-gummed paper, with the result that stamps were up to 0.5 mm larger in size. Of the low values as Type **1** in this series only the 2c. was still current when the "dry" method was introduced.

Stamps as Type **1** can be found perforated either comb or line. The 1c. and 4c. come comb only, the 3c. line only and the 2c. either way.

Examples of Nos. 37/40 are known with part strikes of a forged Sungei Patang postmark dated "14 JY 1920".

For the 2c. Type II see No. 69.

OVERPRINT SETTINGS FOR NOS. 41/51. The low values in Type **1** were overprinted using Setting II as detailed under Straits Settlements. The three listed constant varieties of the typeset block of 12 occur in the same positions for these Kedah stamps as does the No Stop variety from R. 1/5 of the left pane.

For the higher values in Type **2**, which were in sheets of 60 (5×12), a further setting was prepared using the first four vertical rows of the typeset block with each horizontal row completed by a single random impression of the overprint. This means that, in addition to their positions in the truncated typeset block, the Oval last "O" additionally occurs on R. 11/5 and the Raised stop on R. 5/5 of the sheet. In this setting, as for the low values, "BORNEO" was 14 mm long.

Further supplies were subsequently required of the 21, 25 and 50c. values and these were produced using a completely different setting of 20 (5×4), applied three times to each sheet, on which "BORNEO" was 15–15½ mm long.

1922 (Apr). *Malaya-Borneo Exhibition, Singapore. Optd as T* **5** *at Singapore.*

I. "BORNEO" 14 mm long.

(a) Wmk Mult Crown CA *(Nos. 10, 18 and 22/3).*

41	**1**	2c. green (ii)	3·50	25·00
		b. Oval last "O" in "BORNEO"	8·00	45·00
		c. Raised stop after "EXHIBITION"	8·00	45·00
		d. Small second "A" in "MALAYA"	8·00	45·00
		f. No stop	35·00	
42	**2**	21c. mauve and purple	29·00	80·00
		b. Oval last "O" in "BORNEO"	50·00	£130
		c. Raised stop after "EXHIBITION"	50·00	£130
43		25c. blue and purple	29·00	80·00
		a. Opt inverted	£1100	
		b. Oval last "O" in "BORNEO"	50·00	£130
		c. Raised stop after "EXHIBITION"	50·00	£130
44		50c. brown and blue	29·00	95·00
		b. Oval last "O" in "BORNEO"	50·00	£150
		c. Raised stop after "EXHIBITION"	50·00	£150

(b) Wmk Mult Script CA *(Nos. 26 and 28/30).*

45	**1**	1c. brown (ii)	3·75	18·00
		b. Oval last "O" in "BORNEO"	8·00	30·00
		c. Raised stop after "EXHIBITION"	8·00	30·00
		d. Small second "A" in "MALAYA"	8·00	30·00
		f. No stop	32·00	
46		3c. deep purple (ii)	3·00	42·00
		b. Oval last "O" in "BORNEO"	7·00	65·00
		c. Raised stop after "EXHIBITION"	7·00	65·00
		d. Small second "A" in "MALAYA"	7·00	65·00
		f. No stop	32·00	
47		4c. deep carmine (ii)	3·00	25·00
		a. Short sheaf	£120	
		b. Oval last "O" in "BORNEO"	7·00	45·00
		c. Raised stop after "EXHIBITION"	7·00	45·00
		d. Small second "A" in "MALAYA"	7·00	45·00
		f. No stop	32·00	
48		10c. blue and sepia (I)	4·50	45·00
		b. Oval last "O" in "BORNEO"	9·50	70·00
		c. Raised stop after "EXHIBITION"	9·50	70·00
41/8 *Set of 8*			95·00	£375

	II. "BORNEO" 15–15½ mm long. Wmk Mult Crown CA *(Nos. 10 and 22/3).*			
49	**2**	21c. mauve and purple	23·00	£100
50		25c. blue and purple	23·00	£120
51		50c. brown and blue	50·00	£170
49/51 *Set of 3*			85·00	£350

Examples of all values are known with part strikes of the forged postmark mentioned after Nos. 26/40.

1922–**40**. *New colours, etc.* Wmk Mult Script CA (sideways* on 12, 35c.). P 14.

52	**1**	1c. black (ii) (Type I)	1·00	10
53		3c. green (ii) (1924)	2·25	90
54		4c. violet (ii) (1926)	1·00	10
		a. Short sheaf	50·00	10·00
55		5c. yellow (ii)	1·50	10
		w. Wmk inverted	85·00	£100
		x. Wmk reversed	†	£190
		y. Wmk inverted and reversed	†	£190
56		6c. carmine (ii) (1926)	1·75	65
		a. Carmine-red (1926)	12·00	48·00
57		8c. grey-black (ii) (10.36)	13·00	10
58	**2**	12c. black and indigo (II) (1926)	4·75	3·50
59		35c. purple (II) (1926)	9·00	30·00
52/9 *Set of 8*			30·00	32·00
52s/9s Optd or Perf (8c.) "Specimen" *Set of 8*			£300	

*The normal sideways watermark shows Crown to left of CA, *as seen from the back of the stamp.*

With the exception of the 6c. and 8c. the printing plates for the Type **1** values listed above were, as for the previous issue, produced by electrotyping with the face values added to the plates by pantograph. The plates for the 6c. and 8c. values were constructed by the more modern method of using a transfer die to enter each impression.

Printings after November 1933 were normally produced by the "dry" method as described beneath Nos. 26/40. There were late "wet" printings of the 1c. (No. 68a) and 2c. (No. 27) in August 1938. The 3c. only exists from a "wet" printing, the 6c. (No. 56a) and 8c. from dry printings and the remainder from either method.

Stamps as Type **1** can be found perforated either comb or line. The 3c. and 6c. (No. 56) come comb only, the 6c. (No. 56a) and 8c. line only and the 1, 4 and 5c. either way.

For the 1c. Type II see No. 68a.

6 Sultan Abdul Hamid Halimshah

(Recess Waterlow)

1937 (30 June). Wmk Mult Script CA. P 12½.

60	**6**	10c. ultramarine and sepia	4·50	1·25
61		12c. black and violet	40·00	6·50
		a. "A" of "CA" missing from wmk		
62		25c. ultramarine and purple	8·00	4·50
63		30c. green and scarlet	8·00	10·00
64		40c. black and purple	4·00	16·00
65		50c. brown and blue	7·50	4·50
66		$1 black and green	4·00	10·00
67		$2 green and brown	£120	75·00
68		$5 black and scarlet	32·00	£160
60/8 *Set of 9*			£200	£250
60s/8s Perf "Specimen" *Set of 9*			£275	

I   II   I   II

1938 (May)–**40**. *As Nos. 52 and 27, but face values redrawn as Types II.*

68a	**1**	1c. black	£110	3·00
69		2c. bright green (1940)	£225	6·50

1c. Type II. Figures "1" have square-cut corners instead of rounded, and larger top serif. Larger "C". Line perf. Produced from a new electrotyped Plate 2 with different engraved face values. Printings exist from either the "wet" or "dry" methods.

2c. Type II. Figures "2" have circular instead of oval drops and the letters "c" are thin and tall instead of thick and rounded. Produced from a new plate, made from a transfer die, and printed by the "dry" method.

1948 (1 Dec). *Royal Silver Wedding. As Nos. 112/13 of Antigua.*

70		10c. violet	20	40
71		$5 carmine	27·00	38·00

1949 (10 Oct). *75th Anniv of U.P.U. As Nos. 114/17 of Antigua.*

72		10c. purple	25	1·25
73		15c. deep blue	1·75	1·50
74		25c. orange	65	1·75
75		50c. blue-black	1·00	3·25
		a. "A" of "CA" missing from watermark	£750	
72/5 *Set of 4*			3·25	7·00

7 Sheaf of Rice   **8** Sultan Badlishah

1950 (1 June)–**55**. Wmk Mult Script CA. *Chalk-surfaced paper.* P 17½×18.

76	**7**	1c. black	50	30
77		2c. orange	50	15
78		3c. green	2·00	1·00
79		4c. brown	75	10

79a		5c. bright purple (1.9.52)................	2·25	2·25
		ab. Bright mauve (24.9.53)	2·25	1·00
80		6c. grey	70	15
81		8c. scarlet	1·75	3·00
81a		8c. green (1.9.52)	1·00	1·75
		ab. Deep green (24.9.53)	14·00	12·00
82		10c. magenta	70	10
82a		12c. scarlet (1.9.52)	1·00	2·50
83		15c. ultramarine	1·50	35
84		20c. black and green	1·75	25
84a		20c. bright blue (1.9.52)	1·25	10
85	8	25c. purple and orange	1·50	30
85a		30c. scarlet and purple (4.9.55)........	3·25	1·25
85b		35c. scarlet and purple (1.9.52)........	1·50	1·50
86		40c. red and purple	3·00	6·00
87		50c. black and blue	2·50	35
88		$1 blue and purple	3·00	4·75
89		$2 green and scarlet	20·00	23·00
90		$5 green and brown	42·00	48·00
76/90 Set of 21			80·00	90·00

KELANTAN

The Thai monarchy exercised suzerainty over Kelantan and the other northern states of the Malay peninsula from the 16th century onwards.

The first Siamese post office in Kelantan opened at Kota Bharu in 1895. It appears that in the early years this office only accepted letters franked with stamps for delivery within Kelantan.

The initial cancellation, of which no complete example has been discovered, showed Thai characters only. Partial examples have been reported on the 1887–91 8a. and 1896 4a. on 12a.

The operations of the Duff Development Company in Kelantan from 1903 led to a considerable expansion of the postal service based on the company's river steamers. A further post office opened at Batu Mengkebang in 1908, but may have been preceded by manuscript endorsements of "B.M." and date known from early 1907 onwards.

Type E. Double ring. English at top and bottom

For other stamp and postmark types, see under Kedah.

Kota Bharu

Stamps of SIAM cancelled as Type B inscr "KALANTAN" (*from* March 1898).

1887–91. (*Nos. 11/18*).
Z301	9	2a. green and carmine	90·00
Z302		3a. green and blue	95·00
Z303		4a. green and brown	95·00
Z304		8a. green and yellow	95·00
Z305		12a. purple and carmine	85·00
Z306		24a. purple and blue	90·00

1894. *Surch as T 27 with variation of English figures as T 33 (Nos. 37/44).*
Z307	9	2a. on 64a. purple and brown	£130

1894–95. *Surch as T 35 with variation of English figures as T 36 (Nos. 46/50).*
Z308	9	1a. on 64a. purple and brown	£110

1896. *Surch as T 39 (Siamese) and T 40 (English) (No. 51).*
Z309	9	4a. on 12a. purple and carmine	£110

1897. *Surch as T 39 (Siamese) and T 41 (English) (No. 52).*
Z310	9	4a. on 12a. purple and carmine	£110

1898–99. *Surch as T 42 with variation of English section as T 46 (Nos. 53/62).*
Z311	9	3a. on 12a. (11½–11¾ mm long)	£120
Z312		4a. on 12a. purple and carmine (8 mm long)	£110

1899–1904. (*Nos. 67/81*).
Z313	49	1a. olive-green (wide Siamese characters in face value)	90·00
Z314		2a. grass-green	85·00
Z315		2a. scarlet and pale blue	85·00
Z316		3a. red and blue	95·00
Z317		4a. carmine	85·00
Z318		4a. chocolate and pink	95·00
Z319		8a. deep green and orange	85·00
Z320		10a. ultramarine	90·00
Z321		12a. brown-purple and carmine	90·00
Z322		64a. brown-purple and chestnut	£190

1905–09. (*Nos. 92/105*).
Z323	53	1a. green and orange	85·00
Z324		2a. grey and deep violet	85·00
Z325		4a. pale red and sepia	85·00
Z326		4a. scarlet	85·00
Z327		5a. carmine	£100
Z328		8a. olive-bistre and dull black	85·00
Z329		12a. blue	£100
Z330		24a. red-brown	£275
Z331		1t. bistre and deep blue	£275

1907. *Surch with T 56 (No. 109).*
Z332	9	1a. on 24a. purple and blue	£110

Stamps of SIAM cancelled as Type E inscr "Kota Bahru/Kelantan" (*from* July 1908).

1887–91. (*Nos. 11/18*).
Z333	9	12a. purple and carmine	85·00
Z334		24a. purple and blue	£110

1899–1904. (*Nos. 67/81*).
Z335	49	8a. deep green and orange	90·00
Z336		64a. brown-purple and chestnut	£130

1905–09. (*Nos. 92/105*).
Z337	53	1a. green and orange	90·00
Z338		2a. grey and deep violet	90·00
Z339		2a. pale yellow-green	90·00
Z340		4a. pale red and sepia	90·00
Z341		4a. scarlet	90·00
Z342		8a. olive-bistre and dull black	85·00
Z343		9a. blue	95·00
Z344		18a. red-brown	£150

1907. *Surch with T 56 (No. 109).*
Z345	9	1a. on 24a. purple and blue	90·00

1908. *Surch as T 59 (Nos. 110/12).*
Z346	9	2a. on 24a. purple and blue	£130
Z347	53	4a. on 5a. carmine	£160
Z348	49	9a. on 10a. ultramarine	£100

Batu Mengkebang

Stamps of SIAM cancelled as Type E inscr "Batu Menkebang/Kelantan" (*from* July 1908).

1887–91. (*Nos. 11/18*).
Z349	9	12a. purple and carmine	£150

1899–1904. (*Nos. 67/81*).
Z350	49	8a. deep green and orange	£160

1905–09. (*Nos. 92/105*).
Z351	53	1a. green and orange	£150
Z352		2a. grey and deep violet	£150
Z353		2a. pale yellow-green	£160
Z354		4a. pale red and sepia	£160
Z355		4a. scarlet	£150
Z356		8a. olive-bistre and dull black	£130
Z357		9a. blue	£130
Z358		12a. blue	£190
Z359		24a. red-brown	£325
Z360		1t. bistre and deep blue	£350

1907. *Surch with T 56 (No. 109).*
Z361	9	1a. on 24a. purple and blue	£130

1908. *Surch as T 59 (Nos. 110/12).*
Z362	49	9a. on 10a. ultramarine	£190

Suzerainty over Kelantan was transferred by Thailand to Great Britain on 15 July 1909. Siamese stamps were withdrawn from sale and replaced the following day by stamps of the Federated Malay States.

Stamps of the Federated Malay States used in Kelantan

Kota Bahru

Type L   Type M

Cancelled as Type L

1909–11. (*Nos. 29–49*).
Z367	3	1c. green (Die II)	70·00
Z368		3c. carmine	60·00
Z369		4c. black and rose	70·00
Z370		8c. grey-brown and ultramarine	60·00
		a. Wmk upright	75·00
Z373	4	$2 green and carmine	£250

Cancelled as Type M

1909–11. (*Nos. 29–45a*).
Z375	3	1c. green (Die II)	50·00
Z376		3c. carmine	50·00
Z377		4c. black and rose	50·00
Z378		5c. green and carmine/yellow	80·00
Z379		8c. grey-brown and ultramarine	70·00
		a. Wmk upright	80·00
Z380		10c. black and green	90·00
Z381		20c. mauve and black (chalk-surfaced paper)	90·00

Batu Menkebang

Cancelled as Type l inscribed "Batu Menkebang"

1909–11. (*Nos. 34–43d*).
Z385	3	3c. carmine	90·00
Z386		5c. green and carmine/yellow	£100
Z387		10c. black and purple	£100

Cancelled as Type M inscribed "BATU MENKEBANG" *at top*

1909–11. (*Nos. 29–45a*).
Z391	3	1c. green (Die II)	70·00
Z392		3c. carmine	45·00
Z393		4c. black and rose	60·00
Z394		5c. green and carmine/yellow	£100
Z395		8c. grey-brown and ultramarine (wmk upright)	80·00
Z396		20c. mauve and black (chalk-surfaced paper)	£100

Federated Malay States stamps were replaced by those of Kelantan

in January 1911. A British adviser was appointed to Kelantan in 1923 and the state joined the Federation of Malaya on 1 February 1948.

PRICES FOR STAMPS ON COVER TO 1945		
Nos. 1/11	from × 30	
No. 12		
Nos. 14/23	from × 30	
Nos. 30/8	from × 15	
Nos. 39/a	from × 10	
Nos. 40/8	from × 30	
Nos. 49/52	from × 20	
No. 53	from × 3	
No. 54		

1

MALAYA BORNEO EXHIBITION

(2)

1911 (Jan)–**15.** Wmk Mult Crown CA. *Ordinary paper* (1c. to 10c.) *or chalk-surfaced paper* (30c. to $25). P 14.
1	1	1c. yellow-green	7·00	1·00
		a. Blue-green	5·50	30
2		3c. red	4·25	15
3		4c. black and red	1·50	15
4		5c. green and red/yellow	10·00	1·00
		w. Wmk inverted	†	£425
5		8c. ultramarine	5·50	1·00
6		10c. black and mauve	30·00	75
7		30c. dull purple and red	11·00	2·50
		a. Purple and carmine	27·00	14·00
8		50c. black and orange	8·00	2·50
9		$1 green and emerald	48·00	40·00
9a		$1 green and brown (5.15)	55·00	2·00
10		$2 green and carmine	1·50	4·00
11		$5 green and brown	4·00	7·50
12		$25 green and orange	42·00	85·00
1/12 Set of 13			£200	£130
1s/12s Optd "Specimen" Set of 13			£275	

1921 (5 May)–**28.** Wmk Mult Script CA. *Ordinary paper* (1c. to 10c.) *or chalk-surfaced paper* (30c. to $1). P 14.
14	1	1c. dull green (7.21)	4·25	60
15		1c. black (24.2.23)	1·00	50
16		2c. brown (29.7.22)	7·00	3·75
16a		2c. green (24.7.26)	4·25	40
16b		3c. brown (5.3.27)	4·50	1·00
		ba. "C" of "CA" missing from wmk		
17		4c. black and red (15.7.22)	2·75	10
18		5c. green and red/pale yellow (12.22)	1·50	10
19		6c. claret (29.7.22)	3·50	1·50
19a		6c. scarlet (26.5.28)	4·00	5·50
20		10c. black and mauve	3·00	10
21		30c. purple and carmine (24.7.26)	4·00	5·50
22		50c. black and orange (21.3.25)	6·50	45·00
23		$1 green and brown (9.2.24)	28·00	85·00
14/23 Set of 13			65·00	£130
14s/23s Optd "Specimen" Set of 13			£375	

Examples of Nos. 22/3 are known showing part strikes of a forged Kota Bharu postmark dated "27 JUL 11".

For the 4c., 5c. and 6c. surcharged, see issues under "Japanese Occupation".

OVERPRINT SETTINGS FOR NOS. 30/8. All values were overprinted using a triplet of three slightly different types. It is not known if this was applied to the sheets three stamps at a time or if a forme to overprint a pane of 60 was constructed from it.

On the normal setting "MALAYA" is 13 mm long. The 5c. only is also known with "MALAYA" 14 mm from a different triplet setting. It has been suggested that this was a trial overprint on one sheet which was subsequently included in postal stocks.

1922 (31 Mar). *Malaya-Borneo Exhibition, Singapore. Optd with* T 2 ("MALAYA" 13 mm long) by Govt Survey Office, Kkota Bharu.

(a) Wmk Mult Crown CA.
30	1	4c. black and red	5·00	50·00
		a. Opt double	£2500	
31		5c. green and red/pale yellow	6·00	50·00
		a. "MALAYA" 14 mm long	£200	
32		30c. dull purple and red	6·00	70·00
33		50c. black and orange	8·50	75·00
34		$1 green and brown	30·00	£100
35		$2 green and carmine	75·00	£200
36		$5 green and blue	£180	£400

(b) Wmk Mult Script CA.
37	1	1c. green	3·50	50·00
		a. Opt double	£2500	
38		10c. black and mauve	6·00	65·00
30/8 Set of 9			£300	£950

Nos. 30a and 37a show all three lines of the overprint double.

Examples of all values are known showing part strikes of the forged postmark mentioned below Nos. 14/23.

3 Sultan Ismail   4 Sultan Ismail

(Recess Harrison (No. 39) or D.L.R. (No. 39a))

1928–35. Wmk Mult Script CA. P 12.

39	3	$1 blue................................	15·00	80·00
		a. Perf 14 (1935)......................	45·00	42·00
		s. Perf "Specimen"	90·00	

(Recess B.W.)

1937 (July)–40. Wmk Mult Script CA. P 12.

40	4	1c. grey-olive and yellow...............	1·00	55
41		2c. green.................................	5·00	20
42		4c. scarlet...............................	5·50	1·00
43		5c. red-brown............................	4·75	10
44		6c. lake (10.37).........................	11·00	9·50
45		8c. grey-olive...........................	4·75	10
46		10c. purple (10.37).......................	22·00	2·75
47		12c. blue.................................	4·25	6·00
48		25c. vermilion and violet................	6·00	3·50
49		30c. violet and scarlet (10.37).........	42·00	20·00
50		40c. orange and blue-green...............	8·50	27·00
51		50c. grey-olive and orange (10.37)......	65·00	60
52		$1 violet and blue-green (10.37)....	48·00	13·00
53		$2 red-brown and scarlet (3.40)....	£225	£180
54		$5 vermilion and lake (3.40)........	£425	£550
40/54 Set of 15			£800	£750
40s/54s Perf "Specimen" Set of 15			£550	

For above issue surcharged see issues under "Japanese Occupation".

1948 (1 Dec). Royal Silver Wedding. As Nos. 112/13 of Antigua.

55	10c. violet.............................	75	2·75
56	$5 carmine.............................	27·00	48·00

1949 (10 Oct). 75th Anniv of U.P.U. As Nos. 114/17 of Antigua.

57	10c. purple.............................	25	30
58	15c. deep blue.........................	2·00	1·25
59	25c. scarlet............................	40	3·50
60	50c. blue-black........................	70	3·00
57/60 Set of 4		3·00	7·25

Due to the exhaustion of certain B.M.A. values PERAK 2c., 3c., 4c., 6c., 15c., 20c. black and green, 25c., 40c. and 50c. stamps were used in Kelantan from 27 November 1950 until the issue of Nos. 61/81.

5 Sultan Ibrahim	Normal	No. 62a Tiny stop (R. 1/2)

1951 (11 July)–55. Chalk-surfaced paper. Wmk Mult Script CA. P 17½×18.

61	5	1c. black................................	50	30
62		2c. orange..............................	1·25	35
		a. Tiny stop...........................	26·00	
		b. Orange-yellow (11.5.55)............	4·75	2·25
63		3c. green...............................	4·00	1·25
64		4c. brown...............................	1·00	15
65		5c. bright purple (1.9.52).............	1·50	50
		a. Bright mauve (9.12.53).............	2·50	70
66		6c. grey................................	75	20
67		8c. scarlet.............................	2·25	3·50
68		8c. green (1.9.52)......................	1·75	1·75
69		10c. magenta.............................	50	10
70		12c. scarlet (1.9.52)...................	2·75	2·25
71		15c. ultramarine........................	4·25	60
72		20c. black and green...................	1·50	7·00
73		20c. bright blue (1.9.52)..............	1·25	25
74		25c. purple and orange.................	1·50	55
75		30c. scarlet and purple (4.9.55)......	1·25	2·50
76		35c. scarlet and purple (1.9.52)......	1·50	1·50
77		40c. red and purple....................	10·00	14·00
78		50c. black and blue....................	4·00	40
79		$1 blue and purple...................	7·50	7·00
80		$2 green and scarlet.................	27·00	30·00
81		$5 green and brown...................	48·00	45·00
		a. Green and sepia (8.12.53).........	90·00	95·00
61/81 Set of 21			£110	£110

STAMP BOOKLETS

1927 (June). Black on white (No. SB1) or black on grey (No. SB2) covers. Stapled.

SB1	36c. booklet containing thirty-six 1c. (No. 15) in blocks of 6	£2750
SB2	96c. booklet containing twenty-four 4c. (No. 17) in blocks of 6	£2750

1927 (Dec). Black on white (No. SB3) or on grey (No. SB4) covers. Stapled.

SB3	40c. booklet containing forty 1c. (No. 15) in blocks of 10	£2750
SB4	80c. booklet containing twenty 4c. (No. 17) in blocks of 10	£2750

MALACCA

One of the Straits Settlements which joined the Federation of Malaya on 1 February 1948.

1948 (1 Dec). Royal Silver Wedding. As Nos. 112/13 of Antigua.

1	10c. violet.............................	30	1·75
2	$5 brown................................	29·00	38·00

1949 (1 Mar)–52. As T 58 of Straits Settlements, but inscr "MALACCA" at foot. Wmk Mult Script CA. Chalk-surfaced paper. P 17½×18.

3	1c. black..............................	30	70
4	2c. orange.............................	80	45
5	3c. green..............................	30	1·75
6	4c. brown..............................	30	10

6a	5c. bright purple (1.9.52)............	60	1·50
7	6c. grey...............................	75	85
8	8c. scarlet............................	75	6·00
8a	8c. green (1.9.52).....................	2·50	4·75
9	10c. purple.............................	30	10
9a	12c. scarlet (1.9.52)...................	2·50	6·50
10	15c. ultramarine........................	2·50	60
11	20c. black and green...................	60	7·00
11a	20c. bright blue (1.9.52)..............	4·50	2·50
12	25c. purple and orange.................	60	70
12a	35c. scarlet and purple (1.9.52)......	2·75	3·00
13	40c. red and purple....................	1·25	11·00
14	50c. black and blue....................	1·00	1·25
15	$1 blue and purple...................	9·00	22·00
16	$2 green and scarlet.................	21·00	22·00
17	$5 green and brown...................	48·00	35·00
3/17 Set of 20		90·00	£110

1949 (10 Oct). 75th Anniv of U.P.U. As Nos. 114/17 of Antigua.

18	10c. purple.............................	30	50
19	15c. deep blue.........................	2·00	2·00
20	25c. orange............................	40	5·50
21	50c. blue-black........................	60	4·75
18/21 Set of 4		3·00	11·50

NEGRI SEMBILAN

A federation of smaller states reconstituted in 1886. Sungei Ujong, taken under British protection in 1874, was absorbed into Negri Sembilan by Treaty of 8 August 1895. The Negri Sembilan federation joined the Federated Malay States in 1896.

A. SUNGEI UJONG

Until 1 January 1899, when the Federated Malay States joined the U.P.U., mail for addresses outside Malaya was franked with the stamps of the STRAITS SETTLEMENTS.

PRICES FOR STAMPS ON COVER	
Nos. 1/14	—
Nos. 15/27	from × 25
Nos. 28/36	from × 8
Nos. 37/49	from × 10
Nos. 50/5	from × 25

(1)

1878. No. 11 of Straits Settlements handstamped with T 1.

1	2c. brown..............................	£2750	£3000

This overprint on India No. 54 is bogus.

SUNGEI (2) (Narrow letters)   **SUNGEI** (3) ("N" wide)   **SUNGEI** (4) ("S" wide)

UJONG (5) ("N" wide)   **UJONG** (6) (Narrow letters, "UJ" close together)   **UJONG** (7) (Narrow letters, evenly spaced)

1881. No. 11 of Straits Settlements optd with T 2/7.

2	2+5	2c. brown..............................	£4000	£3000
3	3+5	2c. brown..............................	£2500	£2000
4	2+6	2c. brown..............................	£300	
		a. Opt Type 6 double.................	£1700	
5	4+6	2c. brown..............................	£900	
6	2+7	2c. brown..............................	£375	

The two lines of this surcharge were applied as separate operations. On Nos. 2/3 "SUNGEI" was printed as a triplet, probably 2+3+3 "UJONG" being added by a single unit handstamp. Nos. 4 and 5 come from a similar triplet, 4+4+5, completed by another single unit handstamp. No. 6 comes from a single type triplet with the second line added as a triplet instead of by a single unit handstamp.

The 10c. slate overprinted Types 2 + 7 is bogus.

SUNGEI (8) ("N" and "E" wide)   **SUNGEI** (9) ("SUN" and "E" wide)   **SUNGEI** (10) ("SUN" wide)

SUNGEI (11) ("S" wide)   **SUNGEI** (12) (Narrow letters)

UJONG (13) ("U" and "NG" wide)   **UJONG** (14) (Narrow letters)

1881. No. 11 of Straits Settlements optd with T 8/14.

7	8+13	2c. brown..............................	£300	
8	9+13	2c. brown..............................	£325	
9	10+13	2c. brown..............................	£300	
10	11+14	2c. brown..............................	£275	
		a. "S" inverted.......................	£3250	
11	12+14	2c. brown..............................	£180	

Nos. 7/11 also had the two lines of the overprint applied at separate operations. "SUNGEI" as a triplet, either 7+8+9 or 10+11+11, and "UJONG" as a single unit.

S. U.
(15)

1882. Nos. 50/1 of Straits Settlements optd as T 15.

12	2c. brown (with stops).................	£300	
	a. Opt double..........................	£3000	
13	2c. brown (without stops)..............	£275	£325
14	4c. rose (with stops)..................	£3000	£3500

Each of the above was applied by a triplet setting.

Examples of Straits Settlements No. 11 with a similar overprint, including stops, are trials which were not issued.

SUNGEI (16) ("S" and "E" wide)   **SUNGEI** (17) ("E" wide)   **UJONG** (18) ("N" wide)

1882 (Dec)–84. Nos. 12, 50, 52/3 and 63 of Straits Settlements optd with T 11/12, 14 and 16/18.

15	12+14	2c. brown..............................	£800	£375
16	11+14	2c. brown..............................	£1100	£550
17	12+14	2c. pale rose (1884)..................	£180	£180
18	11+14	2c. pale rose (1884)..................	£180	£180
		a. Opt Type 14 double................	£800	
19	16+14	2c. pale rose (1884)..................	£100	£100
20	17+14	2c. pale rose (1884)..................	£110	£120
21	12+18	2c. pale rose (1884)..................	£110	£120
		a. Opt Type 18 double................	£800	
22	12+14	4c. rose...............................	£1600	£1700
		a. Opt Type 12 double................	†	£3250
23	11+14	4c. rose...............................	£2500	£2750
24	11+14	8c. orange.............................	£1800	£1300
25	11+14	8c. orange.............................	£3000	£2500
26	12+14	10c. slate..............................	£550	£475
27	11+14	10c. slate..............................	£850	£750

Nos. 15/27 had the two lines of the overprint applied by separate triplets. Settings so far identified are Nos. 15+16+15, 17+18+19, 19+20+21, 22+23+22, 24+25+24 and 26+27+26.

The 4c. rose overprinted Types 16 + 14 is now believed to be a trial.

UJONG. (19) (With stop. Narrow letters)   **UJONG.** (20) (With stop. "N" wide)   **UJONG** (21) (Without stop. Narrow letters)

1883–84. Nos. 50 and 63/4 of Straits Settlements optd with T 12, 16/17 and 19/21.

28	12+19	2c. brown..............................	48·00	£130
29	16+19	2c. brown..............................	48·00	£130
30	12+20	2c. brown..............................	48·00	£130
		a. Opt Type 12 double................	£1200	
31	16+21	2c. pale rose (1884)..................	90·00	£100
32	17+21	2c. pale rose (1884)..................	90·00	£100
33	12+21	2c. pale rose (1884)..................	90·00	£100
34	16+21	4c. brown (1884)......................	£250	£325
		a. Opt Type 16 double................	£1800	
		b. Opt Type 21 double................		
35	17+21	4c. brown (1884)......................	£250	£325
36	12+21	4c. brown (1884)......................	£250	£325
		a. Opt Type 21 double................	£3750	

Nos. 28/36 had the two lines of the overprint applied by separate triplets. Settings were Nos. 28+29+30, 31+32+33 and 34+35+36.

The 8c. orange overprinted Types 12 + 19 is now believed to be a trial (Price £900 unused).

Sungei Ujong (22)   **SUNGEI UJONG** (23)   **SUNGEI UJONG** (24)

SUNGEI UJONG (25)   **SUNGEI UJONG** (26)   **SUNGEI UJONG** (27)

SUNGEI UJONG (28)   **SUNGEI UJONG.** (29)   **SUNGEI UJONG** (30)

1885–90. Nos. 63/a of Straits Settlements optd with T 22/30.

37	22	2c. pale rose..........................	75·00	85·00
		a. Opt double.........................	£600	£600
38	23	2c. pale rose..........................	35·00	60·00
		a. Opt double.........................	£600	
39	24	2c. pale rose (1886)..................	95·00	£110
40	25	2c. pale rose (1886)..................	£140	£150
		a. Opt double.........................		
41	26	2c. pale rose (1886)..................	90·00	£100
		a. Opt double.........................		
42	27	2c. pale rose (1887)..................	15·00	38·00
43	28	2c. pale rose (1889)..................	9·00	13·00
		a. Narrow "E" (2 mm wide) (R. 3/4 and 4/3)..................	90·00	
		c. Opt double.........................	£1300	
		d. Bright rose (1890).................	13·00	10·00
		da. Narrow "E" (2 mm wide) (R. 3/4 and 4/3)..................	£110	
		db. Antique "N" in "UJONG" (R. 10/6)..	£170	
44	29	2c. pale rose (1889)..................	90·00	70·00
		a. "UNJOG" (R. 7/3)...................	£4250	£2750
45	30	2c. bright rose (1890)................	40·00	17·00
		a. Antique "G" in "SUNGEI" (R. 6/1)..	£325	
		b. Antique "G" in "UJONG" (R. 8/3)...	£325	
		c. Pale rose..........................		

All the above overprints had both lines applied at the same operation. Nos. 37/42 were from different triplet settings. The first printing of Type 28 was from a triplet (No. 43) but this was followed by two further settings of 60 (6×10), the first containing No. 43a and the second Nos. 43d/db. Nos. 44/5 were both from settings of 60.

The antique letter varieties on Types 28 and 30 are similar in style to those on Types 25 and 26.

SUNGEI UJONG Two CENTS
(31)

SUNGEI UJONG Two CENTS
(32)

SUNGEI UJONG Two CENTS
(33)

SUNGEI UJONG Two CENTS
(34)

1891. No. 68 of Straits Settlements surch with T 31/4.

46	**31**	2c. on 24c. green	£800	£900
47	**32**	2c. on 24c. green	£325	£375
		w. Wmk inverted	£550	£600
48	**33**	2c. on 24c. green	£800	£900
49	**34**	2c. on 24c. green	£170	£190
		a. Antique "G" in "SUNGEI" (R. 6/1)	£1000	
		b. Antique "G" in "UJONG" (R. 8/3)	£1000	
		w. Wmk inverted	£375	£400

Nos. 46/9 come from the same setting of 60 on which "SUNGEI UJONG" was from the same type as No. 45. No. 46 occurs in row 1. No. 47 from rows 2 to 4, No. 48 from row 5 and No. 49 from rows 6 to 10.

3 CENTS (36)

35   (36)   37

1891 (Nov)–**94.** Wmk Crown CA. P 14.

50	**35**	2c. rose	30·00	27·00
51		2c. orange (12.94)	1·75	4·25
52		5c. blue (3.93)	5·00	6·50
50/2 Set of 3			32·00	35·00
50s/2s Optd "Specimen" Set of 3			65·00	

1894 (Dec). Surch as T **36** by De La Rue. Wmk Mult Crown CA. P 14.

53	**35**	1c. on 5c. green	1·00	70
54		3c. on 5c. rose	2·50	4·75

1895 (Oct). Wmk Crown CA. P 14.

55	**37**	3c. dull purple and carmine	12·00	3·75
53s/5s Optd "Specimen" Set of 3			65·00	

B. NEGRI SEMBILAN

Stamps of the STRAITS SETTLEMENTS were used in Negri Sembilan during 1891, until replaced by the stamps listed below. Until the Federated Malay States joined the U.P.U. On 1 January 1899 Straits Settlements stamps continued to be used for mail to addresses outside Malaya.

PRICES FOR STAMPS ON COVER TO 1945	
No. 1	from × 200
Nos. 2/4	from × 10
Nos. 5/14	from × 8
Nos. 15/20	from × 10
Nos. 21/49	from × 4

Negri Sembilan
(1)

2   3

1891 (Aug?). No. 63a of Straits Settlements optd with T **1**.

1	2c. bright rose	3·00	6·00

N.SEMBILAN

Short "N" in "SEMBILAN" (Top left pane R. 8/3)

1891 (Nov)–**94.** Wmk Crown CA. P 14.

2	**2**	1c. green (6.93)	3·00	1·00
3		2c. rose	3·25	8·50
		a. Short "N"	80·00	
4		5c. blue (11.94)	30·00	40·00
2/4 Set of 3			32·00	45·00
2s/4s Optd "Specimen" Set of 3			85·00	

1895–99. Wmk Crown CA. P 14.

5	**3**	1c. dull purple and green (1899)	13·00	6·50
6		2c. dull purple and brown (1898)	35·00	£110
7		3c. dull purple and carmine	14·00	1·25
8		5c. dull purple and olive-yellow (1897)	8·50	9·50
9		8c. dull purple and ultramarine (1898)	29·00	17·00

10		10c. dull purple and orange (1897)	27·00	14·00
11		15c. green and violet (1896)	42·00	75·00
12		20c. green and olive (1897)	65·00	38·00
13		25c. green and carmine (1896)	70·00	90·00
14		50c. green and black (1896)	75·00	65·00
5/14 Set of 10			£350	£375
5s/14s Optd "Specimen" Set of 10			£225	

Four cents.

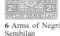
(4)   (5)

1898 (Dec)–**1900.**

(a) Surch as T **4.**

15	**3**	1c. on 15c. green and violet (1900)	£100	£300
		a. Raised stop (R. 5/1 and R. 10/1 of each pane)	£400	£1000
		b. Surch double, one albino		
16	**2**	4c. on 1c. green	2·50	16·00
17	**3**	4c. on 3c. dull purple and carmine	3·25	18·00
		a. Horiz pair, one without surch	£6500	£4250
		b. Surch double	£2000	£1000
		ba. Ditto. "Four cents" albino	†	£1000
		c. Surch inverted	£1700	£1300
		d. "cents" repeated at left	£2000	£1800
		e. "Four" repeated at right	£2000	£1800
		f. Without bar	£800	£650
		g. Bar double	†	£800
18	**2**	4c. on 5c. blue	1·25	15·00

On Nos. 15 and 17 the bar is at the top of the stamp. The surcharges were applied as a setting of 30 (6×5).

(b) Surch as T **5.**

19	**3**	4c. on 8c. dull purple & ultram (G.) (12.98)	6·50	4·25
		a. Vert pair, one without surch	£5000	£3500
		b. Surch double	£2000	£2000
		c. Surch double (G.+R.)	£800	£850
20		4c. on 8c. dull purple & ultramarine (Bk.)	£1100	£1200

Care should be taken in distinguishing the true black surcharge, No. 20, from very deep shades of the green surcharge, No. 19.

Pending the arrival of the permanent Federated Malay States issue the stamps of SELANGOR, FEDERATED MALAY STATES provisional overprints, STRAITS SETTLEMENTS and PERAK were used at various times between October 1899 and April 1901.

The general issues for FEDERATED MALAY STATES were used in Negri Sembilan from 29 April 1901 until 1935.

6 Arms of Negri Sembilan   7 Arms of Negri Sembilan

1935 (2 Dec)–**41.** Wmk Mult Script CA. Ordinary paper (3c., 6c. grey, 15c.) or chalk-surfaced paper (others). P 14.

21	**6**	1c. black (1.1.36)	1·00	20
22		2c. green (1.1.36)	1·00	20
23		2c. orange (11.12.41)	4·25	65·00
24		3c. green	17·00	8·00
		a. Chalk-surfaced paper (12.41)	8·00	8·00
25		4c. orange	1·25	10
26		5c. brown (5.12.35)	1·75	10
27		6c. scarlet (1.1.37)	15·00	2·50
		a. Stop omitted at right (R. 10/4)	£425	£120
28		6c. green (18.12.41)	4·75	75·00
		a. Stop omitted at right (R. 10/4)	£180	£750
29		8c. grey	2·00	10
30		10c. dull purple (1.1.36)	1·00	10
31		12c. bright ultramarine (1.1.36)	2·50	50
32		15c. ultramarine (1.10.41)	10·00	50·00
33		25c. dull purple and scarlet (1.4.36)	1·25	70
34		30c. dull purple and orange (1.1.36)	3·50	2·00
35		40c. scarlet and dull purple	2·50	2·00
36		50c. black/emerald (1.2.36)	5·00	2·25
37		$1 black and red/blue (1.4.36)	4·00	3·75
38		$2 green and scarlet (16.5.36)	32·00	17·00
39		$5 green and red/emerald (16.5.36)	21·00	70·00
21/39 Set of 19			£110	£250
21s/39s Perf "Specimen" Set of 19			£375	

The stamps issued in 1941 were printed by Harrison and Sons following bomb damage to the De La Rue works on 29 December 1940. The used prices quoted for Nos. 23, 28 and 32 are for examples with clearly identifiable 1941 cancellations.

An 8c. scarlet was issued but only with opt during Japanese Occupation of Malaya. Unoverprinted specimens result from leakages.

During shortages in 1941 stamps of STRAITS SETTLEMENTS (2c. green, 25c., 30c.), SELANGOR (2c. green, 2c. orange (both perfs), 8c. grey, 25c.), PERAK (2c. orange, 25c., 50c.) and PAHANG (8c. scarlet) were issued in Negri Sembilan.

1948 (1 Dec). Royal Silver Wedding. As Nos. 112/13 of Antigua.

40		10c. violet	15	50
41		$5 green	20·00	28·00

1949 (1 Apr)–**55.** Chalk-surfaced paper. Wmk Mult Script CA. P 17½×18.

42	**7**	1c. black	30	10
43		2c. orange	30	10
44		3c. green	30	30
45		4c. brown	30	10
46		5c. bright purple (1.9.52)	30	50
		a. Bright mauve (25.8.53)	30	45
47		6c. grey	1·25	10

		a. Pale grey (25.8.53)	5·00	1·25
48		8c. scarlet	50	75
49		8c. green (1.9.52)	2·25	1·60
50		10c. purple	20	10
51		12c. scarlet (1.9.52)	2·25	2·75
52		15c. ultramarine	3·00	10
53		20c. black and green	50	75
54		20c. bright blue (1.9.52)	1·00	50
55		25c. purple and orange	50	10
56		30c. scarlet and purple (4.9.55)	1·25	2·50
57		35c. scarlet and purple (1.9.52)	1·00	1·00
58		40c. red and purple	1·75	4·75
59		50c. black and blue	2·75	20
60		$1 blue and purple	3·75	2·25
61		$2 green and scarlet	12·00	18·00
62		$5 green and brown	50·00	55·00
42/62 Set of 21			75·00	80·00

1949 (10 Oct). 75th Anniv of U.P.U. As Nos. 114/17 of Antigua.

63		10c. purple	20	10
64		15c. deep blue	1·40	2·75
		a. "A" of "CA" missing from wmk	£750	
65		25c. orange	30	2·25
66		50c. blue-black	60	3·25
63/6 Set of 4			2·25	7·50

STAMP BOOKLETS

1935. Stapled.

SB1 $1 booklet containing twenty 5c. (No. 26) in blocks of 10

SB2 $1.30 booklet containing 5c. and 8c. (Nos. 26, 29), each in block of 10

PAHANG

The first British Resident was appointed in 1888. Pahang joined the Federated Malay States in 1896.

Until 1 January 1899, when the Federated Malay States joined the U.P.U., mail for addresses outside Malaya was franked with stamps of the STRAITS SETTLEMENTS.

PRICES FOR STAMPS ON COVER TO 1945	
No. 1	from × 50
Nos. 2/3	—
No. 4	from × 100
No. 5	—
No. 6	from × 100
Nos. 7/10	from × 8
Nos. 11/13	from × 25
Nos. 14/16	from × 20
No. 17/a	—
Nos. 18/d	from × 6
Nos. 19/24	from × 8
No. 25	from × 20
Nos. 26/7	—
No. 28	from × 15
Nos. 29/46	from × 6

PAHANG   **PAHANG**   PAHANG
(1)   (2)   (2a) (Antique letters)

1889 (Jan). Nos. 52/3 and 63 of Straits Settlements optd with T **1**.

1		2c. pale rose	£100	50·00
2		8c. orange	£1700	£1700
3		5c. slate	£225	£250

All three values were overprinted from a triplet setting, but the 2c. also exists from a similar setting of 30 or 60.

1889. No. 63 of Straits Settlements optd with T **2**.

4		2c. pale rose	14·00	18·00
		a. Bright rose	6·00	8·00
		ab. Opt Type **2a**. Antique letters	£850	

No. 4 was overprinted from a setting of 60. No. 4ab usually occurs on R. 10/1, but has also been found on R. 8/1 as the result of revision of the setting.

PAHANG   **PAHANG**
(3)   (4)

1890. No. 63a of Straits Settlements optd.

5	**3**	2c. pale rose	£5500	£1700
6	**4**	2c. bright rose	£100	14·00
		w. Wmk inverted		

No. 5 may have been overprinted from a triplet setting. No. 6 was from a setting of 60.

PAHANG Two CENTS
(5)

PAHANG Two CENTS
(6)

PAHANG Two CENTS
(7)

PAHANG Two CENTS
(8)

1891. No. 68 of Straits Settlements surch with T **5/8**.

7	**5**	2c. on 24c. green	£180	£200
8	**6**	2c. on 24c. green	£850	£1000

9	**7**	2c. on 24c. green......................	£325	£375
10	**8**	2c. on 24c. green......................	£850	£1000

Nos. 7/10 come from one setting used to surcharge the panes of sixty. No. 7 occurs in rows 1 to 5, No. 8 on row 6, No. 9 on rows 7 to 9 and No. 10 on row 10.

9

10

1891 (Nov)–**95**. Wmk Crown CA. P 14.

11	**9**	1c. green (3.95)......................	4·25	3·25
12		2c. rose......................	4·50	3·25
13		5c. blue (6.93)......................	11·00	40·00
11/13		Set of 3	18·00	42·00
11s/13s		Optd "Specimen" Set of 3	80·00	

Following an increase of postage rates on 1 March 1894 1 cent stamps of STRAITS SETTLEMENTS were used in Pahang until the autumn of the following year.

1895–99. Wmk Crown CA. P 14.

14	**10**	3c. dull purple and carmine..........	7·50	2·75
15		4c. dull purple and carmine (1899).	17·00	12·00
16		5c. dull purple and olive-yellow (1897)......................	27·00	21·00
14/16		Set of 3	45·00	32·00
14s/16s		Optd "Specimen" Set of 3	65·00	

1897 (2 Aug). No. 13 bisected, surch in red manuscript at Kuala Lipis and initialled "JFO".

(a) Bisected horizontally.

17		2c. on half of 5c. blue (surch "2" and bar across "5")......................	—	£1700
17a		3c. on half of 5c. blue (surch "3")	£5000	£1700

(b) Bisected diagonally.

18		2c. on half of 5c. blue (surch "2" and bar across "5")......................	£1500	£375
	a.	Unsevered pair. Nos. 18 and 18d......................	£9500	£3750
	b.	Se-tenant pair. Nos. 18 and 18d......................	£4000	£1000
	c.	Surch in black manuscript......................	£8000	£3000
18d		3c. on half of 5c. blue (surch "3")	£1500	£375
	dc.	Surch in black manuscript......................	£8000	£3000

The initials are those of John Fortescue Owen, the District Treasurer at Kuala Lipis.

Nos. 17 and 18 only occur on the bottom half of the 5c. and Nos. 17a and 18d on the top half. No. 18a is a complete example of No. 13 showing the two surcharges. No. 18b is a se-tenant pair of bisects from adjoining stamps.

Pahang.   Pahang.
(11)   **(12)**

1898–99.

(a) Nos. 72/5 of Perak optd with T 11.

19		10c. dull purple and orange (3.98)...........	20·00	25·00
20		25c. green and carmine......................	85·00	£160
21		50c. dull purple and greenish black	£400	£450
22		50c. green and black (1899)......................	£250	£325

(b) Nos. 76 and 79 of Perak optd with T 12.

23		$1 green and pale green......................	£350	£475
24		$5 green and ultramarine......................	£1300	£2000

Pahang
Four cents
(13)

Four cents.
(14)

1898.

(a) No. 71 of Perak surch with T 13.

25		4c. on 8c. dull purple and ultramarine	4·75	5·50
	a.	Surch inverted......................	£3250	£1400
	b.	Surch double......................	£850	

(b) T 13 on plain paper (no stamp), but issued for postage. Imperf.

26		4c. black......................		£3500
27		5c. black......................		£2250

No. 26 also exists pin-perforated.

1899. No. 16 surch with T 14.

28	**10**	4c. on 5c. dull purple and olive-yellow..	17·00	60·00

Pending the arrival of the permanent Federated Malay States issue the stamps of SELANGOR, FEDERATED MALAY STATES provisional overprints and PERAK were used at various times between November 1899 and July 1902. The general issues for the FEDERATED MALAY STATES were used in Pahang from July 1902 until 1935.

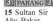
15 Sultan Sir Abu Bakar

16 Sultan Sir Abu Bakar

1935 (2 Dec)–**41**. *Chalk-surfaced paper.* Wmk Mult Script CA. P14.

29	**15**	1c. black (1.1.36)......................	20	40
30		2c. green (1.1.36)......................	1·25	50
31		3c. green (ordinary paper) (21.8.41)......................	38·00	4·25
	a.	Chalk-surfaced paper......................	15·00	15·00
32		4c. orange......................	70	50
33		5c. brown (5.12.35)......................	70	10
34		6c. scarlet (1.1.37)......................	16·00	1·75
35		8c. grey......................	60	10
36		8c. scarlet (11.12.41)......................	2·75	55·00
37		10c. dull purple (1.1.36)......................	80	10
38		12c. bright ultramarine (1.1.36)......................	2·25	1·25
39		15c. ultram (ordinary paper) (1.10.41)......................	15·00	50·00
40		25c. dull purple and scarlet (1.4.36) .	1·25	1·50
41		30c. dull purple and orange (1.1.36).	1·00	1·10
42		40c. scarlet and dull purple......................	85	2·00
43		50c. black/emerald (1.2.36)......................	3·00	1·50
44		$1 black and red/blue (1.4.36)......................	2·50	8·00
45		$2 green and scarlet (16.5.36)......................	22·00	30·00
46		$5 green and red/emerald (16.5.36)......................	8·00	65·00
29/46		Set of 18	80·00	£200
29s/46s		Perf "Specimen" Set of 18	£400	

The stamps issued during 1941 were printed by Harrison and Sons following bomb damage to the De La Rue works on 29 December 1940. The used prices quoted for Nos. 36 and 39 are for examples with clearly identifiable 1941 cancellations.

A 2c. orange and a 6c. grey were prepared but not officially issued. (*Price mint £4 each*).

During shortages in 1941 stamps of STRAITS SETTLEMENTS (2c., 25c.), SELANGOR (2c. orange, 3c., 8c.), NEGRI SEMBILAN (6c.) and PERAK (2c. orange) were issued in Pahang.

1948 (1 Dec). *Royal Silver Wedding. As Nos. 112/13 of Antigua.*

47		10c. violet......................	15	60
48		$5 green......................	25·00	40·00

1949 (10 Oct). *75th Anniv of U.P.U. As Nos. 114/17 of Antigua.*

49		10c. purple......................	30	20
50		15c. deep blue......................	1·10	1·25
51		25c. orange......................	35	10
52		50c. blue-black......................	70	2·00
49/52		Set of 4	2·25	4·50

1950 (1 June)–**56**. Wmk Mult Script CA. *Chalk-surfaced paper.* P 17½×18.

53	**16**	1c. black......................	10	10
54		2c. orange......................	10	10
55		3c. green......................	30	80
56		4c. brown......................	1·00	10
	a.	Chocolate (24.3.54)......................	9·00	2·25
57		5c. bright purple (1.9.52)......................	50	70
	a.	Bright mauve (10.9.53)......................	50	15
58		6c. grey......................	40	30
59		8c. scarlet......................	50	1·50
60		8c. green (1.9.52)......................	85	75
61		10c. magenta......................	25	10
62		12c. scarlet (1.9.52)......................	85	1·25
63		15c. ultramarine......................	75	10
64		20c. black and green......................	50	2·75
65		20c. bright blue (1.9.52)......................	1·00	10
	a.	Ultramarine (8.3.56)......................	7·00	2·75
66		25c. purple and orange......................	50	10
67		30c. scarlet and brown-purple (4.9.55) .	1·25	4·50
	a.	Scarlet and purple (8.3.56)......................	17·00	4·50
68		35c. scarlet and purple (1.9.52)......................	60	25
69		40c. red and purple......................	1·50	7·50
70		50c. black and blue......................	1·50	10
71		$1 blue and purple......................	2·75	3·25
72		$2 green and scarlet......................	13·00	21·00
73		$5 green and brown......................	55·00	70·00
	a.	Green and sepia (24.3.54)......................	90·00	90·00
53/73		Set of 21	75·00	95·00

STAMP BOOKLETS

1935. *Black on buff covers. Stapled.*

SB1		$1 booklet *containing* twenty 5c. (No. 33) in blocks of 10	
SB2		$1.30 booklet containing 5c. and 8c. (Nos. 33, 35) each in block of 10 and pane of airmail labels	£2500

PENANG

One of the Straits Settlements which joined the Federation of Malaya on 1 February 1948.

1948 (1 Dec). *Royal Silver Wedding. As Nos. 112/13 of Antigua.*

1		10c. violet......................	30	20
2		$5 brown......................	30·00	30·00

1949 (21 Feb)–**52**. *As T 58 of Straits Settlements, but inscr "PENANG" at foot.* Wmk Mult Script CA. *Chalk-surfaced paper.* P 17½×18.

3		1c. black......................	30	20
4		2c. orange......................	85	20
5		3c. green......................	30	10
6		4c. brown......................	30	10
7		5c. bright purple (1.9.52)......................	2·25	2·75
8		6c. grey......................	30	20
9		8c. scarlet......................	60	4·00
10		8c. green (1.9.52)......................	1·50	1·75
11		10c. purple......................	30	10
12		12c. scarlet (1.9.52)......................	2·25	6·00
13		15c. ultramarine......................	60	30

14		20c. black and green......................	60	1·25
15		20c. bright blue (1.9.52)......................	70	1·25
16		25c. purple and orange......................	1·75	30
17		35c. scarlet and purple (1.9.52)......................	1·25	1·25
18		40c. red and purple......................	1·75	12·00
19		50c. black and blue......................	2·75	20
20		$1 blue and purple......................	17·00	2·00
21		$2 green and scarlet......................	22·00	8·00
22		$5 green and brown......................	48·00	3·00
3/22		Set of 20	95·00	35·00

1949 (10 Oct). *75th Anniv of U.P.U. As Nos. 114/17 of Antigua.*

23		10c. purple......................	20	10
24		15c. deep blue......................	2·00	3·00
25		25c. orange......................	45	3·00
26		50c. blue-black......................	1·50	3·50
23/6		Set of 4	3·75	8·50

PERAK

Perak accepted a British Resident in 1874, although he was later murdered.

The state joined the Federated Malay States in 1896.

The stamps of the STRAITS SETTLEMENTS were used in Perak during 1877/8. Until 1 January 1899, when the Federated Malay States joined the U.P.U., mail for addresses outside Malaya was franked with stamps of the STRAITS SETTLEMENTS.

PRICES FOR STAMPS ON COVER TO 1945

No. 1	—
Nos. 2/9	from × 60
Nos. 10/13	from × 30
Nos. 14/16	from × 8
Nos. 17/22	from × 20
No. 23	—
Nos. 24/5	—
Nos. 26/8	from × 15
No. 29	from × 75
No. 30	from × 20
Nos. 31/2	—
Nos. 33/40	from × 15
Nos. 43/60	from × 6
Nos. 61/5	from × 20
Nos. 66/79	from × 12
No. 80	—
Nos. 81/7	from × 8
Nos. 88/102	from × 4
Nos 103/21	from × 3

The official stamps of Perak are rare used on cover.

(1)

1878. No. 11 of Straits Settlements handstamped with T **1**.

1		2c. brown......................	£1800 £1400

PERAK   PERAK   PERAK
(2) (14½ mm long)   **(3)** (11 mm long)   **(4)** (10¼ mm long)

PERAK   PERAK   PERAK
(5) (17 mm long)   **(6)** ("RA" narrow)   **(7)** ("R" narrow)

PERAK   PERAK
(8) ("P" and "K" wide)   **(9)** (12 to 13½ mm long)

1880–81. No. 11 (wmk Crown CC) of Straits Settlements optd with T **2/9**.

2	**2**	2c. brown......................	£1900	£900
3	**3**	2c. brown......................	£1700	£650
4	**4**	2c. brown......................	£850	£650
5	**5**	2c. brown (1881)......................	30·00	60·00
6	**6**	2c. brown (1881)......................	£225	£250
7	**7**	2c. brown (1881)......................	£150	£170
8	**8**	2c. brown (1881)......................	£500	£475
	a.	Opt double......................	†	£1700
9	**9**	2c. brown (1881)......................	£140	£150

Of the above No. 2 is from a single unit overprint, No. 5 from a setting of sixty and the remainder from settings applied as horizontal strips of three. Nos. 6/8 come from mixed triplets, either 6+7+7 or 7+7+8. No. 4 is believed to come from a single unit overprint in addition to a triplet.

PERAK   PERAK
(10) ("A" wide)   **(11)** ("E" wide)

1882–83. Nos. 50 (wmk Crown CA) and 63 of Straits Settlements optd with T **9/11**.

10	**9**	2c. brown......................	19·00	55·00
	a.	Opt double......................	£600	
11		2c. pale rose (1883)......................	25·00	48·00
	a.	Opt double......................	£650	
12	**10**	2c. pale rose (1883)......................	25·00	75·00
13	**11**	2c. pale rose (1883)......................	25·00	60·00
	a.	Opt double......................	£650	

The above were all overprinted as triplet settings. Those for the 2c. rose were 11+12+13, 13+11+11 and 13+11+12.

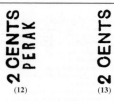

2 CENTS PERAK		2 OENTS
(12)		(13)

1883 (July). *No. 51* (wmk Crown CA) *of Straits Settlements surch.*

(a) Surch with T **12**.

| 14 | | 2c. on 4c. rose .... | £3000 | |
| | a. | On Straits Settlements No. 12 (wmk Crown CC).................................... | £7500 | |

(b) Optd as T **9** *or* **11** *and surch with T* **13**.

| 15 | 11 | 2c. on 4c. rose .... | £950 | £425 |
| 16 | 9 | 2c. on 4c. rose .... | £550 | £250 |

It is believed that No. 14 occurred on the top row of the sheet with the remaining nine rows surcharged with a triplet containing 15+16+16. Only one unused example, with defects, of No. 14a is recorded.

PERAK	PERAK	PERAK
(14) ("E" wide)	(15) ("E" narrow)	(16) (12½–13 mm long)

PERAK	PERAK	PERAK
(17) (12–12½ mm long)	(18) (10½ mm long)	(19) (10 mm long)

PERAK
(20) (13 mm long)

1884–91. *Nos. 63/a of Straits Settlements optd with T* **14/20**.

17	14	2c. pale rose	4·00	3·00
	a.	Opt double	£600	£600
	b.	Opt inverted	£375	£475
	c.	Bright rose	5·50	2·25
18	15	2c. pale rose	65·00	65·00
	b.	Opt inverted	£1400	£1500
	c.	Opt triple	£1400	
	d.	Bright rose		
19	16	2c. pale rose (1886)	£150	30·00
	a.	Bright rose (1891)	2·00	6·50
	ab.	Optd "FERAK"	£350	£450
20	17	2c. pale rose (1886)	7·00	25·00
	a.	Opt double	£1500	
21	18	2c. pale rose (1886)	£120	£130
	a.	Bright rose		
22	19	2c. bright rose (1890)	16·00	50·00
23	20	2c. bright rose (1891)	£3250	

Settings:

Nos. 17/18 – triplets (either 17 + 17 + 17 or 18 + 17 + 17)–30 (3×10) (containing twenty-eight as No. 17 and two as No. 18)–60 (6×10) (containing either fifty-seven as No. 17 and three as No. 18 or all as No. 17)

No. 19 – 60 (6×10) (No. 19a occurs on one position of the setting, it is often found amended in manuscript)

No. 20 – triplet
No. 21 – tripletNo. 22–60 (6×10)
No. 22 – 60 (6×10)
No. 23 – not known

1 CENT
(21)

1886. *No. 17 surch with T* **21**.

| 24 | 14 | 1c. on 2c. pale rose .... | £2500 | £2000 |

ONE CENT PERAK	ONE CENT PERAK.	ONE CENT PERAK.
(22)	(23)	(24) ("N" wide in "ONE" and "CENT")

1886. *No. 63 of Straits Settlements surch with T* **22/4**.

25	22	1c. on 2c. pale rose	£600	£650
26	23	1c. on 2c. pale rose	65·00	85·00
	a.	Surch double	£1000	
27	24	1c. on 2c. pale rose	£110	£130

Nos. 26/7 are from a triplet setting, Types **23-24-23**, in which the two Type 23's can be differentiated by the height of the right upright of the "N" of "CENT", which is short on one. This triplet was used for the top nine rows of the sheet. Type 22 may have been used on the bottom row.

1 CENT PERAK	One CENT PERAK	ONE CENT PERAK
(25)	(26)	(27)

1886. *No. 63 of Straits Settlements surch with T* **25**.

| 28 | | 1c. on 2c. pale rose .... | £130 | £130 |
| | a. | Surch double .... | £1700 | £1700 |

No. 28 comes from a triplet setting.

1886. *No. 63 of Straits Settlements surch with T* **26**.

29		1c. on 2c. pale rose	3·50	10·00
	a.	"One" inverted	£2750	
	b.	Surch double	£1100	

No. 29 comes from a triplet setting. It is believed that No. 29a occurred when the type was dropped and "One" replaced upside down.

1887. *No. 63 of Straits Settlements surch with T* **27** *in blue*.

| 30 | | 1c. on 2c. rose .... | 45·00 | 50·00 |
| | a. | Optd in black .... | £1800 | £1300 |

No. 30 was printed from a setting of 60.

I CENT PERAK	1 CENT PERAK
(28)	(29)

1887. *No. 63 of Straits Settlements surch with T* **28**.

| 31 | | 1c. on 2c. pale rose .... | £800 | £600 |

No. 31 comes from a triplet setting

1887. *No. 63 of Straits Settlements surch with T* **29**.

| 32 | | 1c. on 2c. pale rose .... | £2000 | £2000 |

The size of setting used for No. 32 is not known.

One CENT PERAK	One CENT PERAK	One CENT PERAK	One CENT PERAK
(30)	(31)	(32)	(33)

One CENT PERAK	One CENT PERAK	One CENT PERAK	One CENT PERAK
(34)	(35)	(36)	(37)

1887–89. *No. 63 of Straits Settlements surch with T* **30/7**.

33	30	1c. on 2c. pale rose	2·75	6·00
	a.	Surch double	£1100	
	b.	Bright rose	2·75	2·75
34	31	1c. on 2c. pale rose (1889)	£120	£140
	b.	Bright rose		
35	32	1c. on 2c. pale rose (1889)	13·00	40·00
	a.	"PREAK" (R. 6/1)	£600	£750
	b.	Bright rose	18·00	40·00
	ba.	"PREAK" (R. 6/1)	£750	£1000
	w.	Wmk inverted	£200	
36	33	1c. on 2c. pale rose (1889)	7·50	15·00
	b.	Bright rose	4·50	15·00
37	34	1c. on 2c. pale rose (1889)	9·00	17·00
	b.	Bright rose	4·50	17·00
38	35	1c. on 2c. bright rose (1889) ...	£600	£750
39	36	1c. on 2c. bright rose (1889) ...	£325	£425
40	37	1c. on 2c. bright rose (1889) ...	17·00	35·00
	b.	Bright rose	17·00	29·00

Settings. No. 33 originally appeared as a triplet, then as a block of 30 (3×10) and, finally, as part of a series of composite settings of 60. Specialists recognise four such composite settings:

Setting I contained No. 33 in Rows 1 to 4, R. 5/1 to 5/5 and Row 7; No. 34 on R. 5/6, 6/1 and 6/2; No. 35 on R. 6/3–6; No. 36 on Row 8; No. 37 on Rows 9 and 10.

Setting II was similar, but had the example of No. 33 on R. 3/5 replaced by No. 38 and those on R. 7/4 and R. 7/6 by No. 39.

Setting III contained No. 33 in Rows 1 to 5; No. 35 in Row 6 with the "PREAK" error on the first position; No. 36 in Row 7; No. 37 in Rows 8 and 9; No. 40 in Row 10.

Setting IV was similar, but showed the "PREAK" error on R. 6/1 corrected.

ONE CENT.	ONE CENT
(38)	(39)

1889–90. *No. 17 surch with T* **38/9**.

| 41 | 38 | 1c. on 2c. bright rose .... | £250 | £130 |
| 42 | 39 | 1c. on 2c. bright rose (1890) .... | — | £250 |

PERAK Two CENTS	PERAK One CENT
(40)	(41)

1891. *Nos. 63a, 66 and 68 of Straits Settlements surch.*

(a) As T **30**, **32/4** *and* **37**, *but with "PERAK" at top and a bar through the original value.*

43	30	1c. on 6c. lilac	48·00	27·00
44	32	1c. on 6c. lilac	£170	£160
45	33	1c. on 6c. lilac	£170	£160
46	34	1c. on 6c. lilac	80·00	75·00
47	37	1c. on 6c. lilac	£170	£160

(b) With T **40** *and as T* **32/4** *and* **37** *but with "PERAK" at top, all with a bar through the original value.*

48	40	2c. on 24c. green	18·00	11·00
	w.	Wmk inverted	£225	
49	32	2c. on 24c. green	£100	65·00
	w.	Wmk inverted		
50	33	2c. on 24c. green	£100	65·00
51	34	2c. on 24c. green	65·00	30·00
52	37	2c. on 24c. green	£100	65·00

(c) With T **41** *and as T* **30**, **34** *and* **37**, *but with "PERAK" at top.*

(i) Without bar over original value.

53	30	1c. on 2c. bright rose	£170	
	a.	Narrow "O" in "One" (R. 3/3)	£1800	
54	41	1c. on 2c. bright rose	£2750	
55	34	1c. on 2c. bright rose	£1300	
56	37	1c. on 2c. bright rose	£750	

(ii) With bar through original value.

| 57 | 30 | 1c. on 2c. bright rose .... | 2·25 | 8·00 |

---

			a. Narrow "O" in "One" (R. 3/3)	24·00	65·00
58	41	1c. on 2c. bright rose	7·00	28·00
59	34	1c. on 2c. bright rose	2·25	11·00
60	37	1c. on 2c. bright rose	7·00	28·00

Settings. Nos. 43/7 were arranged as Setting IV described under Nos. 33/40.

Nos. 48/52 were similar except that Type **40** replaced Type **30** on the first five rows.

The first printing of the 1c. on 2c. was without a bar through the original face value. Both printings, Nos. 53/60, were from the same setting with Type **30** on Rows 1 to 5, **41** on Row 6, **34** on Rows 7 to 9 and **37** on Row 10.

3 CENTS
(43)

(42)

1892 (1 Jan)**–95. Wmk Crown CA. P 14.**

61	42	1c. green	2·25	15
62		2c. rose	1·75	30
63		2c. orange (9.9.95)	50	3·25
64		5c. blue	3·25	7·50
61/4 *Set of 4*			7·00	10·00
61s/4s Optd "Specimen" *Set of 4*			£110	

1895 (26 Apr). *Surch with T* **43**. **Wmk Crown CA. P 14.**

| 65 | 42 | 3c. on 5c. rose .... | 3·75 | 3·00 |
| | s. | Optd "Specimen" .... | 30·00 | |

44	45	Malformed "C" in left value tablet (R. 9/3, left pane)

1895 (2 Sept)**–99. P 14.**

(a) Wmk Crown CA.

66	44	1c. dull purple and green..............	2·50	50
	a.	Malformed "C"	£120	60·00
67		2c. dull purple and brown.............	2·75	50
68		3c. dull purple and carmine..........	2·75	50
69		4c. dull purple and carmine (1899)...	12·00	4·75
70		5c. dull purple and olive-green......	4·00	55
71		8c. dull purple and ultramarine	45·00	65
72		10c. dull purple and orange............	15·00	50
73		25c. green and carmine (1897).........	£160	12·00
74		50c. dull purple and greenish black ..	48·00	32·00
75		50c. green and black (12.98)..........	£200	£160

(b) Wmk Crown CC.

76	45	$1 green and pale green (1896).......	£180	£180
77		$2 green and carmine (1896).........	£325	£300
78		$3 green and ochre (1898)...........	£375	£400
79		$5 green and ultramarine (1896)	£500	£500
80		$25 green and orange (1899?)........	£8500	£3000
	s.	Optd "Specimen"	£250	
66/76 *Set of 11*			£600	£350
66s/79s Optd "Specimen" *Set of 14*			£425	

Pending the arrival of the permanent Federated Malay States issue the stamps of FEDERATED MALAY STATES provisional overprints, SELANGOR and STRAITS SETTLEMENTS were used at various times between June 1900 and February 1901.

The general issues for the FEDERATED MALAY STATES were used in Perak from 1901 until 1935.

One Cent.	ONE CENT.
(46)	(47)

Three Cent.	Three Cent.
(48)	(49)

Three Cent.
Thinner "t" in "Cent"

1900. *Stamps of 1895–99 surch.*

81	46	1c. on 2c. dull purple & brown (13 July*)....................	60	2·25
	a.	Antique "e" in "One" (R. 5/2)	60·00	£130
	b.	Antique "e" in "Cent" (R. 9/4)	60·00	£130
82	47	1c. on 4c. dull purple and carmine..	1·00	11·00
	a.	Surch double	£1000	
83	46	1c. on 5c. dull purple & ol-yell (30 June*)	2·25	12·00

		a. Antique "e" in "One" (R. 5/2)	90·00	£250
		b. Antique "e" in "Cent" (R. 9/4)	90·00	£250
84	48	3c. on 8c. dull purple & ultram (26 Sept*)	4·50	9·50
		a. Antique "e" in "Cent" (R. 9/4)	£170	£250
		b. No stop after "Cent" (R. 9/5)	£170	£250
		c. Surch double	£475	£500
85		3c. on 50c. green and black (31 Aug*)	2·75	6·50
		a. Antique "e" in "Cent" (R. 9/4)	£130	£200
		b. No stop after "Cent" (R. 9/5)	£130	£200
86	49	3c. on $1 green and pale green (21 Oct*)	55·00	£140
		a. Thinner "t" in "Cent"	£300	£500
		b. Surch double	£1500	
		w. Wmk inverted	£400	£550
87		3c. on $2 green and carmine (24 Oct*)	30·00	85·00
81/7		*Set of 7*	85·00	£225

*Earliest known postmark date.

With exception of No. 86a, whose sheet position is not known, the remaining surcharge varieties all occur in the left-hand pane.

No. 86b is also known showing the thinner "t" in "Cent" variety. (*Price £4000 unused*).

50 Sultan Iskandar   **51** Sultan Iskandar   Malformed "2c." (R. 10/10)

1935 (2 Dec)–37. *Chalk-surfaced paper.* Wmk Mult Script CA. P 14.

88	50	1c. black (1.1.36)	1·25	10
89		2c. green (1.1.36)	1·25	10
90		4c. orange	1·50	10
91		5c. brown (5.12.35)	60	10
92		6c. scarlet (1.1.37)	11·00	4·25
93		8c. grey	1·00	10
94		10c. dull purple (1.1.36)	70	15
95		12c. bright ultramarine (1.1.36)	2·75	1·00
96		25c. dull purple and scarlet (1.4.36)	2·25	1·00
97		30c. dull purple and orange (1.1.36)	3·00	1·50
98		40c. scarlet and dull purple	4·50	4·50
99		50c. black/*emerald* (1.2.36)	5·00	1·25
100		$1 black and red/*blue* (1.4.36)	2·50	1·00
101		$2 green and scarlet	23·00	8·50
102		$5 green and red/*emerald* (16.5.36)	£100	40·00
88/102		*Set of 15*	£140	55·00
88s/102s		Perf "Specimen" *Set of 15*	£325	

No. 91 exists in coils constructed from normal sheets in 1936.

1938 (2 May)–41. Wmk Mult Script CA. *Chalk-surfaced paper.* P 14.

103	51	1c. black (4.39)	10·00	10
104		2c. green (13.1.39)	5·50	10
105		2c. orange (30.10.41)	3·50	6·00
		a. Malformed "2c"	75·00	£100
		b. Ordinary paper	4·50	17·00
		ba. Malformed "2c"	95·00	£225
106		3c. green (*ordinary paper*) (21.8.41)	—	6·00
		a. Chalk-surfaced paper (10.41)	2·75	5·50
107		4c. orange (5.39)	38·00	10
108		5c. brown (1.2.39)	6·00	10
109		6c. scarlet (12.39)	27·00	10
110		8c. grey (1.12.38)	26·00	10
111		8c. scarlet (18.12.41)	1·00	65·00
112		10c. dull purple (17.10.38)	28·00	10
113		12c. bright ultramarine (17.10.38)	21·00	1·00
114		15c. brt ultram (*ordinary paper*) (8.41)	4·25	13·00
115		25c. dull purple and scarlet (12.39)	50·00	3·25
116		30c. dull purple and orange (17.10.38)	9·50	2·25
117		40c. scarlet and dull purple	50·00	2·00
118		50c. black/*emerald* (17.10.38)	32·00	75
119		$1 black and red/*blue* (7.40)	£130	16·00
120		$2 green and scarlet (9.40)	£150	60·00
121		$5 green and red/*emerald* (1.41)	£225	£300
103/21		*Set of 19*	£750	£425
103s/21s		perf "Specimen" *Set of 19*	£400	

No. 108 exists in coils constructed from normal sheets.

The stamps issued during 1941 were printed by Harrison and Sons following bomb damage to the De La Rue works on 29 December 1940. The used price quoted for No. 111 is for an example with clearly identifiable 1941 cancellation.

During shortages in 1941 stamps of STRAITS SETTLEMENTS (2c. green) and SELANGOR (2c. orange (both perfs), 3c.) were issued in Perak.

1948 (1 Dec). *Royal Silver Wedding. As Nos. 112/13 of Antigua.*

122		10c. violet	15	10
123		$5 green	23·00	29·00

1949 (10 Oct). *75th Anniv of U.P.U. As Nos. 114/17 of Antigua.*

124		10c. purple	15	10
125		15c. deep blue	1·50	2·00
126		25c. orange	30	2·75
127		50c. blue-black	1·25	3·50
124/7		*Set of 4*	2·75	7·50

52 Sultan Yussuf 'Izzuddin Shah

1950 (17 Aug)–56. *Chalk-surfaced paper.* Wmk Mult Script CA. P 17½×18.

128	52	1c. black	10	10
129		2c. orange	20	10
130		3c. green	2·50	10
		a. Yellowish green (15.11.51)	11·00	5·50
131		4c. brown	50	10
		a. Yellow-brown (20.6.56)	7·00	10
132		5c. bright purple (1.9.52)	50	2·00
		a. Bright mauve (10.11.54)	1·25	2·00
133		6c. grey	30	10
134		8c. scarlet	65	2·25
135		8c. green (1.9.52)	1·00	1·00
136		10c. purple	20	10
		a. Brown-purple (20.6.56)	7·00	45
137		12c. scarlet (1.9.52)	1·00	4·00
138		15c. ultramarine	1·00	10
139		20c. black and green	1·00	65
140		20c. bright blue (1.9.52)	75	10
141		25c. purple and orange	60	10
142		30c. scarlet and purple (4.9.55)	1·50	20
143		35c. scarlet and purple (1.9.52)	1·00	25
144		40c. red and purple	3·25	6·00
145		50c. black and blue	3·25	10
146		$1 blue and purple	7·00	1·00
147		$2 green and scarlet	13·00	7·00
148		$5 green and brown	38·00	15·00
128/48		*Set of 21*	70·00	35·00

STAMP BOOKLETS

1935.

SB1	$1 booklet *containing* twenty 5c. (No. 91) in blocks of 10	
SB2	$1.30 booklet containing 5c. and 8c. (Nos. 91, 93), each in block of 10	

1938.

SB3	$1 booklet *containing* twenty 5c. (No. 108) in blocks of 10	
SB4	$1.30 booklet containing 5c. and 8c. (Nos. 108, 110), each in block of 10	

OFFICIAL STAMPS

P.G.S.   **Service.**
(O 1)   (O 2)

1889 (1 Nov). *Stamps of Straits Settlements optd Type O 1.* Wmk Crown CC (Nos. O6 and O8) or Crown CA (others).

O1		2c. bright rose	4·25	5·50
		a. Opt double	£800	£800
		b. Wide space between "G" and "S"	65·00	80·00
		c. No stop after "S"	65·00	80·00
O2		4c. brown	13·00	22·00
		a. Wide space between "G" and "S"	90·00	£120
		b. No stop after "S"	£150	£170
		c. Broken oval	£250	
		w. Wmk inverted	90·00	
O3		6c. lilac	25·00	50·00
		a. Wide space between "G" and "S"	£140	£180
O4		8c. orange	32·00	65·00
		a. Wide space between "G" and "S"	£160	£250
O5		10c. slate	75·00	75·00
		a. Wide space between "G" and "S"	£300	£300
O6		12c. blue (CC)	£200	£250
		a. Wide space between "G" and "S"	£700	
O7		12c. brown-purple (CA)	£250	£325
		a. Wide space between "G" and "S"	£800	
O8		24c. green (CC)	£750	£850
		a. Wide space between "G" and "S"	£2250	
O9		24c. green (CA)	£190	£225
		a. Wide space between "G" and "S"	£650	

Nos. O1/9 were overprinted from a setting of 30 (3×10). The variety "wide space between G and S" occurs on R. 10/3 and R. 10/6 of the original printing. A later printing of the 2c. and 4c. values had this variety corrected, but was without a stop after "S" on R. 10/1 and R. 10/4.

The broken oval flaw occurs on R. 10/5 (lower right pane) of the basic stamp. For illustration see Straits Settlements.

1894 (1 June). *No. 64 optd with Type O 2.*

O10		5c. blue	70·00	1·00
		a. Overprint inverted	£900	£475

1897. *No. 70 optd with Type O 2.*

O11		5c. dull purple and olive-yellow	2·50	50
		a. Overprint double	£600	£400

PERLIS

The Thai monarchy exercised suzerainty over Perlis and the other northern states of the Malay peninsula from the 16th century onwards. The Siamese post office at Kangar is recorded as opening during 1894. It is believed that the initial cancellation showed Thai characters only, but no complete example has so far been discovered.

Stamps of SIAM *cancelled as Type B inscr* "PERLIS" (*from July* 1904).

1887–91. (*Nos. 11/18*).

Z401	9	12a. purple and carmine		£150
Z402		24a. purple and blue		£200

1897. *Surch as T 39 (Siamese) and T 41 (English) (No. 52).*

Z403	9	4a. on 12a. purple and carmine		£275

1899–1904. (*Nos. 67/81*).

Z404	49	1a. olive-green (wide Siamese characters in face value)		£180
Z405		2a. grass-green		£160
Z406		2a. scarlet and pale blue		£160
Z407		3a. red and blue		£250
Z408		4a. carmine		£160
Z409		4a. chocolate and pink		£160
Z410		8a. deep green and orange		£160
Z411		10a. ultramarine		£160
Z412		12a. brown-purple and carmine		£150
Z413		24a. brown-purple and blue		£300

1905–09. (*Nos. 97/105*).

Z416	53	1a. green and orange		£150
Z417		2a. grey and deep violet		£150
Z418		3a. green		£160
Z419		4a. pale red and sepia		£150
Z420		5a. carmine		£160
Z421		8a. olive-bistre and dull black		£150
Z422		12a. blue		£170
Z423		24a. red-brown		£250

Stamps of SIAM *cancelled as Type C inscr* "Perlis" *at foot* (*from Sept.* 1907).

1887–91. (*Nos. 11/18*).

Z425	9	12a. purple and carmine		£170

1899–1904. (*Nos. 67/81*).

Z426	49	1a. olive-green (narrow Siamese characters in face value)		£180
Z427		8a. deep green and orange		£170
Z428		10a. ultramarine		£180

1905–09. (*Nos. 92/105*).

Z429	53	1a. green and orange		£180
Z430		2a. grey and deep violet		£170
Z431		3a. green		£180
Z432		4a. pale red and sepia		£180
Z433		4a. scarlet		£180
Z434		5a. carmine		£180
Z435		8a. olive-bistre and dull black		£180
Z436		9a. blue		£170
Z437		24a. red-brown		£300

1907. *Surch with T 56 (No. 109).*

Z438	9	1a. on 24a. purple and blue		£180

Suzerainty over Perlis was transferred by Thailand to Great Britain on 15 July 1909, although the use of Siamese stamps appears to have extended into early August. Stamps of the Federated Malay States were used there until 1912.

Stamps of the Federated Malay States used in Perlis

Cancelled as Type C inscribed "Perlis" at foot.

1909–12. (*Nos. 29–34*).

Z441	3	1c. green (Die II)		£110
Z442		3c. carmine		£110

Cancelled as Type B inscribed "PERLIS".

1909–12.

Z443	3	1c. green (Die II)		£100
Z444		3c. carmine		60·00
Z445		4c. black and rose		£100

Federated Malay States stamps were withdrawn on 15 June 1912. A Treaty of Friendship between Great Britain and Perlis was signed on 28 April 1930 and the state joined the Federation of Malaya on 1 February 1948.

The stamps of Kedah were in use in Perlis between 1912 and 1941.

1948 (1 Dec). *Royal Silver Wedding. As Nos. 112/13 of Antigua.*

1		10c. violet	30	2·75
2		$5 brown	29·00	48·00

1949 (10 Oct). *75th Anniv of U.P.U. As Nos. 114/17 of Antigua.*

3		10c. purple	30	1·50
4		15c. deep blue	1·25	3·75
5		25c. orange	45	2·00
6		50c. blue-black	1·00	3·75
3/6		*Set of 4*	2·75	10·00

1 Raja Syed Putra

1951 (26 Mar)–55. *Chalk-surfaced paper.* Wmk Mult Script CA. P 17½×18.

7	1	1c. black	20	1·00
8		2c. orange	75	50
9		3c. green	1·50	2·75
10		4c. brown	1·25	30
11		5c. bright purple (1.9.52)	50	3·00
12		6c. grey	1·50	1·25
13		8c. scarlet	2·25	4·75
14		8c. green (1.9.52)	75	3·50
15		10c. purple	50	30
		a. Error. St Edward's Crown W9*b*	£4000	
16		12c. scarlet (1.9.52)	75	3·00
17		15c. ultramarine	4·00	4·75
18		20c. black and green	2·25	7·50
19		20c. bright blue (1.9.52)	1·00	70
20		25c. purple and orange	1·75	25
21		30c. scarlet and purple (4.9.55)	1·75	10·00
22		35c. scarlet and purple (1.9.52)	1·75	4·00
23		40c. red and purple	3·25	20·00
24		50c. black and blue	4·00	4·25
25		$1 blue and purple	7·50	22·00
26		$2 green and scarlet	14·00	38·00
27		$5 green and brown	50·00	95·00
7/27		*Set of 21*	90·00	£200

SELANGOR

The first British Resident was appointed in 1874. Selangor joined the Federated Malay States in 1896.

The stamps of the STRAITS SETTLEMENTS were used in Selangor from 1879 until 1881. Until 1 January 1899, when the Federated Malay States joined the U.P.U., mail for addresses outside Malaya was franked with stamps of the STRAITS SETTLEMENTS.

PRICES FOR STAMPS ON COVER TO 1945	
Nos. 1/8	—
Nos. 9/19	from × 10
Nos. 20/30	from × 12
Nos. 31/3	from × 25
Nos. 34/6	from × 20
Nos. 37/8	from × 15
Nos. 38a/40	—
Nos. 41/2	from × 8
Nos. 43	—
Nos. 44/8	from × 8
Nos. 49/53	from × 30
Nos. 54/66	from × 10
Nos. 66a/7	from × 4
Nos. 68/85	from × 3
Nos. 86/7	from × 4

The Straits Settlements 1867 2c. brown with Crown CC watermark (No. 11) has been known since 1881 overprinted in black with a crescent and star over a capital S, all within an oval, similar in style to the overprints listed for Perak and Sungei Ujong.

The status of this item remains unclear, but it may well represent the first issue of distinctive stamps for Selangor. A similar overprint in red on the Straits Settlements 2c. brown with Crown CA watermark also exists and may have been produced for sale to collectors (*Price £275, unused*).

This overprint should not be confused with a somewhat similar cancellation used on Selangor stamps of the same period. This cancellation differs in having a circular frame with the capital S shown above the crescent and star. It is usually struck in red.

SELANGOR **SELANGOR** **SELANGOR**
(1) ("S" inverted and narrow letters) (2) ("S" wide) (3) (narrow letters)

SELANGOR **SELANGOR** **SELANGOR**
(4) ("N" wide) (5) ("SE" and "AN" wide) (6) ("SEL" and "N" wide)

SELANGOR
(7) ("SELAN" wide)

1881–82. *No. 11 (wmk Crown CC) of Straits Settlements optd with T 1/7.*

1	1	2c. brown	£475	£500
2	2	2c. brown	£170	£180
3	3	2c. brown	£100	£100
4	4	2c. brown	£5500	£2000
5	5	2c. brown (1882)	£200	£225
6	6	2c. brown (1882)	£200	£225
7	7	2c. brown (1882)	£200	£225

Nos. 1/3 and 5/7 have been identified as coming from triplet settings, either Nos. 1+2+3, 2+3+3 or 5+6+7. The setting for No. 4 is unknown.

S.
(8)

1882. *No. 50 (wmk Crown CA) of Straits Settlements optd with T 8.*

8	8	2c. brown	—	£2500

SELANGOR **SELANGOR** **SELANGOR**
(9) ("SEL" and "NG" wide) (10) ("E" and "ANG" wide) (11) ("ELANG" wide)

SELANGOR **SELANGOR** **SELANGOR**
(12) ("S" and "L" wide) (13) ("S" and "A" wide) (14) ("E" wide)

SELANGOR **SELANGOR** **SELANGOR**
(15) ("EL" wide) (16) ("SE" and "N" wide) (17) ("S" and "N" wide)

1882–83. *No. 50 (wmk Crown CA) of Straits Settlements optd with T 2/3 and 9/17.*

9	9	2c. brown	£250	£275
10	10	2c. brown	£250	£275
11	11	2c. brown	£250	£275
12	2	2c. brown (1883)	£150	£120
13	3	2c. brown (1883)	£275	£120
14	12	2c. brown (1883)	—	£3000
15	13	2c. brown (1883)	£500	£450
16	14	2c. brown (1883)	£350	£275
17	15	2c. brown (1883)	£350	£275
18	16	2c. brown (1883)	£160	£150
		a. Opt double	£900	
19	17	2c. brown (1883)	£160	£150

The above were all printed from triplet settings. Those so far identified are Nos. 9+10+11, 12 (with defective "G") +13+13, 15+16+17 and 18+12+19. No. 14 occurs as the first position of a triplet, but the second and third units are not yet known.

SELANGOR **SELANGOR** **SELANGOR**
(18) ("E" and "A" wide) (19) ("A" wide) (20) ("L" wide)

SELANGOR **SELANGOR** **SELANGOR**
(21) ("L" narrow) (22) ("A" narrow) (23) (wide letters)

1883–85. *No. 63 of Straits Settlements optd with T 2, 4, 12, 14/15 and 18/23.*

20	12	2c. pale rose	£190	£150
21	14	2c. pale rose	£120	£100
		a. Opt double		
22	4	2c. pale rose (1884)	£180	£150
23	15	2c. pale rose (1884)	£100	90·00
		a. Opt double	£800	
		b. Opt triple		
24	2	2c. pale rose (1884)	£120	95·00
25	18	2c. pale rose (1884)	£120	95·00
26	19	2c. pale rose (1884)	£350	£160
27	20	2c. pale rose (1884)	£450	£190
28	21	2c. pale rose (1885)	95·00	85·00
29	22	2c. pale rose (1885)	£170	£140
30	23	2c. pale rose (1885)	£425	£190

The above come from triplet settings with Nos. 20+21+21, 22+22+23, 23+26 (with defective "A") +26, 24+25+23 and 28+29+28 so far identified. The triplets for Nos. 27 and 30 are not known.

SELANGOR *Selangor* **SELANGOR**
(24) (25) (26)

SELANGOR **SELANGOR** *SELANGOR* **SELANGOR**
(27) (28) (29) (30)

SELANGOR **SELANGOR** **SELANGOR** *SELANGOR*
(31) (32) (33) (34)

1885–91. *Nos. 63/a of Straits Settlements optd with T 24/34.*

31	24	2c. pale rose	12·00	23·00
		a. Opt double	£850	£750
		w. Wmk inverted	—	£300
32	25	2c. pale rose	£1200	£1300
33	26	2c. pale rose	35·00	42·00
34	27	2c. pale rose (1886)	55·00	55·00
		a. Opt double	†	£700
35	28	2c. pale rose (horiz opt without stop) (1887)	11·00	2·75
		a. Opt double	£700	
		b. Bright rose	12·00	2·25
36		2c. pale rose (horiz opt with stop) (1887)	£100	70·00
		a. Bright rose		
37	29	2c. pale rose (1889)	£200	80·00
38	30	2c. pale rose (vert opt) (1889)	75·00	6·00
		a. Bright rose		
38b		2c. bright rose (horiz opt) (1889)	£3250	
39	31	2c. pale rose (diagonal opt) (1889)	£1800	
40	32	2c. pale rose (1889)	£500	30·00
41	28	2c. brt rose (vert opt without stop) (1890)	18·00	30·00
42	33	2c. bright rose (1890)	£110	3·00
		a. Opt double		
43	34	2c. bright rose (1891)	£325	£150

Settings:

Nos. 31/4 – each in triplet containing three examples of the same stamp
No. 35 – triplet or 60 (6×10)
No. 36 – 60 (6×10)
Nos. 37/8 – 60 (6×10) containing both overprints in an unknown combination, but with No. 38 predominating
Nos. 38b/9 – not known
Nos. 40/3 – each in 60 (6×10)

SELANGOR **SELANGOR** **SELANGOR**
Two *Two* *Two*
CENTS CENTS CENTS
(35) (36) (37)

SELANGOR **SELANGOR**
Two Two
CENTS CENTS
(38) (39)

1891. *No. 68 of Straits Settlements, surch with T 35/9, each with bar obliterating old value.*

44	35	2c. on 24c. green	30·00	65·00
45	36	2c. on 24c. green	£180	£225
46	37	2c. on 24c. green	£180	£225
47	38	2c. on 24c. green	95·00	£130
		a. "SELANGCR"		
48	39	2c. on 24c. green	£180	£225

Nos. 44/8 come from the one setting used to surcharge the panes of sixty. No. 44 occurs in rows 1 to 5, No. 45 on row 6, No. 46 on row 7, No. 47 on rows 8 and 9, and No. 48 on row 10.

The error, No. 47a, occurs in the first printing only and is No. 45 (R. 8/3) on the pane.

40

3 CENTS
(41)

1891 (1 Nov)–**95**. Wmk Crown CA. P 14.

49	40	1c. green (5.93)	1·50	25
50		2c. rose	3·50	1·00
51		2c. orange (27.5.95)	2·50	80
52		5c. blue (8.92)	24·00	4·75
49/52 Set of 4			28·00	6·00
49s/52s Optd "Specimen" Set of 4			95·00	

1894 (Dec). Surch with T 41. Wmk Crown CA. P 14.

53	40	3c. on 5c. rose	3·75	50
		s. Optd "Specimen"	35·00	

42   43

Dented frame above "A" of "SELANGOR" (left pane R. 4/5)

1895–99. Wmk Crown CA or Crown CC (dollar values). P 14.

54	42	3c. dull purple and carmine	6·50	30
55		5c. dull purple and olive-yellow	6·00	30
56		8c. dull purple and ultramarine (1898)	48·00	7·00
57		10c. dull purple and orange	10·00	1·75
58		25c. green and carmine (1896)	80·00	50·00
59		50c. dull purple and greenish black (1896)	65·00	24·00
		a. Dented frame	£375	
60		50c. green and black (1898)	£425	£120
		a. Dented frame		
61	43	$1 green and yellow-green	50·00	£130
62		$2 green and carmine (1897)	£225	£225
63		$3 green and ochre (1897)	£500	£400
64		$5 green and blue	£250	£300
65		$10 green and purple (1899)	£650	£800
		s. Optd "Specimen"	£130	
66		$25 green and orange (1897)	£3000	£3000
		s. Optd "Specimen"	£250	
54/62 Set of 9			£850	£500
54s/64s Optd "Specimen" Set of 11			£375	

Pending the arrival of the permanent Federated Malay States issue the stamps of STRAITS SETTLEMENTS and PERAK were used at various times between July 1900 and March 1901.

The general issues for the FEDERATED MALAY STATES were used in Selangor from 1901 until 1935.

One cent. **Three cents.**
(44) (45)

Antique "t" (R. 3/4 and 8/4)

1900 (Oct). Nos. 55 and 59 surch with T 44 or 45.

66a	42	1c. on 5c. dull purple & ol-yell (31 Oct*)	60·00	£120
66b		1c. on 50c. green and black (22 Oct*)	3·00	23·00
		bc. "cent" repeated at left	£2250	
		bd. Dented frame	95·00	
67		3c. on 50c. green and black (30 Oct*)	4·00	23·00
		a. Antique "t" in "cents"	£300	£450
		b. Dented frame	£225	

*Earliest known postmark date.

It is believed that these stamps were surcharged from settings of 30, repeated four times to complete the sheet of 120.

No. 66bc occurred on two separate vertical strips of five stamps where two impressions of the setting overlapped.

46 Mosque at Palace, Klang   47 Sultan Suleiman

Joined script (R. 2/1)

(Selangor)

(Des E. J. McNaughton)

1935 (2 Dec)–**41**. Wmk Mult Script CA (sideways on *T* 46). *Chalk-surfaced paper.* P 14 or 14×14½ (No. 70).

68	**46**	1c. black (1.1.36)	30	10
69		2c. green (1.1.36)	90	10
		a. Joined script	50·00	20·00
70		2c. orange (*ordinary paper*) (P 14×14½) (21.8.41)	3·50	75
		aa. Joined script	£110	30·00
		a. Perf 14. Ordinary paper (9.41)	20·00	1·50
		ab. Joined script	£225	55·00
71		3c. green (*ordinary paper*) (21.8.41)	1·25	8·00
		a. Chalk-surfaced paper (10.41)	16·00	2·75
72		4c. orange	50	10
73		5c. brown (5.12.35)	70	10
74		6c. scarlet (1.1.37)	5·50	10
75		8c. grey	60	10
76		10c. dull purple (1.1.36)	60	10
77		12c. bright ultramarine (1.1.36)	1·25	10
78		15c. brt ultram (*ordinary paper*) (1.10.41)	12·00	32·00
79		25c. dull purple and scarlet (1.4.36)	1·00	60
80		30c. dull purple and orange (1.1.36)	1·00	85
81		40c. scarlet and dull purple	1·50	1·00
82		50c. black/*emerald* (1.2.36)	1·00	15
83	**47**	$1 black and rose/*blue* (1.4.36)	7·50	90
84		$2 green and scarlet (16.5.36)	25·00	8·00
85		$5 green and red/*emerald* (16.5.36)	75·00	23·00
		68/85 *Set of* 18	£120	60·00
		68s/85s Perf "Specimen" *Set of* 18	£400	

The stamps issued during 1941 were printed by Harrison and Sons following bomb damage to the De La Rue works on 29 December 1940.

No. 69 exists in coils constructed from normal sheets.

Supplies of an unissued 8c. scarlet were diverted to Australia in 1941. Examples circulating result from leakages of this supply (*Price* £600).

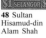

48 Sultan Hisamud-din Alam Shah

49 Sultan Hisamud-din Alam Shah

1941. Wmk Mult Script CA. *Chalk-surfaced paper.* P 14.

86	**48**	$1 black and red/*blue* (15.4.41)	17·00	6·00
87		$2 green and scarlet (7.7.41)	48·00	28·00
		s. Perf "Specimen"	70·00	

A $5 green and red on emerald, *T* 48, was issued overprinted during the Japanese occupation of Malaya. Unoverprinted examples are known, but were not issued (*Price* £120).

During shortages in 1941 stamps of STRAITS SETTLEMENTS (2c.) and PERAK (25c.) were issued in Selangor.

1948 (1 Dec). *Royal Silver Wedding. As Nos.* 112/13 *of Antigua.*

88		10c. violet	20	30
89		$5 green	27·00	17·00

1949 (12 Sept)–**55**. Wmk Mult Script CA. *Chalk-surfaced paper.* P 17½×18.

90	**49**	1c. black	10	60
91		2c. orange	10	70
92		3c. green	2·00	1·50
93		4c. brown	30	10
94		5c. bright purple (1.9.52)	30	2·00
		a. Bright mauve (17.9.53)	30	60
95		6c. grey	30	40
96		8c. scarlet	50	65
97		8c. green (1.9.52)	65	1·75
98		10c. purple	20	10
99		12c. scarlet (1.9.52)	80	3·50
		w. Wmk inverted	£400	
100		15c. ultramarine	4·75	10
101		20c. black and green	2·75	35
102		20c. bright blue (1.9.52)	80	10
103		25c. purple and orange	2·00	20
104		30c. scarlet and purple (4.9.55)	2·00	2·25
105		35c. scarlet and purple (1.9.52)	70	1·50
106		40c. scarlet and purple	8·00	6·00
107		50c. black and blue	2·50	10
108		$1 blue and purple	3·00	60
109		$2 green and scarlet	13·00	60
110		$5 green and brown	45·00	2·25
		90/110 *Set of* 21	80·00	21·00

1949 (10 Oct). *75th Anniv of U.P.U. As Nos.* 114/17 *of Antigua.*

111		10c. purple	30	10
112		15c. deep blue	2·00	2·50
113		25c. orange	35	3·75
114		50c. blue-black	1·00	3·75
		111/14 *Set of* 4	3·25	9·00

STAMP BOOKLETS

1935. *Stapled.*

SB1	$1 booklet *containing* twenty 5c. (No. 73) in blocks of 10	
SB2	$1.30 booklet containing 5c. and 8c. (Nos. 73, 75), each in block of 10	

TRENGGANU

Suzerainty over Trengganu was transferred by Thailand to Great Britain in 1909. A British adviser was appointed in 1919.

The state joined the Federation of Malaya on 1 February 1948.

PRICES FOR STAMPS ON COVER TO 1945	
Nos. 1/15	*from* × 12
No. 16/18	—
Nos. 19/22	*from* × 10
Nos. 23/33	*from* × 12
Nos. 34/6	—
Nos. 37/47	*from* × 15
Nos. 48/60	*from* × 6
Nos. D1/4	—

RED CROSS

2c.

(3)

1 Sultan Zain ul ab din

2 Sultan Zain ul ab din

1910 (14 Dec)–**19**. Wmk Mult Crown CA. *Ordinary paper* (1c. to 10c.) or chalk-surfaced paper (20c. to $25). P 14.

1	**1**	1c. blue-green	1·75	1·00
		a. Green	2·75	1·25
2		2c. brown and purple (1915)	1·00	90
3		3c. carmine-red	2·25	2·25
4		4c. orange	3·50	5·50
5		4c. red-brown and green (1915)	2·00	3·75
5a		4c. carmine-red (1919)	1·25	1·75
6		5c. grey	1·25	3·50
7		5c. grey and brown (1915)	2·25	2·00
8		8c. ultramarine	1·25	9·00
9		10c. purple/*yellow*	5·00	14·00
		a. On pale yellow	3·25	6·50
10		10c. green and red/*yellow* (1915)	1·25	2·25
11		20c. dull and bright purple	3·50	4·50
12		25c. green and dull purple (1915)	8·00	32·00
13		30c. dull purple and black (1915)	6·50	55·00
14		50c. black/*green*	4·50	9·00
15		$1 black and carmine/*blue*	17·00	24·00
16		$3 green and red/*green* (1915)	£170	£400
17	**2**	$5 green and red/*green* (1912)	£180	£550
18		$25 rose-carmine and green (1912)	£950	£2000
		s. Optd "Specimen"	£250	
		1/17 *Set of* 18	£375	£1000
		1s/17s Optd "Specimen" *Set of* 18	£550	

The 8c. is known used bisected at Kretai in December 1918. Such use was not officially authorised.

1917 (June)–**18**. *Surch with T* 3.

19	**1**	2c. on 3c. carmine-red	50	8·00
		a. Comma after "2c."	10·00	40·00
		b. "SS" in "CROSS" inverted	£375	£450
		c. "CSOSS" for "CROSS"	95·00	£200
		d. "2" in thick block type	22·00	70·00
		e. Surch inverted	£850	£950
		f. Pair, one without surch	£3500	£3000
		g. "RED CROSS" omitted	£300	
		h. "RED CROSS" twice	£375	
		i. "2c." omitted	£300	
		j. "2c." twice	£350	
20		2c. on 4c. orange	1·50	15·00
		a. Comma after "2c."	18·00	70·00
		b. "SS" in "CROSS" inverted	£1800	£1300
		c. "CSOSS" for "CROSS"	£170	£400
		d. Surch double	£950	
		e. "RED CROSS" omitted	£350	
		f. "RED CROSS" twice	£500	
		g. "2c." omitted	£350	
		h. "2c." twice	£450	
21		2c. on 4c. red-brown and green (1918)	3·75	42·00
		a. Pair, one without surch	£2500	
		b. "RED CROSS" omitted	£650	
		c. "RED CROSS" twice	£650	
22		2c. on 8c. ultramarine (1917)	1·25	30·00
		a. Comma after "2c."	11·00	85·00
		b. "SS" in "CROSS" inverted	£750	
		c. "CSOSS" for "CROSS"	£150	£425
		d. "RED CROSS" omitted	£350	
		e. "RED CROSS" twice	£450	
		f. "2c." omitted	£350	
		g. "2c." twice	£425	

The surcharges on Nos. 19/22 were arranged in settings of 18 (6×3) applied three times to cover the top nine rows of the sheet with the tenth row completed by a further impression so that "RED CROSS" from the centre row of the setting appears on the bottom sheet margin. Specialists recognise six different settings:

Setting I – Shows comma after "2" on both R. 1/3 and 1/5, "SS" inverted on R. 1/6 and "CSOSS" for "CROSS" on R. 2/1. Used for 4c. orange and 8c.

Setting Ia – Inverted "SS" on R. 1/6 corrected. Other varieties as Setting I. Used for 3c., 4c. orange and 8c.

Setting II – "CSOSS" on R. 2/1 corrected. Comma varieties as Setting I. Used for 3c., 4c. orange and 8c.

Setting III – Both comma varieties now corrected. Used for 3c., both 4c. and 8c.

Setting IIIa – "SS" inverted on R. 2/5. Used for 3c. only.

Setting IV – Thick block "2" on R. 2/2. Inverted "SS" on R. 2/5 corrected. Used for 3c. only.

Nos. 19g/j, 20e/h and 22d/g result from the misplacement of the surcharge.

During a temporary shortage between March and August 1921 2c., 4c. and 6c. stamps of the STRAITS SETTLEMENTS were authorised for use in Trengganu.

4 Sultan Suleiman

5 Sultan Suleiman

2 CENTS

(6)

1921–**41**. *Chalk-surfaced paper.* P 14.

(a) Wmk Mult Crown CA.

23	**4**	$1 purple and blue/*blue*	12·00	23·00
24		$3 green and red/*emerald*	£110	£250
25	**5**	$5 green and red/*pale yellow*	£120	£350
		23/5 *Set of* 3	£225	£600
		23s/5s Optd "Specimen" *Set of* 3	£140	

(b) Wmk Mult Script CA.

26	**4**	1c. black (1926)	1·75	1·50
		a. Ordinary paper (1941)	—	50·00
27		2c. green	1·25	2·00
		a. Ordinary paper (1941)	—	50·00
28		3c. green (1926)	2·00	1·00
29		3c. reddish brown (1938)	25·00	14·00
		a. Ordinary paper. *Chestnut* (1941)	—	20·00
30		4c. rose-red	1·75	1·25
		a. Ordinary paper. *Scarlet-verm* (1941)	£225	28·00
31		5c. grey and deep brown	2·00	5·00
32		5c. purple/*yellow* (1926)	1·75	1·25
		a. *Deep reddish purple/brt yellow* (1939)	£225	5·00
33		6c. orange (1924)	4·00	50
		a. Ordinary paper (1941)	—	85·00
34		8c. grey (1938)	30·00	6·00
		a. Ordinary paper (1941)	—	26·00
35		10c. bright blue (1926)	2·00	1·00
36		12c. bright ultramarine (1926)	4·25	4·50
37		20c. dull purple and orange	2·25	1·50
38		25c. green and deep purple	2·25	3·00
39		30c. dull purple and black	3·25	3·75
40		35c. carmine/*yellow* (1926)	4·75	8·00
41		50c. green and bright carmine	9·00	3·25
42		$1 purple and blue/*blue* (1929)	9·00	3·75
43		$3 green and lake/*green* (1926)	55·00	£160
		a. *Green and brown-red/green* (1938)	£150	
44	**5**	$5 green and red/*yellow* (1938)	£350	£2000
45		$25 purple and blue	£700	£1300
		s. Optd "Specimen"	£160	
46		$50 green and yellow	£1800	£3250
		s. Optd "Specimen"	£350	
47		$100 green and scarlet	£5500	£6500
		s. Optd "Specimen"	£650	
		26/43 *Set of* 18	£140	£200
		26s/44s Optd or Perf (3c. reddish brown, 8c., $1, $5) "Specimen" *Set of* 19	£750	

The used price quoted for No. 44 is for an example with an identifiable cancellation from 1938–41.

Printings of the 2c. yellow-orange, 3c. blue-green, 4c. purple/*yellow*, 6c. slate-grey, 8c. rose, 15c. ultramarine and $1 black and red/*blue* on ordinary paper were despatched to Malaya in late 1941, but did not arrive before the Japanese occupation. Unused examples are known of the 2, 3, 6, 8 and 15c. (*Prices*, 3c. £425, *others* £180 *each, unused*).

The 12c. bright ultramarine was also printed on ordinary paper, and exists overprinted during the Japanese occupation. See No. J107b.

OVERPRINT SETTINGS FOR NOS. 48/58. The low values in Types 1 and 4 were overprinted using Setting II as detailed under Straits Settlements. The three listed constant varieties from the original typeset block of 12 occur in the same positions for these Trengganu stamps as does the No stop variety from R. 1/5 of the left pane.

A separate setting, believed to be of 30 (6×5), was required for the $5 in the larger design. This was constructed by duplicating the second horizontal row of the original typeset block five times so that the raised stop after "EXHIBITION" variety occurs on all stamps in the second vertical row and the small second "A" in "MALAYA" on all stamps in the sixth.

1922 (Apr). *Malaya-Borneo Exhibition, Singapore. Optd as T* 56 *of Straits Settlements at Singapore.*

48	**4**	2c. green	4·75	27·00
		b. Oval last "O" in "BORNEO"	9·50	48·00
		c. Raised stop after "EXHIBITION"	9·50	48·00
		d. Small second "A" in "MALAYA"	9·50	48·00
		f. No stop		
49		4c. rose-red	6·50	40·00
		b. Oval last "O" in "BORNEO"	13·00	70·00
		c. Raised stop after "EXHIBITION"	13·00	70·00
		d. Small second "A" in "MALAYA"	13·00	70·00
		f. No stop		
50	**1**	5c. grey and brown	3·25	42·00
		b. Oval last "O" in "BORNEO"	7·00	70·00
		c. Raised stop after "EXHIBITION"	7·00	70·00
		d. Small second "A" in "MALAYA"	7·00	70·00
		f. No stop		
51		10c. red/*yellow*	5·50	32·00
		b. Oval last "O" in "BORNEO"	11·00	55·00
		c. Raised stop after "EXHIBITION"	11·00	55·00
		d. Small second "A" in "MALAYA"	11·00	55·00
		f. No stop		
52		20c. dull and bright purple	5·50	35·00
		b. Oval last "O" in "BORNEO"	11·00	60·00
		c. Raised stop after "EXHIBITION"	11·00	60·00
		d. Small second "A" in "MALAYA"	11·00	60·00
		f. No stop		

53		25c. green and dull purple................	4·75	35·00
		b. Oval last "O" in "BORNEO"....	9·50	60·00
		c. Raised stop after		
		"EXHIBITION"......................	9·50	60·00
		d. Small second "A" in		
		"MALAYA"..........................	9·50	60·00
		f. No stop.		
54		30c. dull purple and black..............	5·50	35·00
		b. Oval last "O" in "BORNEO"....	11·00	60·00
		c. Raised stop after		
		"EXHIBITION"......................	11·00	60·00
		d. Small second "A" in		
		"MALAYA"..........................	11·00	60·00
		f. No stop.		
55		50 c. black/green...........................	5·50	40·00
		b. Oval last "O" in "BORNEO"....	11·00	70·00
		c. Raised stop after		
		"EXHIBITION"......................	11·00	70·00
		d. Small second "A" in		
		"MALAYA"..........................	11·00	70·00
		f. No stop.		
56		$1 black and carmine/blue..............	14·00	70·00
		b. Oval last "O" in "BORNEO"....	24·00	£120
		c. Raised stop after		
		"EXHIBITION"......................	24·00	£120
		d. Small second "A" in		
		"MALAYA"..........................	24·00	£120
		f. No stop.		
57		$3 green and red/green	£140	£375
		b. Oval last "O" in "BORNEO"....	£250	£650
		c. Raised stop after		
		"EXHIBITION"......................	£250	£650
		d. Small second "A" in		
		"MALAYA"..........................	£250	£650
58	2	$5 green and dull purple................	£250	£650
		c. Raised stop after		
		"EXHIBITION"......................	£375	£1000
		d. Small second "A" in		
		"MALAYA"..........................	£375	£1000
48/58 Set of 11			£400	£1200

1941 (1 May). Nos. 32a and 35 surch as T **6**.

59	**4**	2c. on 5c. deep reddish purple/brt		
		yellow	6·50	3·50
60		8c. on 10c. bright blue.................	7·00	4·00

1948 (2 Dec). Royal Silver Wedding. As Nos. 112/13 of Antigua.

61		10c. violet	15	1·75
62		$5 carmine	25·00	42·00

1949 (10 Oct). 75th Anniv of U.P.U. As Nos. 114/17 of Antigua.

63		10c. purple	30	75
64		15c. deep blue	1·90	3·00
65		25c. orange	40	2·25
66		50c. blue-black...........................	1·00	3·50
		a. "C" of "CA" missing from wmk....	£750	
63/6 Set of 4			3·25	8·50

7 Sultan Ismail

1949 (27 Dec)–**55**. Wmk Mult Script CA. Chalk-surfaced paper. P 17½×18.

67	**7**	1c. black	30	75
68		2c. orange	30	75
69		3c. green	1·50	3·25
70		4c. brown	30	60
71		5c. bright purple (1.9.52).............	30	1·75
72		6c. grey	1·25	60
73		8c. scarlet	40	2·50
74		8c. green (1.9.52).......................	65	1·75
		a. Deep green (11.8.53)...............	10·00	10·00
75		10c. purple	30	30
76		12c. scarlet (1.9.52)	65	2·75
77		15c. ultramarine	2·50	30
78		20c. black and green	3·00	3·75
79		20c. bright blue (1.9.52)...............	80	40
80		25c. purple and orange	2·00	2·00
81		30c. scarlet and purple (4.9.55)........	1·25	2·25
82		35c. scarlet and purple (1.9.52)........	85	2·25
83		40c. red and purple	6·00	15·00
84		50c. black and blue	2·00	2·25
85		$1 blue and purple	7·00	8·00
86		$2 green and scarlet	29·00	25·00
87		$5 green and brown	50·00	60·00
67/87 Set of 21			£100	£120

POSTAGE DUE STAMPS

D 1

1937 (10 Aug). Wmk Mult Script CA (sideways). P 14.

D1	D **1**	1c. scarlet	7·50	55·00
D2		4c. green	9·50	60·00
D3		8c. yellow	55·00	£325
D4		10c. brown	£110	95·00
D1/4 Set of 4			£160	£475
D1s/4s Perf "Specimen" Set of 4			£150	

VI. JAPANESE OCCUPATION OF MALAYA

PRICES FOR STAMPS ON COVER

Nos. J1/55	from × 10
Nos. J56/76	from × 12

PRICES FOR STAMPS ON COVER

Nos. J77/89	from × 20
Nos. J90/1	from × 6
Nos. J92/115	from × 6
Nos. J116/18	—
Nos. J119/32	from × 12
Nos. J133/45	from × 10
Nos. J146/223	from × 6
Nos. J224/58	from × 12
No. J259	from × 15
Nos. J260/96	from × 12
Nos. J297/310	from × 20
Nos. J311/17	
Nos. JD1/10	from × 30
Nos. JD11/16	from × 12
Nos. JD17/20	from × 30
Nos. JD21/7	from × 20
Nos. JD28/33	from × 30
Nos. JD34/41	from × 60

Japanese forces invaded Malaya on 8 December 1941 with the initial landings taking place at Kota Bharu on the east coast. Penang fell, to a force which crossed the border from Thailand, on 19 December, Kuala Lumpur on 11 January 1942 and the conquest of the Malay peninsula was completed by the capture of Singapore on 15 February.

During the Japanese Occupation various small Dutch East Indies islands near Singapore were administered as part of Malaya. Stamps of the Japanese Occupation of Malaya were issued to the post offices of Dabo Singkep, Puloe Samboe, Tanjong Balei, Tanjong Batu, Tanjong Pinang and Terempa between 1942 and 1945. The overprinted issues were also used by a number of districts at Atjeh (Northern Sumatra) whose postal services were administered from Singapore until the end of March 1943.

Malayan post offices were also opened in October 1943 to serve camps of civilians working on railway construction and maintenance in Thailand. Overprinted stamps of the Japanese Occupation of Malaya were used at these offices between October 1943 and the end of the year after which mail from the camps was carried free. Their postmarks were inscribed in Japanese Katakana characters, and, uniquely, showed the Japanese postal symbol.

JOHORE

The postal service in Johore was reconstituted in mid-April 1942 using Nos. J146/60 and subsequently other general issues. Stamps of Johore overprinted "DAI NIPPON 2602" were, however, only used for fiscal purposes. Overprinted Johore postage due stamps were not issued for use elsewhere in Malaya.

POSTAGE DUE STAMPS

(1) (Upright)　(2)　Second character sideways (R. 6/3)

1942 (1 Apr). Nos. D1/5 of Johore optd as T **1** in brown.

JD1	D **1**	1c. carmine................................	50·00	85·00
		a. Black opt...........................	20·00	70·00
JD2		4c. green.................................	80·00	95·00
		a. Black opt...........................	65·00	80·00
JD3		8c. orange..............................	£140	£150
		a. Black opt...........................	80·00	95·00
JD4		10c. brown...............................	50·00	70·00
		a. Black opt...........................	16·00	50·00
JD5		12c. purple...............................	90·00	£100
		a. Black opt...........................	42·00	50·00

1943. Nos. D1/5 of Johore optd with T **2**.

JD6	D **1**	1c. carmine..............................	8·00	28·00
		a. Second character sideways......	£300	£550
JD7		4c. green.................................	7·50	30·00
		a. Second character sideways......	£325	£550
JD8		8c. orange..............................	9·00	30·00
		a. Second character sideways......	£400	£650
JD9		10c. brown	8·50	40·00
		a. Second character sideways......	£375	£700
JD10		12c. purple...............................	10·00	60·00
		a. Second character sideways......	£425	£800
JD6/10 Set of 5			38·00	£170

KEDAH

Postal services resumed by 31 January 1942 using unoverprinted Kedah values from 1c. to 8c. which were accepted for postage until 13 May 1942.

During the Japanese occupation Perlis was administered as part of Kedah.

DAI NIPPON　　DAI NIPPON

2602　　2602

(3)　　(4)

1942 (13 May)–**43**. Stamps of Kedah (Script wmk) optd with T **3** (1c. to 8c.) or **4** (10c. to $5), both in red.

J1	**1**	1c. black (No. 68a)....................	5·50	8·50
J2		2c. bright green (No. 69)............	27·00	30·00
J3		4c. violet	6·00	4·00
		a. Short sheaf........................	£170	£150
		b. Black opt (1943).................	£200	£225
J4		5c. yellow................................	5·50	4·50
		a. Black opt (1943).................	£200	£225
J5		6c. carmine (No. 56) (Blk.).........	4·25	14·00
		a. Carmine-red (No. 56a)...........	50·00	75·00
J6		8c. grey-black	4·25	2·50
J7	**6**	10c. ultramarine and sepia............	14·00	14·00

J8		12c. black and violet......................	30·00	42·00
J9		25c. ultramarine and purple.............	9·50	15·00
		a. Black opt (1943)	£275	£250
J10		30c. green and scarlet	70·00	80·00
J11		40c. black and purple....................	35·00	50·00
J12		50c. brown and blue	35·00	50·00
J13		$1 black and green	£140	£150
		a. Opt inverted	£650	£750
J14		$2 green and brown	£170	£170
J15		$5 black and scarlet	65·00	95·00
		a. Black opt (1943)	£950	£900
J1/15 Set of 15			£650	£650

Nos. J1/15 were gradually replaced by issues intended for use throughout Malaya. Kedah and Perlis were ceded to Thailand by the Japanese on 19 October 1943.

KELANTAN

Postal services resumed on 1 June 1942. Stamps used in Kelantan were overprinted with the personal seals of Sunagawa, the Japanese Governor, and of Handa, the Assistant Governor.

(5) Sunagawa Seal　　(6) Handa Seal

$1.00

40 CENTS
(7)　　(8)

1　Cents
(9)

1942 (June). Stamps of Kelantan surch.

(a) As T **7** or **8** (dollar values). Optd with T **5** in red.

J16	**4**	1c. on 50c. grey-olive and orange............	£225	£180
J17		2c. on 40c. orange and blue-green	£700	£300
J18		4c. on 30c. violet and scarlet.................	£1800	£1200
J19		5c. on 12c. blue (R.)...........................	£250	£190
J20		6c. on 25c. vermilion and violet..............	£300	£190
J21		8c. on 5c. red-brown (R.).....................	£375	£140
J22		10c. on 6c. lake................................	75·00	£120
		a. "CENST" for "CENTS"	£5000	
J23		12c. on 8c. grey-olive (R.)....................	50·00	£110
J24		25c. on 10c. purple (R.).......................	£1300	£1300
J25		30c. on 4c. scarlet	£1900	£2000
J26		40c. on 6c. green (R.).........................	60·00	85·00
		a. Surch double (B.+R.)...............	£3250	
J27		50c. on 1c. grey-olive and yellow	£1500	£1300
J28	**1**	$1 on 4c. black and red (R., bars Blk.)....	50·00	80·00
J29		$2 on 5c. green and red/yellow	50·00	80·00
J30		$5 on 6c. scarlet	50·00	80·00
		a. Surch double	£400	

(b) As T **7**. Optd with T **6** in red.

J31	**4**	12c. on 8c. grey-olive	£190	£325
		a. Type 6 omitted (in horiz pair		
		with normal).....................	£3250	

(c) As T **9**. Optd with T **5** in red.

J32	**4**	1c. on 50c. grey-olive and orange	£170	95·00
		a. "Cente" for "Cents" (R. 5/1).......	£2000	£1100
J33		2c. on 40c. orange and blue-green	£170	£110
		a. "Cente" for "Cents" (R. 5/1).......	£2000	£1200
J34		5c. on 12c. blue (R.)	£150	£140
		a. "Cente" for "Cents" (R. 5/1).......	£1700	
J35		8c. on 5c. red-brown (R.)	£120	75·00
		a. "Cente" for "Cents" (R. 5/1).......	£1400	£950
J36		10c. on 6c. lake	£375	£400
		a. "Cente" for "Cents" (R. 5/1).......	£3000	

(d) As T **9**. Optd with T **6** in red.

J41	**4**	1c. on 50c. grey-olive and orange	£110	£160
		a. "Cente" for "Cents" (R. 5/1).......	£1300	
J42		2c. on 40c. orange and blue-green	£120	£170
		a. "Cente" for "Cents" (R. 5/1).......	£1400	
J43		8c. on 5c. red-brown (R.)	65·00	£130
		a. "Cente" for "Cents" (R. 5/1).......	£1200	
J44		10c. on 6c. lake	90·00	£160
		a. "Cente" for "Cents" (R. 5/1).......	£1300	

As stamps of the above series became exhausted the equivalent values from the series intended for use throughout Malaya were introduced. Stamps as Nos. J28/30, J32/3 and J35/6, but without Type **5** or **6**, are from remainders sent to Singapore or Kuala Lumpur after the state had been ceded to Thailand (Price from £16 each unused). Nos. J19, J21, J23 and J25/6 have also been seen without Type **5** (Price from £70 each unused).

The 12c. on 8c., 30c. on 4c., 40c. on 2c. and 50c. on 1c. surcharged with Type **9**, formerly listed as Nos. J37/40, are now believed to exist only as remainders without the Type **5** red handstamp (Price from £20 each, unused).

Kelantan was ceded to Thailand by the Japanese on 19 October 1943.

MALACCA

Postal services from Malacca resumed on 21 April 1942, but there were no stamps available for two days.

PRICES. Those quoted are for single stamps. Blocks of four showing complete handstamp are worth from five times the price of a single stamp.

(10) "Military Administration Malacca State Government Seal"

1942 (23 Apr). *Stamps of Straits Settlements handstamped as T **10**, in red, each impression covering four stamps.*

J45	**58**	1c. black	90·00	70·00
J46		2c. orange	60·00	65·00
J47		3c. green	60·00	70·00
J48		5c. brown	£130	£130
J49		8c. grey	£190	£110
J50		10c. dull purple	85·00	90·00
J51		12c. ultramarine	95·00	£100
J52		15c. ultramarine	70·00	85·00
J53		40c. scarlet and dull purple	£550	£600
J54		50c. black/*emerald*	£850	£850
J55		$1 black and red/*blue*	£900	£850

The 30c., $2 and $5 also exist with this overprint, but these values were not available to the public. (*Price for set of 3 £10000 unused*)

POSTAGE DUE STAMPS

1942 (23 Apr). *Postage Due stamps of Malayan Postal Union handstamped as T **10**, in red, each impression covering four stamps.*

JD11	D 1	1c. slate-purple	£200	£180
JD12		4c. scarlet	£225	£225
JD13		8c. scarlet	£2500	£1600
JD14		10c. yellow-orange	£425	£400
JD15		12c. ultramarine	£600	£550
JD16		50c. black	£2250	£1400

Nos. J45/55 and JD11/16 were replaced during May 1942 by the overprinted issues intended for use throughout Malaya.

PENANG

Postal services on Penang Island resumed on 30 March 1942 using Straits Settlements stamps overprinted by Japanese seals of the Government Accountant, Mr. A. Okugawa, and his assistant, Mr. Itchiburi.

(11)	**(12)** Itchiburi	DAI NIPPON
Okugawa	Seal	2602
Seal		PENANG
		(13)

1942 (30 Mar). *Straits Settlements stamps optd.*

*(a) As T **11** (three forms of the seal).*

J56	**58**	1c. black	9·50	11·00
J57		2c. orange	24·00	22·00
		a. Pair, one without handstamp	£1200	
J58		3c. green	20·00	22·00
J59		5c. brown	24·00	25·00
J60		8c. grey	26·00	35·00
J61		10c. dull purple	50·00	50·00
J62		12c. ultramarine	35·00	50·00
J63		15c. ultramarine	50·00	50·00
J64		40c. scarlet and dull purple	90·00	£110
J65		50c. black/*emerald*	£200	£225
J66		$1 black and red/*blue*	£225	£275
J67		$2 green and scarlet	£700	£700
J68		$5 green and red/*emerald*	£2000	£1500

*(b) With T **12**.*

J69	**58**	1c. black	£140	£120
J70		2c. orange	£140	£140
J71		3c. green	95·00	95·00
J72		5c. brown	£1900	£1900
J73		8c. grey	80·00	90·00
J74		10c. dull purple	£140	£150
J75		12c. ultramarine	90·00	£110
J76		15c. ultramarine	£110	£120

Straits Settlements 1, 2, 3, 4 and 5c. values exist with a similar but circular seal containing four characters, but these were not available to the public.

1942 (15 Apr). *Straits Settlements stamps optd with T **13** by Penang Premier Press.*

J77	**58**	1c. black (R.)	5·00	3·00
		a. Opt inverted	£425	£425
		b. Opt double	£300	£300
J78		2c. orange	4·50	4·00
		a. "PE" for "PENANG"	£100	85·00
		b. Opt inverted	£160	
		c. Opt double	£425	
J79		3c. green (R.)	4·75	4·25
		a. Opt double, one inverted	£375	
J80		5c. brown (R.)	2·75	7·50
		a. "N PPON"	£180	
		b. Opt double	£425	£375
J81		8c. grey (R.)	2·25	1·40
		a. "N JPPON"	50·00	55·00
		b. Opt double, one inverted	£425	
J82		10c. dull purple (R.)	1·50	2·25
		a. Opt double	£400	£400
		b. Opt double, one inverted	£400	£400
J83		12c. ultramarine (R.)	3·75	16·00
		a. "N PPON"	£475	
		b. Opt double	£375	
		c. Opt double, one inverted	£500	£500
J84		15c. ultramarine (R.)	1·75	3·50

		a. "N PPON"	£100	£110
		b. Opt inverted	£400	£400
		c. Opt double	£475	£475
J85		40c. scarlet and dull purple	4·75	5·00
J86		50c. black/*emerald* (R.)	3·75	28·00
J87		$1 black and red/*blue*	6·00	38·00
		a. Opt inverted	£950	
J88		$2 green and scarlet	50·00	80·00
J89		$5 green and red/*emerald*	£500	£600
J77/89 Set of 13			£550	£700

Nos. J77/89 were replaced by the overprinted issues intended for use throughout Malaya.

SELANGOR

Postal services resumed in the Kuala Lumpur area on 3 April 1942 and gradually extended to the remainder of the state. Stamps of the general overprinted issue were used, but the following commemorative set was only available in Selangor.

```
SELANGOR
EXHIBITION
DAI NIPPON
2602
MALAYA
(14)
```

1942 (3 Nov). *Selangor Agri-horticultural Exhibition. Nos. 294 and 283 of Straits Settlements optd with T **14**.*

J90	**58**	2c. orange	12·00	24·00
		a. "C" for "G" in "SELANGOR" (R. 1/9)	£375	£425
		b. Opt inverted	£300	£400
J91		8c. grey	13·00	24·00
		a. "C" for "G" in "SELANGOR" (R. 1/9)	£375	£425
		b. Opt inverted	£300	£400

SINGAPORE

The first post offices re-opened in Singapore on 16 March 1942.

(15) "Malaya Military Government Division Postal Services Bureau Seal"

(Handstamped at Singapore)

1942 (16 Mar). *Stamps of Straits Settlements optd with T **15** in red.*

J92	**58**	1c. black	14·00	15·00
J93		2c. orange	13·00	13·00
		a. Pair, one without handstamp	£2000	
J94		3c. green	50·00	70·00
J95		8c. grey	22·00	18·00
J96		15c. ultramarine	16·00	15·00
J92/6 Set of 5			£100	£120

The overprint Type **15** has a double-lined frame, although the two lines are not always apparent, as in the illustration. Three chops were used, differing slightly in the shape of the characters, but forgeries also exist. It is distinguishable from Type **1**, used for the general issues, by its extra width, measuring approximately 14 mm against 12½ mm.

The 6, 10, 30, 40, 50c., $2 and $5 also exist with this overprint, but were not sold to the public.

Nos. J92/6 were replaced on the 3 May 1942 by the stamps overprinted with Type **1** which were intended for use throughout Malaya.

TRENGGANU

Postal services resumed in Trengganu on 5 March 1942 using unoverprinted stamps up to the 35c. value. These remained in use until September 1942.

1942 (Sept). *Stamps of Trengganu (Script wmk) optd as T **1** at Kuala Lumpur.*

J97	**4**	1c. black (No. 26a)	90·00	90·00
		a. Chalk-surfaced paper (No. 26)		£150
		b. Red opt	£190	£200
		c. Brown opt (chalk-surfaced paper)	£450	£275
J98		2c. green (No. 27a)	£140	£140
		a. Chalk-surfaced paper (No. 27)	—	£225
		b. Red opt	£250	£275
		c. Brown opt	£500	£325
J99		2c. on 5c. deep reddish purple/*bright yellow* (No. 59)	40·00	40·00
		a. Red opt	50·00	75·00
J100		3c. chestnut (No. 29a)	85·00	80·00
		a. Brown opt	£650	£450
J101		4c. scarlet-vermilion (No. 30a)	£160	£140
J102		5c. dp reddish purple/*brt yell* (No. 32a)	10·00	19·00
		a. Purple/*yellow* (No. 32)	£120	£130
		b. Red opt	27·00	
J103		6c. orange (No. 33a)	9·00	25·00
		a. Red opt	£170	
		b. Brown opt	£650	£650
J104		8c. grey (No. 34a)	9·00	13·00
		a. Chalk-surfaced paper (No. 34)	£150	
		b. Brown to red opt	55·00	70·00
J105		8c. on 10c. bright blue (No. 60)	13·00	50·00
		a. Red opt	21·00	
J106		10c. bright blue	24·00	42·00
		a. Red opt	£190	
		b. Brown opt	£700	£700

J107		12c. bright ultramarine (No. 36)	8·00	42·00
		a. Red opt	27·00	60·00
		b. Ordinary paper	30·00	
J108		20c. dull purple and orange	8·50	38·00
		a. Red opt	21·00	
J109		25c. green and deep purple	7·50	45·00
		a. Red opt	22·00	
		b. Brown opt	£750	£750
J110		30c. dull purple and black	9·00	38·00
		a. Red opt	30·00	55·00
J111		35c. carmine/*yellow*	27·00	50·00
		a. Red opt	29·00	
J112		50c. green and bright carmine	75·00	90·00
J113		$1 purple and blue/*blue*	£3250	£3250
J114		$3 green & brown-red/*green* (No. 43a)	60·00	£100
		a. Green and lake/*green* (No. 43)	£190	
		b. Red opt	65·00	
J115	**5**	$5 green and red/*yellow*	£170	£225
J116		$25 purple and blue	£1300	
		a. Red opt	£4250	
J117		$50 green and yellow	£10000	
J118		$100 green and scarlet	£1400	

```
DAI NIPPON
2602
MALAYA
(16)
```

1942 (Sept). *Stamps of Trengganu (Script wmk) optd with T **16**.*

J119	**4**	1c. black (No. 26a)	13·00	12·00
J120		2c. green (No. 27a)	£200	£200
J121		2c. on 5c. deep reddish purple/*bright yellow* (No. 59)	6·00	8·00
J122		3c. chestnut (No. 29a)	13·00	25·00
J123		4c. scarlet-vermilion (No. 30a)	13·00	11·00
J124		5c. dp reddish purple/*brt yell* (No. 32a)	5·50	13·00
J125		6c. orange (No. 33a)	5·50	13·00
J126		8c. grey (No. 34a)	80·00	27·00
J127		8c. on 10c. bright blue (No. 60)	5·50	10·00
J128		12c. bright ultramarine (No. 36)	5·00	27·00
J129		20c. dull purple and orange	15·00	16·00
J130		25c. green and deep purple	7·00	35·00
J131		30c. dull purple and black	7·50	32·00
J132		$3 green & brown-red/*green* (No. 43a)	75·00	£140
J119/32 Set of 14			£425	£500

1943. *Stamps of Trengganu (Script wmk) optd with T **2**.*

J133	**4**	1c. black (No. 26a)	15·00	17·00
		a. Chalk-surfaced paper	40·00	
J134		2c. green (No. 27a)	13·00	30·00
J135		2c. on 5c. bright reddish purple/*bright yellow* (No. 59)	9·00	22·00
J136		5c. brt reddish purple/*brt yell* (No. 32a)	11·00	30·00
J137		6c. orange (No. 33a)	12·00	35·00
J138		8c. grey (No. 34a)	60·00	£100
J139		8c. on 10c. bright blue (No. 60)	25·00	50·00
J140		10c. bright blue	90·00	£225
J141		12c. bright ultramarine (No. 36)	15·00	48·00
J142		20c. dull purple and orange	20·00	48·00
J143		25c. green and deep purple	17·00	50·00
J144		30c. dull purple and black	22·00	50·00
J145		35c. carmine/*yellow*	22·00	65·00
J133/45 Set of 13			£300	£700

POSTAGE DUE STAMPS

1942 (Sept). *Nos. D1/4 of Trengganu optd with T **1** sideways.*

JD17	D 1	1c. scarlet	50·00	85·00
JD18		4c. green	90·00	£130
		a. Brown opt	50·00	90·00
JD19		8c. yellow	14·00	50·00
JD20		10c. brown	14·00	50·00

The Trengganu 8c. postage due also exists overprinted with Type **16**, but this was not issued (*Price £600 unused*).

Trengganu was ceded to Thailand by the Japanese on 19 October 1943.

GENERAL ISSUES

The following stamps were produced for use throughout Malaya, except for Trengganu.

1942 (3 Apr). *Stamps optd as T **1**.*

(a) On Straits Settlements.

J146	**58**	1c. black (R.)	3·25	3·25
		a. Black opt	£375	£375
		b. Violet opt	£900	£600
J147		2c. orange (V.)	£2750	£1800
J148		2c. orange (R.)	3·00	2·25
		a. Black opt	£120	£130
		b. Violet opt	£225	£200
		c. Brown opt	£800	£600
J149		3c. green (R.)	2·75	2·25
		a. Black opt	£350	£350
		b. Violet opt	£900	£700
J150		5c. brown (R.)	22·00	28·00
		a. Black opt	£500	£500
J151		8c. grey (R.)	4·25	2·25
		a. Pair, one without handstamp	†	£1800
		b. Black opt	£250	£250
J152		10c. dull purple (R.)	48·00	45·00
		a. Black opt	£900	£700
J153		12c. ultramarine (R.)	80·00	£130
J154		15c. ultramarine (R.)	3·50	3·75
		a. Violet opt	£600	£500
J155		30c. dull purple and orange (R.)	£2250	£2250
J156		40c. scarlet and dull purple (R.)	95·00	95·00
		a. Brown opt	£700	£375
J157		50c. black/*emerald* (R.)	50·00	48·00
J158		$1 black and red/*blue* (R.)	75·00	75·00
J159		$2 green and scarlet (R.)	£130	£160
J160		$5 green and red/*emerald* (R.)	£170	£190

The 2c. green is known with the overprint in red, but this was not available to the public (*Price, £350 unused*).

(b) On Negri Sembilan.

J161	**6**	1c. black (R.)	19·00	13·00
		a. Violet opt	22·00	20·00
		b. Brown opt	13·00	17·00
		c. Black opt	55·00	38·00
		d. Pair. Nos. J161/a	£275	
		e. Pair. Nos. J161 and J161b	£350	
J162		2c. orange (R.)	27·00	19·00
		a. Red opt	50·00	27·00
		b. Black opt	35·00	28·00
		c. Brown opt	65·00	50·00
J163		3c. green (R.)	38·00	20·00
		a. Violet opt	23·00	29·00
		c. Brown opt	£150	60·00
		d. Black opt	60·00	45·00
J164		5c. brown	38·00	21·00
		a. Pair, one without opt	£1700	
		b. Brown opt	17·00	15·00
		c. Red opt	15·00	11·00
		d. Violet opt	50·00	38·00
		e. Pair. Nos. J164c/d	£325	
J165		6c. grey	£140	£120
		b. Brown opt	£325	£325
J166		8c. scarlet	£130	£110
J167		10c. dull purple	£190	£180
		a. Red opt	£350	£320
		b. Brown opt	£475	£350
J168		12c. bright ultramarine (Br.)	£1400	£1400
J169		15c. ultramarine (R.)	22·00	8·00
		a. Violet opt	90·00	30·00
		b. Brown opt	27·00	12·00
J170		25c. dull purple and scarlet	28·00	38·00
		a. Red opt	60·00	75·00
		b. Brown opt	£450	£350
J171		30c. dull purple and orange	£225	£180
		a. Brown opt	£1100	£850
J172		40c. scarlet and dull purple	£1100	£900
		a. Brown opt	£900	£850
J173		50c. black/*emerald*	£950	£950
J174		$1 black and red/*blue*	£200	£225
		a. Red opt	£170	£190
		b. Brown opt	£400	£400
J175		$5 green and red/*emerald*	£500	£600
		a. Red opt	£950	£950

Nos. J161a and J163a exist with the handstamped overprint sideways.

(c) On Pahang.

J176	**15**	1c. black	50·00	45·00
		a. Red opt	55·00	50·00
		b. Violet opt	£325	£250
		c. Brown opt	£250	£250
J177		3c. green	£375	£300
		a. Red opt	£225	£275
		b. Violet opt	£650	£475
J178		5c. brown	14·00	12·00
		a. Red opt	£190	£110
		b. Brown opt	£250	£110
		c. Violet opt	£450	£250
		d. Pair. Nos. J178/b	£800	
J179		8c. grey	£850	£650
J180		8c. scarlet	20·00	8·00
		a. Red opt	£110	50·00
		b. Violet opt	£100	55·00
		c. Brown opt	£110	65·00
		d. Pair. Nos. J180a/c	£400	
J181		10c. dull purple	£325	£140
		a. Red opt	£275	£225
		b. Brown opt	£375	£250
J182		12c. bright ultramarine	£1600	£1600
		a. Red opt	£1200	£1200
J183		15c. ultramarine	£140	£110
		a. Red opt	£375	£250
		b. Violet opt	£650	£475
		c. Brown opt	£500	£325
J184		25c. dull purple and scarlet	21·00	29·00
J185		30c. dull purple and orange	12·00	28·00
		a. Red opt	£140	£170
J186		40c. scarlet and dull purple	20·00	32·00
		a. Brown opt	£425	£300
		b. Red opt	85·00	90·00
J187		50c. black/*emerald*	£950	£950
		a. Red opt	£1000	£1000
J188		$1 black and red/*blue* (R.)	£140	£150
		a. Black opt	£300	£300
		b. Brown opt	£650	£650
J189		$5 green and red/*emerald*	£650	£800
		a. Red opt	£950	£900

(d) On Perak.

J190	**51**	1c. black	55·00	35·00
		a. Violet opt	£250	£100
		b. Brown opt	80·00	80·00
J191		2c. orange	30·00	20·00
		a. Violet opt	70·00	70·00
		b. Red opt	60·00	40·00
		c. Brown opt	55·00	55·00
J192		3c. green	26·00	28·00
		a. Violet opt	£475	£300
		b. Brown opt	£180	£150
		c. Red opt	£325	£280
J193		5c. brown	7·00	6·00
		a. Pair, one without opt	£1000	
		b. Brown opt	40·00	28·00
		c. Violet opt	£250	£200
		d. Red opt	£225	£200
J194		8c. grey	75·00	48·00
		a. Red opt	£375	£250
		b. Brown opt	£350	£250
J195		8c. scarlet	40·00	42·00
		a. Violet opt	£475	£275
J196		10c. dull purple	26·00	24·00
		a. Red opt	£350	£225
J197		12c. bright ultramarine	£225	£225
J198		15c. ultramarine	24·00	31·00
		a. Red opt	£225	£200
		b. Violet opt	£425	£300
		c. Brown opt	£375	£275
J199		25c. dull purple and scarlet	14·00	25·00
		a. Red opt	£275	
J200		30c. dull purple and orange	17·00	32·00

		a. Pair, one without opt	£1600	
		b. Brown opt	£550	£400
		c. Red opt	35·00	55·00
		ca. Pair, one without opt	£2000	
J201		40c. scarlet and dull purple	£425	£350
		a. Brown opt	£500	£425
J202		50c. black/*emerald*	40·00	50·00
		a. Red opt	50·00	60·00
		b. Brown opt	£450	£350
J203		$1 black and red/*blue*	£425	£400
		a. Brown opt	£450	£375
J204		$2 green and scarlet	£3250	£3250
J205		$5 green and red/*emerald*	£475	
		a. Brown opt	£1700	

(e) On Selangor.

J206	**46**	1c. black, S	12·00	25·00
		a. Red opt, S	42·00	38·00
		b. Violet opt, SU	45·00	42·00
J207		2c. green, SU	£1500	£1200
		a. Violet opt, SU	£1800	£1200
J208		2c. orange (P 14×14½), S	95·00	60·00
		a. Red opt, U	£200	£170
		b. Violet opt, U	£225	£160
		c. Brown opt, S	85·00	80·00
J209		2c. orange (P 14), S	£120	80·00
		a. Red opt, U	£225	£170
		b. Violet opt, U	£375	£170
		c. Brown opt, U	—	£170
J210		3c. green, SU	23·00	15·00
		a. Red opt, SU	18·00	15·00
		b. Violet opt, SU	65·00	50·00
		c. Brown opt, SU	18·00	15·00
J211		5c. brown, SU	6·00	5·50
		a. Red opt, SU	13·00	16·00
		b. Violet opt, SU	21·00	22·00
		c. Brown opt, SU	60·00	50·00
J212		6c. scarlet, SU	£375	£375
		a. Red opt, S	£200	£250
		b. Brown opt, S	£800	£800
J213		8c. grey, S	£170	17·00
		a. Red opt, SU	60·00	40·00
		b. Violet opt, U	35·00	35·00
		c. Brown opt, S	£170	75·00
J214		10c. dull purple, S	13·00	21·00
		a. Red opt, S	75·00	60·00
		b. Brown opt, S	£150	85·00
J215		12c. bright ultramarine, S	60·00	70·00
		a. Red opt, S	£120	£130
		b. Brown opt, S	£130	£120
J216		15c. ultramarine, S	16·00	22·00
		a. Red opt, SU	55·00	55·00
		b. Violet opt, U	£150	£150
		c. Brown opt, U	£100	65·00
J217		25c. dull purple and scarlet, S	80·00	£100
		a. Red opt, S	60·00	80·00
J218		30c. dull purple and orange, S	11·00	24·00
		a. Red opt, S	£450	£275
J219		40c. scarlet and dull purple, S	£140	£140
		a. Brown opt, S	£400	£200
		b. Red opt, S	£300	
J220		50c. black/*emerald*, S	£140	£150
		a. Red opt	£150	£160
		b. Brown opt, S	£500	£375
J221	**48**	$1 black and red/*blue*	30·00	45·00
		a. Red opt	£120	£150
J222		$2 green and scarlet	35·00	60·00
		a. Pair, one without opt	£1700	
		b. Red opt	£650	£700
J223		$5 green and red/*emerald*	65·00	90·00

On *T* **46** the overprint is normally sideways (with "top" to either right or left), but on *T* **48** it is always upright.

S = Sideways
U = Upright
SU = Sideways or upright (our prices being for the cheaper).

Specialists recognise nine slightly different chops as Type **1**. Initial supplies with the overprint in red were produced at Singapore. Later overprintings took place at Kuala Lumpur in violet, red or brown and finally, black. No. J155 was from the Kuala Lumpur printing only. Except where noted, these overprints were used widely in Malaya and, in some instances, Sumatra.

The following stamps also exist with this overprint, but were not available to the public:

Straits Settlements (in red) 6, 25c.
Kelantan (in black) 10c.
Negri Sembilan 2c. green (Blk. or Brn.), 4c. (Blk.), 6c. scarlet (Blk.), 8c. grey (Blk.), 12c. (Blk.), $2 (Blk. or Brn.)
Pahang (in black, 2c. also in brown) 2, 4, 6c., $2
Perak 2c. green (R.), 6c. (Blk.)
Selangor 4c. (Blk.)

1942 (May). *Optd with T* **16**.

(a) On Straits Settlements.

J224	**58**	2c. orange	2·25	60
		a. Opt inverted	12·00	21·00
		b. Opt double, one inverted	50·00	60·00
J225		3c. green	50·00	65·00
J226		8c. grey	6·00	3·00
		a. Opt inverted	17·00	32·00
J227		15c. blue	15·00	9·50
J224/7 *Set of 4*			65·00	70·00

(b) On Negri Sembilan.

J228	**6**	1c. black	2·50	60
		a. Opt inverted	9·00	25·00
		b. Opt double, one inverted	35·00	50·00
J229		2c. orange	7·50	50
J230		3c. green	5·50	50
J231		5c. brown	1·75	3·00
J232		6c. grey	3·50	2·25
			†	£1400
		b. Stop omitted at right (R. 10/4)	£100	£110
J233		8c. scarlet	6·50	1·25
J234		10c. dull purple	3·00	2·50
J235		15c. ultramarine	16·00	2·50
J236		25c. dull purple and scarlet	5·00	16·00
J237		30c. dull purple and orange	7·50	3·00
J238		$1 black and red/*blue*	80·00	95·00
J228/38 *Set of 11*			£120	£110

(c) On Pahang.

J239	**15**	1c. black	3·00	3·25

		a. Opt omitted (in pair with normal)	£500	
J240		5c. brown	1·25	70
J241		8c. scarlet	26·00	2·75
		a. Opt omitted (in pair with normal)	£1300	
J242		10c. dull purple	11·00	7·00
J243		12c. bright ultramarine	2·75	15·00
J244		25c. dull purple and scarlet	5·00	22·00
J245		30c. dull purple and orange	3·00	10·00
J239/45 *Set of 7*			48·00	55·00

(d) On Perak.

J246	**51**	2c. orange	3·25	2·50
		a. Opt inverted	45·00	48·00
J247		3c. green	1·25	1·50
		a. Opt inverted	15·00	26·00
		b. Opt omitted (in pair with normal)	£500	
J248		8c. scarlet	70	50
		a. Opt inverted	4·50	7·00
		b. Opt double, one inverted	£225	£250
		c. Opt omitted (in horiz pair with normal)	£400	
J249		10c. dull purple	15·00	6·50
J250		15c. ultramarine	7·50	2·00
J251		50c. black/*emerald*	3·25	4·50
J252		$1 black and red/*blue*	£425	£450
J253		$5 green and red/*emerald*	42·00	70·00
		a. Opt inverted	£275	£350
J246/53 *Set of 8*			£450	£500

(e) On Selangor.

J254	**46**	3c. green	2·00	3·50
J255		12c. bright ultramarine	1·10	14·00
J256		15c. ultramarine	6·50	1·50
J257		40c. scarlet and dull purple	2·00	4·75
J258	**48**	$2 green and scarlet	10·00	45·00
J254/8 *Set of 5*			19·00	60·00

On *T* **46** the overprint is sideways, with "top" to left or right. The following stamps also exist with this overprint, but were not available to the public.

Perak 1, 5, 30c. (*Price for set of 3 £375 unused*).
Selangor 1, 5, 10, 30c., $1, $5 (*Price for set of 6 £700 unused*).

DAI NIPPON 2602 MALAYA **2 Cents** (17)	DAI NIPPON YUBIN **2 Cents** (18) "Japanese Postal Service"

1942 (Nov.). *No. 108 of Perak surch with T* **17**.

J259	**51**	2c. on 5c. brown	1·25	3·25
		a. Inverted "s" in "Cents" (R. 3/5)	55·00	80·00

1942 (Nov.). *Perak stamps surch or opt only, as in T* **18**.

J260	**51**	1c. black	5·50	10·00
		a. Opt inverted	19·00	40·00
J261		2c. on 5c. brown	2·00	6·50
		a. "DAI NIPPON YUBIN" inverted	17·00	38·00
		b. Ditto and "2 Cents" omitted	45·00	65·00
		c. Inverted "s" in "Cents" (R. 3/5)	60·00	£110
J262		8c. scarlet	50	2·25
		a. Opt inverted	11·00	24·00
J260/2 *Set of 3*			11·50	17·00

A similar overprint exists on the Selangor 3c. but this was not available to the public (*Price £350 unused*).

On 8 December 1942 contemporary Japanese 3, 5, 8 and 25s. stamps were issued without overprint in Malaya and the 1, 2, 4, 6, 7, 10, 30 and 50s. and 1y. values followed on 15 February 1943.

大日本郵便 (19)		
6 cts. (20)	**6 cts.** (21)	**2 Cents** (22)
6 cts. (23)	**$1·00** (24)	

1942 (4 Dec).-**44**. *Stamps of various Malayan territories optd "Japanese Postal Service" in Kanji characters as T* **2** *or* **19**, *some additionally surch as T* **20** *to* **24**.

(a) Stamps of Straits Settlements optd with T **2**.

J263	**58**	8c. grey (Blk.) (1943)	1·40	50
		a. Opt inverted	50·00	65·00
		b. Opt omitted (in pair with normal)	£850	
		c. Red opt	2·50	3·25
J264		12c. ultramarine (1943)	1·25	50
J265		40c. scarlet and dull purple (1943)	2·25	4·75
J263/5 *Set of 3*			4·50	14·50

(b) Stamps of Negri Sembilan optd with T **2** *or surch also.*

J266	**6**	1c. black	30	2·50
		a. Opt inverted	11·00	27·00
		b. Sideways second character	20·00	35·00
		ba. Opt inverted with sideways second character	£750	
J267		2c. on 5c. brown (surch as T 20)	80	1·25
J268		6c. on 5c. brown (surch as T 21) (1943)	40	1·50
		a. Opt Type 2 and surch as Type 21 both inverted	£225	£225
J269		25c. dull purple and scarlet (1943)	1·10	19·00
J266/9 *Set of 4*			2·25	19·00

(c) Stamp of Pahang optd with T **2** *and surch also.*

J270	**15**	6c. on 5c. brown (surch T 20) (1943)	50	75

J271		6c. on 5c. brown (surch T 21) (1943)	1·00	1·75

(d) Stamps of Perak optd with T 2 or surch also.

J272	**51**	1c. black..	1·00	70
J273		a. Sideways second character	£200	£225
		2c. on 5c. brown (surch as T 20)....	60	50
		a. Opt Type 2 and surch Type 20 both inverted....................	18·00	32·00
		b. Opt Type 2 inverted.............	18·00	32·00
		c. Sideways second character....	50·00	50·00
J274		2c. on 5c. brown (surch T 22)...............	60	50
		a. Surch Type 22 inverted.......	18·00	32·00
		b. Opt Type 2 and surch Type 22 both inverted....................	23·00	35·00
		c. Sideways second character	25·00	32·00
		ca. Surch Type 22 inverted.......	£1300	
		cb. Opt Type 2 with sideways second character and surch Type 22 both inverted............	£1300	
J275		5c. brown..	55	65
		a. Opt inverted........................	35·00	40·00
		b. Sideways second character....	£500	£375
J276		8c. scarlet......................................	55	2·00
		a. Opt inverted........................	15·00	28·00
		b. Sideways second character....	50·00	70·00
		ba. Opt inverted with sideways second character................	£700	
		c. Opt omitted (in pair with normal)...............................	£1000	
J277		10c. dull purple (1943)...................	60	50
J278		30c. dull purple and orange (1943)..	4·50	6·50
J279		50c. black/emerald (1943).............	3·75	20·00
J280		$5 green and red/emerald (1943) ...	60·00	£100
J272/80		Set of 9	65·00	£120

(e) Stamps of Selangor optd with T 2 (sideways on T 46).

J281	**46**	1c. black (1943)	1·00	2·75
J282		3c. green..	40	45
		a. Sideways second character........	17·00	26·00
J283		12c. bright ultramarine	45	1·60
		a. Sideways second character........	60·00	75·00
J284		15c. ultramarine	3·75	3·25
		a. Sideways second character........	50·00	55·00
J285	**48**	$1 black and red/*blue*....................	3·00	22·00
		a. Opt inverted........................	£225	£225
		b. Sideways second character........	£375	£400
J286		$2 green and scarlet (1943).............	10·00	48·00
J287		$5 green and red/*emerald* (1943) ...	22·00	80·00
		a. Opt inverted........................	£250	£300
J281/7		Set of 7	35·00	£140

(f) Stamps of Selangor optd with T 19 or surch also.

J288	**46**	1c. black (R.) (1943)...................	35	50
J289		2c. on 5c. brown (surch as T 21) (R.) (1943)...............................	1·00	50
J290		3c. on 5c. brown (surch as T 21) (1943)	30	4·50
		a. "s" in "cts". inverted (R. 4/3)	30·00	60·00
		b. Comma after "cts" (R. 9/3)...	30·00	60·00
J291		5c. brown (R.) (1944)...................	1·60	4·50
J292		6c. on 5c. brown (surch T 21) (1944)	80	1·75

J293		6c. on 5c. brown (surch T 23) (1944)	40	70
		a. "6" inverted (R. 7/8).............	£850	
		b. Full stop between "6" and "cts" (R. 8/6)......................	£450	
		c. Surch and opt double.............	£450	
J294		15c. ultramarine	4·00	4·00
J295		$1 on 10c. dull purple (surch T 24) (18.12.1944)...................	40	1·00
J296		$1.50 on dull purple and orange (surch 30c. T 24) (18.12.1944)...............	40	1·00
J288/96		Set of 9	8·25	17·00

The error showing the second character in Type **2** sideways occurred on R. 6/3 in the first of four settings only.

The 2c. orange, 3c. and 8c. grey of Perak also exist overprinted with Type **2**, but these stamps were not available to the public (*Price for set of 3 £100 unused*).

Examples of No. J275 are known postally used from the Shan States (part of pre-war Burma).

25 Tapping Rubber

26 Fruit

27 Japanese Shrine, Singapore

(Litho Kolff & Co, Batavia)

1943 (29 Apr–1 Oct). *T 25/7 and similar designs. P 12½.*

J297	**25**	1c. grey-green (1 Oct)	1·50	55
J298	**26**	2c. pale emerald (1 June)	1·00	20
J299	**25**	3c. drab (1 Oct)........................	40	20
J300	–	4c. carmine-rose.......................	2·25	20
J301	–	8c. dull blue	40	20
J302	–	10c. brown-purple (1 Oct).............	50	20
J303	**27**	15c. violet (1 Oct).......................	70	4·00
J304	–	30c. olive-green (1 Oct)...............	1·25	35
J305	–	50c. blue (1 Oct)........................	4·00	4·00
J306	–	70c. blue (1 Oct)........................	17·00	11·00
J297/306		Set of 10	26·00	19·00

Designs: *Vert*—4c. Tin dredger; 8c. War Memorial, Bukit Batok, Singapore; 10c. Fishing village; 30c. Sago palms; 50c. Straits of Johore. *Horiz*—70c. Malay Mosque, Kuala Lumpur.

The 2c. and 4c. values exist, printed by typography, in paler shades either imperforate or rouletted. It is suggested that these may have been available in Singapore at the very end of the Japanese Occupation.

28 Ploughman

29 Rice-planting

1943 (1 Sept). *Savings Campaign. Litho. P 12½.*

J307	**28**	8c. violet	9·50	2·75
J308		15c. scarlet	6·50	2·75

(Des Hon Chin. Litho)

1944 (15 Feb). *"Re-birth" of Malaya. P 12½.*

J309	**29**	8c. rose-red	15·00	3·25
J310		15c. magenta	4·00	3·25

(30)   (31)   (32)

1944 (16 Dec). *Stamps intended for use on Red Cross letters. Surch with T 30/2 in red.*

(a) On Straits Settlements.

J311	**58**	50c. on 50c. black/*emerald*..................	10·00	24·00
J312		$1 on $1 black and red/*blue*.............	21·00	35·00
J313		$1.50 on $2 green and scarlet...............	32·00	70·00

(b) On Johore.

J314	**29**	50c. on 50c. dull purple and red............	7·00	20·00
J315		$1.50 on $2 green and carmine.............	4·00	12·00

(c) On Selangor.

J316	**48**	$1 on $1 black and red/*blue*..............	3·50	14·00
J317		$1.50 on $2 green and scarlet.............	5·00	20·00
J311/17		Set of 7	75·00	£180

Nos. J311/17 were issued in Singapore but were withdrawn after one day, probably because supplies of Nos. J295/6 were received and issued on the 18 December.

A similar 6c. surcharge exists on the Straits Settlements 5c. but this was not available to the public (*Price £500 unused*).

STAMP BOOKLETS

1942. *Nos. SB3/4 of Perak and SB2 of Selangor with covers optd with T* **1**.

SB1	$1 booklet *containing* twenty 5c. (No. J193) in blocks of 10	£2500
SB2	$1.30 booklet containing 5c. and 8c. (Nos. J193/4), each in block of 10	£2500
SB3	$1.30 booklet containing 5c. and 8c. (Nos. J211 and J213), each in block of 10	£2500

POSTAGE DUE STAMPS

Postage Due stamps of the Malayan Postal Union overprinted.

1942 (3 Apr). *Handstamped as T* **1** *in black.*

JD21	D 1	1c. slate-purple.................................	12·00	26·00
		a. Red opt...................................	£140	£140
		b. Brown opt................................	£130	£140
JD22		3c. green.....................................	65·00	70·00
		a. Red opt...................................	£225	£250
JD23		4c. green.....................................	55·00	38·00
		a. Red opt...................................	55·00	50·00
		b. Brown opt................................	£150	£150
JD24		8c. scarlet...................................	95·00	80·00
		a. Red opt...................................	£150	£120
		b. Brown opt................................	£180	£180
JD25		10c. yellow-orange............................	27·00	48·00
		a. Red opt...................................	£225	£225
		b. Brown opt................................	£225	£225
JD26		12c. ultramarine..............................	25·00	50·00
		a. Red opt...................................	£225	£225
JD27		50c. black....................................	60·00	80·00
		a. Red opt...................................	£425	£450

1942. *Optd with T* **16**.

JD28	D 1	1c. slate-purple.................................	2·75	9·50
JD29		3c. green.....................................	16·00	22·00
JD30		4c. green.....................................	15·00	11·00
JD31		8c. scarlet...................................	22·00	19·00
JD32		10c. yellow-orange	1·75	16·00
JD33		12c. ultramarine	1·75	30·00
JD28/33 *Set of 6*			55·00	95·00

The 9c. and 15c. also exist with this overprint, but these were not issued (*Price £600 each unused*).

1943–45. *Optd with T* **2**.

JD34	D 1	1c. slate-purple.................................	2·00	4·50
JD35		3c. green.....................................	2·00	4·50
		a. Opt omitted (in pair with normal)..................................	£650	
JD36		4c. green.....................................	55·00	42·00
JD37		5c. scarlet...................................	1·50	4·75
JD38		9c. yellow-orange............................	80	8·00
		a. Opt inverted	21·00	28·00
JD39		10c. yellow-orange............................	2·00	8·50
		a. Opt inverted	70·00	70·00
JD40		12c. ultramarine..............................	2·00	16·00
JD41		15c. ultramarine..............................	2·00	8·50
JD34/41 *Set of 8*			60·00	85·00

VII. THAI OCCUPATION OF MALAYA

Stamps issued for use in the Malay States of Kedah (renamed Syburi), Kelantan, Perlis and Trengganu, ceded by Japan to Thailand on 19 October 1943. British rule was restored on 9 (Kelantan), 18 (Perlis), 22 (Kedah) and 24 September 1945 (Trengganu). Nos TM1/6 continued to be used for postage until replaced by the overprinted B.M.A. Malaya issues on 10 October 1945.

PRICES FOR STAMPS ON COVER	
Nos. TK1/5	*from* × 30
Nos. TM1/6	*from* × 25
Nos. TT1/35	—

KELANTAN

TK 1

(Typo Kelantan Ptg Dept, Khota Baru)

1943 (15 Nov). *Handstamped with State arms in violet. No gum.* P 11.

TK1	TK 1	1c. black....................................	£200	£300
TK2		2c. black....................................	£250	£250
		a. Handstamp omitted....................	£700	
TK3		4c. black....................................	£250	£300
		a. Handstamp omitted....................	£850	
TK4		8c. black....................................	£250	£250
		a. Handstamp omitted....................	£550	
TK5		10c. black....................................	£325	£425
TK1/5 *Set of 5*....................................			£1100	£1400

Nos. TK1/5 were printed in sheets of 84 (12×7) and have sheet watermarks in the form of "STANDARD" in block capitals with curved "CROWN" above and "AGENTS" below in double-lined capitals. This watermark occurs four times in the sheet.
Sheets were imperforate at top and left so that stamps exist imperforate at top, left or at top and left.
Genuine examples have a solid star at the top centre of the arms, as shown in Type TK **1**. Examples with a hollow outline star in this position are forgeries.
Similar stamps, but with red handstamps, were for fiscal use.

GENERAL ISSUE

TM 1 War Memorial

(Litho Defence Ministry, Bangkok)

1944 (15 Jan–4 Mar). *Thick opaque, or thin semi-transparent paper. Gummed or ungummed.* P 12½.

TM1	TM 1	1c. yellow (4 Mar)........................	30·00	32·00
TM2		2c. red-brown.............................	12·00	20·00
		a. Imperf (pair).........................	£850	
		b. Perf 12½×11.........................	20·00	20·00
TM3		3c. green (4 Mar)..........................	20·00	38·00
		a. Perf 12½×11...........................	30·00	42·00
TM4		4c. purple (4 Mar)..........................	14·00	28·00
		a. Perf 12½×11...........................	20·00	35·00
TM5		8c. carmine (4 Mar).........................	14·00	20·00
		a. Perf 12½×11...........................	20·00	20·00
TM6		15c. blue (4 Mar)............................	38·00	60·00
		a. Perf 12½×11...........................	42·00	60·00
TM1/6 *Set of 6*..			£110	£180

5c. and 10c. stamps in this design were prepared, but never issued.

TRENGGANU

TRENGGANU
(TT **1**)

(Overprinted at Trengganu Survey Office)

1944 (1 Oct). *Various stamps optd with Type TT* **1**.

(a) On Trengganu without Japanese opt.

TT1	4	1c. black (26a)		
TT2		30c. dull purple and black (39)		

(b) On Trengganu stamps optd as T **1** *of Japanese Occupation.*

TT2a	4	1c. black (J97)	—	£1300
TT3		8c. grey (J104)	£550	£400

(c) On stamps optd with T **16** *of Japanese Occupation.*

(i) Pahang.

TT4	15	12c. bright ultramarine (J243)...........	£450	£130

(ii) Trengganu.

TT5	4	2c. on 5c. deep reddish purple/bright yellow (J121)*.....................	£500	£500
TT6		8c. on 10c. brt blue (J127) (inverted)....	£425	£425
TT7		12c. brt ultramarine (J128) (inverted)..............................	£425	£425

This is spelt "TRENGANU" with one "G".

(d) On stamps optd with T **2** *of Japanese Occupation.*

(i) Straits Settlements.

TT8	58	12c. ultramarine (J264)...................	£450	£450
TT9		40c. scarlet and dull purple (J265)....	£450	£450

(ii) Negri Sembilan.

TT9a	6	25c. dull purple and scarlet (J269)....	—	£1300

(iii) Pahang.

TT10	15	6c. on 5c. brown (J271).................		

(iv) Perak.

TT11	51	1c. black (J272).........................		
TT12		10c. dull purple (J277)...................		
TT13		30c. dull purple and orange (J278) ...	£750	£450
TT13a		50c. black/emerald (J279)	—	£1300

(v) Selangor.

TT14	46	3c. green (J282).........................	£350	£350
TT15		12c. brt ultramarine (J283) (L. to R.)	£190	£110
TT16		12c. brt ultramarine (J283) (R. to L.)	£180	£110
		a. Sideways second character........	£1900	£1900

(e) On Selangor stamps optd with T **19** *of Japanese Occupation.*

TT16b	46	1c. black (J288)	—	£1300
TT17		2c. on 5c. brown (J289).................	£450	£450
TT18		3c. on 5c. brown (J290).................	£450	£450

(f) On pictorials of 1943 (Nos. J297/306).

TT19	25	1c. grey-green	£350	£300
TT20	26	2c. pale emerald...........................	£350	£160
TT21	25	3c. drab....................................	£190	£120
TT22	—	4c. carmine-rose...........................	£300	£160
TT23	—	8c. dull blue...............................	£500	£475
TT24	—	10c. brown-purple..........................	£950	£600
TT25	27	15c. violet.................................	£300	£160
TT26	—	30c. olive-green............................	£450	£140
TT27	—	50c. blue...................................	£450	£250
TT28	—	70c. blue...................................	£900	£650

(g) On Savings Campaign stamps (Nos. J307/8).

TT29	28	8c. violet..................................	£500	£500
TT30		15c. scarlet................................	£350	£160

(h) On stamps of Japan.

TT31	—	3s. green (No. 319)........................		
TT32	—	5s. claret (No. 396).......................	£450	£375
TT33	—	25c. brown and chocolate (No. 329).	£300	£110
TT34	—	30c. blue-green (No. 330).................	£450	£160

(i) On Trengganu Postage Due stamp optd with T **1** *of Japanese Occupation.*

TT35	D 1	1c. scarlet (JD17)...........................	£1700	£1700

Maldive Islands

BRITISH PROTECTORATE

(Currency. 100 cents = 1 Ceylon rupee)

MALDIVES
(1)

2 Minaret, Juma Mosque, Malé

3

1906 (9 Sept). *Nos. 277/9. 280a and 283/4 of Ceylon optd with T* **1**. *Wmk Mult Crown CA. P* 14.

1	**44**	2c. red-brown	16·00	42·00
2	**45**	3c. green	23·00	42·00
3		4c. orange and ultramarine	40·00	85·00
4	**46**	5c. dull purple	4·00	6·50
5	**48**	15c. blue	80·00	£160
6		25c. bistre	90·00	£170
1/6 Set of 6			£225	£450

The *T* **1** opt has been extensively forged.

Supplies of Nos. 1/6 were exhausted by March 1907 and the stamps of CEYLON were used until 1909.

(Recess D.L.R.)

1909 (May). *T* **2** (18½×22½ mm). *W* **3**. *P* 14×13½ (2c., 5c.) or 13½×14 (3c., 10c.).

7	**2**	2c. orange-brown	2·25	3·50
		a. Perf 13½×14	2·50	90
8		3c. deep myrtle	50	70
9		5c. purple	50	35
10		10c. carmine	7·50	80
7/10 Set of 4			9·50	2·50

These stamps perforated 14×13½ (14×13.7) are from a line machine and those perforated 13½×14 (13.7×13.9) from a comb machine.

4

(Photo Harrison)

1933. *T* **2** *redrawn (reduced to* 18×21½ mm*). W* **4**. *P* 15×14.

A. Wmk upright.

11A	**2**	2c. grey	2·75	2·00
12A		3c. red-brown	70	2·75
14A		5c. mauve	25·00	10·00
15A		6c. scarlet	1·50	5·50
16A		10c. green	85	55
17A		15c. black	6·50	14·00
18A		25c. brown	6·50	14·00
19A		50c. purple	6·50	18·00
20A		1r. deep blue	11·00	16·00
11A/20A Set of 9			55·00	75·00

B. Wmk sideways.

11B	**2**	2c. grey	6·00	5·00
12B		3c. red-brown	5·00	1·75
13B		5c. claret	40·00	32·00
15B		6c. scarlet	10·00	5·50
16B		10c. green	3·75	5·50
17B		15c. black	15·00	18·00
18B		25c. brown	11·00	18·00
19B		50c. purple	16·00	18·00
20B		1r. deep blue	16·00	3·25
11B/20B Set of 9			£110	95·00

(New Currency. 100 larees = 1 rupee)

5 Palm Tree and Dhow

(Recess B.W.)

1950 (24 Dec). *P* 13.

21	**5**	2l. olive-green	2·25	2·00
		a. Olive-brown (1952)	5·50	6·00
22		3l. blue	10·00	50
23		5l. emerald-green	10·00	50
24		6l. red-brown	1·25	1·00
25		10l. scarlet	1·25	70
26		15l. orange	1·25	70
27		25l. purple	1·25	1·50
28		50l. violet	1·25	2·25
29		1r. chocolate	12·00	32·00
21/9 Set of 9			35·00	35·00

7 Fish

8 Native Products

1952. *P* 13.

30	**7**	3l. blue	2·00	60
31	**8**	5l. emerald	1·00	2·00

Malta

Early records of the postal services under the British Occupation are fragmentary, but it is known that an Island Postmaster was appointed in 1802. A British Packet Agency was established in 1806 and it later became customary for the same individual to hold the two appointments together. The inland posts continued to be the responsibility of the local administration, but the overseas mails formed part of the British G.P.O. system.

The stamps of Great Britain were used on overseas mails from September 1857. Previously during the period of the Crimean War letters franked with Great Britain stamps from the Crimea were cancelled at Malta with a wavy line obliterator. Such postmarks are known between April 1855 and September 1856.

The British G.P.O. relinquished control of the overseas posts on 31 December 1884 when Great Britain stamps were replaced by those of Malta.

Z 1

Z 2

1855–56. *Stamps of* GREAT BRITAIN *cancelled with wavy lines obliteration, Type Z* **1**.

Z1	1d. red-brown (1854), Die I, wmk Small Crown, perf 16		£800
Z2	1d. red-brown (1855), Die II, wmk Small Crown, perf 14		£800
	a. Very blued paper		
Z3	1d. red-brown (1855), Die II, wmk Large Crown, perf 16		£800
Z3a	1d. red-brown (1855), Die II, wmk Large Crown, perf 14		£800
Z4	2d. blue (1855), wmk Large Crown, perf 14. Plate No. 5		
Z5	6d. (1854) embossed		£4000
Z6	1s. (1847) embossed		£4500

It is now established that this obliterator was sent to Malta and used on mail in transit emanating from the Crimea.

1857 (18 Aug)–**59**. *Stamps of* GREAT BRITAIN *cancelled "M", Type Z* **2**.

Z7	1d. red-brown (1841), imperf		£1600
Z8	1d. red-brown, Die I, wmk Small Crown, perf 16		£130
Z9	1d. red-brown, Die II, wmk Small Crown, perf 16		£900
Z10	1d. red-brown, Die II (1855), wmk Small Crown, perf 14		£225
Z11	1d. red-brown, Die II (1855), wmk Large Crown, perf 14		75·00
Z12	1d. rose-red (1857), wmk Large Crown, perf 14		20·00
Z13	2d. blue (1841)		£3000
Z14	2d. blue (1854) wmk Small Crown, perf 16. Plate No. 4.		£750
Z15	2d. blue (1855), wmk Large Crown, perf 14 ... From Plate Nos. 5, 6.		55·00
Z16	2d. blue (1858), wmk Large Crown, perf 16. Plate No. 6.		£300
Z17	2d. blue (1858) (Plate No. 7, 8, 9) ... From		40·00
Z18	4d. rose (1857)		35·00
	a. Thick glazed paper		£180
Z19	6d. violet (1854), embossed		£3500
Z20	6d. lilac (1856)		40·00
	a. Thick paper		£200
Z21	6d. lilac (1856) (blued paper)		£850
Z22	1s. green (1856)		£120
	a. Thick paper		£180

Z 3

Z 6

Z 4

Z 5

Z 7

1859–84. *Stamps of* GREAT BRITAIN *cancelled "A 25" as in Types Z* **3/7**.

Z23	½d. rose-red (1870–79) ... From Plate Nos. 4, 5, 6, 8, 9, 10, 11, 12, 13, 14, 15, 19, 20.		23·00
Z24	1d. red-brown (1841), imperf		£2750
Z25	1d. red-brown (1854), wmk Small Crown, perf 16		£325
Z26	1d. red-brown (1855), wmk Large Crown, perf 14		75·00
Z27	1d. rose-red (1857), wmk Large Crown, perf 14		7·50
Z28	1d. rose-red (1861), Alphabet IV		£450
Z30	1d. rose-red (1864–79) ... From Plate Nos, 71, 72, 73, 74, 76, 78, 79, 80, 81, 82, 83, 84, 85, 86, 87, 88, 89, 90, 91, 92, 93, 94, 95, 96, 97, 98, 99, 100, 101, 102, 103, 104, 105, 106, 107, 108, 109, 110, 111, 112, 113, 114, 115, 116, 117, 118, 119, 120, 121, 122, 123, 124, 125, 127, 129, 130, 131, 132, 133, 134, 135, 136, 137, 138, 139, 140, 141, 142, 143, 144, 145, 146, 147, 148, 149, 150, 151, 152, 153, 154, 155, 156, 157, 158, 159, 160, 161, 162, 163, 164, 165, 166, 167, 168, 169, 170, 171, 172, 173, 174, 175, 176, 177, 178, 179, 180, 181, 182, 183, 184, 185, 186, 187, 188, 189, 190, 191, 192, 193, 194, 195, 196, 197, 198, 199, 200, 201, 202, 203, 204, 205, 206, 207, 208, 209, 210, 211, 212, 213, 214, 215, 216, 217, 218, 219, 220, 221, 222, 223, 224		15·00
Z31	1½d. lake-red (1870–79) (Plate Nos. 1, 3) ... From		£450
Z32	2d. blue (1841), imperf		£4000
Z33	2d. blue (1855) wmk Large Crown perf 14		70·00
Z34	2d. blue (1858–69) ... From Plate Nos. 7, 8, 9, 12, 13, 14, 15.		15·00
Z35	2½d. rosy mauve (1875) (blued paper) ... From Plate Nos. 1, 2.		70·00
Z36	2½d. rosy mauve (1875–76) ... From Plate Nos. 1, 2, 3.		32·00
Z37	2½d. rosy mauve (Error of Lettering)		£2250
Z38	2½d. rosy mauve (1876–79) ... From Plate Nos. 3, 4, 5, 6, 7, 8, 9, 10, 11, 12, 13, 14, 15, 16, 17.		16·00
Z39	2½d. blue (1880–81) ... From Plate Nos. 17, 18, 19, 20.		10·00
Z40	2½d. blue (1881) (Plate Nos. 21, 22, 23) ... From		7·50
Z41	3d. carmine-rose (1862)		£120
Z42	3d. rose (1865) (Plate No. 4)		75·00
Z43	3d. rose (1867–73) ... From Plate Nos. 4, 5, 6, 7, 8, 9, 10.		24·00
Z44	3d. rose (1873–76) ... From Plate Nos. 11, 12, 14, 15, 16, 17, 18, 19, 20.		32·00
Z45	3d. rose (1881) (Plate Nos. 20, 21) ... From		£900
Z46	3d. on 3d. lilac (1883)		£475
Z47	4d. rose (or rose-carmine) (1857)		30·00
	a. Thick glazed paper		£120
Z48	4d. red (1862) (Plate Nos. 3, 4) ... From		32·00
Z49	4d. vermilion (1865–73) ... From Plate Nos. 7, 8, 9, 10, 11, 12, 13, 14.		16·00
Z50	4d. vermilion (1876) (Plate No. 15)		£180
Z51	4d. sage-green (1877) (Plate Nos. 15, 16) From		95·00
Z52	4d. grey-brown (1880) wmk Large Garter ... Plate No. 17.		£140
Z53	4d. grey-brown (1880) wmk Crown ... From Plate Nos. 17, 18.		48·00
Z54	6d. violet (1854), embossed		£2500
Z55	6d. lilac (1856)		42·00
	a. Thick paper		
Z56	6d. lilac (1862) (Plate Nos. 3, 4) ... From		35·00
Z57	6d. lilac (1865–67) (Plate Nos. 5, 6) ... From		28·00
Z58	6d. lilac (1865–67) (Wmk error)		£1200
Z59	6d. lilac (1867) (Plate No. 6)		32·00
Z60	6d. violet (1867–70) (Plate Nos. 6, 8, 9) ... From		25·00
Z61	6d. buff (1872–73) (Plate Nos. 11, 12) ... From		£100
Z62	6d. chestnut (1872) (Plate No. 11)		30·00
Z63	6d. grey (1873) (Plate No. 12)		75·00
Z64	6d. grey (1873–80) ... From Plate Nos. 13, 14, 15, 16, 17.		32·00
Z65	6d. grey (1881–82) (Plate Nos. 17, 18) ... From		60·00
Z66	6d. on 6d. lilac (1883)		£120
Z67	6d. orange (1876)		£375
Z68	9d. straw (1862)		£600

Z69	9d. bistre (1862)			£550
Z70	9d. straw (1865)			£550
Z71	9d. straw (1867)			£700
Z72	10d. red-brown (1867)			£130
Z73	1s. (1847), embossed			£2750
Z74	1s. green (1856)			70·00
Z75	1s. green (1856) (*thick paper*)			£275
Z76	1s. green (1862)			60·00
Z77	1s. green ("K" *variety*)			£2250
Z78	1s. green (1865) (Plate No. 4)			40·00
Z79	1s. green (1867–73) (Plate No. 4, 5, 6, 7)		*From*	27·00
Z80	1s. green (1873–77)		*From*	40·00
	Plate Nos. 8, 9, 10, 11, 12, 13.			
Z81	1s. orange-brown (1880) (Plate No. 13)			£250
Z82	1s. orange-brown (1881)		*From*	75·00
	Plate Nos. 13, 14.			
Z83	2s. blue (*shades*) (1867)		*From*	£140
Z84	2s. brown (1880)			£2500
Z85	5s. rose (1867–74) (Plate Nos. 1, 2)		*From*	£350
Z86	5s. rose (1882) (Plate No. 4), *blued paper*			£1700
Z87	5s. rose (1882) (Plate No. 4), *white paper*			£1400
Z88	10s. grey-green (1878)			£2500

1880.

Z89	½d. deep green	13·00
Z90	½d. pale green	13·00
Z91	1d. Venetian red	12·00
Z92	1½d. Venetian red	£400
Z93	2d. pale rose	38·00
Z94	2d. deep rose	38·00
Z95	5d. indigo	65·00

1881.

Z96	1d. lilac (14 *dots*)	24·00
Z97	1d. lilac (16 *dots*)	8·00

1883–84.

Z98	½d. slate-blue	14·00
Z99	1½d. lilac	
Z100	2d. lilac	85·00
Z101	2½d. lilac	12·00
Z102	3d. lilac	
Z103	4d. dull green	£160
Z104	5d. dull green	£140
Z105	6d. dull green	
Z106	9d. dull green	
Z107	1s. dull green	
Z108	5s. rose (*blued paper*)	£1600
Z109	5s. rose (*white paper*)	£950

POSTAL FISCALS

Z109a	1d. reddish lilac (Type F **8**) (1867) wmk Anchor.	
Z110	1d. purple (Type F **12**) (1871) wmk Anchor	£800
Z111	1d. purple (Type F **12**) (1881) wmk Orb	£600

PRICES FOR STAMPS ON COVER TO 1945	
Nos. 1/3	*from* × 4
Nos. 4/19	*from* × 5
Nos. 20/9	*from* × 6
No. 30	
Nos. 31/3	*from* × 4
Nos. 34/7	*from* × 10
Nos. 38/88	*from* × 4
Nos. 92/3	*from* × 5
Nos. 97/103	*from* × 3
Nos. 104/5	—
Nos. 106/20	*from* × 3
No. 121	—
Nos. 122/38	*from* × 3
Nos. 139/40	—
Nos. 141/72	*from* × 4
Nos. 173/209	*from* × 3
Nos. 210/31	*from* × 2
Nos. D1/10	*from* × 30
Nos. D11/20	*from* × 15

CROWN COLONY

PRINTERS. Nos. 1/156. Printed by De La Rue; typographed *except where otherwise stated.*

Type **1**

The first Government local post was established on 10 June 1853 and, as an experiment, mail was carried free of charge. During 1859 the Council of Government decided that a rate of ½d. per ½ ounce should be charged for this service and stamps in Type I were ordered for this purpose. Both the new rate and the stamps were introduced on 1 December 1860. Until 1 January 1885 the ½d. stamps were intended for the local service only; mail for abroad being handled by the British Post Office on Malta, using G.B. stamps.

Specialists now recognise 29 printings in shades of yellow and one in green during the period to 1884. These printings can be linked to the changes in watermark and perforation as follows:

Ptg 1—Blued paper without wmk. P 14.
Ptgs 2 and 3—White paper without wmk. P 14.
Ptgs 4 to 9, 11, 13 to 19, 22 to 24—Crown CC wmk. P 14.
Ptg 10—Crown CC wmk. P 12½ (rough).
Ptg 12—Crown CC wmk. P 12½ (clean-cut).
Ptgs 20 and 21—Crown CC wmk. P 14×12½.
Ptgs 25 to 28, 30—Crown CA wmk. P 14.
Ptg 29—In green (No. 20).

(Des E. Fuchs)

1860 (1 Dec)–**63.** No wmk. P 14.

(a) Blued paper.

1	½d. buff (1.12.60)	£950	£475

(b) Thin, hard white paper.

2	½d. brown-orange (11.61)	£900	£375
3	½d. buff (1.63)	£650	£325
	a. Pale buff	£650	£325

No. 1 is printed in fugitive ink. It is known imperforate but was not issued in that state (*Price £10000 unused*).

The printing on No. 2 gives a very blurred and muddy impression; on Nos. 3/3a the impression is clear.

Specks of carmine can often be detected with a magnifying glass on Nos. 2/3a, and also on No. 4. Examples also exist on which parts of the design are in pure rose, due to defective mixing of the ink.

1863–81. Wmk Crown CC.

(a) P 14.

4	½d. buff (6.63)		85·00	55·00
	w. Wmk inverted		£325	£325
	x. Wmk reversed		£850	
5	½d. bright orange (11.64)		£475	£140
	w. Wmk inverted		†	£650
6	½d. orange-brown (4.67)		£325	90·00
7	½d. dull orange (4.70)		£200	70·00
	w. Wmk inverted		†	£425
	x. Wmk reversed		£800	
8	½d. orange-buff (5.72)		£140	60·00
9	½d. golden yellow (aniline) (10.74)		£275	£325
10	½d. yellow-buff (9.75)		65·00	55·00
11	½d. pale buff (3.77)		£160	55·00
	w. Wmk inverted		†	£450
12	½d. bright orange-yellow (4.80)		£170	90·00
13	½d. yellow (4.81)		95·00	55·00
	w. Wmk inverted		†	£425

(b) P 12½ rough (No. 14) or clean-cut (No. 15).

14	½d. buff-brown (11.68)	£130	95·00
15	½d. yellow-orange (5.71)	£275	£160

(c) P 14×12½.

16	½d. yellow-buff (7.78)	£160	85·00
	w. Wmk inverted	†	£800
17	½d. yellow (2.78)	£180	90·00

Examples of No. 4 from the 1863 printing are on thin, surfaced paper; later printings in the same shade were on unsurfaced paper.

The ink used for No. 5 is mineral and, unlike that on No. 9, does not stain the paper.

Some variations of shade on No. 6 may be described as chestnut. The ink of No. 6 is clear and never muddy, although some examples are over-inked. Deeper shades of No. 4, with which examples of No. 6 might be confused, have muddy ink.

It is believed that there are no surviving pairs of the buff-brown imperforate between variety previously listed.

The Royal Collection contains an unused horizontal pair of the yellow-buff perforated 12½×14.

1882 (Mar)–**84.** Wmk Crown CA. P 14.

18	½d. orange-yellow	35·00	35·00
19	½d. red-orange (9.84)	17·00	48·00

2   3

4   5

1885 (1 Jan)–**90.** Wmk Crown CA. P 14.

20	**1**	½d. green	2·75	50
		w. Wmk inverted	£110	85·00
21	**2**	1d. rose	85·00	26·00
		w. Wmk inverted	£1300	
22		1d. carmine (*shades*) (1890)	5·00	35
		w. Wmk inverted	†	£1000
23	**3**	2d. grey	5·50	1·50
24	**4**	2½d. dull blue	55·00	2·50
25		2½d. bright blue	40·00	1·00
26		2½d. ultramarine	40·00	1·00
27	**3**	4d. brown	11·00	3·00
		a. Imperf (pair)	£5000	£5000
		w. Wmk inverted	£1300	
28		1s. violet	38·00	9·50
29		1s. pale violet (1890)	60·00	19·00
		w. Wmk inverted	£650	£250
20/8	Set of 6		90·00	14·00
20s/8s Optd "Specimen" Set of 6			£3500	

Although not valid for postage until 1 January 1885 these stamps were available at the G.P.O., Valletta from 27 December 1884.

Three unused examples of the ½d. green, No. 20, are known line perforated 12. It is believed that these originated from proof books, the stamp not being issued for use with this perforation.

The Royal Collection includes an example of the 1d. carmine printed on the gummed side.

1886 (1 Jan). Wmk Crown CC. P 14.

30	**5**	5s. rose	£110	80·00
		s. Optd "Specimen"	£600	
		w. Wmk inverted	£150	£110

6 Harbour of Valletta   **7** Gozo Fishing Boat   **8** Galley of Knights of St. John

9 Emblematic figure of Malta   **10** Shipwreck of St. Paul

(T **6/10** recess)

1899 (4 Feb)–**1901.** P 14.

(a) Wmk Crown CA (sideways* on ¼d).

31	**6**	¼d. brown (4.1.01)	4·50	2·50
		a. Red-brown	1·50	40
		w. Wmk Crown to left of CA	2·50	75
		x. Wmk sideways reversed	38·00	20·00
		y. Wmk Crown to left of CA and reversed	48·00	25·00
32	**7**	4½d. sepia	18·00	13·00
33	**8**	5d. vermilion	35·00	15·00
		x. Wmk reversed	£170	£170

(b) Wmk Crown CC.

34	**9**	2s.6d. olive-grey	40·00	12·00
35	**10**	10s. blue-black	90·00	65·00
		x. Wmk reversed	—	£450
		y. Wmk inverted and reversed	£425	£350
31/5 Set of 5			£170	95·00
31s/5s Optd "Specimen" Set of 5			£225	

The normal sideways watermark shows Crown to right of CA, as seen from the back of the stamp.

One Penny

(11)   12

1902 (4 July). Nos. 24 and 25 surch locally at Govt Ptg Office with T **11**.

36	1d. on 2½d. dull blue	1·00	1·40
	a. Surch double	£15000	£3750
	b. "One Pnney" (R. 9/2)	28·00	55·00
	ba. Surch double, with "One Pnney"	£30000	
	s. Optd "Specimen"	70·00	
37	1d. on 2½d. bright blue	1·00	1·75
	a. "One Pnney" (R. 9/2)	30·00	55·00

(Des E. Fuchs)

1903 (12 Mar)–**04.** Wmk Crown CA. P 14.

38	**12**	½d. green	8·50	85
39		1d. blackish brown and red (7.5.03)	15·00	40
40		2d. purple and grey	27·00	6·00
41		2½d. maroon and blue (9.03)	23·00	4·50
42		3d. grey and purple (26.3.03)	1·75	50
43		4d. blackish brown and brown (19.5.04)	26·00	16·00
44		1s. grey and violet (6.4.03)	19·00	7·00
38/44 Set of 7			£110	32·00
38s/44s Optd "Specimen" Set of 7			£150	

1904–14. Wmk Mult Crown CA (sideways* on ¼d.). P 14.

45	**6**	¼d. red-brown (10.10.05)	6·00	80
		a. Deep brown (2.4.10†)	3·00	10
		aw. Wmk Crown to left of CA	8·50	1·50
		ax. Wmk reversed		
		ay. Wmk Crown to left of CA and reversed		
47	**12**	½d. green (6.11.04)	5·00	30
		aw. Wmk inverted		
		b. Deep green (1909)	4·50	10
		bw. Wmk inverted		
48		1d. black and red (24.4.05)	19·00	20
49		1d. red (2.4.07)	2·50	10
50		2d. purple and grey (22.2.05)	10·00	2·25
51		2d. grey (4.10.11)	3·25	5·50
52		2½d. maroon and blue (8.10.04)	21·00	60
53		2½d. bright blue (15.1.11)	5·50	3·25
54		4d. black and brown (1.4.06)	11·00	5·50
		w. Wmk inverted		
55		4d. black and red/*yellow* (21.11.11)	4·00	3·50
57	**7**	4½d. brown (27.2.05)	28·00	5·50
		w. Wmk inverted	£250	£200
58		4½d. orange (6.3.12†)	4·50	3·50
59	**8**	5d. vermilion (20.2.05)	4·25	3·50
60		5d. pale sage-green (1909)	4·25	3·50
		a. Deep sage-green (1914)	11·00	14·00
61		1s. grey and violet (14.12.04)	50·00	2·00
62		1s. black/*green* (15.3.11)	7·50	3·25
63		5s. green and red/*yellow* (22.3.11)	65·00	75·00
45/63 Set of 17			£250	£100
45as, 47bs, 49s, 51s, 53s, 55s, 58s, 60s, 62s/3s Optd "Specimen" Set of 10			£375	

The normal sideways watermark shows Crown to right of CA, as seen from the back of the stamp.

†These are the earliest known dates of use.

13	14	15

1914–21. *Ordinary paper (¼d. to 2½d., 2s.6d.) or chalk-surfaced paper (others).* Wmk Mult Crown CA. P 14.

69	13	¼d. brown (2.1.14)	1·00	10
		a. Deep brown (1919)	1·75	60
		x. Wmk reversed	†	£600
71		½d. green (20.1.14)	2·25	30
		aa. Wmk sideways	†	£8000
		a. Deep green (1919)	3·25	1·00
		aw. Wmk inverted	†	£250
73		1d. carmine-red (15.4.14)	1·50	10
		a. Scarlet (1915)	1·50	40
		w. Wmk inverted	†	£250
75		2d. grey (12.8.14)	9·50	4·00
		aw. Wmk inverted	†	£600
		b. Deep slate (1919)	9·00	13·00
77		2½d. bright blue (11.3.14)	2·25	50
		w. Wmk inverted	†	£150
78	14	3d. purple/*yellow* (1.5.20)	2·50	10·00
		a. On orange-buff	60·00	42·00
79	6	4d. black (21.8.15)	15·00	4·00
		a. Grey-black (28.10.16)	27·00	8·00
80	13	6d. dull and bright purple (10.3.14)	11·00	18·00
		a. Dull purple and magenta (1918)	15·00	18·00
		w. Wmk inverted		
81	14	1s. black/*emerald (white back)* (2.1.14)	14·00	27·00
		a. On green, green back (1915)	12·00	17·00
		ab. Wmk sideways	†	£2000
		as. Optd "Specimen"	50·00	
		b. On blue-green, olive back (1918)	19·00	23·00
		c. On emerald surface (1920)	8·50	24·00
		d. On emerald back (1921)	32·00	70·00
86	15	2s. purple and bright blue/*blue* (15.4.14)	50·00	30·00
		a. Break in scroll	£325	
		b. Broken crown and scroll	£350	
		c. Nick in top right scroll	£325	
		d. Dull purple and blue/blue (1921)	85·00	60·00
		da. Break in scroll	£375	
		db. Broken crown and scroll	£425	
		de. Break in lines below left scroll	£375	
		df. Damaged leaf at bottom right	£375	
87	9	2s.6d. olive-green (1914)	60·00	80·00
		a. Olive-grey (1920)	70·00	£100
88	15	5s. green and red/*yellow* (21.3.17)	90·00	£100
		a. Break in scroll	£425	
		b. Broken crown and scroll	£475	
		e. Break in lines below left scroll	£425	
		f. Damaged leaf at bottom right	£425	
69/88		Set of 12	£225	£225
69s/88s		(ex 2s.6d.) Optd "Specimen" Set of 11	£450	

The design of Nos. 79/*a* differs in various details from that of Type **6**. We have only seen one copy of No. 71aa; it is in used condition.

A 3d. purple on yellow on white back, Type **14**, was prepared for use but not issued. It exists overprinted "Specimen" (*Price* £250).

An example of the 2s.6d. olive-grey with bottom margin attached exists with the "A" omitted from "CA" in the watermark on the margin.

For illustrations of the varieties on Nos. 86 and 88 see above No. 51*b* of Bermuda.

WAR TAX
(16)

17	18

1917–18. *Optd with T* **16** *by De La Rue.*

92	13	½d. deep green (14.12.17*)	1·75	15
		w. Wmk inverted	£450	
		y. Wmk inverted and reversed	£750	
93	12	3d. grey and purple (15.2.18*)	1·75	9·00
92s/3s		Optd "Specimen" Set of 2	£140	

*These are the earliest known dates of use.

(T **17** recess)

1919 (6 Mar). Wmk Mult Crown CA. P 14.

96	17	10s. black	£2750	£3750
		s. Optd "Specimen"	£800	

Dark flaw on scroll (R. 2/4 1st state)   Lines omitted from scroll (R. 2/4 2nd state)

1921 (16 Feb)–**22.** *Chalk-surfaced paper (6d., 2s.) or ordinary paper (others).* Wmk Mult Script CA. P 14.

97	13	¼d. brown (12.1.22)	3·50	29·00
98		½d. green (19.1.22)	4·00	21·00
99		1d. scarlet (24.12.21)	3·75	1·75
		w. Wmk inverted	£600	£225
100	18	2d. grey	5·50	1·75
101	13	2½d. bright blue (15.1.22)	4·25	30·00
102		6d. dull purple & brt purple (19.1.22)	29·00	70·00
103	15	2s. purple and blue/*blue* (19.1.22)	65·00	£200
		a. Break in scroll	£275	£550
		b. Broken crown and scroll	£275	
		c. Dark flaw on scroll	£2000	
		d. Lines omitted from scroll	£425	
		e. Break in lines below left scroll	£275	
		f. Damaged leaf at bottom right	£275	
104	17	10s. black (19.1.22)	£350	£700
97/104		Set of 8	£425	£950
97s/104s		Optd "Specimen" Set of 8	£425	

For illustrations of other varieties on No. 103 see above No. 51*b* of Bermuda.

Examples of all values are known showing a forged G.P.O. Malta postmark dated "MY 10 22".

SELF-GOVERNMENT	SELF-GOVERNMENT
(19)	**(20)**

1922 (12 Jan–Apr). *Optd with T* **19** *or T* **20** *(large stamps), at Govt Printing Office, Valletta.*

(a) On No. 35. Wmk Crown CC.

105	10	10s. blue-black (R.)	£190	£375

(b) On Nos. 71, 77, 78a, 80, 81d, 86c, 87a and 88. Wmk Mult Crown CA.

106	13	½d. green	1·00	1·75
		w. Wmk inverted	£100	
107		2½d. bright blue	10·00	32·00
108	14	3d. purple/*orange-buff*	3·50	19·00
109	13	6d. dull and bright purple	3·00	18·00
		x. Wmk reversed	†	£850
110	14	1s. black/*emerald*	3·75	18·00
111	15	2s. purple and blue/*blue* (R.)	£250	£475
		a. Break in scroll	£750	
		b. Broken crown and scroll	£750	
		e. Break in lines below left scroll	£750	
		f. Damaged leaf at bottom right	£750	
112	9	2s.6d. olive-grey	24·00	45·00
		a. "C" of "CA" missing from wmk.	£900	
113	15	5s. green and red/*yellow*	50·00	80·00
		a. Break in scroll	£325	
		b. Broken crown and scroll	£325	
		c. Lines omitted from scroll	£325	
		e. Break in lines below left scroll	£325	
		f. Damaged leaf at bottom right	£325	
106/13		Set of 8	£300	£600

(c) On Nos. 97/104. Wmk Mult Script CA.

114	13	¼d. brown	30	75
		w. Wmk inverted		
115		½d. green (29.4)	2·50	6·50
116		1d. scarlet	1·00	20
117	18	2d. grey	2·75	45
118	13	2½d. bright blue (15.1)	1·10	45
119		6d. dull and bright purple (19.4)	14·00	38·00
120	15	2s. purple and blue/*blue* (R.) (25.1)	42·00	85·00
		a. Break in scroll	£250	
		b. Broken crown and scroll	£250	
		c. Lines omitted from scroll	£350	
		e. Break in lines below left scroll	£250	
		f. Damaged leaf at bottom right	£250	
121	17	10s. black (R.) (9.3)	£140	£225
114/21		Set of 8	£180	£325

Examples of all values are known showing a forged G.P.O. Malta postmark dated "MY 10 22".

3d.	1/-

One Farthing
(21)   **22**   **23**

1922 (15 Apr). *No. 100 surch with T* **21**, *at Govt Printing Office, Valletta.*

122	18	¼d. on 2d. grey	85	30

(Des C. Dingli (*T* **22**) and G. Vella (**23**))

1922 (1 Aug)–**26.** Wmk Mult Script CA (sideways* on *T* **22**, except No. 140). P 14.

(a) Typo. Chalk-surfaced paper.

123	22	¼d. brown (22.8.22)	2·50	60
		a. Chocolate-brown	3·75	70
		w. Wmk Crown to right of CA	—	70·00
124		½d. green	2·50	15
		w. Wmk Crown to right of CA	—	70·00
125		1d. orange and purple	3·50	20
		w. Wmk Crown to right of CA	—	50·00
126		1d. bright violet (25.4.24)	3·50	80
127		1½d. brown-red (1.10.23)	4·50	15
128		2d. bistre-brown & turquoise (28.8.22)	2·75	1·25
		w. Wmk Crown to right of CA	—	95·00
129		2½d. ultramarine (16.2.26)	3·50	8·50

130		3d. cobalt (28.8.22)	4·25	1·50
		a. Bright ultramarine	3·75	1·50
131		3d. black/*yellow* (16.2.26)	3·25	15·00
132		4d. yellow and bright blue (28.8.22)	2·25	3·00
		w. Wmk Crown to right of CA	£160	
133		6d. olive-green and reddish violet	3·25	2·50
134	23	1s. indigo and sepia	8·00	2·50
135		2s. brown and blue	12·00	12·00
136		2s.6d. brt magenta & black (28.8.22)	11·00	15·00
137		5s. orange-yell & brt ultram (28.8.22)	21·00	45·00
138		10s. slate-grey and brown (28.8.22)	60·00	£160

(b) Recess.

139	22	£1 black and carmine-red (wmk sideways) (28.8.22)	£120	£300
140		£1 black and bright carmine (wmk upright) (14.5.25)	£100	£300
123/40		Set of 17	£200	£500
123s/39s		Optd "Specimen" Set of 17	£500	

*The normal sideways watermark shows Crown to left of CA, *as seen from the back of the stamp.*

Two pence halfpenny   POSTAGE
(24)   **(25)**

1925. *Surch with T* **24**, *at Govt Printing Office, Valletta.*

141	22	2½d. on 3d. cobalt (3 Dec)	1·75	3·75
142		2½d. on 3d. bright ultramarine (9 Dec)	1·75	3·50

1926 (1 Apr). *Optd with T* **25** *at Govt Printing Office, Valletta.*

143	22	¼d. brown	70	4·00
144		½d. green	70	15
		w. Wmk Crown to right of CA	80·00	
145		1d. bright violet	1·00	25
146		1½d. brown-red	1·25	60
147		2d. bistre-brown and turquoise	75	1·40
148		2½d. ultramarine	1·25	1·00
149		3d. black/*yellow*	75	80
		a. Opt inverted	£170	£475
150		4d. yellow and bright blue	8·50	20·00
		w. Wmk Crown to right of CA	£150	
151		6d. olive-green and violet	2·75	4·00
152	23	1s. indigo and sepia	5·50	13·00
153		2s. brown and blue	50·00	£140
154		2s.6d. bright magenta and black	15·00	40·00
155		5s. orange-yellow & brt ultramarine	9·00	40·00
156		10s. slate-grey and brown	7·00	18·00
143/56		Set of 14	95·00	£250

26	27 Valletta Harbour

28 St. Publius	29 Mdina (Notabile)

30 Gozo fishing boat	31 Neptune

32 Neolithic temple, Mnajdra	33 St. Paul

(*T* **26** typo, others recess Waterlow)

1926 (6 Apr)–**27.** *T* **26/33.** Inscr "POSTAGE". Wmk Mult Script CA. P 15×14 (*T* **26**) or 12½ (others).

157	26	¼d. brown	80	15
158		½d. yellow-green (5.8.26)	60	15
		a. Printed on the gummed side	£900	
		w. Wmk inverted	†	£650
159		1d. rose-red (1.4.27)	3·00	1·00
160		1½d. chestnut (7.10.26)	2·00	10
161		2d. greenish grey (1.4.27)	4·50	10·00
162		2½d. blue (1.4.27)	4·50	1·50
162a		3d. violet (1.4.27)	4·25	3·00
163		4d. black and red	3·25	11·00
164		4½d. lavender and ochre	3·50	3·25
165		6d. violet and scarlet (5.5.26)	4·25	4·25

166	27	1s. black	6·50	5·50
167	28	1s.6d. black and green	6·50	15·00
168	29	2s. black and purple	6·50	17·00
169	30	2s.6d. black and vermilion	15·00	48·00
170	31	3s. black and blue	17·00	30·00
171	32	5s. black and green (5.5.26)	22·00	60·00
172	33	10s. black and carmine (9.2.27)	55·00	£100
157/72 *Set of* 17			£140	£275
157s/72s Optd "Specimen" *Set of* 17				£325

POSTAGE

| AIR MAIL (34) | AND REVENUE (35) | POSTAGE AND REVENUE. (36) |

1928 (1 Apr). *Air. Optd with T* **34**.

| 173 | 26 | 6d. violet and scarlet | 1·75 | 1·00 |

1928 (1 Oct–5 Dec). *As Nos.* 157/72, *optd.*

174	35	¼d. brown	1·50	10
175		½d. yellow-green	1·50	10
176		1d. rose-red	1·75	3·25
177		1d. chestnut (5.12.28)	4·50	10
178		1½d. chestnut	2·00	85
179		1½d. rose-red (5.12.28)	4·25	10
180		2d. greeenish grey	4·25	9·00
181		2½d. blue	2·00	10
182		3d. violet	2·00	80
183		4d. black and red	2·00	1·75
184		4½d. lavender and ochre	2·25	1·00
185		6d. violet and scarlet	2·25	1·50
186	36	1s. black (R.)	5·50	2·50
187		1s.6d. black and green (R.)	7·00	9·50
188		2s. black and purple (R.)	24·00	55·00
189		2s.6d. black and vermilion (R.)	17·00	21·00
190		3s. black and blue (R.)	19·00	24·00
191		5s. black and green (R.)	30·00	65·00
192		10s. black and carmine (R.)	60·00	90·00
174/92 *Set of* 19			£170	£250
174s/92s Optd "Specimen" *Set of* 19				£350

1930 (20 Oct). *As Nos.* 157/172, *but inscr* "POSTAGE (&) REVENUE".

193		¼d. brown	60	10
194		½d. yellow-green	60	10
195		1d. chestnut	60	10
196		1½d. rose-red	70	10
197		2d. greenish grey	1·25	50
198		2½d. blue	2·00	10
199		3d. violet	1·50	20
200		4d. black and red	1·25	4·00
201		4½d. lavender and ochre	3·25	1·25
202		6d. violet and scarlet	2·75	1·25
203		1s. black	10·00	14·00
204		1s.6d. black and green	8·50	20·00
205		2s. black and purple	10·00	21·00
206		2s.6d. black and vermilion	17·00	48·00
207		3s. black and blue	29·00	55·00
208		5s. black and green	38·00	65·00
209		10s. black and carmine	85·00	£170
193/209 *Set of* 17			£190	£350
193s/209s Perf "Specimen" *Set of* 17				£350

1935 (6 May). *Silver Jubilee. As Nos.* 91/4 *of Antigua, but printed by B.W.* P 11×12.

210		½d. black and green	50	70
		a. Extra flagstaff	22·00	38·00
		b. Short extra flagstaff	45·00	
		c. Lightning conductor	35·00	
211		2½d. brown and deep blue	2·50	4·50
		a. Extra flagstaff	£130	£160
		b. Short extra flagstaff	£180	
		c. Lightning conductor	£140	
212		6d. light blue and olive-green	7·00	6·00
		a. Extra flagstaff	£180	£225
		b. Short extra flagstaff	£300	
		c. Lightning conductor	£170	
213		1s. slate and purple	12·00	18·00
		a. Extra flagstaff	£425	£475
		b. Short extra flagstaff	£375	
		c. Lightning conductor	£300	
210/13 *Set of* 4			20·00	26·00
210s/13s Perf "Specimen" *Set of* 4				£160

For illustrations of plate varieties see Omnibus section following Zanzibar.

Sheets from the second printing of the ½d., 6d. and 1s. in November 1935 had the extra flagstaff partially erased from the stamp with a sharp point.

1937 (12 May). *Coronation. As Nos.* 95/7 *of Antigua, but printed by D.L.R.* P 14.

214		½d. green	10	20
215		1½d. scarlet	1·25	65
		a. Brown-lake	£600	£600
216		2½d. bright blue	1·00	80
214/16 *Set of* 3			2·00	1·50
214s/16s Perf "Specimen" *Set of* 3				80·00

37 Grand Harbour, Valletta

38 H.M.S. *St. Angelo*

39 Verdala Palace

40 Hypogeum, Hal Saflieni

41 Victoria and Citadel, Gozo

42 De L'Isle Adam entering Mdina

43 St. John's Co-Cathedral

44 Ruins at Mnajdra

45 Statue of Manoel de Vilhena

46 Maltese girl wearing faldetta

47 St. Publius

48 Mdina Cathedral

49 Statue of Neptune

50 Palace Square, Valletta

51 St. Paul

Broken cross (Right pane R. 5/7)

Extra windows (R. 2/7) (corrected in 1945)

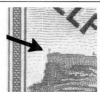

Flag on citadel (R. 5/8)

Damaged value tablet (R. 4/9)

Semaphore flaw (R. 2/7)

(Recess Waterlow)

1938 (17 Feb*)–**43**. *T* **37/51**. *Wmk Mult Script CA* (*sideways on No.* 217). P 12½.

217	37	¼d. brown	10	10
218	38	½d. green	2·25	30
218a		½d. red-brown (8.3.43)	55	30
219	39	1d. red-brown	4·25	40
219a		1d. green (8.3.43)	60	10
220	40	1½d. scarlet	1·00	30
		a. Broken cross	£120	60·00
220b		1½d. slate-black (8.3.43)	30	15
		ba. Broken cross	65·00	50·00
221	41	2d. slate-black	40	2·00
		a. Extra windows	50·00	
221b		2d. scarlet (8.3.43)	40	30
		ba. Extra windows	50·00	
		bb. Flag on citadel	55·00	
222	42	2½d. greyish blue	1·25	60
222a		2½d. dull violet (8.3.43)	60	10
223	43	3d. dull violet	1·00	80
223a		3d. blue (8.3.43)	30	20
224	44	4½d. olive-green and yellow-brown	50	30
225	45	6d. olive-green and scarlet	1·25	30
226	46	1s. black	1·25	30
227	47	1s.6d. black and olive-green	7·00	4·00
228	48	2s. green and deep blue	4·50	4·00
229	49	2s.6d. black and scarlet	8·50	5·50
		a. Damaged value tablet	£225	£140
230	50	5s. black and green	4·50	6·50
		a. Semaphore flaw	75·00	
231	51	10s. black and carmine	17·00	15·00
217/31 *Set of* 21			50·00	38·00
217s/31s Perf "Specimen" *Set of* 21				£400

*This is the local date of issue but the stamps were released in London on 15 February.

1946 (3 Dec). *Victory. As Nos.* 110/11 *of Antigua, but inscr* "MALTA" *between Maltese Cross and George Cross.*

232		1d. green	15	10
		w. Wmk inverted	£700	
233		3d. blue	40	1·00
232s/3s Perf "Specimen" *Set of* 2			70·00	

SELF-GOVERNMENT

SELF-GOVERNMENT 1947

(52)

"NT" joined (R. 4/10)

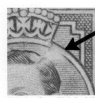

Halation flaw (Pl 2 R. 2/5) (ptg of 8 Jan 1953)

Cracked plate (Pl 2 R. 5/1) (ptg of 8 Jan 1953)

(Optd by Waterlow)

1948 (25 Nov)–**53**. *New Constitution. As Nos.* 217/31 *but optd as T* **52**; *reading up on ½d. and 5s., down on other values, and smaller on ¼d. value.*

234	37	¼d. brown	30	20
235	38	½d. red-brown	30	10
		a. "NT" joined	19·00	
236	39	1d. green	30	10
236a		1d. grey (R.) (8.1.53)	30	10
237	40	1½d. blue-black (R.)	1·25	10
		a. Broken cross	85·00	40·00
237b		1½d. green (8.1.53)	30	10
		ba. Albino opt	†	£12000
238	41	2d. scarlet	1·25	10
		a. Extra windows	75·00	
		b. Flag on citadel	65·00	
238c		2d. yellow-ochre (8.1.53)	30	10
		ca. Halation flaw	£130	
		cc. Cracked plate	£120	
239	42	2½d. dull violet (R.)	80	10
239a		2½d. scarlet-vermilion (8.1.53)	50	1·50

240	**43**	3d. blue (R.)	2·00	15
240a		3d. dull violet (R.) (8.1.53)	50	15
241	**44**	4½d. olive-green and yellow-brown...	2·00	1·50
241a		4½d. olive-grn and dp ultram (R.) (8.1.53)	50	90
242	**45**	6d. olive-green and scarlet	3·25	15
243	**46**	1s. black	3·25	40
244	**47**	1s.6d. black and olive-green	2·50	50
245	**48**	2s. green and deep blue (R.)	5·00	2·50
246	**49**	2s.6d. black and scarlet	12·00	2·50
		a. Damaged value tablet	£750	
247	**50**	5s. black and green (R.)	21·00	3·50
		a. "NT" joined	£225	£120
		b. Semaphore flaw	—	£2500
248	**51**	10s. black and carmine	21·00	22·00
234/48		Set of 21	70·00	32·00

1949 (4 Jan). *Royal Silver Wedding. As Nos. 112/13 of Antigua, but inscr "MALTA" between Maltese Cross and George Cross and with £1 ptd in recess.*

249		1d. green	50	10
250		£1 indigo	38·00	35·00

1949 (10 Oct). *75th Anniv of U.P.U. As Nos. 114/17 of Antigua, but inscr "MALTA" in recess.*

251		2½d. violet	30	10
252		3d. deep blue	3·00	1·00
253		6d. carmine-red	60	1·00
254		1s. blue-black	60	2·50
251/4		Set of 4	4·00	4·25

53 Queen Elizabeth II when Princess

54 "Our Lady of Mount Carmel" (attrib Palladino)

(*T* **53/4**. Recess B.W.)

1950 (1 Dec). *Visit of Princess Elizabeth to Malta.* Wmk Mult Script CA. P 12×11½.

255	**53**	1d. green	10	15
256		3d. blue	20	20
257		1s. black	65	1·25
255/7		Set of 3	80	1·40

1951 (12 July). *Seventh Centenary of the Scapular.* Wmk Mult Script CA. P 12×11½.

258	**54**	1d. green	15	20
259		3d. violet	50	10
260		1s. black	1·10	1·10
258/60		Set of 3	1·60	1·25

POSTAGE DUE STAMPS

D 1   **D 2**

1925 (16 Apr). *Typeset by Govt Printing Office, Valletta. Imperf.*

D1	**D 1**	½d. black	1·25	7·50
		a. Tête-bêche (horiz pair)	5·00	20·00
D2		1d. black	3·25	3·00
		a. Tête-bêche (horiz pair)	10·00	12·00
D3		1½d. black	3·00	3·75
		a. Tête-bêche (horiz pair)	10·00	15·00
D4		2d. black	8·00	15·00
		a. Tête-bêche (horiz pair)	18·00	40·00
D5		2½d. black	2·75	2·75
		a. "2" of "½" omitted	£850	£1200
		b. Tête-bêche (horiz pair)	12·00	15·00
D6		3d. black/*grey*	9·00	15·00
		a. Tête-bêche (horiz pair)	30·00	48·00
D7		4d. black/*buff*	5·00	9·50
		a. Tête-bêche (horiz pair)	17·00	38·00
D8		6d. black/*buff*	5·00	18·00
		a. Tête-bêche (horiz pair)	17·00	50·00
D9		1s. black/*buff*	7·50	22·00
		a. Tête-bêche (horiz pair)	25·00	60·00
D10		1s.6d. black/*buff*	14·00	55·00
		a. Tête-bêche (horiz pair)	40·00	£140
D1/10		Set of 10	50·00	£130

Nos. D1/10 were each issued in sheets containing 4 panes (6×7) printed separately, the impressions in the two right-hand panes being inverted. Fourteen horizontal *tête-bêche* pairs occur from the junction of the left and right-hand panes.

No. D5a occurred on R. 4/4 of the last 2½d. pane position to be printed. Forgeries exist, but can be detected by comparison with a normal example under ultra-violet light. They are often found in pair with normal, showing forged cancellations of "VALLETTA AP20 25" or "G.P.O MY 7 25".

(Typo B.W.)

1925 (20 July). Wmk Mult Script CA (sideways). P 12.

D11	**D 2**	½d. green	1·25	60
D12		1d. violet	1·25	45
D13		1½d. brown	1·50	80
D14		2d. grey	11·00	1·00
D15		2½d. orange	2·00	1·25
		x. Wmk reversed	85·00	
D16		3d. blue	3·50	4·50
D17		4d. olive-green	12·00	16·00
D18		6d. purple	3·00	4·50

D19		1s. black	6·50	13·00
D20		1s.6d. carmine	8·50	30·00
D11/20		Set of 10	45·00	60·00
D11s/20s		Optd "Specimen" Set of 10	£200	

Mauritius

GREAT BRITAIN STAMPS USED IN MAURITIUS. We no longer list the Great Britain stamps with obliteration "B 53" as there is no evidence that British stamps were available from the Mauritius Post Office

See under SEYCHELLES for stamps of Mauritius used at Victoria with "B 64" cancellations between 1861 and 1890.

A similar "B 65" cancellation was used on the island of Rodrigues, a dependency of Mauritius, from 11 December 1861 onwards.

PRICES FOR STAMPS ON COVER TO 1945	
Nos. 1/5	*from* × 2
Nos. 6/9	*from* × 4
Nos. 10/15	*from* × 4
Nos. 16/25	*from* × 5
Nos. 26/9	*from* × 3
Nos. 30/1	—
Nos. 32/5	*from* × 4
Nos. 36/44	*from* × 5
Nos. 46/72	*from* × 3
Nos. 76/82	*from* × 5
Nos. 83/91	*from* × 4
Nos. 92/100	*from* × 3
Nos. 101/11	*from* × 3
Nos. 117/24	*from* × 8
Nos. 127/32	*from* × 4
No. 133	*from* × 7
Nos. 134/5	*from* × 10
No. 136	*from* × 8
Nos. 137/56	*from* × 6
Nos. 157/63	*from* × 5
Nos. 164/221	*from* × 3
No. 222	—
Nos. 223/41	*from* × 3
Nos. 242/4	*from* × 10
Nos. 245/8	*from* × 3
Nos. 249/63	*from* × 2
Nos. E1/6	*from* × 10
Nos. D1/7	*from* × 40
Nos. R1/3	*from* × 15

CROWN COLONY

Nos. 1/25b and 36/44 were printed in Mauritius.

1 ("POST OFFICE")   **2** ("POST PAID")

(Engraved on copper by J. O. Barnard)

1847 (21 Sept). *Head of Queen on groundwork of diagonal and perpendicular lines. Imperf.*

1	**1**	1d. orange-red	—	£450000
2		2d. deep blue	—	£550000

A single plate contained one example of each value.

It is generally agreed that fifteen examples of No. 1 have survived (including two unused) and twelve of No. 2 (including four unused). Most are now in permanent museum collections.

NOTE. Our prices for early Mauritius are for stamps in very fine condition. Exceptional copies are worth more, poorer copies considerably less.

(Engraved on copper by J. O. Barnard)

1848 (June)–*59. Imperf.*

A. Earliest impressions. Design deep, sharp and clear. Diagonal lines predominate. Thick paper (Period of use: 1d. 1853–54, 2d. 1848–49).

3	**2**	1d. orange-vermilion/*yellowish*	£38000	£13000
4		2d. indigo-blue/*grey to bluish*	£32000	£15000
		a. "PENOE" for "PENCE" (R. 3/1)	£65000	£23000
5		2d. deep blue/*grey to bluish*	£32000	£15000
		a. "PENOE" for "PENCE" (R. 3/1)	£65000	£26000

B. Early impressions. Design sharp and clear but some lines slightly weakened. Paper not so thick, grey to yellowish white or bluish (Period of use: 1d. 1853–55, 2d. 1849–54).

6	**2**	1d. vermilion	£17000	£5500
7		1d. orange-vermilion	£18000	£5000
8		2d. blue	£19000	£6000
		a. "PENOE" for "PENCE" (R. 3/1)	£30000	£9500
9		2d. deep blue	£23000	£6500

C. Intermediate impressions. White patches appear where design has worn. Paper yellowish white, grey or bluish, of poorish quality (Period of use: 1d and 2d. 1854–57).

10	**2**	1d. bright vermilion	£10000	£2000
11		1d. dull vermilion	£10000	£2000
12		1d. red	£10000	£2000
13		2d. deep blue	£14000	£3000
14		2d. blue	£10000	£2250
		a. "PENOE" for "PENCE" (R. 3/1)	*from* £17000	£4750
15		2d. light blue	£10000	£2250

D. Worn impressions. Much of design worn away but some diagonal lines distinct. Paper yellowish, grey or bluish, of poorish quality (Period of use: 1d. 1857–59, 2d. 1855–58).

16	**2**	1d. red/*yellowish or grey*	£4000	£500
17		1d. red-brown/*yellowish or grey*	£4000	£500
18		1d. red/*bluish*	£3000	£450
		a. Doubly printed		
19		1d. red-brown/*bluish*	£3000	£450
20		2d. blue (*shades*)/*yellowish or grey*	£4500	£950
		a. "PENOE" for "PENCE" (R. 3/1)	*from*	£1600
21		2d. grey-blue/*yellowish or grey*	£4750	£900
22		2d. blue (*shades*)/*bluish*	£4500	£900
		a. Doubly printed		

E. Latest impressions. Almost none of design showing except part of Queen's head and frame. Paper yellowish, grey or bluish, of poorish quality (Period of use: 1d. 1859, 2d. 1856–58).

23	**2**	1d. red	£2500	£425
24		1d. red-brown	£2500	£425
25		2d. grey-blue/*bluish*	£3250	£650
		a. "PENOE" for "PENCE" (R. 3/1)	£5500	£1100

Earliest known use of the 2d. value is on 19 June 1848, but the 1d. value is not known used before 27 September 1853.

There were separate plates for the 1d. and 2d. values, each of 12 (3×4).

3   **(4)**   **5**

(Eng G. Fairman. Recess P.B.)

1858*. Surch with *T* **4**. *Imperf.*

26	**3**	4d. green	£1100	£425

*Although originally gazetted for use from 8 April 1854, research into the archives indicates that No. 26 was not actually issued until 1858, when the stamps were mentioned in an ordinance of 30 April. The earliest dated postmark known is 27 March 1858.

PERKINS BACON "CANCELLED". For notes on these handstamps, showing "CANCELLED" between horizontal bars forming an oval, see Catalogue Introduction.

1858–62. *No value expressed. Imperf.*

27	**3**	(4d.) green	£450	£200
28		(6d.) vermilion	38·00	70·00
29		(9d.) dull magenta (1859)	£650	£200
		a. Reissued as (1d.) value (11.62).	†	£160

Prepared for use but not issued.

30	**3**	(No value), red-brown	19·00	
31		(No value), blue (H/S "CANCELLED" in oval £9500)	5·50	

Use of the dull magenta as a 1d. value can be confirmed by the presence of the "B 53" cancellation which was first introduced in 1861.

Remainders of Nos. 30/1, overprinted "L.P.E. 1890" in red, were perforated at the London Philatelic Exhibition and sold as souvenirs.

(Recess P.B.)

1859–61. *Imperf.*

32	**5**	6d. bl (H/S "CANCELLED" in oval £12000)	£600	42·00
33		6d. dull purple-slate (1861)	24·00	48·00
34		1s. vermilion (H/S "CANCELLED" in oval £7500)	£2250	45·00
35		1s. yellow-green (1861)	£550	£120

The 1859 printings had the colours transposed by mistake.

6   **7**   **8**

(Engraved on copper by J. Lapirot)

1859 (Mar–Nov). Imperf.

(a) Early impressions.

36	**6**	2d. deep blue	£7500	£2000
37		2d. blue	£6000	£1800

(b) Intermediate prints. Lines of background, etc, partly worn away (July).

38	**6**	2d. blue	£3750	£750

(c) Worn impressions, bluish-paper (Oct).

39	**6**	2d. blue	£2000	£475

(d) Retouched impression (Nov).

39a	**6**	2d. blue	†	—
		ab. "MAURITUIS" (R. 2/4)	†	£100000
		ac. "MAURITUS" (R. 3/1)	†	£100000

Nos. 36/9a were printed from a plate of 12 (4×3).

Research by Mr A. Rudge has established the existence of an initial state of the plate, before the lines were deepened to produce the "Early impression". Only one stamp from this state has so far been identified.

The plate became worn through use, and was eventually extensively re-engraved. Only two pairs (one on cover) have been recorded from this retouched impression. The errors made in the re-engraving of the inscriptions probably resulted in it being withdrawn from use.

(1848 plate re-engraved by R. Sherwin)

1859 (Oct). *Bluish paper. Imperf.*

40	**7**	2d. deep blue	£110000	£4250

The 1d. plate was also re-engraved, but was not put into use. Reprints

in black were made in 1877 from both 1d. and 2d. re-engraved plates. Coloured autotype illustrations were prepared from these reprints and 600 were included in the R.P.S.L. handbook on *British Africa* in 1900. Further reprints in black were made in 1911 after the plates had been presented to the R.P.S.L. and defaced.

(Lithographed by L. A. Dardenne)

1859 (12 Dec). *White laid paper. Imperf.*

41	**8**	1d. deep red	£7000	£1500
41a		1d. red	£5000	£1000
42		1d. dull vermilion	£4000	£850
43		2d. slate-blue	£4250	£800
43a		2d. blue	£2500	£600
44		2d. pale blue	£2250	£475
		a. Heavy retouch on neck	—	£1300
		b. Retouched below "TWO"	—	£700

The neck retouch shows a prominent curved white line running from the base of the chignon to the nape of the neck. No. 44b shows several diagonal lines in the margin below "TWO".

| 9 | 10 |

(Typo D.L.R.)

1860 (7 Apr)–**63**. *No wmk. P 14.*

46	**9**	1d. purple-brown	£225	24·00
47		2d. blue	£250	42·00
48		4d. rose	£250	28·00
49		6d. green (1862)	£700	£130
50		6d. slate (1863)	£275	95·00
51		9d. dull purple	£130	40·00
52		1s. buff (1862)	£275	85·00
53		1s. green (1863)	£600	£160

1862. *Intermediate perf 14 to 16.*

54	**5**	6d. slate	23·00	70·00
		Imperf between (horiz pair)	£6000	
55		1s. deep green	£2000	£325

1863–**72**. *Wmk Crown CC. P 14.*

56	**9**	1d. purple-brown	70·00	13·00
		w. Wmk inverted	90·00	26·00
		y. Wmk inverted and reversed		
57		1d. brown	90·00	8·00
58		1d. bistre (1872)	£120	10·00
		w. Wmk inverted		
59		2d. pale blue	70·00	9·00
		z. Imperf (pair)	£1500	£1900
		x. Wmk reversed	£140	26·00
		y. Wmk inverted and reversed		
60		2d. bright blue	80·00	9·00
61		3d. deep red	£150	26·00
61a		3d. dull red	60·00	13·00
		aw. Wmk inverted	£120	32·00
62		4d. rose	80·00	3·25
		w. Wmk inverted	£150	20·00
63		6d. dull violet	£250	30·00
		w. Wmk inverted		
		x. Wmk inverted		
64		6d. yellow-green (1865)	£170	13·00
65		6d. blue-green	£150	5·50
		w. Wmk inverted	£225	32·00
		y. Wmk inverted and reversed		
66		9d. yellow-green (1872)	£140	£225
67	**10**	10d. maroon (1872)	£275	40·00
		w. Wmk inverted		
68	**9**	1s. yellow	£225	23·00
		w. Wmk inverted	£300	45·00
69		1s. blue (1866)	£130	23·00
		w. Wmk inverted	—	50·00
		x. Wmk reversed	—	£130
70		1s. orange (1872)	£190	12·00
		w. Wmk inverted	£325	45·00
		y. Wmk inverted and reversed		
71		5s. rosy mauve	£180	55·00
		w. Wmk inverted	£325	
72		5s. bright mauve (1865)	£250	55·00
		w. Wmk inverted	£350	

HALF PENNY
(11)

½ d

HALF PENNY
(12)

1876.

(a) Nos. 51 and 67 surch with T **11** *locally.*

76	**9**	½d. on 9d. dull purple	10·00	15·00
		a. Surch inverted	£500	
		b. Surch double	—	£1600
77	**10**	½d. on 10d. maroon	1·75	20·00
		y. Wmk inverted and reversed		

(b) Prepared for use, but not issued. No. 51 surch with T **12**.

78	**9**	½d. on 9d. dull purple (R.)	£1900	
		a. "PRNNY"	—	
		b. Black surch	£3000	

HALF PENNY
(13)

One Penny
(14)

OneShilling
(15)

Shill
Wrong fount "S"

1877 (Apr–Dec). *Nos. 62, 67 (colour changed) and 71/2 surch T* **13** *by D.L.R. or T* **14/15** *locally.*

79	**10**	½d. on 10d. rose	5·00	32·00
		w. Wmk inverted		70·00
80	**9**	1d. on 4d. rose-carmine (6 Dec)	11·00	16·00
		w. Wmk inverted	—	70·00
81		1s. on 5s. rosy mauve (6 Dec)	£250	95·00
		w. Wmk inverted	£325	£130
82		1s. on 5s. bright mauve (6 Dec)	£225	£110
		a. Wrong fount "S"		
		w. Wmk inverted		

(New Currency. 100 cents = 1 rupee)

"CANCELLED" OVERPRINTS. Following the change of currency in 1878 various issues with face values in sterling were overprinted "CANCELLED" in serifed type and sold as remainders. The stamps involved were Nos. 51, 56/62, 65, 67/8, 71/2, 76, 78/b, 79 and 81/2. Examples of such overprints on stamps between Nos. 51 and 72 are worth about the same as the prices quoted for used, on Nos. 78/b they are worth 6% of the unused price, on No. 79 65% and on Nos. 81/2 20%.

2 CENTS **2 Rs. 50 C.**
(16) (17)

1878 (3 Jan). *Surch as T* **16** *or* **17** *(No. 91). Wmk Crown CC. P 14.*

83	**10**	2c. dull rose (lower label blank)	9·00	6·00
		w. Wmk inverted	70·00	45·00
84	**9**	4c. on 1d. bistre	17·00	6·00
85		8c. on 2d. blue	70·00	2·50
86		13c. on 3d. orange-red	14·00	29·00
87		17c. on 4d. rose	£160	3·00
88		25c. on 6d. slate-blue	£200	6·00
89		38c. on 9d. pale violet	24·00	70·00
90		50c. on 1s. green	85·00	3·25
		w. Wmk inverted		
91		2r.50 on 5s. bright mauve	15·00	18·00
		83/91 Set of 9	£550	£130

| 18 | 19 | 20 |

| 21 | 22 | 23 |

| 24 | 25 | 26 |

(Typo D.L.R.)

1879 (Mar)–**80**. *Wmk Crown CC. P 14.*

92	**18**	2c. Venetian red (1.80)	42·00	17·00
93	**19**	4c. orange	60·00	3·50
		w. Wmk inverted		
94	**20**	8c. blue (1.80)	20·00	3·00
		w. Wmk inverted		90·00
95	**21**	13c. slate (1.80)	£130	£170
96	**22**	17c. rose (1.80)	65·00	6·00
		w. Wmk inverted	—	£130
97	**23**	25c. olive-yellow	£350	10·00
98	**24**	38c. bright purple (1.80)	£160	£250
99	**25**	50c. green (1.80)	3·75	3·25
		w. Wmk inverted	95·00	
100	**26**	2r.50 brown-purple (1.80)	40·00	60·00
		92/100 Set of 9	£800	£475

27

(Typo D.L.R.)

1883–**94**. *Wmk Crown CA. P 14.*

101	**18**	1c. pale violet (1893)	1·75	45
102		2c. Venetian red	30·00	4·75
103		2c. green (1885)	2·50	60
104	**19**	4c. orange	70·00	3·50
		w. Wmk inverted		
105		4c. carmine (1885)	2·75	1·00
		w. Wmk inverted		
		x. Wmk reversed	†	£160
106	**20**	8c. blue (1891)	2·00	1·50
		w. Wmk inverted		
		x. Wmk reversed		
107	**27**	15c. chestnut (1893)	4·50	1·25
		w. Wmk inverted		95·00
108		15c. blue (1894)	5·50	1·25
109		16c. chestnut (1885)	1·75	75
110	**23**	25c. olive-yellow	6·50	2·25
		w. Wmk inverted	£250	£130

111	**25**	50c. orange (1887)	29·00	11·00
		w. Wmk inverted		
101/11		Set of 11	£140	26·00
101s, 103s, 105s, 107s/9s, 111s Optd "Specimen" Set of 7			£475	

16 CENTS **16 CENTS**
(28) (28a)

1883 (26 Feb). *No. 96 surch with T* **28/a** *locally.*

112	**22**	16c. on 17c. rose (surch T **28**–14½ mm long)	£140	50·00
		a. Surch double	†	£1900
		b. Horiz pair. Nos. 112/13	£475	£475
113		16c. on 17c. rose (surch T **28**–15½ mm long)	£150	50·00
		a. Surch double	—	£2000
114		16c. on 17c. rose (surch T **28a**)	£300	£100

These stamps were surcharged using two different settings, each of which produced three horizontal rows at a time.

The length of the surcharge in the first setting (Type **28**) is either 14½ mm or 15½ mm and these exist in horizontal *se-tenant* pairs. In Type **28** the height of the surcharge is 3.25 mm. On the second setting (Type **28a**) the type differs, especially the numerals and "S", with the surcharge measuring 15-15½ mm long and 3 mm high.

SIXTEEN CENTS **2 CENTS** **2 CENTS**
(29) (30) (31)

1883 (14 July). *Surch with T* **29** *by D.L.R. Wmk Crown CA. P 14.*

115	**22**	16c. on 17c. rose	80·00	2·00
		w. Wmk inverted		

1886 (11 May). *No. 98 surch with T* **30** *locally.*

116	**24**	2c. on 38c. bright purple	£110	35·00
		a. Without bar	—	£160
		b. Surch inverted	£800	£750
		c. Surch double	£850	

1887 (6 July). *No. 95 surch with T* **31** *locally.*

117	**21**	2c. on 13c. slate (R.)	50·00	90·00
		a. Surch inverted	£170	£180
		b. Surch double	£750	£650
		c. Surch double, one on back of stamp	£750	
		d. Surch double, both inverted	†	£1200

TWO CENTS

TWO CENTS
(32)

TWO CENTS
(33)

1891 (10–16 Sept). *Nos. 88, 96, 98 and 105 surch locally as T* **32** *(Nos. 118/19, 121) or T* **33** *(No. 120).*

118	**19**	2c. on 4c. carmine (No. 105) (12 Sept)	1·50	60
		a. Surch inverted	75·00	
		b. Surch double	80·00	75·00
		c. Surch double, one inverted	80·00	75·00
119	**22**	2c. on 17c. rose (No. 96) (16 Sept)	£100	£110
		a. Surch inverted	£375	
		b. Surch double	£700	£700
120	**9**	2c. on 38c. on 9d. pale violet (No. 89) (16 Sept)	4·00	4·25
		a. Surch inverted	£400	
		b. Surch double	£700	£700
		c. Surch double, one inverted	£150	£160
		w. Wmk inverted	†	£200
121	**24**	2c. on 38c. bright purple (No. 98)	5·00	6·00
		a. Surch inverted	£800	
		b. Surch double	£180	£190
		c. Surch double, one inverted	£700	£700

Minor varieties are also known with portions of the surcharge missing, due to defective printing.

ONE CENT
(34)

ONE CENT
(35)

1893 (1–7 Jan). *Surch with T* **34** *by D.L.R. or T* **35** *locally. Wmk Crown CA. P 14.*

123	**18**	1c. on 2c. pale violet	1·75	60
		s. Optd "Specimen"	28·00	
124	**27**	1c. on 16c. chestnut (7 Jan)	1·75	3·00
		w. Wmk inverted	48·00	

| 36 | 37 |

(Typo D.L.R.)

1895–**99**. *Wmk Crown CA. P 14.*

127	**36**	1c. dull purple and ultramarine (8.7.97)	75	1·50
128		2c. dull purple and orange (8.7.97)	4·00	50
129		3c. dull purple and deep purple	70	50
130		4c. dull purple and emerald (8.7.97)	3·75	50
131		6c. green and rose-red (1899)	4·50	4·00
132	**37**	18c. green and ultramarine (8.7.97)	12·00	3·50
127/32 Set of 6			23·00	9·50
127s/32s Optd "Specimen" Set of 6			£100	

(Des L. Duvergé. Typo D.L.R.)

1898 (15 Apr). *Diamond Jubilee. Wmk CA over Crown (sideways).*
P 14.

133	**37**	36c. orange and ultramarine...............	11·00	20·00
		s. Optd "Specimen"......................	45·00	

6
CENTS
(38)

15
CENTS
(39)

1899 (23–28 May). *Nos. 132/3 surcharged with T 38/9 locally.*

134	**36**	6c. on 18c. green and ultramarine (R.)...................................	1·00	1·00
		a. Surch inverted...............	£500	£250
135	**37**	15c. on 36c. orge & ultram (B) (28 May)................................	1·60	1·75
		a. Bar of surch omitted......	£350	

The space between "6" and "CENTS" varies from 2½ to 4 mm.

40 Admiral Mahé
de Labourdonnais,
Governor of Mauritius,
1735–46

4
Cents
(41)

(Recess D.L.R.)

1899 (13 Dec). *Birth Bicentenary of Labourdonnais. Wmk Crown
CC. P 14.*

136	**40**	15c. ultramarine	15·00	4·00
		s. Optd "Specimen"..............	70·00	
		w. Wmk inverted	80·00	

1900. *No. 109 surch with T 41 locally.*

137	**27**	4c. on 16c. chestnut	4·75	15·00

12
CENTS
(43)

42

(Typo D.L.R.)

1900–05. *Ordinary paper. Wmk Crown CC (1r.) or Crown CA
(others) (sideways on 2r.50, 5r.). P 14.*

138	**36**	1c. grey and black (1901)...............	50	10
139		2c. dull purple and bright purple (4.01)................................	75	20
140		3c. green and carmine/*yellow* (1902)..............................	3·75	1·25
141		4c. purple and carmine/*yellow*.........	1·50	40
142		4c. grey-green and violet (1903).....	1·00	2·00
		w. Wmk inverted		
143		4c. black and carmine/*blue* (14.10.04)...........................	8·00	60
		w. Wmk inverted	17·00	17·00
144		5c. dull purple & brt pur/*buff* (8.10.02)............................	6·50	50·00
145		5c. dull purple and black/*buff* (2.03).................................	2·50	2·50
146		6c. purple and carmine/*red* (1902)..	2·00	80
		a. Wmk sideways................	£2000	
		w. Wmk inverted	22·00	17·00
147		8c. green and black/*buff* (16.7.02)..	2·00	8·00
148		12c. grey-black and carmine (16.7.02)........................	1·75	2·25
149		15c. green and orange	13·00	6·00
		w. Wmk inverted		
150		15c. black and blue/*blue* (1905).......	50·00	1·25
151		25c. green and carmine/*green* (1902)	12·00	27·00
		a. Chalk-surfaced paper.........	4·00	16·00
152		50c. dull green & dp green /*yellow* (1902).............................	17·00	48·00
153	**42**	1r. grey-black and carmine (1902)..	50·00	50·00
		w. Wmk inverted	95·00	
154		2r.50 green and black/*blue* (1902)......	22·00	£100
155		5r. purple and carmine/*red* (1902)..	75·00	£100
138/55 *Set of 18*			£225	£350
138s/55s Optd "Specimen" *Set of 18*......................			£300	

Examples of Nos. 144 and 151/5 are known showing a forged Port
Louis postmark dated "SP 29 10".

1902. *No. 132 surch with T 43.*

156	**36**	12c. on 18c. green and ultramarine....	2·00	5·50

The bar cancelling the original value seems in some cases to be one
thick bar and in others two thin ones.

Postage & Revenue.
(44)

1902 (7 July). *Various stamps optd with T 44 locally.*

157	**36**	4c. purple and carmine/*yellow* (No. 141)................................	1·25	20
158		6c. green and rose-red (No. 131)...	1·25	2·75
159		15c. green and orange (No. 149)......	3·50	75
160	**23**	25c. olive-yellow (No. 110)..........	4·25	2·75
161	**25**	50c. green (No. 99)...................	6·00	3·50
162	**26**	2r.50 brown-purple (No. 100).........	95·00	£150
157/62 *Set of 6*			£100	£150

Nos. 157/62 were overprinted to make surplus stocks of postage
stamps available for revenue (fiscal) purposes also.

1902 (22 Sept). *No. 133 surch as T 43, but with longer bar.*

163	**37**	12c. on 36c. orange and ultramarine ...	1·25	1·25
		a. Surch inverted.................	£550	£400

The note below No. 156 also applies to No. 163.

Forged double surcharge errors show a straight, instead of a curved,
serif to the "1" of "12".

1904–07. *Ordinary paper (2c., 4c., 6c.) or chalk-surfaced paper
(others). Wmk Mult Crown CA. P 14.*

164	**36**	1c. grey and black (1907).............	8·00	3·75
165		2c. dull and bright purple (1905)	26·00	3·00
		a. Chalk-surfaced paper.........	26·00	1·75
166		3c. green and carmine/*yellow*	21·00	9·00
167		4c. black and carmine/*blue*	20·00	1·50
		a. Chalk-surfaced paper.........	5·00	10
168		6c. purple and carmine/*red*	11·00	30
		a. Chalk-surfaced paper.........	6·00	10
171		15c. black and blue/*blue* (1907)........	4·00	35
174		50c. green and deep green/*yellow*	2·00	2·75
175	**42**	1r. grey-black and carmine (1907)..	27·00	48·00
164/75 *Set of 8*			90·00	60·00

46

47

(Typo D.L.R.)

1910 (17 Jan). *Ordinary paper (1c. to 15c.) or chalk-surfaced paper
(25c. to 10r.). Wmk Mult Crown CA. P 14.*

181	**46**	1c. black	2·75	30
182		2c. brown	2·75	10
183		3c. green	3·00	10
		a. "A" of "CA" missing from wmk............................	†	—
		w. Wmk inverted	28·00	
184		4c. pale yellow-green and carmine..	3·50	10
		w. Wmk inverted	—	48·00
185	**47**	5c. grey and carmine	2·75	3·00
186	**46**	6c. carmine-red	2·50	20
		a. *Pale red*	3·50	1·50
		ab. "A" of "CA" missing from wmk............................	†	—
187		8c. orange	3·00	1·25
188	**47**	12c. greyish slate	2·50	2·75
189	**46**	15c. blue	17·00	20
190	**47**	25c. black and red/*yellow*	2·00	12·00
191		50c. dull purple and black	2·25	18·00
192		1r. black/*green*	7·50	12·00
193		2r.50 black and red/*blue*	15·00	70·00
194		5r. green and red/*yellow*	26·00	95·00
195		10r. green and red/*green*	£100	£180
181/95 *Set of 15*			£170	£350
181s/95s Optd "Specimen" *Set of 15*......................			£300	

On Nos. 185, 191, 192, 193 and 194 the value labels are as in *T* **48**.

48

49

(Typo D.L.R.)

1913–22. *Die I. Ordinary paper (5c., 12c.) or chalk-surfaced paper
(others). Wmk Mult Crown CA. P 14.*

196	**48**	5c. grey and carmine (1913)...........	1·75	4·00
		a. *Slate-grey and carmine*............	10·00	10·00
198	**49**	12c. greyish slate (1914)	5·00	1·00
199		25c. black and red/*yellow* (1913).....	40	1·40
		a. *White back* (1914)...............	80	17·00
		aw. Wmk inverted and reversed....	32·00	
		b. *On orange-buff* (1920)...........	32·00	60·00
		c. *On pale yellow* (1921)...........	32·00	40·00
		cs. Optd "Specimen"..............	38·00	
		cw. Wmk inverted	£100	
		d. Die II. *On pale yellow* (1921) ...	80	19·00
		ds. Optd "Specimen"..............	38·00	
200	**48**	50c. dull purple and black (1920)	42·00	90·00
201		1r. black/*blue-green (olive back)* (1917)............................	3·25	17·00
		a. *On emerald (olive back)* (1921)	7·50	48·00
		b. Die II. *On emerald (emerald back)* (1921)...................	2·25	7·50
		bs. Optd "Specimen"..............	38·00	
202		2r.50 black and red/*blue* (1916)........	22·00	65·00
203		5r. green and red/*orange-buff* (1921)............................	90·00	£140
		a. *On pale yellow* (1921)...........	80·00	£140
		b. Die II. *On pale yellow* (1922) ...	50·00	£160
204	**49**	10r. grn and red/*grn (bl-grn back)* (1913)............................	75·00	£150
		a. *On blue-green (olive back)* (1919)............................	£800	
		b. *On emerald (olive back)* (1921)	90·00	£150
		c. *On emerald (emerald back)* (1921)............................	50·00	£140
		d. Die II. *On emerald (emerald back)* (1922)...................	30·00	£120
		ds. Optd "Specimen"..............	45·00	

196/204 *Set of 8*			£140	£375
196s/202s, 203s, 204s Optd "Specimen" *Set of 8*......			£225	

Examples of Nos. 200/4d are known showing part strikes of the forged
Port Louis postmark mentioned after Nos. 138/55.

1921–26. *Chalk-surfaced paper (50r.). Wmk Mult Script CA. P 14.*

205	**46**	1c. black	1·00	1·00
		w. Wmk inverted	24·00	
206		2c. brown	1·00	10
		w. Wmk inverted		
207		2c. purple/*yellow* (1926).............	1·25	40
		w. Wmk inverted	20·00	
208		3c. green (1926)......................	2·75	1·75
209		4c. pale olive-green and carmine.....	1·50	1·75
		x. Wmk reversed	70·00	
210		4c. green (1922)......................	1·00	10
		w. Wmk inverted		
		x. Wmk reversed		
211		4c. brown (1926)	2·75	1·50
212		6c. carmine	12·00	6·50
		x. Wmk reversed	75·00	
213		6c. bright mauve (1922)	1·25	10
214		8c. orange (1925)....................	2·25	17·00
215		10c. grey (1922)......................	2·00	3·25
216		10c. carmine-red (1926)	5·00	2·00
217		12c. carmine-red (1922)	1·50	40
218		12c. grey (1926)......................	1·75	3·50
219		15c. blue	5·50	4·75
		ax. Wmk reversed	80·00	
		b. *Cobalt* (1926)....................	75	25
220		20c. blue (1922)......................	2·00	80
221		20c. purple (1926)...................	8·50	10·00
222	—	50r. dull purple and green (1924)......	£700	£1800
		s. Optd "Specimen"..............	£200	
205/21 *Set of 17*			42·00	42·00
205s/21s Optd "Specimen" *Set of 17*			£325	

No. 222 is as Type **46**, but measures 25×35 mm.

4c
Normal

4c
Open "C" (R. 9/6 of
right pane)

MAURITIUS
12c
A

MAURITIUS
12c
B

Two types of duty plate in the 12c. In Type B the letters of
"MAURITIUS" are larger; the extremities of the downstroke and the
tail of the "2" are pointed, instead of square, and the "c" is larger.

1921–34. *Die II. Chalk-surfaced paper (25c. to 10r.). Wmk Mult
Script CA. P 14.*

223	**49**	1c. black (1926)	1·00	1·75
224		2c. brown (1926).....................	70	10
225		3c. green (1926)......................	1·00	40
226		4c. sage-green and carmine (1926) .	1·25	30
		a. Open "C".......................	50·00	
		b. Die I (1932)...................	7·50	48·00
		ba. Open "C".......................	£120	
226c		4c. green (Die I) (1932)...........	6·50	45
		ca. Open "C".......................	£110	
227	**48**	5c. grey and carmine (1922).........	90	10
		a. Die I (1932)...................	6·00	6·00
228	**49**	6c. sepia (1927).....................	3·00	60
229		8c. orange (1926)	1·00	10·00
230		10c. carmine-red (1926)	1·75	20
		a. Die I (1932)...................	8·50	10·00
231		12c. grey (Type A) (1922)	1·40	17·00
232		12c. carmine-red (Type A) (1922).....	30	3·50
232a		12c. pale grey (Type A) (1926)	1·60	16·00
		as. Optd "Specimen"..............	38·00	
232b		12c. grey (Type B) (1934)	7·00	20
233		15c. Prussian blue (1926)	2·00	20
234		20c. purple (1926)	1·25	40
235		20c. Prussian blue (Die I) (1932).....	9·50	1·10
		a. Die II (1934).................	17·00	40
236		25c. black and red/*pale yellow* (1922)...........................	70	15
		a. Die II (1934).................	3·75	42·00
237	**48**	50c. dull purple and black (1921)	7·50	3·50
238		1r. black/*emerald* (1924)	3·50	50
		a. Die I (1932)...................	17·00	42·00
239		2r.50 black and red/*blue* (1922)........	20·00	8·00
240	**49**	5r. green and red/*yellow* (1924)......	29·00	75·00
241		10r. green and red/*emerald* (1924) ...	90·00	£250
223/41 *Set of 20*			£160	£325
223s/41s Optd or Perf (Nos. 226cs, 235s) "Specimen" *Set of 20*			£425	

3
Cents
(50)

51

1925 (25 Nov). *Nos. 210, 217 and 220 surch locally as T 50.*

242	**46**	3c. on 4c. green.....................	3·50	3·75
243		10c. on 12c. carmine-red	35	70
244		15c. on 20c. blue....................	55	20
242/4 *Set of 3*			4·00	4·25
242s/4s Optd "Specimen" *Set of 3*...............			80·00	

1935 (6 May). *Silver Jubilee. As Nos. 91/4 of Antigua. P 13½×14.*

245		5c. ultramarine and grey	50	10
		f. Diagonal line by turret.........	55·00	25·00
		g. Dot to left of chapel..........	£100	50·00
		h. Dot by flagstaff...............	£100	50·00

246	12c. green and indigo	4·50	10
	f. Diagonal line by turret	£110	40·00
	g. Dot to left of chapel	£190	60·00
247	20c. brown and deep blue	5·50	20
	f. Diagonal line by turret	£140	50·00
	g. Dot to left of chapel	£200	70·00
248	1r. slate and purple	29·00	45·00
	h. Dot by flagstaff	£400	£475
245/8	Set of 4	35·00	45·00
245s/8s Perf "Specimen" Set of 4		£110	

For illustrations of plate varieties see Omnibus section following Zanzibar.

Line through sword (R. 2/2) Line by sceptre (R. 5/3)

1937 (12 May). *Coronation. As Nos. 95/7 of Antigua, but printed by D.L.R.* P 14.

249	5c. violet	40	10
250	12c. scarlet	50	2·25
251	20c. bright blue	85	10
	a. Line through sword	70·00	35·00
	b. Line by sceptre	70·00	35·00
249/51	Set of 3	1·60	2·25
249s/51s Perf "Specimen" Set of 3		75·00	

Sliced "S" at right (R. 2/2, 3/2, right pane) Sliced "S" at top (R. 4/1, left pane and R. 8/4, right pane)

Broken frame under "A" of "MAURITIUS" (R. 9/3 left pane, Key Plate 2)

"IJ" flaw (R. 3/6 of right pane) Battered "A" (R. 6/1 of right pane)

(Typo D.L.R.)

1938–49. *T 51 and similar types. Chalk-surfaced paper (25c. to 10r.).* Wmk Mult Script CA. P 14.

252	2c. olive-grey (9.3.38)	30	10
	a. Perf 15×14 (1942)	1·00	10
253	3c. reddish purple and scarlet (27.10.38)	2·00	2·00
	a. Sliced "S" at right	85·00	85·00
	b. Reddish lilac and red (4.43)	3·50	3·50
	ba. Sliced "S" at right	£150	£150
254	4c. dull green (26.2.38)	3·25	2·00
	a. Open "C"	£130	85·00
	b. Deep dull green (4.43)	2·00	2·00
	ba. Open "C"	90·00	85·00
255	5c. slate-lilac (23.2.38)	11·00	85
	a. Pale lilac (shades) (4.43)	3·25	20
	b. Perf 15×14 (1942)	55·00	10
256	10c. rose-red (9.3.38)	2·75	30
	a. Sliced "S" at top	£140	40·00
	b. Deep reddish rose (shades) (4.43)	2·50	20
	ba. Sliced "S" at top	£130	30·00
	c. Perf 15×14. Pale reddish rose (1942)	28·00	1·25
	ca. Sliced "S" at top	£425	£100
257	12c. salmon (shades) (26.2.38)	1·00	20
	a. Perf 15×14 (1942)	55·00	75
258	20c. blue (26.2.38)	1·00	10
	a. Broken frame	£200	70·00
259	25c. brown-purple (2.3.38)	13·00	20
	a. "IJ" flaw	£325	50·00
	b. Ordinary paper (8.4.43)	7·00	10
	ba. "IJ" flaw	£170	40·00
260	1r. grey-brown (2.3.38)	29·00	2·00
	a. Battered "A"	£450	£130
	b. Ordinary paper (8.4.43)	19·00	1·25
	ba. Battered "A"	£375	£100
	c. Drab (4.49)	35·00	6·00
	ca. Battered "A"	£475	£170
261	2r.50 pale violet (2.3.38)	40·00	15·00
	a. Ordinary paper (8.4.43)	30·00	15·00
	b. Slate-violet (4.48)	55·00	29·00
262	5r. olive-green (2.3.38)	48·00	26·00
	a. Ordinary paper. Sage-green (8.4.43)	27·00	26·00

263	10r. reddish purple (shades) (2.3.38)	50·00	40·00
	a. Ordinary paper (8.4.43)	12·00	26·00
252/63a	Set of 12	95·00	65·00
252s/63s Perf "Specimen" Set of 12		£250	

The stamps perf 15×14 were printed by Bradbury, Wilkinson from De La Rue plates and issued only in the colony in 1942. De La Rue printings of the 2c. to 20c. in 1943–45 were on thin, whiter paper. 1943–45 printings of the 25c. to 10r. were on unsurfaced paper.

1946 (20 Nov). *Victory. As Nos. 110/11 of Antigua.*

264	5c. lilac	10	60
265	20c. blue	20	25
264s/5s Perf "Specimen" Set of 2		70·00	

52 1d. "Post Office" Mauritius and King George VI

(Recess B.W.)

1948 (22 Mar). *Centenary of First British Colonial Postage Stamp.* Wmk Mult Script CA. P 11½×11.

266	52	5c. orange and magenta	10	50
267		12c. orange and green	15	25
268	–	20c. blue and light blue	15	10
269	–	1r. blue and red-brown	25	30
266/9	Set of 4		60	1·00
266s/9s Perf "Specimen" Set of 4			£110	

Design:—20c., 1r. As *T 52* but showing 2d. "Post Office" Mauritius.

1948 (25 Oct). *Royal Silver Wedding. As Nos. 112/13 of Antigua.*

270	5c. violet	10	10
271	10r. magenta	12·00	26·00

1949 (10 Oct). *75th Anniv of U.P.U. As Nos. 114/17 of Antigua.*

272	12c. carmine	50	1·50
273	20c. deep blue	2·25	2·50
274	35c. purple	60	1·50
275	1r. sepia	50	20
272/5	Set of 4	3·50	5·00

53 Labourdonnais Sugar Factory 54 Grand Port

55 Aloe Plant 56 Tamarind Falls

57 Rempart Mountain 58 Transporting cane

59 Mauritius Dodo and map 60 Legend of Paul and Virginie

61 Labourdonnais statue 62 Government House, Reduit

63 Pieter Both Mountain 64 Timor Deer

65 Port Louis 66 Beach scene

67 Arms of Mauritius

(Photo Harrison)

1950 (1 July). *T 53/67. Chalk-surfaced paper.* Wmk Mult Script CA. P 13½×14½ (horiz.), 14½×13½ (vert.).

276	53	1c. bright purple	10	50
277	54	2c. rose-carmine	15	10
278	55	3c. yellow-green	60	3·25
279	56	4c. green	20	2·00
280	57	5c. blue	15	10
281	58	10c. scarlet	30	75
282	59	12c. olive-green	1·50	2·75
283	60	20c. ultramarine	1·00	15
284	61	25c. brown-purple	2·00	40
285	62	35c. violet	30	10
286	63	50c. emerald-green	2·75	50
287	64	1r. sepia	6·50	10
288	65	2r. orange	12·00	12·00
289	66	5r. red-brown	14·00	15·00
290	67	10r. dull blue	15·00	24·00
276/290 Set of 15			50·00	55·00

The latitude is incorrectly shown on No. 282 and No. 283 is incorrectly inscribed "VIRGINIA".

EXPRESS DELIVERY STAMPS

EXPRESS DELIVERY 15c. (E 1) EXPRESS DELIVERY (INLAND) 15c. (E 2)

EXPRESS DELIVERY (INLAND) 15 c. (E 3) EXPRESS DELIVERY (INLAND) 15 c (E 4)

Type E 2. "(INLAND)" was inserted at a second printing on stamps already surcharged with Type E 1 (No. E1).

Type E 3. New setting made at one printing. More space above and below "(INLAND)".

Type E 4. New setting with smaller "15c" and no stop.

1903 (10 Aug)–04. *No. 136 surch locally in red.*

E1	E 1	15c. on 15c. ultramarine	9·00	25·00
E2	E 2	15c. on 15c. ultramarine (28.3.04)	45·00	65·00
		a. "A" inverted	£1200	£850
		b. "(INLAND)" inverted	†	£2500
E3	E 3	15c. on 15c. ultramarine (4.04)	7·50	3·00
		a. Surch inverted	£800	£500
		aw. Surch and wmk inverted	—	£550
		b. Surch double, both inverted	£1400	£1400
		c. Imperf between (vert pair)	£3750	
		w. Wmk inverted		
E4	E 4	15c. on 15c. ultramarine (1904)	£600	£550
		a. Surch inverted	—	£1300
		b. Surch double	—	£2500
		c. Surch double, both inverted	—	£4250
		d. "c" omitted	—	£1900

(FOREIGN) EXPRESS DELIVERY 18 CENTS

(E 5)

1904. *T 42 (without value in label), surch with Type E 5 locally.* Wmk Crown CC. P 14.

E5		18c. green	2·00	26·00
	a.	Exclamation mark for "I" in "FOREIGN"		£500

1904. *T 42 (without value in label) surch with Type E 3 locally.*

E6		15c. grey-green (R.)	5·00	4·75
	a.	Surch inverted	£700	600
	b.	Surch double	£500	£550
	c.	Surch double, one "LNIAND"	£600	£550

POSTAGE DUE STAMPS

D 1

(Typo Waterlow)

1933–54. Wmk Mult Script CA. P 15×14.

D1	2c. black		1·25	50
D2	4c. violet		50	65
D3	6c. scarlet		60	80
D4	10c. green		70	1·25
D5	20c. bright blue		50	1·50
D6	50c. deep magenta (1.3.54)		55	16·00
D7	1r. orange (1.3.54)		70	16·00
D1/7	Set of 7		4·25	32·00
D1s/5s	Perf "Specimen" Set of 5		75·00	

Stamps in a similar design on Block CA paper were issued between 1966 and 1972.

FISCALS USED FOR POSTAGE

INLAND REVENUE (F 1)   INLAND REVENUE (F 2)   F 3

1889. *T 19, wmk Crown CA, optd.* P 14.

R1	F 1	4c. carmine	18·00	5·00
R2	F 2	4c. lilac	4·50	12·00

(Typo D.L.R.)

1896. Wmk Crown CA. P 14.

R3	F 3	4c. dull purple	27·00	45·00

Montserrat

A local post office operated on Montserrat from 1702, although the first recorded postal marking does not occur until 1791. A branch of the British G.P.O. was established at Plymouth, the island capital, in 1852.

The stamps of Great Britain were used from 1858 until the overseas postal service reverted to local control on 1 April 1860.

In the interim period between 1860 and the introduction of Montserrat stamps in 1876 No. CC1 and a similar "uncrowned" handstamp were again used.

PLYMOUTH

CROWNED-CIRCLE HANDSTAMPS

C 1

CC1   C 1   MONTSERRAT (R.) (15.7.1852)

Price on cover   £4000

No. CC1 was used as an emergency measure, struck in black, during 1886.

Stamps of GREAT BRITAIN *cancelled* "A 08" *as Type Z 1 of Jamaica.*

1858 (8 May)**–60.**

Z1	1d. rose-red (1857), perf 14		£1200
Z2	4d. rose (1857)		
Z3	6d. lilac (1856)		£500
Z4	1s. green (1856)		£1600

MONTSERRAT

1   (2)   3 (Die I)

(T 1 recess D.L.R.)

1876 (Sept)**–83.** *Stamps of Antigua optd with T 2.* Wmk Crown CC. P 14.

1	1	1d. red	24·00	17·00
	a.	Bisected (½d.) (1883) (on cover)	†	£1400
	b.	Inverted "S"	£1000	£750
	w.	Wmk inverted	50·00	
	x.	Wmk reversed	28·00	22·00
	y.	Wmk inverted and reversed	45·00	50·00
2		6d. green	70·00	45·00
	a.	Trisected (used as 2d.) (12.83) (on cover)	†	£5500
	b.	Inverted "S"	£1700	£1000
	x.	Wmk reversed	—	85·00
3		6d. blue-green	£1200	
	a.	Inverted "S"	£9000	

Nos. 1/3 were overprinted either from a setting of 120 (12×10) or from a setting of 60 (6×10) applied twice to each sheet. This setting of 60 had an inverted "S" on R. 2/3. The same setting was subsequently used for some sheets of Nos. 6 and 8.

No. 1 was bisected and used for a ½d. in 1883. This bisected stamp is found surcharged with a small "½" in *black* and also in *red*; both were unofficial and they did not emanate from the Montserrat P.O.

The 6d. in blue-green is only known unused.

(T 3 typo D.L.R.)

1880 (Jan). Wmk Crown CC. P 14.

4	3	2½d. red-brown	£250	£180
5		4d. blue	£150	40·00
	w.	Wmk inverted	—	£150
	x.	Wmk reversed		£375

1883 (Mar). Wmk Crown CA. P 12.

6	1	1d. red	70·00	55·00
	a.	Inverted "S"	£2000	£1300
	b.	Bisected (½d.) (on cover)	†	£1600
	x.	Wmk reversed	—	50·00

Top left triangle detached (Pl 2 R. 3/3 of right pane)

1884–85. Wmk Crown CA. P 14.

7	3	½d. dull green	1·00	9·00
	a.	Top left triangle detached	£130	
8	1	1d. red	17·00	19·00
	a.	Inverted "S"	£1000	£1000
	bx.	Wmk reversed	—	26·00
	c.	Rose-red (1885)	18·00	15·00
	ca.	Bisected vert (½d.) (on cover)	†	£1300
	cb.	Inverted "S"	£1100	£1000
	ex.	Wmk reversed	21·00	21·00
9	3	2½d. red-brown	£250	65·00
10		2½d. ultramarine (1885)	23·00	21·00
	a.	Top left triangle detached	£425	
	w.	Wmk inverted		£100
11		4d. blue	£1800	£250
12		4d. mauve (1885)	5·50	3·00
	a.	Top left triangle detached	£250	
10s, 12s	Optd "Specimen" Set of 2	£425	

The stamps for Montserrat were superseded by the general issue for Leeward Islands in November 1890, but the following issues were in concurrent use with the stamps inscribed "LEEWARD ISLANDS" until 1 July 1956, when Leeward Islands stamps were withdrawn and invalidated.

4 Device of the Colony   5

(Typo D.L.R.)

1903 (Aug).

(a) Wmk Crown CA. P 14.

14	4	½d. grey-green and green	75	14·00
15		1d. grey-black and red	75	40
	w.	Wmk inverted		
16		2d. grey and brown	5·50	35·00
17		2½d. grey and blue	1·50	1·75
18		3d. dull orange and deep purple	4·50	38·00
19		6d. dull purple and olive	5·50	48·00
20		1s. green and bright purple	10·00	17·00
21		2s. green and brown-orange	25·00	17·00
22		2s.6d. green and black	21·00	40·00

(b) Wmk Crown CC. P 14.

23	5	5s. black and scarlet	£110	£160
14/23	Set of 10		£170	£350
14s/23s	Optd "Specimen" Set of 10		£170	

1904–08. *Ordinary paper (½d., 2d., 3d., 6d.) or chalk-surfaced paper (others).* Wmk Mult Crown CA. P 14.

24	4	½d. grey-green and green	6·00	2·00
	a.	Chalk-surfaced paper (3.06)	1·00	1·25
25		1d. grey-black and red (11.07)	17·00	24·00
26		2d. grey and brown	1·25	7·00
	a.	Chalk-surfaced paper (5.06)	2·25	1·25
27		2½d. grey and blue (12.05)	2·50	6·50
28		3d. dull orange and deep purple	7·00	7·50
	a.	Chalk-surfaced paper (5.08)	9·50	2·50
29		6d. dull purple and olive	4·25	26·00
	a.	Chalk-surfaced paper (5.08)	11·00	5·50
30		1s. green and bright purple (5.08)	11·00	7·00
31		2s. green and orange (5.08)	35·00	42·00
32		2s.6d. green and black (5.08)	48·00	48·00
33	5	5s. black and red (9.07)	£100	£110
24/33	Set of 10		£200	£225

1908 (June)**–14.** *Ordinary paper (½d. to 2½d.) or chalk-surfaced paper (3d. to 5s.).* Wmk Mult Crown CA. P 14.

35	4	½d. deep green (4.10)	7·00	1·00
36		1d. rose-red	1·40	30
38		2d. greyish slate (9.09)	1·75	15·00
39		2½d. blue	2·25	3·50
40		3d. purple/yellow (9.09)	1·00	18·00
		a. White back (1.14)	4·00	35·00
		as. Optd "Specimen"	27·00	
43		6d. dull and deep purple (9.09)	6·50	55·00
	a.	Dull and bright purple (1914)	11·00	55·00
44		1s. black/green (9.09)	8·50	45·00
45		2s. purple and bright blue/blue (9.09)	35·00	55·00
46		2s.6d. black and red/blue (9.09)	35·00	70·00
47	5	5s. red and green/yellow (9.09)	50·00	70·00
35/47	Set of 10		£130	£300
35s/47s	Optd "Specimen" Set of 10		£225	

Examples of most values are known showing forged Montserrat postmarks dated "OC 16 1909" or "NO 26 1910".

WAR STAMP

7   8   (9)

(T 7/8 typo D.L.R.)

1914. *Chalk-surfaced paper.* Wmk Mult Crown CA. P 14.

48	7	5s. red and green/yellow	65·00	95·00
	s.	Optd "Specimen"	75·00	

1916 (10 Oct)**–22.** *Ordinary paper (½d. to 2½d.) or chalk-surfaced paper (3d. to 5s.).* Wmk Mult Crown CA. P 14.

49	8	½d. green	30	2·50
50		1d. scarlet	1·50	75
		a. Carmine-red	22·00	8·00
51		2d. grey	2·00	4·00
52		2½d. bright blue	1·50	20·00
53		3d. purple/yellow	1·25	14·00
		a. On pale yellow (13.7.22)	75	14·00
		as. Optd "Specimen"	26·00	
54		4d. grey-black & red/pale yell (13.7.22)	5·50	38·00
55		6d. dull and deep purple	2·75	23·00
56		1s. black/blue-green (olive back)	3·00	26·00
57		2s. purple and blue/blue	14·00	35·00
58		2s.6d. black and red/blue	24·00	65·00
59		5s. green and red/yellow	38·00	65·00
49/59	Set of 11		85·00	£275
49s/59s	Optd "Specimen" Set of 11		£180	

1917 (8 Oct)**–18.** *No. 49 optd with T 9.*

60	8	½d. green (R.)	10	1·50
	a.	Short opt (right pane R. 10/1)	10·00	
	y.	Wmk inverted and reversed	50·00	
61		½d. green (Blk.) (5.18)	1·00	3·00
	a.	Short opt (right pane R. 10/1)	18·00	
	b.	Deep green (10.18)	15	1·75
	ba.	"C" and "A" missing from wmk	£1100	
	bb.	Short opt (right pane R. 10/1)	10·00	
	w.	Wmk inverted		

Nos. 60a, 61a, and 61bb show the overprint 2 mm high instead of 2½ mm.

No. 61ba shows the "C" omitted from one impression and the "A" missing from the next. The price quoted is for a horizontal pair.

1919 (4 Mar). *T 8. Special printing in orange. Value and "WAR STAMP" as T 9 inserted in black at one printing.*

62		1½d. black and orange	10	30
60s/2s	Optd "Specimen" Set of 3		85·00	

1922 (13 July)–**29**. *Ordinary paper (¼d. to 3d.) (No. 73) or chalk-surfaced paper (others).* Wmk Mult Script CA. P 14.

63	**8**	¼d. brown	15	5·50
64		½d. green (5.4.23)	30	30
65		1d. bright violet (5.4.23)	30	60
66		1d. carmine (1929)	75	1·50
67		1½d. orange-yellow	1·75	9·50
68		1½d. carmine (5.4.23)	30	4·00
69		1½d. red-brown (1929)	2·25	50
70		2d. grey	50	2·00
71		2½d. deep bright blue	8·00	16·00
		a. *Pale bright blue* (17.8.26)	60	90
		as. Optd "Specimen"	32·00	
72		2½d. orange-yellow (5.4.23)	1·25	19·00
73		3d. dull blue (5.4.23)	75	16·00
74		3d. purple (2.1.27)	1·10	4·75
75		4d. black and red/*pale yellow*	75	12·00
76		5d. dull purple and olive	3·75	10·00
77		6d. pale and bright purple (5.4.23)	3·00	7·50
78		1s. black/*emerald* (5.4.23)	3·00	7·00
79		2s. purple and blue/*blue*	7·00	17·00
80		2s.6d. black and red/*blue* (5.4.23)	12·00	50·00
81		3s. green and violet	12·00	19·00
82		4s. black and scarlet	15·00	38·00
83		5s. green and red/*pale yellow* (6.23)	27·00	48·00
63/83		Set of 21	85·00	£250
63s/83s		Optd or Perf (Nos. 66s, 69s) "Specimen" Set of 21	£325	

10 Plymouth

(Recess D.L.R.)

1932 (18 Apr). *300th Anniv of Settlement of Montserrat.* Wmk Mult Script CA. P 14.

84	**10**	½d. green	75	8·50
85		1d. scarlet	75	5·50
86		1½d. red-brown	1·25	2·50
87		2d. grey	1·50	16·00
88		2½d. ultramarine	1·25	15·00
89		3d. orange	1·50	19·00
90		6d. violet	2·25	30·00
91		1s. olive-brown	12·00	42·00
92		2s.6d. purple	48·00	70·00
93		5s. chocolate	£100	£160
84/93		Set of 10	£150	£325
84s/93s		Perf "Specimen" Set of 10	£225	

Examples of all values are known showing a forged G.P.O. Plymouth postmark dated "MY 13 32".

1935 (6 May). *Silver Jubilee. As Nos. 91/4 of Antigua, but ptd by Waterlow & Sons.* P 11×12.

94		1d. deep blue and scarlet	85	3·25
95		1½d. ultramarine and grey	1·50	2·75
96		2½d. brown and deep blue	2·25	3·25
97		1s. slate and purple	3·00	14·00
94/7		Set of 4	7·00	21·00
94s/7s		Perf "Specimen" Set of 4	95·00	

1937 (12 May). *Coronation. As Nos. 95/7 of Antigua, but printed by D.L.R.* P 14.

98		1d. scarlet	30	1·50
99		1½d. yellow-brown	40	40
100		2½d. bright blue	40	1·50
98/100		Set of 3	1·00	3·00
98s/100s		Perf "Specimen" Set of 3	70·00	

11 Carr's Bay

12 Sea Island Cotton

13 Botanic Station

(Recess D.L.R.)

1938 (2 Aug)–**48**. Wmk Mult Script CA. P 12 (10s., £1) or 13 (others).

101	**11**	½d. blue-green	3·75	1·50
		a. Perf 14 (1942)	15	20
102	**12**	1d. carmine	3·75	40
		a. Perf 14 (1943)	50	30
103		1½d. purple	17·00	50
		a. Perf 14 (1942)	50	50
		ab. "A" of "CA" missing from wmk.		
104	**13**	2d. orange	17·00	60
		a. Perf 14 (1942)	1·50	70
105	**12**	2½d. ultramarine	1·50	60
		a. Perf 14 (1942)	50	30
106	**11**	3d. brown	4·00	1·00
		a. Perf 14. *Red-brown* (1942)	2·00	40
		ab. *Deep brown* (1943)	1·75	5·50
107	**13**	6d. violet	18·00	80
		a. Perf 14 (1943)	2·50	60
108	**11**	1s. lake	18·00	70
		a. Perf 14 (1942)	2·25	30
109	**13**	2s.6d. slate-blue	30·00	80
		a. Perf 14 (1943)	17·00	2·50
110	**11**	5s. rose-carmine	40·00	8·00

111	**13**	a. Perf 14 (1942)	21·00	3·00
111	**13**	10s. pale blue (1.4.48)	13·00	19·00
112	**11**	£1 black (1.4.48)	13·00	27·00
101a/12		Set of 12	65·00	50·00
101s/12s		Perf "Specimen" Set of 12	£275	

Nos. 101/2 exist in coils constructed from normal sheets.

1946 (1 Nov). *Victory. As Nos. 110/11 of Antigua.*

113		1½d. purple	10	10
114		3d. chocolate	10	10
113s/14s		Perf "Specimen" Set of 2	65·00	

1949 (3 Jan). *Royal Silver Wedding. As Nos. 112/13 of Antigua.*

115		2½d. ultramarine	10	10
116		5s. carmine	4·75	9·50

1949 (10 Oct). *75th Anniv of U.P.U. As Nos. 114/17 of Antigua.*

117		2½d. ultramarine	15	1·25
118		3d. brown	1·75	60
119		6d. purple	30	50
120		1s. purple	30	60
117/20		Set of 4	2·25	2·75

(New Currency. 100 cents = 1 West Indies, later Eastern Caribbean dollar)

1951 (16 Feb). *Inauguration of B.W.I. University College. As Nos. 118/19 of Antigua.*

121		3c. black and purple	20	1·25
122		12c. black and violet	20	1·25

14 Government House

18 Badge of Presidency

(Recess B.W.)

1951 (17 Sept). *T* **14**, **18** *and similar horiz designs.* Wmk Mult Script CA. P 11½×11.

123	**14**	1c. black	10	2·00
124	–	2c. green	15	70
125	–	3c. orange-brown	30	70
126	–	4c. carmine	30	1·25
127	–	5c. reddish violet	30	70
128	**18**	6c. olive-brown	30	30
129	–	8c. deep blue	1·50	20
130	–	12c. blue and chocolate	75	30
131	–	24c. carmine and yellow-green	1·25	30
132	–	60c. black and carmine	7·00	3·75
133	–	$1.20 yellow-green and blue	7·00	6·00
134	–	$2.40 black and green	9·00	13·00
135	**18**	$4.80 black and purple	17·00	17·00
123/135		Set of 13	40·00	42·00

Designs:—2c., $1.20, Sea Island cotton: cultivation; 3c. Map of colony; 4, 24c. Picking tomatoes; 5, 12c. St. Anthony's Church; 8, 60c. Sea Island cotton: ginning; $2.40, Government House.

Morocco Agencies (British Post Offices)

I. GIBRALTAR USED IN MOROCCO

With the growth of trade and commerce during the 19th century European powers opened post offices or postal agencies in various ports along the Moroccan coast from the early 1850's onwards. French and, in the north, Spanish influence eventually became predominant, leading to the protectorates of 1912. The British, who had inaugurated a regular postal service between Gibraltar and Tangier or Tetuan in May 1778, established their first postal agency in 1857. German offices followed around the turn of the century.

Before 1892 there was no indigenous postal service and those towns where there was no foreign agency were served by a number of private local posts which continued to flourish until 1900. In November 1892 the Sultan of Morocco established the Cherifian postal service, but this was little used until after its reorganization at the end of 1911. The Sultan's post was absorbed by the French postal service on 1 October 1913. Issues of the local posts and of the Sultan's post can occasionally be found used on cover in combination with stamps of Gibraltar or the Morocco Agencies.

In 1857 the first British postal agency was established at Tangier within the precincts of the Legation and was run by the official interpreter. From 1 March 1858 all letters for Great Britain sent via the British mail packets from Gibraltar required franking with Great Britain stamps.

In 1872 the Tangier office was relocated away from the Legation and the interpreter was appointed British Postal Agent. At the same time the agency was placed under the control of the Gibraltar postmaster. When the colonial posts became independent of the British G.P.O. on 1 January 1886 Gibraltar retained responsibility for the Morocco Agencies. Further offices, each under the control of the local Vice-Consul, were opened from 1886 onwards.

I. GIBRALTAR USED IN MOROCCO

Details of the various agencies are given below. Type C, the "A26" killer, is very similar to postmarks used at Gibraltar during this period. In addition to the town name, postmarks as Types A, B and D from Fez, Mazagan, Saffi and Tetuan were also inscribed "MOROCCO".

Postmark Types used on Gibraltar issues.

Type A Circular datestamp   Type C "A26" killer

Type B Duplex cancellation

Type D Registered oval

BISECTS. The 10c., 40c. and 50c. values of the 1889 surcharges and of the 1889–96 issue are known bisected and used for half their value from various of the Morocco Agencies. These bisects were never authorised by the Gibraltar Post Office.

CASABLANCA

The British postal agency opened on 1 January 1887 and was initially supplied with ½d., 4d. and 6d. stamps from the Gibraltar 1886 overprinted on Bermuda issue and 1d., 2d. and 2½d. values from the 1886–87 set.

Stamps of GIBRALTAR cancelled with Types A (*without code or code* "C"), B (*without code or code* "A") *or* D.

1886. *Optd on Bermuda (Nos. 1/7).*

Z1	½d. dull green	70·00	
Z2	4d. orange-brown	£325	
Z3	6d. deep lilac	£325	

1886–87. *Queen Victoria £sd issue (Nos. 8/14).*

Z4	½d. dull green	30·00	
Z5	1d. rose	35·00	
Z6	2d. brown-purple	75·00	
Z7	2½d. blue	45·00	
Z8	4d. orange-brown	£110	
Z10	1s. bistre	£325	

1889. *Surch in Spanish currency (Nos. 15/21).*

Z11	5c. on ½d. green	50·00	
Z12	10c. on 1d. rose	42·00	
Z13	25c. on 2d. brown-purple	65·00	
Z14	25c. on 2½d. bright blue	40·00	
Z15	40c. on 4d. orange-brown	£120	
Z16	50c. on 6d. bright lilac	£110	
Z17	75c. on 1s. bistre	£140	

1889–96. *Queen Victoria Spanish currency issue (Nos. 22/33).*

Z18	5c. green	14·00	
Z19	10c. carmine	14·00	
Z20	20c. olive-green and brown	32·00	
Z22	25c. ultramarine	14·00	
Z23	40c. orange-brown	38·00	
Z24	50c. bright lilac	28·00	
Z25	75c. olive-green	85·00	
Z26	1p. bistre	75·00	
Z28	1p. bistre and ultramarine	38·00	
Z29	2p. black and carmine	55·00	

FEZ

The British postal agency in this inland town opened on 13 February 1892 and was initially supplied with stamps up to the 50c. value from the Gibraltar 1889–96 issue.

Stamps of GIBRALTAR cancelled with Types A (*without code*) *or* D.

1889–96. *Queen Victoria Spanish currency issue (Nos. 22/33).*

Z31	5c. green	30·00	
Z32	10c. carmine	32·00	
Z33	20c. olive-green and brown	60·00	
Z35	25c. ultramarine	45·00	
Z36	40c. orange-brown	80·00	
Z37	50c. bright lilac	60·00	

LARAICHE

The British postal agency at Laraiche opened in March 1886, although the first postmark, an "A26" killer, was not supplied until May.

Stamps of GIBRALTAR cancelled with Types B (*without code*) *or* D.

1886. *Optd on Bermuda (Nos. 1/7).*

Z39	½d. dull green		
Z40	1d. rose-red		
Z41	2½d. ultramarine		

1886–87. *Queen Victoria £sd issue (Nos. 8/14).*
Z42 ½d. dull green .... 95·00
Z43 1d. rose .... 90·00
Z45 2½d. blue .... 95·00

1889. *Surch in Spanish currency (Nos. 15/21).*
Z47 5c. on ½d. green .... 65·00
Z48 10c. on 1d. rose
Z49 25c. on 2½d. bright blue ....

It is believed that the other surcharges in this series were not supplied to Laraiche.

1889–96. *Queen Victoria Spanish currency issue (Nos. 22/33).*
Z50 5c. green .... 32·00
Z51 10c. carmine .... 42·00
Z52 20c. olive-green and brown ....
Z54 25c. ultramarine .... 42·00
Z55 40c. orange-brown ....
Z56 50c. bright-lilac .... 85·00
Z57 1p. bistre and ultramarine ....

MAZAGAN

This was the main port for the inland city of Marrakesh. The British postal agency opened on 1 March 1888 and was initially supplied with stamps from the Gibraltar 1886–87 series.

Stamps of GIBRALTAR *cancelled with Types* A (*codes* "A" *or* "C") *or* D (*without code, code* "A" *or code* "C").

1886–87. *Queen Victoria £sd issue (Nos. 8/14).*
Z58 ½d. dull green .... 32·00
Z59 1d. rose .... 32·00
Z60 2d. brown-purple ....
Z61 2½d. blue .... 40·00
Z62 4d. orange-brown £120
Z63 6d. lilac £140

1889. *Surch in Spanish currency (Nos. 15/21).*
Z64 5c. on ½d. green
Z65 10c. on 1d. rose
Z66 25c. on 2½d. bright blue

It is believed that the other surcharges in this series were not supplied to Mazagan.

1889–96. *Queen Victoria Spanish currency issue (Nos. 22/33).*
Z67 5c. green .... 20·00
Z68 10c. carmine .... 18·00
Z69 20c. olive-green and brown .... 55·00
Z70 25c. ultramarine .... 45·00
Z71 40c. orange-brown .... 80·00
Z72 50c. bright lilac ....
Z74 1p. bistre and ultramarine ....
Z75 2p. black and carmine ....

MOGADOR

The British postal agency at this port opened on 1 April 1887 and was initially supplied with stamps from the Gibraltar 1886–87 series.

Stamps of GIBRALTAR *cancelled with Types* A (*code* "C"), B (*code* "C") *or* D.

1886–87. *Queen Victoria £sd issue (Nos. 8/14).*
Z76 ½d. dull green .... 30·00
Z77 1d. rose .... 40·00
Z78 2d. brown-purple .... 75·00
Z79 2½d. blue .... 40·00

1889. *Surch in Spanish currency (Nos. 15/21).*
Z80 5c. on ½d. green .... 50·00
Z81 10c. on 1d. rose .... 50·00
Z82 25c. on 2½d. bright blue .... 50·00

It is believed that the other surcharges in this series were not supplied to Mogador.

1889–96. *Queen Victoria Spanish currency issue (Nos. 22/33).*
Z83 5c. green .... 14·00
Z84 10c. carmine .... 16·00
Z85 20c. olive-green and brown ....
Z87 25c. ultramarine .... 20·00
Z88 40c. orange-brown .... 35·00
Z89 50c. bright lilac .... 35·00
Z90 1p. bistre and ultramarine .... 55·00

RABAT

The British postal agency at this port on the north-west coast of Morocco opened in March 1886, although the first cancellation, an "A26" killer, was not supplied until May. The initial stock of stamps was from the Gibraltar 1886 overprinted on Bermuda issue.

Stamps of GIBRALTAR *cancelled with Types* B (*code* "O") *or* D.

1886. *Optd on Bermuda (Nos. 1/7).*
Z92 ½d. dull green ....
Z93 1d. rose-red ....
Z94 2½d. ultramarine £140

1886–87. *Queen Victoria £sd issue (Nos. 8/14).*
Z 95 ½d. dull green .... 32·00
Z 96 1d. rose .... 32·00
Z 97 2d. brown-purple .... 75·00
Z 98 2½d. blue .... 42·00
Z101 1s. bistre £375

1889. *Surch in Spanish currency (Nos. 15/21).*
Z102 5c. on ½d. green .... 50·00
Z103 10c. on 1d. rose .... 45·00
Z104 25c. on 2½d. bright blue .... 50·00

It is believed that the other surcharges in this series were not supplied to Rabat.

1889–96. *Queen Victoria Spanish currency issue (Nos. 22/33).*
Z105 5c. green .... 20·00
Z106 10c. carmine .... 20·00
Z107 20c. olive-green and brown .... 42·00
Z108 25c. ultramarine .... 21·00
Z109 40c. orange-brown .... 48·00
Z110 50c. bright lilac .... 42·00

SAFFI

The British postal agency at this port opened on 1 July 1891 and was supplied with stamps from the Gibraltar 1889–96 series.

Stamps of GIBRALTAR *cancelled with Types* B (*code* "C") *or* D (*code* "C").

1889–96. *Queen Victoria Spanish currency issue (Nos. 22/33).*
Z111 5c. green .... 21·00
Z112 10c. carmine .... 21·00
Z113 20c. olive-green and brown .... 48·00
Z115 25c. ultramarine .... 23·00
Z116 40c. orange-brown .... 80·00
Z117 50c. bright lilac .... 60·00
Z118 1p. bistre and ultramarine .... 65·00
Z119 2p. black and carmine .... 75·00

TANGIER

The British postal agency in Tangier opened on 1 April 1857 and from 1 March of the following year letters from it sent via the packet service to Great Britain required franking with Great Britain stamps.

No identifiable postmark was supplied to Tangier until 1872 and all earlier mail was cancelled with one of the Gibraltar marks. In April 1872 a postmark as Type A was supplied on which the "N" of "TANGIER" was reversed. A corrected version, with code letter "A", followed in 1878, but both were used as origin or arrival marks and the Great Britain stamps continued to be cancelled with Gibraltar obliterators. The Type A postmarks generally fell into disuse after 1880 and very few identifiable marks occur on mail from Tangier until the introduction of Gibraltar stamps on 1 January 1886.

Stamps of GIBRALTAR *cancelled with Types* A (*codes* "A" *or* "C"), B (*code* "A") *or* D.

1886. *Optd on Bermuda (Nos. 1/7).*
Z120 ½d. dull green .... 42·00
Z121 1d. rose-red .... 65·00
Z122 2d. purple-brown £140
Z123 2½d. ultramarine .... 42·00
Z124 4d. orange-brown £170
Z125 6d. deep lilac £225
Z126 1s. yellow-brown £500

1886–87. *Queen Victoria £sd issue (Nos. 8/14).*
Z127 ½d. dull green .... 18·00
Z128 1d. rose .... 18·00
Z129 2d. brown-purple .... 48·00
Z130 2½d. blue .... 27·00
Z131 4d. orange-brown .... 80·00
Z132 6d. lilac £120
Z133 1s. bistre £275

1889. *Surch in Spanish currency (Nos. 15/21).*
Z134 5c. on ½d. green .... 29·00
Z135 10c. on 1d. rose .... 20·00
Z136 25c. on 2d. brown-purple .... 38·00
Z137 25c. on 2½d. bright blue .... 29·00
Z138 40c. on 4d. orange-brown .... 95·00
Z139 50c. on 6d. bright lilac .... 90·00
Z140 75c. on 1s. bistre £120

1889–96. *Queen Victoria Spanish currency issue (Nos. 22/33).*
Z141 5c. green .... 5·00
Z142 10c. carmine .... 5·00
Z143 20c. olive-green and brown .... 22·00
Z144 20c. olive-green .... 70·00
Z145 25c. ultramarine .... 8·00
Z146 40c. orange-brown .... 13·00
Z147 50c. bright lilac .... 12·00
Z148 75c. olive-green .... 50·00
Z149 1p. bistre .... 60·00
Z150 1p. bistre and ultramarine .... 20·00
Z151 2p. black and carmine .... 40·00
Z152 5p. slate-grey £110

TETUAN

The British postal agency in this northern town opened on 1 April 1890 and was supplied with stamps from the Gibraltar 1889–96 series.

Stamps of GIBRALTAR *cancelled with Types* A (*code* "C"), B (*code* "C" *often inverted*) *or* D (*code* "C").

1889–96. *Queen Victoria Spanish currency issue (Nos. 22/33).*
Z153 5c. green .... 26·00
Z154 10c. carmine .... 30·00
Z155 20c. olive-green and brown .... 55·00
Z157 25c. ultramarine .... 35·00
Z158 40c. orange-brown .... 65·00
Z159 50c. bright lilac .... 65·00
Z161 1p. bistre and ultramarine ....

PRICES FOR STAMPS ON COVER TO 1945	
Nos. 1/16	*from* × 7
Nos. 17/30	*from* × 3
Nos. 31/74	*from* × 3
Nos. 75/6	*from* × 4
Nos. 112/24	*from* × 4
No. 125	
Nos. 126/35	*from* × 5
Nos. 136/42	*from* × 2
Nos. 143/59	*from* × 3
Nos. 160/75	*from* × 8
Nos. 191/9	*from* × 5
Nos. 200/1	*from* × 3
Nos. 202/11	*from* × 4
Nos. 212/15	*from* × 5
Nos. 216/24	*from* × 8
Nos. 225/6	*from* × 2
Nos. 227/30	*from* × 8
Nos. 231/52	*from* × 6

The above prices apply to stamps used on cover from Morocco. Examples of Nos. 31/76 & 231/52 used on cover in G.B. after 1950 have little value.

II. GIBRALTAR ISSUES OVERPRINTED

With the reversion of Gibraltar to sterling in 1898 it became necessary to provide separate issues for the Morocco Agencies which continued to use Spanish currency.

The following were used in all the British postal agencies.

Morocco	**Morocco**
Agencies	**Agencies**
(1)	(2)
Agencies	**Agencies**
Inverted "V" for "A" (Right-hand pane R. 6/6)	Long tail to "S" (Right-hand pane R. 8/2)

Broken "M" (Pl 2 R. 4/5)

Flat top to "C" (Pl 2 R. 4/4)

1898 (1 June)–**1900.** *Nos. 22/8 and 31/2 (Queen Victoria) of Gibraltar optd Typographically (No. 2e) or by lithography (others) with T* 1 (*wide "M" and ear of "g" projecting upwards*), *in black at Gibraltar Chronicle office.*

1	5c. green	3·25	2·75
	a. Inverted "V" for "A"	38·00	45·00
	b. Long tail to "S"	40·00	48·00
	c. Broken "M" in "CENTIMOS"	55·00	
2	10c. carmine	5·00	75
	b. Bisected (5c.) (on cover)	†	£1100
	c. Inverted "V" for "A"	£225	£275
	d. Long tail to "S"	£225	
	e. Lines of opt 5 mm apart (6.00)	6·00	3·25
	ea. Opt double	£600	
3	20c. olive-green and brown	9·50	1·75
	a. Inverted "V" for "A"	70·00	75·00
	b. Long tail to "S"	75·00	80·00
3c	20c. olive-green	11·00	5·50
	ca. Opt double	£475	£600
	cb. Inverted "V" for "A"	80·00	90·00
	cc. Long tail to "S"	85·00	95·00
	cd. Flat top to "C" in "CENTIMOS"	£110	
4	25c. ultramarine	4·50	60
	a. Inverted "V" for "A"	£130	£130
	b. Long tail to "S"	£140	£140
5	40c. orange-brown (2.6.98)	6·00	3·25
	a. Inverted "V" for "A"	£170	£190
	b. Long tail to "S"	£180	£200
	c. Blue opt (7.98)	45·00	32·00
	ca. "Morocco" omitted (R. 1/1)		
6	50c. bright lilac (2.6.98)	17·00	23·00
	a. Inverted "V" for "A"	£250	£325
	b. Long tail to "S"	£300	£350
	c. Blue opt (7.98)	12·00	12·00
7	1p. bistre and ultramarine (2.6.98)	18·00	27·00
	a. Inverted "V" for "A"	£250	£350
	b. Long tail to "S"	£275	£350
	c. Blue opt (7.98)	£150	£190
8	2p. black and carmine (4.6.98)	24·00	27·00
	a. Inverted "V" for "A"	£325	£375
	b. Long tail to "S"	£350	£375
1/8	Set of 8	75·00	65·00

The blue overprint can be easily distinguished by looking through the stamp in front of a strong light.

The listed varieties of overprint occur from the first litho setting. They were corrected on the second setting of July 1898, which produced Nos. 5c, 6c, 7c and further supplies of No. 8. The corrected type was subsequently used to produce additional stocks of Nos. 1/2. Numerous more minor varieties exist from these settings.

No. 2e comes from two further printings in 1900 using a third setting on which the two lines of the overprint were 5 mm apart instead of the 4 mm space used previously and applied typographically.

Agencies	**Morocco**	**Agencies**
"CD" sideways flaw (Left-hand pane R. 1/5)	Broad top to "M" (Left-hand pane R. 7/3)	Hyphen between "nc" (Right-hand pane R. 3/5)

1899 (Feb)–**1902.** *Nos. 22/3, 25/8 and 31/2 (Queen Victoria) of Gibraltar optd typographically with T* 2 (*narrow "M" and ear of "g" horizontal*), *in black by D.L.R., London.*

9	5c. green (4.99)	50	1·00
	a. "CD" sideways	17·00	21·00
	b. Broad top to "M"	9·50	14·00
	c. Hyphen between "nc"	9·50	14·00
	d. Broken "M" in "CENTIMOS"	42·00	
10	10c. carmine	2·75	30
	a. "CD" sideways	27·00	21·00
	b. Broad top to "M"	12·00	13·00
	c. Hyphen between "nc"	12·00	13·00
	d. Opt double	£750	£750
11	20c. olive-green (5.02)	7·50	1·00
	b. Broad top to "M"	38·00	40·00
	c. Hyphen between "nc"	38·00	40·00
	d. Flat top to "C" in "CENTIMOS"	£110	
12	25c. ultramarine (10.99)	11·00	90
	a. "CD" sideways	65·00	55·00
	b. Broad top to "M"	48·00	50·00
	c. Hyphen between "nc"	48·00	50·00
13	40c. orange-brown (3.02)	45·00	35·00
	b. Broad top to "M"	£225	£250
	c. Hyphen between "nc"	£225	£250
14	50c. bright lilac (4.99)	10·00	3·50
	b. Broad top to "M"	£120	£130
	c. Hyphen between "nc"	£120	£130

15		1p. bistre and ultramarine (4.99)	29·00	48·00
	b.	Broad top to "M"	£160	£250
	c.	Hyphen between "nc"	£160	£250
16		2p. black and carmine (3.01)	60·00	48·00
	b.	Broad top to "M"	£350	£375
	c.	Hyphen between "nc"	£350	£375
		9/16 Set of 8	£150	£120
		9s/16s Optd "Specimen" Set of 8	£200	

1903–05. As Nos. 46/51 (King Edward VII) of Gibraltar, but with value in Spanish currency, optd with T 2. Wmk Crown CA. P 14.

17		5c. grey-green and green (1.03)	10·00	3·50
	a.	"CD" sideways	60·00	55·00
	b.	Broad top to "M"	55·00	60·00
	c.	Hyphen between "nc"	55·00	60·00
18		10c. dull purple/red (8.03)	9·00	40
	a.	"CD" sideways	55·00	42·00
	b.	Broad top to "M"	50·00	42·00
	c.	Hyphen between "nc"	50·00	42·00
	w.	Wmk inverted	40·00	
19		20c. grey-green and carmine (9.04)	17·00	45·00
	a.	"CD" sideways	£120	£190
	b.	Broad top to "M"	£110	£190
	c.	Hyphen between "nc"	£110	£190
20		25c. purple and black/blue (1.7.03)	8·00	30
	a.	"CD" sideways	60·00	48·00
	b.	Broad top to "M"	55·00	48·00
	c.	Hyphen between "nc"	55·00	48·00
21		50c. purple and violet (3.7.05)	90·00	£160
	a.	"CD" sideways	£375	£600
	b.	Broad top to "M"	£350	£600
	c.	Hyphen between "nc"	£350	£600
22		1p. black and carmine (19.11.05)	40·00	£150
	a.	"CD" sideways	£250	£500
	b.	Broad top to "M"	£225	£500
	c.	Hyphen between "nc"	£225	£500
23		2p. black and blue (19.11.05)	50·00	£120
	a.	"CD" sideways	£300	£475
	b.	Broad top to "M"	£275	£475
	c.	Hyphen between "nc"	£275	£475
		17/23 Set of 7	£200	£425
		17s/23s Optd "Specimen" Set of 7	£200	

Examples of Nos. 19 and 21/3 are known showing a forged Registered Mazagan postmark dated "15 SP 10".

1905 (Jan)–06. As Nos. 17/23 but wmk Mult Crown CA. Ordinary paper (5, 10, 20c.) or chalk-surfaced paper (others).

24		5c. grey-green and green (4.05)	11·00	3·50
	a.	"CD" sideways	65·00	48·00
	b.	Broad top to "M"	65·00	48·00
	c.	Hyphen between "nc"	£850	£950
	d.	Chalk-surfaced paper (1.06)	8·50	5·00
	da.	"CD" sideways	55·00	55·00
	db.	Broad top to "M"	55·00	55·00
25		10c. dull purple/red	12·00	2·00
	a.	"CD" sideways	65·00	40·00
	b.	Broad top to "M"	65·00	40·00
	cw.	Wmk inverted	26·00	20·00
	d.	Chalk-surfaced paper (12.05)	6·00	2·00
	da.	"CD" sideways	45·00	40·00
	db.	Broad top to "M"	45·00	40·00
26		20c. grey-green and carmine (1.06)	5·50	30·00
	a.	"CD" sideways	55·00	£160
	b.	Broad top to "M"	55·00	£160
27		25c. purple and black/blue (6.06)	45·00	8·50
	a.	"CD" sideways	£325	£160
	b.	Broad top to "M"	£325	£160
28		50c. purple and violet (7.06)	7·50	48·00
	a.	"CD" sideways	£150	£275
	b.	Broad top to "M"	£150	£275
29		1p. black and carmine (11.05)	32·00	80·00
	a.	"CD" sideways	£225	£325
	b.	Broad top to "M"	£225	£325
30		2p. black and blue (11.05)	17·00	35·00
	a.	"CD" sideways	£180	£250
	b.	Broad top to "M"	£180	£250
		24/30 Set of 7	£110	£190

Examples of Nos. 26 and 28/30 are known showing a forged Registered Mazagan postmark dated "15 SP 10".

Control of the British postal agencies in Morocco returned to the G.P.O., London, from 1 January 1907.

All the following issues are overprinted on Great Britain

III. BRITISH CURRENCY

Stamps overprinted "MOROCCO AGENCIES" only were primarily intended for use on parcels (and later, air-mail correspondence), and were on sale at British P.Os throughout Morocco including Tangier, until 1937.

PRICES. Our prices for used stamps with these overprints are for specimens used in Morocco. These stamps were valid for postal purposes in Great Britain from the summer of 1950 onwards. Examples with G.B. postmarks are worth 50 per cent of the used prices quoted.

MOROCCO AGENCIES (4)	**MOROCCO AGENCIES** (5)	MOROCCO AGENCIES (6)

1907 (30 Apr)–13. King Edward VII optd as T 4 or 5 (2s.6d.).

(a) De La Rue printings. Ordinary paper (½d., 1d., 4d. (No. 35) or chalk-surfaced paper (others).

31		½d. pale yellowish green (1.6.07)	2·25	8·50
32		1d. scarlet (5.5.07)	9·50	5·50
33		2d. pale grey-green and carmine-red	10·00	5·50
34		4d. green and chocolate-brown (29.10.07)	3·75	4·25
35		4d. orange (3.12)	12·00	13·00
	a.	Orange-red	10·00	12·00
36		6d. pale dull purple (5.5.07)	15·00	19·00
	a.	Dull purple	17·00	20·00
37		1s. dull green and carmine (5.5.07)	26·00	17·00
38		2s.6d. pale dull purple (5.5.07)	85·00	£130
	a.	Dull purple	85·00	£130
		31/8 Set of 8	£150	£180
		37s/8s Optd "Specimen" Set of 2	£140	

(b) Harrison printing. Ordinary paper.

40		4d. bright orange (No. 286) (1913)	24·00	25·00

(c) Somerset House printing. Ordinary paper.

41		2s.6d. dull greyish purple (No. 315) (1913)	£100	£190

1914–31. King George V.

(a) W 100 (Simple Cypher). Optd with T 4.

42		½d. green	4·00	50
43		1d. scarlet	85	20
44		1½d. red-brown (1921)	3·25	12·00
45		2d. orange (Die I)	4·00	60
46		3d. bluish violet (1921)	1·25	35
47		4d. grey-green (1921)	3·25	1·50
48		6d. reddish purple (chalk-surfaced paper) (1921)	4·75	15·00
49		1s. bistre-brown (1917)	6·00	1·25
	a.	Opt triple, two albino	£120	

(b) W 110 (Single Cypher). Optd with T 6.

50		2s.6d. sepia-brown (Waterlow ptg) (No. 400) (1914)	45·00	55·00
	a.	Re-entry (R. 2/1)	£800	£950
	b.	Opt double, one albino	£180	
51		2s.6d. yellow-brown (D.L.R. ptg) (No. 406) (1917)	48·00	30·00
	a.	Opt double	£1600	£1200
	b.	Opt triple, two albino	£225	
	c.	Pale brown (No. 407)	40·00	50·00
53		2s.6d. chocolate-brown (B.W. ptg) (No. 414)	38·00	25·00
	a.	Opt double, one albino*	£170	
54		5s. rose-red (B.W. ptg) (No. 416) (1931)	55·00	90·00
	a.	Opt triple, two albino	£300	
		42/54 Set of 10	£110	£130
		49s/50s, 54s Optd "Specimen" Set of 3	£200	

*The albino overprint is quite clear, with "MOROCCO" appearing just below "AGENCIES" on the normal overprint and a little to the right as seen from the back. There is also a second faint albino impression just below the normal overprint.

MOROCCO AGENCIES **S** (7)	MOROCCO AGENCIES **S** (8)

Type 7: Opt 14 mm long; ends of "s" cut off diagonally.
Type 8: Opt 15½ mm long; ends of "s" cut off horizontally

1925–36. King George V (W 111 (Block Cypher)) optd with T 8 (4d.) or 7 (others).

55		½d. green	2·00	50
	aw.	Wmk inverted	75·00	
	b.	Optd with Type 8	9·00	42·00
56		1½d. chestnut (1931)	12·00	13·00
57		2d. orange	2·25	1·00
58		2½d. blue	2·50	5·00
	a.	Optd with Type 8	£100	30·00
59		4d. grey-green (1.36)	7·50	35·00
60		6d. purple (1931)	2·00	8·50
	a.	Opt double, one albino	£120	
	b.	Optd with Type 8	1·00	60
61		1s. bistre-brown	17·00	5·00
	as.	Optd "Specimen"	60·00	
	b.	Optd with Type 8	55·00	50·00
		55/61 Set of 7	40·00	55·00

1935 (8 May). Silver Jubilee (Nos. 453/6) optd "MOROCCO AGENCIES" only, as in T 17.

62		½d. green (B.)	1·25	6·50
63		1d. scarlet (B.)	1·25	6·50
64		1½d. red-brown (B.)	2·50	11·00
65		2½d. blue (R.)	2·75	2·50
		62/5 Set of 4	7·00	24·00

1935–37. King George V.

(a) Harrison photo ptgs (Nos. 440/5 and 449). W 111 (Block Cypher). Optd with T 8.

66		1d. scarlet (4.35)	3·25	14·00
67		1½d. red-brown (28.4.36)	3·25	17·00
68		2d. orange (1.5.36)	1·25	8·50
69		2½d. ultramarine (11.2.36)	1·75	4·25
70		3d. violet (2.3.36)	50	30
71		4d. deep grey-green (14.5.36)	50	30
72		1s. bistre-brown (31.8.36)	80	3·75
	s.	Optd "Specimen"	60·00	

(b) Waterlow re-engraved ptgs. W 110 (Single Cypher) optd with T 6.

73		2s.6d. chocolate-brown (No. 450)	42·00	60·00
	s.	Optd "Specimen"	70·00	
74		5s. bright rose-red (No. 451) (2.3.37)	23·00	£100
		66/74 Set of 9	70·00	£190

1936 (26 Oct)–37. King Edward VIII, optd "MOROCCO AGENCIES" only, as in T 18 with "MOROCCO" 14¼ mm long.

75		1d. scarlet	10	30
	a.	"MOROCCO" 15¼ mm long (5.1.37)	6·00	17·00
76		2½d. bright blue	10	15
	a.	"MOROCCO" 15¼ mm long (5.1.37)	1·00	4·25

The first two printings of both values showed all the stamps with the short overprint, Nos. 75/6.

On 5 January 1937 a further printing of both values was placed on sale in London which had the 24 stamps from the bottom two horizontal rows (Rows 19 and 20) with the long overprint, Nos. 75a/6a. Subsequent printings increased the number of long overprints in the sheet to 25 by the addition of R. 8/9, and, finally, to 31 (R. 1/7, R. 7/1, R. 8/1, R. 13/3, 4 and 10, R. 14/6, but without R. 8/9).

For the 1d. value all sheets from cylinder 2 show the first setting. Sheets from cylinder 6 were also used for the first, and for all subsequent settings. The 2½d. value was overprinted on sheets from cylinder 2 throughout.

From 3 June 1937 unoverprinted stamps of Great Britain were supplied to the post offices at Tangier and Tetuan (Spanish Zone) as local stocks of issues overprinted "MOROCCO AGENCIES" were exhausted.

Type E   Type F

Stamps of GREAT BRITAIN cancelled as Types E or F at Tangier.

1937. King George V.

Z170	1½d. red-brown (No. 441)		
Z171	2d. orange (No. 442)		12·00
Z172	3d. violet (No. 444)		12·00
Z173	4d. deep grey-green (No. 445)		9·00
Z174	6d. purple (No. 426a)		9·00
Z175	1s. bistre-brown (No. 449)		32·00
Z176	2s.6d. chocolate-brown (No. 450)		70·00
Z177	5s. bright rose-red (No. 451)		

1937–39. King George VI (Nos. 462/75).

Z178	½d. green		13·00
Z179	1d. scarlet		13·00
Z180	1½d. red-brown		11·00
Z181	2d. orange		11·00
Z182	2½d. ultramarine		8·50
Z183	3d. violet		8·50
Z184	4d. grey-green		8·50
Z185	5d. brown		11·00
Z186	6d. purple		5·50
Z187	7d. emerald-green		9·00
Z188	8d. bright carmine		17·00
Z189	9d. deep olive-green		12·00
Z190	10d. turquoise-blue		17·00
Z191	1s. bistre-brown		5·50

1939–42. King George VI (Nos. 476/8a).

Z192	2s.6d. brown		42·00
Z193	2s.6d. yellow-green		13·00
Z194	5s. red		19·00
Z195	10s. dark blue		80·00
Z196	10s. ultramarine		35·00

1941–42. King George VI pale colours (Nos. 485/90).

Z197	½d. pale green		8·50
Z198	1d. pale scarlet		8·50
Z199	1½d. pale red-brown		8·50
Z200	2d. pale orange		8·50
Z201	2½d. light ultramarine		7·50
Z202	3d. pale violet		5·50

1946. Victory (Nos. 491/2).

Z203	2½d. ultramarine		7·50
Z204	3d. violet		7·50

Type G

Stamps of GREAT BRITAIN cancelled as Type G at Tetuan.

1937. King George V.

Z208	4d. deep grey-green (No. 445)		20·00
Z209	6d. purple (No. 426a)		20·00
Z210	1s. bistre-brown (No. 449)		

1937–39. King George VI (Nos. 465/75).

Z211	2d. orange		17·00
Z212	2½d. ultramarine		
Z213	3d. violet		
Z214	4d. grey-green		17·00
Z215	6d. purple		11·00
Z216	9d. deep olive-green		
Z217	1s. bistre-brown		11·00

1939–42. King George VI (Nos. 476/7).

Z218	2s.6d. brown		
Z219	2s.6d. yellow-green		35·00
Z220	5s. red		45·00

1941. King George VI pale colours (Nos. 485/90).

Z221	½d. pale green		
Z222	2d. pale orange		
Z223	2½d. light ultramarine		
Z224	3d. pale violet		11·00

Other unoverprinted stamps of Great Britain are known with Morocco Agencies postmarks during this period, but it is believed that only Nos. Z170/224 were sold by the local post offices.

The use of unoverprinted stamps in Tangier ceased with the issue of Nos. 261/75 on 1 January 1949. Stamps overprinted "MOROCCO AGENCIES" replaced the unoverprinted values at Tetuan on 16 August 1949.

MOROCCO AGENCIES (9)	**MOROCCO AGENCIES** (10)

1949 (16 Aug). King George VI, optd with T 9 or 10 (2s.6d., 5s.).

77		½d. pale green	1·75	7·00
78		1d. pale scarlet	2·75	9·00
79		1½d. pale red-brown	2·75	9·00
80		2d. pale orange	3·00	9·00
81		2½d. light ultramarine	3·25	10·00

82	3d. pale violet	1·50	1·75
83	4d. grey-green	50	1·25
84	5d. brown	3·00	15·00
85	6d. purple	1·50	1·50
86	7d. emerald-green	50	16·00
87	8d. bright carmine	3·00	6·50
88	9d. deep olive-green	50	11·00
89	10d. turquoise-blue	50	6·50
90	11d. plum	70	7·50
91	1s. bistre-brown	2·75	6·00
92	2s.6d. yellow-green	17·00	35·00
93	5s. red	30·00	60·00
	77/93 Set of 17	65·00	£180

1951 (3 May). *King George VI (Nos. 503/7, 509/10), optd with T* **9** *or* **10** *(2s.6d., 5s.).*

94	½d. pale orange	2·00	1·00
95	1d. light ultramarine	2·00	1·40
96	1½d. pale green	2·00	3·00
97	2d. pale red-brown	2·25	4·00
98	2½d. pale scarlet	2·00	4·25
99	2s.6d. yellow-green (H.M.S. *Victory*)	13·00	21·00
100	5s. red (Dover)	13·00	23·00
	94/100 Set of 7	32·00	50·00

IV. SPANISH CURRENCY

Stamps surcharged in Spanish currency were sold at British P.Os. throughout Morocco until the establishment of the French Zone and the Tangier International Zone, when their use was confined to the Spanish Zone.

During this period further British postal agencies were opened at Alcazar (1907–1916), Fez–Mellah (Jewish quarter) (1909), Marrakesh (1909), Marrakesh–Mellah (Jewish quarter) (1909–17) and Mequinez (1907–1916).

MOROCCO AGENCIES | **MOROCCO AGENCIES**

5 CENTIMOS (11) | **6 PESETAS** (12)

1907 (1 Jan)–**12**. *King Edward VII surch as T* **11** *(5c. to 1p.) or* **12** *(3p. to 12p.).*

(a) De La Rue printings. Ordinary paper (Nos. 112/13, 116, 118, 122/3) or chalk-surfaced paper (others).

112	5c. on ½d. pale yellowish green	9·00	20
	a. Yellowish green	9·00	20
113	10c. on 1d. scarlet	13·00	10
	a. Bright scarlet	13·00	10
114	15c. on 1½d. pale dull purple and green	6·00	1·00
	a. Slate-purple and bluish green	3·25	20
	b. "1" of "15" omitted	£5000	
115	20c. on 2d. pale grey-green and carmine-red	3·00	30
	a. Pale grey-green and scarlet	3·75	70
116	25c. on 2½d. ultramarine	3·00	20
	a. Pale ultramarine	1·75	20
117	40c. on 4d. green & chocolate-brn (29.10.07)	1·25	3·00
	a. Deep green and chocolate-brown	2·00	1·75
118	40c. on 4d. pale orange (12.5.10)	2·50	1·25
	a. Orange-red	1·00	60
119	50c. on 5d. dull purple and ultramarine	4·00	3·75
	a. Slate-purple and ultramarine	2·50	3·50
120	1p. on 10d. dull purple and carmine	28·00	15·00
	a. Slate-purple and carmine	22·00	12·00
	b. No cross on crown		
121	3p. on 2s.6d. pale dull purple	21·00	25·00
	a. Dull purple	21·00	25·00
122	6p. on 5s. bright carmine	35·00	45·00
	a. Deep bright carmine	35·00	45·00
123	12p. on 10s. ultramarine (30.4.07)	80·00	75·00
	112/23 Set of 12	£170	£140
	117s, 123s Optd "Specimen" Set of 2	£140	

(b) Harrison printing. Ordinary paper.

124	25c. on 2½d. bright blue (No. 283) (1912)	40·00	27·00
	a. Dull blue	26·00	27·00

(c) Somerset House printing. Ordinary paper.

125	12p. on 10s. blue (No. 319) (1912)	£180	£225

No. 114b occurred on stamps from the first vertical row of one sheet.

1912. *King George V (W* **49** *(Imperial Crown)) surch as T* **11**.

126	5c. on ½d. green (No. 339)	3·00	20
127	10c. on 1d. scarlet (No. 342)	1·00	10
	a. No cross on crown	£110	55·00

MOROCCO AGENCIES

3 CENTIMOS (13) | **MOROCCO AGENCIES** | **10 CENTIMOS** (14)

MOROCCO AGENCIES | **MOROCCO AGENCIES**

15 CENTIMOS (15) | **6 PESETAS** (16)

1914–26. *King George V.*

(a) W **100** *(Simple Cypher). Surch as T* **11** *(5c.),* **13** *(3c. and 40c.)*,* **15** *(15c.) and* **14** *(remainder).*

128	3c. on ½d. green (1917)	1·25	5·00
129	5c. on ½d. green	75	10
130	10c. on 1d. scarlet	1·50	10
	y. Wmk inverted and reversed	—	£160
131	15c. on 1½d. red-brown (1915)	1·00	10
	a. Surch double, one albino	80·00	
132	20c. on 2d. orange (Die I)	1·00	25
	a. Surch double, one albino	80·00	
133	25c. on 2½d. blue (*shades*)	1·75	25
	a. Surch double, one albino	60·00	
	w. Wmk inverted		
134	40c. on 4d. grey-green (1917)	3·50	4·00
	a. Surch double, one albino		
135	1p. on 10d. turquoise-blue	3·75	7·50
	a. Surch double, one albino	85·00	

*The surcharge on Nos. 134, 148 and 158 is as T **713** *for the value and T* **715** *for "MOROCCO AGENCIES".*

(b) W **110** *(Single Cypher). Surch as T* **16**.

(i) Waterlow printings.

136	6p. on 5s. rose-carmine	29·00	48·00
	a. Surch double, one albino	£140	
	b. Surch triple, two albino	£160	
137	6p. on 5s. pale rose-carmine	£130	£180
	a. Surch double, one albino	£190	
138	12p. on 10s. indigo-blue (R.)	£100	£170
	a. Surch double, one albino	£225	
	b. Surch triple, two albino		
	136s, 138s Optd "Specimen" Set of 2	£180	

(ii) De La Rue printings.

139	3p. on 2s.6d. grey-brown (1918)	38·00	£110
	a. Surch double, one albino		
140	3p. on 2s.6d. yellow-brown	35·00	£140
	a. Surch double, one albino	£150	
141	12p. on 10s. blue (R.)	90·00	£160
	a. Surch double, one albino	£275	

(iii) Bradbury Wilkinson printings.

142	3p. on 2s.6d. chocolate-brown (1926)	23·00	75·00
	128/42 Set of 11	£140	£275

1925–31. *King George V (W* **111** *(Block Cypher)), surch as T* **11**, **13**, **14** *or* **15**.

143	5c. on ½d. green (1931)	3·00	16·00
144	10c. on 1d. scarlet (1929)	20·00	27·00
145	15c. on 1½d. red-brown	7·50	23·00
146	20c. on 2d. orange (1931)	3·00	9·00
	a. Surch double, one albino	85·00	
147	25c. on 2½d. blue	2·50	2·50
	a. Surch double, one albino	60·00	
	w. Wmk inverted	55·00	
148	40c. on 4d. grey-green (1930)	2·50	2·50
	a. Surch double, one albino		
	143/8 Set of 6	35·00	70·00

MOROCCO AGENCIES | **10 CENTIMOS** (17) | **MOROCCO AGENCIES** | **10 CENTIMOS** (18)

1935 (8 May). *Silver Jubilee (Nos. 453/6). Surch as T* **17**.

149	5c. on ½d. green (B.)	1·00	1·25
150	10c. on 1d. scarlet (B.)	2·75	2·25
	a. Pair, one with "CENTIMES"	£1500	£1800
151	15c. on 1½d. red-brown (B.)	5·50	19·00
152	25c. on 2½d. blue (R.)	3·50	2·25
	149/52 Set of 4	11·50	22·00

No. 150a occurred on R. 5/4 of a small second printing made in June 1935. The error can only be identified when *se-tenant* with a normal No. 150. Beware of forgeries.

1935–37. *King George V (Harrison photo ptgs) (Nos. 439/43, 445 and 448). Surch as T* **11**, **13**, **14** *or* **15**. *W* **111** *(Block Cypher).*

153	5c. on ½d. green (9.6.36)	1·00	1·00
154	10c. on 1d. scarlet (11.36)	2·50	11·00
155	15c. on 1½d. red-brown (4.35)	6·00	3·25
156	20c. on 2d. orange (26.10.36)	50	25
157	25c. on 2½d. ultramarine (8.9.36)	1·25	4·75
158	40c. on 4d. deep grey-green (18.5.37)	50	3·50
159	1p. on 10d. turquoise-blue (14.4.37)	6·00	30
	153/9 Set of 7	16·00	38·00

1936 (26 Oct)–**37**. *King Edward VIII surch as T* **18** *with "MOROCCO" 14¼ mm long.*

160	5c. on ½d. green	10	10
161	10c. on 1d. scarlet	50	2·00
	a. "MOROCCO" 15¼ mm long (5.1.37)	3·50	15·00
162	15c. on 1½d. red-brown	10	15
163	25c. on 2½d. bright blue	10	10
	160/3 Set of 4	65	2·00

The first three printings of the 10c. on 1d. (from cyls 4, 5 and 6) showed all stamps with the short surcharge (No. 161).

On 5 January 1937 a further printing was placed on sale in London which had 49 stamps in the sheet (R. 1/2 to 11, R. 2/1, 5 and 6, 8 and 9, R. 3/5, R. 4/5, R. 5/4 and 5, 10, R. 6/6 and 7, R. 7/8, R. 8/8, R. 9/8, R. 11/7, 9, R. 13/2 to 5, 7 and 8, R. 14/1, 7, R. 15/7, 11, R. 16/5, 10, R. 17/4, 10 and 11, R. 18/1, R. 19/2, R. 20/1 and 2, 3, 7, 9) with long

---

surcharge (No. 161a). The next printing increased the number of long surcharges in the sheet to 50 (R. 10/2), but the final version, although retaining 50 long surcharges, showed them on R. 1/2 to 11, R. 17/5 to 8 and the entire rows 18, 19 and 20. The first two printings with long surcharges were from cylinder 6 and the last from cylinder 13.

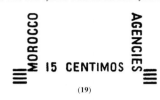

MOROCCO AGENCIES 15 CENTIMOS (19)

1937 (13 May). *Coronation (No. 461), surch as T* **19**.

164	15c. on 1½d. maroon (B.)	70	70

MOROCCO AGENCIES | **MOROCCO AGENCIES**

10 CENTIMOS (20) | **10 CENTIMOS** (21)

1937 (June)–**52**. *King George VI (Nos. 462/4, 466, 468, 471 and 474), surch as T* **20**.

165	5c. on ½d. green (B.)	1·25	30
166	10c. on 1d. scarlet	1·00	10
167	15c. on 1½d. red-brown (B.) (4.8.37)	1·50	25
168	25c. on 2½d. ultramarine	2·00	1·25
169	40c. on 4d. grey-green (9.40)	30·00	13·00
170	70c. on 7d. emerald-green (9.40)	1·75	15·00
171	1p. on 10d. turquoise-blue (16.6.52)	2·25	3·75
	165/71 Set of 7	35·00	30·00

1940 (6 May). *Centenary of First Adhesive Postage Stamps (Nos. 479/81 and 483), surch as T* **21**.

172	5c. on ½d. green (B.)	30	2·75
173	10c. on 1d. scarlet	3·75	2·50
174	15c. on 1½d. red-brown (B.)	70	3·00
175	25c. on 2½d. ultramarine	80	1·75
	172/5 Set of 4	5·00	9·00

25 CENTIMOS (22) | **45 PESETAS MOROCCO AGENCIES** (23)

MOROCCO AGENCIES

1948 (26 Apr). *Silver Wedding (Nos. 493/4), surch with T* **22** *or* **23**.

176	25c. on 2½d. ultramarine	1·00	30
177	45p. on £1 blue	17·00	22·00

1948 (29 July). *Olympic Games (Nos. 495/8), variously surch as T* **22**.

178	25c. on 2½d. ultramarine	50	1·50
179	30c. on 3d. violet	50	1·50
	a. Crown flaw	55·00	
180	60c. on 6d. bright purple	50	1·50
181	1p.20c. on 1s. brown	60	1·50
	a. Surch double	£850	
	178/81 Set of 4	1·90	5·50

1951 (3 May)–**52**. *King George VI (Nos. 503/5 and 507/8), surch as T* **20**.

182	5c. on ½d. pale orange	2·00	5·00
183	10c. on 1d. light ultramarine	3·25	8·00
184	15c. on 1½d. pale green	1·75	18·00
185	25c. on 2½d. pale scarlet	1·75	11·00
186	40c. on 4d. light ultramarine (26.5.52)	60	11·00
	182/6 Set of 5	8·50	48·00

V. FRENCH CURRENCY

For use in the British postal agencies at Casablanca (closed 14.8.37), Fez (closed 8.1.38), Fez–Mellah (closed after 1930), Marrakesh (closed 14.8.37), Mazagan (closed 14.8.37), Mogador (closed 31.10.33), Rabat (closed 8.1.38) and Saffi (closed 14.8.37).

MOROCCO AGENCIES | **MOROCCO AGENCIES**

25 CENTIMES (24) | **1 FRANC** (25)

1917–24. *King George V (W* **100** *(Simple Cypher)), surch as T* **24** *or* **25** *(1f.).*

191	3c. on ½d. green (R.)	1·00	2·50
192	5c. on ½d. green	40	20
193	10c. on 1d. scarlet	3·25	40
194	15c. on 1½d. red-brown	2·50	20
195	25c. on 2½d. blue	2·00	20
196	40c. on 4d. slate-green	2·50	20
197	50c. on 5d. yellow-brown (1923)	80	2·75
198	75c. on 9d. olive-green (1924)	1·00	75
	a. Surch double, one albino	£100	
199	1f. on 10d. turquoise-blue	7·00	3·00
	a. Surch double, one albino	85·00	
	191/9 Set of 9	18·00	10·50

1924–32. *King George V (B.W. ptg).* W **110** (*Single Cypher*), *surch as T* **25**, *but closer vertical spacing.*

200	3f. on 2s.6d. chocolate-brown	7·50	1·50
	a. Major re-entry (R. 1/2)	£425	£425
	b. Surch double, one albino		
	c. Reddish brown	13·00	10·00
201	6f. on 5s. rose-red (1932)	38·00	42·00
200s/1s Optd "Specimen" Set of 2		£130	

1925–34. *King George V (*W **111** (*Block Cypher*)), *surch as T* **24** *or* **25** (*1f.*).

202	5c. on ½d. green	30	6·50
203	10c. on 1d. scarlet	30	2·00
	a. Surch double, one albino	90·00	
204	15c. on 1½d. red-brown	1·00	1·75
205	25c. on 2½d. blue	1·50	50
206	40c. on 4d. grey-green	60	80
	a. Surch double, one albino	65·00	
207	50c. on 5d. yellow-brown	1·50	10
	w. Wmk inverted	75·00	
208	75c. on 9d. olive-green	4·00	15
	a. Surch double, one albino	£130	
	w. Wmk inverted	—	£120
209	90c. on 9d. olive-green	17·00	7·50
210	1f. on 10d. turquoise-blue	1·25	10
	a. Surch double, one albino	£100	
211	1f.50 on 1s. bistre-brown	10·00	2·25
	s. Optd "Specimen"	55·00	
202/11 Set of 10		32·00	19·00

1935 (8 May). *Silver Jubilee (Nos. 453/6), surch as T* **17**, *but in French currency.*

212	5c. on ½d. green (B.)	15	15
213	10c. on 1d. scarlet (B.)	3·00	50
214	15c. on 1½d. red-brown (B.)	35	50
215	25c. on 2½d. blue (R.)	30	25
212/15 Set of 4		3·50	1·25

1935–37. *King George V (Harrison photo ptgs.* W **111** (*Block Cypher*)), *surch as T* **24** *or* **25** (*1f.*).

216	5c. on ½d. green (10.35)	50	5·00
217	10c. on 1d. scarlet (2.3.36)	35	30
218	15c. on 1½d. red-brown	4·75	5·50
219	25c. on 2½d. ultramarine (25.9.36)	30	15
220	40c. on 4d. deep grey-green (2.12.36)	30	15
221	50c. on 5d. yellow-brown (15.9.36)	30	15
222	90c. on 9d. deep olive-green (15.2.37)	35	1·75
223	1f. on 10d. turquoise-blue (10.2.37)	30	30
224	1f.50 on 1s. bistre-brown (20.7.37)	75	3·25
	s. Optd "Specimen"	55·00	

1935–36. *King George V (Waterlow re-engraved ptgs.* W **100** (*Single Cypher*), *surch as T* **25**, *but closer vertical spacing.*

225	3f. on 2s.6d. chocolate-brown (No. 450)	4·75	12·00
226	6f. on 5s. bright rose-red (No. 451) (17.6.36)	6·00	21·00
216/26 Set of 11		17·00	45·00
225s/6s Optd "Specimen" Set of 2		£130	

1936 (26 Oct). *King Edward VIII, surch as T* **18**, *but in French currency.*

227	5c. in ½d. green	10	15
	a. Bar through "POSTAGE"	£550	
228	15c. on 1½d. red-brown	10	15

No. 227a involved R. 18/10 to 12 on a total of eight sheets. The bar, probably a printers rule, became progressively longer so that on four of the sheets it extends over all three stamps. Price quoted is for an example with the bar through the entire word.

1937 (13 May). *Coronation (No. 461), surch as T* **19**, *but in French currency.*

229	15c. on 1½d. maroon (B.)	30	20

1937 (June). *King George VI, surch as T* **20**, *but in French currency.*

230	5c. on ½d. green (B.)	2·25	2·50

Stamps surcharged in French currency were withdrawn from sale on 8 January 1938.

VI. TANGIER INTERNATIONAL ZONE

By an agreement between Great Britain, France and Spain, Tangier was declared an international zone in 1924. Stamps overprinted "Morocco Agencies" or surcharged in Spanish currency were used there until replaced by Nos. 231/4.

PRICES. Our note *re* U.K. usage (at beginning of Section III) also applies to "TANGIER" optd stamps.

TANGIER
(26)

TANGIER
(27)

1927. *King George V (*W **111** (*Block Cypher*)), *optd with T* **26**.

231	½d. green	3·50	20
	a. Opt double, one albino		
232	1d. scarlet	3·50	25
	a. Inverted "Q" for "O" (R. 20/3)	£800	
233	1½d. chestnut	6·00	3·75
234	2d. orange	3·25	20
	a. Opt double, one albino	80·00	
231/4 Set of 4		15·00	4·00

1934 (Dec)–**35.** *King George V (Harrison photo ptgs.* W **111** (*Block Cypher*)), *optd with T* **26**.

235	½d. green (2.35)	1·25	1·60
236	1d. scarlet	4·50	2·50
237	1½d. red-brown	75	20
235/7 Set of 3		6·00	3·75

1935 (8 May). *Silver Jubilee (Nos. 453/5), optd with T* **27**.

238	½d. green (B.)	1·50	5·50
239	1d. scarlet	15·00	16·00

240	1½d. red-brown (B.)	1·25	1·25
238/40 Set of 3		16·00	20·00

1936 (26 Oct). *King Edward VIII, optd with T* **26**.

241	½d. green	10	20
242	1d. scarlet	10	10
243	1½d. red-brown	15	10
241/3 Set of 3		30	30

TANGIER (28) **TANGIER** (29) **TANGIER**

1937 (13 May). *Coronation (No. 461), optd with T* **28**.

244	1½d. maroon (B.)	50	50

1937. *King George VI (Nos. 462/4), optd with T* **29**.

245	½d. green (B.) (June)	2·50	1·75
246	1d. scarlet (June)	8·00	1·75
247	1½d. red-brown (B.) (4 Aug)	2·50	40
245/7 Set of 3		11·50	3·50

TANGIER (30) **TANGIER** (31)

1940 (6 May). *Centenary of First Adhesive Postage Stamps (Nos. 479/81), optd with T* **30**.

248	½d. green (B.)	30	5·00
249	1d. scarlet	45	60
250	1½d. red-brown (B.)	2·00	6·00
248/50 Set of 3		2·50	10·50

1944. *King George VI pale colours (Nos. 485/6), optd with T* **29**.

251	½d. pale green (B.)	12·00	5·00
252	1d. pale scarlet	12·00	3·50

1946 (11 June). *Victory (Nos. 491/2), optd as T* **31**.

253	2½d. ultramarine	65	65
254	3d. violet	65	2·00

The opt on No. 254 is smaller (23×2½ mm).

1948 (26 Apr). *Royal Silver Wedding (Nos. 493/4), optd with T* **30**.

255	2½d. ultramarine	50	15
	a. Opt omitted (in vert pair with stamp optd at top)	£5000	
256	£1 blue	20·00	25·00

No. 255a comes from a sheet on which the overprint is misplaced downwards resulting in the complete absence of the opt from the six stamps of the top row. On the rest of the sheet the opt falls at the top of each stamp instead of at the foot (*Price £250, unused, £350 used*).

1948 (29 July). *Olympic Games (Nos. 495/8), optd with T* **30**.

257	2½d. ultramarine	1·00	2·00
258	3d. violet	1·00	2·25
	a. Crown flaw	65·00	
259	6d. bright purple	1·00	2·25
260	1s. brown	1·00	1·75
257/60 Set of 4		3·50	7·50

1949 (1 Jan). *King George VI, optd with T* **29**.

261	2d. pale orange	5·00	6·50
262	2½d. light ultramarine	1·75	6·50
263	3d. pale violet	70	70
264	4d. grey-green	11·00	11·00
265	5d. brown	3·75	21·00
266	6d. purple	70	30
267	7d. emerald-green	1·25	14·00
268	8d. bright carmine	3·75	12·00
269	9d. deep olive-green	1·50	13·00
270	10d. turquoise-blue	1·25	13·00
271	11d. plum	1·75	12·00
272	1s. bistre-brown	1·25	2·75
273	2s.6d. yellow-green	4·50	13·00
274	5s. red	13·00	38·00
275	10s. ultramarine	48·00	£110
261/75 Set of 15		90·00	£250

1949 (10 Oct). *75th Anniv of U.P.U. (Nos. 499/502), optd with T* **30**.

276	2½d. ultramarine	70	2·75
	a. Lake in India	55·00	
277	3d. violet	70	1·75
278	6d. bright purple	70	1·25
279	1s. brown	70	3·25
276/9 Set of 4		2·50	8·00

1950 (2 Oct)–**51.** *King George VI, optd with T* **29** *or* **30** (*shilling values*).

280	½d. pale orange (3.5.51)	85	1·50
281	1d. pale ultramarine (3.5.51)	1·00	3·00
282	1½d. pale green (3.5.51)	1·00	14·00
283	2d. pale red-brown (3.5.51)	1·00	2·50
284	2½d. pale scarlet (3.5.51)	1·00	5·00
285	4d. light ultramarine	3·00	3·00
286	2s.6d. yell-grn (H.M.S. Victory) (3.5.51)	9·50	5·00
287	5s. red (Dover) (3.5.51)	15·00	17·00
288	10s. ultramarine (St. George) (3.5.51)	20·00	17·00
280/8 Set of 9		48·00	60·00

Muscat

An independent Arab Sultanate in Eastern Arabia with an Indian postal administration.

The Indian post office at Muscat town is officially recorded as having opened on 1 May 1864. Stamps of India were provided for its use, most surviving examples being of the ½a. value, although others to the 8a. are known.

The office was initially included in the Bombay Postal Circle and the first postmark, so far only recorded on stampless covers, was a single circle, 21½ mm in diameter, broken at the top by "MUSCAT" and with the date in two lines across the centre. This was followed by a cancellation showing the post office number, "309", within a diamond of 13, later 16, bars. It is believed that this was used in conjunction with a single ring date stamp inscribed "MUSCAT".

1864 Diamond

In 1869 the office was transferred to the Sind Circle, assigned a new number, "23", and issued with a duplex cancellation. Major reorganisation of the postal service in 1873 resulted in Muscat becoming office "K-4". For ten years from 1873 the cancellations do not, very confusingly, carry any indication of the year of use.

1869 Duplex

1873 Duplex

Muscat rejoined the Bombay Circle in 1879 and was issued with a cancellation showing a "B" within a square of horizontal bars. The date stamp used at this time was unique in that it carried the inscription "MASKAT", although the spelling reverted to the more usual form by 1882. The square cancellation had been replaced by a similar circular mark by 1884.

Subsequent postmarks were of various circular types, all inscribed "MUSCAT".

There was only one Indian post office in Muscat, but a further office did exist, from 12 April 1868, at the Muscat dependency of Guadur, a port on the Mekran coast of Baluchistan.

No cancellations have been reported from Guadur before its transfer to the Sind Circle in 1869. Cancellations are all similar in style to those for Muscat, Guadur being initially assigned number "24", although an office in Southern India is also known to have used this numeral. The 1869 duplex is interesting in that it is inscribed "GWADUR". Under the 1873 reorganisation the office became "4/K-1", this postmark using the "GUADUR" spelling.

1869 Duplex

(Currency 12 pies = 1 anna; 16 annas = 1 Indian rupee)

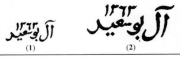

(1) (2)

1944 (20 Nov). *Bicentenary of Al-Busaid Dynasty. Nos. 259/60, 265/8 and 269a/77 (King George VI) of India optd ("AL BUSAID 1363" in Arabic script) as T 1 or 2 (rupee values).*

1	3p. slate	30	7·00
	w. Wmk inverted	5·00	
2	½a. purple	30	7·00
3	9p. green	30	7·00
4	1a. carmine	30	7·00
5	1½a. dull violet	30	7·00
6	2a. vermilion	40	7·00
	w. Wmk inverted		
7	3a. bright violet	1·00	7·00
	w. Wmk inverted	5·00	
8	3½a. bright blue	1·00	7·00
9	4a. brown	1·00	7·00
10	6a. turquoise-green	1·00	7·00
11	8a. slate-violet	1·25	7·00
12	12a. lake	1·25	7·00
13	14a. purple	4·00	11·00
14	1r. grey and red-brown	1·50	11·00
15	2r. purple and brown	3·50	17·00
1/15	Set of 15	16·00	£110

OFFICIAL STAMPS

1944 (20 Nov). *Bicentenary of Al-Busaid Dynasty. Nos. O138, O143, O144a/6 and 146b/50 of India optd as T 1 or 2 (1r.).*

O 1	3p. slate	60	13·00
O 2	½a. purple	70	13·00
O 3	9p. green	70	13·00
O 4	1a. carmine	70	13·00
O 5	1½a. dull violet	75	13·00
O 6	2a. vermilion	1·00	13·00
O 7	2½a. bright violet	4·25	13·00
O 8	4a. brown	2·25	13·00
O 9	8a. slate-violet	4·25	15·00
O10	1r. grey and red-brown	2·50	23·00
O1/10	Set of 10	16·00	£130

Used prices quoted for Nos. 1/15 and O1/10 are for stamps cancelled with contemporary postmarks of the Indian postal administration. Those with cancellations of the subsequent British post office are worth considerably less. Collectors are warned against forged overprints and cancellations.

From December 1947 there was a Pakistani postal administration and stamps of Pakistan were used until 31 March 1948. The subsequent British administration operated from 1 April 1948 to 29 April 1966 when the stamps of the BRITISH POSTAL AGENCIES IN EASTERN ARABIA were used. Guadur, however, continued to use the stamps of Pakistan until the dependency was finally ceded to that country in 1953.

Natal *see* South Africa

Nauru *see after* Australia

Nevis *see* St. Kitts-Nevis

New Brunswick *see* Canada

Newfoundland *see* Canada

New Guinea *see after* Australia

New Hebrides

Stamps of NEW SOUTH WALES were used by various Postal Agencies in the New Hebrides from August 1891 onwards. From late 1892 the N.S.W. agency at Port Vila was run by the Australian New Hebrides Company who, from 1897, issued local 1d. and 2d. stamps for the carriage of mail on the Company's ships. These can be found used in combination with N.S.W. issues. Similar Postal Agencies supplying the stamps of NEW CALEDONIA were opened from 1903 onwards. The use of New South Wales and New Caledonia stamps was prohibited after 1 December 1908.

PRICES FOR STAMPS ON COVER TO 1945	
Nos. 1/8 (F1/5)	from × 10
No. 9	from × 2
Nos. 10/16 (F6/10)	from × 8
Nos. 18/28 (F11/32)	from × 6
Nos. 30/4 (F33/7)	from × 4
No. 35 (F32a)	
Nos. 36/9	from × 3
Nos. 40/2 (F38/41)	from × 4
Nos. 43/51 (F42/52)	from × 5
Nos. 52/63 (F53/64)	from × 3
Nos. D1/5 (FD53/7)	from × 100
Nos. D6/10 (FD65/9)	from × 8

ANGLO-FRENCH CONDOMINIUM

The New Hebrides, an island group in the south-west Pacific, were recognised as an area of joint Anglo-French influence in 1878. The position was regularised by the Convention of 20 October 1906 which created a Condominium, the two nations having equal rights and shares in the administration of the islands.

Stamps inscribed in English or French were issued concurrently and had equal validity throughout the islands. A common currency was reflected in the face values from 1938.

Where common designs were used, the main differences between stamps inscribed in English and those in French are as follows:
(a) Inscriptions in English or French.
(b) Position of cyphers. French issues normally have "RF" to the right or above the British royal cypher.
(c) French issues are without watermark, *unless otherwise stated.*

Inscriptions in English	Inscriptions in French

I. STAMPS INSCRIBED IN ENGLISH

NEW HEBRIDES.   **NEWHEBRIDES**

CONDOMINIUM.   **CONDOMINIUM**
(1)   (2)

1908 (29 Oct). *T* **23** *and* **24** *of Fiji optd with T* **1** *by Govt Printing Establishment, Suva. On the bicoloured stamps the word "FIJI" obliterated by a bar in the colour of the word. P* 14.

(a) Wmk Multiple Crown CA. Ordinary paper (½d., 1d.) or chalk-surfaced paper (1s.).
1	½d. green and pale green (No. 115)	4·50	15·00
1a	½d. green (No. 118)	40	7·00
2	1d. red	50	40
	a. Opt omitted (in vert pair with normal)	£6000	
3	1s. green and carmine	19·00	3·75

(b) Wmk Crown CA.
4	½d. green and grey-green	50·00	80·00
5	2d. dull purple and orange	60	70
6	2½d. dull purple and blue/*blue*	60	70
7	5d. dull purple and olive	80	2·00
8	6d. dull purple and carmine	70	1·25
9	1s. green and carmine	£130	£250
1/9 *Set of 9*		£180	£300

1910 (15 Dec). *Types as last optd with T* **2** *by D.L.R. Ordinary paper (½d. to 2½d.) or chalk-surfaced paper (5d., 6d., 1s.). Wmk Multiple Crown CA. P* 14.
10	½d. green	3·50	24·00
11	1d. red	10·00	8·50
12	2d. grey	60	3·00
13	2½d. bright blue	65	4·25
14	5d. dull purple and olive-green	1·50	5·50
15	6d. dull and deep purple	1·25	5·00
16	1s. black/*green* (R.)	1·25	7·50
10/16 *Set of 7*		17·00	50·00
10s/16s Optd "Specimen" *Set of 7*		£275	

1d.
(4)

3 Weapons and Idols

(*Des J. Giraud. Recess D.L.R.*)
1911 (25 July). *Wmk Mult Crown CA. P* 14.
18	**3**	½d. green	85	1·75
19		1d. red	3·75	2·00
20		2d. grey	8·00	4·00

21		2½d. ultramarine	3·00	5·50
24		5d. sage-green	4·50	7·00
25		6d. purple	3·00	5·00
26		1s. black/*green*	2·75	13·00
27		2s. purple/*blue*	24·00	22·00
28		5s. green/*yellow*	35·00	48·00
18/28 *Set of 9*			75·00	95·00
18s/28s Optd "Specimen"*Set of 9*			£190	

1920 (June)–**21**. *Surch with T* **4** *at Govt Printing Establishment, Suva.*

(a) On Nos. 24 *and* 26/8.
30	**3**	1d. on 5d. sage-green (10.3.21)	7·00	60·00
		a. Surch inverted	£2500	
31		1d. on 1s. black/*green*	1·25	13·00
32		1d. on 2s. purple/*blue*	1·00	10·00
33		1d. on 5s. green/*yellow*	1·00	10·00

(b) On No. F16.
34	**3**	2d. on 40c. red/*yellow*	1·00	19·00

(c) On No. F27.
35	**3**	2d. on 40c. red/*yellow*	£130	£700

1921 (Sept–Oct). *Wmk Mult Script CA. P* 14.
36	**3**	1d. scarlet	2·50	14·00
37		2d. slate-grey	4·25	38·00
39		6d. purple	14·00	75·00
36/9 *Set of 3*			19·00	£110
36s/9s Optd "Specimen" *Set of 3*			75·00	

1924 (1 May). *Surch as T* **4**, *at Suva.*
40	**3**	1d. on ½d. green (No. 18)	4·00	22·00
41		3d. on 1d. scarlet (No. 36)	4·00	11·00
42		5d. on 2½d. ultramarine (No. 21)	7·50	21·00
		a. Surch inverted	£2250	
40/2 *Set of 3*			14·00	48·00

5

(*Recess D.L.R.*)
1925 (June). *Wmk Mult Script CA. P* 14.
43	**5**	½d. (5c.) black	1·25	14·00
44		1d. (10c.) green	1·00	12·00
45		2d. (20c.) slate-grey	1·75	2·50
46		2½d. (25c.) brown	1·00	13·00
47		5d. (50c.) ultramarine	3·00	2·75
48		6d. (60c.) purple	3·50	14·00
49		1s. (1.25fr.) black/emerald	3·25	19·00
50		2s. (2.50fr.) purple/blue	6·00	22·00
51		5s. (6.25fr.) green/yellow	6·00	25·00
43/51 *Set of 9*			23·00	£110
43s/51s Optd "Specimen" *Set of 9*			£190	

(New Currency. 100 gold centimes = 1 gold franc)

The currency used for the face values of issues to 1977 was an artificial, rather than an actual, monetary unit. The actual currencies in use were Australian dollars and the local franc.

6 Lopevi Island and Outrigger Canoe

(*Des J. Kerhor. Eng J. G. Hall. Recess B.W.*)
1938 (1 June). *Gold Currency. Wmk Mult Script CA. P* 12.
52	**6**	5c. blue-green	2·50	4·50
53		10c. orange	1·25	2·25
54		15c. bright violet	3·50	4·50
55		20c. scarlet	1·60	2·75
56		25c. reddish brown	1·60	3·00
57		30c. blue	2·50	2·75
58		40c. grey-olive	4·50	6·50
59		50c. purple	1·60	2·75
60		1f. red/*green*	4·00	9·00
61		2f. blue/*green*	30·00	19·00
62		5f. red/*yellow*	70·00	48·00
63		10f. violet/*blue*	£200	75·00
52/63 *Set of 12*			£300	£160
52s/63s Perf "Specimen" *Set of 12*			£225	

(*Recess Waterlow*)
1949 (10 Oct). *75th Anniv of U.P.U. As No. 117 of Antigua. Wmk Mult Script CA. P* 13½×14.
64	10c. red-orange	30	1·00
65	15c. violet	30	1·00
66	30c. ultramarine	30	1·00
67	50c. purple	40	1·00
64/7 *Set of 4*		1·10	3·50

POSTAGE DUE STAMPS

POSTAGE DUE   **POSTAGE DUE**   **POSTAGE DUE**
(D 1)   (D 2)   (D 3)

1925 (June). *Optd with Type D* **1**, *by D.L.R.*
D1	**5**	10d. (10c.) orange	30·00	1·00
D2		2d. (20c.) slate-grey	32·00	1·00
D3		3d. (30c.) red	32·00	2·50
D4		5d. (50c.) ultramarine	35·00	4·50
D5		10d. (1f.) carmine/blue	40·00	5·50

D1/5 *Set of 5*		£150	13·00
D1s/5s Optd "Specimen" *Set of 5*		£180	

1938 (1 June). *Optd with Type D* **2**, *by B.W.*
D6	**6**	5c. blue-green	25·00	40·00
D7		10c. orange	25·00	40·00
D8		20c. scarlet	28·00	55·00
D9		40c. grey-olive	35·00	65·00
D10		1f. red/*green*	45·00	75·00
D6/10 *Set of 5*		£140	£250
D6s/10s Perf "Specimen" *Set of 5*		£130	

II. STAMPS INSCRIBED IN FRENCH

(Currency. 100 centimes = 1 French franc)

NOUVELLES

HÉBRIDES   **NOUVELLES-HÉBRIDES**
(F 1)   (F 2)

1908 (21 Nov). *T* **15/17** *of New Caledonia. optd with Types F* **1** *or F* **2** *(1f.), by Govt Ptg Wks, Paris.*
F1	5c. green	5·50	4·75
F2	10c. carmine	7·00	3·50
F3	25c. blue/*greenish* (R.)	7·00	2·25
F4	50c. red/*orange*	7·00	4·75
F5	1f. blue/*green* (R.)	17·00	20·00
F1/5 *Set of 5*		40·00	30·00

CONDOMINIUM   **10c.**
(F 3)   (F 6)

1910 (Aug)–**11**. *Nos. F1/5 further optd with Type F* **3**, *or larger (1f.), by Govt Ptg Wks, Paris.*
F6	5c. green	3·25	3·00
F7	10c. carmine	3·25	1·25
F8	25c. blue/*greenish* (R.) (1911)	2·25	3·75
F9	50c. red/*orange* (1911)	6·50	9·75
F10	1f. blue/*green* (R.)	15·00	22·00
F6/10 *Set of 5*		27·00	35·00

All the above were released in Paris on 16 March 1910. The 5c., 10c. and 1f. were issued in New Hebrides in August but the 25c. and 50c. were not received until 1911 after the issue of the definitive stamps and they were placed in reserve, although some may have been issued on request.

1911 (12 July). *Wmk Mult Crown CA. P* 14.
F11	**3**	5c. green	1·00	2·75
F12		10c. carmine	50	75
F13		20c. greyish slate	1·00	2·25
F14		25c. ultramarine	2·50	7·00
F15		30c. brown/*yellow*	6·50	5·25
F16		40c. red/*yellow*	1·40	3·75
F17		50c. sage-green	2·00	4·00
F18		75c. orange	7·00	23·00
F19		1f. red/*blue*	2·50	3·00
F20		2f. violet	8·50	22·00
F21		5f. red/*green*	12·00	35·00
F11/21 *Set of 11*			40·00	95·00

1913. *As last but wmk "R F" in sheet or without wmk.*
F22	**3**	5c. green	1·25	5·00
F23		10c. carmine	1·00	4·00
F24		20c. greyish slate	1·00	2·40
F25		25c. ultramarine	1·25	5·50
F26		30c. brown/*yellow*	1·90	10·00
F27		40c. red/*yellow*	22·00	70·00
F28		50c. sage-green	10·00	27·00
F29		75c. orange	9·00	40·00
F30		1f. red/*blue*	6·00	10·00
F31		2f. violet	9·00	42·00
F32		5f. red/*green*	22·00	48·00
F22/32 *Set of 11*			75·00	£225

The above were placed on sale in Paris on 29 April 1912.

1920–21. *Surch as Type F* **6**, *at Govt Printing Establishment, Suva, Fiji.*

(a) On stamps of 1908–11 (June 1920).
F32a	5c. on 50c. red/orange (F4)	£450	£475
F33	5c. on 50c. red/orange (F9)	2·40	13·00
F33a	10c. on 25c. blue/greenish (F8)	50	1·50

(b) On stamps of 1911–13 (10.3.21).
F34	**3**	5c. on 40c. red/yellow (F27)	27·00	95·00
F35		20c. on 30c. brown/yellow (F15)	11·00	65·00
F36		20c. on 30c. brown/yellow (F26)	6·50	70·00

(c) On Inscr in English (10.3.21).
F37	**3**	10c. on 5d. sage-green (24)	11·00	50·00

1924 (1 May). *Stamps of 1911–13 surch as Type F* **6**, *at Suva.*
F38	**3**	5c. on 5c. green (F22)	1·00	6·00
F39		30c. on 10c. carmine (F23)	1·00	2·50
F40		50c. on 25c. ultramarine (F14)	32·00	90·00
F41		50c. on 25c. ultramarine (F25)	2·50	24·00
F38/41 *Set of 4*			32·00	£110

F 7   **France Libre**
(F 9)

(*Recess D.L.R.*)
1925 (June). *Wmk "R F" in sheet or without wmk. P* 14.
F42	F **7**	5c. (½d.) black	75	10·00
F43		10c. (1d.) green	1·00	9·00
F44		20c. (2d.) greyish slate	1·75	2·75
F45		25c. (2½d.) brown	1·50	9·00
F46		30c. (3d.) red	1·50	9·00

F47		40c. (4d.) red/yellow	1·50	9·00
F48		50c. (5d.) ultramarine	1·50	1·75
F49		75c. (7½d.) yellow-brown	1·50	15·00
F50		1f. (10d.) carmine/blue	1·50	2·50
F51		2f. (1/8) violet	2·50	25·00
F52		5f. (4s.) carmine/green	3·50	25·00
F42/52 Set of 11			17·00	£110
F42s/52s Optd "Specimen" Set of 11				£250

In July 1929 a batch of mail was carried by aircraft from Port Vila to the French cruiser *Tourville* for sorting and forwarding at Nouméa, New Caledonia. Stamps of the above issue (including those with English inscriptions) were affixed to covers and handstamped "PAR AVION" before cancellation.

(New Currency. 100 gold centimes = 1 gold franc)

1938 (1 June). *Gold Currency.* Wmk "R F" in sheet or without wmk. P 12.

F53	**6**	5c. blue-green	2·50	6·50
F54		10c. orange	2·25	1·75
F55		15c. bright violet	2·25	4·00
F56		20c. scarlet	2·50	3·50
F57		25c. reddish brown	5·50	4·50
F58		30c. blue	5·50	5·00
F59		40c. grey-olive	2·25	9·00
F60		50c. purple	2·25	3·25
F61		1f. lake/*pale green (shades)*	2·75	5·50
F62		2f. blue/*pale green (shades)*	30·00	30·00
F63		5f. red/*yellow*	50·00	50·00
F64		10f. violet/*blue*	£120	£100
F53/64 Set of 12			£200	£200
F53s/64s Perf "Specimen" Set of 12				£300

1941 (15 Apr). *Adherence to General de Gaulle. Optd with Type F 9, at Nouméa, New Caledonia.*

F65	**6**	5c. blue-green	2·00	25·00
F66		10c. orange	3·75	24·00
F67		15c. bright violet	6·50	40·00
F68		20c. scarlet	18·00	32·00
F69		25c. reddish brown	21·00	42·00
F70		30c. blue	21·00	38·00
F71		40c. grey-olive	21·00	40·00
F72		50c. purple	19·00	38·00
F73		1f. lake/*pale green*	20·00	38·00
F74		2f. blue/*pale green*	18·00	38·00
F75		5f. red/*yellow*	17·00	38·00
F76		10f. violet/*blue*	17·00	38·00
F65/76 Set of 12			£170	£375

1949 (10 Oct). *75th Anniv of U.P.U. As Nos. 64/7.* Wmk "R F" in sheet or without wmk. P 13½.

F77		10c. red-orange	2·50	5·50
F78		15c. violet	3·75	9·00
F79		30c. ultramarine	5·50	12·00
F80		50c. purple	6·50	15·00
F77/80 Set of 4			16·00	38·00

POSTAGE DUE STAMPS

CHIFFRE TAXE	**CHIFFRE TAXE**	**TIMBRE-TAXE**
(FD **1**)	(FD **2**)	(FD **3**)

1925 (June). *Optd with Type FD 1, by D.L.R.*

FD53	**F 7**	10c. (1d.) green	50·00	3·00
FD54		20c. (2d.) greyish slate	55·00	3·00
FD55		30c. (3d.) red	55·00	3·00
FD56		50c. (5d.) ultramarine	50·00	3·00
FD57		1f. (10d.) carmine/blue	50·00	3·00
FD53/7 Set of 5			£225	13·50
FD53s/7s Optd "Specimen" Set of 5				£250

Although on sale in Paris, the Postmaster would not issue any in unused condition for about a year and most copies are cancelled-to-order.

1938 (1 June). *Optd with Type FD 2, by Bradbury, Wilkinson.*

FD65	**6**	5c. blue-green	14·00	60·00
FD66		10c. orange	17·00	60·00
FD67		20c. scarlet	23·00	65·00
FD68		40c. grey-olive	48·00	£130
FD69		1f. lake/*pale green*	48·00	£140
FD65/9 Set of 5			£130	£400
FD65s/9s Perf "Specimen" Set of 5				£200

1941 (15 Apr). *Nos. FD65/9 optd with Type F 9 at Nouméa, New Caledonia.*

FD77	**6**	5c. blue-green	15·00	38·00
FD78		10c. orange	15·00	38·00
FD79		20c. scarlet	15·00	38·00
FD80		40c. grey-olive	19·00	38·00
FD81		1f. lake/*pale green*	18·00	38·00
FD77/81 Set of 5			75·00	£170

New Republic
see South Africa

New South Wales
see Australia

New Zealand

From 1831 mail from New Zealand was sent to Sydney, New South Wales, routed through an unofficial postmaster at Kororareka.

The first official post office opened at Kororareka in January 1840 to be followed by others at Auckland, Britannia, Coromandel Harbour, Hokianga, Port Nicholson, Russell and Waimate during the same year. New South Wales relinquished control of the postal service when New Zealand became a separate colony on 3 May 1841.

The British G.P.O. was responsible for the operation of the overseas mails from 11 October 1841 until the postal service once again passed under colonial control on 18 November 1848.

CC 1   CC 2

AUCKLAND

CROWNED-CIRCLE HANDSTAMPS

CC1	CC 1	AUCKLAND NEW ZEALAND (R.) (31.10.1846) ... *Price on cover*	£300

NELSON

CROWNED-CIRCLE HANDSTAMPS

CC2	CC 1	NELSON NEW ZEALAND (R.) (31.10.1846) ... *Price on cover*	£1100

NEW PLYMOUTH

CROWNED-CIRCLE HANDSTAMPS

CC3	CC 1	NEW PLYMOUTH NEW ZEALAND (R. or Black) (31.10.1846) ... *Price on cover*	£2750
CC3a	CC 2	NEW PLYMOUTH NEW ZEALAND (R. or Black) (1854) ... *Price on cover*	£3250

OTAGO

CROWNED-CIRCLE HANDSTAMPS

CC4	CC 2	OTAGO NEW ZEALAND (R.) (1851) ... *Price on cover*	£1900

PETRE

CROWNED-CIRCLE HANDSTAMPS

CC5	CC 1	PETRE NEW ZEALAND (R.) (31.10.1846) ... *Price on cover*	£1400

PORT VICTORIA

CROWNED-CIRCLE HANDSTAMPS

CC6	CC 2	PORT VICTORIA NEW ZEALAND (R.) (1851) ... *Price on cover*	£1200

RUSSELL

CROWNED-CIRCLE HANDSTAMPS

CC7	CC 1	RUSSELL NEW ZEALAND (R.) (31.10.1846) ... *Price on cover*	£7000

WELLINGTON

CROWNED-CIRCLE HANDSTAMPS

CC8	CC 1	WELLINGTON NEW ZEALAND (R.) (31.10.1846) ... *Price on cover*	£350

A similar mark for Christchurch as Type CC 2 is only known struck, in black, as a cancellation after the introduction of adhesive stamps. No. CC3a is a locally-cut replacement with the office name around the circumference, but a straight "PAID AT" in the centre.

PRICES FOR STAMPS ON COVER TO 1945

Nos. 1/125	*from* × 2
Nos. 126/36	*from* × 3
Nos. 137/9	*from* × 2
No. 140	—
No. 141	*from* × 2
No. 142	—
Nos. 143/8	*from* × 3
Nos. 149/51	*from* × 10
Nos. 152/84	*from* × 2
Nos. 185/6	—
Nos. 187/203	*from* × 3
No. 205/7e	—
Nos. 208/13	*from* × 2
Nos. 214/16j	—
Nos. 217/58	*from* × 3
No. 259	—
Nos. 260/9	*from* × 3
No. 270	—
Nos. 271/6	*from* × 4
Nos. 277/307	*from* × 2
Nos. 308/16	*from* × 3
No. 317	—
Nos. 318/28	—
Nos. 329/48	—
No. 349	*from* × 5
Nos. 350/1	—
No. 352	*from* × 5
No. 353/69	—
Nos. 370/86	*from* × 2
No. 387	*from* × 4
Nos. 388/99	*from* × 3
Nos. 400/666	*from* × 2
Nos. E1/5	*from* × 5
No. E6	*from* × 10
Nos. D1/8	*from* × 3
Nos. D9/16	*from* × 5

PRICES FOR STAMPS ON COVER TO 1945

Nos. D17/20	*from* × 3
Nos. D21/47	*from* × 6
Nos. O1/24	*from* × 12
Nos. O59/66	*from* × 4
Nos. O67/8	—
Nos. O69/81	*from* × 5
Nos. O82/7	—
Nos. O88/93	*from* × 20
Nos. O94/9	*from* × 12
Nos. O100/11	*from* × 5
Nos. O112/13	—
Nos. O115/19	*from* × 15
Nos. O120/33	*from* × 10
Nos. O134/51	*from* × 4
Nos. P1/7	*from* × 8
Nos. L1/9	*from* × 10
Nos. L9a/12	—
Nos. L13/20	*from* × 15
Nos. L21/3	—
Nos. L24/41	*from* × 12
No. F1	—
No. F2	*from* × 5
Nos. F3/144	—
Nos. F145/58	*from* × 3
Nos. F159/68	—
Nos. F169/79	*from* × 3
Nos. F180/6	—
Nos. F187/90	*from* × 2
Nos. F191/203	*from* × 3
Nos. F204/11	—
Nos. F212/18	*from* × 2
Nos. A1/3	*from* × 2

CROWN COLONY

PERKINS BACON "CANCELLED". For notes on these handstamps, showing "CANCELLED" between horizontal bars forming an oval, see Catalogue Introduction.

1   2

(Eng by Humphreys. Recess P.B.)

1855 (20 July). Wmk Large Star, W w **1**.

1	**1**	1d. dull carmine (*white paper*) (H/S "CANCELLED" in oval £27000)	£60000	£12000
2		2d. dull blue (*blued paper*) (H/S "CANCELLED" in oval £28000)	£30000	£600
3		1s. pale yellow-green (*blued paper*) (H/S "CANCELLED" in oval £24000)	£40000	£5500
		a. Bisected (6d.) (on cover)	†	£38000

The 2d. and 1s. on white paper formerly listed are now known to be stamps printed on blued paper which have had the bluing washed out. Nos. 3a and 6a were used at Dunedin between March 1857, when the rate for ½ oz. letters to Great Britain was reduced to 6d., and August 1859. All known examples are bisected vertically.

(Printed by J. Richardson, Auckland, N.Z.)

1855 (Dec). *First printing. White paper.* Wmk Large Star. Imperf.

3b	**1**	1d. orange	£30000

1855 (Dec)–**57**. *Blue paper. No wmk. Imperf.*

4	**1**	1d. red	£11000	£1800
5		2d. blue (3.56)	£3000	£300
		a. Without value		—
6		1s. green (9.57)	£35000	£3750
		a. Bisected (6d.) (on cover)	†	£25000

These stamps on blue paper may occasionally be found watermarked double-lined letters, being portions of the papermaker's name.

1857 (Jan). *White paper similar to the issue of July 1855.* Wmk Large Star.

7	**1**	1d. dull orange	†	£20000

This stamp is in the precise shade of the 1d. of the 1858 printing by Richardson on *no wmk* white paper. An unsevered pair is known with Dunedin cancellation on a cover front showing an Auckland arrival postmark of 19.1.1857.

1857–**63**. *Hard or soft white paper. No wmk.*

(a) Imperf.

8	**1**	1d. dull orange (1858)	£2500	£600
8a		2d. deep ultramarine (1858)	£2000	£800
9		2d. pale blue	£1000	£180
10		2d. blue (12.57)	£1000	£180
11		2d. dull deep blue	£1500	£275
12		6d. bistre-brown (8.59)	£3250	£500
13		6d. brown	£1800	£300
14		6d. pale brown	£1800	£300
15		6d. chestnut	£3500	£550
16		1s. dull emerald-green (1858)	£15000	£1700
17		1s. blue-green	£14000	£1700

(b) Pin-roulette, about 10 at Nelson (1860).

18	**1**	1d. dull orange	†	£5500
19		2d. blue	†	£3500
20		6d. brown	†	£4250
20a		1s. dull emerald-green	†	£6500
21		1s. blue-green	†	£6500

(c) Serrated perf about 16 or 18 at Nelson (1862).

22	**1**	1d. dull orange	†	£4750
23		2d. blue	†	£3500

24		6d. brown	†	£3250
25		6d. chestnut	†	£6500
26		1s. blue-green	†	£6000

(d) Rouletted 7 at Auckland (April 1859).

27	1	1d. dull orange	£7000	£4750
28		2d. blue	£7000	£3250
29		6d. brown	£6500	£2750
		a. Imperf between (pair)	£20000	£11000
30		1s. dull emerald-green	†	£4500
31		1s. blue-green	†	£4500

(e) P 13 at Dunedin (1863).

31a	1	1d. dull orange	†	£6000
31b		2d. pale blue	£3750	£2250
32		6d. pale brown	†	£6000

(f) "H" roulette 16 at Nelson.

32a	1	2d. blue	†	£4250
32b		6d. brown	†	£4500

(g) "Y" roulette 18 at Nelson.

32c	1	1d. dull orange	†	£5000
32d		2d. blue	†	£3750
32e		6d. brown	†	£4250
32f		6d. chestnut	†	£4250
32g		1s. blue-green	†	£7000

(h) Oblique roulette 13 at Wellington.

32h	1	1d. dull orange	†	£5500

The various separations detailed above were all applied by hand to imperforate sheets. The results were often poorly cut and badly aligned. Nos. 32a/b and 32c/g were produced using roulette wheels fitted with cutting edges in the shape of "H" or "Y".

(Printed by John Davies at the G.P.O., Auckland, N.Z.)

1862 (Feb–Dec). Wmk Large Star.

(a) Imperf.

33	1	1d. orange-vermilion	£750	£225
34		1d. vermilion	£600	£225
35		1d. carmine-vermilion	£400	£250
36		2d. deep blue (Plate I)	£600	80·00
		a. Double print	—	£3000
37		2d. slate-blue (Plate I)	£1800	£200
37a		2d. milky blue (Plate I, worn)	—	£225
38		2d. pale blue (Plate I, worn)	£500	80·00
39		2d. blue (to deep) (Plate I, very worn)	£500	80·00
40		3d. brown-lilac (Dec 1862)	£450	£150
41		6d. black-brown	£1300	£130
42		6d. brown	£1100	£110
43		6d. red-brown	£1000	£100
44		1s. green	£1500	£300
45		1s. yellow-green	£1300	£325
46		1s. deep green	£1600	£375

The 2d. in a distinctive deep bright blue on white paper wmkd. Large Star is believed by experts to have been printed by Richardson in 1861 or 1862. This also exists doubly printed and with serrated perf.

No. 37 shows traces of plate wear to the right of the Queen's head. This is more pronounced on Nos. 37a/8 and quite extensive on No. 39.

(b) Rouletted 7 at Auckland (5.62).

47	1	1d. orange-vermilion	£4250	£800
48		1d. vermilion	£2750	£800
48a		1d. carmine-vermilion	£4250	£950
49		2d. deep blue	£2750	£450
50		2d. slate-blue	£3750	£800
51		2d. pale blue	£2250	£600
52		3d. brown-lilac	£2750	£750
53		6d. black-brown	£3000	£475
54		6d. brown	£2750	£600
55		6d. red-brown	£2750	£475
56		1s. green	£3250	£850
57		1s. yellow-green	£3250	£850
58		1s. deep green	£4250	£950

(c) Serrated perf 16 or 18 at Nelson (8.62).

59	1	1d. orange-vermilion	£8500	£2000
60		2d. deep blue	†	£1200
		a. Imperf between (pair)	£13000	£5000
61		2d. slate-blue	†	£1200
62		3d. brown-lilac	£4000	£1700
63		6d. black-brown	†	£1800
64		6d. brown	†	£2000
65		1s. yellow-green	†	£3750

(d) Pin-perf 10 at Nelson (8.62).

66	1	2d. deep blue	†	£2750
67		6d. black-brown	†	£3750

(e) "H" roulette 16 at Nelson.

67a	1	2d. deep blue (Plate I)	†	£2000
67b		6d. black-brown	†	£2000
67c		1s. green	—	£3500

(f) "Y" roulette 18 at Nelson.

67d	1	1d. orange-vermilion	†	£2250
67e		2d. deep blue (Plate I)	†	£1900
67f		2d. slate-blue (Plate I)	†	£1900
67g		3d. brown-lilac	†	£2500
67h		6d. brown	†	£1900
67i		6d. brown	†	£1900
67j		1s. yellow-green	†	£3500

(g) Oblique roulette 13 at Wellington.

67k	1	2d. deep blue (Plate I)	†	£2000
67l		2d. slate-blue (Plate I)	†	
67m		3d. brown-lilac	†	£2750
67n		6d. black-brown	†	£2000

(h) Square roulette 14 at Auckland.

67o	1	1d. orange-vermilion	†	£2250
67p		2d. deep blue (Plate I)	†	£1900
67q		3d. brown-lilac	†	£2750
67r		6d. black-brown	†	£2000

(i) Serrated perf 13 at Dunedin.

67s	1	1d. orange-vermilion	†	£2750
67t		2d. deep blue (Plate I)	†	£1900
67u		3d. brown-lilac	£3500	£1800
67v		6d. black-brown	†	£1900
67w		1s. yellow-green	†	£3500

The dates put to above varieties are the earliest that have been met with.

1862. Wmk Large Star. P 13 (at Dunedin).

68	1	1d. orange-vermilion	£1800	£325
		a. Imperf between (horiz pair)	†	£8000
69		1d. orange-vermilion	£1800	£325
70		2d. deep blue (Plate I)	£500	95·00
71		2d. slate-blue (Plate I)	†	
72		2d. blue (Plate I)	£400	70·00
72a		2d. milky blue (Plate I)	—	£500
73		2d. pale blue (Plate I)	£400	70·00
74		3d. brown-lilac	£1500	£400
75		6d. black-brown	£1300	£225
		a. Imperf between (horiz pair)	†	
76		6d. brown	£1100	£140
77		6d. red-brown	£1000	£110
78		1s. dull green	£1700	£425
79		1s. deep green	£1800	£400
80		1s. yellow-green	£1800	£375

See also Nos. 110/25 and the note that follows these.

1862–63. Pelure paper. No wmk.

(a) Imperf.

81	1	1d. orange-vermilion (1863)	£8500	£2250
82		2d. ultramarine	£5000	£850
83		2d. pale ultramarine	£4750	£800
84		3d. lilac	£40000	†
85		6d. black-brown	£2500	£250
86		1s. deep green	£10000	£1100

The 3d. is known only unused.

(b) Rouletted 7 at Auckland.

87	1	1d. orange-vermilion	†	£5500
88		6d. black-brown	£3000	£475
89		1s. deep green	£11000	£1700

(c) P 13 at Dunedin.

90	1	1d. orange-vermilion	£13000	£3250
91		2d. ultramarine	£6000	£700
92		2d. pale ultramarine	£6000	£700
93		6d. black-brown	£5000	£400
94		1s. deep green	£11000	£1600

(d) Serrated perf 16 at Nelson.

95	1	6d. black-brown	—	£5000

(e) Serrated perf 13 at Dunedin.

95a	9	1d. orange-vermilion	†	£8000

1863 (early). Thick soft white paper. No wmk.

(a) Imperf.

96	1	2d. dull deep blue (shades)	£2750	£800

(b) P 13.

96a	1	2d. dull deep blue (shades)	£1800	£475

These stamps show slight beginnings of wear of the printing plate in the background to right of the Queen's ear, as one looks at the stamps. By the early part of 1864, the wear of the plate had spread, more or less, all over the background of the circle containing the head. The major portion of the stamps of this printing appears to have been consigned to Dunedin and to have been there perforated 13.

1864. Wmk "N Z", W 2.

(a) Imperf.

97	1	1d. carmine-vermilion	£800	£325
98		2d. pale blue (Plate I worn)	£1200	£250
99		6d. red-brown	£4250	£650
100		1s. green	£1400	£275

(b) Rouletted 7 at Auckland.

101	1	1d. carmine-vermilion	£5550	£3000
102		2d. pale blue (Plate I worn)	£1800	£750
103		6d. red-brown	£6000	£3000
104		1s. green	£4000	£1100

(c) P 13 at Dunedin.

104a	1	1d. carmine-vermilion	£10000	£5500
105		2d. pale blue (Plate I worn)	£800	£180
106		1s. green	£1800	£500
		a. Imperf between (horiz pair)	£13000	
		aa. Perf 6½×13	†	£3500

(d) "Y" roulette 18 at Nelson.

106b	1	1d. carmine-vermilion	—	£5500

(e) P 12½ at Auckland.

106c	1	1d. carmine-vermilion	£10000	£4750
107		2d. pale blue (Plate I worn)	£375	70·00
108		6d. red-brown	£450	55·00
109		1s. yellow-green	£7000	£2500

The "NZ" watermark is frequently found inverted.

1864–67. Wmk Large Star. P 12½ (at Auckland).

110	1	1d. carmine-vermilion (1864)	£180	35·00
111		1d. pale orange-vermilion	£225	35·00
		a. Imperf (pair)	£3500	£2250
112		1d. orange	£500	90·00
113		2d. pale blue (Plate I worn) (1864)	£225	25·00
114		2d. deep blue (Plate II) (1866)	£180	22·00
		a. Imperf vert (horiz pair)	†	£4250
115		2d. blue (Plate II)	£180	22·00
		a. Retouched (Plate II) (1867)	£275	50·00
		c. Imperf (pair) (Plate II)	£2250	£1700
		d. Retouched. Imperf (pair)	£3500	£3750
116		3d. brown-lilac (1864)	£1800	£600
117		3d. lilac (1867)	£120	35·00
		a. Imperf (pair)	£3500	£1700
118		3d. deep mauve (1867)	£550	70·00
		a. Imperf (pair)	£3750	£1700
119		4d. deep rose (1865)	£2750	£250
120		4d. yellow (1865)	£190	£110
121		4d. orange	£2250	£1000
122		6d. red-brown (1864)	£250	28·00
122a		6d. brown	£275	40·00
		b. Imperf (pair)	£2000	£2000
123		1s. deep green (1864)	£1000	£325
124		1s. green	£500	£130
125		1s. green	£225	£225

The above issue is sometimes difficult to distinguish from Nos. 68/80 because the vertical perforations usually gauge 12¾ and sometimes a full

13. However, stamps of this issue invariably gauge 12½ horizontally, whereas the 1862 stamps measure a full 13.

Nos. 111a, 115c/d, 117a, 118a and 122b were issued during problems with the perforation machine which occurred in 1866–67, 1869–70 and 1871–73. Imperforate sheets of the 1s. were also released, but these stamps are very similar to Nos. 44/6.

The new plate of the 2d. showed signs of deterioration during 1866 and thirty positions in rows 13 and 16 to 20 were retouched by a local engraver.

The 1d., 2d. and 6d. were officially reprinted imperforate, without gum, in 1884 for presentation purposes. They can be distinguished from the errors listed by their shades which are pale orange, dull blue and dull chocolate-brown respectively, and by the worn state of the plates from which they were printed (Prices £75 each unused).

1871. Wmk Large Star.

(a) P 10.

126	1	1d. brown	£700	£120

(b) P 12½×10.

127	1	1d. deep brown	†	£3250

(c) P 10×12½.

128	1	1d. brown	£250	55·00
		a. Perf 12½ comp 10 (1 side)	£550	£170
129		2d. deep blue (Plate II)	†	£9000
		a. Perf 10*	†	£16000
130		2d. vermilion	£250	35·00
		a. Retouched	£375	55·00
		b. Perf 12½ comp 10 (1 side)	£1700	£425
		c. Perf 10*	†	£16000
131		6d. deep blue	£2250	£800
		a. Blue	£1500	£550
		b. Imperf between (vert pair)	—	£7500
		c. Perf 12½ comp 10 (1 side)	£1300	£450
		ca. Imperf vert (horiz pair)	†	

(d) P 12½.

132	1	1d. red-brown	£180	38·00
		a. Brown (shades, worn plate)	£180	38·00
		b. Imperf horiz (vert pair)	—	£4500
133		2d. orange	£160	29·00
		a. Retouched	£250	50·00
134		2d. vermilion	£200	32·00
		a. Retouched	£300	60·00
135		6d. blue	£250	60·00
136		6d. pale blue	£180	55·00

*Only one used copy each of Nos. 129a and 130c have been reported.

1872. No wmk. P 12½.

137	1	1d. brown	£750	£170
		a. Watermarked (script letters)*	£3750	£2250
		b. Watermarked (double-lined capitals)*	£1800	£550
138		2d. vermilion	£120	55·00
		a. Retouched	£200	85·00
		b. Watermarked (script letters)*	£3500	£1300
		c. Watermarked (double-lined capitals)*	£1700	£750
139		4d. orange-yellow	£180	£700
		a. Watermarked (double-lined capitals)*		£275

*In or about 1872, 1d., 2d. and 4d. stamps were printed on paper showing sheet watermarks of either "W. T. & Co." (Wiggins Teape & Co.) in script letters or "T. H. Saunders" in double-lined capitals; portions of these letters are occasionally found on stamps.

1872. Wmk "N Z", W 2. P 12½.

140	1	1d. brown	†	£4500
141		2d. vermilion	£850	£300
		a. Retouched	£1300	£400

1872. Wmk Lozenges, with "INVICTA" in double-lined capitals four times in the sheet. P 12½.

142	1	2d. vermilion	£3000	£500
		a. Retouched	£4500	£750

3	4

(Des John Davies. Die eng on wood in Melbourne. Printed from electrotypes at Govt Ptg Office, Wellington)

1873 (1 Jan). (a) Wmk "NZ", W 2.

143	3	½d. pale dull rose (P 10)	£110	50·00
144		½d. pale dull rose (P 12½)	£180	85·00
145		½d. pale dull rose (P 12½×10)	£110	75·00
		a. Perf 10×12½	£150	80·00

(b) No wmk.

146	3	½d. pale dull rose (P 10)	£200	65·00
147		½d. pale dull rose (P 12½)	£250	£100
148		½d. pale dull rose (P 12½×10)	£150	85·00
		a. Perf 10×12½	£300	£120

As the paper used for Nos. 143/5 was originally intended for fiscal stamps which were more than twice as large, about one-third of the impressions fall on portions of the sheet showing no watermark, giving rise to varieties Nos. 146/8. In later printings of No. 151 a few stamps in each sheet are without watermark. These can be distinguished from No. 147 by the shade.

1875 (Jan). Wmk Star, W 4.

149	3	½d. pale dull rose (P 12½)	20·00	2·75
		a. Imperf horiz (vert pair)	£750	£425
		b. Imperf between (horiz pair)	†	£700
		c. Perf compound of 12½ and 10...	†	
150		½d. dull pale rose (p nearly 12)	70·00	12·00

1892 (May). Wmk "NZ and Star". W 12b. P 12½.

151	3	½d. bright rose (shades)	12·00	1·75
		a. No Wmk	17·00	10·00
		w. Wmk inverted	60·00	40·00
		x. Wmk reversed	—	£120

5 6 7

8 9 10

11 12 12a 6 mm

12b 7 mm 12c 4 mm

(T 5/10 eng De La Rue. T 11 and 12 des, eng & plates by W. R. Bock. Typo Govt Ptg Office, Wellington)

1874 (2 Jan)–**78**. *A. White paper.* W **12**a.

(a) P 12½.

152	5	1d. lilac	60·00	8·00
		a. Imperf	£450	
		w. Wmk inverted	†	55·00
		x. Wmk reversed	†	£130
		y. Wmk inverted and reversed	†	£300
153	6	2d. rose	60·00	6·00
154	7	3d. brown	£110	60·00
155	8	4d. maroon	£275	70·00
		w. Wmk inverted	£500	£120
156	9	6d. blue	£180	11·00
		w. Wmk inverted	—	60·00
		x. Wmk reversed	†	£200
157	10	1s. green	£550	30·00
		w. Wmk inverted		£275

(b) Perf nearly 12.

158	6	2d. rose (1878)	£600	£180

(c) Perf compound of 12½ and 10.

159	5	1d. lilac	£150	40·00
		w. Wmk inverted	—	70·00
160	6	2d. rose	£200	80·00
		w. Wmk inverted	—	£110
161	7	3d. brown	£160	65·00
162	8	4d. maroon	£425	£110
163	9	6d. blue	£250	48·00
		w. Wmk inverted	—	85·00
164	10	1s. green	£600	£120
		a. Imperf between (vert pair)	†	£4500
		bw. Wmk inverted	†	£325

(d) Perf nearly 12×12½.

164c	5	1d. lilac (1875)	£650	£250
165	6	2d. rose (1878)	£650	£225

B. Blued paper.

(a) P 12½.

166	5	1d. lilac	£100	32·00
167	6	2d. rose	£120	32·00
		w. Wmk inverted	—	60·00
		x. Wmk reversed	†	£100
168	7	3d. brown	£250	85·00
169	8	4d. maroon	£425	£110
170	9	6d. blue	£325	55·00
171		1s. green	£1000	£190

(b) Perf compound of 12½ and 10.

172	5	1d. lilac	£190	55·00
173	6	2d. rose	£550	85·00
174	7	3d. brown	£275	85·00
175	8	4d. maroon	£500	£130
176	9	6d. blue	£325	95·00
177	10	1s. green	£1000	£225

1875. Wmk Large Star, W w **1**. P 12½.

178	5	1d. deep lilac	£800	£130
179	6	2d. rose	£350	25·00

1878. W **12**a. P 12×11½ (comb).

180	5	1d. mauve-lilac	50·00	6·00
181	6	2d. rose	50·00	6·00
182	8	4d. maroon	£140	45·00
183	9	6d. blue	85·00	11·00
184	10	1s. green	£130	42·00
		w. Wmk inverted	†	£350
185	11	2s. deep rose (1 July)	£350	£300
186	12	5s. grey (1 July)	£375	£300

This perforation is made by a horizontal "comb" machine, giving a gauge of 12 horizontally and about 11¾ vertically. Single specimens can be found apparently gauging 11½ all round or 12 all round, but these are all from the same machine. The perforation described above as "nearly 12" was from a single-line machine.

13 14 15

16 17 18

19 20 21

22

Description of Watermarks

W **12**a. 6 mm between "N Z" and star; broad irregular star; comparatively wide "N"; "N Z" 11½ mm wide.

W **12**b. 7 mm between "N Z" and star; narrower star; narrow "N"; "N Z" 10 mm wide.

W **12**c. 4 mm between "N Z" and star; narrow star; wide "N"; "N Z" 11½ mm wide.

Description of Papers

1882–88. Smooth paper with horizontal mesh. W **12**a.

1888–98. Smooth paper with vertical mesh. W **12**b.

1890–91. Smooth paper with vertical mesh. W **12**c.

1898. Thin yellowish toned, coarse paper with clear vertical mesh. W **12**b. Perf 11 only.

In 1899–1900 stamps appeared on medium to thick white coarse paper but we do not differentiate these (except where identifiable by shade) as they are more difficult to distinguish.

PAPER MESH. This shows on the back of the stamp as a series of parallel grooves, either vertical or horizontal. It is caused by the use of a wire gauze conveyor-belt during paper-making.

Description of Dies

1d.

Die 1

Die 2

Die 3

1882.	Die 1.	Background shading complete and heavy.
1886.	Die 2.	Background lines thinner. Two lines of shading weak or missing left of Queen's forehead.
1889.	Die 3.	Shading on head reduced; ornament in crown left of chignon clearer, with unshaded "arrow" more prominent.

"Ellipse" flaw (Die 3, lower left pane, R. 9/2)

2d.

Die 1

Die 2

Die 3

1882. Die 1. Background shading complete and heavy.

1886. Die 2. Weak line of shading left of forehead and missing shading lines below "TA".

1889. Die 3. As Die 2 but with comma-like white notch in hair below "&".

6d.

Die 1

Die 2

1882. Die 1. Shading heavy. Top of head merges into shading. Second ornament from the right on the crown shows a line in its left portion.

1892. Die 2. Background lines thinner. Shading on head more regular with clear line of demarcation between head and background shading. Second ornament from the right in the crown shows small dots in its left portion. Most examples also show a break in the back line of the neck immediately above its base.

STAMPS WITH ADVERTISEMENTS. During November 1891 the New Zealand Post Office invited tenders for the printing of advertisements on the reverse of the current 1d. to 1s. stamps. The contract was awarded to Messrs Miller, Truebridge & Reich and the first sheets with advertisements on the reverse appeared in February 1893. Different advertisements were applied to the backs of the individual stamps within the sheets of 240 (four panes of 60).

On the first setting those in a vertical format were inverted in relation to the stamps and each of the horizontal advertisements had its base at the left-hand side of the stamp when seen from the back. For the second and third settings the vertical advertisements were the same way up as the stamps and the bases of those in the horizontal format were at the right as seen from the back. The third setting only differs from the second in the order of the individual advertisements.

The experiment was not, however, a success and the contract was cancelled at the end of 1893.

(Des F. W. Sears (½d.), A. E. Cousins (2½d.), A. W. Jones (5d.); others adapted from 1874 issue by W. H. Norris. Dies eng A. E. Cousins (½d., 2½d., 5d.), W. R. Bock (others). Typo Govt Ptg Office)

1882–1900. Inscr "POSTAGE & REVENUE". A. Paper with horiz mesh (1.4.82–86). W **12**a.

(a) P 12×11½.

187	14	1d. rose to rose-red (Die 1)	42·00	6·00
		a. Imperf (pair)	£550	
		b. Imperf between (vert pair)	£600	
		cw. Wmk inverted		
		d. Die 2. Pale rose to carm-rose (1886)	40·00	6·00
		dw. Wmk inverted	†	30·00
		dx. Wmk reversed	80·00	35·00
188	15	2d. lilac to lilac-purple (Die 1)	55·00	4·00
		a. Imperf (pair)	£600	
		b. Imperf between (vert pair)	£600	
		cw. Wmk inverted	85·00	16·00
		d. Die 2. Lilac (1886)	60·00	8·50
189	17	3d. yellow (1884)	65·00	9·50
190	18	4d. blue-green	85·00	6·50
191	20	6d. brown (Die 1)	90·00	3·75
		w. Wmk inverted	£180	30·00
192	21	8d. blue	85·00	48·00
193	22	1s. red-brown	£110	14·00

(b) P 12½ (1884?).

193a	14	1d. rose to rose-red (Die 1)	£225	95·00

B. Paper with vert mesh (1888–95) W**12**b.

(a) P 12×11½ (1888–95).

194	13	½d. black (1.4.95)	32·00	80·00
195	14	1d. rose to rosine (Die 2)	48·00	3·75
		aw. Wmk inverted	£160	16·00
		b. Die 3. Rose to carmine (1889)	48·00	3·75
		bb. Red-brn advert (1st setting) (2.93)	90·00	25·00
		bc. Red advert (1st setting) (3.93)	90·00	25·00
		bd. Blue advert (2nd setting) (4.93)	£110	50·00
		be. Mauve advert (2nd setting) (5.93)	80·00	27·00

No.	Type	Description	Un	Used
		bf. Green advert (2nd setting) (6.93)		
		bg. Brn-red advert (3rd setting) (9.93)	80·00	27·00
		bh. "Ellipse" flaw	75·00	20·00
		bw. Wmk inverted	80·00	17·00
		bx. Wmk reversed	90·00	22·00
196	15	2d. lilac (Die 2)	55·00	4·75
		a. Die 3. *Lilac to purple* (1889)	55·00	5·00
		ab. Red advert (1st setting) (3.93)	£100	27·00
		ac. Mauve advert (2nd setting) (5.93)	90·00	27·00
		ad. Sepia advert (2nd setting) (5.93)	90·00	27·00
		ae. Green advert (2nd setting) (6.93)	—	85·00
		af. Brn-red advert (3rd setting) (9.93)	90·00	27·00
		aw. Wmk inverted	85·00	9·50
197	16	2½d. pale blue (1891)	75·00	5·50
		a. Brn-red advert (3rd setting) (4.93)	£150	40·00
		ax. Wmk reversed	£180	50·00
		b. *Ultramarine* (green advert. 2nd setting) (6.93)	£150	42·00
198	17	3d. yellow	48·00	8·00
		a. Brn-red advert (3rd setting) (4.93)	£120	65·00
		b. Sepia advert (2nd setting) (5.93)	—	£130
199	18	4d. green *to bluish green*	65·00	3·75
		a. Sepia advert (2nd setting) (5.93)	£120	40·00
		aw. Wmk inverted	†	£110
200	19	5d. olive-black (1.2.91)	60·00	15·00
		a. Imperf (pair)	£550	
		b. Brn-pur advert (3rd setting) (9.93)	£160	55·00
201	20	6d. brown (Die 1)	80·00	3·75
		a. Die 2 (1892)	£130	60·00
		ab. Sepia advert (2nd setting) (5.93)		
		ac. Brn-red advert (3rd setting) (9.93)	£375	£130
		ax. Wmk reversed	†	—
202	21	8d. blue	70·00	45·00
203	22	1s. red-brown	95·00	6·00
		a. Black advert (2nd setting) (5.93)	£375	£170
		b. Brn-pur advert (3rd setting) (9.93)	£225	20·00
		w. Wmk inverted	£180	22·00

(b) P 12×12½ (1888–91).

No.	Type	Description	Un	Used
204	14	1d. rose (Die 2)	£225	95·00
		a. Die 3 (1889)		

(c) P 12½ (1888–89).

No.	Type	Description	Un	Used
205	14	1d. rose (Die 3) (1889)	£190	£110
		a. Mauve advert (2nd setting) (5.93)	†	—
		x. Wmk reversed	£170	£110
206	15	2d. lilac (Die 2)	£120	80·00
		a. Die 3. *Deep lilac* (1889)	£120	80·00
		ab. Brn-red advert (3rd setting) (9.93)	£350	£150
207	16	2½d. blue (1891)	£200	£110

(d) Mixed perfs 12×11½ and 12½×11½ (1891–93).

No.	Type	Description	Un	Used
207a	14	1d. rose (Die 3) (brn-red advert. 3rd setting)	£110	65·00
207b	15	2d. lilac (Die 3)	†	£325
		ba. Brn-red advert (3rd setting) (9.93)	†	—
207c	18	4d. green	†	80·00
207d	19	5d. olive-black	†	£110
207e	20	6d. brown (Die 1)	†	£120
		ea. Die 2	†	£180

C. Paper with vert mesh (1890). W12c.

(a) P 12×11½.

No.	Type	Description	Un	Used
208	14	1d. rose (Die 3)	80·00	14·00
		a. "Ellipse" flaw	£150	35·00
209	15	2d. purple (Die 3)	80·00	13·00
		x. Wmk reversed		
210	16	2½d. ultramarine (27.12)	60·00	9·50
		x. Wmk reversed	†	45·00
211	17	3d. yellow	85·00	21·00
		a. *Lemon-yellow*	85·00	25·00
212	20	6d. brown (Die 1)	£140	28·00
213	22	1s. deep red-brown	£170	70·00

(b) P 12½.

No.	Type	Description	Un	Used
214	14	1d. rose (Die 3)	£200	£120
215	15	2d. purple (Die 3)	£180	£120
216	16	2½d. ultramarine	£250	£120

(c) P 12×12½.

No.	Type	Description	Un	Used
216a	20	6d. brown (Die 1)	£225	£160

D. Paper with vert mesh (1891–1900) Continuation of W12b.

(a) P 10×12½ (1891–94).

No.	Type	Description	Un	Used
216b	14	1d. rose (Die 3)	£200	£130
		ba. Perf 12½×10	£225	£140
		baa. "Ellipse" flaw	£500	
		bb. Red-brn advert (1st setting) (2.93)	£375	£250
		bc. Brn-red advert (2nd setting) (4.93)	£375	£250
		bd. Mauve advert (2nd setting) (5.93)	£375	£250
		be. Green advert (2nd setting) (6.93)	£375	£250
216c	15	2d. lilac (Die 3)	£180	70·00
216d	16	2½d. blue (1893)	£160	75·00
		da. Perf 12½×10	£180	
216e	17	3d. yellow	£180	85·00
		ea. Perf 12½×10		
216f	18	4d. green	£200	£160
216g	19	5d. olive-black (1894)	£200	£180
		ga. Perf 12½×10	£250	£180
216h	20	6d. brown (Die 1)	£250	£250
		i. Die 2 (1892)	£180	£180
		ia. Brn-pur advert (3rd setting) (9.93)	£375	£275
216j	22	1s. red-brown	£190	£190
		ja. Perf 12½×10	†	

(b) P 10 (1891–95).

No.	Type	Description	Un	Used
217	13	½d. black (1895)	6·00	1·75
218	14	1d. rose (Die 3)	8·00	1·00
		a. *Carmine*	10·00	1·50
		c. Imperf (pair)	£500	£500
		d. Imperf between (pair)	£550	
		d. Imperf horiz (vert pair)	£500	
		e. Mixed perfs 10 and 12½	£250	£130
		f. Red-brn advert (1st setting) (2.93)	20·00	4·75
		g. Red advert (1st setting) (3.93)	20·00	6·50
		h. Brown-red advert (2nd and 3rd settings) (4.93)	17·00	3·00
		i. Blue advert (2nd setting) (4.93)	70·00	32·00
		j. Mauve advert (2nd setting) (5.93)	17·00	3·00
		k. Green advert (2nd setting) (6.93)	60·00	17·00
		l. Brn-pur advert (3rd setting) (9.93)	17·00	4·00
		m. "Ellipse" flaw	35·00	10·00
		w. Wmk inverted	32·00	13·00
		x. Wmk reversed	38·00	17·00
219	15	2d. lilac (Die 3)	17·00	1·25
		a. *Purple*	18·00	1·25
		b. Imperf between (pair)	£600	
		c. Mixed perfs 10 and 12½	—	£110
		d. Red-brn advert (1st setting) (2.93)	30·00	9·00
		e. Red advert (1st setting) (3.93)	30·00	6·50
		f. Brown-red advert (2nd and 3rd settings) (4.93)	24·00	3·25
		g. Sepia advert (2nd setting) (5.93)	26·00	3·75
		h. Green advert (2nd setting) (6.93)	45·00	11·00
		i. Brn-pur advert (3rd setting) (9.93)	24·00	3·25
		x. Wmk reversed	70·00	22·00
220	16	2½d. blue (1892)	55·00	3·50
		a. *Ultramarine*	55·00	4·00
		b. Mixed perfs 10 and 12½	£200	£110
		c. Mauve advert (2nd setting) (5.93)	£140	10·00
		d. Green advert (2nd setting) (6.93)	£150	12·00
		e. Brn-pur advert (3rd setting) (9.93)	£120	9·00
		ex. Wmk reversed	£160	45·00
221	17	3d. pale orange-yellow	55·00	8·50
		a. *Orange*	55·00	12·00
		b. *Lemon-yellow*	55·00	14·00
		c. Mixed perfs 10 and 12½	£190	£130
		d. Brown-red advert (2nd and 3rd settings) (4.93)	95·00	18·00
		e. Sepia advert (2nd setting) (5.93)	£110	35·00
		f. Brn-pur advert (3rd setting) (9.93)	95·00	16·00
222	18	4d. green (1892)	55·00	4·25
		a. *Blue-green*	55·00	4·50
		b. Mixed perfs 10 and 12½	£225	85·00
		c. Brn-red advert (2nd and 3rd settings) (4.93)	£100	5·00
		d. Brn-pur advert (3rd setting) (9.93)	£100	4·25
223	19	5d. olive-black (1893)	50·00	15·00
		a. Brn-pur advert (3rd setting) (9.93)	£130	27·00
		ab. Mixed perfs 10 and 12½	£180	£110
224	20	6d. brown (Die 1)	£100	28·00
		a. Mixed perfs 10 and 12½		
		b. Die 2 (1892)	60·00	8·50
		ba. *Black-brown*	60·00	8·50
		bb. Imperf (pair)	£600	
		bc. Mixed perfs 10 and 12½	£170	65·00
		bd. Sepia advert (2nd setting) (4.93)	£250	15·00
		be. Brn-red advert (3rd setting) (9.93)	£250	15·00
		bf. Brn-pur advert (3rd setting) (9.93)	£250	15·00
		bx. Wmk reversed (with brown-purple advert)	†	50·00
225	21	8d. blue (brown-purple advert. 3rd setting) (9.93)	75·00	48·00
226	22	1s. red-brown	90·00	7·50
		a. Imperf between (pair)	£900	
		b. Mixed perfs 10 and 12½	£225	£150
		c. Sepia advert (2nd setting) (5.93)	£190	26·00
		d. Black advert (2nd setting) (5.93)	£250	£120
		e. Brn-red advert (3rd setting) (9.93)	£190	26·00
		f. Brn-pur advert (3rd setting) (9.93)	£190	26·00

(c) P 10×11 (1895–97).

No.	Type	Description	Un	Used
227	13	½d. black (1896)	3·25	50
		a. Mixed perfs 10 and 11	£100	45·00
		b. Perf 11×10	35·00	15·00
228	14	1d. rose (Die 3)	4·75	15
		a. Mixed perfs 10 and 11	£110	60·00
		b. Perf 11×10	60·00	10·00
		c. "Ellipse" flaw	30·00	10·00
		x. Wmk reversed	55·00	22·00
229	15	2d. purple (Die 3)	14·00	30
		a. Mixed perfs 10 and 11	70·00	50·00
230	16	2½d. blue (1896)	55·00	3·75
		a. *Ultramarine*	55·00	4·50
		b. Mixed perfs 10 and 11	—	90·00
231	17	3d. lemon-yellow (1896)	65·00	13·00
232	18	4d. pale green (1896)	75·00	12·00
		a. Mixed perfs 10 and 11	—	£120
233	19	5d. olive-black (1896)	55·00	12·00
234	20	6d. deep brown (Die 2) (1896)	70·00	8·50
		a. Mixed perfs 10 and 11	£170	55·00
		b. Perf 11×10		
235	22	1s. red-brown (1896)	80·00	9·00
		a. Mixed perfs 10 and 11	£180	80·00

(d) P 11 (1895–1900).

No.	Type	Description	Un	Used
236	13	½d. black (1897)	4·50	15
		aw. Wmk inverted	45·00	16·00
		ax. Wmk reversed	55·00	22·00
		b. Thin coarse toned paper (1898)	28·00	4·00
		ba. Wmk sideways	—	£300
237	14	1d. rose (Die 3)	4·00	10
		a. *Deep carmine*	5·50	1·50
		b. Imperf between (pair)	£550	
		c. *Dp carm/thin coarse toned* (1898)	9·50	2·00
		ca. Wmk sideways	—	£275
		d. "Ellipse" flaw	30·00	10·00
		w. Wmk inverted	22·00	18·00
		x. Wmk reversed	38·00	18·00
		y. Wmk inverted and reversed	70·00	42·00
238	15	2d. mauve (Die 3)	13·00	75
		a. *Purple*	13·00	75
		b. *Dp purple/thin coarse toned* (1898)	13·00	2·75
		ba. Wmk sideways	£200	£275
		w. Wmk inverted	18·00	6·00
		x. Wmk reversed	70·00	22·00
239	16	2½d. blue (1897)	50·00	3·75
		a. Thin coarse toned paper (1898)	80·00	18·00
240	17	3d. pale yellow (1897)	55·00	7·50
		a. *Pale dull yellow/thin coarse toned* (1898)	70·00	17·00
		b. *Orange* (1899)	45·00	11·00
		c. *Dull orange-yellow* (1900)	50·00	18·00
241	18	4d. yellowish green	50·00	4·50
		a. *Bluish green* (1897)	50·00	4·25
		w. Wmk inverted	85·00	12·00
242	19	5d. olive-black/*thin coarse toned* (1899)	55·00	26·00
243	20	6d. brown (Die 2) (1897)	70·00	4·25
		a. *Black-brown*	70·00	4·25
		b. *Brown/thin coarse toned* (1898)	90·00	8·50
		x. Wmk reversed	†	32·00
244	21	8d. blue (1898)	70·00	48·00
245	22	1s. red-brown (1897)	80·00	7·00

Only the more prominent shades have been included.

Stamps perf compound of 11 and 12½ exist.

For the ½d. and 2d. with double-lined watermark, see Nos. 271/2.

23 Mount Cook or Aorangi

24 Lake Taupo and Mount Ruapehu

25 Pembroke Peak, Milford Sound

26 Lake Wakatipu and Mount Earnslaw, inscribed "WAKITIPU"

27 Lake Wakatipu and Mount Earnslaw, inscribed "WAKATIPU"

28 Huia

29 White Terrace, Rotomahana

30 Otira Gorge and Mount Ruapehu

31 Brown Kiwi

32 Maori War Canoe

33 Pink Terrace, Rotomahana   **34** Kea and Kaka

35 Milford Sound

36 Mount Cook

(Des H. Young (½d.), J. Gaut (1d.), W. Bock (2d., 3d., 9d., 1s.), E. Howard (4d., 6d., 8d.), E. Luke (others). Eng A. Hill (2½d., 1s.), J. A. C. Harrison (5d.), Rapkin (others). Recess Waterlow)

1898 (5 Apr). No Wmk. P 12 to 16.

246	23	½d. purple-brown	7·00	1·25
		a. Imperf between (pair)	£1500	£1100
		b. Purple-slate	7·00	1·25
		c. Purple-black	8·50	2·75
247	24	1d. blue and yellow-brown	5·50	40
		a. Imperf between (horiz pair)	£1100	
		b. Imperf vert (horiz pair)	£800	£850
		c. Imperf horiz (vert pair)	£800	£850
		d. Blue and brown	6·00	80
		da. Imperf between (pair)	£1100	
248	25	2d. lake	30·00	25
		a. Imperf vert (horiz pair)	£500	
		b. Rosy lake	30·00	25
		ba. Imperf between (vert pair)	£1000	
		bb. Imperf vert (horiz pair)	£500	
249	26	2½d. sky-blue (inscr "WAKITIPU")	9·50	32·00
		a. Blue	9·50	32·00
250	27	2½d. blue (inscr "WAKATIPU")	30·00	3·50
		a. Deep blue	30·00	3·50
251	28	3d. yellow-brown	25·00	7·50
252	29	4d. bright rose	14·00	19·00
		a. Lake-rose	17·00	20·00
		b. Dull rose	14·00	19·00
253	30	5d. sepia	70·00	£170
		a. Purple-brown	45·00	18·00
254	31	6d. green	60·00	35·00
		a. Grass-green	£130	£140
255	32	8d. indigo	42·00	40·00
		a. Prussian blue	48·00	35·00
256	33	9d. purple	48·00	30·00
257	34	1s. vermilion	70·00	24·00
		a. Dull red	70·00	24·00
		ab. Imperf between (pair)	£3500	
258	35	2s. grey-green	£120	£120
		a. Imperf between (vert pair)	£3500	£3500
259	36	5s. vermilion	£200	£350
246/59 Set of 13			£650	£600

37 Lake Taupo and Mount Ruapehu

(Recess Govt Printer, Wellington)

1899 (May)–**03**. Thick, soft ("Pirie") paper. No wmk. P 11.

260	27	2½d. blue (6.99)	15·00	3·50
		a. Imperf between (horiz pair)	£950	
		b. Imperf horiz (vert pair)	£550	
		c. Deep blue	15·00	3·50
261	28	3d. yellow-brown (5.00)	23·00	2·00
		a. Imperf between (pair)	£1100	
		b. Imperf vert (horiz pair)	£550	
		c. Deep brown	23·00	2·00
		ca. Imperf between (pair)	£1100	
262	37	4d. indigo and brown (8.99)	5·50	3·00
		a. Bright blue and chestnut	5·50	3·00
		b. Deep blue and bistre-brown	5·50	3·00
263	30	5d. purple-brown (6.99)	25·00	3·25
		a. Deep purple-brown	25·00	3·25
		ab. Imperf between (pair)	£1800	
264	31	6d. deep green	65·00	65·00
		a. Yellow-green	85·00	£110
265		6d. pale rose (5.5.00)	38·00	4·25
		a. Imperf vert (horiz pair)	£500	
		b. Imperf between (horiz pair)	£500	
		c. Rose-red	38·00	4·25
		ca. Printed double	£600	£650
		cb. Imperf between (vert pair)	£1000	
		cc. Imperf vert (horiz pair)	£375	
		cd. Showing part of sheet wmk (7.02)*	£100	90·00
		d. Scarlet	75·00	20·00
		da. Imperf vert (horiz pair)	£650	
266	32	8d. indigo	30·00	13·00
		a. Prussian blue	30·00	13·00
267	33	9d. deep purple (8.99)	45·00	25·00
		a. Rosy purple	42·00	9·50
268	34	1s. red (5.00)	55·00	8·50
		a. Dull orange-red	60·00	4·00
		b. Dull brown-red	60·00	9·50
		c. Bright red	65·00	32·00
269	35	2s. blue-green (7.99)	£100	42·00
		a. Laid paper (1.03)	£190	£225
		b. Grey-green	£100	55·00
270	36	5s. vermilion (7.99)	£200	£275
		a. Carmine-red	£275	£325
260/70 Set of 11			£550	£375

*No. 265cd is on paper without general watermark, but showing the words "LISBON SUPERFINE" wmkd once in the sheet; the paper was obtained from Parsons Bros, an American firm with a branch at Auckland.

38

1900. Thick, soft ("Pirie") paper. Wmk double-lined "NZ" and Star, W **38** (sideways*). P 11.

271	13	½d. black	9·00	12·00
		x. Wmk reversed	80·00	65·00
272	15	2d. bright purple	23·00	10·00
		w. Wmk sideways inverted	35·00	16·00
		y. Wmk sideways inverted and reversed	—	60·00

*The normal sideways wmk on Nos. 271/2 shows the star to the right of NZ, as seen from the back of the stamp.

39 White Terrace, Rotomahana

41

40 Commemorative of the New Zealand Contingent in the South African War

(Des J. Nairn (1½d.). Recess Govt Printer, Wellington)

1900 (Mar–Dec). Thick, soft ("Pirie") paper. W **38**. P 11.

273	23	½d. pale yellow-green (7.3.00)	10·00	4·25
		a. Yellow-green	6·50	1·25
		b. Green	6·00	1·00
		ba. Imperf between (pair)	£400	
		c. Deep green	6·00	1·00
		w. Wmk inverted	22·00	11·00
		y. Wmk inverted and reversed	55·00	27·00
274	39	1d. crimson (7.3.00)	13·00	20
		a. Rose-red	13·00	20
		ab. Imperf between (pair)	£1200	£1100
		ac. Imperf vert (horiz pair)	£500	
		b. Lake	30·00	4·00
		w. Wmk inverted	†	£130
		x. Wmk reversed	†	
275	40	1½d. khaki (7.12.00)	£800	£550
		a. Brown	50·00	50·00
		ab. Imperf vert (horiz pair)	£1000	
		ac. Imperf (pair)	£1100	
		b. Chestnut	9·50	4·00
		ba. Imperf vert (horiz pair)	£1000	
		bb. Imperf horiz (vert pair)	£1200	
		c. Pale chestnut	9·50	4·00
		ca. Imperf (pair)	£1100	
276	41	2d. dull violet (3.00)	11·00	65
		a. Imperf between (pair)	£1100	
		b. Mauve	12·00	1·50
		c. Purple	10·00	75
		ca. Imperf between (pair)	£1000	

The above ½d. stamps are slightly smaller than those of the previous printing. A new plate was made to print 240 stamps instead of 120 as previously, and to make these fit the watermarked paper, the border design was redrawn and contracted, the centre vignette remaining as before. The 2d. stamp is also from a new plate providing smaller designs.

42

(Des G. Bach and G. Drummond. Eng J. A. C. Harrison. Recess Waterlow)

1901 (1 Jan). Universal Penny Postage. No Wmk. P 12 to 16.

277	42	1d. carmine	3·50	4·25

All examples of No. 277 show a minute dot above the upper left corner of the value tablet which is not present on later printings.

(Recess Govt Printer, Wellington)

1901 (Feb–Dec). Thick, soft ("Pirie") paper with vertical mesh. W **38**.

(a) P 11.

278	42	1d. carmine	6·00	15
		a. Imperf vert (horiz pair)	£300	
		b. Deep carmine	6·00	15
		ba. Imperf vert (horiz pair)	£300	
		c. Carmine-lake	20·00	10·00
		x. Wmk reversed	†	40·00
		y. Wmk inverted and reversed	—	60·00

(b) P 14.

279	23	½d. green (11.01)	15·00	4·75
280	42	1d. carmine	50·00	14·00
		a. Imperf vert (horiz pair)	£275	
		y. Wmk inverted and reversed	£100	35·00

(c) P 14×11.

281	23	½d. green	8·00	9·00

		a. Deep green	8·00	9·00
		b. Perf 11×14	12·00	18·00
282	42	1d. carmine	£200	80·00
		a. Perf 11×14	£1300	£550

(d) P 11 and 14 mixed*.

283	23	½d. green	45·00	60·00
284	42	1d. carmine	£200	80·00

*The term "mixed" is applied to stamps from sheets which were at first perforated 14, or 14×11, and either incompletely or defectively perforated. These sheets were patched on the back with strips of paper, and re-perforated 11 in those parts where the original perforation was defective.

Nos. 278/84 were printed from new plates supplied by Waterlow. These were subsequently used for Nos. 285/307 with later printings on Cowan paper showing considerable plate wear.

WATERMARK VARIETIES. The watermark on the Basted Mills version of the W **38** paper used for Nos. 285/92 occurs indiscriminately normal, reversed, inverted etc.

(Recess Govt Printer, Wellington)

1901 (Dec). Thin, hard ("Basted Mills") paper with vertical mesh. W **38**.

(a) P 11.

285	23	½d. green	55·00	65·00
286	42	1d. carmine	80·00	£100

(b) P 14.

287	23	½d. green	25·00	27·00
		a. Imperf vert (horiz pair)	£350	
288	42	1d. carmine	14·00	4·75
		a. Imperf vert (horiz pair)	£275	
		b. Imperf horiz (vert pair)	£275	

(c) P 14×11.

289	23	½d. green	22·00	55·00
		a. Deep green	22·00	55·00
		b. Perf 11×14	20·00	50·00
290	42	1d. carmine	23·00	11·00
		a. Perf 11×14	12·00	3·50

(d) Mixed perfs.

291	23	½d. green	55·00	65·00
292	42	1d. carmine	75·00	75·00

(Recess Govt Printer, Wellington)

1902 (Jan). Thin, hard ("Cowan") paper with horizontal mesh. No Wmk.

(a) P 11.

293	23	½d. green	£120	£170

(b) P 14.

294	23	½d. green	14·00	5·00
295	42	1d. carmine	12·00	2·75

(c) P 14×11.

296	23	½d. green	85·00	£150
		a. Perf 11×14	£120	£190
297	42	1d. carmine	£110	£120
		a. Perf 11×14	£120	£150

(d) Mixed perfs.

298	23	½d. green	£110	£140
299	42	1d. carmine	£120	£140

43 "Single" Wmk

SIDEWAYS WATERMARKS. In its sideways format the single NZ and Star watermark W **43**, exists indiscriminately sideways, sideways inverted, sideways reversed and sideways inverted plus reversed.

(Recess Govt Printer, Wellington)

1902 (Apr). Thin, hard ("Cowan") paper. W **43**.

(a) P 11.

300	23	½d. green	60·00	85·00
301	42	1d. carmine	£650	£475

(b) P 14.

302	23	½d. green	6·50	80
		a. Imperf vert (horiz pair)	£200	
		b. Deep green	6·50	1·00
		ba. Imperf vert (horiz pair)	£200	
		c. Yellow green	7·50	1·00
		d. Pale yellow-green	15·00	3·25
		w. Wmk inverted	24·00	14·00
		x. Wmk reversed	32·00	23·00
		y. Wmk inverted and reversed	45·00	30·00
303	42	1d. carmine	3·00	10
		a. Imperf horiz (vert pair)	£170	
		b. Booklet pane of 6 (21.8.02)	£250	
		c. Pale carmine	3·00	10
		ca. Imperf vert (horiz pair)	£170	
		cb. Booklet pane of 6	£250	
		d. Deep carmine*	32·00	4·00
		w. Wmk inverted	70·00	35·00
		x. Wmk reversed	70·00	35·00
		y. Wmk inverted and reversed	50·00	15·00

(c) P 14×11.

304	23	½d. green	19·00	95·00
		a. Deep green	25·00	
		b. Perf 11×14	22·00	75·00
305	42	1d. carmine	£100	£120

a. Perf 11×14 .... £130 £130
ab. *Deep carmine** £425 £425

(d) Mixed perfs.
306 23 ½d. green .... 26·00 50·00
         a. *Deep green* .... 32·00
307 42 1d. carmine .... 25·00 48·00
         a. *Pale carmine* .... 25·00 48·00
         b. *Deep carmine** £275 £300
         y. Wmk inverted and reversed.......

*Nos. 303*d*, 305*a* and 307*b* were printed from a plate made by Waterlow & Sons, known as the "Reserve" plate. The stamps do not show evidence of wearing and the area surrounding the upper part of the figure is more deeply shaded. This plate was subsequently used to produce Nos. 362, 364 and 366/9.

A special plate, made by W. R. Royle & Sons, showing a minute dot between the horizontal rows, was introduced in 1902 to print the booklet pane, No. 303*b*. A special characteristic of the booklet pane was that the pearl in the top left-hand corner was large. Some panes exist with the outer edges imperforate.

(Recess Govt Printer, Wellington)

1902 (28 Aug)–09. *Thin, hard ("Cowan") paper. W* **43** *(sideways on 3d., 5d., 6d., 8d., 1s. and 5s.).*

(a) P 11.
308 27 2½d. blue (5.03) .... 14·00 12·00
         a. *Deep blue* .... 16·00 12·00
         w. Wmk inverted .... £110 55·00
         x. Wmk reversed .... 70·00 27·00
         y. Wmk inverted and reversed ...... 90·00 42·00
309 28 3d. yellow-brown .... 27·00 1·50
         a. *Bistre-brown* .... 28·00 1·50
         b. *Pale bistre* .... 35·00 4·00
310 37 4d. dp blue & dp brn/*bluish* ..... 6·00 55·00
         (27.11.02)
         a. Imperf vert (horiz pair) £550
311 30 5d. red-brown (4.03) .... 32·00 9·50
         a. *Deep brown* .... 29·00 6·00
         b. *Sepia* .... 45·00 16·00
312 31 6d. rose (9.02) .... 38·00 7·00
         a. *Rose-red* .... 38·00 7·50
         ab. Wmk upright £1300 £1000
         b. *Rose-carmine* .... 42·00 7·50
         ba. Imperf vert (horiz pair) £650
         c. *Bright carmine-pink* .... 50·00 8·00
         d. *Scarlet* .... 60·00 16·00
313 32 8d. blue (2.03) .... 35·00 11·00
         a. *Steel-blue* .... 35·00 11·00
         ab. Imperf vert (horiz pair) £1100
         ac. Imperf vert (vert pair) £1100
314 33 9d. purple (5.03) .... 50·00 12·00
         w. Wmk inverted .... 80·00 48·00
         x. Wmk reversed £120 £100
         y. Wmk inverted and reversed ...... £120 90·00
315 34 1s. brown-red (11.02) .... 55·00 12·00
         a. *Bright red* .... 55·00 13·00
         b. *Orange-red* .... 55·00 4·50
         ba. Error. Wmk W **12***b* (inverted) .. † £1500
         c. *Orange-brown* .... 60·00 14·00
316 35 2s. green (4.03) .... £100 55·00
         a. *Blue-green* .... 90·00 45·00
         x. Wmk reversed £350
         w. Wmk inverted .... £350 90·00
317 36 5s. deep red (6.03) £200 £250
         a. Wmk upright £225 £275
         b. *Vermilion* £200 £250
         ba. Wmk upright £225 £275
         w. Wmk inverted £650 £550

(b) P 14.
318 40 1½d. chestnut (2.07) .... 19·00 50·00
319 41 2d. grey-purple (12.02) .... 5·50 1·75
         a. *Purple* .... 5·50 1·75
         ab. Imperf vert (horiz pair) £425 £600
         ac. Imperf horiz (vert pair) £450
         b. *Bright reddish purple* .... 6·50 2·50
320 27 2½d. blue (1906) .... 18·00 3·50
         a. *Deep blue* .... 18·00 3·50
         w. Wmk inverted .... £110 80·00
         x. Wmk reversed .... † £130
         y. Wmk inverted and reversed £150 £110
321 28 3d. bistre-brown (1906) .... 27·00 5·50
         a. Imperf vert (horiz pair) £750
         b. *Bistre* .... 27·00 5·50
         c. *Pale yellow-bistre* .... 50·00 14·00
322 37 4d. dp blue & dp brown/*bluish* ... 6·50 3·00
         (1903)
         a. Imperf vert (horiz pair) £550
         b. Imperf horiz (vert pair) £500
         c. *Centre inverted* .... † *
         d. *Blue and chestnut/bluish* ..... 4·00 2·50
         e. *Blue and ochre-brown/bluish* .. 4·00 2·50
         w. Wmk inverted .... 27·00 11·00
         x. Wmk reversed .... 70·00 60·00
         y. Wmk inverted and reversed ...... 70·00 60·00
323 30 5d. black-brown (1906) .... 55·00 25·00
         a. *Red-brown* .... 32·00 12·00
324 31 6d. bright carmine-pink (1906) .... 55·00 9·50
         a. Imperf vert (horiz pair) £600
         b. *Rose-carmine* .... 55·00 9·50
325 32 8d. steel-blue (1907) .... 27·00 11·00
326 33 9d. purple (1906) .... 27·00 8·00
         w. Wmk inverted .... £110 38·00
327 34 1s. orange-brown (1906) .... 65·00 7·50
         a. *Orange-red* .... 60·00 7·50
         b. *Pale red* .... £100 50·00
328 35 2s. green (1.06) .... 85·00 24·00
         a. *blue-green* .... 90·00 32·00
         aw. Wmk inverted .... £300 80·00
         ax. Wmk reversed .... †
         ay. Wmk inverted and reversed ..... £325 85·00
329 38 5s. deep red (1906) £190 £225
         a. Wmk upright £200 £250
         b. *Dull red* £190 £225
         ba. Wmk upright £200 £250

(c) Perf compound of 11 and 14.
330 40 1½d. chestnut (1907) £1000
331 41 2d. purple (1903) £325 £325
332 28 3d. bistre-brown (1906) £650 £550
333 37 4d. blue and yellow-brown (1903).. £325 £375

334 30 5d. red-brown (1906) £1100 £950
335 31 6d. rose-carmine (1907) £350 £250
336 32 8d. steel-blue (1907) £900 £950
337 33 9d. purple (1906) £1200 £1100
338 36 5s. deep red (1906) £2500

(d) Mixed perfs.
339 40 1½d. chestnut (1907) £1000
340 41 2d. purple (1903) £275 £300
341 28 3d. bistre-brown (1906) £650 £550
342 37 4d. blue and chestnut/*bluish* (1904) £275 £325
         a. *Blue and yellow-brown/bluish* ... £275 £325
         w. Wmk inverted £550 £550
         x. Wmk reversed £650 £650
343 30 5d. red-brown (1906) £900 £750
344 31 6d. rose-carmine (1907) £325 £275
         a. *Bright carmine-pink* £350 £275
345 32 8d. steel-blue (1907) £850 £900
346 33 9d. purple (1906) £1000 £1000
347 35 2s. blue-green (1906) £1200 £1300
348 36 5s. vermilion (Wmk upright) (1906) £1800
         w. Wmk inverted ....

Two sizes of paper were used for the above stamps:—
(1) A sheet containing 240 wmks, with a space of 9 mm between each.
(2) A sheet containing 120 wmks, with a space of 24 mm between each vertical row.

Size (1) was used for the ½d., 1d., 2d. and 4d., and size (2) for 2½d., 5d., 6d., 8d. and 2s. The paper in each case exactly fitted the plates, and had the watermark in register, though in the case of the 4d., the plate of which contained only 80 stamps, the paper was cut up to print it. The 3d., 6d., 8d. and 1s. were printed on variety (1), but with watermark sideways: by reason of this, specimens from the margins of the sheets show parts of the words "NEW ZEALAND POSTAGE" in large letters, and some copies have no watermark at all. For the 1½d. and 5s. stamps variety (1) was also used, but two watermarks appear on each stamp.

*The only known example of No. 322*c*, postmarked at Picton on 21 March 1904, was purchased for the New Zealand Post archive collection in 1998.

(Recess Govt Printer, Wellington)

1904 (Feb). *Printed from new "dot" plates made by W. R. Royle & Sons. Thin, hard ("Cowan") paper. W* **43**.

(a) P 14.
349 42 1d. rose-carmine .... 8·00 50
         a. *Pale carmine* .... 8·00 50
         w. Wmk inverted .... 75·00 27·00
         y. Wmk inverted and reversed ...... 85·00 35·00

(b) P 11×14.
350 42 1d. rose-carmine £140 £120

(c) Mixed perfs.
351 42 1d. rose-carmine .... 28·00 35·00
         a. *Pale carmine* .... 28·00 35·00

These plates have a dot in the margins between stamps, level with the small pearls at the side of the design, but it is frequently cut out by the perforations. However, they can be further distinguished by the notes below.

In 1906 fresh printings were made from four new plates, two of which, marked in the margin "W1" and "W2", were supplied by Waterlow Bros and Layton, and the other two, marked "R1" and "R2", by W. R. Royle & Son. The intention was to note which pair of plates wore the best and produced the best results. They can be distinguished as follows:—

(a) *(b)* *(c)*
(d) *(e)* *(f)*

(*a*) Four o'clock flaw in rosette at top right corner. Occurs in all these plates but not in the original Waterlow plates.
(*b*) Pearl at right strong.
(*c*) Pearl at right weak.
(*d*) Dot at left and S-shaped ornament unshaded.
(*e*) S-shaped ornament with one line of shading within.
(*f*) As (*e*) but with line from left pearl to edge of stamp.
"Dot" plates comprise (*a*) and (*d*).
Waterlow plates comprise (*a*), (*b*) and (*e*).
Royle plates comprise (*a*), (*c*) and (*e*) and the line in (*f*) on many stamps but not all.

(Recess Govt Printer, Wellington)

1906. *Thin, hard ("Cowan") paper. W* **43**.

(a) Printed from new Waterlow plates.
(i) P 14.
352 42 1d. deep rose-carmine .... 30·00 2·00
         a. Imperf horiz (vert pair) £250
         b. *Aniline carmine* .... 29·00 2·00
         ba. Imperf vert (horiz pair) £250
         c. *Rose-carmine* .... 29·00 2·00
         y. Wmk inverted and reversed ....
(ii) P 11.
353 42 1d. aniline carmine £600 £700
(iii) P 11×14.
354 42 1d. rose-carmine £425 £475
         a. Perf 14×11 .... £425 £750
(iv) Mixed perfs.
355 42 1d. deep rose-carmine £400 £450

(b) Printed from new Royle plates. (i) P 14 .
356 42 1d. rose-carmine .... 11·00 1·25
         a. Imperf horiz (vert pair) £225 £250
         b. *Bright rose-carmine* .... 12·00 1·40
         w. Wmk inverted ....
         y. Wmk inverted and reversed ...... — £180
(ii) P 11.
357 42 1d. bright rose-carmine £100 £180
(iii) P 11×14.
358 42 1d. rose-carmine £100
         a. Perf 14×11 .... £110 £160
(iv) Mixed perfs.
359 42 1d. rose-carmine £100 £140
(v) P 14×14½ (comb).
360 42 1d. bright rose-carmine .... 65·00 55·00
         a. *Rose-carmine* .... 65·00 55·00

Nos. 360/*a* are known both with and without the small dot. See also No. 386.

1905 (15 June)–06. *Stamps supplied to penny-in-the-slot machines.*
(i) "Dot" plates of 1904.
(ii) Waterlow "reserve" plate of 1902.

(a) Imperf top and bottom; zigzag roulette 9½ on one or both sides, two large holes at sides.
361 42 1d. rose-carmine (i) £150
362 42 1d. deep carmine (ii) £170

(b) As last but rouletted 14½ (8.7.05).
363 42 1d. rose-carmine (i) £160
364 42 1d. deep carmine (ii) £325

(c) Imperf all round, two large holes each side (6.3.06).
365 42 1d. rose-carmine (i) £130
366 42 1d. deep carmine (ii) £130

(d) Imperf all round (21.6.06).
367 42 1d. deep carmine (ii) £140

(e) Imperf all round. Two small indentations on back of stamp (1.06).
368 42 1d. deep carmine (ii) £170 £150

(f) Imperf all round; two small pin-holes in stamp (21.6.06).
369 42 1d. deep carmine (ii) £150 £150

No. 365 *only* exists from strips of Nos. 361 or 363 (resulting from the use of successive coins) which have been separated by scissors. Similarly strips of Nos. 362 and 364 can produce single copies of No. 366 but this also exists in singles from a different machine.

Most used copies of Nos. 361/7 are forgeries and they should only be collected on cover.

44 Maori Canoe, *Te Arawa*

(Des L. J. Steele. Eng W. R. Bock. Typo Govt Printer, Wellington)

1906 (1–17 Nov). *New Zealand Exhibition, Christchurch. T* **44** *and similar horiz designs. W* **43** *(sideways). P 14.*
370 ½d. emerald-green .... 24·00 32·00
371 1d. vermilion .... 16·00 16·00
         a. *Claret* £6500 £9500
372 3d. brown and blue .... 50·00 80·00
373 6d. pink and olive-green (17.11) .. £180 £275
370/3 Set of 4 .... £250 £350

Designs:—1d. Maori art; 3d. Landing of Cook; 6d. Annexation of New Zealand.

The 1d. in claret was the original printing, which was considered unsatisfactory.

47 (T **28** reduced)   **48** (T **31** reduced)   **49** (T **34** reduced)

(New plates (except 4d.), supplied by Perkins Bacon. Recess Govt Printer, Wellington).

1907–08. *Thin, hard ("Cowan") paper. W* **43**.

(a) P 14 (line).
374 23 ½d. green (1907) .... 26·00 9·50
         a. Imperf (pair) £200
         b. *Yellow-green* .... 17·00 3·75
         c. *Deep yellow-green* .... 17·00 3·75
375 47 3d. brown (6.07) .... 55·00 25·00
376 48 6d. carmine-pink (3.07) .... 40·00 8·00
         a. *Red* .... 50·00 35·00

(b) P 14×13, 13½ (comb).
377 23 ½d. green (1907) .... 17·00 11·00
         a. *Yellow-green* .... 8·00 4·00
         b. Imperf three sides (top stamp of vert pair) £300
378 47 3d. brown (2.08) .... 50·00 35·00
         a. *Yellow-brown* .... 50·00 35·00
379 37 4d. blue and yellow-brown/*bluish* (6.08) .... 29·00 38·00
380 48 6d. pink (2.08) £275 £120
381 49 1s. orange-red (12.07) .... £120 50·00

(c) P 14×15 (comb).
382 23 ½d. yellow-green (1907) .... 8·00 1·00
         a. Imperf three sides (top stamp of vert pair) £300
         y. Wmk inverted and reversed ..... — £170

383	**47**	3d. brown (8.08)	35·00	15·00
		a. *Yellow-brown*	35·00	15·00
384	**48**	6d. carmine-pink (8.08)	40·00	11·00
385	**49**	1s. orange-red (8.08)	£110	24·00
		a. *Deep orange-brown*	£325	£750

The ½d. stamps of this 1907–8 issue have a minute dot in the margin between the stamps, where not removed by the perforation. (See note after No. 351a). Those perforated 14 can be distinguished from the earlier stamps, Nos. 302/d, by the absence of plate wear. This is most noticeable on the 1902 printings as a white patch at far left, level with the bottom of the "P" in "POSTAGE". Such damage is not present on the new plates used for Nos. 374/c.

Stamps of T 47, 48 and 49 also have a small dot as described in note after No. 351a.

TYPOGRAPHY PAPERS. 1908–30. De La Rue paper is chalk-surfaced and has a smooth finish. The watermark is as illustrated. The gum is toned and strongly resistant to soaking.

Jones paper is chalk-surfaced and has a coarser texture, is poorly surfaced and the ink tends to peel. The outline of the watermark commonly shows on the surface of the stamp. The gum is colourless or only slightly toned and washes off readily.

Cowan paper is chalk-surfaced and is white and opaque. The watermark is usually smaller than in the "Jones" paper and is often barely visible.

Wiggins Teape paper is chalk-surfaced and is thin and hard. It has a vertical mesh with a narrow watermark, whereas the other papers have a horizontal mesh and a wider watermark.

50

(Typo Govt Printer, Wellington, from Perkins Bacon plate).

1908 (1 Dec). *De La Rue chalk-surfaced paper.* W **43**. P 14×15 (comb).

386	**50**	1d. carmine	23·00	2·00
		w. Wmk inverted	—	60·00

The design of Type **50** differs from Type **42** by alterations in the corner rosettes and by the lines on the globe which are diagonal instead of vertical.

51   **52**   **53**

(Eng. P.B. Typo Govt Printer, Wellington)

1909 (8 Nov)–**12**. *De La Rue chalk-surfaced paper with toned gum.* W **43**. P 14×15 (comb).

387	**51**	½d. yellow-green	4·25	50
		aa. *Deep green*	4·25	50
		a. Imperf (pair)	£190	
		b. Booklet pane. Five stamps plus label in position 1 (4.10)	£650	
		c. Ditto, but label in position 6 (4.10)	£650	
		d. Booklet pane of 6 (4.10)	£180	
		e. Ditto, but with coloured bars on selvedge (5.12)	£170	
		w. Wmk inverted	†	£350

Stamps with blurred and heavy appearance are from booklets.

(Eng W. R. Royle & Son, London. Recess Govt Printer, Wellington)

1909 (8 Nov)–**16**. *T* **52** *and similar portraits.*

(a) W **43**. P 14×14½ (comb).

388		2d. mauve	9·50	6·50
		a. *Deep mauve*	18·00	6·50
		w. Wmk inverted	†	—
389		3d. chestnut	23·00	1·25
390		4d. orange-red	26·00	27·00
		a. *Orange-yellow* (5.1.12)	6·00	6·50
		aw. Wmk inverted	£300	80·00
391		5d. brown (1910)	17·00	3·50
		a. *Red-brown*	17·00	3·50
		w. Wmk inverted	†	—
392		6d. carmine (1910)	40·00	1·25
		a. *Deep carmine* (29.10.13)	45·00	3·00
393		8d. indigo-blue	11·00	1·75
		a. *Deep bright blue*	13·00	1·75
		w. Wmk inverted	50·00	30·00
394		1s. vermilion (1910)	48·00	2·75
		w. Wmk inverted	£180	75·00
388/94 *Set of 8*			£160	45·00

(b) W **43**. P 14 (line)*.

395		3d. chestnut (1910)	48·00	12·00
396		4d. orange (1910)	20·00	14·00
397		5d. brown	26·00	4·50
		a. *Red-brown* (15.9.11)	26·00	5·00
		w. Wmk inverted		—
398		6d. carmine	40·00	10·00
399		1s. vermilion	55·00	13·00
395/9 *Set of 5*			£170	48·00

(c) W **43** (sideways) *(paper with widely spaced wmk as used for Nos. 308 and 320 – see note below No. 348).* P 14 (line)*.

400		8d. indigo-blue (8.16)	25·00	55·00
		a. No wmk	85·00	£150

(d) W **43**. P 14×13½ (comb)†.

401		3d. chestnut (1915)	60·00	75·00
		a. Vert pair. P 14×13½ and 14×14½	£225	£275
		w. Wmk inverted	£160	£150
402		5d. red-brown (1916)	19·00	3·00
		a. Vert pair. P 14×13½ and 14×14½	50·00	70·00
403		6d. carmine (1915)	70·00	75·00
		a. Vert pair. P 14×13½ and 14×14½	£225	£275

404		8d. indigo-blue (3.16)	28·00	3·00
		a. Vert pair. P 14×13½ and 14×14½	50·00	70·00
		b. *Deep bright blue*	30·00	3·25
		ba. Vert pair. P 14×13½ and 14×14½	60·00	80·00
		w. Wmk inverted	50·00	30·00
401/4 *Set of 4*			£150	£140

*In addition to showing the usual characteristics of a line perforation, these stamps may be distinguished by their vertical perforation which measures 13.8. Nos. 388/94 generally measure vertically 14 to 14.3. An exception is 13.8 one vertical side but 14 the other.

†The 3d. and 6d. come in full sheets perf 14×13½. The 3d., 5d. and 6d. values also exist in two combinations: (*a*) five top rows perf 14×13½ with five bottom rows perf 14×14½ and (*b*) four top rows perf 14×13½ with six bottom rows perf 14×14½. The 8d. perf 14×13½ only exists from combination (*b*).

(Eng P.B. Typo Govt Printer, Wellington)

1909 (8 Nov)–**26**. P 14×15 (comb).

(a) W **43**. *De La Rue chalk-surfaced paper with toned gum.*

405	**53**	1d. carmine	1·75	10
		a. Imperf (pair)	£350	
		b. Booklet pane of 6 (4.10)	£150	
		c. Ditto, but with coloured bars on selvedge (5.12)	£110	
		w. Wmk inverted	30·00	23·00
		y. Wmk inverted and reversed		

Examples of No. 405 with a blurred and heavy appearance are from booklets.

(b) W **43**. *Jones chalk-surfaced paper with white gum.*

406	**53**	1d. deep carmine (6.24)	14·00	7·00
		a. On unsurfaced paper. *Pale carmine*	£375	
		b. Booklet pane of 6 with bars on selvedge (1.12.24)	£110	
		w. Wmk inverted	42·00	30·00

No. 406a comes from a sheet on which the paper coating was missing from the right-hand half.

(c) W **43**. *De La Rue unsurfaced medium paper with toned gum.*

407	**53**	1d. rose-carmine (4.25)	35·00	£120

(d) W **43** (sideways). *De La Rue chalk-surfaced paper with toned gum.*

408	**53**	1d. bright carmine (4.25)	9·50	45·00
		a. No Wmk	20·00	60·00
		b. Imperf (pair)	65·00	

Many stamps from the sheets of No. 408 were without watermark or showed portions of "NEW ZEALAND POSTAGE" in double-lined capitals.

(e) No Wmk, but bluish "NZ" and Star lithographed on back. *Art paper.*

409	**53**	1d. rose-carmine (7.25)	2·50	4·25
		a. "NZ" and Star in black	13·00	
		b. "NZ" and Star colourless	24·00	

(f) W **43**. *Cowan thick, opaque, chalk-surfaced paper with white gum.*

410	**53**	1d. deep carmine (8.25)	5·00	1·10
		a. Imperf (pair)	£100	£130
		b. Booklet pane of 6 with bars and adverts on selvedge	£140	
		w. Wmk inverted	38·00	28·00
		x. Wmk reversed (1926)	9·00	3·00
		xa. Booklet pane of 6 with bars and adverts on selvedge (1927)	£130	
		y. Wmk inverted and reversed (1926)	45·00	32·00

(g) W **43**. *Wiggins Teape thin, hard, chalk-surfaced paper with white gum.*

411	**53**	1d. rose-carmine (6.26)	28·00	20·00
		w. Wmk inverted	42·00	27·00

(59)   **60**

1913 (1 Dec). *Auckland Industrial Exhibition. Nos.* 387aa, 389, 392 *and* 405 *optd with T* **59** *by Govt Printer, Wellington.*

412	**51**	½d. deep green	15·00	55·00
413	**53**	1d. carmine	21·00	45·00
414	**52**	3d. chestnut	£130	£250
415		6d. carmine	£160	£300
412/15 *Set of 4*			£300	£600

These overprinted stamps were only available for letters in New Zealand and to Australia.

(Des H. L. Richardson. Recess Govt Printer, Wellington, from plates made in London by P.B.)

1915 (30 July)–**30**. W **43**. P 14×13½ (comb) (see notes below).

(a) Cowan unsurfaced paper.

416	**60**	1½d. grey-slate	3·00	1·75
		a. Perf 14×14½ (1915)	4·00	1·75
		aw. Wmk inverted	60·00	60·00
		b. Vert pair. Nos. 416/a	35·00	90·00
417		2d. bright violet	8·00	45·00
		a. Perf 14×14½	7·00	35·00
		b. Vert pair. Nos. 417/a	24·00	£160
418		2d. yellow (15.1.16)	7·00	30·00
		a. Perf 14×14½	7·00	30·00
		b. Vert pair. Nos. 418/a	18·00	£250
419		2½d. blue	3·25	5·00
		a. Perf 14×14½ (1916)	9·50	25·00
		b. Vert pair. Nos. 419/a	40·00	£160
420		3d. chocolate	16·00	1·25
		aw. Wmk inverted	£140	£110
		ax. Wmk reversed		
		b. *Deep chocolate*	13·00	2·00
		bw. Wmk inverted	£140	£110
		bx. Wmk reversed	£275	
		c. Vert pair. Nos. 420 and 420b	45·00	£140
		cw. Wmk inverted		
		cx. Wmk reversed		

421		4d. yellow	4·25	50·00
		a. Re-entry (Pl 20 R. 1/6)	45·00	
		b. Re-entry (Pl 20 R. 4/10)	60·00	
		c. Perf 14×14½	4·25	55·00
		d. Vert pair. Nos. 421 and 421c	26·00	£250
422		4d. bright violet (7.4.16)	9·00	50
		a. Imperf three sides (top stamp of vertical pair)	£1500	
		b. Perf 14×14½	45·00	24·00
		c. Re-entry (Pl 20 R. 4/10)	60·00	28·00
		dx. Wmk reversed		
		e. Perf 14×14½	7·00	50
		ew. Wmk inverted	†	
		ex. Wmk reversed		£170
		f. Vert pair. Nos. 422 and 422e	60·00	£140
		fx. Wmk reversed		
423		4½d. deep green	12·00	24·00
		a. Perf 14×14½ (1915)	12·00	42·00
		b. Vert pair. Nos. 423/a	50·00	£170
424		5d. light blue (4.22)	6·50	1·00
		a. Imperf (pair)	£140	£180
		aa. Imperf (top stamp of vertical pair)	£850	
		bw. Wmk inverted	—	£120
		c. Perf 14×14½	12·00	38·00
		d. *Pale ultramarine* (5.30)	13·00	11·00
		da. Perf 14×14½	20·00	21·00
		db. Vert pair. Nos. 424d/da	65·00	£180
425		6d. carmine	8·50	50
		a. Imperf three sides (top stamp of vert pair)	£1500	
		bw. Wmk inverted	£130	75·00
		bx. Wmk reversed	—	£130
		by. Wmk inverted and reversed		
		c. *Carmine-lake* (11.27)	£500	£400
		d. Perf 14×14½ (1915)	8·50	60
		dw. Wmk inverted	55·00	42·00
		e. Vert pair. Nos. 425 and 425d	65·00	£140
426		7½d. red-brown	10·00	23·00
		a. Perf 14×14½ (10.20)	11·00	55·00
		b. Vert pair. Nos. 426/a	48·00	£200
427		8d. indigo-blue (19.4.21)	11·00	50·00
		a. Perf 14×14½	11·00	50·00
		b. Vert pair. Nos. 427/a	38·00	£180
428		8d. red-brown (3.22)	20·00	1·50
429		9d. sage-green	17·00	2·75
		a. Imperf (pair)	£1500	
		b. Imperf three sides (top stamp of vert pair)	£1500	
		c. *Yellowish olive* (12.25)	20·00	16·00
		d. Perf 14×14½	17·00	18·00
		e. Vert pair. Nos. 429 and 429d	75·00	£225
430		1s. vermilion	14·00	2·25
		a. Imperf (pair)	£2250	
		aa. Imperf (top stamp of vertical pair)	£2000	
		bw. Wmk inverted	£250	£140
		c. Perf 14×14½ (1915)	14·00	50
		ca. *Pale orange-red* (4.24)	30·00	21·00
		cb. Imperf (pair)	£325	
		cba. Imperf (top stamp of vertical pair)	£750	
		cc. *Orange-brown* (1.2.28)	£550	£400
		cw. Wmk inverted	£225	
		d. Vert pair. Nos. 430 and 430c	75·00	£250
		dw. Wmk inverted		
416/30 *Set of 15*			£130	£200

(b) W **43** (sideways on 2d., 3d. and 6d.). *Thin paper with widely spaced watermark as used for Nos. 308 and 320 (see note below No. 348).* P 14×13½ (comb) (see notes below) (1½d.) or 14 (line) (others).

431	**60**	1½d. grey-slate (3.16)	3·00	8·00
		a. No wmk	4·00	17·00
		b. Perf 14×14½	3·00	8·00
		ba. No wmk	4·00	17·00
		by. Wmk inverted and reversed		
		c. Vert pair. Nos. 431 and 431b	22·00	£100
		ca. Vert pair. Nos. 431a and 431ba	60·00	£150
432		2d. yellow (6.16)	6·50	55·00
		a. No wmk	75·00	£150
433		3d. chocolate (6.16)	9·00	35·00
		a. No wmk	75·00	£150
434		6d. carmine (6.16)	9·00	75·00
		a. No wmk	£100	£200
431/4 *Set of 4*			23·00	£160

The 1½d., 2½d., 4½d. and 7½d. have value tablets as shown in Type **60**. For the other values the tablets are shortened and the ornamental border each side of the crown correspondingly extended.

With the exception of Nos. 432/4 stamps in this issue are comb-perforated 14×13½, 14×14½ or a combination of the two.

The 1½d. (No. 416), 2½d., 4d. (both), 4½d., 5d., 6d., 7½d., 8d. red-brown, 9d. and 1s. are known to have been produced in sheets perforated 14×13½ throughout with the 4d. bright violet, 5d., 6d. and 1s. known perforated 14×14½ throughout.

On the sheets showing the two perforations combined, the top four rows are usually perforated 14×13½ and the bottom six 14×14½. Combination sheets are known to have been produced in this form for the 1½d. (Nos. 416 and 431), 2d. (both), 2½d., 3d., 4d. (both), 4½d., 6d., 7½d., 8d. indigo-blue, 9d. and 1s. On a late printing of the 4d. bright violet and 5d. pale ultramarine the arrangement is different with the top five rows perforated 14×14½ and the bottom five 14×13½.

With the exception of Nos. 432/4 any with perforations measuring 14×14 or nearly must be classed as 14×14½, this being an irregularity of the comb machine, and not a product of the 14-line machine.

During the laying-down of plate 20 for the 4d., from the roller-die which also contained dies of other values, an impression of the 4½d. value was placed on R. 1/6 and of the 2½d. on R. 4/10. These errors were subsequently corrected by re-entries of the 4d. impression, but on R. 1/6 traces of the original impression can be found in the right-hand value tablet and above the top frame line, while on R. 4/10 the foot of the "2" is visible in the left-hand value tablet with traces of "½" to its right.

61   **62**   **WAR STAMP**

                                (63)

Type **62** (from local plates) can be identified from Type **61** (prepared by Perkins Bacon) by the shading on the portrait. This is diagonal on Type **62** and horizontal on Type **61**.

(Die eng W. R. Bock. Typo Govt Printer, Wellington, from plates made by P.B. (*T* **61**) or locally (*T* **62**))

1915 (30 July)–**33**. W **43**. P 14×15.

(a) De La Rue chalk-surfaced paper with toned gum.

435	**61**	½d. green............................	1·25	20
		a. Booklet pane of 6 with bars on selvedge.................................	£120	
		b. *Yellow-green*.............................	3·75	1·40
		ba. Booklet pane of 6 with bars on selvedge.................................	£100	
		c. Very thick, highly surfaced paper with white gum (12.15)..	12·00	45·00
		w. Wmk inverted	40·00	70·00
		x. Wmk reversed	—	70·00
		y. Wmk inverted and reversed.......	—	70·00
436	**62**	1½d. grey-black (4.16)......................	9·00	1·25
		a. *Black*......................................	10·00	1·40
		w. Wmk inverted and reversed.......		£140
437	**61**	1½d. slate (5.9.16)........................	7·50	20
		x. Wmk reversed		£140
438		1½d. orange-brown (9.18)................	2·25	20
		w. Wmk inverted	£130	90·00
		x. Wmk reversed	†	—
		y. Wmk inverted and reversed.......	£150	95·00
439		2d. yellow (9.16).........................	2·25	20
		a. *Pale yellow*.............................	3·75	70
		w. Wmk inverted	90·00	
440		3d. chocolate (5.19)....................	7·00	75
435/40		Set of 6..................................	26·00	2·50

(b) W **43**. *Jones chalk-surfaced paper with white gum.*

441	**61**	1d. green (10.24).........................	9·00	9·50
		a. Booklet pane of 6 with bars on selvedge (1.12.24)...................	£110	
		w. Wmk inverted	50·00	30·00
442		2d. dull yellow (7.24)...................	7·00	32·00
		w. Wmk inverted	38·00	
443		3d. deep chocolate (3.25)...............	22·00	19·00
441/3		Set of 3..................................	35·00	55·00

(c) No Wmk, but bluish "NZ" and Star lithographed on back. Art paper.

444	**61**	½d. apple-green (4.25)...................	3·00	4·00
		a. "NZ" and Star almost colourless...............................	4·50	
445		2d. yellow (7.25).........................	7·00	55·00

(d) W **43**. *Cowan thick, opaque, chalk-surfaced paper with white gum.*

446	**61**	½d. green (8.25)...........................	1·50	30
		a. Booklet pane of 6 with bars and adverts on selvedge.................	£140	
		ab. Booklet pane of 6 with bars on selvedge (1928)...................	£325	
		bw. Wmk inverted	55·00	45·00
		bx. Wmk reversed (1926)................	4·00	2·25
		bxa. Booklet pane of 6 with bars and adverts on selvedge (1927)........	£100	
		by. Wmk inverted and reversed (1926)................................	45·00	30·00
		c. Perf 14 (1927).........................	1·50	35
		ca. Booklet pane of 6 with bars on selvedge (1928)...................	95·00	
		cb. Booklet pane of 6 with bars and adverts on selvedge (1928)........	95·00	
		cc. Imperf three sides (horiz pair)..	£550	
		cw. Wmk inverted	45·00	38·00
447		1½d. orange-brown (P 14) (8.29).......	8·50	25·00
		a. Perf 14×15 (7.33).....................	35·00	75·00
448		2d. yellow (8.25).........................	7·50	50
		ax. Wmk reversed (1927)................	12·00	65·00
		ay. Wmk inverted and reversed (1927)................................	£120	
		b. Perf 14 (1929).........................	2·75	20
		bw. Wmk inverted	40·00	30·00
449		3d. chocolate (8.25).....................	7·50	1·00
		aw. Wmk inverted	60·00	
		b. Perf 14 (1929).........................	7·50	2·75
446/9		Set of 4..................................	18·00	25·00

(e) W **43**. *Wiggins Teape thin, hard, chalk-surfaced paper.*

450	**61**	1½d. orange-brown (P 14) (1930).......	35·00	70·00
451		2d. yellow (5.26).........................	9·00	20·00
		aw. Wmk inverted	28·00	28·00
		b. Perf 14 (10.27)........................	8·50	20·00
		bw. Wmk inverted	38·00	35·00

The designs of these stamps also differ as described beneath No. 434.

Stamps from booklet panes often have blurred, heavy impressions. Different advertisements can be found on the listed booklet panes.

Examples of No. 446cc, which occur in booklet panes, show the stamps perforated at top.

The ½d. and 2d. (Nos. 446c and 448b) are known showing ½d. and 1d. local surcharges from 1932 applied diagonally in blue to stamps previously stuck on to envelopes or cards at Christchurch (½d.) or Wellington (1d.).

1915 (24 Sept). No. 435 optd with *T* **63**.

452	**61**	½d. green..................................	2·25	50

64 "Peace" and Lion **65** "Peace" and Lion

(Des and typo D.L.R. from plates by P.B., Waterlow and D.L.R.)

1920 (27 Jan). Victory. *T* **64**/**5** *and similar designs. De La Rue chalk-surfaced paper.* W **43** (sideways on ½d., 1½d., 3d. and 1s.). P 14.

453		½d. green..................................	3·00	2·50

454		a. *Pale yellow-green*	26·00	27·00
		1d. carmine-red............................	4·50	60
		a. *Bright carmine*.........................	6·00	70
		w. Wmk inverted	16·00	8·50
		x. Wmk reversed	55·00	24·00
455		1½d. brown-orange	3·00	50
456		3d. chocolate	12·00	14·00
457		6d. violet	13·00	17·00
		a. Wmk sideways...........................	†	£500
		w. Wmk inverted	—	£130
458		1s. orange-red	20·00	48·00
453/8		Set of 6..................................	50·00	75·00

Designs: *Horiz* (as *T* **65**)—1½d. Maori chief. (As *T* **64**)—3d. Lion; 1s. King George V. *Vert* (as *T* **64**)—6d. "Peace" and "Progress".

The above stamps were placed on sale in London in November, 1919.

2d. 2d.

TWOPENCE **69**
(68)

1922 (Mar). No. 453 surch with *T* **68**.

459	**64**	2d. on ½d. green (R.)...................	3·75	1·40

(Des and eng W. R. Bock, Typo Govt Printer, Wellington)

1923 (1 Oct)–**25**. *Restoration of Penny Postage.* W **43**. P 14×15.

(a) De La Rue chalk-surfaced paper with toned gum.

460	**69**	1d. carmine..............................	3·00	60

(b) Jones chalk-surfaced paper with white gum.

461	**69**	1d. carmine (3.24)......................	8·50	5·50
		a. Wmk sideways.........................	†	£350
		w. Wmk inverted	55·00	45·00

(c) Cowan unsurfaced paper with very shiny gum.

462	**69**	1d. carmine-pink (4.25)	30·00	27·00

The paper used for No. 462 is similar to that of Nos. 416/30.

70 Exhibition Buildings

(Des H. L. Richardson. Eng and typo Govt Printer, Wellington)

1925 (17 Nov). *Dunedin Exhibition. Cowan chalk-surfaced paper.* W **43**. P 14×15.

463	**70**	½d. yellow-green/*green*	3·00	11·00
		w. Wmk inverted	£120	£100
464		1d. carmine/*rose*	3·75	5·50
		w. Wmk inverted	£120	£100
465		4d. mauve/*pale mauve*	30·00	70·00
		a. "POSTAGF" at right (R. 1/2, R. 10/1)...............................	£100	£170
463/5		Set of 3..................................	32·00	80·00

71 **72**

(Des H. L. Richardson; plates by B.W. (1d. from sheets), P.B. (1d. from booklets), Royal Mint, London (others). Typo Govt Printer, Wellington)

1926 (12 July)–**34**. W **43**. P 14.

(a) Jones chalk-surfaced paper with white gum.

466	**72**	2s. deep blue	50·00	55·00
		w. Wmk inverted	50·00	55·00
467		3s. mauve	80·00	£160
		w. Wmk inverted	80·00	£160

(b) Cowan thick, opaque, chalk-surfaced paper with white gum.

468	**71**	1d. rose-carmine (15.11.26)............	75	20
		a. Imperf (pair)...........................	£160	
		b. Booklet pane of 6 with bars on selvedge (1928).....................	£100	
		c. Booklet pane of 6 with bars and adverts on selvedge (1928)........	85·00	
		dw. Wmk inverted	26·00	15·00
		e. Perf 14×15 (3.27).....................	65	50
		ea. Booklet pane of 6 with bars and adverts on selvedge (1934)........	95·00	
		ew. Wmk inverted	26·00	15·00
		ex. Wmk reversed	11·00	
469	**72**	2s. light blue (5.27)...................	55·00	25·00
470		3s. pale mauve (9.27)..................	90·00	£150
468/70		Set of 3................................	£130	£160

(c) Wiggins Teape thin, hard, chalk-surfaced paper with white gum.

471	**71**	1d. rose-carmine (6.30)................	18·00	12·00
		w. Wmk inverted	65·00	26·00

No. 468ex exists in a range of colours including scarlet and deep carmine to magenta but we have insufficient evidence to show that these were issued.

Following the reduction of the postage rate to ½d. on 1 June 1932 the firm of R. H. White & Co. Ltd. of Stratford returned a quantity of envelopes stamped with 1d. stamps (No. 468) to the New Plymouth post office who surcharged the stamps "HALFPENNY" in purple using a handstamp. The covers were then returned to the firm for normal use. Similar local surcharges were applied diagonally to 1d. stamps stuck on to postcards or lettercards at Dunedin, Greymouth and Invercargill in blue or at Palmerston North in purple. With the exception of the Greymouth provisional, where forty mint examples were acquired by a stamp dealer these local surcharges are only found unused, no gum, or used.

73 Nurse **74** Smiling Boy

(Typo Govt Printing Office, Wellington)

1929–**30**. *Anti-Tuberculosis Fund. T* **73** *and similar design.* W **43**. P 14.

(a) Inscribed "HELP STAMP OUT TUBERCULOSIS".

544		1d.+1d. scarlet (11.12.29)	11·00	18·00
		w. Wmk inverted	£225	£170

(b) Inscribed "HELP PROMOTE HEALTH".

545		1d.+1d. scarlet (29.10.30)	20·00	38·00

(Des L. C, Mitchell. Dies eng and plates made Royal Mint, London (1d.), Govt Ptg Office, Wellington from W. R. Bock die (2d.). Typo Govt Ptg Office, Wellington)

1931 (31 Oct). *Health Stamps.* W **43** (sideways). P 14½×14.

546	**74**	1d.+1d. scarlet	75·00	75·00
547		2d.+1d. blue...........................	75·00	60·00

75 New Zealand Lake Scenery FIVE PENCE
(76)

(Des L. C. Mitchell. Plates, Royal Mint, London. Typo Govt Ptg Office)

1931 (10 Nov)–**35**. *Air.* W **43**. P 14×14½.

548	**75**	3d. chocolate	25·00	15·00
		a. Perf 14×15 (4.35)....................	£130	£425
549		4d. blackish purple	25·00	20·00
550		7d. brown-orange	27·00	9·00
548/50		Set of 3...............................	70·00	40·00

1931 (18 Dec). *Air. Surch with T* **76**. W **43**. P 14×14½.

551	**75**	5d. on 3d. green (R.)..................	10·00	8·00

77 Hygeia, Goddess of Health **78** The Path to Health

(Des R. E. Tripe and W. J. Cooch. Eng H. T. Peat. Recess Govt Printing Office, Wellington)

1932 (18 Nov). *Health Stamp.* W **43**. P 14.

552	**77**	1d.+1d. carmine	20·00	27·00
		w. Wmk inverted	£250	£130
		x. Wmk reversed	†	£300

(Des J. Berry. Eng H. T. Peat. Recess Govt Printing Office, Wellington)

1933 (8 Nov). *Health Stamp.* W **43**. P 14.

553	**78**	1d.+1d. carmine	13·00	17·00
		w. Wmk inverted	£180	£120

TRANS-TASMAN AIR MAIL "FAITH IN AUSTRALIA." **80** Crusader
(79)

1934 (17 Jan). *Air. T* **75** *in new colour optd with T* **79**. W **43**. P 14×14½.

554	**75**	7d. light blue (B.)....................	35·00	40·00

(Des J. Berry. Recess D.L.R.)

1934 (25 Oct). *Health Stamp.* W **43** (sideways). P 14×13½.

555	**80**	1d.+1d. carmine	11·00	17·00

81 Collared
Grey Fantail

82 Brown Kiwi

83 Maori
Woman

84 Maori Carved
House

85 Mt. Cook

86 Maori Girl

87 Mitre Peak

88 Striped Marlin

89 Harvesting

90 Tuatara Lizard

91 Maori Panel

92 Parson Bird

93 Capt. Cook at Poverty Bay

94 Mt. Egmont

Die I   Die II

"Captain Coqk" (R. 1/4)

(Des J. Fitzgerald (½d., 4d.), C. H. and R. J. G. Collins (1d.) M.
Matthews (1½d.), H. W. Young (2d.), L. C. Mitchell (2½d., 3d., 8d.,
1s., 3s.), W. J. Cooch and R. E. Tripe (5d.), T. I. Archer (6d.), I. F.
Calder (9d.) and I. H. Jenkins (2s.). Litho Waterlow (9d.). Recess
D.L.R. (remainder))

1935 (1 May)–36. W **43** (sideways on. 8d.).

556	81	½d. bright green, P 14×13½	1·50	1·25
		w. Wmk inverted	2·75	3·50
557	82	1d. scarlet (Die I), P 14×13½	1·75	1·00
		aw. Wmk inverted	5·00	3·25
		b. Perf 13½×14 (1936)	75·00	50·00
		c. Die II. Perf 14×13½ (1935)	6·50	3·00
		ca. Die II. Booklet pane of 6 with adverts on selvedge	60·00	
		cw. Wmk inverted	13·00	3·75
558	83	1½d. red-brown, P 14×13½	9·00	14·00
		a. Perf 13½×14 (1935)	6·50	8·50
		ay. Wmk inverted and reversed (2.36)	19·00	27·00
559	84	2d. orange, P 14×13½	4·50	1·50
		w. Wmk inverted	£160	65·00
560	85	2½d. chocolate and slate, P 13–14×13½	6·50	32·00
		aw. Wmk inverted	24·00	45·00
		b. Perf 13½×14 (11.35)	5·50	21·00
		bx. Wmk reversed	†	£750
561	86	3d. brown, P 14×13½	12·00	3·25
		w. Wmk inverted	£550	£250
562	87	4d. black and sepia, P 14	3·75	2·25
		w. Wmk inverted	£425	£160
563	88	5d. ultramarine, P 13–14×13½	23·00	30·00
		aw. Wmk inverted	†	£200
		b. Perf 13½×14	26·00	42·00
564	89	6d. scarlet, P 13½×14	8·00	7·50
		w. Wmk inverted	£300	£100

565	90	8d. chocolate, P 14×13½	9·50	13·00
566	91	9d. scarlet and black, P 14×14½	11·00	3·75
567	92	1s. deep green, P 14×13½	20·00	13·00
		w. Wmk inverted	—	£160
568	93	2s. olive-green, P 13–14×13½	45·00	42·00
		a. "CAPTAIN COQK"	£130	
		bw. Wmk inverted	£110	55·00
		c. Perf 13½×14 (1935)	55·00	50·00
		ca. "CAPTAIN COQK"	£140	
569	94	3s. choc & yell-brn, P 13–14×13½	17·00	48·00
		a. Perf 13½×14 (11.35)	19·00	48·00
		aw. Wmk inverted	†	£225
		ay. Wmk inverted and reversed (1936)	£350	£375
556/69		Set of 14	£150	£180

Some stamps from sheets perforated 14×13½ by De La Rue sometimes
show the horizontal perforations nearer 13½.

In the 2½d., 5d., 2s. and 3s. perf 13–14×13½ the horizontal
perforations of each stamp are in two sizes, one half of each horizontal
side measuring 13 and the other 14.

See also Nos. 577/90 and 630/1.

95 Bell Block Aerodrome

96 King George V and Queen
Mary

(Des J. Berry. Eng Stamp Printing Office, Melbourne. Recess Govt
Printing Office, Wellington)

1935 (4 May). *Air.* W **43**. P 14.

570	95	1d. carmine	1·00	70
		w. Wmk inverted	75·00	45·00
571		3d. violet	5·00	5·00
		w. Wmk inverted	£100	50·00
572		6d. blue	9·50	9·50
		w. Wmk inverted	£120	70·00
570/2		Set of 3	14·00	6·00

(Frame by J. Berry. Recess B.W.)

1935 (7 May). *Silver Jubilee.* W **43**. P 11×11½.

573	96	½d. green	75	1·00
574		1d. carmine	1·00	80
575		6d. red-orange	18·00	28·00
573/5		Set of 3	18·00	28·00

97 "The Key to
Health"

98 "Multiple Wmk"

(Des S. Hall. Recess John Ash, Melbourne)

1935 (30 Sept). *Health Stamp.* W **43**. P 11.

576	97	1d.+1d. scarlet	2·50	2·75

WATERMARKS. In W **43** the wmk units are in vertical columns
widely spaced and the sheet margins are unwatermarked or wmkd "NEW
ZEALAND POSTAGE" in large letters.

In W **98** the wmk units are arranged alternately in horizontal rows
closely spaced and are continued into the sheet margins.

Stamps with W **98** sideways show the star to the left of NZ, *as seen
from the back.* Sideways inverted varieties have the star to right *as
seen from the back.*

(Litho Govt Ptg Office, Wellington (9d). Recess Waterlow or D.L.R.
(others))

1936–42. W **98**.

577	81	½d. bright green, P 14×13½	3·25	10
		w. Wmk inverted	5·50	2·75
578	82	1d. scarlet (Die II), P 14×13½ (4.36)	2·50	10
		w. Wmk inverted	7·00	3·00
579	83	1½d. red-brown, P 14×13½ (6.36)	11·00	5·50
580	84	2d. orange, P 14×13½ (3.36)	30	10
		aw. Wmk inverted	£170	80·00
		b. Perf 12½† (6.41)	5·00	10
		bw. Wmk inverted	†	
		c. Perf 14 (6.41)	25·00	1·25
		d. Perf 14×15 (6.41)	38·00	22·00
581	85	2½d. chocolate and slate, P 13–14×13½	8·00	19·00
		aw. Wmk inverted	32·00	50·00
		b. Perf 14 (11.36)	6·50	1·50
		bw. Wmk inverted	18·00	21·00
		c. Perf 14×13½ (11.42)	50	4·00
582	86	3d. brown, P 14×13½	35·00	70
		w. Wmk inverted	60·00	40·00
583	87	4d. black and sepia, P 14×13½	7·00	50
		aw. Wmk inverted	15·00	16·00
		b. Perf 12½* (1941)	30·00	14·00
		bw. Wmk inverted	†	
		c. Perf 14, line (1941)	65·00	£100
		d. Perf 14×14½ comb (7.42)	1·00	20
		cw. Wmk inverted	£150	80·00
584	88	5d. ultramarine, P 13–14×13½ (8.36)	20·00	3·00
		aw. Wmk inverted	38·00	17·00
		b. Perf 12½*† (7.41)	17·00	3·50
		ba. Perf 14×13½ (11.42)	2·00	1·75
		ca. Double print, one albino	£650	
		cw. Wmk inverted	£160	£160
585	89	6d. scarlet, P 13½×14 (8.36)	18·00	1·75

		aw. Wmk inverted	42·00	16·00
		b. Perf 12½* (10.41)	3·00	3·50
		c. Perf 14½×14 (6.42)	1·25	20
		cw. Wmk inverted	£300	£250
586	90	8d. choc, P 14×13½ (wmk sideways)	11·00	4·25
		aw. Wmk sideways inverted	27·00	28·00
		b. Wmk upright (7.39)	4·00	4·25
		bw. Wmk inverted	†	
		c. Perf 12½* (wmk sideways) (7.41)	3·75	1·50
		d. Perf 14×14½ (wmk sideways) (7.42)	3·75	1·25
		dw. Wmk sideways inverted	—	80·00
587	91	9d. red and grey, P 14×15 (wmk sideways)	48·00	3·25
		ay. Wmk sideways inverted and reversed	—	£140
		b. Wmk upright. *Red and grey-black*, P 13½×14 (1.3.38)	55·00	3·25
		bw. Wmk inverted	£110	60·00
588	92	1s. deep green, P 14×13½	2·50	60
		aw. Wmk inverted	55·00	35·00
		b. Perf 12½* (11.41)	65·00	21·00
589	93	2s. olive-green, P 13–14×13½ (8.36)	38·00	7·50
		a. "CAPTAIN COQK"	75·00	
		bw. Wmk inverted	£300	£150
		c. Perf 13½×14 (3.39)	£300	3·00
		ca. "CAPTAIN COQK"	£300	
		d. Perf 12½*† (7.41)	19·00	8·50
		da. "CAPTAIN COQK"	70·00	
		e. Perf 14×13½ (10.42)	5·50	1·50
		ea. "CAPTAIN COQK"	£120	
		ew. Wmk inverted	—	£160
590	94	3s. chocolate & yellow-brown, P 13–14×13½	50·00	8·50
		aw. Wmk inverted	£100	22·00
		b. Perf 12½* (1941)	80·00	50·00
		c. Perf 14×13½ (1942)	3·50	2·25
577/90c		Set of 14	£110	17·00

*†Stamps indicated with an asterisk were printed and perforated by
Waterlow; those having a dagger were printed by D.L.R. and perforated
by Waterlow. No. 580d was printed by D.L.R. and perforated by Harrison
and No. 583c was printed by Waterlow and perforated by D.L.R. These
are all known as "Blitz perfs" because De La Rue were unable to
maintain supplies after their works were damaged by enemy action.
All the rest, except the 9d., were printed and perforated by D.L.R.

On stamps printed and perforated by De La Rue the perf 14×13½
varies in the sheet and is sometimes nearer 13½. 2d. perf 14×15 is
sometimes nearer 14×14½.

2½d., 5d., 2s. and 3s. in perf 13–14×13½ one half the length of each
horizontal perforation measures 13 and the other 14. In perf 14×13½
the horizontal perforation is regular.

4d. No. 583c is line-perf measuring 14 exactly and has a blackish
sepia frame. No. 583d is a comb-perf measuring 14×14.3 or 14×14.2
and the frame is a warmer shade.

2s. No. 589c is comb-perf and measures 13.5×13.75.

For 9d. typographed, see Nos. 630/1.

99 N.Z. Soldier at
Anzac Cove

100 Wool

(Des L. C. Mitchell. Recess John Ash, Melbourne)

1936 (27 Apr). *Charity. 21st Anniv of "Anzac" Landing at Gallipoli.*
W **43**. P 11.

591	99	½d.+½d. green	60	1·75
592		1d.+1d. scarlet	60	1·40

(Des L. C. Mitchell. Recess John Ash, Melbourne)

1936 (1 Oct). *Congress of British Empire Chambers of Commerce,
Wellington. Industries Issue.* T **100** *and similar horiz designs.*
W **43** (sideways). P 11½.

593		½d. emerald-green	30	30
594		1d. scarlet	30	20
595		2½d. blue	1·25	8·00
596		4d. violet	1·00	5·50
597		6d. red-brown	2·50	4·50
593/7		Set of 5	4·75	17·00

Designs:—1d. Butter; 2½d. Sheep; 4d. Apples; 6d. Exports.

105 Health Camp

106 King George VI and
Queen Elizabeth

(Des J. Berry. Recess John Ash, Melbourne)

1936 (2 Nov). *Health Stamp.* W **43** (sideways). P 11.

598	105	1d.+1d. scarlet	1·75	3·75

(Recess B.W.)

1937 (13 May). *Coronation.* W **98**. P 14×13½.

599	106	1d. carmine	30	10
600		2½d. Prussian blue	80	2·50
601		6d. red-orange	1·10	2·25
599/601		Set of 3	2·00	5·00

107 Rock climbing   **108** King George VI   **108a** King George VI

(Des G. Bull and J. Berry. Recess John Ash, Melbourne)

1937 (1 Oct). *Health Stamp.* W **43**. P 11.
602 **107** 1d.+1d. scarlet .... 3·00   3·75

Broken ribbon flaw (R. 6/6 of Pl 8)

(Des W. J. Cooch. Recess B.W.)

1938–44. W **98**. P 14×13½.
603 **108** ½d. green (1.3.38)............................ 6·50   10
    w. Wmk inverted .... 16·00   3·00
604   ½d. orange-brown (10.7.41) 20   40
    w. Wmk inverted ....
605   1d. scarlet (1.7.38) .... 5·00   10
    a. Broken ribbon .... 65·00
    w. Wmk inverted .... 16·00   3·00
606   1d. green (21.7.41).......................... 20   10
    w. Wmk inverted .... 55·00   20·00
607 **108a** 1½d. purple-brown (26.7.38)............. 26·00   2·75
    w. Wmk inverted .... 38·00   4·50
608   1½d. scarlet (1.2.44)...................... 20   60
    w. Wmk inverted .... —   65·00
609   3d. blue (26.9.41) 20   10
    w. Wmk inverted .... —   80·00
603/9 *Set of 7* .... 35·00   3·50

For other values see Nos. 680/9.

109 Children playing   **110** Beach Ball

(Des J. Berry. Recess B.W.)

1938 (1 Oct). *Health Stamp.* W **98**. P 14×13½.
610 **109** 1d.+1d. scarlet .... 6·50   3·00

(Des S. Hall. Recess Note Printing Branch, Commonwealth Bank of Australia, Melbourne)

1939 (16 Oct). *Health Stamps. Surcharged with new value.* W **43**. P 11.
611 **110** 1d. on ½d.+½d. green .... 4·75   4·50
612   2d. on 1d.+1d. scarlet .... 5·50   4·50

111 Arrival of the Maoris, 1350   **115** Signing Treaty of Waitangi, 1840

(Des L. C. Mitchell (½d., 3d., 4d.); J. Berry (others). Recess BW.)

1940 (2 Jan–8 Mar). *Centenary of Proclamation of British Sovereignty.* T **111, 115** *and similar designs.* W **98**. P 14×13½ (2½d.), 13½×14 (5d.) or 13½ (others).
613   ½d. blue-green 30   10
614   1d. chocolate and scarlet .... 2·75   10
615   1½d. light blue and mauve 30   60
616   2d. blue-green and chocolate........... 1·50   10
617   2½d. blue-green and blue .... 2·00   1·00
618   3d. purple and carmine .... 3·75   1·00
619   4d. chocolate and lake .... 13·00   1·50
620   5d. pale blue and brown .... 7·00   3·75
621   6d. emerald-green and violet .... 11·00   1·25
622   7d. black and red .... 1·75   4·00
623   8d. black and red (8.3).................... 11·00   3·00
624   9d. olive-green and orange .... 7·50   2·00
625   1s. sage-green and deep green .... 13·00   3·75
613/25 *Set of 13* .... 65·00   19·00

Designs: *Horiz* (as T **111**)—1d. *Endeavour*, Chart of N.Z., and Capt. Cook; 1½d. British Monarchs; 2d. Tasman with his ship and chart; 3d. Landing of immigrants, 1840; 4d. Road, Rail, Sea and Air Transport; 6d. *Dunedin* and "Frozen Mutton Route" to London; 7d., 8d. Maori council; 9d. Gold mining in 1861 and 1940. (*As T* **115**)—5d. H.M.S. *Britomar* at Akaroa, 1840. *Vert* (as T **111**)—1s. Giant Kauri tree.

1940 (1 Oct). *Health Stamps. As T* **110**, *but without extra surcharge.* W **43**. P 11.
626 **110** 1d.+½d. blue-green .... 14·00   16·00
627   2d.+1d. brown-orange .... 14·00   16·00

(123)   Inserted "2"   (124)

1941. Nos. 603 and 607 surch as T **123**.
628 **108** 1d. on ½d. green (1.5.41)................... 1·75   10
629 **108a** 2d. on 1½d. purple-brown (4.41).......... 1·75   10
    a. Inserted "2" £550   £300

The surcharge on No. 629 has only one figure, at top left, and there is only one square to obliterate the original value at bottom right.

The variety "Inserted 2" occurs on the 10th stamp, 10th row. It is identified by the presence of remnants of the damaged "2", and by the spacing of "2" and "D" which is variable and different from the normal.

(Typo Govt Printing Office, Wellington)

1941. *As T* **91**, *but smaller* (17½×20½ mm). *Chalk-surfaced paper.* P 14×15.

(a) W **43**.
630 **91** 9d. scarlet and black (5.41) .... 95·00   30·00
    w. Wmk inverted .... †   £250

(b) W **98**.
631 **91** 9d. scarlet and black (29.9.41) .... 3·75   3·50
    w. Wmk inverted £250   £180

1941 (4 Oct). *Health Stamps. Nos. 626/7 optd with T* **124**.
632 **110** 1d.+½d. blue-green 50   2·25
633   2d.+1d. brown-orange 50   2·25

125 Boy and Girl on Swing   **126** Princess Margaret

(Des S. Hall. Recess Note Printing Branch, Commonwealth Bank of Australia, Melbourne)

1942 (1 Oct). *Health Stamps.* W **43**. P 11.
634 **125** 1d.+½d. blue-green 30   1·25
635   2d.+1d. orange-red 30   1·25

(Des J. Berry. Recess B.W.)

1943 (1 Oct). *Health Stamps. T* **126** *and similar triangular design.* W **98**. P 12.
636   1d.+½d. green 20   1·50
    a. Imperf between (vert pair)............ £8000
637   2d.+1d. red-brown 20   25
    a. Imperf between (vert pair)............ £10000   £10000

Design:— 2d. Queen Elizabeth II as Princess.

❖ TENPENCE ❖
(128)

1944 (1 May). *No. 615 surch with T* **128**.
662 10d. on 1½d. light blue and mauve 15   30

129 Queen Elizabeth II as Princess and Princess Margaret   **130** Statue of Peter Pan, Kensington Gardens

(Recess B.W.)

1944 (9 Oct). *Health Stamps.* W **98**. P 13½.
663 **129** 1d.+1d. green 30   40
664   2d.+1d. blue 30   30

(Des J. Berry. Recess B.W.)

1945 (1 Oct). *Health Stamps.* W **98**. P 13½.
665 **130** 1d.+½d. green and buff 15   20
    w. Wmk inverted .... 55·00   45·00
666   2d.+1d. carmine and buff 15   20
    w. Wmk inverted .... £110   65·00

---

131 Lake Matheson   **132** King George VI and Parliament House, Wellington

133 St. Paul's Cathedral   **139** "St. George" (Wellington College War Memorial Window)   Printer's guide mark (R. 12/3)

Completed rudder (R. 2/4 of Pl 42883 and R. 3/2 of Pl 42796)

(Des J. Berry. Photo Harrison (1½d. and 1s.). Recess B.W. (1d. and 2d.) and Waterlow (others))

1946 (1 Apr). *Peace issue.* T **131/3**, **139** *and similar designs.* W **98** (sideways on 1½d.). P 13 (1d., 2d.), 14×14½ (1½d., 1s.), 13½ (others)
667   ½d. green and brown 20   65
    a. Printer's guide mark .... 15·00
    w. Wmk inverted .... 70·00   45·00
668   1d. green. 10   10
    w. Wmk inverted .... 45·00   24·00
669   1½d. scarlet 10   50
    w. Wmk sideways inverted................. 10   50
670   2d. purple 15   10
671   3d. ultramarine and grey 30   15
    a. Completed rudder .... 9·50
    b. Ultramarine omitted ....
672   4d. bronze-green and orange 20   20
    w. Wmk inverted .... £120   48·00
673   5d. green and ultramarine 50   1·00
674   6d. chocolate and vermilion 15   30
675   8d. black and carmine 15   30
676   9d. blue and black 15   30
677   1s. grey-black 40   40
667/77 *Set of 11* .... 2·10   3·50

Designs: *Horiz* (as T **132**)—2d. The Royal Family. (*As T* **131**)—3d. R.N.Z.A.F. badge and airplanes; 4d. Army badge, tank and plough; 5d. Navy badge, H.M.N.Z.S. *Achilles* (cruiser) and *Dominion Monarch* (liner); 6d. N.Z. coat of arms, foundry and farm; 9d. Southern Alps and Franz Josef Glacier. *Vert* (as T **139**)—1s. National Memorial Campanile.

Only one example of No. 671b is known. It was caused by a paper fold.

142 Soldier helping Child over Stile

(Des J. Berry. Recess Waterlow)

1946 (24 Oct). *Health Stamps.* W **98**. P 13½.
678 **142** 1d.+½d. green and orange-brown 15   15
    a. Yellow-green and orange-brown .... 4·50   5·00
    w. Wmk inverted .... 20·00   20·00
679   2d.+1d. chocolate and orange-brown.. 15   15

144 King George VI   **145** Statue of Eros

Plate 1   Plate 2

(Des W. J. Cooch. Recess *T* 108*a*, B.W.; *T* 144, D.L.R.)

1947 (1 May)–**52**. W **98** (sideways on "shilling" values).

(a) P 14×13½..

680	108a	2d. orange	15	10
681		4d. bright purple	70	60
682		5d. slate	50	90
683		6d. carmine	50	10
		w. Wmk inverted	£110	32·00
684		8d. violet	75	65
685		9d. purple-brown	1·75	1·00
		w. Wmk inverted	45·00	12·00

(b) P 14.

686	144	1s. red-brown and carmine (Plate 1)	1·60	1·00
		aw. Wmk sideways inverted	16·00	9·00
		b. Wmk upright (Plate 1)	50	80
		c. Wmk upright (Plate 2) (1950)	2·25	1·25
		cw. Wmk inverted	80·00	23·00
687		1s.3d. red-brown and blue (Plate 2)	1·25	1·25
		aw. Wmk sideways inverted	12·00	6·00
		b. Wmk upright (14.1.52)	2·25	4·50
		bw. Wmk inverted	†	—
688		2s. brown-orange and green (Plate 1)	3·75	2·50
		aw. Wmk sideways inverted	18·00	12·00
		b. Wmk upright (Plate 1)	5·50	9·00
689		3s. red-brown and grey (Plate 2)	4·50	3·50
		w. Wmk sideways inverted	35·00	16·00
680/9		Set of 10	13·00	9·75

In head-plate 2 the diagonal lines of the background have been strengthened and result in the upper corners and sides appearing more deeply shaded.

(Des J. Berry. Recess Waterlow)

1947 (1 Oct). *Health Stamps.* W **98** (sideways). P 13½.

690	145	1d.+½d. green	15	15
		w. Wmk sideways inverted	42·00	42·00
691		2d.+1d. carmine	15	15
		w. Wmk sideways inverted	65·00	65·00

146 Port Chalmers, 1848   148 First Church, Dunedin

(Des J. Berry. Recess B.W.)

1948 (23 Feb). *Centennial of Otago.* T **146**, **148** *and similar designs.* W **98** (sideways on 3d.). P 13½.

692		1d. blue and green	25	35
		w. Wmk inverted	50·00	50·00
693		2d. green and brown	25	35
694		3d. purple	30	60
695		6d. black and rose	30	60
		w. Wmk inverted	—	£180
692/5		Set of 4	1·00	1·75

Designs: *Horiz*—2d. Cromwell, Otago; 6d. University of Otago.

150 Boy Sunbathing and   151 Nurse and
Children Playing   Child

(Des E. Linzell. Recess B.W.)

1948 (1 Oct). *Health Stamps.* W **98**. P 13½.

696	150	1d.+½d. blue and green	15	20
		w. Wmk inverted	42·00	32·00
697		2d.+1d. purple and scarlet	15	20

1949 ROYAL VISIT ISSUE. Four stamps were prepared to commemorate this event: 2d. Treaty House, Waitangi; 3d. H.M.S. Vanguard; 5d. Royal portraits; 6d. Crown and sceptre. The visit did not take place and the stamps were destroyed, although a few examples of the 3d. later appeared on the market. A similar set was prepared in 1952, but was, likewise, not issued.

(Des J. Berry. Photo Harrison)

1949 (3 Oct). *Health Stamps.* W **98**. P 14×14½.

698	151	1d.+½d. ultramarine	25	20
699		2d.+1d.	25	20

---

a. No stop below "D" of "1D." (R. 1/2)		6·50	17·00

1½d.
POSTAGE
(152)

153 Queen Elizabeth II and Prince Charles

1950 (28 July). *As Type F* **6**, *but without value, surch with T* **152**. *Chalk-surfaced paper.* W **98** (inverted). P 14.

700	F 6	1½d. carmine	40	30
		w. Wmk upright	3·00	3·75

(Des J. Berry and R. S. Phillips. Photo Harrison)

1950 (2 Oct). *Health Stamps.* W **98**. P 14×14½.

701	153	1d.+½d. green	25	20
		w. Wmk inverted	5·00	5·00
702		2d.+1d. plum	25	20
		w. Wmk inverted	27·00	32·00

154 Christchurch   155 Cairn on Lyttleton Hills
Cathedral

(Des L. C. Mitchell (2d.), J. A. Johnstone (3d.) and J. Berry (others). Recess B.W.)

1950 (20 Nov). *Centennial of Canterbury, N.Z. T* **154/5** *and similar designs.* W **98** (sideways on 1d. and 3d.). P 13½.

703		1d. green and blue	40	55
704		2d. carmine and orange	40	55
705		3d. dark blue and blue	40	75
706		6d. brown and blue	50	75
707		1s. reddish purple and blue	50	1·00
703/7		Set of 5	2·00	3·25

Designs: *Vert (as T* **154**)—3d. John Robert Godley. *Horiz (as T* **155**)—6d. Canterbury University College; 1s. Aerial view of Timaru.

159 "Takapuna" class Yachts

(Des J. Berry and R. S. Phillips. Recess B.W.)

1951 (1 Nov). *Health Stamps.* W **98**. P 13½.

708	159	1½d.+½d. scarlet and yellow	25	1·00
709		2d.+1d. deep green and yellow	25	25
		w. Wmk inverted	48·00	48·00

STAMP BOOKLETS

Nos. SB1 to SB19 are stapled.
Nos. SB1/5 were sold at ½d. above the face value of the stamps to cover the cost of manufacture.

1901 (1 Apr). *White card covers with postage rates.*

SB1	1s.½d. booklet containing twelve 1d. (No. 278) in blocks of 6 .... £2250
SB2	2s.6½d. booklet containing thirty 1d. (No. 278) in blocks of 6 .... £3000

Original printings of Nos. SB1/2 showed the face value on the cover in small figures. Subsequent printings show large figures of value on the covers and the prices quoted are for this type.

1902 (21 Aug)–**05**. *White card covers with postage rates.*

SB3	1s.½d. booklet containing twelve 1d. in panes of 6 (Nos. 303b or 303cb) £1800
SB4	2s.½d. booklet containing twenty-four 1d. in panes of 6 (Nos. 303b or 303cb) (21.3.05) £2250
SB5	2s.6½d. booklet containing thirty 1d. in panes of 6 (Nos. 303b or 303cb) £2750

1910 (Apr). *White card cover with postage rates.*

SB6	2s. booklet containing eleven ½d. in pane of 5 with 1 label (Nos. 387b or 387c) and pane of 6 (No. 387d), and eighteen 1d. in three panes of 6 (No. 405b) £3750

1912 (May). *White card cover.*

SB7	2s. booklet containing twelve ½d. and eighteen 1d. in panes of 6 with bars on the selvedge (Nos. 387c, 405c) £2750
	a. Blue cover ....

1915 (Feb). *Red card cover.*

SB8	2s. booklet containing twelve ½d. and eighteen 1d. in panes of 6 with bars on the selvedge (Nos. 435a or 435ba, 405c) £1500
	a. Grey cover ....

---

	b. Blue cover ....
	c. Yellow-buff cover ....
	d. Purple-buff cover ....

1924 (1 Dec)–**25**. *Cover inscription within frame.*

SB9	2s. booklet containing twelve ½d. and eighteen 1d. in panes of 6 with bars on the selvedge (Nos. 441a, 406b) (lilac cover) £1600
	a. Grey cover ....
SB10	2s. booklet containing twelve ½d. and eighteen 1d. in panes of 6 with bars and advertisements on the selvedge (Nos. 446a, 410b) (yellow-buff cover) (1925) £1800
	a. Grey-green cover £1800
	b. Grey-buff cover ....
	c. Grey-pink cover £2000

1928–34.

SB11	2s. booklet containing twelve ½d. (P 14×15) and eighteen 1d. in panes of 6 with bars on the selvedge (Nos. 446ab, 468b) £2250
	a. As No. SB11, but ½d. (P 14) (Nos. 446ca, 468b) £1500
	b. As No. SB11 but panes with bars and advertisements on the selvedge (Nos. 446cb, 468c) £1500
SB12	2s. booklet containing twenty-four 1d (P 14) in panes of 6 with bars and advertisements on the selvedge (No.468c) (1930) £1500
	a. As No. SB12, but 1d. (P 14×15) (No. 468ea) (1934) £1400

1935.

SB15	2s. booklet containing twenty-four 1d, in panes of 6 with advertisements on the selvedge (No. 557ca) £375

1936.

SB16	2s. booklet containing twenty-four 1d. (No. 578) in blocks of 6 .... £250

B 1

1938 (1 July). *Cream cover as Type* B **1**.

SB17	2s. booklet containing twenty-four 1d. (No. 605) in blocks of 6 .... £325

1938 (Nov). *Cream (No. SB18) or blue (No. SB19) covers as Type* B **1**.

SB18	2s. booklet containing twelve ½d. and eighteen 1d. (Nos. 603, 605) in blocks of 6 .... £425
SB19	2s. 3d. booklet containing eighteen 1½d. (No. 607) in blocks of 6 .... £375

EXPRESS DELIVERY STAMPS

E 1

(Typo Govt Printing Office, Wellington)

1903 (9 Feb). *Value in first colour.* W **43** (sideways). P 11.

E1	E 1	6d. red and violet	38·00	23·00

1926–36. *Thick, white, opaque chalk-surfaced "Cowan" paper.* W **43**.

(a) P 14×14½.

E2	E 1	6d. vermilion and bright violet	42·00	26·00
		w. Wmk inverted	£140	

(b) P 14×15 (1936).

E3	E 1	6d. carmine and bright violet	60·00	60·00

1937–39. *Thin, hard, chalk-surfaced "Wiggins Teape" paper.*

(a) P 14×14½.

E4	E 1	6d. carmine and bright violet	85·00	48·00

(b) P 14×15 (1939).

E5	E 1	6d. vermilion and bright violet	£150	£250

E 2 Express Post Delivery Car

(Des J. Berry. Eng Stamp Ptg Office, Melbourne Recess Govt Ptg Office, Wellington)

1939 (16 Aug). W **43**. P.14.

E6	E 2	6d. violet	1·50	1·75
		w. Wmk inverted	80·00	

No. E6 was withdrawn on 30 June 1948, when the Express Delivery service ceased.

POSTAGE DUE STAMPS

D 1   (I)

(II)

3D.   **5**D.

(a) Large "D"   *(b) Small "D"*

(Typo Govt Printing Office, Wellington)

1899 (1 Dec). *Coarse paper.* W **12b**. P 11.

I. Type I. Circle of 14 ornaments, 17 dots over "N.Z.", "N.Z." large.

(a) Large "D".

D1	D **1**	½d. carmine and green......................	18·00	28·00
		a. No stop after "D" (Right pane R. 2/3)..............................	95·00	£150
D2		8d. carmine and green......................	60·00	80·00
		a. Carmine "8D." printed double.......		
D3		1s. carmine and green......................	65·00	90·00
D4		2s. carmine and green......................	£120	£150
D1/4 *Set of 4*..........................			£225	£325

To avoid further subdivision the 1s. and 2s. are placed with the *pence* values, although the two types of "D" do not apply to the higher values.

(b) Small "D".

D6	D **1**	5d. carmine and green......................	23·00	28·00
D7		6d. carmine and green......................	30·00	32·00
D8		10d. carmine and green....................	70·00	95·00
D6/8 *Set of 3*..........................			£110	£140

II. Type II. Circle of 13 ornaments, 15 dots over "N.Z.", "N.Z." small.

(a) Large "D".

D9	D **1**	½d. vermilion and green..................	3·00	16·00
		a. No stop after "D" (Right pane R. 2/3)..............................	60·00	£100
D10		1d. vermilion and green..................	14·00	2·25
D11		2d. vermilion and green..................	48·00	9·00
D12		3d. vermilion and green..................	13·00	3·75
D9/12 *Set of 4*........................			70·00	28·00

(b) Small "D".

D14	D **1**	1d. vermilion and green..................	15·00	2·00
D15		2d. vermilion and green..................	48·00	6·50
D16		4d. vermilion and green..................	32·00	10·00
D14/16 *Set of 3*......................			85·00	17·00

Nos. D9/16 were printed from a common frame plate of 240 (4 panes of 60) used in conjunction with centre plates of 120 (2 panes of 60) for the ½d. and 4d. or 240 for the other values. Sheets of the 1d. and 2d. each contained two panes with large "D" and two panes with small "D".

D **2**   D **3**

(Des W. R. Bock. Typo Govt Printing Office, Wellington)

1902 (28 Feb). *No wmk.* P 11.

D17	D **2**	½d. red and deep green................	1·75	7·50

1904–08. *"Cowan" unsurfaced paper.* W **43** (sideways).

(a) P 11.

D18	D **2**	½d. red and green (4.04)................	1·75	2·50
		a. Imperf between (horiz pair).......	£750	
D19		1d. red and green (5.12.05)..........	11·00	3·50
D20		2d. red and green (5.4.06)............	90·00	£100
D18/20 *Set of 3*....................			90·00	£100

(b) P 14.

D21	D **2**	1d. carmine and green (12.06)........	14·00	1·50
		a. Rose-pink and green (9.07).......	13·00	1·50
D22		2d. carmine and green (10.06)........	9·00	7·00
		a. Rose-pink and green (6.08).......	5·50	2·50

1919 (Jan)–**20**. *"De La Rue" chalky paper. Toned gum.* W **43**. P 14×15.

D23	D **2**	½d. carmine and green (6.19).........	3·25	3·75
D24		1d. carmine and green...................	7·00	50
		w. Wmk inverted	†	—
D25		2d. carmine and green (8.20).........	15·00	3·00
D23/5 *Set of 3*......................			23·00	6·50

1925 (May). *"Jones" chalky paper. White gum.* W **43**. P 14×15.

D26	D **2**	½d. carmine and green...................	35·00	45·00

1925 (July). *No wmk, but bluish "N Z" and Star lithographed on back.* P 14×15.

D27	D **2**	½d. carmine and green...................	2·00	23·00
D28		2d. carmine and green...................	3·50	25·00

1925 (Nov)–**35**. *"Cowan" thick, opaque chalky paper.* W **43**.

(a) P 14×15.

D29	D **2**	½d. carmine and green (12.26)........	1·75	9·00
D30		1d. carmine and green...................	3·75	80
D31		2d. carmine and green (6.26)..........	19·00	4·25
		x. Wmk reversed.........................	32·00	21·00

D32		3d. carmine and green (1.35).........	48·00	55·00
D29/32 *Set of 4*.....................			65·00	60·00

(b) P 14.

D33	D **2**	½d. carmine and green (10.28)........	48·00	30·00
D34		1d. rose and pale yellow-green (6.28)................................	4·00	1·25
D35		2d. carmine and green (10.29)........	7·00	3·00
D36		3d. carmine and green (5.28).........	15·00	42·00
D33/6 *Set of 4*......................			65·00	70·00

1937–38. *"Wiggins Teape" thin, hard chalky paper.* W **43**. P 14×15.

D37	D **2**	½d. carmine and yellow-green (2.38)................................	27·00	38·00
D38		1d. carmine and yellow-green (1.37)................................	11·00	3·75
D39		2d. carmine and yellow-green (6.37)................................	42·00	13·00
D40		3d. carmine and yellow-green (11.37)...............................	£100	70·00
D37/40 *Set of 4*....................			£160	£110

(Des J. Berry. Typo Govt Printing Office, Wellington)

1939–49. P 15×14.

(a) W **43** (sideways inverted) (16.8.39).

D41	D **3**	½d. turquoise-green.....................	5·00	5·00
D42		1d. carmine..............................	2·75	1·25
		w. Wmk sideways.......................	£150	4·25
D43		2d. bright blue..........................	6·00	2·75
D44		3d. orange-brown.......................	23·00	25·00
		w. Wmk sideways.......................		
D41/4 *Set of 4*......................			32·00	30·00

(b) W **98** (sideways (1d.), sideways inverted (2d.) or upright (3d.))

D45	D **3**	1d. carmine (4.49)......................	16·00	5·50*
D46		2d. bright blue (12.46).................	8·00	2·00
		w. Wmk sideways (4.49)................	2·75	9·00
D47		3d. orange-brown (1943)................	55·00	35·00
		a. Wmk sideways inverted (6.45).....	21·00	7·00
		aw. Wmk sideways (28.11.49).........	9·00	10·00
D45/7 *Set of 3*......................			25·00	13·00*

The use of Postage Due stamps ceased on 30 September 1951, our used price for No. D45 being for stamps postmarked after this date (price for examples clearly cancelled 1949–51, £27).

OFFICIAL STAMPS

1891 (Dec)–**1906**. *Contemporary issues handstamped "O.P.S.O." diagonally.*

(a) Stamps of 1873 type. W **12b**. P 12½.

O1	**3**	½d. rose (V.)............................	—	£550

(b) Stamps of 1882–97 optd in rose or magenta. W **12b**.

O2	**13**	½d. black (P 10)........................	—	£325
		a. Violet opt	—	£375
O3		½d. black (P 10×11)....................	—	£325
O4	**14**	1d. rose (P 12×11½)....................	—	£325
O5		1d. rose (P 11).........................	—	£325
O6	**15**	2d. purple (P 11).......................	—	£425
O7		2d. mauve-lilac (P 10).................	—	£425
		a. Violet opt		
O8	**16**	2½d. blue (P 11)........................	—	£375
O9		2½d. ultramarine (P 10)...............	—	£375
O10		2½d. ultramarine (P 10×11)...........	—	£375
O11	**19**	5d. olive-black (P 12×11½)............	—	£500
O12	**20**	6d. brown (P 12×11½)...................	—	£700

(c) Stamps of 1898–1903 optd in violet. P 11.

(i) No wmk.

O13	**23**	½d. green (P 14) (No. 294)............	—	£325
O14	**26**	2½d. blue (P 12–16) (No. 249a).......	—	£600
O15	**27**	2½d. blue (No. 260).....................	—	£500
O16	**37**	4d. indigo and brown (No. 262).......	—	£550
O17	**30**	5d. purple-brown (No. 263)............	—	£550
		a. Green opt	—	£500
O18	**32**	8d. indigo (No. 266)...................	—	£650

(ii) W **38**.

O19	**42**	1d. carmine (No. 278)..................	—	£350

(iii) W **43** (sideways on 3d., 1s.).

O20	**42**	1d. carmine (P 14) (No. 303).........	—	£350
		a. Green opt	—	£350
O21	**27**	2½d. blue (No. 308).....................	—	£400
O22	**28**	3d. yellow-brown (No 309)............	—	£550
O23	**34**	1s. orange-red (No. 315b).............	—	£1100
O24	**36**	2s. green (No. 316)....................	—	£1800

The letters signify "On Public Service Only", and stamps so overprinted were used by the Post Office Department at Wellington on official correspondence to foreign countries.

Unused examples with the "O.P.S.O." handstamp are generally considered to be reprints.

OFFICIAL.

(O **3**)

1907–11. *Stamps of 1902–6 optd with Type O 3 (vertically, upwards).* W **43** (sideways on 3d., 6d., 1s. and 5s.). P 14.

O59	**23**	½d. yellow-green.......................	9·00	75
		a. Perf 14×14..........................	£150	
		b. Mixed perfs........................	£150	
O60	**42**	1d. carmine (No. 303) (1.7.07*).....	8·50	12·00
		a. Booklet pane of 6..................	55·00	
		ab. Imperf horiz (booklet pane of 6)................................	£2500	
O60b		1d. rose-carmine (Waterlow) (No. 352)................................	12·00	50
		ba. Perf 11×14..........................	—	£300
		bb. Mixed perfs........................	—	£300
O60c		1d. carmine (Royle)....................	24·00	50
		ca. Perf 11×14..........................	£250	£300

O61	**41**	cb. Mixed perfs........................	£250	£300
		2d. purple................................	9·50	1·75
		a. Bright reddish purple.............	8·50	1·60
		b. Mixed perfs........................	£275	£275
O63	**28**	3d. bistre-brown........................	48·00	1·75
		a. Mixed perfs........................	—	£1000
O64	**31**	6d. bright carmine-pink...............	£170	21·00
		a. Imperf vert (horiz pair)...........	£900	
		b. Mixed perfs........................	£650	£500
O65	**34**	1s. orange-red..........................	95·00	15·00
O66	**35**	2s. blue-green..........................	80·00	£100
		a. Imperf between (pair).............	£2500	
		b. Imperf vert (horiz pair)..........	£2000	
		w. Wmk inverted......................	£375	£300
O67	**36**	5s. deep red............................	£150	£180
		w. Wmk upright (1911)................	£900	£1000

Though issued in 1907 a large quantity of booklets was mislaid and not utilized until they were found in 1930.

1908–09. *Optd as Type O 3*. W **43**.

O69	**23**	½d. green (P 14×15)...................	8·00	3·25
O70	**50**	1d. carmine (P 14×15).................	65·00	3·25
O71	**48**	6d. pink (P 14×15)....................	£160	45·00
O72		6d. pink (P 14×15) (1909)............	£160	35·00
O72a	F **4**	£1 rose-pink (P 14) (No. F89).......	£550	£400

1910. *No. 387 optd with Type O 3*.

O73	**51**	½d. yellow-green.......................	6·50	30
		a. Opt inverted (reading downwards)...........................	†	£1600

1910–16. *Nos. 389 and 392/4 optd with Type O 3*. P 14×14½.

O74	**52**	3d. chestnut............................	14·00	80
		a. Perf 14×13½ (1915)................	60·00	80·00
		ab. Vert pair. Nos. O74/a..............	£300	£475
O75	—	6d. carmine............................	19·00	5·50
		b. Perf 14 (line) (No. 398)..........	†	
		c. Deep carmine.......................	25·00	5·50
		w. Wmk inverted......................		
O76		8d. indigo-blue (R.) (5.16)...........	12·00	20·00
		aw. Wmk inverted......................	45·00	45·00
		b. Perf 14×13½.........................	12·00	20·00
		bw. Wmk inverted......................	40·00	40·00
		c. Vert pair, Nos. O76 and O76b.....	48·00	95·00
		cw. Wmk inverted......................	£120	£150
O77		1s. vermilion...........................	48·00	15·00
O74/7 *Set of 4*......................			85·00	38·00

1910–26. *Optd with Type O 3*.

(a) W **43**. *De La Rue chalk-surfaced paper with toned gum.*

O78	**53**	1d. carmine (No. 405).................	3·25	10
		y. Wmk inverted and reversed.......		

(b) W **43**. *Jones chalk-surfaced paper with white gum.*

O79	**53**	1d. deep carmine (No. 406) (1925)...	11·00	6·50

(c) No wmk, but bluish "NZ" and Star lithographed on back. Art paper.

O80	**53**	1d. rose-carmine (No. 409) (1925)...	6·00	19·00

(d) W **43**. *Cowan thick, opaque, chalk-surfaced paper with white gum.*

O81	**53**	1d. deep carmine (No. 410) (1925)...	8·00	1·25
		x. Wmk reversed (1926)...............	35·00	22·00

1913–25. *Postal Fiscal stamps optd with Type O 3*.

(i) Chalk-surfaced De La Rue paper.

(a) P 14 (1913–14).

O82	F **4**	2s. blue (30.9.14)......................	50·00	48·00
O83		5s. yellow-green (13.6.13)............	75·00	£100
O84		£1 rose-carmine (1913)................	£600	£550
O82/4 *Set of 3*......................			£650	£650

(b) P 14½×14, comb (1915).

O85	F **4**	2s. deep blue (Aug)....................	55·00	48·00
		a. No stop after "OFFICIAL".........	£140	£110
O86		5s. yellow-green (Jan).................	70·00	85·00
		a. No stop after "OFFICIAL".........	£225	£250

(ii) Thick, white, opaque chalk-surfaced Cowan paper. P 14½×14 (1925).

O87	F **4**	2s. blue...................................	80·00	75·00
		a. No stop after "OFFICIAL".........	£200	£200

The overprint on these last, and on Nos. O69 and O72a is from a new set of type, giving a rather sharper impression than Type O 3, but otherwise resembling it closely.

1915 (12 Oct)–**34**. *Optd with Type O 3*. P 14×15.

(a) On Nos. 435/40 (De La Rue chalk-surfaced paper with toned gum).

O88	**61**	½d. green...............................	1·25	20
O89	**62**	1½d. grey-black (6.16).................	7·50	2·50
O90	**61**	1½d. slate (12.16).....................	5·50	1·00
O91		1½d. orange-brown (4.19).............	5·00	30
O92		2d. yellow (4.17)......................	6·00	20
O93		3d. chocolate (11.19).................	12·00	1·00
O88/93 *Set of 6*.....................			32·00	4·75

(b) On Nos. 441 and 443 (Jones chalk-surfaced paper with white gum).

O94	**61**	½d. green (1924).......................	4·50	3·50
O95		3d. deep chocolate (1924)............	38·00	9·50

(c) On Nos. 446/7 and 448a/9 (Cowan thick, opaque, chalk surfaced paper with white gum).

O96	**61**	½d. green (1925).......................	2·00	10
		ax. Wmk reversed (1927).............	15·00	15·00
		ay. Wmk inverted and reversed (1927)...............................	40·00	27·00
		b. Perf 14 (1929).....................	3·75	40
		ba. No stop after "OFFICIAL"........	25·00	32·00
O97		1½d. orange-brown (4.19) (1929).....	10·00	15·00
		a. No stop after "OFFICIAL".........	60·00	75·00
		b. Perf 14×15 (1934).................	28·00	32·00
O98		2d. yellow (P 14) (1931)..............	2·50	50
		a. No stop after "OFFICIAL".........	55·00	55·00
O99		3d. chocolate (1925)..................	5·00	50
		a. No stop after "OFFICIAL".........	70·00	50·00

	b. Perf 14 (1930)............		45·00	3·00
	ba. No stop after "OFFICIAL"......		£140	65·00
O96/9	Set of 4		18·00	15·00

1915 (Dec)–**27**. *Optd with Type* O **3**. P 14×13½.

(a) Nos. 420, 422, 425, 428 and 429/30 (Cowan unsurfaced paper).

O100	60	3d. chocolate	4·50	1·50
		aw. Wmk inverted	17·00	5·00
		b. Perf 14×14½	4·50	1·75
		bw. Wmk inverted	17·00	5·00
		c. Vert pair, Nos. O100 and O100b	40·00	£110
		cw. Wmk inverted	£100	£150
		d. Opt double	†	£1200
O101		4d. bright violet (4.25)	14·00	4·00
		a. Re-entry (Pl 20 R. 1/6).....	55·00	40·00
		b. Re-entry (Pl 20 R. 4/10).....	60·00	48·00
		c. Perf 14×14½ (4.27)..	27·00	1·00
O102		6d. carmine (6.16)	5·00	75
		aw. Wmk inverted	95·00	
		b. Perf 14×14½	5·00	1·25
		c. Vert pair, Nos. O102 and O102b	55·00	£140
O103		8d. red-brown (8.22)	65·00	£180
O104		9d. sage-green (4.25)	40·00	38·00
O105		1s. vermilion (9.16)	18·00	13·00
		aw. Wmk inverted	£180	£120
		b. Perf 14×14½	7·00	2·00
		ba. *Pale orange-red*	15·00	20·00
		bw. Wmk inverted	£180	£180
		c. Vert pair. Nos. O105 and O105b	65·00	£180
		cw. Wmk inverted	£475	
O100/5	Set of 6		£120	£200

(b) No. 433 (Thin paper with widely spaced sideways wmk).

O106	60	3d. chocolate (P 14) (7.16)	3·00	15·00
		a. No wmk	50·00	75·00

1927–33. *Optd with Type* O **3**. W **43**. P 14.

O111	71	1d. rose-carmine (No. 468)......	2·00	20
		a. No stop after "OFFICIAL"......	28·00	65·00
		bw. Wmk inverted	†	35·00
		c. Perf 14×15	3·25	20
O112	72	2s. light blue (No. 469) (2.28)	75·00	£110
O113	F 6	5s. green (1933)	£250	£300
O111/13	Set of 3		£300	£375

Official   Official
(O **4**)   (O **5**)

1936–61. *Pictorial issue optd horiz or vert (2s.) with Type* O **4**.

(a) W **43** *(Single "N Z" and Star).*

O115	82	1d. scarlet (Die I) (P 14×13½)........	4·25	1·25
		a. Perf 13½×14	£100	70·00
O116	83	1½d. red-brown (P 13½×14)....	28·00	30·00
		a. Perf 14×13½	£10000	
O118	92	1s. deep green (P 14×13½)........	32·00	48·00
		w. Wmk inverted	†	£160
O119	F 6	5s. green (P 14) (12.38)	£130	48·00
O115/19	Set of 4		£170	£110

The watermark of No. O119 is almost invisible.

Only four examples of No. O116a exist. The error occurred when a sheet of No. 558a was found to have a block of four missing. This was replaced by a block of No. 558 and the sheet was then sent for overprinting.

(b) W **98** *(Mult "N Z" and Star).*

O120	81	½d. bright green, P 14×13½ (7.37) ..	7·50	4·50
O121	82	1d. scarlet (Die II), P 14×13½ (11.36)....................	7·00	50
		w. Wmk inverted	28·00	24·00
O122	83	1½d. red-brown, P 14×13½ (7.36)..	24·00	15
O123	84	2d. orange, P 14×13½ (1.38)	4·75	10
		aw. Wmk inverted	—	£140
		b. Perf 12½ (1942)..........	£190	55·00
		c. Perf 14 (1942)..........	50·00	15·00
O124	85	2½d. chocolate & slate, P 13–14×13½ (26.7.38) ..	60·00	90·00
		a. Perf 14 (1938)...........	14·00	21·00
O125	86	3d. brown, P 14×13½ (1.3.38)...	48·00	3·50
		w. Wmk inverted	—	£130
O126	87	4d. black and sepia, P 14×13½ (8.36)....................	10·00	1·10
		a. Perf 14 (8.41)...........	12·00	4·50
		b. Perf 12½ (1941).........	10·00	6·50
		c. Perf 14×14½ (10.42)...	4·50	1·00
		cw. Wmk inverted	—	£160
O127	89	6d. scarlet, P 13½×14 (12.37)...	23·00	80
		aw. Wmk inverted	†	—
		b. Perf 12½ (1941).........	15·00	5·50
		c. Perf 14½×14 (7.42)...	12·00	30
O128	90	8d. chocolate, P 12½ (wmk sideways) (1942)	15·00	17·00
		a. Perf 14×14½ (wmk sideways) (1945)...................	8·50	16·00
		b. Perf 14×13½	†	£2500
O129	91	9d. red & grey-black (G.) (No. 587a), P 13½×14 (1.3.38)...	80·00	38·00
O130		9d. scar & blk (*chalk-surfaced paper*) (Blk.) (No. 631), P 14×15 (1943).......	20·00	22·00
O131	92	1s. deep green, P 14×13½ (2.37)...	50·00	1·50
		aw. Wmk inverted	£200	
		b. Perf 12½ (1942).........	28·00	2·25
O132	93	2s. olive-green, P 13–14×13½ (5.37)....................	80·00	40·00
		a. "CAPTAIN COQK"	£150	
		b. Perf 13½×14 (1939)......	£190	6·50
		ba. "CAPTAIN COQK"	£225	
		c. Perf 12½ (1942).........	80·00	22·00
		ca. "CAPTAIN COQK"	£140	
		d. Perf 14×13½ (1944)......	42·00	8·50
		da. "CAPTAIN COQK"	£325	
O133	F 6	5s. green (*chalk-surfaced paper*), P 14 (3.43)............	42·00	6·00
		aw. Wmk inverted	40·00	6·00

	b. Perf 14×13½. Yellow-green (*ordinary paper*) (10.61)...........		17·00	32·00
O120/33	Set of 14		£275	£110

The opt on No. O127a was sometimes applied at the top of the stamp, instead of always at the bottom as on No. O127.

All examples of No. O128b were used by a government office in Whangerei.

The 5s. value on ordinary paper perforated 14×13½ does not exist without the "Official" overprint.

See notes on perforations after No. 590b.

1938–51. *Nos. 603 etc., optd with Type* O **4**.

O134	108	½d. green (1.3.38)	20·00	2·25
O135		½d. brown-orange (1946)	1·60	3·50
O136		1d. scarlet (1.7.38)	21·00	15
O137		1d. green (10.7.41)	3·50	10
O138	108a	1½d. purple-brown (26.7.38)...	75·00	18·00
O139		1½d. scarlet (2.4.51)	10·00	6·50
O140		3d. blue (16.10.41)	3·50	10
O134/40	Set of 7		£120	27·00

1940 (2 Jan–8 Mar). *Centennial. Nos. 613, etc., optd with Type* O **5**.

O141		½d. blue-green (R.)...........	2·75	35
O142		1d. chocolate and scarlet	6·00	10
		a. "ff" joined, as Type O **4**	50·00	60·00
O143		1½d. light blue and mauve	3·75	2·00
		a. "ff" joined, as Type O **4**	50·00	60·00
O144		2d. blue-green and chocolate	5·50	10
		a. "ff" joined, as Type O **4**	60·00	60·00
O145		2½d. blue-green and ultramarine ..	5·00	2·75
		a. "ff" joined, as Type O **4**	50·00	65·00
O146		3d. purple and carmine (R.).....	8·00	1·00
		a. "ff" joined, as Type O **4**	42·00	48·00
O147		4d. chocolate and lake	40·00	1·50
		a. "ff" joined, as Type O **4**	£120	90·00
O148		6d. emerald-green and violet	26·00	1·50
		a. "ff" joined, as Type O **4**	70·00	70·00
O149		8d. black and red (8.3).......	30·00	17·00
		a. "ff" joined, as Type O **4**	70·00	£100
O150		9d. olive-green and vermilion ...	11·00	5·00
O151		1s. sage-green and deep green	48·00	3·00
O141/51	Set of 11		£160	30·00

For this issue the Type O **4** overprint occurs on R. 4/3 of the 2½d. and on R. 1/10 of the other values.

1947 (1 May)–**51**. *Nos. 680, etc., optd with Type* O **4**.

O152	108a	2d. orange.......................	2·75	10
O153		4d. bright purple..............	4·25	2·50
O154		6d. carmine....................	14·00	50
O155		8d. violet......................	8·00	6·50
O156		9d. purple-brown...............	9·00	6·50
O157	144	1s. red-brown and carmine (wmk upright) (Plate 1)	17·00	1·00
		a. Wmk sideways (Plate 1) (1949)	8·50	9·00
		aw. Wmk sideways inverted	40·00	16·00
		b. Wmk upright (Plate 2) (4.51)..	24·00	7·50
		bw. Wmk inverted	95·00	30·00
O158		2s. brown-orange and green (wmk sideways) (Plate 1)...........	30·00	16·00
		a. Wmk upright (Plate 1)...........	32·00	48·00
O152/8	Set of 7		70·00	30·00

STAMP BOOKLET

1907 (1 July). *White card cover.*

OB1	10s. booklet containing one hundred and twenty 1d. in panes of 6 (No. O60a)	£1100	

PROVISIONALS ISSUED AT REEFTON AND USED BY THE POLICE DEPARTMENT

1907 (Jan). *Current stamps of 1906, optd "Official", in red manuscript and handstamped with a circular "Greymouth—PAID—3". P 14.*

P1	23	½d. green (R.)................	£1100	£1300
P2	40	1d. carmine.................	£1200	£1200
P3	38	2d. purple....................	£1400	£1600
P4	28	3d. bistre....................	£2000	
P5	31	6d. pink......................	£2000	
P6	34	1s. orange-red..............	£2500	
P7	35	5s. green.....................	£7000	

Only the ½d., 1d. and 2d. are known postally used, cancelled with the Reefton squared circle postmark. The 3d. and 6d. were later cancelled by favour at Wanganui.

LIFE INSURANCE DEPARTMENT

L **1** Lighthouse   L **2** Lighthouse

(Des W. B. Hudson and J. F. Rogers; Eng. A. E. Cousins. Typo Govt Printing Office, Wellington)

1891 (2 Jan)–**98**.

A. W **12c**. P 12×11½.

L1	L **1**	½d. bright purple	75·00	6·00
		a. Mixed perf 12×11 and 12½..	†	—
		x. Wmk reversed	†	
L2		1d. blue......................	60·00	4·00
		ax. Wmk reversed	†	
		ay. Wmk inverted and reversed......	£100	38·00
		b. Wmk **12b**	£100	21·00
		bx. Wmk reversed	†	
L3		2d. brown-red	95·00	8·50
		ax. Wmk reversed		90·00
		b. Wmk **12b**	£110	16·00
L4		3d. deep brown	£180	23·00
L5		6d. green	£300	60·00
L6		1s. rose	£500	£120
L1/6	Set of 6		£1100	£200

B. W **12b** (1893–98).

(a) P 10 (1893).

L7	L **1**	½d. bright purple	70·00	10·00
L8		1d. blue.......................	60·00	1·75
L9		2d. brown-red	85·00	3·75
L7/9	Set of 3		£190	14·00

(b) P 11×10.

L10	L **1**	½d. bright purple (1896)....	95·00	28·00
		a. Perf 10×11	£170	70·00
L11		1d. blue (1897)..............	†	45·00
		a. Perf 10×11	65·00	14·00

(c) Mixed perfs 10 and 11 (1897).

L12	L **1**	2d. brown-red	£700	£700

(d) P 11 (1897–98).

L13	L **1**	½d. bright purple	60·00	4·00
		a. Thin coarse toned paper (1898)	85·00	6·00
L14		1d. blue.......................	60·00	75
		a. Thin coarse toned paper (1898)	85·00	2·75
		x. Wmk reversed	£130	15·00
		y. Wmk inverted and reversed......	£130	25·00
L15		2d. brown-red	90·00	3·50
		a. *Chocolate*	£120	24·00
		b. Thin coarse toned paper (1898)	£150	4·25
L13/15	Set of 3		£190	7·50

1902–04. W **43** (sideways).

(a) P 11.

L16	L **1**	½d. bright purple (1903)......	65·00	7·00
L17		1d. blue (1902)..............	60·00	1·50
L18		2d. brown-red (1904)........	£110	10·00
L16/18	Set of 3		£200	17·00

(b) P 14×11.

L19	L **1**	½d. bright purple (1903)......	£1500	
L20		1d. blue (1904)..............	£110	11·00

Nos. L16/17 and L20 are known without watermark from the margins of the sheet.

1905–06. *Redrawn, with "V.R." omitted.* W **43** (sideways).

(a) P 11.

L21	L **2**	2d. brown-red (12.05)........	£1100	95·00

(b) P 14.

L22	L **2**	1d. blue (7.06)..............	£170	30·00

(c) P 14×11.

L23	L **2**	1d. blue (7.06)..............	£500	£150
		a. Mixed perfs	†	£425

Between January 1907 and the end of 1912 the Life Insurance Department used ordinary Official stamps.

1913 (2 Jan)–**37**. *New values and colours.* W **43**.

(a) "De La Rue" paper. P 14×15.

L24	L **1**	½d. green.....................	16·00	2·25
		a. *Yellow-green*.............	16·00	2·25
L25		1d. carmine..................	10·00	1·25
		a. *Carmine-pink*.............	16·00	1·75
L26		1½d. black (1917)............	40·00	8·50
L27		1½d. chestnut-brown (1919)....	1·50	3·00
L28		2d. bright purple..............	50·00	29·00
L29		2d. yellow (1920).............	†	£100
L30		3d. yellow-brown.............	7·00	2·00
L31		6d. carmine-pink.............	35·00	24·00
L24/31	Set of 8		£180	90·00

(b) "Cowan" paper. (i) P 14×15.

L31a	L **2**	½d. yellow-green (1925)......	32·00	4·50
L31b		1d. carmine-pink (1925)......	32·00	3·50
		bw. Wmk inverted	45·00	6·00

(ii) P 14.

L32	L **2**	½d. yellow-green (1926)......	10·00	3·00
		w. Wmk inverted	†	20·00
L33		1d. scarlet (1931)............	7·50	2·00
		w. Wmk inverted	16·00	4·00
L34		2d. yellow (1937).............	7·00	7·00
		w. Wmk inverted	35·00	28·00
L35		3d. brown-lake (1931)........	18·00	24·00
L36		6d. pink (1925)..............	35·00	38·00
L32/6	Set of 5		70·00	65·00

(c) "Wiggins Teape" paper. P 14×15.

L36a	L **2**	½d. yellow-green (3.37)......	8·00	12·00
L36b		1d. scarlet (3.37)............	15·00	3·25
L36c		6d. pink (7.37)..............	35·00	40·00
L36a/c	Set of 3		50·00	50·00

For descriptions of the various types of paper, see after No. 385. In the 1½d. the word "POSTAGE" is in both the side-labels instead of at left only.

1944–47. W **98**. P 14×15.

L37	L **2**	½d. yellow-green (7.47)......	6·00	9·00
L38		1d. scarlet (6.44)............	3·25	2·00
L39		2d. yellow (1946).............	14·00	18·00
L40		3d. brown-lake (10.46)........	20·00	38·00
L41		6d. pink (7.47)..............	14·00	35·00
L37/41	Set of 5		50·00	90·00

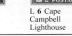

L **3** Castlepoint Lighthouse   L **6** Cape Campbell Lighthouse

(Des J. Berry. Recess B.W.).

1947 (1 Aug)–**65**. *Type L 3, L 6 and similar designs.* W **98** (sideways inverted on 1d., 2d., sideways on 2½d.). P 13½.

L42	½d. grey-green and orange-red	1·75	70
L43	1d. olive-green and pale blue	1·75	1·25
L44	2d. deep blue and grey-black	1·50	1·00
L45	2½d. black and bright blue (*white opaque paper*) (4.11.63)	9·50	13·00
L46	3d. mauve and pale blue	3·50	1·00
L47	4d. brown and yellow-orange	4·25	1·75
	a. Wmk sideways (*white opaque paper*) (13.10.65)	4·00	14·00
L48	6d. chocolate and blue	4·00	2·75
L49	1s. red-brown and blue	4·00	3·50
L42/49 *Set of 8*		27·00	22·00

Designs: *Horiz* (as Type L **3**)—1d. Taiaroa lighthouse; 2d. Cape Palliser lighthouse; 6d. The Brothers lighthouse. *Vert* (as Type L **6**)—3d. Eddystone lighthouse; 4d. Stephens Island lighthouse; 1s. Cape Brett lighthouse.

POSTAL FISCAL STAMPS

As from 1 April 1882 fiscal stamps were authorised for postal use and conversely postage stamps became valid for fiscal use. Stamps in the designs of 1867 with "STAMP DUTY" above the Queen's head were withdrawn and although some passed through the mail quite legitimately they were mainly "philatelic" and we no longer list them. The issue which was specifically authorised for postal use in 1882 was the one which had originally been put on sale for fiscal use in 1880.

There is strong evidence that the authorities used up existing low value revenue stamps for postage, delaying the general release of the new "Postage and Revenue" low values (T **14, 15** and **18–22**) to achieve this. Used prices for such stamps are for examples with 1882–3 postal cancellations.

Although all fiscal stamps were legally valid for postage, only values between 2s. and £1 were stocked at ordinary post offices. Other values could only be obtained by request from the G.P.O, Wellington or from offices of the Stamp Duties Department. Later the Arms types above £1 could also be obtained from the head post offices in Auckland, Christchurch, Dunedin and also a branch post office at Christchurch North where there was a local demand for them.

It seems sensible to list under Postal Fiscals the Queen Victoria stamps up to the £1 value and the Arms types up to the £5 because by 1931 the higher values were genuinely needed for postal purposes. Even the £10 was occasionally used on insured airmail parcels.

Although 2s. and 5s. values were included in the 1898 pictorial issue, it was the general practice for the Postal Department to limit the postage issues to 1s. until 1926 when the 2s. and 3s. appeared. These were then dropped from the fiscal issues and when in turn the 5s. and 10s. were introduced in 1953 and the £1 in 1960 no further printings of these values occurred in the fiscal series.

FORGED POSTMARKS. Our prices are for stamps with genuine postal cancellations. Beware of forged postmarks on stamps from which fiscal cancellations have been cleaned off.

Many small post offices acted as agents for government departments and it was the practice to use ordinary postal date-stamps on stamps used fiscally, so that when they are removed from documents they are indistinguishable from postally used specimens unless impressed with the embossed seal of the Stamp Duties Department.

Date-stamps very similar to postal date-stamps were sometimes supplied to offices of the Stamp Duties Department and it is not clear when this practice ceased. Prior to the Arms types the only sure proof of the postal use of off-cover fiscal stamps is when they bear a distinctive duplex, registered or parcel post cancellation, but beware of forgeries of the first two.

F 1   F 2   F 3

(Die eng W. R. Bock. Typo Govt Ptg Office)

1882 (Feb). W **12a**. P 12×11½.

F1	F **1**	1d. lilac	£650	£375
F2		1d. blue	£150	30·00
		w. Wmk inverted		

The 1d. fiscal was specifically authorised for postal use in February 1882 owing to a shortage of the 1d. Type **5** and pending the introduction of the 1d. Type **14** on 1 April.

The 1d. lilac fiscal had been replaced by the 1d. blue in 1878 but postally used copies with 1882 duplex postmarks are known although most postally used examples are dated from 1890 and these must have been philatelic.

1882 (early). W **12a**. P 12×11½.

F3	F **2**	1s. grey-green	
F4	F **3**	1s. grey-green and red	
F4a		2s. rose and blue	

Examples of these are known postally used in 1882 and although not specifically authorised for postal use it is believed that their use was permitted where there was a shortage of the appropriate postage value.

WMK TYPE F 5. The balance of the paper employed for the 1867 issue was used for early printings of Type F **4** introduced in 1880 before changing the "N Z" and Star watermark. The values we list with this watermark are known with 1882–83 postal date stamps. Others have later dates and are considered to be philatelic but should they be found with 1882–83 postal dates we would be prepared to add them to the list.

F 4   F 5

The 12s.6d. value has the head in an oval (as Type **10**), and the 15s. and £1 values have it in a broken circle (as Type **7**).

(Dies eng W.R. Bock. Typo Govt Ptg Office)

1882 (1 Apr). *Type F **4** and similar types.* "De La Rue" paper.

A. W **12a** (6 mm).

(a) P 12 (1882).

F5	4d. orange-red (Wmk F **5**)	—	£275
F6	6d. lake-brown	—	£180
	a. Wmk F **5**	—	£600
F7	8d. green (Wmk F **5**)	—	£600
F8	1s. pink	—	£225
	a. Wmk F **5**	—	£225
F9	2s. blue	60·00	5·50
F10	2s.6d. grey-brown	95·00	5·50
	a. Wmk F **5**		
F11	3s. mauve	£120	7·00
F12	4s. brown-rose	£130	12·00
	a. Wmk F **5**		
F13	5s. green	£160	13·00
	a. Yellow-green	£160	13·00
F14	6s. rose	£170	32·00
F15	7s. ultramarine	£180	60·00
F16	7s.6d. bronze-grey	£375	£120
F17	8s. deep blue	£190	65·00
F18	9s. orange	£225	60·00
F19	10s. brown-red	£160	23·00
	a. Wmk F **5**		
F20	15s. green	£375	£100
F21	£1 rose-pink	£225	60·00

(b) P 12½ (1886).

F22	2s. blue	60·00	5·50
F23	2s.6d. grey-brown	95·00	5·50
F24	3s. mauve	£130	7·00
F25	4s. purple-claret	£130	12·00
	a. Brown-rose	£130	12·00
F26	5s. green	£160	13·00
	a. Yellow-green	£160	13·00
F27	6s. rose	£170	32·00
F28	7s. ultramarine	£180	60·00
F29	8s. deep blue	£190	65·00
F30	9s. orange	£225	60·00
F31	10s. brown-red	£160	23·00
F32	15s. green	£375	£100
F33	£1 rose-pink	£225	60·00

B. W **12b** (7 mm). P 12½ (1888).

F34	2s. blue	60·00	5·50
F35	2s.6d. grey-brown	95·00	5·50
F36	3s. mauve	£120	7·00
F37	4s. brown-rose	£120	12·00
	a. Brown-red	£120	12·00
F38	5s. green	£150	13·00
	a. Yellow-green	£150	13·00
F39	6s. rose	£170	32·00
F40	7s. ultramarine	£180	60·00
F41	7s.6d. bronze-grey	£375	£120
F42	8s. deep blue	£190	65·00
F43	9s. orange	£225	60·00
F44	10s. brown-red	£160	22·00
	a. Maroon	£160	22·00
F45	£1 pink	£225	60·00

C. W **12c** (4 mm). P 12½ (1890).

F46	2s. blue	85·00	12·00
F46a	2s.6d. grey-brown	£130	14·00
F47	3s. mauve	£170	32·00
F48	4s. brown-red	£140	18·00
F49	5s. green	£160	14·00
F50	6s. rose	£190	35·00
F51	7s. ultramarine	£200	65·00
F52	8s. deep blue	£225	75·00
F53	9s. orange	£275	80·00
F54	10s. brown-red	£180	24·00
F55	£1 pink	£400	£120

D. Continuation of W **12b**. P 11 (1895–1901).

F56	2s. blue	35·00	6·00
F57	2s.6d. grey-brown	90·00	5·50
	a. Inscr "COUNTERPART" (1901)*	£160	£180
F58	3s. mauve	£120	7·00
F59	4s. brown-red	£120	11·00
F60	5s. yellow-green	£150	14·00
F61	6s. rose	£160	32·00
F62	7s. pale blue	£180	60·00
F63	7s.6d. bronze-grey	£375	£120
F64	8s. deep blue	£190	65·00
F65	9s. orange	£225	60·00
	a. Imperf between (horiz pair)	£1000	
F66	10s. brown-red	£160	22·00
	a. Maroon	£160	22·00
F67	15s. green	£375	£100
F68	£1 rose-pink	£225	60·00

*The plate normally printed in yellow and inscribed "COUNTERPART" just above the bottom value panel, was for use on the counterparts of documents but was issued in error in the colour of the normal fiscal stamp and accepted for use.

E. W **43** (*sideways*).

(i) Unsurfaced "Cowan" paper.

(a) P 11 (1903).

F69	2s.6d. grey-brown	90·00	5·50
F70	3s. mauve	£120	7·00
F71	4s. orange-red	£120	11·00

F72	6s. rose	£160	32·00
F73	7s. pale blue	£180	60·00
F74	8s. deep blue	£190	65·00
F75	10s. brown-red	£150	22·00
	a. Maroon	£150	22·00
F76	15s. green	£375	£100
F77	£1 rose-pink	£200	60·00

(b) P 14 (1906).

F78	2s.6d. grey-brown	85·00	5·50
F79	3s. mauve	£110	7·00
F80	4s. orange-red	£110	9·00
F81	5s. yellow-green	95·00	10·00
F82	6s. rose	£150	32·00
F83	7s. pale blue	£160	60·00
F84	7s.6d. bronze-grey	£350	£100
F85	8s. deep blue	£180	65·00
F86	9s. orange	£190	60·00
F87	10s. maroon	£140	22·00
F88	15s. green	£375	£100
F89	£1 rose-pink	£190	60·00

(c) P 14½×14, comb (clean-cut) (1907).

F90	2s. blue	35·00	5·00
F91	2s.6d. grey-brown	90·00	5·50
F92	3s. mauve	£120	7·00
F93	4s. orange-red	£110	10·00
F94	6s. rose	£160	32·00
F95	10s. maroon	£150	20·00
F96	15s. green	£375	£100
F97	£1 rose-pink	£190	60·00

(ii) Chalk-surfaced "De la Rue" paper.

(a) P 14 (1913).

F98	2s. blue	30·00	4·50
F99	2s.6d. grey-brown	35·00	5·50
F100	3s. purple	80·00	7·00
F101	4s. orange-red	80·00	8·00
F102	5s. yellow-green	80·00	9·50
F103	6s. rose	£130	17·00
F104	7s. pale blue	£140	35·00
F105	7s.6d. bronze-grey	£375	£110
F106	8s. deep blue	£170	38·00
F107	9s. orange	£200	60·00
F108	10s. maroon	£140	18·00
F109	15s. green	£375	£100
F110	£1 rose-carmine	£190	60·00

(b) P 14½×14, comb (1913–21).

F111	2s. deep blue	30·00	4·50
F112	2s.6d. grey-brown	35·00	5·50
F113	3s. purple	80·00	7·00
F114	4s. orange-red	80·00	8·50
F115	5s. yellow-green	80·00	9·50
F116	6s. rose	£130	17·00
F117	7s. pale blue	£140	35·00
F118	8s. deep blue	£170	38·00
F119	9s. orange	£180	60·00
F120	10s. maroon	£140	18·00
F121	12s.6d. deep plum (1921)	£5500	£2500
F122	15s. green	£375	£100
F123	£1 rose-carmine	£180	60·00

The "De La Rue" paper has a smooth finish and has toned gum which is strongly resistant to soaking.

(iii) Chalk-surfaced "Jones" paper. P 14½×14, comb (1924).

F124	2s. deep blue	38·00	6·00
F125	2s.6d. deep grey-brown	42·00	6·50
F126	3s. purple	95·00	7·50
F127	5s. yellow-green	95·00	11·00
F128	10s. brown-red	£160	18·00
F129	12s.6d. deep purple	£5500	£2500
F130	15s. green	£350	£110

The "Jones" paper has a coarser texture, is poorly surfaced and the ink tends to peel. The outline of the watermark commonly shows on the surface of the stamp. The gum is colourless or only slightly toned and washes off readily.

(iv) Thick, opaque, chalk-surfaced "Cowan" paper. P 14½×14, comb (1925–30).

F131	2s. blue	32·00	5·50
F132	2s.6d. deep grey-brown	35·00	6·00
F133	3s. mauve	£110	11·00
F134	4s. orange-red	80·00	11·00
F135	5s. yellow-green	80·00	13·00
	x. Wmk reversed (1927)	£110	23·00
F136	6s. rose	£130	21·00
F137	7s. pale blue	£140	35·00
F138	8s. deep blue	£170	38·00
	a. Error. Blue (as 2s.) (1930)	£500	
F139	10s. brown-red	£140	18·00
	x. Wmk reversed (1927)	£200	£150
F140	12s.6d. blackish purple	£5500	£2500
F141	15s. green	£350	£110
F142	£1 rose-pink	£180	60·00

The "Cowan" paper is white and opaque and the watermark, which is usually smaller than in the "Jones" paper, is often barely visible.

(v) Thin, hard, chalk-surfaced "Wiggins Teape" paper. P 14½×14, comb (1926).

F143	4s. orange-red	85·00	14·00
F144	£1 rose-pink	£200	£110

The "Wiggins Teape" paper has a horizontal mesh, in relation to the design, with narrow watermark, whereas other chalk-surfaced papers with this perforation have a vertical mesh and wider watermark.

F **6**   (F **7**)

35/-

(Des H. L. Richardson. Typo Govt Ptg Office)

1931–40. *As Type F* **6** *(various frames).* W **43**. P 14.

(i) Thick, opaque, chalk-surfaced "Cowan" paper, with horizontal mesh (1931–35).

F145	1s.3d. lemon (4.31)	6·00	40·00
F146	1s.3d. orange-yellow	7·50	9·00
F147	2s.6d. deep brown	15·00	4·50
F148	4s. red	15·00	6·50
F149	5s. green	20·00	12·00
F150	6s. carmine-rose	32·00	13·00
F151	7s. blue	28·00	24·00
F152	7s.6d. olive-grey	70·00	80·00
F153	8s. slate-violet	28·00	32·00
F154	9s. brown-orange	30·00	29·00
F155	10s. carmine-lake	24·00	9·00
F156	12s. deep plum (9.35)	£130	£130
F157	15s. sage-green	65·00	38·00
F158	£1 pink	65·00	19·00
F159	25s. greenish blue	£375	£475
F160	30s. brown (1935)	£250	£140
F161	35s. orange-yellow	£3000	£3500
F162	£2 bright purple	£300	60·00
F163	£2 10s. red	£350	£400
F164	£3 green	£400	£225
F165	£3 10s. rose (1935)	£1400	£1400
F166	£4 light blue (1935)	£375	£150
F167	£4 10s. deep olive-grey (1935)	£1200	£1300
F168	£5 indigo-blue	£325	£100

(ii) Thin, hard 'Wiggins Teape' paper with vertical mesh (1936–40).

(a) Chalk-surfaced (1936–39).

F169	1s.3d. pale orange-yellow	22·00	3·50
F170	2s.6d. dull brown	70·00	3·75
F171	4s. pale red-brown	85·00	8·50
F172	5s. green	85·00	7·00
	w. Wmk inverted	—	£200
F173	6s. carmine-rose	85·00	30·00
F174	7s. pale blue	£120	32·00
F175	8s. slate-violet	£140	48·00
F176	9s. brown-orange	£150	70·00
F177	10s. pale carmine-lake	£140	7·00
F178	15s. sage-green	£200	50·00
F179	£1 pink	£160	26·00
F180	30s. brown (1.39)	£450	£160
F181	35s. orange-yellow	£3750	£4000
F182	£2 bright purple (1937)	£700	£100
	w. Wmk inverted		
F183	£3 green (1937)	£800	£300
F184	£5 indigo-blue (1937)	£950	£200

(b) Unsurfaced (1940).

F185	7s.6d. olive-grey	£170	75·00

Not all values listed above were stocked at ordinary post offices as some of them were primarily required for fiscal purposes but all were valid for postage.

1939. *No. F161 surch with Type F* **7**.

F186	35/- on 35s. orange-yellow	£475	£250

Because the 35s. orange-yellow could so easily be confused with the 1s.3d. in the same colour, it was surcharged.

1940 *(June). New values surch as Type F* **7**. *"Wiggins Teape" chalk-surfaced paper.* W **43**. P 14.

F187	3/6 on 3s.6d. grey-green	55·00	21·00
F188	5/6 on 5s.6d. lilac	95·00	50·00
F189	11/- on 11s. yellow	£170	£130
F190	22/- on 22s. scarlet	£425	£300
F187/90 Set of 4		£650	£450

These values were primarily needed for fiscal use.

1940–58. *As Type F* **6** *(various frames).* W **98** P 14.

(i) "Wiggins Teape" chalk-surfaced paper with vertical mesh (1940–56).

F191	1s.3d. orange-yellow	13·00	2·25
	w. Wmk inverted		£150
F192	1s.3d. yellow and black (wmk inverted) (14.6.55)	4·00	1·25
	aw. Wmk upright (9.9.55)	32·00	32·00
	b. Error. Yellow and blue (wmk inverted) (7.56)	4·50	5·50
F193	2s.6d. deep brown	8·50	80
	w. Wmk inverted (3.49)	8·50	80
F194	4s. red-brown	19·00	1·50
	w. Wmk inverted (3.49)	21·00	1·75
F195	5s. green	20·00	1·00
	w. Wmk inverted (1.5.50)	23·00	1·00
F196	6s. carmine-rose	35·00	3·25
	w. Wmk inverted (1948)	35·00	3·25
F197	7s. pale blue	32·00	5·50
F198	7s.6d. ol-grey (wmk inverted) (21.12.50)	65·00	55·00
F199	8s. slate-violet	55·00	17·00
	w. Wmk inverted (6.12.50)	55·00	18·00
F200	9s. brown-orange (1.46)	26·00	42·00
	w. Wmk inverted (9.1.51)	55·00	42·00
F201	10s. carmine-lake	35·00	2·25
	w. Wmk inverted (4.50)	38·00	2·50
F202	15s. sage-green	45·00	19·00
	w. Wmk inverted (8.12.50)	65·00	26·00
F203	£1 pink	28·00	3·75
	w. Wmk inverted (1.2.50)	42·00	4·25
F204	25s. greenish blue (1946)	£400	£400
	w. Wmk inverted (7.53)	£475	£475
F205	30s. brown (1946)	£275	£110
	w. Wmk inverted (9.49)	£250	£110
F206	£2 bright purple (1946)	£110	22·00
	w. Wmk inverted (17.6.52)	£110	22·00
F207	£2 10s. red (wmk inverted) (9.8.51)	£300	£325
F208	£3 green (1946)	£160	48·00
	w. Wmk inverted (17.6.52)	£150	48·00
F209	£3 10s. rose (11.48)	£1700	£1200
	w. Wmk inverted (5.52)	£1800	£1200
F210	£4 light blue (wmk inverted) (12.2.52)	£160	£120
	w. Wmk upright	†	£750
F211	£5 indigo-blue	£350	70·00
	w. Wmk inverted (11.9.50)	£200	45·00
F191/211 Set of 21		£3250	£2250

THREE SHILLINGS

THREE SHILLINGS

3s.6d.

Type I. Broad serifed capitals

Type II. Taller capitals, without serifs

Surcharged as Type F **7**.

F212	3/6 on 3s.6d. grey-green (I) (1942)	20·00	7·00
	w. Wmk inverted (12.10.50)	38·00	11·00
F213	3/6 on 3s.6d. grey-green (II) (6.53)	14·00	38·00
	w. Wmk inverted (6.53)	45·00	45·00
F214	5/6 on 5s.6d. lilac (1944)	48·00	18·00
	w. Wmk inverted (13.9.50)	60·00	18·00
F215	11/- on 11s. yellow (1942)	80·00	48·00
F216	22/- on 22s. scarlet (1945)	£300	£140
	w. Wmk inverted (1.3.50)	£325	£150
F212/16 Set of 5		£425	£225

(ii) P 14×13½. *"Wiggins Teape" unsurfaced paper with horizontal mesh (1956–58).*

F217	1s.3d. yellow and black (11.56)	2·75	3·25
	w. Wmk inverted	24·00	24·00
F218	£1 pink (20.10.58)	35·00	12·00

No. F192b had the inscription printed in blue in error but as many as 378,000 were printed.

From 1949–53 inferior paper had to be used and for technical reasons it was necessary to feed the paper into the machine in a certain way which resulted in whole printings with the watermark inverted for most values.

ANTARCTIC EXPEDITIONS

VICTORIA LAND

These issues were made under authority of the New Zealand Postal Department and, while not strictly necessary, they actually franked correspondence to New Zealand. They were sold to the public at a premium.

1908 *(15 Jan). Shackleton Expedition. T* **42** *of New Zealand (P* 14*), optd "King Edward VII Land", in two lines, reading up, by Coulls, Culling and Co., Wellington.*

A1		1d. rose-carmine (No. 356 Royle) (G.)	£425	38·00
		a. Opt double	†	£1600
A1b		1d. rose-carmine (No. 352c Waterlow) (G.)	£1400	£850

Nos. A1/1b were used on board the expedition ship, *Nimrod*, and at the Cape Royds base in McMurdo Sound. Due to adverse conditions Shackleton landed in Victoria Land rather than King Edward VII Land, the intended destination.

1911 *(9 Feb)–13. Scott Expedition. Stamps of New Zealand optd "VICTORIA LAND.", in two lines by Govt Printer, Wellington.*

A2	**51**	½d. deep green (No. 387aa) (18.1.13)	£600	£700
A3	**53**	1d. carmine (No. 405)	50·00	95·00
		a. No stop after "LAND" (R. 7/5).	£325	£700

Nos. A2/3 were used at the Cape Evans base on McMurdo Sound or on the *Terra Nova*.

AITUTAKI

The island of Aitutaki, under British protection from 1888, was annexed by New Zealand on 11 June 1901.

NEW ZEALAND DEPENDENCY

Stamps of COOK ISLANDS were used in Aitutaki from 1892 until 1903.

PRICES FOR STAMPS ON COVER TO 1945	
Nos. 1/7	*from* × 4
Nos. 9/14	*from* × 3
Nos. 15/29	*from* × 4
Nos. 30/2	*from* × 6

Stamps of New Zealand overprinted or surcharged. For illustrations of watermarks and definitive types see New Zealand.

AITUTAKI. (1) **Ava Pene.** (2) ½d.

Tai Pene. (3) 1d. **Rua Pene Ma Te Ava.** (4) 2½d.

Toru Pene. (5) 3d. **Ono Pene.** (6) 6d.

Tai Tiringi. (7) 1s.

1903 *(29 June)–11. T* 23, 27/8, 31, 34 *and* 42 *surch with T* **1** *at top and T* **2** *to* **7** *at foot. Thin, hard Cowan paper.* W **43**.

(a) P 14.

1	½d. green (No. 302) (R.)	4·50	6·50
2	1d. carmine (No. 303) (B.)	4·75	5·50
3	2½d. deep blue (No. 320a) (R.) (9.11)	8·00	18·00
	a. "Ava" without stop	£150	£225
1/3 Set of 3		15·00	27·00

4	2½d. blue (No. 308) (R.)		11·00	12·00
5	3d. yellow-brown (No. 309) (B.)		18·00	15·00
6	6d. rose-red (No. 312a) (B.)		30·00	25·00
7	1s. bright red (No. 315a) (B.)		50·00	85·00
	a. "Tiringi" without stop (R. 7/12)		£600	£800
	b. *Orange-red*		65·00	95·00
	ba. "Tiringi" without stop (R. 7/12)		£750	£900
4/7 Set of 4			£100	£120

Nos. 1/2 and 4/7 were placed on sale in Auckland on 12 June 1903. There were four states of the overprint used for No. 3. On the first the "no stop" variety (No. 3a) occurs on R. 6/8, on the second it appears on R. 1/4, 2/4 and 6/8, on the third on R. 5/8 and 6/8, and on the fourth all stops are present.

AITUTAKI.

Ono Pene.
(8)

1911–16. *T* **51** *and* **53** *surch with T* **1** *at top and T* **2** *or* **3** *at foot and T* **52** *surch as T* **8**. P 14×15 *(½d., 1d.) or* 14×14½ *(others).*

9	½d. green (No. 387) (R.) (9.11)	1·00	4·50
10	1d. carmine (No. 405) (B.) (2.13)	3·00	12·00
11	6d. carmine (No. 392) (B.) (23.5.16)	45·00	£120
12	1s. vermilion (No. 394) (B.) (9.14)	50·00	£140
9/12 Set of 4		90·00	£250

1916–17. *T* **60** *(recess) surch as T* **8**. W **43**. P 14×13½.

13	6d. carmine (No. 425) (B.) (6.6.16)	10·00	50·00
	a. Perf 14×14½	7·50	27·00
	b. Vert pair. Nos. 13/13a	50·00	£160
14	1s. vermilion (No. 430) (B.) (3.17)	14·00	90·00
	a. Perf 14×14½	17·00	90·00
	ab. "Tai" without dot (R. 8/9, 9/12, 10/12)	£225	£500
	ac. "Tiringi" without dot on second "i" (R. 8/12, 10/7).	£300	£600
	ad. "Tiringi" without dot on third "i" (R. 8/11)	£425	£800
	b. Vert pair. Nos. 14/14a	£120	£375

1917–18. *T* **60** *(recess) optd "AITUTAKI" only, as in T* **8**. W **43**. P 14×13½.

15	2½d. blue (No. 419) (R.) (12.18)	2·00	18·00
	a. Perf 14×14½	1·75	15·00
	b. Vert pair. Nos. 15/15a	30·00	£130
16	3d. chocolate (No. 420) (B.) (1.18)	1·75	26·00
	a. Perf 14×14½	1·50	24·00
	b. Vert pair. Nos. 16/16a	30·00	£140
17	6d. carmine (No. 425) (B.) (11.17)	6·00	21·00
	a. Perf 14×14½	4·75	21·00
	b. Vert pair. Nos. 17/17a	40·00	£140
18	1s. vermilion (No. 430) (B.) (11.17).	14·00	42·00
	a. Perf 14×14½	12·00	32·00
	b. Vert pair. Nos. 18/18a	65·00	£190
15/18 Set of 4		18·00	85·00

1917–20. *T* **53** *and* **61** *(typo) optd "AITUTAKI" only, as in T* **8**. W **43**. P 14×15.

19	½d. green (No. 435) (R.) (2.20)	1·00	6·00
20	1d. carmine (No. 405) (B.) (5.20)	4·25	28·00
21	1½d. slate (No. 437) (R.) (11.17)	3·75	30·00
22	1½d. orange-brown (No. 438) (R.) (2.19)..	80	7·00
23	3d. chocolate (No. 440) (B.) (6.19)	3·50	17·00
19/23 Set of 5		12·00	80·00

(Des and recess Perkins, Bacon & Co)

1920 *(23 Aug). T* **9/14** *of Cook Islands, but inscr "AITUTAKI". No wmk.* P 14.

24	½d. black and green	3·50	25·00
25	1d. black and dull carmine	3·50	17·00
	a. Double derrick flaw (R.2/8, 3/6 or 5/2)	11·00	
26	1½d. black and sepia	6·00	12·00
27	3d. black and deep blue	2·50	14·00
28	6d. red-brown and slate	5·50	14·00
29	1s. black and purple	9·50	16·00
24/9 Set of 6		27·00	90·00

(Recess Govt Printing Office, Wellington)

1924–27. *T* **9/10** *and* **16** *of Cook Islands, but inscr "AITUTAKI".* W **43** *of New Zealand.* P 14.

30	½d. black and green (5.27)	2·00	15·00
31	1d. black and deep carmine (10.24)	6·00	7·50
	a. Double derrick flaw (R. 2/8, 3/6 or 5/2)	16·00	
32	2½d. black and dull blue (10.27)	7·50	65·00
30/2 Set of 3		14·00	80·00

Cook Islands stamps superseded those of Aitutaki on 15 March 1932. Separate issues were resumed in 1972.

COOK ISLANDS

A British Protectorate was declared over this group of fifteen islands by the local Vice-Consul on 20 September 1888.

Before the introduction of the Cook Islands Post Office, mail was forwarded via Auckland, New Zealand.

PRICES FOR STAMPS ON COVER TO 1945	
Nos. 1/4	*from* × 5
Nos. 5/74	*from* × 4
Nos. 75/145	*from* × 3

BRITISH PROTECTORATE

1   **2** Queen   **3** White Tern or
Makea Takau   Torea

(Des F. Moss. Typo Govt Printing Office, Wellington)

1892 (19 Apr). No wmk. *Toned or white paper.* P 12½.

1	**1**	1d. black	27·00	26·00
		a. Imperf between (vert pair)	£9000	
2		1½d. mauve	40·00	38·00
		a. Imperf (pair)	£9500	
3		2½d. blue	40·00	38·00
4		10d. carmine	£140	£130
1/4 *Set of 4*			£200	£200

Nos. 1/4 were printed in sheets of 60 (6×10) from plates constructed from a matrix of 6 slightly different types.

(Eng A. E. Cousins. Typo Govt Printing Office, Wellington)

1893 (28 July)–**1900**. W **12b** of New Zealand (N Z and Star wide apart) (sideways on *T* **3**).

(a) P 12×11½.

5	**2**	1d. brown	40·00	45·00
6		1d. blue (3.4.94)	10·00	2·00
		a. Perf 12×11½ and 12½ mixed	†	£1300
7		1½d. mauve	9·00	7·00
8		2½d. rose	38·00	23·00
		a. Rose-carmine	60·00	48·00
		ab. Perf 12×11½ and 12½ mixed	£1900	
9		5d. olive-black	18·00	13·00
10		10d. green	70·00	48·00
5/10 *Set of 6*			£160	£120

(b) P 11 (July 1896–1900).

11	**3**	½d. steel blue (1st setting) (11.99)	32·00	45·00
		a. Upper right "d" omitted	£1500	
		b. Second setting	21·00	22·00
		ba. Deep blue (1900)	5·00	6·50
12	**2**	1d. blue	5·00	4·50
13		1d. deep brown/cream (4.99)	18·00	17·00
		a. Wmk sideways	21·00	21·00
		b. Bistre-brown (1900)	21·00	21·00
14		1½d. deep lilac	9·00	6·50
		a. Deep mauve (1900)	9·00	6·50
15	**3**	2d. brown/thin toned (7.98)	11·00	6·50
		a. Deep brown (1900)	8·50	6·50
16	**2**	2½d. pale rose	48·00	38·00
		a. Deep rose (1900)	18·00	9·00
17		5d. olive-black	24·00	18·00
18	**3**	6d. purple/thin toned (7.98)	26·00	29·00
		a. Bright purple (1900)	19·00	23·00
19		10d. green	18·00	48·00
20	**3**	1s. red/thin toned (7.98)	60·00	70·00
		a. Deep carmine (1900)	48·00	48·00
11/20a *Set of 10*			£150	£170

Examples of the 1d., 1½d., 2½d. and 5d. perforated 11 and on laid paper are perforation trials. On the 1st setting of the ½d. the face values are misplaced in each corner. As corrected in the second setting the face values are correctly positioned in each corner.

ONE
HALF
PENNY
(4)   (5)

1899 (24 Apr). No. 12 surch with T **4** by Govt Printer, Rarotonga.

21	**2**	½d. on 1d. blue	32·00	42·00
		a. Surch inverted	£850	£900
		b. Surch double	£1000	£850

NEW ZEALAND TERRITORY

On 8 and 9 October 1900 the chiefs of all the main islands, except Aitutaki, ceded their territory to the British Crown. On 11 June 1901 all the islands, including Aitutaki, were transferred by Great Britain to New Zealand control.

1901 (8 Oct). No. 13 optd with T **5** by Govt Printer, Rarotonga.

22	**2**	1d. brown	£180	£140
		a. Crown inverted	£1900	£1500
		c. Optd with crown twice	£1600	£1600

1902. No wmk. P 11.

(a) Medium white Cowan paper (Feb).

23	**3**	½d. blue-green	6·50	7·00
		a. Imperf horiz (vert pair)	£1200	
24	**2**	1d. dull rose	9·00	15·00

(b) Thick white Pirie paper (May).

25	**3**	½d. yellow-green	4·25	4·25
26	**2**	1d. rose-red	12·00	11·00
		a. Rose-lake	11·00	6·50
27		2½d. dull blue	13·00	21·00

NEW ZEALAND WATERMARKS. In W **43** the wmk units are in vertical columns widely spaced and the sheet margins are unwatermarked or wmkd "NEW ZEALAND POSTAGE" in large letters.

In W **98** the wmk units are arranged alternately in horizontal rows closely spaced and are continued into the sheet margins. Stamps with W **98** sideways show the star to the left of NZ, *as seen from the back.* Sideways inverted varieties have the star to the right, *as seen from the back.*

1902 (Sept). W **43** of New Zealand (single-lined NZ and Star, close together; sideways on *T* **2**). P 11.

28	**3**	½d. yellow-green	2·75	3·25
		a. Grey-green	21·00	48·00
29	**2**	1d. rose-pink	4·00	3·00
30		1½d. deep mauve	4·00	8·50
31	**3**	2d. deep brown	5·00	10·00
		a. No figures of value	£2250	£3000
		b. Perf 11×14	£1700	
32	**2**	2½d. deep blue	3·75	7·00
33		5d. olive-black	35·00	48·00
34	**3**	6d. purple	32·00	28·00
35	**2**	10d. green	48·00	95·00
36	**3**	1s. carmine	48·00	70·00
		a. Perf 11×14	£1900	
28/36 *Set of 9*			£150	£250

Stamps in Type **3** were printed from a master plate with the value added by a series of separate duty plates. One sheet of the 2d. missed this second pass through the press and was issued without value.

For Nos. 28/36 Type **3** exists with the watermark in equal quantities either upright or inverted and for Type **2**, on which the watermark is sideways, in equal quantities with the star to the right or left of NZ.

1909–11. W **43** of New Zealand.

37	**3**	½d. green (P 14½×14) (1911)	6·00	8·00
38	**2**	1d. deep red (P 14)	35·00	30·00
		a. Wmk sideways (24.12.09)	14·00	7·00

For Nos. 37/8 the watermark is either upright or inverted. For No. 38a it is sideways, either with star to right or left of NZ.

1913–19. W **43** of New Zealand (sideways on *T* **3**). *Chalk-surfaced paper.*

39	**3**	½d. deep green (P 14) (1915)	5·50	15·00
		a. Wmk upright	7·00	13·00
40	**2**	1d. red (P 14) (7.13)	5·50	4·25
41		1d. red (P 14×14½) (1914)	5·50	6·00
42		1½d. deep mauve (P 14) (1915)	75·00	32·00
43		1½d. deep mauve (P 14×15) (1916)	10·00	4·00
44	**3**	2d. deep brown (P 15×14) (1919)	5·00	45·00
45	**2**	10d. green (P 14×15) (1918)	18·00	90·00
46	**3**	1s. carmine (P 15×14) (1919)	27·00	90·00
39/46 *Set of 6*			65·00	£225

RAROTONGA

APA PENE
(8)

1919 (Apr–July). *Stamps of New Zealand surch as T* **8**.

(a) T **53**. W **43**. *De La Rue chalk-surfaced paper.* P 14×15.

47		1d. carmine (No. 405) (B.) (June)	1·00	3·00

(b) T **60** *(recess).* W **43**. *Cowan unsurfaced paper.* P 14×13½.

48		2½d. blue (No. 419) (R.) (June)	2·25	6·50
		a. Perf 14×14½	2·00	8·50
		b. Vert pair. Nos. 48/a	20·00	48·00
49		3d. chocolate (No. 420) (B.)	2·00	8·00
		a. Perf 14×14½	2·25	2·00
		b. Vert pair. Nos. 49/a	22·00	55·00
50		4d. bright violet (No. 422) (B.)	2·00	5·50
		a. Re-entry (Pl 20 R. 1/6)	60·00	
		b. Re-entry (Pl 20 R. 4/10)	60·00	
		c. Perf 14×14½	1·75	4·25
		d. Vert (pair Nos. 50 and 50c)	20·00	60·00
51		4½d. deep green (No. 423) (B.)	2·00	7·00
		a. Perf 14×14½	1·75	8·00
		b. Vert pair. Nos. 51/a	20·00	70·00
52		6d. carmine (No. 425) (B.) (June)	3·00	8·50
		a. Perf 14×14½	1·75	5·50
		b. Vert pair. Nos. 52/a	38·00	85·00
53		7½d. red-brown (No. 426a) (B.)	1·50	5·50
54		9d. sage-green (No. 429) (R.)	3·25	15·00
		a. Perf 14×14½	2·00	15·00
		b. Vert pair. Nos. 54/a	38·00	£110
55		1s. vermilion (No. 430) (B.) (June)	11·00	30·00
		a. Perf 14×14½	2·75	18·00
		b. Vert pair. Nos. 55/a	48·00	£120

(c) T **61** *(typo).* W **43**. *De La Rue chalk-surfaced paper.* P 14×15.

56		½d. green (No. 435) (R.) (June)	40	1·00
57		1½d. orange-brown (No. 438) (R.) (June)	50	75
58		2d. yellow (No. 439) (R.)	1·50	1·75
59		3d. chocolate (No. 440) (B.) (July)	2·75	13·00
47/59 *Set of 13*			19·00	70·00

9 Capt. Cook   **10** Wharf at Avarua
landing

11 "Capt. Cook"   **12** Palm Tree
(Dance)

---

13 Huts at Arorangi   **14** Avarua Harbour

R. 2/8   R. 3/6 Double   R. 5/2
derrick flaws

(Des, eng and recess Perkins, Bacon & Co)

1920 (23 Aug). No wmk. P 14.

70	**9**	½d. black and green	4·00	21·00
71	**10**	1d. black and carmine-red	4·75	21·00
		a. Double derrick flaw (R. 2/8, 3/6 or 5/2)	12·00	
72	**11**	1½d. black and dull blue	8·50	8·50
73	**12**	3d. black and chocolate	2·25	5·50
74	**13**	6d. brown and yellow-orange	3·00	8·50
75	**14**	1s. black and violet	5·00	17·00
70/5 *Set of 6*			24·00	75·00

Examples of the 1d. and 1s. with centre inverted were not supplied to the Post Office.

RAROTONGA
(15)

RAROTONGA
Trimmed overprint (R. 1/6 and R. 3/7)

1921 (Oct)–**23**. *Postal Fiscal stamps as Type F* **4** *of New Zealand optd with T* **15**. W **43** (sideways). *Chalk-surfaced "De La Rue" paper.* P 14½×14.

76		2s. deep blue (No. F111) (R.)	27·00	55·00
		a. Trimmed opt	£100	
		b. Carmine opt (1923)	£150	£170
		ba. Trimmed opt	£425	£475
77		2s.6d. grey-brown (No. F112) (B.)	19·00	50·00
		a. Trimmed opt	80·00	
78		5s. yellow-green (No. F115) (R.)	27·00	65·00
		a. Trimmed opt	£100	
79		10s. maroon (No. F120) (B.)	70·00	£110
		a. Trimmed opt	£180	
80		£1 rose-carmine (No. F123) (B.)	£110	£190
		a. Trimmed opt	£300	
76/80 *Set of 5*			£225	£425

See also Nos. 85/9.

16 Te Po,   **17** Harbour, Rarotonga
Rarotongan Chief   and Mt. Ikurangi

(2½d. from a print; 4d. des A. H. Messenger. Plates by P. B. Recess Govt Ptg Office, Wellington)

1924–27. W **43** of New Zealand (sideways on 4d.). P 14.

81	**9**	½d. black and green (13.5.26)	4·50	8·50
82	**10**	1d. black and deep carmine (10.11.24)	6·00	2·25
		a. Double derrick flaw (R. 2/8, 3/6 or 5/2)	16·00	
		x. Wmk reversed	£160	
83	**16**	2½d. red-brown and steel blue (15.10.27)	5·00	24·00
84	**17**	4d. green and violet (15.10.27)	8·00	16·00
81/4 *Set of 4*			21·00	45·00

1926 (Feb–May). *As Nos. 76/80, but on thick, opaque white chalk-surfaced "Cowan" paper.*

85		2s. blue (No. F131) (C.)	£140	£200
		a. Trimmed opt	£400	
86		2s.6d. deep grey-brown (No. F132) (B.)	80·00	£130
87		5s. yellow-green (No. F135) (R.) (May)	85·00	£130
		a. Trimmed opt	£225	
88		10s. brown-red (No. F139) (B.) (May)	90·00	£150
89		£1 rose-pink (No. F142) (B.) (May)	£130	£200
		a. Trimmed opt	£400	
85/9 *Set of 5*			£475	£750

1926 (Oct)–**28**. *T* **72** of New Zealand, overprinted with T **15**.

(a) Jones chalk-surfaced paper.

90		2s. deep blue (No. 466) (R.)	10·00	40·00
		w. Wmk inverted		

(b) Cowan thick, opaque chalk-surfaced paper.

91		2s. light blue (No. 469) (R.) (18.6.27)	15·00	40·00
92		3s. pale mauve (No. 470) (R.) (30.1.28)	16·00	42·00
90/2 *Set of 3*			38·00	£110

TWO PENCE   COOK ISLANDS.
(18)   (19)

1931 (1 Mar). Surch with *T* **18**. P 14.

(a) No wmk.

93	**11**	2d. on 1½d. black and blue (R.)	9·50	2·75

(b) W **43** *of New Zealand.*

94	**11**	2d. on 1½d. black and blue (R.)	4·75	11·00

1931 (12 Nov)–**32**. *Postal Fiscal stamps as Type F* **6** *of New Zealand.* W **43**. *Thick, opaque, white chalk-surfaced "Cowan" paper.* P 14.

(a) Optd with T **15**.

95	2s.6d. deep brown (No. F147) (B.)		10·00	22·00
96	5s. green (No. F149) (R.)		18·00	55·00
97	10s. carmine-lake (No. F155) (B.)		38·00	95·00
98	£1 pink (No. F158) (B.)		90·00	£160

(b) Optd with T **19** *(3.32).*

98a	£3 green (No. F164) (R.)		£325	£550
98b	£5 indigo-blue (No. F168) (R.)		£190	£325

The £3 and £5 values were mainly used for fiscal purposes.

20 Capt. Cook landing

21 Capt. Cook

22 Double Maori Canoe

23 Natives working Cargo

24 Port of Avarua

25 R.M.S. *Monowai*

26 King George V

(Des L. C. Mitchell. Recess P.B.)

1932 (15 Mar–2 May). No wmk. P 13.

99	**20**	½d. black and deep green	3·50	16·00
		a. Perf 14	28·00	90·00
100	**21**	1d. black and lake	6·50	4·50
		a. Centre inverted	£5000	£5000
		b. Perf compound of 13 and 14........	£180	£200
		c. Perf 14	15·00	23·00
101	**22**	2d. black and brown........................	3·00	5·50
		a. Perf 14	9·00	20·00
102	**23**	2½d. black and deep blue	13·00	50·00
		a. Perf 14	14·00	50·00
103	**24**	4d. black and bright blue	20·00	60·00
		a. Perf 14	10·00	50·00
		b. Perf 14×13	30·00	£100
		c. Perf compound of 14 and 13........	50·00	£110
104	**25**	6d. black and orange........................	24·00	48·00
		a. Perf 14	4·25	15·00
105	**26**	1s. black and violet (P 14) (2 May)	10·00	22·00
99/105 *Set of 7*			45·00	£140

Nos. 100b and 103c come from sheets reperforated 14 on arrival at Wellington. No. 100b comes from the first vertical column of a sheet and has 14 at left and No. 103c from the third or fourth vertical column with 13 at left or right.

Other major errors exist on this issue, but these are not listed as they originated from printer's waste which appeared on the market in 1935.

(Recess from P.B. plates at Govt Printing Office, Wellington)

1933–36. W **43** of New Zealand (Single N Z and Star). P 14.

106	**20**	½d. black and deep green	1·00	4·50
		w. Wmk inverted	—	75·00
107	**21**	1d. black and scarlet (1935)	1·25	2·00
		w. Wmk inverted and reversed.......		
108	**22**	2d. black and brown (1936)..............	1·50	50
		w. Wmk inverted		
109	**23**	2½d. black and deep blue	1·50	2·25
110	**24**	4d. black and bright blue	1·50	50
111	**25**	6d. black and orange-yellow (1936)	1·75	2·25
112	**26**	1s. black and violet (1936).............	22·00	38·00
106/12 *Set of 7*			28·00	45·00

SILVER JUBILEE
OF
KING GEORGE V.
1910–1935.

	Normal Letters
	B K E N
	B K E N
	Narrow Letters

(27)

1935 (7 May). *Silver Jubilee. Optd with T* **27** *(wider vertical spacing on 6d.). Colours changed.* W **43** *of New Zealand.* P 14.

113	**21**	1d. red-brown and lake	60	1·40
		a. Narrow "K" in "KING".............	2·75	5·50
		b. Narrow "B" in "JUBILEE".......	8·00	11·00
114	**23**	2½d. dull and deep blue (R.)............	1·00	2·50
		a. Narrow first "E" in "GEORGE"	3·50	6·00
115	**25**	6d. green and orange.....................	3·50	6·00
		a. Narrow "N" in KING	13·00	20·00
113/15 *Set of 3*			4·50	9·00

1936 (15 July)–**44**. *Stamps of New Zealand optd with T* **19**. W **43**. P 14.

(a) T **72**. *Cowan thick, opaque chalk-surfaced paper.*

116		2s. light blue (No. 469)	13·00	45·00
117		3s. pale mauve (No. 470)	13·00	70·00

(b) Type F **6**. *Cowan thick, opaque chalk-surfaced paper.*

118		2s.6d. deep brown (No. F147)	20·00	70·00
119		5s. green (No. F149) (R.)	25·00	90·00
120		10s. carmine-lake (No. F155)...........	55·00	£170
121		£1 pink (No. F158)	85·00	£190
118/21 *Set of 4*			£170	£475

(c) Type F **6**. *Thin, hard, chalk-surfaced Wiggins Teape paper.*

122		2s.6d. dull brown (No. F170) (12.40)...	£110	£110
123		5s. green (No. F172) (R.) (10.40).....	£400	£350
123a		10s. pale carmine-lake (No. F177) (11.44)............	£130	£180
123b		£3 green (No. F183) (R.) (date?)........	£375	£600
122/3b *Set of 4*			£900	£1100

COOK IS'DS. (28)

IS'DS. Small second "S" (R. 1/2)

1937 (1 June). *Coronation. Nos. 599/601 of New Zealand (inscr "12th MAY 1937") optd with T* **28**.

124	1d. carmine		40	80
	a. Small second "S"		14·00	
125	2½d. Prussian blue		80	1·40
	a. Small second "S"		24·00	
126	6d. red-orange		80	60
	a. Small second "S"		24·00	
124/6 *Set of 3*			1·75	2·50

29 King George VI

30 Native Village

31 Native Canoe

32 Tropical Landscape

(Des J. Berry (2s., 3s., and frame of 1s.). Eng B.W. Recess Govt Ptg. Office, Wellington)

1938 (2 May). W **43** of New Zealand. P 14.

127	**29**	1s. black and violet	8·50	12·00
128	**30**	2s. black and red-brown	18·00	13·00
		w. Wmk inverted		
129	**31**	3s. greenish blue and green	48·00	35·00
127/9 *Set of 3*			65·00	55·00

(Recess B.W.)

1940 (2 Sept). *Surch as in T* **32**. W **98** *of New Zealand.* P 13½×14.

130	**32**	3d. on black and purple....................		
		1½d.	75	60

Type 32 was not issued without surcharge.

1943–54. *Postal Fiscal stamps as Type F* **6** *of New Zealand optd with T* **19**. W **98**. *Wiggins Teape chalk-surfaced paper.* P 14.

131	2s.6d. dull brown (No. F193) (3.46)......		65·00	75·00
	w. Wmk inverted (2.4.51)...............		23·00	
132	5s. green (No. F195) (R.) (11.43).....		10·00	22·00
	w. Wmk inverted (5.54)..................		25·00	28·00
133	10s. pale carmine-lake (No. F201) (10.48).........		75·00	£100
	w. Wmk inverted (10.51).................		55·00	80·00
134	£1 pink (No. F203) (R.)		60·00	90·00
	w. Wmk inverted (19.5.54).............		65·00	95·00
135	£3 green (No. F208) (R.) (1946?).....		£700	£850
	w. Wmk inverted (28.5.53)..............		60·00	£160
136	£5 indigo-blue (No. F211) (R.) (25.10.50)..............		£300	£400
	w. Wmk inverted (19.5.54)..............		£250	£375
131/6 *Set of 6*			£400	£650

The £3 and £5 were mainly used for fiscal purposes.

(Recess Govt Ptg Office, Wellington)

1944–46. W **98** of New Zealand (sideways on ½d. 1d., 1s., and 2s.). P 14.

137	**20**	½d. black and deep green (11.44)	1·75	4·00
		w. Wmk sideways inverted	5·00	9·00
138	**21**	1d. black and scarlet (3.45)	2·00	1·00
		w. Wmk sideways inverted	7·00	2·50
		x. Wmk sideways reversed		
139	**22**	2d. black and brown (3.44)	1·75	8·00
140	**23**	2½d. black and deep blue (5.45)........	1·00	2·00
141	**24**	4d. black and blue (4.44).................	5·00	14·00

		y. Wmk inverted and reversed.......	40·00	40·00
142	**25**	6d. black and orange (6.44).............	2·75	2·00
143	**29**	1s. black and violet (9.44)..............	2·50	2·50
144	**30**	2s. black and red-brown (8.45)........	35·00	45·00
145	**31**	3s. greenish blue and green (6.45)...	35·00	32·00
		w. Wmk inverted	95·00	
137/45 *Set of 9*			75·00	£100

The normal sideways watermark shows the star to the right of NZ as seen from the back of the stamp.

COOK ISLANDS

(33)

1946 (4 June). *Peace. Nos. 668, 670, 674/5 of New Zealand optd with T* **33** *(reading up and down at sides on 2d.).*

146		1d. green (Parliament House)	30	10
147		2d. purple (Royal family) (B.).........	30	50
148		6d. chocolate and vermilion (Coat of arms, foundry and farm).........	1·00	75
149		8d. black and carmine ("St. George") (B.)...............	60	75
146/9 *Set of 4*			2·00	1·75

34 Ngatangiia Channel, Rarotonga

35 Capt. Cook and map of Hervey Islands

36 Rartonga and Revd. John Williams

37 Aitutaki and palm trees

38 Rarotonga Airfield

39 Penrhyn village

40 Native hut

41 Map and Statue of Capt. Cook

42 Native hut and palms

43 *Matua* (inter-island freighter)

(Des J. Berry. Recess Waterlow)

1949 (1 Aug)–**61**. *T* **34/43**. W **98** of New Zealand (sideways on shilling values). P 13½×13 (horiz) or 13×13½ (vert).

150	**34**	½d. violet and brown	10	1·00
151	**35**	1d. chestnut and green	3·50	2·00
152	**36**	2d. reddish brown and scarlet..........	2·00	2·00
153	**37**	3d. green and ultramarine	2·00	2·00
		aw. Wmk inverted	£100	
		b. Wmk sideways (white opaque paper) (22.5.61)	3·75	2·50
154	**38**	5d. emerald-green and violet	6·00	1·50
155	**39**	6d. black and carmine	5·50	2·75
156	**40**	8d. olive-green and orange	55	3·75
		w. Wmk inverted	£100	50·00
157	**41**	1s. light blue and chocolate	4·25	3·75
158	**42**	2s. yellow-brown and carmine	3·00	13·00
		w. Wmk sideways inverted.............		
159	**43**	3s. light blue and bluish green	10·00	24·00
150/9 *Set of 10*			32·00	50·00

NIUE

Niue became a British Protectorate on 20 April 1900 and was transferred to New Zealand control on 11 June 1901. There was considerable local resentment at attempts to incorporate Niue into the Cook Islands and, in consequence, the island was recognised as a separate New Zealand dependency from 1902.

PRICES FOR STAMPS ON COVER TO 1945

No. 1	from × 3
Nos. 2/5	from × 8
Nos. 6/7	—
Nos. 8/9	from × 30
Nos. 10/12	—
Nos. 13/31	from × 3
Nos. 32/7c	—
Nos. 38/47	from × 5
Nos. 48/9	—
No. 50	from × 15
Nos. 51/4	—
Nos. 55/61	from × 8
Nos. 62/8	from × 12
Nos. 69/71	from × 3
Nos. 72/4	from × 10
Nos. 75/8	from × 8
Nos. 79/88	—
Nos. 89/97	from × 2

NEW ZEALAND DEPENDENCY
Stamps of New Zealand overprinted

NIUE
(1)

1902 (4 Jan). *Handstamped with T* **1** *in green or bluish green. Pirie paper. Wmk double-lined "N Z" and Star, W* **38** *of New Zealand. P* 11.

| 1 | 42 | 1d. carmine | £300 | £300 |

A few overprints were made with a *greenish violet* ink. These occurred only in the first vertical row and part of the second row of the first sheet overprinted owing to violet ink having been applied to the pad (*Price* £1400 *un*).

NIUE. ½ PENI.
(2)

NIUE. TAHA PENI.
(3) 1d.

NIUE. 2½ PENI.
(4)

1902 (4 Apr). *Type-set surcharges. T* **2**, **3**, *and* **4**.

(i) Pirie paper. No wmk. P 11.

2	27	2½d. blue (R.)	1·50	4·00
		a. No stop after "PENI"	26·00	50·00
		b. Surch double	£2500	

(ii) Basted Mills paper. Wmk double-lined "N Z" and Star, W **38** *of New Zealand.*

(a) P 14.

3	23	½d. green (R.)	2·50	4·50
		a. Spaced "U" and "E" (R. 3/3, 3/6, 8/3, 8/6)	14·00	22·00
		b. Surch inverted	£325	£550
		c. Surch double	£950	
4	42	1d. carmine (B.)	25·00	27·00
		a. Spaced "U" and "E" (R.3/3, 3/6, 8/6)	£130	£140
		b. No stop after "PENI" (R. 9/3)	£350	£375
		c. Varieties a. and b. on same stamp (R. 8/3)	£350	£375

(b) P 11×14.

5	42	1d. carmine (B.)	1·75	2·50
		a. Spaced "U" and "E" (R. 3/3, 3/6, 8/3, 8/6)	12·00	16·00
		c. No stop after "PENI" (R. 9/3)	32·00	48·00
		d. Varieties b. and c. on same stamp (R. 8/3)	32·00	48·00

(c) Mixed perfs.

| 6 | 23 | ½d. green (R.) | £1200 | |
| 7 | 42 | 1d. carmine (B.) | £700 | |

1902 (2 May). *Type-set surcharges, T* **2**, **3**. *Cowan paper. Wmk single-lined "N Z" and Star, W* **43** *of New Zealand.*

(a) P 14.

8	23	½d. green (R.)	1·00	1·00
		a. Spaced "U" and "E" (R. 3/3, 3/6, 8/6)	7·50	9·50
9	42	1d. carmine (B.)	60	1·00
		a. Surch double	£1500	£1600
		b. Spaced "U" and "E" (R. 3/3, 3/6, 8/6)	9·50	16·00
		c. No stop after "PENI" (R. 5/3, 7/3, 9/3, 10/3, 10/6)	9·00	15·00
		d. Varieties b. and c. on same stamp (R. 8/3)	30·00	45·00
		e. "I" of "NIUE" omitted (R. 6/5 from end of last ptg)	£750	

(b) P 14×11.

| 10 | 23 | ½d. green (R.) | | |

(c) Mixed perfs.

11	23	½d. green (R.)	£1100	
12	42	1d. carmine (B.)	£180	
		a. Spaced "U" and "E" (R. 3/3, 3/6, 8/3, 8/6)	£500	
		b. No stop after "PENI" (R. 5/3, 7/3, 9/3, 10/3, 10/6)	£475	

NIUE. (5) Tolu e Pene. (6) 3d.

Ono e Pene. (7) 6d. Taha e Sileni. (8) 1s.

1903 (2 July). *Optd with name at top, T* **5**, *and values at foot, T* **6**/**8**, *in blue. W* **43** *of New Zealand (sideways). P* 11.

| 13 | 28 | 3d. yellow-brown | 9·50 | 5·00 |
| 14 | 31 | 6d. rose-red | 12·00 | 11·00 |

15	34	1s. brown-red ("Tahae" joined)	£650	
		a. Surch double, one albino	£850	
16		1s. bright red	35·00	35·00
		a. Orange-red	45·00	48·00
13/16 Set of 3			50·00	45·00

NIUE. ½ PENI.
(9)

NIUE. 2½ PENI.
(9a)

NIUE.
(10)

1911 (30 Nov). *½d. surch with T* **9**, *others optd at top as T* **5** *and values at foot as T* **7**, **8**. *W* **43** *of New Zealand. P* 14×15 (½d.) *or* 14×14½ (*others*).

17	51	½d. green (C.)	50	50
18	52	6d. carmine (B.)	2·00	7·00
19		1s. vermilion (B.)	6·50	48·00
17/19 Set of 3			8·00	50·00

1915 (Sept). *Surch with T* **9a**. *W* **43** *of New Zealand. P* 14.

| 20 | 27 | 2½d. deep blue (C.) | 17·00 | 38·00 |

1917 (Aug). *1d. surch as T* **3**, *3d. optd as T* **5** *with value as T* **6**. *W* **43** *of New Zealand.*

21	53	1d. carmine (P 14×15) (Br.)	14·00	5·00
		a. No stop after "PENI" (R. 10/16)	£425	
22	60	3d. chocolate (P 14×14½) (B.)	45·00	85·00
		a. No stop after "Pene" (R. 10/4)	£800	
		b. Perf 14×13½	55·00	95·00
		c. Vert pair, Nos. 22/b	£160	

1917–21. *Optd with T* **10**. *W* **43** *of New Zealand.*

(a) P 14×15.

23	61	½d. green (R.) (2.20)	70	2·50
24	53	1d. carmine (B.) (10.17)	10·00	8·50
25	61	1½d. slate (R.) (11.17)	1·00	2·25
26		1½d. orange-brown (R.) (2.19)	70	4·50
27		3d. chocolate (B.) (6.19)	1·40	29·00

(b) P 14×13½.

28	60	2½d. blue (R.) (10.20)	3·00	9·00
		a. Perf 14×14½	1·25	7·00
		ab. Opt double, one albino		
		b. Vert pair, Nos. 28/a	18·00	60·00
29		3d. chocolate (B.) (10.17)	1·60	9·00
		a. Perf 14×14½	1·25	1·50
		b. Vert pair, Nos. 29/a	22·00	48·00
30		6d. carmine (B.) (8.21)	6·50	24·00
		a. Perf 14×14½	4·75	24·00
		b. Vert pair, Nos. 30/a	32·00	£100
31		1s. vermilion (B.) (10.18)	8·50	27·00
		a. Perf 14×14½	5·50	27·00
		b. Vert pair, Nos. 31/a	40·00	£110
23/31 Set of 9			24·00	95·00

1918–29. *Postal Fiscal stamps as Type* F **4** *of New Zealand optd with T* **10** *of New Zealand (sideways).*

(i) Chalk-surfaced "De La Rue" paper.

(a) P 14.

| 32 | | 5s. yellow-green (R.) (7.18) | £100 | £110 |

(b) P 14½×14, comb.

33		2s. deep blue (R.) (9.18)	16·00	32·00
34		2s.6d. grey-brown (B.) (2.23)	21·00	48·00
35		5s. yellow-green (R.) (10.18)	25·00	50·00
36		10s. maroon (B.) (2.23)	£120	£160
37		£1 rose-carmine (B.) (2.23)	£150	£225
33/7 Set of 5			£300	£450

(ii) Thick, opaque, white chalk-surfaced "Cowan" paper. P 14½×14.

37a		5s. yellow-green (R.) (10.29)	27·00	60·00
37b		10s. brown-red (B.) (2.27)	90·00	£140
37c		£1 rose-pink (B.) (2.28)	£160	£225
37a/c Set of 3			£250	£375

11 Landing of Captain Cook

12 Landing of Captain Cook

R. 2/8   R. 3/6   R. 5/2

Double derrick flaws

(Des, eng and recess P.B.)

1920 (23 Aug). *T* **11** *and similar designs. No wmk. P* 14.

38		½d. black and green	3·75	3·75
39		1d. black and dull carmine	2·00	1·25
		a. Double derrick flaw (R. 2/8, 3/6 or 5/2)	6·50	6·50
40		1½d. black and blue	2·50	9·50
41		3d. black and blue	75	14·00
42		6d. red-brown and green	1·75	18·00
43		1s. black and sepia	1·75	18·00
38/43 Set of 6			11·00	55·00

Designs: *Vert*—1d. Wharf at Avarua; 1½d. "Capt Cook (Dance)"; 3d. Palm tree. *Horiz*—6d. Huts at Arorangi; 1s. Avarua Harbour.

Examples of the 6d. with inverted centre were not supplied to the Post Office.

1925–27. *As Nos. 38/9 and new values. W* **43** *of New Zealand (sideways on 4d.) P* 14.

44		½d. black and green (1927)	1·50	8·00
45		1d. black and deep carmine (1925)	1·75	1·00
		a. Double derrick flaw (R. 2/8, 3/6 or 5/2)	5·50	4·50
46		2½d. black and blue (10.27)	4·25	11·00
47		4d. black and violet (10.27)	7·00	20·00
44/7 Set of 4			13·00	35·00

Designs: *Vert*—2½d. Te Po, Rarotongan chief. *Horiz*—4d. Harbour, Rarotonga, and Mount Ikurangi.

1927–28. *Admiral type of New Zealand optd as T* **10**. *W* **43** *of New Zealand. P* 14.

(a) "Jones" paper (wmk inverted).

| 48 | 72 | 2s. deep blue (2.27) (R.) | 15·00 | 48·00 |

(b) "Cowan" paper.

| 49 | 72 | 2s. light blue (R.) (2.28) | 18·00 | 32·00 |

1931 (1 Apr). *No. 40 surch as T* **18** *of Cook Is.*

| 50 | | 2d. on 1½d. black and red | 3·00 | 1·00 |

1931 (12 Nov). *Postal Fiscal stamps as Type* F **6** *of New Zealand optd as T* **10**. *W* **43** *of New Zealand. Thick, opaque, chalk-surfaced "Cowan" paper. P* 14.

51		2s.6d. deep brown (B.)	4·00	11·00
52		5s. green (B.)	35·00	70·00
53		10s. carmine-lake (B.)	35·00	£100
54		£1 pink (B.)	65·00	£150
51/4 Set of 4			£130	£300

See also Nos. 79/82 for different type of overprint.

(Des L. C. Mitchell. Recess P.B.)

1932 (16 Mar). *T* **12** *and similar designs inscr "NIUE" and "COOK ISLANDS". No wmk. P* 13.

55		½d. black and emerald	9·50	22·00
		a. Perf 13×14×13×13	£250	
56		1d. black and deep lake	1·00	50
57		2d. black and red-brown	2·50	4·00
		a. Perf 14×13×13×13	£110	£160
58		2½d. black and slate-blue	8·00	75·00
59		4d. black and greenish blue	14·00	60·00
		a. Perf 14	16·00	55·00
60		6d. black and orange-vermilion	2·50	2·00
61		1s. black and purple (P 14)	2·25	5·00
55/61 Set of 7			35·00	£150

Designs: *Vert*—1d. Capt. Cook; 1s. King George V. *Horiz*—2d. Double Maori canoe; 2½d. Islanders working cargo; 4d. Port of Avarua; 6d. R.M.S. *Monowai*.

Examples of the 2½d. with inverted centre were not supplied to the Post Office.

Nos. 55a and 57a are mixed perforations, each having one side perforated 14 where the original perforation, 13, was inadequate.

(Recess from Perkins Bacon's plates at Govt Ptg Office, Wellington, N.Z.)

1932–36. *As Nos. 55/61, but W* **43** *of New Zealand. P* 14.

62		½d. black and emerald	50	3·50
63		1d. black and deep lake	50	1·75
		w. Wmk inverted	45·00	
64		2d. black and yellow-brown (1.4.36)	50	1·75
		w. Wmk inverted	25·00	45·00
65		2½d. black and slate-blue	50	4·25
		w. Wmk inverted	45·00	
66		4d. black and greenish blue	1·75	4·25
		w. Wmk inverted		
67		6d. black and red-orange (1.4.36)	70	75
68		1s. black and purple (1.4.36)	8·50	24·00
62/8 Set of 7			11·50	35·00

Imperforate proofs of No. 65 are known used on registered mail from Niue postmarked 30 August 1945 or 29 October 1945.

See also Nos. 89/97.

SILVER JUBILEE OF KING GEORGE V 1910–1935.
(13)

| | Normal Letters | B K E N |
| | Narrow Letters | B K E N |

1935 (7 May). *Silver Jubilee. Designs as Nos. 63, 65 and 67 (colours changed) optd with T* **13** *(wider vertical spacing on 6d.). W* **43** *of New Zealand. P* 14.

69		1d. red-brown and lake	60	3·50
		a. Narrow "K" in "KING"	2·75	9·00
		b. Narrow "B" in "JUBILEE"	3·25	11·00
70		2½d. dull and deep blue (R.)	3·50	8·00
		a. Narrow first "E" in "GEORGE"	4·00	13·00
71		6d. green and orange	3·25	6·50
		a. Narrow "N" in "KING"	15·00	35·00
69/71 Set of 3			6·50	16·00

Examples of No. 70 imperforate horizontally are from proof sheets not issued through the Post and Telegraph Department (*Price* £250 *for vert pair*).

NIUE (14) NIUE

Short opt (R. 9/4)

1937 (13 May). *Coronation. Nos. 599/601 of New Zealand optd with T* **14**.

72		1d. carmine	30	10
		a. Short opt	8·00	
73		2½d. Prussian blue	40	1·50
		a. Short opt	10·00	
74		6d. red-orange	40	20
		a. Short opt	10·00	
72/4 Set of 3			1·00	1·60

15 King George VI   **16** Tropical Landscape

1938 (2 May). *T* **15** *and similar designs inscr* "NIUE COOK ISLANDS". W **43** *of New Zealand. P* 14.

75	1s. black and violet	12·00	8·00
76	2s. black and red-brown	12·00	17·00
77	3s. blue and yellowish green	35·00	17·00
75/7 *Set of 3*		55·00	38·00

Designs: *Vert*—2s. Island village. *Horiz*—3s. Cook Islands canoe.

1940 (2 Sept). *Unissued stamp surch as in T* **16**. W **98** *of New Zealand. P* 13½×14.

78	3d. on 1½d. black and purple	75	20

NIUE.
(17)

1941–67. *Postal Fiscal stamps as Type F* **6** *of New Zealand with thin opt, T* **17**. P 14.

(i) Thin, hard, chalk-surfaced "Wiggins Teape" paper with vertical mesh (1941–43).

(a) W **43** *of New Zealand.*

79	2s.6d. deep brown (B.) (4.41)	85·00	85·00
80	5s. green (R.) (4.41)	£300	£225
81	10s. pale carmine-lake (B.) (6.42)	£120	£200
82	£1 pink (B.) (2.43?)	£190	£350
79/82 *Set of 4*		£600	£750

(b) W **98** *of New Zealand (1944–54).*

83	2s.6d. deep brown (B.) (3.45)	3·50	10·00
	w. Wmk inverted (11.51)	13·00	18·00
84	5s. green (R.) (11.44)	7·50	11·00
	w. Wmk inverted (19.5.54)	7·50	13·00
85	10s. carmine-lake (B.) (11.45)	55·00	£100
	w. Wmk inverted	60·00	£100
86	£1 pink (B.) (6.42)	48·00	60·00
83/6 *Set of 4*		£100	£160

(ii) Unsurfaced "Wiggins Teape" paper with horizontal mesh. W **98** *of New Zealand (1957–67).*

87	2s.6d. deep brown (P 14×13½) (1.11.57)	9·50	10·00
88	5s. pale yellowish green (wmk sideways) (6.67)	20·00	75·00

No. 88 came from a late printing made to fill demands from Wellington, but no supplies were sent to Niue. It exists in both line and comb perf.

1944–46. *As Nos.* 62/7 *and* 75/7, *but* W **98** *of New Zealand (sideways on ½d., 1d., 1s. and 2s.).*

89	**12**	½d. black and emerald	50	2·50
90	–	1d. black and deep lake	50	1·75
91	–	2d. black and red-brown	5·50	6·50
92	–	2½d. black and slate-blue (1946) ...	60	1·25
93	–	4d. black and greenish blue	4·25	1·00
		w. Wmk inverted and reversed.......	17·00	
94	–	6d. black and red-orange	2·25	1·40
95	**15**	1s. black and violet	1·50	85
96	–	2s. black and red-brown (1945)......	8·50	3·00
97	–	3s. blue and yellowish green (1945).................................	15·00	7·00
89/97 *Set of 9*			35·00	23·00

1946 (4 June). *Peace. Nos.* 668, 670, 674/5 *of New Zealand optd as T* **17** *without stop (twice, reading up and down on 2d.).*

98	1d. green (Blk.)............................	40	10
99	2d. purple (Blk.)............................	40	10
100	6d. chocolate and vermilion (Blk.)...........	40	80
	a. Opt double, one albino	£250	
101	8d. black and carmine (B.)....................	50	80
98/101 *Set of 4*		1·50	1·60

Nos. 102/112 are no longer used.

18 Map of Niue   **19** H.M.S. *Resolution*

20 Alofi landing   **20a** Native hut

21 Arch at Hikutavake   **21a** Alofi Bay

---

22 Spearing fish   **22a** Cave, Makefu

23 Bananas   **24** Matapa Chasm

(Des J. Berry. Recess B.W.)

1950 (3 July). *T* **18/24**. W **98** *of New Zealand (sideways inverted on* 1d., 2d., 3d., 4d., 6d. *and* 1s.). P 13½×14 *(horiz.) or* 14×13½ *(vert.).*

113	**18**	½d. orange and blue......................	10	1·00
114	**19**	1d. brown and blue-green	2·25	2·25
115	**20**	2d. black and carmine....................	1·25	1·75
116	**20a**	3d. blue and violet-blue	10	20
117	**21**	4d. olive-green and purple-brown ...	10	20
118	**21a**	6d. green and brown-orange	80	1·25
119	**22**	9d. orange and brown	10	1·40
120	**22a**	1s. purple and black...................	10	20
121	**23**	2s. brown-orange and dull green ...	2·50	4·75
122	**24**	3s. blue and black......................	4·50	4·75
113/22 *Set of 10*			10·50	16·00

PENRHYN ISLAND

Stamps of COOK ISLANDS were used on Penrhyn Island from late 1901 until the issue of the surcharged stamps in May 1902.

PRICES FOR STAMPS ON COVER TO 1945

No. 1	*from* × 25
No. 3	—
Nos. 4/5	*from* × 25
Nos. 6/8	—
Nos. 9/10	*from* × 50
Nos. 11/13	—
Nos. 14/18	*from* × 3
Nos. 19/23	*from* × 2
Nos. 24/37	*from* × 3
Nos. 38/40	*from* × 5

NEW ZEALAND DEPENDENCY

The island of Penrhyn, under British protection from 20 September 1888, was annexed by New Zealand on 11 June 1901.

Stamps of New Zealand overprinted or surcharged. For illustrations of New Zealand watermarks and definitive types see the beginning of Cook Islands.

PENRHYN ISLAND.

½ PENI.

(1)

PENRHYN ISLAND.

TAI PENI.

(2) 1d.

PENRHYN ISLAND.

2½ PENI.

(3)

1902 (5 May). *T* **23**, **27** *and* **42** *surch with T* **1**, **2** *and* **3**.

(a) Thick, soft Pirie paper. No wmk. P 11.

1	2½d. blue (No. 260) (R.)	4·00	8·00
	a. "½" and "P" spaced (all stamps in 8th vert row)........................	17·00	32·00

(b) Thin, hard Basted Mills paper. W **38** *of New Zealand.*

(i) P 11.

3	1d. carmine (No. 286) (Br.)	£850	£1000

(ii) P 14.

4	½d. green (No. 287) (R.)	80	7·00
	a. No stop after "ISLAND"....................	£150	£225
5	1d. carmine (No. 288) (Br.)	3·25	17·00

(iii) Perf compound of 11 *and* 14.

6	1d. carmine (No. 290) (Br.)	£950	£1000

(iv) Mixed perfs.

7	½d. green (No. 291) (R.)	£1300	
8	1d. carmine (No. 292) (Br.)	£1500	

(c) Thin, hard Cowan paper. W **43** *of New Zealand.*

(i) P 14.

9	½d. green (No. 302) (R.)	2·25	7·00
	a. No stop after "ISLAND" (R. 10/6)	£140	£250
10	1d. carmine (No. 303) (B.)	1·25	4·50
	a. No stop after "ISLAND" (R. 10/6)	48·00	£100

(ii) Perf compound of 11 *and* 14.

11	1d. carmine (No. 305) (B.)	£7000	

(iii) Mixed perfs.

12	½d. green (No. 306) (R.)	£1400	£1500
13	1d. carmine (No. 307) (B.)	£650	£700

PENRHYN ISLAND.
(4)

Toru Pene.
(5) 3d.

Ono Pene.
(6) 6d.

Tahi Silingi.
(7) 1s.

1903 (28 Feb). *T* **28**, **31** *and* **34** *surch with name at top, T* **4**, *and values at foot, T* **5**/**7**. *Thin, hard Cowan paper.* W **43** (sideways) *of New Zealand. P* 11.

14	3d. yellow-brown (No. 309) (B.)............	10·00	24·00
15	6d. rose-red (No. 312a) (B.)............	15·00	35·00
16	1s. brown-red (No. 315) (B.)............	55·00	55·00
	a. Bright red....................	42·00	42·00
	b. Orange-red....................	55·00	55·00
14/16a *Set of 3*		60·00	90·00

1914 (May)–**15**. *T* **51**/**2** *surch with T* **1** (½d.) *or optd with T* **4** *at top and surch with T* **6**/**7** *at foot.*

19	½d. yellow-green (No. 387) (C.) (5.14)...	80	8·00
	a. No stop after "ISLAND"...................	25·00	75·00
	b. No stop after "PENI" (R. 3/17).......	90·00	£170
	c. Vermilion opt (1.15)....................	80	8·00
	ca. No stop after "ISLAND"................	10·00	48·00
	cb. No stop after "PENI" (R. 3/5, 3/17) .	40·00	£120
22	6d. carmine (No. 393) (B.) (8.14)...........	23·00	70·00
23	1s. vermilion (No. 394) (B.) (8.14)...........	42·00	95·00
19/23 *Set of 3*		60·00	£150

The "no stop after ISLAND" variety occurs on R. 1/4, 1/10, 1/16, 1/22, 6/4, 6/10, 6/16 and 6/22 of the carmine surcharge, No. 19, and on these positions plus R. 1/12, 1/24, 6/12 and 6/24 for the vermilion, No. 19c.

1917 (Nov)–**20**. *Optd as T* **4**.

(a) T **60** *(recess).* W **43** *of New Zealand. P* 14×13½.

24	2½d. blue (No. 419) (R.) (10.20)...........	3·00	11·00
	a. Perf 14×14½	2·00	7·00
	ab. No stop after "ISLAND" (R. 10/8) ..	£190	£375
	b. Vert pair. Nos. 24/4a	45·00	90·00
25	3d. chocolate (No. 420) (B.) (6.18)........	12·00	70·00
	a. Perf 14×14½	9·50	70·00
	b. Vert pair. Nos. 25/5a	70·00	£225
26	6d. carmine (No. 425) (B.) (1.18)	8·00	25·00
	a. Perf 14×14½	5·00	20·00
	ab. No stop after "ISLAND" (R. 10/8) ..	£425	£700
	b. Vert pair. Nos. 26/6a	55·00	£140
27	1s. vermilion (No. 430) (B.) (12.17)........	15·00	42·00
	a. Perf 14×14½	12·00	32·00
	ab. No stop after "ISLAND" (R. 10/8) ..	£500	£750
	b. Vert pair. Nos. 27/7a	£100	£225
24/7 *Set of 4*		25·00	£110

(b) T **61** *(typo).* W **43** *of New Zealand. P* 14×15.

28	½d. green (No. 435) (R.) (2.20)...........	1·00	2·00
	a. No stop after "ISLAND" (R. 2/24)...	£120	£170
	b. Narrow spacing	7·00	12·00
29	1½d. slate (No. 437) (R.)...........	6·50	20·00
	a. Narrow spacing	18·00	45·00
30	1½d. orange-brown (No. 438) (R.) (2.19)...	60	7·00
	a. Narrow spacing	5·00	45·00
31	3d. chocolate (No. 440) (B.) (6.19)........	3·50	24·00
	a. Narrow spacing	16·00	60·00
28/31 *Set of 4*		10·50	60·00

The narrow spacing variety occurs on R. 1/5–8, 4/21–4, 7/5–8 and 9/21–4.

(Recess P.B.)

1920 (23 Aug). *As T* **9**/**14** *of Cook Islands, but inscr* "PENRHYN". No wmk. P 14.

32	½d. black and emerald............................	1·00	17·00
	a. Part imperf block of 4	£1400	
33	1d. black and deep red............................	1·50	15·00
	a. Double derrick flaw (R. 2/8, 3/6 or 5/2)....................	5·50	45·00
34	1½d. black and deep violet............	6·50	19·00
35	3d. black and red............	2·50	8·50
36	6d. red-brown and sepia............	3·25	20·00
37	1s. black and slate-blue............	10·00	26·00
32/7 *Set of 6*		22·00	95·00

No. 32a comes from sheets on which two rows were imperforate between horizontally and the second row additionally imperforate vertically.

Examples of the ½d. and 1d. with centre inverted were not supplied to the Post Office.

(Recess Govt Printing Office, Wellington)

1927–29. *As T* **9**/**10** *and* **16** *of Cook Islands, but inscr* "PENRHYN". W **43**. P 14.

38	½d. black and green (5.29)............	5·50	21·00
39	1d. black and deep carmine (14.3.28)...	5·50	18·00
	a. Double derrick flaw (R. 2/8, 3/6 or 5/2)....................	16·00	
40	2½d. red-brown and dull blue (10.27).......	5·00	28·00
38/40 *Set of 3*		14·50	60·00

Cook Islands stamps superseded those of Penrhyn Island on 15 March 1932.

TOKELAU ISLANDS

Formerly known as the Union Islands, and administered as part of the Gilbert & Ellice Islands Colony, Tokelau was transferred to New Zealand on 4 November 1925 and administered with Western Samoa. The Islands were finally incorporated in New Zealand on 1 January 1949 and became a dependency. The name Tokelau was officially adopted on 7 May 1946.

Stamps of GILBERT AND ELLICE ISLANDS were used in Tokelau from Feburary 1911 until June 1926 when they were replaced by those of SAMOA. These were current until 1948.

The post office on Atafu opened in 1911, but the cancellations for the other two islands, Fakaofo and Nukunono, did not appear until 1926.

NEW ZEALAND ADMINISTRATION

1 Atafu village and map

2 Nukunono hut and map

3 Fakaofo village and map

(Des J. Berry from photographs by T. T. C. Humphrey. Recess B.W.)

1948 (22 June). *T* **1/3**. Wmk *T* **98** of New Zealand (Mult N Z and Star). P 13½.

1		½d. red-brown and purple	15	75
2		1d. chestnut and green	15	50
		w. Wmk inverted	£275	
3		2d. green and ultramarine	15	50
1/3		Set of 3	40	1·60

Covers are known postmarked 16 June 1948, but this was in error for 16 July.

WESTERN SAMOA

PRICES FOR STAMPS ON COVER TO 1945

Nos. 1/20 are very rare used on cover.

Nos. 21/40	*from* × 20
Nos. 41/8	*from* × 100
Nos. 49/56	*from* × 4
Nos. 57/64	*from* × 12
Nos. 65/8	*from* × 2
Nos. 69/97	*from* × 20
Nos. 101/9	*from* × 3
Nos. 110/14	—
Nos. 115/21	*from* × 3
Nos. 122/32	—
Nos. 134/64	*from* × 3
Nos. 165/76	—
Nos. 177/214	*from* × 2

INDEPENDENT KINGDOM OF SAMOA

The first postal service in Samoa was organised by C. L. Griffiths, who had earlier run the *Fiji Times* Express post in Suva. In both instances the principal purpose of the service was the distribution of newspapers of which Griffiths was the proprietor. The first issue of the *Samoa Times* (later the *Samoa Times and South Sea Gazette*) appeared on 6 October 1877 and the newspaper continued in weekly publication until 27 August 1881.

Mail from the Samoa Express post to addresses overseas was routed via New South Wales, New Zealand or U.S.A. and received additional franking with stamps of the receiving country on landing.

Cancellations, inscribed "APIA SAMOA", did not arrive until March 1878 so that examples of Nos. 1/9 used before that date were cancelled in manuscript. the Samoa Express stamps may also be found cancelled at Fiji, Auckland and Sydney.

1

A 2nd State (Nos. 4/9)

B 3rd State (Nos. 10/19)

(Des H. H. Glover. Litho S. T. Leigh & Co, Sydney, N.S.W.)

1877 (1 Oct)–**80**. *A. 1st state: white line above "X" in "EXPRESS" not broken.* P 12½.

1	**1**	1d. ultramarine	£250	£150
2		3d. deep scarlet	£300	£140
3		6d. bright violet	£300	£140
		a. Pale lilac	£325	£140

B. 2nd state: white line above "X" usually broken by a spot of colour, and dot between top of "M" and "O" of "SAMOA". P 12½ (1878–79).

4	**1**	1d. ultramarine	90·00	£150
5		3d. bright scarlet	£325	£450
6		6d. bright violet	£450	£500
7		1s. dull yellow	£200	90·00
		b. Perf 12 (1879)	80·00	£150
		c. Orange-yellow	£200	£200
8		2s. red-brown	£275	£375
		a. Chocolate	£300	£375
9		5s. green	£1600	£1100

C. 3rd state: line above "X" repaired, dot merged with upper right serif of "M" (1879).

(a) P 12½.

10	**1**	1d. ultramarine	£150	90·00
11		3d. vermilion	£275	£120
12		6d. lilac	£300	85·00
13		2s. brown	£250	£250
		a. Chocolate	£250	£250
14		5s. green	£1000	£600
		a. Line above "X" not repaired (R. 2/3)	£1300	

(b) P 12.

15	**1**	1d. blue	24·00	
		a. Deep blue	32·00	
		b. Ultramarine	28·00	
16		3d. vermilion	48·00	
		a. Carmine-vermilion	48·00	
17		6d. bright violet	40·00	
		a. Deep violet	40·00	
18		2s. deep brown	£150	
19		5s. yellow-green	£400	
		a. Deep green	£550	
		b. Line above "X" not repaired (R. 2/3)	£500	

D. 4th state: spot of colour under middle stroke of "M". P 12 (1880).

20	**1**	9d. orange-brown	60·00	£350

Originals exist imperf, but are not known used in this state.

On sheets of the 1d., 1st state, at least eight stamps have a stop after "PENNY". In the 2nd state, three stamps have the stop, and in the 3rd state, only one.

In the 1st state, all the stamps, 1d., 3d. and 6d., were in sheets of 20 (5×4) and also the 1d. in the 3rd state.

All values in the 2nd state, all values except the 1d. in the 3rd state and No. 20 were in sheets of 10 (5×2).

As all sheets of all printings of the originals were imperf at the outer edges, the only stamps which can have perforations on all four sides are Nos. 1 to 3a, 10 and 15 to 15b, all other originals being imperf on one or two dates.

The perf 12 stamps, which gauge 11.8, are generally very rough but later the machine was repaired and the 1d., 3d. and 6d. are known with clean-cut perforations.

Remainders of the 1d., unissued 2d. rose, 6d. (in sheets of 21 (7×3), 3d., 9d., 5s. (in sheets of 12 (4×3) and of the 1s. and 2s. (sheet format unknown) were found in the Samoan post office when the service closed down in 1881. The remainders are rare in complete sheets.

Reprints of all values, in sheets of 40 (8×5), were made after the originals had been withdrawn from sale. These are practically worthless.

The majority of both reprints and remainders are in the 4th state as the 9d. with the spot of colour under the middle stroke of the "M", but a few stamps (both remainders and reprints) do not show this, while on some it is very faint.

There are six known types of forgery, one of which is rather dangerous, the others being crude.

The last mail despatch organised by the proprietors of the Samoa Express took place on 31 August 1881, although one cover is recorded postmarked 24 September 1881.

After the withdrawal of the Samoa Express service it would appear that the Apia municipality appointed a postmaster to continue the overseas post. Covers are known franked with U.S.A. or New Zealand stamps in Samoa, or routed via Fiji.

In December 1886 the municipal postmaster, John Davis, was appointed Postmaster of the Kingdom of Samoa by King Malietoa. Overseas mail sent via New Zealand was subsequently accepted without the addition of New Zealand stamps, although letters to the U.S.A. continued to require such franking until August 1891.

2 Palm Trees

3 King Malietoa Laupepa

4a 6 mm

4b 7 mm

4c 4 mm

Description of Watermarks

(These are the same as W **12a/c** of New Zealand)

W **4a**. 6 mm between "N Z" and star; broad irregular star; comparatively wide "N"; "N Z" 11½ mm wide, with horizontal mesh.

W **4b**. 7 mm between "N Z" and star; narrower star; narrow "N"; "N Z" 10 mm wide, with vertical mesh.

W **4c**. 4 mm between "N Z" and star; narrow star; wide "N"; "N Z" 11 mm wide, with vertical mesh.

(Des A. E. Cousins (*T* **3**). Dies eng W. R. Bock and A. E. Cousins (*T* **2**) or A. E. Cousins (*T* **3**). Typo Govt Ptg Office, Wellington)

1886–1900.

(i) W **4a**.

(a) P 12½(15 Oct–Nov 1886).

21	**2**	½d. purple-brown	24·00	55·00
22		1d. yellow-green	11·00	12·00
23		2d. dull orange	28·00	10·00
24		4d. blue	48·00	10·00
25		1s. rose-carmine	65·00	11·00
		a. Bisected (2½d.) (on cover)*	†	£325
26		2s.6d. reddish lilac	55·00	75·00

(b) P 12×11½(6 July–Nov 1887).

27	**2**	½d. purple-brown	70·00	80·00
28		1d. yellow-green	£100	28·00
29		2d. yellow	95·00	£140
30		4d. blue	£250	£200
31		6d. brown-lake	29·00	15·00
32		1s. rose-carmine	—	£190
33		2s.6d. reddish lilac	£1000	

(ii) W **4c**. P 12×11½ (9 May 1890).

34	**2**	½d. purple-brown	75·00	30·00
35		1d. green	55·00	40·00
36		2d. brown-orange	80·00	40·00
37		4d. blue	£140	5·00
38		6d. brown-lake	£300	11·00
39		1s. rose-carmine	£350	13·00
		x. Wmk reversed	£450	£100
40		2s.6d. reddish lilac	£450	8·50

(iii) W **4b**.

(a) P 12×11½ (9 May 1890–92).

41	**2**	½d. pale purple-brown	4·50	4·50
		a. Blackish purple	4·50	4·50
42		1d. myrtle-green	26·00	1·40
		a. Green	26·00	1·40
		b. Yellow-green	26·00	1·40
43		2d. dull orange	35·00	1·75
		x. Wmk reversed	£100	£100
44	**3**	2½d. rose (22.11.92)	75·00	4·00
		a. Pale rose	75·00	4·00
45	**2**	4d. blue	£225	20·00
46		6d. brown-lake	£110	9·50
47		1s. rose-carmine	£225	5·00
48		2s.6d. slate-lilac	—	9·00

(b) P 12½ (Mar 1891–92).

49	**2**	½d. purple-brown		
50		1d. green		
51		2d. orange-yellow	—	£350
52	**3**	2½d. rose (7.1.92)	26·00	4·50
53	**2**	4d. blue	£2750	£450
54		6d. brown-purple	£2750	£1300
55		1s. rose-carmine	£1000	£1000
56		2s.6d. slate-lilac	£2750	

(c) P 11 (May 1895–1900).

57	**2**	½d. purple-brown	2·75	1·75
		a. Deep purple-brown	2·25	1·75
		b. Blackish purple (1900)	2·25	35·00
58		1d. green	8·00	1·75
		a. Bluish green (1897)	7·50	1·75
		b. Deep green (1900)	2·75	22·00
59		2d. pale yellow	40·00	40·00
		a. Orange (1896)	20·00	20·00
		b. Bright yellow (1.97)	13·00	8·00
		c. Pale ochre (10.97)	5·00	8·00
		d. Dull orange (1900)	7·50	
60	**3**	2½d. rose	2·75	10·00
		a. Deep rose-carmine (1900)	2·25	42·00
61	**2**	4d. blue	15·00	7·50
		a. Deep blue (1900)	1·25	50·00
62		6d. brown-lake	10·00	3·00
		a. Brown-purple (1900)	1·75	60·00
63		1s. rose	10·00	3·75
		a. Dull rose-carmine/toned (5.98)	3·25	35·00
		b. Carmine (1900)	1·50	
64		2s.6d. purple	55·00	10·00
		a. Reddish lilac (wmk inverted) (1897)	11·00	8·50
		b. Deep purple/toned (wmk reversed) (17.5.98)	4·75	9·50
		ba. Imperf between (vert pair)	£400	
		c. Slate-violet	£120	

*Following a fire on 1 April 1895 which destroyed stocks of all stamps except the 1s. value perf 12½, this was bisected diagonally and used as a 2½d. stamp for overseas letters between 24 April and May 1895, and was cancelled in blue. Fresh supplies of the 2½d. did not arrive until July 1895, although other values were available from 23 May.

Examples of the 1s. rose perforated 11, No. 63, were subsequently bisected and supplied cancelled-to-order by the post office to collectors, often with backdated cancellations. Most of these examples were bisected vertically and all were cancelled in black (*Price* £7).

The dates given relate to the earliest dates of printing in the various watermarks and perforations and not to issue dates.

The perf 11 issues (including those later surcharged or overprinted), are very unevenly perforated owing to the large size of the pins. Evenly perforated copies are extremely hard to find.

For the 2½d. black, see Nos. 81/2 and for the ½d. green and 1d. red-brown, see Nos. 88/9.

(5)	(6)	(7)

1893 (Nov–Dec). *Handstamped singly, at Apia.*

(a) In two operations.

65	**5**	5d. on 4d. blue (37)	70·00	45·00
66		5d. on 4d. blue (45)	55·00	£100
67	**6**	5d. on 4d. blue (37)	£100	£110

| 68 | | 5d. on 4d. blue (45)............................ | 70·00 | |

(b) In three operations (Dec.)

| 69 | 7 | 5d. on 4d. blue (37) (R.)...................... | 26·00 | 50·00 |
| 70 | | 5d. on 4d. blue (45) (R.)...................... | 29·00 | 32·00 |

In Types **5** and **6** the bars obliterating the original value vary in length from 13½ to 16½ mm and can occur with either the thick bar over the thin one or vice versa. Example can be found with the bars omitted.

Double handstamps exist but we do not list them.

A surcharge as Type **7** but with stop after "d" is now considered to be a trial. It exists in black and in red. Where the "d" was applied separately its position in relation to the "5" naturally varies.

Surcharged

| **8** | **R** | **1½d.** | **3d.** |
| | | **(9)** | **(10)** |

The "R" in Type **10** indicates use for registration fee.

(Des and die eng A. E. Cousins. Typo New Zealand Govt Ptg Office)

1894 (26 Feb)–**1900**. W **4b** (sideways).

(a) P 11½×12.

71	8	5d. dull vermilion............................	20·00	2·75
		a. Dull red......................................	20·00	3·75
		ab. Mixed perfs 11½×12 and 12½ ..		

(b) P 11.

| 72 | 8 | 5d. dull red (1895)............................ | 25·00 | 9·00 |
| | | a. Deep red (1900)........................... | 3·50 | 15·00 |

1895–1900. W **4b**.

*(i) Handstamped with T **9** or **10**.*

(a) P 12×11½ (28.1.95).

| 73 | 2 | 1½d. on 2d. dull orange (B.)............ | 16·00 | 8·00 |
| 74 | | 3d. on 2d. dull orange.................... | 48·00 | 13·00 |

(b) P 11 (6.95).

75	2	1½d. on 2d. orange (B.)...................	3·00	7·00
		a. Pair, one without handstamp .	£450	
		b. On 2d. yellow...........................	7·00	7·00
76		3d. on 2d. orange............................	8·00	10·00
		a. On 2d. yellow............................	10·00	10·00

*(ii) Handstamped as T **9** or **10**. P 11 (1896).*

78	2	1½d. on 2d. orange-yellow (B.).......	3·00	23·00
79		3d. on 2d. orange-yellow...............	3·75	48·00
		a. Imperf between (vert pair).....	£450	
		b. Pair, one without handstamp .		

*(iv) Surch typo as T **10**. P 11 (7 Feb 1900).*

| 80 | 2 | 3d. on 2d. deep red-orange (G.)...... | 1·50 | £130 |

†In No. 78 the "2" has a serif and the handstamp is in pale greenish blue instead of deep blue. In No. 79 the "R" is slightly narrower. In both instances the stamp is in a different shade.

A special printing in a distinctly different colour was made for No. 80 and the surcharge is in green.

Most of the handstamps exist double.

1896 (Aug). *Printed in the wrong colour.* W **4b**.

(a) P 10×11.

| 81 | 3 | 2½d. black....................................... | 1·50 | 3·00 |

(b) P 11.

| 82 | 3 | 2½d. black....................................... | 75·00 | 65·00 |
| | | a. Mixed perfs 10 and 11.............. | £375 | |

Surcharged

2½d.	**PROVISIONAL**
(11)	**GOVT.**
	(12)

1898–99. W **4b**. P 11.

*(a) Handstamped as T **11** (10.98).*

| 83 | 2 | 2½d. on 1s. dull rose-carmine/toned .... | 48·00 | 50·00 |

*(b) Surch as T **11** (1899).*

84	2	2½d. on 1d. bluish green (R.)....................	75	3·00
		a. Surch inverted.........................	£750	£375
85		2½d. on 1s. dull rose-carmine/toned (R.)..	8·00	13·00
		a. Surch double............................	£350	
86		2½d. on 1s. dull rose-carmine/toned (Blk.)...	8·00	13·00
		a. Surch double............................	£450	
87		2½d. on 2s.6d. deep purple/toned (wmk reversed)....	9·00	18·00

The typographed surcharge was applied in a setting of nine, giving seven types differing in the angle and length of the fractional line, the type of stop, etc.

1899 (18 July). *Colours changed.* W **4b**. P 11.

88		½d. dull blue-green............................	1·75	2·25
		a. Deep green.................................	1·75	2·25
89		1d. deep red-brown...........................	2·50	2·50

1899 (20 Sept)–**1900**. *Provisional Government. New printings optd with T **12** (longer words and shorter letters on 5d.)* W **4b**. P 11.

90	2	½d. dull blue-green (R.)....................	2·00	3·50
		a. Yellowish green (1900).............	2·25	5·50
91		1d. chestnut (R.).............................	2·50	9·00
92		2d. dull orange (R.).........................	2·50	7·50
		a. Orange-yellow (1900)................	2·50	9·00
93		4d. deep dull blue (R.)....................	70	15·00
94	8	5d. dull vermilion............................	3·00	9·00
		a. Red (1900).................................	2·75	9·00
95	2	6d. brown-lake (B.).........................	1·50	8·50
96		1s. rose-carmine (B.)......................	1·50	28·00

| 97 | | 2s.6d. reddish purple (R.).................... | 4·75 | 21·00 |
| 90/7 | | Set of 8 .... | 16·00 | 90·00 |

The Samoan group of islands was partitioned on 1 March 1900: Western Samoa (Upolu, Savaii Apolima and Manono) to Germany and Eastern Samoa (Tutuila, the Manu'a Is and Rose Is) to the United States. German issues of 1900–14 will be found listed in Part 7 (*Germany*) of this catalogue; previously there were no U.S. issues.

The Samoan Kingdom post office run by John Davis was suspended in March 1900.

NEW ZEALAND OCCUPATION

The German Islands of Samoa surrendered to the New Zealand Expeditionary Force on 30 August 1914 and were administered by New Zealand until 1962.

G.R.I.	**G.R.I.**
1 d.	**1 Shillings.**
(13)	**(14)**

SETTINGS. Nos. 101/9 were surcharged by a vertical setting of ten, repeated ten times across the sheet. Nos. 110/14 were from a horizontal setting of four repeated five times in the sheet.

Nos. 101b, 102a and 104a occurred on position 6. The error was corrected during the printing of No. 102.

Nos. 101c, 102c, 104d and 105b are from position 10.

Nos. 101d, 102e and 104b are from position 1.

No. 108b is from position 9.

(Surch by Samoanische Zeitung, Apia)

1914 (3 Sept). *German Colonial issue (ship) (no wmk) inscr "SAMOA" surch as T **13** or **14** (mark values).*

101		½d. on 3pf. brown............................	40·00	10·00
		a. Surch double............................	£650	£500
		b. No fraction bar.........................	60·00	32·00
		c. Comma after "I"........................	£650	£400
		d. "1" to left of "2" in "½".............	60·00	32·00
102		½d. on 5pf. green.............................	50·00	14·00
		a. No fraction bar.........................	£120	55·00
		b. Comma after "I"........................	£375	£170
		d. Surch double............................	£650	£500
		e. "1" to left of "2" in "½".............	£100	40·00
103		1d. on 10pf. carmine.......................	95·00	40·00
		a. Surch double............................	£750	£600
104		2½d. on 20pf. ultramarine.................	42·00	10·00
		a. No fraction bar.........................	75·00	38·00
		b. "1" to left of "2" in "½".............	75·00	38·00
		c. Surch inverted..........................	£900	£800
		d. Comma after "I"........................	£475	£325
		e. Surch double............................	£650	£550
105		3d. on 25pf. black and red/yellow....	55·00	40·00
		a. Surch double............................	£950	£700
		b. Comma after "I"........................	£4750	£1000
106		4d. on 30pf. black and orange/buff....	£110	60·00
107		5d. on 40pf. black and carmine........	£110	70·00
108		6d. on 50pf. black and purple/buff....	60·00	35·00
		a. Surch double............................	£950	£900
		b. Inverted "9" for "6"..................	£180	£100
109		9d. on 80pf. black and carmine/rose ..	£200	£100
110		"1 shillings" on 1m. carmine...........	£3250	£3500
111		"1 shilling" on 1m. carmine............	£11000	£7000
112		2s. on 2m. blue...............................	£3250	£2750
113		3s. on 3m. violet-black....................	£1400	£1200
		a. Surch double............................	£8000	£9000
114		5s. on 5m. carmine and black..........	£1100	£1000
		a. Surch double............................	£11000	£12000

No. 108b is distinguishable from 108, as the "d" and the "9" are not in a line, and the upper loop of the "9" turns downwards to the left.

UNAUTHORISED SURCHARGES. Examples of the 2d. on 20pf., 3d. on 30pf., 3d. on 40pf., 4d. on 40pf., 6d. on 80pf., 2s. on 3m. and 2s. on Marshall Islands 2m., together with a number of errors not listed above, were produced by the printer on stamps supplied by local collectors. These were not authorised by the New Zealand Military Administration.

SAMOA.
(15)

1914 (29 Sept)–**15**. *Stamps of New Zealand. T **50**, **51**, **52** and **27**, optd as T **15**, but opt only 14 mm long on all except 2½d. Wmk "N Z" and Star, W **43** of New Zealand.*

115		½d. yellow-green (R.) (P 14×15).............	1·00	30
116		1d. carmine (B.) (P 14×15)....................	1·00	10
117		2d. mauve (R.) (P 14×14½) (10.14)........	1·00	1·00
118		2½d. deep blue (R.) (P 14) (10.14)	1·75	1·75
		w. Wmk inverted		
119		6d. carmine (B.) (P 14×14½) (10.14)......	1·75	1·75
		a. Perf 14×13½	17·00	23·00
		b. Vert pair. Nos. 119/a (1915).....	50·00	90·00
120		6d. pale carmine (B.) (P 14×14½) (10.14)............................	10·00	10·00
121		1s. vermilion (B.) (P 14×14½) (10.14)....	5·50	19·00
115/21		Set of 6	11·00	21·00

1914–24. *Postal Fiscal stamps as Type F **4** of New Zealand optd with T **15**. W **43** of New Zealand (sideways). Chalk-surfaced "De La Rue" paper.*

(a) P 14 (Nov 1914–17).

122		2s. blue (R.) (9.17)............................	£100	£100
123		2s.6d. grey-brown (B.) (9.17).................	5·50	9·00
124		5s. yellow-green (R.)..........................	13·00	11·00
125		10s. maroon (B.).................................	28·00	28·00
126		£1 rose-carmine (R.)...........................	70·00	45·00

(b) P 14½×14, comb (1917–24).

127		2s. deep blue (3.18)...........................	5·50	5·50
128		2s.6d. grey-brown (B.) (10.24)................	£325	£150
129		3s. purple (R.) (6.23)..........................	16·00	9·00
130		5s. yellow-green (9.17)........................	17·00	15·00

| 131 | | 10s. maroon (B.) (11.17)....................... | 70·00 | 45·00 |
| 132 | | £1 rose-carmine (B.) (3.18)................... | 80·00 | 70·00 |

We no longer list the £2 value as it is doubtful if this was used for postal purposes.

See also Nos. 165/6e.

1916–19. *King George V stamps of New Zealand optd as T **15**, but 14 mm long.*

(a) Typo. P 14×15.

134	61	½d. yellow-green (R.).....................	60	1·25
135		1½d. slate (R.) (1917)....................	50	25
136		1½d. orange-brown (R.) (1919)........	30	50
137		2d. yellow (R.).............................	1·50	20
138		3d. chocolate (B.) (1919)..............	1·75	15·00

(b) Recess. P 14×13½.

139	60	2½d. blue (R.)...............................	60	50
		a. Perf 14×14½	1·25	60
		b. Vert pair. Nos. 139/a............	16·00	26·00
140		3d. chocolate (B.) (1917)............	50	1·00
		a. Perf 14×14½	50	1·00
		b. Vert pair. Nos. 140/a............	16·00	29·00
141		6d. carmine (B.) (5.5.17).............	1·50	3·25
		a. Perf 14×14½	1·50	1·25
		b. Vert pair. Nos. 141/a............	18·00	38·00
142		1s. vermilion (B.).......................	2·00	1·50
		a. Perf 14×14½	4·75	9·00
		b. Vert pair. Nos. 142/a............	25·00	50·00
134/42		Set of 9	8·25	19·00

LEAGUE OF NATIONS MANDATE

Administered by New Zealand.

1920 (July). *Victory. Nos. 453/8 of New Zealand optd as T **15**, but 14 mm long.*

143		½d. green (R.)...............................	4·00	11·00
144		1d. carmine (B.)...........................	2·75	11·00
145		1½d. brown-orange (R.)...................	1·50	9·00
146		3d. chocolate (R.)........................	8·00	9·00
147		6d. violet (R.)..............................	4·50	7·00
148		1s. orange-red (B.).......................	13·00	11·00
143/8		Set of 6	30·00	50·00

SILVER JUBILEE OF KING GEORGE V 1910 - 1935.

| **16** Native Hut | **(17)** |

(Eng B.W. Recess-printed at Wellington, NZ)

1921 (23 Dec). W **43** of New Zealand.

(a) P 14×14½.

149	16	½d. green...................................	2·50	8·00
150		1d. lake.....................................	3·75	40
151		1½d. chestnut..............................	1·25	15·00
152		2d. yellow..................................	2·25	2·00
149/52		Set of 4	8·75	23·00

(b) P 14×13½.

153	16	½d. green...................................	4·50	1·75
154		1d. lake.....................................	20	50
155		1½d. chestnut..............................	11·00	9·50
156		2d. yellow..................................	13·00	80
157		2½d. grey-blue............................	1·75	8·00
158		3d. sepia...................................	1·75	4·50
159		4d. violet..................................	1·75	3·50
160		5d. light blue.............................	1·75	7·00
161		6d. bright carmine......................	1·75	6·00
162		8d. red-brown............................	1·75	12·00
163		9d. olive-green..........................	2·00	30·00
164		1s. vermilion.............................	1·75	26·00
153/64		Set of 12	42·00	£100

1925–28. *Postal Fiscal stamps as Type F **4** of New Zealand optd with T **15**. W **43** of New Zealand (sideways). P 14½×14.*

(a) Thick, opaque, white chalk-surfaced "Cowan" paper.

165		2s. blue (R.) (12.25)....................	£180	£200
166		2s.6d. deep grey-brown (B.) (10.28)...	65·00	£110
166a		3s. mauve (R.) (9.25)...................	65·00	95·00
166b		5s. yellow-green (R.) (11.26)........	20·00	42·00
		ba. Opt at top of stamp................	£1100	
166c		10s. brown-red (B.) (12.25)...........	£180	£130
166d		£1 rose-pink (B.) (11.26).............	80·00	£110
165/6d		Set of 6	£550	£600

(b) Thin, hard, chalk-surfaced "Wiggins Teape" paper.

| 166e | | £1 rose-pink (B.) (1928)............... | — | £900 |

1926–27. *T **72** of New Zealand, optd with T **15**, in red.*

(a) "Jones" paper.

167		2s. deep blue (11.26)....................	5·00	18·00
168		3s. mauve (10.26)........................	18·00	45·00
		w. Wmk inverted	18·00	48·00

(b) "Cowan" paper.

| 169 | | 2s. light blue (10.11.27).............. | 6·00 | 45·00 |
| 170 | | 3s. pale mauve (10.11.27)............ | 50·00 | 95·00 |

1932 (Aug). *Postal Fiscal stamps as Type F **6** of New Zealand optd with T **15**. W **43** of New Zealand. Thick, opaque, white chalk-surfaced "Cowan" paper. P 14.*

171		2s.6d. deep brown (B.).......................	16·00	48·00
172		5s. mauve (B.)..............................	20·00	50·00
173		10s. carmine-lake (B.).....................	45·00	£100
174		£1 pink (R.)..................................	70·00	£140
175		£2 bright purple (R.).....................		£750
176		£5 indigo-blue (R.)........................		£2250

The £2 and £5 values were primarily for fiscal use.

1935 (7 May). *Silver Jubilee. Optd with T **17**. P 14×13½.*

| 177 | 16 | 1d. lake..................................... | 30 | 30 |
| | | a. Perf 14×14½ .... | 90·00 | £170 |

178		2½d. grey-blue	60	65
179		6d. bright carmine	2·75	2·75
177/9 *Set of 3*			3·25	3·25

18 Samoan Girl

19 Apia

20 River scene

21 Chief and Wife

22 Canoe and house

23 R. L. Stevenson's home "Vaillma"

24 Stevenson's tomb

25 Lake Lanuto'o

26 Falefa Falls

(Recess D.L.R.)

1935 (7 Aug). *T* **18/26**. W **43** of New Zealand ("N Z" and Star). P 14×13½ (½d., 2½d., 2s., 3s.), 14 (2d.) or 13½×14 (others).

180	**18**	½d. green	10	35
		w. Wmk inverted		
181	**19**	1d. black and carmine	10	10
182	**20**	2d. black and orange	3·50	3·25
		aw. Wmk inverted		
		b. Perf 13½×14	4·00	4·25
		bw. Wmk inverted		
183	**21**	2½d. black and blue	10	10
184	**22**	4d. slate and sepia	70	15
185	**23**	6d. bright magenta	50	10
186	**24**	1s. violet and brown	30	10
187	**25**	2s. green and purple-brown	80	50
188	**26**	3s. blue and brown-orange	1·50	3·50
180/8 *Set of 9*			6·50	7·00

See also Nos. 200/3.

WESTERN SAMOA.
(27)

1935–42. Postal Fiscal stamps as Type F **6** of New Zealand optd with T **27**. W **43** of New Zealand. P 14.

(a) Thick, opaque chalk-surfaced "Cowan" paper (7.8.35).

189		2s.6d. deep brown (B.)	6·00	16·00
190		5s. green (B.)	13·00	23·00
191		10s. carmine-lake (B.)	60·00	75·00
192		£1 pink (B.)	55·00	£100
193		£2 bright purple (R.)	£160	£350
194		£5 indigo-blue (R.)	£225	£450

(b) Thin, hard chalk-surfaced "Wiggins Teape" paper (1941–42).

194*a*		5s. green (B.) (6.42)	£110	£120
194*b*		10s. pale carmine-lake (B.) (6.41)	£130	£140
194*c*		£2 bright purple (R.) (2.42)	£450	£700
194*d*		£5 indigo-blue (R.) (2.42)	£1100	£1400

The £2 and £5 values were primarily for fiscal use.
See also Nos. 207/14.

28 Coastal Scene

29 Map of Western Samoa

30 Samoan dancing party

31 Robert Louis Stevenson

(Des J. Berry (1d. and 1½d.). L. C. Mitchell (2½d. and 7d.). Recess B.W.)

1939 (29 Aug). *25th Anniv of New Zealand Control.* T **28/31**. W **98** of New Zealand. P 13½×14 or 14×13½ (7d.).

195	**28**	1d. olive-green and scarlet	1·00	25
196	**29**	1½d. light blue and red-brown	1·50	75
197	**30**	2½d. red-brown and blue	1·25	75
198	**31**	7d. violet and slate-green	8·00	4·00
195/8 *Set of 4*			10·50	5·25

32 Samoan Chief

33 Apia Post Office

(Recess B.W.)

1940 (2 Sept). W **98** of New Zealand (Mult "N Z" and Star). P 14×13½.

199	**32**	3d. on 1½d. brown	75	10

T **32** was not issued without surcharge.

(*T* **33**. Des L. C. Mitchell. Recess B.W.)

1944–49. As Nos. 180, 182/3 and T **33**. W **98** of New Zealand (Mult "N Z" and Star) (sideways on 2½d.). P 14 or 13½×14 (5d.)

200		½d. green	30	18·00
202		2d. black and orange	3·50	5·50
203		2½d. black and blue (1948)	4·75	35·00
205		5d. sepia and blue (8.6.49)	1·75	50
200/5 *Set of 4*			9·25	55·00

1945–53. Postal Fiscal stamps as Type F **6** of New Zealand optd with T **27**. W **98** of New Zealand. *Thin hard, chalk-surfaced "Wiggins Teape" paper.* P 14.

207		2s.6d. deep brown (B.) (6.45)	7·50	16·00
		w. Wmk inverted	9·50	13·00
208		5s. green (B.) (5.45)	16·00	16·00
		w. Wmk inverted	17·00	17·00
209		10s. carmine-lake (B.) (4.46)	20·00	17·00
		w. Wmk inverted	28·00	30·00
210		£1 pink (B.) (6.48)	£110	£170
		w. Wmk inverted		
211		30s. brown (8.48)	£180	£300
		w. Wmk inverted	£400	£550
212		£2 bright purple (R.) (11.47)	£190	£275
		w. Wmk inverted	£325	£425
213		£3 green (8.48)	£225	£375
		w. Wmk inverted	£425	£700
214		£5 indigo-blue (R) (1946)	£350	£450
		w. Wmk inverted (5.53)	£350	£450
207/10 *Set of 4*			£140	£190

The £2 to £5 values were mainly used for fiscal purposes.
The 5s., 10s., £1 and £2 were reissued in 1955 with a larger overprint, omitting the stop after "SAMOA".

WESTERN SAMOA
(34)

1946 (4 June). *Peace Issue.* Nos. 668, 670 and 674/5 of New Zealand optd with T **34** (reading up and down at sides on 2d.).

215		1d. green	40	15
		w. Wmk inverted	£150	
216		2d. purple (B.)	40	15
217		6d. chocolate and vermilion	40	15
218		8d. black and carmine (B.)	40	15
215/18 *Set of 4*			1·40	55

Nigeria

LAGOS

A British Consul was established at Lagos during 1853 as part of the anti-slavery policy, but the territory was not placed under British administration until occupied by the Royal Navy in August 1861. From 19 February 1866 Lagos was administered with Sierra Leone and from July 1874 as part of Gold Coast. It became a separate colony on 13 January 1886.

Although a postal service had been established by the British G.P.O. in April 1852 no postal markings were supplied to Lagos until 1859. The British G.P.O. retained control of the postal service until June 1863, when it became the responsibility of the colonial authorities.

CROWNED-CIRCLE HANDSTAMPS

CC 1

CC1   CC 1 LAGOS (19.12.1859) .... Price on cover   £3250

First recorded use of No. CC1 is 12 December 1871. It is later known used as a cancellation.

PRICES FOR STAMPS ON COVER	
Nos. 1/9	from × 10
Nos. 10/26	from × 8
Nos. 27/9	—
Nos. 30/8	from × 10
Nos. 39/41	—
No. 42	from × 20
Nos. 44/50	from × 8
Nos. 51/3	—
Nos. 54/60	from × 8
Nos. 61/3	—

PRINTERS. All the stamps of Lagos were typographed by D.L.R.

1

1874 (10 June)–**75**. Wmk Crown CC. P 12½.

1	1	1d. lilac-mauve	55·00	35·00
2		2d. blue	55·00	28·00
3		3d. red-brown (2.75)	85·00	42·00
5		4d. carmine	90·00	40·00
6		6d. blue-green	95·00	13·00
8		1s. orange (15½ mm) (2.75)..	£450	£140
		a. Value 16½ mm long (7.75)..	£300	60·00
1/8a Set of 6			£600	£200

1876–**79**. Wmk Crown CC. P 14.

10	1	1d. lilac-mauve	38·00	18·00
11		2d. blue	48·00	13·00
12		3d. red-brown	£100	18·00
13		3d. chestnut	£110	35·00
14		4d. carmine	£190	11·00
		a. Wmk sideways	£1100	£130
15		6d. green	95·00	6·00
16		1s. orange (value 16½ mm long) (1879)	£650	85·00
10/16 Set of 6			£1000	£130

1882 (June). Wmk Crown CA. P 14.

17	1	1d. lilac-mauve	20·00	11·00
18		2d. blue	£160	5·00
19		3d. chestnut	15·00	5·00
20		4d. carmine	£150	12·00
17/20 Set of 4			£300	30·00

1884 (Dec)–**86**. *New values and colours.* Wmk Crown CA. P 14.

21	1	½d. dull green (1885)	2·00	80
22		1d. rose-carmine	2·00	80
		w. Wmk inverted	£110	95·00
23		2d. grey	65·00	6·00
24		4d. pale violet	£110	8·50
25		6d. olive-green	8·00	45·00
26		1s. orange (3.85)	7·50	20·00
27		2s.6d. olive-black (1886)	£325	£275
28		5s. blue (1886)	£600	£450
29		10s. purple-brown (1886)	£1600	£1000
21/9 Set of 9			£2500	£1600
27s/9s Optd "Specimen" Set of 3			£425	

We would warn collectors against clever forgeries of Nos. 27 to 29 on genuinely watermarked paper.

A

2½ PENNY

B

1887 (Mar)–**1902**. Wmk Crown CA. P 14.

30	1	2d. dull mauve and blue	3·75	2·00
31		2½d. ultramarine (A) (1891)	4·00	1·75
		a. Larger letters of value (B)	22·00	17·00
		b. Blue (A)	80·00	50·00
32		3d. dull mauve and chestnut (4.91)	2·50	3·25
33		4d. dull mauve and black	2·25	1·75
34		5d. dull mauve and green (2.94)	2·00	11·00
35		6d. dull mauve and mauve	4·75	3·00
		a. Dull mauve and carmine (10.02)	5·00	12·00
36		7½d. dull mauve and carmine (2.94)	2·25	30·00
37		10d. dull mauve and yellow (2.94)	3·25	13·00
38		1s. yellow-green and black	5·50	24·00
		a. Blue-green and black	5·00	26·00
39		2s.6d. green and carmine	23·00	80·00
40		5s. green and blue	40·00	£150
41		10s. green and brown	85·00	£200
30/41 Set of 12			£160	£475
30s/41s Optd "Specimen" Set of 12			£275	

HALF PENNY

(2)   3

1893 (2 Aug). No. 33 surch with T 2 locally.

42	1	½d. on 4d. dull mauve and black	4·25	2·50
		a. Surch double	55·00	55·00
		b. Surch treble	£130	
		c. Error. ½d. on 2d. (No. 30)	—	£20000

There were two separate settings of No. 42. The most common, of which there were five separate printings, shows "HALF PENNY" 16 mm long and was applied as a horizontal pair or triplet. The scarcer setting, also applied as a triplet, shows "HALF PENNY" 16½ mm long.

Three examples of No. 42c are known, two unused and one used. Only the latter is in private hands.

1904 (22 Jan–Nov). Wmk Crown CA. P 14.

44	3	½d. dull green and green	1·50	5·50
45		1d. purple and black/red	1·00	15
46		2d. dull purple and blue	6·00	6·00
47		2½d. dull purple and blue/blue (B)	1·00	1·50
		aw. Wmk inverted	—	85·00
		b. Smaller letters of value as A	4·50	8·50
		bw. Wmk inverted	£130	£130
48		3d. dull purple and brown	2·25	1·75
49		6d. dull purple and mauve	35·00	10·00
50		1s. green and black	35·00	42·00
51		2s.6d. green and carmine	£100	£200
52		5s. green and blue	£130	£275
53		10s. green and brown (Nov)	£275	£750
44/53 Set of 10			£500	£1200
44s/53s Optd "Specimen" Set of 10			£180	

1904–**06**. Ordinary paper. Wmk Mult Crown CA. P 14.

54	3	½d. dull green and green (30.10.04)	7·50	2·50
		a. Chalk-surfaced paper (12.3.06)	10·00	1·75
55		1d. purple and black/red (22.10.04)	7·00	10
		a. Chalk-surfaced paper (21.9.05)	1·50	10
		aw. Wmk inverted	—	80·00
56		2d. dull purple and blue (2.05)	2·25	2·00
		a. Chalk-surfaced paper (25.9.06)	13·00	11·00
		aw. Wmk inverted		£120
57		2½d. dull purple and blue/blue (B) (chalk-surfaced paper) (13.10.05)	1·75	16·00
		a. Smaller letters of value as A	55·00	£120
58		3d. dull purple and brown (27.4.05)	3·50	1·25
		a. Chalk-surfaced paper (2.8.06)	15·00	1·75
		w. Wmk inverted		
59		6d. dull purple and mauve (31.10.04)	6·50	2·50
		a. Chalk-surfaced paper (1.3.06)	4·25	1·50
60		1s. green and black (15.10.04)	13·00	21·00
		a. Chalk-surfaced paper (4.06)	23·00	2·25
		w. Wmk inverted		
61		2s.6d. green and carmine (3.12.04)	16·00	60·00
		a. Chalk-surfaced paper (21.10.06)	35·00	60·00
62		5s. green and blue (1.05)	22·00	£100
		a. Chalk-surfaced paper (21.10.06)	70·00	£170
63		10s. green and brown (3.12.04)	65·00	£200
		a. Chalk-surfaced paper (12.3.06)	80·00	£190
54/63 Set of 10			£120	£350

Lagos was incorporated into the Colony and Protectorate of Southern Nigeria, previously formed from Niger Coast Protectorate and part of the Niger Company territories, on 16 February 1906. Stamps of Lagos were then authorised for use throughout Southern Nigeria.

NIGER COAST PROTECTORATE

OIL RIVERS PROTECTORATE

A British consulate for the Bights of Benin and Biafra was established in 1849 on the off-shore Spanish island of Fernando Po. In 1853 the appointment was divided with a consul for the Bight of Benin at Lagos. The consulate for the Bight of Biafra was transferred to Old Calabar in 1882.

A British protectorate was proclaimed over the coastal area, with the exceptions of the colony of Lagos and the centre of the Niger delta, on 5 June 1885. It was not, however, until July 1891 that steps were taken to set up an administration with a consul-general at Old Calabar and vice-consuls at some of the river ports.

The consulate-general at Old Calabar and the vice-consulates at Benin, Bonny, Brass, Forcados and Opobo acted as collection and distribution

centres for mail from November 1891, but were not recognised as post offices until 20 July 1892.

For a few months from July 1892 local administrative handstamps, as Type Z 1, were in use either as obliterators or in conjunction with the c.d.s.

Z 1

These oval handstamps are usually found on the 1892 overprinted issue, but the following are known on unoverprinted stamps of Great Britain:

1892.

BENIN

Stamps of GREAT BRITAIN cancelled with oval postmark, Type Z 1, inscribed "BENIN".

Z1	2½d. purple/blue (V.)	£1000

BONNY

Stamps of GREAT BRITAIN cancelled with oval postmark, Type Z 1, inscribed "BONNY".

Z2	2½d. purple/blue (V.)	£1000

BRASS RIVER

Stamps of GREAT BRITAIN cancelled with oval postmark, Type Z 1, inscribed "BRASS".

Z3	2½d. purple/blue (Blk.)	£750

OLD CALABAR RIVER

Stamps of GREAT BRITAIN cancelled with oval postmark, Type Z 1, inscribed "OLD CALABAR".

Z4	2d. purple/blue (Blk.)	£750

Stamps of GREAT BRITAIN cancelled "BRITISH VICE-CONSULATE OLD CALABAR" within double-lined circle.

Z5	2½d. purple/blue (V.)	£450
Z6	5d. dull purple and blue (V.)	

For later use of Type Z 1 and the circular Vice-Consulate marks see note beneath No. 6.

Z 2

Unoverprinted stamps of Great Britain remained officially valid for postage in the Protectorate until 30 September 1892, but were available from post offices in the Niger Company Territories up to the end of 1899. The two areas were so closely linked geographically that offices in the Protectorate continued to accept letters franked with Great Britain stamps until the reorganisation of 1900. The listing below covers confirmed examples, known on cover or piece, the prices quoted being for the latter.

1892–**99**. Stamps of GREAT BRITAIN cancelled with circular postmarks as Type Z 2.

BENIN RIVER

Z7	2d. green and carmine	
Z8	2½d. purple/blue	£550
Z9	3d. purple/yellow	£550
Z10	5d. dull purple and blue	
Z11	1s. green	

BONNY RIVER

Z12	½d. vermilion	£375
Z12a	1d. lilac	£325
Z13	2½d. purple/blue	£275
Z14	5d. dull purple and blue	£375
Z15	6d. deep purple/red	£750

BRASS RIVER

Z16	1½d. dull purple and green	£800
Z17	2½d. purple/blue	£700
Z17a	2½d. purple/blue (squared-circle cancellation)	£850
Z18	6d. purple/red	£750

FORCADOS RIVER

Z19	1d. lilac	£600
Z20	2½d. purple/blue	
Z21	5d. dull purple and blue (m/s cancellation)	
Z22	10d. dull purple and carmine	

OLD CALABAR RIVER

Z23	½d. vermilion	£325
Z24	1d. lilac	£275
Z25	1½d. dull purple and green	£375
Z26	2d. green and vermilion	£375
Z27	2½d. purple/blue	£275
Z28	5d. dull purple and blue	£375
Z29	6d. purple/red	£375
Z30	1s. green	£500

OPOBO RIVER

Z31	2½d. purple/blue	£300
Z32	10d. dull purple and carmine	£600

Some later covers are known franked with G.B. stamps, but the origin of the stamps involved is uncertain.

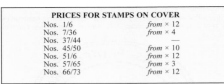

PRICES FOR STAMPS ON COVER

Nos. 1/6	from × 12
Nos. 7/36	from × 4
Nos. 37/44	
Nos. 45/50	from × 10
Nos. 51/6	from × 12
Nos. 57/65	from × 3
Nos. 66/73	from × 12

BRITISH PROTECTORATE

(1) (2)

OIL RIVERS

1892 (20 July)–94. *Nos. 172, 197, 200/1, 207a and 211 of Great Britain optd by D.L.R. with T* **1**.

1	½d. vermilion	12·00	8·00
2	1d. lilac	7·00	8·00
	a. Opt reversed "OIL RIVERS" at top	£7500	
	b. Bisected (½d.) (on cover)	†	£2500
3	2d. grey-green and carmine	25·00	8·00
	a. Bisected (1d.) (on cover)	†	£2500
4	2½d. purple/*blue*	6·50	2·25
5	5d. dull purple and blue (Die II (No. 207a))	10·00	6·50
	a. On Die I (No. 207)		
6	1s. dull green	55·00	80·00
1/6 *Set of 6*		£100	£100
1s/6s H/S "Specimen" *Set of 6*		£275	

Nos. 2b and 3a were used at Bonny River during August and September 1894.

Die II of the 5d. shows thin vertical lines to the right of "5d.". On Die I there are square dots in this position.

OVAL HANDSTAMPS. In addition to Nos. Z1/4 postmarks as Type Z **1** are also known used on the 1892–94 overprinted issue from the following offices:

Bakana (Nos. 2, 4/6)
Benin (Nos. 1/6)
Bonny (No. 2)
Brass (Nos. 3/5)
Buguma (Nos. 4 and 6)
Old Calabar (No. 4)
Opobo (Nos. 1/3)
Sombreiro River (Nos. 1/6)

The Vice-Consulate marks, as Nos. Z5/6, are also known struck on examples of No. 4 from Bonny, Forcados or Old Calabar.

Nos. 2 to 6 surcharged locally

1893 (3 Sept). *Issued at Old Calabar. Surch with T* **2** *and then bisected.*

7	½d. on half of 1d. (R.)	£150	£140
	a. Unsevered pair	£475	£450
	ab. Surch inverted and dividing line reversed (unsevered pair)	—	£13000
	b. Surch reversed (dividing line running from left to right) (unsevered pair)	—	£13000
	c. Straight top to "1" in ½	£350	£350
	d. "½" omitted		
	e. Surch double (unsevered pair with normal)	—	£1600
	f. Vert *se-tenant* pair. Nos. 7a/8a	—	£16000
8	½d. on half of 1d. (V.)	£4750	£4250
	a. Unsevered pair	£13000	£12000
	b. Surch double (pair)	£19000	

The surcharge was applied in a setting covering one horizontal row at a time. Violet ink was used for the top row in the first sheet, but was then replaced with red.

(3) (4)

In T **3** "HALF" measures 9½ mm and "PENNY" 12½ mm with space 1½ mm between the words. Bar 14½ mm ending below the stop. The "F" is nearly always defective.

In T **4** "HALF" is 8½ mm, "PENNY" 12½ mm, spacing 2½ mm, and bar 16 mm, extending beyond the stop.

HALF PENNY.
5 (Stop after "N")

HALF PENNY
6 (No stop after "N")

In T **5** the "P" and "Y" are raised, and the space between the words is about 4 mm. Bar is short, approx 13½ mm. T **6** is similar but without the stop after "N".

Half Penny
(7)

Half Penny
(8)

In T **7** the "a" and "e" are narrow and have a short upward terminal hook. The "1" has a very small hook. The letters "nny" have curved serifs, and the distance between the words is 5½ mm.

In T **8** the "a" and "e" are wider. The "1" has a wider hook. The letters "nny" have straight serifs, and the distance between the words is 4¼ mm.

HALF PENNY.
(9)

HALF PENNY
(10)

1893 (Dec). *Issue at Old Calabar. Nos. 3/4 handstamped.*

(a) With T **3**.

9	½d. on 2d. (V.)	£500	£325
	a. Surch inverted	£11000	
	b. Surch diagonal (up or down)	£5000	
	c. Surch vertical (up or down)	£6500	
10	½d. on 2½d. (Verm.)	£11000	
10a	½d. on 2½d. (Verm.)	£27000	

(b) With T **4**.

11	½d. on 2½d. (G.)	£300	£250
	a. Surch double	£2500	£2500
	b. Surch diagonally inverted	£11000	
12	½d. on 2½d. (C.)	£1000	£300
13	½d. on 2½d. (C.)	£400	£425
	a. Surch omitted (in pair)		
14	½d. on 2½d. (B.)	£350	£400
15	½d. on 2½d. (Blk.)	£4000	
	a. Surch inverted	£11000	
	b. Surch diagonal inverted (up or down)	£9000	
16	½d. on 2½d. (B.-Blk.)	£4750	

(c) With T **5**.

17	½d. on 2½d. (Verm.)	£1200	£200
	a. Surch double	—	£1600
	b. Surch vertical (up)	—	£5500

(d) With T **6**.

18	½d. on 2d. (V.)	£750	£400
19	½d. on 2½d. (Verm.)	£400	£300
	a. Surch inverted	£6500	
	b. Surch double	—	£2000
	c. Surch diagonal (up or down)	£3750	
	d. Surch omitted (in strip of 3)	£22000	
	e. Surch vertical (up or down)	£11000	
	f. Surch diagonal, inverted (up or down)	£5500	

(e) With T **7**.

20	½d. on 2d. (V.)	£400	£250
	a. Surch double	—	£6500
	b. Surch vertical (up or down)	£6500	
	c. Surch diagonal (up or down)	£6500	
	d. Surch diagonal (inverted)	£11000	
	e. Surch inverted		
21	½d. on 2½d. (Verm.)	£325	£180
	a. Surch double	£4500	
	b. Surch vertical (up or down)	£6500	
	c. Surch inverted	£8500	
	d. Surch diagonal (up or down)	£4750	
	e. Surch diagonal, inverted (up)	£11000	
22	½d. on 2½d. (B.)	£16000	£16000
23	½d. on 2½d. (C.)	£16000	
24	½d. on 2½d. (V.)	£7500	

(f) With T **8**.

25	½d. on 2½d. (Verm)	£475	£600
	a. Surch diagonal (up)	£6500	
26	½d. on 2½d. (B.)	£27000	
27	½d. on 2½d. (G.)	£425	£550
	a. Surch double	£5500	
28	½d. on 2½d. (C.)	£20000	£20000

(g) With T **9**.

29	½d. on 2d. (V.)	£375	£325
30	½d. on 2d. (B.)	£1700	£700
	a. Surch double		
31	½d. on 2½d. (Verm.)	£500	£600
	a. Surch double		
32	½d. on 2½d. (B.)	£400	£350
33	½d. on 2½d. (G.)	£425	£450
	a. Surch double (G.)	£2000	
	b. Surch double (G. + Verm.)		
34	½d. on 2½d. (V.)	£5500	

(h) With T **10**.

35	½d. on 2½d. (G.)	£475	£450
36	½d. on 2½d. (Verm.)	£7500	

Various types of surcharges on Nos. 9 to 36 were printed on the same sheet, and different types in different colours may be found *se-tenant* (*Prices, from £3750 per pair, unused*).

Unused examples of Nos. 11, 12 and 31 with surcharge omitted in pair with normal (No. 11) or as the first and third stamps in a strip of three (Nos. 12 and 31) exist in the Royal collection.

One Shilling
(11)

5/-
(12)

1893 (Dec). *Issued at Old Calabar. Nos. 3 and 5/6 handstamped.*

(a) With T **11**.

37	1s. on 2d. (V.)	£450	£350
	a. Surch inverted	£8500	
	b. Surch vertical (up or down)	£5500	
	c. Surch diagonal (up or down)	£6500	
	d. Surch diagonal, inverted (up or down)	£6500	
	e. Pair, Nos. 37 and 38	£4250	
38	1s. on 2d. (Verm.)	£600	£3750
	a. Surch inverted	£11000	
	b. Surch diagonal (up or down)	£8500	
	c. Surch vertical (up or down)	£11000	
39	1s. on 2d. (Blk.)	£5500	
	a. Surch inverted	£16000	
	b. Surch vertical (up or down)	£13000	
	c. Surch diagonal (up)	£13000	

(b) As T **12**.

40	5s. on 2d. (V.)	£9000	£10000
	a. Surch inverted	£38000	
	b. Surch vertical (up or down)	£32000	£32000
	c. Surch diagonal (down)	£32000	
41	10s. on 5d. (Verm.)	£6500	£8500
	a. Surch inverted	£32000	
	b. Surch vertical (up or down)	£32000	
	c. Surch diagonal (down)		
42	20s. on 1s. (V.)	£110000	
	a. Surch inverted	£130000	
43	20s. on 1s. (Verm.)	£110000	
44	20s. on 1s. (Blk.)	£110000	

There are two main settings of the "One Shilling" surcharge:—

Type A. The "O" is over the "hi" of "Shilling" and the downstrokes on the "n" in "One", if extended, would meet the "ll" of "Shilling". The "g" is always raised. Type A is known in all three colours from one sheet of 120.

Type B. The "O" is over the first "i" of "Shilling" and the downstrokes of the "n" would meet the "li" of "Shilling". Type B is known in violet (two sheets) and vermilion (one sheet).

An example of No. 38 with surcharge diagonal, inverted exists on the Royal collection.

NIGER COAST PROTECTORATE

The protectorate was extended into the interior and the name changed to Niger Coast Protectorate on 12 May 1893.

PERFORATION. There are a number of small variations in the perforation of the Waterlow issues of 1893 to 1898 which were due to irregularity of the pins rather than different perforators.

In the following lists, stamps perf 12, 12½, 13 or compound are described as perf 12–13, stamps perf 13½, 14 or compound are described as perf 13½–14 and those perf 14½, 15 or compound are listed as perf 14½–15. In addition the 13½–14 perforation exists compound with 14½–15 and with 12–13, whilst perf 15½–16 comes from a separate perforator.

13 14

(Des G. D. Drummond. Recess Waterlow)

1894 (1 Jan). *T* **13** *(with* "OIL RIVERS" *obliterated and* "NIGER COAST" *in top margin). Various frames. Thick and thin papers. No wmk. P* 14½–15.

45	½d. vermilion	4·25	4·75
	a. Perf 13½–14	7·00	9·00
46	1d. pale blue	6·00	3·25
	a. Bisected (½d.) (on cover)	†	£550
	b. Dull blue	3·75	3·25
	ba. Bisected (½d.) (on cover)	†	£450
	c. Perf 13½–14	4·00	
	d. Perf 13½–14, comp 12–13	—	20·00
	e. Perf 12–13		55·00
47	2d. green	30·00	27·00
	a. Imperf between (horiz pair)	†	£14000
	b. Bisected (1d.) (on cover)	†	£700
	c. Perf 14½–15, comp 13½–14		
	d. Perf 13½–14	19·00	13·00
	e. Perf 13½–14, comp 12–13	48·00	29·00
	f. Perf 12–13		
48	2½d. carmine-lake	8·50	3·50
	a. Perf 13½–14	15·00	12·00
	b. Perf 13½–14, comp 12–13	25·00	25·00
	c. Perf 12–13	£100	£100
49	5d. grey-lilac	17·00	12·00
	a. Lilac (1894)	14·00	18·00
	b. Perf 13½–14	14·00	13·00
	c. Perf 13½–14, comp 12–13	45·00	
50	1s. black	14·00	12·00
	a. Perf 14½–15, comp 13½–14	60·00	
	b. Perf 13½–14	28·00	22·00
	c. Perf 13½–14, comp 12–13	28·00	25·00
	d. Perf 14½–15, comp 13½–14	50·00	38·00
45/50 *Set of 6*		55·00	42·00

There were three printings of each value, in November 1893, Jan 1894 and March 1894.

Nos. 46a, 46ba and 47b were used at Bonny River during August and September 1894.

(Recess Waterlow)

1894 (May). *T* **14** *(various frames). No wmk. P* 14½–15.

51	½d. yellow-green	4·75	5·00
	a. Deep green	5·50	6·00
	b. Perf 14½–15, comp 13½–14		
	c. Perf 13½–14	9·50	9·00
	d. Perf 13½–14, comp 12–13	24·00	20·00
52	1d. orange-vermilion	16·00	10·00
	a. Vermilion	13·00	8·50
	b. Bisected diagonally (½d.) (on cover)	†	£500
	c. Perf 15½–16		50·00
	d. Perf 13½–14	24·00	

53	e. Perf 13½–14, comp 12–13	—	18·00
	2d. lake	30·00	6·50
	a. Bisected diagonally (1d.) (on cover).		
	b. Perf 13½–14	40·00	9·00
	c. Perf 13½–14, comp 12–13	50·00	20·00
54	2½d. blue	15·00	3·75
	a. Pale blue	8·50	7·50
	b. Perf 13½–14	24·00	15·00
55	5d. purple	6·50	5·50
	a. Deep violet	6·00	5·50
56	1s. black	48·00	17·00
	b. Perf 13½–14	48·00	7·00
	b. Perf 13½–14, comp 12–13	60·00	35·00
51/6	Set of 6	£100	32·00

Nos. 52b and 53a were used at Bonny River during August and September 1894.

(15) (16) (17)

1894. Provisionals. Issued at Opobo.

(a) Nos. 46b and 46 bisected vertically and surch with T **15** *(May–June).*

57	"½" on half of 1d. dull blue (R.) (May)...	£1400	£475
	a. Surch inverted (in strip of 3 with normals)	£13000	
58	"½" on half of 1d. pale blue (R.) (June)...	£800	£325
	a. Surch tête-bêche (pair)	£4750	
	b. Surcharge inverted		£350
	c. Perf 13½–14	—	£350
	d. Perf 13½–14, comp 12–13	—	£400

(b) No. 3 bisected vertically and surch.

(i) With T **16** *(12 mm high). (June–Oct).*

59	"1" on half of 2d. (Verm.)	£1700	£350
	a. Surch double	£5500	£1200
	b. Surch inverted	—	£1600
	c. Unsevered pair	†	£2500

(ii) Smaller "1" *(4¾ mm high).*

60	"1" on half of 2d. (C.)	—	£7500

(iii) Smaller "1" *(3¾ mm high).*

61	"1" on half of 2d. (C.)		

Nos. 60 and 61 exist se-tenant. *(Price £27000 used)*

(c) No. 52a (Perf 14½–15) bisected, surch with T **15** *(Aug–Sept).*

62	"½" on half of 1d. vermilion (Blk.)..........	£4500	£1000
63	"½" on half of 1d. vermilion (V.)	£3250	£650
64	"½" on half of 1d. vermilion (B.)	£2500	£425
	a. "½" double	—	£2500
	b. Perf 13½–14		£2500
	c. Perf 13½–14, comp 12–13		

The stamp is found divided down the middle and also diagonally.

1894 (10 Aug). Issued at Old Calabar. No. 54 surch with T **17** and two bars through value at foot.

65	½d. on 2½d. blue	£375	£225
	a. Surch double	£4250	£1500
	b. "OIE" for "ONE"	£1600	£1000
	c. Ditto. Surch double	—	£6500

There are eight types in the setting of Type **17**, arranged as a horizontal row. No. 65b occurred on No. 8 in the setting at some point during surcharging.

(Recess Waterlow)

1897 (Mar)**–98.** As T **14** (various frames). Wmk Crown CA. P 14½–15.

66	½d. green (7.97)	3·50	1·50
	a. Sage-green	4·25	2·25
	b. Perf 13½–14	3·25	3·00
	c. Perf 15½–16	12·00	6·50
	d. Perf 13½–14, comp 12–13	24·00	15·00
	x. Wmk reversed	90·00	
67	1d. orange–vermilion	4·50	1·50
	a. Vermilion	4·50	1·50
	b. Imperf vert (horiz pair)	£10000	
	c. Perf 15½–16	8·50	7·50
	d. Perf 13½–14	2·50	2·75
	e. Perf 13½–14, comp 12–13	18·00	11·00
	f. Perf 13½–14, comp 14½–15	—	20·00
68	2d. lake (7.97)	1·75	2·00
	a. Perf 15½–16	4·00	2·50
	b. Perf 13½–14	4·00	3·75
	c. Perf 13½–14, comp 12–13	27·00	
	x. Wmk reversed	90·00	90·00
69	2½d. slate-blue (8.97)	7·50	2·00
	a. Deep bright blue	9·00	2·25
	b. Perf 13½–14	6·00	4·00
	c. Perf 15½–16	—	35·00
	w. Wmk inverted	—	£150
70	5d. red-violet (p 13½–14) (1898)..........	9·00	65·00
	a. Purple	9·00	70·00
	b. Perf 13½–14, comp 12–13	21·00	£110
	b. Perf 14½–15		£120
71	6d. yellow-brown (6.98)	7·00	6·50
	a. Perf 15½–16	8·50	12·00
	b. Perf 13½–14	50·00	30·00
	x. Wmk reversed		
72	1s. black (1898)	15·00	29·00
	a. Perf 13½–14	14·00	30·00
	b. Perf 13½–14, comp 12–13	45·00	
73	2s.6d. olive-bistre (6.98)	60·00	£130
	a. Perf 15½–16	60·00	£140
	b. Perf 13½–14	22·00	80·00
74	10s. deep violet (6.98)	£110	£180
	a. Bright violet	£110	£180
	b. Perf 13½–14	90·00	£170
	ba. Bright violet	90·00	£170
	c. Perf 13½–14, comp 12–13	£180	£275
66/74	Set of 9	£140	£325
71s, 73s/4s Optd "Specimen" Set of 3		£250	

Owing to temporary shortages in Southern Nigeria, the above issue was again in use at various times from 1902 until 1907.

On 1 January 1900 the Niger Coast Protectorate together with the southern portion of the Niger Company Territories became the protectorate of Southern Nigeria.

NIGER COMPANY TERRITORIES

Following the development of trade along the Niger, British commercial interests formed the United African Company in 1879 which became the National African Company in 1882 and the Royal Niger Company in 1886. A charter was granted to the Company in the same year to administer territory along the Rivers Niger and Benue over which a British protectorate had been proclaimed in June 1885. The Company's territories extended to the Niger delta to provide access to the interior.

Post Offices were opened at Akassa (1887), Burutu (1896), Lokoja (1899) and Abutshi (1899). The stamps of Great Britain were used from 1888.

On the establishment of postal services in 1887 the Company arranged with the British G.P.O. that unstamped mail marked with their handstamps would be delivered in Great Britain, the recipients only being charged the normal rate of postage from West Africa. This system was difficult to administer, however, so the British authorities agreed in 1888 to the supply of G.B. stamps for use at the Company post offices.

Initially the stamps on such covers were left uncancelled until the mail arrived in the United Kingdom, the Company handstamp being struck elsewhere on the address side. This method continued to be used until early 1896, although a number of covers from the twelve months prior to that date do show the Company handstamp cancelling the stamps. Some of these covers were later recancelled on arrival in Great Britain. From May 1896 the postage stamps were cancelled in the Niger Territories.

In the following listings no attempt has been made to cover the use of the Company marks on the reverse of envelopes.

Dates given are those of earliest known postmarks. Colour of postmarks in brackets. Where two or more colours are given, price is for cheapest. Illustrations are reduced to two-thirds linear of the actual size.

Stamps of GREAT BRITAIN *cancelled as indicated below.*

ABUTSHI

1899. Cancelled as T **8**, but inscribed "THE ROYAL NIGER CO. C. & L. ABUTSHI" with "CUSTOMS (date) OFFICE" in central oval.

Z1	½d. vermilion (V.)	£700	
Z2	1d. lilac (V.)	£475	
Z3	2½d. purple/blue (V.)	£700	
Z4	5d. dull purple and blue (V.)	£750	
Z5	10d. dull purple and carmine (V.)	£850	
Z6	2s.6d. deep lilac (V.)	£950	

AKASSA

The listings for Nos. Z7/15a are for *covers* on which the Akassa handstamp appears on the front, but is *not* used as a cancellation for the G.B. stamps. Examples of Nos. Z16/26 occur, from 1895–96, with the handstamp struck on the front of the cover away from the stamps, or, from 1896, used as a cancellation. The prices quoted are for *single stamps* showing the cancellation; covers from either period being worth considerably more. On Nos. Z29/42b the handstamp was used as a cancellation and the prices quoted are for *single stamps*.

1   2

1888–90. Cancelled as T **3**, but with Maltese cross each side of "AKASSA". Size 36× 22 mm.

Z7	6d. deep purple/red (V.)	£1300	

1889–94. Size 39× 24 mm.

Z8	1	2½d. purple/blue (V.)	£650
Z9		3d. purple/yellow (V.)	
Z10		5d. dull purple and blue (V.)	
Z11		6d. deep purple/red (V.)	£425
Z12		10d. dull purple and carmine (V.)	
Z12a		1s. green (V.)	
Z13		2s.6d. deep lilac (V.)	

1894–95.

Z14	2	1d. lilac (V.)	£450
Z15		2½d. purple/lilac (V.)	
Z15a		2s.6d. deep lilac (V.)	

3   4

1895. Size 39× 25 mm.

Z16	3	2½d. purple/blue (V.)	

1895–99.

Z17	4	½d. vermilion (V.)	90·00
Z18		1d. lilac (V.)	85·00
Z19		2d. green and carmine (V.)	£450
Z20		2½d. purple/blue (V.)	42·00
Z21		3d. purple/yellow (V.)	£325
Z22		5d. dull purple and blue (V.)	65·00
Z23		6d. deep purple/red (V.)	£325
Z24		9d. dull purple and blue (V.)	£450
Z25		10d. dull purple and carmine (V.)	£110
Z26		2s.6d. deep lilac (V.)	£250

5

1897–99.

Z29	5	½d. vermilion (V.)	70·00
Z30		1d. lilac (V.)	55·00
		a. "RECD" for year in postmark	£650
Z31		2d. green and carmine (V.)	£250
Z32		2½d. purple/blue (V.)	65·00
		a. "RECD" for year in postmark (1898)....	£1000
Z33		3d. purple/yellow (V.)	£225
Z34		4d. green and brown (V.)	£325
Z35		4½d. green and carmine (V.)	£900
Z36		5d. dull purple and blue (V.)	85·00
Z37		6d. deep purple/red (V.)	£275
Z38		9d. dull purple and blue (V.)	£450
Z39		10d. dull purple and carmine (V.)	£190
Z40		1s. green (V.)	£850
Z41		2s.6d. deep lilac (V.)	£350

1899. Cancelled as T **7** but inscribed "AKASSA".

Z42	5d. dull purple and blue (V.)	£1000	

1899. Cancelled as T **4**, but "CUSTOMS DEPT" in place of "POST OFFICE".

Z42a	1d. lilac (V.)	£700	
Z42b	2½d. purple/blue (V.)	£700	

BURUTU

6

1896–99. Cancelled as T **6**, "BURUTU" in sans-serif caps. Size 44× 24 mm.

Z43	6	½d. vermilion (V., Blk)	£110
Z44		1d. lilac (V.)	95·00
Z45		1½d. dull purple and green (V.)	£425
Z46		2d. green and carmine (V.)	£250
Z47		2½d. purple/blue (V., Blk.)	42·00
Z48		3d. purple/yellow (V., Blk)	£250
Z49		4d. green and brown (V.)	£275
Z50		5d. dull purple and blue (V., Blk.)	90·00
Z51		6d. deep purple/red (V.)	£300
Z52		9d. dull purple and blue (V.)	£450
Z53		10d. dull purple and carmine (V., Blk.)....	£150
Z54		1s. green (V.)	£800
Z55		2s.6d. lilac (V.)	£300

1898–99. Cancelled as T **4**, but inscribed "BURUTU" in serifed caps. Size 44× 27 mm.

Z56	½d. vermilion (V., Blk)	75·00	
Z57	1d. lilac (V., Blk.)	55·00	
Z58	2d. green and carmine (V.)	£350	
Z59	2½d. purple/blue (V., Blk.)	60·00	
Z60	3d. purple/yellow (V.)	£300	
Z61	4d. green and brown (V.)	£325	
Z62	4½d. green and carmine (V.)	£900	
Z63	5d. dull purple and blue (V.)	90·00	
Z64	6d. deep purple/red (V.)	£325	
Z65	9d. dull purple and blue (V.)	£475	
Z66	10d. dull purple and carmine (V., Blk) ...	£140	
Z67	2s.6d. lilac (V., Blk.)	£350	

7

1898–99.

Z68	7	1d. lilac (V.)	
Z69		2½d. purple/blue (V.)	£325

1899. Cancelled as T **4**, but inscribed "CUSTOM DEPT. BURUTU".

Z70	1d. lilac (V.)		

LOKOJA

8

1899.

Z71	8	½d. vermilion (V.)	£120
Z72		1d. lilac (V.)	85·00
Z73		2½d. purple/blue (V.)	£275
Z74		5d. dull purple and blue (V.)	£450
Z75		10d. dull purple and carmine (V.)	£500
Z76		2s.6d. deep lilac (V.)	£650

AGENT GENERAL NIGER TERRITORIES

The listings for Nos. Z78/9 are for covers showing a handstamp struck on the address side, but *not* used as a cancellation for the G.B. stamp.

1894–99. *Cancelled as T* **8**, *but inscribed* "AGENT GENERAL NIGER TERRITORIES".

Z77	1d. lilac (V.)		
Z78	2½d. purple/*blue* (V.)		£1300

1895–96. *Cancelled as T* **7**, *but inscribed as Nos.* Z77/8.

Z79	2½d. purple/*blue* (V.)		£1300
Z80	5d. dull purple and blue (V.)		
Z81	10d. dull purple and carmine (V.)		
Z82	2s.6d. deep lilac (V.)		

It is now believed that these cancellations may have been used at Asaba. They all occur on covers with Akassa handstamps, often of different dates.

The British Government purchased the Royal Niger Company territories and from 1 January 1900 they were incorporated into the protectorates of Northern and Southern Nigeria. Of the post offices listed above, only Lokoja was then situated in Northern Nigeria, the remainder joining Niger Coast in forming Southern Nigeria.

Issues for Northern Nigeria did not reach Lokoja until sometime in March 1900 and the post office there continued to use unoverprinted stamps of Great Britain until these supplies arrived.

NORTHERN NIGERIA

The protectorate of Northern Nigeria was formed on 1 January 1900 from the northern part of the Niger Company Territories. Only one post office existed in this area, at Lokoja, and this continued to use unoverprinted stamps of GREAT BRITAIN until the arrival of Nos. 1/9 during April 1900.

PRICES FOR STAMPS ON COVER	
Nos. 1/7	*from* × 6
Nos. 8/9	—
Nos. 10/16	*from* × 5
Nos. 17/19	—
Nos. 20/6	*from* × 5
No. 27	—
Nos. 28/37	*from* × 5
Nos. 38/9	—
Nos. 40/9	*from* × 5
Nos. 50/2	—

PRINTERS. All issues were typographed by De La Rue & Co.

1 2

1900 (Apr). Wmk Crown CA. P 14.

1	**1**	½d. dull mauve and green	3·25	14·00
2		1d. dull mauve and carmine	3·50	3·75
3		2d. dull mauve and yellow	12·00	48·00
4		2½d. dull mauve and ultramarine	10·00	38·00
5	**2**	5d. dull mauve and chestnut	24·00	50·00
6		6d. dull mauve and violet	21·00	32·00
7	**1**	1s. green and black	24·00	70·00
8		2s.6d. green and ultramarine	£110	£450
9		10s. green and brown	£250	£650
1/9 *Set of 9*			£400	£1200
1s/9s Optd "Specimen" *Set of 9*			£190	

Examples of all values are known showing a forged Northern Nigeria postmark dated "AU 14 1900".

3 4

1902 (1 July). Wmk Crown CA. P 14.

10	**3**	½d. dull purple and green	2·00	1·00
		w. Wmk inverted	—	£225
11		1d. dull purple and carmine	2·25	75
12		2d. dull purple and yellow	2·00	3·00
13		2½d. dull purple and ultramarine	1·50	9·50
14	**4**	5d. dull purple and chestnut	3·00	5·00
15		6d. dull purple and violet	9·00	4·50
16	**3**	1s. green and black	3·50	6·00
17		2s.6d. green and ultramarine	8·00	50·00
18		10s. green and brown	48·00	55·00
10/18 *Set of 9*			70·00	£120
10s/18s Optd "Specimen" *Set of 9*			£150	

1904 (Apr). Wmk Mult Crown CA. P 14.

19	**4**	£25 green and carmine		£48000

No. 19, although utilising the "POSTAGE & REVENUE" Key type, was intended to pay the fiscal fee for liquor licences.

1905 (Aug)–**07.** *Ordinary paper.* Wmk Mult Crown CA. P 14.

20	**3**	½d. dull purple and green (10.05)	21·00	8·00
		a. Chalk-surfaced paper (1906)	5·50	5·00
21		1d. dull purple and carmine	20·00	1·00
		a. Chalk-surfaced paper (1906)	5·50	1·25
22		2d. dull purple and yellow (10.05)	14·00	32·00
		a. Chalk-surfaced paper (1907)	19·00	27·00
23		2½d. dull purple and ultramarine (10.05)	6·50	8·00
24	**4**	5d. dull purple and chestnut (10.05)	24·00	70·00
		a. Chalk-surfaced paper (1907)	35·00	70·00
25		6d. dull purple and violet (10.05)	27·00	55·00
		a. Chalk-surfaced paper (1906)	40·00	40·00
26	**3**	1s. green and black (10.05)	55·00	90·00

---

		a. Chalk-surfaced paper (1906)	22·00	48·00
27		2s.6d. green and ultramarine (10.05)	48·00	50·00
		a. Chalk-surfaced paper (1906)	30·00	48·00
20/7 *Set of 8*			£120	£225

5 6

1910 (30 Jan)–**11.** *Ordinary paper* (½d. *to* 2½d.) *or chalk-surfaced paper (others).* Wmk Mult Crown. CA. P 14.

28	**3**	½d. green (15.4.10)	2·00	1·25
29		1d. carmine	2·00	1·25
30		2d. grey (26.10.11)	4·50	2·25
31		2½d. blue (10.10)	2·25	7·00
32	**4**	3d. purple/*yellow*	3·50	75
34		5d. dull purple and olive-green (26.2.11)	4·00	13·00
35		6d. dull purple and purple (10.11.10)	6·00	17·00
		a. Dull and bright purple (1911)	5·00	6·00
36	**3**	1s. black/*green* (10.11.10)	2·25	75
37		2s.6d. black and red/*blue* (15.3.11)	10·00	30·00
38	**4**	5s. green and red/*yellow* (10.9.11)	23·00	75·00
39	**3**	10s. green and red/*green* (15.3.11)	42·00	48·00
28/39 *Set of 11*			90·00	£170
28s/39s Optd "Specimen" *Set of 11*			£250	

1912. *Ordinary paper* (½d., 1d., 2d.) *or chalk-surfaced paper (others).* Wmk Mult Crown CA. P 14.

40	**5**	½d. deep green	1·75	60
41		1d. red	1·75	60
42		2d. grey	3·00	8·50
43	**6**	3d. purple/*yellow*	2·25	1·25
44		4d. black and red/*yellow*	1·25	2·25
45		5d. dull purple and olive–green	4·00	12·00
46		6d. dull and bright purple	4·00	4·25
47		9d. dull purple and carmine	2·00	2·00
48	**5**	1s. black/*green*	4·50	2·25
49		2s.6d. black and red/*blue*	7·00	45·00
50	**6**	5s. green and red/*yellow*	20·00	80·00
51	**5**	10s. green and red/*green*	38·00	48·00
52	**6**	£1 purple and black/*red*	£170	£110
40/52 *Set of 13*			£225	£275
40s/52s Optd "Specimen" *Set of 13*			£200	

Examples of most values are known showing forged postmarks of Lokoja dated "MR 22 12" or Minna dated "JN 16 1913". These forged postmarks have also been seen on examples of earlier issues.

On 1 January 1914 Northern Nigeria became part of Nigeria.

SOUTHERN NIGERIA

The Colony and Protectorate of Southern Nigeria was formed on 1 January 1900 by the amalgamation of Niger Coast Protectorate with the southern part of the Niger Territories. Lagos was incorporated into the territory on 1 May 1906.

The stamps of NIGER COAST PROTECTORATE were used in Southern Nigeria until the introduction of Nos. 1/9, and also during a shortage of these values in mid-1902. The issues of LAGOS were utilized throughout Southern Nigeria after 1 May 1906 until supplies were exhausted.

PRICES FOR STAMPS ON COVER	
Nos. 1/7	*from* × 8
Nos. 8/9	—
Nos. 10/18	*from* × 4
Nos. 19/20	—
Nos. 21/30	*from* × 4
Nos. 31/2	—
Nos. 33/42	*from* × 4
Nos. 43/4	—
Nos. 45/53	*from* × 4
Nos. 55/6	—

PRINTERS. All issues of Southern Nigeria were typographed by De La Rue & Co, Ltd, London.

1 2 3

1901 (Mar)–**02.** Wmk Crown CA. P 14.

1	**1**	½d. black and pale green	1·75	2·25
		a. Sepia and green (1902)	2·25	2·50
2		1d. black and carmine	1·40	1·50
		a. Sepia and carmine (1902)	2·25	1·75
3		2d. black and red-brown	3·25	3·75
4		4d. black and sage-green	2·75	19·00
5		6d. black and purple	2·75	6·50
6		1s. green and black	8·00	26·00
7		2s.6d. black and brown	48·00	85·00
8		5s. black and orange-yellow	48·00	£110
9		10s. black and purple/*yellow*	95·00	£190
1/9 *Set of 9*			£190	£400
1s/9s Optd "Specimen" *Set of 9*			£160	

1903 (Mar)–**04.** Wmk Crown CA. P 14.

10	**2**	½d. grey-black and pale green	1·00	30
		w. Wmk inverted		
11		1d. grey-black and carmine	1·25	70
12		2d. grey-black and chestnut	7·50	1·50
13		2½d. grey-black and blue (1904)	2·00	1·00
14		4d. grey-black and olive-green	2·75	5·50
15		6d. grey-black and purple	4·25	8·00
16		1s. green and black	30·00	19·00

17		2s.6d. grey-black and brown	30·00	65·00
18		5s. grey-black and yellow	70·00	£160
19		10s. grey-black and purple/*yellow*	30·00	95·00
20		£1 green and violet	£350	£700
10/20 *Set of 11*			£475	£950
10s/20s Optd "Specimen" *Set of 11*			£225	

Two Dies of Head Plate:

A B

In Head A the fifth line of shading on the king's cheek shows as a line of dots and the lines of shading up to the king's hair are broken in places. In Head B the lines of shading are more regular, especially the fifth line.

1904 (June)–**09.** *Head Die A. Ordinary paper.* Wmk Mult Crown CA. P 14.

21	**2**	½d. grey-black and pale green	60	10
		a. Chalk-surfaced paper (1905)	1·25	90
22		1d. grey-black and carmine	12·00	10
		a. Chalk-surfaced paper (1905)	12·00	10
23		2d. grey-black and chestnut (1905)	2·50	45
		a. Pale grey and chestnut (Head Die B) (1907)	4·50	40
24		2½d. grey-black and bright blue (9.09)	1·00	1·00
25		3d. orange-brown & bright purple (chalk-surfaced paper) (Head Die B) (18.8.07)	9·50	1·25
		s. Optd "Specimen"	20·00	
26		4d. grey-black and olive-green (12.05)	14·00	25·00
		a. Chalk-surfaced paper (1906)	26·00	30·00
		ab. Grey-black and pale olive-green (Head Die B) (1907)	38·00	35·00
27		6d. grey-black and bright purple (9.05)	13·00	3·50
		a. Chalk-surfaced paper (1906)	13·00	7·00
		ab. Head Die B (1907)	18·00	2·25
28		1s. grey-green and black (19.9.07)	3·25	3·50
		a. Chalk-surfaced paper (Head Die B) (1907)	38·00	3·25
29		2s.6d. grey-black and brown (30.4.06)	24·00	17·00
		a. Chalk-surfaced paper (1906)	14·00	13·00
		ab. Head Die B (1907)	40·00	18·00
30		5s. grey-black and yellow (10.12.07)	40·00	75·00
		a. Chalk-surfaced paper (Head Die B) (1908)	55·00	75·00
31		10s. grey-black and purple/*yellow* (chalk-surfaced paper) (Head Die B) (9.08)	£110	£180
32		£1 green and violet (19.3.06)	£225	£275
		a. Chalk-surfaced paper (1906)	£225	£300
		ab. Head Die B (1907)	£190	£250
21/32 *Set of 12*			£375	£500

I II

Die I. Thick "1", small "d". (double working plate.)
Die II. Thinner "1", larger "d" (single working plate.)

1907–11. *Colours changed. Head Die B. Ordinary paper* (½d. *to* 2½d.) *or chalk-surfaced paper (others).* Wmk Mult Crown CA. P 14.

33	**2**	½d. pale green (1907)	2·50	20
		a. Head Die A	8·00	1·25
		b. Blue-green (1910)	2·25	20
34		1d. carmine (I) (12.8.07)	4·00	60
		a. Head Die A	13·00	1·50
		ab. Die II. Carmine-red (1910)	75	10
35		2d. greyish slate (9.09)	2·50	70
36		2½d. blue (9.09)	2·50	3·75
37		3d. purple/*yellow* (7.09)	2·00	30
38		4d. black and red/*yellow* (9.09)	2·25	80
39		6d. dull purple and purple (9.09)	27·00	3·25
		a. Dull purple and bright purple (1911)	26·00	3·25
		aw. Wmk inverted		
40		1s. black/*green* (7.09)	7·00	40
41		2s.6d. black and red/*blue* (9.09)	5·00	1·00
42		5s. green and red/*yellow* (9.09)	38·00	48·00
43		10s. green and red/*green* (9.09)	70·00	£100
44		£1 purple and black/*red* (9.09)	£200	£225
33/44 *Set of 12*			£325	£350
33s/44s Optd "Specimen" *Set of 12*			£275	

1912. Wmk Mult Crown CA. P 14.

45	**3**	½d. green	2·25	10
46		1d. red	2·00	10
		w. Wmk inverted	£150	£140
47		2d. grey	75	85
48		2½d. bright blue	2·75	2·75
49		3d. purple/*yellow*	1·00	30
50		4d. black and red/*yellow*	1·25	2·00
51		6d. dull and bright purple	1·25	1·25
52		1s. black/*green*	2·75	75
53		2s.6d. black and red/*blue*	8·00	35·00
54		5s. green and red/*yellow*	20·00	75·00
55		10s. green and red/*green*	45·00	90·00
56		£1 purple and black/*red*	£180	£225
45/56 *Set of 12*			£225	£375
45s/56s Optd "Specimen" *Set of 12*			£200	

STAMP BOOKLETS

1904. *Black on red cover. Stapled.*
SB1 2s.1d. booklet containing twenty-four 1d. (No. 11) in blocks of 6

1905 (1 June)–**06.** *Black on red cover. Stapled.*
SB2 2s.1d. booklet containing twenty-four 1d. (No. 22) in blocks of 6 .... £1800
    a. As No. SB2 but containing No. 22a (1906).... £1500

1907 (7 Oct). *Black on red cover. Stapled.*
SB3 2s.1d. booklet containing twenty-four 1d. (No. 34) in blocks of 6 .... £2000

1910 (19 Sept). *Black on red cover. Stapled.*
SB4 2s. booklet containing eleven ½d. and eighteen 1d. (Nos. 33b, 34ab) in blocks of 6 or 5 ....

1912 (Oct). *Black on red cover. Stapled.*
SB5 2s. booklet containing twelve ½d. and eighteen 1d. (Nos. 45/6) in blocks of 6 .... £1500

On 1 January 1914 Southern Nigeria became part of Nigeria.

NIGERIA

Nigeria was formed on 1 January 1914 from the former protectorates of Northern and Southern Nigeria.

PRICES FOR STAMPS ON COVER TO 1945	
Nos. 1/10	
Nos. 11/12	*from* × 3
Nos. 15/28	
Nos. 29/a	*from* × 3
Nos. 30/3	*from* × 3
Nos. 34/59	*from* × 2

CROWN COLONY

       1   2

(Typo D.L.R.)

1914 (1 June)–**29.** *Die I. Ordinary paper (½d. to 2½d.) or chalk-surfaced paper (others). Wmk Mult Crown CA. P 14.*
1	**1**	½d. green...................................	5·00	70
2		1d. carmine-red..........................	4·75	10
		a. Scarlet (1916)	7·50	20
		w. Wmk inverted..........................	95·00	£100
3		2d. grey.......................................	8·00	1·75
		a. Slate-grey (1918)......................	9·00	75
4		2½d. bright blue..........................	7·00	3·00
		a. Dull blue (1915)........................	15·00	4·75
5	**2**	3d. purple/yellow (white back)........	3·25	10·00
		a. Lemon back (19.8.15).................	1·50	2·75
		b. On deep yellow (yellow back) (thick paper) (1915)..............	32·00	7·50
		bs. Optd "Specimen".....................	45·00	
		c. On orange-buff (1920)...............	9·00	22·00
		d. On buff (1920)...........................	11·00	
		e. On pale yellow (1921)................	11·00	15·00
6		4d. black and red/yellow (white back)..	1·40	10·00
		a. Lemon back (19.8.15).................	1·00	4·25
		b. On deep yellow (yellow back) (thick paper) (1915)..............	32·00	8·00
		bs. Optd "Specimen".....................	45·00	
		c. On orange-buff (1920)...............	11·00	11·00
		d. On buff (1920)...........................	11·00	
		e. On pale yellow (1921)................	10·00	18·00
7		6d. dull purple and bright purple.....	9·00	10·00
8	**1**	1s. black/blue-green (white back).......	1·50	23·00
		a. On yellow-green (white back) (1915).........................	£150	
		b. Yellow-green back (19.8.15)......	40·00	40·00
		c. Blue-green back (1915)............	1·00	9·50
		cs. Optd "Specimen".....................	45·00	
		d. Pale olive back (1917)...............	28·00	30·00
		dw. Wmk inverted		
		e. On emerald (pale olive back) (1920)................................	8·00	38·00
		f. On emerald (emerald back) (1920)................................	1·25	15·00
9		2s.6d. black and red/blue................	16·00	6·50
10	**2**	5s. green and red/yellow (white back)..	13·00	55·00
		a. Lemon back (19.8.15).................	21·00	55·00
		b. On deep yellow (yellow back) (thick paper) (1915)...............	50·00	65·00
		bs. Optd "Specimen".....................	48·00	
		c. On orange-buff (1920)...............	48·00	85·00
		d. On buff (1920)...........................	55·00	
		e. On pale yellow (1921)	75·00	£140
11	**1**	10s. green and red/blue-green (white back).................................	45·00	£150
		a. Blue-green back (19.8.15)........	50·00	85·00
		as. Optd "Specimen".....................	55·00	
		b. Pale olive back (1917)...............	£850	£1400
		c. On emerald (pale olive back) (1920)................................	£110	£160
		d. On emerald (emerald back) (1921)................................	35·00	£100
12	**2**	£1 deep purple and black/red...........	£180	£225
		a. Purple and black/red (1917).....	£170	£200
		b. Die II. Dp purple & blk/red (19.1.27)..............................	£200	£300
		ba. Purple and black/red (1929)...	£190	£275
1/12 *Set of 12*			£250	£325
1s/12s Optd "Specimen" *Set of 12*			£325	

The ½d. and 1d. were printed in sheets of 240 using two plates one above the other.

1921–32. *Ordinary paper (½d. to 3d.) or chalk-surfaced paper (others). Wmk Mult Script CA. P 14.*
15	**1**	½d. green (Die I) (1921).................	1·25	40
		aw. Wmk inverted	85·00	85·00
		b. Die II (1925).............................	4·00	85
		c. Vert gutter pair. Die I and Die II. Nos. 15/b (1925).............	£325	
16		1d. rose-carmine (Die I) (1921).......	3·25	30
		aw. Wmk inverted..........................	80·00	80·00
		b. Die II (1925).............................	1·75	35
		c. Vert gutter pair. Die I and Die II. Nos. 16/b (1925)..............	£325	
17	**2**	1½d. orange (Die II) (1.4.31)	4·50	15
18	**1**	2d. grey (Die I) (1921)...................	1·50	6·00
19		a. Die II (1924).............................	8·00	40
		2d. chestnut (Die II) (1.10.27)........	4·50	15
20		2d. chocolate (Die II) (1.7.28)........	1·50	15
		a. Die I (1932).............................	5·50	75
21		2½d. bright blue (Die I) (1921)..........	1·00	7·00
22	**2**	3d. bright violet (Die I) (1924)........	5·00	3·25
		a. Die II (1925).............................	10·00	1·00
23		3d. bright blue (Die I) (1.4.31)........	6·50	1·00
24		4d. black & red/pale yellow (Die II) (1923)................................	65	55
		a. Die I (1932).............................	5·50	7·00
25		6d. dull purple & brt purple (Die I) (1921)................................	12·00	23·00
		a. Die II (1923).............................	7·00	8·00
		aw. Wmk inverted	£100	
26	**1**	1s. black/emerald (Die II) (1924) ...	1·25	2·00
27		2s.6d. black and red/blue (Die II) (1925)................................	6·50	28·00
		a. Die I (1932).............................	40·00	70·00
28	**2**	5s. green & red/pale yellow (Die I) (1926)................................	15·00	65·00
		a. Die I (1932).............................	65·00	£190
29	**1**	10s. green and red/green (Die II) (1925)................................	60·00	£190
		a. Die I (1932).............................	£100	£425
15/29 *Set of 15*			£110	£275
15s/29s (ex 2d. chocolate) Optd or Perf (1½d., 3d. blue) "Specimen" *Set of 14*			£400	

The ½d. and 1d., together with the 1½d. from 1932, were printed in sheets of 240 using two plates one above the other. Nos. 15c and 16c come from printings in November 1924 which combined Key Plate No. 7 (Die I) above Key Plate No. 12 (Die II).

1935 (6 May). *Silver Jubilee. As Nos. 91/4 of Antigua, but ptd by Waterlow. P 11×12.*
30		1½d. ultramarine and grey..........................	80	1·00
31		2d. green and indigo...........................	1·50	1·00
		k. Kite and vertical log	85·00	85·00
32		3d. brown and deep blue...................	3·00	15·00
33		1s. slate and purple...........................	3·00	30·00
30/3 *Set of 4*			7·50	42·00
30s/3s Perf "Specimen" *Set of 4*			85·00	

For illustration of plate variety see Omnibus section following Zanzibar.

3 Apapa Wharf

4 Cocoa

5 Tin dredger

6 Timber industry

7 Fishing Village

8 Cotton ginnery

9 Habe Minaret

10 Fulani cattle

---

11 Victoria-Buea Road

12 Oil Palms

13 River Niger at Jebba

14 Canoe pulling

(Recess D.L.R.)

1936 (1 Feb). *T 3/14. Wmk Mult Script CA.*

(a) P 11½×13.
34	**3**	½d. green...............................	1·50	1·40
35	**4**	1d. carmine...........................	50	40
36	**5**	1½d. brown............................	2·00	40
		a. Perf 12½×13½...................	60·00	4·00
37	**6**	2d. black...............................	50	80
38	**7**	3d. blue.................................	2·00	1·50
		a. Perf 12½×13½...................	£120	24·00
39	**8**	4d. red-brown.......................	2·00	2·00
40	**9**	6d. dull violet......................	50	60
41	**10**	1s. sage-green......................	1·75	4·75

(b) P 14.
42	**11**	2s.6d. black and ultramarine	3·75	25·00
43	**12**	5s. black and olive-green.............	9·00	32·00
44	**13**	10s. black and grey.......................	55·00	80·00
45	**14**	£1 black and orange...................	80·00	£160
34/45 *Set of 12*			£140	£275
34s/45s Perf "Specimen" *Set of 12*			£225	

1937 (12 May). *Coronation. As Nos. 95/7 of Antigua. P 11×11½.*
46		1d. carmine................................	60	2·50
47		1½d. brown.................................	1·60	3·00
48		3d. blue.....................................	1·60	3·00
46/8 *Set of 3*			3·50	7·75
46s/8s Perf "Specimen" *Set of 3*			75·00	

15 King George VI

16 Victoria-Buea Road

(Recess B.W. (T **15**), D.L.R. (others))

1938 (1 May)–**51.** *Designs as T 15/16. Wmk Mult Script CA. P 12 (T 15) or 13×11½ (others).*
49	**15**	½d. green....................................	10	10
		a. Perf 11½ (15.2.50).................	1·75	40
50		1d. carmine...............................	19·00	2·50
		a. Rose-red (shades) (1940).......	75	30
		ab. "A" of "CA" missing from wmk.......................................		
50b		1d. bright purple (1.12.44)..........	10	20
		ba. Perf 11½ (15.2.50).................	30	50
		bw. Wmk inverted (P 12).............		
51		1½d. brown................................	20	10
		a. Perf 11½ (15.11.50)...............	10	10
52		2d. black....................................	10	1·60
52a		2d. rose-red (1.12.44).................	10	1·60
		ab. Perf 11½ (15.2.50).................	10	50
52b		2½d. orange (4.41).......................	10	1·50
53		3d. blue......................................	10	10
		a. Wmk sideways........................	†	£3750
53b		3d. black (1.12.44)......................	15	1·25
54		4d. orange...................................	48·00	3·00
54a		4d. blue (1.12.44)........................	15	2·50
55		6d. blackish purple.....................	40	10
		a. Perf 11½ (17.4.51)..................	1·50	60
56		1s. sage-green............................	60	10
		a. Perf 11½ (15.2.50)..................	30	10
57		1s.3d. light blue (1940)................	90	30
		a. Perf 11½ (14.6.50)..................	80	70
		aw. Wmk sideways.......................	†	£3500
58	**16**	2s.6d. black and blue...................	60·00	17·00
		a. Perf 13½ (6.42).......................	3·75	4·25
		ab. Black and deep blue (1947)......	55·00	55·00
		b. Perf 14 (1942).........................	2·25	3·50
		c. Perf 12 (15.8.51).....................	2·00	4·50
59	**13**	5s. black and orange...................	£110	14·00
		a. Perf 13½ (8.42).......................	5·50	4·50
		b. Perf 14 (1948).........................	7·50	3·00
		c. Perf 12 (19.5.49).....................	5·50	4·00
49/59c *Set of 16*			55·00	16·00
49s/59s (ex 2½d.) Perf "Specimen" *Set of 15*..........			£250	

The 1d., No. 50ba, exists in coils constructed from normal sheets.

1946 (21 Oct). *Victory. As Nos. 110/11 of Antigua.*
60		1½d. chocolate	35	10
61		4d. blue..................................	35	2·25
60s/1s Perf "Specimen" *Set of 2*			65·00	

1948 (20 Dec). *Royal Silver Wedding. As Nos. 112/13 of Antigua.*
62		1d. bright purple.......................	35	30
63		5s. brown-orange......................	6·00	12·00

1949 (10 Oct). *75th Anniv of U.P.U. As Nos. 114/17 of Antigua.*
64		1d. bright reddish purple............	15	25
65		3d. deep blue...........................	1·25	3·00
66		6d. purple...............................	30	10
67		1s. olive..................................	50	2·00
64/7 *Set of 4*			2·00	7·50

STAMP BOOKLETS

1915. *Crimson cover, inscribed* "NIGERIA".
SB1 2s. booklet containing twelve ½d. and eighteen 1d. (Nos 1/2) in blocks of 6. .... £2000

1921–26. *Black on scarlet cover, inscribed* "NIGERIA" .
SB2 4s. booklet containing twelve 1d. and eighteen 2d. grey (both Die I) (Nos. 16, 18) in blocks of 6 £2000
  a. Containing Nos. 16 and 18a (Die II) (1924)... £1800
  b. Containing Nos. 16b and 18a (both Die II) (1926) £1800

1926 (?). *Black on scarlet cover, inscribed* "STAMPS BOOKLET/ NIGERIA."
SB3 4s. booklet containing twelve 1d. and eighteen 2d. grey (both Die II) (Nos. 16b, 18a) in blocks of 6... £1800

1928. *Black on scarlet cover, inscribed* "STAMPS BOOKLET/ NIGERIA."
SB5 4s. booklet containing twelve 1d. (Die II) and eighteen 2d. chestnut (Nos. 16b, 19) in blocks of 6... £2000

1929. *Black on scarlet cover, inscribed* "STAMPS BOOKLET/ NIGERIA."
SB6 4s. booklet containing twleve 1d. (Die II) and eighteen 2d. chocolate (Nos. 16b, 20) in blocks of 6... £1600

1931 (Jan). *Black on scarlet cover, inscribed* "STAMPS BOOKLET/NIGERIA".
SB7 4s. booklet containing twelve 1d. and twenty-four 1½ d. (Nos. 16a, 17) in blocks of 6 .... £2000

Niue *see after* New Zealand

Norfolk Island *see after* Australia

North Borneo

BRITISH NORTH BORNEO COMPANY ADMINISTRATION

PRINTERS. The stamps of this country up to 1894 were designed by T. Macdonald and printed in lithography by Blades, East and Blades, London.

1	(2)	(3)

1883 (Mar). P 12.
1 1 2c. red-brown............................ 29·00 65·00
    a. Imperf between (horiz pair).......

The figure "2" varies in size.

1883 (June). *No. 1 surch as T* **2** *or* **3**.
2 2 8c. on 2c. red-brown £1000 £650
3 3 8c. on 2c. red-brown £475 £190
    a. Surch double .... † £4250

Type **2** was handstamped and stamps without stop are generally forgeries. Type **3** was a setting of 50 (10×5) providing ten varieties; it normally has a stop which sometimes failed to print.

CANCELLED-TO-ORDER—Prices are separately indicated in a third price column, for stamps showing the recognisable black bars remainder mark cancellation. The issues since 1916 have not been thus cancelled.

It should be noted, however, that a postmark of this form was in use for postal purposes up to this period, and was used at one or two of the smaller post-offices until 1949. A small oval with five bars was used to mark railway mail during 1945/55 and also as a paquebot mark at Jesselton *c.* 1950.

4	5	(6)

1883. P 14.
4 4 50c. violet .... £150 — 27·00
    a. Inverted "L" for first "F" in "FIFTY" (R. 5/2) .... £1000 — £190
5 5 $1 scarlet .... £130 — 14·00

1883 (July). P 12.
6 1 4c. pink .... 55·00 60·00
    a. Imperf (horiz pair) .... † —
7 8c. green .... 80·00 60·00

1886. P 14.
8 1 ½c. magenta .... 95·00 £180
9 1c. orange £180 £325
    a. Imperf (pair)........................ £275 £275
    b. Imperf horiz (vert pair)............ £950
10 2c. brown .... 30·00 27·00
    a. Imperf between (horiz pair)....... £600
11 4c. pink .... 17·00 50·00
12 8c. green .... 19·00 50·00
    a. Imperf between (horiz pair)....... £800
13 10c. blue .... 32·00 50·00
    a. Imperf (pair) £350
8/13 *Set of 6* £325 £600

Imperforate examples of the 4c. pink are listed under No. 6a.

1886 (Sept). *Nos.* **8** *and* **13** *optd with T* **6**.
14 ½c. magenta £140 £225
15 10c. blue £190 £225

(7)	(8)	Small "3" variety (R. 3/1, 3/4, 3/7)

(Surchd by *North Borneo Herald*, Sandakan)

1886 (Sept). *T* **1** *surch as T* **7/8**.

(a) P 12.
16 7 3c. on 4c. pink £225 £300
    a. Small "3" .... — £6000
17 8 5c. on 8c. green £250 £300

(b) P 14.
18 7 3c. on 4c. pink £120 £130
    a. Small "3" £1800
19 8 5c. on 8c. green £120 £130
    a. Surch inverted...................... £2250

9

10	11

12	13

1886–87.

(a) P14.
No.	Type	Description		
21b	9	½c. magenta	16·00	50·00
22		½c. rose	3·50	13·00
		a. Imperf (pair)..................	42·00	
23		1c. orange-yellow	12·00	29·00
		a. Imperf between (vert pair)........	£325	
		b. Imperf (pair)...................	50·00	
24		1c. orange.........................	2·00	9·00
		a. Imperf (pair)...................	40·00	
25		2c. brown	2·00	8·50
		a. Imperf (pair)...................	40·00	
26		4c. pink	3·00	12·00
		a. Imperf (pair)...................	42·00	
		b. Imperf between (horiz or vert pair)........................	£275	
		c. Imperf vert (horiz pair)...........	£275	
		d. Error. 1c. pink (R. 2/3) (centre stamp of strip of 3)	£250	£650
		da. Imperf between (pair).............		
		db. Imperf (pair)...................	£4250	
27		8c. green	14·00	21·00
		a. Imperf (pair)...................	42·00	
28		10c. blue	7·50	28·00
		a. Imperf between (vert pair).......	£350	
		b. Imperf (pair)...................	42·00	
29	10	25c. indigo	£225	16·00
		a. Imperf between (vert pair).......		
		b. Imperf (pair)...................	£350	32·00
30	11	50c. violet	£300	17·00
		a. Imperf (pair)...................	£400	32·00
31	12	$1 scarlet	£325	16·00
		a. Imperf (pair)...................	£425	32·00
32	13	$2 sage-green	£400	22·00
		a. Imperf (pair)...................	£325	35·00
22/32		*Set of 10*	£1200	£150

(b) P 12.
| 34 | 9 | ½c. magenta .... | £200 | £375 |
| 35 | | 1c. orange......................... | £170 | £225 |

Nos. 21b/32 are known to have been sold as cancelled remainders, but these are difficult to distinguish from postally used. Values above 10c. are infrequently found postally used so that the used prices quoted are for the remainders.

14

15	16

17	18

1888–92. *T* **14** (*as T* **9** *but inscr* "POSTAGE & REVENUE") *and* *T* **15/18** (*T* **10/13** *redrawn*). P 14.
36	14	½c. magenta (1889)	4·00	26·00	2·25
		a. Imperf vert (horiz pair)	†	†	£225
		b. Rose	1·50	4·75	60
		ba. Imperf between (horiz pair)........................	£375		
		c. Imperf (pair)...................	38·00	—	11·00
37		1c. orange (1892)	2·75	4·25	50
		a. Imperf vert (horiz pair)	£325		
		b. Imperf (pair)...................	38·00	—	9·50
38		2c. brown (1889)	9·50	16·00	90

		a. Imperf between (horiz pair)	†	†	£375
		b. *Lake-brown*	4·25	16·00	50
		c. Imperf (pair)	38·00	—	9·00
39		3c. violet (1889)	2·50	12·00	50
		b. Imperf (pair)	29·00	—	9·00
40		4c. rose-pink (1889)	6·00	32·00	50
		a. Imperf between (pair).	—	£200	
		b. Imperf (pair)	38·00	—	9·50
41		5c. slate (1889)	2·75	23·00	50
		a. Imperf between (pair).			
		b. Imperf (pair)	38·00	—	9·50
42		6c. lake (1892)	9·00	23·00	50
		a. Imperf (pair)	38·00	—	12·00
43		8c. blue-green (1891)	28·00	35·00	1·00
		a. Yellow-green	21·00	27·00	50
		c. Imperf (pair)	38·00	—	12·00
44		10c. blue (1891)	8·00	29·00	1·00
		a. Imperf between (vert pair)	†	†	£225
		b. *Dull blue*	6·50	21·00	50
		ba. Imperf between (horiz pair)			
		d. Imperf (pair)	38·00	—	11·00
45	15	25c. indigo	65·00	80·00	75
		a. Imperf (pair)	£250	†	18·00
		b. Imperf vert (horiz pair)	†	†	£275
46	16	50c. violet	90·00	£130	75
		a. Imperf (pair)	£350	†	18·00
		b. *Chalky blue*	£110	£120	†
47	17	$1 scarlet	30·00	£110	75
		a. Imperf (pair)	£250	†	18·00
48	18	$2 dull green	£140	£180	1·50
		a. Imperf (pair)	£400	†	21·00
36*b*/48 *Set of 13*			£325	£600	7·50

Nos. 39, 43 and 44 showing stamps printed double or triple, one inverted, are from waste sheets subsequently sold by the British North Borneo Company to collectors.

These stamps to the 10c. value were forged on several occasions. Most forgeries of the ½c. value can be identified by the presence of a diagonal line joining the top two horizontal strokes of the uppermost Chinese character.

The new 25c. has the inscription "BRITISH NORTH BORNEO" in taller capitals. In the 50c. the "0" of the numerals "50" in the two upper corners is square-shaped at the top and bottom instead of being oval. The 1 dollar has 14 pearls instead of 13 at each side, and on the 2 dollars the word "BRITISH" measures 10½ to 11 mm in length in place of 12 mm.

19   20

1889. P 14.

49	19	$5 bright purple	£200	£225	8·50
		a. Imperf (pair)	£500	†	40·00
50	20	$10 brown	£275	£350	12·00
		a. Imperf (pair)	£700	†	48·00
		b. "DOLLAPS" for "DOLLARS" (R. 2/1).	£1300	£1600	£325
		ba. Ditto. Imperf (pair)	£3000	†	£700

Two Cents. (21)   6 cents. (22)   1 cent. (23)

1890 (Dec). *Surch as T 21, in red.*

51	15	2c. on 25c. indigo	70·00	90·00
		a. Surch inverted	£425	£425
52		8c. on 25c. indigo	95·00	£110

The first printing of Nos. 51/2 had the two lines of the surcharge 3.5 mm apart. On a second printing of both values this gap widened to 5 mm.

1891–92. *Surch with T 22.*

54	9	6c. on 8c. green (1892)	£8000	£4250
		a. Large "s" in "cents"	£15000	
55	14	6c. on 8c. yellow-green	24·00	10·00
		a. Surch inverted	£450	£500
		b. Inverted "c" in "cents" (R. 5/4).	£500	£600
		c. "cetns." for "cents" (R. 3/7)..	£500	£600
		d. Large "s" in "cents" (R. 2/9 or 3/7).	£225	£200
56	9	6c. on 10c. blue	60·00	22·00
		a. Surch inverted	£275	£275
		b. Surch double		
		c. Surch treble	£475	
		d. Large "s" in "cents"	£275	£170
57	14	6c. on 10c. blue	£170	26·00
		a. Large "s" in "cents"	£650	£225

Unused examples of Nos. 55 and 57 are normally without gum.

There were three settings of the surcharge for No. 55. On the first two the large "s" in "cents" occurred on R. 2/9 with the other two listed varieties also included. Nos. 55b/c were corrected on the third setting and the large "s" in cents occurred on R. 3/7.

1892 (Mar–Nov). *Surch as T 23 ("Cents." with capital "C" as in T 21 on No. 65), in red.*

63	14	1c. on 4c. rose-pink	23·00	14·00
		a. Surch double	£1300	
		b. Surch on back and on front	—	£600
		ba. As b, but with surch double on front		

64		1c. on 5c. slate (Nov)	7·00	6·00
65	15	8c. on 25c. indigo (date?)	£150	£160

Unused examples of Nos. 63/5 are normally without gum.

24 Dyak Chief   **25** Sambar Stag (*Cervus unicolor*)   **26** Sago Palm

27 Great Argus Pheasant   **28** Arms of the Company

29 Malay Dhow   **30** Estuarine Crocodile

31 Mount Kinabalu   **32** Arms of the Company with Supporters

PERFORATION. There are a number of small variations in the perforation of the Waterlow issues of 1894 to 1922 which we believe were due to irregularity of the pins rather than different perforators.

In the following lists, stamps perf 12, 12½, 13 or compound are described as perf 12–13, stamps perf 13½, 14 or compound are described as perf 13½–14 and those perf 14½, 15 or compound are listed as perf 14½–15. In addition the 13½–14 perforation exists compound with 14½–15 and with 12–13, whilst perf 15½–16 comes from a separate perforator.

(Recess Waterlow)

1894 (Feb). P 14½–15.

66	24	1c. black and olive-bistre..	1·25	9·50	50
		a. Imperf between (horiz or vert pair)	£750		
		b. Perf 13½–14	1·75	12·00	50
		c. Perf 13½–14, comp 14½–15	45·00	55·00	—
		d. Perf 13½–14, comp 12–13	24·00	50·00	
		e. Perf 12–13			
67		1c. black and bistre-brown	1·75	15·00	50
		a. Perf 13½–14	2·50	15·00	50
		b. Perf 13½–14, comp 12–13	27·00	55·00	
		c. Perf 12–13			
68	25	2c. black and rose-lake	5·50	4·75	50
		a. Imperf between (horiz or vert pair)	£750	£750	†
		b. Perf 13½–14	40·00	45·00	75
		c. Perf 13½–14, comp 14½–15			
69		2c. black and lake	5·50	4·75	50
		a. Perf 13½–14	40·00	40·00	1·50
		b. Perf 13½–14, comp 12–13	30·00	32·00	
		c. Imperf between (horiz pair)			
70	26	3c. olive-green and dull purple	2·75	8·50	50
		a. Imperf between (horiz pair)	—	£750	†
		aa. Perf 13½–14, comp 14½–15			
		b. Bronze-green and dull purple	5·00	—	50
		c. Perf 13½–14			
71		3c. olive-green & violet (P 13½–14)	20·00	50·00	1·25
		a. Imperf between (horiz pair)			
72	27	5c. black and vermilion	14·00	11·00	60
		a. Imperf between (horiz or vert pair)	£650		
		b. Perf 13½–14	45·00	60·00	1·25
		c. Perf 13½–14, comp 12–13	—	65·00	5·50
		d. Perf 13½–14, comp 14½–15			
73	28	6c. black and bistre-brown	60·00	80·00	60
		a. Perf 13½–14	4·50	18·00	60
		b. Perf 13½–14, comp 12–13	—	65·00	5·50
		c. Perf 13½–14, comp 14½–15	60·00		
		d. Imperf between (horiz pair)			
74	29	8c. black and dull purple..	6·50	11·00	60
		a. Imperf between (vert pair)	£650		

		b. Perf 13½–14	9·50	38·00	1·00
		ba. Imperf between (vert pair)	£450	†	£300
		d. Perf 13½–14, comp 12–13			
75	30	12c. black and blue	28·00	85·00	2·50
		a. Perf 13½–14	28·00	80·00	2·50
		b. Imperf between (horiz pair)	£1000	†	£600
		c. Perf 13½–14, comp 14½–15			5·00
76		12c. black and ultramarine .	42·00	85·00	3·00
		a. Perf 13½–14	40·00	85·00	3·00
		b. Imperf between (pair).			
78	31	18c. black and deep green..	27·00	50·00	2·00
		a. Perf 13½–14	29·00	50·00	2·00
		b. Perf 13½–14, comp 14½–15			5·00
79	32	24c. blue and rose-lake	23·00	85·00	2·00
		a. Imperf between (vert pair)	—	—	£400
		b. Imperf between (vert strip of 3)	†	†	£550
		c. Perf 13½–14	23·00	70·00	2·00
		d. Perf 13½–14, comp 14½–15			
66/79 *Set of 9*			£100	£225	9·00

32a   32b

32c   32d

(Litho Blades, East & Blades, London)

1894 (Feb). *T 32a to 32d and T 19/20, but inscribed* "THE STATE OF NORTH BORNEO". P 14.

81		25c. indigo	9·00	30·00	1·00
		a. Imperf (pair)	42·00	†	9·50
		b. Imperf between (horiz or vert pair)	£750	—	£100
82		50c. deep slate-purple	26·00	60·00	2·00
		a. Imperf (pair)	—	†	9·50
		b. Imperf between (horiz pair)	—	60·00	
		d. Chalky blue			
83		$1 scarlet	12·00	24·00	1·25
		a. Perf 14×11	£250		
		b. Imperf (pair)	38·00	†	9·50
84		$2 dull green	20·00	75·00	2·50
		a. Imperf (pair)	—	†	15·00
85		$5 bright purple	£225	£300	16·00
		a. Imperf (pair)	£425	†	45·00
		b. Dull purple	£225	£300	9·00
86		$10 brown	£250	£350	28·00
		a. Imperf (pair)	£425	†	45·00
81/6 *Set of 6*			£450	£700	28·00
81s/6s Optd "Specimen" *Set of 6*			£150		

For Nos. 81 to 83 in other colours, see Labuan 80a, 81a and 82a.

Nos. 81/4 showing stamps printed double, double, one inverted, or on both sides, are from waste sheets subsequently sold by the British North Borneo Company to collectors.

4 CENTS

(33 (3½ mm between lines of surcharge))

(Surcharged by Waterlow)

1895 (June). *No. 83 surch as T 33.*

87	32	4 cents on $1 scarlet	6·50	1·50	50
		a. Surch double, one diagonal....	£950		
88		10 cents on $1 scarlet	23·00	1·75	50
89		20 cents on $1 scarlet	42·00	17·00	50
90		30 cents on $1 scarlet	30·00	28·00	65
91		40 cents on $1 scarlet	32·00	48·00	65
87/91 *Set of 5*			£120	85·00	2·50
87s/91s Optd "Specimen" *Set of 5*			85·00		

For $1 with wider spacing see No. 121. No. 88 exists with the figures of the surcharge 2½ mm away from "CENTS". The normal setting has a space of 3½ mm. Examples of the narrow setting have, so far, only been seen on cancelled-to-order stamps.

34   **35**   **36**

37 Orang-Utan   **38**   **39**

40   **41** Sun Bear

42   **43** Borneo Railway Train

44   **45**

(Recess Waterlow)

1897 (Mar)–**1902**. *T* **34** *to* **45**. *New frames.* P 13½–14.

92		1c. black and bistre-brown	15·00	3·75	40
	aa.	Perf 16	11·00	2·75	40
	a.	Perf 14½–15			
	b.	Perf 13½–14, comp 12–13	65·00	50·00	—
	c.	Imperf between (horiz pair)	†	†	£550
	d.	Perf 12–13	£120		
93		1c. black and ochre	50·00	14·00	50
	a.	Perf 14½–15	32·00	13·00	50
	ab.	Imperf between (horiz pair)	†	†	£550
	b.	Perf 13½–14 comp 12–13	—		
94		2c. black and lake	40·00	3·50	40
	a.	Perf 14½–15	22·00	2·50	40
	ab.	Imperf between (horiz pair)	†	†	£600
	b.	Perf 13½–14, comp 12–13	—	17·00	1·25
	c.	Perf 12–13			
	d.	Imperf between (vert pair)	†	†	£650
	e.	Perf 13½–14, comp 14½–15	—		3·00
95		2c. black and green (1900)	48·00	2·00	60
	a.	Perf 14½–15	95·00	17·00	2·00
	b.	Perf 13½–14, comp 12–13	£120	28·00	—
	c.	Perf 12–13			
	d.	Imperf between (horiz pair)	—	£900	†
96		3c. green and rosy mauve	50·00	13·00	40
	a.	Perf 14½–15	55·00	50·00	1·00
	b.	Perf 13½–14, comp 12–13	75·00	75·00	—
97		3c. green & dull mauve (P 14½–15)	18·00	3·00	50
98		4c. black and green (1900)	9·00		1·50
	a.	Perf 13½–14, comp 12–13			
99		4c. black and carmine (1900)	35·00	9·00	50
	a.	Perf 16	80·00	48·00	50
	b.	Perf 14½–15	55·00	2·25	50
	c.	Perf 13½–14, comp 12–13	38·00	45·00	2·00
	d.	Perf 12–13			
100		5c. black and orange-vermilion	95·00	3·50	60
	a.	Perf 14½–15	95·00	3·00	60
	b.	Imperf between (horiz pair)	†	£1400	†
	b.	Perf 13½–14, comp 12–13	£100	14·00	70
	c.	Perf 12–13			
101		6c. black and bistre-brown	50·00	24·00	50
	a.	Perf 14½–15	32·00	4·00	50
	b.	Perf 13½–14, comp 12–13	—		3·00
102		8c. black and brown-purple	75·00	50·00	60
	a.	Perf 16	£110	£140	70
	ab.	Imperf between (vert pair)	£375	£375	—
	b.	Perf 14½–15	45·00	2·75	60
103		8c. black and brown	12·00	28·00	75
	a.	Perf 14½–15	65·00	80·00	
	b.	Perf 16			
104		10c. brown and slate-lilac (1902)	£100	42·00	2·75
	a.	Imperf between (vert pair)			
105		10c. brown and slate-blue (1902)	£225	85·00	1·50
106		12c. black and dull blue	£130	48·00	1·75
	a.	Imperf between (vert pair)	†	†	£600
	b.	Perf 14½–15	90·00	35·00	1·50
	c.	Perf 13½–14, comp 12–13	£160	55·00	—
	d.	Perf 12–13			
107		16c. green and chestnut (1902)	£130	90·00	3·25
	a.	Perf 14½–15	£170	£140	10·00
108		18c. black and green (P 16)	22·00	75·00	2·00
	a.	Imperf between (horiz pair)	†	†	85·00
	b.	Imperf between (vert pair)	†	†	£325
	c.	Imperf (pair)	†	†	£180
	d.	Perf 14½–15	—		10·00

109		24c. blue and lake	20·00	90·00	2·00
	a.	Perf 13½–14, comp 12–13	45·00	£100	2·00
	b.	Perf 12–13	£150		
92/109		(one of each value) Set of 12	£500	£300	11·50
92s/109s		(excl 93, 97, 103, 105) Optd "Specimen" Set of 14	£300		

No. 98 was printed in an incorrect frame colour and it is doubtful if it was issued for postal purposes in North Borneo. Used examples come from dealers' stock sent to the territory for cancellation.

In the above the 18c. has "POSTAL REVENUE" instead of "POSTAGE AND REVENUE" and the 24c. has those words omitted. These stamps were replaced by others with corrected inscriptions; see Nos. 110 and 111.

46   **47**

1897. *Corrected inscriptions.* P 13½–14.

110	**46**	18c. black and green	£110	28·00	2·25
	a.	Imperf between (horiz pair)	†	†	£550
	b.	Perf 14½–15	80·00	12·00	1·50
	c.	Perf 13½–14, comp 12–13	—		2·75
111	**47**	24c. blue and lake	80·00	45·00	2·25
	a.	Perf 16	£140	£120	2·00
	b.	Perf 14½–15	45·00	55·00	2·50
	c.	Perf 13½–14, comp 12–13	—		3·25
	d.	Perf 12–13			
110s/11s		Optd "Specimen" Set of 2	50·00		

BRITISH
4 CENTS   PROTECTORATE.   **4** cents
(48) (4½ mm between lines of surcharge)   (49)   (50)

1899 (22 July–Oct). *Surch with T* **48**. P 14½–15 (Nos. 112/17) or 14 (Nos. 118/26).

(a) 4½ mm between lines of surch.

112		4c. on 5c. (No. 100a)	48·00	48·00	
	a.	Perf 13½–14	28·00	10·00	
	b.	Perf 13½–14, comp 12–13	40·00	32·00	
113		4c. on 6c. (No. 101a) (date?)	19·00	24·00	
	a.	Perf 13½–14	18·00	48·00	
	b.	Perf 13½–14, comp 14½–15			
114		4c. on 8c. (No. 102b) (Oct)	15·00	10·00	
115		4c. on 12c. (No. 106b) (Oct)	24·00	13·00	
	a.	Imperf between (horiz pair)	£700		
	b.	Imperf between (vert pair)	—	£750	
	c.	Perf 13½–14	42·00	50·00	
	d.	Perf 12–13			
	e.	Perf 13½–14, comp 12–13	40·00	40·00	
116		4c. on 18c. (No. 110a) (Oct)	12·00	14·00	
	a.	Perf 13½–14	30·00	35·00	
117		4c. on 24c. (No. 111b) (Oct)	24·00	18·00	
	a.	Perf 16	50·00	50·00	
	b.	Perf 14½–15	20·00	38·00	
	c.	Perf 13½–14, comp 12–13	35·00	38·00	
	d.	Perf 12–13	90·00	£100	
118		4c. on 25c. indigo (No. 81)	5·50	8·50	
	a.	Imperf between (horiz strip of 3)	£950		
119		4c. on 50c. deep slate-purple (No. 82)	11·00	16·00	
	a.	Chalky blue	28·00	38·00	
121		4c. on $1 scarlet (No. 83)	5·50	12·00	
122		4c. on $2 dull green (No. 84)	5·50	13·00	
123		4c. on $5 bright purple (No. 85)	£150	£225	
	a.	Dull purple	£225	£250	
124		4c. on $10 brown (No. 86)	£110	£225	
112/24		Set of 9	£350	£500	
112s/24s		Optd "Specimen" Set of 12	£190		

(b) 8½ mm between lines of surch. P 14.

125		4c. on $5 (No. 85)		6·50	14·00
126		4c. on $10 (No. 86)		6·50	14·00

No. 121 differs only from No. 87 in having the "4" and "cents" wider apart.

Examples of the Kudat postmark dated "AU 15 1899" struck on Nos. 112/24 are generally considered to be faked.

A new setting of the surcharge, with 2½ mm between "4" and "CENTS" for values to $2 and 3½ mm on the $5 and $10, was used for the Specimen overprints, including unissued surcharges on the 1c., 2c. and 3c. values (price £110 the set of three).

(Optd by Waterlow)

1901 (8 Oct)–**05**. *Optd as T* **49**.

(a) P 13½–14.

127		1c. (No. 92) (R.)	3·50	1·50	30
	a.	Perf 14½–15	2·50	1·75	30
128		2c. (No. 95) (R.)	3·75	1·25	30
	a.	Perf 16	3·50	14·00	40
	b.	Perf 14½–15	12·00	12·00	30
129		3c. (No. 96)	1·75	5·50	30
	a.	Imperf between (vert pair)	†	†	£1000
	b.	Perf 14½–15	9·00	2·75	30
	c.	Perf 13½–14, comp 14½–15	50·00		30
130		4c. on 99 (G.)		1·50	30
	a.	Perf 14½–15	23·00	1·50	40
131		5c. (No. 100) (G.)	48·00	3·50	30
	a.	Perf 14½–15	14·00	2·50	30
132		6c. (No. 101) (R.)	50·00	65·00	1·25

	a.	No stop after "Protectorate"	80·00	80·00	1·25
	b.	Perf 16	4·00	15·00	70
133		8c. (No. 103) (B.)	3·75	3·75	50
	a.	No stop after "Protectorate"	3·00	24·00	1·50
	b.	Perf 13½–14, comp 12–13	60·00	25·00	
	c.	Imperf horiz (vert pair)	†	†	£350
134		10c. (No. 104) (R.) (7.02)	60·00	5·00	1·00
	a.	Perf 14½–15	£100	32·00	1·75
	c.	Perf 13½–14. No stop after "Protectorate"	£190	—	8·50
	d.	Opt double	£750	†	£325
	e.	(No. 105)	£200	—	1·00
	f.	Imperf vert (horiz pair)	†	†	£550
135		12c. (No. 106) (R.)	50·00	12·00	1·50
	a.	Perf 14½–15			
136		16c. (No. 107) (7.02)	£140	26·00	2·25
	a.	Perf 14½–15	£130	50·00	2·25
	b.	Perf 13½–14 comp 12–13	£200	75·00	
137		18c. (No. 110) (R.)	12·00	25·00	1·25
	a.	No stop after "Protectorate"			
	b.	Perf 13½–14, comp 12–13	50·00		1·50
138		24c. (No. 111)	16·00	40·00	1·50
	a.	Perf 14½–15	60·00	90·00	1·75
	b.	Imperf between (horiz pair)			

(b) P 14.

139		25c. (No. 81) (R.)	2·00	10·00	50
	a.	No stop after "Protectorate"	£170	£190	24·00
	b.	Overprints tête-bêche (horiz pair)			
	c.	Overprint inverted	£500		
140		50c. (No. 82) (R.)	2·75	11·00	55
	a.	No stop after "Protectorate"	85·00	£150	—
	b.	Chalky blue			
141		$1 (No. 83) (R.) (1.04)	10·00	65·00	
142		$1 (No. 83)	6·50	38·00	2·50
	a.	Imperf horiz (vert pair)	£700	†	£375
	b.	Opt double			
	c.	Opt treble			
143		$2 (No. 84) (R.) (1903)	30·00	95·00	3·50
	a.	Opt double	£1200	†	£425
144		$5 (No. 85b) (R.) (2.05)	£225	£475	8·00
145		$10 (No. 86) (R.) (2.05)	£425	£750	11·00
	a.	Opt inverted	£1900	†	£450
127/45		Set of 18	£900	£1400	30·00
127s/40s		Optd "Specimen" Set of 14	£275		

There was more than one setting of the overprint for some of the values. Full sheets of the 6c. and 8c. are known, without stop throughout.

1904–05. *Surch locally with T* **50**.

(a) P 14½–15.

146		4c. on 5c. (No. 100a)	38·00	48·00	12·00
	a.	Surch omitted (in pair with normal)			
147		4c. on 6c. (No. 101a)	7·00	21·00	12·00
	a.	Surch inverted	£225		
148		4c. on 8c. (No. 102b)	13·00	26·00	12·00
	a.	Surch inverted	£300		
149		4c. on 12c. (No. 106b)	28·00	40·00	12·00
	a.	Perf 13½–14	48·00	60·00	12·00
	b.	Perf 13½–14 comp 12–13	28·00	60·00	—
	c.	Surch omitted (in pair with normal)			
150		4c. on 18c. (No. 110b)	14·00	38·00	12·00
	a.	Perf 13½–14			
151		4c. on 24c. (No. 111b)	23·00	50·00	12·00
	a.	Perf 16	17·00	50·00	12·00
	b.	Perf 13½–14	23·00	50·00	12·00
	c.	Perf 12–13			

(b) P 14.

152		4c. on 25c. (No. 81)	4·50	25·00	12·00
153		4c. on 50c. (No. 82)	5·00	38·00	12·00
154		4c. on $1 (No. 83)	6·00	48·00	12·00
155		4c. on $2 (No. 84)	6·00	48·00	12·00
156		4c. on $5 (No. 85)	12·00	48·00	12·00
	a.	Surch on No. 85b	30·00	50·00	—
157		4c. on $10 (No. 86)	12·00	48·00	12·00
	a.	Surch inverted	£2000		
	b.	Surch omitted (in pair with normal)			
146/57		Set of 12	£140	£425	£130

51 Malayan Tapir   **52** Travellers' Tree

53 Jesselton Railway Station   **54** The Sultan of Sulu, his staff and W. C. Cowie, Managing Director of the Company

55 Indian Elephant

56 Sumatran Rhinoceros

57 Ploughing with Buffalo

58 Wild Boar

59 Palm Cockatoo

60 Rhinoceros Hornbill

61 Banteng

62 Dwarf Cassowary

(Recess Waterlow)

1909 (1 July)–**23**. *Centres in black.* P 13½–14.

158	51	1c. chocolate-brown	7·00	1·50	30
		a. Perf 14½–15	42·00	13·00	40
159		1c. brown	18·00	1·60	30
		a. Perf 14½–15	35·00	4·00	30
		b. Imperf between (vert pair)	£1500		
160	52	2c. green	1·00	70	30
		a. Imperf between (pair)			
		a. Perf 14½–15	2·50	70	30
161	53	3c. lake	3·25	75	30
162		3c. rose-lake	2·75	2·75	50
		a. Perf 14½–15	35·00		55
163		3c. green (1923)	25·00	1·50	—
164	54	4c. scarlet	2·75	30	30
		a. Imperf between (vert pair)			35
		b. Perf 14½–15	17·00	2·00	
165	55	5c. yellow-brown	11·00	4·00	40
		a. Perf 14½–15			
166		5c. dark brown	23·00	5·50	
167	56	6c. olive-green	10·00	1·75	30
		a. Perf 14½–15	75·00	6·50	60
168		6c. apple-green	38·00	3·50	60
169	57	8c. lake	4·00	1·75	60
		a. Perf 14½–15			10·00
170	58	10c. greyish blue	45·00	8·00	1·25
		a. Perf 14½–15	90·00	35·00	—
171		10c. blue	50·00	3·75	—
172		10c. turquoise-blue	38·00	2·00	1·50
		a. Perf 14½–15	60·00	5·50	
173	59	12c. deep blue	28·00	3·50	1·00
		a. Perf 14½–15			10·00
		b. Imperf between (horiz pair).	†	†	£550
173c		12c. deep bright blue			
174	60	16c. brown-lake	26·00	7·00	1·00
175	61	18c. blue-green	95·00	32·00	1·00
176	62	24c. deep rose-lilac	28·00	3·50	1·75
		a. Deep lilac	38·00	6·00	
158/76		Set of 13	£250	55·00	
158s/76s		Optd "Specimen" Set of 13	£275		

For this issue perf 12½ see Nos. 277, etc.

20
CENTS
(63)   (64)   (65)

1909 (7 Sept). *No. 175 surch with T 63 by Waterlow.* P 13½–14.

177		20c. on 18c. blue-green (R.)	7·00	1·00	30
		a. Perf 14½–15	£200	65·00	
		s. Optd "Specimen"	45·00		

(Recess Waterlow)

1911 (7 Mar). P 13½–14.

178	64	25c. black and yellow-green	12·00	4·75	2·00
		a. Perf 14½–15	14·00	38·00	
		b. Imperf (pair)	50·00		
178c		25c. black and yellow-green	45·00		
179		50c. black and steel-blue	12·00	4·50	2·25
		a. Perf 14½–15	21·00	22·00	—

---

		ab. Imperf between (horiz pair)		£2500	
		c. Imperf (pair)	85·00		
180		$1 black and chestnut	17·00	4·00	3·00
		a. Perf 14½–15	50·00	15·00	6·50
		b. Imperf (pair)	£140		
181		$2 black and lilac	65·00	17·00	4·75
182	65	$5 black and lake	£120	£130	32·00
		a. Imperf (pair)	£180		
183		$10 black and brick-red	£400	£450	75·00
		a. Imperf (pair)	£425		
178/83		Set of 6	£550	£550	£100
178s/83s		Optd "Specimen" Set of 6	£300		

BRITISH

2 PROTECTORATE cents ✠
(66)   (67)   (68)

1912 (July). *Nos. 85b and 86 optd with T 66.*

184		$5 dull purple (R.)	£1200	£1400	8·50
185		$10 brown (R.)	£1600	—	8·50
		a. Opt inverted	†	†	—

1916 (Feb). *Nos. 162, 167 and 173 surch as T 67 by Govt Printing Office, Sandakan.* P 13½–14.

186	53	2c. on 3c. black and rose-lake	25·00	15·00
		a. "s" inverted (R. 2/5)	£100	95·00
		b. Surch double	£1600	
187	56	4c. on 6c. black and olive-green (R.)	22·00	17·00
		a. "s" inverted (R. 2/5)	95·00	95·00
		b. "s" inserted by hand	—	£900
		c. Perf 14½–15	£170	£170
		ca. "s" inverted (R. 2/5)	£160	£170
188	59	10c. on 12c. black and deep blue (R.)	55·00	65·00
		a. "s" inverted (R. 2/5)	£160	£170
		b. "s" inserted by hand	£1100	
186/8		Set of 3	90·00	85·00
186s/8s		Optd "Specimen" Set of 3	£120	

Nos. 186/8 were surcharged from a setting of 25 (5×5) on which the required face values were inserted.

1916 (May). *Stamps of 1909–11 optd with T 68 by Waterlow. Centres in black.* P 13½–14.

(a) Cross in vermilion (thick shiny ink).

189	51	1c. brown	7·50	35·00
190	52	2c. green	48·00	80·00
		a. Perf 14½–15	32·00	80·00
		ab. Opt double, one albino	£300	
191	53	3c. rose-lake	27·00	48·00
		a. Nos. 191 and 204 se-tenant (vert pair)	£2750	
192	54	4c. scarlet	5·50	32·00
		a. Perf 14½–15	£225	£160
193	55	5c. yellow-brown	40·00	55·00
		a. Perf 14½–15		
194	56	6c. apple-green	60·00	65·00
		a. Perf 14½–15	£200	£200
195	57	8c. lake	23·00	60·00
196	58	10c. blue	45·00	70·00
197	59	12c. deep blue	90·00	90·00
198	60	16c. brown-lake	90·00	90·00
199	61	20c. on18c. blue-green	42·00	90·00
200	62	24c. dull mauve	£110	£110
201	64	25c. green (P 14½–15)	£350	£425
		a. Imperf between (vert pair)		
189/201		Set of 13	£800	£1100

(b) Cross in shades of carmine (matt ink).

202	51	1c. brown	26·00	65·00
		a. Perf 14½–15	£200	
203	52	2c. green	27·00	50·00
		b. Perf 14½–15	£170	
		ba. Opt double	†	£1400
204	53	3c. rose-lake	42·00	65·00
204a	54	4c. scarlet	£700	£800
205	55	5c. yellow-brown	55·00	70·00
206	56	6c. apple-green	50·00	65·00
		a. Perf 14½–15	£170	£190
207	57	8c. lake	27·00	55·00
208	58	10c. blue	50·00	70·00
209	59	12c. deep blue	85·00	£110
210	60	16c. brown-lake	95·00	£110
211	61	20c. on18c. blue-green	85·00	£100
212	62	24c. dull mauve	£100	£140
213	64	25c. green	£750	
		a. Perf 14½–15	£425	£475
202/13a		(ex 4c.) Set of 12	£900	£1200

The British North Borneo Company donated a proportion of the above issue to be sold by the National Philatelic War Fund for the benefit of the Red Cross and St. John's Ambulance Brigade.

RED CROSS   ✚

TWO CENTS   FOUR CENTS
(69)   (70)

1918 (Aug). *Stamps of 1909–11 surch as T 69.* P 13½–14.

(a) Lines of surcharge 9 mm apart.

214	51	1c.+2c. brown	3·50	12·00
		a. Imperf between (horiz pair)	£2250	
215	52	2c.+2c. green	1·00	8·50
		a. Imperf between (horiz or vert pair)	£3000	
		b. Imperf (pair)		
		c. Perf 14½–15		
216	53	3c.+2c. rose-red	14·00	19·00
		a. Imperf between (horiz pair)	£3000	

217		b. Perf 14½–15	25·00	65·00
		3c.+2c. dull rose-carmine	£150	
		a. Perf 14½–15	£190	
218	54	4c.+2c. scarlet	70	5·00
		a. Surch inverted	£425	
219	55	5c.+2c. deep brown	8·00	23·00
220		5c.+2c. pale brown	8·50	28·00
221	56	6c.+2c. olive-green	5·00	24·00
		a. Perf 14½–15	£200	£225
221b		6c.+2c. apple-green	£275	
		a. Perf 14½–15	£275	
222	57	8c.+2c. lake	5·50	11·00
		a. Inverted figure "3" for "C" in "CENTS"		
223	58	10c.+2c. blue	8·00	24·00
224	59	12c.+2c. deep bright blue	21·00	45·00
		a. Surch inverted	£650	
225	60	16c.+2c. brown-lake	22·00	45·00
226	62	24c.+2c. mauve	22·00	45·00

(b) Lines of surch 13–14 mm apart.

227	52	2c.+2c. green	85·00	£160
228	56	6c.+2c. olive-green	£475	£850
228	64	25c.+2c. green	10·00	42·00
230		50c.+2c. steel-blue	12·00	42·00
231		$1+2c. chestnut	45·00	50·00
		a. Surcharge double, one albino	£275	
232		$2+2c. lilac	75·00	95·00
233	65	$5+2c. lake	£350	£550
234		$10+2c. brick-red	£375	£550
214/34		Set of 17	£850	£1400

The above stamps were dispatched from London in three consignments, of which two were lost through enemy action at sea.

Only one sheet was found of No. 228.

These stamps were sold at a premium of 2c. per stamp, which went to the Red Cross Society.

1918 (Oct). *Stamps of 1909–11 surch with T 70, in red.* P 13½–14.

235	51	1c.+4c. chocolate	60	5·00
		a. Imperf between (horiz pair)	£2000	
236	52	2c.+4c. green	65	8·00
237	53	3c.+4c. rose-lake	1·00	3·75
238	54	4c.+4c. scarlet	40	4·75
239	55	5c.+4c. brown	2·00	22·00
240	56	6c.+4c. apple-green	1·90	12·00
		a. Imperf between (vert pair)	£1800	
241	57	8c.+4c. lake	1·25	9·50
242	58	10c.+4c. turquoise-blue	3·75	12·00
242a		10c.+4c. greenish blue	8·50	40·00
243	59	12c.+4c. deep blue	14·00	14·00
		a. Surch double	£1100	
244	60	16c.+4c. brown-lake	8·00	16·00
245	62	24c.+4c. mauve	11·00	20·00
246	64	25c.+4c. yellow-green	6·00	50·00
247		25c.+4c. blue-green	27·00	75·00
248		50c.+4c. steel-blue	15·00	45·00
		a. Perf 14½–15	60·00	
249		$1+4c. chestnut	18·00	60·00
		a. Perf 14½–15	£130	
250		$2+4c. lilac	50·00	80·00
251	65	$5+4c. lake	£275	£400
252		$10+4c. brick-red	£300	£400
235/52		Set of 17	£650	£1000

Nos. 235/52 were sold at face, plus 4c. on each stamp for Red Cross Funds.

Examples of a double-ring "SANDAKAN N. BORNEO" postmark dated "1 NOV 1918" on these stamps are generally considered to be faked.

THREE

MALAYA-BORNEO EXHIBITION 1922.
▬CENTS▬
(71)   (72)

1922 (31 Mar). *Malaya-Borneo Exhibition, Singapore. Stamps of 1909–22 some in different shades, optd as T 71 by Govt Printing Office, Sandakan.* P 13½–14.

253	51	1c. brown (R.)	14·00	65·00
		a. "BORHEO"	£325	£425
		b. "BORNEQ"	£475	£600
		c. Stop after "EXHIBITION."	80·00	
		d. Raised stop after "1922"	£550	£650
		e. "EXHIBITICN." with stop	£650	
		f. Perf 14½–15	30·00	70·00
		fa. "BORHEO"	£550	
		fb. "BORNEQ"	£800	
		fc. Raised stop after "1922"	£800	
		fd. "EXHIBITICN." with stop	£1000	
		fe. "MHLAYA" and stop after "EXHIBITION"	£3000	
		ff. Stop after "EXHIBITION."	£140	
253g		1c. brown (B.) (P 14½–15)	£1300	
		ga. Vert pair, with and without opt	£3500	
		gb. Raised stop after "1922."	£3500	
		gc. "BORHEO"	£3000	
		gd. "BORNEQ"	£3750	
		gf. "EXHIBITICN." with stop	£3750	
		gg. "MHLAYA" and stop after "EXHIBITION"		
254		1c. orange-brown (R.)	30·00	65·00
255	52	2c. green (R.)	2·00	23·00
		a. Stop after "EXHIBITION."	32·00	
256	53	3c. rose-lake (B.)	15·00	60·00
		a. Stop after "EXHIBITION."	80·00	£225
		b. "EXHIBITICN." with stop	£2750	

257	**54**	c. Raised stop after "1922"	£1800		
		4c. scarlet (B.)....................	3·00	38·00
		a. Stop after "EXHIBITION."	38·00	
		b. Perf 14½–15	80·00	
		ba. Stop after "EXHIBITION."	£375	
258	**55**	5c. orange-brown (B.)..........	9·00	60·00
		a. Imperf between (vert pair)	£1400	£1500
		b. Stop after "EXHIBITION."	70·00	
		c. Opt double	£1900	
		d. Opt double (with stop)	£4250	
259		5c. chestnut (B.)..........	20·00	65·00
		a. Stop after "EXHIBITION."	95·00	
260	**56**	6c. apple-green (R.).....	9·00	65·00
		a. Stop after "EXHIBITION."	60·00	
		b. Opt double	£1800	
		c. Opt double (with stop)	£4250	
261	**57**	8c. dull rose (B.).....	6·00	42·00
		a. Stop after "EXHIBITION."	75·00	
262		8c. deep rose-lake (B.).....	7·00	50·00
		a. Stop after "EXHIBITION."	80·00	
263	**58**	10c. turquoise-blue (R.)..........	14·00	60·00
		a. Stop after "EXHIBITION."	90·00	
		b. Perf 14½–15	38·00	
		ba. Stop after "EXHIBITION."	£200	
264		10c. greenish blue (R.)	14·00	75·00
		a. Stop after "EXHIBITION."	90·00	
265	**59**	12c. deep blue (R.)	9·00	21·00
		a. Stop after "EXHIBITION."	80·00	£160
266		12c. deep bright blue (R.)	38·00	
		a. Stop after "EXHIBITION."	£200	
267	**60**	16c. brown-lake (B.).................	20·00	65·00
		a. Stop after "EXHIBITION."	£110	
		b. Opt in red	£7000	
268	**61**	20c. on 18c. blue-green (B.).....	21·00	80·00
		a. Stop after "EXHIBITION."	£190	
269		20c. on 18c. blue-green (R.).....	21·00	£140
		a. Stop after "EXHIBITION."	£225	£400
270	**62**	24c. mauve (R.).....	38·00	70·00
		a. Stop after "EXHIBITION."	£180	£325
271		24c. lilac (R.)	38·00	70·00
		a. Stop after "EXHIBITION."	£180	
272		24c. reddish lilac (R.)	45·00	80·00
		a. Stop after "EXHIBITION."	£200	
273	**64**	25c. blue-green (R.).....	21·00	75·00
		a. Stop after "EXHIBITION."	£170	
274		25c. yellow-green (R.)...........	8·00	60·00
		a. Stop after "EXHIBITION."	£120	
		b. Opt double	£3000	
		c. Perf 14½–15	13·00	70·00
		ca. Stop after "EXHIBITION."	£200	
		cb. Opt double	£3250	
275		50c. steel-blue (R.).....	12·00	60·00
		a. Stop after "EXHIBITION."	£140	
		b. Perf 14½–15	23·00	80·00
		ba. Stop after "EXHIBITION."	£180	
253/75 *Set of 14*			£160	£700
253s/75s *Optd* "Specimen" *Set of 14*			£450	

These overprints were applied from a number of settings covering 10, 20, 25 or 30 stamps at a time.

Of the ten settings known for the horizontal stamps the earliest were only used for the 1c. on which most of the varieties occur. Of the others the vast majority come from settings of 20 (10×2) with the stop after "EXHIBITION" variety on R. 2/7, or 25 (5×5) on which the same variety can be found on R. 5/4. In addition the 3c. comes from a different setting of 20 (10×2) on which there is a raised stop after "1922" on R. 2/8 and EXHIBITICN. on R. 2/9.

The 1c. sequence is complicated, but additionally includes a setting of 10 with "BORHEO" on stamps 3 and 10, BORNEQ" on stamp 4, raised stop on stamp 8 and "EXHIBITICN." on stamp 9. A setting of 20 repeats this sequence on its bottom line as does one of 30, although in this instance "MHLAYA" replaces "EXHIBITICN" as the variety on stamp 9.

For the vertical stamps (2, 6, 10, 12, 16 and 20c. on 18c.) the settings were of 20 (10×2) or 25 (5×5). The stop after "EXHIBITION" occurs on R. 2/7 of the former and R. 5/4 of the latter.

The 25c. and 50c. high values were overprinted from a setting of 20 (10×2), with the stop after "EXHIBITION" on R. 2/7, or 25 (5×5).

1923 (Oct). T **54** *surch with* T **72**.

276		3c. on 4c. black and scarlet	1·50	6·00
		a. Surch double	£1000	
		s. Optd "Specimen"	50·00	

1925–28. *Designs as 1909–22 issue with centres in black and some frame colours changed.* P 12½.

277	**51**	1c. chocolate-brown................	1·00	70
		Imperf between (horiz pair).........................	£1200	
278	**52**	2c. claret	85	60
		a. Imperf between (vert pair).	—	£950
		b. Imperf between (horiz pair).........................		
279	**53**	3c. green	3·00	75
		a. Imperf between (horiz pair).........................	†	£1300
280	**54**	4c. scarlet	50	10
		a. Imperf between (vert pair).	£275	£375

---

		b. Imperf between (horiz pair)..........	£750	
		c. Imperf between (vert strip of three)..........	£1100	
281	**55**	5c. yellow-brown..................	5·50	2·75
		a. Imperf between (vert pair).	£950	
282	**56**	6c. olive-green..................	6·50	90
283	**57**	8c. carmine..................	3·50	50
		a. Imperf between (vert pair).	£500	
		b. Imperf between (horiz pair)..........		
		c. Imperf between (vert strip of four)..........	£1600	
284	**58**	10c. turquoise-blue..................	3·75	90
		a. Imperf between (horiz pair)..........	£900	£1200
		b. Imperf between (vert pair).		
285	**59**	12c. deep blue..................	21·00	80
286	**60**	16c. red-brown..................	28·00	£170
287	**61**	20c. on18c. blue-green (R.)..........	9·50	3·00
288	**62**	24c. violet..................	55·00	£140
289	**64**	25c. green..................	9·50	4·25
290		50c. steel-blue..................	16·00	14·00
291		$1 chestnut..................	19·00	£350
292		$2 mauve..................	65·00	£400
293	**65**	$5 lake (1928)..........	£160	£900
294		$10 orange-red (1928)	£400	£950
277/94 *Set of 18*			£700	£2500

Examples of No. 278 were supplied for U.P.U. distribution punched with a 3½ mm diameter hole. Examples of the 16c., 24c., $1, $2, $5 and $10 in this perforation were not supplied to the territory for postal purposes. Used examples exist from covers prepared by stamp dealers.

73 Head of a Murut

74 Orang-Utan

75 Dyak warrior

76 Mount Kinabalu

77 Clouded Leopard

78 Badge of the Company

79 Arms of the Company

80 Arms of the Company

(Eng J. A. C. Harrison. Recess Waterlow)

1931 (1 Jan). *50th Anniv of British North Borneo Company.* T **73/80**. P 12½.

295	**73**	3c. black and blue-green..................	1·25	80
296	**74**	6c. black and orange..................	16·00	3·25
297	**75**	9c. black and scarlet..................	4·25	13·00
298	**76**	12c. black and ultramarine..........	4·75	8·00
299	**77**	25c. black and violet..................	38·00	35·00
300	**78**	$1 black and yellow-green..........	27·00	£100
301	**79**	$2 black and chestnut..................	48·00	£110
302	**80**	$5 black and purple..................	£150	£450
295/302 *Set of 8*			£250	£650
295s/302s *Optd* "Specimen" *Set of 8*			£300	

Examples of all values are known showing a forged Jesselton postmark dated "22 AUG 1931".

---

81 Buffalo Transport

82 Palm Cockatoo

83 Native

84 Proboscis Monkey

85 Mounted Bajaus

86 Eastern Archipelago

87 Orang-Utan

88 Murut with blowpipe

89 Dyak

90 River scene

91 Native boat

92 Mt. Kinabalu

93 Badge of the Company

94 Arms of the Company

95 Arms of the Company

(Eng J. A. C. Harrison. Recess Waterlow)

1939 (1 Jan). T **81/95**. P 12½.

303	**81**	1c. green and red-brown..................	3·50	1·75
304	**82**	2c. purple and greenish blue..........	5·00	1·75
305	**83**	3c. slate-blue and green..........	4·00	2·00
306	**84**	4c. bronze-green and violet..........	9·00	50
307	**85**	6c. deep blue and claret..........	8·50	9·50
308	**86**	8c. scarlet..................	12·00	1·50
309	**87**	10c. violet and bronze-green..........	38·00	6·00
310	**88**	12c. green and royal blue..........	30·00	6·50
		a. Green and blue	55·00	8·00
311	**89**	15c. blue-green and brown..........	25·00	9·00
312	**90**	20c. violet and slate-blue..........	18·00	4·50
313	**91**	25c. green and chocolate..........	23·00	12·00
		a. Vignette printed double, one albino.		
314	**92**	50c. chocolate and violet..........	26·00	9·50
315	**93**	$1 brown and carmine..........	85·00	19·00
316	**94**	$2 green and olive-green..........	£130	£110
317	**95**	$5 indigo and pale blue..........	£350	£225
303/17 *Set of 15*			£700	£375
303s/17s Perf "Specimen" *Set of 15*			£425	

Examples of most values are known showing forged Jesselton

postmarks dated "22 AUG 1941" or "15 JA 48".

No. 313a has the albino impression sideways.

WAR TAX (96) WAR TAX (97)

1941 (24 Feb). *Nos.* 303/4 *optd at Sandakan with T* **96**/**7**.
318		1c. green and red-brown	1·75	3·50
		a. Optd front and back	£450	
319		2c. purple and greenish blue	7·00	4·00

The 1c. was for compulsory use on internal mail and the 2c. on overseas mail, both in addition to normal postage.

BRITISH MILITARY ADMINISTRATION

North Borneo, including Labuan, was occupied by the Japanese in January 1942. Australian forces landed on Labuan on 10 June 1945 and by the end of the war against Japan on 14 August had liberated much of western North Borneo. The territory was placed under British Military Administration on 5 January 1946.

BMA (98)   𝒢𝓡 (99)

1945 (17 Dec). *Nos.* 303/17 *optd with T* **98**.
320	81	1c. green and red-brown	9·00	2·00
321	82	2c. purple and greenish blue	14·00	2·00
		a. Opt double	£6500	
322	83	3c. slate-blue and green	1·25	1·25
323	84	4c. bronze-green and violet	16·00	16·00
324	85	6c. deep blue and claret	1·25	1·25
325	86	8c. scarlet	3·00	75
326	87	10c. violet and bronze-green	3·00	40
327	88	12c. green and blue	6·00	2·75
		a. Green and royal blue	9·00	1·25
328	89	15c. blue-green and brown	1·50	1·00
329	90	20c. violet and slate-blue	1·50	1·50
330	91	25c. green and chocolate	6·50	1·50
331	92	50c. chocolate and violet	3·00	1·75
332	93	$1 brown and carmine	48·00	40·00
333	94	$2 violet and olive-green	50·00	32·00
		a. Opt double	£3250	
334	95	$5 indigo and pale blue	23·00	14·00
320/34	*Set of 15*		£170	£100

These stamps and the similarly overprinted stamps of Sarawak were obtainable at all post offices throughout British Borneo (Brunei, Labuan, North Borneo and Sarawak), for use on local and overseas mail.

CROWN COLONY

North Borneo became a Crown Colony on 15 July 1946.

Lower bar broken at right (R. 8/3)   Lower bar broken at left (R. 8/4 and R. 8/8)

1947 (1 Sept–22 Dec). *Nos.* 303 *to* 317 *optd with T* **99** *and bars obliterating words* "THE STATE OF" *and* "BRITISH PROTECTORATE".
335	81	1c. green and red-brown (15.12)	15	1·00
		b. Lower bar broken at right	20·00	38·00
		c. Lower bar broken at left	18·00	35·00
336	82	2c. purple and greenish blue (22.12)	1·75	90
337	83	3c. slate-blue and green (R.) (22.12)	15	90
338	84	4c. bronze-green and violet	70	90
339	85	6c. deep blue and claret (R.) (22.12)	25	20
340	86	8c. scarlet	30	20
		b. Lower bar broken at right	22·00	22·00
341	87	10c. violet and bronze-green (15.12)	1·50	40
342	88	12c. green and royal blue (22.12)	2·00	2·75
		a. Green and blue	8·00	7·00
343	89	15c. blue-green and brown (22.12)	2·25	30
344	90	20c. violet and slate-blue (22.12)	2·75	85
		b. Lower bar broken at right	45·00	32·00
345	91	25c. green and chocolate (22.12)	2·75	50
		b. Lower bar broken at right	65·00	32·00
346	92	50c. chocolate and violet (22.12)	2·75	85
		b. Lower bar broken at right	65·00	32·00
		c. Lower bar broken at left	60·00	30·00
347	93	$1 brown and carmine (22.12)	6·50	1·75
348	94	$2 violet and olive-green (22.12)	15·00	17·00
349	95	$5 indigo and pale blue (R.) (22.12)	23·00	17·00
		b. Lower bar broken at right	£160	£160
335/49	*Set of 15*		55·00	40·00
335s/49s	Perf "Specimen" *Set of 15*		£275	

1948 (1 Nov). *Royal Silver Wedding. As Nos.* 112/13 *of Antigua.*
350		8c. scarlet	30	80
351		$10 mauve	23·00	35·00

1949 (10 Oct). *75th Anniv of U.P.U. As Nos.* 114/17 *of Antigua.*
352		8c. carmine	60	30
353		10c. brown	3·25	1·50
354		30c. orange-brown	1·25	1·75
355		55c. blue	1·25	2·50
352/5	*Set of 4*		5·50	5·50

100 Mount Kinabalu   101 Native musical instrument

102 Coconut Grove   103 Hemp drying

104 Cattle at Kota Belud   105 Map

106 Log pond   107 Malay prau, Sandakan

108 Bajau Chief   109 Suluk river canoe, Lahad Datu

110 Clock Tower Jesselton   111 Bajau horsemen

112 Murut with blowpipe   113 Net-fishing

114 Arms of North Borneo

(Photo Harrison)

1950 (1 July)–**52**. *T* **100**/**114**. *Chalk-surfaced paper.* Wmk Mult Script CA. P 13½×14½ (horiz), 14½×13½ (vert).
356	100	1c. red-brown	15	1·25
357	101	2c. blue	15	50
358	102	3c. green	15	15
359	103	4c. bright purple	15	10
360	104	5c. violet	15	10
361	105	8c. scarlet	1·25	85
362	106	10c. maroon	1·50	15
363	107	15c. ultramarine	2·00	65
364	108	20c. brown	1·75	10
365	109	30c. olive-brown	40	20
366	110	50c. rose-carmine ("JESSLETON")	1·00	3·25
366a		50c. rose-carmine ("JESSELTON") (1.5.52)	10·00	2·75
367	111	$1 red-orange	4·00	1·00
368	112	$2 grey-green	7·00	14·00
369	113	$5 emerald-green	16·00	22·00
370	114	$10 dull blue	40·00	65·00
356/70	*Set of 16*		80·00	£100

POSTAL FISCALS

Three Cents. Revenue (F 1) (Raised stop)   Ten Cents. Revenue (F 2)

1886. *Regular issues surch as Type F* **1** *or F* **2**.
F1	1	3c. on 4c. pink (No. 6)	£130	£180
		a. Raised stop after "Cents"	£110	£170
F2		5c. on 8c. green (No. 7)	£130	£180

		a. Raised stop after "Cents"	£110	£170
F3	4	10c. on 50c. violet (No. 4)	£170	£1100
		a. Surch double	—	£1100
		b. No stop after "Cents" and stop after "Revenue."	£450	£500
		c. Inverted "L" for first "F" in "FIFTY" (R. 5/2)	—	£850

It is believed that Nos. F1/2 were each surcharged from a horizontal setting of five so that the raised stop variety occurs on every stamp in the first, second, third, sixth, seventh and eighth vertical columns in the sheets of 50 (10×5).

POSTAGE DUE STAMPS

POSTAGE DUE (D 1)

1895 (1 Aug)–**97**. *Nos.* 68/79 *optd with Type* D **1** *horizontally (8, 12, 18 and 24c.) or vertically, reading upwards (others). P* 14½–15.
D1	25	2c. black and rose-lake	23·00	40·00	2·75
		a. Opt double*	†	†	£300
		b. Opt vertical, reading downwards*	†	†	£350
D2		2c. black and lake	18·00	24·00	2·25
		a. Perf 13½–14			
		b. Perf 13½–14, comp 12–13*	†	†	10·00
		c. Opt omitted (in vert pair with normal)*	†	†	£1700
D3	26	3c. olive-green and dull purple	6·00	16·00	1·00
		a. Bronze-green and dull purple			
		b. Opt vertical, reading downwards*	†	†	
D4		3c. olive-green and violet			
		a. Perf 13½–14	†	†	£425
		b. Opt double*	†	†	
D5	27	5c. black and vermilion	55·00	25·00	3·00
		a. Printed double	—	—	
		b. With stop after "DUE" in opt (1897)	£225		
		c. Opt double	£700	£750	†
		d. Perf 13½–14	—	50·00	2·50
		e. Perf 13½–14, comp 12–13	—	55·00	
D6	28	6c. black and bistre-brown	55·00	70·00	2·50
		a. Perf 13½–14	16·00	48·00	2·50
		b. Perf 12–13*	†	†	
		c. Perf 13½–14, comp 12–13			
		d. Opt vertical, reading downwards*	†	†	
D7	29	8c. black and dull purple	50·00	50·00	2·75
		a. Opt double*	†	†	£350
		b. Perf 13½–14			
		ba. Opt inverted*	†	†	£190
		c. Perf 13½–14, comp 12–13	65·00		
D8	30	12c. black and blue	—	50·00	2·50
		a. Opt double*	†	†	£375
		b. Perf 13½–14	70·00	50·00	2·50
		c. Perf 13½–14, comp 14½–15	90·00		
D9		12c. black & ultram (P 13½–14)	80·00	60·00	
D10	31	18c. black and deep green	70·00	60·00	4·00
		a. Opt inverted	£350	£400	†
		b. Perf 13½–14	75·00	80·00	4·00
		ba. Opt double*	†	†	£300
		c. Opt vertical, reading upwards (1897)	75·00	95·00	4·50
		ca. Opt vertical, reading downwards	£450	£325	†
D11	32	24c. blue and rose-lake	70·00	85·00	4·00
		a. Opt double*	†	†	£325
		b. Perf 13½–14	29·00	55·00	4·00
		c. Perf 13½–14, comp 14½–15			

D3s, D5s, D8s, D10cs, D11s Optd "Specimen" *Set of 5* ... £150

There were two local overprintings of these stamps which show variations in the distance between the two words. Further overprints were produced in London for sale to dealers by the British North Borneo Company. Those listings marked with an * only exist from the London overprinting and are usually only known cancelled-to-order.

No. D5b comes from at least one sheet which was included in a later overprinting.

1897–99. *Nos.* 94/7, 99/103, 106, 108/11 *optd with Type* D **1** *horizontally (8c.) or vertically reading upwards (others).* P 14½–15.
D12	35	2c. black and lake (1898)	8·50	9·00	1·50
		a. Perf 13½–14	32·00		
		b. Opt horizontal*	†	†	£140
		s. Optd "Specimen"	27·00		
D13		2c. black and green (P 13½–14)*	50·00		70
		a. Perf 13½–14, comp 12–13*	†	†	90
		b. Perf 16*	†	†	
		c. Perf 12–13*	†	†	
		d. Opt vertical, reading downwards*			
		e. Opt horizontal*	£140		
D14	36	3c. green and rosy mauve*	20·00	†	50
		a. Perf 13½–14*	35·00	†	1·25
		b. Perf 13½–14, comp 14½–15*			
		c. Opt double*			
D15		3c. green and dull mauve	21·00	40·00	
D16	37	4c. black and carmine *	—	†	1·00
		a. Perf 13½–14	45·00	†	50
D17	38	5c. black & orange-verm (1899)	60·00	60·00	90
		a. Perf 13½–14	20·00	48·00	1·75
D18	39	6c. black and bistre-brown	5·50	30·00	70
		a. Perf 13½–14	—	35·00	50
		b. Perf 13½–14, comp 12–13*	—	†	2·00

D19	40	s. Optd "Specimen"	27·00		
		8c. black & brown-purple (1898)	65·00	80·00	†
		a. Opt vertical, reading upwards (P 16)*		†	£275
		s. Optd "Specimen"	27·00		
D20		8c. blk & brn (opt vert, reading upwards)*			
			7·00	†	50
		a. Opt vertical, reading downwards*		†	£600
		b. Perf 13½–14*		†	
D21	42	12c. black and dull blue*	—	†	5·00
		a. Perf 13½–14*	£100	†	4·00
D22	44	18c. black and green (P 16)*		†	£750
D23	46	18c. black and green (P 13½–14)*	55·00	†	4·00
		a. Perf 13½–14, comp 12–13*	£100	†	4·00
D24	45	24c. blue and lake*		†	£375
D25	47	24c. blue and lake*	27·00	†	2·25
		a. Perf 13½–14*		†	

In addition to local overprints, stamps from the 1897–1902 series were also overprinted by Waterlow on two occasions for sale by the British North Borneo Company to dealers from London. These Waterlow overprints were not supplied to North Borneo for postal purposes and are indicated by an * in the above listing.

1901–02. Nos. 96/7, 100 and 102/3 optd locally as Type D **1**, but with stop after "DUE", horizontally (8c.) or vertically reading upwards (others). P 13½–14.

D26	36	3c. green and rosy mauve (1902)	50·00	70·00
		a. Opt double	£250	
D27		3c. green & dull mve (P 14½–15) (1902)	50·00	70·00
		a. Opt double	£250	£275
D28	38	5c. black & orange-verm (P 14½–15)	60·00	
D29	40	8c. black and brown-purple (P 14½–15)	23·00	75·00
D30		8c. black and brown (P 14½–15)	£160	£190

1902 (10 Oct)–**12.** Stamps of 1901–05 (optd "BRITISH PROTECTORATE") further optd with Type D **1** locally (No. D31) or by Waterlow (others). P 13½–14.

(a) Optd horizontally showing stop after "DUE".

D31	34	1c. black and bistre-brown	4·50	55·00
		a. With raised stop after "DUE"	4·75	60·00

(b) Optd vertically reading upwards.

D32	35	2c. black and green (P 16)	£400	£190
D33	36	3c. green and rosy mauve	£100	£120
D34	38	5c. black & orange-verm (P 14½–15)	£180	£120
D35	40	8c. black and brown	£160	95·00
D36	47	24c. blue and lake	£200	£100

(c) Optd horizontally at centre of stamp.

D37	34	1c. black and bistre-brown*	—	†	28·00
		a. Perf 14½–15*	£225	†	28·00
D38	35	2c. black and green (1909)	16·00	3·75	30
		a. Perf 14½–15 (1903)	50·00	45·00	†
D39	36	3c. green and rosy mauve (1912)	5·50	3·25	30
		a. Perf 14½–15 (1904)	50·00	38·00	†
		ab. Type D **1** opt double	£425		
D40	37	4c. black and carmine (1912)	14·00	6·50	30
		a. Type D **1** opt double*	£550	†	£150
		b. Perf 14½–15 (1.3.03)	7·50	17·00	1·00
D41	38	5c. black & orange-verm (1905)	26·00	4·50	30
		a. Perf 14½–15 (1905)	70·00	27·00	†
D42	39	6c. black & bistre-brown (1912)	18·00	11·00	40
		a. Type D **1** opt inverted*	£450	†	£110
		b. Type D **1** opt double	£650	—	
		c. No stop after "PROTECTORATE" (1912)			
		d. Perf 16 (1906)	75·00	38·00	†
D43	40	8c. black and brown (1912)	20·00	4·25	40
		a. No stop after "PROTECTORATE" (1903)	50·00	60·00	†
D44	41	10c. brown and slate-lilac (1906)	£200	70·00	4·25
		a. No stop after "PROTECTORATE" (1906)	—		†
D45		10c. brown and slate-blue (1912)	90·00	20·00	1·40
D46	42	12c. black and dull blue (2.12.10)	28·00	17·00	2·50
D47	43	16c. green and chestnut (2.12.10)	48·00	22·00	2·50
D48	46	18c. black and green (2.12.10)	11·00	19·00	1·50
		a. Type D **1** opt double*	£500	†	70·00
		b. Imperf between (vert pair)	—	†	£700
D49	47	24c. blue and lake (1905)	11·00	26·00	2·50
		a. Perf 14½–15 (1909)	—	—	†
		b. Type D **1** opt double*	£300	†	90·00

(d) Optd horizontally at top of stamp.

D50	35	2c. black and green (P 16) (1906)	85·00	40·00	
		a. Perf 14½–15 (1908)	70·00	45·00	
D51	37	4c. black and carmine (1906)	65·00	23·00	

Items marked * only occur in stocks obtained from the British North Borneo Company in London.

POSTAGE DUE   POSTAGE DUE
(D **2**)   (D **3**)

Type D **2**. Thick letters. Ends of "S" and top of "G" straight. Pointed beard to "G".

Type D **3**. Thinner letters. Ends of "S" and top of "G" slanted. Square beard to "G".

1918–30. Opt with Type D **2** locally.

(a) On stamps of 1909–23. P 13½–14.

D52	52	2c. black and green (opt at foot) (1.24)	11·00	75·00
		a. Perf 14½–15	20·00	80·00
		s. Optd "Specimen"	28·00	
D53	53	3c. black and green (opt at foot) (1.9.23)	4·50	42·00
D54	54	4c. black and scarlet (opt at top) (10.18)	90·00	17·00
D55		4c. black and scarlet (opt at foot) (1.22)	1·00	1·25
D56		4c. black & scarlet (opt in centre) (5.23)	—	14·00
D57	55	5c. black & yell-brn (opt at foot) (1.22)	9·50	24·00
D58		5c. blk & yell-brn (opt in centre) (1.23)	13·00	24·00
D59	56	6c. black & ol-grn (opt at foot) (1.9.23)	11·00	12·00
D60		6c. black & ol-grn (opt in centre) (6.23)	17·00	7·50
D61	—	6c. blk & apple-grn (opt at foot) (1.9.23)	10·00	16·00
D62	57	8c. blk & rose-lake (opt at foot) (1.9.23)	1·50	1·50
		a. Opt double	£900	
D63	58	10c. black & turq-bl (opt at foot) (1.8.24)	13·00	19·00
		a. Perf 14½–15	80·00	£160
D64	59	12c. black and deep blue (1.8.24)	60·00	50·00
		a. Horiz pair, one without opt	£13000	
D65	60	16c. black and brown-lake (2.29)	19·00	50·00
		a. Black and red-brown		
		s. Optd "Specimen"	30·00	

(b) On stamps of 1925–28 with opt at foot. P 12½ (1928–30).

D66	52	2c. black and claret (3.30)	75	1·75
D67	53	3c. black and green (1926)	9·00	27·00
D68	54	4c. black and scarlet (1926)	1·50	2·00
D69	55	5c. black and yellow-brown (1926)	8·00	90·00
D70	56	6c. black and olive-green (3.28)	8·50	2·75
D71	57	8c. black and carmine (2.28)	4·25	18·00
D72	58	10c. black and turquoise-blue (1926)	11·00	90·00
D73	59	12c. black and deep blue (1926)	32·00	£160

Dates given as month and year only indicate first known postmark where recorded.

1930–38. Optd with Type D **3**, locally, at foot of stamp.

(a) On stamps of 1909–23. P 13½–14.

D74	57	8c. black and carmine (1931)	—	1·50
D75	60	16c. black and brown-lake (11.31)	17·00	75·00
		a. Black and red-brown	6·50	

(b) On stamps of 1925–28. P 12½.

D76	52	2c. black and claret (5.31)	50	2·00
D77	53	3c. black and green (11.38)	8·00	27·00
D78	54	4c. black and scarlet (6.36)		2·25
D79	55	5c. black and yellow-brown	15·00	
D80	56	6c. black and olive-green (12.30)	6·50	2·50
D81	57	8c. black and carmine (9.31)	3·75	18·00
D82	58	10c. black and turquoise-blue (12.32)	15·00	90·00
D83	59	12c. black and deep blue	40·00	
D84	60	16c. black and red-brown	65·00	£200

Dates given are those of earliest postmark where recorded.

D **4** Crest of the Company

(Recess Waterlow)

1939 (1 Jan). P 12½.

D85	D **4**	2c. brown	6·50	75·00
D86		4c. scarlet	6·50	£100
D87		6c. violet	23·00	£130
D88		8c. green	24·00	£225
D89		10c. blue	55·00	£350
D85/9 Set of 5			£100	£800
D85s/9s Perf "Specimen" Set of 5			£160	

LABUAN
CROWN COLONY

The island of Labuan, off the northern coast of Borneo, was ceded to Great Britain by the Sultan of Brunei in December 1846.

Stamps of STRAITS SETTLEMENTS were used from 1867 until 1879. Covers of 1864 and 1865 are known from Labuan franked with stamps of INDIA or HONG KONG.

PRICES FOR STAMPS ON COVER

Nos. 1/4	
Nos. 5/10	from × 50
Nos. 11/13	
Nos. 14/21	from × 40
Nos. 22/5	
Nos. 26/35	from × 50
Nos. 36/8	
Nos. 39/47	from × 100
Nos. 49/50	from × 15
Nos. 51/7	from × 60
Nos. 62/74	from × 15
Nos. 75/9	from × 40
Nos. 80/8	from × 20
Nos. 89/97	from × 15
Nos. 98/116	from × 10

PRICES FOR STAMPS ON COVER

Nos. 117/28	from × 30
Nos. 129/37	from × 10
Nos. 138/42	from × —
Nos. D1/9	from × 30

1   (2)   (3)

(Recess D.L.R.)

1879 (May). Wmk CA over Crown, sideways. P 14.

1	**1**	2c. blue-green	£1100	£800
2		6c. orange-brown	£200	£170
		a. No dot at upper left (R. 2/4)	£450	£375
3		12c. carmine	£1600	£700
		a. No right foot to second Chinese character (R. 2/3)	£3000	£1200
4		16c. blue	60·00	£130

This watermark is always found sideways, and extends over two stamps, a single specimen showing only a portion of the Crown or the letters CA, these being tall and far apart. This paper was chiefly used for long fiscal stamps.

1880 (Jan)–**82.** Wmk Crown CC (reversed on 8c.). P 14.

5	**1**	2c. yellow-green	23·00	32·00
		x. Wmk reversed	48·00	60·00
		y. Wmk inverted and reversed	80·00	80·00
6		6c. orange-brown	£110	£120
		a. No dot at upper left	£225	£225
		x. Wmk reversed	£190	
7		8c. carmine (4.82)	£110	£110
		a. No dot at lower left (R. 2/5)	£200	£200
		x. Wmk normal (not reversed)	£250	£250
8		10c. brown	£160	85·00
		w. Wmk inverted	£130	90·00
		x. Wmk reversed		
9		12c. carmine	£275	£325
		a. No right foot to second Chinese character	£475	£550
		w. Wmk inverted	£375	
		x. Wmk reversed	£275	£325
		y. Wmk inverted and reversed		
10		16c. blue (1881)	80·00	80·00
		w. Wmk inverted	£170	£170
		x. Wmk reversed	£140	£150
		y. Wmk inverted and reversed	£200	
5/10 Set of 6			£650	£650

1880 (Aug).

*(a) No. 9 surch with T **2** in black and with the original value obliterated by manuscript bar in red or black.*

11		8c. on 12c. carmine	£1400	£850
		a. Type 2 inverted	£1700	£1000
		b. "12" not obliterated	£2500	£1600
		c. As b. with Type 2 inverted		
		d. No right foot to second Chinese character	£2500	£1500
		x. Wmk reversed	£1300	£850

*(b) No. 4 surch with two upright figures and No. 9 surch with two at right angles as T **3**.*

12		6c. on 16c. blue (R.)	£2500	£1000
		a. With one "6" only		
13		8c. on 12c. carmine	£1700	£1100
		a. Both "8"s upright	£1800	£1200
		b. Upright "8" inverted		
		c. No right foot to second Chinese character	£2750	£1800
		w. Wmk inverted	†	£1500
		x. Wmk reversed	£1700	£1100
		y. Wmk inverted and reversed		

EIGHT CENTS   Eight Cents
(4)   (5)   (6)

1881 (Mar). No. 9 handstamped with T **4**.

14		8c. on 12c. carmine	£325	£375
		a. No right foot to second Chinese character	£600	£700
		w. Wmk inverted	£425	
		x. Wmk reversed	£325	£375

1881 (June). No. 9 surch with T **5**.

15		8c. on 12c. carmine	£120	£130
		a. Surch double	£1600	£1600
		b. Surch inverted	£11000	
		c. "Eighr"	£17000	
		d. No right foot to second Chinese character	£250	£300
		w. Wmk inverted	£250	
		x. Wmk reversed	£120	£130

The error "Eighr" occurred on R. 2/1 of the first printing, but was soon corrected.

Only one sheet of 10 has been reported of No. 15b, which also shows wmk inverted and reversed.

1883. Wmk Crown CA (reversed on 8c.). P 14.

17	**1**	2c. yellow-green	20·00	28·00
		a. Imperf between (horiz pair)	£9500	
		w. Wmk inverted	55·00	
		x. Wmk reversed	21·00	42·00

18   8c. carmine....... £275 £100
   a. No dot at lower left £475 £190
19   10c. yellow-brown........ 32·00 42·00
   w. Wmk inverted........ 70·00 80·00
   x. Wmk reversed........ 70·00 80·00
20   16c. blue........ 95·00 £180
21   40c. amber........ 18·00 £100
   x. Wmk reversed........ 26·00 £100
17/21 Set of 5........ £400 £400

1883 (May). *No.* 10 *surch* "One Dollar A.S.H." *by hand as* T **6**.
22   1 $1 on 16c. blue (**R.**)........ £3750
The initials are those of the postmaster, Mr. A. S. Hamilton.

2 CENTS   2 Cents   2 Cents
(7)   (8)   (9)

1885 (June). *Nos.* 18 *and* 10 *handstamped as* T **7**.
23   1   2c. on 8c. carmine........ £225 £425
   a. No dot at lower left £400
24   2c. on 16c. blue........ £950 £900
   w. Wmk inverted........ £1000
   x. Wmk reversed........ † £900

1885 (July). *No.* 20 *surch as* T **8**.
25   1   2c. on 16c. blue........ £110 £160
   a. Surch double........ † £4250
   b. "2" inserted........ £1800
   w. Wmk inverted........
No. 25b shows a second "2" applied by a separate handstamp to correct indistinct impressions of Type 8.

1885 (Sept). *No.* 18 *handstamped diag as* T **9**.
26   1   2c. on 8c. carmine........ 65·00 £110
   a. No dot at lower left £130 £250
   x. Wmk normal (not reversed) .. £130

1885 (Sept)–86. Wmk Crown CA. P 14.
30   1   2c. rose-red........ 3·00 11·00
   a. *Pale rose-red* (1886)........ 3·00 9·50
   x. Wmk reversed........ 8·00
31   8c. deep violet........ 24·00 7·00
   a. No dot at lower left........ 50·00 20·00
   b. *Mauve* (1886)........ 27·00 8·00
   ba. No dot at lower left........ 60·00 22·00
   bw. Wmk inverted........ 70·00
32   10c. sepia (1886)........ 12·00 40·00
   w. Wmk inverted........ 40·00
   x. Wmk reversed........ 25·00
33   16c. grey (1886)........ £130
   x. Wmk reversed........ £110 £160
30/3 Set of 4........ £130 £190
30s/3s Optd "Specimen" Set of 4........ £475

ISSUES OF BRITISH NORTH BORNEO COMPANY

From 1 January 1890 while remaining a Crown Colony, the administration of Labuan was transferred to the British North Borneo Co, which issued the following stamps.

6   Two   Six
Cents   CENTS   CENTS
(10)   (11)   (12)

1891 (July)–92. *Handstamped with* T **10**.
34   1   6c. on 8c. deep violet (No. 31)........ £130 £110
   a. Surch inverted........ £225 £200
   b. Surch double........ £500
   c. Surch double, one inverted.... £950
   d. "Cents" omitted........ £450 £450
   f. Pair, one without surch, one surch inverted........ £1600
   g. No dot at lower left........ £275 £250
35   6c. on 8c. mauve (No. 31b)........ 10·00 9·00
   a. Surch inverted........ 75·00 70·00
   b. Surch double, one inverted........ £900
   c. Surch double, both inverted... £900
   d. "6" omitted........ £500
   e. Pair, one without surcharge ... £1400 £1400
   f. Surch inverted with "Cents" omitted........ £500
   g. Pair, one without surch, one surch inverted........ £1600 £1600
   h. Surch double........ £325
   i. No dot at lower left........ 24·00 24·00
   j. Imperf between (horiz pair)...
   w. Wmk inverted........ 50·00 50·00
   x. Wmk reversed........ 30·00
36   6c. on 8c. mauve (R.) (No. 31b) (2.92).. £1000 £475
   .... £1400 £700
37   6c. on 16c. blue (No. 4) (3.92)........ £2000 £1800
   .... £8500 £6500
38   6c. on 40c. amber (No. 21)........ £9500 £4750
   a. Surch inverted........ £8500 £7500

There are two different versions of Type 10 with the lines of the surcharge either 1 mm or 2 mm apart.

(Recess D.L.R.)
1892–93. No wmk. P 14.
39   1   2c. rose-lake........ 5·50 3·50
40   6c. bright green........ 8·00 4·50
   a. No dot at upper left........ 20·00 15·00
41   8c. violet........ 6·00 10·00
   a. *Pale violet* (1893)........ 6·50 10·00
43   10c. brown........ 13·00 8·00
   a. *Sepia-brown* (1893)........ 13·00 10·00
45   12c. bright blue........ 7·00 6·50
   a. No right foot to second Chinese character........ 18·00 18·00

46   16c. grey........ 7·00 10·00
47   40c. ochre........ 20·00 32·00
   a. *Brown-buff* (1893)........ 42·00 25·00
39/47 Set of 7........ 60·00 60·00

The 6c., 12c., 16c. and 40c. are in sheets of 10, as are all the earlier issues. The other values are in sheets of 30.

1892 (Dec). *Nos.* 47 *and* 46 *surch locally as* T **11** *or* **12**.
49   1   2c. on 40c. ochre (13 December)............ £170 90·00
   a. Surch inverted........ £425 £550
50   6c. on 16c. grey (20 December)............ £375 £150
   a. Surch inverted........ £500 £300
   b. Surch sideways........ £500 £300
   c. Surch "Six Cents"........ £1900

There are 10 slightly different versions of each of these surcharges which were applied in settings of 5×2, although instances of single handstamps are known.
A "SIX CENTS" handstamp with Roman "I" in "SIX" (without dot) is a clandestine surcharge, although it can be found with genuine postmarks. It also exists sideways or inverted.
The "Six Cents" surcharge of No. 50c was handstamped onto examples where the Type **12** surcharge had failed to print or where it was partially or completely albino.

CANCELLED-TO-ORDER. Prices are separately indicated, in a third price column, for stamps showing the recognisable black bars remainder cancellation. Earlier issues of the Company administration were also so treated, but, as postal cancellations were used, these cannot be identified.

(Litho D.L.R.)
1894 (Apr). No wmk. P 14.
51   1   2c. carmine-pink........ 1·60 12·00 50
52   6c. bright green........ 13·00 32·00 50
   a. Imperf between (horiz pair)........ £6500
   b. No dot at upper left ..... 26·00 70·00 1·25
53   8c. bright mauve........ 14·00 32·00 50
54   10c. brown........ 45·00 48·00 50
55   12c. pale blue........ 21·00 60·00 60
   a. No right foot to second Chinese character........ 45·00 £100 1·25
56   16c. grey........ 25·00 £100 50
57   40c. orange-buff........ 50·00 £110 50
51/7 Set of 7........ £150 £325 3·25
51s/7s H/S "Specimen" Set of 7........ £120

Collectors are warned against forgeries of this issue.

PERFORATION. There are a number of small variations in the perforation of the Waterlow issues of 1894 to 1905 which we believe to be due to irregularity of the pins rather than different perforators.
In the following lists, stamps perf 12, 12½, 13 or compound are described as perf 12–13, stamps perf 13½, 14 or compound are described as perf 13½–14 and those perf 14½, 15 or compound are listed as perf 14½–15. In addition the 13½–14 perforation exists compound with 14½–15 and with 12–13, whilst perf 16 comes from a separate perforator.

LABUAN

40
CENTS
13   (14)

1894 (May)–96. T **24/32** *of North Borneo (colours changed), with* "LABUAN" *engraved on vignette plate as* T **13** (8, 12, 24c.) *or horizontally (others).* P 14½–15.

(a) Name and central part of design in black.
62   24   1c. grey-mauve........ 1·50 9·00 50
   a. Imperf between (vert pair).. † † £650
   b. Perf 13½–14........ 9·50 9·50 —
   ba. Imperf between (vert pair).. £950 £475
   c. Perf 13½–14, comp 14½–15........
   d. Perf 13½–14, comp 12–13 . 24·00 11·00 90
   e. Perf 12–13........
63   25   2c. blue........ 2·50 8·50 50
   a. Imperf (pair)........ £600
   b. Perf 13½–14........ 4·00 8·50 —
   c. Perf 13½–14, comp 14½–15........ 27·00
   d. Perf 13½–14, comp 12–13 . £100
64   26   3c. ochre........ 3·75 17·00 50
   a. Perf 13½–14........ 9·00 9·00 —
   b. Perf 13½–14, comp 14½–15........
   c. Perf 13½–14, comp 12–13 . 40·00
   d. Perf 12–13........
65   27   5c. green........ 32·00 25·00 65
   a. Perf 13½–14........ 38·00 15·00 —
   ab. Imperf between (horiz pair) £1100
   b. Perf 13½–14, comp 12–13 . 50·00
   c. Perf 12–13........ £120
67   28   6c. brown-lake........ 2·50 16·00 50
   a. Imperf (pair)........ £550 † £300
   b. Perf 13½–14........ — 1·50
   c. Perf 13½–14, comp 14½–15........ — 90
   d. Perf 13½–14, comp 12–13 .
   e. Perf 12–13........
68   29   8c. rose-red........ 23·00 27·00 50
   a. Perf 13½–14........ 27·00 45·00 —
69   8c. pink (1896)........ 7·00 24·00 50
   a. Perf 13½–14........ 28·00 32·00 —
70   30   12c. orange-vermilion........ 23·00 48·00 50
   a. Imperf between (vert pair).. † † £2500
   b. Perf 13½–14........ 65·00 70·00 2·00
   c. Perf 13½–14, comp 14½–15........ £180
   d. Perf 13½–14, comp 12–13 . 80·00 85·00 —
71   31   18c. olive-brown........ 22·00 55·00 50
   .... 70·00
72   18c. olive-bistre (1896)........ 55·00 70·00 50
   a. Perf 13½–14........ 27·00 65·00 —
   b. Perf 13½–14, comp 12–13 .

   c. Imperf between (vert pair).. † † £1500
   d. Perf 13½–14, comp 14½–15........ † † 1·50

(b) Name and central part in blue.
73   32   24c. pale mauve........ 23·00 55·00 50
   a. Perf 13½–14........ 22·00 50·00 —
   b. Perf 13½–14 comp 14½–15........
74   24c. dull lilac (1896)........ 15·00 45·00 50
   a. Perf 13½–14........ 13·00 45·00 —
62/74 Set of 9........ 95·00 £200 4·00
62s/74s Optd "Specimen" Set of 9........ £150

1895 (June). *No.* 83 *of North Borneo* ($1 *inscr* "STATE OF NORTH BORNEO") *surch as* T **14**.
75   32   4c. on $1 scarlet........ 1·25 2·25 40
76   10c. on $1 scarlet........ 4·50 1·40 40
77   20c. on $1 scarlet........ 29·00 10·00 40
78   30c. on $1 scarlet........ 32·00 42·00 50
79   40c. on $1 scarlet........ 30·00 32·00 50
75/9 Set of 5........ 85·00 80·00 2·00
75s/9s Optd "Specimen" Set of 5........ 80·00

No. 76 exists with the figures of the surcharge 2½ mm away from "CENTS". The normal setting has a space of 4 mm. Examples of the narrow setting have, so far, only been seen on cancelled-to-order stamps (*Price* £20 c.t.o.).

1846   4
JUBILEE
LABUAN   1896   CENTS
(15)   (16)   (17)

1896. T **32a** *to* **32c** *of North Borneo (as Nos. 81 to 83, but colours changed) optd with* T **15**.
80   25c. green........ 26·00 30·00 60
   a. Opt omitted........ 23·00 — 1·25
   b. Imperf (pair)........ 42·00 — 60·00
81   50c. maroon........ 26·00 30·00 60
   a. Opt omitted........ 21·00 — 1·25
   b. Imperf (pair)........ — 60·00
   ba. Opt omitted........ 40·00 —
82    $1 blue........ 60·00 55·00 60
   a. Opt omitted........ 30·00 — 1·25
   b. Imperf (pair)........ — 60·00
   ba. Opt omitted........ 45·00 —
80s/2s Optd "Specimen" Set of 3........ 60·00

Nos. 80/1 showing stamps either printed double or double, one inverted, are from waste sheets subsequently sold by the British North Borneo Company to collectors.

1896 (24 Sept). *Jubilee of Cession of Labuan to Gt Britain. Nos.* 62 *to* 68 *optd with* T **16**. P 14½–15.
83   1c. black and grey-mauve........ 18·00 22·00 80
   b. Opt in orange........ £200 £200 20·00
   c. "JEBILEE" (R. 8/7)........ £1100 £550 £300
   d. "JUBILE" (R. 3/10)........ £1900
   e. Perf 13½–14........ 24·00 22·00 —
   ea. Opt double .... £375 £375 —
   eb. Opt in orange........ £250 £250 †
   f. Perf 13½–14, comp 12–13 . 29·00 18·00 —
   fa. Opt in orange .... £200 †
   g. Perf 12–13........
84   2c. black and blue........ 38·00 24·00 1·00
   a. Imperf horiz (vert pair)........ £800 £900 †
   b. "JEBILEE" (R. 8/7)........ £1200 £1100 —
   c. "JUBILE" (R. 3/10)........ £2250 £2000
   d. Perf 13½–14........ 38·00 16·00 —
   e. Perf 13½–14, comp 14½–15........ 38·00 —
   f. Perf 13½–14, comp 12–13 . 45·00
85   3c. black and ochre........ 35·00 22·00 80
   a. "JEBILEE" (R. 8/7)........ £1600 £1500 £700
   b. "JUBILE" (R. 3/10)........
   d. Perf 13½–14........ 40·00 28·00 90
   db. Opt treble........ £650
   e. Perf 13½–14, comp 14½–15........
   fa. Opt double £375 £375 £160
   fb. Opt treble........ £650
86   5c. black and green........ 55·00 16·00 1·00
   a. Opt double........ £650 £500 —
   b. Perf 13½–14........ 60·00 22·00 1·00
   c. Perf 13½–14, comp 12–13 .
   d. Perf 13½–14, comp 14½–15........ — 3·00
87   6c. black and brown-lake........ 27·00 21·00 80
   a. Opt double........ £750 £500 †
   b. "JUBILE" (R. 3/10)........ £2500
   c. Perf 13½–14, comp 14½–15........ — 70·00
   d. Perf 12–13........
88   8c. black and pink........ 45·00 13·00 80
   a. Opt double........ † £2500 †
   b. Perf 13½–14........ 40·00 12·00 80
   c. Perf 13½–14, comp 14½–15........ 50·00 18·00 —
83/8 Set of 6........ £190 £100 4·75
83s/8s Optd "Specimen" Set of 6........ £150

The normal overprint on the 1c. varies in appearance from pure black to brownish black owing to a mixing of the inks. The orange overprint on this value is in a clear, bright, unadulterated ink.
No. 84b is known in a vertical strip of 3 imperf horizontally except at the base of the bottom stamp (*Price* £6000 *unused*).

1897 (Apr)–1901. T **34/45** *of North Borneo (colours changed), with* "LABUAN" *engraved on vignette plate as* T **13** (8, 10, 12, 24c.) *or horizontally (others). Name and central part in black (24c. in blue).* P 13½–14.
89   34   1c. dull claret (P 14½–15)........ 4·00 4·75 50
   a. Perf 13½–14, comp 14½–15........

		ab. Perf 16	—	—	2·00
		b. *Brown* (1901)	17·00	19·00	65
		ba. Perf 14½–15	3·00		
		bb. Perf 16	14·00	13·00	
90	35	2c. blue	16·00	4·25	65
		a. Imperf between (vert pair)	†	†	£700
		b. Imperf between (horiz pair)	†	†	£750
		c. Perf 14½–15	23·00		75
		d. Perf 13½–14, comp 12–13	40·00	19·00	—
		e. Perf 16	—	—	7·00
91	36	3c. ochre	8·50	21·00	50
		a. Imperf between (vert pair)	£900	†	£550
		b. Perf 14½–15	8·50	6·50	50
		c. Perf 13½–14, comp 12–13	20·00	30·00	1·00
		d. Perf 12–13	75·00		
92	38	5c. green	55·00	55·00	70
		a. Perf 14½–15	50·00	55·00	
		b. Perf 13½–14, comp 12–13			
93	39	6c. brown-lake	6·50	32·00	50
		b. Perf 14½–15	7·00	21·00	50
		ba. Imperf between (vert pair)	†	†	£700
		c. Perf 13½–14, comp 12–13	—	—	6·00
94	40	8c. rose-red	50·00		50
		a. Perf 14½–15	18·00	12·00	
		b. Perf 13½–14, comp 12–13	32·00	—	2·75
		c. *Vermilion*	12·00		50
		ca. Perf 16	—	—	5·00
95	42	12c. vermilion	80·00	90·00	1·25
		a. Perf 14½–15	32·00	50·00	1·00
96	44	18c. olive-bistre	70·00	70·00	70
		a. Imperf between (vert pair)	†	†	
		b. Perf 16	12·00	45·00	50
97	45	24c. grey-lilac	45·00	75·00	75
		a. Perf 14½–15	12·00	50·00	50
89/97 Set of 9			£140	£225	4·75
89s/97s Optd "Specimen" Set of 9			£160		

The 12, 18 and 24c. above were errors; in the 12c., "LABUAN" is over the value at the top; the 18c. has "POSTAL REVENUE" instead of "POSTAGE AND REVENUE", and the 24c. is without "POSTAGE AND REVENUE".

1897 (Nov)–98.*(a) Types of North Borneo (colours changed), with "LABUAN" engraved on the vignette plate as in T* **13**. *P* 13½–14.

98	42	12c. black and vermilion (3.98)	†	—	3·25
		a. Perf 14½–15, comp 14½–15	42·00	50·00	
		b. Perf 13½–14, comp 14½–15			
		c. Perf 16	55·00	60·00	—
99	46	18c. black and olive-bistre			
		a. Perf 14½–15	80·00	60·00	2·00
		b. Perf 13½–14, comp 12–13	£100		
		c. Perf 16	†	—	8·50
100	47	24c. blue and lilac-brown	30·00	55·00	2·00
		a. Perf 14½–15	30·00	55·00	
		b. Perf 13½–14, comp 12–13	—	65·00	—
		c. Perf 16	32·00		
		d. *Blue and ochre* (P 14½–15)	—	—	3·00

In the 12c., "LABUAN" is now correctly placed at foot of stamp. The 18c. and 24c. have the inscriptions on the stamps corrected, but the 18c. still has "LABUAN" over the value at foot, and was further corrected as follows.

(b) As No. 99, but "LABUAN" at top.

101	46	18c. black and olive-bistre (3.98)	60·00	60·00	
		a. Perf 14½–15	27·00	70·00	2·75
		b. Perf 13½–14, comp 12–13	38·00	55·00	
		c. Perf 12–13			

98s, 100s/1as Optd "Specimen" Set of 3 .... 70·00

1899 (July). *Surch with T* **17**.

(a) P 14½–15.

102	38	4c. on 5c. (No. 92a)	38·00	26·00	
103	39	4c. on 6c. (No. 93b)	23·00	19·00	
		a. Perf 13½–14	32·00	38·00	
		b. Perf 13½–14 comp 12–13	50·00	60·00	
104	40	4c. on 8c. (No. 94a)	60·00	40·00	
		a. Perf 13½–14	30·00	32·00	
		b. Perf 13½–14, comp 12–13	29·00	35·00	
		c. Perf 12–13			
105	42	4c. on 12c. (No. 98a)	40·00	35·00	
		a. Perf 13½–14	40·00	42·00	
		b. Perf 16	40·00	40·00	
		c. Perf 13½–14, comp 12–13	55·00	65·00	
106	46	4c. on 18c. (No. 101a)	26·00	18·00	
		a. Surch double	£400	£450	
107	47	4c. on 24c. (No. 100a)	25·00	30·00	
		a. Perf 13½–14	20·00	25·00	
		b. Perf 13½–14, comp 12–13	30·00	30·00	
		c. Perf 16	45·00	48·00	

(b) P 14.

108	32	4c. on 25c. (No. 80)	6·00	7·50	
109	32	4c. on 50c. (No. 81)	6·50	7·50	
110	32	4c. on $1 (No. 82)	6·50	7·50	
102/10 Set of 9			£170	£160	
102s/10s Optd "Specimen" Set of 9			£150		

A new setting of the surcharge with closer spacing (2½ mm) between "4" and "CENTS" was used for the Specimen overprints, including unissued surcharges on the 1c., 2c. and 3c. values (*price £140 for the set of three*).

1900–02. *Types of North Borneo with "LABUAN" engraved on the vignette plate as in T* **13**, *in green on 16c. P* 13½–14.

111	35	2c. black and green	3·75	2·50	30
		a. Imperf between (horiz pair)	£2500		
		b. Perf 13½–14, comp 12–13			
112	37	4c. black and yellow-brown	8·50	42·00	60
		a. Imperf between (vert pair)	£1100		
		b. Perf 13½–14, comp 12–13	32·00		

113		4c. black and carmine (8.1900)	12·00	2·75	75
		a. Perf 14½–15	5·00	9·50	50
		b. Perf 13½–14, comp 12–13	32·00	8·00	75
		c. Perf 16			
114	38	5c. black and pale blue	20·00	18·00	65
		a. Perf 13½–14, comp 12–13	—	85·00	—
		b. Perf 12–13	£120		
115	41	10c. green and slate-lilac (P 14½–15) (1902)	50·00	80·00	60
116	43	16c. green and chestnut (1902)	50·00	£110	2·50
		a. Perf 13½–14, comp 12–13	85·00	£110	
		b. Perf 12–13	£225		
		c. Perf 14½–15	£110		
111/16 Set of 6			£120	£225	4·75
111s/16s Optd "Specimen" Set of 6			£150		

No. 112 was printed in an incorrect frame colour and was not issued for postal purposes in Labuan. Used examples come from dealers' stock sent to the island for cancellation.

18 Line through "B" (R. 5/10)

(Recess Waterlow)

1902 (Sept)–03. *P* 13½–14.

117	18	1c. black and purple (10.03)	4·50	7·00	50
		a. Perf 14½–15	80·00	7·50	—
		b. Perf 13½–14 comp 12–13	75·00	50·00	
		c. Line through "B"	65·00	90·00	7·00
118		2c. black and green	4·00	5·00	30
		a. Perf 14½–15	£100	5·00	—
		aa. Perf 13½–14, comp 12–13	£100		
		b. Line through "B"	60·00	75·00	7·00
119		3c. black and sepia (10.03)	3·25	13·00	30
		a. Line through "B"	60·00	£100	7·00
120		4c. black and carmine	3·25	3·50	30
		a. Perf 14½–15	7·00	9·00	—
		b. Perf 13½–14 comp 12–13	65·00	50·00	—
		c. Line through "B"	60·00	65·00	7·00
121		8c. black and vermilion	11·00	9·00	50
		a. Perf 14½–15	8·00		
		b. Line through "B"	85·00	£100	7·00
122		10c. brown and slate-blue	3·25	13·00	30
		a. Perf 14½–15	5·50	15·00	—
		ba. Imperf between (vert pair)	†	†	£700
		c. Line through "B"	60·00	£130	7·00
123		12c. black and yellow	8·00	15·00	30
		a. Imperf between (vert strip of 3)	†	†	£3250
		b. Perf 16	8·00	19·00	50
		c. Line through "B"	85·00	£140	7·00
124		16c. green and brown	4·75	19·00	30
		a. Imperf between (vert pair)	†	†	£1900
		b. Line through "B"	80·00	£160	7·00
125		18c. black and pale brown	3·25	23·00	30
		a. Line through "B"	65·00	£180	7·00
126		25c. green and greenish blue	7·50	18·00	50
		a. Perf 14½–15	15·00	30·00	60
		b. Error. Black and greenish blue	—	†	£450
		c. Line through "B"	95·00	£180	8·00
127		50c. dull purple and lilac	10·00	42·00	1·00
		a. Perf 13½–14 comp 12–13	16·00	48·00	—
		b. Line through "B"	£170	£375	12·00
128		$1 claret and orange	8·50	50·00	1·00
		a. Perf 14½–15	10·00	—	1·00
		b. Line through "B"	£140	£400	12·00
117/28 Set of 12			60·00	£200	5·00
117s/28s Optd "Specimen" Set of 12			£190		

4 cents
(19)

1904 (Dec). *Issues of 1895 and 1897–8 surch with T* **19**.

(a) P 14½–15.

129	38	4c. on 5c. (No. 92a)	42·00	40·00	14·00
130	39	4c. on 6c. (No. 93b)	12·00	38·00	14·00
131	40	4c. on 8c. (No. 94a)	25·00	42·00	14·00
132	42	4c. on 12c. (No. 98a)	20·00	42·00	14·00
		a. Perf 16	28·00	45·00	—
133	46	4c. on 18c. (No. 101) (P 13½–14)	23·00	45·00	14·00
		a. Perf 13½–14, comp 12–13	27·00	45·00	—
		b. Perf 12–13			
134	47	4c. on 24c. (No. 100a)	16·00	50·00	14·00
		a. Perf 13½–14	27·00	38·00	—
		b. Perf 13½–14, comp 12–13	35·00	48·00	—
		c. Perf 16	26·00	40·00	14·00

(b) P 14.

135	32	4c. on 25c. (No. 80)	8·50	24·00	14·00
136	32	4c. on 50c. (No. 81)	8·50	24·00	14·00

		a. Surch double	£325		
137	32	4c. on $1 (No. 82)	8·50	24·00	14·00
129/37 Set of 9			£140	£300	£110

No. 136a usually shows one complete surcharge and parts of two further examples due to the position of the second impression.

The barred cancels can be found used on "philatelic" covers of this issue.

LABUAN LABUAN
(20)   (21)

1904 (12 Oct)–05. *Nos. 81, 83 (in Labuan colour), and 84/6 of North Borneo optd locally with T* **20** (25c. $2) *or* **21** (*others*).

138	32	25c. indigo (2.05)	£1100	†	£900
139	32	$1 blue (2.05)	†	†	£850
140	32	$2 dull green	£3250	£3250	
141	14	$5 bright purple (2.05)	£6000	£6500	£1400
142	15	$10 brown (11.05)	£26000	†	£9000

Dangerous forgeries exist.
The overprint on No. 140 is 12 mm long.

POSTAGE DUE STAMPS

POSTAGE DUE
(D 1)

1901. *Optd with Type D* **1**, *reading vertically upwards. P* 13½–14.

D1	35	2c. black and green (111)	17·00	25·00	50
		a. Opt double	£350		
		b. Perf 13½–14, comp 12–13	75·00	80·00	10·00
D2	36	3c. black and ochre (91)	21·00	90·00	70
		a. Perf 13½–14, comp 12–13	75·00	—	2·00
D3	37	4c. black and carmine (113)	38·00	—	1·25
		a. Opt double	†	†	£700
		b. Perf 14½–15	38·00	90·00	50
D4	38	5c. black and pale blue (114)	50·00	£110	75
		a. Perf 14½–15	—	—	1·00
		b. Perf 13½–14, comp 12–13	80·00	£150	—
D5	39	6c. black and brown-lake (93)	32·00	£100	75
		a. Perf 14½–15	45·00	90·00	—
		b. Perf 16	55·00	—	65
D6	40	8c. black and vermilion (94c)	65·00	95·00	1·25
		a. Perf 14½–15	75·00	£130	85
		ba. Frame inverted	†	†	£9000
		c. Perf 16	75·00	95·00	—
		d. *Black and rose-red* (94)	80·00	£120	—
		da. Perf 14½–15	£100	—	7·00
		e. Perf 13½–14, comp 12–13	£100	—	—
D7	42	12c. black and vermilion (98)	95·00	—	4·00
		a. Opt reading downwards	†	†	£650
		b. Perf 14½–15	90·00	£120	12·00
D8	46	18c. black and olive-bistre (101) (P 14½–15)	24·00	£110	1·25
D9	47	24c. blue and lilac-brown (100)	48·00	£120	5·00
		a. Perf 13½–14, comp 12–13	75·00		
		b. Perf 14½–15	32·00		
		ba. *Blue and ochre*	75·00	—	1·25
		c. Perf 16	50·00	90·00	—
D1/9 Set of 9			£350	£750	9·50

No. D6ba only exists cancelled-to-order.

The administration of Labuan reverted to Colonial Office control, as part of an agreement with Brunei on 1 January 1906. By Letters Patent dated 30 October 1906 Labuan was incorporated with Straits Settlements and ceased issuing its own stamps. In 1946 it became part of the Colony of North Borneo.

JAPANESE OCCUPATION OF NORTH BORNEO

Japanese forces landed in Northern Borneo on 15 December 1941 and the whole of North Borneo had been occupied by 19 January 1942.

Brunei, North Borneo, Sarawak and, after a short period, Labuan, were administered as a single territory by the Japanese. Until 12 December 1942, previous stamp issues, without overprint, continued to be used in conjunction with existing postmarks. From November 1942 onwards unoverprinted stamps of Japan were made available and examples can be found used from the area for much of the remainder of the War. Japanese Occupation issues for Brunei, North Borneo and Sarawak were equally valid throughout the combined territory but not, in practice, equally available.

PRICES FOR STAMPS ON COVER	
Nos. J1/17	*from* × 5
Nos. J18/19	*from* × 6
Nos. J20/32	*from* × 25
Nos. J33/4	*from* × 2
Nos. J35/48	*from* × 12

(1)   **2** Mt. Kinabalu   **3** Borneo Scene

1942 (30 Sept). *Stamps of North Borneo handstamped with T* **1**.

(a) In violet on Nos. 303/17.

J1		1c. green and red-brown	£160	£225
		a. Black opt	£275	£200
		ab. Pair, one without opt	£3000	
J2		2c. purple and greenish blue	£160	£225
		a. Black opt	£350	£225
J3		3c. slate-blue and green	£130	£225
		a. Black opt	£375	£300
J4		4c. bronze-green and violet	£180	£275
		a. Black opt	50·00	£130
J5		6c. deep blue and claret	£140	£275
		a. Black opt	£375	£300
J6		8c. scarlet	£180	£190
		a. Pair, one without opt	£3000	
		b. Black opt	£250	£190

J7	10c. violet and bronze-green	£160	£275
	a. Black opt	£350	£275
J8	12c. green and bright blue	£180	£425
	a. Black opt	£550	£425
J9	15c. blue-green and brown	£170	£425
	a. Pair, one without opt	£3000	
	b. Black opt	£600	£425
J10	20c. violet and slate-blue	£200	£500
	a. Black opt	£700	£500
J11	25c. green and chocolate	£200	£500
	a. Black opt	£700	£500
J12	50c. chocolate and violet	£275	£600
	a. Black opt	£800	£600
J13	$1 brown and carmine	£275	£750
	a. Black opt	£900	£750
J14	$2 violet and olive-green	£475	£950
	a. Pair, one without opt	£4250	
	b. Black opt	£1200	£950
J15	$5 indigo and pale blue	£550	£1000
	a. Black opt	£1500	£1200

(b) In black on Nos. 318/19 ("WAR TAX")

J16	1c. green and red-brown	£550	£300
	a. Pair, one without opt	†	£3000
	b. Violet opt		£700
J17	2c. purple and greenish blue	£1400	£500
	a. Violet opt	—	£850

(Litho Kolff & Co., Batavia)

1943 (29 Apr). P 12½.

J18	**2**	4c. red	19·00	42·00
J19	**3**	4c. blue	16·00	42·00

(4)   (5)

("Imperial Japanese Postal Service North Borneo")

1944 (30 Sept). *Nos. 303/15 of North Borneo optd with T **4** at Chinese Press, Kuching.*

J20	1c.	green and red-brown	5·00	12·00
J21	2c.	purple and greenish blue	7·50	9·00
		a. Optd on No. J2	£425	
J22	3c.	slate-blue and green	4·75	9·50
		a. Optd on No. J3	£425	
J23	4c.	bronze-green and violet	9·00	17·00
J24	6c.	deep blue and claret	6·00	6·50
J25	8c.	scarlet	8·50	17·00
		a. Optd on No. J6	£425	
J26	10c.	violet and bronze-green	8·50	13·00
		a. Optd on No. J7	£425	
		b. Optd on No. J7a	£200	£375
J27	12c.	green and bright blue	12·00	13·00
		a. Optd on No. J8	£425	
J28	15c.	blue-green and brown	11·00	16·00
		a. Optd on No. J9	£425	
J29	20c.	violet and slate-blue	24·00	45·00
		a. Optd on No. J10	£1600	
J30	25c.	green and chocolate	24·00	45·00
		a. Optd on No. J11	£1600	
J31	50c.	chocolate and violet	70·00	£120
		a. Optd on No. J12	£2250	
J32	$1	brown and carmine	90·00	£150
J20/32		Set of 13	£250	£425

The spacing between the second and third lines of the overprint is 12 mm on the horizontal stamps, and 15 mm on the upright.

1944 (11 May). *No. J1 surch with T **5**.*

J33	**81**	$2 on 1c. green and red-brown	£4500	£3750

(6)   7 Girl War-worker   (8) ("North Borneo")

1944 (11 May). *North Borneo No. 315 surch with T **6**.*

J34	$5 on $1 brown and carmine	£4000	£2750
	a. Surch on No. J13	£6000	£4500

1944 (2 Oct)–**45**. *Contemporary stamps of Japan as T **7** (various subjects) optd with T **8** at Chinese Press, Kuching.*

J35	1s. red-brown (No. 391) (1.45)	8·00	24·00
J36	2s. scarlet (No. 392b) (10.44)	7·00	19·00
J37	3s. emerald-green (No. 316) (8.45)	7·00	24·00
J38	4s. yellow-green (No. 395) (10.44)	12·00	20·00
J39	5s. claret (No. 318) (1.45)	9·00	23·00
J40	6s. orange (No. 319) (8.45)	12·00	24·00
	a. Opt double, one inverted	£425	£425
J41	8s. violet (No. 321) (11.44)	6·50	24·00
	a. Opt double	£350	
J42	10s. carmine and pink (No. 399) (1.45)	7·50	24·00
J43	15s. blue (No. 401) (11.44)	9·50	24·00
J44	20s. blue-slate (No. 325) (11.44)	80·00	90·00
J45	25s. brown and chocolate (No. 326) (2.45)	55·00	75·00
J46	30s. turquoise-blue (No. 327) (8.45)	£170	95·00
J47	50s. olive and bistre (No. 328) (8.45)	65·00	70·00

J48	1y. red-brown & chocolate (No. 329) (5.45)	65·00	£100
J35/48	Set of 14	£450	£550

Designs:—2s. General Nogi; 3s. Hydro-electric Works; 4s. Hyuga Monument and Mt Fuji; 5s. Admiral Togo; 6s. Garambi Lighthouse, Formosa; 8s. Meiji Shrine; 10s. Palms and map of S.E. Asia; 15s. Airman; 20s. Mt Fuji and cherry blossoms; 25s. Horyu Temple; 30s. Torii, Itsukushima Shrine at Miyajima; 50s. Kinkaku Temple; 1y. Great Buddha, Kamakura.

Examples of some values have been found with hand-painted forged overprints.

POSTAGE DUE STAMPS

1942 (30 Sept). *Nos. D66/7 and D69 of North Borneo handstamped with T **1** in black.*

JD1	D **2**	2c. brown	—	£3250
JD2		4c. scarlet	—	£3250
JD3		8c. green	—	£3250

Northern Nigeria
see Nigeria

Northern Rhodesia

The north-eastern and north-western provinces of Rhodesia, previously administered by the British South Africa Company, became a Crown Colony on 1 April 1924.

The current stamps of Rhodesia (the "Admiral design" first issued in 1913) remained in use until 31 March 1925 and continued to be valid for postal purposes until 30 September of that year.

PRICES FOR STAMPS ON COVER TO 1945	
Nos. 1/21	*from* × 2
Nos. 22/4	*from* × 5
Nos. 25/45	*from* × 2
Nos. D1/4	*from* × 15

1   2

(Des W. Fairweather. Eng J. A. C. Harrison. Recess Waterlow)

1925 (1 April)–**29**. Wmk Mult Script CA. P 12½.

1	**1**	½d. green	1·75	80
2		1d. brown	1·75	10
3		1½d. carmine-red	2·00	30
4		2d. yellow-brown	2·00	10
5		3d. ultramarine	2·00	1·25
6		4d. violet	4·25	50
7		6d. slate-grey	4·50	40
8		8d. rose-purple	4·00	48·00
9		10d. olive-green	4·50	42·00
10	**2**	1s. yellow-brown and black	3·75	1·75
11		2s. brown and ultramarine	16·00	25·00
12		2s.6d. black and green	17·00	10·00
13		3s. violet and blue (1929)	24·00	19·00
14		5s. slate-grey and violet	35·00	19·00
15		7s.6d. rose-purple and black	£120	£170
16		10s. green and black	75·00	80·00
17		20s. carmine-red and rose-purple	£170	£190
1/17		Set of 17	£425	£550
1s/17s		Optd or Perf (3s.) "Specimen" Set of 17	£800	

A used example of the 4d. exists imperforate between the stamp and a fragment of another below it.

1935 (6 May). *Silver Jubilee. As Nos. 91/4 of Antigua.* P 13½×14.

18	1d. light blue and olive-green	80	1·50
	f. Diagonal line by turret	60·00	80·00
	h. Dot by flagstaff	£100	£140
	i. Dash by turret	£100	£140
19	2d. green and indigo	1·25	1·50
	f. Diagonal line by turret	75·00	95·00
	g. Dot to left of chapel	£130	£160
20	3d. brown and deep blue	2·50	5·50
	f. Diagonal line by turret	£120	£170
	g. Dot to left of chapel	£225	£300
21	6d. slate and purple	4·75	1·50
	a. Frame printed double, one albino	£1800	
	h. Dot by flagstaff	£275	£190
18/21	Set of 4	8·50	9·00
18s/21s	Perf "Specimen" Set of 4	£140	

For illustrations of plate varieties see Omnibus section following Zanzibar.

THERN_RHODE

Hyphen between "NORTHERN" AND "RHODESIA" (R. 9/6)

3   4

"Tick bird" flaw (Pl 1 R. 7/1 of ptgs from Sept 1938 onwards)

(Recess Waterlow)

1938 (1 Mar)–**52**. Wmk Mult Script CA. P 12½.

25	**3**	½d. green	10	10
		a. "C" of "CA" missing from wmk		
26		½d. chocolate (15.11.51)	75	1·50
		a. Perf 12½×14 (22.10.52)	1·40	6·00
27		1d. brown	20	20
		a. Chocolate (1948)	1·75	75
28		1d. green (15.11.51)	75	1·50
29		1½d. carmine-red	45·00	75
		a. Imperf between (horiz pair)	£15000	
		b. "Tick bird" flaw	£2750	£275
30		1½d. yellow-brown (10.1.41)	30	10
		b. "Tick bird" flaw	75·00	32·00
31		2d. yellow-brown	45·00	1·75
32		2d. carmine-red (10.1.41)	30	50
33		2d. purple (1.12.51)	45	1·50
34		3d. ultramarine	40	30
35		3d. scarlet (1.12.51)	50	2·75
36		4d. dull violet	30	40
37		4½d. blue (5.5.52)	1·00	7·00
38		6d. grey	30	10
39		9d. violet (5.5.52)	1·00	5·50
40	**4**	1s. yellow-brown and black	3·50	60
41		2s.6d. black and green	7·00	4·25
42		3s. violet and blue	15·00	10·00
43		5s. grey and dull violet	15·00	10·00
44		10s. green and black	18·00	15·00
45		20s. carmine-red and rose-purple	45·00	48·00
25/45		Set of 21	£180	£100
25s/45s		Perf "Specimen" Set of 15	£350	

Nos. 26a and 28 exist in coils, constructed from normal sheets.

1946 (26 Nov). *Victory. As Nos. 110/11 of Antigua.* P 13½×14.

46	1½d. red-orange	50	50
	a. Perf 13½	14·00	12·00
47	2d. carmine	10	50
46s/7s	Perf "Specimen" Set of 2	80·00	

The decimal perforation gauge for Nos. 46/7 is 13.7×14.1 and for No. 46a 13.7×13.4.

1948 (1 Dec). *Royal Silver Wedding. As Nos. 112/13 of Antigua, but 20s. ptd in recess.*

48	1½d. orange	30	10
49	20s. brown-lake	45·00	50·00

1949 (10 Oct). *75th Anniv of U.P.U. As Nos. 114/17 of Antigua.*

50	2d. carmine	20	30
51	3d. deep blue	1·50	1·75
52	6d. grey	55	1·75
53	1s. red-orange	55	1·00
50/3	Set of 4	2·50	4·25

POSTAGE DUE STAMPS

D **1**

1929 (June)–**52**. *Ordinary paper.* Wmk Mult Script CA. P 14.

D1	D **1**	1d. grey-black	2·50	2·50
		a. Chalk-surfaced paper. *Black* (22.1.52)	24·00	75·00
		ab. Error. St. Edward's Crown, W9*b*	£2250	
D2		2d. grey-black	3·50	3·00
		a. Bisected (1d.) (on cover)	†	£550
D3		3d. grey-black	3·00	26·00
		a. Chalk-surfaced paper. *Black* (22.1.52)	7·00	65·00
		ab. Error. Crown missing, W9*b*	£325	
		ac. Error. St. Edward's Crown, W9*b*	£180	
D4		4d. grey-black	9·50	30·00
D1/4		Set of 4	17·00	55·00
D1s/4s		Perf "Specimen" Set of 4	£110	

The 2d. is known bisected and used as a 1d. at Luanshya or Nkana

on various dates between 1937 and 1951 and on understamped letters from South Africa at Chingola in May 1950 (*Price on cover* £850).

Following an increase in the internal letter rate from 1½d. to 2d. on 1 July 1953 stocks of postage due stamps at Mkushi became exhausted. As an emergency measure the sub-postmaster was authorised to surcharge examples of No. 28 "POSTAGE DUE (or "postage due") 1d." in red by typewriter. No. 55, the 1d. Rhodes Centenary stamp, was also surcharged. Examples properly used on cover between 23 July and 15 September 1953 are of considerable scarcity (*Price on cover* £3750). No unused examples exist.

North-West Pacific Islands
see New Guinea
after Australia

Nova Scotia *see* Canada

Nyasaland

PRICES FOR STAMPS ON COVER TO 1945	
Nos. 1/9a	*from* × 15
Nos. 10/19	—
No. 20	*from* × 10
Nos. 21/6	*from* × 5
Nos. 27/31	—
No. 32/7	*from* × 6
Nos. 38/42	—
Nos. 43/7	*from* × 12
Nos. 48/52	—
No. 53	*from* × 15
No. 54	*from* × 2
No. 55	*from* × 4
Nos. 55b/7a	*from* × 7
Nos. 57d/63	*from* × 6
Nos. 64/71	—
Nos. 72/9	*from* × 5
Nos. 80/2	—
Nos. 83/95	*from* × 4
Nos. 96/9	—
Nos. 100/57	*from* × 2

By 1891 the territory west of Lake Nyasa was recognised as being under British protection and the southern, eastern and northern borders had been delineated with the Portuguese and German governments.

BRITISH CENTRAL AFRICA

A protectorate under the name "Nyassaland Districts" was declared on 14 May 1891, the title being changed to the "British Central Africa Protectorate" on 22 February 1893. Such a description had been in use for some time previously and the handwritten notice of 20 July 1891, announcing the introduction of postal services, described the area as "British Central Africa".

Until 1895 the British South Africa Company contributed to the revenues of the protectorate administration which, in return governed North-eastern Rhodesia. Stamps of the British South Africa Company overprinted "B.C.A.", in addition to use in British Central Africa, were issued to post offices at Fife, Fort Rosebery, Katwe, Johnston Falls, Rhodesia (later Kalungwisi) and Tanganyika (later Abercorn) in North-eastern Rhodesia from 1893 until 1899.

B.C.A.	**B.C.A.**	**FOUR SHILLINGS.**	**ONE PENNY.**	
	(1)	(2)	(3)	

1891 (20 July)–**95**. *Stamps of Rhodesia optd as T* 1. P 14, 14½.

1	**1**	1d. black	7·00	5·50
2	**4**	2d. sea-green and vermilion	7·00	4·00
		a. Bisected (1d.) (on cover) (1895)	†	£3250
3		4d. reddish chestnut and black	7·50	5·00
4	**1**	6d. ultramarine	50·00	20·00
5		6d. deep blue	10·00	8·00
6	**4**	8d. rose-lake and ultramarine	15·00	28·00
6a		8d. red and ultramarine	27·00	45·00
7		1s. grey-brown	17·00	12·00
8		2s. vermilion	28·00	50·00
9		2s.6d. grey-purple	65·00	85·00
9a		2s.6d. lilac	65·00	85·00
10	**4**	3s. brown and green (1895)	65·00	65·00
11		4s. grey-black and vermilion (2.93)	60·00	85·00
12	**1**	5s. orange-yellow	70·00	75·00
13		10s. deep green	£140	£190
14	**2**	£1 deep blue	£700	£550
15		£2 rose-red	£950	
16		£5 sage-green	£1600	
17		£10 brown	£3500	£4500
1/14 *Set of 13*			£1000	£1000

The overprint varies on values up to 10s. Sets may be made with thin or thick letters. The bisected 2d, No. 2a, was authorised for use at Blantyre, Chiromo and Zomba in July and October 1895.

1892 (Aug)–**93**. *Stamps of Rhodesia surch as T* 2.

18	**4**	3s. on 4s. grey-black and vermilion (10.93)	£325	£325
19	**1**	4s. on 5s. orange-yellow	75·00	85·00

1895. *No.* 2 surch at Cape Town with T **3**.

20	**4**	1d. on 2d. sea-green and vermilion	11·00	35·00
		a. Surch double	£5500	£3500

Specimens are known with double surcharge, without stop after "PENNY". These are from a trial printing made at Blantyre, but it is believed that they were not issued to the public (*Price* £550 *un.*).

5 Arms of the Protectorate

6 Arms of the Protectorate

(Des Sir Harry Johnston. Litho D.L.R.)

1895. No wmk. P 14.

21	**5**	1d. black	14·00	12·00
22		2d. black and green	26·00	12·00
23		4d. black and reddish buff	55·00	40·00
24		6d. black and blue	65·00	8·00
25		1s. black and rose	75·00	32·00
26	**6**	2s.6d. black and bright magenta	£200	£300
27		3s. black and yellow	£140	50·00
28		5s. black and olive	£170	£200
29		£1 black and yellow-orange	£950	£375
30		£10 black and orange-vermilion	£5500	£4000
31		£25 black and blue-green	£10000	
21/8 *Set of 8*			£650	£600
21s/9s Optd "Specimen" *Set of 9*			£375	

Cancellations inscribed "BRITISH CENTRAL AFRICA" within a double-circle and with the name of a town across the centre or at foot were intended for use on stamps presented for the payment of the hut tax. Such marks can be found in black, violet or blue and are without date. Stamps with such fiscal obliterations are of little value. Prices quoted are for postally used.

1896 (Feb). Wmk Crown CA (T **5**) or CC (sideways) (T **6**). P 14.

32	**5**	1d. black	3·25	5·50
		y. Wmk inverted and reversed	†	£375
33		2d. black and green	15·00	5·00
34		4d. black and orange-brown	24·00	17·00
35		6d. black and blue	28·00	13·00
36		1s. black and rose	28·00	17·00
37	**6**	2s.6d. black and magenta	£140	£130
38		3s. black and yellow	£110	55·00
39		5s. black and olive	£160	£200
40		£1 black and blue	£900	£500
41		£10 black and orange	£6500	£3750
		s. Optd "Specimen"	£180	
42		£25 black and green	£14000	
		s. Optd "Specimen"	£325	
32/9 *Set of 8*			£450	£375
32s/40s Optd "Specimen" *Set of 9*			£375	

7

8

(Typo D.L.R.)

1897 (Aug)–**1900**. T **7** (wmk Crown CA) and **8** (wmk Crown CC). P 14.

43	**7**	1d. black and ultramarine	3·25	1·25
		w. Wmk inverted	£170	£225
44		2d. black and yellow	2·00	2·00
45		4d. black and carmine	6·50	1·50
46		6d. black and green	45·00	4·25
47		1s. black and dull purple	11·00	7·00
48	**8**	2s.6d. black and ultramarine	55·00	42·00
49		3s. black and sea-green	£200	£250
50		4s. black and carmine	70·00	80·00
50a		10s. black and olive-green (1900)	£160	£170
51		£1 black and dull purple	£275	£160
52		£10 black and yellow	£4750	£1800
		s. Optd "Specimen"	£200	
43/51 *Set of 10*			£750	£650
43s/51s Optd "Specimen" *Set of 10*			£275	

INTERNAL

ONE PENNY

POSTAGE.

(9)

ONE PENNY

10

1897 (31 Dec). *No.* 49 surch with T **9**, in red.

53	**8**	1d. on. 3s. black and sea-green	6·50	9·50
		a. "PNNEY" (R. 4/2)	£3500	£3000
		b. "PENN"	£2000	£1600
		c. Surch double	£500	£850

No. 53b shows an albino impression of the "Y".

1898 (11 Mar). Imperf.

(a) Setting I. The vertical frame lines of the stamps cross the space between the two rows of the sheet.

(i) With the initials "J.G." or "J.T.G." on the back in black ink.

54	**10**	1d. vermilion and grey-blue	£7500	£850
		a. Without the initials	£4000	
		b. Without the initials and centre inverted	£14000	

(ii) With a control number and letter or letters, printed in plain relief at the back.

55	**10**	1d. vermilion and grey-blue	—	£600

(b) Setting II. The vertical frame lines do not cross the space between the rows except at the extreme ends of the sheet. Control as No. 55.

55b	**10**	1d. vermilion and pale ultramarine	—	£120
		c. Control on face	—	£3250
		d. Centre omitted (vert pair with normal)	£15000	
56		1d. vermilion and deep ultramarine	—	£120
		a. Without Control at back	£3000	£170
		b. Control doubly impressed	—	£425

1898 (June). Setting II. Control as No. 55. P 12.

57	**10**	1d. vermilion and pale ultramarine	£3000	23·00
57a		1d. vermilion and deep ultramarine	—	38·00
		ab. Without Control at back	£3000	90·00
		ac. Two different Controls on back.	—	£600
		ad. Control printed in black	£4000	

The two different settings of these stamps are each in 30 types, issued without gum.

1901. Wmk Crown CA. P 14.

57d	**7**	1d. dull purple and carmine-rose	2·50	50
57e		4d. dull purple and olive-green	8·50	11·00
58		6d. dull purple and brown	3·75	3·00
57d/8 *Set of 3*			13·00	13·00
57ds/8s Optd "Specimen" *Set of 3*			60·00	

11

12

(Typo D.L.R.)

1903–04. T **11** (Wmk Crown CA) and **12** (Wmk Crown CC). P 14.

59	**11**	1d. grey and carmine	7·50	1·75
60		2d. dull and bright purple	3·50	1·00
61		4d. grey-green and black	2·50	9·00
62		6d. grey and reddish buff	3·25	2·00
		aw. Wmk inverted	£130	
62b		1s. grey and blue	3·75	12·00
63	**12**	2s.6d. grey-green and green	50·00	80·00
64		4s. dull and bright purple	70·00	80·00
		w. Wmk inverted	£800	
65		10s. grey-green and black	£140	£225
66		£1 grey and carmine	£275	£180
67		£10 grey and blue	£5000	£3500
		s. Optd "Specimen"	£400	
59/66 *Set of 9*			£500	£500
59s/66s Optd "Specimen" *Set of 9*			£325	

1907. Chalk-surfaced paper. Wmk Mult Crown CA. P 14.

68	**11**	1d. grey and carmine	6·50	2·75
69		2d. dull and bright purple	£12000	
70		4d. grey-green and black	£12000	
71		6d. grey and reddish buff	29·00	48·00

Nos. 69/70 were prepared, but not issued in Nyasaland due to the Protectorate's name being changed. It is estimated that no more than a dozen examples of each remain in collectors' hands.

NYASALAND PROTECTORATE

The title of the Protectorate was changed again from 6 July 1907.

13

14

Serif on "G" (R. 4/5. All ptgs of £1 Duty plate)

(Typo D.L.R.)

1908 (22 July)–**11**. P 14.

(a) Wmk Crown CA. *Chalk-surfaced paper.*

72	**13**	1s. black/green	2·75	13·00

(b) Wmk Mult Crown CA. *Ordinary paper (½d., 1d.) or chalk-surfaced paper (others).*

73	**13**	½d. green	1·75	2·25
74		1d. carmine	4·00	1·00
75		3d. purple/yellow	1·50	4·25
		w. Wmk inverted	£225	
76		4d. black and red/yellow	1·50	1·50
		w. Wmk inverted	£120	£140

77		6d. dull purple and bright purple.....	3·75	11·00
78	14	2s.6d. brownish black & carm-red/blue.....	55·00	85·00
		a. Brownish black and deep rose-red/pale blue (1911).....	£200	£225
79		4s. carmine and black.....	85·00	£130
80		10s. green and red/green	£130	£250
81		£1 purple and black/red	£475	£600
		c. Serif on "G"	£1900	£2250
82		£10 purple and ultramarine.....	£8500	£6000
		s. Optd "Specimen".....	£750	
72/81 Set of 10			£700	£1000
72s/81s Optd "Specimen" Set of 10			£550	

15   16

"Bullet holes" flaw (R. 5/2. March 1919 ptgs)

Triangle flaw (R. 3/5. March 1919 ptg of 4s.)

1913 (1 Apr)–**19**. Wmk Mult Crown CA. *Ordinary paper (½d. to 2½d.) or chalk-surfaced paper (others).* P 14.

83	15	½d. green.....	1·25	1·75
84		½d. blue-green (1918).....	1·75	2·00
85		1d. carmine-red.....	1·50	2·00
86		1d. scarlet (1916).....	2·75	1·00
87		2d. grey (1916).....	3·75	1·00
88		2d. slate.....	8·00	2·50
89		2½d. bright blue.....	2·25	7·00
90		3d. purple/yellow (1914).....	4·50	4·50
		a. On pale yellow	4·25	9·50
		w. Wmk inverted		
91		4d. black and red/yellow (shades) ..	2·00	2·50
		a. On pale yellow	6·00	8·00
92		6d. dull and bright purple.....	3·50	9·50
92a		6d. dull purple and bright violet.....	12·00	10·00
93		1s. black/green.....	1·75	8·50
		a. On blue-green, olive back.....	5·50	1·50
		aw. Wmk inverted	£130	£170
		b. On emerald back.....	3·75	6·50
		bs. Optd "Specimen".....	55·00	
94	16	2s.6d. black and red/blue.....	11·00	15·00
		a. Break in scroll.....	£180	
		b. Broken crown and scroll.....	£250	
		c. Nick in top right scroll	£190	£250
		f. Damaged leaf at bottom right.....	£190	
		h. "Bullet-holes" flaw	£325	
		x. Wmk reversed	†	£1300
95		4s. carmine and black.....	16·00	55·00
		a. Break in scroll.....	£200	
		b. Broken crown and scroll.....	£275	
		c. Nick in top right scroll	£225	
		e. Break in lines below left scroll .	£350	
		f. Damaged leaf at bottom right.....	£225	
		h. "Bullet-holes" flaw	£350	
		i. Triangle flaw	£350	
96		10s. pale green and deep scarlet/green.....	90·00	£120
		d. Nick in top right scroll	£500	
		e. Green and deep scarlet/green (1919).....	90·00	£120
		ea. Break in scroll.....	£475	
		eb. Broken crown and scroll.....	£475	
		ef. Damaged leaf at bottom right.....	£475	
		eh. "Bullet holes" flaw.....	£600	
98		£1 purple and black/red	£180	£140
		a. Break in scroll.....	£750	
		b. Broken crown and scroll.....	£750	£650
		c. Nick in top right scroll	£800	
		e. Break in lines below left scroll .	£850	
		f. Damaged leaf at bottom right.....	£750	
		h. "Bullet holes" flaw.....	£1200	
		i. Serif on "G".....	£800	£650

99		w. Wmk inverted	£5500	
		c. Nick in top right scroll	£6500	
		e. Purple and dull ultramarine	£3250	£1700
		e. Purple and royal blue (1919).....	£3250	£3000
		ea. Break in scroll.....	£5000	£3000
		eb. Broken crown and scroll.....	£5000	
		ef. Damaged leaf at bottom right.....		
		eh. "Bullet holes" flaw.....	£425	
		s. Optd "Specimen".....		
83/98 Set of 12			£275	£300
83s/98s Optd "Specimen" Set of 12			£475	

For illustrations of the other varieties on Nos. 94/9 see above Bermuda No. 51b.

For stamps overprinted "N.F." see TANZANIA.

Damaged crown (R. 4/1. 2s.6d. ptg of June 1924)

1921–33. Wmk Mult Script CA. *Ordinary paper (½d. to 2d.) or chalk-surfaced paper (others).* P 14.

100	15	½d. green.....	1·50	50
		w. Wmk inverted	—	£180
101		1d. carmine.....	2·25	50
102		1½d. orange.....	3·25	17·00
103		2d. grey.....	1·00	50
105		3d. purple/pale yellow.....	10·00	3·25
106		4d. black and red/yellow.....	3·00	11·00
107		6d. dull and bright purple.....	3·00	3·25
108		1s. black/emerald (1930).....	9·00	4·50
109	16	2s. purple and blue/blue (1926)	15·00	12·00
		a. Break in scroll.....	£160	£160
		b. Broken crown and scroll.....	£160	£160
		d. Break through scroll (Oct 1933 ptg only).....	£300	£300
		e. Break in lines below left scroll .	£160	£160
		f. Damaged leaf at bottom right.....	£160	£160
		g. Gash in fruit and leaf (Oct 1933 ptg only).....	£300	£300
		h. Breaks in scrolls at right (Oct 1933 ptg only).....	£300	£300
110		2s.6d. black and red/blue (30.9.24).....	21·00	16·00
		a. Break in scroll.....	£170	£170
		b. Broken crown and scroll.....	£170	£170
		c. Nick in top right scroll	£170	£170
		d. Break through scroll (Oct 1933 ptg only).....	£325	£325
		e. Break in lines below left scroll .	£170	£170
		f. Damaged leaf at bottom right.....	£170	£170
		g. Gash in fruit and leaf (Oct 1933 ptg only).....	£325	£325
		h. Breaks in scrolls at right (Oct 1933 ptg only).....	£325	£325
111		4s. carmine and black (1927).....	19·00	28·00
		a. Break in scroll.....	£170	
		b. Broken crown and scroll.....	£170	
		c. Nick in top right scroll	£170	
		e. Break in lines below left scroll .	£170	
		f. Damaged leaf at bottom right.....	£170	
112		5s. green and red/yellow (1929).....	40·00	75·00
		a. Break in scroll.....	£300	
		b. Broken crown and scroll.....	£300	
		c. Nick in top right scroll	£300	
		e. Break in lines below left scroll .	£300	
		f. Damaged leaf at bottom right.....	£300	
113		10s. Green and red/pale emerald (1926).....	90·00	95·00
		a. Break in scroll.....	£425	£475
		b. Broken crown and scroll.....	£425	£475
		c. Nick in top right scroll	£425	£475
		e. Break in lines below left scroll .	£425	£475
		f. Damaged leaf at bottom right.....	£425	£475
		g. Green and scarlet/emerald (1927).....	£475	£650
		ga. Break in scroll.....	£1400	
		gb. Broken crown and scroll.....	£1400	
		ge. Break in lines below left scroll .	£1400	
		gf. Damaged leaf at bottom right.....	£1400	
100/13 Set of 13			£200	£225
100s/13s Optd or Perf (1s., 5s.) "Specimen" Set of 13.....			£425	

For illustrations of the other varieties on Nos. 109/13 see above Bermuda No. 51b.

17 King George V and Symbol of the Protectorate

(Des Major H. E. Green. Recess Waterlow)

1934 (June)–**35**. Wmk Mult Script CA. P 12½.

114	17	½d. green.....	75	1·25
115		1d. brown.....	75	75
116		1½d. carmine.....	75	3·00
117		2d. pale grey.....	80	1·25

118		3d. blue.....	2·50	1·75
119		4d. bright magenta (20.5.35).....	2·50	3·50
120		6d. violet.....	2·50	50
121		9d. olive-bistre (20.5.35).....	6·50	9·00
122		1s. black and orange.....	9·50	14·00
114/22 Set of 9			24·00	32·00
114s/22s Perf "Specimen" Set of 9.....			£200	

1935 (6 May). *Silver Jubilee. As Nos. 91/4 of Antigua, but ptd by Waterlow.* P 11×12.

123		1d. ultramarine and grey.....	1·00	2·00
		k. Kite and vertical log	£120	£160
		m. "Bird" by turret	£160	
124		2d. green and indigo	1·00	1·50
		m. "Bird" by turret	£160	
125		3d. brown and deep blue.....	7·00	17·00
		k. Kite and vertical log	£275	£375
126		1s. slate and purple.....	20·00	50·00
		k. Kite and vertical log	£350	£350
123/6 Set of 4			26·00	65·00
123s/6s Perf "Specimen" Set of 4			£130	

For illustrations of plate varieties see Omnibus section following Zanzibar.

1937 (12 May). *Coronation. As Nos. 95/7 of Antigua.* P 11×11½.

127		½d. green.....	30	1·50
128		1d. brown.....	50	1·00
129		2d. grey-black.....	50	2·50
127/9 Set of 3			1·10	4·50
127s/9s Perf "Specimen" Set of 3			85·00	

18 Symbol of the Protectorate   **19**

(T **18** recess Waterlow; T **19** typo D.L.R.)

1938 (1 Jan)–**44**. *Chalk-surfaced paper (2s. to £1).* P 12½ (T **18**) or 14 (T **19**).

(a) Wmk Mult Script CA.

130	18	½d. green.....	30	1·50
130a		½d. brown (12.12.42).....	10	2·25
131		1d. brown.....	2·75	30
131a		1d. green (12.12.42).....	30	1·25
132		1½d. carmine.....	4·75	4·50
132a		1½d. grey (12.12.42).....	30	6·00
133		2d. grey.....	8·00	1·25
133a		2d. carmine (12.12.42).....	30	1·75
		b. "A" of "CA" missing from wmk.....		
134		3d. blue.....	60	70
135		4d. bright magenta	2·75	1·50
136		6d. violet.....	2·75	1·00
137		9d. olive-bistre.....	2·75	3·25
138		1s. black and orange.....	3·50	2·00
139	19	2s. purple and blue/blue.....	10·00	12·00
140		2s.6d. black and red/blue.....	12·00	14·00
141		5s. pale green and red/yellow	45·00	23·00
		a. Ordinary paper. Green and red/pale yellow (3.44).....	80·00	£110
142		10s. emerald and deep red/pale green.....	50·00	50·00
		a. Ordinary paper. Bluish green and brown-red/pale green (1.38).....	£350	£325

(b) Wmk Mult Crown CA.

143	19	£1 purple and black/red	40·00	32·00
		c. Serif on "G"	£750	£550
130/43 Set of 18			£170	£140
130s/43s Perf "Specimen" Set of 18			£700	

No. 141a has a yellow surfacing often applied in horizontal lines giving the appearance of laid paper

The printer's archives record the despatch of No. 142a to Nyasaland in January 1938, but no examples have been reported used before 1945. The paper coating on this printing varied considerably across the sheet. It is reported that some examples show a faint reaction to the silver test.

20 Lake Nyasa   **21** King's African Rifles

22 Tea estate   **23** Map of Nyasaland

24 Fishing village

25 Tobacco

25a Badge of Nyasaland

(Recess B.W.)

1945 (1 Sept). T **20/25a**. Wmk Mult Script CA (sideways on horiz designs). P 12.

144	20	½d. black and chocolate	50	10
145	21	1d. black and emerald	20	70
146	22	1½d. black and grey-green	30	50
147	23	2d. black and scarlet	1·50	85
148	24	3d. black and light blue	20	30
149	25	4d. black and claret	2·00	80
150	22	6d. black and violet	2·50	90
151	20	9d. black and olive	1·75	3·00
152	23	1s. indigo and deep green	1·50	20
153	24	2s. emerald and maroon	6·00	4·75
154	25	2s.6d. emerald and blue	7·50	5·00
155	25a	5s. purple and blue	4·50	6·50
156	23	10s. claret and emerald	15·00	14·00
157	25a	20s. scarlet and black	21·00	28·00
144/57 Set of 14			60·00	60·00
144s/57s Perf "Specimen" Set of 14			£325	

1946 (16 Dec). Victory. As Nos. 110/11 of Antigua.

158		1d. green	10	30
159		2d. red-orange	30	10
158s/9s Perf "Specimen" Set of 2			75·00	

26 Symbol of the Protectorate
27 Arms in 1891 and 1951

(Recess B.W.)

1947 (20 Oct). Wmk Mult Script CA. P 12.

160	26	1d. red-brown and yellow-green	50	20
		a. Perf "Specimen"	55·00	

1948 (15 Dec). Royal Silver Wedding. As Nos. 112/13 of Antigua.

161		1d. green	15	10
162		10s. mauve	15·00	26·00

1949 (21 Nov). 75th Anniv of U.P.U. As Nos. 114/17 of Antigua.

163		1d. blue-green	30	20
		a. "A" of "CA" missing from wmk	£600	
164		3d. greenish blue	2·00	3·25
165		6d. purple	50	50
166		1s. ultramarine	30	50
163/6 Set of 4			2·75	4·00

As on other examples of this variety, No. 163a shows traces of the left leg of the "A".

(Des C. Twynam. Recess B.W.)

1951 (15 May). Diamond Jubilee of Protectorate. Wmk Mult Script CA. P 11×12.

167	27	2d. black and scarlet	1·25	1·50
168		3d. black and turquoise-blue	1·25	1·50
169		6d. black and violet	1·25	2·00
170		5s. black and indigo	3·75	7·00
167/70 Set of 4			6·75	11·00

POSTAGE DUE STAMPS

D 1

(Typo D.L.R.)

1950 (1 July). Wmk Mult Script CA. P 14.

D1	D 1	1d. scarlet	3·75	25·00
D2		2d. ultramarine	13·00	25·00
D3		3d. green	13·00	6·00
D4		4d. purple	23·00	48·00
D5		6d. yellow-orange	30·00	£130
D1/5 Set of 5			75·00	£200

Orange Free State see South Africa

Pakistan

(Currency. 12 pies = 1 anna; 16 annas = 1 rupee)

DOMINION

PAKISTAN (1)   **PAKISTAN** (2)

1947 (1 Oct). Nos. 259/68 and 269a/77 (King George VI) of India optd by litho at Nasik, as T **1** (3p. to 12a.) or **2** (14a. and rupee values).

1		3p. slate	10	10
2		½a. purple	10	10
3		9p. green	10	10
4		1a. carmine	10	10
5		1½a. dull violet	30	10
		w. Wmk inverted		
6		2a. vermilion	10	20
7		3a. bright violet	10	20
8		3½a. bright blue	65	2·25
9		4a. brown	20	20
10		6a. turquoise-green	1·00	1·25
11		8a. slate-violet	30	60
12		12a. lake	1·00	20
13		14a. purple	3·00	3·50
14		1r. grey and red-brown	2·50	1·25
		w. Wmk inverted	60·00	
15		2r. purple and brown	3·25	20
16		5r. green and blue	4·00	4·00
17		10r. purple and claret	4·00	3·50
18		15r. brown and green	55·00	80·00
19		25r. slate-violet and purple	60·00	45·00
1/19 Set of 19			£120	£130

Numerous provisional "PAKISTAN" overprints, both handstamped and machine-printed, in various sizes and colours, on Postage and Official stamps, also exist.

These were made under authority of Provincial Governments, District Head Postmasters or Local Postmasters and are of considerable philatelic interest.

The 1a.3p. (India No. 269) exists only as a local issue (Price, Karachi opt £1. unused; £1.75 used).

The 12a., as No. 12 but overprinted at Karachi, exists with overprint inverted (Price £60 unused).

The 1r. value with Karachi local overprint exists with overprint inverted (Price £150 unused) or as a vertical pair with one stamp without overprint (Price £600 unused).

3 Constituent Assembly Building, Karachi   6 Crescent and Stars

(Des R ud Dim (1½a., 3a.) and A. Chughtai (1r.). Recess D.L.R.)

1948 (9 July). Independence. T **3**, **6** and similar horiz designs. P 13½×14 or 11½ (1r.).

20		1½a. ultramarine	1·25	1·25
21		2½a. green	1·25	20
22		3a. purple-brown	1·25	35
23		1r. scarlet	1·25	70
		a. Perf 14×13½	4·75	18·00
20/3 Set of 4			4·50	2·25

Designs:—2½a. Karachi Airport entrance; 3a. Gateway to Lahore Fort.

7 Scales of Justice   8 Star and Crescent   9 Lloyds Barrage

---

10 Karachi Airport

13 Khyber Pass

(Des M. Suharwardi (T **8**). Recess Pakistan Security Ptg Corp Ltd, Karachi (P 13 and 13½), D.L.R. (others))

1948 (14 Aug)—56?. T **7/10**, **13** and similar designs. P 13½×14 or 11½ (1r.).

24	7	3p. red (P 12½)	10	10
		a. Perf 13½ (1954?)	1·00	1·00
25		6p. violet (P 12½)	80	10
		a. Perf 13½ (1954?)	3·00	2·50
26		9p. green (P 12½)	50	10
		a. Perf 13½ (1954?)	2·00	1·75
27	8	1a. blue (P 12½)	10	50
28		1½a. grey-green (P 12½)	10	10
29		2a. red (P 12½)	1·50	70
30	9	2½a. green (P 14×13½)	3·25	6·50
31	10	3a. green (P 14)	7·50	1·00
32	9	3½a. bright blue (P 14×13½)	3·75	5·50
33		4a. reddish brown (P 12½)	65	10
34	—	6a. blue (P 14×13½)	1·00	50
35	—	8a. black (P 12½)	65	1·25
36	10	10a. scarlet (P 14)	5·50	8·00
37		12a. scarlet (P 14×13½)	7·50	1·00
38		1r. ultramarine (P 14)	6·50	10
		a. Perf 13½ (1954?)	16·00	5·50
39		2r. chocolate (P 14)	20·00	60
		a. perf 13½ (1954?)	26·00	2·00
40		5r. carmine (P 14)	17·00	1·25
		a. Perf 13½ (7.53)	12·00	25
41	13	10r. magenta (P 14)	10·00	20·00
		a. Perf 12	85·00	6·50
		b. Perf 13 (1951)	18·00	1·50
42		15r. blue-green (P 12)	18·00	17·00
		a. Perf 14	18·00	48·00
		b. Perf 13 (1956?)	21·00	15·00
43		25r. violet (P 14)	55·00	80·00
		a. Perf 12	32·00	55·00
		b. Perf 13 (1954)	45·00	30·00
24/43 Set of 20			£120	65·00

Designs: Vert (as T **7**)—6a., 8a., 12a. Karachi Port Trust. (As T **10**)—1r., 2r., 5r. Salimullah Hostel, Dacca.
For 25r. with W **98**, see No. 210.

14 Star and Crescent   15 Karachi Airport

(Recess Pakistan Security Ptg Corp (P 13½), D.L.R. (others).

1949 (Feb)—53?. Redrawn. Crescent moon with points to left as T **14/15**.

44	14	1a. blue (P 12½)	4·00	85
		a. Perf 13½ (1953?)	4·50	10
45		1½a. grey-green (P 12½)	3·75	85
		a. Perf 13½ (1952?)	3·00	10
		ab. Printed on the gummed side	55·00	
46		2a. red (P 12½)	4·50	10
		a. Perf 13½ (1953?)	4·00	10
47	15	3a. green (P 14)	13·00	1·00
48	—	6a. blue (as No. 34) (P 14×13½)	10·00	1·50
49	—	8a. black (as No. 35) (P 12½)	10·00	2·00
50	15	10a. scarlet (P 14)	19·00	2·50
51	—	12a. scarlet (as No. 37) (P 14×13½)	23·00	50
44/51 Set of 8			75·00	6·75

16

(Recess D.L.R.)

1949 (11 Sept). First Death Anniv of Mohammed Ali Jinnah. T **16** and similar design. P 14.

52	16	1½a. brown	2·00	1·50
53		3a. green	2·00	1·50
54		10a. black	6·00	8·00
52/4 Set of 3			9·00	10·00

Design:—10a. Similar inscription reading "QUAID-I-AZAM/ MOHAMMAD ALI JINNAH" etc.

17 Pottery   18 Aeroplane and Hourglass

Two Types of 3½a.:

I

II

19 Saracenic Leaf Pattern

20 Archway and Lamp

(Des A. Chughtai. Recess D.L.R., later printings, Pakistan Security Ptg Corp)

1951 (14 Aug)–56. *Fourth Anniv of Independence.* P 13.

55	**17**	2½a. carmine	1·75	1·25
56	**18**	3a. purple	1·00	10
57	**17**	3½a. blue (I)	1·25	4·50
57a		3½a. blue (II) (12.56)	3·50	5·00
58	**19**	4a. green	75	10
59		6a. brown-orange	1·00	10
60	**20**	8a. sepia	4·50	25
61		10a. violet	2·00	1·75
62	**18**	12a. slate	2·00	10
55/62 Set of 8			16·00	11·50

The above and the stamps issued on the 14 August 1954, 1955 and 1956, are basically definitive issues, although issued on the Anniversary date of Independence

OFFICIAL STAMPS

PAKISTAN
(O 1)

1947. *Nos. O138/41 and O143/50 (King George VI) of India, optd as Type O 1 (Nos. O1/9) or as T 2 (Nos. O10/13) both in litho by Nasik.*

O1		3p. slate	2·00	1·50
O2		½a. purple	30	10
O3		9p. green	5·00	3·25
O4		1a. carmine	30	10
O5		1½a. dull violet	30	10
		w. Wmk inverted	20·00	
O6		2a. vermilion	30	30
O7		2½a. bright violet	7·00	9·00
O8		4a. brown	1·25	10
O9		8a. slate-violet	1·75	2·50
O10		1r. grey and red-brown	80	2·00
O11		2r. purple and brown	5·50	4·50
O12		5r. green and blue	21·00	38·00
O13		10r. purple and claret	55·00	£110
O1/13 Set of 13			90·00	£150

See note after No. 19. The 1a.3p. (India No. O146a) exists as a local issue (*Price*, Karachi opt, £8 mint, £25 used).

SERVICE
(O 2)

SERVICE
(O 3)

NOTE. Apart from a slight difference in size, Types O 2 and O 3 can easily be distinguished by the difference in the shape of the "c".

PRINTERS. Type O 2 was overprinted by De La Rue and Type O 3 by the Pakistan Security Ptg Corp.

1948 (14 Aug)–54?. *Optd with Type O 2.*

O14	**7**	3p. red (No. 24)	10	10
O15		6p. violet (No. 25) (R.)	10	10
O16		9p. green (No. 26) (R.)	10	10
O17	**8**	1a. blue (No. 27) (R.)	3·75	10
O18		1½a. grey-green (No. 28) (R.)	3·50	10
O19		2a. red (No. 29)	1·50	10
O20	**10**	3a. green (No. 31)	26·00	10·00
O21	**9**	4a. reddish brown (No. 33)	1·25	10
O22	–	8a. black (No. 35) (R.)	2·25	9·50
O23	–	1r. ultramarine (No. 38)	1·25	10
O24	–	2r. chocolate (No. 39)	14·00	10·00
O25	–	5r. carmine (No. 40)	45·00	12·00
O26	**13**	10r. magenta (No. 41)	17·00	48·00
		a. Perf 12 (10.10.51)	22·00	50·00
		b. Perf 13 (1954?)	15·00	55·00
O14/26 Set of 13			£100	80·00

1949. *Optd with Type O 2.*

O27		1a. blue (No. 44) (R.)	2·50	10
O28		1½a. grey-green (No. 45) (R.)	1·50	10
		a. Opt inverted	£275	42·00
O29		2a. red (No. 46)	1·75	10
		a. Opt omitted (in pair with normal)	—	£160
O30		3a. green (No. 47)	29·00	6·00
O31		8a. black (No. 49) (R.)	48·00	19·00
O27/31 Set of 5			75·00	23·00

1951 (14 Aug). *4th Anniv of Independence. As Nos. 56, 58 and 60, but inscr "SERVICE" instead of "PAKISTAN POSTAGE".*

O32	**18**	3a. purple	7·50	10·00
O33	**19**	4a. green	2·00	10
O34	**20**	8a. sepia	8·00	4·00
O32/4 Set of 3			16·00	12·50

1953. *Optd with Type O 3.*

O35		3p. red (No. 24a)	10	10
O36		6p. violet (No. 25a) (R.)	10	10
O37		9p. green (No. 26a) (R.)	10	10
O38		1a. blue (No. 44a) (R.)	10	10
O39		1½a. grey-green (No. 45a) (R.)	10	10
O40		2a. red (No. 46a) (1953?)	15	10
O41		1r. ultramarine (No. 38a)	10·00	4·25
O42		2r. chocolate (No. 39a)	4·25	20

O43		5r. carmine (No. 40a)	42·00	19·00
O44		10r. magenta (No. 41b) (date?)	22·00	55·00
O35/44 Set of 10			70·00	70·00

BAHAWALPUR

Bahawalpur, a former feudatory state situated to the west of the Punjab, was briefly independent following the partition of India on 15 August 1947 before acceding to Pakistan on 3 October of the same year.

East India Company and later Indian Empire post offices operated in Bahawalpur from 1854. By a postal agreement of 1879 internal mail from the state administration was carried unstamped, but this arrangement was superseded by the issue of Official stamps in 1945.

These had been preceded by a series of pictorial stamps prepared in 1933–34 on unwatermarked paper. It was intended that these would be used as state postage stamps, but permission for such use was withheld by the Indian Government so they were used for revenue purposes. The same designs were utilised for the 1945 Official series, Nos. O1/6, on paper watermarked Star and Crescent. Residual stocks of the unwatermarked 1a., 8a., 1r. and 2r. were used for the provisionalOfficials, Nos. O7 and O11/13.

A commemorative 1a. Receipt stamp was produced to mark the centenary of the alliance with Great Britain. This may not have been ready until 1935, but an example of this stamp is known used on cover from Deh Rawal to Sadiq Garh and postmarked 14 August 1933. Both this 1a. and the same value from the unwatermarked set also exist with Official Arabic overprint in black. These were not issued for postal purposes although one used example of the latter has been recorded postmarked 22 February 1933 also from Deh Rawal.

Stamps of India were overprinted in the interim period between 15 August and 3 October 1947. After the state joined Pakistan postage stamps were issued for internal use until 1950.

PRICES FOR STAMPS ON COVER
The postage and Official stamps of Bahawalpur are rare used **on cover.**

Nawab (from 1947 Amir) Sadiq Mohammad Khan Abbasi V, 1907–1966

(1)

1947 (15 Aug). *Nos. 265/8, 269a/77 and 259/62 (King George VI) of India optd locally with T 1.*

1		3p. slate (R.)	22·00
2		½a. purple	22·00
3		9p. green (R.)	22·00
4		1a. carmine	22·00
5		1½a. dull violet (R.)	22·00
6		2a. vermilion	22·00
		a. Opt double	£2500
7		3a. bright violet (R.)	22·00
8		3½a. bright blue (R.)	22·00
9		4a. brown	22·00
10		6a. turquoise-green (R.)	22·00
		a. Opt double	£2500
11		8a. slate-violet (R.)	22·00
12		12a. lake	22·00
13		14a. purple	65·00
14		1r. grey and red-brown	25·00
		a. Opt double, one albino	£300
15		2r. purple *and* brown (R.)	£1600
16		5r. green and blue (R.)	£1600
17		10r. purple and claret	£1600
1/17 Set of 17			£4500

Nos. 1/17 were issued during the interim period, following the implementation of the Indian Independence Act, during which time Bahawalpur was part of neither of the two Dominions created. The Amir acceded to the Dominion of Pakistan on 3 October 1947 and these overprinted stamps of India were then withdrawn.

The stamps of Bahawalpur only had validity for use within the state. For external mail Pakistan stamps were used.

PRINTERS. All the following issues were recess-printed by De La Rue & Co, Ltd, London.

2 Amir Muhammad Bahawal Khan I Abbasi

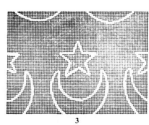
3

1947 (1 Dec). *Bicentenary Commemoration.* W 3 (sideways). P 12½×11½.

18	**2**	½a. black and carmine	2·50	3·75

---

4 H.H. the Amir of Bahawalpur

5 The Tombs of the Amirs

6 Mosque in Sadiq-Garh

7 Fort Derawar from the Lake

8 Nur-Mahal Palace

9 The Palace, Sadiq-Garh

10 H.H. the Amir of Bahawalpur

11 Three Generations of Rulers; H.H. the Amir in centre

1948 (1 Apr). W 3 (sideways on vert designs). P 12½ (T 4), 11½×12½ (T 5, 7, 8 and 9), 12½×11½ (T 6 and 10) or 13½×14 (T 11).

19	**4**	3p. black and blue	2·00	20·00
20		½a. black and claret	2·00	20·00
21		9p. black and green	2·00	20·00
22		1a. black and carmine	2·00	20·00
23		1½a. black and violet	2·25	16·00
24	**5**	2a. green and claret	2·25	20·00
25	**6**	4a. orange and brown	2·25	20·00
26	**7**	6a. violet and blue	2·50	20·00
27	**8**	8a. carmine and violet	2·50	20·00
28	**9**	12a. green and carmine	3·00	30·00
29	**10**	1r. violet and brown	19·00	42·00
30		2r. green and claret	48·00	70·00
31		5r. black and violet	48·00	85·00
32	**11**	10r. scarlet and black	32·00	£100
19/32 Set of 14			£150	£450

12 H.H. The Amir of Bahawalpur and Mohammed Ali Jinnah

13 Soldiers of 1848 and 1948

1948 (3 Oct). *First Anniv of Union of Bahawalpur with Pakistan.* W 3. P 13.

33	**12**	1½a. carmine and blue-green	1·50	3·50

1948 (15 Oct). *Multan Campaign Centenary.* W 3. P 11½.

34	**13**	1½a. black and lake	1·25	9·50

1948. *As Nos. 29/32, but colours changed.*

35	**10**	1r. deep green and orange	1·75	18·00
36		2r. black and carmine	1·75	22·00
37		5r. chocolate and ultramarine	1·90	40·00
38	**11**	10r. red-brown and green	2·00	45·00
35/8 Set of 4			6·75	£110

14 Irrigation

17 U.P.U. Monument, Berne

1949 (3 Mar). *Silver Jubilee of Accession of H.H. the Amir of*

Bahawalpur. T 14 and similar horiz designs. W 3. P 14.

39		3p. black and ultramarine	10	8·00
40		½a. black and brown-orange	10	8·00
41		9p. black and green	10	8·00
42		1a. black and carmine	10	8·00
39/42	Set of 4		30	29·00

Designs:—½a. Wheat; 9p. Cotton; 1a. Sahiwal bull.
Nos. 39/42 exist imperforate (*Prices, £20 per pair, unused*).

1949 (10 Oct). *75th Anniv of Universal Postal Union. W 3. P 13.*

43	17	9p. black and green	20	1·25
		a. Perf 17½×17	1·25	17·00
44		1a. black and magenta	20	1·25
		a. Perf 17½×17	1·25	17·00
45		1½a. black and orange	20	1·25
		a. Perf 17½×17	1·25	17·00
46		2½a. black and blue	20	1·25
		a. Perf 17½×17	1·25	17·00
43/6	Set of 4		70	4·50
43a/6a	Set of 4		4·50	60·00

Nos. 43/6 exist imperforate (*Prices, £10 per pair, unused*).

OFFICIAL STAMPS

O 1 Panjnad Weir

O 2 Dromedary and Calf

O 3 Blackbuck

O 4 Eastern White Pelicans

O 5 Friday Mosque, Fort Derawar

O 6 Temple at Pattan Munara

1945 (1 Mar). *Various horizontal pictorial designs, with red Arabic opt. W 3. P 14.*

O1	O 1	½a. black and green	4·25	14·00
O2	O 2	1a. black and carmine	3·75	9·00
		a. Opt omitted	†	£1100
O3	O 3	2a. black and violet	3·25	12·00
O4	O 4	4a. black and olive-green	12·00	26·00
O5	O 5	8a. black and brown	23·00	16·00
O6	O 6	1r. black and orange	23·00	16·00
O1/6	Set of 6		60·00	85·00

Permission for the introduction of Nos. O1/6 was granted by the Imperial Government as from 1 January 1945, but the stamps were not used until 1 March. First Day covers exist showing the January date.
Examples of No. O2a come from a sheet used at Rahimya Khan.
It is believed that examples of Nos. O1/2 in different shades and with white gum appeared in 1949 and were included in the Silver Jubilee Presentation Booklet.

O 7 Baggage Camels

(O 8)

1945 (10 Mar). *Revenue stamp with red Arabic opt. No wmk. P 14.*

O7	O 7	1a. black and brown	45·00	55·00

1945 (Mar–June). *Surch as Type O 8 (at Security Printing Press, Nasik) instead of red Arabic opt. No wmk. P 14.*

O11	O 5	½a. on 8a. black and purple	5·50	5·50
O12	O 6	1a. on 1r. black and orange	40·00	11·00
O13	O 1	1½a. on 2r. black and blue (1 June)	£130	8·50
O11/13	Set of 3		£160	23·00

The stamps used as a basis for Nos. O7 and O11/13 were part of the Revenue series issued in 1933–34.

(O 9)

O 10 H.H. the Amir of Bahawalpur

1945. *Optd with Type O 9 (by D.L.R.) instead of red Arabic opt. No wmk. P 14.*

O14	O 1	½a. black and carmine	1·25	11·00
O15	O 2	1a. black and carmine	2·00	13·00
O16	O 3	2a. black and orange	3·25	45·00
O14/16	Set of 3		6·00	60·00

1945. P 14.

O17	O 10	3p. black and blue	3·50	9·00
O18		1½a. black and violet	20·00	8·00

O 11 Allied Banners

(Des E. Meronti. Recess, background litho)

1946 (1 May). *Victory. P 14.*

O19	O 11	1½a. green and grey	3·00	4·00

1948. *Nos. 19, 22, 24/5 and 35/8 optd as Nos. O1/6.*

O20	4	3p. black and blue (R.)	80	12·00
O21		1a. black and carmine (Blk.)	80	11·00
O22	5	2a. green and carmine (Blk.)	80	12·00
O23	6	4a. orange and brown (Blk.)	80	16·00
O24	10	1r. deep green and orange (R.)	80	18·00
O25		2r. black and carmine (R.)	80	24·00
O26		5r. chocolate and ultramarine (R.)	80	40·00
O27	11	10r. red-brown and green (R.)	80	40·00
O20/7	Set of 8		5·75	£150

1949 (10 Oct). *75th Anniv of Universal Postal Union. Nos. 43/6 optd as Nos. O1/6.*

O28	17	9p. black and green	15	4·50
		aw. Wmk inverted	†	£300
		b. Perf 17½×17	2·50	29·00
O29		1a. black and magenta	15	4·50
		b. Perf 17½×17	2·50	29·00
O30		1½a. black and orange	15	4·50
		b. Perf 17½×17	2·50	29·00
O31		2½a. black and blue	15	4·50
		b. Perf 17½×17	2·50	29·00
O28/31	Set of 4		55	16·00
O28b/31b	Set of 4		9·00	£100

Nos. O28/31 exist imperforate (*Prices, £10 per pair, unused*)

From 1947 stamps of Pakistan were used on all external mail. Bahawalpur issues continued to be used on internal mail until 1953.

Palestine

The stamps of TURKEY were used in Palestine from 1865. In addition various European Powers, and Egypt, maintained post offices at Jerusalem (Austria, France, Germany, Italy, Russia), Jaffa (Austria, Egypt, France, Germany, Russia) and Haifa (Austria, France) using their own stamps or issues specially prepared for Levant post offices. All foreign post offices had closed by the time of the British Occupation.

PRICES FOR STAMPS ON COVER TO 1945	
No. 1	*from × 6*
No. 2	*from × 4*
Nos. 3/4	*from × 5*
Nos. 5/15	*from × 4*
Nos. 16/29	*from × 3*
Nos. 30/42	*from × 2*
No. 43	
Nos. 44/57	*from × 2*
Nos. 58/9	
Nos. 60/8	*from × 3*
Nos. 69/70	
Nos. 71/89	*from × 3*
Nos. 90/103	*from × 4*
Nos. 104/11	*from × 8*
Nos. D1/5	*from × 30*
Nos. D6/20	*from × 10*

BRITISH MILITARY OCCUPATION

British and allied forces invaded Palestine in November 1917 capturing Gaza (7 November), Jaffa (16 November) and Jerusalem (9 December). The front line then stabilised until the second British offensive of September 1918.

Nos. 1/15 were issued by the British military authorities for use by the civilian population in areas they controlled previously, part of the Ottoman Empire. Before the issue of Nos. 1/2 in February 1918, civilian mail was carried free. In addition to Palestine the stamps were available from E.E.F. post offices in Syria (including what subsequently became Transjordan) from 23 September 1918 to 23 February 1922, Lebanon from 21 October 1918 to September 1920 and Cilicia from 2 September 1919 to 16 July 1920. Use in the following post offices outside Palestine is recorded in *British Empire Campaigns and Occupations in the Near East, 1914–1924* by John Firebrace:

Adana, Cilicia	Hasbaya, Lebanon
Akkari ("Akkar"), Syria	Hasine, Cilicia
Aleih ("Alie"), Lebanon	Hommana, Lebanon
Aleppo ("Alep, Halep"), Syria	Homs, Syria
Alexandretta, Syria	Kozan, Cilicia
Antakie, Syria	Lattakia ("Laskie,Lattaquie"), Syria
Baalbek, Lebanon	Massel el Chouf ("Moussalc"), Lebanon
Bab, Syria	Merdjajoun Lebanon
Babitoma, Syria	Mersina ("Mersine"), Cilicia
Ba'abda, Lebanon	Mounboudje, Syria
Behamdoun, Lebanon	Nabatti, Lebanon
Beit ed Dine, Lebanon	Nebk ("Nebik"), Syria
Beit Mery, Beyrouth, Lebanon	Payass, Syria
Bekaa, Lebanon	Racheya, Lebanon
Beyrouth, Lebanon	Safita, Syria
Bouzanti, Syria	Savour, Tyre, Lebanon
Broumana, Lebanon	Selimie, Syria
Damascus ("Damas"), Syria	Sidan ("Saida (Echelle)"), Lebanon
Damour ("Damor"), Lebanon	Suweidiya ("Suvedie"), Syria
Der'a ("Deraa"), Syria	Talia, Syria
Deurt-Yol, Syria	Tarsous, Cilicia
Djey Han, Syria	Tartous, Syria
Djezzin ("Djezzine"), Lebanon	Tibnin, Lebanon
Djon, Lebanon	Tripoli, Syria
Djounie, Lebanon	Zahle, Lebanon
Djubeil, Lebanon	Zebdani, Syria
Douma, Syria	
Edleb, Syria	
Feke, Turkey	
Habib Souk, Syria	
Hajjin ("Hadjin"), Cilicia	
Hama, Syria	

This information is reproduced here by permission of the publishers, Robson Lowe Publications.

(Currency. 10 milliemes = 1 piastre)

1 (2) 3

"E.E.F." = Egyptian Expeditionary Force

W 100 of Great Britain

(Des G. Rowntree. Litho Typographical Dept, Survey of Egypt, Giza, Cairo)

1918 (10 Feb). *Wmk Royal Cypher in column (W 100 of Great Britain). Ungummed. Roul 20.*

1	1	1p. indigo	£180	£100
		a. Deep blue	£150	90·00
		b. Blue	£150	90·00
		s. Optd "Specimen"	£300	

Control: A 18 (*Prices, corner block of* 4; No. 1 £850. No. 1a, £750. No. 1b, £850).

1918 (16 Feb). *As last (ungummed) surch with T 2.*

2	1	5m. on 1p. cobalt-blue	90·00	£475
		a. "MILLILMES" (R. 1/10)	£3250	£9000
		s. Optd "Specimen"	£300	
		w. Wmk inverted		

Control: B 18 A (*Corner block, £1100*)

1918 (5 Mar). *As No. 1 but colour changed. With gum.*

3	1	1p. ultramarine (*shades*)	2·00	2·00
		a. Crown missing from wmk	40·00	
		b. Printed on the gummed side		
		w. Wmk inverted	£180	£225

Control: C 18. (*Corner block, £70*).

1918 (5 Mar–13 May). *No. 3 surch with T 2.*

4	1	5m. on 1p. ultramarine	4·75	2·75
		a. Arabic surch wholly or partly missing (R. 1/11)	£300	£400
		b. Crown missing from wmk	60·00	
		w. Wmk inverted	£250	

Controls: C 18 B (Mar). (*Corner block, £700*). D 18 C (May). (*Corner block, £200*).

(Typo Stamping Dept, Board of Inland Revenue, Somerset House, London)

1918 (16 July–27 Dec). Wmk Royal Cypher in column (W **100** of Great Britain). P 15×14.

5	**3**	1m. sepia	30	40
		a. Deep brown	40	40
6		2m. blue-green	30	45
		a. Deep green	1·50	80·
7		3m. yellow-brown (17 Dec)	35	35
		a. Chestnut	13·00	6·00
8		4m. scarlet	35	40
9		5m. yellow-orange (25 Sept)	2·50	30
		a. Orange	65	30
		b. Crown missing from wmk	£140	
		w. Wmk inverted	—	£1500
10		1p. deep indigo (9 Nov)	35	25
		a. Crown missing from wmk	£120	
		w. Wmk inverted	£150	£160
11		2p. pale olive	1·25	60
		a. Olive	1·75	1·10
12		5p. purple	1·75	2·25
13		9p. ochre (17 Dec)	4·75	5·00
14		10p. ultramarine (17 Dec)	4·25	3·25
		w. Wmk inverted	£400	
15		20p. pale grey (27 Dec)	11·00	16·00
		a. Slate-grey	16·00	22·00
5/15 Set of 11			24·00	26·00

There are two sizes of the design of this issue:
19×23 mm. 1, 2, and 4m., and 2 and 5p.
18×21½ mm. 3 and 5m., and 1, 9, 10 and 20p.
There are numerous minor plate varieties in this issue, such as stops omitted in "E.E.F.", malformed Arabic characters, etc.

CIVIL ADMINISTRATION UNDER BRITISH HIGH COMMISSIONER

Palestine was placed under civil administration by a British High Commissioner on 1 July 1920.

(4)	(5)	(6)

Differences:—

T **5**. 20 mm vert and 7 mm between English and Hebrew.
T **6**. 19 mm and 6 mm respectively.

Two settings of Type **4**:

Setting I (used for Nos. 16/26). This consisted of two horizontal rows of 12 of which the first setting row appeared on Rows 1, 3/7, 15, 17/18 and 20 of the sheet and the second on Rows 2, 8/14, 16 and 19.

On the first position in the top setting row the Arabic "t" (third character from the left) is incorrectly shown as an Arabic "z" by the addition of a dot to its right. On the eleventh position in the same row the first two letters in the Hebrew overprint were transposed so that " character appears first. On row 12 stamp 1 the final "E" of "PALESTINE" appears as a "B" on certain values. Once the errors were noticed vertical columns one and eleven were removed from the remaining sheets.

Setting II (used for Nos. 16/29). This consisted of a single horizontal row of 12 reproduced to overprint the complete sheet of 240. The order in which the horizontal rows were used was changed several times during overprinting. During one such re-arrangement a damaged impression was replaced by one from Setting I showing the Arabic "z" error. (R. 14/8 for 1, 2, 3, 4, 5m (P 14), 20p.). The "B" error also occurs in the second setting, once in each sheet on either R. 17/8, 18/8 or 19/8.

(Optd at Greek Orthodox Convent, Jerusalem)

1920 (1 Sept). Optd with T **4** (Arabic 8 mm long).

(a) P 15×14.

16	**3**	1m. sepia	4·25	1·90
		b. Arabic "z" (Settings I and II)	£1000	
		c. Hebrew characters transposed (I)	£1000	
		d. "PALESTINB" (II)	75·00	
17		2m. blue-green	7·50	4·50
		b. "Arabic "z" (Settings I and II)	£850	
		c. Hebrew characters transposed (I)	£850	
		d. "PALESTINB" (II)	85·00	
18		3m. chestnut	9·00	4·75
		a. Opt inverted	£450	£600
		b. Arabic "z" (Settings I and II)	£1500	
		c. Hebrew characters transposed (I)	£1500	
		d. "PALESTINB" (II)	45·00	
19		4m. scarlet	2·50	1·25
		b. Arabic "z" (Settings I and II)	£1500	
		c. Hebrew characters transposed (I)	£1500	
		d. PALESTINB" (II)	45·00	
20		5m. yellow-orange	17·00	4·25
		c. Hebrew characters transposed (I)	†	£2500
		d. "PALESTINB" (II)	85·00	
21		1p. deep indigo (Sil.)	3·75	80
		d. "PALESTINB" (II)	20·00	
		w. Wmk inverted	£120	£130
22		2p. deep olive	3·50	1·90
		a. Crown missing from wmk	£500	
		b. Arabic "z" (I)	£180	
		c. Hebrew characters transposed (I)	£180	
		d. "PALESTINB" (Settings I and II)	90·00	
23		5p. deep purple	19·00	22·00
		b. Arabic "z" (I)	£900	
		c. Hebrew characters transposed (I)	£500	
		d. "PALESTINB" (Setting I and II)	£140	
24		9p. ochre	10·00	20·00
		b. Arabic "z" (I)	£400	
		c. Hebrew characters transposed (I)	£450	
		d. "PALESTINB" (Settings I and II)	£160	
25		10p. ultramarine	10·00	17·00
		b. Arabic "z" (I)	£300	
		c. Hebrew characters transposed (I)	£400	
		d. "PALESTINB" (Settings I and II)	£200	
26		20p. pale grey	27·00	42·00
		b. Arabic "z" (Settings I and II)	£800	

		c. Hebrew characters transposed (I)	£900	
		d. "PALESTINB" (Settings I and II)	£1800	
16/26 Set of 11			£100	£110

(b) P 14.

27	**3**	2m. blue-green	1·60	1·40
		d. "PALESTINB" (II)	30·00	
28		3m. chestnut	55·00	55·00
29		5m. orange	3·00	65
		d. "PALESTINB" (II)	70·00	

Faulty registration of the overprint in this issue has resulted in numerous misplaced overprints, either vertically or horizontally, which are not of great importance with the exception of Nos. 21 and 29 which exist with the overprint out of sequence, i.e. Hebrew/Arabic/English or English/Arabic/Hebrew or English/Hebrew only. Also all values are known with Arabic/English only.

1920 (Dec)–**21**. Optd with T **5*** (Arabic 10 mm long).

(a) P 15×14.

30	**3**	1m. sepia (27.12.20)	1·75	1·00
		a. Opt inverted	£400	†
31		2m. blue-green (27.12.20)	7·00	4·00
		a. Opt double		
32		3m. yellow-brown (27.12.20)	3·00	1·00
33		4m. scarlet (27.12.20)	4·25	1·25
34		5m. yellow-orange	2·25	75
35		1p. deep indigo (Silver) (21.6.21)	£450	27·00
36		2p. olive (21.6.21)	60·00	27·00
37		5p. deep purple (21.6.21)	42·00	9·50

(b) P 14.

38	**3**	1m. sepia	£550	£750
39		2m. blue-green	3·25	4·00
40		4m. scarlet	55·00	75·00
41		5m. orange	85·00	9·00
		a. Yellow-orange	7·50	1·10
42		1p. deep indigo (Silver)	50·00	1·25
43		5p. purple	£200	£450

*In this setting the Arabic and Hebrew characters are badly worn and blunted, the Arabic "S" and "T" are joined (i.e. there is no break in the position indicated by the arrow in our illustration); the letters of "PALESTINE" are often irregular or broken; and the space between the two groups of Hebrew characters varies from 1 mm to over 1¾ mm. The " character in the left-hand Hebrew word extends above the remainder of the line (For clear, sharp overprint, see Nos. 47/59.)

The dates of issue given are irrespective of the perforations, i.e. one or both perfs could have been issued on the dates shown.

Nos. 31 and 39 exist with any one line of the overprint partly missing.

1920 (6 Dec). Optd with T **6**.

(a) P 15×14.

44	**3**	3m. yellow-brown	50·00	32·00
44a		5m. yellow-orange	£14000	£12000

(b) P 14.

45	**3**	1m. sepia	50·00	32·00
46		5m. orange	£350	30·00

(6a)	(7)	(8)

1921 (29 May–4 Aug). Optd as T **6a**.

(a) P 15×14.

47	**3**	1m. sepia (23.6)	11·00	3·50
48		2m. blue-green (18.6)	21·00	5·50
49		3m. yellow-brown (23.6)	28·00	3·00
50		4m. scarlet (23.6)	29·00	3·50
51		5m. yellow-orange	60·00	1·00
52		1p. deep indigo (Silver) (1.7)	18·00	75
53		2p. olive (4.8)	23·00	6·00
54		5p. purple (4.8)	25·00	8·00
55		9p. ochre (4.8)	50·00	90·00
56		10p. ultramarine (4.8)	55·00	14·00
57		20p. pale grey (4.8)	85·00	50·00
47/57 Set of 11			£350	£160

(b) P 14.

58	**3**	1m. sepia	—	£2000
59		20p. pale grey	£12000	£2500

In this setting the Arabic and Hebrew characters are sharp and pointed and there is usually a break between the Arabic "S" and "T", though this is sometimes filled with ink. The space between the two groups of Hebrew characters is always 1¾ mm. The top of the " character in the Hebrew aligns with the remainder of the word.

The 3m. with "PALESTINE" omitted is an essay (Price £2500 unused).

1921 (26 Sept)–**22**. Optd with T **7** ("PALESTINE" in sans-serif letters) by Stamping Dept, Board of Inland Revenue, Somerset House, London. Wmk Royal Cypher in column (W **100** of Great Britain). P 15×14.

60	**3**	1m. sepia (5.10.21)	1·25	30
61		2m. blue-green (11.10.21)	1·75	30
62		3m. yellow-brown (17.10.21)	1·75	30
63		4m. scarlet (15.10.21)	2·25	60
64		5m. yellow-orange	2·00	30
65		1p. bright turquoise-blue (14.11.21)	1·75	35
66		2p. olive (7.12.21)	2·50	40
67		5p. deep purple (11.12.21)	7·00	5·00
68		9p. ochre (10.3.22)	14·00	14·00
69		10p. ultramarine (10.3.22)	19·00	£500
		w. Wmk inverted	†	
70		20p. pale grey (10.3.22)	50·00	£1400
60/70 Set of 11			95·00	

Dates quoted are of earliest known postmarks.

(Printed and optd by Waterlow & Sons from new plates)

1922 (Sept–Nov). T **3** (redrawn), optd with T **8**. Wmk Mult Script CA.

(a) P 14.

71	**3**	1m. sepia	1·00	30
		a. Deep brown	1·50	30
		b. Opt inverted	—	£12000
		c. Opt double	£225	£425
		w. Wmk inverted	35·00	25·00
72		2m. yellow	1·00	30
		a. Orange-yellow	3·50	50
		b. Wmk sideways	†	£1500
		w. Wmk inverted	30·00	30·00
73		3m. greenish blue	1·75	15
		w. Wmk inverted	30·00	30·00
74		4m. carmine-pink	1·75	20
		w. Wmk inverted	38·00	38·00
75		5m. orange	2·00	30
		w. Wmk inverted	50·00	38·00
76		6m. blue-green	1·75	30
		w. Wmk inverted	40·00	40·00
77		7m. yellow-brown	1·50	30
		w. Wmk inverted	£200	£200
78		8m. scarlet	1·50	30
		w. Wmk inverted	45·00	50·00
79		1p. grey	2·00	30
		w. Wmk inverted	50·00	50·00
80		13m. ultramarine	2·25	15
		w. Wmk inverted	30·00	20·00
81		2p. olive	2·50	35
		a. Opt inverted	£300	£500
		b. Ochre	£120	6·50
		w. Wmk inverted	£180	£140
82		5p. deep purple	4·75	1·25
		aw. Wmk inverted	†	£550
82b		9p. ochre	£900	£200
83		10p. light blue	65·00	13·00
		a. "E.E.F." for "E.E.F." in bottom panel (R. 10/3)	£650	£400
84		20p. bright violet	£150	£100

(b) P 15×14.

86	**3**	5p. deep purple	55·00	4·00
87		9p. ochre	9·00	9·00
88		10p. light blue	7·50	2·50
		a. "E.E.F." for "E.E.F." in bottom panel (R. 10/3)	£375	£275
		w. Wmk inverted	£425	£225
89		20p. bright violet	9·00	5·50
71s/89s Optd "Specimen" Set of 15			£400	

Most values can be found on thin paper.

In this issue the design of all denominations is the same size, 18×21½ mm. Varieties may be found with one or other of the stops between "E.E.F." missing.

BRITISH MANDATE TO THE LEAGUE OF NATIONS

The League of Nations granted a mandate to Great Britain for the administration of Palestine on 29 September 1923.

(New Currency. 1,000 mils = 1 Palestine pound)

9 Rachel's Tomb	**10** Dome of the Rock

11 Citadel, Jerusalem	**12** Sea of Galilee

(Des F. Taylor. Typo Harrison)

1927 (1 June)–**45**. Wmk Mult Script CA. P 13½×14½ (2m. to 20m.) or 14.

90	**9**	2m. greenish blue (14.8.27)	1·50	10
		w. Wmk inverted	†	£500
91		3m. yellow-green	1·00	10
		w. Wmk inverted	—	£225
92	**10**	4m. rose-pink (14.8.27)	5·50	1·25
93	**11**	5m. orange (14.8.27)	2·50	10
		a. From coils. Perf 14½×14 (1936)	14·00	18·00
		ac. Yellow. From coils. Perf 14½×14 (1945)	35·00	28·00
		aw. Wmk inverted	16·00	25·00
		b. Yellow (12.44)	2·50	15
		w. Wmk inverted	25·00	27·00
94	**10**	6m. pale green (14.8.27)	4·00	1·75
		a. Deep green	75	20
95	**11**	7m. scarlet (14.8.27)	7·00	60
96	**10**	8m. yellow-brown (14.8.27)	13·00	6·00
97	**9**	10m. slate (14.8.27)	1·50	10
		a. Grey. From coils. Perf 14½×14 (11.38)	20·00	24·00
		aw. Wmk inverted		
		b. Grey (1944)	1·50	10
98	**10**	13m. ultramarine	8·00	30
99	**11**	20m. dull olive-green (14.8.27)	2·25	15
		a. Bright olive-green (12.44)	1·50	15
		w. Wmk inverted	—	£325
100	**12**	50m. deep dull purple (14.8.27)	1·50	30
		a. Bright purple (12.44)	3·00	30
		w. Wmk inverted	—	£375
101		90m. bistre (14.8.27)	60·00	60·00
102		100m. turquoise-blue (14.8.27)	2·25	70
103		200m. deep violet (14.8.27)	8·00	5·00
		a. Bright violet (1928)	30·00	16·00

b. Blackish violet (12.44)............... 9·00 3·50
90/103b Set of 14................................ £100 65·00
90s/103s Handstamped "Specimen" Set of 14.......... £350

Three sets may be made of the above issue; one on thin paper, one thicker paper with a ribbed appearance, and another on thick white paper without ribbing.

2m. stamps in the grey colour of the 10m., including an example postmarked in 1935, exist as do 50m. stamps in blue, but it has not been established whether they were issued.

Nos. 90/1 and 93 exist in coils, constructed from normal sheets.

1932 (1 June)–**44**. *New values and colours.* Wmk Mult Script CA.
P 13½×14½ (4m. to 15m.) or 14.

104	**10**	4m. purple (1.11.32).................	1·25	10
		w. Wmk inverted........................	†	£400
105	**11**	7m. deep violet........................	75	10
106	**10**	8m. scarlet............................	1·25	20
		w. Wmk inverted........................	†	£500
107		13m. bistre (1.8.32)...................	1·25	10
108		15m. ultramarine (1.8.32)..............	4·00	10
		a. Grey-blue (12.44)..................	3·25	40
		b. Greenish blue......................	3·25	40
		w. Wmk inverted.......................	†	£500
109	**12**	250m. brown (15.1.42).................	4·00	2·25
110		500m. scarlet (15.1.42)...............	4·50	3·00
111		£1 black (15.1.42)....................	6·00	3·50
104/11 Set of 8................................			20·00	8·00
104s/11s Perf "Specimen" Set of 8.............			£375	

No. 108 exists in coils, constructed from normal sheets.

STAMP BOOKLETS

1929. *Blue cover inscr "PALESTINE POSTAGE STAMP BOOKLET" and contents in English. Without advertisements on front. Stitched.*
SB1   150m. booklet containing twelve 2m., 3m. and eighteen 5m. (Nos. 90/1, 93) in blocks of 6..   £2000
   a. As No. SB1, but stapled................................. £1600

1933. *Blue cover inscr "PALESTINE POSTS & TELEGRAPHS POSTAGE STAMP BOOKLET" and contents all in English, Arabic and Hebrew. Without advertisements on front. Stapled.*
SB2   150m. booklet. Contents as No. SB1 ....

1937–38. *Red cover inscr "POSTAGE STAMP BOOKLET" and contents in English, Hebrew and Arabic. With advertisements on front. Stapled.*
SB3   150m. booklet containing 2m., 3m., 5m. and 15m. (Nos. 90/1, 93, 108) in blocks of 6................ £1600
   a. Blue cover (1938)................................ £1600

1939. *Pink cover inscr "POSTAGE STAMP BOOKLET" and contents in English, Hebrew and Arabic. With advertisements on front. Stapled.*
SB4   120m. booklet containing six 10m. and twelve 5m. (Nos. 93, 97) in blocks of 6 .... £1500

POSTAL FISCALS

Type-set stamps inscribed "O.P.D.A." (= Ottoman Public Debt Administration) or "H.J.Z." (Hejaz Railway); British 1d. stamps of 1912–24 and Palestine stamps overprinted with one or other of the above groups of letters, with the word "Devair", with or without surcharge of new value, are fiscal stamps. They are known used as postage stamps, alone, or with other stamps to make up the correct rates, and were passed by the postal authorities, although they were not definitely authorised for postal use.

POSTAGE DUE STAMPS

D 1	D 2 (MILLIEME)	D 3 (MIL)

(Typo Greek Orthodox Convent Press, Jerusalem)

1923 (1 Apr.). P 11.

D1	D **1**	1m. yellow-brown	16·00	25·00
		a. Imperf (pair).....................	£300	
		b. Imperf between (horiz pair).......	£1100	
D2		2m. blue-green.......................	12·00	10·00
		a. Imperf (pair).....................	£425	
D3		4m. scarlet..........................	10·00	10·00
D4		8m. mauve............................	7·00	7·00
		a. Imperf (pair).....................	£130	
		b. Imperf between (horiz pair).......	†	£2000
D5		13m. steel blue......................	6·00	6·00
		a. Imperf between (horiz pair).......	£900	
D1/5 Set of 5................................			45·00	50·00

Perfectly centred and perforated stamps of this issue are worth considerably more than the above prices, which are for average specimens.

(Types D **2/3**. Typo D.L.R.)

1924 (3 Oct). Wmk Mult Script CA. P 14.

D 6	D **2**	1m. deep brown.......................	90	2·00
D 7		2m. yellow...........................	2·25	1·75
		w. Wmk inverted......................	†	£450
D 8		4m. green............................	2·00	1·25
D 9		8m. scarlet..........................	3·00	90
D10		13m. ultramarine.....................	2·75	2·50
D11		5p. violet...........................	8·50	1·75
D6/11 Set of 6................................			17·00	9·00
D6s/11s Optd "Specimen" Set of 6............			£275	

1928 (1 Feb)–**45**. Wmk Mult Script CA. P 14.

D12	D **3**	1m. brown............................	1·00	·85
		a. Perf 15×14 (1944).................	35·00	70·00
D13		2m. yellow...........................	1·50	60
		w. Wmk inverted......................	†	£450
D14		4m. green............................	2·00	1·60
		a. Perf 15×14 (1945).................	60·00	85·00

D15	6m. orange-brown (10.33)		16·00	5·00
D16	8m. carmine............................		2·00	1·00
D17	10m. pale grey.........................		1·50	60
D18	13m. ultramarine.......................		2·50	1·75
D19	20m. pale olive-green..................		2·50	1·25
D20	50m. violet............................		2·75	1·25
D12/20 Set of 9........................			28·00	14·00
D12s/20s Optd or Perf (6m.) "Specimen" Set of 9...			£325	

Nos. D12a and D14a were printed and perforated by Harrison and Sons following bomb damage to the De La Rue works on 29 December 1940.

The British Mandate terminated on 14 May 1948. Later issues of stamps and occupation issues will be found listed under Gaza, Israel and Jordan in Part 19 (*Middle East*) of this catalogue.

Papua *see after* Australia

Penrhyn Island *see after* New Zealand

Pitcairn Islands

CROWN COLONY

The settlement of Pitcairn Island by the *Bounty* mutineers in 1790 was not discovered until the American whaler *Topaz*, Capt. Mayhew Folger, called there in 1808. A visit by two Royal Navy frigates followed in 1814 and reports from their captains resulted in considerable interest being taken in the inhabitants' welfare by religious and philanthropic circles in Great Britain.

Due to overcrowding the population was resettled on Tahiti in 1831, but many soon returned to Pitcairn which was taken under British protection in 1838. The island was again evacuated in 1856, when the inhabitants were moved to Norfolk Island, but a number of families sailed back to their original home in 1859 and 1864.

The earliest surviving letter from the island dated 1849. Before 1921 the mail service was irregular, as it depended on passing ships, and mail for the island was often sent via Tahiti. Some covers, purportedly sent from Pitcairn between 1883 and 1890 are known handstamped "Pitcairn Island" or "PITCAIRN ISLAND", but these are now believed to be forgeries.

In 1920 a regular mail service was introduced. As there were no stamps available, letters were allowed free postage as long as they carried a cachet, or manuscript endorsement, indicating their origin. Illustrations of Cachets I/VI, VIII, VIIIa, X and XIII are taken from *Pitcairn Islands Postal Markings 1883–1991*, published by the Pitcairn Islands Study Group, and are reproduced by permission of the author, Mr. Cy Kitching. Cachets I to XIII are shown three-quarter size.

POSTED IN PITCAIRN NO STAMPS AVAILABLE
Cachet I

			Value on cover
Cat No.			
C1	**1920-25.** Cachet I (62×8 mm) (*violet or black*)............		£3250

POSTED AT PITCAIRN ISLAND NO STAMPS AVAILABLE.
Cachet II

C2	1921-25. Cachet II (*violet or red*)................................	£2750

POSTED AT PITCAIRN ISLAND NO STAMPS AVAILABLE.
Cachet III

C3	1922-28. Cachet III (49×8½ mm) (*vio, pur or blk*)	£2000

POSTED IN PITCAIRN ISLAND 1923 NO STAMPS AVAILABLE
Cachet IV

C4	1923. Cachet IV. (black)........................	£2750

Posted at Pitcairn Island no Stamps Available
Cachet IVa

C4a	1923. Cachet IVa. (73½×22 mm) (*red*)....................	£2750

POSTED AT PITCAIRN ISLAND NO STAMPS AVAILABLE
Cachet V

C5	1923-28. (Aug). Cachet V (47×9 mm) (*red, violet or black*).......................................	£2500
C5a	1925-26. As Cachet V, but second line shown as "No Stamps Available" (*black*)	

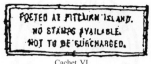

POSTED AT PITCAIRN ISLAND. NO STAMPS AVAILABLE. NOT TO BE SURCHARGED.
Cachet VI

C6	1923. Cachet VI (*blue-green or red*)......................	
C7	1923. As Cachet V, but in three lines (*red*).............	

POSTED AT PITCAIRN ISLAND NO STAMPS AVAILABLE.
Cachet VII

C8	1923-27. Cachet VII. (*violet or black*)	£1900
C9	1924. As Cachet IV, but dated "1924" (*black*)	£2500

POSTED AT PITCAIRN ISLAND. NO STAMPS AVAILABLE.
Cachet VIII

C10	1924-26.. Cachet VIII (36×8 mm) (*vio, blk or red*)	£2500

POSTED AT PITCAIRN NO STAMPS AVAILABLE
Cachet VIIIa

C10a	1924-26. Cachet VIIIa (36×8¾ mm) (*vio or blk*)	£2000

POSTED AT PITCAIRN ISLAND NO STAMPS AVAILABLE.
Cachet IX

C11	1924-26. (Feb)–25. Cachet IX (63×7 mm) (vio or blk).	£2750

POSTED IN PITCAIRN. NO STAMPS AVAILABLE
Cachet IXa

C11a	1924. Cachet IXa (58×8½ mm) (*vio or blk*)	
C12	1925. (Sept). As Cachet IV, but dated "1925" (*blk*).	£2500

POSTED IN PITCAIRN NO STAMPS AVAILABLE.
Cachet X

C13	1925. Cachet X (48×5 *mm*)	£2250

POSTED AT PITCAIRN ISLAND, NO STAMPS AVAILABLE.
Cachet XI

C14	1925-26. Cachet XI (50×10 mm) (*violet or blk*)............	£2500

Posted at PITCAIRN ISLAND No Stamps Available
Cachet XII

C15	1925. Cachet XII (55×7½ mm) (*violet*)	

POSTED IN PITCAIRN NO STAMPS AVAILABLE.
Cachet XIII

C16	1926. (Jan). Cachet XIII (64×8 mm) (*pur or blk*)	£3000

The New Zealand Government withdrew the free postage concession on 12 May 1926, but after representations from the islanders, opened a postal agency on Pitcairn using New Zealand stamps cancelled with Type Z 1. Some impressions of this postmark appear to show a double ring, but this is the result of heavy or uneven use of the handstamp. The postal agency operated from 7 June 1927 until 14 October 1940.

PRICES. Those quoted for Nos. Z1/72 and ZF1 are for examples showing a virtually complete strike of Type Z 1. Due to the size of the cancellation such examples will usually be on piece.

Z 1

Stamps of New Zealand cancelled with Type Z 1.

1915–29. *King George V (Nos. 419, 422/6, 428/31 and 446/9).*
Z 1	½d. green	25·00
Z 2	1½d. grey-slate	55·00
Z 3	1½d. orange-brown	45·00
Z 4	2d. yellow	40·00
Z 5	2½d. blue	75·00
Z 6	3d. chocolate	80·00
Z 7	4d. bright violet	75·00
Z 8	4½d. deep green	90·00
Z 9	5d. light blue	75·00
Z10	6d. carmine	90·00
Z11	7½d. red-brown	95·00
Z12	8d. red-brown	£130
Z13	9d. yellowish olive	£130
Z14	1s. vermilion	£130

1926–27. *King George V in Admiral's uniform (Nos. 468/9).*
Z15	1d. rose-carmine	25·00
Z16	2s. light blue	£200

1929. *Anti-Tuberculosis Fund (No. 544).*
Z17	1d.+1d. scarlet	£120

1931. *Air (Nos.548/9).*
Z18	3d. chocolate	£200
Z19	4d. blackish purple	£250

1932. *Health (No. 552).*
Z21	1d.+1d. carmine	£120

1935. *Pictorials (Nos. 556/8 and 560/9). W 43.*
Z22	½d. bright green	55·00
Z23	1d. scarlet	35·00
Z24	1½d. red-brown	85·00
Z26	2½d. chocolate and slate	75·00
Z27	3d. brown	85·00
Z28	4d. black and sepia	95·00
Z29	5d. ultramarine	£100
Z30	6d. scarlet	95·00
Z31	8d. chocolate	£100
Z32	9d. scarlet and black	£100
Z33	1s. deep green	90·00
Z34	2s. olive-green	£200
Z35	3s. chocolate and yellow-brown	£250

1935. *Silver Jubilee (Nos. 573/5).*
Z36	½d. green	40·00
Z37	1d. carmine	40·00
Z38	6d. red-orange	75·00

1935. *Health (No. 576).*
Z39	1d.+1d. scarlet	65·00

1936. *Pictorials (Nos. 577/82). W 98.*
Z40	½d. bright green	45·00
Z41	1d. scarlet	15·00
Z42	1½d. red-brown	75·00
Z43	2d. orange	60·00
Z44	2½d. chocolate and slate	65·00
Z45	3d. brown	70·00

1936. *21st Anniv of "Anzac" Landing at Gallipoli (Nos. 591/2).*
Z46	½d.+½d. green	42·00
Z47	1d.+1d. scarlet	42·00

1936. *Congress of British Empire Chambers of Commerce (Nos. 593/7).*
Z48	½d. emerald-green	40·00
Z49	1d. scarlet	40·00
Z50	2½d. blue	45·00
Z51	4d. violet	70·00
Z52	6d. red-brown	70·00

1936. *Health (No. 598).*
Z53	1d.+1d. scarlet	65·00

1937. *Coronation (Nos. 599/601).*
Z54	1d. carmine	30·00
Z55	2½d. Prussian blue	32·00
Z56	6d. red-orange	32·00

1937. *Health (No. 602).*
Z57	1d.+1d. scarlet	65·00

1938. *King George VI (Nos. 603, 605, 607).*
Z58	½d. green	65·00
Z59	1d. scarlet	65·00
Z60	1½d. purple-brown	75·00

1940. *Centenary of British Sovereignty (Nos. 613/22, 624/5).*
Z61	½d. blue-green	32·00
Z62	1d. chocolate and scarlet	38·00
Z63	1½d. light blue and mauve	40·00
Z64	2d. blue-green and chocolate	40·00
Z65	2½d. blue-green and blue	42·00
Z66	3d. purple and carmine	42·00
Z67	4d. chocolate and lake	65·00
Z68	5d. pale blue and mauve	70·00
Z69	6d. emerald-green and violet	70·00
Z70	7d. black *and* red	90·00
Z71	9d. olive-green and orange	90·00
Z72	1s. sage-green and deep green	90·00

POSTAL FISCAL STAMPS

1932. *Arms (No. F147).*
ZF1	2s.6d. deep brown	£250

PRICES FOR STAMPS ON COVER TO 1945	
Nos. 1/8	from × 10

1 Cluster of Oranges

2 Christian on *Bounty* and Pitcairn Island

3 John Adams and his house

4 Lt. Bligh and H.M.S. *Bounty*

5 Pitcairn Islands and Pacific Ocean

5a *Bounty* Bible

6 H.M.S. *Bounty*

6a School, 1949

7 Fletcher Christian and Pitcairn Island

8 Christian on H.M.S. *Bounty* and Pitcairn Coast

(Recess B.W. (1d., 3d., 4d., 8d. and 2s.6d.), and Waterlow (others))

1940 (15 Oct)–**51**. *T 1/8.* Wmk Mult Script CA. P 11½×11 (1d., 3d., 4d., 8d. and 2s.6d.) or 12½ (others).
1	**1**	½d. orange and green	40	60
2	**2**	1d. mauve and magenta	55	80
3	**3**	1½d. grey and carmine	55	50
4	**4**	2d. green and brown	2·00	1·40
5	**5**	3d. yellow-green and blue	1·25	1·40
		aw. Wmk inverted	£3250	
5b	**5a**	4d. black and emerald-green (1.9.51)	16·00	11·00
6	**6**	6d. brown and grey-blue	5·00	1·50
6a	**6a**	8d. olive-green and magenta (1.9.51)	19·00	7·00
7	**7**	1s. violet and grey	3·50	2·25
8	**8**	2s.6d. green and brown	8·50	3·75
1/8 *Set of 10*			50·00	27·00
1s/8s (*ex* 4d., 8d.) Perf "Specimen" *Set of 8*			£1100	

Flagstaff flaw (R. 8/2)

1946 (2 Dec). *Victory. As Nos. 110/11 of Antigua.*
9	2d. brown	70	30
10	3d. blue	70	30
	a. Flagstaff flaw	35·00	35·00
9s/10s Perf "Specimen" *Set of 2*		£300	

1949 (1 Aug). *Royal Silver Wedding. As Nos. 112/13 of Antigua.*
11	1½d. scarlet	2·00	1·50
12	10s. mauve	38·00	50·00

1949 (10 Oct). *75th Anniv of U.P.U. As Nos. 114/17 of Antigua.*
13	2½d. red-brown	1·00	4·25
14	3d. deep blue	8·00	4·25
15	6d. deep blue-green	4·00	4·25
16	1s. purple	4·00	4·25
13/16 *Set of 4*		15·00	15·00

STAMP BOOKLETS

1940 (15 Oct). *Black on deep green cover. Stapled.*
SB1	4s.8d. booklet containing one each ½d., 1d., 1½d., 2d., 3d., 6d., 1s. and 2s.6d. (Nos. 1/5, 6, 7/8)	£2750

Genuine examples of No. SB1 are interleaved with ordinary kitchen wax-paper, which frequently tones the stamps, and are secured with staples 17 mm long.

The status of other booklets using different size staples or paper fasteners is uncertain although it is believed that some empty booklet covers were available on the island.

Prince Edward Island
see **Canada**

Queensland *see* **Australia**

Rhodesia

Stamps of BECHUANALAND (see BOTSWANA) were used in Matabeleland on the runner post between Gubulawayo and Mafeking (Bechuanaland) from 9 August 1888 until 5 May 1894. Such stamps were cancelled "GUBULAWAYO" or by the barred oval "678" obliteration.

Between 27 June 1890 and 13 May 1892 external mail from Mashonaland sent via Bechuanaland was franked with that territory's stamps. A similar arrangement, using the stamps of MOZAMBIQUE existed for the route via Beira inaugurated on 29 August 1891. In both instances the stamps were cancelled by the post offices receiving the mail from Mashonaland. From 14 May until 31 July 1892 letters via Bechuanaland were franked with a combination of B.S.A Company and Bechuanaland issues.

Rhodesia joined the South African Postal Union on 1 August 1892 when its stamps became valid for international mail. Combination frankings with Mozambique stamps continued to be required until April 1894.

For the use of British Central Africa overprints in North-eastern Rhodesia from 1893 to 1899 see MALAWI (NYASALAND).

PRICES FOR STAMPS ON COVER TO 1945

Nos. 1/7	from × 5
Nos. 8/13	—
Nos. 14/17	from × 2
Nos. 18/24	from × 10
Nos. 25/6	—
Nos. 27/8	from × 7
Nos. 29/35	from × 10
Nos. 36/7	—
Nos. 41/6	from × 6
Nos. 47/50	—
Nos. 51/3	from × 2
Nos. 58/64	from × 3
Nos. 66/72	from × 8
Nos. 73/4	—
Nos. 75/87	from × 6
Nos. 88/93a	—
Nos. 94/9	from × 3
Nos. 100/10	from × 5
Nos. 111/13e	—
Nos. 114/18	from × 7
Nos. 119/60a	from × 10
Nos. 160b/6b	—
Nos. 167/78	from × 6
Nos. 179/81a	—
Nos. 182/5a	from × 4
Nos. 186/208	from × 8
Nos. 209/41	from × 8
Nos. 242/54a	—
Nos. 255/77	from × 8
Nos. 278/9c	—
Nos. 280/1	from × 15
Nos. 282/310	from × 8
Nos. 311/22	—

A. ISSUES FOR THE BRITISH SOUTH AFRICA COMPANY TERRITORY

	1	2	(3)

(Recess B.W.)

1892 (2 Jan*)–**93**. *Thin wove paper.* P 14, 14½.

1	**1**	1d. black	10·00	2·75
2		6d. ultramarine	50·00	25·00
3		6d. deep blue (1893)	29·00	3·75
4		1s. grey-brown	40·00	9·00
5		2s. vermilion	48·00	27·00
6		2s.6d. grey-purple	30·00	42·00
7		2s.6d. lilac (1893)	48·00	42·00
8		5s. orange-yellow	65·00	50·00
9		10s. deep green	80·00	£100
10	**2**	£1 deep blue	£190	£130
11		£2 rose-red**	£425	£150
12		£5 sage-green	£1600	£450
13		£10 brown	£2750	£700
1/10 Set of 8			£400	£300

Great caution is needed in buying the high values in either used or unused condition, many stamps offered being revenue stamps cleaned and re-gummed or with forged postmarks.

*Printing of stamps in Types **1**, **2** and **4** commenced in 1890, although none were used for postal purposes before 2 January 1892 when the route to the East Coast was inaugurated.

**For later printings of the £2 see No. 74.

The following sheet watermarks are known on Nos. 1/26: (1) William Collins, Sons & Co's paper watermarked with the firm's monogram, and "PURE LINEN WOVE BANK" in double-lined capitals (1890 and 1891 ptgs). (2) As (1) with "EXTRA STRONG" and "139" added (1892 ptgs). (3) Paper by Wiggins Teape & Co, watermarked "W T & Co" in script letters in double-lined wavy border (1893 ptgs). (4) The same firm's paper, watermarked "1011" in double-lined figures (1894 ptgs except ½d.). (5) "WIGGINS TEAPE & CO LONDON" in double-lined block capitals (1894 ptg of No. 18). Many values can also be found on a slightly thicker paper without wmk, but single specimens are not easily distinguishable.

1892 (2 Jan). Nos. 2 and 4 surch as T **3**.

14	**1**	½d. on 6d. ultramarine	£110	£375
15		2d. on 6d. ultramarine	£130	£500
16		4d. on 6d. ultramarine	£160	£600
17		8d. on 1s. grey-brown	£160	£700
14/17 Set of 4			£500	£2000

Caution is needed in buying these surcharges as both forged surcharges and forged postmarks exist.

4	5 (ends of scrolls behind legs of springboks)

(T **4**. Centre recess; value B.W.)

1892 (2 Jan)–**94**. *Thin wove paper (wmks as note after No. 13).* P 14, 14½.

18	**4**	½d. dull blue and vermilion	2·50	3·50
19		½d. deep blue and vermilion (1893)	2·75	4·75
20		2d. deep dull green and vermilion	19·00	3·00
21		3d. grey-black and green (8.92)	13·00	4·50
22		4d. chestnut and black	25·00	3·00
23		8d. rose-lake and ultramarine	13·00	13·00
24		8d. red and ultramarine (1892)	12·00	13·00
25		3s. brown and green (1894)	£150	80·00
26		4s. grey-black and vermilion (1893)	32·00	50·00
18/26 Set of 7			£225	£140

(Recess P.B. from the Bradbury, Wilkinson plates)

1895. *Thick soft wove paper.* P 12½.

27	**4**	2d. green and red	23·00	13·00
28		4d. yellow-brown and black	23·00	15·00
		a. Imperf (pair)	£1800	

(Centre recess; value typo P.B.)

1896–97. *Wove paper.* P 14.

(a) Die I. Plates 1 and 2. Small dot to the right of the tail of the right-hand supporter in the coat of arms. Body of lion only partly shaded.

29	**5**	1d. scarlet and emerald	15·00	4·50
		a. Carmine-red and emerald		
30		2d. brown and mauve	24·00	2·00
31		3d. chocolate and ultramarine	5·00	1·75
32		4d. ultramarine and mauve	55·00	
		a. Imperf between (pair)		
		b. Blue and mauve	26·00	17·00
33		6d. mauve and pink	80·00	19·00
34		8d. green and mauve/buff	7·00	60
		a. Imperf between (pair)		
		b. Imperf (pair)	£3000	
35		1s. green and blue	15·00	2·75
36		3s. green and mauve/blue	65·00	35·00
		a. Imperf (pair)	£8000	
37		4s. orange-red and blue/green	50·00	2·75
29/37 Set of 9			£250	75·00

(b) Die II. Plates 3 and 4. No dot. Body of lion heavily shaded all over.

41	**5**	½d. slate and violet	3·00	3·25
42		1d. scarlet and emerald	4·50	3·75
43		2d. brown and mauve	10·00	4·50
44		4d. ultramarine and mauve	75·00	12·00
		a. Blue and mauve	11·00	50
46		6d. mauve and rose	9·00	75
47		2s. indigo and green/buff	26·00	8·50
48		2s.6d. brown and purple/yellow	70·00	50·00
49		5s. chestnut and emerald	50·00	9·00
50		10s. slate and vermilion/rose	£100	65·00
41/50 Set of 9			£250	£130

(6)	(7)

(Surchd by *Bulawayo Chronicle*)

1896 (April). *Matabele Rebellion provisionals. Surch with T **6** and **7**.*

51	**6**	1d. on 3d. (No. 21)	£475	£600
		a. "P" in "Penny" inverted	£35000	
		b. "y" in "Penny" inverted		
52		1d. on 4s. (No. 26)	£250	£275
		a. "P" in "Penny" inverted	£30000	
		b. "y" in "Penny" inverted	£30000	
		c. Single bar through original value	£1100	£1200
53	**7**	3d. on 5s. (No. 8)	£170	£225
		a. "R" in "THREE" inverted	£30000	
		b. "T" in "THREE" inverted	£35000	

Nos. 51 and 52 occur in two settings, one with 9¾ mm between value and upper bar, the other with 11 mm between value and upper bar.

BRITISH
SOUTH AFRICA
COMPANY.

(8)	9 (ends of scrolls between legs of springboks)

1896 (22 May–Aug). *Cape of Good Hope stamps optd by Argus Printing Co, Cape Town, with T **8**. Wmk Anchor (3d. wmk Crown CA).* P 14.

58	**6**	½d. grey-black (No. 48a)	13·00	19·00
59	**17**	1d. rose-red (No. 58)	15·00	20·00
60	**6**	2d. deep bistre (No. 50a)	18·00	11·00
61		3d. pale claret (No. 40)	50·00	75·00
62		4d. blue (No. 51)	20·00	20·00
		a. "COMPANY," omitted	£9000	
63	**4**	6d. deep purple (No. 52a)	50·00	65·00
64	**6**	1s. yellow-ochre (No. 65) (Aug)	£140	£140
58/64 Set of 7			£275	£325

No. 62 also exists with "COMPANY" partially omitted. Examples with the word completely omitted, as No. 62a, are known from positions 1 to 6 of the setting.

Forgeries of this overprint show a narrow final "A" in "AFRICA" and have a rectangular full stop. On the genuine overprint both "As" are the same and the stop is oval.

(Eng J. A. C. Harrison (vignette), Bain or Rapkin (£1) (frames). Recess Waterlow)

1897. P 13½ to 16.

66	**9**	½d. grey-black and purple	3·25	5·50
67		1d. scarlet and emerald	3·50	5·00
68		2d. brown and mauve	9·00	2·25
69		3d. brown-red and slate-blue	3·00	50
		a. Imperf between (horiz pair)	£2750	
70		4d. ultramarine and claret	12·00	2·25
		a. Imperf between (horiz pair)	£12000	£12000
71		6d. dull purple and pink	7·50	3·50
72		8d. green and mauve/buff	13·00	50
		a. Imperf between (vert pair)	†	£2750
73		£1 black and red-brown/green	£350	£225

(Recess Waterlow, from the Bradbury plate)

1897 (Jan). P 15.

74	**2**	£2 rosy red	£1700	£425

10	11	12

(Recess Waterlow)

1898–1908. P 13½ to 15½.

75	**10**	½d. dull bluish green	5·00	1·50
		a. Yellow green (1904)	2·75	1·50
		aa. Imperf between (horiz pair)	£700	
		ab. Imperf (pair)	£750	
		ac. Imperf between (vert pair)	£950	
76		½d. deep green (shades) (1908)	24·00	2·00
77		1d. rose (shades)	4·50	50
		a. Imperf (pair)	£650	£750
		b. Imperf between (vert pair)	£500	
78		1d. red (shades) (1905)	5·50	50
		a. Imperf vert (horiz pair)	£350	£400
		ab. Imperf horiz (vert pair)	£900	
		b. Imperf (pair)	£500	£600
		c. Imperf between (horiz pair)	£750	£450
		d. Imperf between (vert strip of 4)	£1800	
79		2d. brown	3·25	60
80		2½d. dull blue (shades)	5·50	80
		a. Imperf vert (horiz pair)	£850	£950
		b. Grey-blue (shades) (1903)	12·00	1·00
81		3d. claret	5·00	80
		a. Imperf between (vert pair)	£700	
82		4d. olive	4·75	30
		a. Imperf between (vert pair)	£700	
83		6d. reddish purple	12·00	1·75
		a. Reddish mauve (1902)	16·00	5·50
84	**11**	1s. bistre	17·00	2·75
		a. Imperf between (vert pair)	£2750	
		ab. Imperf between (horiz pair)	£3000	
		b. Deep olive-bistre (1907)	£2750	
		bc. Imperf (pair)	£2750	
		bd. Imperf between (horiz pair)	£3750	
		c. Bistre-brown (1908)	55·00	14·00
		d. Brownish yellow (1908)	19·00	7·50
85		2s.6d. bluish grey (11.06)	45·00	1·00
		a. Imperf between (vert pair)	£1000	£500
86		3s. violet (1902)	16·00	2·25
		a. Deep bluish violet (1908)	60·00	11·00
87		5s. brown-orange	42·00	12·00
88		7s.6d. black (11.01)	70·00	21·00
89		10s. grey-green	29·00	1·00
90	**12**	£1 greyish red-purple (p 15½) (7.01)	£275	95·00
91		a. Perf 14. Blackish purple (1902)	£450	£100
92		£2 brown (5.08)	85·00	6·50
93		£5 deep blue (7.01)	£3250	£2500
		£10 lilac (7.01)	£3250	£2250
93a		£20 yellow-bistre (1901?)	£14000	
75/90 Set of 14			£475	£130
80s/1s, 85s/6s, 88s/93s Perf "Specimen" Set of 10				£900

A £100 cherry-red, perf 13½, was ordered in June 1901, a number of mint, together with several examples showing fiscal cancellations being known.

13 Victoria Falls	(14)

(Recess Waterlow)

1905 (13 July). *Visit of British Association and Opening of Victoria Falls Bridge.* P 14½ to 15 (5d.), 14 (others).

94	**13**	1d. red	4·50	5·00
		a. Perf 14½ to 15.	11·00	12·00
95		2½d. deep blue	10·00	7·00
		a. Perf 14½ to 15.	16·00	12·00
96		5d. claret	24·00	48·00
		a. Perf 14	42·00	60·00
		sa. Optd "Specimen"	£150	
97		1s. blue-green	27·00	42·00
		a. Imperf (pair)	£21000	
		b. Imperf between (horiz pair)	£27000	
		c. Imperf between (vert pair)	£27000	
		d. Imperf vert (horiz pair)	£22000	
		e. Perf 14½ to 15	—	£225
98		2s.6d. black	£100	£150
99		5s. violet	90·00	40·00
		a. Perf 14½ to 15		£275
94/9 Set of 6			£225	£250
94s/9s Optd or Perf (5d.) "Specimen" Set of 6			£400	

1909 (15 Apr)–**12**. Optd as T **14**. P 13½ to 15.

100	**10**	½d. green to deep green	2·25	1·25
		a. No stop	50·00	32·00
		b. Yellow-green (1911)	35·00	27·00
101		1d. carmine-rose	3·75	1·00
		a. No stop	60·00	25·00
		b. Imperf between (horiz pair)	£400	
		c. Deep carmine-rose	3·75	1·00
		cd. Imperf between (horiz pair)	£400	
102		2d. brown	1·75	4·00
		a. No stop	£100	75·00
103		2½d. pale dull blue	1·25	80
		a. No stop	38·00	24·00
104		3d. claret	1·60	80
		a. No stop	£160	70·00
		b. Opt inverted	†	15·00
		c. Opt double	†	£1000
105		4d. olive	4·25	1·75
		a. No stop	65·00	55·00
		b. Opt inverted	†	15·00
106		6d. reddish purple	5·00	4·75
		a. No stop	60·00	
		b. Reddish mauve		
		c. Dull purple	17·00	4·75
		ca. No stop	80·00	48·00
107	**11**	1s. bistre	18·00	
		a. No stop	£150	
		b. Bistre-brown		
		ba. No stop		
		c. Deep brownish bistre	8·50	4·00
		ca. No stop	85·00	42·00
108		2s.6d. bluish grey	20·00	10·00
		a. No stop	90·00	60·00
		b. Opt inverted	†	20·00
109		3s. deep violet	15·00	10·00
110		5s. orange	28·00	42·00
		a. No stop	£100	£120
111		7s.6d. black	90·00	21·00
112		10s. dull green	38·00	14·00
		a. No stop	£250	£180
113	**12**	£1 grey-purple	£150	80·00
		a. Vert pair, lower stamp without opt	£30000	
		b. Opt in violet	£375	£190
113c		£2 brown	£4000	£300
113d		£2 rosy brown (bluish paper) (P 14½×15) (1912)	£3250	£275
113e		£5 deep blue (bluish paper)	£7000	£4250
100/13 Set of 14			£325	£170
100s/13s Perf "Specimen" Set of 14			£350	

In some values the no stop variety occurs on every stamp in a vertical row of a sheet, in other values only once in a sheet. Other varieties, such as no serif to right of apex of "A", no serif to top of "E", etc., exist in some values.

No. 113a comes from a sheet with the overprint omitted from the bottom row.

(15)	(16)

1909 (April)–**11**. *Surch as T* **15** *and* **16** (*2s.*) *in black.*

114	**10**	5d. on 6d. reddish purple	7·00	12·00
		a. Surcharge in violet	90·00	
		b. Reddish mauve		
		c. Dull purple	14·00	12·00
116	**11**	7½d. on 2s.6d. bluish grey	3·50	3·75
		a. Surcharge in violet	17·00	9·00
		ab. Surch double	†	£6500
117		10d. on 3s. deep violet	13·00	16·00
		a. Surcharge in violet	4·25	3·75
118		2s. on 5s. orange	12·00	7·50
114s/18s Perf "Specimen" Set of 4			£180	

In the 7½d. and 10d. surcharges the bars are spaced as in T **16**.

17	18

(Recess Waterlow)

1910 (11 Nov)–**13**.

(a) P 14.

119	**17**	½d. yellow-green	12·00	1·75
		a. Imperf between (horiz pair)	£20000	

120		½d. bluish green	22·00	3·00
		a. Imperf (pair)	£12000	£4750
121		½d. olive-green	30·00	3·00
122		½d. dull green	70·00	50·00
123		1d. bright carmine	22·00	3·00
		a. Imperf between (vert pair)	£17000	£11000
		b. Imperf between (horiz pair)		
124		1d. carmine-lake	50·00	2·75
125		1d. rose-red	24·00	2·50
126		2d. black and grey	50·00	10·00
127		2d. black-purple and slate-grey	£160	£750
128		2d. black and slate-grey	55·00	7·00
129		2d. black and slate	70·00	8·50
130		2d. black and grey-black	80·00	15·00
131		2½d. ultramarine	24·00	7·00
131a		2½d. bright ultramarine	22·00	7·00
132		2½d. dull blue	26·00	8·00
133		2½d. chalky blue	20·00	16·00
134		3d. purple and ochre	32·00	32·00
135		3d. purple and yellow-ochre	40·00	14·00
136		3d. magenta and yellow-ochre	£150	14·00
137		3d. violet and ochre	£110	75·00
138		4d. greenish black and olive	90·00	90·00
139		4d. brown-purple and orange	70·00	55·00
140		4d. black and orange	40·00	15·00
141		5d. purple-brown and olive-green	29·00	48·00
141a		5d. purple-brown and olive-yellow	29·00	50·00
		ab. Error. Purple-brown and ochre	£600	£150
143		5d. lake-brown and olive	£275	60·00
143a		5d. lake-brown and green (9.12)	£20000	£1600
144		6d. red-brown and mauve	38·00	38·00
145		6d. brown and purple	35·00	16·00
145a		6d. bright chestnut and mauve	£700	60·00
146		8d. black and purple	£5000	
147		8d. dull purple and purple	£170	90·00
148		8d. greenish black and purple	£140	90·00
149		10d. scarlet and reddish mauve	38·00	48·00
150		10d. carmine and deep purple	£650	60·00
151		1s. grey-black and deep blue-green	42·00	22·00
151a		1s. black and deep blue-green	£150	28·00
152		1s. black and pale blue-green	48·00	13·00
152a		1s. purple-black and blue-green	£250	50·00
153		2s. black and ultramarine	80·00	55·00
154		2s. black and dull blue	£1100	65·00
154a		2s. purple-black and ultramarine	£3000	£225
155		2s.6d. black and lake	£325	£350
155a		2s.6d. black and crimson	£325	£275
156		2s.6d. sepia and deep crimson	£400	£325
156a		2s.6d. bistre-brown and crimson	£1100	£600
157		2s.6d. black and rose-carmine	£300	£325
158		3s. green and violet (shades)	£170	£170
158a		3s. bright green and magenta	£1200	£650
159		5s. vermilion and deep green	£275	£325
160		5s. scarlet and pale yellow-green	£275	£190
160a		5s. crimson and yellow-green	£225	£190
160b		7s.6d. carmine and pale blue	£600	£425
161		7s.6d. carmine and light blue	£700	£800
162		7s.6d. carmine and bright blue	£2500	£1000
163		10s. deep myrtle and orange	£600	£275
164		10s. blue-green and orange	£375	£240
165		£1 carmine-red and bluish black	£1100	£500
166		£1 rose-scarlet and bluish black	£1200	£375
166a		£1 crimson and slate-black	£1400	£950
		b. Error. Scarlet and reddish mauve	£9500	

(b) P 15.

167	**17**	½d. blue-green	£300	13·00
168		½d. yellow-green	£350	11·00
169		½d. apple-green	£600	27·00
170		1d. carmine	£300	8·50
170a		1d. carmine-lake	£425	15·00
170b		1d. rose-carmine	£325	11·00
171		2d. black and grey-black	£900	32·00
171a		2d. black and grey	£900	32·00
171b		2d. black and slate	£1000	32·00
172		2½d. ultramarine (shades)	70·00	35·00
173		3d. purple and yellow-ochre	£6000	70·00
173a		3d. claret and pale yellow-ochre	£2750	50·00
174		4d. black and orange (shades)	50·00	60·00
175		5d. lake-brown and olive	£750	75·00
176		6d. brown and mauve	£850	60·00
177		1s. black and blue-green (shades)	£1100	55·00
178		2s. black and dull blue	£2250	£325
179		£1 red and black	£16000	£3000

(c) P 14×15 (½d., 3d., 1s.) or 15×14 (1d., 4d.)

179a	**17**	½d. yellow-green	†	£2750
179b		1d. carmine	†	£5500
180		3d. purple and ochre	£6000	£225
181		4d. black and orange	£450	
181a		1s. black and blue-green	£24000	£2500

(d) P 13½.

182	**17**	½d. yellow-green	£300	40·00
182a		½d. green	£350	40·00
183		1d. bright carmine	£2000	48·00
184		2½d. ultramarine (shades)	35·00	60·00
185		8d. black and purple (shades)	60·00	£250
185a	**17**	8d. grey-purple and dull purple	£375	£450
119s/85s Optd "Specimen" (all perf 14 except 2½d. and 8d. perf 13½) Set of 18			£3500	

Plate varieties in T **17** are:—½d., double dot below "D" in right-hand value tablet (R. 3/9) (from £500 un. £350 used); 2d. to £1 excluding 2½d., straight stroke in Queen's right ear known as the "gash in ear" variety (R. 1/2) (from 3 to 5 times normal).

Stamps from the above and the next issue are known compound perf with 14 or 15 on one side only or on adjoining sides but we no longer list them.

Examples of some values are known with a forged registered Bulawayo postmark dated "JA 10 11".

(Recess Waterlow)

1913 (1 Sept)–**22**. No wmk.

(i) From single working plates.

(a) P 14.

186	**18**	½d. blue-green	7·00	2·00
187		½d. deep green	5·00	2·00
		a. Imperf horiz (vert pair)	£750	
		b. Imperf between (vert strip of 5)	£2500	
188		½d. yellow-green	13·00	2·00

		a. Imperf between (horiz pair)	£800	
188b		½d. dull green	10·00	2·00
		ba. Imperf vert (horiz pair)	£800	£800
		bb. Imperf between (horiz pair)	£1100	
189		½d. bright green	19·00	2·00
		a. Imperf between (vert pair)	£1300	
190		1d. rose-carmine	6·50	2·00
		a. Imperf between (horiz pair)	£800	£700
191		1d. carmine-red (shades)	9·50	2·00
		a. Imperf between (pair)	£1100	
192		1d. brown-red	4·00	2·00
193		1d. red	5·50	2·00
		a. Imperf between (horiz pair)	£750	
194		1d. scarlet	15·00	2·25
		a. Imperf between (horiz pair)	£900	
195		1d. rose-red	10·00	2·00
		a. Imperf between (horiz pair)	£700	£750
		b. Imperf between (vert pair)	£1800	
196		1d. rosine	£500	20·00
197		1½d. brown-ochre (1919)	5·00	2·00
		a. Imperf between (horiz pair)	£700	£700
198		1½d. bistre-brown (1917)	5·00	2·00
		a. Imperf between (horiz pair)	£700	£700
199		1½d. drab-brown (1917)	5·50	2·00
		a. Imperf between (horiz pair)	£700	
		b. Imperf between (vert pair)	£1900	
200		2½d. deep blue	5·50	26·00
201		2½d. bright blue	5·50	26·00

(b) P 15.

202	**18**	½d. blue-green	8·50	16·00
203		½d. green	14·00	15·00
204		1d. rose-red	£550	22·00
		a. Imperf between (horiz pair)	£14000	
205		1d. brown-red	4·00	6·00
206		1½d. bistre-brown (1919)	32·00	7·00
		a. Imperf between (horiz pair)	£18000	
206b		1½d. brown-ochre (1917)	40·00	11·00
207		2½d. deep blue	19·00	45·00
208		2½d. bright blue	16·00	42·00

(c) P 14×15.

208a	**18**	½d. green	£6500	£180

(d) P 15×14.

208b	**18**	½d. green	£6500	£350
208c		1½d. drab-brown		

(e) P 13½.

208d	**18**	1d. red (1914)	†	£500

Die I	Die II	Die III

The remaining values were printed from double, i.e. head and duty, plates. There are at least four different head plates made from three different dies, which may be distinguished as follows:—

Die I. The King's left ear is neither shaded nor outlined; no outline to top of cap. Shank of anchor in cap badge is complete.

Die II. The ear is shaded all over, but has no outline. The top of the cap has a faint outline. Anchor as Die I.

Die III. The ear is shaded and outlined; a heavy continuous outline round the cap. Shank of anchor is broken just below the lowest line which crosses it.

(ii) Printed from double plates. Head Die I.

(a) P 14.

209	**18**	2d. black and grey	12·00	8·00
210		3d. black and yellow	75·00	9·00
211		4d. black and orange-red	8·00	29·00
212		5d. black and green	4·75	13·00
213		6d. black and mauve	£200	23·00
213a		8d. violet and green	£5000	
214		2s. black and brown	95·00	75·00

(b) P 15.

215	**18**	3d. black and yellow	5·50	19·00
216		4d. black and orange-red	£140	19·00
217		6d. black and mauve	6·50	7·00
217a		8d. violet and green	£18000	£22000
218		2s. black and brown	10·00	38·00

(iii) Head Die II.

(a) P 14.

219	**18**	2d. black and grey	14·00	4·00
220		2d. black and brownish grey	48·00	7·00
221		3d. black and deep yellow	30·00	6·00
222		3d. black and yellow	65·00	6·00
223		3d. black and buff	8·50	6·00
224		4d. black and orange-red	20·00	8·00
225		4d. black and deep orange-red	14·00	8·00
226		5d. black and grey-green	15·00	32·00
227		5d. black and bright green	13·00	32·00
228		6d. black and mauve	30·00	3·50
229		6d. black and purple	75·00	4·50
230		8d. violet and green	14·00	55·00
231		10d. blue and carmine-red	20·00	45·00
232		1s. black and greenish blue	55·00	48·00
233		1s. black and turquoise-blue	12·00	11·00
234		2s. black and brown	75·00	10·00
235		2s. black and yellow-brown	£325	30·00
236		2s.6d. indigo and grey-brown	50·00	32·00
236a		2s.6d. pale blue and brown	£950	55·00
236b		3s. brown and blue	90·00	£110
237		3s. chestnut and bright blue	85·00	£120
238		5s. blue and yellow-green	£130	70·00
239		5s. blue and blue-green	55·00	60·00
240		7s.6d. blackish purple and slate-black	£300	£325
241		10s. crimson and yellow-green	£180	£300
242		£1 black and purple	£400	£550
243		£1 black and violet	£350	£600

(b) P 15.

244	18	2d. black and grey	8·50	8·50
245		4d. black and deep orange-vermilion	£1100	£250
246		8d. violet and green	£190	£170
247		10d. blue and red	9·00	29·00
248		1s. black and greenish blue	55·00	12·00
249		2s.6d. indigo and grey-brown	42·00	80·00
250		3s. chocolate and blue	£700	£550
251		5s. blue and yellow-green	£140	£150
251a		5s. blue and blue-green	£1600	
252		7s.6d. blackish purple and slate-black	£140	£190
253		10s. red and green	£180	£375
		a. Frame double, one albino	£550	
254		£1 black and purple	£1300	£1400
254a		£1 black and deep purple	£3000	£2500

186s, 190s, 198s, 208s, 209s, 211s/12s, 215s, 217s/18s, 230s, 232s, 237s/8s, 240s/2s, 247s, 249s Optd "Specimen" *Set of* 19 .... £2250

(iv) Head Die III (1919). Toned paper, yellowish gum.

(a) P 14.

255	18	2d. black and brownish grey	11·00	5·50
256		2d. black and grey-black	9·00	3·25
		a. Imperf between (horiz pair)	£4750	
		b. Imperf between (horiz strip of 3)	£9500	
		c. Imperf vert (horiz pair)	£4250	£4250
257		2d. black and grey	11·00	4·00
258		2d. black and sepia	42·00	8·50
259		3d. black and yellow	11·00	2·50
260		3d. black and ochre	11·00	2·50
261		4d. black and orange-red	14·00	5·50
262		4d. black and dull red	13·00	7·00
263		5d. black and pale green	7·50	30·00
		a. Imperf between (horiz strip of 3)	£17000	
264		5d. black and green	7·50	30·00
265		6d. black and reddish mauve	7·00	7·00
		a. Imperf between (horiz pair)	£14000	
266		6d. black and dull mauve	7·00	7·00
267		8d. mauve and dull blue-green	19·00	55·00
268		8d. mauve and greenish blue	17·00	55·00
		a. Imperf vert (horiz pair)	£10000	
269		10d. indigo and carmine	15·00	50·00
270		10d. blue and red	13·00	50·00
271		1s. black and greenish blue	9·50	8·50
272		1s. black and pale blue-green	9·00	7·00
272a		1s. black and light blue	11·00	15·00
272b		1s. black and green	70·00	30·00
273		2s. black and brown	12·00	15·00
		aa. Imperf between (vert pair)	†	£28000
273a		2s. black and yellow-brown	£3000	£140
274		2s.6d. dp ultramarine & grey-brn	35·00	65·00
274a		2s.6d. pale blue and pale bistre-brown	£100	£550
274b		3s. chestnut and light blue	£225	£150
275		5s. deep blue and blue-green (*shades*)	80·00	60·00
276		5s. blue & pale yell-grn (*shades*)	£100	65·00
276a		7s.6d. maroon and slate-black	£800	£1200
277		10s. carmine-lake and yellow-green	£325	£190
278		£1 black and bright purple	£450	£600
279		£1 black and deep purple	£475	£600
279a		£1 black and violet-indigo	£550	£700
279b		£1 black and deep violet	£600	£700

(b) P 15.

279c	18	2d. black and brownish grey	£5500	£500

Half Penny (19)   **Half- Penny.** (20)

1917 (15 Aug). *No. 190 surch at the Northern Rhodesian Administrative Press, Livingstone, with T* **19**, *in violet or violet-black.*

280	18	½d. on 1d. rose-carmine (shades)	2·50	7·50
		a. Surch inverted	£1400	£1500
		b. Letters "n n" spaced wider	11·00	27·00
		c. Letters "n y" spaced wider	7·50	22·00

The setting was in two rows of 10 repeated three times in the sheet. The two colours of the surcharge occur on the same sheet.

1917 (22 Sept). *No. 190 surch as T* **20** *(new setting with hyphen, and full stop after "Penny"), in deep violet.*

281	18	½d. on 1d. rose-carmine (shades)	1·75	8·00

1922–24. *New printings on white paper with clear white gum.*

(i) Single working plates.

(a) P 14.

282	18	½d. dull green (1922)	5·50	6·50
283		½d. deep blue-green (1922)	5·50	7·00
284		1d. bright rose (1922)	9·00	5·50
285		1d. bright rose-scarlet (1923)	9·00	5·50
		a. Imperf between (horiz pair)	£1800	
		b. Imperf between (vert pair)	£2250	
286		1d. aniline red (8.24)	20·00	8·50
287		1½d. brown-ochre (1923)	8·00	7·50
		a. Imperf between (vert pair)	£2500	£1500

(b) P 15.

288	18	½d. dull green (1923)	45·00	
289		1d. bright rose-scarlet (1923)	48·00	
290		1½d. brown-ochre (1923)	48·00	

(ii) Double plates. Head Die III.

(a) P 14.

291	18	2d. black and grey-purple (1922)	7·50	4·25
292		2d. black and slate-purple (1923)	7·50	5·50
293		3d. black and yellow (1922)	10·00	27·00
294		4d. black and orange-vermilion (1922–3)	14·00	35·00
295		6d. jet-black and lilac (1922–3)	5·00	4·25

296		8d. mauve and pale blue-green (1922)	32·00	70·00
297		8d. violet and grey-green (1923)	35·00	70·00
298		10d. bright ultramarine and red (1922)	10·00	55·00
299		10d. brt ultramarine and carm-red (1923)	17·00	60·00
300		1s. black and dull blue (1922–3)	9·00	11·00
		a. Imperf between (horiz pair)	£12000	
		b. Imperf between (vert pair)	£14000	
301		2s. black and brown (1922–3)	19·00	48·00
302		2s.6d. ultramarine and sepia (1922)	42·00	75·00
303		2s.6d. violet-blue and grey-brown (1923)	55·00	75·00
304		3s. red-brown and turquoise-blue (1922)	90·00	£110
305		3s. red-brown and grey-blue (1923)	£120	£140
306		5s. brt ultramarine and emerald (1922)	£100	£130
307		5s. deep blue and bright green (1923)	£110	£130
308		7s.6d. brown-purple and slate (1922)	£200	£300
309		10s. crimson and brt yellow-green (1922)	£180	£225
310		10s. carmine and yellow-green (1923)	£200	£275
311		£1 black and magenta (1922)	£550	£750
311a		£1 black and deep magenta (1923)	£600	£850

(b) P 15 (1923).

312	18	2d. black and slate-purple	38·00
313		4d. black and orange-vermilion	40·00
314		6d. jet-black and lilac	50·00
315		8d. violet and grey-green	60·00
316		10d. bright ultramarine & carmine-red	65·00
317		1s. black and dull blue	75·00
318		2s. black and brown	£100
319		2s.6d. violet-blue and grey-brown	£120
320		3s. red-brown and grey-blue	£150
321		5s. deep blue and bright green	£190
322		£1 black and deep magenta	£850

The 1922 printing shows the mesh of the paper very clearly through the gum. In the 1923 printing the gum is very smooth and the mesh of the paper is not so clearly seen. Where date is given as "(1922–23)" two printings were made, which do not differ sufficiently in colour to be listed separately.

Nos. 288/90 and 312/22 were never sent out to Rhodesia, but only issued in London. Any used copies could, therefore, only have been obtained by favour.

Southern Rhodesia, that part of the Company's territory south of the River Zambesi, became a self-governing colony on 1 October 1923. British South Africa Company rule continued in Northern Rhodesia until the administration was transferred to the Colonial Office on 1 April 1924.

The current stamps of Rhodesia, the Admiral series first issued in 1913, continued to be used in Southern Rhodesia until 1 April 1924 (invalidated 1 May 1924) and in Northern Rhodesia until 1 April 1925 (invalidated 30 September 1925).

St. Christopher
see **St. Kitts-Nevis**

St. Helena

CROWN COLONY

PRICES FOR STAMPS ON COVER TO 1945	
Nos. 1/5	*from* × 12
Nos. 6/30	*from* × 10
Nos. 34/45	*from* × 15
Nos. 46/52	*from* × 6
Nos. 53/67	*from* × 5
No. 71	—
Nos. 72/86	*from* × 5
Nos. 87/8	*from* × 12
Nos. 89/95	*from* × 5
No. 96	—
Nos. 97/110	*from* × 5
Nos. 111/13	—
Nos. 114/40	*from* × 4

PERKINS BACON "CANCELLED". For notes on these handstamps, showing "CANCELLED" between horizontal bars forming an oval, see Catalogue Introduction.

ONE PENNY (2)   **FOUR PENCE** (3)

(Recess P.B.)

1856 (1 Jan). Wmk Large Star, W w **1**. Imperf.

1	1	6d. bl (H/S "CANCELLED" in oval £8500)	£500	£180

1861 (April (?)). Wmk Large Star, W w **1**.

(a) Clean-cut perf 14 to 16.

2	1	6d. blue	£1700	£275

(b) Rough perf 14 to 16.

2a	1	6d. blue	£425	£130

> **NOTE:** The issues which follow consist of 6d. stamps, T **1**, printed in various colours and (except in the case of the 6d. values) surcharged with a new value, as T **2** to **10**, *e.g.* stamps described as "1d." are, in fact, 1d. on 6d. stamps, and so on.
> The numbers in the Type column below refer to the *types of the lettering* of the surcharged value.

(Printed by D.L.R. from P.B. plate)

Two Types of Bar on 1d. value:
A. Bar 16–17 mm long.
B. Bar 18½–19 mm long.

1863 (July). *Surch as T* **2/3** *with thin bar approximately the same length as the words. Wmk Crown CC. Imperf.*

3	2	1d. lake (Type A)	£110	£160
		a. Surch double	£5500	£3250
		b. Surch omitted	£18000	
		w. Wmk inverted	£325	
4		1d. lake (Type B)	£120	£170
		a. Vert pair. Nos. 3/4	£9000	
5	3	4d. carmine (bar 15½–16½ mm)	£500	£250
		a. Surch double	£13000	£9000

ONE PENNY (4 (A))   **ONE PENNY** (4 (B))   **ONE PENNY** (4 (C))

TWO PENCE (5)   **THREE PENCE** (6)   **FOUR PENCE** (7)

ONE SHILLING (8)   **FIVE SHILLINGS** (9)

Three Types of Bar:
A. Thin bar (16½ to 17 mm) nearly the same length as the words.
B. Thick bar (14 to 14½ mm) much shorter than the words, except on the 2d. (Nos. 9, 22, 28) where it is nearly the same length.
C. Long bar (17 to 18 mm) same length as the words.

1864–80. *6d. as T* **1**, *without surcharge. Wmk Crown CC.*

(a) P 12½ (1864–73).

6	4	1d. lake (Type A) (1864)	50·00	26·00
		a. Surch double	£8500	
7		1d. lake (Type B) (1868)	£160	55·00
		a. Surch double	£2500	
		w. Wmk inverted		£120
8		1d. lake (Type C) (1871)	£100	17·00
		a. Surch in blue-black	£1000	£550
		x. Wmk reversed	£160	
		y. Wmk inverted and reversed		£225
9	5	2d. yellow (Type B) (1868)	£170	60·00
		a. Imperf	£10000	
		x. Wmk reversed	£300	
10		2d. yellow (Type C) (1873)	£100	42·00
		a. Surch in blue-black	£4000	£2250
		b. Surch double, one albino		
		x. Wmk reversed	£150	70·00
11	6	3d. deep dull purple (Type B) (1868)	85·00	50·00
		a. Surch double	—	£6000
		b. Imperf	£800	
		c. Light purple	£2750	£750
		x. Wmk reversed	£160	
12		3d. deep dull purple (Type A) (1873)	£100	60·00
13	7	4d. carmine (Type A) (words 17 mm long) (1864)	£140	50·00
		a. Surch double	†	£5500
14		4d. carmine (Type B) (words 18 mm long) (1868)	95·00	55·00
		a. Surch double		£5000
		b. Surch double (18+19 mm widths)	£21000	£9000
		c. Imperf	£11000	
		x. Wmk reversed	£170	90·00
15		4d. carmine-rose (Type B) (words 19 mm long) (1868)	£200	£120
		a. Surch omitted	†	
16	—	6d. dull blue (1871)	£700	£100
		a. Ultramarine (1873)	£400	80·00
		x. Wmk reversed	†	£170
17	8	1s. deep yellow-green (Type A) (1864)	£300	28·00
		a. Surch double	†	£20000
		w. Wmk inverted	—	65·00
18		1s. deep yellow-green (Type B) (1868)	£600	£130
		a. Surch double	£15000	
		b. Imperf	£13000	
		c. Surch omitted*	£15000	
19		1s. deep green (Type C) (1871)	£475	16·00
		a. Surch in blue-black	£550	55·00
		x. Wmk reversed		
20	9	5s. orange (Type B) (1868)	50·00	60·00
		a. Yellow	£450	£375
		x. Wmk reversed	£120	£140

(b) P 14×12½ (1876).

21	4	1d. lake (Type A)	75·00	15·00
		w. Wmk inverted	£140	
22	5	2d. yellow (Type B)	£100	50·00
23		3d. purple (Type B)	£200	70·00
24		4d. carmine (Type B) (words 16½ mm long)	£110	60·00
		y. Wmk inverted and reversed	£110	60·00

25	–	6d. milky blue	£375	50·00
26	8	1s. deep green (Type C)	£650	24·00

(c) P 14 (1880).

27	4	1d. lake (Type B)	90·00	18·00
28	5	2d. yellow (Type B)	£110	30·00
29	–	6d. milky blue (Type B)	£400	50·00
		x. Wmk reversed	†	£110
30	8	1s. milky blue (Type B)	21·00	12·00
		y. Wmk inverted and reversed	—	85·00

Two used examples of No. 15a are known, one being in the Royal Collection and the other damaged at bottom right.

*No. 18c is from a sheet of the 1s. with surcharge misplaced, the fifth row of 12 stamps being thus doubly surcharged and the tenth row without surcharge.

(10) 11 12

1884–94. T **1** *surch. Bars similar to Type B above (except 2½d., T **10**, and the 1s., in which the bar is nearly the same length as the words). The 6d. as before without surcharge.* Wmk Crown CA. P 14.

34	–	½d. emerald (*words* 17 *mm*) (1884)	12·00	16·00
		a. "N" and "Y" spaced	£1100	
		b. Surch double	£1200	£1300
		ba. Ditto. "N" and "Y" spaced	£11000	
		w. Wmk inverted	—	35·00
		y. Wmk inverted and reversed	—	35·00
35	–	½d. green (*words* 17 *mm*) (1885)	9·50	16·00
		a. "N" and "Y" spaced	£450	£650
		x. Wmk reversed	11·00	18·00
36	–	½d. green (*words* 14½ *mm*) (1893)	2·50	2·75
		a. "N" and "Y" spaced	£1500	
37	4	1d. red (1887)	4·75	3·75
		x. Wmk reversed	5·00	4·50
38		1d. pale red (1890)	6·00	3·00
		x. Wmk reversed	7·00	4·00
39	5	2d. yellow (1894)	2·50	8·00
40	10	2½d. ultramarine (1893)	3·00	5·50
		a. Surch double	£18000	
		b. Stamp doubly printed	£9500	
		w. Wmk inverted	21·00	
41	6	3d. deep mauve (1887)	7·50	11·00
		a. Surch double	—	£9000
42		3d. deep reddish lilac (1887)	5·00	5·00
		a. Surch double	£9500	£6000
		w. Wmk reversed	7·00	4·75
43	7	4d. pale brn (*words* 16½ *mm*) (1890)	22·00	24·00
		a. Additional thin bar in surch (R. 7/4)	£650	
		by. Wmk inverted and reversed	30·00	
43c		4d. sepia (*words* 17 *mm*) (1894)	25·00	17·00
		cx. Wmk reversed	28·00	
44	–	6d. grey (1887)	22·00	5·00
		x. Wmk reversed	28·00	4·75
45	8	1s. yellow-green (1894)	50·00	25·00
		a. Surch double	£4750	
34/45		*Set of 8*	£100	65·00
40s/1s, 43bys, 44s Optd "Specimen" *Set of 4*			£180	

Examples of the above are sometimes found showing no watermark; these are from the bottom row of the sheet, which had escaped the watermark, the paper being intended for stamps of a different size to Type **1**.

Some are found without bar and others with bar at top of stamp, due to careless overprinting.

Nos. 34a and 35a occur on R. 18/12 and show a minimum space between the letters of 0.8 mm. Normal examples are spaced 0.5 mm, but some stamps show intermediate measurements due to loose type, On No. 34ba only one impression of the surcharge shows "N" and "Y" spaced. On the reset surcharge, No. 36, a similar variety occurs on R. 5/9.

Of the 2½d. with double surcharge only six copies exist, and of the 2½d. double printed, one row of 12 stamps existed on one sheet only.

CANCELLATIONS. Nos. 40/5 and No. 20 were sold as remainders in 1904 cancelled with a violet diamond-shaped grill with four interior bars extending over two stamps. These cannot be considered as *used* stamps, and they are consequently not priced in the list.

This violet obliteration is easily removed and many of these remainders have been cleaned and offered as unused; some are repostmarked with a date and name in thin type rather larger than the original, a usual date being "Ap.4.01."

(Typo D.L.R.)

1890–97. *Plate I for the 1½d. Plate II for the other values (for differences see Seychelles).* Wmk Crown CA. P 14.

46	11	½d. green (1897)	2·75	6·50
47		1d. carmine (1896)	16·00	2·00
48		1½d. red-brown and green (1890)	4·50	8·00
49		2d. orange-yellow (1896)	5·00	12·00
50		2½d. ultramarine (1896)	14·00	12·00
51		5d. mauve (1896)	11·00	30·00
52		10d. brown (1896)	24·00	60·00
46/52		*Set of 7*	70·00	£120
46s/52s Optd "Specimen" *Set of 7*			£300	

The note below No. 45a *re* violet diamond-shaped grill cancellation also applies to Nos. 48/52.

1902. Wmk Crown CA. P 14.

53	12	½d. green (Mar)	1·50	2·50
54		1d. carmine (24 Feb)	8·00	70
53s/4s Optd "Specimen" *Set of 2*			75·00	

13 Government House   14 The Wharf

(Typo D.L.R.)

1903 (May). Wmk Crown CC. P 14.

55	13	½d. brown and grey-green	2·00	3·25
		w. Wmk inverted	£130	£160
56	14	1d. black and carmine	1·50	35
57	13	2d. black and sage-green	6·50	1·25
58	14	4d. black and brown	22·00	32·00
59	13	1s. brown and brown-orange	23·00	40·00
60	14	2s. black and violet	48·00	85·00
55/60		*Set of 6*	90·00	£150
55s/60s Optd "Specimen" *Set of 6*			£225	

A printing of the 1d. value in Type **14** in red only on Mult Crown CA paper was made in 1911, but not sold to the public. Examples are known overprinted "SPECIMEN" (*Price* £325).

15

(Typo D.L.R.)

1908 (May)–11. *Ordinary paper (2½d.) or chalk-surfaced paper (4d., 6d.).* P 14.

(a) Wmk Mult Crown CA.

64	15	2½d. blue	1·50	1·50
66		4d. black and red/*yellow*	8·00	19·00
		a. Ordinary paper (1911)	3·00	18·00
67		6d. dull and deep purple	14·00	30·00
		a. Ordinary paper (1911)	5·50	14·00

(b) Wmk Crown CA. Chalk-surfaced paper.

71	15	10s. green and red/*green*	£200	£250
64/71		*Set of 4*	£200	£250
64s/71s Optd "Specimen" *Set of 4*			£250	

Examples of Nos. 58/60 and 66/71 are known showing a forged St. Helena postmark dated "JY 28 1".

16   17

(Typo D.L.R.)

1912–16. Wmk Mult Crown CA. P 14.

72	16	½d. black and green	2·25	10·00
73	17	1d. black and carmine-red	4·75	1·75
		a. Black and scarlet (1916)	12·00	20·00
74		1½d. black and dull orange (1913)	3·50	6·50
75	16	2d. black and greyish slate	4·50	1·75
76	17	2½d. black and bright blue	3·50	5·50
77	16	3d. black and purple/*yellow* (1913)	3·50	5·00
78	17	8d. black and dull purple	7·00	50·00
79	16	1s. black/*green*	9·00	35·00
80	17	2s. black and blue/*blue*	40·00	80·00
81		3s. black and violet (1913)	55·00	£130
72/81		*Set of 10*	£120	£275
72s/81s Optd "Specimen" *Set of 10*			£300	

No. 73*a* is on thicker paper than 73.

18   19   Split "A" (R. 8/3 of left pane)

(Typo D.L.R.)

1912. *Chalk-surfaced paper.* Wmk Mult Crown CA. P 14.

83	18	4d. black and red/*yellow*	12·00	25·00
84		6d. dull and deep purple	4·00	5·00
83s/4s Optd "Specimen" *Set of 2*			90·00	

1913. Wmk Mult Crown CA. P 14.

85	19	4d. black and red/*yellow*	8·00	2·75
		a. Split "A"	£250	£180
86		6d. dull and deep purple	14·00	28·00
		a. Split "A"	£400	
85s/6s Optd "Specimen" *Set of 2*			90·00	

WAR TAX WAR TAX

ONE PENNY 1 d.
(20) (21)

1916 (Sept). *As No. 73a, on thin paper, surch with* T **20**.

87	17	1d.+1d. black and scarlet	2·00	3·25
		a. Surch double	†	£15000
		s. Optd "Specimen"	55·00	

1919. *No. 73 on thicker paper, surch with* T **21**.

88	17	1d.+1d. black and carmine-red (shades)	1·75	4·50
		s. Optd "Specimen"	55·00	

1922 (Jan). *Printed in one colour.* Wmk Mult Script CA. P 14.

89	17	1d. green	1·75	30·00
		w. Wmk inverted	£180	
		y. Wmk inverted and reversed	£170	
90		1½d. rose-scarlet	10·00	30·00
91	16	3d. bright blue	19·00	60·00
		y. Wmk inverted and reversed	£180	
89/91		*Set of 3*	28·00	£110
89s/91s Optd "Specimen" *Set of 3*			£110	

22 Badge of St. Helena

PLATE FLAWS ON THE 1922–37 ISSUE. Many constant plate varieties exist on both the vignette and duty plates of this issue. The three major varieties are illustrated and listed below.

a. Broken mainmast. Occurs on R. 2/1 of all sheets from the second printing onwards. It does not appear on Nos. 93/6 and 112/13 as these stamps only exist from the initial printing invoiced in May 1922.

b. Torn flag. Occurs on R. 4/6 of all sheets from printings up to and including that invoiced in December 1922. The flaw was retouched for the printing invoiced in December 1926 and so does not occur on Nos. 97f, 99e, 103d, 107/10 and 111d.

c. Cleft rock. Occurs on R. 5/1 of all sheets from the second printing onwards. It does not appear on Nos. 93/6 and 112/13 as these stamps only exist from the initial printing invoiced in May 1922.

(Des T. Bruce. Typo D.L.R.)

1922 (June)–37. P 14.

(a) Wmk Mult Crown CA. *Chalk-surfaced paper.*

92	22	4d. grey and black/*yellow* (2.23)	11·00	6·00
		a. Broken mainmast	£160	£170

		b. Torn flag	£160	£170
		c. Cleft rock	£140	£160
93		1s.6d. grey and green/*blue-green*	22·00	55·00
		b. Torn flag	£400	£650
94		2s.6d. grey and red/*yellow*	25·00	60·00
		b. Torn flag	£450	
95		5s. grey and green/*yellow*	38·00	85·00
		b. Torn flag	£600	
96		£1 grey and purple/*red*	£400	£475
		b. Torn flag	£2000	

92/6 *Set of 5*			£450	£600
92s/6s Optd "Specimen" *Set of 5*			£500	

The paper of No. 93 is bluish on the surface with a full green back.

(b) Wmk Mult Script CA. *Ordinary paper (1s.6d., 2s.6d., 5s.) or chalk-surfaced paper (others).*

97	22	½d. grey and black (2.23)	2·25	2·50
		a. Broken mainmast	50·00	75·00
		b. Torn flag	£170	£225
		c. Cleft rock	42·00	75·00
		d. "A" of "CA" missing from wmk.		†
		ew. Wmk inverted	£350	£375
		f. Grey-black and black (1937)	6·50	4·00
		fa. Broken mainmast	£130	£140
		fc. Cleft rock	£120	£130
98		1d. grey and green	2·50	1·60
		a. Broken mainmast	55·00	70·00
		b. Torn flag	£150	£180
		c Cleft rock	48·00	
99		1½d. rose-red (*shades*) (2.23)	2·75	13·00
		a. Broken mainmast	80·00	£140
		b. Torn flag	80·00	£140
		c. Cleft rock	75·00	£140
		dw. Wmk inverted	£800	
		dx. Wmk reversed	£900	
		e. Deep carmine-red (1937)	80·00	85·00
		ea. Broken mainmast	£750	£850
		ec. Cleft rock	£750	£850
100		2d. grey and slate (2.23)	3·75	2·00
		a. Broken mainmast	95·00	£110
		b. Torn flag	£180	£225
		c. Cleft rock	90·00	£100
101		3d. bright blue (2.23)	2·00	4·00
		a. Broken mainmast	90·00	£130
		b. Torn flag	95·00	£130
		c. Cleft rock	75·00	£120
		x. Wmk reversed	£425	
103		5d. green and deep carmine/*green* (1927)	3·00	5·50
		a. Broken mainmast	£150	£200
		c. Cleft rock	£140	£200
		d. Green and carmine-red/green (1936)	3·00	5·50
		da. Broken mainmast	£150	£200
		dc. Cleft rock	£140	£200
104		6d. grey and bright purple	4·50	8·00
		a. Broken mainmast	£180	£275
		b. Torn flag	£225	£325
		c. Cleft rock	£160	£275
105		8d. grey and bright violet (2.23)	3·75	7·00
		a. Broken mainmast	£150	£250
		b. Torn flag	£150	£250
		c. Cleft rock	£130	£250
106		1s. grey and brown	6·50	9·00
		a. Broken mainmast	£225	£300
		b. Torn flag	£300	£350
		c. Cleft rock	£200	£275
107		1s.6d. grey and green/*green* (1927)	15·00	45·00
		a. Broken mainmast	£275	
		c. Cleft rock	£250	
108		2s. purple and blue/*blue* (1927)	18·00	42·00
		a. Broken mainmast	£300	
		c. Cleft rock	£275	
109		2s.6d. grey and red/*yellow* (1927)	14·00	60·00
		a. Broken mainmast	£275	
		c. Cleft rock	£250	
110		5s. grey and green/*yellow* (1927)	38·00	75·00
		a. Broken mainmast	£450	
		c. Cleft rock	£425	
111		7s.6d. grey-brown and yellow-orange	85·00	£130
		b. Torn flag	£700	£1400
		d. Brownish grey and orange (1937)	£650	£850
		da. Broken mainmast	£5000	
		dc. Cleft rock	£5000	
112		10s. grey and olive-green	£110	£170
		b. Torn flag	£1200	
113		15s. grey and purple/*blue*	£850	£1500
		b. Torn flag	£3750	£6000

97/112 *Set of 15*			£275	£500
97s/113s Optd "Specimen" *Set of 16*			£1100	

Examples of all values are known showing a forged St. Helena postmark dated "DE 18 27".

23 Lot and Lot's Wife

24 The "Plantation"

25 Map of St. Helena

26 Quay at Jamestown

27 James Valley

28 Jamestown

29 Munden's Promontory

30 St. Helena

31 High Knoll

32 Badge of St. Helena

(Recess B.W.)

1934 (23 April). *Centenary of British Colonisation.* T **23/32**. Wmk Mult Script CA. P 12.

114	23	½d. black and purple	1·00	80
115	24	1d. black and green	65	85
116	25	1½d. black and scarlet	2·50	3·25
117	26	2d. black and orange	2·25	1·25
118	27	3d. black and blue	1·40	4·50
119	28	6d. black and light blue	3·25	3·00
120	29	1s. black and chocolate	6·50	18·00
121	30	2s.6d. black and lake	35·00	48·00
122	31	5s. black and chocolate	75·00	80·00
123	32	10s. black and purple	£225	£250

114/23 *Set of 10*			£325	£375
114s/23s Perf "Specimen" *Set of 10*			£375	

Examples of all values are known showing a forged St. Helena postmark dated "MY 12 34".

1935 (6 May). *Silver Jubilee. As Nos. 91/4 of Antigua.* P 13½×14.

124		1½d. deep blue and carmine	1·00	5·50
		f. Diagonal line by turret	80·00	£170
125		2d. ultramarine and grey	1·75	90
		f. Diagonal line by turret	£100	
		g. Dot to left of chapel	£150	
126		6d. green and indigo	7·00	3·25
		a. Frame printed double, one albino	£1600	
		f. Diagonal line by turret	£200	
		h. Dot by flagstaff	£325	
127		1s. slate and purple	14·00	16·00
		h. Dot by flagstaff	£425	
		i. Dash by turret	£425	

124/7 *Set of 4*			21·00	23·00
124s/7s Perf "Specimen" *Set of 4*			£140	

For illustrations of plate varieties see Omnibus section following Zanzibar.

1937 (19 May). *Coronation. As Nos. 95/7 of Antigua, but ptd by D.L.R.* P 14.

128		1d. green	40	75
129		2d. orange	55	45
130		3d. bright blue	80	50

128/30 *Set of 3*			1·60	1·50
128s/30s Perf "Specimen" *Set of 3*			80·00	

33 Badge of St. Helena

(Recess Waterlow)

1938 (12 May)–**44**. Wmk Mult Script CA. P 12½.

131	33	½d. violet	15	65
132		1d. green	9·00	2·25
132*a*		1d. yellow-orange (8.7.40)	30	30
133		1½d. scarlet	30	40
134		2d. red-orange	30	15
135		3d. ultramarine	80·00	18·00
135*a*		3d. grey (8.7.40)	30	30
135*b*		4d. ultramarine (8.7.40)	2·00	1·25
136		6d. light blue	2·00	1·50
136*a*		8d. sage-green (8.7.40)	3·25	1·00
		b. Olive-green (24.5.44)	4·50	4·00
137		1s. sepia	1·25	50
138		2s.6d. maroon	18·00	6·50
139		5s. chocolate	18·00	12·00
140		10s. purple	18·00	18·00

131/40 *Set of 14*			£140	55·00
131s/40s Perf "Specimen" *Set of 14*			£350	

See also Nos. 149/51.

1946 (21 Oct). *Victory. As Nos. 110/11 of Antigua..*

141		2d. red-orange	40	40
142		4d. blue	40	30
141s/2s Perf "Specimen" *Set of 2*			80·00	

1948 (20 Oct). *Royal Silver Wedding. As Nos. 112/13 of Antigua.*

143		3d. black	30	30
144		10s. violet-blue	25·00	32·00

1949 (10 Oct). *75th Anniv of U.P.U. As Nos. 114/17 of Antigua.*

145		3d. carmine	25	1·00
146		4d. deep blue	3·00	1·40
147		6d. olive	45	2·00
148		1s. blue-black	35	1·10
145/8 *Set of 4*			3·50	5·00

1949 (1 Nov). Wmk Mult Script CA. P 12½.

149	33	1d. black and green	1·25	1·50
150		1½d. black and carmine	1·25	1·50
151		2d. black and scarlet	1·25	1·50
149/51 *Set of 3*			3·25	4·00

St. Kitts-Nevis

ST. CHRISTOPHER

From 1760 the postal service for St. Christopher was organised by the Deputy Postmaster General on Antigua. It was not until May 1779 that the first postmaster was appointed to the island and the use of postmarks on outgoing mail commenced.

Stamps of Great Britain were used between May 1858 and the end of March 1860 when control of the postal services passed to the local authorities. In the years which followed, prior to the introduction of St. Christopher stamps in April 1870, a circular "PAID" handstamp was used on overseas mail.

BASSETERRE

Stamps of GREAT BRITAIN *cancelled* "A 12" *as Type Z* **1** *of Jamaica.*

1858–60.

Z1		1d. rose-red (1857), *perf* 14	£650
Z2		2d. blue (1858) (Plate No. 7)	£1000
Z3		4d. rose (1857)	£350
Z4		6d. lilac (1856)	£200
Z5		1s. green (1856)	£1700

PRICES FOR STAMPS ON COVER	
Nos. 1/9	*from* × 25
Nos. 11/21	*from* × 30
Nos. 22/6	*from* × 25
No. 27	
No. 28	*from* × 30
Nos. R1/6	—

1

Distorted "E" (R. 2/1)

1870 (1 Apr)–**79**. Wmk Crown CC.

(a) P 12½.

1	1	1d. dull rose	85·00	48·00
		a. Wmk sideways	£225	£160
		w. Wmk inverted		
2		1d. magenta (*shades*) (1871)	75·00	30·00
		a. Wmk sideways	†	£600
		w. Wmk inverted	£120	65·00
		x. Wmk reversed		
4		6d. yellow-green	£120	19·00
		w. Wmk inverted		
5		6d. green (1871)	£120	7·50

(b) P 14.

6	1	1d. magenta (*shades*) (1875)	65·00	7·00
		a. Bisected diag or vert (½d.) (on cover) (3.82)	†	£2000
		w. Wmk inverted		
7		2¼d. red-brown (11.79)	£180	£250
8		4d. blue (11.79)	£200	15·00
		a. Wmk sideways	£1100	£170
		w. Wmk inverted	£375	50·00
9		6d. green (1876)	55·00	5·00
		a. Imperf between (pair)	£650	£150
		b. Wmk sideways		
		x. Wmk reversed	£200	

The magenta used for the 1d. was a fugitive colour which reacts to both light and water.

No. 6a was authorised for use between March and June 1882 to make up the 2¼d. letter rate and for ½d. book post.

1882 (June)–**90**. Wmk Crown CA. P 14.

11	1	½d. dull green	2·25	2·00
		a. Wmk sideways	£300	
		x. Wmk reversed		
12		1d. dull magenta	£550	70·00
		a. Bisected diagonally (½d.) (on cover)		
13		1d. carmine-rose (2.84)	1·75	2·25
		a. Bisected (½d.) (on cover)		
		b. Distorted "E"	20·00	
		x. Wmk reversed		
14		2½d. pale red-brown	£180	60·00
15		2½d. deep red-brown	£190	65·00
16		2½d. ultramarine (2.84)	2·50	1·50
17		4d. blue	£475	20·00
18		4d. grey (10.84)	1·50	1·00
19		6d. olive-brown (3.90)	85·00	£375
		w. Wmk inverted		
20		1s. mauve (6.86)	95·00	65·00
		w. Wmk inverted	—	£150
21		1s. bright mauve (1890)	85·00	£160
19s/20s Optd "Specimen" *Set of 2*			£120	

FOUR PENCE (2)	Halfpenny (3)

1884 (Dec). No. 9 surch with T **2** by The Advertiser Press.

22	**1**	4d. on 6d. green............	65·00	50·00
		a. Full stop after "PENCE"	65·00	50·00
		b. Surch double	—	£2750

No. 22a occurred on alternate stamps.

1885 (Mar). No. 13 bisected and each half diagonally surch with T **3**.

23	**1**	½d. on half of 1d. carmine-rose	25·00	40·00
		a. Unsevered pair..............	£120	£120
		ab. Ditto, one surch inverted ...	£400	£275
		b. Surch inverted..............	£225	£110
		ba. Ditto, unsevered pair......	£1000	
		c. Surch double.................		

ONE PENNY. (4)	4d. (5)

1886 (June). No. 9 surch with T **4** or **5** each showing a manuscript line through the original value.

24	**1**	1d. on 6d. green............	20·00	32·00
		a. Surch inverted................	£8000	
		b. Surch double	—	£1500
25		4d. on 6d. green............	55·00	95·00
		a. No stop after "d"	£225	£300
		b. Surch double	£2500	£2750

No. 24b is only known penmarked with dates between 21 July and 3 August 1886, or with violet handstamp.

1887 (May). No. 11 surch with T **4** showing a manuscript line through the original value.

26	**1**	1d. on ½d. dull green	40·00	45·00

ONE PENNY. (7)

1888 (May). No. 16 surch.

(a) With T **4**. Original value unobliterated.

27	**1**	1d. on 2½d. ultramarine	£18000	£12000

(b) With T **7** showing a manuscript line through the original value.

28	**1**	1d. on 2½d. ultramarine	65·00	65·00
		a. Surch inverted................	£15000	£8500

The 1d. of Antigua was used provisionally in St. Christopher between February and March 1890 during a shortage of 1d. stamps. Such use can be distinguished by the postmark, which is "A 12" in place of "A02" (price from £130 used).

REVENUE STAMPS USED FOR POSTAGE

Saint Christopher (R 1)	SAINT KITTS NEVIS / REVENUE (R 2)

1883. Nos. F6 and F8 of Nevis optd with Type R **1**, in violet. Wmk Crown CA. P 14.

R1		1d. lilac-mauve............	£375	
R2		6d. green............	85·00	£140

1885. Optd with Type R **2**. Wmk Crown CA. P 14.

R3	**1**	1d. rose............	2·75	16·00
R4		3d. mauve............	16·00	65·00
R5		6d. orange-brown	10·00	50·00
R6		1s. olive............	3·00	42·00

Other fiscal stamps with overprints as above also exist, but none of these were ever available for postal purposes.

The stamps for St. Christopher were superseded by the general issue for Leeward Islands on 31 October 1890.

Stamps for St. Kitts, issued from 1980 onwards will be found listed after those for the combined colony.

NEVIS

Little is known concerning the early postal affairs of Nevis, although several covers exist from the island in the 1660s. It is recorded that the British G.P.O. was to establish a branch office on the island under an Act of Parliament of 1710, although arrangements may not have been finalised for a number of years afterwards. Nevis appears as "a new office" in the P.O. Accounts of 1787.

Stamps of Great Britain were used on the island from May 1858 until the colonial authorities assumed control of the postal service on 1 May 1860. Between this date and the introduction of Nevis stamps in 1861 No. CC1 was again used on overseas mail.

CHARLESTOWN

CROWNED-CIRCLE HANDSTAMPS

CC 1

CC1	CC **1**	NEVIS (R.) (9.1852) .....Price on cover	£4000

No. CC1, struck in black or red (1882) was later used on several occasions up to 1882 when there were shortages of adhesive stamps.

Stamps of GREAT BRITAIN cancelled "A 09" as Type Z **1** of Jamaica.

1858–60.

Z1		1d. rose-red (1857), perf 14	£450
Z2		2d. blue (1858) (Plate Nos. 7, 8)	£1800
Z3		4d. rose (1857)	£425
Z4		6d. lilac (1856)	£300
Z5		1s. green (1856)	£300

PRICES FOR STAMPS ON COVER	
Nos. 5/22	from × 20
Nos. 23/4	from × 10
Nos. 25/34	from × 20
Nos. 35/6	from × 10
Nos. F1/8	from × 30

The designs on the stamps refer to a medicinal spring on the island

(Recess Nissen & Parker, London)

1861. Greyish paper. P 13.

5	**1**	1d. dull lake............	85·00	50·00
		a. On blued paper............	£275	£120
6	**2**	4d. rose............	£120	65·00
		a. On blued paper............	£800	£170
7	**3**	6d. grey-lilac............	£120	55·00
		a. On blued paper............	£650	£225
8	**4**	1s. green............	£300	75·00
		a. On blued paper............	£950	£200

Nos. 5/8 and later printings of Types **1/4** were in sheets of 12 (3×4).

1866–76. White paper. P 15.

9	**1**	1d. pale red............	48·00	42·00
10		1d. deep red............	48·00	42·00
11	**2**	4d. orange............	£120	23·00
12		4d. deep orange............	£120	23·00
13	**4**	1s. blue-green............	£275	32·00
14		1s. yellow-green (1876)............	£850	£110
		a. Vertically laid paper............	£18000	£6000
		b. No. 9 on sheet with crossed lines on hill............	£3500	£500
		c. Ditto. On laid paper	†	£14000

Examples of the 4d. exist showing part of a papermakers watermark reading "A. COWAN & SONS EXTRA SUPERFINE".

(Lithographed by transfer from the engraved plates Nissen and Parker, London)

1876–78.

(a) P 15.

15	**1**	1d. pale rose-red............	22·00	17·00
		a. Imperf (pair)............	£850	
16		1d. deep rose-red............	32·00	27·00
17		1d. vermilion-red............	27·00	27·00
		a. Bisected (½d.) (on cover).........	†	£2500
18	**2**	4d. orange-yellow (1878)............	£170	32·00
		a. Imperf between (vert pair)........	£6500	
19	**3**	6d. grey (1878)............	£225	£190
20	**4**	1s. pale green (1878)............	90·00	£110
		a. Imperf............		
		b. Imperf between (horiz strip of three)............	£10000	
		c. No. 9 on sheet with crossed lines on hill............		£250
21		1s. deep green............	£100	£140
		c. No. 9 on sheet with crossed lines on hill............		£900

(b) P 11½.

22	**1**	1d. vermilion-red (1878)............	48·00	55·00
		a. Bisected (½d.) (on cover).........	†	£2500
		b. Imperf (pair)............	£500	
		c. Imperf between (horiz pair)............		

No. 21c occurs on a small part of the deep green printing only.

RETOUCHES. 1d. Lithograph.

i.	No. 1 on sheet. Top of hill over kneeling figure redrawn by five thick lines and eight small slanting lines	£140	£150
ii.	No. 1 on sheet. Another retouch. Three series of short vertical strokes behind the kneeling figure	£140	£150
iii.	No. 3 on sheet. Right upper corner star and border below star retouched	£140	£150
iv.	No. 9 on sheet. Retouch in same position as on No. 3 but differing in detail	£160	£170
v.	No. 12 on sheet. Dress of standing figure retouched by a number of horizontal and vertical lines...................	£140	£150

5 (Die I)	(6)

(Typo D.L.R.)

1879–80. Wmk Crown CC. P 14.

23	**5**	1d. lilac-mauve (1880)............	75·00	38·00
		a. Bisected (½d.) (on cover) ...	†	£950
		w. Wmk inverted............		
24		2½d. red-brown............	£130	85·00

1882–90. Wmk Crown CA. P 14.

25	**5**	½d. dull green (11.83)............	5·50	15·00
		a. Top left triangle detached........	£225	
26		1d. lilac-mauve............	£100	30·00
		a. Bisected (½d.) on cover (1883).	†	£700
27		1d. dull rose (11.83)............	26·00	18·00
		a. Carmine (1884)............	11·00	11·00
		ab. Top left triangle detached........	£325	
28		2½d. red-brown............	£120	50·00
29		2½d. ultramarine (11.83)............	19·00	19·00
		a. Top left triangle detached........	£500	
30		4d. blue............	£325	50·00
31		4d. grey (1884)............	12·00	4·00
		a. Top left triangle detached........	£425	£350
32		6d. green (11.83)............	£400	£350
33		6d. chestnut (10.88)............	24·00	60·00
		a. Top left triangle detached........	£600	
34		1s. pale violet (3.90)............	£110	£180
		a. Top left triangle detached........	£1300	
33s/4s		Optd "Specimen" Set of 2	£110	

For illustration of the "top left triangle detached" variety, which occurs on Plate 2 R. 3/3 of the right pane, see below Montserrat No. 5.

1883 (4 Sept). No. 26 bisected vertically and surch with T **6**, reading upwards or downwards.

35		½d. on half 1d. lilac-mauve (V.)	£850	48·00
		a. Surch double............	—	£300
		b. Surch on half "REVENUE" stamp No. F6		£550
36		½d. on half 1d. lilac-mauve............	£1000	45·00
		a. Surch double............	—	£300
		b. Unsevered pair............	£3750	£600
		c. Surch on half "REVENUE" stamp No. F6	—	£550

FISCALS USED FOR POSTAGE

Revenue (F 1)	REVENUE (F 2)

1882. (a) Stamps of 1876–78 optd with Type F **1** by Nissen & Parker, London.

F1	**1**	1d. bright red............	60·00	
F2	**2**	1d. rose............	60·00	26·00
F3		4d. orange............	£100	
F4	**3**	6d. grey............	£170	
F5	**4**	1s. green............	£190	
		a. No. 9 on sheet with crossed lines on hill............		

(b) Nos. 26, 30 and 32 optd with Type F **2** by D.L.R.

F6	**5**	1d. lilac-mauve............	60·00	55·00
		a. Bisected (½d.) (on cover)............		
F7		4d. blue............	38·00	60·00
F8		1s. green............	23·00	65·00

Nos. F1/5 were produced from fresh transfers. Similar "REVENUE" handstamps, both with and without stop, were also applied to postage issues.

The stamps of Nevis were superseded by the general issue for Leeward Islands on 31 October 1890.

ST. KITTS-NEVIS

CROWN COLONY

Stamps for the combined colony were introduced in 1903, and were used concurrently with the general issues of Leeward Islands until the latter were withdrawn on 1 July 1956.

PRICES FOR STAMPS ON COVER TO 1945	
Nos. 1/9	from × 3
No. 10	—
Nos. 11/20	from × 3
No. 21	—
Nos. 22/3	from × 15
Nos. 24/34	from × 3
Nos. 35/6	—
Nos. 37/47	from × 2
No. 47a/b	—
Nos. 48/57	from × 2
Nos. 58/60	—
Nos. 61/4	from × 2
Nos. 65/7	from × 5
Nos. 68/77	from × 2

1 Christopher Columbus

2 Medicinal Spring

(Typo D.L.R.)

1903. Wmk Crown CA. P 14.

1	1	½d. dull purple and deep green	1·75	70
2	2	1d. grey-black and carmine	4·75	20
3	1	2d. dull purple and brown	2·50	11·00
4		2½d. grey-black and blue	17·00	4·25
5	2	3d. deep green and orange	15·00	28·00
6	1	6d. grey-black and bright purple	4·75	38·00
7		1s. grey-green and orange	6·50	11·00
8	2	2s. deep green and grey-black	12·00	20·00
9	1	2s.6d. deep green and violet	18·00	42·00
10	2	5s. dull purple and sage-green	55·00	55·00
1/10 Set of 10			£120	£190
1s/10s Optd "Specimen" Set of 10			£130	

1905–18. Chalk-surfaced paper (1d. (No. 13), 5s.) or ordinary paper (others). Wmk Mult Crown CA. P 14.

11	1	½d. dull purple and deep green	7·50	5·50
12		½d. grey-green (1907)	1·00	60
		a. Dull blue-green (1916)	50	1·75
13	2	1d. grey-black and carmine (1906)	2·25	25
14		1d. carmine (1907)	2·25	15
		a. Scarlet (1916)	80	20
15	1	2d. dull purple and brown	10·00	8·00
		a. Chalk-surfaced paper (1906)	6·50	8·00
16		2½d. grey-black and blue (1907)	14·00	3·25
17		2½d. bright blue (1907)	2·50	50
18	2	3d. deep green and orange	10·00	9·00
		a. Chalk-surfaced paper (1906)	2·75	2·75
19	1	6d. grey-black and deep violet	23·00	48·00
		a. Chalk-surfaced paper. Grey-black and deep purple (1908)	17·00	25·00
		ab. Grey-black and bright purple (1916)	6·00	25·00
20	1	1s. grey-green and orange (1909)	24·00	42·00
		a. Chalk-surfaced paper	3·50	30·00
21	2	5s. dull purple and sage-green (11.18)	32·00	80·00
11/21 Set of 11			70·00	£140
12s, 14s, 17s Optd "Specimen" Set of 3			60·00	

WAR TAX   WAR STAMP

(3)

(3a)

1916 (Oct). Optd with T 3. Wmk Mult Crown CA. P 14.

22	1	½d. dull blue-green (No. 12a)	1·00	50
		a. Deep green	1·00	50
		s. Optd "Specimen"	40·00	
		x. Wmk reversed	35·00	

No. 22a was a special printing produced for this overprint.

1918 (26 July). Optd with T 3a. Wmk Mult Crown CA. P 14.

23	1	1½d. orange	80	80
		a. Short opt (right pane R. 10/1)	17·00	
		s. Optd "Specimen"	45·00	

No. 23 was a special printing produced for this overprint.
No. 23a shows the overprint 2 mm high instead of 2½ mm.

4 **5**

(Typo D.L.R.)

1920–22. Ordinary paper (½d. to 2½d.) or chalk-surfaced paper (others). Wmk Mult Crown CA (sideways*). P 14.

24	4	½d. blue-green	3·75	5·50
25	5	1d. scarlet	2·25	6·00
26	4	1½d. orange-yellow	1·25	1·75
		x. Wmk sideways reversed	85·00	
27	5	y. Wmk sideways inverted and reversed		
		2d. slate-grey	3·00	3·75
28	4	2½d. ultramarine	2·25	9·00
		a. "A" of "CA" missing from wmk	£400	
29	5	3d. purple/yellow	1·75	11·00
30	4	6d. dull purple and bright mauve	3·50	11·00
31	5	1s. grey and black/green	3·50	4·00
32	4	2s. dull purple and blue/blue	15·00	24·00
		x. Wmk sideways reversed	£170	
33	5	2s.6d. grey and red/blue	5·00	32·00
		y. Wmk sideways inverted and reversed	£170	
34	4	5s. green and red/pale yellow	5·00	40·00
		x. Wmk sideways reversed	£120	
35	5	10s. green and red/green	12·00	48·00
36	4	£1 purple and black/red (1922)	£225	£300
24/36 Set of 13			£250	£400
24s/36s Optd "Specimen" Set of 13			£325	

*The normal sideways watermark shows Crown to left of CA, as seen from the back of the stamp.

Examples of most values are known showing a forged St. Kitts postmark dated "8 DE 23".

1921–29. Chalk-surfaced paper (2½d. (No. 44), 3d. (No. 45a) and 6d. to 5s.) or ordinary. Wmk Mult Script CA (sideways*).

37	4	½d. blue-green	2·25	1·50
		a. Yellow-green (1922)	1·50	80
38	5	1d. rose-carmine	65	15

39		sa. Perf "Specimen" (1929)	70·00	
		1d. deep violet (1922)	5·00	1·00
		a. Pale violet (1929)	7·00	1·50
40	4	1½d. red (1925)	2·75	2·75
40a		1½d. red-brown (1929)	1·00	30
41	5	2d. slate-grey (1922)	50	60
42	4	2½d. pale bright blue (1922)	3·00	2·25
43		2½d. brown (1922)	2·25	9·00
44		2½d. ultramarine (1927)	1·50	1·50
45	5	3d. dull ultramarine (1922)	1·00	4·25
45a		3d. purple/yellow (1927)	75	4·50
46	4	6d. dull and bright purple (1924)	5·00	6·00
		aw. Wmk Crown to right of CA	4·00	6·00
46b	5	1s. black/green (1929)	3·75	6·50
47	4	2s. purple and blue/blue (1922)	8·00	23·00
47a	5	2s.6d. black and red/blue (1927)	15·00	29·00
47b	4	5s. green and red/yellow (1929)	40·00	70·00
37/47b Set of 16			85·00	£150
37s/47bs Optd or Perf (1½d. red-brown, 1s., 5s.) "Specimen" Set of 16			£375	

*The normal watermark shows Crown to left of CA, as seen from the back of the stamp.

6 Old Road Bay and Mount Misery

(Typo D.L.R.)

1923. Tercentenary of Colony. Chalk-surfaced paper. P 14.

(a) Wmk Mult Script CA (sideways).

48	6	½d. black and green	2·25	7·00
49		1d. black and bright violet	4·50	1·50
50		1½d. black and scarlet	4·50	10·00
51		2d. black and slate-grey	3·75	1·50
52		2½d. black and brown	6·00	32·00
53		3d. black and ultramarine	3·75	15·00
54		6d. black and bright purple	9·50	32·00
55		1s. black and sage-green	14·00	32·00
56		2s. black and blue/blue	45·00	65·00
57		2s.6d. black and red/blue	48·00	80·00
58		10s. black and red/emerald	£275	£425

(b) Wmk Mult Crown CA (sideways).

59	6	5s. black and red/pale yellow	80·00	£180
60		£1 black and purple/red	£700	£1500
48/60 Set of 13			£1100	£2000
48s/60s Optd "Specimen" Set of 13			£700	

Examples of all values are known showing a forged St. Kitts postmark dated "8 DE 23."

1935 (6 May). Silver Jubilee. As Nos. 91/4 of Antigua, but ptd by Waterlow. P 11×12.

61		1d. deep blue and scarlet	1·00	70
		k. Kite and vertical log	80·00	
		l. Kite and horizontal log	£120	
62		1½d. ultramarine and grey	75	75
		k. Kite and vertical log	75·00	85·00
63		2½d. brown and deep blue	1·00	80
64		1s. slate and purple	5·50	15·00
		k. Kite and vertical log	£250	
		l. Kite and horizontal log	£275	£375
61/4 Set of 4			7·50	15·00
61s/4s Perf "Specimen" Set of 4			95·00	

For illustrations of plate varieties see Omnibus section following Zanzibar.

1937 (12 May). Coronation. As Nos. 95/7 of Antigua, but ptd by D.L.R. P 14.

65		1d. scarlet	30	25
66		1½d. buff	40	10
67		2½d. bright blue	60	1·00
65/7 Set of 3			1·10	1·25
65s/7s Perf "Specimen" Set of 3			75·00	

Nos. 61/7 are inscribed "ST. CHRISTOPHER AND NEVIS".

7 King George VI

8 King George VI and Medicinal Spring

9 King George VI and Christopher Columbus

10 King George VI and Anguilla Island

Break in value tablet (R. 12/5) (1947 ptg only)

Break in oval (R. 12/1) (1938 ptg only)

Break in value tablet frame (R. 3/2)

Break in value tablet frame (R. 12/3) (ptgs between 1941 and 1945)

Break in frame above ornament (R. 2/4) (ptgs between 1941 and 1950)

Break in oval at foot (R. 12/5) (ptgs between 1941 and 1945 only). Sometimes touched-in by hand painting

Break in oval at left (R. 7/1) (ptgs between 1941 and 1945 only)

(Typo; centre litho (T **10**). D.L.R.)

1938 (15 Aug)–**50**. Chalk-surfaced paper (10s., £1). Wmk Mult Script CA (sideways on T **8** and **9**). P 14 (T **7** and **10**) or 13×12 (T **8/9**).

68	7	½d. green	4·00	20
		a. Blue-green (5.4.43)	10	10
69		1d. scarlet	6·00	70
		a. Carmine (5.43)	1·50	50
		b. Carmine-pink (4.47)	60·00	16·00
		c. Rose-red (7.47)	1·50	80
70		1½d. orange	20	30
71	8	2d. scarlet and grey	23·00	2·75
		a. Chalk-surfaced paper. Carmine and deep grey (18.2.41*)	55·00	10·00
		b. Perf 14. Scarlet and pale grey (6.43*)	1·25	1·25
		ba. Scarlet and deep grey (6.42*)	24·00	4·00
		c. Perf 14. Chalk-surfaced paper. Scarlet and pale grey (2.50*)	3·50	3·50
72	7	2½d. ultramarine	4·00	30
		a. Bright ultramarine (5.4.43)	70	30
73	8	3d. dull reddish purple and scarlet	19·00	4·50
		a. Chalk-surfaced paper. Brown-purple and carmine-red (1940)	23·00	6·50
		b. Perf 14. Chalk-surfaced paper. Dull reddish purple and carm-red (6.43*)	35·00	4·00
		c. Perf 14. Ordinary paper. Reddish lilac and scarlet (8.46*)	3·75	12·00
		d. Perf 14. Ordinary paper. Purple and bright scarlet (1.46*)	12·00	7·50
		da. Break in value tablet	£170	
		e. Perf 14. Chalk-surfaced paper. Deep purple and scarlet (12.47*)	75·00	19·00
		f. Perf 14. Ordinary paper. Rose-lilac and bright scarlet (1.49*)	9·00	9·00
		g. Perf 14. Chalk-surfaced paper. Deep reddish purple and brt scarlet (8.50*)	7·00	7·00
74	9	6d. green and bright purple	6·50	2·25
		a. Break in oval	£150	
		b. Perf 14. Chalk-surfaced paper. Green and deep claret (17.5.43*)	55·00	11·00
		c. Perf 14. Ordinary paper. Green and purple (10.44*)	5·00	1·50
		d. Perf 14. Chalk-surfaced paper. Green and purple (11.48*)	5·00	3·50
75	8	1s. black and green	12·00	1·50
		a. Break in value tablet frame	£225	
		b. Perf 14 (8.43*)	4·00	85
		ba. Break in value tablet frame	£120	75·00
		c. Perf 14. Chalk-surfaced paper (7.50*)	6·50	5·50
		ca. Break in value tablet frame	£140	
76		2s.6d. black and scarlet	32·00	9·00
		a. Perf 14. Chalk-surfaced paper (12.43*)	17·00	6·00
		ab. Ordinary paper (5.45*)	12·00	3·75
77	9	5s. grey-green and scarlet	65·00	20·00
		a. Perf 14. Chalk-surfaced paper (25.10.43*)	£130	30·00
		ab. Break in value tablet frame	£700	£275
		ac. Break in frame above ornament	£700	£275
		ad. Break in oval at foot	£700	£275
		ae. Break in oval at left	£700	£275
		b. Perf 14. Ordinary paper. Bluish green and scarlet (7.11.45*)	24·00	12·00
		ba. Break in value tablet frame	£300	£160
		bb. Break in frame above ornament	£325	£170
		bc. Break in oval at foot	£300	£150
		bd. Break in oval at left	£300	£160
		c. Perf 14. Chalk-surfaced paper. Green and scarlet-vermilion (10.50*)	45·00	48·00
		cb. Break in frame above ornament	£400	
77e	10	10s. black and ultramarine (1.9.48)	13·00	19·00
77f		£1 black and brown (1.9.48)	13·00	23·00
68a/77f Set of 12			70·00	60·00
68s/77fs Perf "Specimen" Set of 10			£200	

*Earliest postmark date. Many printings were supplied to St. Kitts-Nevis considerably earlier. Details of many of the dates are taken, with permission, from *A Study of the King George VI Stamps of St. Kitts-Nevis* by P. L. Baldwin (2nd edition 1997).

1946 (1 Nov). *Victory. As Nos. 110/11 of Antigua.*
78	1½d. red-orange		10	10
79	3d. carmine		10	10
	78s/9s Perf "Specimen" Set of 2		75·00	

1949 (3 Jan). *Royal Silver Wedding. As Nos. 112/13 of Antigua.*
80	2½d. ultramarine		10	50
81	5s. carmine		6·50	3·50

1949 (10 Oct). *75th Anniv of U.P.U. As Nos. 114/17 of Antigua.*
82	2½d. ultramarine		15	30
83	3d. carmine-red		1·50	1·75
84	6d. magenta		20	1·00
85	1s. blue-green		20	40
	a. "A" of "CA" missing from wmk		£500	
	82/5 Set of 4		1·90	3·00

ANGUILLA

ANGUILLA

TERCENTENARY 1650-1950
(11)

TERCENTENARY 1650—1950
(12)

1950 (10 Nov). *Tercentenary of British Settlement in Anguilla. Nos. 69c, 70 and 72a (perf 14) optd as T 11 and new ptgs of T 8/9 on chalk-surfaced paper perf 13×12½ optd as T 12.*
86	7	1d. rose-red	10	20
87		1½d. orange	10	50
		a. Error. Crown missing, W 9a	£2000	
		b. Error. St. Edward's Crown, W 9b	£1000	
88		2½d. bright ultramarine	15	20
89	8	3d. dull purple and scarlet	20	75
90	9	6d. green and bright purple	20	20
91	8	1s. black and green (R.)	70	25
		a. Break in value tablet frame	12·00	
		86/91 Set of 6	1·25	1·90

Nos. 87a/b occur on a row in the watermark, in which the crowns and letters "CA" alternate.

(New Currency. 100 cents = 1 West Indian dollar)

1951 (16 Feb). *Inauguration of B.W.I. University College. As Nos. 118/19 of Antigua.*
92		3c. black and yellow-orange	30	15
93		12c. turquoise-green and magenta	30	1·50

ST. CHRISTOPHER, NEVIS AND ANGUILLA

LEGISLATIVE COUNCIL

13 Bath House and Spa, Nevis

14 Warner Park

15 Map of the Islands

16 Brimstone Hill

17 Nevis from the Sea, North

18 Pinney's Beach

19 Sir Thomas Warner's Tomb

20 Old Road Bay

21 Sea Island Cotton

22 The Treasury

23 Salt Pond, Anguilla

24 Sugar Factory

(Recess Waterlow)

1952 (14 June). *Vert designs as T 13/24. Wmk Mult Script CA. P 12½.*
94	13	1c. deep green and ochre	15	1·25
95	14	2c. green	1·00	1·00
96	15	3c. carmine-red and violet	30	1·25
97	16	4c. scarlet	20	20
98	17	5c. bright blue and grey	30	10
99	18	6c. ultramarine	30	15
100	19	12c. deep blue and reddish brown	1·25	10
101	20	24c. black and carmine-red	30	10
102	21	48c. olive and chocolate	2·25	2·50
103	22	60c. ochre and deep green	2·00	3·00
104	23	$1.20 deep green and ultramarine	7·00	2·75
105	24	$4.80 green and carmine	13·00	18·00
		94/105 Set of 12	25·00	27·00

St. Lucia

Although a branch office of the British G.P.O. was not opened at Castries, the island capital, until 1844 some form of postal arrangements for overseas mails existed from at least 1841 when the issue of a Ship Letter handstamp is recorded.

The stamps of Great Britain were used on the island from May 1858 until the end of April 1860 when the local authorities assumed responsibility for the postal service. No. CC1 was again used on overseas mail between 1 May and the introduction of St. Lucia stamps in December 1860.

CASTRIES

CROWN-CIRCLE HANDSTAMPS

CC 1

CC1	CC 1 ST. LUCIA (R.) (1.5.1844)		*Price on cover*	£900

No. CC1 was utilised, struck in black, during a shortage of 1d. stamps in late April and early May 1904. *Price on cover* £325

Stamps of GREAT BRITAIN *cancelled* "A 11" *as Type Z 1 of Jamaica.*

1858–60.
Z1		1d. rose-red (1857), *perf 14*	£1000
Z2		2d. blue (1855)	£425
Z3		4d. rose (1857)	£425
Z4		6d. lilac (1856)	£225
Z5		1s. green (1856)	£1400

PRICES FOR STAMPS ON COVER TO 1945	
Nos. 1/3	*from* × 60
Nos. 5/8	*from* × 30
Nos. 9/10	†
Nos. 11/24	*from* × 15
Nos. 25/30	*from* × 10
Nos. 31/6	*from* × 6
Nos. 39/42	*from* × 10
Nos. 43/50	*from* × 15
Nos. 51/2	—
Nos. 53/62	*from* × 6
No. 63	*from* × 15
Nos. 64/75	*from* × 4
Nos. 76/7	—
Nos. 78/88	*from* × 3
No. 89	*from* × 4
No. 90	*from* × 20
Nos. 91/112	*from* × 3
Nos. 113/24	*from* × 2
Nos. 125/7	*from* × 10
Nos. 128/41	*from* × 2
Nos. D1/6	*from* × 10
Nos. F1/28	—

CROWN COLONY

PERKINS BACON "CANCELLED". For notes on these handstamps, showing "CANCELLED" between horizontal bars forming an oval, see Catalogue Introduction.

1

Half penny
(2)

(Recess P.B.)

1860 (18 Dec). *Wmk Small Star, W w 2. P 14 to 16.*
1	1	(1d.) rose-red (H/S "CANCELLED" in oval £8000)	£100	65·00
		a. Imperf vert (horiz pair)		
		b. Double impression	£2000	
2		(4d.) blue (H/S "CANCELLED" in oval £9000)	£225	£150
		a. Deep blue		
		b. Imperf vert (horiz pair)		
3		(6d.) green (H/S "CANCELLED" in oval £9000)	£300	£200
		a. Imperf vert (horiz pair)		
		b. Deep green	£350	£225

(Recess D.L.R.)

1863. *Wmk Crown CC. P 12½.*
5	1	(1d.) lake	75·00	90·00
		ax. Wmk reversed	70·00	85·00
		b. Brownish lake	90·00	90·00
		bx. Wmk reversed	85·00	85·00
7		(4d.) indigo	£120	£130
		x. Wmk reversed		
8		(6d.) emerald-green	£170	£170
		w. Wmk inverted		
		x. Wmk reversed	£180	£170

Prepared for use, but not issued. Surch as T 2.
9	1	½d. on (6d.) emerald-green	70·00	
		x. Wmk reversed	85·00	
10		6d. on (4d.) indigo	£1100	

All three values exist imperforate from proof sheets.

1864 (19 Nov)–**76.** *Wmk Crown CC.*

(a) P 12½.
11	1	(1d.) black	22·00	12·00
		a. Intense black	21·00	11·00
		ax. Wmk reversed	28·00	15·00
12		(4d.) yellow	£170	38·00
		b. Lemon-yellow	£1500	
		c. Chrome-yellow	£200	38·00
		d. Olive-yellow	£375	90·00
		w. Wmk inverted		
		x. Wmk inverted	£225	45·00
		y. Wmk inverted and reversed		
13		(6d.) violet	£120	32·00
		a. Mauve	£190	30·00
		b. Deep lilac	£150	35·00
		x. Wmk reversed	£150	
14		(1s.) brown-orange	£325	28·00
		b. Orange	£250	28·00
		c. Pale orange	£225	28·00
		ca. Imperf between (horiz pair)		
		x. Wmk reversed	£250	

(b) P 14.
15	1	(1d.) black (6.76)	28·00	18·00
		a. Imperf between (horiz pair)		
		x. Wmk reversed	30·00	18·00
16		(4d.) yellow (6.76)	£110	21·00
		a. Olive-yellow	£300	95·00
		w. Wmk inverted		
		x. Wmk reversed		
17		(6d.) mauve (6.76)	£110	38·00
		a. Pale lilac	£110	20·00
		b. Violet	£250	70·00
		x. Wmk reversed		
18		(1s.) orange (10.76)	£225	22·00
		a. Deep orange	£150	16·00
		w. Wmk inverted		
		x. Wmk reversed	—	25·00

All four values exist imperforate from proof sheets.

ST. LUCIA
THREE PENCE
5

HALFPENNY
(3)

2½ PENCE
(4)

1881 (Sept). *Surch with T 3 or 4. Wmk Crown CC. P 14.*
23	1	½d. green	70·00	90·00
		x. Wmk reversed		
24		2½d. brown-red	35·00	23·00

The 1d. black is known surcharged "1d." in violet ink by hand, but there is no evidence that this was done officially.

1882–84. *Surch as T 3. Wmk Crown CA.*

(a) P 14.
25	1	½d. green (1882)	21·00	29·00
26		1d. black (C.)	28·00	11·00
		a. Bisected (on cover)	†	—
27		4d. yellow	£300	20·00
28		6d. violet	30·00	29·00
29		1s. orange	£275	£170

(b) P 12.
30	1	4d. yellow	£275	28·00

Deep blue stamps, wmk Crown CA, perf 14 or 12 are fiscals from which the overprint "THREE PENCE—REVENUE", or "REVENUE", has been fraudulently removed.

(Typo D.L.R.)

1883 (6 July)–**86.** *Die I. Wmk Crown CA. P 14.*
31	5	½d. dull green	8·50	4·50

32		a. Top left triangle detached	£275	
		1d. carmine-rose	40·00	11·00
33		2½d. blue	42·00	2·00
		a. Top left triangle detached	£650	150
34		4d. brown (1885)	32·00	1·25
		a. Top left triangle detached	£650	120
35		6d. lilac (1886)	£250	£200
36		1s. orange-brown (1885)	£375	£150
31/6		Set of 6	£650	£325

The 4d. and 6d. exist imperforate from proof sheets. For illustration of "top left triangle detached" variety on this and the following issue see above No. 6 of Montserrat.

1886–87. *Die I.* Wmk Crown CA. P 14.

39	**5**	1d. dull mauve	7·50	6·00
		a. Top left triangle detached	£225	
40		3d. dull mauve and green	£120	17·00
		a. Top left triangle detached	—	£450
41		6d. dull mauve and blue (1887)	4·25	10·00
		a. Top left triangle detached	£200	£275
42		1s. dull mauve and red (1887)	£110	27·00
		a. Top left triangle detached	£900	
39/42		Set of 4	£225	55·00
39s/42s		Optd "Specimen" *Set of 4*	£180	

The 1d. exists imperforate from proof sheets.

1891–98. *Die II.* Wmk Crown CA. P 14.

43	**5**	½d. dull green	2·50	1·00
44		1d. dull mauve	4·00	30
45		2d. ultramarine and orange (1898)	3·75	1·00
46		2½d. ultramarine	5·00	1·00
47		3d. dull mauve and green	4·75	5·50
48		4d. brown	3·00	2·25
49		6d. dull mauve and blue	24·00	24·00
50		1s. dull mauve and red	7·00	5·00
51		5s. dull mauve and orange	50·00	£130
52		10s. dull mauve and black	90·00	£140
43/52		Set of 10	£170	£275
45s, 51s/2s		Optd "Specimen" *Set of 3*	£120	

For description and illustration of differences between Die I and Die II see Introduction.

ONE HALF PENNY (6) ½d (7) ONE PENNY (8)

N
Normal "N"

N
Thick "N"

Three types of T **8**

I. All letters "N" normal.
II. Thick diagonal stroke in first "N".
III. Thick diagonal stroke in second "N".

1891–92.

(a) Stamps of Die I surch.

53	**6**	½d. on 3d. dull mauve and green	£140	70·00
		a. Small "A" in "HALF"	£350	150
		b. Small "O" in "ONE"	£350	150
		c. Top left triangle detached	£950	
54	**7**	½d. on half dull mauve and blue 6d.	24·00	3·25
		a. No fraction bar	£250	£130
		b. Surch sideways	£1300	
		c. Surch double	£600	£600
		d. "2" in fraction omitted	£475	£500
		e. Thick "1" with sloping serif	£200	£120
		f. Surch triple	£1100	
		g. Figure "1" used as fraction bar	£475	£275
		h. Top left triangle detached	£300	
55	**8**	1d. on 4d. brown (I) (12.91)	5·00	3·50
		a. Surch double	£225	
		b. Surch inverted	£800	£700
		c. Type II	23·00	20·00
		ca. Surch double	£350	
		cb. Surch inverted	—	£800
		d. Type III	22·00	20·00
		e. Top left triangle detached	£190	£160

(b) Stamp of Die II surch.

56	**6**	½d. on 3d. dull mauve and green	80·00	24·00
		a. Surch double	£800	£600
		b. Surch inverted	£1700	£600
		c. Surch both sides	—	£700
		d. Small "O" in "ONE"	£180	90·00
		e. Small "A" in "HALF"	£180	90·00
		f. "ONE" misplaced ("O" over "H")	£180	90·00

9

10

(Typo D.L.R.)

1902–03. Wmk Crown CA. P 14.

58	**9**	½d. dull purple and green	2·75	1·50
59		1d. dull purple and carmine	5·00	50
60		2d. dull purple and ultramarine	24·00	5·50
61	**10**	3d. dull purple and yellow	6·00	8·50
62		1s. green and black	10·00	30·00
58/62		Set of 5	42·00	42·00
58s/62s		Optd "Specimen" *Set of 5*	£100	

11 The Pitons

(Recess D.L.R.)

1902 (15 Dec). *400th Anniv of Discovery by Columbus.* Wmk Crown CC (sideways). P 14.

63	**11**	2d. green and brown	9·50	1·75
		s. Optd "Specimen"	60·00	

This stamp was formerly thought to have been issued on 16 December but it has been seen on a postcard clearly postmarked 15 December.

1904–10. *Chalk-surfaced paper (Nos. 71, 73/5 and 77) or ordinary paper (others).* Wmk Mult Crown CA. P 14.

64	**9**	½d. dull purple and green	4·50	60
		a. Chalk-surfaced paper	5·50	1·25
65		½d. green (1907)	1·75	1·00
66		1d. dull purple and carmine	6·00	1·25
		a. Chalk-surfaced paper	5·00	1·25
67		1d. carmine (1907)	4·25	30
68		2½d. dull purple and ultramarine	18·00	1·25
		a. Chalk-surfaced paper	12·00	4·50
69		2½d. blue (1907)	3·75	1·75
70	**10**	3d. dull purple and yellow	7·50	3·00
71		3d. purple/*yellow* (1909)	3·00	13·00
72		6d. dull purple and violet (1905)	17·00	20·00
		a. Chalk-surfaced paper	20·00	26·00
		ab. Dull purple and bright purple (1907)	8·50	28·00
73		6d. dull purple (1910)	60·00	75·00
74		1s. green and black (1905)	32·00	26·00
75		1s. black/*green* (1909)	4·75	8·00
76		5s. green and carmine (1905)	70·00	£170
77		5s. green and red/*yellow* (1907)	60·00	70·00
64/77		Set of 14	£225	£350
65s, 67s, 69s, 71s/2s, 72abs and 75s/7s		Optd "Specimen" *Set of 9*	£250	

Examples of Nos. 71/7 are known with a forged Castries postmark dated "JA 21 09".

12

13

14

15

16

(Typo D.L.R.)

1912–21. *Die I. Chalk-surfaced paper (3d. to 5s.).* Wmk Mult Crown CA. P 14.

78	**12**	½d. deep green	70	50
		a. Yellow-green (1916)	1·00	30
79		1d. carmine-red	1·90	10
		a. Scarlet (1916)	4·00	10
		b. Rose-red	7·00	1·00
80	**13**	2d. grey	1·50	4·25
		a. Slate-grey (1916)	17·00	13·00
81	**12**	2½d. ultramarine	3·75	2·75
		a. Bright blue	2·75	2·75
		b. Deep bright blue (1916)	11·00	10·00
82	**15**	3d. purple/*yellow*	1·25	2·25
		b. Die II. On pale yellow (1921)	12·00	42·00
		bw. Wmk inverted		
83	**14**	4d. black and red/*yellow*	1·00	2·00
		a. White back	70	1·50
		as. Optd "Specimen"	28·00	
84	**15**	6d. dull and bright purple	2·00	13·00
		a. Grey-purple and purple (1918)	16·00	17·00
85		1s. black/*green*	3·25	5·00
		a. On blue-green (olive back) (1918)	9·00	9·00
86		1s. orange-brown (1920)	11·00	45·00
87	**16**	2s.6d. black and red/*blue*	23·00	40·00
88	**15**	5s. green and red/*yellow*	24·00	75·00
78/88		Set of 11	65·00	£170
78s/88s		Optd "Specimen" *Set of 11*	£200	

WAR TAX
(17)

WAR TAX
(18)

1916 (1 June). *No. 79a optd locally with T* **17**.

89	**12**	1d. scarlet	11·00	11·00
		a. Opt double	£425	£425
		b. Carmine-red	60·00	42·00

For overprinting with Type **17** the sheets were vertically divided to the left of the centre margin and the top margin of the sheet was folded beneath the top row of stamps so that the marginal examples from this row show an inverted albino impression of the overprint in

the top margin.

Examples are also recorded of similar albino overprints in the right-hand and bottom margins but it is unclear if some sheets had all margins folded under before overprinting.

1916 (Sept). *No. 79a optd in London with T* **18**.

90	**12**	1d. scarlet	1·25	30
		s. Optd "Specimen"	42·00	

1921–30. *Die II. Chalk-surfaced paper (3d. (No. 100) to 5s.).* Wmk Mult Script CA. P 14.

91	**12**	½d. green	75	50
92		1d. rose-carmine	11·00	16·00
93		1d. deep brown (1922)	1·40	15
94	**14**	1½d. dull carmine (1922)	75	2·50
95	**13**	2d. slate-grey	75	15
96	**12**	2½d. bright blue	4·00	2·75
97		2½d. orange (1925)	11·00	50·00
98		2½d. dull blue (1926)	3·75	2·50
99	**15**	3d. bright blue (1922)	5·00	16·00
		a. Dull blue (1924)	2·75	11·00
100		3d. purple/*pale yellow* (1926)	1·25	12·00
		a. Deep purple/*pale yellow* (1930)	17·00	12·00
101	**14**	4d. black and red/*yellow* (1924)	1·25	2·50
102	**15**	6d. grey-purple and purple	2·00	4·75
103		1s. orange-brown	2·00	3·25
104	**16**	2s.6d. black and red/*blue* (1924)	18·00	27·00
105	**15**	5s. green and red/*pale yellow* (1923)	48·00	75·00
91/105		Set of 15	95·00	£190
91s/105s		Optd "Specimen" *Set of 15*	£300	

1935 (6 May). *Silver Jubilee. As Nos.* 91/4 *of Antigua.* P 13½×14.

109		½d. black and green	20	1·25
		f. Diagonal line by turret	32·00	
110		2d. ultramarine and grey	60	1·00
		f. Diagonal line by turret	50·00	
111		2½d. brown and deep blue	1·00	1·25
		a. Frame printed double, one albino	†	
		f. Diagonal line by turret	75·00	
		g. Dot to left of chapel	£110	
112		1s. slate and purple	8·50	10·00
		h. Dot by flagstaff	£300	
109/12		Set of 4	9·25	12·00
109s/12s		Perf "Specimen" *Set of 4*	90·00	

For illustrations of plate varieties see Omnibus section following Zanzibar.

19 Port Castries

20 Columbus Square, Castries (inscr "COLOMBUS SQUARE" in error)

21 Ventine Falls

22 Fort Rodney, Pigeon Island

23 Inniskilling monument

24 Government House

25 The Badge of the Colony

(Recess D.L.R.)

1936 (1 Mar–Apr). *T* **19/25**. Wmk Mult Script CA. P 14 or 13×12 (1s. and 10s.).

113	**19**	½d. black and bright green	30	50
		a. Perf 13×12 (8.4.36)	2·75	14·00
114	**20**	1d. black and brown	40	10
		a. Perf 13×12 (8.4.36)	3·50	2·75
115	**21**	1½d. black and scarlet	55	30
		a. Perf 12×13	8·00	2·25
116	**19**	2d. black and grey	50	20
117	**20**	2½d. black and blue	50	15
118	**21**	3d. black and dull green	1·25	70
119	**19**	4d. black and red-brown	50	1·00
120	**20**	6d. black and orange	1·00	1·00
121	**22**	1s. black and light blue	1·25	2·50
122	**23**	2s.6d. black and ultramarine	9·00	14·00

123	**24**	5s. black and violet....................		11·00	20·00
124	**25**	10s. black and carmine................		50·00	70·00
113/24 Set of 12				70·00	£100
113s/24s Perf "Specimen" Set of 12					£190

Examples of most values are known with a forged Castries postmark dated "1 MR 36".

1937 (12 May). *Coronation. As Nos. 95/7 of Antigua.* P 11×11½.

125		1d. violet...................................		30	35
126		1½d. carmine..............................		55	20
127		2½d. blue...................................		55	1·25
125/7 Set of 3				1·25	1·60
125s/7s Perf "Specimen" Set of 3				75·00	

26 King George VI   **27** Columbus Square

28 Government House   **29** The Pitons

30 *Lady Hawkins* loading bananas   **31** Device of St. Lucia

(Des E. Crafer (T **26**), H. Fleury (5s.). Recess Waterlow (½d. to 3½d., 8d., 3s., 5s., £1), D.L.R. (6d., 1s.) and B.W. (2s., 10s.))

1938 (22 Sept)–48.T **26/31**.Wmk Mult Script CA (sideways on 2s.).

128	**26**	½d. green (P 14½×14)...........		2·00	10
		a. Perf 12½ (1943)................		10	10
129		1d. violet (P 14½×14)...........		2·50	75
		a. Perf 12½ (1938)................		10	15
129b		1d. scarlet (P 12½) (1947)......		1·00	10
		c. Perf 14½×14 (1948)..........		10	10
130		1½d. scarlet (P 14½×14).........		2·00	40
		a. Perf 12½ (1943)................		1·25	1·00
131		2d. grey (P 14½×14).............		3·25	1·50
		a. Perf 12½ (1943)................		10	10
132		2½d. ultramarine (P 14½×14)....		4·25	15
		a. Perf 12½ (1943)................		10	10
132b		2½d. violet (P 12½) (1947).......		1·00	10
133		3d. orange (P 14½×14)...........		1·25	10
		a. Perf 12½ (1943)................		10	10
133b		3½d. ultramarine (P 12½) (1947).......		1·00	15
134	**27**	6d. claret (P 13½)................		6·00	75
		a. Carmine-lake (P 13½) (1945)...		3·00	35
		b. Perf 12. Claret (1948)......		2·50	1·75
134c	**26**	8d. brown (P 12½) (1946).......		3·50	30
135	**28**	1s. brown (P 13½)................		75	30
		a. Perf 12 (1948).................		75	30
136	**29**	2s. blue and purple (P 12).....		3·50	1·25
136a	**26**	3s. bright purple (P 12½) (1946)....		8·00	1·75
137	**30**	5s. black and mauve (P 12½)....		14·00	9·00
138	**31**	10s. black/yellow (P 12).........		8·50	9·00
141	**26**	£1 sepia (P 12½) (1946)........		11·00	8·00
128a/41 Set of 17				48·00	28·00
128s/41s Perf "Specimen" Set of 17				£350	

1946 (8 Oct). *Victory. As Nos. 110/11 of Antigua.*

142		1d. lilac....................................		10	10
143		3½d. blue.................................		10	10
142s/3s Perf "Specimen" Set of 2				70·00	

1948 (26 Nov). *Royal Silver Wedding. As Nos. 112/13 of Antigua.*

144		1d. scarlet................................		15	10
145		£1 purple-brown......................		16·00	35·00

(New Currency. 100 cents = 1 West Indian dollar)

32 King George VI   **33** Device of St. Lucia

(Recess Waterlow (**32**), B.W. (**33**))

1949 (1 Oct)–**50**. *Value in cents or dollars.* Wmk Mult Script CA. P 12½ (1c. to 16c.), 11×11½ (others).

146	**32**	1c. green.................................		25	10
		a. Perf 14 (1949).................		2·50	40
147		2c. magenta............................		1·00	10
		a. Perf 14½×14 (1949)........		2·50	1·00
148		3c. scarlet..............................		1·00	1·75
149		4c. grey.................................		75	10

		a. Perf 14½×14		†	£9000
150		5c. violet		1·25	10
151		6c. orange		75	2·75
152		7c. ultramarine		3·00	21
153		12c. claret		5·50	3·00
		a. Perf 14½×14 (1950).........		£550	£425
154		16c. brown		4·00	50
155	**33**	24c. light blue		50	10
156		48c. olive-green		1·50	1·25
157		$1.20 purple		2·25	8·00
158		$2.40 blue-green		3·25	17·00
159		$4.80 rose-carmine		9·00	18·00
146/159 Set of 14				30·00	48·00

Most examples of Nos. 146a and 147a were produced as coils, but a few sheets in these perforations were distributed and blocks of four are scarce.

No genuine mint example of No. 149a is known. Photographic forgeries do, however, exist.

1949 (10 Oct). *75th Anniv of U.P.U. As Nos. 114/17 of Antigua.*

160		5c. violet		15	60
161		6c. orange		1·60	2·00
		a. "A" of "CA" missing from wmk		£500	
162		12c. magenta		20	20
163		24c. blue-green		30	20
160/3 Set of 4				2·00	2·75

1951 (16 Feb). *Inauguration of B.W.I. University College. As Nos. 118/19 of Antigua.*

164		3c. black and scarlet		45	50
165		12c. black and deep carmine ...		65	50

34 Phoenix rising from Burning Buildings   **N E W 1951 CONSTITUTION** (**35**)

(Flames typo, rest recess B.W.)

1951 (19 June). *Reconstruction of Castries.* Wmk Mult Script CA. P 13½×13.

166	**34**	12c. red and blue		25	1·00

1951 (25 Sept). *New Constitution. Nos. 147, 149/50 and 153 optd with T **35** by Waterlow.* P 12½.

167	**32**	2c. magenta		20	80
168		4c. grey		20	60
169		5c. violet		20	80
170		12c. claret		75	60
167/70 Set of 4				1·25	2·50

POSTAGE DUE STAMPS

D 2   **D 3**

No. 4545 ST. LUCIA. 1d. POSTAGE DUE

D 1

(Type-set Government Printing Office)

1930. *Each stamp individually handstamped with different number. No gum. No wmk. Rough perf 12.*

(a) Horizontally laid paper.

D1	**D 1**	1d. black/blue		5·50	15·00
		b. Wide, wrong fount "No."		18·00	38·00
		c. Missing stop after "ST"		£150	£225
		d. Missing stop after "LUCIA" ...		£150	£225
		e. Handstamped number double		£700	
		f. Handstamped number triple.......			
		g. Incorrect number with correction above ..			
		h. Two different numbers on same stamp		£850	
		i. Number omitted		£2500	

(b) Wove paper.

D2	**D 1**	2d. black/yellow		13·00	40·00
		a. Imperf between (vert pair)........		£6000	
		b. Wide, wrong fount "No."		35·00	95·00
		c. Missing stop after "ST"		£300	£500
		d. Missing stop after "LUCIA" ...		£450	
		g. Incorrect number with correction above		£1200	
		h. Two different numbers on same stamp		£1400	

Nos. D1/2 were produced in sheets of 60 (6×10) usually with imperforate outer edges at the top, at right and at foot. It would appear that the sheets were bound into books from which they could be detached

using the line of perforations along the left-hand side.

There were three printings of each value, utilising the same basic type. The paper for the first two printings of the 1d. and the first printing of the 2d. showed papermaker's watermarks, that for the 1d. being "KINGSCLERE" in double-lined capitals below a crown with parts occurring on between ten and fourteen stamps in each sheet.

Details of the printings are as follows:

1d.

First printing. On paper with sheet watermark. Shows wide fount "No." on R. 10/3–6 and missing stop after "ST" on R. 5/3.

Second printing. On paper with sheet watermark. Shows wide fount "No." on R. 10/2–6 and missing stop after "ST" on R. 5/3. The first two printings of the 1d. were numbered together as 1 to 12000.

Third printing. On paper without watermark. Shows wide fount "No." on all stamps in Row 10. Missing stop after "ST" on R. 5/3 corrected, but missing stop after "LUCIA" occurs on R. 9/2. Numbered 12001 to 24000.

2d.

First printing. On paper with sheet watermark. Shows wide fount "No." on R. 10/2–6 and missing stop after "ST" on R. 5/3 (as 1d. second printing). Numbered 1 to 4800.

Second printing. On paper without watermark. Shows wide fount "No." on all stamps in Row 10. Missing stop after "ST" corrected (printed *before* 1d. third printing). Numbered 4801 to 14820.

Third printing. On paper without watermark. Shows wide fount "No." on all stamps in Row 10. Missing stop after "ST" corrected, but missing stop after "LUCIA" occurs on R. 4/4 and 9/2 (printed *after* 1d. third printing). Numbered 14821 to 16800.

The handstamped numbers were applied at the Post Office using a numbering machine. Mistakes in the numbering on the 1d. were sometimes partially erased and then corrected with a second strike, either of the complete number or of incorrect digits, using a machine with a smaller font.

D 2   **D 3**

(Typo D.L.R.)

1933–47. Wmk Mult Script CA. P 14.

D3	**D 2**	1d. black..............................		4·75	6·00
D4		2d. black..............................		19·00	8·00
D5		4d. black (28.6.47)...............		5·50	45·00
D6		8d. black (28.6.47)...............		5·50	55·00
D3/6 Set of 4				32·00	£100
D3s/6s Perf "Specimen" Set of 4				£130	

1949 (1 Oct)–**52**. *Value in cents.* Typo. Wmk Mult Script CA. P 14.

D7	**D 3**	2c. black..............................		1·75	27·00
		a. Chalk-surfaced paper (27.11.52)...............		10	8·50
		ab. Error. Crown missing, W 9a...		£130	
		ac. Error. St. Edward's Crown, W 9b..		32·00	
D8		4c. black..............................		3·50	21·00
		a. Chalk-surfaced paper (27.11.52)...............		50	11·00
		ab. Error. Crown missing, W 9a..		£180	
		ac. Error. St. Edward's Crown, W 9b..		45·00	
D9		8c. black..............................		3·25	25·00
		a. Chalk-surfaced paper (27.11.52)...............		3·00	38·00
		ac. Error. St. Edward's Crown, W 9b..		£325	
D10		16c. black.............................		15·00	65·00
		a. Chalk-surfaced paper (27.11.52)...............		4·50	50·00
		ac. Error. St. Edward's Crown, W 9b..		£450	
D7/10 Set of 4				21·00	£120
D7a/10a Set of 4				7·25	95·00

The 2c. and 4c. watermarked Block CA were issued in 1965.

POSTAL FISCAL STAMPS

Nos. F1/28 were authorised for postal use from 14 April 1885.

CANCELLATIONS. Many used examples of the Postal Fiscal stamps have had previous pen cancellations removed before being used postally.

SHILLING STAMP (F **1**)	**One Penny Stamp** (F **2**)	**HALFPENNY Stamp** (F **3**)

1881. Wmk Crown CC. P 14.

*(a) Surch as Type F **1**.*

F1	**1**	ONE PENNY STAMP, black (C.)...........................		65·00	48·00
		a. Surch inverted.....................		£700	£700
		b. Surch double......................		£650	£700
F2		FOUR PENNY STAMP, yellow...		£100	70·00
		a. Bisected (2d.) (on cover)...........		†	
F3		SIX PENCE STAMP, mauve.....		£170	£130
F4		SHILLING STAMP, orange		£100	70·00
		a. "SHILEING"......................		£650	£600
		b. "SHILDING"......................		£650	£600

*(b) Surch as Type F **2**.*

F7	**1**	One Penny Stamp, black (R.)...		65·00	50·00
		a. Surch double......................		£700	
		w. Wmk inverted			
F8		Four Pence Stamp, yellow........		95·00	65·00
		x. Wmk reversed			
F9		Six Pence Stamp, mauve........		£100	65·00
F10		Shilling Stamp, orange..........		£110	85·00

*(c) Surch as Type F **3**.*

F11	**1**	Halfpenny Stamp, green.........		65·00	55·00
		a. "Stamp" double.................		£450	£450

NO. Normal   **No.** Wide fount

F12		One Shilling Stamp, orange (wmk Crown CA)......................	£110	75·00
		a. "Stamp" double......................	£450	£500

A fiscally used example of No. F1b is known showing one red and one black surcharge.

FOUR PENCE
REVENUE Revenue REVENUE
(F **4**)　　　(F **5**)　　　(F **6**)

1882. *Surch as Type F* **4**. *Wmk Crown CA*.

(a) P 14.

F13	**1**	1d. black (C.)......................	45·00	24·00
F14		2d. pale blue......................	30·00	11·00
F15		3d. deep blue (C.)......................	85·00	48·00
F16		4d. yellow......................	35·00	4·00
F17		6d. mauve......................	60·00	28·00

(b) P 12.

F18	**1**	1d. black (C.)......................	45·00	25·00
F19		3d. deep blue (C.)......................	65·00	20·00
F20		1s. orange......................	65·00	13·00

The 1d. and 2d. exist as imperforate proofs.

1883. Nos. 25, 26, 30 and 32 optd locally as Type F **5**.

(a) Word 11 mm long.

F21		1d. black (C.)......................	35·00	40·00
		a. Opt inverted......................		
		b. Opt double......................	£275	£350

(b) Word 13 mm

F22		1d. black (C.)......................	—	65·00

(c) Word 15½ mm

F23		½d. green......................	—	60·00
		a. "Revenue" double......................		£275
F24		1d. black (C.)......................	35·00	10·00
		a. "Revenue" double......................	£150	
		b. "Revenue" triple......................	£300	
		c. "Revenue" double, one inverted......	£275	£300
F25		1d. rose (No. 32)......................	—	65·00
F26		4d. yellow......................	—	85·00

1884–85. *Optd with Type F* **6**. *Wmk Crown CA.* P 14.

F27	**5**	1d. slate (C.)......................	25·00	16·00
F28		1d. dull mauve (Die I) (1885).........	25·00	8·50

No. F27 exists as an imperforate proof.

St. Vincent

Although postal markings for St. Vincent are recorded as early as 1793 it was not until 1852 that the British G.P.O. opened a branch office at Kingstown, the island's capital.

The stamps of Great Britain were used between May 1858 and the end of April 1860. From 1 May in that year the local authorities assumed responsibility for the postal services and fell back on the use of No. CC 1 until the introduction of St. Vincent stamps in 1861.

KINGSTOWN

CROWNED-CIRCLE HANDSTAMPS

CC **1**

CC1 CC **1** ST. *VINCENT* (R.) (30.1.1852)... Price on cover £950

Stamps of GREAT BRITAIN *cancelled* "A 10" *as Type Z* **1** *of Jamaica.*

1858–60.

Z1	1d. rose-red (1857), *perf* 14......................		£650
Z2	2d. blue (1855)......................		
Z3	4d. rose (1857)......................		£400
Z4	6d. lilac (1856)......................		£300
Z5	1s. green (1856)......................		£1600

PRICES FOR STAMPS ON COVER TO 1945

No. 1	from × 50
No. 2	from × 15
Nos. 4/5	from × 40
Nos. 6/7	from × 20
No. 8	—
No. 9	from × 12
No. 10	—
No. 11	from × 15
Nos. 12/13	from × 20
No. 14	from × 10
No. 15	from × 50
No. 16	from × 15
No. 17	from × 10
No. 18	from × 20
No. 19	from × 20
Nos. 20/21	from × 7
No. 22	from × 100
Nos. 149/59	from × 2

PRICES FOR STAMPS ON COVER TO 1945

No. 23	from × 25
No. 24	from × 15
No. 25	from × 25
No. 26	
No. 26a	from × 50
Nos. 27/28	—
No. 29	from × 100
Nos. 30/31	from × 30
Nos. 32/34	—
No. 35	from × 30
No. 36/7	from × 10
No. 38	from × 50
Nos. 39/40	from × 100
No. 41	from × 25
Nos. 42/5	from × 8
No. 46	from × 15
Nos. 47/54	from × 4
Nos. 55/8	from × 8
No. 59	from × 10
No. 60	from × 6
Nos. 61/3	from × 8
Nos. 67/75	from × 3
Nos. 76/84	from × 2
Nos. 85/92	from × 3
No. 93	—
Nos. 94/8	from × 3
Nos. 99/107	from × 2
Nos. 108/19	from × 3
No. 120	—
No. 121	from × 3
No. 122	from × 5
No. 123	—
No. 124	from × 5
Nos. 126/9	from × 10
Nos. 131/45	from × 3
Nos. 146/8	from × 6
Nos. 149/59	from × 2

CROWN COLONY

1　　　　(2)　　　3

(T **1**, **3** *and* **7** *recess P.B*)

1861 (8 May). No Wmk. Rough to intermediate perf 14 to 16.

1	**1**	1d. rose-red......................	48·00	14·00
		a. Imperf vert (horiz pair)............	£350	
		b. Imperf (pair)......................	£275	
2		6d. deep yellow-green......................	£7500	£200

The perforations on the 1d. are usually rough, but individual examples can be found on which some, or all, of the holes have the appearance of the intermediate perforations. All examples of the 6d. show intermediate perforations.

Imperforate examples, possibly proofs, exist of the 1d. rose-red and 6d. deep green handstamped "CANCELLED" in oval of bars (see note on Perkins Bacon "CANCELLED" in Catalogue Introduction). (*Price* 1d. £7500, 6d. £8500)

1862 (Sept). No wmk. Rough perf 14 to 16.

4	**1**	6d. deep green......................	55·00	19·00
		a. Imperf between (horiz pair)......	£10000	£11000
		b. Imperf (pair)......................	£1000	

1863–68. No wmk.

(a) P 11 to 12½.

5	**1**	1d. rose-red (3.63)......................	40·00	16·00
6		4d. deep blue (*shades*) (1866).........	£275	£110
		a. Imperf between (horiz pair)......	†	
7		6d. deep green (7.68)......................	£225	75·00
8		1s. slate-grey (8.66)......................	£2500	£900

(b) P 14 to 16.

9	**1**	1s. slate-grey (*shades*) (8.66).........	£350	£140

(c) P 11 to 12½×14 to 16.

10	**1**	1d. rose-red (1866)......................	£5500	£1100
11		1s. slate-grey (*shades*) (8.66).........	£275	£120

1869 (Apr–Sep). *Colours changed.* No wmk. P 11 to 12½.

12	**1**	4d. yellow (9.69)......................	£350	£160
13		1s. indigo......................	£375	90·00
14		1s. brown (9.69)......................	£500	£160

1871 (Apr). Wmk Small Star, W w **2**. Rough perf 14 to 16.

15	**1**	1d. black......................	55·00	12·00
		a. Imperf between (vert pair)........	£14000	
16		6d. deep green......................	£325	70·00
		a. Wmk sideways......................	—	85·00

1872 (June). *Colour changed.* W w **2** (sideways). P 11 to 12½.

17	**1**	1s. deep rose-red......................	£750	£140

1872–75. W w **2** (sideways).

(a) Perf about 15.

18	**1**	1d. black (*shades*) (11.72)............	55·00	10·00
		a. Wmk upright......................	65·00	11·00
19		6d. dull blue-green (*shades*) (1873)...	£2000	50·00
		b. *Deep blue-green* (1875)......	£1500	48·00
		c. Wmk upright......................	£2250	

(b) P 11 to 12½×15.

20	**1**	1s. lilac-rose (1873)......................	£5500	£350

1875. *Colour changed.* W w **2** (sideways). P 11 to 12½.

21		1s. claret......................	£600	£250

1875–78. W w **2** (sideways).

(a) P 11 to 12½×15.

22	**1**	1d. black (*shades*) (4.75)......................	80·00	10·00
		a. Imperf between (horiz pair)......	†	£20000
		b. Wmk upright......................	£150	50·00
23		6d. pale green (1877)......................	£650	50·00
24		1s. vermilion (2.77)......................	£950	85·00
		a. Imperf vert (horiz pair)............		

(b) P 11 to 12½.

25	**1**	4d. deep blue (7.77)......................	£500	90·00

(c) Perf about 15.

26	**1**	6d. pale green (3.77)......................	£1600	£450
		a. Wmk upright. Lt yellow-green (1878)......	£700	26·00
27		1s. vermilion (1878?)......................	†	£40000

Only two examples of No. 27 have been recorded. The 1s vermilion is also known apparently imperforate and used.

1880 (May). *No. 19b divided vertically by a line of perforation gauging* 12, *and surch locally with T* **2** *in red*.

28	**1**	1d. on half 6d. deep blue-green......................	£500	£350
		a. Unsevered pair......................	£2000	£1200

1880 (June). W w **2** (sideways on 1d., 6d. and 1s.). P 11 to 12½.

29	**1**	1d. olive-green......................	£160	4·50
30		6d. bright green......................	£450	70·00
31		1s. bright vermilion......................	£750	55·00
		a. Imperf between (horiz pair)......	£20000	
32	**3**	5s. rose-red......................	£1000	£1400
		a. Imperf......................	£6000	

d
1
2
(4)

ONE PENNY
(5)

4d
(6)

1881. *Nos. 30/1 surch locally. No. 33 is divided vertically as No. 28.*

33	**4**	½d. on half 6d. bright green (R.) (1.9)........	£160	£170
		a. Unsevered pair......................	£450	£475
		b. Fraction bar omitted (with and without bar)........	£4250	£5000
34	**5**	1d. on 6d. bright green (30.11)......	£450	£350
35	**6**	4d. on 1s. bright vermilion (28.11).....	£1600	£800

No. 33 exists showing the "1" of "½" with a straight serif. Some examples come from a constant variety on R. 6/20, but others are the result of faulty type.

It is believed that Type **4** was applied as a setting of 36 (6×6) surcharges repeated three times on each sheet across rows 1 to 9. The missing fraction bar occurs on R. 6/3 of the setting.

The tenth vertical row of stamps appears to have been surcharged from a separate setting of 12 (2×6) on which the constant "straight serif" flaw occurs on the bottom right half-stamp.

Three unused single copies of No. 33 are known with the surcharge omitted.

It is believed that Nos. 34 and 35 were surcharged in settings of 30 (10×3).

No. 34 was only on sale between the 30 November and 3 December when supplies of No. 37 became available.

7　　　2½ PENCE　　　1d 2½ PENCE
(8)　　　(9)

1881 (3 Dec). W w **2**. P 11 to 12½.

36	**7**	½d. orange (*shades*)......................	7·00	4·50
37	**1**	1d. drab (*shades*)......................	£700	10·00
38		4d. bright blue......................	£1200	£120
		a. Imperf between (horiz pair)......		

(Recess D.L.R. from Perkins, Bacon plates)

1882 (Nov)–**83**. *No. 40 is surch with T* **8**. *Wmk Crown CA.* P 14.

39	**1**	1d. drab......................	55·00	2·50
		x. Wmk reversed......................	85·00	10·00
40		2½d. on 1d. lake (1883)......................	19·00	1·00
		w. Wmk inverted......................	60·00	10·00
		x. Wmk reversed......................	28·00	5·00
		y. Wmk inverted and reversed......		
41		4d. ultramarine......................	£650	75·00
		a. *Dull ultramarine* (wmk reversed)......................	£1000	£350
		w. Wmk inverted......................		
		x. Wmk reversed......................	£450	40·00
		y. Wmk inverted and reversed......		

1883–84. Wmk Crown CA. P 12.

42	**7**	½d. green (1884)......................	80·00	26·00
		x. Wmk reversed......................		£150
43	**1**	4d. ultramarine-blue......................	£750	40·00
		a. *Grey-blue*......................	£2000	£250
		w. Wmk inverted......................		
		x. Wmk reversed......................	£450	22·00
		y. Wmk inverted and reversed......		
44		6d. bright green......................	£150	£300
		x. Wmk reversed......................	£325	
45		1s. orange-vermilion......................	£130	60·00

333

		x. Wmk reversed	£275	

The ½d. orange, 1d. rose-red, 1d. milky blue (without surcharge) and 5s. carmine-lake which were formerly listed are now considered to be colour trials. They are, however, of great interest (*Prices un.* ½d. £950, 1d. red £1000, 1d. blue £1300, 5s. £2500).

1885 (Mar). *No. 40 further surch locally as in T* **9**.

46	1	1d. on 2½d. on 1d. lake	22·00	18·00
		w. Wmk inverted		
		x. Wmk reversed	25·00	20·00

Stamps with three cancelling bars instead of two are considered to be proofs.

1885–93. *No. 49 is surch with T* **8**. Wmk Crown CA. P 14.

47	7	½d. green	1·00	60
		a. Deep green	2·50	60
		w. Wmk inverted	35·00	15·00
		x. Wmk reversed	15·00	
48	1	1d. rose-red	3·00	1·00
		a. Rose (1886)	4·75	1·75
		b. Red (1887)	1·60	85
		c. Carmine-red (1889)	24·00	3·75
		w. Wmk inverted		
		x. Wmk reversed	5·00	1·50
49		2½d. on 1d. milky blue (1889)	23·00	5·50
		x. Wmk reversed		
50		4d. red-brown	£950	22·00
		x. Wmk reversed	—	75·00
51		4d. purple-brown (1886)	70·00	75
		a. Chocolate (1887)	70·00	1·40
		w. Wmk inverted		
		x. Wmk reversed	£150	10·00
		y. Wmk inverted and reversed...		
52		6d. violet (1888)	£150	£170
		w. Wmk inverted	£170	£200
		ws. Optd "Specimen"	75·00	
		x. Wmk reversed	£500	
53	3	5s. lake (1888)	27·00	50·00
		a. Printed both sides.................	£6000	
		b. Brown-lake (1893).................	30·00	50·00
		x. Wmk reversed	£400	
		49s, 51s/2s Optd "Specimen" *Set of 3*	£180	

2½d. (10)	**5 PENCE** (11)

1890 (Aug). *No. 51a surch locally with T* **10**.

54	1	2½d. on 4d. chocolate	80·00	£110
		a. No fraction bar (R. 1/7, 2/4) .	£400	£475

1890–93. *No. 55 is surch with T* **8**. *Colours changed.* Wmk Crown CA. P 14.

55	1	2½d. on 1d. grey-blue (1890)	20·00	55
		a. Blue (1893)	1·50	35
		w. Wmk inverted		
		x. Wmk reversed		
56		4d. yellow (1893)........................	1·60	8·50
		s. Optd "Specimen"	30·00	
57		6d. dull purple (1891)	2·25	15·00
58		1s. orange (1891)	5·50	11·00
		a. Red-orange (1892)	11·00	17·00

1892 (Nov). *No. 51a surch locally with T* **11**, *in purple.*

59	1	5d. on 4d. chocolate	22·00	35·00
		s. Optd "Specimen"	40·00	
		sa. Error. "Spicemen"	£1200	

Some letters are known double due to loose type, the best known being the first "E", but they are not constant.

FIVE PENCE (12)	**St VINCENT** ½d **13**	**St VINCENT** 1s **14**

Short "F" (R. 5/1)

1893–94. *Surch with T* **12**. Wmk Crown CA. P 14.

60	1	5d. on 6d. carmine-lake................	20·00	30·00
		a. Deep lake (1893)	1·00	1·75
		b. Lake (1894)	1·75	4·25
		c. Surch double	£5500	£3500
		d. Short "F"	30·00	40·00
		s. Optd "Specimen"	45·00	

(Recess D.L.R.)

1897 (13 July). *New values.* Wmk Crown CA. P 14.

61	1	2½d. blue	5·00	1·75
62		5d. sepia	5·50	23·00
		61s/2s Optd "Specimen" *Set of 2*	60·00	

1897 (6 Oct). *Surch as T* **12**. Wmk Crown CA. P 14.

63	1	3d. on 1d. mauve	5·00	18·00
		a. Red-mauve	10·00	30·00
		s. Optd "Specimen"	40·00	

(Typo D.L.R.)

1899 (1 Jan). Wmk Crown CA. P 14.

67	13	½d. dull mauve and green	2·75	2·50
68		1d. dull mauve and carmine	4·50	1·25
		w. Wmk inverted	£250	

69		2½d. dull mauve and blue	4·00	2·00
70		3d. dull mauve and olive	4·00	13·00
71		4d. dull mauve and orange	4·00	17·00
72		5d. dull mauve and black	7·00	13·00
73		6d. dull mauve and brown	13·00	38·00
74	14	1s. green and carmine	13·00	48·00
75		5s. green and blue	80·00	£140
		67/75 *Set of 9*	£120	£250
		67s/75s Optd "Specimen" *Set of 9*	£170	

St VINCENT ½d **15**	**St VINCENT** 2d **16**

(Typo D.L.R.)

1902. Wmk Crown CA. P 14.

76	15	½d. dull purple and green..............	3·50	70
77		1d. dull purple and carmine	4·25	30
78	16	2d. dull purple and black	3·25	2·75
79	15	2½d. dull purple and blue	5·00	3·50
80		3d. dull purple and olive	5·00	3·75
81		6d. dull purple and brown	11·00	30·00
82	16	1s. green and carmine	24·00	55·00
83	15	2s. green and violet	25·00	55·00
84	16	5s. green and blue	70·00	£120
		76/84 *Set of 9*	£130	£225
		76s/84s Optd "Specimen" *Set of 9*	£225	

1904–11. *Ordinary paper (½d., 1d., 1s.) or chalk-surfaced paper (others).* Wmk Mult Crown CA. P 14.

85	15	½d. dull purple and green (1905).....	7·50	4·00
		a. Chalk-surfaced paper	1·25	1·25
86		1d. dull purple and carmine	24·00	1·50
		a. Chalk-surfaced paper	21·00	1·50
88		2½d. dull purple and blue (1906).......	16·00	42·00
89		6d. dull purple and brown (1905)....	16·00	42·00
90	16	1s. green and carmine (1906).......	19·00	48·00
		a. Chalk-surfaced paper	11·00	55·00
91	15	2s. purple and bright blue/*blue* (3.09?)	23·00	42·00
92	16	5s. green and red/*yellow* (3.09?)	17·00	50·00
93		£1 purple and black/*red* (22.7.11) ..	£275	£325
		85/93 *Set of 8*	£350	£475
		91s/3s Optd "Specimen" *Set of 3*	£190	

Examples of most values are known showing a forged Kingstown postmark code letter "O", dated "JA 7 10" or a forged Calliaqua postmark dated "SP 20 09". Both have also been seen on some values of the 1899 and 1902 issues.

St VINCENT 1d **17**	**St VINCENT** 1d **18**

(Recess D.L.R.)

1907–08. Wmk Mult Crown CA. P 14.

94	17	½d. green (2.7.07)	3·25	2·25
95		1d. carmine (26.4.07)..................	3·50	15
96		2d. orange (5.08).......................	1·50	6·50
97		2½d. blue (8.07)..........................	28·00	8·50
98		3d. violet (1.6.07)	8·00	15·00
		94/8 *Set of 5*	40·00	29·00
		94s/8s Optd "Specimen" *Set of 5*	£110	

1909. *No dot below "d".* Wmk Mult Crown CA. P 14.

99	18	1d. carmine (3.09)......................	1·25	30
100		6d. dull purple (16.1.09)	5·50	32·00
101		1s. black/*green* (16.1.09)	4·25	8·50
		99/101 *Set of 3*	10·00	38·00
		99s/101s Optd "Specimen" *Set of 3*	70·00	

1909 (Nov)–**11**. *T* **18**, *redrawn (dot below "d", as in T* **17**). Wmk Mult Crown CA. P 14.

102	18	½d. green (31.10.10)....................	1·50	60
		w. Wmk inverted	£100	
103		1d. carmine..............................	1·00	40
104		2d. grey (3.8.11)	4·00	8·50
105		2½d. ultramarine (25.7.10)	8·00	3·50
106		3d. purple/*yellow*....................	2·50	8·00
107		6d. dull purple	10·00	5·00
		102/7 *Set of 6*	25·00	23·00
		102s, 104s/6s Optd "Specimen" *Set of 4*	85·00	

St VINCENT ½d **19**	**ONE PENNY.** (20)

(Recess D.L.R.)

1913 (1 Jan)–**17**. Wmk Mult Crown CA. P 14.

108	19	½d. green...............................	75	20
109		1d. red	80	75
		a. Rose-red	1·00	75
		b. Scarlet (1.17)	14·00	5·00
		w. Wmk inverted	90·00	
		y. Wmk inverted and reversed ..	90·00	
110		2d. grey	7·00	30·00
		a. Slate	3·00	30·00
111		2½d. ultramarine	50	75
		x. Wmk reversed	£140	
112		3d. purple/*yellow*	80	5·00
		a. On lemon	2·75	12·00
		aw. Wmk inverted	£100	

		ax. Wmk reversed......................	£100	
		b. On pale yellow	2·50	9·00
113		4d. red/yellow	80	2·00
114		5d. olive-green (7.11.13)...........	2·25	14·00
		x. Wmk reversed......................	£110	
115		6d. claret...............................	2·00	4·50
116		1s. black/*green*	1·50	3·75
117		1s. bistre (1.5.14)	4·00	24·00
118	18	2s. blue and purple	4·75	27·00
119		5s. carmine and myrtle	13·00	50·00
120		£1 mauve and black	85·00	£160
		108/20 *Set of 13*	£110	£275
		108s/20s Optd "Specimen" *Set of 13*	£250	

Nos. 118/20 are from new centre and frame dies, the motto "PAX ET JUSTITIA" being slightly over 7 mm long, as against just over 8 mm in Nos. 99 to 107. Nos. 139/41 are also from the new dies. Examples of several values are known showing part strikes of the forged postmarks mentioned below Nos. 85/93.

1915 (30 Jan). *No. 116 surch locally with T* **20**.

121	19	1d. on 1s. black/*green* (R.)	7·50	28·00
		a. "ONE" omitted	£1000	£850
		b. "ONE" double......................	£650	
		c. "PENNY" and bar double.......	£650	£650

The two lines of the surcharge were applied in separate operations, so that the spacing between them varies considerably.

WAR STAMP. (21)	**WAR STAMP.** (22)	**WAR STAMP** (24)

1916 (June). *No. 109 optd locally with T* **21**.

(a) First and second settings; words 2 to 2½ mm apart.

122	19	1d. red	7·50	10·00
		a. Opt double	£160	£160
		b. Comma for stop	8·50	17·00
		w. Wmk inverted		

In the first printing every second stamp has the comma for stop. The second printing of this setting has full stops only. These two printings can therefore only be distinguished in blocks or pairs.

(b) Third setting; words only 1½ mm apart.

123	19	1d. red	85·00	
		a. Opt double	£1100	

Stamps of the first setting are offered as this rare one. Care must be taken to see that the distance between the lines is not over 1½ mm.

(c) Fourth setting; optd with T **22**. *Words 3½ mm apart.*

124	19	1d. carmine-red	3·00	15·00
		a. Opt double	£225	
		w. Wmk inverted		
		y. Wmk inverted and reversed.......		

1916 (Aug)–**18**. *T* **19**, *from new printings, optd with T* **24** *by De La Rue.*

126		1d. carmine-red	30	80
		s. Optd "Specimen"	60·00	
		w. Wmk inverted		
		x. Wmk reversed.....................		
		y. Wmk inverted and reversed	£100	
127		1d. pale rose-red	80	80
		w. Wmk inverted	60·00	
		x. Wmk reversed.....................		
128		1d. deep rose-red	1·00	80
129		1d. pale scarlet (1918)	60	1·25

1921–32. Wmk Mult Script CA. P 14.

131	19	½d. green (3.21).......................	1·75	30
132		1d. carmine (6.21)	1·00	80
		a. Red	2·50	15
132b		1½d. brown (1.12.32)	3·25	15
133		2d. grey (3.22)	2·50	60
133a		2½d. bright blue (12.25)	1·25	1·50
134		3d. bright blue (3.22)................	1·00	6·00
135		3d. purple/*yellow* (1.12.26)	1·00	1·50
135a		4d. red/*yellow* (9.30)..............	1·75	6·00
136		5d. sage-green (8.3.24)	1·00	6·50
137		6d. claret (1.11.27)	1·50	3·50
138		1s. bistre-brown (9.21)..............	6·00	25·00
		a. Ochre (1927)	3·25	17·00
139	18	2s. blue and purple (8.3.24)	7·50	13·00
140		5s. carmine and myrtle (8.3.24)..	18·00	32·00
141		£1 mauve and black (9.28)	90·00	£130
		131/41 *Set of 14*	£120	£200
		131s/41s Optd or Perf (1½d., 4d., £1) "Specimen" *Set of 14*	£300	

Examples of Nos. 140/1 are known with forged postmarks, including part strikes of those mentioned above, and others from Kingstown dated "6 MY 35" and "16 MY 41".

1935 (6 May). *Silver Jubilee. As Nos. 91/4 of Antigua, but ptd by Waterlow.* P 11×12.

142		1d. deep blue and scarlet	40	3·00
143		1½d. ultramarine and grey	1·00	3·75
144		2½d. brown and deep blue	1·90	3·75
145		1s. slate and purple	2·25	3·75
		l. Kite and horizontal log	£375	
		142/5 *Set of 4*	5·00	13·00
		142s/5s Perf "Specimen" *Set of 4*	90·00	

For illustration of plate variety see Omnibus section following Zanzibar.

1937 (12 May). *Coronation. As Nos. 95/7 of Antigua.* P 11×11½.

146		1d. violet	35	1·25
147		1½d. carmine	40	1·25
148		2½d. blue	45	2·25
		146/8 *Set of 3*	1·10	4·25
		146s/8s Perf "Specimen" *Set of 3*	70·00	

25

26 Young's Island and Fort Duvernette

27 Kingstown and Fort Charlotte

28 Bathing Beach at Villa

29 Victoria Park, Kingstown

NEW
CONSTITUTION
1951
(29a)

(Recess B.W.)

1938 (11 Mar)–47. Wmk Mult Script CA. P 12.

149	25	½d. blue and green	20	10
150	26	1d. blue and lake-brown	20	10
151	27	1½d. green and scarlet	20	10
152	25	2d. green and black	40	35
153	28	2½d. blue-black and blue-green	20	40
153a	29	2½d. green and purple-brown (14.1.47)	40	20
154	25	3d. orange and purple	20	10
154a	28	3½d. blue-black and blue-green (1.4.47)	40	2·50
155	25	6d. black and lake	1·00	40
156	29	1s. purple and green	1·00	80
157	25	2s. blue and purple	6·00	75
157a		2s.6d. red-brown and blue (14.1.47)	1·25	3·50
158		5s. scarlet and deep green	10·00	2·50
158a		10s. violet and brown (14.1.47)	4·00	9·00
		aw. Wmk inverted	£5000	£2000
159		£1 purple and black	18·00	15·00
149/59 Set of 15			40·00	32·00
149s/59s Perf "Specimen" Set of 15			£275	

1946 (15 Oct). Victory. As Nos. 110/11 of Antigua.

160	1½d. carmine	10	10
161	3½d. blue	10	10
160s/1s Perf "Specimen" Set of 2		70·00	

1948 (30 Nov). Royal Silver Wedding. As Nos. 112/13 of Antigua.

162	1½d. scarlet	10	10
163	£1 bright purple	18·00	22·00

No. 163 was originally printed in black, but the supply of these was stolen in transit. A few archive examples exist, some perforated "Specimen".

(New Currency. 100 cents = 1 West Indian dollar)

1949 (26 Mar)–52. Value in cents and dollars. Wmk Mult Script CA. P 12.

164	25	1c. blue and green	20	1·75
164a		1c. green and black (10.6.52)	30	2·50
165	26	2c. blue and lake-brown	15	50
166	27	3c. green and scarlet	50	1·00
166a	25	3c. orange and purple (10.6.52)	30	2·50
167		4c. green and black	35	20
167a		4c. blue and green (10.6.52)	30	20
168	29	5c. green and purple-brown	15	10
169	25	6c. orange and green	50	1·25
169a	27	6c. green and scarlet (10.6.52)	30	2·25
170	28	7c. blue-black and blue-green	5·50	1·50
170a		10c. blue-black and blue-green (10.6.52)	50	20
171	25	12c. black and lake	35	15
172	29	24c. green and green	35	55
173	25	48c. blue and purple	2·75	3·00
174		60c. red-brown and blue	2·00	4·00
175		$1.20, scarlet and deep green	4·25	4·25
176		$2.40, violet and brown	6·00	10·00
177		$4.80, purple and black	12·00	20·00
164/77 Set of 19			32·00	48·00

1949 (10 Oct). 75th Anniv of U.P.U. As Nos. 114/17 of Antigua.

178	5c. blue	20	20
179	6c. purple	1·25	2·25
180	12c. magenta	20	2·25
181	24c. blue-green	20	1·00
178/81 Set of 4		1·60	5·25

1951 (16 Feb). Inauguration of B.W.I. University College. As Nos. 118/19 of Antigua.

182	3c. deep green and scarlet	30	65
183	12c. black and purple	30	1·75

1951 (21 Sept). New Constitution. Optd with T 29a by B.W.

184	27	3c. green and scarlet	20	1·75
185	25	4c. green and black	20	60
186	29	5c. green and purple-brown	20	60
187	25	12c. black and lake	1·25	1·25
184/7 Set of 4			1·60	3·75

Samoa
see after New Zealand

Sarawak

Sarawak was placed under British protection in 1888. It was ceded to Great Britain on 1 July 1946 and was administered as a Crown Colony until 16 September 1963 when it became a state of the Federation of Malaysia.

From 1859 letters from Sarawak to overseas addresses, other than to other British possessions in Borneo and Singapore, were franked by stamps of INDIA and, after 1867, STRAITS SETTLEMENTS, a stock of which was kept by the Sarawak Post Office. The stamps of Sarawak continued to have this limited validity until 1 July 1897 when the country joined the U.P.U.

PRICES FOR STAMPS ON COVER TO 1945	
No. 1	—
Nos. 2/7	from × 50
Nos. 8/21	from × 8
Nos. 22/6	from × 6
No. 27	from × 40
Nos. 28/35	from × 6
Nos. 36/47	from × 8
No. 48	†
No. 49	from × 10
Nos. 50/61	from × 6
No. 62	†
Nos. 63/71	from × 4
Nos. 72/3	from × 8
Nos. 74/5	—
Nos. 76/90	from × 7
Nos. 91/105	from × 5
Nos. 106/25	from × 3
Nos. 126/45	from × 2

BROOKE FAMILY ADMINISTRATION

Sir James Brooke. 1842–11 June 1868

Sir Charles Brooke. 11 June 1868–17 May 1917

UNUSED PRICES. Nos. 1/7, 27 and 32/5 in unused condition are normally found to be without gum. Prices in the unused column are for stamps in this state. Examples of these issues with original gum are worth considerably more.

1 Sir James Brooke

2 Sir Charles Brooke

The initials in the corners of T **1** and **2** stand for "James (Charles) Brooke, Rajah (of) Sarawak".

(T **1** and **2**. Die eng Wm. Ridgeway. Litho Maclure, Macdonald & Co, Glasgow)

1869 (1 Mar). P 11.

1	1	3c. brown/yellow	48·00	£225

Similar stamps are known printed from the engraved die in orange-brown on orange surface-coloured paper, and perf 12. These are specimens submitted to the Sarawak authorities and exist both with and without obliterations.

1871 (1 Jan). P 11 (irregular).

2	2	3c. brown/yellow	1·75	3·50
		a. Stop after "THREE"	45·00	60·00
		b. Imperf between (vert pair)	£500	
		c. Imperf between (horiz pair)	£800	

The "stop" variety, No. 2a, which occurs on R. 10/7 is of no more philatelic importance than any of the numerous other variations, such as narrow first "A" in "SARAWAK" (R. 2/7) and "R" with long tail in left lower corner (R. 9/10), but it has been accepted by collectors for many years, and we therefore retain it. The papermaker's wmk "L N L" appears once or twice in sheets of No. 2.

Specimens are known, recess-printed, similar to those mentioned in the note after No. 1.

TWO CENTS

Copies of No. 2 surcharged as above were first reported in 1876 but following the discovery of dies for forgeries and faked postmarks in 1891 it was concluded that the issue was bogus, especially as the availability of the 2c. of 1875 made it unnecessary to issue a provisional. It has now been established that a 2c. postal rate was introduced from 1 August 1874 for the carriage of newspapers. Moreover four examples are known with a stop after "CENTS." and showing other minor differences from the forgery illustrated. This version could be genuine and if others come to light we will reconsider listing it.

1875 (1 Jan). P 11½–12.

3	2	2c. mauve/lilac (shades)	9·00	17·00
4		4c. red-brown/yellow	3·50	3·00
		a. Imperf between (vert pair)	£750	£850
5		6c. green/green	3·75	3·50
6		8c. bright blue/blue	3·75	3·75
7		12c. red/pale rose	7·50	6·50
3/7 Set of 5			25·00	30·00

4 Sir Charles Brooke

(Typo D.L.R.)

1888 (10 Nov)–97. No wmk. P 14.

8	4	1c. purple and black (6.6.92)	2·50	50
9		2c. purple and carmine (11.11.88)	3·50	2·00
		a. Purple and rosine (1897)	10·00	4·25
10		3c. purple and blue (11.11.88)	4·00	3·50
11		4c. purple and yellow	20·00	55·00
12		5c. purple and green (12.6.91)	15·00	3·00
13		6c. purple and brown (11.11.88)	16·00	55·00
14		8c. green and carmine (11.11.88)	12·00	3·50
		a. Green and rosine (1897)	23·00	15·00
15		10c. green and purple (12.6.91)	38·00	14·00
16		12c. green and blue (11.11.88)	10·00	9·00
17		16c. green and orange (28.12.97)	48·00	75·00
18		25c. green and brown (19.11.88)	45·00	42·00
19		32c. green and black (28.12.97)	32·00	55·00
20		50c. green (26.7.97)	45·00	90·00
21		$1 green and black (2.11.97)	80·00	85·00
8/21 Set of 14			£325	£450

Prepared for use but not issued.

21a	$2 green and blue	£750
21b	$5 green and violet	£750
21c	$10 green and carmine	£750

On No. 21 the value is in black on an uncoloured ground. The tablet of value in this and later similar issues is in the second colour given.

One Cent.
(5)

one cent.
(6)

2ᶜ.
(7)

5ᶜ
(8)

5ᶜ.
(9)

1889 (3 Aug)–92. T 4 surch. P 14.

22	5	1c. on 3c. purple and blue (12.1.92)	50·00	29·00
		a. Surch double	£700	£600
23	6	1c. on 3c. purple and blue (2.92)	3·00	2·75
		a. No stop after "cent" (R. 2/6)	£200	
24	7	2c. on 8c. green and carmine (3.8.89)	3·00	5·50
		a. Surch double	£425	
		b. Surch inverted	£2750	
		c. Surch omitted (in pair with normal)	£5000	
25	8	5c. on 12c. green and blue (with stop after "C") (17.2.91)	24·00	45·00
		a. No stop after "C"	28·00	50·00
		b. "C" omitted	£475	£475
		c. Surch double	£1100	
		d. Surch double, one vertical	£3000	
		e. Surch omitted (in pair with normal)	£8500	
26	9	5c. on 12c. green and blue (17.2.91)	£200	£225
		a. No stop after "C"	95·00	120
		b. "C" omitted	£650	£700
		c. Surch double	£1200	

ONE CENT
(10)

1892 (23 May). No. 2 surch with T 10.

27	2	1c. on 3c. brown/yellow	1·40	2·00
		a. Stop after "THREE."	40·00	42·00
		b. Imperf between (vert pair)	£650	
		c. Imperf horiz (vert pair)	£600	
		d. Bar omitted (1st ptg)	£225	£250
		e. Bar at top and bottom (1st ptg)	£375	
		f. Surch double (2nd ptg)	£425	£475

No. 27 was surcharged with a setting of 100 (10×10). It was originally intended that there should be no bar at foot, but this was then added at a second operation before the stamps were issued. Subsequent supplies were surcharged with "ONE CENT" and bar at one operation.

Varieties with part of the surcharge missing are due to gum on the face of the unsurcharged stamps receiving part of the surcharge, which was afterwards washed off.

Nos. 3, 4, 6 and 7 have the watermark "L N L" in the sheet, as No. 2. No. 5 is watermarked "L N T".

All values exist imperf and can be distinguished from the proofs by shade and impression. Stamps rouletted, pin-perf, or roughly perf 6½ to 7 are proofs clandestinely perforated.

The 12c. "laid" paper, formerly listed, is not on a true laid paper, the "laid" effect being accidental and not consistent.

The lithographic stones for Nos. 3 to 7 were made up from strips of five distinct impressions hence there are five types of each value differing mainly in the lettering of the tablets of value. There are flaws on nearly every individual stamp, from which they can be plated.

11   12

13 Sir Charles   14
Brooke

(Die eng Wm. Ridgeway. Recess P.B.)

1895 (12 Feb–Sept). *No wmk. P 11½–12.*

28	**11**	2c. brown-red	9·50	9·00
		a. Imperf between (vert pair)	£450	
		b. Imperf between (horiz pair)	£375	
		c. Second ptg. Perf 12½ (Sept)	13·00	4·50
		ca. Perf 12½. Imperf between (horiz pair)	£500	
29	**12**	4c. black	9·50	3·50
		a. Imperf between (horiz pair)	£650	
30	**13**	6c. violet	11·00	9·00
31	**14**	8c. green	28·00	6·00
28/31	Set of 4		50·00	21·00

Stamps of these types, printed in wrong colours, are trials and these, when surcharged with values in "pence", are from waste sheets that were used by Perkins, Bacon & Co as trial paper when preparing an issue of stamps for British South Africa.

4
CENTS.
(15)   16

1899 (29 June–16 Nov). *Surch as T 15.*

32	**2**	2c. on 3c. brown/*yellow* (19 Sept)	1·60	1·75
		a. Stop after "THREE"	60·00	60·00
		b. Imperf between (vert pair)	£900	
33		2c. on 12c. red/*pale rose*	2·75	3·00
		a. Surch inverted	£850	£1300
34		4c. on 6c. green/*green* (R.)	29·00	75·00
		(16 Nov)		
35		4c. on 8c. bright blue/*blue* (R.)	3·75	8·00
32/5	Set of 4		32·00	80·00

A variety of surcharge with small "S" in "CENTS" may be found in the 2c. on 12c. and 4c. on 8c. and a raised stop after "CENTS" on the 4c. on 6c.

The omission of parts of the surcharge is due to gum on the surface of the stamps (see note after No. 27).

A block of 50 of No. 35 from the right of the pane is known line perforated 12.7 between the stamps and the margins at top and right.

(Typo D.L.R.)

1899 (10 Nov)–**1908**. *Inscribed "POSTAGE POSTAGE." No wmk. P 14.*

36	**4**	1c. grey blue and rosine (1.1.01)	1·25	1·25
		a. Grey-blue and red	4·50	1·75
		b. Ultramarine and rosine	7·50	2·75
		c. Dull blue and carmine	15·00	4·50
37		2c. green (16.12.99)	2·00	90
38		3c. dull purple (1.2.08)	11·00	65
39		4c. rose-carmine (10.11.99)	10·00	2·50
		a. Aniline carmine	2·50	15
40		8c. yellow and black (6.12.99)	2·25	80
41		10c. ultramarine (10.11.99)	2·75	1·00
42		12c. mauve (16.12.99)	4·75	4·50
		a. Bright mauve (1905)	26·00	8·50
43		16c. chestnut and green (16.12.99)	4·00	1·75
44		20c. bistre and bright mauve (4.00)	5·50	4·25
45		25c. brown and blue (16.12.99)	6·00	5·00
46		50c. sage-green and carmine (16.12.99)	22·00	26·00
47		$1 rose-carmine and green (16.12.99)	55·00	£110
		a. Rosine and pale green	75·00	£120
36/47	Set of 12		£110	£140

Prepared for use but not issued.

48	**4**	5c. olive-grey and green	12·00

The figures of value in the $1 are in colour on an uncoloured ground.

1902. *Inscribed "POSTAGE POSTAGE". W 16. P 14.*

49	**4**	2c. green	26·00	14·00

Sir Charles Vyner Brooke. 17 May 1917–1 June 1946

ONE
cent

17 Sir Charles   (18)
Vyner Brooke

(Typo D.L.R.)

1918 (24 Mar–Apr). *Chalk-surfaced paper. No wmk. P 14.*

50	**17**	1c. slate-blue and red	2·25	2·50
		a. Dull blue and carmine	2·25	2·50
51		2c. green	2·50	1·50
52		3c. brown-purple (Apr)	3·25	2·75
53		4c. rose-carmine (Apr)	4·00	3·00
		a. Rose-red	5·50	3·00
54		8c. yellow and black (Apr)	12·00	60·00
55		10c. blue (*shades*) (Apr)	3·00	3·25
56		12c. purple (Apr)	12·00	29·00
57		16c. chestnut and green (Apr)	5·50	7·50
58		20c. olive and violet (*shades*) (Apr)	7·00	6·50
59		25c. brown and bright blue (Apr)	8·00	15·00
60		50c. olive-green and carmine (Apr)	10·00	15·00
61		$1 bright rose and green (Apr)	21·00	28·00
50/61	Set of 12		75·00	£150
50s/61s	Optd "Specimen" Set of 12		£275	

Prepared for use but not issued.

62	**17**	1c. slate-blue and slate	22·00

On the $1 the figures of value are in colour on an uncoloured ground.

Most values are known with part strikes of a forged Kuching postmark dated "12 MAR 90".

1922 (Jan)–**23**. *New colours and values. Chalk-surfaced paper. No wmk. P 14.*

63	**17**	2c. purple (5.3.23)	2·00	2·75
64		3c. dull green (23.3.22)	1·75	1·25
65		4c. brown-purple (10.4.23)	1·50	85
66		5c. yellow-orange	1·75	90
67		6c. claret	1·50	1·40
68		8c. bright rose-red (1922)	4·50	32·00
69		10c. black (1923)	2·00	4·00
70		12c. bright blue (12.22)	10·00	18·00
		a. Pale dull blue	10·00	19·00
71		30c. ochre-brown and slate	3·75	4·25
63/71	Set of 9		26·00	60·00

1923 (Jan). *Surch as T 18.*

(a) First printing. Bars 1¼ mm apart.

72	**17**	1c. on 10c. dull blue	10·00	55·00
		a. "cnet" for "cent" (R. 9/5)	£375	£850
73		2c. on 12c. purple	6·50	42·00
		a. Thick, narrower "W" in "TWO"	19·00	90·00

(b) Second printing. Bars ¾ mm apart.

74	**17**	1c. on 10c. dull blue	£350	
		b. "cnet" for "cent" (R. 9/5)	£14000	
		c. Bright blue	£140	£400
		ca. "en" of "cent" scratched out and "ne" overprinted (R. 9/5)	£5000	
75		2c. on 12c. purple	80·00	£250
		a. Thick, narrower "W" in "TWO"	£150	

In the 2c. on 12c. the words of the surcharge are about 7½ mm from the bars.

The "cnet" error occurred on R. 9/5 of all sheets from the first printing of the 1c. on 10c. A single example of the error, No. 74b, is known from the second printing, but the error was then corrected, as shown by the evidence of a surviving plate block, only to have the correct spelling scratched out by a local employee, and "ne" substituted (No. 74ca).

The thick "W" variety occurs on all stamps of the last two horizontal rows of the first printing (12 stamps per sheet), and in the last two vertical rows of the second (20 stamps per sheet).

1928 (7 Apr)–**29**. *Chalk-surfaced paper. W 16 (Multiple). P 14.*

76	**17**	1c. slate-blue and carmine	1·50	35
77		2c. bright purple	2·00	1·25
78		3c. green	2·25	5·00
79		4c. brown-purple	1·75	10
80		5c. yellow-orange (7.8.29)	11·00	5·00
81		6c. claret	1·25	30
82		8c. bright rose-red	3·25	18·00
83		10c. black	1·75	1·25
84		12c. bright blue	3·25	25·00
85		16c. chestnut and green	3·25	4·00
86		20c. olive-bistre and violet	3·25	6·00
87		25c. brown and bright blue	5·50	8·50
88		30c. bistre-brown and slate	4·50	10·00
89		50c. olive-green and carmine	5·50	16·00
90		$1 bright rose and green	15·00	24·00
76/90	Set of 15		60·00	£110
76s/90s	Optd or Perf (5c.) "Specimen" Set of 15		£275	

In the $1 the value is as before.

1 c

19 Sir Charles   20
Vyner Brooke

(Recess Waterlow)

1932 (1 Jan). *W 20. P 12½.*

91	**19**	1c. indigo	80	1·00
92		2c. green	1·00	1·50
93		3c. violet	4·00	1·00
94		4c. red-orange	4·00	75
95		5c. deep lake	6·50	1·25
96		6c. scarlet	7·00	9·50
97		8c. orange-yellow	9·00	8·50
98		10c. black	2·25	3·25
99		12c. deep ultramarine	4·00	9·50
100		15c. chestnut	6·50	8·50
101		20c. red-orange and violet	6·50	6·00
102		25c. orange-yellow and chestnut	10·00	22·00
103		30c. sepia and vermilion	9·50	8·00
104		50c. carmine-red and olive-green	14·00	13·00
105		$1 green and carmine	22·00	35·00
91/105	Set of 15		95·00	£130
91s/105s	Perf "Specimen" Set of 15		£325	

21 Sir Charles   B M A
Vyner Brooke   (22)

(Recess B.W.)

1934 (1 May)–**41**. *No wmk. P 12.*

106	**21**	1c. purple	1·25	10
107		2c. green	1·50	10
107a		2c. black (1.3.41)	3·75	1·60
108		3c. black	1·25	10
108a		3c. green (1.3.41)	7·00	4·50
109		4c. bright purple	2·00	15
110		5c. violet	2·00	10
111		6c. carmine	2·75	60
111a		6c. lake-brown (1.3.41)	7·50	8·00
112		8c. red-brown	2·25	10
112a		8c. carmine (1.3.41)	8·00	10
113		10c. scarlet	3·00	40
114		12c. blue	3·00	25
114a		12c. orange (1.3.41)	6·00	4·50
115		15c. orange	4·50	10·00
115a		15c. blue (1.3.41)	8·50	15·00
116		20c. olive-green and carmine	4·50	1·25
117		25c. violet and orange	4·50	1·50
118		30c. red-brown and violet	4·50	2·50
119		50c. violet and scarlet	5·50	75
120		$1 scarlet and sepia	2·00	75
121		$2 bright purple and violet	16·00	13·00
122		$3 carmine and green	32·00	35·00
123		$4 blue and scarlet	32·00	55·00
124		$5 scarlet and red-brown	38·00	55·00
125		$10 black and yellow	24·00	60·00
106/25	Set of 26		£200	£250
106s/25s	Perf "Specimen" Set of 26		£550	

For the 3c. green, wmkd Mult Script CA, see No. 152a.

BRITISH MILITARY ADMINISTRATION

Following the Japanese surrender, elements of the British Military Administration reached Kuching on 11 September 1945. From 5 November 1945 current Australian 1d., 3d., 6d. and 1s. stamps were made available for civilian use until replaced by Nos. 126/45. Other Australian stamps were also accepted as valid for postage during this period.

1945 (17 Dec). *Optd with T 22.*

126	**21**	1c. purple	1·25	60
127		2c. black (R.)	1·75	1·25
		a. Opt double	†	£6000
128		3c. green	1·25	1·50
129		4c. bright purple	1·75	30
		a. Opt double, one albino	£1900	
130		5c. violet (R.)	2·75	1·00
131		6c. lake-brown	2·75	75
132		8c. carmine	13·00	13·00
133		10c. scarlet	1·50	70
134		12c. orange	2·00	3·75
135		15c. blue	4·25	40
136		20c. olive-green and carmine	2·50	2·50
137		25c. violet and orange (R.)	3·00	2·75
138		30c. red-brown and violet	6·00	2·75
139		50c. violet and scarlet	1·25	35
140		$1 scarlet and sepia	2·50	2·00
141		$2 bright purple and violet	9·00	13·00
142		$3 carmine and green	18·00	65·00
143		$4 blue and scarlet	26·00	48·00
144		$5 scarlet and red-brown	£160	£225
145		$10 black and yellow	£150	£225
126/45	Set of 20		£375	£550

These stamps, and the similarly overprinted stamps of North Borneo, were obtainable at all post offices throughout British Borneo (Brunei, Labuan, North Borneo and Sarawak), for use on local and overseas mail.

The administration of Sarawak was returned to the Brooke family on 15 April 1946, but the Rajah, after consulting the inhabitants, ceded the territory to Great Britain on 1 June 1946. Values from the 1934–41 issue were used until replaced by Nos. 150/64.

23 Sir James Brooke, Sir Charles   (24)
Vyner Brooke and Sir Charles
Brooke

(Recess B.W.)

1946 (18 May). *Centenary Issue. P 12.*

146	**23**	8c. lake	1·50	1·00
147		15c. blue	1·75	2·00
148		50c. black and scarlet	2·00	2·50
149		$1 black and sepia	2·50	22·00
146/9	Set of 4		7·00	25·00
146s/9s	Perf "Specimen" Set of 4		£140	

CROWN COLONY

1947 (16 Apr). *Optd with T 24, typo by B.W. in blue-black or red. Wmk Mult Script CA. P 12.*

150	**21**	1c. purple	15	30
151		2c. black (R.)	15	15
152		3c. green (R.)	15	15
		a. Albino opt	£5000	
153		4c. bright purple	15	15
154		6c. lake-brown	20	90
155		8c. carmine	75	10
156		10c. scarlet	20	20
157		12c. orange	20	1·00
158		15c. blue (R.)	20	40

159		20c. olive-green and carmine (R.).....	2·00	50
160		25c. violet and orange (R.)................	40	30
161		50c. violet and scarlet (R.)	70	40
162		$1 scarlet and sepia	1·25	90
163		$2 bright purple and violet	2·50	3·25
164		$5 scarlet and red-brown	3·00	3·25
150/64		*Set of 15*	10·50	10·50
150s/64s		Perf "Specimen" *Set of 15*	£300	

No. 152a shows an uninked impression of T 24.

1948 (25 Oct). *Royal Silver Wedding. As Nos. 112/13 of Antigua.*

165		8c. scarlet	30	30
166		$5 brown	32·00	42·00

1949 (10 Oct). *75th Anniv of U.P.U. As Nos. 114/17 of Antigua.*

167		8c. carmine	1·25	60
168		15c. deep blue	3·00	2·50
169		25c. deep blue-green...................	2·00	1·50
170		50c. violet	2·00	5·00
167/70		*Set of 4*	7·50	8·75

25 *Trogonoptera brookiana*   **26** Western Tarsier

27 Kayan tomb   **28** Kayan girl and boy

29 Bead work   **30** Dyak dancer

31 Malayan Pangolin   **32** Kenyah boys

33 Fire making   **34** Kelemantan rice barn

35 Pepper vines   **36** Iban woman

37 Kelabit smithy   **38** Map of Sarawak

39 Arms of Sarawak

(Recess; Arms typo B.W.)

1950 (3 Jan). *T* **25**/39. Wmk Mult Script CA. P 11½×11 (horiz) or 11×11½ (vert).

171	25	1c. black..............................	40	30
172	26	2c. red-orange	30	40
173	27	3c. green..............................	30	60
174	28	4c. chocolate	30	20
175	29	6c. turquoise-blue	30	15
176	30	8c. scarlet............................	40	30
177	31	10c. orange............................	1·50	4·00
178	32	12c. violet..............................	3·50	1·50
179	33	15c. blue...............................	2·50	15
180	34	20c. purple-brown and red-orange	2·00	30
181	35	25c. green and scarlet	3·25	30
182	36	50c. brown and violet,...............	4·50	25
183	37	$1 green and chocolate	20·00	4·50
184	38	$2 blue and carmine	26·00	15·00
185	39	$5 black, yellow, red and purple	19·00	15·00
171/85		*Set of 15*	75·00	38·00

40 Map of Sarawak

(Recess B.W.)

1952 (1 Feb). Wmk Mult Script CA. P 11½×11.

186	40	10c. orange..........................	1·75	50

JAPANESE OCCUPATION OF SARAWAK

Japanese forces landed in North Borneo on 16 December 1941 and Sarawak was attacked on 23 December 1941.

Brunei, North Borneo, Sarawak and after a short period, Labuan, were administered as a single territory by the Japanese. Until September–October 1942, previous stamp issues, without overprint, continued to be used in conjunction with existing postmarks. From 1 October 1942 onwards unoverprinted stamps of Japan were made available and examples can be found used from the area for much of the remainder of the War. Japanese Occupation issues for Brunei, North Borneo and Sarawak were equally valid throughout the combined territory but not, in practice, equally available.

PRICES FOR STAMPS ON COVER	
Nos. J1/21	*from* × 8
Nos. J22/6	—

大日本帝国郵便

(1) ("Imperial Japanese Government")

1942 (Oct). *Stamps of Sarawak handstamped with T* **1** *in violet.*

J1	21	1c. purple	32·00	75·00
		a. Pair, one without opt................	£2000	
J2		2c. green..........................	£110	£170
		a. Black opt........................	£100	
J3		2c. black..........................	£100	£120
		a. Black opt........................	£150	£170
J4		3c. black..........................	£375	£375
J5		3c. green..........................	60·00	95·00
		a. Black opt........................	£130	
J6		4c. bright purple	75·00	95·00
		a. Black opt........................	£130	
J7		5c. violet..........................	90·00	£100
		a. Black opt........................	£130	
J8		6c. carmine	£140	£140
J9		6c. lake-brown	90·00	£100
		a. Black opt........................	£120	£130
J10		8c. red-brown	£375	£375
		a. Black opt........................	£550	
J11		8c. carmine	75·00	£120
		a. Black opt........................	£250	£325
J12		10c. scarlet	85·00	£110
		a. Black opt........................	£130	
J13		12c. blue	£160	£180
		a. Black opt........................	£250	
J14		12c. orange.........................	£160	£190
J15		15c. orange.........................	£400	£400
		a. Black opt........................	£450	
J16		15c. blue	£110	£130
J17		20c. olive-green and carmine	65·00	£100
		a. Black opt........................	£130	
J18		25c. violet and orange	£100	£110
		a. Black opt........................	£140	
J19		30c. red-brown and violet	65·00	£100
		a. Black opt........................	£130	
J20		50c. violet and scarlet	70·00	£100
		a. Black opt........................	£250	
		b. Blue opt.........................	£450	
J21		$1 scarlet and sepia	£100	£140
		a. Black opt........................	£325	
J22		$2 bright purple and violet	£200	£300
		a. Blue opt.........................	£375	
J23		$3 carmine and green	£1600	£1600
		a. Black opt........................	£2250	
J24		$4 blue and scarlet	£225	£375
J25		$5 scarlet and red-brown	£250	£375
J26		$10 black and yellow	£250	£375

The overprint, being handstamped, exists inverted or double on some values. Those on Nos. J20b, J21a and J22a are diagonal. The remainder are horizontal.

Stamps of T **21** optd with Japanese symbols within an oval frame are revenue stamps, while the same stamps overprinted with three Japanese characters between two vertical double rules, were used as seals.

"Nos. J1/26 have been extensively forged. Recent research indicates that complete or part sets on cover cancelled by Japanese circular postmarks in violet dated "17 11 21" (21 Nov 1942) or "18 3 1" (1 Mar 1943) have forged overprints."

Seychelles

Seychelles was administered as a dependency of Mauritius from 1810 until 1903, although separate stamp issues were provided from April 1890 onwards.

The first post office was opened, at Victoria on Mahé, on 11 December 1861 and the stamps of Mauritius were used there until 1890. No further post offices were opened until 1901.

B 6 4

Z 1

Stamps of MAURITIUS *cancelled with Type* Z **1**.

1848–59.

Z1		2d. blue (*intermediate* impression) (No. 14)........	£10000

1859–61.

Z2		6d. blue (*No. 32*)	£900
Z3		6d. dull purple-slate (*No. 33*)	£2250
Z4		1s. vermilion (*No. 34*)	£1400

1860–63. (*Nos. 46/53*).

Z5		1d. purple-brown	£200
Z6		1d. blue.................................	£250
Z7		4d. rose	£200
Z8		6d. green	£900
Z9		6d. slate	£600
Z10		9d. dull purple	£110
Z11		1s. buff	£300
Z12		1s. green	£700

1862.

Z13		6d. slate (*No. 54*)	£800

1863–72. (*Nos. 56/72*).

Z14		1d. purple-brown	£110
Z14a		1d. brown	95·00
Z15		1d. bistre	£100
Z16		2d. pale blue	£120
Z17		2d. bright blue	£120
Z18		3d. deep red	£150
Z19		3d. dull red	85·00
Z20		4d. rose	48·00
Z21		6d. dull violet	£250
Z22		6d. yellow-green	£110
Z23		6d. blue-green	75·00
Z24		9d. yellow-green	£1500
Z25		10d. maroon	£325
Z26		1s. yellow	£100
Z27		1s. blue	£300
Z28		1s. orange	£110
Z29		5s. rosy mauve	£850
Z30		5s. bright mauve	£850

1876. (*Nos. 76/7*).

Z31		½d. on 9d. dull purple	£300
Z32		½d. on 10d. maroon	£275

1877. (*Nos. 79/82*).

Z33		½d. on 10d. rose	£600
Z34		1d. on 4d. rose-carmine	
Z35		1s. on 5s. rosy mauve	
Z36		1s. on 5s. bright mauve	

1878. (*Nos. 83/91*).

Z37		2c. dull rose (lower label blank)	90·00
Z38		4c. on 1d. bistre	£375
Z39		8c. on 2d. blue	40·00
Z40		13c. on 3d. orange-red	£120
Z41		17c. on 4d. rose	40·00
Z42		25c. on 6d. slate-blue	£100
Z43		38c. on 9d. pale violet	£475
Z44		50c. on 1s. green	£110
Z45		2r.50 on 5s. bright mauve	£500

1879–80. (*Nos. 92/100*).

Z46		2c. Venetian red	£130
Z47		4c. orange	£130
Z48		8c. blue	40·00
Z49		13c. slate	£1200
Z50		17c. rose	90·00
Z51		25c. olive-yellow	£190
Z52		38c. bright purple	£1700
Z53		50c. green	£850
Z54		2r.50 brown-purple	£850

1883–90.

Z55		2c. Venetian red (No. 102)	95·00
Z56		2c. green (No. 103)	£180
Z57		4c. orange (No. 104)	65·00
Z58		4c. carmine (No. 105)	95·00
Z59		16c. chestnut (*No. 109*)	55·00

Z60		25c. olive-yellow (No. 110)		£110
Z61		50c. orange (No. 111)		£900

1883.
Z62		16c. on 17c. rose (No. 112)		£120

1883.
Z63		16c. on 17c. rose (No. 115)		45·00

1885.
Z64		2c. on 38c. bright purple (No. 116)		

1887.
Z65		2c. on 13c. slate (No. 117)		

POSTAL FISCAL

1889.
ZR1		4c. lilac *(No. R2)*		£1200

Mauritius stamps are occasionally found cancelled with the "SEYCHELLES" cds. Examples are known dated between 25 and 29 February 1884 when it seems that Type Z **1** may have been mislaid (*Price from* £425).

We no longer list the G.B. 1862 6d. lilac with this obliteration as there is no evidence that the stamps of Great Britain were sold by the Victoria post office.

PRICES FOR STAMPS ON COVER TO 1945

Nos. 1/8	*from* × 20
Nos. 9/24	*from* × 30
No. 25	*from* × 10
No. 26	*from* × 20
No. 27	*from* × 10
Nos. 28/32	*from* × 20
No. 33	*from* × 5
No. 34	*from* × 30
Nos. 35/6	—
Nos. 37/40	*from* × 40
Nos. 41/2	*from* × 25
Nos. 43/5	*from* × 10
Nos. 46/50	*from* × 30
Nos. 51/4	*from* × 10
Nos. 55/6	—
Nos. 57/9	*from* × 10
Nos. 60/7	*from* × 20
Nos. 68/70	—
Nos. 71/81	*from* × 10
Nos. 82/131	*from* × 5
Nos. 132/4	*from* × 10
Nos. 135/49	*from* × 3

(Currency: 100 cents = 1 Mauritius, later Seychelles rupee)

DEPENDENCY OF MAURITIUS

PRINTERS. Nos. 1 to 123 were typographed by De La Rue & Co.

1

Die I   Die II

In Die I there are lines of shading in the middle compartment of the diadem which are absent from Die II.

Normal   Malformed "S"   Repaired "S"

The malformed "S" occurs on R. 7/3 of the left pane from Key Plate 2. It is believed that the repair to it took place in mid-1898. Both states may occur on other stamps in Types **1** and **4**. Stamps subsequently printed from Key Plate 3 showed the "S" normal.

1890 (5 April)–**92**. Wmk Crown CA. P 14.

(i) Die I.
1	**1**	2c. green and carmine	3·50	10·00
2		4c. carmine and green	28·00	12·00
3		8c. brown-purple and blue	10·00	3·50
4		10c. ultramarine and brown	7·00	20·00
5		13c. grey and black	6·00	11·00
6		16c. chestnut and blue	7·00	4·25
7		48c. ochre and green	20·00	10·00
8		96c. mauve and carmine	60·00	48·00
1/8 *Set of 8*			£130	£110
1s/8s *Optd "Specimen" Set of 8*			£190	

(ii) Die II (1892).
9	**1**	2c. green and rosine	2·50	1·00
10		4c. carmine and green	2·50	1·00
11		8c. brown-purple and ultramarine	8·50	1·75
12		10c. bright ultramarine and brown	10·00	3·25
		a. Malformed "S"		
13		13c. grey and black	3·25	1·75
14		16c. chestnut and ultramarine	42·00	11·00
		a. Malformed "S"		
9/14 *Set of 6*			60·00	18·00

The 10c. Die I also exists in ultramarine and chestnut, but has so far only been found with "SPECIMEN" overprint (*Price* £650).

3 cents	**18 CENTS**	
(2)	(3)	4

1893 (1 Jan). *Surch locally as T* **2**.
15		3c. on 4c. (No. 10)	1·10	1·50
		a. Surch inverted	£300	£375
		b. Surch double	£475	
		c. Surch omitted (in horiz pair with normal)	£11000	
16		12c. on 16c. (No. 6)	2·50	3·75
		a. Surch inverted	£475	
		b. Surch double	£13000	£9000
17		12c. on 16c. (No. 14)	15·00	2·50
		a. Surch inverted	£4500	£4500
		b. Surch omitted (in pair with normal)		
18		15c. on 16c. (No. 6)	9·50	13·00
		a. Surch inverted	£325	£300
		b. Surch double	£1300	£1300
19		15c. on 16c. (No. 14)	16·00	3·00
		a. Surch inverted	£900	£1000
		b. Surch double	£700	£750
		c. Surch triple	£4250	
20		45c. on 48c. (No. 7)	27·00	5·50
21		90c. on 96c. (No. 8)	60·00	32·00
		a. Wide "O" (3½ mm wide instead of 3 mm) (R. 1/1, 2/1 of setting)	£300	£300
15/21 *Set of 7*			£120	55·00

Nos. 15/21 were each produced from settings of 30.

Nos. 15, 16, 18, 19 and 20 exist with "cents" omitted and with "cents" above value due to misplacement of the surcharge.

Some examples of No. 15b occur in the same sheet as No. 15c with the double surcharge on stamps from the last vertical row of the left pane and the surcharge omitted from stamps from the last vertical row of the right pane.

Most examples of the inverted surcharge error No. 16a were officially defaced with a red vertical ink line (*Price* £200, *unused*). Similarly examples of No. 19a exist defaced with a horizontal ink line (*Price* £400, *unused*).

1893 (Nov). *New values. Die II. Wmk Crown CA. P 14.*
22	**1**	3c. dull purple and orange	1·50	50
23		12c. sepia and green	2·50	60
24		15c. sage-green and lilac	4·50	2·00
25		45c. brown and carmine	23·00	35·00
22/5 *Set of 4*			28·00	35·00
22s/5s *Optd "Specimen" Set of 4*			95·00	

1896 (1 Aug). *No. 25 surch locally as T* **3**.
26	**1**	18c. on 45c. brown and carmine	7·00	2·75
		a. Surch double	£1400	£1400
		b. Surch triple	£2000	
27		36c. on 45c. brown and carmine	8·00	50·00
		a. Surch double	£1700	
26s/7s *Optd "Specimen" Set of 2*			70·00	

1897–1900. *Colours changed and new values. Die II. Wmk Crown CA. P 14.*
28	**1**	2c. orange-brown and green (1900)	2·00	1·25
		a. Repaired "S"	£275	£275
29		6c. carmine (1900)	3·50	50
		a. Repaired "S"	£350	£275
30		15c. ultramarine (1900)	6·50	3·50
		a. Repaired "S"	£400	£325
31		18c. ultramarine	5·50	1·00
32		36c. brown and carmine	28·00	4·50
33	**4**	75c. yellow and violet (1900)	55·00	70·00
		a. Repaired "S"	£550	
34		1r. bright mauve and deep red	13·00	4·25
35		1r.50 grey and carmine (1900)	75·00	85·00
		a. Repaired "S"	£600	£800
36		2r.25 bright mauve and green (1900)	£100	85·00
		a. Repaired "S"	£800	
28/36 *Set of 9*			£250	£225
28s/36s *Optd "Specimen" Set of 9*			£250	

3 cents	**6 cents**
(5)	(5a)

1901 (21 June–Oct). *Surch locally with T* **5** *or* **5a**.
37		3c. on 10c. bright ultramarine and brown (No. 12) (9.01)	1·50	60
		a. Surch double	£900	
		b. Surch triple	£2750	
		c. Malformed "S"	£250	
38		3c. on 16c. chestnut and ultramarine (No. 14) (8.01)	3·25	4·50
		a. Surch inverted	£700	£700
		b. Surch double	£500	£550
		c. "3 cents" omitted	£550	£550
		d. Malformed "S"	£300	£350
39		3c. on 36c. brown and carmine (No. 32)	70	80
		a. Surch double	£750	£850
		b. "3 cents" omitted	£650	£700

40		6c. on 8c. brn-pur and ultram (No. 11) (7.01)	2·25	3·00
		a. Surch inverted	£650	£750
37/40 *Set of 4*			7·00	8·00
37s/40s H/S "Specimen" *Set of 4*			£100	

1902 (June). *Surch locally as T* **5**.
41	**1**	2c. on 4c. carmine and green (No. 10)	1·75	2·75
42	**4**	30c. on 75c. yellow and violet (No. 33)	1·50	4·00
		a. Narrow "0" in "30" (R. 3/6, 5/2-4)	8·00	45·00
		b. Repaired "S"	£300	
43		30c. on 1r. bright mauve and dp red (No. 34)	7·50	30·00
		a. Narrow "0" in "30" (R. 3/6, 5/2-4)	26·00	90·00
		b. Surch double	£1500	
44		45c. on 1r. bright mauve and dp red (No. 34)	3·50	32·00
45		45c. on 2r.25 brt mauve and grn (No. 36)	42·00	90·00
		a. Narrow "5" in "45" (R. 4/1)	£200	£375
		b. Repaired "S"	£700	£950
41/5 *Set of 5*			50·00	£140
41s/5s *Optd "Specimen" Set of 5*			£120	

6	7	**3 cents** (8)

Dented frame (R. 1/6 of left pane)

1903 (26 May). Wmk Crown CA. P 14.
46	**6**	2c. chestnut and green	1·75	2·00
		a. Dented frame	£120	£140
47		3c. dull green	1·00	1·25
		a. Dented frame	£100	£120
48		6c. carmine	2·75	1·25
		a. Dented frame	£160	£130
49		12c. olive-sepia and dull green	2·75	2·50
		a. Dented frame	£160	£170
50		15c. ultramarine	4·00	2·50
		a. Dented frame	£225	£180
51		18c. sage-green and carmine	4·25	6·50
		a. Dented frame	£225	£300
52		30c. violet and dull green	7·00	11·00
		a. Dented frame	£275	£400
53		45c. brown and carmine	7·00	11·00
		a. Dented frame	£325	£400
		w. Wmk inverted	£350	£400
54	**7**	75c. yellow and violet	10·00	28·00
		a. Dented frame	£350	
55		1r.50 black and carmine	48·00	70·00
		a. Dented frame	£650	£850
56		2r.25 purple and green	35·00	85·00
		a. Dented frame	£600	£900
46/56 *Set of 11*			£110	£200
46s/56s *Optd "Specimen" Set of 11*			£200	

1903. *Surch locally with T* **8**.
57	**6**	3c. on 15c. ultramarine (3.7)	1·00	3·25
		a. Dented frame	£190	
58		3c. on 18c. sage-green and carmine (2.9)	2·75	40·00
		a. Dented frame	£275	£850
59		3c. on 45c. brown and carmine (21.7)	3·00	3·25
		a. Dented frame	£275	
57/9 *Set of 3*			6·00	42·00
57s/9s H/S "Specimen" *Set of 3*			80·00	

CROWN COLONY

The Seychelles became a Seperate Crown Colony by Letters Patent dated 31 August 1903.

1906. Wmk Mult Crown CA. P 14.
60	**6**	2c. chestnut and green	1·50	4·25
		a. Dented frame	£100	£170
61		3c. dull green	1·50	1·50
		a. Dented frame	£120	£140
62		6c. carmine	2·00	80
		a. Dented frame	£140	£100
63		12c. olive-sepia and dull green	3·00	3·25
		a. Dented frame	£190	£225
64		15c. ultramarine	3·00	2·00
		a. Dented frame	£170	£170
65		18c. sage-green and carmine	3·00	6·50
		a. Dented frame	£170	£275
66		30c. violet and dull green	6·00	8·00
		a. Dented frame	£300	£325
67		45c. brown and carmine	3·00	6·50
		a. Dented frame	£275	£325
68	**7**	75c. yellow and violet	8·50	55·00
		a. Dented frame	£375	
69		1r.50 black and carmine	55·00	60·00
		a. Dented frame	£700	£700
70		2r.25 purple and green	35·00	60·00
		a. Dented frame	£650	
60/70 *Set of 11*			£110	£180

9	10

1912 (Apr)–**16**. Wmk Mult Crown CA. P 14.

71	**9**	2c. chestnut and green	70	5·50
		a. Split "A"	85·00	£190
72		3c. green	2·50	60
		a. Split "A"	£110	90·00
73		6c. Carmine-red (6.13)	4·25	1·00
		a. Aniline-carmine (1916)	13·00	4·50
		b. Split "A"	£180	95·00
74		12c. olive-sepia and dull green (1.13)	1·25	4·00
		a. Split "A"	£130	£190
75		15c. ultramarine	3·75	1·00
		a. Split "A"	£180	95·00
76		18c. sage-green and carmine (1.13)..	3·25	6·50
		a. Split "A"	£170	£275
77		30c. violet and green (1.13)	5·50	1·25
		a. Split "A"	£225	£140
78		45c. brown and carmine (1.13)	2·75	35·00
		a. Split "A"	£190	
79	**10**	75c. yellow and violet (1.13)	2·75	5·50
		a. Split "A"	£190	£275
80		1r.50 black and carmine (1.13)	7·50	1·00
		a. Split "A"	£325	£120
81		2r.25 dp magenta and grn (shades) (1.13)	60·00	2·50
		a. Split "A"	£650	£190
71/81 Set of 11			85·00	55·00
71s/81s Optd "Specimen" Set of 11			£225	

For illustration of "Split A" flaw see above St. Helena No. 83.

11	**12**	**13**

1917–22. Die I. Chalk-surfaced paper (18c. to 5r.). Wmk Mult Crown CA. P 14.

82	**11**	2c. chestnut and green	50	2·75
83		3c. green	2·00	1·25
84	**12**	5c. deep brown (1920)	2·25	6·50
85	**11**	6c. carmine	2·50	1·50
		a. Rose (1919)	5·00	2·50
86		12c. grey (1919)	1·25	1·00
87		15c. ultramarine	1·75	1·50
88		18c. purple/yellow (1919)	3·50	26·00
		a. On orange-buff (1920)	14·00	55·00
		b. On buff (1920)		
		c. Die II. On pale yellow (1922)	1·25	17·00
89	**13**	25c. black and red/buff (1920)	1·75	32·00
		a. On orange buff (1920)	40·00	75·00
		b. Die II. On pale yellow (1922)	1·75	9·50
90	**11**	30c. dull purple and olive (1918)	1·50	8·50
91		45c. dull purple and orange (1919)	3·00	35·00
92	**13**	50c. dull purple and black (1920)	5·50	30·00
93		75c. black/blue-green (olive back) (1918)	1·60	15·00
		a. Die II. On emerald back (1922)	1·40	20·00
94		1r. dull purple and red (1920)	11·00	45·00
95		1r.50 reddish purple and blue/blue (1918)	9·00	50·00
		a. Die II. Blue-pur and blue/blue (1922)	14·00	32·00
96		2r.25 yellow-green and violet (1918)	48·00	£130
97		5r. green and blue (1920)	95·00	£250
82/97 Set of 16			£170	£500
82s/97s Optd "Specimen" Set of 16			£300	

Examples of most values are known showing forged postmarks. These include part strikes of Seychelles postmarks dated "24 AP 93" and "AU 6 1903", and Victoria postmarks dated "NO 27" or "MY 6 35".

1921–32. Die II. Chalk-surfaced paper (18c. and 25c. to 5r.). Wmk Mult Script CA. P 14.

98	**11**	2c. chestnut and green	25	15
99		3c. green	1·75	15
100		3c. black (1922)	1·00	30
101		4c. green (1922)	1·00	2·50
102		4c. sage-green and carmine (1928)	6·50	17·00
103	**12**	5c. deep brown	75	5·50
104	**11**	6c. carmine	2·75	9·00
		w. Wmk inverted	£160	
105		6c. deep mauve (1922)	80	10
106	**13**	9c. red (1927)	3·25	4·25
107	**11**	12c. grey	2·75	20
		a. Die I (1932)	15·00	65
108		12c. carmine-red (1922)	1·25	30
110		15c. bright blue	2·00	55·00
111		15c. yellow (1922)	1·00	2·75
112		18c. purple/pale yellow (1925)	2·50	12·00
113	**13**	20c. bright blue (1922)	1·50	35
		a. Dull blue	8·00	55
114		25c. black and red/pale yellow (1925)	2·75	17·00
115	**11**	30c. dull purple and olive	1·25	15·00
		w. Wmk inverted		
116		45c. dull purple and orange	1·25	5·00
117	**13**	50c. dull purple and black	2·50	2·25
118		75c. black/emerald (1924)	8·00	21·00
119		1r. dull purple and red	15·00	18·00
		a. Die I (1932)	12·00	35·00
121		1r.50 purple and blue/blue (1924)	14·00	22·00
122		2r.25 yellow-green and violet	14·00	14·00
123		5r. yellow-green and blue	90·00	£170
98/123 Set of 24			£160	£350
98s/123s Optd "Specimen" Set of 24			£400	

The 3c. green and 12c. grey (Die II) were reissued in 1927. "Specimen" overprints on these printings are 15.5×1.75 mm instead of the 14.5×2.5 mm of the original issue. (Price, 3c. £350, 12c. £110).

Examples of most values are known showing the forged postmarks mentioned above.

1935 (6 May). Silver Jubilee. As Nos. 91/4 of Antigua, but ptd by B.W. P 11×12.

128		6c. ultramarine and grey-black	1·00	2·00
		a. Extra flagstaff	£225	£300
		b. Short extra flagstaff	£250	£300
		c. Lightning conductor	£325	

		d. Flagstaff on right-hand turret	£350	£325
		e. Double flagstaff	£375	£325
129		12c. green and indigo	3·25	1·50
		a. Extra flagstaff	£3500	£3000
		b. Short extra flagstaff	£375	£275
		c. Lightning conductor	£2250	
		d. Flagstaff on right-hand turret	£475	
		e. Double flagstaff	£475	
130		20c. brown and deep blue	2·50	3·00
		a. Extra flagstaff	£350	£400
		b. Short extra flagstaff	£275	
		c. Lightning conductor	£425	£425
		d. Flagstaff on right-hand turret	£450	
		e. Double flagstaff	£450	
131		1r. slate and purple	7·00	16·00
		a. Extra flagstaff	£180	£250
		b. Short extra flagstaff	£375	
		c. Lightning conductor	£275	
		d. Flagstaff on right-hand turret	£475	
128/31 Set of 4			12·50	20·00
128s/31s Perf "Specimen" Set of 4			£130	

For illustrations of plate varieties see Omnibus section following Zanzibar.

Examples are known showing forged Victoria "B MY 6 35" postmarks.

1937 (12 May). Coronation. As Nos. 95/7 of Antigua. P 11×11½.

132		6c. sage-green	35	15
133		12c. orange	50	50
134		20c. blue	70	1·00
132/4 Set of 3			1·40	1·50
132s/4s Perf "Specimen" Set of 3			80·00	

14 Coco-de-mer Palm   **15** Giant Tortoise

16 Fishing Pirogue

"Handkerchief" on oar flaw (R. 6/2)

(Photo Harrison)

1938 (1 Jan)–**49**. Wmk Mult Script CA. Chalk-surfaced paper. P 14½×13½ (vert) or 13½×14½ (horiz).

135	**14**	2c. purple-brown (10.2.38)	1·50	40
		a. Ordinary paper (18.11.42)	30	1·75
136	**15**	3c. green	8·50	1·75
136a		3c. orange (8.8.41)	1·25	1·00
		ab. Ordinary paper (18.11.42)	55	1·50
137	**16**	6c. orange	9·50	3·50
137a		6c. greyish green (8.8.41)	4·00	1·25
		aw. Wmk inverted	£900	
		b. Ordinary paper. Green (18.11.42)	55	2·25
		c. Green (5.4.49)	6·50	1·25
138	**14**	9c. scarlet (10.2.38)	10·00	2·25
138a		9c. grey-blue (8.8.41)	11·00	40
		ab. Ordinary paper (18.11.42)	13·00	1·50
		ac. Ordinary paper. Dull blue (19.11.45)	6·50	2·50
		ad. Dull blue (5.4.49)	16·00	6·00
		aw. Wmk inverted		
139	**15**	12c. reddish violet	45·00	1·25
139a		15c. brown-carmine (8.8.41)	15·00	40
		ab. Ordinary paper. Brown-red (18.11.42)	6·50	3·25
139c	**14**	18c. carmine-lake (8.8.41)	10·00	60
		ca. Ordinary paper (18.11.42)	7·00	2·75
		cb. Rose-carmine (5.4.49)	19·00	12·00
140	**16**	20c. blue	42·00	6·00
140a		20c. brown-ochre (8.8.41)	11·00	65
		ab. Ordinary paper (18.11.42)	2·50	35
		ac. "Handkerchief" flaw	£150	90·00
141	**14**	30c. brown-ochre	50·00	14·00
142	**15**	30c. carmine (10.2.38)	50·00	10·00
142a		30c. blue (8.8.41)	11·00	50
		ab. Ordinary paper (18.11.42)	2·25	3·75
143	**16**	45c. chocolate (10.2.38)	19·00	2·00
		a. Ordinary paper. Purple-brown (18.11.42)	2·75	1·75
		b. Purple-brown (5.4.49)	23·00	12·00
144	**14**	50c. deep reddish violet (10.2.38)	12·00	60
		a. Ordinary paper (18.11.42)	1·75	3·25
144b		50c. bright lilac (13.6.49)	2·50	2·25
145	**15**	75c. slate-blue (10.2.38)	85·00	38·00
145a		75c. deep slate-lilac (8.8.41)	14·00	3·00
		ab. Ordinary paper (18.11.42)	2·50	3·50

146	**16**	1r. yellow-green (10.2.38)	£100	60·00
146a		1r. grey-black (8.8.41)	24·00	2·75
		ab. Ordinary paper (18.11.42)	1·50	3·50
147	**14**	1r.50 ultramarine (10.2.38)	25·00	3·75
		a. Ordinary paper (18.11.42)	4·50	8·50
		aw. Wmk inverted	£2250	
148	**15**	2r.25 olive (10.2.38)	45·00	9·00
		a. Ordinary paper (18.11.42)	21·00	23·00
149		5r. red (10.2.38)	13·00	5·00
		a. Ordinary paper (18.11.42)	20·00	27·00
135/49 Set of 25			£425	£150
135s/49s (ex 50c. bright lilac) Perf "Specimen" Set of 24			£500	

Examples of most values are known showing forged Victoria postmarks dated "NO 27", "SP 17 41", "DE 12 41", "SP 14 42", "DE 21 42" or "NO 16 43".

Lamp on mast flaw (R. 1/5)

1946 (23 Sept). Victory. As Nos. 110/11 of Antigua.

150		9c. light blue	10	10
151		30c. deep blue	30	10
		a. Lamp on mast flaw	26·00	
150s/1s Perf "Specimen" Set of 2			70·00	

Line by crown (R. 1/3)

1948 (5 Nov). Royal Silver Wedding. As Nos. 112/13 of Antigua.

152		9c. ultramarine	15	60
		a. Line by crown	26·00	
153		5r. carmine	12·00	30·00

Examples are known showing forged Victoria "C 11 NOV 48" postmarks.

1949 (10 Oct). 75th Anniv of U.P.U. As Nos. 114/17 of Antigua, but inscribed "SEYCHELLES" in recess.

154		18c. bright reddish purple	15	25
155		50c. purple	1·75	1·00
156		1r. grey	25	25
157		2r.25 olive	30	1·25
154/7 Set of 4			2·25	2·50

17 Sailfish   **18** Map of Indian Ocean

(Photo Harrison)

1952 (3 Mar). Various designs as T **14/16** but with new portrait and crown as in T **17/18**. Chalk-surfaced paper. Wmk Mult Script CA. P 14½×13½ (vert) or 13½×14½ (horiz).

158	**17**	2c. lilac	60	70
		a. Error. Crown missing, W 9a	£650	
		b. Error. St. Edward's Crown, W 9b	£130	£170
159	**15**	3c. orange	60	30
		a. Error. Crown missing, W 9a	£500	£500
		b. Error. St. Edward's Crown, W 9b	£150	£150
160	**14**	9c. chalky blue	60	1·75
		a. Error. Crown missing, W 9a	£950	
		b. Error. St. Edward's Crown, W 9b	£275	£350
161	**16**	15c. deep yellow-green	50	75
		a. Error. Crown missing, W 9a	£650	
		b. Error. St. Edward's Crown, W 9b	£250	£300
162	**18**	18c. carmine-lake	1·50	20
		a. Error. Crown missing, W 9a	£900	
		b. Error. St. Edward's Crown, W 9b	£300	£275
163	**16**	20c. orange-yellow	1·00	1·50
		a. Error. Crown missing, W 9a	£1100	£950
		b. Error. St. Edward's Crown, W 9b	£375	£400
164	**15**	25c. vermilion	70	1·50
		a. Error. Crown missing, W 9a	£1200	
		b. Error. St. Edward's Crown, W 9b	£400	
165	**17**	40c. ultramarine	1·00	1·25
		a. Error. Crown missing, W 9a	£1300	
		b. Error. St. Edward's Crown, W 9b	£550	
166	**16**	45c. purple-brown	1·00	30
		a. Error. Crown missing, W 9a	£1300	
		b. Error. St. Edward's Crown, W 9b	£475	£475
167	**14**	50c. reddish violet	1·25	1·75
		a. Error. Crown missing, W 9a	£1500	£1400
		b. Error. St. Edward's Crown, W 9b	£550	£650
168	**18**	1r. grey-black	3·25	3·00
		b. Error. St. Edward's Crown, W 9b	£1100	
169	**14**	1r.50 blue	7·00	12·00
		b. Error. St. Edward's Crown, W 9b	£2000	
170	**15**	2r.25 brown-olive	12·00	12·00
		b. Error. St. Edward's Crown, W 9b	£1400	
171	**18**	5r. red	13·00	14·00
		b. Error. St. Edward's Crown, W 9b	£1000	
172	**17**	10r. green	20·00	35·00
158/72 Set of 15			60·00	75·00

See *Introduction* re the watermark errors.

POSTAGE DUE STAMPS

D 1

(Frame recess, value typo B.W.)

1951 (1 Mar). Wmk Mult Script CA. P 11½.

D1	D 1	2c. scarlet and carmine	80	1·50
D2		3c. scarlet and green	2·00	1·50
D3		6c. scarlet and bistre	2·00	1·25
D4		9c. scarlet and orange	2·00	1·25
D5		15c. scarlet and violet	1·75	12·00
D6		18c. scarlet and blue	1·75	12·00
D7		20c. scarlet and brown	1·75	12·00
D8		30c. scarlet and claret	1·75	7·50
D1/8 Set of 8			12·50	45·00

The 2c. and 3c. were issued on Block CA watermark in 1964–65.

Sierra Leone

PRICES FOR STAMPS ON COVER TO 1945

Nos. 1/15	from × 10
Nos. 16/26	from × 15
Nos. 27/34	from × 20
Nos. 35/7	from × 10
No. 38	—
No. 39	from × 15
Nos. 41/52	from × 8
No. 53	—
No. 54	from × 40
Nos. 55/63	from × 5
Nos. 64/71	—
Nos. 73/84	from × 4
No. 85	—
Nos. 86/97	from × 4
No. 98	—
Nos. 99/110	from × 4
No. 111	—
Nos. 112/26	from × 2
Nos. 127/30	—
Nos. 131/45	from × 2
Nos. 146/8	—
Nos. 155/66	from × 2
No. 167	—
Nos. 168/78	from × 2
Nos. 179/80	—
Nos. 181/4	from × 6
Nos. 185/7	from × 5
Nos. 188/200	from × 2

CROWN COLONY AND PROTECTORATE

The first settlement in Sierra Leone intended as a home for repatriated Africans, and subsequently those released by the Royal Navy from slave ships, was established in 1787. The Sierra Leone Company was created by Act of Parliment in 1791, but its charter was surrendered in 1808 and the coastal settlements then became a Crown Colony. The inland region was proclaimed a British protectorate on 21 August 1896.

A post office was established in 1843 but, until the inclusion of Freetown in the British Post Office packet system in 1850, overseas mail was carried at irregular intervals by passing merchant or naval vessels.

The stamps of GREAT BRITAIN were not sold at Sierra Leone post offices, although examples from ships of the West African Squadron do exist with local cancellations.

PRINTERS. All issues of Sierra Leone until 1932 were typographed by De La Rue & Co. Ltd, London. .

HALF
PENNY

1   2   (3)

SIX.

Dot after "SIX" and break in octagonal frame (R. 19/11)

1859 (21 Sept)–**74**. No wmk. P 14.

1	1	6d. dull purple	£200	50·00
		a. Dot after "SIX"	£1000	£400
2		6d. grey-lilac (1865)	£250	40·00
		a. Dot after "SIX"		£350
3		6d. reddish violet (P 12½) (1872) ..	£375	60·00
		a. Dot after "SIX"		£450
4		6d. reddish lilac (1874)	50·00	27·00
		a. Dot after "SIX"	£350	£180

Imperforate proofs exist.

The paper used for the 6d. value often shows varying degrees of blueing, caused by a chemical reaction.

The 6d. plate contained 240 stamps arranged in panes of 20 (4×5) with the sheets containing 12 such panes in four horizontal rows of three.

1872–73. Wmk Crown CC. P 12½.

(a) Wmk sideways (April 1872).

7	2	1d. rose-red	75·00	35·00
8		3d. buff	£140	38·00
9		4d. blue	£180	38·00
10		1s. green	£475	55·00

(b) Wmk upright (Sept 1873).

11	2	1d. rose-red	£130	30·00
		w. Wmk inverted	£225	90·00
12		2d. magenta	£130	50·00
13		3d. saffron-yellow	£500	85·00
14		4d. blue	£325	90·00
15		1s. green	£475	90·00

1876. Wmk Crown CC. P 14.

16	2	½d. brown	3·00	8·50
		w. Wmk inverted	£140	
17		1d. rose-red	50·00	15·00
18		1½d. lilac (Nov)	50·00	9·00
19		2d. magenta	65·00	4·00
20		3d. buff	50·00	4·50
		w. Wmk inverted		
21		4d. blue	£170	6·50
		w. Wmk inverted		
22		1s. green	60·00	6·50
16/22 Set of 7			£400	48·00

1883 (June–19 Sept). Wmk Crown CA. P 14.

23	2	½d. brown	25·00	50·00
24		1d. rose-red (3.9.83*)	£200	35·00
25		2d. magenta	50·00	8·50
26		4d. blue	£900	28·00

*Earliest known postmark date.

1884 SIERRA 5s. LEONE SURCHARGE. From 2 June 1884 the administration decided that, as a temporary measure, revenue and fiscal duties were to be paid with ordinary postage stamps. At that time there was no postage value higher than 1s., so a local surcharge, reading "SIERRA 5s. LEONE", was applied to No. 22 (*Price £200 unused*). Until withdrawal on 1 March 1885 this surcharge was valid for both fiscal and postal purposes, although no genuine postal cover or piece has yet been found. One mint example is known with overprint inverted (*Price £850*).

Remainders of the surcharge were cancelled by a horizontal red brush stroke (*Price £32 with upright surcharge, £160 with inverted surcharge*).

1884 (July)–**91**. Wmk Crown CA. P 14.

27	2	½d. dull green	3·00	1·75
		w. Wmk inverted	£190	£140
28		1d. carmine	5·00	1·00
		a. Rose-carmine (1885?)	28·00	8·50
		aw. Wmk inverted	†	£140
29		1½d. pale violet (1889)	3·50	6·50
30		2d. grey	38·00	2·75
31		2½d. ultramarine (1891)	12·00	1·50
		w. Wmk inverted	†	£170
32		3d. yellow (1889)	3·50	10·00
33		4d. brown	2·50	2·00
		w. Wmk inverted	£225	
		ws. Ditto, optd "Specimen"	£200	
34		1s. red-brown (1888)	22·00	12·00
27/34 Set of 8			80·00	35·00
27s/34s (ex 1½d., 3d.) Optd "Specimen" Set of 6			£600	
27s/8sa, 30sa, 33sa Optd "Specimen" (perf 12) Set of 4			£1100	

1885–96. Wmk Crown CC. P 14.

35	1	6d. dull violet (1885)	60·00	24·00
		a. Bisected (3d.) (on cover)	†	£2500
		b. Dot after "SIX"	—	£180
36		6d. brown-purple (1890)	19·00	14·00
		a. Dot after "SIX"	£130	£110
		s. Optd "Specimen"	70·00	
		w. Wmk inverted		
37		6d. purple-lake (1896)	2·75	7·00
		a. Dot after "SIX"	55·00	80·00

Proofs of the 6d. brown-purple exist from 1889 on Crown CA watermark and perforated 12 (*Price £1500, unused*).

1893 (8 Jan). *Surch with T 3 by Govt Printer, Freetown.*

(a) On No. 18. Wmk Crown CC.

38	2	½d. on 1½d. lilac	£475	£700
		a. "PFNNY" (R.3/1)	£3000	£4000

(b) On No. 29. Wmk Crown CA.

39	2	½d. on 1½d. pale violet	4·50	3·00
		a. Surch inverted	£110	£110
		b. "PFNNY" (R. 3/1)	75·00	75·00
		ba. Ditto. Surch inverted	£2500	£5000

On Nos. 38/9 the surcharge and the cancelling bars were often applied separately using a separate forme. When the bar missed its intended position across the value tablet, second, or even third bars were added, sometimes by pen or brush. No. 39a exists with the bars either normal or inverted with the rest of the surcharge.

Forged surcharges with "HALF PENNY" shown on one line were prepared by employees of the printer. It is believed that only a single example of this forgery still exists.

The 6d. fiscal, inscribed "STAMP DUTY" as Type 6 surcharged "ONE-PENNY" is known used for postage between May and August 1894, but no official sanction for such usage has been found.

---

4   5

1896–97. Wmk Crown CA. P 14.

41	4	½d. dull mauve and green (1897).....	2·50	3·00
42		1d. dull mauve and carmine	4·25	1·75
43		1½d. dull mauve and black (1897).....	4·00	21·00
44		2d. dull mauve and orange	2·50	5·00
45		2½d. dull mauve and ultramarine......	2·50	1·25
46	5	3d. dull mauve and slate	8·50	7·00
47		4d. dull mauve and carmine (1897)..	9·50	13·00
48		5d. dull mauve and black (1897)....	13·00	15·00
49		6d. dull mauve (1897)	8·00	24·00
		w. Wmk inverted		£160
50		1s. green and black	6·00	20·00
51		2s. green and ultramarine	25·00	60·00
52		5s. green and carmine	70·00	£180
53		£1 purple/*red*	£170	£450
41/53 Set of 13			£300	£700
41s/53s Optd "Specimen" Set of 13			£225	

Examples of most values are known showing forged oval registered postmarks dated "16 JUL 11" or "4 SP 11".

POSTAGE
AND
REVENUE
(7)

6

2½d.   2½d.   2½d.
(8)   (9)   (10)

2½d.   2½d.   2½d.
(11)   (12)   (13)

POSTAGE AND   REVENUE
REVENUE   *Italic "N" (R. 3/4 of the setting)*
(14)

1897. *Fiscal stamps as T 6*. Wmk CA over Crown, w 7. P 14.

(a) Optd with T 7 (26 Feb*).

54		1d. dull purple and green	4·25	3·50
		a. Opt double	£1500	£1500

(b) Optd with T 7 and surch T 8, 10, 11 (with square stop) or 12 with six thin bars across the original face value (27 Feb*).

55	8	2½d. on 3d. dull purple and green	11·00	14·00
		a. Surch double	£29000	
		b. Surch double (Types 8+10)..	£24000	
		c. Surch double (Types 8+11)..	£38000	
		d. Bars omitted	£38000	
56	10	2½d. on 3d. dull purple and green..........	55·00	65·00
57	11	2½d. on 3d. dull purple and green..........	£160	£180
58	12	2½d. on 3d. dull purple and green..........	£325	£425
59	8	2½d. on 6d. dull purple and green..........	8·50	14·00
60	10	2½d. on 6d. dull purple and green..........	42·00	55·00
61	11	2½d. on 6d. dull purple and green..........	£120	£140
62	12	2½d. on 6d. dull purple and green..........	£275	£325

*Earliest known postmark date.

Nos. 55/8 and 59/62 were surcharged from a setting of 30 (10×3) which contained 22 examples of Type 8 (including three with square stops), five of Type 10, two of Type 11 and one of Type 12.

Two examples are known of No. 55a, five of No. 55b (of which two are in the Royal Collection) and two of No. 55c (one in the Royal Collection). A unique example of a double surcharge on No. 55 showing Types 8+12 is also in the Royal Collection.

No. 55d comes from the top row of a setting and was caused by the downward displacement of the overprint. Stamps in the lower rows show the overprint transposed with the obliterating bars at the top of the stamp.

(c) Optd with T 14 and surch T 8, 9, 10, 11 (with round stop) or 13 with five thin bars across the original face value (1 Mar).

63	8	2½d. on 1s. dull lilac	90·00	65·00
64	9	2½d. on 1s. dull lilac	£1400	£1200
65	10	2½d. on 1s. dull lilac	£800	£700
66	11	2½d. on 1s. dull lilac	£425	£400
		a. Italic "N"	£1300	£1200
66b	13	2½d. on 1s. dull lilac	£1400	£1200
67	8	2½d. on 2s. dull lilac	£1700	£2000
68	9	2½d. on 2s. dull lilac	£38000	£42000
69	10	2½d. on 2s. dull lilac	£16000	
70	11	2½d. on 2s. dull lilac	£9500	£11000
		a. Italic "N"	£20000	£20000
71	13	2½d. on 2s. dull lilac	£38000	£42000

The setting of 30 (10×3) used for both Nos. 63/6b and 67/71 contained 22 examples of Type 8 (including one with square stop), two examples of Type 9, two of Type 10, four of Type 11 (including one with italic "N") and one of Type 13.

Most examples of Nos. 63/6b are water-stained. Stamps in this condition are worth about 25% of the price quoted.

15   16

1903. Wmk Crown CA. P 14.

73	15	½d. dull purple and green	3·00	4·50
74		1d. dull purple and rosine	2·00	1·00
75		1½d. dull purple and black	1·25	12·00
76		2d. dull purple and brown-orange	3·75	16·00
77		2½d. dull purple and ultramarine	4·50	8·00
78	16	3d. dull purple and grey	9·50	13·00
79		4d. dull purple and rosine	7·00	14·00
80		5d. dull purple and black	8·00	35·00
81		6d. dull purple	11·00	19·00
82		1s. green and black	16·00	55·00
83		2s. green and ultramarine	50·00	65·00
84		5s. green and carmine	70·00	£110
85		£1 purple/*red*	£225	£250
73/85 *Set of 13*			£375	£550
73s/85s Optd "Specimen" *Set of 13*			£180	

1904–05. *Ordinary paper (1d.) or chalk-surfaced paper (others).* Wmk Mult Crown CA. P 14.

86	15	½d. dull purple and green (1905)	5·00	4·50
87		1d. dull purple and rosine (1905)	1·50	1·00
		a. Chalk-surfaced paper (1905)	4·50	1·50
88		1½d. dull purple and black (1905)	3·00	13·00
89		2d. dull purple and brown-orange (1905)	4·25	4·00
90		2½d. dull purple and ultramarine (1905)	4·50	2·00
91	16	3d. dull purple and grey (1905)	42·00	3·50
92		w. Wmk inverted	40·00	30·00
		4d. dull purple and rosine (1905)	7·50	7·00
		w. Wmk inverted	£100	
93		5d. dull purple and black (1905)	12·00	26·00
94		6d. dull purple (1905)	4·00	3·25
95		1s. green and black (1905)	7·50	9·00
96		2s. green and ultramarine (1905)	24·00	27·00
97		5s. green and carmine (1905)	30·00	50·00
98		£1 purple/*red* (1905)	£225	£250
86/98 *Set of 13*			£300	£325

1907–12. *Ordinary paper (½d. to 2½d.) or chalk-surfaced paper (others).* Wmk Mult Crown CA. P 14.

99	15	½d. green	1·00	50
100		1d. carmine	11·00	75
		a. Red	8·50	60
101		1½d. orange (1910)	1·25	2·00
102		2d. greyish slate (1909)	1·25	1·50
103		2½d. blue	3·75	3·00
104	16	3d. purple/*yellow* (1909)	7·50	2·75
		a. Ordinary paper (1912)	14·00	12·00
105		4d. black and red/*yellow* (1908)	2·25	1·60
106		5d. purple and olive-green (1908)	11·00	5·00
107		6d. dull and bright purple (1908)	11·00	8·00
108		1s. black/*green* (1908)	5·50	5·00
109		2s. purple and bright blue/*blue* (1908)	15·00	19·00
110		5s. green and red/*yellow* (1908)	40·00	55·00
111		£1 purple and black/*red* (1911)	£250	£180
99/111 *Set of 13*			£325	£250
99s/111s Optd "Specimen" *Set of 13*			£300	

Most values from the 1903, 1904–05 and 1907–12 issues are known with forged postmarks. These include oval registered examples dated "16 JUL 11" or "4 SP 11".

USED HIGH VALUES. The £2 and £5 values of the King George V series were intended for fiscal use only. Before the introduction of the airmail service at the end of 1926 there was no postal rate for which they could be used. Under the airmail rates used between 1926 and 1932 it is just possible that a very heavy letter may have required a £2 value. Postmarks on the £5 and on the £2 before December 1926 can only have been applied "by favour" or, in the case of the cds type, are on stamps removed from telegraph forms. Used prices quoted for Nos. 129/30 and 147/8 are for "by favour" cancellations.

17   18

19   20

1912–21. *Die I. Chalk-surfaced paper (3d. and 6d. to £5).* Wmk Mult Crown CA. P 14.

112	17	½d. blue-green	3·00	2·50
		a. Yellow-green (1914)	3·50	2·50
		b. Deep green (1919)	5·00	3·00
113		1d. carmine-red	2·25	30
		a. Scarlet (1916)	5·00	1·00
		b. Rose-red (1918)	5·00	80
		bw. Wmk inverted	†	£150
		bx. Wmk reversed	£140	£140
114		1½d. orange (1913)	2·00	2·50
		a. Orange-yellow (1919)	5·00	1·00
115		2d. greyish slate	1·25	20
		a. "A" of "CA" missing from wmk.		

116		w. Wmk inverted	35·00	35·00
		2½d. deep blue	11·00	2·50
		a. Ultramarine (1917)	1·00	80
116b	20	3d. purple/*yellow*	3·00	3·25
		ba. On pale yellow (1921)	3·25	3·25
117	18	4d. black and red/*yellow*	2·75	10·00
		a. On lemon (1915)	4·00	6·50
		b. Die II. On pale yellow (1921)	4·25	5·50
118		5d. purple and olive-green	1·25	7·00
119		6d. dull and bright purple	3·25	6·00
120	19	7d. purple and orange	3·00	8·50
121		9d. purple and black	5·00	12·00
122	18	10d. purple and red	3·00	18·00
124	20	1s. black/*green*	5·00	4·50
		a. On blue-green, green back	4·50	3·25
		w. Wmk inverted	55·00	55·00
125		2s. blue and purple/*blue*	13·00	5·50
126		5s. red and green/*yellow*	13·00	26·00
127		10s. red and green/*green*	70·00	£120
		a. Carmine and blue-green/*green*	95·00	£150
		b. Carmine and yellow-green/*green*	£100	£170
128		£1 black and purple/*red*	£160	£225
129		£2 blue and dull purple	£550	£750
		s. Optd "Specimen"	£110	
130		£5 orange and green	£1500	£2000
		s. Optd "Specimen"	£300	
112/28 *Set of 17*			£250	£400
112s/28s Optd "Specimen" *Set of 17*			£300	

Examples of Nos. 127/8 are known with part strikes of the forged postmarks mentioned after Nos. 99/111.

1921–27. *Die II. Chalk-surfaced paper (6d. to £5).* Wmk Mult Script CA. P 14.

131	17	½d. dull green	1·25	1·00
		a. Bright green	3·50	1·50
132		1d. bright violet (Die I) (1924)	2·00	2·25
		a. Die II (1925)	3·00	20
133		1½d. scarlet (1925)	1·75	1·25
134		2d. grey (1922)	1·25	20
135		2½d. ultramarine	1·75	11·00
136	18	3d. bright blue (1922)	1·25	1·25
137		4d. black and red/*pale yellow* (1925)	2·00	3·25
138		5d. purple and olive-green	1·25	1·25
139		6d. grey-purple and bright purple	1·25	2·50
		y. Wmk inverted and reversed		
140	19	7d. purple and orange (1927)	2·75	23·00
141		9d. purple and black (1922)	3·00	17·00
142	18	10d. purple and red (1925)	3·25	28·00
143	20	1s. black/*emerald* (1925)	9·50	7·00
144		2s. blue and dull purple/*blue*	9·50	10·00
		w. Wmk inverted	£130	£140
145		5s. red and green/*yellow* (1927)	9·50	55·00
146		10s. red and green/*green* (1927)	£100	£200
147		£2 blue and dull purple (1923)	£500	£700
		s. Optd "Specimen"	£110	
148		£5 orange and green (1923)	£1400	£1900
		s. Optd "Specimen"	£275	
131/46 *Set of 16*			£140	£325
131s/46s Optd "Specimen" *Set of 16*			£300	

21 Rice Field   22 Palms and Cola Tree

(Eng J.A.C. Harrison (T 21))

1932 (1 Mar). Wmk Mult Script CA.

(a) Recess Waterlow. P 12½.

155	21	½d. green	20	30
156		1d. violet	30	30
157		1½d. carmine	30	1·25
		a. Imperf between (horiz pair)		
158		2d. brown	30	30
159		3d. blue	70	1·75
160		4d. orange	70	8·50
161		5d. bronze-green	85	4·00
162		6d. light blue	70	3·25
163		1s. lake	3·00	7·50

(b) Recess B.W. P 12.

164	22	2s. chocolate	5·00	5·50
165		5s. deep blue	12·00	19·00
166		10s. green	65·00	£130
167		£1 purple	£120	£200
155/67 *Set of 13*			£190	£350
155s/67s Perf "Specimen" *Set of 13*			£190	

23 Arms of Sierra Leone   23a "Freedom"

23b Map of Sierra Leone   24 Old Slave Market. Freetown

25 Native fruit seller   25a Government sanatorium

25b Bullom canoe   26 Punting near Banana Islands

26a Government buildings, Freetown   26b Bunce Island

27 African Elephant   28 King George V

29 Freetown harbour

(Des Father F. Welsh. Recess B.W.)

1933 (2 Oct). *Centenary of Abolition of Slavery and of Death of William Wilberforce.* T **23/29**. Wmk Mult Script CA (sideways on horiz designs). P 12.

168	23	½d. green	1·00	1·25
169	23a	1d. black and brown	65	10
170	23b	1½d. chestnut	5·00	4·50
171	24	2d. purple	3·00	20
172	25	3d. blue	3·75	1·75
173	25a	4d. brown	6·50	10·00
174	25b	5d. green and chestnut	7·00	13·00
175	26	6d. black and brown-orange	8·00	8·00
176	26a	1s. violet	4·75	18·00
177	26b	2s. brown and light blue	26·00	40·00
178	27	5s. black and purple	£150	£170
179	28	10s. black and sage-green	£190	£275
180	29	£1 violet and orange	£375	£450
168/80 *Set of 13*			£700	£900
168s/80s Perf "Specimen" *Set of 13*			£500	

1935 (6 May). *Silver Jubilee. As Nos. 91/4 of Antigua, but ptd by B.W.* P 11×12.

181		1d. ultramarine and grey-black	1·00	2·50
		a. Extra flagstaff	50·00	75·00
		b. Short extra flagstaff	£150	
		c. Lightning conductor	45·00	
182		3d. brown and deep blue	1·25	8·50
		a. Extra flagstaff	70·00	£110
		b. Short extra flagstaff	£350	
		c. Lightning conductor	85·00	
183		5d. green and indigo	2·00	17·00
		a. Extra flagstaff	£110	£190
		b. Short extra flagstaff	£425	
		c. Lightning conductor	£120	
184		1s. slate and purple	11·00	7·50
		a. Extra flagstaff	£325	£250
		b. Short extra flagstaff	£375	
		c. Lightning conductor	£300	£250
181/4 *Set of 4*			14·00	32·00
181s/4s Perf "Specimen" *Set of 4*			£190	

For illustrations of plate varieties see Omnibus section following Zanzibar.

1937 (12 May). *Coronation. As Nos. 95/7 of Antigua.* P 11×11½.

185		1d. orange	70	1·00

186	2d. purple		90	1·00
187	3d. blue		1·50	3·75
185/7 Set of 3			2·75	5·25
185s/7s Perf "Specimen" Set of 3			75·00	

30 Freetown from the Harbour   **31** Rice Harvesting

(Recess Waterlow)

1938 (1 May)–44. Wmk Mult Script CA (sideways). P 12½.

188	30	½d. black and blue-green	15	40
189		1d. black and lake	40	60
		a. Imperf between (vert pair)	†	
190	31	1½d. scarlet	20·00	1·00
190a		1½d. mauve (1.2.41)	30	60
191		2d. mauve	40·00	2·50
191a		2d. scarlet (1.2.41)	30	2·00
192	30	3d. black and ultramarine	55	50
193		4d. black and red-brown (20.6.38)..	1·50	4·50
194	31	5d. olive-green (20.6.38)	5·00	4·00
195		6d. grey (20.6.38)	1·50	50
196	30	1s. black and olive-green (20.6.38).	2·25	70
196a		1s.3d. yellow-orange (1.7.44)	75	60
197	30	2s. black and sepia (20.6.38)	4·50	2·75
198	31	5s. red-brown (20.6.38)	10·00	10·00
199		10s. emerald-green (20.6.38)	19·00	12·00
200	30	£1 deep blue (20.6.38)	17·00	23·00
188/200 Set of 16			£110	60·00
188s/200s Perf "Specimen" Set of 16			£300	

1946 (1 Oct). Victory. As Nos. 110/11 of Antigua.

201	1½d. lilac		20	10
202	3d. ultramarine		20	30
201s/2s Perf "Specimen" Set of 2			70·00	

1948 (1 Dec). Royal Silver Wedding. As Nos. 112/13 of Antigua.

203	1½d. bright purple		15	15
204	£1 indigo		18·00	17·00

1949 (10 Oct). 75th Anniv of U.P.U. As Nos. 114/17 of Antigua.

205	1½d. purple		20	50
206	3d. deep blue		1·50	4·50
207	6d. grey		35	4·75
208	1s. olive		35	1·00
205/8 Set of 4			2·25	9·75

STAMP BOOKLETS

1929.

SB1	1s. booklet containing twelve 1d. (No. 132a)	
SB2	2s. booklet containing twelve 2d. (No. 134)	

Singapore

A Crown Colony until the end of 1957. From 1 August 1958, an internally self-governing territory designated the State of Singapore. From 16 September 1963, part of the Malaysian Federation until 9 August 1965, when it became an independent republic within the Commonwealth.

Stamps in the Crown Colony Victory design with face values of 8c. and 15c. were prepared for Singapore in 1946, but were not issued.

(Currency. 100 cents = 1 Malayan, dollar)

CROWN COLONY

(Typo D.L.R.)

1948 (1 Sept)–52. As T 58 of Malaysia (Straits Settlements), but inscribed "SINGAPORE" at foot. Chalk-surfaced paper. Wmk Mult Script CA.

(a) P 14.

1	1c. black	15	1·00
2	2c. orange	15	60
3	3c. green	50	1·00
4	4c. brown	20	1·25
5	6c. grey	40	1·00
6	8c. scarlet (1.10.48)	50	1·00
7	10c. purple	30	10
8	15c. ultramarine (1.10.48)	11·00	10
9	20c. black and green (1.10 48)	5·50	50
10	25c. purple and orange (1.10.48)	7·00	40
11	40c. red and purple (1.10.48)	9·50	5·00
12	50c. black and blue (1.10.48)	3·25	15
13	$1 blue and purple (1.10.48)	10·00	3·75
14	$2 green and scarlet (25.10.48)	48·00	4·75
15	$5 green and brown (1.10.48)	£110	5·50
1/15 Set of 15		£180	23·00

(b) P 17½×18

16	1c. black (21.5.52)	1·50	4·25
17	2c. orange (31.10.49)	1·50	2·00
19	4c. brown (1.7.49)	1·50	10
19a	5c. bright purple (1.9.52)	3·00	2·00
20	6c. grey (10.12.52)	2·00	2·00
21	8c. green (1.9.52)	7·50	3·50
21a	10c. purple (9.2.50)	60	10
22	12c. scarlet (1.9.52)	9·50	11·00
22a	15c. ultramarine (9.2.50)	17·00	10
23	20c. black and green (31.10.49)	8·00	3·50
24	20c. bright blue (1.9.52)	5·00	10
24a	25c. purple and orange (9.2.50)	1·50	10
25	35c. scarlet and purple (1.9.52)	5·00	30
25a	40c. red and purple (30.4.51*)	42·00	16·00
26	50c. black and blue (9.2.50)	8·50	10
27			

28	$1 blue and purple (31.10.49)		17·00	20
	a. Error. St. Edward's Crown. W **9**b		£7000	£3000
29	$2 green and scarlet (24.5.51)		90·00	1·25
	a. Error. St. Edward's Crown. W **9**b		£7000	
	w. Wmk inverted			
30	$5 green and brown (19.12.51)		£190	1·50
	w. Wmk inverted			
16/30 Set of 18			£375	42·00

*Earliest known postmark date.

Single-colour values were from single plate printings (Die II) and all bi-colour, except the 25c., from separate head and duty plates (Die I). For differences between the Dies see after Nos. 278/98 of Malaysia (Straits Settlements). The 25c. is unique in this series in that it combines a Die II frame with a separate head plate.

Nos. 28a and 29a occur on rows in the watermark in which the crowns and letters "CA" alternate.

Postal forgeries of the 50c., $1 and $2 exist on unwatermarked paper and perforated 14×14½.

1948 (25 Oct). Royal Silver Wedding. As Nos. 112/13 of Antigua.

31	10c. violet	75	80
32	$5. brown	£110	45·00

1949 (10 Oct). 75th Anniv of U.P.U. As Nos. 114/17 of Antigua.

33	10c. purple	75	60
34	15c. deep blue	6·00	3·25
35	25c. orange	6·00	3·00
36	50c. blue-black	6·00	3·25
33/6 Set of 4		17·00	9·00

Somaliland Protectorate

Egyptian post offices were opened in Somaliland during 1876 and the stamps of Egypt were used there until the garrisons were withdrawn in 1884.

Cancellations for these offices have been identified as follows (for illustrations of postmark types see SUDAN).

BARBARA (Berbera). Open 1876 to 1 November 1884. Circular datestamp as Sudan Type I.

ZEILA. Open 1876 to 1 November 1884. Circular datestamp as Sudan Types G and I, sometimes inscr ZEJLA. One example with seal type cancellation as Sudan Type B is also known.

Stamps of India were used at the two post offices from 1 January 1887 until 1903 usually cancelled with circular datestamps or the "B" obliterator used by all offices controlled from Bombay.

The Protectorate Post Office was established on 1 June 1903, when control of British Somaliland was transferred from the Indian Government to the British Foreign Office.

PRICES FOR STAMPS ON COVER TO 1945	
Nos. 1/11	from × 25
Nos. 12/13	
Nos. 18/22	from × 12
Nos. 23/4	
Nos. 25/30	from × 30
Nos. 32/59	from × 12
Nos. 60/92	from × 6
Nos. 93/104	from × 3
Nos. 105/16	from × 4
Nos. O1/13	from × 8
Nos. O14/15	—

(Currency. 12 pies = 1 anna; 16 annas = 1 rupee)

BRITISH SOMALILAND
(1)   2   3

SETTINGS OF TYPE 1

In all printings the ½, 1, 2, 2½, 3, 4, 8, 12a. and 1r. values were overprinted from a setting of 240 (2 panes 12×10, one above the other), covering the entire sheet at one operation.

The 6a., which was in sheets of 320 (4 panes, each 8×10), had a modified setting of 160, applied twice to each sheet.

The high values were overprinted in sheets of 96 (8 panes, each 4×3).

The settings for the low value stamps contained two slightly different styles of overprint, identified by the position of "B" of "BRITISH". Type A shows this letter over the "M" of "SOMALILAND" and Type B over the "OM".

For the first printing with the overprint at the top of the design the 240 position setting showed all the stamps in the upper pane and 63 in the lower as Type A, with the remaining 57 as Type B. When the setting was used for the printing with overprint at foot it was amended slightly so that one of the Type A examples in the upper pane became a Type B.

The 6a. value with overprint at top shows 250 examples of Type A and 70 as Type B in each sheet. This proportion altered in the printing with overprint at foot to 256 as Type A and 64 as Type B.

OVERPRINT VARIETIES

Missing second "I" in "BRITISH"—Occurs on the stamps with overprint at top from R. 2/6 of the upper pane and R. 5/1 of the lower, although it is believed that the example on the 2½a. (No. 4a) only occurs from the second position. On the later printing with overprint at foot a similar error can be found on R. 7/12 of the upper pane. Some examples of both these errors show traces of the letter remaining, but the prices quoted are for stamps with it completely omitted.

Figure "1" for first "I" in "BRITISH"—Occurs on R. 6/4 of the upper pane for all printings of the 240 impression setting. In addition it has been reported from R. 7/12 of the Queen Victoria 2½, 12a. and 1r. with overprint at foot. Both versions of the 6a. show the variety on

---

R. 6/4 of the upper left and upper right panes.

Curved overprint—Occurs on R. 3/4 of the top right-hand pane of the high values.

"SUMALILAND"—Occurs on R. 2/9 of the upper pane for all low values with the overprint at foot, except the 6a. A similar variety occurs on the high values from the same series on R. 1/3 of the top left pane.

"SOMAL.LAND"—Occurs on R. 7/5 of the lower pane from the 240 impression setting with the overprint at foot. In addition the Edwardian values of this series also have an example on R. 6/7. The 6a. has examples of the flaw on R. 6/9 and R. 7/5 of both the lower right and left panes. A similar variety occurs on the high values from the same series at R. 3/4 of the third pane in the right-hand column.

1903 (1 June). Nos. 80, 94, 96, 98, 100, 106/9, 114/16 and 118 of India (Queen Victoria) optd with T **1**, at top of stamp, in Calcutta. Wmk Elephant Head (6a.) or Star (others).

1	½a. yellow-green		2·75	4·25
	a. "BRIT SH"		£170	
	b. "BRITISH"		£150	£225
2	1a. carmine		2·75	3·75
	a. "BRIT SH"		£200	£275
	b. "BRITISH"		£150	
3	2a. pale violet		2·25	1·50
	a. "BRIT SH"		£350	£425
	b. "BRITISH"		£300	
	c. Opt double		£750	
4	2½a. ultramarine		2·00	1·75
	a. "BRIT SH"		£550	
	b. "BRITISH"		£325	
5	3a. brown-orange		3·25	3·00
	a. "BRIT SH"		£700	
	b. "BRITISH"		£350	£375
6	4a. slate-green		3·50	2·75
	a. "BRITISH"		£350	£325
7	6a. olive-bistre		5·50	4·50
	a. "BRITISH"		£250	£275
8	8a. dull mauve		3·75	5·00
	a. "BRITISH"		£350	
9	12a. purple/red		3·50	7·00
	a. "BRITISH"		£350	£450
10	1r. green and aniline carmine		7·00	10·00
	a. "BRITISH"		£425	
11	2r. carmine and yellow-brown		26·00	42·00
	a. Curved opt		£375	
12	3r. brown and green		22·00	48·00
	a. Curved opt		£375	
13	5r. ultramarine and violet		38·00	55·00
	a. Curved opt		£400	
1/13 Set of 13			£110	£170

1903 (1 Sept–2 Nov). Stamps of India optd with T **1**, at bottom of stamp, in Calcutta.

(a) On Nos. 80, 100, 106/9 and 118 (Queen Victoria).

18	2½a. ultramarine (2.11)		4·00	7·50
	a. "BR1TISH"		£190	
	b. "SUMALILAND"		£250	
	c. "SOMAL.LAND"		£250	
19	6a. olive-bistre (2.11)		7·00	6·00
	a. "BR1TISH"		£275	
	b. "SOMAL.LAND"		£160	
20	12a. purple/red (2.11)		8·50	13·00
	a. "BR1TISH"		£250	
	b. "SUMALILAND"		£325	
	c. "SOMAL.LAND"		£325	
21	1r. green and aniline carmine (2.11)		4·50	11·00
	a. "BR1TISH"		£300	
	b. "SUMALILAND"		£400	
	c. "SOMAL.LAND"		£400	
22	2r. carmine and yellow-brown (2.11)		90·00	£140
	a. Curved opt		£550	
	b. "SUMALILAND"		£550	
	c. "SOMAL.LAND"		£550	
23	3r. brown and green (2.11)		90·00	£150
	a. Opt double, both inverted with one albino		£700	
	b. Curved opt		£650	
	c. "SUMALILAND"		£650	
	d. "SOMAL.LAND"		£650	
24	5r. ultramarine and violet (2.11)		·85·00	£120
	a. Curved opt		£500	
	b. "SUMALILAND"		£500	
	c. "SOMAL.LAND"		£500	

(b) On Nos. 122/4, 127/8 and 133 (King Edward VII).

25	½a. green		2·25	55
	a. "BRIT SH"		£400	
	b. "BRITISH"		90·00	
	c. "SUMALILAND"		90·00	
	d. "SOMAL.LAND"		55·00	60·00
26	1a. carmine (8.10)		1·25	30
	a. "BRIT SH"		£275	
	b. "BRITISH"		90·00	90·00
	c. "SUMALILAND"		90·00	
	d. "SOMAL.LAND"		50·00	50·00
27	2a. violet (2.11)		1·75	2·50
	a. "BRIT SH"		£1000	
	b. "BRITISH"		£180	
	c. "SUMALILAND"		£180	
	d. "SOMAL.LAND"		95·00	
28	3a. orange-brown (2.11)		2·50	2·50
	a. "BRITISH"		£190	£250
	b. "SUMALILAND"		£190	
	c. "SOMAL.LAND"		95·00	
29	4a. olive (2.11)		1·50	4·00
	a. "BR1TISH"		£180	
	b. "SUMALILAND"		£180	
	c. "SOMAL.LAND"		95·00	
30	8a. purple (2.11)		1·75	2·25
	a. "BR1TISH"		£250	
	b. "SUMALILAND"		£250	
	c. "SOMAL.LAND"		£140	
18/30 Set of 13			£275	£400

(Typo D.L.R.)

1904 (15 Feb–3 Sept).

(a) Wmk Crown CA, P 14.

32	2	½a. dull green and green	2·00	4·25
33		1a. grey-black and red (3.9)	12·00	3·25
34		2a. dull and bright purple (3.9)	2·00	2·25

35		2½a. bright blue (3.9)......		4·25	3·75
36		3a. chocolate and grey-green (3.9)..		2·25	2·75
37		4a. green and black (3.9)...		2·25	4·75
38		6a. green and violet (3.9)........		5·50	17·00
39		8a. grey-black and pale blue (3.9)..		4·00	5·50
40		12a. grey-black and orange-buff (3.9)...		7·50	11·00

(b) Wmk Crown CC. P 14.

41	3	1r. green (3.9).............	12·00	40·00
42		2r. dull and bright purple (3.9)..	42·00	75·00
43		3r. green and black (3.9)...	42·00	90·00
44		5r. grey-black and red (3.9).....	42·00	90·00
32/44	*Set of 13*		£160	£325
32s/44s	Optd "Specimen" *Set of 13*		£180	

1905 (July)–11. *Ordinary paper. Wmk Mult Crown CA. P 14.*

45	2	½a. dull green and green........	1·25	7·50
46		1a. grey-black and red (10.7.05)..	15·00	6·00
		a. Chalk-surfaced paper (1906)	12·00	1·60
47		2a. dull and bright purple...	7·50	11·00
		a. Chalk-surfaced paper (1909)	13·00	14·00
48		2½a. bright blue........	3·00	10·00
49		3a. chocolate and grey-green...	2·00	15·00
		a. Chalk-surfaced paper (1911)	10·00	29·00
50		4a. green and black.......	4·00	16·00
		a. Chalk-surfaced paper (1911)	14·00	38·00
51		6a. green and violet........	3·00	25·00
		a. Chalk-surfaced paper (1911)	26·00	55·00
52		8a. grey-black and pale blue..	7·00	10·00
		a. Chalk-surfaced paper. *Black and blue* (27.1.11)...	27·00	70·00
53		12a. grey-black and orange-buff..	6·50	10·00
		a. Chalk-surfaced paper. *Black and orange-brown* (9.11.11)...	17·00	65·00

1909 (30 Apr–May). *Wmk Mult Crown CA. P 14.*

58	2	½a. bluish green (May)......	26·00	28·00
59		1a. red........	2·50	2·00
		s. Optd "Specimen".....	28·00	
45/59	*Set of 11*.......		65·00	£120

4   5

(Typo D.L.R.)

1912 (Sept)–19. *Chalk-surfaced paper (2a. and 3a. to 5r.). Wmk Mult Crown CA. P 14.*

60	4	½a. green (11.13)........	65	8·00
		w. Wmk inverted........	15·00	60·00
61		1a. red........	2·50	50
		a. *Scarlet* (1917).......	3·00	1·25
62		2a. dull and bright purple (12.13)...	3·50	16·00
		a. *Dull purple and violet-purple* (4.19)...	22·00	35·00
63		2½a. bright blue (10.13)..	1·00	8·50
64		3a. chocolate and grey-green (10.13)...	2·25	6·50
		w. Wmk inverted....	85·00	
65		4a. green and black (12.12)...	2·50	10·00
66		6a. green and violet (4.13)...	2·50	5·00
67		8a. grey-black and pale blue (10.13)...	3·50	15·00
68		12a. grey-black and orange-buff (10.13)...	3·50	21·00
69	5	1r. green (11.12).....	12·00	16·00
70		2r. dull purple and purple (4.19)..	20·00	70·00
71		3r. green and black (4.19)...	65·00	£130
72		5r. black and scarlet (4.19)..	60·00	£170
60/72	*Set of 13*........		£160	£425
60s/72s	Optd "Specimen" *Set of 13*...		£200	

1921. *Chalk-surfaced paper (2a. and 3a. to 5r.). Wmk Mult Script CA. P 14.*

73	4	½a. blue-green.........	2·75	12·00
74		1a. carmine-red.......	3·50	70
75		2a. dull and bright purple...	4·25	1·00
76		2½a. bright blue......	1·00	5·00
77		3a. chocolate and green....	2·50	7·50
78		4a. green and black......	2·50	7·50
79		6a. green and violet......	1·50	13·00
80		8a. grey-black and pale blue..	2·00	5·50
81		12a. grey-black and orange-buff..	8·50	15·00
82	5	1r. dull green......	8·50	48·00
83		2r. dull purple and purple....	23·00	55·00
84		3r. dull green and black...	35·00	£110
85		5r. black and scarlet....	70·00	£180
73/85	*Set of 13*........		£150	£425
73s/85s	Optd "Specimen" *Set of 13*....		£200	

Examples of most values are known showing a forged Berbera postmark dated "21 OC 1932".

1935 (6 May). *Silver Jubilee. As Nos. 91/4 of Antigua. but ptd by Waterlow. P 11×12.*

86		1a. deep blue and scarlet......	2·25	3·50
		m. "Bird" by turret.....	95·00	
87		2a. ultramarine and grey...	2·75	3·50
		k. Kite and vertical log....	75·00	
88		3a. brown and deep blue....	2·25	15·00
		k. Kite and vertical log....	£110	
		l. Kite and horizontal log....	£100	
89		1r. slate and purple....	7·00	16·00
		k. Kite and vertical log....	£140	
		l. Kite and horizontal log....	£150	£225
86/9	*Set of 4*........		13·00	35·00
86s/9s	Perf "Specimen" *Set of 4*...		90·00	

For illustrations of plate varieties see Omnibus section following Zanzibar.

1937 (13 May). *Coronation. As Nos. 95/7 of Antigua. but ptd by D.L.R. P 14.*

90		1a. scarlet........	15	25
91		2a. grey-black.....	55	2·00
92		3a. bright blue.....	1·10	1·00
90/2	*Set of 3*........		1·60	3·00
90s/2s	Perf "Specimen" *Set of 3*......		75·00	

6 Berbera Blackhead Sheep   7 Lesser Kudu

8 Somaliland Protectorate

(Des H. W. Claxton. Recess Waterlow)

1938 (10 May). *Portrait to left. Wmk Mult Script CA. P 12½.*

93	6	½a. green.......	50	5·00
94		1a. scarlet......	50	2·00
95		2a. maroon.....	2·50	3·00
96		3a. bright blue....	11·00	13·00
97	7	4a. sepia.....	5·50	10·00
98		6a. violet.....	9·00	12·00
99		8a. grey.....	2·25	12·00
100		12a. red-orange....	9·00	20·00
101	8	1r. green.....	8·50	55·00
102		2r. purple.....	19·00	55·00
103		3r. bright blue....	19·00	35·00
104		5r. black.....	22·00	35·00
		a. Imperf between (horiz pair)......	£18000	
93/104	*Set of 12*.......		95·00	£225
93s/104s	Perf "Specimen" *Set of 12*........		£190	

Examples of most values are known showing a forged Berbera postmark dated "15 AU 38".

> Following the Italian Occupation, from 19 August 1940 until 16 March 1941, the stamps of ADEN were used at Berbera from 1 July 1941 until 26 April 1942.

9 Berbera Blackhead Sheep

5 Cents (10)   1 Shilling (11)

(Recess Waterlow)

1942 (27 Apr). *As T 6/8 but with full-face portrait of King George VI, as in T 9. Wmk Mult Script CA. P 12½.*

105	9	½a. green.......	20	40
106		1a. scarlet.....	20	10
107		2a. maroon.....	50	20
108		3a. bright blue....	2·00	20
109	7	4a. sepia.....	3·00	30
110		6a. violet....	3·00	20
111		8a. grey....	3·25	20
112		12a. red-orange....	3·25	50
113	8	1r. green....	2·00	1·00
114		2r. purple....	2·25	4·75
115		3r. bright blue....	3·75	9·00
116		5r. black....	8·00	8·00
105/16	*Set of 12*.......		28·00	22·00
105s/16s	Perf "Specimen" *Set of 12*......		£190	

1946 (15 Oct). *Victory. As Nos. 110/11 of Antigua.*

117		1a. carmine.......	10	10
		a. Perf 13½.....	14·00	45·00
118		3a. blue....	10	10
117s/18s	Perf "Specimen" *Set of 2*...		65·00	

1949 (28 Jan). *Royal Silver Wedding. As Nos. 112/13 of Antigua.*

119		1a. scarlet.....	10	10
120		5r. black....	3·75	4·00

1949 (24 Oct*). *75th Anniv of U.P.U. As Nos. 114/17 of Antigua. Surch with face values in annas.*

121		1a. on 10c. carmine......	20	40
122		3a. on 30c. deep blue (R.)...	1·25	1·75
123		6a. on 50c. purple.....	35	2·25
124		12a. on 1s. red-orange....	35	1·25
121/4	*Set of 4*........		1·90	5·00

*This is the local date of issue. The Crown Agents released these stamps in London on 10 October.

(New Currency. 100 cents = 1 shilling)

1951 (1 Apr). *1942 issue surch as T 10/11.*

125		5c. on ½a. green......	30	1·50
126		10c. on 2a. maroon....	30	70
127		15c. on 3a. bright blue....	1·75	2·00
128		20c. on 4a. sepia....	2·00	20
129		30c. on 6a. violet....	1·75	1·00
130		50c. on 8a. grey....	2·50	20
131		70c. on 12a. red-orange....	4·00	5·00
132		1s. on 1r. green....	2·00	75
133		2s. on 2r. purple....	5·50	16·00
134		2s. on 3r. bright blue....	7·00	6·00
135		5s. on 5r. black (R.)......	9·50	8·50
125/35	*Set of 11*......		32·00	38·00

OFFICIAL STAMPS

SERVICE

BRITISH	BRITISH	
SOMALILAND	SOMALILAND	**O.H.M.S.**
(O 1)	(O 2)	(O 3)

SETTING OF TYPE O 1

The 240 impression setting used for the Official stamps differs considerably from that on the contemporary postage issue with overprint at foot, although the "BR1TISH" error can still be found on R. 6/4 of the upper pane. The Official setting is recorded as consisting of 217 overprints as Type A and 23 as Type B.

OVERPRINT VARIETIES

Figure "1" for first "I" in "BRITISH"—Occurs on R. 6/4 of the upper pane as for the postage issue.

"BRITIS H"—Occurs on R. 8, stamps 4 and 10 of the lower pane.

1903 (1 June). *Nos. O45, O48, O49a and O50/1 of India (Queen Victoria optd "O.H.M.S.".) additionally optd with Type O 1 in Calcutta.*

O1	½a. yellow-green........	6·50	48·00
	a. "BR1TISH".....	£350	
	b. "BRITIS H".....	£160	
O2	1a. carmine....	15·00	9·00
	a. "BR1TISH".....	£375	£325
	b. "BRITIS H".....	£180	
O3	2a. pale violet....	8·00	50·00
	a. "BR1TISH".....	£425	
	b. "BRITIS H".....	£200	
O4	8a. dull mauve....	10·00	£375
	a. "BR1TISH".....	£1100	
	b. "BRITIS H".....	£500	
	c. Stop omitted after "M" of "O.H.M.S." (lower pane R. 12/10)	£2000	
O5	1r. green and carmine....	10·00	£550
	a. "BR1TISH".....	£1100	
	b. "BRITIS H".....	£500	
O1/5	*Set of 5*........	45·00	£900

No. O4c was caused by an attempt to correct a minor spacing error of the "O.H.M.S." overprint which is known on the equivalent India Official stamp.

SETTING OF TYPE O 2

This 240 impression setting of "BRITISH SOMALILAND" also differs from that used to prepare the postage issue with overprint at foot, although many of the errors from the latter still occur in the same positions for the Official stamps. The setting used for Nos. O6/9f contained 180 overprints as Type A and 60 as Type B.

OVERPRINT VARIETIES

Missing second "I" in "BRITISH"—Occurs R. 7/12 of upper pane as for the postage issue.

Figure "1" for first "I" in "BRITISH"—Occurs R. 6/4 of upper pane as for the postage issue.

"SUMALILAND"—Occurs R. 2/9 of the upper pane as for the postage issue.

"SOMAL.LAND"—Occurs R. 6/7 of the lower pane as for the postage issue.

SERVICE
(O 2a)

"SERVICE" in wrong fount (Type O 2a)—Occurs R. 1/7 of lower pane.

1903. *Prepared for use but not issued. Nos. 106, 122/4 and 133 of India (1r. Queen Victoria, rest King Edward VII), optd with Type O 2 in Calcutta.*

O6	½a. green.......	40	
	a. "BRIT SH".....	70·00	
	b. "BR1TISH".....	55·00	
	c. "SUMALILAND".....	55·00	
	d. "SOMAL.LAND".....	45·00	
	e. "SERVICE" as Type O 2a..	50·00	
O7	1a. carmine....	40	
	a. "BRIT SH".....	70·00	
	b. "BR1TISH".....	55·00	
	c. "SUMALILAND".....	55·00	
	d. "SOMAL.LAND".....	45·00	
	e. "SERVICE" as Type O 2a..	50·00	
O8	2a. violet....	70	
	a. "BRIT SH".....	£100	
	b. "BR1TISH".....	85·00	
	c. "SUMALILAND".....	85·00	
	d. "SERVICE" as Type O 2a..	75·00	
O9	8a. purple....	4·00	
	a. "BRIT SH".....	£1800	
	b. "BR1TISH".....	£850	
	c. "SUMALILAND".....	£850	
	d. "SERVICE" as Type O 2a..	£850	
O9f	1r. green and aniline carmine..	17·00	
	fa. "BRIT SH".....	£1800	
	fb. "BR1TISH".....	£850	
	fc. "SUMALILAND".....	£850	
	fd. "SOMAL.LAND".....	£850	
	fe. "SERVICE" as Type O 2a..	£850	
O6/9f	*Set of 5*........	20·00	

Used examples of Nos. O6/9f are known, but there is no evidence that such stamps did postal duty.

SETTING OF TYPE O 3

The anna values were overprinted in sheets of 120 (2 panes 6×10) from a setting matching the pane size. The full stop after the "M" on the fifth vertical column was either very faint or completely omitted. The prices quoted are for stamps with the stop missing; examples with partial stop are worth much less.

The 1r. value was overprinted from a separate setting of 60 which did not show the "missing stop" varieties.

1904 (1 Sept)–**05**. *Stamps of Somaliland Protectorate optd with Type* O **3**.

(a) Wmk Crown CA. P 14.

O10	**2**	½a. dull green and green	4·25	48·00
		a. No stop after "M"	£275	
O11		1a. grey-black and carmine	3·25	7·00
		a. No stop after "M"	£200	£275
O12		2a. dull and bright purple	£180	65·00
		a. No stop after "M"	£2000	£700
O13		8a. grey-black and pale blue...........	60·00	£140
		a. No stop after "M"	£550	£700

(b) Wmk Mult Crown CA.

O14	**2**	2a. dull and bright purple, **O** (7.05?)...	80·00	£800
		a. No stop after "M"	£1900	

(c) Wmk Crown CC.

O15	**3**	1r. green..	£170	£600
O10s/13s , O15s Optd "Specimen" *Set of 5*			£130	

South Africa

South Africa as a nation, rather than a geographical term, came into being with the creation of the Union of South Africa on 31 May 1910.

The development, both political and philatelic, of the area is very complex and the method adopted by the catalogue is to first list, in alphabetical order, the various colonies and republics which formed this federation, followed by stamps for the Union of South Africa.

The section is divided as follows:

I. CAPE OF GOOD HOPE. British Kaffraria. Mafeking Siege Stamps. Vryburg
II. GRIQUALAND WEST
III. NATAL
IV. NEW REPUBLIC
V. ORANGE FREE STATE. Orange River Colony
VI. TRANSVAAL. Pietersburg. Local British Occupation Issues
VII. ZULULAND
VIII. BRITISH ARMY FIELD OFFICES DURING SOUTH AFRICAN WAR
IX. UNION OF SOUTH AFRICA

I. CAPE OF GOOD HOPE

PRICES FOR STAMPS ON COVER

Nos. 1/4	from × 4
Nos. 5/14	from × 3
Nos. 18/21	from × 5
No. 22	
Nos. 23/6	from × 5
Nos. 27/31	from × 8
Nos. 32/3	from × 10
No. 34	from × 25
No. 35	from × 20
No. 36	from × 10
Nos. 37/8	from × 25
Nos. 39/45	from × 10
Nos. 46/7	from × 12
Nos. 48/54	from × 10
Nos. 55/6	from × 25
No. 57	from × 50
Nos. 58/69	from × 10
Nos. 70/8	from × 6

PRICES. Our prices for early Cape of Good Hope are for stamps in very fine condition. Exceptional copies are worth more, poorer copies considerably less.

1 Hope

2

(Des Charles Bell, Surveyor-General. Eng W. Humphrys. Recess P.B.)

1853 (1 Sept). W **2**. Imperf.

(a) Paper deeply blued.

1	1	1d. pale brick-red	£3750	£300
		a. Deep brick-red	£5000	£325
		b. Wmk sideways	†	£400
2		4d. deep blue	£2250	£160
		a. Wmk sideways	£3000	£250

Plate proofs of the 4d. in a shade similar to the issued stamp exist on ungummed watermarked paper. The blueing on the reverse of these proofs is uneven giving a blotchy appearance.

(b) Paper slightly blued (blueing not pronounced at back).

3	1	1d. brick-red	£3000	£200
		a. Brown-red	£3250	£225
		b. Wmk sideways	†	£325
4		4d. deep blue	£1300	£110
		a. Blue	£1400	£150
		b. Wmk sideways	†	£275

PERKINS BACON "CANCELLED". For notes on these handstamps showing "CANCELLED" between horizontal bars forming an oval, see Catalogue Introduction.

1855–63. W **2**.

(a) Imperf.

5	1	1d. brick-red/*cream toned paper* (1857)	£5000	£900
		a. Rose (1858) (H/S "CANCELLED" in oval £17000)	£450	£200
		ab. Wmk sideways	—	£425
		b. Deep rose-red	£650	£250
		ba. Wmk sideways	—	£425

6		4d. deep blue/*white paper* (1855)	£650	50·00
		a. Blue (H/S "CANCELLED" in oval £17000)	£475	50·00
		b. Bisected (on cover)	†	£35000
		c. Wmk sideways	†	£170
7		6d. pale rose-lilac/*white paper* (18.2.58) (H/S "CANCELLED" in oval £13000)	£800	£200
		a. Wmk sideways	†	£900
		b. Deep rose-lilac/white paper	£1700	£300
		c. Slate-lilac/blued paper (1862)	£4250	£450
		d. Slate-purple/blued paper (1863)	£3500	£1000
		e. Bisected (on cover)	†	—
8		1s. brt yellow-green/*white paper* (18.2.58) (H/S "CANCELLED" in oval £17000)	£2750	£180
		a. Wmk sideways	†	£1000
		b. Deep dark green (1859)	£275	£500

The method adopted for producing the plate of the 4d., 6d and 1s. stamps involved the use of two dies, so that there are two types of each of these values differing slightly in detail, but produced in equal numbers.

The 1d. value in dull rose on ungummed watermarked paper with the watermark sideways is a plate proof.

The 4d. is known bisected in 1858 and used with two other 4d. values to pay the inland registered fee. The 6d. is known bisected and used with 1d. for 4d. rate.

The paper of No. 5 is similar to that of Nos. 1/4, but is without the blueing. It is much thicker than the white paper used for later printings of the 1d. The evolution of the paper on these Cape of Good Hope stamps is similar to that on the line-engraved issues of Great Britain. Examples of the 6d. slate-lilac apparently on white paper have had the blueing washed out.

The 4d. value is known printed in black on white watermarked paper. Twelve authenticated copies have been recorded, the majority of which show cancellations or, at least, some indication that they have been used.

It was, at one time, believed that these stamps came from a small supply printed. in black to mark the death of the Prince Consort, but references to examples can be found in the philatelic press before news of this event reached Cape Town.

It is now thought that these stamps represent proof sheets, possibly pressed into service during a shortage of stamps in 1861. (*Price* £35000 *un*, £30000 *with obliteration*).

(b) Unofficially rouletted.

9	1	1d. brick-red	†	£3000
10		4d. blue	†	£2250
11		6d. rose-lilac	†	£1500
12		1s. bright yellow-green	†	£3250
		a. Deep dark green	†	£3500

These rouletted stamps are best collected on cover.

3 Hope

(Local provisional (so-called "wood-block") issue. Engraved on steel by C. J. Roberts. Printed from stereotyped plates by Saul Solomon & Co, Cape Town)

1861 (Feb–Apr). *Laid paper.* Imperf.

13	3	1d. vermilion (27 February)	£14000	£2250
		a. Carmine (7 March)	£24000	£3000
		b. Brick-red (10 April)	£35000	£4250
		c. Error. Pale milky blue	£150000	£28000
		ca. Pale bright blue	—	£30000
14		4d. pale milky blue (23 February)	£20000	£1700
		aa. Retouch or repair to right-hand corner	—	£6000
		a. Pale grey-blue (March?)	£21000	£1700
		b. Pale bright blue (March?)	£21000	£2000
		ba. Retouch or repair to right-hand corner	—	£6000
		c. Deep bright blue (12 April)	£95000	£4500
		d. Blue	£25000	£3000
		e. Error. Vermilion	£150000	£40000
		ea. Carmine	—	£95000
		f. Sideways tête-bêche (pair)	†	£120000

Nos. 13/14 were each issued in *tête-bêche* pairs normally joined at edges bearing the same inscription ("POSTAGE" against "POSTAGE", etc). No. 14f, of which only one used example is known, comes from the first printing and shows the right-hand stamp misplaced so that "FOUR PENCE" adjoins "POSTAGE".

Nos. 13c/ca and 14e/ea were caused by the inclusion of incorrect clichés in the plates of the 1d. or 4d. values.

Both values were officially reprinted in March 1883, on wove paper. The 1d. is in deep red, and the 4d. in a deeper blue than that of the deepest shade of the issued stamp.

Specimens of the reprints have done postal duty, but their use thus was not intended. There are no reprints of the errors or of the retouched 4d.

Further reprints were made privately but with official permission, in 1940/41, in colours much deeper than those of any of the original printings, and on thick carton paper.

Examples of the 4d. are known unofficially rouletted.

Early in 1863, Perkins Bacon Ltd handed over the four plates used for printing the triangular Cape of Good Hope stamps to De La Rue & Co, Ltd, who made all the subsequent printings.

(Printed from the P.B. plates by D.L.R.)

1863–64. Imperf.

*(a) W **2**.*

18	1	1d. deep carmine-red (1864)	£160	£225
		a. Wmk sideways	£300	£300
		b. Deep brown-red	£375	£250
		ba. Wmk sideways	£500	£300
		c. Brownish red	£375	£225
		ca. Wmk sideways	£500	£275

19		4d. deep blue (1864)	£160	55·00
		a. Blue	£170	65·00
		b. Slate-blue	£2000	£500
		c. Steel-blue	£2000	£250
		d. Wmk sideways	£500	£180
20		6d. bright mauve (1864)	£200	£450
		a. Wmk sideways	†	£1200
21		1s. bright emerald-green	£400	£450
		a. Pale emerald-green	£1000	

(b) Wmk Crown CC (sideways).

22	1	1d. deep carmine-red	—	£22000

No. 22 was a trial printing, and is only known unused.

Our prices for the 4d. blue are for stamps which are blue by comparison with the other listed shades. An exceptionally pale shade is recognised by specialists and is rare.

With the exception of the 4d., these stamps may be easily distinguished from those printed by Perkins Bacon by their colours, which are quite distinct.

The De La Rue stamps of all values are less clearly printed, the figure of Hope and the lettering of the inscriptions standing out less boldly, while the fine lines of the background appear blurred and broken when examined under a glass. The background as a whole often shows irregularity in the apparent depth of colour, due to wear of the plates.

For note regarding the two dies of the 4d., 6d., and 1s. values, see after No. 8.

All the triangular stamps were demonetised as from 1 October 1900.

4 "Hope" seated, with vine and ram. (With outer frame-line)   (5)

(Des Charles Bell. Die engraved on steel and stamps typo by D.L.R.)

1864–77. *With outer frame-line surrounding the design.* Wmk Crown CC. P 14.

23	4	1d. carmine-red (5.65)	85·00	25·00
		a. Rose-red	80·00	24·00
		w. Wmk inverted	£275	£130
24		4d. pale blue (8.65)	£100	3·25
		a. Blue	£100	3·25
		b. Ultramarine	£250	55·00
		c. Deep blue (1872)	£150	3·50
		w. Wmk inverted	£400	£150
25		6d. pale lilac (before 21.3.64)	£110	22·00
		a. Deep lilac	£200	7·00
		b. Violet (to bright) (1877)	£130	1·50
		w. Wmk inverted	†	£275
26		1s. deep green (1.64)	£500	18·00
		a. Green	£110	3·50
		ax. Wmk reversed		
		b. Blue-green	£120	4·50
		w. Wmk inverted	£600	£150

The 1d. rose-red, 6d. lilac, and 1s. blue-green are known imperf, probably from proof sheets.

The 1d. and 4d. stamps of this issue may be found with side and/or top outer frame-lines missing, due to wear of the plates.

See also Nos. 44 and 52/3.

(Surch by Saul Solomon & Co, Cape Town)

1868 (17 Nov). *No. 25a surch with T **5**.*

27	4	4d. on 6d. deep lilac (R.)	£250	16·00
		a. "Peuce" for "Pence"	£1800	£700
		b. "Fonr" for "Four"	—	£700
		w. Wmk inverted	—	£275

Specimens may also be found with bars omitted or at the top of the stamp, due to misplacement of the sheet.

The space between the words and bars varies from 12½ to 16 mm, stamps with spacing 15½ and 16 mm being rare. There were two printings, one of 120,000 in November 1868 and another of 1,000,000 in December. Stamps showing widest spacings are probably from the earlier printing.

6 (No outer frame-line)

(Die re-engraved. Typo D.L.R.)

1871–76. *Outer frame-line removed.* Wmk Crown CC. P 14.

28	6	½d. grey-black (*shades*) (12.75)	18·00	8·00
		w. Wmk inverted	—	£100
29		1d. carmine-red (*shades*) (2.72)	32·00	60
		w. Wmk inverted	£275	£120
30		4d. dull blue (*shades*) (12.76)	£100	75
		b. Ultramarine	£200	50·00
		w. Wmk inverted	£325	90·00
31		5s. yellow-orange (25.8.71)	£350	16·00

The ½d., 1d. and 5s. are known imperf, probably from proof sheets.

See also Nos. 36, 39, 40/3, 48/51, 54, 61/2 and 64/8.

ONE PENNY   **THREE PENCE**

(7)   (8)

(Surch by Saul Solomon & Co, Cape Town)

1874-76. *Nos. 25a and 26a surch with T* **7**.

32	**4**	1d. on 6d. deep lilac (R.) (1.9.74)	£500	90·00
		a. "E" of "PENNY" omitted	—	£1000
33		1d. on 1s. green (11.76)	80·00	50·00

These provisionals are found with the bar only, either across the centre of the stamp or at top, with value only; or with value and bar close together, either at top or foot. Such varieties are due to misplacement of sheets during surcharging.

1879 (1 Nov). *No. 30 surch with T* **8**.

34	**6**	3d. on 4d. blue (R.)	£100	1·75
		a. "PENCB" for "PENCE"	£1700	£225
		b. "THE.EE" for "THREE"	£2000	£275
		c. Surch double	£8500	£3250
		d. Variety b. double		

The double surcharge must also have existed showing variety *a*. but only variety *b*. is known.

There are numerous minor varieties, including letters broken or out of alignment, due to defective printing and use of poor type.

The spacing between the bar and the words varies from 16½ to 18 mm.

THREEPENCE (9)   **3** (10)   **3** (11)

(Surch by D.L.R.)

1880 (Feb). *Special printing of the 4d. in new colour, surch, with T* **9**. *Wmk Crown CC.*

35	**6**	3d. on 4d. pale dull rose	70·00	1·75
		w. Wmk inverted	—	£200

A minor constant variety exists with foot of "P" in "PENCE" broken off, making the letter appear shorter.

1880 (1 July). *Wmk Crown CC. P* 14.

36	**6**	3d. pale dull rose	£190	25·00
		w. Wmk inverted	—	£300

(Surch by Saul Solomon & Co, Cape Town)

1880 (Aug). *No. 36 surch.*

37	**10**	"3" on 3d. pale dull rose	75·00	1·50
		a. Surch inverted	£900	40·00
		b. Vert pair. Nos. 37/8	£950	£400
		w. Wmk inverted	—	£150
38	**11**	"3" on 3d. pale dull rose	£190	7·00
		a. Surch inverted	£8000	£950
		w. Wmk inverted	—	£400

The "3" (T **10**) is sometimes found broken. Vert pairs are known showing the two types of surcharge *se-tenant*, and vertical strips of three exist, the top stamp having surcharge T **10**, the middle stamp being without surcharge, and the lower stamp having surcharge T **11** (*Price for strip of 3* £4250 *un.*).

1881 (Jan). *Wmk Crown CC. P* 14.

39	**6**	3d. pale claret	£140	2·75
		a. Deep claret	£110	2·50
		w. Wmk inverted		

This was a definite colour change made at the request of the Postmaster-General owing to the similarity between the colours of the 1d. stamp and the 3d. in pale dull rose. Imperf copies are probably from proof sheets.

Proofs of this value were printed in brown, on unwatermarked wove paper and imperf, but the colour was rejected as unsuitable.

1882 (July)-**83**. *Wmk Crown CA. P* 14.

40	**6**	3d. black (1.9.82)	25·00	2·25
		a. Grey-black	22·00	2·25
		w. Wmk inverted	—	£140
41		1d. rose-red	55·00	1·50
		a. Deep rose-red	50·00	1·50
		w. Wmk inverted	—	£170
42		2d. pale bistre (1.9.82)	95·00	60
		a. Deep bistre	£100	60
		w. Wmk inverted	—	£170
43		3d. pale claret	7·00	1·25
		a. Deep claret	11·00	75
		aw. Wmk inverted	—	£100
44	**4**	6d. mauve (to bright) (8.82)	90·00	70
45	**6**	5s. orange (8.83)	£800	£225

Imperf pairs of the ½d., 1d. and 2d. are known, probably from proof sheets.

One Half-penny. (12)   **13** "Cabled Anchor"

(Surch by Saul Solomon & Co, Cape Town)

1882 (July). *Nos. 39a and 43a surch with T* **12**.

46	**6**	½d. on 3d. deep claret (Wmk CC)	£3250	£130
		a. Hyphen omitted	—	£3250
47		½d. on 3d. deep claret (Wmk CA)	28·00	3·75
		a. "p" in "penny" omitted	£2000	£700
		b. "y" in "penny" omitted	£1000	£600
		c. Hyphen omitted	£650	£350
		w. Wmk inverted	—	£300

Varieties also exist with broken and defective letters, and with the obliterating bar omitted or at the top of the stamp.

1884-90. *W* **13**. *P* 14.

48	**6**	½d. black (1.86)	5·00	10
		a. Grey-black	4·75	10
		w. Wmk inverted	—	£375
49		1d. rose-red (12.85)	5·50	10
		a. Carmine-red	5·50	10
		w. Wmk inverted	—	£170
50		2d. pale bistre (12.84)	25·00	1·25
		a. Deep bistre	6·50	10
		w. Wmk inverted	—	£130

51		4d. blue (6.90)	12·00	50
		a. Deep blue	12·00	50
52	**4**	6d. reddish purple (12.84)	60·00	1·60
		a. Purple (shades)	11·00	20
		b. Bright mauve	11·00	50
		w. Wmk inverted	—	£300
53		1s. green (12.85)	£140	5·00
		a. Blue-green (1889)	90·00	50
		w. Wmk inverted	—	£375
54	**6**	5s. orange (7.87)	90·00	5·50
48/54		Set of 7	£200	6·25

All the above stamps are known in imperf pairs, probably from proof sheets.

For later shade and colour changes, etc., see Nos. 61, etc.

2½d (14)   **15**   (16)

(Surch by D.L.R.)

1891 (Mar). *Special printing of the 3d. in new colour, surch with T* **14**.

55	**6**	2½d. on 3d. pale magenta	7·00	1·50
		a. Deep magenta	4·00	20
		b. "1" with horiz serif	55·00	32·00

No. 55b occurs on two stamps (Nos. 8 and 49) of the pane of 60.

Two types of "d" are found in the surcharge, one with square end to serif at top, and the other with pointed serif.

1892 (June). *W* **13**. *P* 14.

56	**15**	2½d. sage-green	11·00	10
		a. Olive-green	13·00	55

See also No. 63.

(Surch by W. A. Richards & Sons, Cape Town)

1893 (Mar). *Nos. 50/a surch with T* **16**.

57	**6**	1d. on 2d. pale bistre	5·00	1·50
		a. Deep bistre	3·25	50
		b. No stop after "PENNY"	55·00	13·00
		c. Surch double	—	£425

No. 57b occurs on stamp No. 42 of the upper left-hand pane, and on No. 6 of the lower right-hand pane.

Minor varieties exist showing broken letters and letters out of alignment or widely spaced. Also with obliterating bar omitted, due to misplacement of the sheet during surcharging.

17 "Hope" standing. Table Bay in background   **18** Table Mountain and Bay with Arms of the Colony

(Des Mr. Mountford. Typo D.L.R.)

1893 (Oct)-**1902**. *W* **13**. *P* 14.

58	**17**	½d. green (9.98)	3·00	10
59		1d. rose-red	4·00	1·50
		a. Carmine	1·25	10
		aw. Wmk inverted	†	£120
60		3d. magenta (3.02)	4·00	1·75

The 1d. is known in imperf pairs, probably from proof sheets.

1893-98. *New colours, etc. W* **13**. *P* 14.

61	**6**	½d. yellow-green (12.96)	1·50	50
		a. Green	2·75	50
62		2d. chocolate-brown (3.97)	2·00	75
63	**15**	2½d. pale ultramarine (3.96)	5·00	15
		a. Ultramarine	5·00	10
64	**6**	3d. bright magenta (9.98)	9·00	85
65		4d. sage-green (3.97)	4·50	2·25
66		1s. blue-green (12.93)	65·00	4·50
		a. Deep blue-green	80·00	9·00
67		1s. yellow-ochre (5.96)	10·00	50
68		5s. brown-orange (6.96)	75·00	3·50
61/8		Set of 8	£160	12·50

(Des E. Sturman. Typo D.L.R.)

1900 (Jan). *W* **13**. *P* 14.

69	**18**	1d. carmine	3·25	10
		w. Wmk inverted	—	£120

19   **20**   **21**

22   **23**   **24**

25   **26**   **27**

(Typo D.L.R.)

1902 (Dec)-**04**. *W* **13**. *P* 14.

70	**19**	½d. green	2·25	10
71	**20**	1d. carmine	2·00	10
		w. Wmk inverted		
		y. Wmk inverted and reversed		
72	**21**	2d. brown (10.04)	12·00	80
		w. Wmk inverted		
73	**22**	2½d. ultramarine (3.04)	2·75	6·50
74	**23**	3d. magenta (4.03)	7·50	75
75	**24**	4d. olive-green (2.03)	9·50	65
76	**25**	6d. bright mauve (3.03)	17·00	30
77	**26**	1s. yellow-ochre	13·00	50
78	**27**	5s. brown-orange (2.03)	85·00	17·00
70/8		Set of 9	£140	24·00

All values exist in imperf pairs, from proof sheets.

The ½d. exists from coils constructed from normal sheets for use in stamp machines introduced in 1911.

STAMP BOOKLET

1905 (Dec). *Black on red cover. Stapled.*

SB1	2s.7d. booklet containing thirty 1d. (No. 71) in blocks of 6	£2000

OFFICIAL STAMPS

The following stamps, punctured with a double triangle device, were used by the Stationery and Printed Forms Branch of the Cape of Good Hope Colonial Secretary's Department between 1904 and 1906. Later South Africa issues may have been similarly treated, but this has not been confirmed.

(O **1**)

1904. *Various issues punctured as Type O* **1**.

(a) Nos. 50 and 52a.

O1	**6**	2d. pale bistre	17·00
O2	**4**	6d. purple	20·00

(b) Nos. 58 and 60.

O3	**17**	½d. green	22·00
O4		3d. magenta	17·00

(c) Nos. 62 and 64/5.

O5	**6**	2d. chocolate-brown	17·00
O6		3d. bright magenta	22·00
O7		4d. sage-green	22·00

(d) No. 69.

O8	**18**	1d. carmine	17·00

(e) Nos. 70/2 and 74/8.

O9	**19**	½d. green	22·00
O10	**20**	1d. carmine	13·00
O11	**21**	2d. brown	20·00
O12	**23**	3d. magenta	16·00
O13	**24**	4d. olive-green	17·00
O14	**25**	6d. bright mauve	18·00
O15	**26**	1s. yellow-ochre	22·00
O16	**27**	5s. brown-orange	55·00

Nos. O1/16 are only known used.

Cape of Good Hope became a province of the Union of South Africa on 31 May 1910.

BRITISH KAFFRARIA

The history of the Cape eastern frontier was punctuated by a series of armed conflicts with the native population, known as the Kaffir Wars. After a particularly violent outbreak in 1846 the Governor, Sir Harry Smith, advanced the line of the Cape frontier to the Keikama and Tyumie Rivers. In the area between the new frontier and the Kei River a buffer state, British Kaffraria, was established on 17 December 1847. This area was not annexed to the Cape, but was administered as a separate Crown dependency by the Governor of Cape Colony in his capacity as High Commissioner for South Africa.

The territory, with its administration based on King William's Town, used the stamps of the Cape of Good Hope from 1853 onwards, the mail being sent via Port Elizabeth or overland from the Cape. Covers from British Kaffraria franked with the triangular issues are rare.

The first postal marking known from British Kaffraria is the 1849 type octagonal numeral No 47 from Port Beaufort. Oval post-marks of the 1853 type were used at Alice, Aliwal North, Bedford, Fort Beaufort, King William's Town and Queenstown. In 1864 numeral cancellations were issued to all post offices within the Cape system and it is known that the following numbers were initially assigned to post towns in Kaffraria: 4 (King William's Town), 7 (Bedford), 11 (Queenstown), 29 (East London), 32 (Fort Beaufort), 38 (Aliwal North) and 104 (Cathcart).

It is believed that post offices may have also existed at Adelaide, Barkly East, Sterkstoom and Stutterheim, but, to date, no examples of handstamps or cancellations are known from them during the British Kaffraria period.

Following the decimation by famine of the Xhosa tribes in 1857 British Kaffraria was annexed to Cape Colony in 1865. The area eventually formed the basis of the Ciskei independent "homeland".

MAFEKING SIEGE STAMPS

PRICES FOR STAMPS ON COVER

Nos. 1/16	*from* × 12
Nos. 17/18	*from* × 25
Nos. 19/20	*from* × 15
Nos. 21/2	*from* × 12

23 MARCH to 17 MAY 1900

There are numerous forgeries of the Mafeking overprints, many of which were brought home by soldiers returning from the Boer War.

MAFEKING,
3d.
BESIEGED.
(1)

MAFEKING
3d.
BESIEGED.
(2)

(Surcharged by Townsend & Co, Mafeking)

1900 (23 Mar–28 Apr). *Various stamps surch as T* **1** *and* **2**.

(a) Cape of Good Hope stamps surch as T **1** *(23 Mar)*.

1	**6**	1d. on ½d. green	£200	65·00
2	**17**	1d. on ½d. green (24.3)	£250	75·00
3		3d. on 1d. carmine	£225	50·00
4	**6**	6d. on 3d. magenta (24.3)	£32000	£250
5		1s. on 4d. sage-green (24.3)	£6000	£350

A variety in the setting of each value exists without comma after "MAFEKING".

(b) Nos. 59 and 61/3 of Bechuanaland Protectorate (previously optd on Great Britain) surch as T **1**.

6		1d. on ½d. vermilion (28.3)	£200	60·00
		a. Surch inverted	†	£4500
		b. Vert pair, surch *tête-bêche*	†	£27000
7		3d. on 1d. lilac (4.4)	£850	90·00
		a. Surch double	†	£22000
8		6d. on 2d. green and carmine (6.4)	£1900	75·00
9		6d. on 3d. purple/*yellow* (30.3)	£5000	£275
		a. Surch inverted	†	£27000
		b. Surch double		

(c) Nos. 12 and 35 of British Bechuanaland (4d. previously optd on Great Britain) surch as T **1**.

10		6d. on 3d. lilac and black (27.3)	£350	65·00
11		1s. on 4d. green and purple-brown (29.3)	£1300	80·00
		a. Surch double (both Type **1**)	†	£21000
		ab. Surch double (Type **1** and Type **2**)	£8500	£5000
		b. Surch treble	†	£21000
		c. Surch double, one inverted	†	£21000

(d) Nos. 61/2 and 65 of Bechuanaland Protectorate (previously optd on Great Britain) surch as T **2**.

12		3d. on 1d. lilac (1 Apr)	£900	75·00
		a. Surch double	†	£7000
13		6d. on 2d. green and carmine (25 Apr)	£1100	75·00
14		1s. on 6d. purple/*rose-red* (12 Apr)	£4500	90·00

(e) Nos. 36/7 of British Bechuanaland (previously optd on Great Britain) surch as T **2**.

15		1s. on 6d. purple/*rose-red* (28 Apr)	£17000	£700
16		2s. on 1s. green (13 Apr)	£8500	£400

On the stamps overprinted "BECHUANALAND PROTECTORATE" and "BRITISH BECHUANALAND" the local surcharge is so adjusted as not to overlap the original overprint.

Two examples of British Bechuanaland No. 37 are known surcharged 2s. as T1 but their status is uncertain.

3 Cadet Sergt.-major Goodyear

4 General Baden-Powell

(Des Dr. W. A. Hayes (T **3**), Capt. H. Greener (T **4**))

1900 (6–11 Apr). *Produced photographically by Dr. D. Taylor. Horiz laid paper with sheet wmk "OCEANA FINE". P* 12.

(a) 18½ mm wide. (b) 21 mm wide.

17	**3**	1d. pale blue/*blue* (7.4)	£800	£275
18		1d. deep blue/*blue*	£800	£275
19	**4**	3d. pale blue/*blue (a)*	£1200	£400
		a. Reversed design	£60000	£35000
20		3d. deep blue/*blue (a)*	£1200	£350
		a. Imperf between (horiz pair)	†	£60000
		b. Double print	†	£16000
21		3d. pale blue/*blue (b)* (11.4)	£7500	£800
		a. Vert laid paper	£11000	
22		3d. deep blue/*blue (b)* (11.4)	£8000	£950

These stamps vary a great deal in colour from deep blue to pale grey.

No. 18 imperforate and without gum is believed to be a proof (*Price for unused pair* £17000).

No. 19a comes from a sheet of 12 printed in reverse of which nine, three mint and six used, are known to have survived.

VRYBURG

PRICES FOR STAMPS ON COVER

Nos. 1/4	*from* × 5
Nos. 11/12	*from* × 2

BOER OCCUPATION

Vryburg was occupied by Boer forces on 15 October 1899. Unoverprinted stamps of Transvaal were used initially. Nos. 1/4 were only available from 24 to 29 November. The Boers evacuated the town on 7 May 1900.

½ PENCE
Z.A.R.
(1)

1899 (24 Nov). *Cape stamps surch as T* **1**. *Surch* 12 *mm high on No. 3 and* 10 *mm on all other values.*

1	**6**	½ PENCE green	£200	80·00
		a. Italic "Z"	£1700	£700
		b. Surch 12 mm high	£1700	£700
2	**17**	1 PENCE rose	£225	£100
		a. Italic "Z"	£1900	£800
		b. Surch 12 mm high	£1900	£800
		c. "I" for "1"	£1200	£500
3	**4**	2 PENCE on 6d. mauve	£2000	£500
		a. Italic "Z"	£10000	£4250
4	**15**	2½ PENCE on 2½d. blue	£1700	£425
		a. Italic "Z"	£10000	£4250
		b. Surch 12 mm high	£10000	£4250

The "2 PENCE" on 6d. shows the surcharge 12 mm high. It is possible that this was the first value surcharged as the remaining three show the height reduced to 10 mm with the exception of one position in the second vertical row of the setting. The italic "Z" occurs on one position in the sixth vertical row. It is believed that the setting was of 60 (6×10).

BRITISH REOCCUPATION

V. R.
SPECIAL
POST
(2)

1900 (16 May). *Provisionals issued by the Military Authorities. Stamps of Transvaal handstamped with T* **2**.

11	**30**	½d. green	—	£2250
11a		1d. rose-red (No. 206)		
12		1d. rose-red and green (No. 217)	£9000	£4250
13		2d. brown and green		
14		2½d. dull blue and green		

No. 11 is known used with double handstamp and Nos. 11/12 with the overprint reading downwards.

II. GRIQUALAND WEST

Griqualand West was situated to the North of Cape Colony, bounded on the north by what became British Bechuanaland and on the east by the Orange Free State.

The area was settled the early nineteenth century by the Griqua tribal group, although many members of the tribe, including the paramount chief, migrated to Griqualand East (between Basutoland and the east coast of South Africa) in 1861–63. There was little European involvement in Griqualand West before 1866, but in that year the diamond fields along the Vaal River were discovered. Sovereignty was subsequently claimed by the Griqua Chief, the Orange Free State and the South African Republic (Transvaal). In 1871 the British authorities arbitrated in favour of the Griqua Chief who promptly ceded his territory to Great Britain. Griqualand West became a separate Crown Colony in January 1873.

During the initial stages of the prospecting boom, mail was passed via the Orange Free State, but a post office connected to the Cape Colony postal system was opened at Klip Drift (subsequently Barkly) in late 1870. Further offices at De Beer's New Rush (subsequently Kimberley), Douglas and Du Toit's Pan (subsequently Beaconsfield) were open by September 1873.

Cape of Good Hope stamps to the 5s. value were in use from October 1871, but those originating in Griqualand West can only be identified after the introduction of Barred Oval Diamond Numeral cancellations in 1873. Numbers known to have been issued in the territory are:

1 De Beers N.R. (New Rush) (subsequently Kimberley)
3 Junction R. & M. (Riet and Modder Rivers)
4 Barkly
6 or 9 Du Toit's Pan (subsequently Beaconsfield)
8 Langford (transferred to Douglas)
10 Thornhill

PRICES FOR STAMPS ON COVER. The stamps of Griqualand West are worth from ×10 the price quoted for used stamps, when on cover from the territory.

FORGED OVERPRINTS. Many stamps show forged overprints. Great care should be taken when purchasing the scarcer items.

Stamps of the Cape of Good Hope, Crown CC, perf 14, overprinted.

1874 (Sept). *No. 24a of Cape of Good Hope surch "1d." in red manuscript by the Kimberley postmaster.*

1		1d. on 4d. blue	£1300	£2250

G. W.
(1)

1877 (Mar). *Nos. 29/30 of Cape of Good Hope optd with T* **1**.

2		1d. carmine-red	£500	85·00
		a. Opt double	†	£2000
3		4d. dull blue (R.)	£400	75·00
		w. Wmk inverted	£1300	£275

G (1a) **G** (2) **G** (3) **G** (4) **G** (5) **G** (6)

G (7) **G** (8) **G** (9) **G** (10) **G** (11)

G (12) **G** (13) **G** (14)

1877 (Mar)–**78**. *Nos. 24a, 25a, 26a and 28/31 of Cape of Good Hope optd with capital "G".*

(a) First printing. Optd with T **1a/6** *and* **8** *in black (1d.) or red (others).*

4		½d. grey-black		
		a. Opt Type **1a**	23·00	27·00
		b. Opt Type **2**	55·00	70·00
		c. Opt Type **3**	29·00	38·00
		d. Opt Type **4**	55·00	70·00
		e. Opt Type **5**	65·00	80·00
		f. Opt Type **6**	27·00	32·00
		g. Opt Type **8**	£500	£550
5		1d. carmine-red		
		a. Opt Type **1a**	24·00	18·00
		b. Opt Type **2**	60·00	40·00
		c. Opt Type **3**	29·00	25·00
		d. Opt Type **4**	60·00	40·00
		e. Opt Type **5**	70·00	48·00
		f. Opt Type **6**	24·00	18·00
		g. Opt Type **8**	*	
6		4d. blue (with frame-line) (No. 24a)		
		a. Opt Type **1a**	£250	40·00
		b. Opt Type **2**	£650	£110
		c. Opt Type **3**	£425	55·00
		d. Opt Type **4**	£650	£110
		e. Opt Type **5**	£750	£140
		f. Opt Type **6**	£325	50·00
		g. Opt Type **8**	£2000	£650
7		4d. dull blue (without frame-line) (No. 30)		
		a. Opt Type **1a**	£170	25·00
		b. Opt Type **2**	£450	75·00
		c. Opt Type **3**	£300	32·00
		d. Opt Type **4**	£425	75·00
		e. Opt Type **5**	£500	90·00
		f. Opt Type **6**	£275	30·00
		g. Opt Type **8**	£1700	£450
8		6d. deep lilac		
		a. Opt Type **1a**	£130	27·00
		b. Opt Type **2**	£300	80·00
		c. Opt Type **3**	£190	40·00
		cw. Wmk inverted	†	£300
		d. Opt Type **4**	£300	80·00
		e. Opt Type **5**	£375	95·00
		f. Opt Type **6**	£170	38·00
		g. Opt Type **8**	£1500	£550
9		1s. green		
		a. Opt Type **1a**	£160	24·00
		ab. Opt inverted	—	£475
		b. Opt Type **2**	£375	55·00
		ba. Opt inverted	—	£800
		c. Opt Type **3**	£275	30·00
		d. Opt Type **4**	£375	55·00
		da. Opt inverted	—	£800
		e. Opt Type **5**	£450	70·00
		f. Opt Type **6**	£250	27·00
		fa. Opt inverted	—	£550
		g. Opt Type **8**	£2750	£550
10		5s. yellow-orange		
		a. Opt Type **1a**	£600	29·00
		b. Opt Type **2**	£950	65·00
		c. Opt Type **3**	£800	35·00
		cw. Wmk inverted	†	£750
		d. Opt Type **4**	£950	65·00
		dw. Wmk inverted	†	£1000
		e. Opt Type **5**	£1400	80·00
		f. Opt Type **6**	£750	32·00
		g. Opt Type **8**	£2750	£700

*The 1d. with overprint Type **8** from this setting can only be distinguished from that of the second printing when *se-tenant* with overprint Type **3**.

Nos. 4/10 were overprinted by a setting of 120 covering two panes of 60 (6×10). This setting contained 41 examples of Type **1a**, 10 of Type **2**, 23 of Type **3**, 10 of Type **4**, 8 of Type **5**, 27 of Type **6** and 1 of Type **8**. Sub-types of Types **1a** and **2** exist. The single example of Type **8** occurs on R.7/4 of the right-hand pane.

It is believed that there may have been an additional setting used for the 5s. which was in considerable demand for the postage and registration on diamond consignments. It is also possible that single panes of this value and of the 1s. were overprinted using the right-hand half of the normal 120 setting.

(b) Second printing. Optd with T **6/14** *in black (1878).*

11		1d. carmine-red		
		a. Opt Type **6**	*	
		b. Opt Type **7**	26·00	19·00
		c. Opt Type **8**	55·00	32·00
		d. Opt Type **9**	27·00	20·00
		e. Opt Type **10**	75·00	70·00
		f. Opt Type **11**	65·00	45·00
		g. Opt Type **12**	70·00	65·00
		h. Opt Type **13**	£110	£100
		i. Opt Type **14**	£375	£325

12		4d. dull blue (without frame-line) (No. 30)		£325	65·00
		a. Opt Type **6**		£120	25·00
		b. Opt Type **7**		£300	55·00
		c. Opt Type **8**		£140	26·00
		d. Opt Type **9**		£375	80·00
		e. Opt Type **10**		£325	70·00
		f. Opt Type **11**		£350	75·00
		g. Opt Type **12**		£500	£140
		h. Opt Type **13**		£1800	£450
		i. Opt Type **14**			
13		6d. deep lilac		£450	£100
		a. Opt Type **6**		£225	55·00
		b. Opt Type **7**			
		ba. Opt double		£425	90·00
		c. Opt Type **8**		£275	65·00
		d. Opt Type **9**		—	£800
		da. Opt double		£500	£140
		e. Opt Type **10**		—	£950
		ea. Opt double		£450	£100
		f. Opt Type **11**		£450	£130
		g. Opt Type **12**		£700	£200
		h. Opt Type **13**		£2000	£600
		i. Opt Type **14**			

*The 1d. with overprint Type **6** from this setting can only be distinguished from that of the first printing when *se-tenant* with Types **11**, **12** or **13**.

Nos. 11/13 were overprinted by another double-pane setting of 120 in which only Types **6** and **8** were repeated from that used for the first printing. The second printing setting contained 12 examples of Type **6**, 30 of Type **7**, 13 of Type **8**, 27 of Type **9**, 9 of Type **10**, 11 of Type **11**, 11 of Type **12**, 6 of Type **13** and 1 of Type **14**. Sub-types of Types **7** and **12** exist.

G (15) *G* (16) *G* (17)

1878 (June). *Nos. 24a, 25a and 28/30 of Cape of Good Hope optd with small capital "G", T **15/16**.*

14	15	½d. grey-black (R.)		11·00	11·00
		a. Opt inverted		13·00	13·00
		b. Opt double		48·00	60·00
		c. Opt double, both inverted		90·00	£110
		d. Black opt		£190	£110
		da. Opt inverted		£200	
		db. Opt double, one inverted in red		£375	
		dc. Opt double, one inverted (Type **16**) in red		£180	
15	16	½d. grey-black (R.)		12·00	12·00
		a. Opt inverted		12·00	13·00
		b. Opt double		80·00	80·00
		c. Opt double, both inverted		65·00	75·00
		d. Black opt		48·00	48·00
		da. Opt inverted		£100	75·00
		db. Opt double, one inverted (Type **15**) in red		£180	
16	15	1d. carmine-red		12·00	10·00
		a. Opt inverted		12·00	12·00
		b. Opt double		£190	50·00
		c. Opt double, both inverted		£190	70·00
		d. Opt double, both inverted with one in red		40·00	42·00
		e. Opt double, both inverted with one (Type **16**) in red			
17	16	1d. carmine-red		12·00	12·00
		a. Opt inverted		85·00	30·00
		b. Opt double		—	90·00
		c. Opt double, both inverted		—	£110
		d. Opt double, both inverted with one in red		85·00	85·00
18	15	4d. blue (with frame-line) (No. 24a)		—	£150
19	16	4d. blue (with frame-line) (No. 24a)		—	£150
20	15	4d. dull blue (without frame-line) (No. 30)		£130	30·00
		a. Opt inverted		£200	90·00
		b. Opt double		—	£200
		c. Opt double, both inverted		—	£275
		d. Red opt		£325	£100
		da. Opt inverted		£375	85·00
21	16	4d. dull blue (without frame-line) (No. 30)		£150	13·00
		a. Opt inverted		£225	30·00
		b. Opt double		—	£200
		c. Opt double, both inverted		—	£275
		d. Red opt		—	90·00
		da. Opt inverted		£350	90·00
22	15	6d. deep lilac		£130	27·00
23	16	6d. deep lilac		—	27·00

Nos. 14/23 were also overprinted using a double-pane setting of 120. Based on evidence from surviving ½d. and 1d. sheets all overprints in the left-hand pane were roman, Type **15**, and all those in the right-hand pane italic, Type **16**, except for R.1/6, 4/5, 6/6, 7/6, 8/6, 9/6 and 10/6 which were Type **15**. There is considerable evidence to suggest that after the ½d. value had been overprinted the setting was amended to show a Type **15**, instead of a Type **16**, on R.10/5 of the right-hand pane. Two strikes of the setting were required to overprint the sheets of 240 and it would appear that on many sheets the bottom two panes had the overprints inverted.

1879. *Nos. 25b, 26b and 28/31 of Cape of Good Hope optd with small capital "G", T **17**.*

24		½d. grey-black		15·00	7·50
		a. Opt double		£400	£275
25		1d. carmine-red		16·00	5·50
		a. Opt inverted		—	90·00
		b. Opt double		—	£140
		c. Opt treble		—	£225
		w. Wmk inverted		†	£250
26		4d. dull blue		30·00	5·50
		a. Opt double		—	£120
27		6d. violet		£140	8·50
		a. Opt inverted		—	35·00
		b. Opt double		£650	£180
28		1s. green		£120	6·00
		a. Opt double		£350	95·00
29		5s. yellow-orange		£425	13·00
		a. Opt double		£550	80·00
		b. Opt treble		—	£300

Nos. 24/9 were also overprinted using a setting of 120 which contained a number of minor type varieties.

Griqualand West was merged with Cape Colony in October 1880. The remaining stock of the overprinted stamps was returned from Kimberley to Cape Town and redistributed among various post offices in Cape Colony where they were used as ordinary Cape stamps.

III. NATAL

PRICES FOR STAMPS ON COVER	
Nos. 1/7	*from* × 2
Nos. 9/25	*from* × 3
Nos. 26/56	*from* × 4
Nos. 57/8	
Nos. 59/73	*from* × 5
Nos. 76/84	*from* × 4
Nos. 85/93	*from* × 3
Nos. 96/103	*from* × 6
Nos. 104/5	*from* × 4
Nos. 106/25	*from* × 6
Nos. 127/42	*from* × 4
Nos. 143/5a	
Nos. 146/57	*from* × 4
No. 162	
Nos. 165/71	*from* × 3
No. F1	—
Nos. O1/6	*from* × 10

(Embossed in plain relief on coloured wove paper)

1857 (26 May)–**61**. Imperf.

1	1	1d. blue (9.59)	—	£1100
2		1d. rose (1859)	—	£1700
3		1d. buff (1861)	—	£1000
4	2	3d. rose	—	£400
		a. Tête-bêche (pair)	—	£35000
5	3	6d. green	—	£1100
6	4	9d. blue	—	£7000
7	5	1s. buff	—	£5500

All the above have been reprinted more than once, and the early reprints of some values cannot always be distinguished with certainty from originals.

Stamps on surface-coloured paper with higher face values and perforated 12½ are fiscals.

NOTE. The value of the above stamps depends on their dimensions, and the clearness of the embossing, but our prices are for fine used.

PERKINS BACON "CANCELLED". For notes on these handstamps showing "CANCELLED" between horizontal bars forming an oval, see Catalogue Introduction.

(Eng C. H. Jeens. Recess P.B.)

1859–60. No wmk. P 14.

9	6	1d. rose-red (1860) (H/S "CANCELLED" in oval £10000)	£130	70·00
10		3d. blue	£160	42·00
		a. Imperf between (vert pair)	†	£7500

No. 10a is only known from a cover of 1867 franked with two such pairs.

The 3d. also exists with "CANCELLED" in oval, but no examples are believed to be in private hands.

1861. No wmk. Intermediate perf 14 to 16.

11	6	3d. blue	£225	65·00

1861–62. No wmk. Rough perf 14 to 16.

12	6	3d. blue	£110	32·00
		a. Imperf between (horiz pair)	£3750	
		b. Imperf (pair)	—	£3500
13		6d. grey (1862)	£190	50·00

1862. Wmk Small Star. Rough perf 14 to 16.

15	6	1d. rose-red	£140	65·00

The 1d. without watermark and the 3d. watermark Small Star, both imperforate, are proofs.

(Recess D.L.R.)

1863. *Thick paper.* No wmk. P 13.

18	6	1d. lake	90·00	27·00
19		1d. carmine-red	90·00	27·00

1863–65. Wmk Crown CC. P 12½.

20	6	1d. brown-red	£140	38·00
		y. Wmk inverted and reversed	—	£100
21		1d. rose	90·00	35·00
		x. Wmk reversed	90·00	35·00
22		1d. bright rose	90·00	38·00
		x. Wmk reversed	90·00	38·00
23		6d. lilac	70·00	17·00
24		6d. violet	55·00	28·00
		x. Wmk reversed	55·00	28·00

(Typo D.L.R.)

1867 (Apr). Wmk Crown CC. P 14.

25	7	1s. green	£160	30·00
		w. Wmk inverted	—	£275

POSTAGE (7a) Postage. (7b) Postage. (7c)

Postage. (7d) POSTAGE. (7e)

1869 (23 Aug). Optd horiz in Natal. No wmk (3d.), wmk Crown CC (others). P 14 or 14–16 (3d.), 12½ (1d., 6d.) or 14 (1s.).

*(a) With T **7a** (tall capitals without stop).*

26	6	1d. rose	£375	80·00
		x. Wmk reversed	£375	80·00
27		1d. bright red	£325	70·00
		x. Wmk reversed	—	70·00
28		3d. blue (No. 10)	£2000	£600
28a		3d. blue (No. 11)	£650	£250
28b		3d. blue (No. 12)	£650	90·00
29		6d. lilac	£550	70·00
30		6d. violet	£475	80·00
		x. Wmk reversed	£475	80·00
31	7	1s. green	£7000	£1200

*(b) With T **7b** (12¾ mm long).*

32	6	1d. rose	£350	75·00
33		1d. bright red	£300	65·00
		a. Opt double	†	£1300
		x. Wmk reversed	£300	65·00
34		3d. blue (No. 10)	—	£300
34a		3d. blue (No. 11)	£550	£200
34b		3d. blue (No. 12)	£450	80·00
35		6d. lilac	£475	65·00
36		6d. violet	£400	75·00
		x. Wmk reversed	£400	75·00
37	7	1s. green	£5000	£900

*(c) With T **7c** (13¾ mm long).*

38	6	1d. rose	£700	£200
39		1d. bright red	£750	£180
		x. Wmk reversed	—	£180
40		3d. blue (No. 10)	—	£700
40a		3d. blue (No. 11)		
40b		3d. blue (No. 12)	£1500	£350
41		6d. lilac	£1600	£150
42		6d. violet	£1500	£140
		x. Wmk reversed	—	£160
43	7	1s. green	—	£1800

*(d) With T **7d** (14½ to 15½ mm long).*

44	6	1d. rose	£600	£170
45		1d. bright red	£600	£150
46		3d. blue (No. 10)		
46a		3d. blue (No. 11)	—	£450
46b		3d. blue (No. 12)	—	£275
47		6d. lilac	—	£100
48		6d. violet	£1200	95·00
49	7	1s. green	£13000	£1600

*(e) With T **7e** (small capitals with stop).*

50	6	1d. rose	£100	42·00
		x. Wmk reversed	£100	42·00
51		1d. bright red	£150	42·00
		x. Wmk reversed	£150	42·00
52		3d. blue (No. 10)	£300	75·00
53		3d. blue (No. 11)	£160	48·00
54		3d. blue (No. 12)	£180	42·00
		a. Opt double	†	£1000
54b		6d. lilac	£180	60·00
55		6d. violet	£140	50·00
		x. Wmk reversed	£140	50·00
56	7	1s. green	£200	65·00

It is believed that there were two settings of these overprints.

The first setting, probably of 240, contained 60 examples of Type **7a**, 72 of Type **7b**, 20 of Type **7c**, 28 of Type **7d** and 60 of Type **7e**. The second, probably of 60 (6×10), contained Type **7e** only.

(8)

1870. *No. 25 optd with T **8** by De La Rue.*

57	7	1s. green (C.)	—	£3500
58		1s. green (Blk.)	£2500	£1200
		a. Opt double	—	£2500
59		1s. green (G.)	85·00	10·00

For 1s. orange, see No. 108.

POSTAGE POSTAGE POSTAGE POSTAGE POSTAGE

(9)   (10)   (11)

1870–73. *Optd with T **9** by De La Rue. Wmk Crown CC. P 12½.*
60	**6**	1d. bright red	80·00	13·00
		x. Wmk reversed	80·00	13·00
61		3d. bright blue (R.) (1872)	85·00	13·00
		x. Wmk reversed	85·00	13·00
62		6d. mauve (1873)	£160	27·00
		x. Wmk reversed	—	£180

1873 (July). *Fiscal stamp optd locally with T **10**. Wmk Crown CC. P 14.*
| 63 | **7** | 1s. purple-brown | £200 | 21·00 |
| | | w. Wmk inverted | — | £300 |

1874 (July). *No. 21 optd locally with T **11**.*
65	**6**	1d. rose	£250	75·00
		a. Opt double	—	75·00
		x. Wmk reversed	—	75·00

12   13   14

15   16

(Typo D.L.R.)

1874 (Jan)–**99.** *Wmk Crown CC (sideways on 5s.). P 14.*
66	**12**	1d. dull rose	25·00	3·25
67		1d. bright rose	25·00	3·25
68	**13**	3d. blue	£110	22·00
		a. Perf 14×12½	£1600	£850
69	**14**	4d. brown (1878)	£120	11·00
		aw. Wmk inverted	£350	£100
		b. Perf 12½	£325	65·00
70	**15**	6d. bright reddish violet	55·00	7·00
		w. Wmk inverted	†	£160
71	**16**	5s. maroon (1882)	£180	50·00
		a. Perf 15½×15 (1874)	£350	90·00
72		5s. rose	80·00	32·00
73		5s. carmine (H/S S. £160)	75·00	30·00
		a. Wmk upright (1899)		

POSTAGE   POSTAGE   HALF   ½

(17)   (18)   (19)

1875–76. *Wmk Crown CC. P 14 (1s.) or 12½ (others).*
*(a) Optd locally with T **17**.*
76	**6**	1d. rose	£120	50·00
		x. Opt double	£950	£450
		x. Wmk reversed	£120	50·00
77		1d. bright red	£110	65·00
		x. Wmk reversed	£110	65·00

*(b) Optd locally with T **18** (14½ mm long, without stop).*
81	**6**	1d. rose (1876)	90·00	65·00
		x. Opt inverted	£1000	£450
		x. Wmk reversed	90·00	65·00
82		1d. yellow (1876)	70·00	70·00
		a. Opt double, one albino	£200	
		x. Wmk reversed	80·00	80·00
83		6d. violet (1876)	60·00	7·50
		a. Opt double	—	£600
		b. Opt inverted	£700	£150
		w. Wmk inverted	—	£110
		x. Wmk reversed	60·00	7·50
84	**7**	1s. green (1876)	90·00	7·00
		a. Opt double	—	£325

TYPE 19. There are several varieties of this surcharge, of which T **19** is an example. They may be divided as follows:

(a) "½" 4½ mm high, "2" has straight foot.
(b) As last but "½" is 4 mm high.
(c) As last but "2" has curled foot.
(d) "½" 3½ mm. high, "2" has straight foot.
(e) As last but "2" has curled foot.
(f) As last but "2" smaller.

As the "½" and "HALF" were overprinted separately, they vary in relative position, and are frequently overlapping.

1877 (13 Feb). *No. 66 surch locally as T **19**.*
85	**12**	½d. on 1d. rose (a)	29·00	65·00
		a. "½" double		
86		½d. on 1d. rose (b)	£130	
87		½d. on 1d. rose (c)	£110	
88		½d. on 1d. rose (d)	65·00	90·00
89		½d. on 1d. rose (e)	70·00	
90		½d. on 1d. rose (f)	80·00	

POSTAGE

Half-penny

ONE HALF-PENNY.

(21)   23   (24)

1877 (7 Oct)–**79.** *T **6** (wmk Crown CC. P 12½) surch locally as T **21**.*
91	½d. on 1d. yellow	8·50	15·00
	a. Surch inverted	£275	£190
	b. Surch double	£250	£180
	c. Surch omitted (lower stamp, vertical pair)	£2250	£1300
	d. "POSTAGE" omitted (in pair with normal)	£1600	
	e. "S" of "POSTAGE" omitted (R. 8/3)	£250	£190
	f. "T" of "POSTAGE" omitted	£250	£250
	x. Wmk reversed	8·50	15·00
92	1d. on 6d. violet (10.10.77)	50·00	£150
	a. "S" of "POSTAGE" omitted (R. 8/3)	£375	£400
	x. Wmk reversed	—	10·00
93	1d. on 6d. rose (12.2.79)	£100	45·00
	a. Surch inverted	£550	£300
	b. Surch double	—	£250
	c. Surch double, one inverted	£250	£200
	d. Surch four times	£375	£200
	e. "S" of "POSTAGE" omitted (R. 8/3)	£500	£300
	x. Wmk reversed	—	45·00

No. 93c. is known with one surcharge showing variety "S" of "POSTAGE" omitted.

Other minor varieties exist in these surcharges.

(Typo D.L.R.)

1880 (13 Oct). *Wmk Crown CC. P 14.*
| 96 | **23** | ½d. blue-green | 14·00 | 20·00 |
| | | a. Imperf between (vert pair) | | |

1882 (20 Apr)–**89.** *Wmk Crown CA. P 14.*
97	**23**	½d. blue-green (23.4.84)	95·00	16·00
		a. Dull green (10.4.85)	3·25	1·00
		aw. Wmk inverted	£200	
99	**12**	1d. rose (shades) (1.84)	3·25	20
		a. Carmine	3·75	30
		w. Wmk inverted	†	£160
100	**13**	3d. blue (23.4.84)	£100	17·00
101		3d. grey (11.89)	4·50	2·00
102	**14**	4d. brown	6·00	1·25
103	**15**	6d. mauve	5·50	1·50
		w. Wmk inverted	†	£110
97a/103	Set of 6		£110	21·00
97as, 99as, 101s/3s H/S "Specimen" Set of 5			£250	

1885 (26 Jan). *No. 99 surch locally with T **24**.*
| 104 | **12** | ½d. on 1d. rose | 16·00 | 11·00 |
| | | a. No hyphen after "HALF" | 65·00 | 42·00 |

TWO PENCE   TWOPENCE HALFPENNY

(25)   26   (27)

1886 (7 Jan). *No. 101 surch with T **25** by D.L.R.*
| 105 | **13** | 2d. on 3d. grey | 19·00 | 5·50 |

(Typo D.L.R.)

1887 (Sept)–**89.** *Wmk Crown CA. P 14.*
106	**26**	2d. olive-green (Die I)	35·00	2·25
		a. Top left triangle detached	—	£200
		s. Optd "Specimen"	75·00	
107		2d. olive-green (Die II) (1889)	3·25	1·40
		s. Handstamped "Specimen"	60·00	

The differences between Dies I and II are shown in the introduction.

For illustration of "top left triangle detached" variety see above No. 21 of Antigua.

1888 (16 Mar). *As No. 25, but colour changed and wmk Crown CA, optd with T **8** by D.L.R.*
108	**7**	1s. orange (C.)	4·75	1·50
		a. Opt double	—	£1500
		s. Handstamped "Specimen"	£100	

1891 (22 Apr). *Surch locally with T **27**.*
109	**14**	2½d. on 4d. brown	10·00	13·00
		b. "TWOPENCE"	50·00	
		b. "HALFPENN"	£250	£200
		c. Surch double	£275	£200
		d. Surch inverted	£375	£300
		s. Handstamped "Specimen"	50·00	

POSTAGE.

Half-Penny

POSTAGE.

(28)   (29)

Varieties of long-tailed letters

(Typo D.L.R.)

1891 (June). *Wmk Crown CA. P 14.*
| 113 | **28** | 2½d. bright blue | 6·00 | 1·25 |
| | | s. Handstamped "Specimen" | 60·00 | |

1895 (12 Mar). *No. 24 surch locally with T **29** in carmine.*
114	½d. on 6d. violet	2·00	4·25
	a. "Ealf-Penny"	20·00	32·00
	b. "Half-Penny" and long "P"	18·00	32·00
	ba. "Half Penny" and long "T" and "A"	18·00	32·00
	c. No stop after "POSTAGE" and long "P", "T" and "A"	18·00	32·00
	d. Long "P"	2·25	5·50
	e. Long "T"	2·25	5·50
	f. Long "A"	3·50	7·50
	g. Long "P" and "T"	2·25	5·50
	h. Long "P" and "A"	2·25	5·50
	i. Long "T" and "A"	3·00	7·00
	k. Long "P", "T" and "A"	3·25	7·00
	ka. Long "P", "T" and "A" with comma after "POSTAGE"	9·00	15·00
	l. Surch double	£250	
	la. Surch double, one vertical	£250	
	m. "POSTAGE" omitted	£1000	
	s. Handstamped "Specimen"	50·00	
	x. Wmk reversed	2·00	4·25

The surcharge was applied as a setting of 60 (12×5) which contained seventeen normals, one each of Nos. 114a, 114b, 114ba, 114c, six of No. 114d, six of 114e, three of 114f, six of 114g, seven of No. 114h, five of No. 114i, four of No. 114k and two of No. 114ka.

HALF
(30)   31   32

1895 (18 Mar). *No. 99 surch locally with T **30**.*
125	HALF on 1d. rose (shades)	2·75	2·00
	a. Surch double	£350	£350
	b. "H" with longer left limb	27·00	
	c. Pair, one without surcharge		
	s. Handstamped "Specimen"	50·00	

No. 125b, in which the "A" also has a short right leg, occurs on the second, fourth, sixth etc., stamps of the first vertical column of the right-hand pane of the first printing only.

In the second printing what appears to be a broken "E" (with the top limb removed) was used instead of "L" in "HALF" on the last stamp in the sheet (Price £30), No. 125c also comes from this second printing.

(Typo D.L.R.)

1902–03. *Inscr "POSTAGE REVENUE". Wmk Crown CA. P 14.*
127	**31**	½d. blue-green	3·00	30
128		1d. carmine	8·00	15
129		1½d. green and black	3·50	2·50
130		2d. red and olive-green	2·50	25
131		2½d. bright blue	1·50	3·25
132		3d. purple and grey	1·25	1·50
133		4d. carmine and cinnamon	4·50	18·00
134		5d. black and orange	2·25	2·75
		w. Wmk inverted	£130	75·00
135		6d. green and brown-purple	2·25	2·75
136		1s. carmine and pale blue	3·00	3·25
137		2s. green and bright violet	50·00	9·00
138		2s.6d. purple	40·00	12·00
139		4s. deep rose and maize	70·00	75·00
		a. Imperf between (horiz pair)		
127/39	Set of 13		£170	£120
127s/39s	Optd "Specimen" Set of 13		£170	

No. 139a is also imperforate between stamp and left-hand margin.

(Typo D.L.R.)

1902. *Wmk Crown CC. P 14.*
140	**32**	5s. dull blue and rose	30·00	11·00
141		10s. deep rose and chocolate	70·00	26·00
142		£1 black and bright blue	£180	55·00
143		£1 10s. green and violet	£400	£100
		s. Optd "Specimen"	75·00	
144		£5 mauve and black	£2750	£650
		s. Optd "Specimen"	£120	
145		£10 green and orange	£7500	£3000
		as. Optd "Specimen"	£200	
145b		£20 red and green	£15000	£7500
		bs. Optd "Specimen"	£375	
140s/2s	Optd "Specimen" Set of 3		£110	

USED HIGH VALUES. Collectors are warned against fiscally used high value Natal stamps with penmarks cleaned off and forged postmarks added.

1904–08. *Chalk-surfaced paper (£1 10s.). Wmk Mult Crown CA. P 14.*
146	**31**	½d. blue-green	6·00	15
147		1d. rose-carmine	6·00	15
		a. Booklet pane of 6, one stamp optd "NOT FOR USE" (1907)	£275	
148		1d. deep carmine	8·50	30
		w. Wmk inverted	†	80·00
149		2d. red and olive-green	9·00	3·25
152		4d. carmine and cinnamon	2·75	1·25
153		5d. black and orange (1908)	4·25	4·00
155		1s. carmine and pale blue	80·00	7·00
156		2s. dull green and bright violet	55·00	38·00
157		2s.6d. purple	50·00	38·00
162	**32**	£1 10s. brown-orange & dp pur (1908)	£1200	£2000
		s. Optd "Specimen"	£190	
146/57	Set of 9		£200	80·00

1908–09. *Inscr "POSTAGE POSTAGE". Wmk Mult Crown CA. P 14.*
165	**31**	6d. dull and bright purple	4·50	2·75
166		1s. black/green	6·00	2·50
167		2s. purple and bright blue/blue	15·00	3·00
168		2s.6d. black and red/blue	25·00	9·00
169	**32**	5s. green and red/yellow	22·00	26·00
170		10s. green and red/green	75·00	80·00
171		£1 purple and black/red	£275	£250

165/71	Set of 7	£375	£325
165s/71s	Optd "Specimen" Set of 7	£225	

STAMP BOOKLETS

1906. *Black on red cover. Stapled.*
SB1   2s.7d. booklet containing thirty 1d. (No. 147) in
blocks of 6 .... £2000

1907. *Black on red cover. Stapled.*
SB2   2s.6d. booklet containing thirty 1d. (No. 147) in
blocks of 6 .... £2000

The first stamp of the first pane in No. SB2 was overprinted "NOT FOR USE" (No. 147a), the additional penny being used to defray the cost of production.

FISCALS USED FOR POSTAGE

1869. *Embossed on coloured wove, surfaced paper.* P 12½.
F1   **1**   1d. yellow... 50·00   80·00

Examples of 1d. yellow and 6d. rose values as Type **6**, 1s. purple-brown as Type **7** and various values between 5s, and £10 in the design illustrated above are believed to exist postally used, but, as such use was not authorised, they are not now listed.

OFFICIAL STAMPS

OFFICIAL
(O **1**)

1904. T **31**, wmk Mult Crown CA, optd with Type O **1**. P 14.
O1	½d. blue-green	3·00	35
O2	1d. carmine	4·50	70
O3	2d. red and olive-green	24·00	12·00
O4	3d. purple and grey	14·00	4·00
O5	6d. green and brown-purple	48·00	65·00
O6	1s. carmine and pale blue............	£150	£200
O1/6	Set of 6	£200	£250

The use of stamps overprinted as above was discontinued after 30 May 1907. Stamps perforated with the letters "N.G.R." were for use on Government Railways.

Natal became a province of the Union of South Africa on 31 May 1910.

IV. NEW REPUBLIC

During the unrest following the death of Cetshwayo, the Zulu king, in 1884, a group of Boers from the Transvaal offered their support to his son, Dinizulu. The price for this support was the cession of a sizeable portion of Zulu territory to an independent Boer republic. The New Republic, centred on Vryheid, was proclaimed on 16 August 1884 with the remaining Zulu territory becoming a protectorate of the new administration. The first reference to an organised postal service occurs in December 1884.

Alarmed by these developments the British authorities annexed the southernmost part of the land grant, around St. Lucia Bay, to prevent access to the Indian Ocean. The remainder of the New Republic was, however, recognised as independent on 22 October 1886. Zululand was annexed by the British on 22 May 1887.

Difficulties beset the New Republic, however, and its Volksraad voted for union with the South African Republic (Transvaal). The two republics united on 21 July 1888. In 1903 the territory of the former New Republic was transferred to Natal.

Mail from Vryheid in 1884–85 was franked with issues of Transvaal (for dispatches made via Utrecht) or Natal (for those sent via Dundee from August 1885 onwards). Issues of the New Republic were never accepted as internationally valid by these administrations so that all external mail continued to show Transvaal or Natal stamps used in combination with those of the republic.

PRICES FOR STAMPS ON COVER		
No. 1		—
Nos. 2/5		from × 50
Nos. 6/25		
Nos. 26/9		from × 50
Nos. 30/47		
Nos. 48/50		from × 50
No. 51		—
Nos. 52/3		from × 50
Nos. 72/5		from × 50
Nos. 76/7b		—
Nos. 78/80		from × 50
Nos. 81/95		—

1

Printed with a rubber handstamp on paper bought in Europe and sent out ready gummed and perforated.

1886 (7 Jan)–**87.** *Various dates indicating date of printing.* P 11½.
A. Without Arms. (i) Yellow paper.
1	**1**	1d. black (9.1.86)	—	£3000
2		1d. violet (9.1.86)...........................	11·00	13·00
		a. "1d." omitted (in pair with normal) (24.4.86)	£2000	
3		2d. violet (9.1.86)...........................	15·00	20·00
		a. "d" omitted (13.10.86)	£4000	
4		3d. violet (13.1.86)	30·00	35·00
		a. "d" omitted (13.10.86)	£4000	
		b. Tête-bêche (pair) (13.10.86)	£4000	
5		4d. violet (30.8.86).........................	45·00	
6		6d. violet (20.2.86).........................	40·00	45·00
		a. "6d." omitted (in pair with normal) (2.7.86)....................	£2000	
7		9d. violet (13.1.86)	75·00	
8		1s. violet (30.8.86).........................	75·00	
		a. "1s." omitted (in pair with normal) (6.9.86).....................	£2000	
9		1/s. violet (13.10.86)	£550	
10		1/6. violet (30.8.86)........................	80·00	
11		1s.6d. violet (13.1.86)	£450	
		a. Tête-bêche (pair) (6.9.86)	£100	
		b. "d" omitted (13.10.86)	£100	
12		2s. violet (30.8.86).........................	42·00	
		a. Tête-bêche (pair) (6.9.86)	£750	
13		2/6 violet (13.1.86)	£150	
14		2s.6d. violet (1.86).........................	£120	
15		4/s. violet (17.1.87)........................	£450	
15a		4s. violet (17.1.87).........................		
16		5s. violet (1.86)..............................	30·00	40·00
		a. "s" omitted (in pair with normal) (7.3.86)......................	£3000	
17		5/6 violet (20.2.86)	£140	
18		5s.6d. violet (13.1.86)	£300	
19		7/6 violet (13.1.86)	£180	
20		7s.6d. violet (24.5.86)	£120	
21		10s. violet (13.1.86)	£150	£160
		a. Tête-bêche (pair) (2.7.86)	£150	
22		10s.6d. violet (1.86)........................	£170	
		a. "d" omitted (1.86)	£100	
23		13s. violet (24.11.86)	£450	
24		£1 violet (13.1.86)	£120	
		a. Tête-bêche (pair) (13.10.86)	£500	
25		30s. violet (13.1.86)	£100	
		a. Tête-bêche (pair) (24.11.86)	£500	

(ii) Blue granite paper.
26	**1**	1d. violet (20.1.86)	16·00	18·00
		a. "d" omitted (24.11.86)	£500	
		b. "1" omitted (in pair with normal) (24.11.86)		
27		2d. violet (24.1.86)..........................	16·00	18·00
		a. "d" omitted (24.4.86).................	£1000	
		b. "2d." omitted (in pair with normal) (24.4.86)..................		
28		3d. violet (30.8.86)..........................	22·00	24·00
		a. Tête-bêche (pair) (13.10.86)	£300	
29		4d. violet (24.5.86)..........................	30·00	35·00
30		6d. violet (20.2.86)..........................	50·00	50·00
		a. "6" omitted in pair with normal (24.5.86)......................	£2000	
31		9d. violet (6.9.86)...........................	£110	
32		1s. violet (1.86)..............................	30·00	35·00
		a. Tête-bêche (pair) (21.5.86)	£325	
		b. "1s." omitted (in pair with normal) (29.4.86)	£2000	
33		1s.6d. violet (2.7.86).......................	£100	
		a. Tête-bêche (pair) (6.9.86)	£550	
		b. "d" omitted (13.10.86)		
34		1/6 violet (6.9.86)...........................	£150	
35		2s. violet (21.5.86)..........................	£120	
		a. "2s." omitted (in pair with normal) (24.5.86)...................	£2000	
36		2s.6d. violet (19.8.86).....................	£150	
37		2/6 violet (19.8.86)	£180	
38		4/s. violet (17.1.87)........................	£350	
39		5/6 violet (13.1.87)	£250	
		a. "/" omitted (13.1.87)..................		
40		5s.6d. violet (13.1.86)	£250	
41		7/6 violet (13.1.86)	£250	
41a		7s.6d. violet (13.1.86)	£300	
42		10s. violet (1.86)	£200	£200
		a. Tête-bêche (pair) (2.7.86)	£425	
		b. "s" omitted (13.1.86)		
43		10s.6d. violet (1.86)........................	£200	
		a. Tête-bêche (pair) (13.1.86)	£450	
		b. "d" omitted (1.86)		
44		12s. violet (13.1.86)	£300	
45		13s. violet (17.1.87)	£475	
46		£1 violet (13.1.86)	£275	
47		30s. violet (13.1.86)	£250	

B. With embossed Arms of New Republic.
(i) Yellow paper.
48	**1**	1d. violet (20.1.86)	14·00	16·00
		a. Arms inverted (20.1.86)	27·00	30·00
		b. Arms tête-bêche (pair) (14.4.86)..................................	£100	£120
		c. Tête-bêche (pair) (3.11.86)	£800	

49		2d. violet (30.8.86).........................	16·00	18·00
		a. Arms inverted (24.11.86)	25·00	30·00
50		4d. violet (2.12.86).........................	50·00	60·00
		a. Arms inverted (12.86)	£100	70·00
		b. Arms tête-bêche (pair) (12.86)..	£250	
51		6d. violet (2.12.86).........................	£200	

(ii) Blue granite paper.
52	**1**	1d. violet (20.1.86)	15·00	17·00
		a. Arms inverted (10.2.86)	38·00	42·00
		b. Arms tête-bêche (pair) (3.11.86).................................	£500	
53		2d. violet (24.5.86).........................	15·00	17·00
		a. Arms inverted (30.8.86)	50·00	60·00
		b. Arms tête-bêche (pair) (2.12.86).................................	£500	£500

Stamps as Type **1** were produced as and when stocks were required, each printing including in its design the date on which it was prepared. The dates quoted above for Nos. 1/53 are those on which the various stamps first appeared. Details of the various printing dates are given below. From these dates it can be seen that some values share common printing dates, and, it is believed, that the different values were produced *se-tenant* within the same sheet, at least in some instances. A reported proof sheet in the Pretoria Postal Museum, on yellow paper and embossed, contains 4 examples of the 6d. value and 3 each of the 3d., 4d., 9d., 1s., 1/6, 2/-, 2/6, 3s., 4s., 5s., 5/6, 7/6, 10/-, 10/6, £1 and 30/-.

The date on No. 1 measures 17 mm, on all others it is 15 mm.

The significance, if any, of the two coloured papers and the use of the embossing machine have never been satisfactorily explained. Both the different papers and the embossing machine were introduced in January 1886, and occur throughout the period that the stamps with dates were used.

PRINTINGS

Date	Paper	Face value	Cat. No.	Un.	Us
Jan 86	Yellow	5s.	16	30·00	40·00
		10s.6d.	22	£200	
		10s.6	22a	£150	
	Blue	1s.	32		
		10s.	42	£200	£200
		10s.6d.	43	£200	
		10s.6	43b	£500	
7 Jan 86	Yellow	10s.6d.	22	£170	
	Blue	10s.	42		
		10s.6d.	43	£475	
9 Jan 86	Yellow	1d. blk	1	†	£3000
		1d. vio	2	11·00	13·00
		2d.	3	40·00	50·00
13 Jan 86	Yellow	1d.	2	38·00	
		2d.	3	35·00	38·00
		3d.	4	75·00	
		9d	7	£200	
		1s.6d.	11	£450	
		2/6	13	£160	
		2s.6d.	14	£200	
		5s.6d.	18		
		7/6	19	£180	
		10s.	21		
		£1	24	£150	
		30s.	25	£150	
	Blue	5/6	39	£250	
		5s.6d.	40	£250	
		7/6	41	£250	
		7s.6d.	41a	£300	
		10s.	42	£400	
		10s.6d.	43	£200	
		10s.6d.	43a		
		12s.	44	£300	
		£1	46	£250	
		30s.	47	£250	
20 Jan 86	Yellow	1d.	2		
	Blue	1d.	26	£250	
	Yellow, embossed	1d.	48	75·00	
		1d.	48a	£100	
	Blue, embossed	1d.	52	£130	
Jan 20 86	Blue	1d.	26	25·00	
	Yellow, embossed	1d.	48a		
	Blue, embossed	1d.	52	£120	
24 Jan 86	Blue	1d.	26	30·00	
		2d.	27	50·00	
10 Feb 86	Yellow	1d.	2		
	Yellow, embossed	1d.	48		
		1d.	48a	75·00	
	Blue, embossed	1d.	52	£130	
20 Feb 86	Yellow	1d.	2		
		6d.	6		
		1s.6d.	11		
		2s.6d.	14	£130	
		5/6	17	£140	
		5s.6d.	18		
	Blue	6d.	30		
7 Mar 86	Yellow	1d.	2	£110	
		2/6	13		
		2s.6d.	14	£120	
		5s.	16	£200	90·00
		5s.	16a	£3000	
		5/6	17	£140	
		5s.6d.	18	£300	
	Blue	2d.	27	£100	
		6d.	30		
		1s.	32		
17 Mar 86	Yellow	1d.	2	£100	
	Yellow, embossed	1d.	48	50·00	
	Blue, embossed	1d.	52	£130	
		1d.	52a	£110	
26 Mar 86	Blue, embossed	1d.	52a	£130	
14 Apr 86	Yellow	1d.	2		
	Yellow, embossed	1d.	48	30·00	
		1d.	48a	60·00	
		1d.	48b	£100	£120
	Blue, embossed	1d.	52	50·00	
		1d.	52a		
24 Apr 86	Yellow	1d.	2	£100	
		1d.	2a	£2000	
		5s.	16		
	Blue	2d.	27	75·00	
		2d.	27a	£1000	
		2d.	27b		
29 Apr 86	Blue	1s.	32	£110	
		1s.	32b		
21 May 86	Yellow	6d.	6	£130	
	Blue	1d.	26	90·00	
		1s.	32	30·00	35·00
		1s.	32b	£325	
		1s.	32b	£1500	
		2s.	35	£275	
23 May 86	Blue, embossed	1d.	52a	£100	
24 May 86	Yellow	1d.	2	£100	
		2d.	3	£120	

Date	Paper	Face value	Cat. No.	Un.	Us
		5s.	16	£100	
		7/6	19	£180	
		7s.6d.	20	£120	
	Blue	1d.	26	35·00	38·00
		2d.	27	£300	£300
		4d.	29	£100	
		6d.	30	£120	
		6d.	30a	£2000	
		1s.	32	£200	
		1s.	32b	£2000	
		2s.	35	£150	
		2s.	35a	£2000	
	Blue, embossed	2d.	53	£100	
26 May 86	Yellow	1d.	2		
	Blue	1d.	26	£110	
	Yellow, embossed	1d.	48	£250	
		1d.	48a	£100	
	Blue, embossed	1d.	52	£130	
		1d.	52a	50·00	55·00
28 May 86	Yellow, embossed	1d.	48	£150	
Jun 30 86	Blue	1d.	26	16·00	18·00
	Yellow, embossed	1d.	48	18·00	20·00
		1d.	48a	27·00	30·00
		1d.	48b	£200	£225
	Blue, embossed	1d.	52	48·00	42·00
2 Jul 86	Yellow	6d.	6	£200	
		6d.	6a		
		9d.	7	£200	£200
		10s.	21		
		10s.	21a		
	Blue	1s.6d.	33	£100	
		10s.	42	£200	
		10s.	42a	£425	
		10s.6d.	43		
		10s.6d.	43b	£450	
3 Jul 86	Blue	1d.	26		
Jul 7 86	Yellow	1d.	2		
	Blue	1d.	26		
	Yellow, embossed	1d.	48	75·00	
		1d.	48a	£100	£100
	Blue, embossed	1d.	52	18·00	20·00
		1d.	52a	60·00	42·00
4 Aug 86	Yellow	1d.	2		
	Yellow, embossed	1d.	48	60·00	
	Blue, embossed	1d.	52	60·00	
		1d.	52a		
19 Aug 86	Yellow	2/6	13		
		2s.6d.	14	£140	
	Blue	2s.6d.	36	£150	
		2/6	37	£180	
30 Aug 86	Yellow	1d.	2	11·00	13·00
		2d.	3	75·00	
		3d.	4	80·00	
		4d.	5	55·00	
		6d.	6	£100	
		9d.	7	75·00	
		1s.	8	75·00	
		1/6	10	80·00	
		2s.	12	£100	
		2/6	13	£150	
	Blue	2d.	27	16·00	18·00
		3d.	28		
	Yellow, embossed	2d.	49	£100	
	Blue, embossed	2d.	53	45·00	
		2d.	53a	£110	
6 Sep 86	Yellow	1d.	2	£100	
		2d.	3	35·00	40·00
		3d.	4	40·00	
		4d.	5	45·00	
		6d.	6	75·00	
		9d.	7	75·00	
		1s.	8	£100	
		1s.	8a		
		1/6	10	£140	
		1s.6d.	11	£450	
		1s.6d.	11a		
		2s.	12	£100	
		2s.	12a	£750	
		2/6	13	£150	
		2s.6d.	14	£140	
		5s.	16	£140	
		7s.6d.	20	£200	
		10s.	21	£150	
		£1	24	£140	
	Blue	6d.	30	50·00	50·00
		9d.	31	£110	
		1s.	32	75·00	
		1s.6d.	33	£140	
		1s.6d.	33a	£550	
		1/6	34		
		2s.6d.	36		
		2/6	37	£400	
		7s.6d.	41a	£300	
		10s.6d.	43		
13 Sep 86	Yellow	1d.	2		
	Yellow, embossed	1d.	48	75·00	
		1d.	48a	75·00	
	Blue, embossed	1d.	52	£100	
6 Oct 86	Yellow	1d.	2		
	Blue	1d.	26	90·00	
	Yellow, embossed	1d.	48	75·00	60·00
		1d.	48a		
	Blue, embossed	1d.	52	48·00	20·00
		1d.	52a	90·00	
13 Oct 86	Yellow	1d.	2	25·00	25·00
		2d.	3	25·00	30·00
		2d.	3a	£4000	
		3d.	4	30·00	35·00
		3d.	4a	£4000	
		3d.	4b		
		4d.	5	50·00	
		6d.	6	40·00	45·00
		9d.	7	75·00	
		1s.	8	£150	
		1/s	9	£550	
		1/6	10	£150	
		1s 6.	11b	£100	
		2s.	12	42·00	
		2/6	13	£160	
		5s.	16	75·00	
		10s.	21	£150	£160
		10s.6.	22a	£100	
		£1	24	£120	
		£1	24a	£500	
	Blue	2d.	27	16·00	18·00
		3d.	28	22·00	24·00
		3d.	28a	£300	
		4d.	29	30·00	35·00
		1s.	32	50·00	
		1s 6.	33b		
		1/6	34	£150	
		2s.	35	£120	
3 Nov 86	Yellow	1d.	2	40·00	
	Blue	1d.	26		
	Yellow, embossed	1d.	48	14·00	16·00
		1d.	48a	27·00	30·00

Date	Paper	Face value	Cat. No.	Un.	Us
		1d.	48b	£100	£120
		1d.	48c	£800	
	Blue, embossed	1d.	52	15·00	
		1d.	52a	38·00	42·00
		1d.	52b	£500	
13 Nov 86	Yellow	1d.	2	£120	
24 Nov 86	Yellow	1d.	2	£100	
		2d.	3	15·00	20·00
		3d.	4	35·00	40·00
		1/6	10	£150	
		10s.	21	£200	
		13s.	23	£450	
		30s.	25	£100	
		30s.	25a	£500	
	Blue	1d.	26	40·00	30·00
		1d.	26a	£500	
		1d.	26b		
		2d.	27	50·00	
		2d.	27a		
		4d.	29	30·00	35·00
		6d.	30	60·00	60·00
		9d.	31	£120	
		1s.	32	100·00	110·00
		1/6	34	£200	
		2s.	35	£150	
		2s.	35a	£3000	
	Yellow, embossed	2d.	49	£160	
		2d.	49a		
26 Nov 86	Yellow	1/6	10	£140	
2 Dec 86	Yellow	1d.	2		
		2d.	3		
	Blue	2d.	27		
	Yellow, embossed	1d.	48	25·00	30·00
		1d.	48a	£160	
		2d.	49	16·00	18·00
		2d.	49a	25·00	30·00
		4d.	50	£150	
		6d.	51	£150	
	Blue, embossed	2d.	52	35·00	
		1d.	52a	£160	
		2d.	53	15·00	17·00
		2d.	53a	50·00	60·00
		2d.	53b	£500	£500
3 Dec 86	Yellow, embossed	6d.	51		
Dec 86	Yellow	6d.	6		
	Blue	4d.	29		
	Yellow, embossed	4d.	50	50·00	60·00
		4d.	50a	£100	70·00
		4d.	50b	£250	
		6d.	51	£200	
4 Jan 87	Yellow	1d.	2	£100	
		2d.	3	40·00	
		13s.	23	£450	
	Blue	1d.	26	16·00	18·00
		2d.	27	20·00	20·00
	Blue, embossed	2d.	53	45·00	
13 Jan 87	Yellow	7/6	19		
	Blue	5/6	39	£450	
		5/6	39a		
		7/6	41	£500	
17 Jan 87	Yellow	1d.	2	75·00	
		2d.	3	75·00	
		3d.	4	75·00	
		4/s.	15	£450	
		4s.	15a		
	Blue	1d.	26	80·00	
		4/s.	38	£350	
		13s.	45	£475	
		30s.	47	£275	
20 Jan 87	Blue	2d.	27	38·00	
	Yellow, embossed	2d.	49	55·00	
		2d.	49a	£140	
		2d.	53	45·00	
		2d.	53a	£100	
Jan 20 87	Yellow, embossed	1d.	48a	£400	

1887 (Jan–Mar). *As T* **1**, *but without date. With embossed Arms.*

(a) Blue granite paper.

72	1d. violet			17·00	15·00
	b. Stamps tête-bêche (pair)			£475	
	c. Arms tête-bêche (pair)				
	d. Arms inverted			25·00	25·00
	e. Arms omitted			£110	£110
	f. Arms sideways				
73	2d. violet			10·00	10·00
	a. Stamps tête-bêche (pair)			£325	
	b. Arms inverted			28·00	28·00
	c. Arms omitted			£110	£100
	d. Arms tête-bêche (pair)				
74	3d. violet			17·00	17·00
	a. Stamps tête-bêche (pair)			£375	
	b. Arms tête-bêche (pair)				
	c. Arms inverted			50·00	50·00
75	4d. violet			14·00	14·00
	a. Stamps tête-bêche (pair)			£325	
	b. Arms tête-bêche (pair)			£275	
	c. Arms inverted			85·00	
76	6d. violet			17·00	17·00
	a. Arms inverted			85·00	
77	1/6 violet			24·00	22·00
	a. Arms inverted			£120	
	b. Arms tête-bêche (pair)			£400	
77c	2/6 violet			†	£750

(b) Yellow paper (March 1887).

78	2d. violet (*arms omitted*)			25·00	
79	3d. violet			16·00	17·00
	b. Stamps tête-bêche (pair)			£325	£375
	c. Arms tête-bêche (pair)			£200	
	d. Arms inverted			27·00	27·00
	e. Arms sideways			£300	
80	4d. violet			14·00	14·00
	a. Arms inverted			16·00	16·00
81	6d. violet			9·00	10·00
	a. Arms tête-bêche (pair)			£350	
	b. Arms inverted			45·00	45·00
	c. Arms omitted			80·00	
82	9d. violet			12·00	13·00
	a. Arms inverted			£200	
	b. Arms tête-bêche (pair)			£350	
83	1s. violet			12·00	12·00
	a. Arms inverted			70·00	
84	1/6 violet			22·00	20·00
85	2s. violet			19·00	18·00
	a. Arms inverted			55·00	50·00
	b. Arms omitted			£100	
86	2/6 violet			25·00	25·00

	a. Arms inverted			32·00	32·00
87	3s. violet			48·00	48·00
	a. Arms inverted			55·00	55·00
	b. Stamps tête-bêche (pair)			£450	
88	4s. violet			£300	
	a. Arms omitted				
88b	4/s violet			45·00	45·00
	ba. Arms omitted			£180	
89	5s. violet			40·00	40·00
	b. Arms inverted			—	£100
90	5/6 violet			16·00	17·00
91	7/6 violet			20·00	22·00
	a. Arms tête-bêche (pair)			£100	
	b. Arms inverted				
92	10s. violet			16·00	17·00
	b. Arms tête-bêche (pair)			£120	
	c. Arms inverted			27·00	
	d. Arms omitted			£100	£100
93	10/6 violet			17·00	17·00
	b. Arms inverted			50·00	
94	£1 violet			55·00	55·00
	a. Stamps tête-bêche (pair)			£450	£500
	b. Arms inverted			60·00	
95	30s. violet			£140	

A £15 value as Nos. 78/95 exists, but is only known fiscally used (*Price* £4000).

Many values exist with double impressions of the handstamp.

New Republic united with the South African Republic (Transvaal) on 21 July 1888. In 1903 the territory of the former New Republic was transferred to Natal.

V. ORANGE FREE STATE

PRICES FOR STAMPS on COVER	
Nos. 1/9	*from* × 20
Nos. 10/13	*from* × 30
Nos. 18/19	*from* × 20
No. 20	—
Nos. 21/42	*from* × 40
Nos. 48/51	*from* × 25
Nos. 52/138	*from* × 10
Nos. 139/51	*from* × 7
Nos. F1/17	—
Nos. PF1/3	*from* × 20
No. M1	*from* × 20

Supplies of Cape of Good Hope stamps were available at Bloemfontein and probably elsewhere in the Orange Free State, from mid-1856 onwards for use on mail to Cape Colony and beyond. Such arrangements continued after the introduction of Orange Free State stamps in 1868. It is not known if the dumb cancellations used on the few surviving covers were applied in the Free State or at Cape Town.

1

(Typo D.L.R.)

1868 (1 Jan)–94. P 14.

1	**1**	1d. pale brown		16·00	1·25
2		1d. red-brown		12·00	45
3		1d. deep brown		17·00	45
4		6d. pale rose (1868)		50·00	8·00
5		6d. rose (1871)		19·00	5·50
6		6d. rose-carmine (1891)		19·00	12·00
7		6d. bright carmine (1894)		12·00	2·00
8		1s. orange-buff		80·00	6·50
9		1s. orange-yellow		38·00	1·50
		a. Double print		—	£3000

4 **4** **4** **4**

(2) (a)　　(b)　　(c)　　(d)

1877. *No. 5 surcharged T* **2** (a) to (d).

10	**1**	4d. on 6d. rose (a)		£350	55·00
		a. Surch inverted		—	£550
		b. Surch double (a + c)			
		c. Surch double, one inverted (a + c inverted)		†	£2750
		d. Surch double, one inverted (a inverted + c)		†	£4500
11		4d. on 6d. rose (b)		£1200	£180
		a. Surch inverted		—	£1100
		b. Surch double (b + d)			
12		4d. on 6d. rose (c)		£180	27·00
		a. Surch inverted		—	£350
		b. Surch double			
13		4d. on 6d. rose (d)		£225	35·00
		a. Surch inverted		£1100	£375
		b. Surch double, one inverted (d + c inverted)		†	£3000

The setting of 60 comprised nine stamps as No. 10, four as No. 11, twenty-seven as No. 12 and twenty as No. 13.

1878 (July). P 14.

18	**1**	4d. pale blue		20·00	3·00
19		4d. ultramarine		4·00	2·50
20		5s. green		9·00	11·00

1d. **1d.** **1d.** **1d.** **1d.** **1d.**
(3) (a)   (b)   (c)   (d)   (e)   (f)

Type **3**: (a) Small "1" and "d." (b) Sloping serif. (c) Same size as (b), but "1" with straighter horizontal serif. (d) Taller "1" with horizontal serif and antique "d". (e) Same size as (d) but with sloping serif and thin line at foot. (f) as (d) but with Roman "d".

1881 (19 May). *No. 20 surch T* **3** *(a) to (f) with heavy black bar cancelling the old value.*

21	**1**	1d. on 5s. green (a)	95·00	21·00
22		1d. on 5s. green (b)	55·00	21·00
		a. Surch inverted	—	£800
		b. Surch double		£1100
23		1d. on 5s. green (c)	£200	75·00
		a. Surch inverted	—	£1200
		b. Surch double		£1400
24		1d. on 5s. green (d)	85·00	21·00
		a. Surch inverted	£1600	£800
		b. Surch double		£1100
25		1d. on 5s. green (e)	£500	£250
		a. Surch inverted	†	£2000
		b. Surch double	†	£2000
26		1d. on 5s. green (f)	80·00	21·00
		a. Surch inverted	—	£750
		b. Surch double		£800

No. 21 was the first printing in one type only. Nos. 22 to 25 constitute the second printing about a year later, and are all found on the same sheet; and No. 26 the third printing of which about half have the stop raised.

Owing to defective printing, examples of Nos. 22 and 24/5 may be found with the obliterating bar at the top of the stamps or, from the top row, without the bar.

½d
(4)

1882 (Aug). *No. 20 surch with T* **4** *and with a thin black line cancelling old value.*

36	**1**	½d. on 5s. green	17·00	3·75
		a. Surch double	£400	£325
		b. Surch inverted	£1200	£800

3d **3d** **3d** **3d** **3d**
(5) (a)   (b)   (c)   (d)   (e)

1882. *No. 19 surch with T* **5** *(a) to (e) with thin black line cancelling value.*

38	**1**	3d. on 4d. ultramarine (a)	80·00	25·00
		a. Surch double	†	£1200
39		3d. on 4d. ultramarine (b)	80·00	18·00
		a. Surch double	†	£1200
40		3d. on 4d. ultramarine (c)	32·00	16·00
		a. Surch double	†	£1200
41		3d. on 4d. ultramarine (d)	80·00	19·00
		a. Surch double	†	£1200
42		3d. on 4d. ultramarine (e)	£200	65·00
		a. Surch double	†	£2750

Examples of Nos. 39 and 41/2 exist without the cancelling bar due to the misplacement of the surcharge.

1883–84. P 14.

48	**1**	½d. chestnut	2·50	50
49		2d. pale mauve	14·00	60
50		2d. bright mauve	14·00	30
51		3d. ultramarine	3·00	2·00

For 1d. purple, see No. 68.

2d **2d** **2d**
(6) (a)   (b)   (c)

1888 (Sept–Oct). *No. 51 surch with T* **6** *(a), (b) or (c).*

(a) Wide "2". (b) Narrow "2".

52	**1**	2d. on 3d. ultramarine (a) (Sept)	55·00	9·00
		a. Surch inverted		£750
53		2d. on 3d. ultramarine (b)	35·00	2·00
		a. Surch inverted		£300
		b. "2" with curved foot (c)	£1200	£500

1d **1d** **Id**
(7) (a)   (b)   (c)

1890 (Dec)–**91**. *Nos. 51 and 19 surch with T* **7** *(a) to (c).*

54	**1**	1d. on 3d. ultramarine (a)	6·00	60
		a. Surch double	80·00	70·00
		c. "1" and "d" wide apart	£140	£110
		d. Dropped "d" (Right pane R. 5/6)	£150	£120
55		1d. on 3d. ultramarine (b)	21·00	2·75
		a. Surch double	£250	£250
57		1d. on 4d. ultramarine (a)	27·00	5·50
		a. Surch double	£130	£110
		b. Surch double (a + b)	£375	
		c. Surch triple	—	£1500
		d. Raised "1" (Left pane R. 3/1)		
58		1d. on 4d. ultramarine (b)	75·00	50·00
		a. Surch double	£400	£325
59		1d. on 4d. ultramarine (c)	£1400	£500

The settings of the 1d. on 3d. and on 4d. are not identical. The variety (c) does not exist on the 3d.

2½d.   **2½d.**
(8)

Printers leads after surcharge
(Lower right pane No. 43)

1892 (Oct). *No. 51 surch with T* **8**.

67	**1**	2½d. on 3d. ultramarine	14·00	70
		a. No stop after "d"	75·00	50·00
		b. Printers leads after surcharge	—	50·00

1894 (Sept). *Colour changed.* P 14.

68	**1**	1d. purple	3·00	30

½d **½d** **½d**
(9) (a)   (b)   (c)

½d **½d** **½d** **½d**
(d)   (e)   (f)   (g)

Types (a) and (e) differ from types (b) and (f) respectively, in the serifs of the "1", but owing to faulty overprinting this distinction is not always clearly to be seen.

1896 (Sept). *No. 51 surch with T* **9** *(a) to (g).*

69	**1**	½d. on 3d. ultramarine (a)	4·25	9·00
70		½d. on 3d. ultramarine (b)	10·00	10·00
71		½d. on 3d. ultramarine (c)	9·00	2·50
72		½d. on 3d. ultramarine (d)	9·00	2·25
73		½d. on 3d. ultramarine (e)	9·00	2·25
74		½d. on 3d. ultramarine (f)	11·00	12·00
75		½d. on 3d. ultramarine (g)	6·50	3·50
		a. Surch double	13·00	10·00
		b. Surch triple	70·00	70·00

The double and triple surcharges are often different types, but are always type (g), or in combination with type (g).

Double surcharges in the same type, but without the "d" and bar, also exist, probably from a trial sheet prepared by the printer. Both mint and used examples are known.

Halve Penny.

_____
(10)   **2½**
(11)

1896. *No. 51 surch with T* **10**.

77	**1**	½d. on 3d. ultramarine	1·00	50

(i) Errors in setting.

78	**1**	½d. on 3d. (no stop)	15·00	27·00
79		½d. on 3d. ("Peuny")	15·00	27·00

(ii) Surch inverted.

81	**1**	½d. on 3d.	55·00	60·00
81a		½d. on 3d. (no stop)	£2000	
81b		½d. on 3d. ("Peuny")	£1500	

(iii) Surch double, one inverted.

81c	**1**	½d. on 3d. (Nos. 77 and 81)	£180	£200
81d		½d. on 3d. (Nos. 77 and 81a)	£750	£750
81e		½d. on 3d. (Nos. 77 and 81b)	£850	£850
81f		½d. on 3d. (Nos. 81 and 78)	—	£850
82		½d. on 3d. (Nos. 81 and 79)	—	£850

Examples from the top horizontal row can be found without the bar due to the surcharge being misplaced.

Nos. 69 to 75 also exist surcharged as last but are considered not to have been issued with authority (*Prices from* £30 *each, unused*).

1897 (1 Jan). *No. 51 surch with T* **11**. *(a) As in illustration. (b) With Roman "1" and antique "2" in fraction.*

83	**1**	2½d. on 3d. ultramarine (a)	7·00	80
83a		2½d. on 3d. ultramarine (b)	£160	90·00

1897. P 14.

84	**1**	½d. yellow (March)	2·00	35
85		½d. orange	2·00	35
87		1s. brown (Aug)	21·00	1·50

The 6d. blue was prepared for use in the Orange Free State, but had not been brought into use when the stamps were seized in Bloemfontein. A few have been seen without the "V.R.I." overprint but they were not authorized or available for postage (*Price* £60).

BRITISH OCCUPATION

V. R. I.   **V. R. I.**   **V. R. I.**

4d   **½d**   **½d**
31 (Level stops)   (32) Thin "V"   (33) Thick "V"
(Raised stops)

V. R. I.
Inserted "R"

(Surch by Curling & Co, Bloemfontein)

1900. *T* **1** *surch as T* **31/33** *(2½d. on 3d. optd "V.R.I." only).*

(a) First printings surch as T **31** *with stops level (March).*

101	½d. on ½d. orange	3·00	3·50
	a. No stop after "V"	20·00	24·00
	b. No stop after "I"	£160	£160
	c. "½" omitted	£180	£180
	d. "I" omitted	£200	£200
	e. "V.R.I." omitted	£160	
	f. Value omitted	£100	
	g. Small "½"	55·00	55·00
	h. Surch double	£180	
102	1d. on 1d. purple	2·50	1·25
	a. Surch on 1d. deep brown (No. 3)	£600	£400
	b. No stop after "V"	16·00	13·00
	c. No stop after "R"	£160	£170
	d. No stop after "I"	£180	£190
	e. "1" omitted	£180	£190
	f. "I" omitted	£300	£300
	g. "I" and stop after "R" omitted	£300	£300
	h. "V.R.I." omitted	£150	£160
	i. "d" omitted	£325	£325
	j. Value omitted	85·00	90·00
	k. Inverted stop after "R"	£200	£225
	l. Wider space between "1" and "d"	£100	£100
	m. "V" and "R" close	£160	£160
	n. Pair, one without surch	£450	
	o. "V" inserted	£800	
103	2d. on 2d. bright mauve	2·50	1·00
	a. No stop after "V"	14·00	17·00
	b. No stop after "R"	£250	£250
	c. No stop after "I"	£250	£250
	d. "V.R.I." omitted	£300	£300
	e. Value omitted	£300	
104	2½d. on 3d. ultramarine (a)	15·00	12·00
	a. No stop after "V"	85·00	85·00
105	2½d. on 3d. ultramarine (b)	£200	£200
106	3d. on 3d. ultramarine	2·25	2·00
	a. No stop after "V"	18·00	17·00
	b. Pair, one without surch	£550	
	c. "V.R.I." omitted	£250	£250
	d. Value omitted	£250	£250
107	4d. on 4d. ultramarine	7·50	15·00
	a. No stop after "V"	60·00	70·00
108	6d. on 6d. bright carmine	38·00	35·00
	a. No stop after "V"	£250	£275
	b. "6" omitted	£300	£300
109	6d. on 6d. blue	8·00	3·75
	a. No stop after "V"	40·00	42·00
	b. "6" omitted	75·00	80·00
	c. "V.R.I." omitted	—	£300
110	1s. on 1s. brown	7·00	2·75
	a. Surch on 1s. orange-yellow (No. 9)	£3500	£2500
	b. No stop after "V"	42·00	32·00
	c. "1" omitted	£130	£130
	ca. "1" inserted by hand	†	£1000
	d. "1" omitted and spaced stop after "s"	£140	£150
	e. "V.R.I." omitted	£170	£170
	f. Value omitted	£170	£170
	g. Raised stop after "s"	16·00	11·00
	h. Wider space between "1" and "s"	£150	£150
111	5s. on 5s. green	20·00	42·00
	a. No stop after "V"	£250	£300
	b. "5" omitted	£950	£1000
	c. Inverted stop after "R"	£700	£700
	d. Wider space between "5" and "s"	£130	£140
	e. Value omitted	£375	£400

All values are found with a rectangular, instead of an oval, stop after "R". Misplaced surcharges (upwards or sideways) occur.

No. 110ca shows the missing "1" replaced by a handstamp in a different type face.

(b) Subsequent printings.
(i) Surch as T **32**.

112	½d. on ½d. orange	30	20
	a. Raised and level stops mixed	2·00	2·00
	b. Pair, one with level stops	11·00	15·00
	c. No stop after "V"	2·75	3·00
	d. No stop after "I"	27·00	28·00
	e. "V" omitted	£550	
	f. Small "½"	15·00	17·00
	g. As a, and small "½"	15·00	17·00
	i. Space between "V" and "R"	20·00	22·00
	j. Value omitted	£120	£120
113	1d. on 1d. purple	30	20
	a. Raised and level stops mixed	1·60	2·25
	b. Pair, one with level stops	20·00	21·00
	c. No stop after "V"	3·25	6·00
	d. No stop after "R"	16·00	17·00
	e. No stop after "I"	16·00	17·00
	f. No stops after "V" and "I"	£300	
	g. Surch inverted	£300	
	h. Surch double	£110	£100
	i. Pair, one without surch	£250	
	j. Short figure "1"	£110	£110
	k. Space between "V" and "R"	50·00	55·00
	l. Space between "R" and "I"	£120	£130
	m. Space between "1" and "d"	£190	£190
	n. Inserted "R"	£325	£325
	o. Inserted "V"	£700	
	p. Stamp doubly printed, one impression inverted	£2500	
114	2d. on 2d. bright mauve	1·25	30
	a. Raised and level stops mixed	4·75	4·75
	b. Pair, one with level stops	8·50	9·00
	c. Surch inverted	£325	£325
	d. "1" raised	75·00	75·00
	e. Pair, one without surch	£325	£325
	f. No stop after "V"	£1000	
115	2½d. on 3d. ultramarine (a)	£200	£180
	a. Raised and level stops mixed	£600	
116	2½d. on 3d. ultramarine (b)	£1200	
117	3d. on 3d. ultramarine	60	30
	a. Raised and level stops mixed	7·00	7·00
	b. Pair, one with level stops	18·00	19·00

	c. No stop after "V"	£140	£140
	d. No stop after "R"	£350	£450
	e. "I" omitted	£400	£425
	f. Surch double	£400	
	g. Surch double, one diagonal	£375	
	h. Ditto, diagonal surch with mixed stops	£6500	
	n. Inserted "R"		
	o. Space between "3" and "d"	£140	
118	4d. on 4d. ultramarine	2·75	2·75
	a. Raised and level stops mixed	10·00	13·00
	b. Pair, one with level stops	21·00	29·00
119	6d. on 6d. bright carmine	35·00	48·00
	a. Raised and level stops mixed	£140	£140
	b. Pair, one with level stops	£225	£275
120	6d. on 6d. blue	70	40
	a. Raised and level stops mixed	8·00	8·00
	b. Pair, one with level stops	20·00	22·00
	c. No stop after "V"	£500	£500
	d. No stop after "R"	£300	
	e. Value omitted	£450	
121	1s. on 1s. brown	4·50	45
	a. Surch on 1s. orange-yellow (No. 9)	£1300	£1300
	b. Raised and level stops mixed	18·00	18·00
	c. Pair, one with level stops	35·00	38·00
	f. "s" omitted	£250	
	g. "V.R.I." omitted	£400	
122	5s. on 5s. green	8·00	8·50
	a. Raised and level stops mixed	£325	£325
	b. Pair, one with level stops	£1000	
	c. Short top to "5"	60·00	70·00
	s. Handstamped "Specimen"	50·00	

(ii) Surch as T 33.

123	½d. on ½d. orange	4·00	2·75
124	1d. on 1d. purple	4·25	35
	a. Inverted "1" for "I"	19·00	19·00
	b. No stops after "R" and "I"	90·00	70·00
	c. No stop after "R"	42·00	48·00
	d. Surch double	£325	£325
	n. Inserted "R"	£400	£400
	p. Stamp doubly printed, one impression inverted	£5000	
125	2d. on 2d. bright mauve	9·00	10·00
	a. Inverted "1" for "I"	27·00	30·00
126	2½d. on 3d. ultramarine (a)	£650	£750
127	2½d. on 3d. ultramarine (b)	£3750	
128	3d. on 3d. ultramarine	5·00	11·00
	a. Inverted "1" for "I"	65·00	75·00
	b. Surch double	£550	
	ba. Surch double, one diagonal	£550	
129	6d. on 6d. bright carmine	£425	£425
130	6d. on 6d. blue	12·00	23·00
131	1s. on 1s. brown	21·00	8·00
132	5s. on 5s. green	50·00	48·00
	s. Handstamped "Specimen"	£150	

Stamps with thick "V" occur in certain positions in *later* settings of the type with stops above the line (T **32**). *Earlier* settings with stops above the line have all stamps with thin "V".

Some confusion has previously been caused by the listing of certain varieties as though they occurred on stamps with thick "V" in fact they occur on stamps showing the normal thin "V", included in the settings which also contained the thick "V".

For a short period small blocks of unsurcharged Free State stamps could be handed in for surcharging so that varieties occur which are not found in the complete settings. Nos. 102a, 110a and 121a also occur from such stocks.

The inserted "R" variety occurs on positions 6 (T **32**) and 12 (T **33**) of the forme. The "R" of the original surcharge failed to print and the "R", but not the full stop, was added by the use of a handstamp. Traces of the original letter are often visible. The broken "V" flaw, also shown in the illustration, does not appear on No. 124n.

ORANGE RIVER COLONY

CROWN COLONY

E. R. I.

ORANGE RIVER COLONY.	4d	6d
(34)	(35)	(36)

1900 (10 Aug)–02. *Nos. 58a, 61a and 67 of Cape of Good Hope (wmk Cabled Anchor. P 14) optd with T **34** by W. A. Richards and Sons, Cape Town.*

133	½d. green (13.10.00)	50	10
	a. No stop	7·50	16·00
	b. Opt double	£650	£700
134	1d. carmine (May 1902)	1·50	10
	a. No stop	16·00	21·00
135	2½d. ultramarine	1·50	35
	a. No stop	65·00	75·00
133/5 Set of 3		3·25	50

In the ½d. and 2½d., the "no stop" after "COLONY" variety was the first stamp in the left lower pane. In the 1d. it is the twelfth stamp in the right lower pane on which the stop was present at the beginning of the printing but became damaged and soon failed to print.

1902 (14 Feb). *Surch with T **35** by "Bloemfontein Express".*

136	4d. on 6d. on 6d. blue (No. 120) (R.)	1·50	75
	a. No stop after "R"	35·00	40·00
	b. No stop after "I"	£1200	
	c. Surch on No. 130 (Thick "V")	2·00	6·00
	ca. Inverted "I" for "I"	6·00	16·00

1902 (Aug). *Surch with T **36**.*

137	1 6d. on 6d. blue	3·75	11·00
	a. Surch double, one inverted		
	b. Wide space between "6" and "d" (R. 4/2)	60·00	90·00

One Shilling *(37)*

38 King Edward VII, Springbok and Gnu

1902 (Sept). *Surch with T **37**.*

138	1 1s. on 5s. green (O.)	7·50	14·00
	a. Thick "V"	15·00	35·00
	b. Short top to "5"	70·00	80·00
	c. Surch double		

(Typo D.L.R.)

1903 (3 Feb)–04. *Wmk Crown CA. P 14.*

139	38 ½d. yellow-green (6.7.03)	9·00	1·25
	w. Wmk inverted	£150	85·00
140	1d. scarlet	5·00	10
	w. Wmk inverted	£150	75·00
141	2d. brown (6.7.03)	6·50	80
142	2½d. bright blue (6.7.03)	1·60	50
143	3d. mauve (6.7.03)	8·00	90
144	4d. scarlet and sage-green (6.7.03)	32·00	2·00
	a. "IOSTAGE" for "POSTAGE"	£800	£450
145	6d. scarlet and mauve (6.7.03)	8·50	1·00
146	1s. scarlet and bistre (6.7.03)	28·00	1·75
147	5s. blue and brown (31.10.04)	80·00	22·00
139/47 Set of 9		£160	27·00
139s/47s Optd "Specimen" Set of 9		£170	

No. 144a occurs on R. 10/2 of the upper left pane.

The 2d. exists from coils constructed from normal sheets for use in stamp machines introduced in 1911.

Several of the above values are found with the overprint "C.S.A.R.", in black, for use by the Central South African Railways. Examples also exist perforated "CSAR" or "NGR".

1905 (Nov)–09. *Wmk Mult Crown CA. P 14.*

148	38 ½d. yellow-green (28.7.07)	9·00	50
149	1d. scarlet	9·00	30
150	4d. scarlet and sage-green (8.11.07)	4·50	2·75
	a. "IOSTAGE" for "POSTAGE"	£180	£150
151	1s. scarlet and bistre (2.09)	45·00	16·00
148/51 Set of 4		60·00	18·00

POSTCARD STAMPS

From 1889 onwards the Orange Free State Post Office sold postcards franked with adhesives as Type **1**, some subsequently surcharged, over which the State Arms had been overprinted.

There are five known dies of the Arms overprint which can be identified as follows:
(a) Shield without flags. Three cows (two lying down, one standing) at left. Point of shield complete.
(b) Shield with flags. Four cows (two lying down, two standing) at left (*illustrated*).
(c) Shield with flags. Three cows (one lying down, two standing) at left.
(d) Shield without flags. Three cows (two lying down, one standing) at left.
(e) Shield without flags. Three cows (two lying down, one standing) at left. Point of shield broken.
There are also other differences between the dies.

PRICES. Those in the left-hand column are for unused examples on complete postcard; those on the right for used examples off card. Examples used on postcard are worth more.

1889 (Feb). *No. 2 (placed sideways on card) optd Shield Type (a).*

P1	1 1d. red-brown	90·00	40·00
	a. Optd Shield Type (b)	32·00	7·00

1891 (Aug). *No. 48 optd Shield Type (b).*

P2	1 ½d. chestnut	5·50	1·75
	a. Optd Shield Type (c)	13·00	4·25
	b. Optd Shield Type (d)	6·00	2·25
	c. Optd Shield Type (e)	14·00	5·00

1892 (June). *No. 54 optd Shield Type (b).*

P3	1 1d. on 3d. ultramarine	90·00	48·00
	a. Optd Shield Type (c)	15·00	3·00

1½d.	**1½d.**	**1½d.**
(P 1)	(P 2)	(P 3)

1892 (Sept)–95. *Nos. 50/1 optd Shield Type (b) or (d) (No. P6) and surch with Types P **1/3**.*

P4	1 1½d. on 2d. bright mauve (Type P **1**) (11.92)	8·00	3·75
P5	1½d. on 2d. bright mauve (Type P **2**) (9.93)	6·00	1·75
	a. Surch inverted		
P6	1½d. on 2d. brt mauve (Type P **3**) (R.) (6.95)	13·00	4·25
P7	1½d. on 2d. brt mauve (Type P **3**)	7·50	2·25

No. P5a shows the stamp affixed to the card upside down with the surcharge correctly positioned in relation to the card.

½d. (P 4)

1895 (Aug). *No. 48 optd Shield Type (e) and surch with Type P4.*

P8	1 ½d. on ½d. chestnut	13·00	2·75

1½d. (P 5)   **1½d.** (P 6)

1895 (Dec)–97. *No. 50 optd Shield Type (e) and surch with Types P **5/6**.*

P9	1 1½d. on 2d. bright mauve (Type P **5**)	6·50	2·75
P10	1½d. on 2d. brt mauve (Type P **6**) (12.97)	7·50	3·25
P11	1½d. on 2d. bright mauve (as Type P **6**, but without stop) (12.97)	7·50	3·25

1897 (Mar). *No. 85 optd Shield Type (d).*

P12	1 ½d. orange	13·00	1·75
	a. Optd Shield Type (e)	14·00	2·75

V.R.I. (P 7)

1900. *Nos. P10/11 optd as T **31/2** or with Type P **7**.*

P13	1 1½d. on 2d. bright mauve (No. P10) (T **31**)	28·00	5·50
P14	1½d. on 2d. bright mauve (No. P11) (T **31**)	28·00	5·50
P15	1½d. on 2d. bright mauve (No. P10) (T **32**)	28·00	5·50
P16	1½d. on 2d. bright mauve (No. P11) (T **32**)	28·00	5·50
P17	1½d. on 2d. brt mve (No. P10) (Type P **7**)	40·00	10·00
P18	1½d. on 2d. brt mve (No. P11) (Type P **7**)	40·00	10·00

POLICE FRANK STAMPS

The following frank stamps were issued to members of the Orange Free State Mounted Police ("Rijdende Dienst Macht") for use on official correspondence.

PF **1** (eight ornaments at left and right)   PF **2**

1896. P 12.

PF1	PF **1**	(–) Black	£200	£275

No. PF1 was printed in horizontal strips of 5 surrounded by wide margins.

1898. *As Type PF **1**, but with nine ornaments at left and right.* P 12.

PF2		(–) Black	£140	£200

No. PF2 was printed in blocks of 4 (2×2) surrounded by wide margins.

1899. P 12.

PF3	PF **2**	(–) Black/*yellow*	£130	£150
		a. No stop after "V"	£550	

No. PF3 was printed in sheets of 24 (6×4) with the edges of the sheet imperforate. It is believed that they were produced from a setting of 8 (2×4) repeated three times. No. PF3a occurs on R. 1/1 of the setting.

Examples of No. PF3 are known postmarked as late as 28 April 1900. The O.F.S. Mounted Police were disbanded by the British authorities at the end of the following month.

MILITARY FRANK STAMP

M **1**

(Typeset Curling & Co, Bloemfontein)

1899 (15 Oct). P 12.

M1	M **1**	(–) Black/*bistre-yellow*	17·00	55·00

Supplies of No. M1 were issued to members of the Orange Free State army on active service during the Second Boer War. To pass free through the O.F.S. fieldpost system, letters had to be franked with No. M1 or initialled by the appropriate unit commander. The franks were in use between October 1899 and February 1900.

No. M1 was printed in sheets of 20 (5×4) using a setting of five different types in a horizontal row. The colour in the paper runs in water.

Typeset forgeries can be identified by the appearance of 17 pearls, instead of the 16 of the originals, in the top and bottom frames. Forgeries produced by lithography omit the stops after "BRIEF" and "FRANKO".

FISCAL STAMPS USED FOR POSTAGE

The following were issued in December 1877 (Nos. F1 and F3 in 1882) and were authorised for postal use between 1882 and 1886.

F 1   F 2

F 3

(Typo D.L.R.)

1882–86. P 14.

F1	F 1	6d. pearl-grey	10·00	13·00
F2		6d. purple-brown	35·00	24·00
F3	F 2	1s. purple-brown	11·00	18·00
F4		1s. pearl-grey	50·00	60·00
F5		1s.6d. blue	22·00	17·00
F6		2s. magenta	22·00	17·00
F7		3s. chestnut	27·00	60·00
F8		4s. grey		
F9		5s. rose	28·00	24·00
F10		6s. green	—	70·00
F11		7s. violet		
F12		10s. orange	60·00	40·00
F13	F 3	£1 purple	70·00	40·00
		a. "VRY-STAAT" (R. 1/5)		
F14		£2 red-brown	80·00	90·00
		a. "VRY-STAAT" (R. 1/5)		
F14b		£4 carmine		
		ba. "VRY-STAAT" (R. 1/5)		
F15		£5 green	£110	60·00

Die proofs of Type F 3 showed a hyphen in error between "VRY" and "STAAT". This was removed from each impression on the plate before printing, but was missed on R. 1/5.

A fiscally used example of No. F2 exists showing "ZES PENCE" double, one inverted.

The 8s. yellow was prepared but we have no evidence of its use postally without surcharge Type F 3.

ZES PENCE.

(F 4)

1886. Surch with Type F 4.

F16	F 2	6d. on 4s. grey	
F17		6d. on 8s. yellow	£275

Postage stamps overprinted for use as Telegraph stamps and used postally are omitted as it is impossible to say with certainty which stamps were genuinely used for postal purposes.

Orange Free State became a province of the Union of South Africa on 31 May 1910.

VI. TRANSVAAL

(*formerly* South African Republic)

From 1852 mail from the Transvaal was forwarded to the Cape of Good Hope, via the Orange Free State, by a post office at Potchefstroom. In 1859 the Volksraad voted to set up a regular postal service and arrangements were made for letters sent to the Cape and for overseas to be franked with Cape of Good Hope stamps.

The Potchefstroom postmaster placed his first order for these on 23 August 1859 and examples of all four triangular values are known postmarked there. From 1868 mail via the Orange Free State required franking with their issues also.

A similar arrangement covering mail sent overseas via Natal was in operation from 9 July 1873 until the first British Occupation. Such letters carried combinations of Transvaal stamps, paying the rate to Natal, and Natal issues for the overseas postage. Such Natal stamps were sold, but not postmarked, by Transvaal post offices.

PRICES FOR STAMPS ON COVER

Nos. 1/6 are rare used on cover.	
Nos. 7/80	from × 20
Nos. 86/155	from × 3
Nos. 156/62	from × 6
Nos. 163/9	from × 5
Nos. 170/225	from × 10
Nos. 226/34	from × 20
Nos. 235/7	—
Nos. 238/43	from × 12
Nos. 244/55	from × 4
Nos. 256/7	from × 6
Nos. 258/9	
Nos. 260/76	from × 20
Nos. F1/5	from × 5
Nos. D1/7	from × 20

The issues for Pietersburg, Lydenburg, Rustenburg, Schweizer Renecke and Wolmaransstad are very rare when on cover.

1 (Eagle with spread wings)   2   3

(Typo Adolph Otto, Gustrow, Mecklenburg-Schwerin)

1870 (1 May). *Thin paper, clear and distinct impressions.*

(a) Imperf.

1	1	1d. brown-lake	£425	
		a. Orange-red	£550	£550
2		6d. bright ultramarine	£180	£180
		a. Pale ultramarine	£200	£200
3		1s. deep green	£650	£650
		a. Tête-bêche (pair)		

(b) Fine roulette, 15½ to 16.

4	1	1d. brown-lake	£130	
		a. Brick-red	£100	
		b. Orange-red	£100	
		c. Vermilion	£100	
5		6d. bright ultramarine	90·00	90·00
		a. Pale ultramarine	£100	£100
6		1s. deep green	£180	£200
		a. Yellow-green	£150	£240
		b. Emerald-green	£110	£110

Examples of Nos. 1/6 may have been sold to dealers at some stage between their arrival in Transvaal during August 1869 and the sale of stamps to the public for postal purposes on 1 May 1870.

PLATES. The German printings of the 1d., 6d. and 1s. in Type **1** were from two pairs of plates, each pair printing sheets of 80 in two panes of five horizontal rows of eight.

One pair of plates, used for Nos. 4a, 4c, 5a and 6a, produced stamps spaced 1¼ to 1½ mm apart with the rouletting close to the design on all four sides. The 1d. from these "narrow" plates shows a gap in the outer frame line at the bottom right-hand corner. The second pair, used for Nos. 1/3, 4, 4b, 5/a and 6b, had 2½ to 3½ mm between the stamps. These "wide" plates were sent to the Transvaal in 1869 and were there to produce either single or double pane printings until 1883.

The 6d. and 1s. "wide" plates each had an inverted *cliché*. When printed these occurred on right-hand pane R. 4/1 of the 6d. and right-hand pane R. 1/1 of the 1s. These were never corrected and resulted in *tête-bêche* pairs of these values as late as 1883.

REPRINTS AND IMITATIONS. A number of unauthorised printings were made of these stamps by the German printer. Many of these can be identified by differences in the central arms, unusual colours or, in the case of the 1d., by an extra frame around the numeral tablets at top.

Genuine stamps always show the "D" of "EENDRAGT" higher than the remainder of the word, have no break in the border above "DR" and depict the flagstaff at bottom right, behind "MAGT", stopping short of the central shield. They also show the eagle's eye as a clear white circle. On the forgeries the eye is often blurred.

The most difficult of the reprints to detect is the 1s. yellow-green which was once regarded as genuine, but was subsequently identified, by J. N. Luff in *The Philatelic Record* 1911–12, as coming from an unauthorised plate of four. Stamps from this plate show either a white dot between "EEN" and "SHILLING" or a white flaw below the wagon pole.

(Typo M. J. Viljoen, Pretoria)

1870 (1 May–4 July).

I. Thin gummed paper from Germany. Impressions coarse and defective.

(a) Imperf.

8	1	1d. dull rose-red	90·00	
		a. Reddish pink	70·00	
		b. Carmine-red	60·00	70·00
9		6d. dull ultramarine	£300	70·00
		a. Tête-bêche (pair)		

(b) Fine roulette, 15½ to 16.

10	1	1d. carmine-red	£700	£275
11		6d. dull ultramarine	£200	90·00
		a. Imperf between (vert pair)	£750	

(c) Wide roulette, 6½.

12	1	1d. carmine-red	—	£950

II. Thick, hard paper with thin yellow smooth gum (No. 15) or yellow streaky gum (others).

(a) Imperf.

13	1	1d. pale rose-red	70·00	
		a. Carmine-red	70·00	80·00

14		1s. yellow-green	£110	£100
		a. Tête-bêche (pair)	£20000	
		b. Bisected (6d.) (on cover)	†	£1800

(b) Fine roulette, 15½ to 16.

15	1	1d. carmine-red (24 May)	90·00	
16		6d. ultramarine (10 May)	£100	£100
		a. Tête-bêche (pair)	£25000	£18000
17		1s. yellow-green	£650	£650

III. Medium paper, blotchy heavy printing and whitish gum. Fine roulette 15½ to 16 (4 July).

18	1	1d. rose-red	70·00	85·00
		a. Carmine-red	50·00	55·00
		b. Crimson. From over-inked plate	£140	£240
19		6d. ultramarine	90·00	70·00
		a. Tête-bêche (pair)		
		b. Deep ultram. From over-inked plate	£450	£160
20		1s. deep green	£120	75·00
		a. From over-inked plate	£500	£160

The rouletting machine producing the wide 6½ gauge was not introduced until 1875.

Nos. 18b, 19b and 20a were printed from badly over-inked plates giving heavy blobby impressions.

(Typo J. P. Borrius, Potchefstroom)

1870 (Sept)–**71.** *Stout paper, but with colour often showing through, whitish gum.*

(a) Imperf.

21	1	1d. black	£130	£110

(b) Fine roulette, 15½ to 16.

22	1	1d. black	18·00	27·00
		a. Grey-black	18·00	27·00
23		6d. blackish blue (7.71)	£140	60·00
		a. Dull blue	95·00	80·00

(Typo Adolph Otto, Gustrow, Mecklenburg-Schwerin)

1871 (July). *Thin paper, clear and distinct impressions. Fine roulette, 15½ to 16.*

24	2	3d. pale reddish lilac	80·00	90·00
		a. Deep lilac	90·00	£100
		b. Vert laid paper		

No. 24 and later printings in the Transvaal were produced from a pair of plates in the same format as the 1869 issue. All genuine stamps have a small dot on the left leg of the eagle.

Imperforate examples in the issued shade, without the dot on eagle's leg, had been previously supplied by the printer, probably as essays, but were not issued for postal purposes. (Price £550 unused). They also exist tête-bêche (Price for un pair £3250).

Imperforate and rouletted stamps in other colours are reprints.

(Typo J. P. Borrius, Potchefstroom)

1872–74. *Fine roulette, 15½ to 16.*

(a) Thin transparent paper.

25	1	1d. black	£190	£650
26		1d. bright carmine	£160	55·00
27		6d. ultramarine	£110	45·00
28		1s. green	£140	60·00

(b) Thinnish opaque paper, clear printing (Dec 1872).

29	1	1d. reddish pink	65·00	42·00
		a. Carmine-red	65·00	42·00
30	2	3d. grey-lilac	£100	50·00
31	1	6d. ultramarine	65·00	30·00
		a. Pale ultramarine	75·00	32·00
32		1s. yellow-green	80·00	42·00
		a. Green	80·00	42·00
		aa. Bisected (6d.) (on cover)	†	£1800

(c) Thickish wove paper (1873–74).

33	1	1d. dull rose	£400	75·00
		a. Brownish rose	£500	£120
		b. Printed on both sides		
34		6d. milky blue	£150	48·00
		a. Deep dull blue	90·00	42·00
		aa. Imperf (pair)	£700	
		ab. Imperf between (horiz pair)	£750	
		ac. Wide roulette 6½		

(d) Very thick dense paper (1873–74).

35		1d. dull rose	£550	£130
		a. Brownish rose	£425	£110
36		6d. dull blue	£180	65·00
		a. Bright ultramarine	£200	65·00
37		1s. yellow-green	£850	£650

(Typo P. Davis & Son, Pietermaritzburg)

1874 (Sept). P 12½.

(a) Thin transparent paper.

38	1	1d. pale brick-red	£100	40·00
		a. Brownish red	£100	40·00
39		6d. deep blue	£140	60·00

(b) Thicker opaque paper.

40	1	1d. pale red	£160	75·00
41		6d. blue	£130	55·00
		a. Imperf between (pair)		
		b. Deep blue	£130	55·00

(Typo Adolph Otto, Gustrow, Mecklenburg-Schwerin)

1874 (Oct). *Thin smooth paper, clearly printed. Fine roulette 15½ to 16.*

42	3	6d. bright ultramarine	60·00	24·00
		a. Bisected (3d.) (on cover)	†	£1400

Stamps in other shades of blue, brown or red, often on other types of paper, are reprints.

(Typo J. F. Celliers on behalf of Stamp Commission, Pretoria)

1875 (29 Apr)–**77.**

I. Very thin, soft opaque (semi-pelure) paper.

(a) Imperf.

43	1	1d. orange-red	£130	50·00
		a. Pin-perf	£750	£350
44	2	3d. lilac	90·00	50·00

45	1	6d. blue	85·00	42·00
		a. Milky blue	£130	45·00
		aa. Tête-bêche (pair)	£15000	
		ab. Pin-perf	—	£350

(b) Fine roulette, 15½ to 16.

46	1	1d. orange-red	£500	£140
47	2	3d. lilac	£550	£150
48	1	6d. blue	£500	£140

(c) Wide roulette, 6½.

49	1	1d. orange-red	—	£200
50	2	3d. lilac	£700	£300
51	1	6d. blue	—	£150
		a. Bright blue	—	£150
		b. Milky blue	—	£150

II. Very thin, hard transparent (pelure) paper (1875–76).

(a) Imperf.

52	1	1d. brownish red	55·00	32·00
		a. Orange-red	45·00	25·00
		b. Dull red	50·00	50·00
		ba. Pin-perf	£600	£375
53	2	3d. lilac	50·00	42·00
		a. Pin-perf	—	£400
		b. Deep lilac	60·00	42·00
54	1	6d. pale blue	50·00	50·00
		a. Blue	50·00	42·00
		ab. Tête-bêche (pair)		
		ac. Pin-perf	—	£350
		b. Deep blue	55·00	45·00

(b) Fine roulette 15½ to 16.

55	1	1d. orange-red	£350	£120
		a. Brown-red	£350	£120
56	2	3d. lilac	£400	£130
57	1	6d. blue	£160	95·00
		a. Deep blue	£160	£110

(c) Wide roulette, 6½.

58	1	1d. orange-red	£1000	£200
		a. Bright red	—	£180
59	2	3d. lilac	£900	£250
60	1	6d. deep blue	£1000	£200

III. Stout hard-surfaced paper with smooth, nearly white, gum (1876).

(a) Imperf.

61	1	1d. bright red	24·00	18·00
62	2	3d. lilac	£375	£120
63	1	6d. bright blue	£100	24·00
		a. Tête-bêche (pair)		
		b. Pale blue	£100	24·00
		c. Deep blue (deep brown gum)	60·00	20·00
		ca. Tête-bêche (pair)	—	£17000

(b) Fine roulette, 15½ to 16.

64	1	1d. bright red	£400	£150
65	2	3d. lilac	£350	
66	1	6d. bright blue	£750	£110
		a. Deep blue (deep brown gum)	£600	£275

(c) Wide roulette, 6½.

67	1	1d. bright red	£600	£150
68		6d. pale blue	—	£200
		a. Deep blue (deep brown gum)	£650	£250

IV. Coarse, soft white paper (1876–77).

(a) Imperf.

69	1	1d. brick-red	£130	50·00
70		6d. deep blue	£200	55·00
		a. Milky blue	£350	95·00
71		1s. yellow-green	£350	£110
		a. Bisected (6d.) (on cover)	†	£1600

(b) Fine roulette, 15½ to 16.

72	1	1d. brick-red	—	£375
73		6d. deep blue	—	£160
74		1s. yellow-green	£700	£350

(c) Wide roulette, 6½.

75	1	1d. brick-red	—	£450
76		6d. deep blue	—	£1100
77		1s. yellow-green	—	£1200

(d) Fine × wide roulette.

78	1	1d. brick-red	£700	£350

V. Hard, thick, coarse yellowish paper (1876–77).

79	1	1d. brick-red (imperf)	—	£300
80		1d. brick-red (wide roulette)	—	£400

The pin-perforated stamps have various gauges and were probably produced privately or by one or more post offices other than Pretoria. On Nos. 63c/ca, 66a and 68a the brown gum used was so intense that it caused staining of the paper which is still visible on used examples. See also Nos. 171/4.

FIRST BRITISH OCCUPATION

By 1876 conditions in the Transvaal had deteriorated and the country was faced with economic collapse, native wars and internal dissension. In early 1877 Sir Theophilus Shepstone, appointed Special Commissioner to the South African Republic by the British Government, arrived in Pretoria and on 12 April annexed the Transvaal with the acquiesence of at least part of the European population.

V. R.   V. R.

TRANSVAAL.   TRANSVAAL.

(4)   (5)

T 4 is the normal overprint, but Setting I No. 11 (R. 2/3) has a wider-spaced overprint as T 5.

1877 (Apr). Optd with T 4 in red.

(a) Imperf.

86	2	3d. lilac (*semi-pelure*) (No. 44)	£1300	£300
87		3d. lilac (*pelure*) (No. 53)	£1300	£180
		a. Opt Type 5	£6000	£2500
		b. Opt on back	£3250	£3250
		c. Opt double, in red and in black	£6000	
88	1	6d. milky blue (No. 70)	£1600	£180
		a. Opt inverted	—	£5500
		b. Opt double	£4500	£1000
		c. Opt Type 5	£6500	£3000
		d. Deep blue		£250
89		1s. yellow-green (No. 71)	£600	£180
		a. Bisected (6d.) (on cover)	†	£1800
		b. Opt inverted	—	£4500
		c. Opt Type 5	£4500	£1500
		d. Tête-bêche (pair)		

(b) Fine roulette, 15½ to 16.

90	2	3d. lilac (*pelure*) (No. 56)	—	£1600
91	1	6d. deep blue (No. 73)	—	£1700
92		1s. yellow-green (No. 74)	£1600	£750
		a. Opt Type 5		

(c) Wide roulette, 6½.

93	2	3d. lilac (*pelure*) (No. 59)	—	£2250
		a. Opt Type 5		
94		6d. deep blue (No. 76)	—	£2250
95		1s. yellow-green (No. 77)	£4000	£2000
		a. Opt inverted	—	£5500

Nos. 88a, 89b and 95a occurred on the inverted *cliché* of the basic stamps.

1877 (June). Optd with T 4 in black.

I. Very thin, hard transparent (pelure) paper.

96	1	1d. orange-red (imperf) (No. 52a)	£275	£100
97		1d. orange-red (*fine roulette*) (No. 55)	—	£1000

II. Stout hard-surfaced paper with smooth, nearly white, gum.

98	1	1d. bright red (imperf) (No. 61)	25·00	22·00
		a. Opt inverted	£550	£500
		b. Opt Type 5	£750	£800
99		1d. bright red (*fine roulette*) (No. 64)	£160	50·00
		a. Opt inverted		
		b. Opt double	—	£1100
		c. Imperf between (horiz pair)	£750	
100		1d. bright red (*wide roulette*) (No. 67)	£650	£200
100a		1d. bright red (*fine × wide roulette*) (No. 78)		

III. New ptgs on coarse, soft white paper.

(a) Imperf.

101	1	1d. brick-red (5.77)	25·00	22·00
		a. Opt inverted	—	£1200
		b. Opt Type 5	£800	
102	2	3d. lilac	80·00	42·00
		b. Deep lilac	£170	85·00
103	1	6d. dull blue	90·00	32·00
		a. Opt double	£3500	£2000
		b. Opt inverted	£1400	£170
		c. Opt Type 5	—	£1100
		da. Opt Type 5 inverted		
		e. Blue (bright to deep)	£160	30·00
		ea. Bright blue, opt inverted	—	£500
		f. Pin-perf	—	£600
104		1s. yellow-green	£100	50·00
		a. Opt inverted	£1200	£200
		b. Tête-bêche (pair)	£20000	£20000
		c. Opt Type 5	£5000	£1500
		d. Bisected (6d.) (on cover)	†	£1500

(b) Fine roulette, 15½ to 16.

105	1	1d. brick-red	75·00	75·00
		a. Imperf horiz (vert strip of 3)		
		b. Imperf between (horiz pair)	†	£600
106	2	3d. lilac	£180	65·00
107	1	6d. dull blue	£200	55·00
		a. Opt inverted	—	£750
		b. Opt Type 5	£5000	
108		1s. yellow-green	£200	90·00
		a. Opt inverted	£1100	£450
		b. Opt Type 5	—	£2750

(c) Wide roulette, 6½.

109	1	1d. brick-red	£650	£150
		a. Opt Type 5	—	£1000
110	2	3d. lilac	—	£750
111	1	6d. dull blue	—	£1200
		a. Opt inverted	—	£4000
112		1s. yellow-green	£475	£130
		a. Opt inverted	£1500	£600

1877 (31 Aug). Optd with T 4 in black.

113	1	6d. blue/rose (imperf)	80·00	48·00
		a. Bisected (3d.) (on cover)		
		b. Opt inverted	£100	48·00
		c. Tête-bêche (pair)		
		d. Opt omitted	£3500	£2500
114		6d. blue/rose (*fine roulette*)	£180	70·00
		a. Opt inverted	£550	70·00
		b. Tête-bêche (pair)		
		c. Opt omitted		
		d. Bisected (3d.) (on cover)		
115		6d. blue/rose (*wide roulette*)		
		a. Opt inverted	—	£650
		b. Opt omitted		

Nos. 113/15 were overprinted from a setting of 40 which was applied upright to one pane in each sheet and inverted on the other.

V. R.   V. R.

Transvaal   Transvaal

(6)   (7)

1877 (28 Sept)–79. Optd with T 6 in black.

(a) Imperf.

116	1	1d. red	55·00	30·00
		a. "Transvral" (Right pane R. 2/3)	£5500	£2500
		b. Opt double	£4000	
		c. Opt inverted	£800	£400
		d. Opt omitted		
117		1d. red/orange (6.12.77)	20·00	20·00
		a. Pin-perf		
		b. Printed both sides		
		c. Opt double	£3500	
		d. Optd with Type 7 (15.4.78)	55·00	45·00
		e. Pair. Nos. 117 and 117d	£150	
118	2	3d. mauve/buff (24.10.77)	50·00	27·00
		a. Opt inverted	—	£750
		b. Pin-perf		
		c. Bisected (1½d.) (on cover)	†	—
		d. Optd with Type 7 (15.4.78)	65·00	35·00
		da. Pin-perf	£750	£750
		e. Pair. Nos. 118 and 118d	£200	
119		3d. mauve/green (18.4.79)	£150	42·00
		a. Pin-perf		
		b. Opt inverted	—	£2000
		c. Opt double		
		d. Printed both sides		†
		e. Optd with Type 7	£110	35·00
		ea. Opt inverted	—	£2000
		eb. Printed both sides	—	£1000
		f. Opt omitted	—	£3500
		g. Pair. Nos. 119 and 119e	£475	
120	1	6d. blue/green (27.11.77)	85·00	38·00
		a. Deep blue/green	£100	40·00
		b. Broken "Y" for "V" in "V.R." (Left pane R. 3/7)	—	£750
		c. Small "v" in "Transvaal" (Left pane R. 5/2)	—	£750
		d. "V.R." (Right pane R. 3/4)	—	£750
		e. Tête-bêche (pair)	—	£18000
		f. Opt inverted	—	£1100
		g. Pin-perf		
		h. Bisected (3d.) (on cover)	†	
121		6d. blue/blue (20.3.78)	55·00	27·00
		a. Tête-bêche (pair)		
		b. Opt inverted	—	£1000
		c. Opt omitted	—	£2250
		d. Opt double	—	£3250
		e. Pin-perf		
		f. Bisected (3d.) (on cover)	†	£800
		g. Optd with Type 7	£110	30·00
		ga. Tête-bêche (pair)	£15000	
		gb. Opt inverted	—	£600
		gc. Bisected (3d.) (on cover)	†	
		h. Pair. Nos. 121 and 121g	£350	

(b) Fine roulette, 15½ to 16.

122	1	1d. red/blue	90·00	38·00
		a. "Transvral" (Right pane R. 2/3)	—	£3000
123		1d. red/orange (6.12.77)	32·00	27·00
		a. Imperf between (pair)	£600	
		b. Optd with Type 7 (15.4.78)	£140	£120
		c. Pair. Nos. 123 and 123b	£375	
124	2	3d. mauve/buff (24.10.77)	95·00	27·00
		a. Imperf horiz (vert pair)	£750	
		b. Opt inverted	—	£3000
		c. Optd with Type 7 (15.4.78)	£150	£110
		ca. Imperf between (pair)		
		d. Pair. Nos. 124 and 124c	£500	
125		3d. mauve/green (18.4.79)	£600	£150
		a. Optd with Type 7	£600	£150
		b. Pair. Nos. 125 and 125a		
126	1	6d. blue/green (27.11.77)	85·00	27·00
		a. "V.R" (Right pane R. 3/4)	—	£1200
		b. Tête-bêche (pair)		
		c. Opt inverted	—	£650
		d. Opt omitted	—	£4000
		e. Bisected (3d.) (on cover)	†	£700
127		6d. blue/blue (20.3.78)	£225	55·00
		a. Opt inverted	—	£900
		b. Opt omitted	—	£3500
		c. Imperf between (pair)		
		d. Bisected (3d.) (on cover)	†	£750
		e. Optd with Type 7	£375	£110
		ea. Opt inverted	—	£1100

(c) Wide roulette, 6¼.

128	1	1d. red/orange (15.4.78)	£250	£100
		a. Optd with Type 7	—	£300
129	2	3d. mauve/buff (24.10.77)	—	£100
		a. Optd with Type 7 (15.4.78)	—	£350
130		3d. mauve/green (18.4.79)	£650	£275
		a. Optd with Type 7	—	£300
131	1	6d. blue/green (27.11.77)	—	£1000
132		6d. blue/blue (20.3.78)	—	£300
		a. Opt inverted		
		b. Optd with Type 7	—	£350
		ba. Opt inverted		

(d) Fine × wide roulette.

132c	1	1d. red/orange		£750

Nos. 116/32c were overprinted from various settings covering sheets of 80 or panes of 40 (8×5). Initially these settings contained Type 6 only, but from March 1878 settings also contained examples of Type 7. Details of these mixed settings are as follows:

1d. red/orange (sheets of 80): all Type 6 except for 16 Type 7.
3d. mauve/buff (panes of 40): 16 Type 7.
3d. mauve/green (panes of 40): uncertain, some panes at least contained 27 Type 7.
6d. blue/blue (sheets of 80): either 24 or 27 Type 7.

9

(Recess B.W.)

1878 (26 Aug)–80. P 14, 14½.

133	9	½d. vermilion (1.9.80)	22·00	80·00

134		1d. pale red-brown	12·00	4·00
	a.	Brown-red	12·00	3·50
135		3d. dull rose (25 Nov)	15·00	4·50
	a.	Claret	19·00	6·00
136		4d. sage-green	21·00	5·50
137		6d. olive-black (25 Nov)	11·00	4·00
	a.	Black-brown	13·00	3·50
138		1s. green (25 Nov)	£120	38·00
139		2s. blue (25 Nov)	£160	75·00

The ½d. is printed on paper bearing the sheet watermark 'R TURNER/ CHAFFORD MILLS' in double-lined block capitals. Other values are on unwatermarked paper.

The above prices are for specimens perforated on all four sides. Stamps from margins of sheets, with perforations absent on one or two sides, can be supplied for about 30% less.

The used price quoted for No. 139 is for an example with telegraphic cancel, a 23.5 mm circular datestamp of Pretoria (or more rarely Heidelberg or Standerton). Postally used examples are worth much more.

1 Penny **1 Penny** **1 Penny**
(10)   (11)   (12)

1 Penny   **1 Penny**
(13)   (14)

1 PENNY   *1 Penny*
(15)   (16)

1879 (22 Apr). *No. 137a surch with T 10 to 16 in black.*

140	10	1d. on 6d.	75·00	42·00
	a.	Surch in red	£200	£150
141	11	1d. on 6d.	£180	80·00
	a.	Surch in red	£500	£325
142	12	1d. on 6d.	£180	80·00
	a.	Surch in red	£500	£325
143	13	1d. on 6d.	80·00	48·00
	a.	Surch double		
	b.	Surch in red	£250	£170
144	14	1d. on 6d.	£500	£160
	a.	Surch in red	£5000	£1600
145	15	1d. on 6d.	40·00	23·00
	a.	Surch in red	£130	75·00
146	16	1d. on 6d.	£170	75·00
	a.	Surch in red	£450	£300

Nos. 140/6 were surcharged from a setting of 60 containing eleven examples of Type 10, four of Type 11, four of Type 12, nine of Type 13, two of Type 14 (although there may have been only one in the first two ptgs), twenty-five of Type 15 and five of Type 16.

The red surcharges may have been produced first.

V. R.   **V. R.**

Transvaal   **Transvaal**
(16a)   Small "T" (R. 2/8, 3/8, 4/8, 5/8 on right pane of 1d. and left pane of 3d.)

1879 (Aug–Sept). *Optd with T 16a in black.*

(a) Imperf.

147	1	1d. red/*yellow*	45·00	38·00
	a.	Small "T"	£300	£200
	b.	Red/*orange*	40·00	30·00
	ba.	Small "T"	£250	£170
148	2	3d. mauve/*green* (Sept)	40·00	25·00
	a.	Small "T"	£225	£100
149		3d. mauve/*blue* (Sept)	45·00	30·00
	a.	Small "T"	£250	90·00

(b) Fine roulette 15½ to 16.

150	1	1d. red/*yellow*	£350	£200
	a.	Small "T"	£1000	£650
	b.	Red/*orange*	£750	£375
	ba.	Small "T"	£2000	
151	2	3d. mauve/*green*	£750	£250
	a.	Small "T"	—	£850
152		3d. mauve/*blue*	—	£180
	a.	Small "T"		£650

(c) Wide roulette 6½.

153	1	1d. red/*yellow*	£650	£650
	a.	Small "T"		
	b.	Red/*orange*	—	£1200
154	2	3d. mauve/*green*	£1000	£650
	a.	Small "T"		
155		3d. mauve/*blue*	—	£750

(d) Pin-perf about 17.

156	1	1d. red/*yellow*	—	£750
	a.	Small "T"		
157	2	3d. mauve/*blue*	—	£850

SECOND REPUBLIC

Following the first Boer War the independence of the South African Republic was recognised by the Convention of Pretoria from 8 August 1881.

Nos. 133/9 remained valid and some values were available for postage until 1885.

EEN PENNY
(17)

1882 (11 Aug). *No. 136 surch with T 17.*

170	9	1d. on 4d. sage-green	13·00	4·50
	a.	Surch inverted	£300	£200

Used examples of a similar, but larger, surcharge (width 20 mm) are known. These were previously considered to be forgeries, but it is now believed that some, at least, may represent a trial printing of the "EEN PENNY" surcharge.

(Typo J. F. Celliers)

1883 (20 Feb–3 Aug). *Re-issue of T 1 and 2. P 12.*

171	1	1d. grey (*to black*) (5 Apr)	5·00	1·75
	a.	Imperf vert (horiz pair)	£275	
	b.	Imperf horiz (vert pair)	£550	£350
172	2	3d. grey-black (*to black*)/*rose*	23·00	5·00
		Bisected (1d.) (on cover)	†	£600
173		3d. pale red (7 May)	9·50	2·25
	a.	Bisected (1d.) (on cover)	†	£600
	b.	Imperf horiz (vert pair)	†	£1000
	c.	Chestnut	24·00	4·50
	ca.	Imperf between (horiz pair)	†	—
	d.	Vermilion	24·00	5·00
174	1	1s. green (*to deep*) (3 Aug)	55·00	4·00
	a.	Bisected (6d.) (on cover)	†	£450
	b.	Tête-bêche (pair)	£850	£150

Reprints are known of Nos. 172, 173, 173b and 173c. The paper of the first is *bright rose* in place of *dull rose*, and the impression is brownish black in place of grey-black to deep black. The reprints on white paper have the paper thinner than the originals, and the gum yellowish instead of white. The colour is a dull deep orange-red.

The used price quoted for No. 174b is for an example with telegraphic cancel. Postally used examples are worth much more. (See note below No. 139).

18

PERFORATIONS. Stamps perforated 11½×12 come from the first vertical row of sheets of the initial printing otherwise perforated 12½×12.

REPRINTS. Reprints of the general issues 1885–93, 1894–95, 1895–96 and 1896–97 exist in large quantities produced using the original plates from 1911 onwards. They cannot readily be distinguished from genuine originals except by comparison with used stamps, but the following general characteristics may be noted. The reprints are all perf 12½, large holes; the paper is whiter and thinner than that usually employed for the originals and their colours lack the lustre of those of the genuine stamps.

Forged surcharges have been made on these reprints.

(Des J. Vurtheim. Typo Enschedé)

1885 (13 Mar)–93. *P 12½.*

175	18	½d. grey (30.3.85)	70	10
	a.	Perf 13½	5·00	1·00
	b.	Perf 12½×12	2·00	10
	ba.	Perf 11½×12	24·00	7·00
176		1d. carmine	70	10
	a.	Perf 12½×12	1·00	10
	aa.	Perf 11½×12	15·00	2·75
	b.	Rose	70	10
	ba.	Perf 12½×12	1·00	10
177		2d. brown-purple (P 12½×12) (9.85)	1·75	2·50
178		2d. olive-bistre (14.4.87)	1·25	10
	a.	Perf 12½×12	3·75	10
179		2½d. mauve (*to bright*) (8.93)	2·25	50
180		3d. mauve (*to bright*)	2·50	1·25
	a.	Perf 12½×12	6·00	1·10
	aa.	Perf 11½×12	27·00	17·00
181		4d. bronze-green	3·75	60
	a.	Perf 13½	8·00	1·25
	b.	Perf 12½×12	14·00	80
	ba.	Perf 11½×12	£200	80·00
182		6d. pale dull blue	3·75	2·50
	a.	Perf 13½	5·50	1·00
	b.	Perf 12½×12	7·00	30
	ba.	Perf 11½×12		
183		1s. yellow-green	2·50	60
	a.	Perf 13½	25·00	6·00
	b.	Perf 12½×12	9·00	65
184		2s.6d. orange-buff (*to buff*) (2.12.85)	8·00	2·25
	a.	Perf 12½×12	17·00	7·00
185		5s. slate (2.12.85)	8·00	4·00
	a.	Perf 12½×12	35·00	7·50
186		10s. dull chestnut (2.12.85)	30·00	8·00
	a.	Yellow-brown (1891)		
187		£5 dp grn (3.92)* (Optd "Monster") (£150)	£3250	£180

Singles of the 6d. pale dull blue imperforate have been reported used in 1893.

*Most examples of No. 187 on the market are either forgeries or reprints.

(19)

1885 (22 May–Aug). *Surch with T 19. Reading up or down.*

188	2	3d. (No. 173)	5·00	9·50
189	1	½d. on 1s. (No. 174) (Aug)	22·00	50·00
	a.	Tête-bêche (pair)	£750	£350

Nos. 188/9 were surcharged by a setting of 40. After the left pane had been surcharged reading down, the sheets were turned so that the right pane had the surcharges reading up.

(20)   (21)   (22)

1885 (1 Sept). *No. 137a surch with T 20/1 in red.*

190	9	½d. on 6d. black-brown	55·00	85·00
191		2d. on 6d. black-brown	5·50	11·00

1885 (28 Sept). *No. 180a surch with T 22.*

192	18	½d. on 3d. mauve	4·00	4·00
	a.	"PRNNY" (R. 6/6)	40·00	60·00
	b.	2nd "N" inverted (R. 3/8)	85·00	£100
	c.	Perf 11½×12	12·00	11·00

2d   **2d**
(23)   (24)

1887 (15 Jan). *No. 180a surch with T 23/4.*

193	18	2d. on 3d. mauve (Type 23)	7·50	7·50
	a.	Surch double	—	£275
	b.	Perf 11½×12	24·00	12·00
194		2d. on 3d. mauve (Type 24)	1·50	3·25
	a.	Surch double	£180	£180
	b.	Perf 11½×12	6·50	8·50

Nos. 193/4 were surcharged from the same setting of 60 (10×6) which showed Type 24 on the top five horizontal rows and Type 23 on the sixth horizontal row.

Halve Penny   **1 Penny**
(25)   (26)

2½ Pence   **2½ Pence**
(27)   (28)

Two types of surcharge:
A. Vertical distance between bars 12½ mm.
B. Distance 13½ mm.

1893. *T 18 surch. P 12½.*

(a) In red.

195	25	½d. on 2d. olive-bistre (A) (27 May)	80	1·75
	a.	Surch inverted	2·50	2·50
	b.	Surch Type B	1·50	2·50
	ba.	Surch inverted	5·00	10·00

(b) In black.

196	25	½d. on 2d. olive-bistre (A) (2 July)	85	1·75
	a.	Surch inverted	5·00	5·00
	b.	Extra surch on back inverted	£160	
	c.	Surch Type B	1·10	5·00
	ca.	Surch inverted	20·00	15·00
	cb.	Extra surch on back inverted	£275	

197	**26**	1d. on 6d. blue (A) (26 Jan)	70	75
		a. Surch double	55·00	45·00
		b. Surch inverted	1·60	2·00
		c. Surch treble		
		d. Surch Type B	1·00	1·00
		da. Surch inverted	5·00	4·00
		db. Surch double		80·00
		e. Pair, one without surch	£225	
198	**27**	2½d. on 1s. green (A) (2 Jan)	1·25	3·75
		a. "2½d" for "2½" (R. 1/10)	32·00	60·00
		b. Surch inverted	6·50	7·50
		ba. Surch inverted and "2/½d" for "2½"	£350	£300
		c. Extra surch on back inverted	£450	£450
		d. Surch double, one inverted	£700	
		f. Surch Type B	1·50	3·75
		ea. Surch inverted	7·50	16·00
199	**28**	2½d. on 1s. green (A) (24 June)	4·75	4·25
		a. Surch inverted	45·00	40·00
		b. Surch inverted	7·50	7·50
		c. Surch Type B	8·00	8·50
		ca. Surch double	75·00	85·00
		ea. Surch inverted	19·00	19·00

Surcharge Types **25/8** all show a similar setting of the horizontal bars at top and bottom. on horizontal rows 1 to 4 and 6, the bars are 12½ mm apart and on row 5 the distance is 13½ mm.

29 (Wagon with shafts)

30 (Wagon with pole)

1894 (July). P 12½.

200	**29**	½d. grey	60	45
201		1d. carmine	1·25	10
202		2d. olive-bistre	1·25	10
203		6d. pale dull blue	2·00	40
204		1s. yellow-green	11·00	15·00

For note *re* reprints, see below T **18**.

1895 (16 Mar)–96. P 12½.

205	**30**	½d. pearl-grey (1895)	70	10
		a. Lilac-grey	70	10
206		1d. rose-red	70	10
207		2d. olive-bistre (1895)	80	10
208		3d. mauve (1895)	1·75	65
209		4d. olive-black (1895)	2·25	80
210		6d. pale dull blue (1895)	2·25	70
211		1s. yellow-green (18.3.95)	2·75	1·25
212		5s. slate (1896)	14·00	25·00
212a		10s. pale chestnut (1896)	14·00	5·00
205s/8s, 211s Optd "Monster" *Set of 5*			£150	

For note *re* reprints, see below T **18**.

Halve Penny

(31)

1d. **1d.**

(32—Round dot)   (32a—Square dot)

1895 (July–Aug). *Nos.* 211 *and* 179 *surch with T* **31**/2.

213	**30**	½d. on 1s. green (R.)	80	20
			1·75	1·25
		b. "Pennij" for "Penny" (R. 6/6)	50·00	60·00
		c. Surch inverted	4·00	4·50
		d. Surch double	65·00	90·00
214	**18**	1d. on 2½d. bright mauve (G.)	50	10
		a. Surch inverted	19·00	14·00
		b. Surch double	65·00	65·00
		c. Surch on back only	75·00	
		d. Surch Type 32a	1·50	1·25
		da. Surch inverted	65·00	
		e. Surch treble	£550	

The normal space between "Penny" and the bars is 3 mm. on No. 213a, which comes from the fifth horizontal row of the setting, this is increased to 4 mm. Copies may be found in which one or both of the bars have failed to print.

Type **32a** with square stop occurred on R. 3/3-4, 3/6-8, 4/4-5, 4/7-8, 4/10, 6/3, 6/7-8 and 6/10 of the setting of 60.

33   **34**

1895 (July). *Fiscal stamp optd* "POSTZEGEL". P 11½.

215	**33**	6d. bright rose (G.)	1·50	1·75
		a. Imperf between (pair)		
		b. Opt inverted		

(Litho The Press Printing and Publishing Works, Pretoria)

1895 (6 Sept). *Introduction of Penny Postage.* P 11.

215c	**34**	1d. red (pale *to* deep)	1·50	1·75
		ca. Imperf between (pair)	90·00	95·00
		cb. Imperf vert (horiz pair)		
		cc. Imperf (pair)		

1896–97. P 12½.

216	**30**	½d. green (1896)	70	10
217		1d. rose-red (1896)	70	10
218		2d. brown and green (2.97)	70	10
219		2½d. dull blue and green (6.96)	1·25	10
220		3d. purple and green (3.97)	1·75	2·00
221		4d. sage-green and green (3.97)	1·75	2·00
222		6d. lilac and green (11.96)	1·00	1·25
223		1s. ochre and green (3.96)	1·50	45
224		2s.6d. dull violet and green (6.96)	1·75	2·25

For note *re* reprints, see below T **18**.

SECOND BRITISH OCCUPATION

The Second Boer War began on 11 October 1899 and was concluded by the Peace of Vereeniging on 31 May 1902. Pretoria was occupied by the British on 5 June 1900 and a civilian postal service began operating thirteen days later.

FORGERIES. The forgeries of the "V.R.I." and "E.R.I." overprints most often met with can be recognised by the fact that the type used is perfect and the three stops are always in alignment with the bottom of the letters. In the genuine overprints, which were made from old type, it is impossible to find all three letters perfect and all three stops perfect and in exact alignment with the bottom of the letters.

E. R. I.

Half

V. R. I.   **E. R. I.**   **Penny**

(35)   (36)   (37)

1900 (18 June). *Optd with T* **35**.

226	**30**	½d. green	30	30
		a. No stop after "V"	12·00	12·00
		b. No stop after "R"	9·00	9·00
		c. No stop after "I"	7·50	7·50
		d. Opt inverted	10·00	12·00
		e. Opt double		
		f. "V.I.R." (R. 4/4)	£550	
227		1d. rose-red and green	30	30
		a. No stop after "V"	12·00	12·00
		b. No stop after "R"	9·00	9·00
		c. No stop after "I"	6·00	6·00
		d. Opt inverted	10·00	17·00
		e. Opt double	70·00	85·00
		f. No stops after "R" and "I"	75·00	75·00
		g. Opt omitted (in pair with normal)	£250	
228		2d. brown and green	2·50	1·75
		a. No stop after "V"	27·00	29·00
		c. No stop after "I"	32·00	32·00
		d. Opt inverted	17·00	19·00
		f. "V.I.R." (R. 4/4)	£550	£600
		g. Opt albino		
229		2½d. dull blue and green	1·00	1·75
		a. No stop after "V"	19·00	21·00
		b. No stop after "R"	45·00	50·00
		c. No stop after "I"	15·00	17·00
		d. Opt inverted	11·00	12·00
230		3d. purple and green	1·00	1·50
		a. No stop after "V"	23·00	25·00
		b. No stop after "R"	45·00	50·00
		c. No stop after "I"	30·00	35·00
		d. Opt inverted	70·00	80·00
231		4d. sage-green and green	2·50	1·00
		a. No stop after "V"	40·00	40·00
		b. No stop after "R"	50·00	50·00
		c. No stop after "I"	35·00	35·00
		d. Opt inverted	25·00	28·00
		f. "V.I.R." (R. 4/4)	£550	
232		6d. lilac and green	2·50	1·50
		a. No stop after "V"	19·00	19·00
		b. No stop after "R"	25·00	25·00
		c. No stop after "I"	25·00	25·00
		d. Opt inverted	28·00	32·00
233		1s. ochre and green	2·50	3·00
		a. No stop after "V"	19·00	22·00
		b. No stop after "R"	19·00	22·00
		c. No stop after "I"	35·00	40·00
		d. Opt inverted	35·00	40·00
		e. Opt double	75·00	85·00
234		2s.6d. dull violet and green	3·25	8·50
		a. No stop after "V"	35·00	
		b. No stop after "R"	75·00	
		c. No stop after "I"	—	£425
235		5s. slate	6·00	11·00
		a. No stop after "V"	£100	
236		10s. pale chestnut	8·00	13·00
		a. No stop after "V"	85·00	
		c. No stop after "I"	85·00	
237	**18**	£5 deep green*	£2000	£800
		a. No stop after "V"		
234s/7s Optd "Specimen" *Set of 4*			£200	

*Many examples of No. 237 on the market are forgeries and the stamps should only be purchased if accompanied by a recent expert committee certificate.

The error "V.I.R." occurred on R. 4/4 in the first batch of stamps to be overprinted—a few sheets of the ½d., 2d. and 4d. The error was then corrected and stamps showing it are very rare.

A number of different settings were used to apply the overprint to Nos. 226/37. The missing stop varieties listed above developed during overprinting and occur on different positions in the various settings.

1901 (Jan)–02. *Optd with T* **36**.

238	**30**	½d. green	50	1·00
		a. Opt double		

239		1d. rose-red and green (20.3.01)	50	10
		a. "E" of opt omitted	75·00	
240		3d. purple and green (6.02)	2·25	3·00
241		4d. sage-green and green (6.02)	2·25	3·50
242		2s.6d. dull violet and green (10.02)	9·00	20·00

1901 (July). *Surch with T* **37**.

243	**30**	½d. on 2d. brown and green	65	65
		a. No stop after "E" (R. 4/6)	50·00	55·00

38 (POSTAGE REVENUE)   **39** (POSTAGE POSTAGE)

(Typo D.L.R.)

1902 (1 Apr–17 Dec). Wmk Crown CA. P 14.

244	**38**	½d. black and bluish green	1·50	20
		w. Wmk inverted	85·00	60·00
245		1d. black and carmine	1·25	15
		w. Wmk inverted	65·00	50·00
246		2d. black and purple	3·50	50
247		2½d. black and blue	7·00	1·25
		w. Wmk inverted	60·00	35·00
248		3d. black and sage-green (17.12.02)	7·00	50
249		4d. black and brown (17.12.02)	5·50	1·00
250		6d. black and orange-brown	4·00	60
251		1s. black and sage-green	11·00	10·00
252		2s. black and brown	40·00	45·00
253	**39**	2s.6d. magenta and black	15·00	12·00
254		5s. black and purple/*yellow*	25·00	28·00
255		10s. black and purple/*red*	55·00	29·00
244/55 *Set of 12*			£160	£110
244s/55s (*inc* 247ws) Optd "Specimen" *Set of 12*			£140	

The colour of the "black" centres varies from brownish grey or grey to black.

1903 (1 Feb). Wmk Crown CA. P 14.

256	**39**	1s. grey-black and red-brown	13·00	3·00
257		2s. grey-black and yellow	15·00	12·00
258		£1 green and violet	£190	£120
259		£5 orange-brown and violet	£1400	£650
256s/9s Optd "Specimen" *Set of 4*			£200	

1904–09. *Ordinary paper.* Wmk Mult Crown CA. P 14.

260	**38**	½d. black and bluish green	7·00	2·50
		w. Wmk inverted	£100	65·00
		y. Wmk inverted and reversed	90·00	35·00
261		1d. black and carmine	4·50	20
262		2d. black and purple (*chalk-surfaced paper*) (1906)	9·00	1·00
263		2½d. black and blue (1905)	13·00	7·00
		aw. Wmk inverted	90·00	70·00
		b. Chalk-surfaced paper	12·00	3·00
264		3d. black & sage-green (*chalk-surfaced paper*) (1906)	3·50	50
265		4d. black and brown (*chalk-surfaced paper*) (1906)	4·75	70
		w. Wmk inverted	90·00	60·00
266		6d. black and orange (1905)	8·50	1·50
		a. Chalk-surfaced paper. *Black and brown-orange* (1906)	3·00	50
		w. Wmk inverted	£100	75·00
267	**39**	1s. black and red-brown (1905)	6·50	50
268		2s. black and yellow (1906)	21·00	7·00
269		2s.6d. magenta and black (1909)	48·00	5·00
270		5s. black and purple/*yellow*	20·00	1·50
271		10s. black and purple/*red* (1907)	50·00	2·75
272		£1 green and violet (1908)	£200	29·00
		a. Chalk-surfaced paper	£190	16·00
260/72 *Set of 13*			£350	38·00

There is considerable variation in the "black" centres as in the previous issue.

1905–09. Wmk Mult Crown CA. P 14.

273	**38**	½d. yellow-green	2·00	10
		a. Deep green (1908)	2·50	20
		w. Wmk inverted	£120	75·00
274		1d. scarlet	1·25	10
		aw. Wmk inverted	—	£275
		b. Wmk Cabled Anchor, T **13** of Cape of Good Hope	—	£325
275		2d. purple (1909)	50	60
276		2½d. bright blue (1909)	13·00	5·50
273/6 *Set of 4*			18·00	5·50
273s/6s Optd "Specimen" *Set of 4*			70·00	

A 2d. grey, T **38**, was prepared for use but not issued. It exists overprinted "Specimen", price £140.

The monocoloured ½d. and 1d. are printed from new combined plates. These show a slight alteration in that the frame does not touch the crown.

The ½d., 1d. and 2d. exist from coils constructed from normal sheets for use in stamp machines introduced in 1911. These coils were originally joined horizontally but the 1d. was subsequently issued joined vertically.

Many of the King's Head stamps are found overprinted or perforated "C.S.A.R.", for use by the Central South African Railways.

STAMP BOOKLETS

1905 (July). *Black on red cover showing arms. Stapled.*

SB1	2s.7d. booklet containing thirty 1d. (No. 261) in blocks of 6		£2000

1905. *Black on red cover. Stapled.*

SB2	2s.7d. booklet containing thirty 1d. (No. 274) in blocks of 6		£2250

1909. *Black on red cover. Stapled.*
SB3   2s.6d. booklet containing ten ½d. (No. 273) in block
         of 6 and block of 4, and twenty-four 1d. (No.
         274) in blocks of 6.. £2750

Stocks of No. SB3 were supplied containing twelve examples of the
½d., it being intended that the postal clerks would remove two stamps
before the booklets were sold. In some instances this did not occur.

POSTAL FISCAL STAMPS

1900–02. *Fiscal stamps as in T 33, but optd with T 35. P 11½.*
F1   1d. pale blue .... —   45·00
F2   6d. dull carmine .... —   60·00
F3   1s. olive-bistre .... —   75·00
F4   1s.6d. brown .... —   90·00
F5   2s.6d. dull purple .... —   £100

Nos. F1/5, previously listed as Nos. 1/5 of Volksrust, are fiscal issues
which are known postally used from various Transvaal post offices
between June 1900 and June 1902.

Other fiscal stamps are found apparently postally used, but these were
used on telegrams not on postal matter.

POSTAGE DUE STAMPS

D 1

(Typo D.L.R.)

1907. Wmk Mult Crown CA. P 14.
D1   D 1   ½d. black and blue-green................   3·50   1·25
D2   1d. black and scarlet ....   4·00   85
D3   2d. brown-orange ....   4·50   1·25
D4   3d. black and blue ....   7·50   4·25
D5   5d. black and violet ....   2·00 12·00
              a. Inverted "p" for "d" (Right pane
                 R. 10/6)...................................... 50·00
D6   6d. black and red-brown ....   4·25 12·00
D7   1s. scarlet and black .... 10·00   8·50
D1/7 *Set of 7* .... 32·00 35·00

Transvaal became a province of the Union of South Africa on 31 May
1910.

PIETERSBURG

After the fall of Pretoria to the British in June 1900 the Transvaal
government withdrew to the north of the country. Those post offices in
areas not occupied by the British continued to function, but by early
the following year supplies of stamps were exhausted. The following
stamps were then authorised by the State Secretary and remained in
use in some towns to early May 1901. Pietersburg itself was taken by
British forces on 9 April.

PRICES. Genuinely used examples are very rare. Stamps cancelled by
favour exist and are worth the same as the unused prices quoted.

The issued stamps are initialled by the Controller J. T. de V. Smit. All
values exist without his signature and these are believed to come from
remainders abandoned when the Boers evacuated Pietersburg.

P 1   P 2

P 3

TYPES P 1/3. Each value was printed in sheets of 24 (6×4) of which
the first two horizontal rows as Type P **1**, the third row as Type P **2**
and the fourth as Type P **3**. The stamps were issued to post offices in
blocks of 12.

(Type-set *De Zoutpansberg Wachter* Press, Pietersburg)
1901 (20 Mar (1d.)–3 Apr (others)). A. Imperf.
          (a) Controller's initials in black.
1   P 1   ½d. black/*green*............................... 15·00
              e. Controller's initials omitted................. 95·00

---

2   P **2**   ½d. black/*green* .... 45·00
              d. Controller's initials omitted............. 95·00
3   P **3**   ½d. black/*green* .... 45·00
              d. Controller's initials omitted............. 95·00
4   P 1   1d. black/*red*...............................   3·50
5   P **2**   1d. black/*red*...............................   5·50
6   P **3**   1d. black/*red*...............................   7·00
7   P 1   2d. black/*orange* ....   6·00
8   P **2**   2d. black/*orange* .... 14·00
9   P **3**   2d. black/*orange* .... 22·00
10   P 1   4d. black/*blue* ....   5·50
11   P **2**   4d. black/*blue* ....   9·50
12   P **3**   4d. black/*blue* .... 32·00
13   P 1   6d. black/*green* ....   9·50
14   P **2**   6d. black/*green* .... 15·00
15   P **3**   6d. black/*green* .... 40·00
16   P 1   1s. black/*yellow* ....   8·00
17   P **2**   1s. black/*yellow* .... 14·00
18   P **3**   1s. black/*yellow* .... 25·00

              (b) Controller's initials in red.
19   P 1   ½d. black/*green* .... 15·00
20   P **2**   ½d. black/*green* .... 35·00
21   P **3**   ½d. black/*green* .... 40·00

              B. P 11½.
              (a) Controller's initials in red.
22   P 1   ½d. black/*green* ....   5·50
              c. Imperf vert (horiz pair).................... 95·00
23   P **2**   ½d. black/*green* .... 17·00
              c. Imperf vert (horiz pair).................... £120
24   P **3**   ½d. black/*green* .... 12·00
              b. Imperf vert (horiz pair).................... £120

              (b) Controller's initials in black.
25   P 1   1d. black/*red* ....   2·00
              m. Imperf vert (horiz pair) .... 55·00
              n. Imperf between (vert pair: No. 25 +
                 No. 26)...................................... 75·00
              o. Imperf horiz (vert pair)................. 55·00
26   P **2**   1d. black/*red* ....   2·75
              f. Imperf vert (horiz pair) .... 80·00
              g. Imperf horiz (vert pair: No. 26 +
                 No. 27)....................................... 60·00
27   P **3**   1d. black/*red* ....   4·00
              f. Imperf vert (horiz pair) .... 80·00
28   P 1   2d. black/*orange* ....   5·50
29   P **2**   2d. black/*orange* ....   8·00
30   P **3**   2d. black/*orange* .... 14·00

For the ½d. the First printing had initials in either black or red, those
of the Second printing had them in black and all of the Third were
in red.

CONSTANT VARIETIES

*Rows 1 and 2 are as Type P **1**, Row 3 as Type P **2** and Row 4 as
Type P **3**.*

½d. value
First printing—Imperf

R.1/1   & 4 Top left "½" inverted, no stop
            after right "AFR"............................ (No. 19c) 70·00
R.1/2   Top right "½" inverted....................... (No. 19d) 90·00
R.1/3   "⅓" at lower right .... (No. 19e) 90·00
R.1/5   "POSTZFGEL".............................. (No. 19f) 90·00
R.1/6   Left spray inverted, "AFB" at right .. (No. 19g) 90·00
R.2/1   "REB" at left, left side of inner frame
            3 mm too high................................ (No. 19h) 90·00
R.2/2   "BEP" at left................................... (No. 19i) 90·00
R.2/3   "POSTZEOEL"............................... (No. 19j) 90·00
R.2/4   "AER" at right, left side of inner
            frame 2 mm too high....................... (No. 19k) 90·00
R.2/5   No stop after date .... (No. 19l) 90·00
R.2/6   No stop after "PENNY"................... (No. 19m)
R.3/1   "⅓" at top left, "PE" of "PENNY"
            spaced.. (No. 20c) 90·00
R.3/2   Right spray inverted......................... (No. 20d) 90·00
R.3/3   Top left "½" inverted....................... (No. 20e) 90·00
R.3/4   No stop after "2" at left................... (No. 20f)
R.3/5   Centre figures "½" level.................. (No. 20g)
R.3/6   "POSTZEGFL", no stop after right
            "AFR"... (No. 20h)
R.4/3   "⅓" at top right .... (No. 21b) 90·00
R.4/4   Lower left "½" inverted................... (No. 21c) 90·00
R.4/5   "¼" at top left .... (No. 21d) 90·00
R.4/6   Left spray inverted, "901" for
            "1901" .... (No. 21e)

This printing was produced first and was then adapted for the higher
values.

Second printing

R.1/2   No stop after left "AFR" ...... Imperf (No. 1a) 60·00
R.1/3   "⅓" at top left, no bar over lower right
            "½".. Imperf (No. 1b) 60·00
R.1/6   No stop after date .... Imperf (No. 1c) 60·00
R.2/5   "BEP" at left, no stop after date....
            .... Imperf (No. 1d) 60·00
R.3/3   "AFB" at left.................... Imperf (No. 2a) 60·00
R.3/4   "POSTZEGEI".............. Imperf (No. 2b) 60·00
            .... Perf   (No. 23a)
R.3/6   No bar over lower right "½". Imperf (No. 2c) 60·00
R.4/1   No stop after right "AFR" ..... Imperf (No. 3a) 60·00
R.4/4   No stop after left "Z", no bar under
            top right "½" .... Imperf (No. 3b) 60·00
            .... Perf   (No. 23b)
R.4/5   "POSTZECEL AER" at left .. Imperf (No. 3c) 60·00

Third printing

R.1/4   No stop after right "AFR"..... Imperf (No. 19a) 70·00
            .... Perf   (No. 22a) 40·00
R.2/1   Left side of inner frame too high ....
            ....Imperf (No. 19b) 70·00
            .... Perf   (No. 22b) 40·00

R.3/5   Centre figures "½" level .... Imperf (No. 20a) 70·00
            .... Perf   (No. 23d) 40·00
R.3/6   No stop after right "AFR" ..... Imperf (No. 20b) 70·00
            .... Perf   (No. 23e) 40·00
R.4/6   Hyphen between right "AFR" and
            "REP" .... Imperf (No. 21a) 70·00
            .... Perf   (No. 24a) 40·00

1d. value

First printing

R.1/2   Inverted "1" at lower left, first "1" of
            date dropped....................... Imperf (No. 4a) 35·00
            .... Perf   (No. 25a) 22·00
R.1/3   No bar under top left "1" ..... Imperf (No. 4b) 35·00
            .... Perf   (No. 25b) 22·00
R.1/4   No bar over lower right "1" .. Imperf (No. 4c) 35·00
            .... Perf   (No. 25c) 22·00
R.1/5   "POSTZFGEL" .... Imperf (No. 4d) 35·00
            .... Perf   (No. 25d) 22·00
R.1/6   "AFB" at right .... Imperf (No. 4e) 35·00
            .... Perf   (No. 25e) 22·00
R.2/1   "REB" at left .... Imperf (No. 4f) 35·00
            .... Perf   (No. 25f) 22·00
R.2/2   "BEP" at left .... Imperf (No. 4g) 35·00
            .... Perf   (No. 25g) 22·00
R.2/3   "POSTZEOEL" .... Imperf (No. 4h) 35·00
            .... Perf   (No. 25h) 22·00
R.2/4   "AER" at right .... Imperf (No. 4i) 35·00
            .... Perf   (No. 25i) 22·00
R.2/5   No stop after date .... Imperf (No. 4j) 35·00
            .... Perf   (No. 25j) 22·00
R.2/6   No stop after "PENNY" .... Imperf (No. 4k) 35·00
            .... Perf   (No. 25k) 22·00
R.3/2   Right spray inverted............ Imperf (No. 5a) 35·00
            .... Perf   (No. 26a) 22·00
R.3/3   No bar over lower left "1" ... Imperf (No. 5b) 35·00
            .... Perf   (No. 26b) 22·00
R.3/4   No stop after left "Z" .... Imperf (No. 5c) 35·00
            .... Perf   (No. 26c) 22·00
R.3/6   "POSTZEGFL", no stop after right
            "AFR" .... Imperf (No. 5d) 35·00
            .... Perf   (No. 26d) 22·00
R.4/1   No stop after right "AFR".... Imperf (No. 6a) 35·00
            .... Perf   (No. 27a) 22·00
R.4/2   & 6 Left spray inverted .... Imperf (No. 6b) 35·00
            .... Perf   (No. 27b) 13·00
R.4/3   "POSTZEGEI" .... Imperf (No. 6c) 35·00
            .... Perf   (No. 27c) 22·00
R.4/4   No bar under top right "1" .... Imperf (No. 6d) 35·00
            .... Perf   (No. 27d) 22·00

Second printing

R.1/2   First "1" in date dropped....... Imperf (No. 4l) 35·00
            .... Perf   (No. 25l) 22·00
R.3/6   No stop after right "AFR" ..... Imperf (No. 5e) 35·00
            .... Perf   (No. 26e) 22·00
R.4/5   Dropped "P" in "PENNY" .... Imperf (No. 6e) 35·00
            .... Perf   (No. 27e) 22·00

It has been suggested that there may have been a third printing.

2d. value

First printing—Imperf

R.1/1   "1" at lower right............................ (No. 7a) 45·00
R.1/2   No stop after left "AFR" (*on small
            part of printing*)............................. (No. 7b) 90·00
R.1/3   No bar over lower right "2" (*on small
            part of printing*)............................. (No. 7c) 90·00
R.1/3   "PENNY" for "PENCE"............... (No. 7d) 45·00
R.1/5   "POSTZEGEL"............................. (No. 7e) 45·00
R.1/6   "AFB" at right .... (No. 7f) 45·00
R.2/1   "REB" at left .... (No. 7g) 45·00
R.2/2   "AFB" at left .... (No. 7h) 45·00
R.2/3   "POSTZEOEL" .... (No. 7i) 45·00
R.2/4   "AER" at right .... (No. 7j) 45·00
R.2/5   No stop after date .... (No. 7k) 45·00
R.2/6   No stop after date, vertical line after
            "POSTZEGEL" .... (No. 7l) 45·00
R.3/2   Right spray inverted..................... (No. 8a) 45·00
R.3/3   No bar over lower left "2" .... (No. 8b) 45·00
R.3/4   Centre "2" inverted, no stop after left
            "Z" .... (No. 8c) 45·00
R.3/6   "POSTZEGFL", no stop after right
            "AFR" .... (No. 8d) 45·00
R.4/1   Centre "2" wider, no stop after right
            "AFR" (*occurs on second printing
            also*)... (No. 9a) 38·00
R.4/2   Centre "2" wider, left spray inverted (No. 9b) 45·00
R.4/3   "POSTZEGEI" .... (No. 9c) 45·00
R.4/4   No bar under top right "2" .... (No. 9d) 45·00
R.4/5   "1" at lower left, "P" in "PENCE"
            dropped .... (No. 9e) 45·00
R4/6   Left spray inverted....................... (No. 9f) 45·00

Second printing

R.1/2   First "1" in date dropped....... Imperf (No. 7m) 45·00
            .... Perf   (No. 28a) 30·00
R.2/1   No stop after left "REP"........ Imperf (No. 7n) 45·00
            .... Perf   (No. 28b) 30·00
R.3/4   No stop after left "Z".......... Imperf (No. 8e) 45·00
R.3/6   No stop after right "AFR" ..... Imperf (No. 8f) 45·00
            .... Perf   (No. 29a)
R.4/1   Centre 2 wider, no stop after right
            "AFR" (*occurs on first printing also*)
            .... Imperf (No. 9a) 38·00
            .... Perf   (No. 30a) 30·00
R.4/2   Centre "2" wider...... .... Imperf (No. 9g) 45·00
            .... Perf   (No. 30b) 30·00
R.4/5   "P" in "PENCE" dropped.... Imperf (No. 9h) 45·00
            .... Perf   (No. 30c) 30·00

It has been suggested that there was a third printing of this value.

4d.

First printing

R.1/2	No stop after left "AFR"	(No. 10a)	45·00
R.1/3	No bar over lower right "4"	(No. 10b)	45·00
R.1/3	"PENNY" for "PENCE" (*on small part of printing*)	(No. 10c)	90·00
R.1/5	"POSTZFGEL"	(No. 10d)	45·00
R.1/6	"AFB" at right	(No. 10e)	45·00
R.2/1	"REB" at left	(No. 10f)	45·00
R.2/2	"AFB" at left	(No. 10g)	45·00
R.2/3	"POSTZEOEL"	(No. 10h)	45·00
R.2/4	"AER" at right	(No. 10i)	45·00
R.2/5	No stop after date	(No. 10j)	45·00
R.3/2	Right spray inverted	(No. 11a)	45·00
R.3/3	No bar over lower left "4" (*on small part of printing*)	(No. 11b)	90·00
R.3/4	No stop after left "Z"	(No. 11c)	45·00
R.3/6	"POSTZEGFL"	(No. 11d)	45·00
R.4/1	Centre "4" wider, no stop after right "AFR"	(No. 12a)	45·00
R.4/2	Centre "4" wider, left spray inverted	(No. 12b)	45·00
R.4/3	"POSTZEGEI"	(No. 12c)	45·00
R.4/4	No bar under top right "4"	(No. 12d)	45·00
R.4/5	"AER" at left, "P" in "PENCE" dropped	(No. 12e)	45·00
R.4/6	Left spray inverted	(No. 12f)	45·00

Second printing

R.2/1	Left inner frame too high	(No. 10k)	45·00
R.4/1–2	Centre "4" wider	(No. 12g)	35·00
R.4/5	"P" in "PENCE" dropped	(No. 12h)	45·00

6d. value

First printing

R.1/2	No stop after left "AFR"	(No. 13a)	55·00
R.1/3	No bar over lower right "6"	(No. 13b)	55·00
R.1/3	"PENNY" for "PENCE" (*on small part of printing*)	(No. 13c)	£100
R.1/5	"POSTZFGEL"	(No. 13d)	55·00
R.1/6	"AFB" at right	(No. 13e)	55·00
R.2/1	"REB" at left	(No. 13f)	55·00
R.2/2	"AFB" at left	(No. 13g)	55·00
R.2/3	"POSTZEOEL"	(No. 13h)	55·00
R.2/4	"AER" at right	(No. 13i)	55·00
R.2/5	No stop after date	(No. 13j)	55·00
R.3/2	Right spray inverted	(No. 14a)	55·00
R.3/4	Centre "6" inverted, no stop after left "Z" (*on small part of printing*)	(No. 14b)	£100
R.3/4	No stop after left "Z"	(No. 14c)	55·00
R.3/6	"POSTZEGFL"	(No. 14d)	55·00
R.4/1	Centre "6" wider, no stop after right "AFR"	(No. 15a)	55·00
R.4/2	Centre "6" wider, left spray inverted	(No. 15b)	55·00
R.4/3	"POSTZEGEI"	(No. 15c)	55·00
R.4/4	No bar under top right "6"	(No. 15d)	55·00
R.4/5	"AER" at left. "P" in "PENCE" dropped	(No. 15e)	55·00
R.4/6	Left spray inverted	(No. 15f)	55·00

Second printing

R.2/1	Left inner frame too high, no stop after left "REP"	(No. 13k)	55·00
R.4/1–2	Centre "6" wider	(No. 15g)	40·00
R.4/5	"P" in "PENCE" dropped	(No. 15h)	55·00

1s. value

R.1/2	No stop after left "AFR"	(No. 16a)	40·00
R.1/3	No bar over lower right "1"	(No. 16b)	40·00
R.2/5	No stop after date	(No. 16c)	40·00
R.3/3	Centre "1" inverted (*on small part of printing*)	(No. 17a)	
R.3/4	"POSTZEGEI", no stop after left "Z"	(No. 17b)	40·00
R.4/1	No stop after right "AFR"	(No. 18a)	40·00
R.4/4	No bar under top right "1"	(No. 18b)	40·00
R.4/5	"AER" at left	(No. 18c)	40·00

LOCAL BRITISH OCCUPATION ISSUES DURING THE SOUTH AFRICAN WAR 1900–2

Stamps of the Transvaal Republic, unless otherwise stated, variously overprinted or surcharged.

LYDENBURG

Lydenburg fell to the British on 6 September 1900.

V.R.I.
3d.
(L 1)

1900 (Sept). *Nos. 215b and 217 surch as Type* L **1**, *others optd "V.R.I" only.*

1	**30**	½d. green..............................	£120	£120
2		1d. rose-red and green	£110	£100
2a	**34**	3d. on 1d. red		
3	**30**	2d. brown and green	£1100	£800
4		2½d. blue and green	£2000	£850
5		3d. on 1d. rose-red and green	95·00	85·00
6		3d. purple and green		
7		4d. sage-green and green	£2750	£750
8		6d. lilac and green	£2250	£700
9		1s. ochre and green	£4000	£2500

The above were cancelled by British Army postal service postmarks.

These overprints with Transvaal cancellations are believed to be forgeries.

RUSTENBURG

The British forces in Rustenburg, west of Pretoria, were besieged by the Boers during June 1900. When relieved on the 22 June 1900 no "V.R.I" stamps were available so a local handstamp was applied.

V.R.
(R 1)

1900 (23 June). *Handstamped with Type* R **1** *in violet.*

1	**30**	½d. green..............................	£140	£100
2		1d. rose-red and green	£100	80·00
3		2d. brown and green	£300	£120
4		2½d. blue and green	£170	£100
5		3d. purple and green	£225	£130
6		6d. lilac and green	£1100	£350
7		1s. ochre and green	£1600	£350
8		2s.6d. dull violet and green	£9000	£4500
		a. Handstamp in black	†	£8000

Nos. 2 and 5 exist with the handstamp inverted.

SCHWEIZER RENECKE

BESIEGED
(SR 1)

1900 (Sept). *Handstamped with Type* SR **1** *in black, reading vert up or down.*

(a) on stamps of Transvaal.

1	**30**	½d. green..............................	†	£250
2		1d. rose-red and green	†	£250
3		2d. brown and green	†	£325
4		6d. lilac and green	†	£900

(b) on stamps of Cape of Good Hope.

5	**17**	½d. green..............................	†	£425
6		1d. carmine.........................	†	£425

Schweizer Renecke, near the Bechuanaland border, was under siege from 1 August 1900 to 9 January 1901. The British commander authorised the above stamps shortly after 19 August. All stamps were cancelled with the dated circular town postmark ("Schweizer Renecke, Z.A.R."), usually after having been stuck on paper before use. Unused, without the postmark, do not exist.

No. 4 exists with double handstamp.

WOLMARANSSTAD

A British party occupied this town in the south-west of the Transvaal from 15 June to 27 July 1900. Transvaal stamps, to a face value of £5 2s.6d., were found at the local firm of Thos. Leask and Co. and surcharged as below. The first mail left on 24 June and the last on 21 July.

Cancelled
V-R-I.
(L 3)

Cancelled
V-R-I.
(L 4)

1900 (24 June). *Optd with Type* L **3**.

1	**30**	½d. green (B.)	£225	£350
		a. Opt inverted	£750	
		b. Opt in black		
1c		½d. on 1s. green (B.)		
2		1d. rose-red and green (B.)	£160	£250
		a. Opt in green	£1800	
		b. Opt in black		
3		2d. brown and green (B.)	£1800	£1800
		a. Opt in black	£3000	
4		2½d. blue and green (R.)	£1800	
		a. Opt in blue	£2750	£2750
		b. Opt in black		
5		3d. purple and green (B.)	£3000	£3250
6		4d. sage-green and green (B.)	£3750	£4250
7		6d. lilac and green (B.)	£4000	£4250
8		1s. ochre and green (B.)	—	£8000

The two lines of the overprint were handstamped separately. The ½d. exists with two impressions of the "Cancelled" handstamp, the 2½d. with two impressions of "V-R-I", one in red and one in blue and the 3d. with "Cancelled" in green and "V.R.I." in blue.

1900 (24 June). *Optd with Type* L **4**.

9	**34**	1d. red (B.)	£160	£275

The ½d., 1d. and 3d. in Type **30** are also known with this overprint.

VII. ZULULAND

Zululand remained an independent kingdom until annexed by Great Britain on 19 May 1887 when it was declared a Crown Colony.

The first European postal service was operated by a Natal postal agency at Eshowe opened in 1876 which cancelled Natal stamps with a "No. 56 P.O. Natal" postmark. The agency closed during the Zulu War of 1879 and did not re-open until 1885 when a Eshowe postmark was provided. "ZULULAND" was added to the cancellation in 1887 and stamps of Natal continued to be used until replaced by the overprinted series on 1 May 1888.

PRICES FOR STAMPS ON COVER		
Nos. 1/2	*from*	× 100
Nos. 3/10	*from*	× 20
No. 11		—
Nos. 12/16	*from*	× 20
Nos. 20/3	*from*	× 30
No. 24	*from*	× 20
Nos. 25/6	*from*	× 12
Nos. 27/9		—
No. F1	*from*	× 100

ZULULAND
(1)

ZULULAND.
(2)

1888 (1 May)–93.

(a) Nos. 173, 180, 197, 200/2, 205a, 207a/8, 209 and 211 of Great Britain (Queen Victoria) optd with T **1** *by D.L.R.*

1		½d. vermilion (11.88)	3·75	2·50
2		1d. deep purple	26·00	3·75
3		2d. grey-green and carmine	16·00	28·00
4		2½d. purple/*blue* (9.91)	24·00	20·00
5		3d. purple/*yellow*	25·00	22·00
6		4d. green and deep brown	42·00	60·00
7		5d. dull purple and blue (3.93) ...	90·00	£120
		w. Wmk inverted	†	
8		6d. purple/*rose-red*	13·00	17·00
9		9d. dull purple and blue (4.92) ...	90·00	90·00
10		1s. dull green (4.92)	£110	£130
11		5s. rose (4.92)	£500	£600
1/11		*Set of 11*	£850	£1000
1s/11s		(*ex 1d.*) H/S "Specimen" *Set of 10*	£600	

(b) No. 97a of Natal optd with T **2** *at Pietermaritzburg*

12		½d. dull green (with stop) (7.88) ...	55·00	75·00
		a. Opt double	£1000	£1100
		b. Opt inverted	£1200	
		d. Opt omitted (vert pair with normal)..	£6000	
13		½d. dull green (without stop)	24·00	38·00
		a. Opt double	£1400	£1500

1893 (29 Nov*). T **15** *of Natal optd with* T **1** *by D.L.R. (Wmk Crown CA. P 14).*

16			55·00	55·00

*Earliest known date of use. No. 16 was, apparently, originally supplied in 1889 for fiscal purposes.

3

4

Shaved "Z" (R. 4/3 and R. 6/3)

(Typo D.L.R.)

1894 (18 Apr)–96. Wmk Crown CA. P 14.

20	**3**	½d. dull mauve and green	3·25	4·50
		w. Wmk inverted	£140	£150
21		1d. dull mauve and carmine	5·00	2·00
		a. Shaved "Z"	55·00	35·00
22		2½d. dull mauve and ultramarine....	14·00	8·50
23		3d. dull mauve and olive-brown....	8·00	3·00
24	**4**	6d. dull mauve and black	20·00	20·00
25		1s. green	38·00	38·00
26		2s.6d. green and black (2.96)	75·00	85·00
27		4s. green and carmine	£110	£150
28		£1 purple/*red*	£450	£550
29		£5 purple and black/*red*	£4500	£1500
		s. Optd "Specimen"	£425	
20/8		*Set of 9*	£650	£750
20s/8s		Optd "Specimen" *Set of 9*	£400	

Dangerous forgeries exist of the £1 and £5.

FISCAL STAMP USED FOR POSTAGE

1891 (5 May*). *Fiscal stamp of Natal optd with* T **1**. Wmk Crown CA. P 14.

F1		1d. dull mauve	3·50	3·00
		a. Top left triangle detached	£130	£120
		s. Handstamped "Specimen"	60·00	

*Earliest known date of postal use. A proclamation published in the *Natal Government Gazette* on 27 June 1891 authorised the use of this stamp for postal purposes, but it is clear from the wording that such

use had already commenced.

For illustration of "top left triangle detached" variety see above No. 21 of Antigua.

Other values, 1s. to £20 as No. F1 exist apparently with postmarks, but, as these were never authorised for postal use, they are no longer listed.

Zululand was annexed to Natal on 31 December 1897 and its stamps were withdrawn from sale on 30 June 1898.

VIII. BRITISH ARMY FIELD OFFICES DURING SOUTH AFRICAN WAR, 1899–1902

Z 1   Z 2

Stamps of GREAT BRITAIN used by British Army Field Offices in South Africa cancelled as Types Z 1, Z 2 or similar postmarks.

1881. *Stamp of Queen Victoria.*
Z1   1d. lilac (16 *dots*) .... 5·00

1883–84. *Stamps of Queen Victoria.*
Z1a   2s.6d lilac £200
Z2   5s. rose £225
Z2a   10s. ultramarine £475

1887–92. *Stamps of Queen Victoria.*
Z3   ½d. vermilion .... 6·00
Z4   1½d. dull purple and green .... 22·00
Z5   2d. grey-green and carmine .... 15·00
Z6   2½d. purple/*blue* .... 6·00
Z7   3d. purple/*yellow* .... 12·00
Z8   4d. green and brown .... 17·00
Z9   4½d. green and carmine .... 50·00
Z10   5d. dull purple and blue (Die II) .... 15·00
Z11   6d. purple/*rose-red* .... 12·00
Z12   9d. dull purple and blue .... 55·00
Z13   10d. dull purple and carmine .... 50·00
Z14   1s. dull green .... 75·00
Z15   £1 green £800

1900. *Stamps of Queen Victoria.*
Z16   ½d. blue-green .... 6·00
Z17   1s. green and carmine £140

1902. *Stamps of King Edward VII.*
Z18   ½d. blue-green .... 7·00
Z19   1d. scarlet .... 5·00
Z20   1½d. purple and green
Z21   2d. yellowish green and carmine-red ....
Z22   2½d. ultramarine .... 10·00
Z23   3d. purple/*orange-yellow*
Z24   4d. green and grey-brown ....
Z25   5d. dull purple and ultramarine ....
Z26   6d. pale dull purple .... 18·00
Z27   9d. dull purple and ultramarine ....
Z28   10d. dull purple and carmine ....
Z29   1s. dull green and carmine ....

ARMY OFFICIAL STAMPS

1896–1901. *Stamps of Queen Victoria optd "ARMY OFFICIAL".*
ZO1   ½d. vermilion £100
ZO2   ½d. blue-green £100
ZO3   1d. lilac (16 *dots*) .... 85·00
ZO4   6d. purple/*rose-red* ....

IX. UNION OF SOUTH AFRICA

The province continued to use their existing issues until the introduction of Nos. 3/17. From 19 August 1910 the issues of any province were valid for use throughout the Union until they were demonetised on 31 December 1937.

PRICES FOR STAMPS ON COVER TO 1945	
Nos. 1/15	*from* × 4
Nos. 16/17	—
Nos. 18/21	*from* × 6
Nos. 26/32	*from* × 2
No. 33	*from* × 4
Nos. 34/110	*from* × 1
Nos. D1/7	*from* × 4
Nos. D8/33	*from* × 6
Nos. O1/33	*from* × 4

1

(Des H. S. Wilkinson. Recess D.L.R.)
1910 (4 Nov). *Opening of Union Parliament. Inscribed bilingually.* Wmk Multiple Rosettes. P 14.
1   **1**   2½d. deep blue.............................. 3·00   3·00
            s. Handstamped "Specimen".............. £350
2   2½d. blue.................................. 1·75   1·40

The deep blue shade is generally accompanied by a blueing of the paper.

No. 1s. has the overprint in italic capital and lower case letters which measure 12½ mm in length.

2   3   4 Springbok's Head

(Typo D.L.R.)
1913 (1 Sept)–**24**. *Inscribed bilingually.* W **4**.
(a) P 14.
3   **2**   ½d. green .... 1·25   30
            a. Stamp doubly printed........... £10000
            b. Blue-green .... 2·00   20
            c. Yellow-green .... 2·50   80
            d. Printed on the gummed side...... £650
            w. Wmk inverted .... 2·00   70
4   1d. rose-red (*shades*).................. 1·75   10
            a. Carmine-red .... 2·25   10
            b. Scarlet (shades) .... 2·75   75
            c. Printed on the gummed side...... £700
            w. Wmk inverted .... 2·50   60
5   1½d. chestnut (*shades*) (23.8.20)...... 80   10
            a. Tête-bêche (pair) .... 1·75   18·00
            b. Printed on the gummed side...... £750
            c. Wmk sideways .... †   £1500
            w. Wmk inverted 80   10
6   **3**   2d. dull purple .... 1·75   10
            a. Deep purple .... 2·50   10
            b. Printed on the gummed side...... £750
            w. Wmk inverted .... 3·25   1·60
7   2½d. bright blue .... 3·75   1·25
            a. Deep blue .... 5·50   3·00
            w. Wmk inverted .... 70·00   70·00
8   3d. black and orange-red .... 10·00   30
            a. Black and dull orange-red...... 10·00   70
            w. Wmk inverted .... 18·00   8·00
9   3d. ultramarine (*shades*) (4.10.22)... 3·50   1·75
            w. Wmk inverted .... 9·50   5·50
10   4d. orange-yellow and olive-green .. 9·00   55
            a. Orange-yellow and sage-green.. 6·50   55
            w. Wmk inverted .... 8·00   75
11   6d. black and violet................... 5·50   60
            a. Black and bright violet .... 9·50   1·00
            aw. Wmk inverted .... 16·00   9·50
12   1s. orange.............................. 13·00   80
            a. Orange-yellow .... 20·00   1·00
            w. Wmk inverted .... 18·00   1·25
13   1s.3d. violet (*shades*) (1.9.20)....... 13·00   7·00
            w. Wmk inverted £100   £150
14   2s.6d. purple and green .... 55·00   1·50
15   5s. purple and blue .... £110   7·50
            a. Reddish purple and light blue ... £110   8·50
            w. Wmk inverted £4250   £2500
16   10s. deep blue and olive-green......... £180   7·50
            w. Wmk inverted £4000   £1800
17   £1 green and red (7.16)................ £600   £350
            a. Pale olive-green and red (1924) £800   £1200
3/17 *Set of 15* £900   £350
3s/8s, 10s/17s Optd or H/S (1½d. and 1s.3d. in violet, £1 in green) "Specimen" *Set of 14*.................... £1300

(b) Coil stamps. P 14×imperf.
18   **2**   ½d. green .... 6·00   1·00
            w. Wmk inverted £550   £325
19   1d. rose-red (13.2.14)................. 12·00   3·75
            a. Scarlet .... 16·00   8·50
            w. Wmk inverted £550   £325
20   1½d. chestnut (15.11.20)............... 11·00   15·00
            w. Wmk inverted .... †
21   **3**   2d. dull purple (7.10.21).............. 14·00   4·75
18/21 *Set of 4* .... 38·00   22·00

The 6d. exists with "Z" of "ZUID" wholly or partly missing due to wear of plate (*Price wholly missing, £80 un, £38 us*).

5 De Havilland
D.H.9 Biplane

(Eng A. J. Cooper. Litho *Cape Times* Ltd)
1925 (26 Feb). *Air. Inscr bilingually.* P 12.
26   **5**   1d. carmine............................. 3·75   10·00
27   3d. ultramarine .... 7·00   10·00
28   6d. magenta .... 9·00   11·00
29   9d. green .... 23·00   55·00
26/9 *Set of 4* .... 38·00   75·00

Beware of forgeries of all values perforated 11, 11½ or 13.

INSCRIPTIONS. From 1926 until 1951 most issues were inscribed in English and Afrikaans alternately throughout the sheets.

PRICES for Nos. 30/135 are for unused horizontal pairs, used horizontal pairs and used singles (either inscription), *unless otherwise indicated*. Vertical pairs are worth between 25% and 40% of the prices quoted for horizontal pairs.

6 Springbok   7 *Dromedaris* (Van Riebeeck's ship)

8 Orange Tree   9

(Typo Waterlow until 1927, thereafter Govt Printer, Pretoria)
1926 (2 Jan)–**27**. W 9. P 14½×14.

			Un pair	Used pair	Used single
30	**6**	½d. black and green...........	3·00	4·00	10
		a. Missing "1" in "½"....	£2000		
		b. Centre omitted (in pair with normal)..............	£1500		
		cw. Wmk inverted	4·25	4·50	20
		d. Frame printed double..	£2000		
		e. Perf 13½×14 (1927)....	65·00	65·00	4·00
		ea. Tête-bêche (pair)......	£850		
		ew. Wmk inverted	65·00	65·00	4·00
31	**7**	1d. black and carmine.....	2·00	50	10
		a. Imperf (vert pair)*......	£650		
		b. Imperf 3 sides (vert pair)*........................	£650	£700	
		cw. Wmk inverted	5·00	1·75	20
		d. Perf 13½×14 (1927)....	90·00	75·00	4·00
		da. Tête-bêche (pair)......	£950		
		dw. Wmk inverted	90·00	75·00	4·00
		e. Wmk sideways..........	£2000	£2000	
32	**8**	6d. green and orange (1.5.26)...................	38·00	45·00	1·50
		w. Wmk inverted	70·00	75·00	
30/2 *Set of 3*			40·00	45·00	1·50

No. 30a exists in Afrikaans only. Nos. 30e and 31d were only issued in booklets.

No. 30d occurred on the bottom left-hand corner of one sheet and included the bottom four stamps in the first vertical row and the bottom two in the second. As listed No. 30d shows the left-hand stamp with the frame completely double and the right-hand stamp with two-thirds of the frame double.

*Both Nos. 31a and 31b occur in blocks of four with the other vertical pair imperforate at left.

For ½d. with pale grey centre, see No. 126.

For rotogravure printing see Nos. 42, etc.

10 "Hope"

(Recess B.W.)
1926 (2 Jan). T **10**. *Inscribed in English or Afrikaans.* W **9** (upright or inverted in equal quantities).
33   9   4d. grey-blue (English inscr) (*shades*) .... 1·75   1·25
            a. Inscr in Afrikaans.................... 1·75   1·25

In this value the English and Afrikaans inscriptions are on separate sheets.

This stamp is known with private perforations or roulettes.

11 Union Buildings,   12 Groot Schuur
Pretoria

12a A Native Kraal

13 Black and Blue Wildebeest

14 Ox-wagon inspanned

15 Ox-wagon outspanned

16 Cape Town and Table Bay

(Recess B.W.)

1927 (1 Mar)–30. W **9**. P 14.

			Un pair	Used pair	Used single
34	**11**	2d. grey and maroon	11·00	22·00	60
		aw. Wmk inverted	£450	£500	30·00
		b. Perf 14×13½ (2.30).....	28·00	28·00	70
35	**12**	3d. black and red..............	13·00	26·00	60
		a. Perf 14×13½ (1930)....	55·00	60·00	80
35b	**12a**	4d. brown (23.3.28)	26·00	50·00	1·00
		bw. Wmk inverted	£600	£550	35·00
		c. Perf 14×13½ (1930)...	45·00	55·00	1·25
36	**13**	1s. brown and deep blue...	30·00	55·00	1·00
		a. Perf 14×13½ (1930)..	60·00	75·00	2·00
37	**14**	2s.6d. green and brown	£110	£350	17·00
		a. Perf 14×13½ (1930)...	£300	£500	24·00
38	**15**	5s. black and green..........	£225	£650	35·00
		a. Perf 14×13½ (1930)...	£375	£800	40·00
39	**16**	10s. bright blue and brown	£150	£130	10·00
		a. Centre inverted (single stamp).............	£9500		
		b. Perf 14×13½ (1930)...	£180	£170	12·00
34/9 Set of 7			£500	£1100	55·00
34s/9s H/S "Specimen" Set of 7			£900		

17 De Havilland D.H.60 Cirrus Moth

(Typo Govt Ptg Wks, Pretoria)

1929 (16 Aug). *Air. Inscribed bilingually.* No wmk. P 14×13½.

			Un single	Us single
40	**17**	4d. green.............................	5·50	2·50
41		1s. orange...........................	16·00	13·00

PRINTER. All the following issues, except *where stated otherwise*, are printed by rotogravure (the design having either plain lines or a dotted screen) by the Government Printer, Pretoria.

I

II

The two types of the 1d. differ in the spacing of the horizontal lines in the side panels:—Type I close; Type II wide. The Afrikaans had the spacing of the words POSSEEL-INKOMSTE close in Type I and more widely spaced in Type II.

Window flaw (R. 20/4 on all ptgs before 1937) Spear flaw (R. 9/2)

"Monkey" in tree (R. 2/2)

Twisted horn (Cyl 7020 R. 1/5)

1930–45. *T* **6** *to* **8** *and* **11** *to* **14** *redrawn, "SUIDAFRIKA" (in one word) on Afrikaans stamps.* W **9**. P 15×14 (½d., 1d., and 6d.) or 14.

			Un pair	Used pair	Used single
42		½d. black and green (5.30)........	3·50	3·00	10
		a. Two English or two Afrikaans stamps *se-tenant* (vert strip of 4)	40·00		
		b. *Tête-bêche*	£900		
		w. Wmk inverted	3·50	2·75	10
43		1d. black and carmine (I) (4.30)	4·25	3·00	10
		a. *Tête-bêche*	£1100		
		b. Frame omitted (single stamp)..	£450		
		cw. Wmk inverted	4·25	2·75	10
43d		1d. black and carmine (II) (8.32) ..	42·00	3·75	10
		dw. Wmk inverted	35·00	3·75	10
44		2d. slate-grey and lilac (4.31)........	22·00	17·00	30
		a. *Tête-bêche*	£4000		
		b. Centre omitted (single stamp)....	£2250		
		cw. Wmk inverted	17·00	8·50	20
44d		2d. blue and violet (3.38)..............	£325	75·00	2·50
45		3d. black and red (11.31)...............	60·00	80·00	2·25
		aw. Wmk inverted	32·00	60·00	1·25
		b. Window flaw	£120		
45c		3d. blue (10.33)............................	19·00	7·00	20
		cw. Wmk inverted	6·00	6·00	10
		d. Window flaw	42·00		
		e. Centre omitted			
		f. Frame omitted (single stamp)...			
46		4d. brown (19.11.32)....................	£150	£110	6·00
		aw. Wmk inverted	30·00	30·00	40
		b. Spear flaw	£100		
46c		4d. brown (*shades*) (*again redrawn*) (1936)	3·75	2·75	10
		ca. "Monkey" in tree	35·00		
		cw. Wmk inverted	12·00	7·00	10
47		6d. green and orange (*wmk inverted*) (13.5.31)............................	13·00	4·25	10
		w. Wmk upright (8.32)	38·00	14·00	10
48		1s. brown and deep blue (14.9.32).	75·00	42·00	40
		aw. Wmk inverted	35·00	26·00	25
		b. Twisted horn flaw	£180		
49		2s.6d. grn & brn (*shades*) (24.12.32)..	£110	£110	3·25
		aw. Wmk inverted	£130	£140	3·25
49b		2s.6d. blue and brown (1945)	26·00	11·00	20
42/9b Set of 13			£500	£275	6·50

For similar designs with "SUID-AFRIKA" hyphenated, see Nos. 54 etc. and Nos. 114 etc.

Nos. 42/3, 43d/4 exist in coils.

No. 42a comes from the coil printing on the cylinder for which two horizontal rows were incorrectly etched so that two Afrikaans-inscribed stamps were followed by two English. This variety is normally without a coil join, although some examples do occur showing a repair join.

The 1d. (Type I) exists without watermark from a trial printing (*Price £25 un*).

Although it appears to be printed in one colour No. 45c was produced from vignette and frame cylinders in the same way as the bicoloured version. The clouds in the background, which are present on No. 45e, were printed from the frame cylinder.

Nos. 45b, 45d, 46b and 48b all occur on printings with either upright or inverted watermark. The price quoted is for the cheapest version in each instance.

The Rotogravure printings may be distinguished from the preceding Typographed and Recess printed issues by the following tests:—

TYPO	ROTO	

ROTOGRAVURE:

½d. 1d. and 6d. Leg of "R" in "AFR" ends squarely on the bottom line.
2d. The newly built War Memorial appears to the left of the value.
3d. Two fine lines have been removed from the top part of the frame.
4d. No. 46. The scroll is in solid colour.
No. 46c. The scroll is white with a crooked line running through it. (No. 35b. The scroll is shaded by the diagonal lines.)
1s. The shading of the last "A" partly covers the flower beneath.
2s.6d. The top line of the centre frame is thick and leaves only one white line between it and the name.
5s. (Nos. 64/b). The leg of the "R" is straight. Rotogravure impressions are generally coarser.

18 Church of the Vow

19 "The Great Trek" (C. Michell)

20 A Voortrekker

21 Voortrekker Woman

Blurred "SOUTH AFRICA" and red "comet" flaw (Cyls 6917/6922 R. 2/7)

(Des J. Prentice (½d., 2d., 3d.))

1933 (3 May)–**36**. *Voortrekker Memorial Fund.* W **9** (sideways). P 14.

50	**18**	½d.+½d. black and green (16.1.36).....................	3·50	4·50	50
51	**19**	1d.+½d. grey-black and pink	2·75	1·50	25
		a. Blurred "SOUTH AFRICA" and red "comet" flaw	40·00	42·00	
52	**20**	2d.+1d. grey-green and purple.	3·50	4·00	55
53	**21**	3d.+1½d. grey-green and blue	5·50	5·00	70
50/3 Set of 4			14·00	13·50	1·75

22 Gold Mine

22a Groot Schuur

Dies of 6d.

I

II

III

23 Groot Constantia

"Falling ladder" flaw (R. 5/10)

24

JIPEX
1936
(24a)

"Cleft skull" flaw (R. 14/2)

1933–48. *"SUID-AFRIKA" (hyphenated) on Afrikaans stamps.*
W **9.** P 15×14 (½d., 1d. and 6d.) or 14 (others).

54	**6**	½d. grey and green (*wmk inverted*) (9.35)	4·50	2·00	10
		aw. Wmk upright (1936)	8·50	7·00	10
		b. Coil stamp. Perf 13½×14 (1935)	35·00	55·00	1·00
		bw. Wmk upright	35·00	55·00	1·00
		c. Booklet pane of 6 (with adverts on margins) (*wmk upright*)	25·00		
56	**7**	1d. grey and car (*shades*) (19.4.34)	1·75	1·75	10
		a. Imperf (pair) (*wmk inverted*)	£150		
		b. Frame omitted (*single stamp*)	£250		
		cw. Wmk inverted	1·75	1·75	10
		d. Coil stamp. Perf 13½×14 (1935)	38·00	60·00	1·40
		dw. Wmk inverted	38·00	60·00	1·40
		e. Booklet pane of 6 (with adverts on margins) (1935)	17·00		
		f. Booklet pane of 6 (with blank margins) (1937)	18·00		
		h. Booklet pane of 6 (with postal slogans on margins) (1948)	4·00		
		i. Grey & brt rose-carm (7.48)	70	2·00	10
57	**22**	1½d. green and brt gold (12.11.36)	3·25	2·25	10
		a. Shading omitted from mine dump (in pair with normal)	£180	£140	
		bw. Wmk inverted	1·50	1·75	10
		c. Blue-grn & dull gold (8.40)	6·50	3·00	10
58	**11**	2d. blue and violet (11.38)	75·00	35·00	75
58a		2d. grey and dull purple (5.41)	50·00	80·00	1·25
59	**22a**	3d. ultramarine (2.40)	11·00	3·00	10
61	**8**	6d. green & vermilion (I) (10.37)	70·00	29·00	70
		a. "Falling ladder" flaw	£200	£225	
61b		6d. green & vermilion (II) (6.38)	40·00	1·00	10
61c		6d. grn & red-orge (III) (11.46)	20·00	75	10
62	**13**	1s. brown & chalky blue (2.39)	50·00	12·00	10
		a. Frame omitted (*single stamp*)	£3250		
64	**15**	5s. black and green (10.33)	55·00	70·00	1·75
		aw. Wmk inverted	£120	£130	3·00
		b. Black and blue-green (9.44)	38·00	15·00	35
64c	**23**	10s. blue and sepia (*shades*) / (8.39)	65·00	14·00	70
		ca. Blue and charcoal (1944)	42·00	5·50	30
	54/9, 61c/64ca	Set of 10	£250	£140	2·50

The ½d. and 1d. coil stamps may be found in blocks emanating from the residue of the large rolls which were cut into sheets and distributed to Post Offices.

Nos. 54 and 56 also exist in coils.

1d. Is printed from Type II. Frames of different sizes exist due to reductions made from time to time for the purpose of providing more space for the perforations.

3d. In No. 59 the frame is unscreened and composed of solid lines. Centre is diagonally screened. Scrolls above "3d." are clear lined, light in the middle and dark at sides.

6d. Die I. Green background lines faint. "SUID-AFRIKA" 16¼ mm long.

Die II. Green background lines heavy. "SUID-AFRIKA" 17 mm long. "S" near end of tablet. Scroll open.

Die III. Scroll closed up and design smaller (18×22 mm).

Single specimens of the 1933–48 issue inscribed in English may be distinguished from those of 1930–45 as follows:

½d. and 1d. Centres in grey instead of varying intensities of black.

2d. The letters of "SOUTH AFRICA" are narrower and thinner.

3d. The trees are taller and the sky is without lines.

6d. The frame is vermilion.

1s. The frame is chalky blue.

For similar designs, but printed in screened rotogravure, see Nos. 114 to 122a.

BOOKLET PANES. Booklets issued in 1935 contained ½d. and 1d. stamps in panes with advertisements in the top and bottom margins and no margin at right (Nos. 54b and 56d). These were replaced in 1937 by editions showing blank margins on all four sides (Nos. 56e and 75ba). Following a period when the booklet panes were without margins a further 3s. booklet was issued in 1948 which had four margins on the panes and postal slogans at top and bottom (Nos. 56h, 87b and 114a).

(Des J. Booysen)

1935 (1 May). *Silver Jubilee. Inscr bilingually.* W **9.** P 15×14.

65	**24**	½d. black and blue-green	2·50	12·00	10
		a. "Cleft skull" flaw	7·50		
66		1d. black and carmine	2·50	6·00	10
		a. "Cleft skull" flaw	7·50		
67		3d. blue	14·00	55·00	2·25
		a. "Cleft skull" flaw	45·00		
68		6d. green and orange	27·00	75·00	3·25
		a. "Cleft skull" flaw	70·00		
65/8		Set of 4	42·00	£130	5·00

In stamps with English at top the ½d., 3d. and 6d. have "SILWER JUBILEUM" to left of portrait, and "POSTAGE REVENUE" or "POSTAGE" (3d. and 6d.) in left value tablet. In the 1d., "SILVER JUBILEE" is to the left of portrait. In alternate stamps the positions of English and Afrikaans inscriptions are reversed.

1936 (2 Nov). *Johannesburg International Philatelic Exhibition.* Optd with T **24a**. W **9** (inverted).

		Un sheet	Us sheet
MS69	**6** ½d. grey and green (No. 54)	3·50	10·00
MS70	**7** 1d. grey and carmine (No. 56)	2·75	7·00

Issued each in miniature sheet of six stamps with marginal advertisements. Ten different arrangements of advertisements exist on the ½d. sheets, 21 different on the 1d.

25

"Mouse" flaw (R. 4/1)

(Des J. Prentice)

1937 (12 May). *Coronation.* W **9** (sideways*). P 14.

			Un pair	Used pair	Used single
71	**25**	½d. grey-black and blue-green	80	1·25	10
		w. Wmk horns pointing to left	80	1·25	10
72		1d. grey-black and carmine	80	1·00	10
		w. Wmk horns pointing to left	80	1·00	10
73		1½d. orange and greenish blue	80	80	10
		a. "Mouse" flaw	7·00		
		w. Wmk horns pointing to left	80	80	10
74		3d. ultramarine	1·50	3·00	10
		w. Wmk horns pointing to left	1·50	3·00	10
75		1s. red-brown and turquoise-blue	2·25	5·00	15
		a. Hyphen on Afrikaans stamp omitted (R. 2/13)	55·00		
		bw. Wmk horns pointing to left	2·25	5·00	15
71/5		Set of 5	5·50	10·00	40

*The normal sideways watermark shows the horns of the springbok pointing to the right, *as seen from the back of the stamp.*

No. 75a shows the hyphen completely omitted and the top of the "K" damaged. A less distinct flaw, on which part of the hyphen is still visible and with no damage to the "K", occurs on R. 4/17.

SOUTH AFRICA

25a

"Tick" flaw on ear and spot on nose (multipositive flaw (occurring in 1947) (R. 3/4 or 3/1 on some ptgs of No. 114)

1937–40. W **9.** P 15×14.

75c	**25a**	½d. grey and green	9·50	1·75	10
		ca. Booklet pane of 6 (with blank margins) (1937)	50·00		
		cd. Grey and blue green (1940)	7·00	1·00	10
		ce. "Tick" flaw and spot on nose	55·00		

The lines of shading in T **25a** are all horizontal and thicker than in T **6**. In Nos. 75c and 75cd the design is composed of solid lines. For stamps with designs composed of dotted lines, see No. 114. Later printings of No. 75cd have a smaller design.

26 Voortrekker Ploughing   **27** Wagon crossing Drakensberg

28 Signing of Dingaan–Retief Treaty   **29** Voortrekker Monument

(Des W. Coetzer and J. Prentice)

1938 (14 Dec). *Voortrekker Centenary Memorial Fund.* W **9.** P 14 (Nos. 76/7) or 15×14 (others).

76	**26**	½d.+½d. blue and green	12·00	4·50	30
77	**27**	1d.+1d. blue and carmine	14·00	5·50	40
78	**28**	1½d.+1½d. chocolate & blue-grn	19·00	9·00	80
79	**29**	3d.+3d. bright blue	20·00	9·00	1·00
76/9		Set of 4	60·00	25·00	2·25

30 Wagon Wheel   **31** Voortrekker Family

Three bolts in wheel rim (R. 15/5)

(Des W. Coetzer and J. Prentice)

1938 (14 Dec). *Voortrekker Commemoration.* W **9.** P 15×14.

80	**30**	1d. blue and carmine	6·50	3·50	30
		a. Three bolts in wheel rim	35·00	26·00	
81	**31**	1½d. greenish blue and brown	8·50	3·50	30

32 Old Vicarage, Paarl, now a museum   **33** Symbol of the Reformation

34 Huguenot Dwelling, Drakenstein Mountain Valley

(Des J. Prentice)

1939 (17 July). *250th Anniv of Huguenot Landing in South Africa and Huguenot Commemoration Fund.* W **9**. P 14 (Nos. 82/3) or 15×14 (No. 84).

82	32	½d.+½d. brown and green	4·75	6·50	30
83	33	1d.+1d. green and carmine.......	11·00	7·00	30
84	34	1½d.+1½d. blue-green and purple.	26·00	14·00	1·00
82/4		*Set of 3*	38·00	25·00	1·40

34a Gold Mine

1941 (Aug)–**48**. W **9** (sideways). P 14×15.

87	34a	1½d. blue-grn and yellow-buff (*shades*)	2·25	1·25	10
		a. Yellow-buff (centre) omitted	£2500	£1600	
		b. Booklet pane of 6 (with postal slogans on margins) (1948)..........	8·00		

35 Infantry   **36** Nurse and Ambulance   **37** Airman

38 Sailor, Destroyer and Lifebelts   **39** Women's Auxiliary Services

40 Artillery   **41** Electric Welding

42 Tank Corps   **42a** Signaller

"Stain" on uniform (R. 14/11)

"Cigarette" flaw (R. 18/2)

1941–46. *War Effort.* W **9** (sideways on 2d., 4d., 6d.). P 14 (2d., 4d., 6d.) or 15×14 (others).

(a) Inscr alternately.

88	35	½d. green (19.11.41)..........	1·50	2·75	10
		a. Blue-green (7.42)........	3·75	3·00	10
89	36	1d. carmine (3.10.41)........	2·00	2·75	10
		a. "Stain" on uniform flaw....................	25·00		
90	37	1½d. myrtle-green (12.1.42)	1·50	2·25	10
91	39	3d. blue (1.8.41)	23·00	35·00	70
		a. "Cigarette" flaw	85·00		
92	40	4d. orange-brown (20.8.41)................	22·00	22·00	15
		a. Red-brown (6.42).......	35·00	32·00	1·25
93	41	6d. red-orange (3.9.41)	12·00	14·00	15
94	42a	1s.3d. olive-brown (2.1.43)...	13·00	9·50	20
		a. Blackish brown (5.46).	4·00	8·00	20

(b) Inscr bilingually.

			Un single	Us single
95	38	2d. violet (15.9.41).........................	1·00	75
96	42	1s. brown (27.10.41)	3·75	1·00
88/96		*Set of 7 pairs and 2 singles*	65·00	80·00

43 Infantry   **44** Nurse   **45** Airman   **46** Sailor

47 Women's Auxiliary Services   **48** Electric Welding   **49** Heavy Gun in Concrete Turret

50 Tank Corps

Unit (*pair*)

Unit (*triplet*)

Ear Flap flaw (Cyl 43 R. 13/3)

Apostrophe flaw (Cyl 6931 R. 19/1) (later corrected)   Line on Cap (Cyl 39 R. 12/11)

"Bursting Shell" (Cyl 46 R. 11/20)   Smoking "L" (Cyl 46 R. 8/2)

1942–44. *War Effort. Reduced sizes.* In pairs perf 14 (P) or strips of three, perf 15×14 (T), subdivided by roulette 6½. W **9** (sideways* on 3d., 4d. and 1s.).

(a) Inscr alternately.

			Un unit	Un unit	Us single
97	43	½d. blue-green (T) (10.42)	2·00	1·50	10
		a. Green (3.43)...........	3·00	2·00	10
		b. Greenish blue (7.44)...	2·00	1·75	10
		c. Roulette omitted..........	£800	£550	
98	44	1d. carmine-red (T) (5.1.43)	1·50	1·50	10
		a. Bright carmine (3.44) .	1·00	1·25	10
		b. Both roulettes omitted.	£600	£600	
		ba. Left-hand roulette omitted	£800		
99	45	1½d. red-brown (P) (9.42)...	65	2·25	10
		a. Roulette 13 (8.42)......	1·50	4·25	15
		b. Roulette omitted..........	£275	£300	
		c. Ear flap flaw.............	15·00		
100	46	2d. violet (P) (2.43).........	90	2·00	10
		a. Reddish violet (6.43)...	1·50	1·00	10
		b. Roulette omitted..........	£700	£550	
		c. Apostrophe flaw..........	50·00		
		d. Line on cap	50·00		
101	47	3d. blue (T) (10.42)..........	7·00	18·00	10
102	48	6d. red-orange (P) (10.42) ..	2·00	2·00	10

(b) Inscr bilingually.

103	49	4d. slate-green (T) (10.42) ..	18·00	11·00	10
104	50	1s. brown (P) (11.42)........	15·00	4·00	10
		a. "Bursting shell"	70·00		
		b. Smoking "L"...............	70·00		
97/104		*Set of 8*	40·00	38·00	65

*The sideways watermark shows springbok horns pointing to left on the 3d. and 1s., and to right on the 4d., *all as seen from the back of the stamp.*

52   **53**

1943. *Coil stamps. Redrawn.* In single colours with plain background. W **9**. P 15×14.

			Un pair	Used pair	Used single
105	52	½d. blue-green (18.2.43)....	2·50	4·50	20
106	53	1d. carmine (9.43)............	3·25	3·75	15

Quoted prices are for *vertical* pairs.

54 Union Buildings, Pretoria

1945–47. *Redrawn.* W **9**. P 14.

107	54	2d. slate and deep reddish violet (3.45)................	13·00	2·50	10
		a. Slate and deep lilac (10.46)......................	13·00	5·00	10
		b. Slate and bright violet (1947).........................	3·25	9·50	15

In Nos. 107 to 107b the Union Buildings are shown at a different angle from Nos. 58 and 58a. Only the centre is screened i.e., composed of very small square dots of colour arranged in straight diagonal lines. For whole design screened and colours changed, see No. 116. No. 107a/b also show "2" of "2d." clear of white circle at top.

55 "Victory"   **56** "Peace"

57 "Hope"

1945 (3 Dec). *Victory.* W **9**. P 14.
108	55	1d. brown and carmine	20	1·25	10
109	56	2d. slate-blue and violet....	20	1·25	10
110	57	3d. deep blue and blue......	20	1·50	10
108/10 *Set of 3*			55	3·50	25

58 King George VI

59 King George VI and Queen Elizabeth

60 Queen Elizabeth II as Princess, and Princess Margaret

"Bird" on "2" (Cyl 6912 R. 10/6)

"Black-eyed Princess" (R. 19/2)

(Des J. Prentice)

1947 (17 Feb). *Royal Visit.* W **9**. P 15×14.
111	58	1d. black and carmine.......	10	35	10
112	59	2d. violet	15	60	10
		a. "Bird" on "2" flaw......	3·75	6·00	
113	60	3d. blue	15	60	10
		a. "Black-eyed Princess"	5·00	8·50	
111/13 *Set of 3*			35	1·40	20

"Flying saucer" flaw (Cyl 17 R. 17/2)

I

II 5s.

1947–54. "SUID-AFRIKA" *hyphenated on Afrikaans stamps. Printed from new cylinders with design in screened rotogravure.* W **9**. P 15×14 (½d., 1d. and 6d.) or 14 (others).
114	25a	½d. grey and green (frame only screened) (1947).	2·00	3·50	10
		a. Booklet pane of 6 (with postal slogans on margins) (1948)..........	3·50		
		b. "Tick" flaw and spot on nose	38·00		
		c. Entire design screened (2.49)	2·00	3·50	10
		ca. Booklet pane of 6 (with margin at right) (1951)	3·75		
115	7	1d. grey and carmine (1.9.50)...........................	2·25	3·75	10
		a. Booklet pane of 6 (with margin at right) (1951)	4·25		
116	54	2d. slate-blue and purple (3.50)...........................	3·00	9·00	10
117	22a	3d. dull blue (4.49).............	3·00	5·50	10
117a		3d. blue (3.51)..................	3·50	4·50	10
		ab. "Flying saucer" flaw...	60·00	65·00	
118	12a	4d. brown (22.8.52)	4·00	9·00	10

119	8	6d. grn & red-orge (III) (1.50)...........................	3·75	1·50	10
		a. Grn & brn-orge (III) (1951)	3·25	70	10
120	13	1s. brown and chalky blue (1.50)...........................	10·00	9·00	10
		a. Blackish brown and ultram (4.52)..............	18·00	13·00	15
121	14	2s.6d. green and brown (8.49)...........................	10·00	29·00	1·00
122	15	5s. blk & pale bl-grn (I) (9.49)...........................	45·00	65·00	2·00
122a		5s. blk & dp yell-grn (II) (1.54)...........................	50·00	85·00	4·00
114/22 *Set of 9*			75·00	£120	3·00

In screened rotogravure the design is composed of very small squares of colour arranged in straight diagonal lines.

½d. Size 17¾×21¾ mm. Early printings have only the frame screened.

1d. Size 18×22 mm. For smaller, redrawn design, see No. 135.

2d. For earlier issue with centre only screened, and in different colours, see Nos. 107/a.

3d. No. 117. Whole stamp screened with irregular grain. Scrolls above "3d." solid and toneless. Printed from two cylinders.

No. 117a. Whole stamp diagonally screened. Printed from one cylinder. Clouds more pronounced. Late printings were often in deep shades.

4d. Two groups of white leaves below name tablet and a clear white line down left and right sides of stamp.

61 Gold Mine

62 King George VI and Queen Elizabeth

1948 (1 Apr). In unit of four, perf 14, sub-divided by roulette 6½. W **9** (sideways).
			Un unit of 4	Us unit	Used single
124	61	1½d. blue-green and yellow-buff...........................	3·00	4·50	10

(Des J. Booysen and J. Prentice)

1948 (26 Apr). *Silver Wedding.* W **9**. P 14.
			Un pair	Used pair	Used single
125	62	3d. blue and silver............	50	1·25	10

(Typo Government Printer, Pretoria)

1948 (July). W **9**. P 14½×14.
126	6	½d. pale grey and blue-green...........................	1·50	9·50	75

This was an economy printing made from the old plates of the 1926 issue for the purpose of using up a stock of cut paper. For the original printing in black and green, see No. 30.

63 *Wanderer* (emigrant ship) entering Durban

Extended rigging on mainmast (R. 14/2)

"Pennant" flaw (R. 17/5)

(Des J. Prentice)

1949 (2 May). *Centenary of Arrival of British Settlers in Natal.* W **9**. P 15×14.
127	63	1½d. claret...........................	80	80	10
		a. Extended rigging.........	7·50	7·50	
		b. "Pennant" flaw............	7·50	7·50	

SOUTH AFRICA

64 Hermes

65 Wagons approaching Bingham's Berg

Serif on "C" (R. 1/1)

"Lake" in East Africa (R. 2/19)

(Des J. Booysen and J. Prentice)

1949 (1 Oct). *75th Anniv of Universal Postal Union. As T **64** inscr* "UNIVERSAL POSTAL UNION" *and* "WERELDPOSUNIE" *alternately.* W **9** (sideways). P 14×15.
128	64	½d. blue-green	50	1·00	10
129		1½d. brown-red..................	50	1·00	10
130		3d. bright blue	60	1·00	10
		a. Serif on "C"	35·00		
		b. "Lake" in East Africa .	35·00		
128/30 *Set of 3*			1·40	2·75	25

(Des W. Coetzer and J. Prentice)

1949 (1 Dec). *Inauguration of Voortrekker Monument, Pretoria. T **65** and similar horiz designs.* W **9**. P 15×14.
			Un single	Us single
131		1d. magenta	10	10
132		1½d. blue-green	10	10
133		3d. blue...	15	15
131/3 *Set of 3*			30	30

Designs:—1½d. Voortrekker Monument, Pretoria; 3d. Bible, candle and Voortrekkers.

68 Union Buildings, Pretoria

1950 (Apr)–51. W **9** (sideways). P 14×15.
			Un pair	Used pair	Used single
134	68	2d. blue and violet	40	75	10
		a. Booklet pane of 6 (with margin at right) (1951)	4·00		

1951 (22 Feb). *As No. 115, but redrawn with the horizon clearly defined. Size reduced to 17¼×21¼ mm.*
135	7	1d. grey and carmine	1·40	2·50	10

STAMP BOOKLETS

1913. *Black on red cover. With* "UNION OF SOUTH AFRICA" *at top and* "UNIE VAN ZUID AFRIKA" *at foot. Stapled.*
SB1	2s.6d. booklet containing twelve ½d. and twenty-four 1d. (Nos. 3/4) in blocks of 6 .... £5500

1913–20. *Black on red cover with* "UNION OF SOUTH AFRICA" *and* "UNIE VAN ZUID AFRIKA" *both at top. Stapled.*
SB2	2s.6d. booklet containing twelve ½d. and twenty-four 1d. (Nos. 3/4) in blocks of 6 .... £5500
	a. Black on pink cover (1920)..................... £5500

1921. *Black on salmon-pink cover with* "UNION OF SOUTH AFRICA" *and* "UNIE VAN ZUID AFRIKA" *either side of arms and telegraph rates beneath. Stapled.*
SB3	3s. booklet containing twelve ½d., 1d. and 1½d. (Nos. 3/5) in blocks of 6 .... £475

1922. *Black on salmon-pink cover as No. SB3 surch. Stapled.*
SB4	3s.6d. on 3s. booklet containing twelve ½d., 1d. and 2d. (Nos. 3/4, 6) in blocks of 6 .... £1000

1926. *Black on salmon-pink cover as No. SB3. Stitched.*
SB5	2s.6d. booklet containing twelve ½d. and twenty-four 1d. (Nos. 30/1)... £2000

1927. *Black on salmon-pink cover as No. SB3, but inscr* "Union of South Africa" *and* "Unie van Suidafrika". *Stitched.*
SB6	2s.6d. booklet containing twelve ½d. and twenty-four 1d. (Nos. 30e, 31d)..................................... £4500

1930. *Black on pink cover as No. SB6, but with advertisement at foot instead of telegraph rates. Stitched.*
SB7   2s.6d. booklet containing twelve ½d. and twenty-four 1d. (Nos. 42/3) in blocks of 6 .... £1800

1931. *Black on pink cover. Smaller inscr and advertisement on front cover. Stitched.*
SB8   3s. booklet containing twelve 1d. (No. 43) in blocks of 6 and twelve 2d. (No. 44) in blocks of 4 .... £1900

1935. *Black on lemon cover. Advertisement on front cover. Stitched.*
SB9   2s.6d. booklet containing two panes of six ½d. (No. 54c) and four panes of six 1d. (No. 56e), all with adverts on margins £250

1937. *Black on lemon cover. Advertisement on front cover. Stitched.*
SB10   2s.6d. booklet containing two panes of six ½d. (No. 75ba) and four panes of six 1d. (No. 56f), all with blank margins £550

1937. *Machine vended booklets. Red cover. Stitched.*
SB11   6d. booklet containing four ½d. and 1d. (Nos. 75c, 56) in pairs .... 7·00

1938. *Machine vended booklets. Blue cover. Stitched.*
SB12   3d. booklet containing ½d. and 1d. (Nos. 75c, 56), each in pair .... 40·00

1938. *Black on buff cover. Union arms at top left with advertisement at foot.*
SB13   2s.6d. booklet containing twelve ½d. and twenty-four 1d. (Nos. 75c, 56) in blocks of 6 .... £500

1939. *Black on buff cover. Union arms centred at top with advertisement at foot.*
SB14   2s.6d. booklet containing twelve ½d. and twenty-four 1d. (Nos. 75c, 56) in blocks of 6 .... £425

1939–40. *Green on buff cover. Union arms centred at top with large advertisement at bottom left. Stitched.*
SB15   2s.6d. booklet containing twelve ½d. and twenty-four 1d. (Nos. 75c, 56) in blocks of 6 .... £2250
    a. Blue on buff cover (1940) .... 90·00

1941. *Blue on buff cover as No. SB15. Stitched.*
SB17   2s.6d. booklet containing twelve ½d. and 1d. (Nos. 75c, 56) in blocks of 6 and 1½d. (No. 57) in block of 4 .... £150

1948. *Black on buff cover. With advertisement. Stitched.*
SB18   3s. booklet containing two panes of six ½d., 1d. and 1½d. (Nos. 114a, 56h, 87b), all with postal slogans on margins, and pane of air mail labels .... 30·00

1951. *Black on buff cover. Stitched.*
SB19   3s.6d. booklet containing two panes of six ½d., 1d. and 2d. (Nos. 114ca, 115a, 134a), each with margins at right .... 13·00

POSTAGE DUE STAMPS

D 1

UNION OF SOUTH AFRICA   UNION OF SOUTH AFRICA
(A)   (B)

(Typo D.L.R.)

1914–22. *Inscribed bilingually. Lettering as A. W 4. P 14.*

			Un single	Used single
D1	D 1	½d. black and green (19.3.15)	2·25	3·75
D2		1d. black and scarlet (19.3.15)	2·25	15
		a. Black ptd double	£1500	
		w. Wmk inverted	80·00	
D3		2d. black and reddish violet (12.12.14)	6·50	50
		a. Black and bright violet (1922)	7·00	60
		w. Wmk inverted	£130	
D4		3d. black and bright blue (2.2.15)	2·25	60
		w. Wmk inverted	40·00	
D5		5d. black and sepia (19.3.15)	4·00	27·00
D6		6d. black and slate (19.3.15)	7·00	30·00
D7		1s. red and black (19.3.15)	60·00	£150
D1/7 Set of 7			75·00	£190

There are interesting minor varieties in some of the above values, e.g. ½d. to 3d., thick downstroke to "d"; 1d., short serif to "1"; raised "d"; 2d., forward point of "2" blunted; 3d., raised "d"; very thick "d".

(Litho Govt Printer, Pretoria)

1922. *Lettering as A. No wmk. Rouletted.*

D8	D 1	½d. black and bright green (6.6.22)	1·50	15·00
D9		1d. black and rose-red (3.10.22)	1·00	1·00
D10		1½d. black and yellow-brown (3.6.22)	1·25	1·75
D8/10 Set of 3			3·25	16·00

(Litho Govt Printer, Pretoria)

1922–26. *Type D 1 redrawn. Lettering as B. P 14.*

D11	D 1	½d. black and green (1.8.22)	80	1·75
D12		1d. black and rose (16.5.23)	90	15
D13		1½d. black and yellow-brown (12.1.24)	1·00	1·25

D14		2d. black and pale violet (16.5.23)	1·00	70
		a. Imperf (pair)	£250	£350
		b. Black and deep violet	11·00	2·00
D15		3d. black and blue (3.7.26)	8·00	22·00
D16		6d. black and slate (9.23)	12·00	2·50
D11/16 Set of 6			21·00	25·00

The locally printed stamps, perf 14, differ both in border design and in figures of value from the rouletted stamps. All values except the 3d. and 6d. are known with closed "G" in "POSTAGE" usually referred to as the "POSTADE" variety. This was corrected in later printings.

D 2   D 3   D 4

$\overline{2}$

Blunt "2" (R. 3/6, 8/6)

(Typo Pretoria)

1927–28. *Inscribed bilingually. No wmk. P 13½×14.*

D17	D 2	½d. black and green	1·00	3·25
		a. Blunt "2"	11·00	
D18		1d. black and carmine	1·25	30
D19		2d. black and mauve	1·25	30
		a. Black and purple	18·00	80
D20		3d. black and blue	8·50	24·00
D21		6d. black and slate	21·00	3·50
D17/21 Set of 5			30·00	28·00

1932–42. *Type D 2 redrawn. W 9. P 15×14.*

(a) Frame roto, value typo.

D22		½d. black and blue-green (1934)	2·75	1·75
		w. Wmk inverted	2·25	1·75
D23		2d. black and deep purple (10.4.33)	11·00	2·50
		w. Wmk inverted	11·00	2·50

(b) Whole stamp roto.

D25		1d. black & carmine (wmk inverted) (3.34)	2·25	10
D26		2d. black and deep purple (1940)	27·00	10
		a. Thick (double) "2d." (R. 5/6, R. 18/2)	£300	27·00
		w. Wmk inverted	25·00	10
D27		3d. black and Prussian blue (3.8.32)	25·00	14·00
D28		3d. dp blue & blue (wmk inverted) (1935)	8·00	30
		a. Indigo and milky blue (wmk inverted) (1942)	75·00	3·25
		w. Wmk upright	50·00	2·50
D29		6d. green and brown-ochre (wmk inverted) (7.6.33)	25·00	5·00
		a. Green & brt orge (wmk inverted) (1938)	14·00	3·00
D22/9a Set of 7			80·00	19·00

In No. D26 the value is screened, whereas in No. D23 the black of the value is solid.

1943–44. *Inscr bilingually. Roto. W 9. In units of three, perf 15×14 subdivided by roulette 6½.*

			Un unit	Us unit	Us single
D30	D 3	½d. blue-green (1944)	12·00	45·00	30
D31		1d. carmine (1949)	10·00	5·50	10
D32		2d. dull violet	6·50	11·00	15
		a. Bright violet	16·00	48·00	65
D33		3d. indigo (1943)	50·00	80·00	1·25
D30/3 Set of 4			70·00	£130	1·90

3·D·

Split "D" (R. 7/5 on every fourth sheet)

1948–49. *New figure of value and capital "D". Whole stamp roto. W 9. P 15×14.*

			Un single	Used single
D34	D 4	½d. black and blue-green	6·00	13·00
D35		1d. black and carmine	15·00	5·50
D36		2d. black and violet (1949)	15·00	8·00
		a. Thick (double) "2D." (R. 15/5-6, R. 16/5-6)	70·00	35·00
D37		3d. deep blue and blue	15·00	17·00
		a. Split "D"	£225	£250
D38		6d. green and bright orange (1949)	25·00	8·00
D34/8 Set of 5			70·00	45·00

1950–58. *As Type D 4, but "SUID-AFRIKA" hyphenated. Whole stamp roto. W 9. P 15×14.*

D39		1d. black and carmine (5.50)	70	30
D40		2d. black and violet (4.51)	50	20
		a. Thick (double) "2D." (R. 15/5-6, R. 16/5-6)	8·00	8·00
		b. Black and reddish violet (12.52)	1·00	40
		ba. Thick (double) "2D."	10·00	9·00
		bb. Black (value) omitted	£2500	

D41		3d. deep blue and blue (5.50)	4·50	2·50
		a. Split "D"	£110	60·00
D42		4d. deep myrtle-green and emerald (2.58)	12·00	15·00
D43		6d. green and bright orange (3.50)	7·00	9·00
D44		1s. black-brown and purple-brown (2.58)	12·00	15·00
D39/44 Set of 6			32·00	38·00

No. D40bb occurs in horizontal pair with a normal.

OFFICIAL STAMPS

OFFICIAL.   OFFISIEEL.   OFFISIEEL   OFFICIAL

(O 1)   (O 2)

(Approximate measurements of the space between the two lines of overprint are quoted in millimetres, either in the set headings or after individual listings)

1926 (1 Dec). *Optd with Type O 1 (reading upwards with stops and 12½ mm between lines of opt).*

(a) On 1913 issue (No. 6).

O1	3	2d. purple	21·00	1·75

(b) On 1926 issue (Nos. 30/2).

			Un pair	Us pair	Us single
O2	6	½d. black and green	7·50	16·00	1·50
O3	7	1d. black and carmine	4·00	7·50	50
O4	8	6d. green and orange	£550	75·00	10·00
		w. Wmk inverted	£900	£375	10·00

The overprint occurs on both the London and Pretoria printings of Nos. 30/2. For the lower two values the overprinted London printings are scarcer than the Pretoria, but for the 6d. the ratio is reversed.

1928–30. *Nos. 32 and 34 optd as Type O 1 (reading upwards without stops).*

O5	11	2d. grey & maroon (P 14) (17½ mm)	6·00	22·00	2·00
		a. Lines of opt 19 mm apart (1929)	7·00	17·00	1·50
		ab. On No. 34a (P 14×13½) (1930)	30·00	40·00	5·00
O6	8	6d. green and orange (11½–12 mm)	20·00	40·00	2·75

1929–31. *Optd with Type O 2.*
(a) On 1926 (Typo) issue (Nos. 30/2) (13½–15 mm between lines of opt).

O7	6	½d. black and green	2·50	4·25	35
		a. Stop after "OFFISIEEL" on English inscr stamp (1930)	32·00	40·00	3·25
		b. Ditto, but on Afrikaans inscr stamp (1930)	45·00	50·00	3·25
O8	7	1d. black and carmine	3·00	5·50	45
O9	8	6d. green and orange	8·00	38·00	3·25
		a. Stop after "OFFISIEEL" on English inscr stamp (1930)	65·00	£130	10·00
		b. Ditto, but on Afrikaans inscr stamp (1930)	75·00	£140	12·00

(b) On 1927 (Recess) issue (Nos. 36a/7) (17½–19 mm between lines of opt).

O10	13	1s. brown and deep blue (1931)	38·00	90·00	9·50
		a. Stop after "OFFICIAL" on Afrikaans inscr stamp (R. 10/1, 10/7)	£110	£225	
		b. Lines of opt 22 mm apart	£300	£450	
O11	14	2s.6d. green and brown (1931)	60·00	£150	19·00
		a. Stop after "OFFICIAL" on Afrikaans inscr stamp (R. 10/1)	£275	£475	
O7/11 Set of 5			£100	£250	29·00

The "stop" varieties for the ½d., and 6d. occur on R. 5/3, 5/11, 8/12, 15/3, 15/11, 18/12 with English inscriptions and R. 9/10, 9/12, 19/10, 19/12 with Afrikaans on the 1930 overprinting only.

As only the left-hand panes of the 2s.6d. were overprinted in 1931 the stop variety only occurs once. A further overprinting in 1932 was on both panes, but did not include No. O11a.

1930–47. *Nos. 42/4 and 47/9 ("SUIDAFRIKA" in one word) optd with Type O 2.*

O12	6	½d. black and green (9½–12½ mm) (1931)	2·25	5·00	40
		a. Stop after "OFFISIEEL" on English inscr stamp	35·00	50·00	4·00
		b. Ditto, but on Afrikaans inscr stamp	27·00	45·00	3·50
		w. Wmk inverted (1934)	6·00	10·00	60
O13	7	1d. black & carm (I) (12½ mm)	4·75	5·00	55
		a. Stop after "OFFISIEEL" on English inscr stamp	50·00	60·00	4·00
		b. Ditto, but on Afrikaans inscr stamp	35·00	45·00	3·50
		cw. Wmk inverted (1931)	4·75	5·00	55
		d. On Type II (No. 43d) (12½–13½ mm) (1933)	13·00	9·00	90
		da. Opt double	£275	£350	

No.	Type	Description	Un	Un	Used
O14	11	2d. slate-grey and lilac (20½–22½ mm) (1931)	7·50	11·00	1·50
		w. Wmk inverted (1934)..	55·00	£100	8·00
O15		2d. blue and violet (20½–22½ mm) (1938)	£130	£100	9·00
O16	8	6d. green & orange (12½–13½ mm) (wmk inverted) (1931)	8·50	8·50	85
		a. Stop after "OFFISIEEL" on English inscr stamp	85·00	90·00	6·50
		b. Ditto, but on Afrikaans inscr stamp	70·00	75·00	5·50
		c. "OFFISIEEL" reading upwards (R. 17/12, 18/12, 19/12, 20/12) (1933)		£550	
		w. Wmk upright (1935)...	55·00	90·00	7·00
O17	13	1s. brown and deep blue (19 mm) (wmk inverted) (1932)	45·00	85·00	8·50
		a. Twisted horn flaw		£275	
		b. Lines of opt 21 mm apart (wmk inverted) (1933)	55·00	90·00	7·50
		ba. Twisted horn flaw		£275	
		bw. Wmk upright (1936)...	65·00	£130	10·00
O18	14	2s.6d. green and brown (17½–18½ mm) (1933)	80·00	£140	15·00
		a. Lines of opt 21 mm apart (1934)	55·00	75·00	8·50
		aw. Wmk inverted (1937)..	£275	£325	
O19		2s.6d. blue and brown (19½–20 mm) (11.47)	42·00	90·00	6·50
		a. Diaeresis over second "E" of "OFFISIEEL" on Afrikaans inscr stamp (R. 6/2)	£900	£1000	
		b. Ditto, but on English inscr stamp (R. 6/3)..	£900	£1000	

The stop varieties for the ½d., 1d. and 6d. occur on R. 9/10, 9/12, 19/10, 19/12 with English inscriptions and R. 5/3, 5/11, 8/12, 15/3, 15/11, 18/12 with Afrikaans on the 1930 and 1931 overprintings only.

OFFICIAL · OFFISIEEL · OFFISIEEL · OFFICIAL

(O 3)   (O 4)

1935–49. Nos. 54, 56/8, 61/2 and 64a/b ("SUID-AFRIKA" hyphenated) optd.

(a) With Type O 2 (reading downwards with "OFFICIAL" at right).

No.	Type	Description	Un	Un	Used
O20	6	½d. grey and green (12½ mm) (wmk inverted) (1936)	12·00	28·00	1·75
		w. Wmk upright (1937)...	7·00	27·00	1·75
O21	7	1d. grey and carmine (11½–13 mm) (wmk inverted)	4·25	4·75	35
		aw. Wmk upright (1937)...	3·50	3·00	20
		b. Grey & bright rose-carmine (No. 56i) (1949)	3·50	4·50	30
O22	22	1½d. grey and bright gold (20 mm) (wmk inverted) (1937)	45·00	30·00	1·75
		aw. Wmk upright (1939)...	28·00	23·00	1·00
		b. Blue-green and dull gold (No. 57c) (1941)	45·00	11·00	1·10
O23	11	2d. blue & violet (20 mm) (1939)	£130	30·00	2·25
O24	8	6d. green and vermilion (I) (11½–13 mm) (1937)..	80·00	45·00	3·75
		a. "Falling ladder" flaw	£425	£275	
		b. Die II (No. 61b) (1938)	13·00	10·00	1·25
		c. Die III Green & red-orange (No. 61c) (11.47)	4·00	8·50	85
O25	13	1s. brown and chalky blue (20 mm) (1939)	80·00	42·00	2·25
		a. Diaeresis over second "E" of "OFFISIEEL" on both English and Afrikaans inscr stamps (1941)	£1800	£1300	
		b. Ditto, but on English inscr stamp only (11.47)	£1300	£900	
O26	15	5s. black and blue-green (20 mm) (6.48)	65·00	£160	13·00
O27	23	10s. blue and blackish brown (No. 64ba) (20 mm) (6.48)	£100	£275	23·00

(b) With Type O 3 (reading downwards with "OFFICIAL" at left and 18–19 mm between lines of opt).

No.	Type	Description	Un	Un	Used
O28	15	5s. black and blue-green (1940)	£110	£140	12·00
O29	23	10s. blue and sepia (1940) .	£450	£500	38·00

(c) With Type O 4 (reading upwards with "OFFICIAL" at right and 18½ mm between lines of opt).

No.	Type	Description	Un	Un	Used
O30	11	2d. grey and dull purple (No. 58a) (1941)	11·00	30·00	2·25

No. O25a first appeared in the 1941 overprinting where the variety occurs on stamps 5 and 6 of an unidentified row. The variety reappears in the November 1947 overprinting where the stamps involved are R. 6/1 and 2. No. O25b occurs on R. 6/3 of the same overprinting.

Horizontal rows of 6 of the 1s. exist with "OFFICIAL" twice on the first stamp and "OFFISIEEL" twice on the last stamp. Such rows are believed to come from two half sheets which were overprinted in 1947, but not placed into normal stock (Price for row of 6, £2250, unused).

OFFICIAL · OFFISIEEL · OFFICIAL · OFFISIEEL

(O 5)   (O 6)

1937–44. No. 75c (redrawn design) optd.

(a) With Type O 2 (reading downwards with "OFFICIAL" at right and 11–12½ mm between lines of opt).

No.	Type	Description	Un	Un	Used
O31	25a	½d. grey and green	20·00	17·00	1·25
		a. Grey and blue-green (No. 75cd) (1944)	2·75	9·50	60

(b) With Type O 5 (reading up and down with "OFFICIAL" at left and diaeresis over the second "E" of "OFFISIEEL". 10 mm between lines of opt).

No.	Type	Description	Un	Un	Used
O32	25a	½d. grey and blue-green (No. 75cd) (1944)	38·00	27·00	2·00

1944–50. Nos. 87 and 134 optd.

(a) With Type O 2 (reading downwards with "OFFICIAL" at right).

No.	Type	Description	Un	Un	Used
O33	34a	1½d. blue-green and yellow-buff (14½ mm)	2·50	10·00	80
		a. With diaeresis over second "E" of "OFFISIEEL"	£500	£250	25·00
		b. Lines of opt 16½ mm apart (6.48)	2·25	12·00	60

(b) With Type O 6 (reading upwards with "OFFICIAL" at left and 16 mm between lines of opt).

No.	Type	Description	Un	Un	Used
O34	34a	1½d. bl-green & yell-buff (1949)	60·00	65·00	4·00
O35	68	2d. blue and violet (1950)	£2500	£3000	£225

Two different formes were used to overprint Type 34a between 1944 and 1946. The first, applied to the left halves of sheets only, had a diaeresis over the second "E" of "OFFISIEEL" on all positions of the setting, except for R. 1/2, 2/2 and 3/2. The second form, from which the majority of the stamps came, was applied twice to overprint complete sheets, had no diaeresis.

Examples of T34a overprinted with Type O2 horizontally exist, but their status is unclear. (Price £600, unused pair).

1947 (Nov)–49. No. 107a optd with Type O 2 (reading downwards with "OFFICIAL" at right and 20 mm between lines of opt).

No.	Type	Description	Un	Un	Used
O36	54	2d. slate and deep lilac	5·50	24·00	1·90
		a. With diaeresis over second "E" of "OFFISIEEL" (R. 1/5-6, 11/5-6)	£450	£650	
		b. Slate and bright violet (No. 107b) (1949)	7·50	16·00	1·60

1949–50. Nos. 114 and 120 optd with Type O 2 (reading downwards with "OFFICIAL" at right).

No.	Type	Description	Un	Un	Used
O37	25a	½d. grey and green (11 mm)	4·00	7·50	70
		a. "Tick" flaw and spot on nose		42·00	
O38	13	1s. brown and chalky blue (17½–18½ mm) (1950)	9·50	28·00	2·50

OFFISIEEL · OFFICIAL

(O 7)

1950 (June)–54. Optd as Type O 7 using stereo blocks measuring either 10 (½d., 1d., 6d.), 14½ (1½d., 2d.) or 19 mm (others) between the lines of opt.

No.	Type	Description	Un	Un	Used
O39	25a	½d. grey and green (No. 114c) (6.51)	70	1·50	15
O41	7	1d. grey and bright rose-carmine (No. 56i)	1·00	6·00	50
O42		1d. grey and car (No. 115) (3.51)	1·00	3·25	20
O43		1d. grey and car (No. 135) (6.52)	1·25	2·00	20
O44	34a	1½d. blue-green and yellow-buff (No. 87) (3.51)	2·00	4·50	30
O45	68	2d. blue and violet (No. 134)	1·00	2·00	20
		a. Opt inverted		£1000	
O46	8	6d. green and red-orge (No. 119)	1·25	4·00	35
		a. Green and brown-orange (No. 119a) (6.51)	1·50	3·50	35
O47	13	1s. brn and chalky bl (No. 120)	5·50	18·00	2·00
		a. Blackish brown and ultram (No. 120a) (2.53)	£170	£190	18·00
O48	14	2s.6d. green & brn (No. 121)	8·50	35·00	3·50
O49	15	5s. black and blue-green (No. 64a) (3.51)	£180	£120	9·00
O50		5s. black and pale blue-green (I) (No. 122) (2.53)	65·00	85·00	6·50
		a. Black & deep yellow-green (II) (No. 122a) (1.54)	75·00	£100	9·00
O51	23	10s. blue and charcoal (No. 64ca)	75·00	£250	22·00

The use of the official stamps ceased in January 1955.

South Australia
see Australia

Southern Nigeria
see Nigeria

Southern Rhodesia

PRICES FOR STAMPS ON COVER TO 1945
Nos. 1/61   *from × 2*

SELF-GOVERNMENT

The southern part of Rhodesia, previously administered by the British South Africa Company, was annexed by the British Government and granted the status of a self-governing colony from 1 October 1923.

The existing stamps of Rhodesia (the "Admiral" design first issued in 1913) remained in use until 31 March 1924 and continued to be valid for postal purposes until 30 April of that year.

1   2 King George V   3 Victoria Falls

(Recess Waterlow)

1924 (1 Apr)–29. P 14.

No.	Type	Description	Un	Used
1	1	½d. blue-green	2·25	10
		a. Imperf between (vert pair).......	£850	£950
		b. Imperf between (vert pair).......	£850	£950
		c. Imperf vert (horiz pair)...........	£950	
2		1d. bright rose	1·75	10
		a. Imperf between (horiz pair)......	£750	£850
		b. Imperf between (vert pair).......	£1300	
		c. Perf 12½ (coil) (1929)	2·75	80·00
3		1½d. bistre-brown	2·25	80
		a. Imperf between (horiz pair)......	£9000	
		b. Imperf between (vert pair).......	£5500	
		c. Printed double, once albino	£325	
4		2d. black and purple-grey	3·00	70
		a. Imperf between (horiz pair)......	£11000	
5		3d. blue..............................	2·50	3·25
6		4d. black and orange-red	2·50	2·75
7		6d. black and mauve	2·00	4·25
		a. Imperf between (horiz pair)......	£35000	
8		8d. purple and pale green	11·00	45·00
		a. Frame double, once albino		
9		10d. blue and rose	12·00	50·00
10		1s. black and light blue	5·00	5·00
11		1s.6d. black and yellow	19·00	32·00
12		2s. black and brown	17·00	17·00
13		2s.6d. blue and sepia	30·00	60·00
14		5s. blue and blue-green	60·00	£150
1/14	*Set of 14*		£150	£325

Prices for "imperf between" varieties are for adjacent stamps from the same pane and not for those separated by wide gutter margins between vertical or horizontal pairs, which come from the junction of two panes.

(T 2 recess by B.W.; T 3 typo by Waterlow)

1931 (1 April)–37. T 2 (line perf 12 unless otherwise stated and 3 (comb perf 16×14). (The 11½ perf is comb.).

No.	Type	Description	Un	Used
15	2	½d. green..........................	85	1·00
		a. Perf 11½ (1933).................	65	20
		b. Perf 14 (1935).................	1·60	30
16		1d. scarlet.......................	1·00	70
		a. Perf 11½ (1933).................	2·00	20
		b. Perf 14 (1935).................	50	20
16c		1½d. chocolate (3.3.33).........	55·00	42·00
		d. Perf 11½ (1.4.32)..........	2·50	80
17	3	2d. black and sepia.............	4·25	1·40
18		3d. deep ultramarine............	10·00	11·00
19	2	4d. black and vermilion........	1·25	1·50
		a. Perf 11½ (1935).................	17·00	5·00
		b. Perf 14 (10.37).................	32·00	50·00
20		6d. black and magenta.........	2·25	3·00
		a. Perf 11½ (1933).................	1·50	1·00
		b. Perf 14 (1936).................	7·00	1·00
21		8d. violet and olive-green......	1·75	3·25
		a. Perf 11½ (1934).................	17·00	32·00
21b		9d. vermilion and olive-green (1.9.34)..........................	6·50	9·00
22		10d. blue and scarlet..........	7·00	2·25
		a. Perf 11½ (1933).................	6·00	13·00
23		1s. black and greenish blue...	2·00	2·50
		a. Perf 11½ (1933).................	£110	60·00
		b. Perf 14 (10.37).................	£200	£140
24		1s.6d. black and orange-yellow	10·00	17·00
		a. Perf 11½ (1936).................	50·00	£110
25		2s. black and brown...........	21·00	6·50
		a. Perf 11½ (1933).................	35·00	32·00
26		2s.6d. blue and drab..........	35·00	35·00
		a. Perf 11½ (1933).................	28·00	32·00
27		5s. blue and blue-green........	48·00	48·00
		a. Printed on gummed side......	£4500	
15/27	*Set of 15*		£130	£120

No. 16c was only issued in booklets.

PRINTERS. All stamps from Types **4** to **29** were recess-printed by Waterlow and Sons, Ltd, London, except where otherwise stated.

4

1932 (1 May). P 12½.

29	**4**	2d. green and chocolate	4·25	1·00
30		3d. deep ultramarine	4·25	1·75
		a. Imperf horiz (vert pair).........	£8000	£10000
		b. Imperf between (vert pair)........	£19000	

5 Victoria Falls

1935 (6 May). *Silver Jubilee.* P 11×12.

31	**5**	1d. olive and rose-carmine...............	3·25	2·25
32		2d. emerald and sepia...................	5·50	6·00
33		3d. violet and deep blue	5·50	10·00
34		6d. black and purple....................	8·00	16·00
31/4 *Set of 4*............................			20·00	30·00

1935–41. *Inscr* "POSTAGE AND REVENUE".

35	**4**	2d. green and chocolate (P 12½).....	3·75	12·00
		a. Perf 14 (1941).....................	2·25	10
35b		3d. deep blue (P 14) (1938).........	4·00	70

6 Victoria Falls and Railway Bridge   **7** King George VI

1937 (12 May). *Coronation.* P 12½.

36	**6**	1d. olive and rose-carmine...............	60	70
37		2d. emerald and sepia	60	1·75
38		3d. violet and blue	3·25	8·50
39		6d. black and purple....................	1·75	3·75
36/9 *Set of 4*			5·50	13·00

1937 (25 Nov). P 14.

40	**7**	½d. green..............................	50	10
41		1d. scarlet............................	50	10
42		1½d. red-brown.........................	1·00	30
43		4d. red-orange........................	1·50	10
44		6d. grey-black........................	1·50	50
45		8d. emerald-green	2·00	2·75
46		9d. pale blue.........................	1·50	1·00
47		10d. purple...........................	2·25	2·75
48		1s. black and blue-green..............	2·25	10
		a. Frame double, one albino.........	£1600	
49		1s.6d. black and orange-yellow........	12·00	2·50
50		2s. black and brown..................	18·00	55
51		2s.6d. ultramarine and purple........	9·50	5·50
52		5s. blue and blue-green	18·00	2·50
40/52 *Set of 13*			65·00	16·00

Nos. 40/1 exist in coils, constructed from normal sheets.

On No. 48a the frame appears blurred and over-inked.

8 British South Africa Co's Arms   **9** Fort Salisbury, 1890

10 Cecil John Rhodes (after S. P. Kendrick)   **15** Lobengula's Kraal and Govt House, Salisbury

---

Recut shirt collar (R. 6/1)

"Cave" flaw (R. 6/6)

(Des Mrs. L. E. Curtis (½d., 1d., 1½d., 3d.), Mrs I. Mount (others))

1940 (3 June). *British South Africa Company's Golden Jubilee.* T **8**/**10**, **15** and similar designs. P 14.

53		½d. slate-violet and green..............	10	65
54		1d. violet-blue and scarlet............	10	10
55		1½d. black and red-brown...............	15	80
		a. Recut shirt collar.................	22·00	35·00
56		2d. green and bright violet...........	30	70
57		3d. black and blue....................	30	1·50
		a. Cave flaw.........................	45·00	
58		4d. green and brown	2·25	2·50
59		6d. chocolate and green	1·00	2·00
60		1s. blue and green...................	1·00	2·00
53/60 *Set of 8*............................			4·50	9·00

Designs: *Horiz* (as **78**)—2d. Fort Victoria; 3d. Rhodes makes peace. *Vert* (as T**10**)—4d. Victoria Falls Bridge; 6d. Statue of Sir Charles Coghlan.

16 Mounted Pioneer   Hat brim retouch (P1 1B R. 1/8)

Line under saddlebag (Pl 1B R. 6/10)

(Roto South African Govt Printer, Pretoria)

1943 (1 Nov). *50th Anniv of Occupation of Matabeleland.* W **9** of South Africa (Mult Springbok) sideways. P 14.

61	**18**	2d. brown and green	20	1·00
		a. Hat brim retouch..................	19·00	
		b. Line under saddlebag..............	19·00	

17 Queen Elizabeth II when Princess and Princess Margaret

1947 (1 Apr). *Royal Visit.* T **17** and similar horiz design. P 14.

62		½d. black and green...................	30	60
63		1d. black and scarlet.................	30	60

Design:—1d. King George VI and Queen Elizabeth.

19 Queen Elizabeth   **20** King George VI   **21** Queen Elizabeth II when Princess

22 Princess Margaret   Damage to right-hand frame (R. 1/10)

1947 (8 May). *Victory.* P 14.

64	**19**	1d. carmine...........................	10	10
65	**20**	2d. slate.............................	10	10
		a. Double print......................	£1300	
		b. Damaged frame....................	45·00	
66	**21**	3d. blue..............................	85	1·00
67	**22**	6d. orange............................	30	1·40
64/7 *Set of 4*............................			1·25	2·40

(Recess B.W.)

1949 (10 Oct). *76th Anniv of U.P.U.* As Nos. 115/16 of *Antigua.*

68	2d. slate-green......................	70	20
69	3d. blue.............................	80	3·50

23 Queen Victoria, Arms and King George VI

1950 (12 Sept). *Diamond Jubilee of Southern Rhodesia.* P 14.

70	**23**	2d. green and brown	50	1·00

STAMP BOOKLETS

1928 (1 Jan). *Black on blue cover. Stitched.*
SB1   2s.6d. booklet containing twelve ½d. and twenty four 1d. (Nos. 1/2) in blocks of 6 .... £4000

1931. *Black on blue cover. Stitched.*
SB2   2s.6d. booklet containing twelve ½d. and twentyfour 1d. (Nos. 15/16) in blocks of 6 .... £5000

1933 (3 Mar). *Black on red cover, size 69×53 mm. Stitched.*
SB3   3s. booklet containing twelve ½d., 1d. and 1½d. (Nos. 15, 16, 16c) in blocks of 6 .... £3000

The 1½d. postage rate was reduced to 1d. eight weeks after No. SB3 was issued. Postal officials were instructed to detach the 1½d. panes and use them for other purposes. The remaining stocks of the booklet were then sold for 1s.6d.

1938 (Oct)–**45.** *Black on yellow cover. Stitched.*
SB4   2s.6d. booklet containing twenty-four ½d. and eighteen 1d. (Nos. 40/1) in blocks of 6 with postage rates on inside front cover................ £250
  a. Label with new rates affixed to inside front cover (1945)................................ £275
  b. Inside front cover blank...................... £275

No. SB4b was issued sometime between 1945 and 1949.

POSTAGE DUE STAMPS

SOUTHERN

RHODESIA

(D **1**)

1951 (1 Oct). *Postage Due stamps of Great Britain optd with* Type D**1**.

D1	D **1**	½d. emerald (No. D27)...................	3·25	16·00
D2		1d. violet-blue (No. D36)	3·00	2·00
D3		2d. agate (No.D29)	2·50	1·75
D4		3d. violet (No. D30)...................	2·75	2·75
D5		4d. blue (No. D38)....................	1·75	3·50
D6		4d. dull grey-green (No. D31)........	£190	£600
D7		1s. deep blue (No. D33)...............	2·50	4·25
D1/5, 7 *Set of 6*........................			14·00	27·00

No. D6 is reported to have been issued to Fort Victoria and Gwelo main post offices only.

South West Africa

The stamps of Germany were used in the colony from July 1886 until the introduction of issues for GERMAN SOUTH-WEST AFRICA in May 1897. Following occupation by South African forces in 1914–15 the issues of SOUTH AFRICA were used, being replaced by the overprinted issues in 1923.

Walvis (or Walfish) Bay, the major anchorage on the South West Africa coast, was claimed by Great Britain as early as 1796. In 1878 the 430 sq mile area around the port, together with a number of offshore islands, was annexed to Cape Province, passing to the Union of South Africa in 1910.

Stamps of the Cape of Good Hope and South Africa were used at Walfish Bay, often cancelled with numeral obliterator 300, until the enclave was transferred to the South West Africa administration on 1 October 1922.

The Walfish Bay territory reverted to South Africa on 30 August 1977 and from that date the stamps of South Africa were, once again, in use.

PRICES FOR STAMPS ON COVER TO 1945	
Nos. 1/40a	from × 6
Nos. 41/133	from × 2
Nos. D1/5	from × 10
Nos. D6/51	from × 20
Nos. O1/4	from × 3
Nos. O5/20	from × 15
No. O21	from × 2
No. O22	from × 15

INSCRIPTIONS. Most of the postage stamps up to No. 140 are inscribed alternately in English and Afrikaans throughout the sheets and the same applies to all the Official stamps and to Nos. D30/33.

PRICES for Nos. 1/140 are for unused horizontal pairs, used horizontal pairs or used singles (either inscr), *unless otherwise indicated*

OVERPRINT SETTINGS. Between 1923 and 1928 the King George V definitives of South Africa, Types **2** and **3**, and the various postage due stamps were issued overprinted for use in South West Africa. A number of overprint settings were used:

Setting I – Overprint Types **1** and **2** ("Zuid-West Afrika"). 14 mm between lines of overprint. See Nos. 1/12 and D1/9.

Setting II – As Setting I, but 10 mm between lines of overprint. See Nos. 13/15 and D10/13.

Setting III – Overprint Types **3** ("Zuidwest Afrika") and **4**. "South West" 14 mm long. "Zuidwest" 11 mm long. 14 mm between lines of overprint. See Nos. 16/27 and D14/17.

Setting IV – As Setting III, but "South West" 16 mm long, "Zuidwest" 12 mm long and 14 mm between lines of overprint. See Nos. 28 and D17a/20.

Setting V – As Setting IV, but 12 mm between lines of overprint. See Nos. D21/4.

Setting VI – As Setting IV, but 9½ mm between lines of overprint. See Nos. 29/40 and D25/32.

South West   **Zuid-West**

Africa.   **Afrika.**
(1)   (2)

1923 (1 Jan–17 June). *Nos. 3/4, 6 and 9/17 of South Africa optd alternately with T **1** and **2** by typography.*

(a) Setting I (14 mm between lines of opt).

		Un pair	Us pair	Us single
1	½d. green	2·50	9·00	1·00
	a. "Wes" for "West" (R. 20/8)	90·00	£140	
	b. "Afr ica" (R. 20/2)	£120		
	c. Litho opt in shiny ink (17 June)	9·50	55·00	4·75
2	1d. rose-red	3·25	9·00	1·00
	a. Opt inverted	£500		
	b. "Wes" for "West" (R. 12/2)	£170		
	c. "Af.rica" for "Africa" (R. 20/6)	£170	£275	
	d. Opt double	£900		
	e. "Afr ica" (R. 20/2)	£120		
	f. "Afrika" without stop (R. 17/8)	£275		
3	2d. dull purple	4·25	12·00	1·50
	a. Opt inverted	£600	£700	
	b. "Wes" for "West" (R. 20/8)	£250		
	c. Litho opt in shiny ink (30 Mar)	45·00	£110	10·00
4	3d. ultramarine	7·50	16·00	2·75
5	4d. orange-yellow and sage-green	13·00	45·00	4·00
	a. Litho opt in shiny ink (19 Apr)	35·00	70·00	8·00
6	6d. black and violet	8·00	45·00	4·00
	a. Litho opt in shiny ink (19 Apr)	30·00	75·00	7·50
7	1s. orange-yellow	18·00	48·00	5·00
	a. Litho opt in shiny ink (19 Apr)	60·00	£120	11·00
	b. "Afrika" without stop (R. 17/8)			

8	1s.3d. pale violet	30·00	55·00	5·50
	a. Opt inverted	£375		
	b. Litho opt in shiny ink (19 Apr)	75·00	£140	14·00
9	2s.6d. purple and green	60·00	£130	18·00
	a. Litho opt in shiny ink (19 Apr)	£130	£275	35·00
10	5s. purple and blue	£140	£325	50·00
11	10s. blue and olive-green	£1300	£2750	£400
12	£1 green and red	£700	£1900	£250
1/12 Set of 12		£2000	£4750	£650
1s/12s Optd "Specimen" Set of 12 singles..		£1400		

Nos. 1/12 were overprinted in complete sheets of 240 (4 panes 6×10).

No. 3b shows traces of a type spacer to the right of where the "t" should have been. This spacer is not visible on Nos. 1a and 2b.

Minor varieties, such as broken "t" in "West", were caused by worn type. Stamps showing one line of overprint only or with the lower line above the upper line due to overprint misplacement may also be found. All values exist showing a faint stop after "Afrika" on R. 17/8, but only examples of the 1d. and 1s. have been seen with it completely omitted.

(b) Setting II (10 mm between lines of opt) (31 Mar).

13	5s. purple and blue	£140	£250	45·00
	a. "Afrika" without stop (R. 6/1)	£1000	£1200	£225
14	10s. blue and olive-green	£500	£850	£140
	a. "Afrika" without stop (R. 6/1)	£2250	£2750	£550
15	£1 green and red	£1000	£1400	£200
	a. "Afrika" without stop (R. 6/1)	£4000	£5000	£1000
13/15 Set of 3		£1500	£2250	£350

Nos. 13/15 were overprinted in separate panes of 60 (6×10).

Examples of most values are known showing a forged Windhoek postmark dated "30 SEP 24".

Zuidwest   **South West**

Afrika.   **Africa.**
(3)   (4)

1923 (15 July)–**26.** *Nos. 3/4, 6 and 9/17 of South Africa optd as T **3** ("Zuidwest" in one word, without hyphen) and **4** alternately.*

(a) Setting III ("South West" 14 mm long, "Zuidwest" 11 mm long, 14 mm between lines of opt).

16	½d. green (5.9.24)	7·00	35·00	3·75
	a. "outh" for "South" (R. 1/1)	£1600		
17	1d. rose-red (28.9.23)	5·50	9·00	1·40
	a. "outh" for "South" (R. 1/1)	£1600		
18	2d. dull purple (28.9.23)	6·50	9·00	1·25
	a. Opt double	£1000		
19	3d. ultramarine	5·00	10·00	1·25
20	4d. orange-yellow and sage-green	6·00	21·00	2·75
	w. Wmk inverted	†	†	
21	6d. black and violet (28.9.23)	12·00	45·00	5·00
22	1s. orange-yellow	12·00	45·00	5·00
23	1s.3d. pale violet	22·00	45·00	5·50
24	2s.6d. purple and green	45·00	80·00	10·00
25	5s. purple and blue	60·00	£140	18·00
26	10s. blue and olive-green	£160	£450	40·00
27	£1 green and red (28.9.23)	£300	£400	60·00
16/27 Set of 12		£600	£1000	£140

Nos. 16/27 were overprinted in complete sheets of 240 (4 panes 6×10).

Two sets may be made with this overprint, one with bold lettering, and the other from September 1924, with thinner lettering and smaller stops.

(b) Setting IV ("South West" 16 mm long, "Zuidwest" 12 mm long, 14 mm between lines of opt).

28	2s.6d. purple and green (29.6.24)	80·00	£160	28·00

No. 28 was overprinted on two panes of 60 horizontally side by side.

(c) Setting VI ("South West" 16 mm long, "Zuidwest" 12 mm long, 9½ mm between lines of opt).

29	½d. green (16.12.25)	7·00	40·00	5·00
30	1d. rose-red (9.12.24)	3·25	10·00	1·40
	a. Opt omitted (in pair with normal)	£1400		
31	2d. dull purple (9.12.24)	4·00	22·00	1·75
32	3d. ultramarine (31.1.26)	4·50	29·00	2·75
	a. Deep bright blue (20.4.26)	42·00	£100	12·00
33	4d. orge-yellow & sage-grn (9.12.24)	5·50	45·00	4·00
34	6d. black and violet (9.12.24)	9·00	48·00	5·00
35	1s. orange-yellow (9.12.24)	8·50	48·00	5·00
36	1s.3d. pale violet (9.12.24)	11·00	48·00	5·00
37	2s.6d. purple and green (9.12.24)	29·00	70·00	10·00
38	5s. purple and blue (31.1.26)	42·00	£110	14·00
39	10s. blue and olive-green (9.12.24)	75·00	£150	20·00
40	£1 green and red (9.1.26)	£250	£400	55·00
	a. Pale olive-green and red (8.11.26)	£250	£425	65·00
29/40a Set of 12		£400	£900	£120
35s, 39s/40s H/S "Specimen" Set of 3		£500		

Nos. 29/40 were overprinted in complete sheets of 240 (4 panes of 6×10) with, initially, "South West Africa" 16½ mm long on the upper two panes and 16 mm long on the lower two. This order was subsequently reversed. For printings from 8 November 1926 all four panes showed the 16½ mm measurement. No. 40a only comes from this printing. Examples of most values are known showing a forged Windhoek postmark dated "30 SEP 24".

Suidwes   **Afrika.**   **South West**   **Africa.**
(5)   (6)

1926 (1 Jan–1 May). *Nos. 30/2 of South Africa optd with T **5** (on stamps inscr in Afrikaans) and **6** (on stamps inscr in English) sideways, alternately in black.*

41	½d. black and green	4·25	9·00	1·00
42	1d. black and carmine	3·50	8·00	80
43	6d. green and orange (1 May)..	22·00	48·00	7·00
41/3 Set of 3		26·00	60·00	8·00

SOUTH WEST AFRICA   **SUIDWES-AFRIKA**
(7)   (8)

1926. *No. 33 of South Africa, imperf optd.*

*(a) With T **7** (English).*

		Single stamps	
44A	4d. grey-blue	75	3·00

*(b) With T **8** (Afrikaans).*

44B	4d. grey-blue	75	3·00

1927. *As Nos. 41/3, but Afrikaans opt on stamp inscr in English and vice versa.*

		Un pair	Us pair	Us single
45	½d. black and green	2·00	7·00	80
	a. "Africa" without stop (R. 13/8)	£160		
46	1d. black and carmine	2·50	2·50	50
	a. "Africa" without stop (R. 13/8)	£300		
47	6d. green and orange	9·00	29·00	3·00
	a. "Africa" without stop (R. 13/8)	£180		
45/7 Set of 3		12·00	35·00	3·75

SOUTH WEST AFRICA   **S.W.A.**   **S.W.A.**
(9)   (10)   (11)

1927. *As No. 44A, but overprint T **9**.*

		Single stamps	
48	4d. grey-blue	6·00	19·00
	s. Handstamped "Specimen"	70·00	

1927 (Apr). *Nos. 34/9 of South Africa optd alternately as T **5** and **6**, in blue, with lines of overprint spaced 16 mm.*

		Un pair	Us pair	Us single
49	2d. grey and purple	4·75	15·00	1·75
50	3d. black and red	4·75	27·00	2·50
51	1s. brown and blue	15·00	32·00	4·00
52	2s.6d. green and brown	35·00	90·00	13·00
53	5s. black and green	75·00	£180	20·00
54	10s. blue and bistre-brown	65·00	£150	20·00
49/54 Set of 6		£180	£450	50·00
49s/51s, 54s H/S "Specimen" Set of 4		£375		

A variety of Nos. 49, 50, 51 and 54 with spacing 16½ mm between lines of overprint, occurs in the third vertical row of each sheet.

1927. *As No. 44, but perf 11½ by John Meinert Ltd, Windhoek.*

*(a) Optd with T **7** (English).*

		Single stamps	
55A	4d. grey-blue	1·00	4·75
	a. Imperf between (pair)	35·00	70·00
	s. Handstamped "Specimen"	70·00	

*(b) Optd with T **8** (Afrikaans).*

55B	4d. grey-blue	1·00	4·75
	a. Imperf between (pair)	35·00	70·00
	s. Handstamped "Specimen"	70·00	

1927 (Aug)–**30.** *Optd with T **10**.*

(a) On Nos. 13 and 17a of South Africa.

56	1s.3d. pale violet	1·25	6·50
	a. Without stop after "A" (R. 3/4)	£100	
	s. Handstamped "Specimen"	75·00	
57	£1 pale olive-green and red	90·00	£160
	a. Without stop after "A" (R. 3/4)	£1500	£2250

(b) On Nos. 30/2 and 34/9 of South Africa.

		Un pair	Us pair	Us single
58	½d. black and green	2·50	6·50	80
	a. Without stop after "A"	40·00	75·00	
	b. "S.W.A." opt above value..	2·75	16·00	2·25
	c. As b, in vert pair, top stamp without opt	£550		
59	1d. black and carmine	1·25	3·50	55
	a. Without stop after "A"	40·00	75·00	
	b. "S.W.A." opt at top (30.4.30)	1·75	14·00	1·60
	c. As b, in vert pair, top stamp without opt	£550		
60	2d. grey and maroon	9·00	26·00	1·50
	c. Perf 14×13½	16·00	38·00	
	ca. Without stop after "A"	80·00	£130	
	cb. Opt double, one inverted	£750	£950	
61	3d. black and red	5·00	23·00	3·25
	a. Without stop after "A"	75·00	£120	
	b. Perf 14×13½	11·00	42·00	
	ba. Without stop after "A"	85·00	£150	
	bb. Without stop after "W"	£170		
62	4d. brown (4.28)	12·00	40·00	7·00
	a. Without stop after "A"	90·00	£140	
	b. Perf 14×13½	25·00	55·00	
63	6d. green and orange	8·50	24·00	2·75
	a. Without stop after "A"	£120		

64	1s. brown and deep blue..........	15·00	48·00	5·00
	b. Perf 14×13½	45·00	90·00	
	ba. Without stop after "A"	£1400	£1700	£350
65	2s.6d. green and brown............	40·00	85·00	12·00
	a. Without stop after "A"	£160	£275	
	b. Perf 14×13½	75·00	£130	
	ba. Without stop after "A"	£225	£350	
66	5s. black and green.................	60·00	£120	18·00
	a. Without stop after "A"	£250	£375	
	b. Perf 14×13½	95·00	£160	
	ba. Without stop after "A"	£250	£400	
67	10s. bright blue and brown........	£100	£190	28·00
	a. Without stop after "A"	£375	£600	
58/67 Set of 10		£225	£500	70·00
58s/61s, 63s/7s H/S "Specimen" Set of 9 ...		£600		

On the ½d., 1d. and 6d. the missing stop variety occurs three times on each sheet, R. 1/7, 13/4 and one position not yet identified. For the other values it comes on R. 2/3 of the right pane and, for the 2s.6d., 5s. and 10s., on R. 8/1 of the left pane.

The missing stop after "W" on the 3d. occurs on R. 10/5 of the right pane.

The overprint is normally found at the base of the ½d., 1d., 6d., 1s.3d. and £1 values and at the top of the remainder.

Examples of all values are known showing a forged Windhoek postmark dated "20 MAR 31".

1930–31. *Nos. 42 and 43 of South Africa (rotogravure printing) optd with T* **10**.

68	½d. black and green (1931).......	10·00	29·00	2·75
69	1d. black and carmine..............	8·00	27·00	2·75

1930 (27 Nov–Dec). *Air. Nos. 40/1 of South Africa optd.*

(a) As T **10**.

		Un single	Us single
70	4d. green (*first printing*)..........................	8·00	28·00
	a. No stop after "A" of "S.W.A.".........	70·00	£140
	b. Later printings...........................	6·00	28·00
71	1s. orange (*first printing*)........................	70·00	£120
	a. No stop after "A" of "S.W.A.".........	£450	£600
	b. Later printings...........................	9·00	50·00

First printing: Thick letters, blurred impression. Stops with rounded corners.

Later printings: Thinner letters, clear impression. Clean cut, square stops.

(b) As T **11** (12.30).

72	4d. green..	1·25	6·00
	a. Opt double	£170	
	b. Opt inverted	£170	
73	1s. orange.......................................	3·75	15·00
	a. Opt double	£500	

12 Kori Bustard

13 Cape Cross

14 Bogenfels

15 Windhoek

16 Waterberg

17 Luderitz Bay

18 Bush Scene

19 Elands

20 Mountain Zebra and Blue Wildebeests

21 Herero Huts

22 Welwitschia Plant

23 Okuwahaken Falls

24 Monoplane over Windhoek

25 Biplane over Windhoek

(Recess B.W.)

1931 (5 Mar). *T* **12** *to* **25** (*inscr alternately in English and Afrikaans*). *W* **9** *of South Africa. P* 14×13½.

(a) *Postage*.

		Un pair	Us pair	Us single
74	½d. black and emerald...............	2·25	2·50	10
75	1d. indigo and scarlet...............	2·25	2·50	10
76	2d. blue and brown	70	4·25	15
	w. Wmk inverted	£400		
77	3d. grey-blue and blue...............	70	4·25	15
78	4d. green and purple.................	1·50	9·00	20
79	6d. blue and brown	1·50	9·00	20
80	1s. chocolate and blue	1·75	11·00	25
81	1s.3d. violet and yellow	6·00	11·00	50
82	2s.6d. carmine and grey	20·00	24·00	1·75
83	5s. sage-green and red-brown ...	16·00	40·00	2·75
84	10s. red-brown and emerald.......	45·00	50·00	6·00
85	20s. lake and blue-green............	70·00	80·00	10·00

(b) *Air*.

86	3d. brown and blue	25·00	32·00	2·50
87	10d. black and purple-brown ...	38·00	75·00	10
74/87 Set of 14		£200	£300	28·00

Examples of most values are known showing a forged Windhoek postmark dated "20 MAR 31".

26

(Recess B.W.)

1935 (1 May). *Silver Jubilee. Inscr bilingually. W* **9** *of South Africa. P* 14×13½.

			Un single	Us single
88	**26**	1d. black and scarlet	1·00	25
89		2d. black and sepia...............	1·00	25
90		3d. black and blue	7·50	22·00
91		6d. black and purple..............	3·00	11·00
88/91 Set of 4			11·00	30·00

1935–36. *Voortrekker Memorial Fund. Nos. 50/3 of South Africa optd with T* **10**.

		Un pair	Us pair	Us single
92	½d.+½d. black and green...........	1·50	5·50	75
	a. Opt inverted	£275		
93	1d.+½d. grey-black and pink	1·50	3·25	40
	a. Blurred "SOUTH AFRICA" and red "comet" flaw............	40·00		
94	2d.+1d. grey-green and purple.....	5·50	6·00	80
	a. Without stop after "A"....	£200	£225	
	b. Opt double	£225		
95	3d.+1½d. grey-green and blue	16·00	32·00	4·00
	a. Without stop after "A"....	£250	£325	
92/5 Set of 4		22·00	42·00	5·50

27 Mail Train

28

(Recess B.W.)

1937 (1 Mar). *W* **9** *of South Africa. P* 14×13½.

96	**27**	1½d. purple-brown	24·00	3·50	30

Re-entry (R. 6/3)

(Recess B.W.)

1937 (12 May). *Coronation. W* **9** *of South Africa* (*sideways*). P 13½×14.

97	**28**	½d. black and emerald......	40	15	10
98		1d. black and scarlet.......	40	15	10
99		1½d. black and orange......	40	15	10
100		2d. black and brown........	40	15	10
101		3d. black and blue..........	50	15	10
102		4d. black and purple.......	50	20	10
		a. Re-entry	15·00	15·00	
103		6d. black and yellow.......	50	3·00	20
104		1s. black and grey-black...	55	3·25	45
97/104 Set of 8			3·25	6·50	65

On. No. 102a the frame and leaves at lower left are doubled. The stamp is inscribed in Afrikaans.

1938 (14 Dec). *Voortrekker Centenary Memorial. Nos. 76/9 of South Africa optd as T* **11**.

105	½d.+½d. blue and green............	9·50	20·00	1·75
106	1d.+1d. blue and carmine..........	23·00	16·00	1·00
107	1½d.+1½d. chocolate & blue-green	24·00	27·00	2·75
108	3d.+3d. bright blue.................	48·00	70·00	7·50
105/8 Set of 4	95·00	£120	11·50

1938 (14 Dec). *Voortrekker Commemoration. Nos. 80/1 of South Africa optd as T* **11**.

109	1d. blue and carmine...............	10·00	19·00	1·50
	a. Three bolts in wheel rim	50·00		
110	1½d. greenish blue and brown.....	15·00	23·00	1·75

1939 (17 July). *250th Anniv of Landing of Huguenots in South Africa and Huguenot Commemoration Fund. Nos. 82/4 of South Africa optd as T* **11**.

111	½d.+½d. brown and green	14·00	14·00	1·10
112	1d.+1d. green and carmine........	18·00	14·00	1·25
113	1½d.+1½d. blue-green and purple ..	27·00	14·00	1·25
111/13 Set of 3	55·00	38·00	3·25

SWA	**SWA**	**SWA**	**S W A**
(29)	(30)	(31)	(32)

1941 (1 Oct)–**43**. *War Effort. Nos. 88/96 of South Africa optd with T* **29** *or* **30** (3d. *and* 1s.).

(a) *Inscr alternately.*

114	½d. green (1.12.41)..................	75	4·25	25
	a. Blue-green (1942)...............	65	2·50	15
115	1d. carmine (1.11.41)..............	55	3·25	15
	a. "Stain" on uniform.............	10·00		
116	1½d. myrtle-green (21.1.42).......	55	3·50	15
117	3d. blue................................	22·00	23·00	1·00
	a. Cigarette flaw.................	70·00		
118	4d. orange-brown...................	6·50	15·00	1·00
	a. Red-brown......................	18·00	25·00	3·00
119	6d. red-orange......................	5·00	6·00	50
120	1s.3d. olive-brown (15.1.43)........	13·00	20·00	1·25

(b) *Inscr bilingually.*

		Un single	Us single
121	2d. violet	50	1·25
122	1s. brown (17.11.41)................	1·10	1·50
114/22 Set of 7 pairs and 2 singles	45·00	65·00	

1943–44. *War Effort* (*reduced sizes*). *Nos. 97/104 of South Africa, optd with T* **29** (1½d. *and* 1s., *No.* 130), *or T* **31** (*others*).

(a) *Inscr alternately.*

		Un unit	Us unit	Us single
123	½d. blue-green (T)...................	50	4·50	10
	a. Green..............................	4·75	6·50	15
	b. Greenish blue......................	4·00	5·50	10
124	1d. carmine-red (T).................	2·75	4·50	10
	a. Bright carmine..................	2·75	4·50	10
125	1½d. red-brown (P)..................	50	1·25	10
126	2d. violet (P)........................	7·50	5·00	10
	a. Reddish violet..................	9·00	5·00	10
	b. Apostrophe flaw................	35·00		
127	3d. blue (T)...........................	3·25	17·00	45
128	6d. red-orange (P)..................	6·00	2·75	30
	a. Opt inverted...................	£500		

(b) *Inscr bilingually.*

129	4d. slate-green (T)...................	2·00	19·00	45
	a. Opt inverted...................	£650	£400	50·00
130	1s. brown (opt T **29**) (P)...........	11·00	24·00	2·00
	a. Opt inverted...................	£500	£325	
	b. Opt T **31**(1944).................	4·00	5·50	30
	c. Opt T **31** inverted..............	£450	£300	40·00
	d. "Bursting shell"..............	32·00		
	e. Smoking "L"..................	32·00		
123/30b Set of 8	23·00	55·00	1·75

The "units" referred to above consist of pairs (P) or triplets (T).

No. 128 exists with another type of opt as Type **31**, but with broader "s", narrower "w" and more space between the letters.

1945. *Victory. Nos. 108/10 of South Africa optd with T* **30**.

		Un pair	Us pair	Us single
131	1d. brown and carmine	25	75	10
	a. Opt inverted	£275	£300	
132	2d. slate-blue and violet..........	30	75	10
133	3d. deep blue and blue............	1·50	1·75	10
131/3 Set of 3	1·75	3·00	

1947 (17 Feb). *Royal Visit. Nos. 111/13 of South Africa optd as T* **31**, *but* 8½×2 mm.

134	1d. black and carmine.............	10	10	10
135	2d. violet	10	60	10
	a. "Bird" on "2"..................	6·00		
136	3d. blue..............................	15	40	10
	a. "Black-eyed Princess"........	7·50		
134/6 Set of 3	30	1·00	15

1948 (26 Apr). *Royal Silver Wedding. No. 125 of South Africa, optd as T 31, but 4×2 mm.*
137	3d. blue and silver	1·00	35	10

1949 (1 Oct). *75th Anniv of U.P.U. Nos. 128/30 of South Africa optd as T 30, but 13×4 mm.*
138	½d. blue-green	75	2·25	25
139	1½d. brown-red	75	1·75	15
140	3d. bright blue	1·25	1·00	25
	a. Serif on "C"	35·00		
	b. "Lake" in East Africa	38·00		
138/40	Set of 3	2·50	4·50	60

1949 (1 Dec). *Inauguration of Voortrekker Monument, Pretoria. Nos. 131/3 of South Africa optd with T 32.*
			Un single	Us single
141	1d. magenta		10	10
142	1½d. blue-green		10	10
143	3d. blue		15	60
141/3	Set of 3		30	70

POSTAGE DUE STAMPS

PRICES for Nos. D1/39 are for unused horizontal pairs, used horizontal pairs and used singles.

1923 (1 Jan–July). *Optd with T 1 and 2 alternately.*

(a) Setting I (14 mm between lines of overprint).

(i) On Nos. D5/6 of Transvaal.
		Un pair	Us pair	Us single
D1	5d. black and violet	4·00	50·00	11·00
	a. "Wes" for "West" (R. 8/6, 10/2 left pane)	£170		
	b. "Afrika" without stop (R. 6/1)	£110		
D2	6d. black and red-brown	17·00	50·00	11·00
	a. "Wes" for "West" (R. 10/2)	£350		
	b. "Afrika" without stop (R. 6/1, 7/2)	£190		
	c. 12 mm between lines of opt (R. 1/1)	£225		

(ii) On Nos. D3/4 and D6 of South Africa (De La Rue printing).
D3	2d. black and violet	30·00	48·00	10·00
	a. "Wes" for "West" (R. 10/2)	£225	£350	
	b. "Afrika" without stop (R. 6/1, 7/2)	£225		
D4	3d. black and blue	17·00	48·00	10·00
	a. "Wes" for "West" (R. 8/6, 10/2)	£160		
	b. "Africa" without stop (R. 9/1)	£275		
D5	6d. black and slate (20 Apr)	28·00	55·00	13·00
	a. "Wes" for "West" (R. 8/6)	£190		

(iii) On Nos. D9/10, D11 and D14 of South Africa (Pretoria printings).
D6	½d. black and green (P 14)	6·00	29·00	5·50
	a. Opt inverted	£475		
	b. Opt double	£1000	£1100	
	c. "Wes" for "West" (R. 10/2)	£100		
	d. "Afrika" without stop (R. 6/1, 7/2)	£100		
D7	1d. black and rose (roul)	7·00	30·00	6·00
	a. "Wes" for "West" (R. 10/2)	£110	£275	
	b. "Afrika" without stop (R. 6/1)	£110		
	c. Imperf between (horiz pair)	£1300		
D8	1½d. black and yellow-brown (roul)	1·25	14·00	2·75
	a. "Wes" for "West" (R. 8/6, 10/2)	85·00		
	b. "Afrika" without stop (R. 6/1)	90·00		
D9	2d. black and violet (P 14) (21 June)	3·50	25·00	5·00
	a. "Wes" for "West" (R. 8/6)	£100		
	b. "Afrika" without stop (R. 6/1)	£130		

Nos. D1/9 were initially overprinted as separate panes of 60, but some values were later done as double panes of 120.

A variety of Nos. D1, D4/5 and D9 with 15 mm between the lines of overprint occurs on four positions in each pane from some printings.

(b) Setting II (10 mm between lines of overprint).

(i) On No. D5 of Transvaal.
D10	5d. black and violet (20 Apr)	55·00	£160

(ii) On Nos. D3/4 of South Africa (De La Rue printing).
D11	2d. black and violet (20 Apr)	17·00	45·00	9·00
	a. "Afrika" without stop (R. 6/1)	£190		
D12	3d. black and blue (20 Apr)	7·50	28·00	5·50
	a. "Afrika" without stop (R. 6/1)	95·00		

(iii) On No. D9 of South Africa (Pretoria printing). Roul.
D13	1d. black and rose (July)	£12000	—	£1600

1923 (30 July)–**26**. *Optd as T 3 ("Zuidwest" in one word without hyphen) and 4.*

(a) Setting III ("South West" 14 mm long, "Zuidwest" 11 mm long and 14 mm between lines of overprint).

(i) On No. D6 of Transvaal.
D14	6d. black and red-brown	21·00	90·00	20·00

(ii) On Nos. D9 and D11/12 of South Africa (Pretoria printing).
D15	½d. black and green (P 14)	12·00	32·00	5·50
D16	1d. black and rose (roul)	5·50	32·00	5·50
D17	1d. black and rose (P 14) (2.8.23)	19·00	32·00	5·50

(b) Setting IV ("South West" 16 mm long, "Zuidwest" 12 mm long and 14 mm between lines of overprint).

(i) On No. D5 of Transvaal.
D17a	5d. black and violet (1.7.24)	£500	£1000	

(ii) On Nos. D11/12 and D16 of South Africa (Pretoria printing). P 14.
D18	½d. black and green (1.7.24)	7·50	29·00	5·50
D19	1d. black and rose (1.7.24)	7·00	29·00	5·50
D20	6d. black and slate (1.7.24)	2·25	42·00	9·00
	a. "Africa" without stop (R. 9/5)	£120		

(c) Setting V (12 mm between lines of overprint).

(i) On No. D5 of Transvaal.
D21	5d. black and violet (6.8.24)	4·50	50·00	9·00

(ii) On No. D4 of South Africa (De La Rue printing).
D22	3d. black and blue (6.8.24)	16·00	50·00	11·00

(iii) On Nos. D11 and D13 of South Africa (Pretoria printing). P 14.
D23	½d. black and green (6.8.24)	3·00	29·00	6·50
D24	1½d. black and yellow-brown (6.8.24)	5·00	42·00	7·50

(d) Setting VI (9½ mm between lines of overprint).

(i) On No. D5 of Transvaal.
D25	5d. black and violet (7.9.24)	2·75	20·00	3·50
	a. "Africa" without stop (R. 9/5)	80·00		

(ii) On No. D4 of South Africa (De La Rue printing).
D26	3d. black and blue (3.2.26)	7·50	55·00	11·00

(iii) On Nos. D11/16 of South Africa (Pretoria printing). P 14.
D27	½d. black and green (1.3.26)	9·50	35·00	7·50
D28	1d. black and rose (16.3.25)	2·00	12·00	1·60
	a. "Africa" without stop (R. 9/5 right pane)	85·00		
D29	1½d. black and yellow-brown (1.10.26)	4·50	32·00	6·50
	a. "Africa" without stop (R. 9/5 right pane)	90·00		
D30	2d. black and violet (7.9.24)	2·50	18·00	3·50
	a. "Africa" without stop (R. 9/5) right pane)	75·00		
D31	3d. black and blue (6.5.26)	4·50	19·00	3·75
	a. "Africa" without stop (R. 9/5) right pane)	80·00		
D32	6d. black and slate (1.10.26)	10·00	50·00	14·00
	a. "Africa" without stop (R. 9/5 right pane)	£150		
D27/32	Set of 6	30·00	£150	32·00

For Setting VI the overprint was applied to sheets of 120 (2 panes of 60) of the 1d., 3d. and 6d., and to individual panes of 60 for the other values. The two measurements of "South West", as detailed under No. 40, also occur on the postage dues. Nos. D25 and D31/2 show it 16 mm long, No. 27 16½ mm long and the other stamps can be found with either measurement. In addition to the complete panes the 16½ mm long "South West" also occurs on R. 2/4 in the 16 mm left pane for Nos. D28 and D30/2.

Suidwes   **South West**

Afrika.   **Africa.**
(D 1)   (D 2)

1927 (14 May–27 Sept). *Optd as Types D 1 and D 2, alternately, 12 mm between lines of overprint.*

(a) On No. D5 of Transvaal.
D33	5d. black and violet (27 Sept)	19·00	85·00	23·00

(b) On Nos. D13/16 of South Africa (Pretoria printing). P 14.
D34	1½d. black and yellow-brown	1·00	20·00	3·50
D35	2d. black and pale violet (27 Sept)	4·75	16·00	3·25
	a. Black and deep violet	8·00	17·00	3·50
D37	3d. black and blue (27 Sept)	13·00	45·00	11·00
D38	6d. black and slate (27 Sept)	7·50	35·00	8·50

(c) On No. D18 of South Africa (Pretoria printing). P 14.
D39	1d. black and carmine	1·00	11·00	2·25
D33/9	Set of 6	42·00	£200	45·00

No. D33 was overprinted in panes of 60 and the remainder as complete sheets of 120.

Examples of all values can be found with very small or very faint stops from various positions in the sheet.

1928–29. *Optd with T 10.*

(a) On Nos. D15/16 of South Africa.
			Un single	Us single
D40	3d. black and blue		1·50	16·00
	a. Without stop after "A" (R. 3/6)		35·00	
D41	6d. black and slate		6·00	28·00
	a. Without stop after "A" (R. 3/6)		£130	

(b) On Nos. D17/21 of South Africa.
D42	½d. black and green		50	8·00
D43	1d. black and carmine		50	3·25
	a. Without stop after "A" (R. 3/6)		40·00	
D44	2d. black and mauve		50	4·50
	a. Without stop after "A" (R. 3/6)		55·00	
D45	3d. black and blue		2·25	26·00
D46	6d. black and slate		1·50	20·00
	a. Without stop after "A" (R. 3/6)		£190	
D42/6	Set of 5		4·75	55·00

D 3

(Litho B.W.)

1931 (23 Feb). *Inscribed bilingually. W 9 of South Africa. P 12.*
D47	D 3	½d. black and green		1·00	9·00
D48		1d. black and scarlet		1·00	1·25
D49		2d. black and violet		1·00	2·75
D50		3d. black and blue		4·25	17·00
D51		6d. black and slate		13·00	27·00
D47/51		Set of 5		18·00	50·00

OFFICIAL STAMPS

OFFICIAL   **OFFISIEEL**

South West / Africa. (O 1)   **Suidwes / Afrika.** (O 2)

1926 (Dec). *Nos. 30, 31, 6 and 32 of South Africa optd with Type O 1 on English stamp and O 2 on Afrikaans stamp alternately.*
			Un pair	Us pair	Us single
O1	½d. black and green		75·00	£180	30·00
O2	1d. black and carmine		75·00	£180	30·00
O3	2d. dull purple		£170	£300	45·00
O4	6d. green and orange		95·00	£180	30·00
O1/4	Set of 4		£375	£750	£120

OFFICIAL   **OFFISIEEL**

S.W.A. (O 3)   **S.W.A.** (O 4)

1929 (May). *Nos. 30, 31, 32 and 34 of South Africa optd with Type O 3 on English stamp and O 4 on Afrikaans stamp.*
O5	½d. black and green		1·00	15·00	2·75
O6	1d. black and carmine		1·00	15·00	2·75
	w. Inverted		£250		
O7	2d. grey and purple		1·50	20·00	3·50
	a. Pair, one stamp without stop after "OFFICIAL"		6·00	45·00	
	b. Pair, one stamp without stop after "OFFISIEEL"		6·00	45·00	
	c. Pair, comprising a and b		16·00	85·00	
O8	6d. green and orange		2·00	20·00	3·75
O5/8	Set of 4		5·00	65·00	11·50

Types O 3 and O 4 are normally spaced 17 mm between lines on all except the 2d. value, which is spaced 13 mm.

Except on No. O7, the words "OFFICIAL" or "OFFISIEEL" normally have no stops after them.

OFFICIAL   **S.W.A.** (O 5)   **OFFISIEEL**   **S.W.A.** (O 6)

OFFICIAL. / S.W.A. (O 7)   **OFFISIEEL. / S.W.A.** (O 8)

1929 (Aug). *Nos. 30, 31 and 32 of South Africa optd with Types O 5 and 6, and No. 34 with Types O 7 and O 8, languages to correspond.*
O9	½d. black and green		75	15·00	2·75
O10	1d. black and carmine		1·00	15·00	2·75
O11	2d. grey and purple		1·00	15·00	3·25
	a. Pair, one stamp without stop after "OFFICIAL"		3·75	40·00	
	b. Pair, one stamp without stop after "OFFISIEEL"		3·75	40·00	
	c. Pair, comprising a and b		8·00	90·00	
O12	6d. green and orange		2·50	27·00	6·50
O9/12	Set of 4		4·75	65·00	13·50

Examples of Nos. O1/12 are known showing forged Windhoek postmarks dated "30 SEP 24" or "20 MAR 31".

OFFICIAL (O 9)   **OFFISIEEL** (O 10)

1931. *English stamp optd with Type O 9 and Afrikaans stamp with Type O 10 in red.*

O13	12	½d. black and emerald.......	11·00	19·00	3·50
O14	13	1d. indigo and scarlet........	1·00	18·00	3·50
O15	14	2d. blue and brown	2·25	10·00	2·25
O16	17	6d. blue and brown	3·50	14·00	3·25
O13/16 *Set of* 4			16·00	55·00	11·50

OFFICIAL   **OFFISIEEL**
(O 11)   (O 12)

1938 (1 July). *English stamp optd with Type* O **11** *and Afrikaans with Type* O **12** *in red.*

O17	27	1½d. purple-brown..............	26·00	45·00	6·00

OFFICIAL   **OFFISIEEL**
(O 13)   (O 14)

1945–50. *English stamp optd with Type* O **13**, *and Afrikaans stamp with Type* O **14** *in red.*

O18	12	½d. black and emerald.......	13·00	29·00	5·00
O19	13	1d. indigo and scarlet (1950)......................	8·00	17·00	3·25
		a. Opt double	£450		
O20	27	1½d. purple-brown..............	35·00	48·00	6·50
O21	14	2d. blue and brown (1947?)......................	£550	£700	£100
O22	17	6d. blue and brown	20·00	55·00	7·00
O18/20, O22 *Set of* 4			70·00	£130	20·00

OFFICIAL   **OFFISIEEL**
(O 15)   (O 16)

1951 (16 Nov)–**52**. *English stamp optd with Type* O **15** *and Afrikaans stamp with Type* O **16**, *in red.*

O23	12	½d. black and emerald (1952).........................	15·00	23·00	4·50
		a. Opts transposed...........			
O24	13	1d. indigo and scarlet........	5·00	16·00	1·75
		a. Opts transposed...........	90·00	£180	
O25	27	1½d. purple-brown..............	24·00	27·00	5·00
		a. Opts transposed...........	75·00	95·00	
O26	14	2d. blue and brown	2·00	19·00	3·50
		a. Opts transposed...........	60·00	£180	
O27	17	6d. blue and brown	2·75	42·00	7·50
		a. Opts transposed...........	24·00	£140	
O23/7 *Set of* 5			45·00	£110	20·00

The above errors refer to stamps with the English overprint on Afrikaans stamp and *vice versa*.

The use of official stamps ceased in January 1955.

Sudan

ANGLO-EGYPTIAN CONDOMINIUM

An Egyptian post office was opened at Suakin in 1867 and the stamps of Egypt, including postage dues and the official (No. O64). were used in the Sudan until replaced by the overprinted "SOUDAN" issue of 1897.

Cancellations have been identified from eleven post offices, using the following postmark types:

A   B

C   D

E   F

G   H

I   J

K

L

BERBER (*spelt* BARBAR). *Open* 1 October 1873 *to* 20 May 1884. *Postmark type* G.

DABROUSSA. *Open* 1891 *onwards. Postmark as type* J *but with* 11 *bars in arcs*.

DONGOLA. *Open* 1 October 1873 *to* 13 June 1885 *and* 1896 *onwards. Postmark types* F, G, K, L.

GEDAREF. *Open* August 1878 *to* April 1884. *Postmark type* H.

KASSALA. *Open* 15 May 1875 *to* 30 July 1885. *Postmark type* G.

KHARTOUM. *Open* 1 October 1873 *to* 14 December 1885. *Postmark types* E (*spelt* KARTUM), G (*spelt* HARTUM), I (*with or without line of Arabic above date*).

KORTI. *Open* January *to* March 1885 *and* 1897. *Postmark type* K.

SUAKIN. *Open* November 1867 *onwards. Postmark types* A, B, C (*spelt* SUAKIM), D (*spelt* SUAKIM *and also with year replaced by concentric arcs*), I (*spelt* SOUAKIN), J (*spelt* SAWAKIN, *number of bars differs*).

TANI. *Open* 1885. *Postmark type* K.

TOKAR. *Open* 1891 *onwards. Postmark type* J (7 *bars in arcs*).

WADI HALFA. *Open* 1 October 1873 *onwards. Postmark types* F (*spelt* WADI HALFE), G (*spelt* WADI HALFE), I, J (*number of bars differs*).

WADI HALFA CAMP. *Open* 1896 *onwards. Postmark type* I.

Official records also list post offices at the following locations, but no genuine postal markings from them have yet been reported: Chaka, Dara, Debeira, El Abiad, El Fasher, El Kalabat, Faras, Fashoda, Fazogl, Ishkeit, Kalkal, Karkok, Mesellemia, Sara, Sennar and Taoufikia (not to be confused with the town of the same name in Egypt).

M

The post office at Kassala was operated by Italy from 1894 until 1896, using stamps of Eritrea cancelled with postmark type M.

From the last years of the nineteenth century that part of Sudan lying south of the 5 degree North latitude line was administered by Uganda (the area to the east of the Nile) (until 1912) or by Belgium (the area to the west of the Nile, known as the Lado Enclave) (until 1910).

Stamps of Uganda or East Africa were used at Gondokoro and Nimuli between 1901 and 1911, usually cancelled with circular date stamps or, probably in transit at Khartoum, by a lozenge-shaped grid of 18×17 dots.

Stamps of Belgian Congo were used from the Lado Enclave between 1897 and 1910, as were those of Uganda (1901–10) and Sudan (1902–10), although no local postmarks were supplied, examples being initially cancelled in manuscript.

Stamps of Sudan were used at Gambeila (Ethiopia) between 1910 and 10 June 1940 and from 22 March 1941 until 15 October 1956. Sudan stamps were also used at Sabderat (Eritrea) between March 1910 and 1940.

PRICES FOR STAMPS ON COVER TO 1945

Nos. 1/9	*from* × 20
Nos. 10/17	*from* × 6
Nos. 18/29	*from* × 5
Nos. 30/95	*from* × 2
Nos. D1/11	*from* × 30
Nos. O1/3	*from* × 10
No. O4	*from* × 15
Nos. O5/10	*from* × 50
No. O11	*from* × 10
Nos. O12/31	*from* × 15
Nos. O32/42	*from* × 10
No. A1	*from* × 20
Nos. A2/5	—
Nos. A6/10	*from* × 50
No. A11	*from* × 15
Nos. A12/13	—
No. A14	*from* × 15
Nos. A15/16	—
Nos. A17/22	*from* × 20
Nos. A23/6	—
Nos. A27/8	*from* × 10

(Currency. 10 milliemes = 1 piastre. 100 piastres = £1 Sudanese)

السودان
SOUDAN
(1)

1897 (1 Mar). *Nos.* 54b, 55, 56a, 58/a, 59a, 61/a, 63 *and* 64 *of Egypt optd as* T **1** *by Govt Ptg Wks, Būlaq, Cairo.*

1	1m. pale brown	2·50	2·00
	a. Opt inverted	£200	
	b. Opt omitted (in vert pair with normal)	£1100	
	c. Deep brown	2·50	2·25
	w. Wmk inverted		
3	2m. green	1·25	1·75
4	3m. orange-yellow	1·40	1·50
5	5m. rose-carmine	2·00	70
	a. Opt inverted	£200	£225
	b. Opt omitted (in vert pair with normal)	£1200	
6	1p. ultramarine	7·00	2·00
7	2p. orange-brown	60·00	16·00

8	5p. slate	55·00	20·00
	a. Opt double	£4500	
	b. Opt omitted (in vert pair with normal)	£4500	
9	10p. mauve	35·00	45·00
1/9	Set of 8	£150	80·00

Numerous forgeries exist including some which show the characteristics of the varieties mentioned below.

There are six varieties of the overprint on each value. Vertical strips of 6 showing them are worth a premium.

Four settings of the overprint were previously recognised by specialists, but one of these is now regarded as an unauthorised reprint from the original type. Here reprints can only be detected when in multiples. The 2p. with inverted watermark only exists with this unauthorised overprint so it is not listed.

In some printings the large dot is omitted from the left-hand Arabic character on one stamp in the pane of 60.

Only two examples, one unused and the other used (in the Royal Collection), are known of No. 8a. In both instances one impression is partially albino.

PRINTERS. All stamps of Sudan were printed by De La Rue & Co, Ltd, London, *except where otherwise stated.*

2 Arab Postman   3

(Des E. A. Stanton. Typo)

1898 (1 Mar). W **3**. P 14.

10	2	1m. brown and pink	65	2·25
11		2m. green and brown	2·00	2·75
12		3m. mauve and green	2·00	2·25
13		5m. carmine and black	1·75	1·50
14		1p. blue and brown	7·50	4·00
15		2p. black and blue	27·00	7·50
16		5p. brown and green	35·00	15·00
17		10p. black and mauve	25·00	2·25
10/17		Set of 8	90·00	32·00

5 Milliemes

4   (5)

1902–21. *Ordinary paper*. W **4**. P 14.

18	2	1m. brown and carmine (5.05)	1·25	65
19		2m. green and brown (11.02)	1·75	10
20		3m. mauve and green (3.03)	2·25	25
21		4m. blue and bistre (20.1.07)	1·50	2·50
22		4m. vermilion and brown (10.07)	1·50	75
23		5m. scarlet and black (12.03)	2·00	10
		w. Wmk inverted		£110
24		1p. blue and brown (12.03)	2·25	30
25		2p. black and blue (2.08)	25·00	1·75
26		2p. purple & orge-yellow (*chalk-surfaced paper*) (22.12.21)	4·25	10·00
27		5p. brown and green (2.08)	24·00	30
		a. Chalk-surfaced paper	38·00	4·00
28		10p. black and mauve (2.11)	24·00	3·75
		a. Chalk-surfaced paper	32·00	9·50
18/28		Set of 11	80·00	18·00

1903 (Sept). *No. 16 surch at Khartoum with T* **5**, *in blocks of 30.*

29	2	5m. on 5pi. brown and green	6·50	9·50
		a. Surch inverted	£250	£225

6   7

1921–23. *Chalk-surfaced paper. Typo.* W **4**. P 14.

30	6	1m. black and orange (4.2.22)	80	4·25
31		2m. yellow-orange and chocolate (1922)	9·00	11·00
		a. Yellow and chocolate (1923)	11·00	11·00
32		3m. mauve and green (25.1.22)	2·50	9·00
33		4m. green and chocolate (21.3.22)	6·00	5·50
34		5m. olive-brown and black (4.2.22)	2·25	10
35		10m. carmine and black (1922)	3·25	10
36		15m. bright blue and chestnut (14.12.21)	2·75	1·00
30/36		Set of 7	24·00	28·00

1927–41. *Chalk-surfaced paper.* W **7**. P 14.

37	6	1m. black and orange	70	10
		a. Ordinary paper (1941)	70	10
38		2m. orange and chocolate	75	10
		a. Ordinary paper (1941)	1·50	10
39		3m. mauve and green	70	10
		a. Ordinary paper (1941)	2·75	30

40		4m. green and chocolate	60	10
		a. Ordinary paper (1941)	3·50	40
		aw. Wmk inverted	75·00	75·00
41		5m. olive-brown and black	60	10
		a. Ordinary paper (1941)	2·50	10
42		10m. carmine and black	1·50	10
		a. Ordinary paper (1941)	3·00	10
43		15m. bright blue and chestnut	2·50	10
		aw. Wmk inverted	†	£200
		b. Ordinary paper (1941)	1·75	10
44	2	2p. purple and orange-yellow	2·75	10
		a. Ordinary paper (1941)	4·00	10
44b		3p. red-brown and blue (1.1.40).....	3·50	10
		ba. Ordinary paper (1941)	17·00	10
44c		4p. ultramarine and black (2.11.36).	3·50	10
45		5p. chestnut and green	1·25	10
		a. Ordinary paper (1941)	5·50	2·25
45b		6p. greenish blue and black		
		(2.11.36)	7·00	1·25
		ba. Ordinary paper (1941)	38·00	2·25
45c		8p. emerald and black (2.11.36)......	7·00	3·00
		ca. Ordinary paper (1941)	48·00	4·25
46		10p. black and reddish purple...........	4·25	10
		a. Ordinary paper. Black and bright		
		mauve (1941)	8·50	70
46b		20p. pale blue and blue (17.10.35)....	5·50	10
		ba. Ordinary paper (1941)	5·50	10
37/46b Set of 15			38·00	4·25

The ordinary paper of this issue is thick, smooth and opaque and was a wartime substitute for chalk-surfaced paper.

For similar stamps, but with different Arabic inscriptions, see Nos. 96/111.

AIR MAIL	AIR MAIL	AIR
(8)	(9)	Extended foot to "R" (R. 5/12)

1931 (15 Feb–Mar). *Air. Nos. 41/2 and 44 optd with T 8 or 9 (2p.).*

47	6	5m. olive-brown and black (Mar).....	35	70
48		10m. carmine and black	85	12·00
49	2	2p. purple and orange-yellow	85	7·50
		a. Extended foot to "R"	27·00	
47/9 Set of 3			1·90	18·00

2½   2⅛

AIR MAIL

1½   1½

10 Statue of Gen. Gordon   (11)

1931 (1 Sept)–37. *Air. Recess. W* **7** (sideways*). P 14.

49b	10	3m. green and sepia (1.1.33)	2·50	6·50
50		5m. black and green	1·00	10
51		10m. black and carmine	1·00	20
52		15m. red-brown and sepia..............	40	10
		aw. Wmk sideways inverted (top of		
		G to right)	£120	£110
		b. Perf 11½×12½ (1937)............	4·50	10
53		2p. black and orange	30	10
		ax. Wmk reversed	£150	
		ay. Wmk sideways inverted (top of		
		G to right) and reversed	£150	
		b. Perf 11½×12½ (1937)............	4·50	15·00
53c		2½p. magenta and blue (1.1.33)	3·50	10
		d. Perf 11½×12½ (1936)............	3·00	10
		da. Aniline magenta and blue	8·00	3·50
		dx. Wmk reversed	£110	
		dy. Wmk sideways inverted (top of		
		G to right) and reversed		
54		3p. black and grey	60	15
		a. Perf 11½×12½ (1937)............	85	35
55		3½p. black and violet...................	1·50	80
		a. Perf 11½×12½ (1937)............	2·50	13·00
		ay. Wmk sideways inverted (top of		
		G to right) and reversed	†	—
56		4½p. red-brown and grey	10·00	15·00
57		5p. black and ultramarine	1·00	30
		a. Perf 11½×12½ (1937)............	3·75	35
57b		7½p. green and emerald (17.10.35)....	9·50	5·00
		bx. Wmk reversed	£150	
		by. Wmk sideways inverted (top of		
		G to right) and reversed	£110	£110
		c. Perf 11½×12½ (1937)............	4·00	10·00
57d		10p. brown and greenish blue		
		(17.10.35)	9·00	1·75
		e. Perf 11½×12½ (1937)............	4·00	21·00
		ey. Wmk sideways inverted (top of		
		G to right) and reversed	£150	
49b/57d Set of 12 (P 14)			35·00	26·00
52b/7e Set of 8 (P 11½×12½)			24·00	55·00

*The normal sideways watermark shows the top of the G pointing left *as seen from the back of the stamp.*

1932 (18 July). *Air. No. 44 surch with T* **11**.

58	2	2½p. on 2p. purple and orange-yellow .	1·40	3·50

12 Gen. Gordon (after C. Ouless)   **13** Gordon Memorial College, Khartoum

---

14 Gordon Memorial Service, Khartoum (after R. C. Woodville)

1935 (1 Jan). *50th Death Anniv of General Gordon, Recess. W* **7**. *P* 14.

59	12	5m. green	35	10
60		10m. yellow-brown	85	25
61		13m. ultramarine	85	11·00
62		15m. scarlet	1·75	25
63	13	2p. blue	1·25	20
64		5p. orange-vermilion	1·25	40
65		10p. purple	7·50	8·50
66	14	20p. black	23·00	55·00
67		50p. red-brown	85·00	£120
59/67 Set of 9			£110	£180

7½ PIASTRES   5 MILLIEMES

(15)   (16)

1935. *Air. Nos. 49b/51 and 56 surch as T* **15** *at Khartoum.*

68	10	15m. on 10m. black and carmine (Apr)	40	10
		a. Surch double	£750	£850
69		2½p. on 3m. green and sepia (Apr)	85	4·50
		a. Second arabic letter from		
		left missing......................	50·00	£100
		b. Small "½"	2·25	21·00
70		2½p. on 5m. black and green (Apr).....	50	1·50
		a. Second Arabic letter		
		from left missing.................	25·00	55·00
		b. Small "½"	1·25	8·00
		c. Surch inverted	£800	£900
		d. Ditto with variety a............	£5000	
		e. Ditto with variety b...........	£2000	£2250
71		3p. on 4½p. red-brown and grey		
		(Apr)	1·75	17·00
72		7½p. on 4½p. red-brown and grey		
		(Mar)	6·50	48·00
73		10p. on 4½p. red-brown and grey		
		(Mar)	6·50	48·00
68/73 Set of 6			15·00	£110

Nos. 69a and 70a occur in position 49 of the sheet of 50; the small "½" variety occurs in positions 17, 27, 32, 36, 41, 42 and 46.

The 15m. on 10m. surcharged in red (*Price*, £300) and the 2½p. on 3m. and 2½p., on 5m. in green are from proof sheets; the latter two items being known cancelled (*Price* £200 *each, unused*).

There were four proof sheets of the 7½p. on 4½p, two in red and two in black. The setting on these proof sheets showed three errors subsequently corrected before No. 72 was surcharged. Twelve positions showed an Arabic "⅓" instead of "½", one an English "¼" for "½" and another one of the Arabic letters inverted. (*Price for red surcharge*, £300.)

1938 (1 July). *Air. Nos. 53d, 55, 57b and 57d surch as T* **16** *by De La Rue.*

74	10	5m. on 2½p. mag & bl (P 11½×12½)	3·50	10
		w. Wmk sideways inverted		
		(top of G to right)	—	£100
		x. Wmk reversed		
75		3p. on 3½p. black and violet (P 14) .	35·00	48·00
		a. Perf 11½×12½...................	£450	£550
76		3p. on 7½p. green and emerald		
		(P 14)	7·00	6·50
		ax. Wmk reversed		
		ay. Wmk sideways inverted		
		(top of G to right) and		
		reversed	60·00	60·00
		b. Perf 11½×12½...................	£450	£550
77		5p. on 10p. brown & greenish bl		
		(P 14)	1·75	4·75
		ax. Wmk reversed	£100	
		b. Perf 11½×12½...................	£450	£550
74/7 Set of 4			42·00	55·00

A 5p. on 2½p, perf 11½×12½ exists either mint or cancelled from a trial printing (*Price* £375 *unused*).

5 Mills.

(17)   Normal ("Malime")

"Malmime"   Short "mim"   Broken "lam"
(Left-hand pane   (Right-hand pane   (Right-hand pane
R. 5/1)   R. 3/1)   R. 6/2)

5 M

Inserted "5" (Bottom right-hand pane R. 4/5)

1940 (25 Feb). *No. 42 surch with T* **17** *by McCorquodale (Sudan) Ltd, Khartoum.*

78	6	5m. on 10m. carmine and black	75	40
		a. "Malmime"	60·00	70·00
		b. Two dots omitted (Right-		
		hand pane R. 8/6).................	60·00	70·00
		c. Short "mim"	60·00	70·00
		d. Broken "lam"	60·00	70·00
		e. Inserted "5"	£160	

4½ Piastres

4½ PIASTRES   4½ قرش ٤� ١/٢
(18)   (19)

1940–41. *Nos. 41 and 45c surch as T* **18** *or* **19** *at Khartoum.*

79	6	4½p. on 5m. olive-brown & blk		
		(9.2.41)............................	48·00	7·00
80	2	4½p. on 8p. emerald and black		
		(12.12.40).........................	42·00	9·00

20 Tuti Island, R. Nile, near Khartoum   **21** Tuti Island, R. Nile near Khartoum

(Des Miss H. M. Hebbert. Litho Security Printing Press, Nasik, India)

1941 (25 Mar–10 Aug). *P* 14×13½ (*T* **20**) *or P* 13½×14 (*T* **21**).

81	20	1m. slate and orange (10.8)	2·00	4·00
82		2m. orange and chocolate (10.8)	2·00	4·00
83		3m. mauve and green (10.8)	2·25	20
84		4m. green and chocolate (10.8)	80	60
85		5m. olive-brown and black (10.8) ...	30	10
86		10m. carmine and black (10.8)........	9·00	2·75
87		15m. bright blue and chestnut	1·25	10
88	21	2p. purple and orange-yellow		
		(10.8).............................	6·50	60
89		3p. red-brown and blue	1·25	10
90		4p. ultramarine and black	2·50	10
91		5p. chestnut and green (10.8)	5·50	9·00
92		6p. greenish blue and black (10.8)..	19·00	40
93		8p. emerald and black (10.8)	15·00	45
94		10p. slate and purple (10.8)...........	65·00	75
95		20p. pale blue and blue (10.8)........	60·00	35·00
81/95 Set of 15			£170	50·00

22   23

1948 (1 Jan–June). *Arabic inscriptions below camel altered. Typo. Ordinary paper (8, 10, 20p.) or chalk-surfaced paper (others). W* **7**. *P* 14.

96	22	1m. black and orange	35	3·75
97		2m. orange and chocolate	80	4·50
98		3m. mauve and green	30	5·00
99		4m. deep green and chocolate	50	75
100		5m. olive-brown and black	5·50	2·00
		w. Wmk inverted	75·00	
101		10m. rose-red and black	5·50	10
		a. Centre inverted	†	
102		15m. ultramarine and chestnut	5·00	10
103	23	2p. purple and orange-yellow	8·50	2·50
104		3p. red-brown and deep blue	7·50	30
105		4p. ultramarine and black	4·00	1·75
106		5p. brown-orange and deep green ...	4·00	3·00
107		6p. greenish blue and black	4·00	3·00
108		8p. bluish green and black	4·50	10
109		10p. black and mauve	11·00	4·75
		a. Chalk-surfaced paper (June)	42·00	6·00
110		20p. pale blue and deep blue	4·50	30
		a. Perf 13. Chalk-surfaced paper		
		(June)	50·00	£180
111		50p. carmine and ultramarine	6·50	2·50
96/111 Set of 16			65·00	32·00

A single used example is known of No. 101a.

For similar stamps, but with different Arabic inscriptions, see Nos. 37/46b.

24   25

1948 (1 Oct). *Golden Jubilee of "Camel Postman" design. Chalk-surfaced paper. Typo. W* **7**. *P* 13.

112	24	2p. black and light blue	20	10

1948 (23 Dec). *Opening of Legislative Assembly, Chalk-surfaced paper. Typo. W* **7**. *P* 13.

113	25	10m. rose-red and black	50	10
114		5p. brown-orange and deep green ...	1·00	1·50

26 Blue Nile Bridge, Khartoum

27 Kassala Jebel

28 Sagia (water wheel)

29 Port Sudan

30 Gordon Memorial College

31 *Gordon Pasha* (Nile mail boat)

32 Suakin

33 G.P.O., Khartoum

(Des Col. W. L. Atkinson (2½p., 6p.), G. R. Wilson (3p.), others from photographs. Recess)

1950 (1 July). *Air. T* **26**/**33**. W **7**. P 12.

115	26	2p. black and blue-green	4·50	1·50
116	27	2½p. light blue and red-orange	75	1·25
117	28	3p. reddish purple and blue	3·25	1·25
118	29	3½p. purple-brown and yellow-brown	2·75	3·25
119	30	4p. brown and light blue	1·50	2·75
120	31	4½p. black and ultramarine	2·50	3·75
		a. Black and steel-blue	11·00	7·00
121	32	6p. black and carmine	2·50	3·25
122	33	20p. black and purple	2·25	5·50
115/122		Set of 8	18·00	20·00

34 Ibex

35 Whale-headed stork

36 Giraffe

37 Baggara girl

38 Shilluk warrior

39 Hadendowa

40 Policeman

41 Cotton Picking

42 Ambatch reed canoe

43 Nuba wrestlers

44 Weaving

45 Saluka farming

46 Gum tapping

47 Darfur chief

48 Stack Laboratory

49 Nile Lechwe

50 Camel postman

(Des Col. W. L. Atkinson (1m., 2m., 4m., 5m., 10m., 3p., 3½p., 20p.), Col. E. A. Stanton (50p.) others from photographs. Typo)

1951 (1 Sept)–**61**. *Designs as T* **34**/**50**. *Chalk-surfaced paper.* W **7**. P 14 (millieme values) or 13 (piastre values).

123	34	1m. black and orange	2·00	1·50
124	35	2m. black and bright blue	2·00	1·00
125	36	3m. black and green	7·00	3·50
126	37	4m. black and yellow-green	1·75	3·50
127	38	5m. black and purple	2·25	10
		a. *Black and reddish purple* (8.6.59)	6·00	50
128	39	10m. black and pale blue	30	10
129	40	15m. black and chestnut	4·00	10
		a. *Black and brown-orange* (1961*)	4·50	10
130	41	2p. deep blue and pale blue	30	10
		a. *Deep blue and very pale blue* (9.58*)	4·00	10
131	42	3p. brown and dull ultramarine	8·50	10
		a. *Brown and deep blue* (11.59)	9·00	1·25
132	43	3½p. bright green and red-brown	2·25	10
		a. *Light emerald and red-brown* (11.61*)	4·00	10
133	44	4p. ultramarine and black	1·25	10
		a. *Deep blue and black* (7.59*)	7·00	10
134	45	5p. orange-brown and yellow-green	50	10
135	46	6p. blue and black	8·50	2·50
		a. *Deep blue and black* (8.61*)	16·00	6·50
136	47	8p. blue and brown	14·00	3·50
		a. *Deep blue and brown* (5.60*)	16·00	3·50
137	48	10p. black and green	1·50	40
138	49	20p. blue-green and black	5·50	2·50
139	50	50p. carmine and black	13·00	2·50
123/39		Set of 17	65·00	19·00

*Earliest known postmark date.

STAMP BOOKLETS

Nos. SB1/4 have one cover inscribed in English and one in Arabic. Listings are provided for booklets believed to have been issued, with prices quoted for those known to still exist.

1912 (Dec). *Black on pink cover, size 74×29 mm. Stapled.*
SB1   100m. booklet containing twenty 5m. (No. 23) in pairs £650

1924. *Black on pink cover, size 45×50 mm. Stapled.*
SB2   105m. booklet containing twenty 5m. (No. 34) in blocks of 4 ....

1930. *Black on pink cover, size 45×50 mm. Stapled.*
SB3   100m. booklet containing twenty 5m. (No. 41) in blocks of 4 .... £1200

Some supplies of No. SB3 included a page of air mail labels.

POSTAGE DUE STAMPS

1897 (1 Mar). *Type D* **24** *of Egypt, optd with T* **1** *at Bûlaq.*

D1	2m. green	1·75	5·00
	a. Opt omitted (in horiz pair with normal)	£2500	
D2	4m. maroon	1·75	5·00
	a. Bisected (2m.) (on cover)	†	—
D3	1p. ultramarine	10·00	3·50
D4	2p. orange	10·00	7·00
	a. Bisected (1p.) (on cover)	†	£1200
D1/4	Set of 4	21·00	18·00

In some printings the large dot is omitted from the left-hand Arabic character on one stamp in the pane.

No. D1 has been recorded used as a bisect.

D **1** Gunboat *Zafir*

D **2** Gunboat *Zafir*

1901 (1 Jan)–**26**. *Typo. Ordinary paper.* W **4** (sideways). P 14.

D5	D **1**	2m. black and brown	55	60
		a. Wmk upright (1912)	£150	60·00
		b. Chalk-surfaced paper (6.24*)	75	5·50
D6		4m. brown and green	2·00	90
		a. Chalk-surfaced paper (9.26*)	6·00	3·00
D7		10m. green and mauve	4·00	3·75
		a. Wmk upright (1912)	£100	50·00
		b. Chalk-surfaced paper (6.24*)	10·00	10·00
D8		20m. ultramarine and carmine	3·25	3·25
D5/8		Set of 4	9·00	7·50

*Dates quoted for the chalk-surfaced paper printings are those of the earliest recorded postal use. These printings were despatched to the Sudan in March 1922 (10m.) or September 1922 (others).

The 4m. is known bisected at Khartoum or Omdurman in November/December 1901 and the 20m. at El Obeid in 1904–05.

1927–30. *Chalk-surfaced paper.* W **7.** P 14.

D9	D **1**	2m. black and brown (1930)	2·50	2·50
D10		4m. brown and green	1·00	80
D11		10m. green and mauve	1·25	1·60
		a. Ordinary paper	19·00	
D9/11		Set of 3	4·25	4·50

1948 (1 Jan). *Arabic inscriptions at foot altered. Chalk-surfaced paper. Typo.* W **7.** P 14.

D12	D **2**	2m. black and brown-orange	1·00	35·00
D13		4m. brown and green	2·00	38·00
D14		10m. green and mauve	18·00	20·00
D15		20m. ultramarine and carmine	18·00	32·00
D12/15		Set of 4	35·00	£110

The 10 and 20m. were reissued in 1980 on Sudan arms watermarked paper.

OFFICIAL STAMPS

1900 (8 Feb). *5 mils of 1897 punctured "S G" by hand. The "S" has 14 and the "G" 12 holes.*

O1	5m. rose-carmine	48·00	16·00

1901 (Jan). *1m. wmk Quatrefoil, punctured as No. O1.*

O2	1m. brown and carmine	42·00	30·00

Nos. O1/2 are found with the punctured "SG" inverted, reversed or inverted and reversed.

O.S.G.S.   O.S.G.S.

(O **1**) ("On Sudan Government Service")   (O **2**) ("On Sudan Government Service")

1902. *No. 10 optd at Khartoum as Type O* **1** *in groups of 30 stamps.*

O3	**2**	1m. brown and pink	2·00	8·50
		a. Oval "O" (No. 19)	40·00	£110
		b. Round stops. (Nos. 25 to 30)	7·50	40·00
		c. Opt inverted	£250	£350
		d. Ditto and oval "O"	£3000	£3500
		e. Opt double	£650	£800
		f. Opt double	£375	
		g. Ditto and round stops	£950	
		h. Ditto and oval "O"	£3500	

1903–12. *T* **2** *optd as Type O* **2**, *by D.L.R. in sheets of 120 stamps.*
(i) W **3**.(3.06)

O4		10p. black and mauve	13·00	25·00
		a. Malformed "O"	£120	

(ii) W **4**.

O5		1m. brown and carmine (9.04)	50	10
		a. Opt double		
		b. Malformed "O"	19·00	10·00
O6		3m. mauve and green (2.04)	2·50	15
		a. Opt double	£850	£850
		b. Malformed "O"	42·00	12·00
O7		5m. scarlet and black (1.1.03)	2·50	10
		a. Malformed "O"	42·00	10·00
O8		1p. blue and brown (1.1.03)	3·00	10
		a. Malformed "O"	42·00	10·00
O9		2p. black and blue (1.1.03)	22·00	20
		a. Malformed "O"	£150	14·00
O10		5p. brown and green (1.1.03)	2·00	30
		a. Malformed "O"	45·00	15·00
O11		10p. black and mauve (9.12)	4·00	55·00
		a. Malformed "O"	65·00	
O4/11		Set of 8	45·00	70·00

The malformed "O" is slightly flattened on the left-hand side and occurs on position 7 of the lower pane.

1913 (1 Jan)–**22.** *Nos. 18/20 and 23/8 punctured "SG" by machine. The "S" has 12 holes and the "G" 13.*

O12	**2**	1m. brown and carmine	9·00	25
O13		2m. green and brown (1915)	8·00	7·50
O14		3m. mauve and green	15·00	70
O15		5m. scarlet and black	5·00	15
O16		1p. blue and brown	7·50	35
O17		2p. black and blue	16·00	65
O18		2p. purple and orange-yellow (*chalk-surfaced paper*) (1922)	5·50	8·00
O19		5p. brown and black	32·00	1·50
		a. Chalk-surfaced paper	32·00	4·50
O20		10p. black and mauve (1914)	42·00	32·00
		a. Chalk-surfaced paper	42·00	32·00
O12/20 Set of 9			£130	45·00

1922. *Nos. 32/5 punctured "SG" by machine. The "S" has 9 holes and the "G" 10.*

O21	**6**	3m. mauve and green	17·00	14·00
O22		4m. green and chocolate	22·00	9·00
O23		5m. olive-brown and black	3·00	1·50
O24		10m. carmine and black	3·00	1·50
O21/4 Set of 4			40·00	23·00

1927–30. *Nos. 39/42, 44, 45 and 46 punctured "SG" by machine. Nos. O25/8 have 9 holes in the "S" and 10 in the "G"; Nos. O29/31 12 holes in the "S" and 13 in the "G".*

O25	**6**	3m. mauve and green (1928)	15·00	3·50
O26		4m. green and chocolate (1930)	75·00	48·00
O27		5m. olive-green and black	6·00	10
O28		10m. carmine and black	18·00	35
O29	**2**	2p. purple and orange-yellow	20·00	1·00
O30		5p. chestnut and green	18·00	3·50
O31		10p. black and reddish purple	40·00	10·00
O25/31 Set of 7			£170	60·00

The use of Nos. O25/31 on internal official mail ceased in 1932, but they continued to be required for official mail to foreign destinations until replaced by Nos. O32/46 in 1936.

S.G.	S.G.	S.G.
(O 3)	(O 4)	(O 4a)

1936 (19 Sept)–**46.** *Nos. 37a, 38a, 39/43 optd with Type O **3**, and 44, 44ba, 44c, 45, 45ba, 45ca, 46 and 46ba with Type O **4.** W 7. P 14.*

O32	**6**	1m. black and orange (22.11.46)	2·50	9·50
		a. Opt double	†	£160
O33		2m. orange and chocolate (*ordinary paper*) (4.45)	2·00	5·50
		a. Chalk-surfaced paper	—	70·00
O34		3m. mauve and green (*chalk-surfaced paper*) (1.37)	3·00	10
O35		4m. green and chocolate (*chalk-surfaced paper*)	3·50	2·75
		a. Ordinary paper	35·00	2·00
O36		5m. olive-brown and black (*chalk-surfaced paper*) (3.40)	2·75	10
		a. Ordinary paper	20·00	40
O37		10m. carmine and black (*chalk-surfaced paper*) (6.46)	1·00	10
O38		15m. bright blue and chestnut (*chalk-surfaced paper*) (21.6.37)	7·50	30
		a. Ordinary paper	55·00	2·75
O39	**2**	2p. purple and orange-yellow (*chalk-surfaced paper*) (4.37)	14·00	10
		a. Ordinary paper	35·00	2·00
O39b		3p. red-brown and blue (4.46)	6·50	2·75
O39c		4p. ultramarine and black (*chalk-surfaced paper*) (4.46)	30·00	5·00
		ca. Ordinary paper	60·00	4·00
O40		5p. chestnut and green (*chalk-surfaced paper*)	17·00	10
		a. Ordinary paper	65·00	4·50
O40b		6p. greenish blue and black (4.46)	8·00	7·00
O40c		8p. emerald and black (4.46)	5·50	32·00
O41		10p. black and reddish purple (*chalk-surfaced paper*) (10.37)	32·00	13·00
		a. Ordinary paper. *Black and bright mauve* (1941)	50·00	5·00
O42		20p. pale blue and blue (6.46)	28·00	25·00
O32/42 Set of 15			£140	85·00

1948 (1 Jan). *Nos. 96/102 optd with Type O **3**, and 103/111 with Type O **4**.*

O43	**22**	1m. black and orange	30	3·75
O44		2m. orange and chocolate	1·25	10
O45		3m. mauve and green	3·50	7·50
O46		4m. deep green and chocolate	3·25	4·25
O47		5m. olive-brown and black	3·25	10
O48		10m. rose-red and black	3·25	2·25
O49		15m. ultramarine and chestnut	3·50	10
O50	**23**	2p. purple and orange-yellow	3·50	10
O51		3p. red-brown and deep blue	3·50	10
O52		4p. ultramarine and black	3·25	10
		a. Perf 13 (optd Type O **4a**)	13·00	15·00
O53		5p. brown-orange and deep green	4·25	10
O54		6p. greenish blue and black	3·25	10
O55		8p. bluish green and black	3·25	3·50
O56		10p. black and mauve	3·50	20
O57		20p. pale blue and deep blue	4·50	25
O58		50p. carmine and ultramarine	65·00	60·00
O43/58 Set of 16			£100	75·00

1950 (1 July). *Air. Optd with Type O **4a**.*

O59	**26**	2p. black and blue-green (R.)	15·00	3·25
O60	**27**	2½p. light blue and red-orange	1·50	1·75
O61	**28**	3p. reddish purple and blue	80	1·00
O62	**29**	3½p. purple-brown and yellow-brown	80	8·00
O63	**30**	4p. brown and light blue	80	7·50
O64	**31**	4½p. black and ultramarine (R.)	4·00	17·00
		a. Black and steel-blue	10·00	20·00
O65	**32**	6p. black and carmine (R.)	1·00	4·25
O66	**33**	20p. black and purple (R.)	4·00	12·00
O59/66 Set of 8			25·00	48·00

1951 (1 Sept)–**62?.** *Nos. 123/9 optd with Type O **3**, and 130/9 with Type O **4a.***

O67	**34**	1m. black and orange (R.)	40	3·75
O68	**35**	2m. black and bright blue (R.)	50	1·00
O69	**36**	3m. black and green (R.)	6·50	15·00
O70	**37**	4m. black and yellow-green (R.)	10	5·50
O71	**38**	5m. black and purple (R.)	10	10
O72	**39**	10m. black and pale blue (R.)	10	10
O73	**40**	15m. black and chestnut (R.)	75	10
O74	**41**	2p. deep blue and pale blue	10	10
		a. Opt inverted	£600	
		b. *Deep blue and very pale blue (9.61*)*	1·75	10
O75	**42**	3p. brown and deep blue	12·00	10
		a. *Brown and deep blue (8.60*)*	12·00	2·00
O76	**43**	3½p. bright green and red-brown	25	10
		a. *Light emerald & red-brown (1962?)*	4·00	2·25
O77	**44**	4p. ultramarine and black	2·00	10
		a. *Deep blue and black (1961)*	2·50	10
O78	**45**	5p. orange-brown and yellow-green	25	10
O79	**46**	6p. blue and black	50	2·75
		a. *Deep blue and black (1962?)*	10·00	7·00
O80	**47**	8p. blue and brown	75	10
		a. *Deep blue and brown (1962?)*	5·00	2·75
O81	**48**	10p. black and green (R.)	50	10
O81a		10p. black and green (Blk.) (1958)	13·00	2·00
O82	**49**	20p. blue-green and black	1·25	30
		a. Opt inverted	—	£800
O83	**50**	50p. carmine and black	3·50	1·25
O67/83 Set of 18			38·00	27·00

The 5, 10 and 15m. values were later reissued with a thinner overprint.

*Earliest known postmark date.

ARMY SERVICE STAMPS

(A 1)	(A 2)	(A 3)	

1905 (1 Jan). *T 2 optd at Khartoum as Types A **1** or A **2**. W **4** (Mult Star and Crescent).*

(i) "ARMY" reading up.

A1		1m. brown and carmine (A **1**)	3·25	2·00
		a. "!" for "I"	60·00	35·00
		b. Opt Type A **2**	45·00	24·00
		c. Pair. Types A **1** and A **2** se-tenant	80·00	80·00

(ii) Overprint horizontal.

A2		1m. brown and carmine (A **1**)	£325	
		a. "!" for "I"	£3750	
		b. Opt Type A **2**	£2500	

The horizontal overprint exists with either "ARMY" or "OFFICIAL" reading the right way up. It did not fit the stamps, resulting in misplacements where more than one whole overprint appears, or when the two words are transposed.

(iii) "ARMY" reading down.

A3		1m. brown and carmine (A **1**)	90·00	70·00
		a. "!" for "I"	£800	£800
		b. Opt Type A **2**	£700	£475

1905 (Nov). *As No. A1, but W **3** (Quatrefoil).*

A4		1m. brown and pink (A **1**)	£150	£160
		a. "!" for "I"	£3500	£2000
		b. Opt Type A **2**	£1700	£1700
		c. Pair. Types A **1** and A **2** se-tenant	£3250	

The setting used for overprinting Nos. A1/4 was 30 (6×5). The "!" for "I" variety occurs on R. 5/4 and overprint Type A **2** on R. 1/6 and 2/6 of the setting.

Two varieties of the 1 millieme.

A. 1st Ptg. 14 mm between lines of opt.

B. Later Ptgs. 12 mm between lines.

All other values are Type B.

1906 (Jan)–**11.** *T 2 optd as Type A **3**.*

(i) W **4** (Mult Star and Crescent).

A5		1m. brown and carmine (Type A)	£375	£300
		a. Opt double, one albino	£400	
A6		1m. brown and carmine (Type B)	1·50	20
		a. Opt double, one diagonal	†	£850
		b. Opt inverted	£450	£475
		c. Pair, one without opt	†	£4750
		d. "Service" inverted	†	£3500
		e. "A" for "A" in Army	£250	£160
A7		2m. green and brown	14·00	1·00
		a. Pair, one without opt	£3000	
		b. "Army" omitted	£3250	£3250
A8		3m. mauve and green	17·00	40
		a. Opt inverted	£1900	
A9		5m. scarlet and black	1·50	10
		a. Opt. double	£250	£190
		ab. Opt double, one diagonal	£225	
		b. Opt inverted	†	£225
		c. "Amry"	†	£2250
		d. "A" for "A" in Army	—	£250
		e. Opt double, one inverted	£900	£400
A10		1p. blue and brown	14·00	15
		a. "Army" omitted	—	£2250
A11		2p. black and blue (1.09)	60·00	£175
		a. Opt double	†	£3000
A12		5p. brown and green (5.08)	£120	65·00
A13		10p. black and mauve (5.11)	£500	£600
A6s/10s Optd "Specimen" Set of 5			£110	

There were a number of printings of these Army Service stamps; the earlier are as Type A **3**; the 1908 printing has a narrower "A" in "Army" and the 1910–11 printings have the tail of the "y" in "Army" much shorter.

(ii) W **3** (Quatrefoil).

A14		2p. black and green	70·00	10·00
A15		5p. brown and green	£100	£200
A16		10p. black and mauve	£140	£240
A14/16 Set of 3			£275	£550
A14s/16s Optd "Specimen" Set of 3			£100	

1913 (1 Jan)–**22.** *Nos. 18/20 and 23/8 punctured "AS" by machine. The "A" has 12 holes and the "S" 11.*

A17	**2**	1m. brown and carmine	30·00	3·75
A18		2m. green and brown	7·50	70
A19		3m. mauve and green	48·00	3·00
A20		5m. scarlet and black	11·00	50
		a. On No. 13		
A21		1p. blue and brown	24·00	75
A22		2p. black and blue	55·00	4·50
A23		2p. purple and orange-yellow (*chalk-surfaced paper*) (1922)	60·00	55·00
A24		5p. brown and black	65·00	30·00
		a. Chalk-surfaced paper	65·00	30·00
A25		10p. black and mauve (1914)	£450	£275
A17/25 Set of 9			£650	£325

1922–24. *Nos. 31a and 34/5 punctured "AS" by machine. The "A" has 8 holes and the "S" 9.*

A26	**6**	2m. yellow and chocolate (1924)	70·00	42·00
A27		5m. olive-brown and black (4.2.22)	13·00	4·00
A28		10m. carmine and black	19·00	5·50
A26/8 Set of 3			90·00	48·00

The use of Nos. A17/28 on internal Army mail ceased when the Egyptian units were withdrawn at the end of 1924, but existing stocks continued to be used on Army mail to foreign destinations until supplies were exhausted.

Swaziland

PRICES FOR STAMPS ON COVER TO 1945	
Nos. 1/10	*from* × 40
Nos. 11/20	*from* × 4
Nos. 21/4	*from* × 5
Nos. 25/7	*from* × 10
Nos. 28/38	*from* × 4
Nos. 39/41	*from* × 5
Nos. D1/2	*from* × 30

TRIPARTITE GOVERNMENT

Following internal unrest and problems caused by the multitude of commercial concessions granted by the Swazi king the British and Transvaal governments intervened during 1889 to establish a tripartite administration under which the country was controlled by their representatives, acting with the agent of the Swazi king.

The Pretoria government had previously purchased the concession to run the postal service and, on the establishment of the tripartite administration, provided overprinted Transvaal stamps for use from a post office at Embekelweni and later at Bremersdorp and Darkton.

Swaziland
(1)

1889 (18 Oct)–**90.** *Stamps of Transvaal (South African Republic) optd with T **1**, in black.*

(a) P 12½×12.

1	**18**	1d. carmine	17·00	17·00
		a. Opt inverted	£700	£650
2		2d. olive-bistre	85·00	23·00
		a. Opt inverted	—	£1200
		b. "Swazielan"	£1100	£650
		c. "Swazielan" inverted	£750	£475
3		1s. green	11·00	13·00
		a. Opt inverted	£750	£475

(b) P 12½.

4	**18**	½d. grey	9·00	18·00
		a. Opt inverted	£850	£650
		b. "Swazielan"	£1200	£650
		c. "Swazielan" inverted	—	£4500
5		2d. olive-bistre	18·00	15·00
		a. Opt inverted	£800	£450
		b. "Swazielan"	£475	£400
		c. "Swazielan" inverted	£4500	£4000
6		6d. blue	23·00	45·00
7		2s.6d. buff (20.10.90)	£250	£275
8		5s. slate-blue (20.10.90)	£150	£190
		a. Opt inverted	£1800	£2250
		b. "Swazielan"	£4500	
		c. "Swazielan" inverted		
9		10s. dull chestnut (20.10.90)	£5500	£3500

The variety without "d" occurs on R. 6/1 in each sheet of certain printings.

A printing of the ½d, 1d, 2d and 10s. yellow-brown with stop after "Swaziland" was made in July 1894, but such stamps were not issued.

It is possible that the dates quoted above were those on which the overprinting took place in Pretoria and that the stamps were issued slightly later in Swaziland itself.

1892 (Aug). *Optd in carmine. P 12½.*

10	**18**	½d. grey	7·50	16·00
		a. Opt inverted	£500	
		b. Opt double	£450	£450
		c. Pair, one without opt.	—	£1800

No. 10 was overprinted in Pretoria during August 1892 when Swaziland was under quarantine due to smallpox. It is unlikely that it saw much postal use before all the overprints were withdrawn, although cancelled-to-order examples are plentiful.

It appears likely that no further supplies of stamps overprinted "Swazieland" were provided by Pretoria after December 1892, although stocks held at post offices were used up. The overprinted stamps were declared to be invalid from 7 November 1894. They were replaced by unoverprinted issues of the Transvaal (South African Republic).

Stamps of TRANSVAAL (SOUTH AFRICAN REPUBLIC) used in Swaziland between December 1892 and January 1900.

1885–93. *(Nos. 175/87).*

Z1	½d. grey		30·00
Z2	1d. carmine		30·00
Z3	2d. olive-bistre		15·00
Z4	2½d. mauve		30·00
Z5	3d. mauve		30·00
Z6	4d. bronze-green		30·00
Z9	2s.6d. orange-buff		

1893. *(Nos. 195/9).*

Z10	½d. on 2d. olive-bistre (Type A surch in red)		
Z11	½d. on 2d. olive-bistre (Type A surch in black)		
Z12	1d. on 6d. blue (Type A surch)		32·00
	a. Surch Type B		32·00
Z13	2½d. on green ("2½ Pence" in one line)		
	1s. (Type A surch)		32·00
	a. Surch Type B		32·00

1894. *(Nos. 200/4).*

Z16	1d. carmine		30·00
Z17	2d. olive-bistre		30·00

1895–96. *(Nos. 205/12a).*

Z20	½d. pearl-grey		30·00
Z21	1d. rose-red		15·00
Z22	2d. olive-bistre		15·00
Z25	6d. pale dull blue		30·00

1895. *(Nos. 213/14).*

Z27	½d. on 1s. green		

1895. *Introduction of Penny Postage (No. 215b).*

Z29	1d. red		40·00

1896–97. *(Nos. 216/24).*

Z30	½d. green		30·00
Z31	1d. rose-red and green		15·00
Z35	4d. sage-green and green		30·00
Z36	6d. lilac and green		30·00
Z37	1s. ochre and green		60·00

Prices are for clear and fairly complete postmarks. Examples dated in 1892 and 1893 are worth a premium. For list of post offices open during this period see boxed note below. Most known examples are from Bremersdorp (squared circle inscr "SWAZIEL" later replaced by "Z.A.R." or c.d.s.) or Darkton (c.d.s.).

Shortly after the outbreak of the Boer War in 1899 the Transvaal administration withdrew from Swaziland, although the post office at Darkton, which was on the border, was still operating in early 1900. There was, however, no further organised postal service in Swaziland until the country became a British Protectorate in March 1902. From that date, until the introduction of the 1933 definitives, the stamps of Transvaal and subsequently South Africa were in use.

The following post offices or postal agencies existed in Swaziland before 1933. Dates given are those on which it is generally accepted that the offices were first opened. Some were subsequently closed before the end of the period.

Bremersdorp (1890)	Mankaiana (1913)
Darkton (1891)	Mbabane (*previously*
Dwaleni (1918)	Embabaan) (1905)
Embabaan (1895)	M'dimba (1898)
Embekelweni (1889)	Mhlotsheni (1910)
Ezulweni (1910)	Mooihoek (1918)
Forbes Reef (1906)	Motshane (1929)
Goedgegun (1925)	Nomahasha (1904)
Hlatikulu (1903)	Nsoko (1927)
Hluti (1912)	Piggs Peak (1899)
Ivy (1912)	Sandhlan (1903)
Kubuta (1926)	Sicunusa (1913)
Mahamba (1899)	Stegi (1910)
Malkerns (1914)	Umkwakweni (1898)
Malomba (1928)	White Umbuluzi (1925)

BRITISH PROTECTORATE

2 King George V

3 King George VI

(Des Rev. C. C. Tugman. Recess D.L.R.)

1933 (3 Jan). Wmk Mult Script CA. P 14.

11	**2**	½d. green	30	30
12		1d. carmine	30	20
13		2d. brown	30	45
14		3d. blue	45	3·00
15		4d. orange	2·75	3·50
16		6d. bright purple	1·25	95
17		1s. olive	1·50	2·75
18		2s.6d. bright violet	15·00	22·00
19		5s. grey	30·00	50·00
20		10s. sepia	85·00	£110
11/20 *Set of 10*			£120	£170
11s/20s Perf "Specimen" *Set of 10*			£225	

The ½d., 1d., 2d. and 6d. values exist overprinted "OFFICIAL", but authority for their use was withdrawn before any were actually used. However, some stamps had already been issued to the Secretariat staff before instructions were received to invalidate their use (*Price £21,000 per set un*).

1935 (4 May). *Silver Jubilee. As Nos. 91/4 of Antigua, but ptd by B.W. P 11×12.*

21	1d. deep blue and scarlet	50	1·50
	a. Extra flagstaff	£275	£325
	b. Short extra flagstaff	£375	
	c. Lightning conductor	£375	
	d. Flagstaff on right-hand turret	£100	
	e. Double flagstaff	£100	
22	2d. ultramarine and grey-black	70	1·75
	a. Extra flagstaff	£100	£160
	b. Short extra flagstaff	£130	
	c. Lightning conductor	£100	
23	3d. brown and deep blue	70	5·50
	a. Extra flagstaff	75·00	£190
	b. Short extra flagstaff	95·00	£160
	c. Lightning conductor	85·00	
24	6d. slate and purple	70	2·25
	a. Extra flagstaff	90·00	£150
	b. Short extra flagstaff	£100	
	c. Lightning conductor	£110	
21/4 *Set of 4*		2·40	10·00
21s/4s Perf "Specimen" *Set of 4*		£110	

For illustrations of plate varieties see Omnibus section following Zanzibar.

1937 (12 May). *Coronation. As Nos. 95/7 of Antigua. P 11×11½.*

25	1d. carmine	50	2·25
26	2d. yellow-brown	50	25
27	3d. blue	50	75
25/7 *Set of 3*		1·40	3·00
25s/7s Perf "Specimen" *Set of 3*		80·00	

(Recess D.L.R.)

1938 (1 Apr)–**54**. Wmk Mult Script CA. P 13½×13.

28	**3**	½d. green	2·50	1·25
		a. Perf 13½×14 (1.43)	30	2·75
		b. Perf 13½×14. *Bronze-green* (2.50)	2·00	7·00
29		1d. rose-red	2·75	1·25
		a. Perf 13½×14 (1.43)	30	1·75
30		1½d. light blue	4·25	75
		a. Perf 14 (1941)	2·75	1·00
		b. Perf 13½×14 (1.43)	30	1·00
		ba. Printed on the gummed side	£2750	
31		2d. yellow-brown	2·50	1·25
		a. Perf 13½×14 (1.43)	30	50
32		3d. ultramarine	11·00	1·75
		a. *Deep blue* (10.38)	16·00	1·75
		b. Perf 13½×14 *Ultramarine* (1.43)	4·25	6·00
		c. Perf 13½×14 *Light ultram* (10.46)	21·00	15·00
		d. Perf 13½×14 *Deep blue* (10.47)	11·00	12·00
33		4d. orange	6·00	1·75
		a. Perf 13½×14 (1.43)	50	1·40
34		6d. deep magenta	16·00	2·75
		a. Perf 13½×14 (1.43)	4·50	4·50
		b. Perf 13½×14. *Reddish purple (shades)* (7.44)	4·50	1·50
		c. Perf 13½×14. *Claret* (13.10.54)	7·00	6·00
35		1s. brown-olive	16·00	2·00
		a. Perf 13½×14 (1.43)	1·25	65
36		2s.6d. bright violet	25·00	4·00
		a. Perf 13½×14. *Violet* (1.43)	18·00	2·50
		b. Perf 13½×14. *Reddish violet* (10.47)	18·00	9·50
37		5s. grey	55·00	14·00
		a. Perf 13½×14. *Slate* (1.43)	55·00	50·00
		b. Perf 13½×14. *Grey* (5.44)	30·00	14·00
38		10s. sepia	60·00	6·00
		a. Perf 13½×14 (1.43)	6·50	6·00
28/38a *Set of 11*			60·00	28·00
28s/38s Perf "Specimen" *Set of 11*			£225	

The above perforations vary slightly from stamp to stamp, but the average measurements are respectively: 13.3×13.2 comb (13½×13), 14.2 line (14) and 13.3×13.8 comb (13½×14).

Swaziland
(4)

1945 (3 Dec). *Victory. Nos. 108/10 of South Africa optd with T 4.*

			Un pair	Us pair	Us single
39	1d. brown and carmine		55	80	10
40	2d. slate-blue and violet		55	80	10
41	3d. deep blue and blue		55	2·50	20
39/41 *Set of 3*			1·50	3·50	30

1947 (17 Feb). *Royal Visit. As Nos. 32/5 of Basutoland.*

			Un	Us
42	1d. scarlet		10	10
43	2d. green		10	10
44	3d. ultramarine		10	10
45	1s. mauve		10	10
42/5 *Set of 4*			30	30
42s/5s Perf "Specimen" *Set of 4*		90·00		

1948 (1 Dec). *Royal Silver Wedding. As Nos. 112/13 of Antigua.*

46	1½d. ultramarine	50	60
47	10s. purple-brown	27·00	32·00

1949 (10 Oct). *75th Anniv of U.P.U. As Nos. 114/17 of Antigua.*

48	1½d. blue	15	20
	a. "A" of "CA" missing from wmk		
49	3d. deep blue	2·00	3·00
50	6d. magenta	30	70
51	1s. olive	30	1·25
48/51 *Set of 4*		2·50	4·75

POSTAGE DUE STAMPS

D 1

(Typo D.L.R.)

1933 (23 Jan)–**57**. Wmk Mult Script CA. P 14.

D1	**D 1**	1d. carmine	30	10·00
		a. Chalk-surfaced paper. *Deep carmine* (24.10.51)	20	16·00
		ac. Error. St Edward's Crown, W **9b**	£275	
D2		2d. pale violet	2·25	26·00
		a. Chalk-surfaced paper (22.2.57)	4·75	38·00
		ab. Large "d"	50·00	
D1/2 Perf "Specimen" *Set of 2*			42·00	

For illustrations of No. D2ab see above No. D1 of Basutoland.

Tanganyika

The stamps of GERMANY were used in the colony between October 1890 and July 1893 when issues for GERMAN EAST AFRICA were provided.

PRICES FOR STAMPS ON COVER TO 1945	
The Mafia Island provisionals (No. M1/52) are very rare used on cover.	
Nos. N1/5	*from* × 8
Nos. 45/59	*from* × 6
Nos. 60/2	—
Nos. 63/73	*from* × 6
Nos. 74/86	*from* × 8
Nos. 87/8	—
Nos. 89/92	*from* × 6
Nos. 93/106	*from* × 3
No. 107	—

MAFIA ISLAND

BRITISH OCCUPATION

Mafia Island was captured by the British from the Germans in January 1915. Letters were first sent out unstamped, then with stamps handstamped with Type M **1**. Later the military were supplied with handstamps by the post office in Zanzibar. These were used to produce Nos. M11/52.

(Currency. 100 heller = 1 rupee)

G.B. MAFIA (M 1)   (M 3)

1915 (Jan). *German East Africa Yacht types, handstamped with Type M **1**. Wmk Lozenges, or no wmk* (1r., 2r.). A. *In black* (2½h. *in blackish lilac*). B. *In deep purple.* C. *In reddish violet.*

		A	B	C
M1	2½h. brown	£500	†	£200
	a. Pair, one without handstamp	†	†	£3000
M2	4h. green	£600	£800	£300
	a. Pair, one without handstamp	†	†	£3000

M3	7½h. carmine	£425	£475	£100
	a. Pair, one without			
	handstamp	£5000	†	£2500
M4	15h. ultramarine	£450	£650	£170
	a. Pair, one without			
	handstamp	†	†	£2500
M5	20h. black and red/yellow	£650	£750	£325
	a. Pair, one without			
	handstamp	†	£4500	£3000
M6	30h. black and carmine	£750	£10000	£350
	a. Pair, one without			
	handstamp	£5500	†	£3000
M7	45h. black and mauve	£750	£950	£425
	a. Pair, one without			
	handstamp	£5500	†	£3500
M8	1r. carmine	£10000	†	£7000
M9	2r. green	£11000	†	£8000
M10	3r. blue-black and red	£12000	†	£9000

Prices are for unused examples.

A few contemporary Zanzibar stamps (1, 3, 6 and 15c.) and India – I.E.F. ½a and 1a are known with the above handstamp.

(Currency. 100 cents = 1 rupee)

1915 (May). *German East Africa Yacht types with handstamped four-line surcharge "G.R.—POST—6 CENTS—MAFIA" in black, green or violet. Wmk Lozenges or no wmk (1r., 2r).*

M11	6c. on 2½h. brown	£1400	£1500
	a. Pair, one without handstamp		£5500
M12	6c. on 4h. green	£1500	£1700
	a. Pair, one without handstamp		£5500
M13	6c. on 7½h. carmine	£1400	£1700
	a. Pair, one without handstamp		£5500
M14	6c. on 15h. ultramarine	£1400	£1700
M15	6c. on 20h. black and red/yellow	£1900	£2000
M16	6c. on 30h. black and carmine	£2500	£2750
M17	6c. on 45h. black and mauve	£2500	£2500
	a. Pair, one without handstamp		£6500
M18	6c. on 1r. carmine		£35000
M19	6c. on 2r. green		£40000
M20	6c. on 3r. blue-black and red		£45000

The 5, 20 and 40 pesa values of the 1901 Yacht issue are also known with the above surcharge as are the contemporary 1c. and 6c. Zanzibar stamps.

1915 (Sept). *(a) German East African fiscal stamps. "Statistik des Waaren-Verkehrs" (Trade Statistical Charge) handstamped in bluish green or violet, "O.H.B.M.S. Mafia" in a circle, as Type M 3.*

M21	24 pesa, vermilion/buff	£750	£1000
M22	12½ heller, drab	£800	£1100
	a. Pair, one without handstamp	£5500	
M23	25 heller, dull green	£800	£1100
M24	50 heller, slate	£800	£1100
	a. Pair, one without handstamp	£5500	
M25	1 rupee, lilac	£800	£1100

(b) German East African "Übersetzungs- Gebühren" (Fee) stamp, overprinted as before.

M26	25 heller, grey	£800	£1100

G. R	**G. R.**
POST	**Post**
MAFIA	**MAFIA.**
(M 4)	(M 5)

(c) Stamps as above, but with further opt as Type M 4, in bluish green or violet.

M27	24 pesa, vermilion/buff	£1000
M28	12½ heller, drab	£1100
M29	25 heller, dull green	£1100
M30	50 heller, slate	£1100
M31	1 rupee, lilac	£1100
M32	25 heller, grey (No. M26)	£1100
	a. Pair, one without handstamp	
	Type M 4	£5500

Type M 3 is also known handstamped on the 7½h., 20h. and 30h. values of German East Africa 1905 Yacht issue and also on contemporary 1, 3, 6 and 25c. Zanzibar stamps.

(Currency. 12 pies = 1 anna. 16 annas = 1 rupee)

1915 (Sept). *Nos. E1/2, E4/9, E11 and E13 of Indian Expeditionary Forces (India King George V optd "I.E.F.") with a further opt Type M 4 handstruck in green, greenish black or dull blue.*

M33	3p. grey	35·00	80·00
	a. Pair, one stamp without handstamp	—	£1700
M34	½a. light green	50·00	85·00
	a. Pair, one stamp without handstamp	£2000	£1700
M35	1a. aniline carmine	55·00	85·00
M36	2a. purple	85·00	£140
M37	2½a. ultramarine	£110	£180
M38	3a. orange	£120	£180
	a. Pair, one stamp without handstamp	†	£2750
M39	4a. olive-green	£140	£225
M40	8a. deep magenta	£250	£375
	a. Pair, one stamp without handstamp	†	£3000
M41	12a. carmine-lake	£300	£475
M42	1r. red-brown and deep blue-green	£350	£500
	a. "I.E.F." opt double, one albino	£1000	
M33/42 Set of 10		£1300	£2000

All values exist with the overprint inverted, and several are known with overprint double or sideways.

1916 (Oct). *Nos. E1/2, E4/9, E11 and E13 of Indian Expeditionary Forces (India King George V optd "I.E.F.") with further opt Type M 5 handstruck in green, greenish black, dull blue or violet.*

M43	3p. grey	£130	£150
M44	½a. light green	£140	£140
	a. Pair, one without handstamp		£3000
M45	1a. aniline carmine	£100	£120
M46	2a. purple	£170	£170
M47	2½a. ultramarine	£180	£190
M48	3a. orange	£180	£190
M49	4a. olive-green	£300	£300
M50	8a. deep magenta	£375	£375

M51	12a. carmine-lake	£400	£475
M52	1r. red-brown and deep blue-green	£450	£500
M43/52 Set of 10		£2000	£2250

Stamps with handstamp inverted are known.

Used examples of Nos. M43/52 with black double-ring backdated postmarks of "JA 23 1915" are worth about 60% of the prices quoted.

NYASALAND-RHODESIAN FORCE

This issue was sanctioned for use by the Nyasaland-Rhodesian Force during operations in German East Africa, Mozambique and Nyasaland. Unoverprinted Nyasaland stamps were used by the Force prior to the introduction of Nos. N1/5 and, again, in 1918.

N. F.
(N 1)

1916 (7 Aug–18 Sept*). *Nos. 83, 86, 90/1 and 93 of Malawi (Nyasaland) optd with Type N 1 by Govt Printer, Zomba.*

N1	½d. green	1·50	8·00
N2	1d. scarlet	1·50	3·25
N3	3d. purple/yellow (15 Sept*)	11·00	17·00
	a. Opt double	†	£10000
N4	4d. black and red/yellow (13 Sept*)	30·00	40·00
N5	1s. black/green (18 Sept*)	38·00	48·00
N1/5 Set of 5		75·00	£100
N1s/5s Optd "Specimen" Set of 5		£200	

*Earliest known dates of use.

Of No. N3a only six copies were printed, these being the bottom row on one pane issued at M'bamba Bay F.P.O., German East Africa in March 1918.

This overprint was applied in a setting of 60 (10 rows of 6) and the following minor varieties occur on all values: small stop after "N" (R. 1/1); broken "F" (R. 4/3); very small stop after "F" (R. 6/5); no serifs at top left and bottom of "N" (R. 10/1).

TANGANYIKA

BRITISH OCCUPATION OF GERMAN EAST AFRICA

Following the invasion of German East Africa by Allied forces civilian mail was accepted by the Indian Army postal service, using Indian stamps overprinted "I.E.F.". Some offices reverted to civilian control on 1 June 1917 and these used stamps of East Africa and Uganda until the "G.E.A." overprints were ready. The last field post offices, in the southern part of the country, did not come under civilian control until 15 March 1919.

(Currency. 100 cents = 1 rupee)

G.E.A.	**G.E.A.**	**G.E.A.**
(1)	(2)	(3)

1917 (Oct)–21. *Nos. 44/5, 46a/51, 52b, 53/9 and 61 of Kenya, Uganda and Tanganyika optd with T 1 and 2. Ordinary paper (1c. to 15c.) or chalk-surfaced paper (others). Wmk Mult Crown CA.*

45	1c. black (R.)	15	80
	aw. Wmk inverted	£180	
	ay. Wmk inverted and reversed	£110	
	b. Vermilion opt	20·00	16·00
47	3c. green	15	15
48	6c. scarlet	15	10
	a. Wmk sideways	£2000	£2500
	w. Wmk inverted	†	£190
49	10c. yellow-orange	50	60
	y. Wmk inverted and reversed	£160	
50	12c. slate-grey	50	2·25
	w. Wmk inverted and reversed	£130	
51	15c. bright blue	1·00	2·75
	w. Wmk inverted	£150	
52	25c. black and red/yellow	80	3·50
	a. On pale yellow (1921)	1·40	15·00
	as. Optd "Specimen"	40·00	
53	50c. black and lilac	1·00	3·25
54	75c. black/blue-green, olive back (R.)	1·00	4·50
	a. On emerald back (1921)	3·25	45·00
	as. Optd "Specimen"	50·00	
55	1r. black/green (R.)	3·00	7·00
	a. On emerald back (1919)	7·50	55·00
56	2r. red and black/blue	11·00	55·00
	x. Wmk reversed		
57	3r. violet and green	13·00	80·00
58	4r. red and green/yellow	17·00	90·00
59	5r. blue and dull black	38·00	90·00
60	10r. red and green/green	85·00	£325
	a. On emerald back	£100	£375
61	20r. black and purple/red	£190	£400
62	50r. carmine and green	£475	£800
	s. Optd "Specimen"	£190	
45/61 Set of 16		£325	£950
45s/61s Optd "Specimen" Set of 16		£400	

Early printings of the rupee values exist with very large stop after the "E" in "G.E.A." (R. 5/3). There are round stops after "E" varieties, which in one position of later printings became a small stop.

The only known used example of No. 48a is cancelled at Tanga in August 1918.

Examples of Nos. 45/55 can also be found handstamped with Type M 5, but these were not issued.

1921. *Nos. 69/74 of Kenya, Uganda and Tanganyika optd with T 1 or 2. Chalk-surfaced paper (50c. to 5r.). Wmk Mult Script CA.*

63	12c. slate-grey	6·50	95·00
64	15c. bright blue	3·25	5·50
65	50c. black and dull purple	10·00	85·00
66	2r. red and black/blue	32·00	£120
67	3r. violet and green	70·00	£240
68	5r. blue and dull purple	95·00	£250
63/8 Set of 6		£190	£650
63s/8s Optd "Specimen" Set of 6		£225	

1922. *Nos. 65 and 68 of Kenya, Uganda and Tanganyika optd by the Government Printer at Dar-es-Salaam with T 3. Wmk Mult Script CA.*

72	1c. black (R.)	80	19·00
73	10c. orange	80	14·00
	y. Wmk inverted and reversed	£130	

No. 73 is known with the overprint inverted, but this is of clandestine origin.

BRITISH MANDATED TERRITORY
(New Currency. 100 cents = 1 shilling)

4 Giraffe	5 Giraffe

(Recess B.W.)

1922–24. *Head in black.*

(a) Wmk Mult Script CA. P 15×14.

74	4	5c. slate-purple	2·25	20
75		10c. carmine	2·25	85
76		15c. carmine-red	2·00	10
77		20c. orange	1·75	9
78		25c. black	5·50	6·50
79		30c. blue	5·00	5·00
80		40c. yellow-brown	2·75	4·50
81		50c. slate-grey	2·25	1·50
82		75c. yellow-bistre	3·25	18·00

(b) Wmk Mult Script CA (sideways). P 14.

83	5	1s. green	4·25	14·00
		a. Wmk upright (1923)	3·00	11·00
84		2s. purple	5·50	16·00
		a. Wmk upright (1924)	4·50	25·00
85		3s. black	18·00	28·00
86		5s. scarlet	32·00	85·00
		a. Wmk upright (1923)	16·00	75·00
87		10s. deep blue	£120	£225
		a. Wmk upright (1923)	55·00	£110
88		£1 yellow-orange	£200	£350
		a. Wmk upright (1923)	£170	£325
74/88 Set of 15			£250	£550
74s/88s Optd "Specimen" Set of 15			£250	

On the £1 stamp the words of value are on a curved scroll running across the stamp above the words "POSTAGE AND REVENUE".

Nos. 83/8 are known showing a forged Dodoma postmark, dated "16 JA 22".

1925. *As 1922. Frame colours changed.*

89	4	5c. green	3·25	1·50
90		10c. orange-yellow	4·50	1·50
91		25c. blue	4·00	17·00
92		30c. purple	4·25	14·00
89/92 Set of 4			14·50	30·00
89s/92s Optd "Specimen" Set of 4			70·00	

6	7

(Typo D.L.R.)

1927–31. *Head in black. Chalk-surfaced paper (5s., 10s., £1). Wmk Mult Script CA. P 14.*

93	6	5c. green	1·75	10
94		10c. yellow	2·00	10
95		15c. carmine-red	1·75	10
96		20c. orange-buff	2·75	10
97		25c. bright blue	3·75	2·00
98		30c. dull purple	2·75	2·50
98a		30c. bright blue (1931)	25·00	30
99		40c. yellow-brown	2·00	4·50
100		50c. grey	2·50	1·00
101		75c. olive-green	2·00	15·00
102	7	1s. green	4·25	2·75
103		2s. deep purple	20·00	4·50
104		3s. black	23·00	60·00
105		5s. carmine-red	20·00	18·00
		a. Ordinary paper		
106		10s. deep blue	55·00	£100
107		£1 brown-orange	£160	£300
93/107 Set of 16			£300	£450
93s/107s Optd or Perf (No. 98as) "Specimen" Set of 16			£275	

Examples of Nos. 104/7 are known showing a forged Dar-es-Salaam postmark dated "20 NO 1928".

Tanganyika became part of the joint East African postal administration on 1 January 1933 and subsequently used the stamps of KENYA, UGANDA AND TANGANYIKA.

STAMP BOOKLETS

1922–25. *Black on red cover.*

SB1   3s. booklet containing 5c., 10c., 15c. and 20c. (Nos. 74/7), each in block of 6 .... £2000
    a. As No. SB1, but contents changed (Nos. 89/90, 76/7) (1925)

1922–26. *Black on red cover. Stapled.*

SB2   3s. booklet containing six 10c., and twelve 5c. and 15c. (Nos. 74/6) in blocks of 6
    a. As No. SB2, but contents changed (Nos. 74, 90, 76) (1925)
    b. As No. SB2, but contents changed (Nos. 89/90, 76) (1926) £1400

1927. Black on red covers. Stapled.

SB3	3s. booklet containing six 10c., and twelve 5c. and 15c. (Nos. 93/5) in blocks of 6	£1000
SB4	3s. booklet containing 5c., 10c. and 15c. (Nos. 93/5), each in block of 10	£1500

Tasmania *see* Australia

Tobago
see Trinidad and Tobago

Togo

The stamps of GERMANY were used in the colony from March 1888 until June 1897 when issues for TOGO were provided.

PRICES FOR STAMPS ON COVER
Nos. H1/7	*from* × 6
No. H8	—
No. H9	*from* × 6
No. H10	*from* × 2
No. H11	—
Nos. H12/13	*from* × 6
Nos. H14/16	—
Nos. H17/19	*from* × 12
Nos. H20/6	—
Nos. H27/8	*from* × 20
No. H29	—
Nos. H30/1	*from* × 6
Nos. H32/3	—
Nos. H34/58	*from* × 6

ANGLO-FRENCH OCCUPATION

French forces invaded southern Togo on 8 August 1914 and the British landed at Lomé on 12 August. The German administration surrendered on 26 August 1914.

The territory was jointly administered under martial law, but was formally divided between Great Britain and France, effective 1 October 1920. League of Nations mandates were issued for both areas from 20 July 1922.

(Currency. 100 pfennig = 1 mark)

Stamps of German Colonial issue Yacht Types 1900 and 1909–14 (5pf. and 10pf.)

TOGO
Anglo-French
Occupation (1)   **Half penny** (2)

SETTINGS. Nos. H1/33 were all overprinted or surcharged by the Catholic Mission, Lomé.

The initial setting for the 3pf. to 80pf. was of 50 (10×5), repeated twice on each sheet of 100. Overprints from this setting, used for Nos. H1/9, had the lines of type 3 mm apart.

Nos. H1/2 were subsequently surcharged, also from a setting of 50, to form Nos. H12/13. The surcharge setting showed a thin dropped "y" with small serifs on R. 1/1–2, 2/1, 3/1, 4/1 and 5/1–2.

The type from the overprint and surcharge was then amalgamated in a new setting of 50 on which the lines of the overprint were only 2 mm apart. On this amalgamated setting, used for Nos. H27/8, the thin "y" varieties were still present and R. 4/7 showed the second "O" of "TOGO" omitted.

The surcharge was subsequently removed from this "2 mm" setting which was then used to produce Nos. H17/19. The missing "O" was spotted and corrected before any of the 30pf. stamps were overprinted.

The remaining low values of the second issue, Nos. H14/16 and H20/2, were overprinted from settings of 25 (5×5), either taken from the last setting of 50 or from an amended version on which there was no space either side of the hyphen. This slightly narrower overprint was subsequently used for Nos. H29/33. It shows the top of the second "O" broken so that it resembles a "U" on R. 1/5.

The mark values were overprinted from settings of 20 (5×4), showing the same differences in the spacing of the lines as on the low values.

It is believed that odd examples of some German colonial values were overprinted from individual settings in either spacing.

1914 (17 Sept). Optd with T 1 by Catholic Mission, Lomé. Wide setting. Lines 3 mm apart.*
H1	3pf. brown	£110	95·00
H2	5pf. green	£100	95·00
H3	10pf. carmine (Wmk Lozenges)	£120	£100
	a. Opt inverted	£7500	£3000
	b. Opt tête-bêche in vert pair	†	£8000
	c. No wmk	†	£5500
H4	20pf. ultramarine	28·00	40·00
H5	25pf. black and yellow	28·00	30·00
H6	30pf. black and orange/buff	30·00	48·00
H7	40pf. black and carmine	£225	£250
H8	50pf. black and purple/buff	£10000	£8000
H9	80pf. black and carmine/rose	£225	£275

H10	1m. carmine	£5000	£2500
H11	2m. blue	£8000	£9000
	a. "Occupation" double	£14000	£11000
	b. Opt inverted	£10000	

*The post office at Lomé was open for four hours on 17 September, before closing again on instructions from Accra. It finally reopened on 24 September.

The tête-bêche overprint on the 10pf. is due to the sheet being turned round after the upper 50 stamps had been overprinted so that vertical pairs from the two middle rows have the overprint tête-bêche.

1914 (1 Oct). Nos. H1 and H2 surch as T 2.
H12	½d. on 3pf. brown	£160	£140
	a. Thin "y" in "penny"	£400	£350
H13	1d. on 5pf. green	£160	£140
	a. Thin "y" in "penny"	£400	£350

TOGO
Anglo-French
Occupation (3)

TOGO
Anglo-French
Occupation
Half penny (4)

1914 (Oct). (a) Optd with T 3. Narrow Setting. Lines 2 mm apart. "Anglo-French" measures 16 mm.
H14	3pf. brown	£4500	£900
H15	5pf. green	£1100	£700
H16	10pf. carmine	†	£2750
H17	20pf. ultramarine	20·00	12·00
	a. "TOG"	£3500	£3000
	b. Nos. H4 and H17 se-tenant (vert pair)		£7000
H18	25pf. black and red/yellow	26·00	30·00
	a. "TOG"		£12000
H19	30pf. black and orange/buff	19·00	29·00
H20	40pf. black and carmine	£4500	£1500
H21	50pf. black and purple/buff	†	£6000
H22	80pf. black and carmine/rose	£2000	£1800
H23	1m. carmine	£7000	£4000
H24	2m. blue	†	£9000
H25	3m. violet-black	†	£45000
H26	5m. lake and black	†	£45000

(b) Narrow setting, but including value, as T 4.
H27	½d. on 3pf. brown	35·00	26·00
	a. "TOG"	£425	£300
	b. Thin y" in "penny"	60·00	60·00
H28	1d. on 5pf. green	4·50	4·25
	a. "TOG"	£130	£110
	b. Thin "y" in "penny"	12·00	15·00

In the 20pf. one half of a sheet was overprinted with the wide setting (3 mm), and the other half with the narrow setting (2 mm), so that vertical pairs from the middle of the sheet show the two varieties of the overprint.

TOGO
Anglo-French
Occupation (6)

1915 (7 Jan). Optd as T 6. The words "Anglo-French" measure 15 mm instead of 16 mm as in T 3.
H29	3pf. brown	£8500	£2500
H30	5pf. green	£225	£130
	a. "Occupation" omitted	£12000	
H31	10pf. carmine	£200	£130
	a. No wmk	†	£7000
H32	20pf. ultramarine	£1400	£400
H32a	40pf. black and carmine	†	£9000
H33	50pf. black and purple/buff	£14000	£9500

This printing was made on another batch of German Togo stamps, found at Sansane-Mangu.

TOGO
ANGLO-FRENCH
OCCUPATION (7)   OCOU *Accra opt*   OCCU *London opt*

Stamps of Gold Coast overprinted

1915 (May). Nos. 70/81, 82a and 83/4 of Gold Coast (King George V) optd at Govt Press, Accra, with T 7 ("OCCUPATION" 14½ mm long).
H34	½d. green (shades)	30	1·75
	a. Small "F" in "FRENCH"	1·50	5·00
	b. Thin "G" in "TOGO"	3·25	9·50
	c. No hyphen after "ANGLO"	3·25	9·50
	e. "CUPATION" for "OCCUPATION".	£100	
	f. "CCUPATION" for "OCCUPATION"	60·00	
H35	1d. red	30	50
	a. Small "F" in "FRENCH"	1·75	3·25
	b. Thin "G" in "TOGO"	5·50	9·00
	c. No hyphen after "ANGLO"	5·50	9·00
	f. "CCUPATION" for "OCCUPATION"	£170	
	g. Opt double	£350	£475
	h. Opt inverted	£170	£250
	ha. Ditto. "TOGO" omitted	£7000	
H36	2d. grey	30	1·25
	a. Small "F" in "FRENCH"	1·75	5·00
	b. Thin "G" in "TOGO"	5·50	13·00
	c. No hyphen after "ANGLO"	£150	
	d. Two hyphens after "ANGLO"	55·00	
	f. "CCUPATION" for "OCCUPATION"	£170	
H37	2½d. bright blue	2·00	3·75
	a. Small "F" in "FRENCH"	8·00	25·00
	b. Thin "G" in "TOGO"	10·00	25·00
	c. No hyphen after "ANGLO"	£100	
	d. Two hyphens after "ANGLO"	60·00	
	f. "CCUPATION" for "OCCUPATION"	£140	
H38	3d. purple/yellow	2·00	2·75

	a. Small "F" in "FRENCH"	3·00	7·00
	b. Thin "G" in "TOGO"	13·00	24·00
	c. No hyphen after "ANGLO"	50·00	
	f. "CCUPATION" for "OCCUPATION"	£170	
	g. White back	4·00	19·00
	ga. Small "F" in "FRENCH"	25·00	60·00
	gb. Thin "G" in "TOGO"	65·00	£110
H40	6d. dull and bright purple	1·50	1·75
	a. Small "F" in "FRENCH"	4·25	11·00
	b. Thin "G" in "TOGO"	14·00	27·00
	f. "CCUPATION" for "OCCUPATION"	£250	
H41	1s. black/green	2·25	5·50
	a. Small F" in "FRENCH"	4·25	17·00
	b. Thin "G" in "TOGO"	15·00	42·00
	f. "CCUPATION" for "OCCUPATION"	£140	
	g. Opt double	£1200	
H42	2s. purple and blue/blue	10·00	14·00
	a. Small "F" in "FRENCH"	27·00	48·00
	b. Thin "G" in "TOGO"	65·00	90·00
	c. No hyphen after "ANGLO"	£180	
	f. "CCUPATION" for "OCCUPATION"	£400	
H43	2s.6d. black and red/blue	4·50	23·00
	a. Small "F" in "FRENCH"	18·00	70·00
	b. Thin "G" in "TOGO"	50·00	£140
	c. No hyphen after "ANGLO"	£170	
	f. "CCUPATION" for "OCCUPATION"	£600	
H44	5s. green and red/yellow (white back)	8·00	15·00
	a. Small "F" in "FRENCH"	48·00	70·00
	b. Thin "G" in "TOGO"	80·00	£160
	c. No hyphen after "ANGLO"	£225	
	f. "CCUPATION" for "OCCUPATION"	£400	
H45	10s. green and red/green	38·00	60·00
	a. Small "F" in "FRENCH"	90·00	
	b. Thin "G" in "TOGO"	£200	
	f. "CCUPATION" for "OCCUPATION"	£550	
H46	20s. purple and black/red	£130	£150
	a. Small "F" in "FRENCH"	£350	
	b. Thin "G" in "TOGO"	£650	
	f. "CCUPATION" for "OCCUPATION"	£850	
H34/46 Set of 12		£180	£250

Nos. H34/46 were overprinted in panes of 60 (6×10), using a setting of movable type. There were three printings:
1st printing (all values, 3d. No. H38 only).
2nd printing (all values, 3d. No. H38g only).
3rd printing (recorded on 1d., 3d. (H38), 2s., 2s.6d., 5s. only),

Varieties occur as follows (Nos. indicate position in setting)
a. Small "F" in "FRENCH" (25, 58, 59). Accent in all three printings on pos. 25, and on pos. 58 and 59 in 1st and 2nd printings.
b. Thin "G" in "TOGO" (24) Constant in all three printings. The letter is from a slightly smaller fount.
c. No hyphen after "ANGLO" (5, 28). Occurs on pos. 5 during the 1st printing (½d., 1d., 2d., 2½d., 2d. (No. H38), rare on the 2d. and 2½d.), and again on the 3rd printing (1d., 3d., (No. H38), 2s., 2s.6d., 5s.). It is also found on pos. 28 in the 1st printing (½d. and 1d. only).
d. Two hyphens after "ANGLO" (5). Occurs on pos. 5 during the 1st printing (2d., 2½d. only). The two hyphens vary in character. The same two values are also found with misplaced hyphen from this position.
e. "CUPATION" for "OCCUPATION" (33) ½d. value only, 1st printing.
f. "CCUPATION" for "OCCUPATION" (57). All values, 1st printing.

CHARACTERISTICS OF THE ACCRA OVERPRINT

Being set up from moveable type, no two positions are exactly the same and there are many minor varieties of broken type. The two "C"s in "OCCUPATION" often differ slightly in shape and one or both usually have closed jaws. The word "OCCUPATION" is generally fractionally shorter (at 14½ to 14¾ mm) than in the subsequent London overprint, where the length is consistently 15 mm. The impression is variable, but usually appears weaker than the London overprint, which is normally bold and well-inked.

The position of the overprint on the stamp varies greatly, with the word "TOGO" often encroaching on the crown above the King's head (high position) or the word "OCCUPATION" encroaching on the value tablet (low position). The subsequent London overprint is invariably well-centred, leaving both crown and value tablet clear.

Note that the 3rd (No. H38g) and 5s. (No. H44) with white back do not occur with the London overprint.

Variety c occurs in postion 28 only on the ½d. and 1d.

The 1d. opt inverted (No. H35h) exists with small "F" (*Price* £1400 *unused*), thin "G" (*Price* £4000 *unused*) and "No hyphen" (*Price* £4000 *unused*).

Examples of all values, and especially the varieties, are known showing a forged Lomé postmark dated "22 1 15".

1916 (Apr)–20. Nos. 70/84 of Gold Coast (King George V) optd in London with T 8 ("OCCUPATION" 15 mm long). Heavy type and thicker letters showing through on back.
H47	½d. green	30	2·50
H48	1d. red	30	85
H49	2d. grey	50	80
H50	2½d. bright blue	60	1·50
H51	3d. purple/yellow	2·75	70
	a. On buff-yellow (1919)		
H52	6d. dull and bright purple	2·00	1·00
	w. Wmk inverted	£170	
H53	1s. black/green	3·50	6·50
	a. On blue-green (olive back) (1918)	6·50	16·00
	b. On emerald-green (olive back) (1920)	£600	
	c. On emer-grn (emer-grn back) (1920)	£300	£650
H54	2s. purple and blue/blue	4·50	8·50
	w. Wmk sideways	£2250	£2250
H55	2s.6d. black and red/blue	4·50	7·00

H56		5s. green and red/yellow		19·00	26·00
	a.	On buff-yellow (1919)		16·00	50·00
H57		10s. green and red/green		24·00	65·00
	a.	On blue-green (olive back) (1920)....	18·00	70·00
H58		20s. purple and black/red		£140	£170
H47/58	Set of 12			£170	£250
H47s/58s Optd "Specimen" Set of 12			£325	

Nos. H47/58 were overprinted by De La Rue using a stereotyped plate, probably of 120 (two panes, each 6×10). The overprint is much more consistent than the Accra printings, and is usually bold and well-inked, with letters that appear thicker, particularly in the word "TOGO". "OCCUPATION" measures 15 mm in length. The two "C"s in "OCCUPATION" are identical in size and style, with open jaws.

The overprint is invariably well-centred, with the top of the word "TOGO" placed just below the top of the King's head on the 1d, and just below the base of the crown on the other values, leaving the value tablet completely clear.

Nos. H51a, 53a/c, 56/a and 57a are all shades which were overprinted only in London, and do not exist with the Accra overprint. Nos. H51a and 56a, described as on "buff-yellow" paper, include second printings made in 1920, which are not easy to distinguish. Viewed from the back the paper appears rather pale and dull, in comparison with the bright (almost lemon) yellow of Nos H51 and 56.

Nos. H47/58 were withdrawn in October 1920 when Gold Coast stamps were introduced.

The mandates were transferred to the United Nations in January 1946. The inhabitants of the British mandate voted to join Ghana in 1957.

Tokelau *see after* New Zealand

Tonga

The Tongan Post Office was established in 1885 and FIJI 2d. and 6d. stamps are recorded in use until the arrival of Nos. 1/4.

PRICES FOR STAMPS ON COVER TO 1945

Nos. 1/4	*from* × 60
Nos. 5/9	*from* × 20
Nos. 10/28	*from* × 8
Nos. 29/31	*from* × 7
Nos. 32/7	*from* × 6
Nos. 38/54	*from* × 5
Nos. 55/63	*from* × 6
Nos. 64/70	*from* × 3
Nos. 71/87	*from* × 2
Nos. O1/10	*from* × 25

PROTECTORATE KINGDOM
King George I, 1845–93

1 King George I   **2**

(Eng Bock and Cousins. Plates made and typo Govt Ptg Office, Wellington)

1886–88. W **2**. P 12½ (line) or 12×11½ (comb)*.

1	**1**	1d. carmine (P 12½) (27.8.86)........	£400	6·00
	a.	Perf 12½×10	10·00	3·25
	b.	Perf 12×11½ (15.7.87)	10·00	3·25
	ba.	*Pale carmine* (P 12×11½)...........	16·00	8·50
2		2d. pale violet (P 12½) (27.8.86).....	50·00	10·00
	a.	*Bright violet*	70·00	3·50
	b.	Perf 12×11½ (15.7.87)	35·00	2·75
	ba.	*Bright violet* (P 12×11½)...........	45·00	3·00
3		6d. blue (P 12½) (9.10.86)	60·00	2·25
	a.	Perf 12×11½ (15.10.88)	50·00	2·25
	ab.	*Dull blue* (P 12×11½)	28·00	2·25
4		1s. pale green (P 12½) (9.10.86).....	90·00	4·50
	a.	*Deep green* (P 12½)	£100	2·25
	b.	Perf 12×11½ (15.10.88)	55·00	6·00
	ba.	*Deep green* (P 12×11½)	55·00	3·25

*See note after New Zealand, No. 186.

FOUR PENCE.   EIGHT PENCE.
    (3)   (4)

(Surch Messrs Wilson & Horton, Auckland, N.Z.)

1891 (10 Nov). *Nos. 1b and 2b surch.*

5	**3**	4d. on 1d. carmine	3·00	11·00
	a.	No stop after "PENCE"	50·00	£110
6	**4**	8d. on 2d. violet	35·00	90·00
	a.	Short "T" in "EIGHT"	£170	£300

No. 5a occurred on R. 6/8 and 9, R. 10/11, all from the right-hand pane.

1891 (23 Nov). *Optd with stars in upper right and lower left corners.* P 12½.

7	**1**	1d. carmine	48·00	55·00
	a.	Three stars	£400	
	b.	Four stars	£500	
	c.	Five stars	£750	
	d.	Perf 12×11½	£300	
	da.	Three stars	£500	
	db.	Four stars	£650	
	dc.	Five stars	£900	
8		2d. violet	70·00	38·00
	a.	Perf 12×11½	£375	

1892 (15 Aug). W **2**. P 12×11½.

9	**1**	6d. yellow-orange	16·00	26·00

5 Arms of Tonga   **6** King George I

Damaged "O" in "TONGA" (R. 1/1, later corrected)

(Dies eng A. E. Cousins. Typo at Govt Printing Office, Wellington, N.Z.)

1892 (10 Nov). W **2**. P 12×11½.

10	**5**	1d. pale rose	13·00	20·00
	a.	*Bright rose*	12·00	20·00
	b.	Bisected diag (½d.) (1893) (on cover)	†	£850
	c.	Damaged "O"	£100	
11	**6**	2d. olive	19·00	16·00
12	**5**	4d. chestnut	48·00	70·00
13	**6**	8d. bright mauve	55·00	£170
14		1s. brown	80·00	£110
10/14	Set of 5		£190	£350

No. 10b was used from 31 May 1893 to provide a 2½d. rate before the arrival of No. 15, and on subsequent occasions up to 1895.

½d.   2½d.   FIVE PENCE.   7½d.
 (7)   (8)   (9)   (10)

1893. *Printed in new colours and surch with T* **7/10** *by Govt Printing Office, Wellington.*

(a) In carmine. P 12½ (21 Aug).

15	**5**	½d. on 1d. bright ultramarine	23·00	27·00
	a.	Surch omitted		
16	**6**	2½d. on 2d. green	14·00	12·00
17	**5**	5d. on 4d. orange	4·00	6·50
18	**6**	7½d. on 8d. carmine	24·00	80·00

(b) In black. P 12×11½ (Nov).

19	**5**	½d. on 1d. dull blue	45·00	48·00
20	**6**	2½d. on 2d. green	17·00	17·00
	a.	Surch double	£1800	£1800
	b.	Fraction bar completely omitted (R. 3/3)		

King George II, 1893–1918

SURCHARGE.   HALF-PENNY   SURCHARGE, 2½d.   HALF-PEI
  (11)   (12)   Small "F" in "HALF"

(Surch at the *Star* Office, Auckland, N.Z.)

1894 (June–Nov). *Surch with T* **11** *or* **12**.

21	**5**	½d. on 4d. chestnut (B.) (Nov)	2·00	7·00
	a.	"SURCHARGE"	9·00	21·00
	b.	Small "F"	9·00	21·00
22	**6**	½d. on 1s. brown	2·50	11·00
	a.	"SURCHARGE"	11·00	42·00
	b.	Small "F"	11·00	42·00
	c.	Surch double	£275	
	d.	Surch double with "SURCHARGE"	£900	
	e.	Surch double with small "F"...	£750	
23		2½d. on 8d. mauve	5·50	8·00
	a.	No stop after "SURCHARGE"	32·00	55·00
24		2½d. on 1s. deep green (No. 4a) (Nov)	55·00	27·00
	a.	No stop after "SURCHARGE"	£170	
	b.	Perf 12×11½	15·00	45·00
	ba.	No stop after "SURCHARGE"	55·00	

Nos. 21/4 were surcharged in panes of 60 (6×10) with No. 21a occurring on R. 2/6, 4/6, 5/6, 8/6 and 10/6, No. 21b on R. 1/4, 3/4, 6/4, 7/4 and 9/4, No. 22a on R. 1/6, 3/6, 5/6, 8/6 and 10/6, No. 22b on R. 2/4,

---

4/4, 6/4, 7/4 and 9/4 (both after the setting had been rearranged), No. 23a on R. 3/1–3 and Nos. 24a and 24ba on R. 6/3 and R. 7/3 or R. 7/1–2.

Sheets used for these provisionals were surcharged with the remains of the tissue interleaving still in place. This sometimes subsequently fell away taking parts of the surcharge with it.

Deformed "E" in "PENI" (R. 2/2)

(Design resembling No. 11 litho and surch at *Star* Office Auckland, N.Z.)

1895 (22 May*). *As T* **6** *surch as T* **11** *and* **12**. No wmk. P 12.

25	**11**	1d. on 2d. pale blue (C.)	50·00	25·00
	a.	Deformed "E"	£120	
26	**12**	1½d. on 2d. pale blue (C.)	60·00	32·00
	a.	Deformed "E"	£150	
	b.	Perf 12×11	50·00	32·00
	ba.	Deformed "E"	£120	
27		2½d. on 2d. pale blue (C.)†	40·00	48·00
	a.	No stop after "SURCHARGE"	£225	£225
	b.	Deformed "E"	£110	
28		7½d. on 2d. pale blue (C.)	£425	
	a.	Deformed "E"		
	b.	Perf 12×11	60·00	48·00
	ba.	Deformed "E"	£150	

*Earliest known date of use.

†The 2½d. on 2d. is the only value which normally has a stop after the word "SURCHARGE".

No. 27a occurs on R. 1/3 of the right-hand pane.

12a King George II   **13** King George II   (14)

"BU" joined (R. 1/1)   Missing eyebrow (R. 2/4)

"7" for "1" in "'½d." (R. 2/1)

1895 (20 June*). *Unissued stamp surch as in T* **12a**. No wmk. P 12.

29	**11**	½d. on 2½d. vermilion	35·00	32·00
	a.	"BU" joined	75·00	
	b.	"SURCHARCE"	70·00	
	c.	Missing eyebrow	75·00	
	d.	Stop after "POSTAGE" (R. 2/5)	75·00	
	e.	"7" for "1" in "½d."	75·00	
30		1d. on 2½d. vermilion	70·00	42·00
	a.	"BU" joined	£110	
	c.	Missing eyebrow	£110	
	d.	Stop after "POSTAGE" (R. 2/5)	£110	
	e.	"7" for "1" in "½d."	£110	
31	**12**	7½d. on 2½d. vermilion	55·00	65·00
	a.	"BU" joined	£100	
	c.	Missing eyebrow	£100	
	d.	Stop after "POSTAGE" (R. 2/5)	£100	
	e.	"7" for "1" in "½d."	£100	

*Earliest known date of use.

No. 29b occurs on R. 1/6 and 3/6 of both the right and the left pane.

In the ½d. surcharge there is a stop after "SURCHARGE" and not after "PENNY". In the 1d. and 7½d. the stop is after the value only.

"Black Eye" flaw (Rt pane R. 2/4)

(Litho *Star* Office, Auckland, N.Z.)

1895 (9 July–Sept). No wmk. P 12.

32	**13**	1d. olive-green	22·00	26·00
		a. Bisected diagonally (½d.) (on cover) (9.95)	†	£750
		b. Imperf between (horiz pair)	—	£6500
33		2½d. rose	20·00	13·00
		a. Stop (flaw) after "POSTAGE" (R. 4/5)	60·00	60·00
34		5d. blue	25·00	50·00
		a. "Black eye" flaw	65·00	
		b. Perf 12×11	23·00	50·00
		ba. "Black eye" flaw	65·00	
		c. Perf 11	£375	
		ca. "Black eye" flaw		
35		7½d. orange-yellow	30·00	48·00
		a. Yellow	30·00	48·00

1896 (May). *Nos. 26b and 28b with typewritten surcharge "Half-Penny-", in violet, and Tongan surcharge, in black, as T* **14**.

A. Tongan surch reading downwards (right panes).

36A	**6**	½d. on 1½d. on 2d.	£450	
		a. Perf 12	£425	£425
		e. "Halef"	£5500	
		f. "H" over "G"		
		g. "Pen?y"	£4500	
37A		½d. on 7½d. on 2d.	85·00	£110
		a. "Hafl" for "Half"	£2250	£2500
		b. "Hafl" ("Penny" omitted)	£4000	
		c. "PPenny"	£750	
		d. Stops instead of hyphens	£1000	
		e. "Halyf"		
		f. "Half-Penny-" inverted	£2250	
		g. No hyphen after "Penny"		
		i. No hyphen after "Half"	£1000	
		l. Capital "P" over small "p"		
		m. Hyphen after "Penny" over capital "Y"	£2250	
		p. Perf 12	£800	
		pa. No hyphen after "Half"		

B. Tongan surch reading upwards (left panes).

36B	**6**	½d. on 1½d. on 2d.	£450	£450
		a. Perf 12	£475	£475
		ab. "Haalf"	£2500	
		c. "H" double		
		d. Tongan surch omitted	£5000	
		e. "Penyny"	£2500	
37B		½d. on 7½d. on 2d.	85·00	£110
		c. "PPenny"	£950	
		d. Stops instead of hyphens	£1000	
		f. "Half-Penny-" inverted	£3500	
		g. Comma instead of hyphen after "Penny"	£750	
		h. "Hwlf"		
		i. No hyphen after "Half"	£1500	
		j. "Penny" double		
		k. "Penny" twice, with "Half" on top of upper "Penny"	£3750	
		m. "Half H"	£1000	
		n. Tongan surch double	£1500	
		o. Two hyphens between "Half" and "Penny"		
		p. Perf 12	£800	

Nos. 26b and 28b were in sheets of 48 (2 panes 6×4). The panes were separated before the surcharges were applied. There are variations in the relative positions of the words "Half" and "Penny", both vertically and horizontally.

15 Arms

16 Ovava Tree, Kana-Kubolu

17 King George II

18 Prehistoric Trilith at Haamonga

19 Bread Fruit

20 Coral

21 View of Haapai

22 Red Shining Parrot

23 View of Vavau Harbour

24 Tortoises (*upright*)

Types of Type **17**:

Type I. Top of hilt showing

Type II. No sword hilt

Normal

Lopped branch (R. 8/5) (ptgs from 1934 onwards)

Normal

Small "2" (R. 1/2, 1/4–5, 2/8, 4/4, 5/4 and 6/1)

HOGOFULU

Normal

HOGOFULU

Both "O"s small in "HOGOFULU" (R. 1/7)

HOGOFULU

Small second "O" in "HOGOFULU" (R. 2/7)

WATERMARKS. Stamps with W **24** upright show all the tortoise heads pointing upwards, or downwards if inverted. On stamps with sideways watermark the heads point upwards or downwards alternately. Stamps with inverted or sideways inverted watermarks are not separately listed.

(Recess D.L.R.)

1897 (1 June). W **24**. P 14.

38	**15**	½d. indigo	5·00	2·75
		a. Wmk sideways	70	3·00
39	**16**	1d. black and scarlet	80	80
		a. Wmk sideways	7·00	3·50
		b. Lopped branch	55·00	
40	**17**	2d. sepia and bistre (I)	19·00	6·00
		a. Wmk sideways	15·00	3·50
		b. Small "2"	35·00	15·00
41		2d. sepia and bistre (II)	32·00	9·00
		a. Wmk sideways	24·00	9·00
		b. Small "2"	55·00	25·00
42		2d. grey and bistre (II)	32·00	3·25
		a. Wmk sideways	18·00	3·50
		b. Small "2"	38·00	6·00

43		2½d. black and blue	6·00	1·40
		a. No fraction bar in "½" (R. 2/10)	£100	60·00
		b. Wmk sideways	5·00	1·60
		ba. No fraction bar in "½" (R. 2/10)	80·00	60·00
44	**18**	3d. black and yellow-green	3·50	11·00
		a. Wmk sideways	2·50	6·50
45	**19**	4d. green and purple	3·75	4·00
		a. Wmk sideways	4·00	4·50
46	**17**	5d. black with orange (II)	32·00	14·00
		a. Wmk sideways		
47	**20**	6d. red	13·00	6·00
		a. Wmk sideways	8·50	7·00
48	**17**	7½d. black and green (II)	16·00	23·00
		a. Centre inverted	£4500	
49		10d. black and lake (II)	45·00	48·00
		a. Wmk sideways		
		b. Both "O"'s small	£225	£225
		c. Small second "O"	£225	£225
50		1s. black and red-brown (II)	14·00	7·50
		a. No hyphen before "TAHA" (R. 3/5)	£160	£140
51	**21**	2s. black and ultramarine	70·00	75·00
		a. Wmk sideways	22·00	30·00
52	**22**	2s.6d. deep purple	50·00	30·00
		a. Wmk sideways	65·00	50·00
53	**23**	5s. black and brown-red	48·00	48·00
		a. Wmk sideways	26·00	32·00
38a/53a		*Set of 14*	£200	£180

The 1d., 3d. and 4d. are known bisected and used for half their value.

T – L

1 June, 1899.

(25)

26 Queen Salote

1899 (1 June). *Royal Wedding. No. 39a optd with T* **25** *at "Star" Office, Auckland, N.Z.*

54	**16**	1d. black and scarlet (hyphen 2 mm long)	29·00	55·00
		a. "1889" for "1899" (R. 8/1, 8/4)	£225	£375
		b. Hyphen 3 mm long	45·00	80·00
		c. Wmk upright	50·00	85·00
		ca. "1889" for "1899" (R. 8/1, 8/4)	£400	£650
		cb. Hyphen 3 mm long	75·00	£130

The letters "T L" stand for Taufa'ahau, the King's family name, and Lavinia, the bride.

No. 54 was overprinted from a setting of 30 (3×10) applied twice to the sheets of 60. The setting contains twenty-one examples of the 2 mm hyphen and nine of the 3 mm.

Queen Salote, 1918–65

Dies of the 2d.:

Die I (As used for 1897 issue)

Die II

Normal

"2½" recut (note lines on "2" and different "½") (R. 1/1)

Retouched (small) hyphen (R. 3/5)

(Recess D.L.R.)

1920 (Apr)–**35**. W **24** (sideways). P 14.

55	**15**	½d. yellow-green (1934)	1·00	1·25
		a. Wmk upright	26·00	38·00
56	**26**	1½d. grey-black (1935)	50	3·00
57		2d. agate and aniline violet (Die I)	9·00	9·00
		a. Wmk upright	22·00	42·00
		b. Small "2"	60·00	85·00
		c. *Black and slate-violet* (1924)	10·00	2·25
		ca. Wmk upright		
		cb. Small "2"	55·00	20·00
		d. *Black and deep purple* (1925)	11·00	3·00
		db. Small "2"	65·00	25·00
57e		2d. black & blackish lilac (Die II) (1932)	4·50	7·50
58		2½d. black and blue (3.21)	4·75	40·00

381

59		2½d. bright ultramarine (1934)...........	2·00	1·00
		a. Recut "2½"	20·00	9·50
60		5d. black and orange-vermilion		
		(1921)	3·25	4·75
61		7½d. black and yellow-green (1922)..	1·75	1·75
62		10d. black and lake (1922)	2·50	4·75
		a. Both "O"'s small.....................	28·00	45·00
		b. Small second "O"	28·00	45·00
		c. Black and aniline carmine		
		(9.25).............................	7·00	
		ca. Both "O"'s small....................	75·00	
		cb. Small second "O"	75·00	
63		1s. black and red-brown (1922)	1·25	2·50
		a. Retouched (small) hyphen	15·00	24·00
		b. Wmk upright	28·00	28·00
		ba. Retouched (small) hyphen	£130	£130
55/63		Set of 10	26·00	55·00
55s/63s		Optd or Perf (Nos. 55s/6s and 59s)		
		"Specimen" Set of 9		£180

In Die II the ball of the "2" is larger and the word "PENI-E-UA" is re-engraved and slightly shorter; the "U" has a spur on the left side.

For illustration of No. 62a see above No. 38.

TWO PENCE

TWO PENCE

PENI·E·UA	**PENI·E·UA**
(27)	(28)

1923 (20 Oct)–24. Nos. 46, 48/9, 50, 51/2 and 53a surch as T **27** (vert stamps) or **28** (horiz stamps).

64	17	2d. on 5d. black and orange (II) (B.)...	1·00	85
		a. Wmk sideways....................	12·00	8·00
65		2d. on 7½d. black and green (II) (B.)....	22·00	28·00
		a. Wmk sideways....................	65·00	75·00
66		2d. on 10d. black and lake (II) (B.)......	15·00	50·00
		a. Wmk sideways....................	50·00	70·00
		b. Both "O"'s small.................	80·00	
		c. Small second "O"	80·00	
67		2d. on 1s. black and red-brown (II)		
		(B.)...............................	60·00	22·00
		a. No hyphen before "TAHA"		
		(R. 3/5)	£350	£200
		b. Wmk sideways...................	75·00	55·00
68	21	2d. on 2s. black and ultramarine (R)...	25·00	24·00
		a. Wmk sideways....................	11·00	6·00
69	22	2d. on 2s.6d. deep purple (R.)	32·00	6·50
		a. Wmk sideways....................	£110	60·00
70	23	2d. on 5s. black and brown-red (R.)....	18·00	18·00
		a. Wmk sideways....................	3·25	2·50
64/70a		Set of 7	£130	£100

29 Queen Salote

(Recess D.L.R.)

1938 (12 Oct). 20th Anniv of Queen Salote's Accession. Tablet at foot dated "1918–1938". W **24** (sideways). P 13½.

71	29	1d. black and scarlet	1·00	4·25
72		2d. black and purple	9·50	3·75
73		2½d. black and ultramarine	9·50	4·25
71/3		Set of 3	18·00	11·00
71s/3s		Perf "Specimen" Set of 3		70·00

For Silver Jubilee issue in a similar design, see Nos. 83/7.

Further die of 2d.:

2D
PENI·E·UA
Die III

(Recess D.L.R.)

1942–49. Wmk Mult Script CA (sideways on 5s.). P 14.

74	15	½d. yellow-green	30	3·00
		a. "A" of "CA" missing from		
		wmk................................	£600	
75	16	1d. black and scarlet	2·50	3·00
		a. Lopped branch	65·00	
76	26	2d. black and purple (Die II)	7·00	2·75
		a. Die III (4.49).......................	5·00	9·00
77		2½d. bright ultramarine	1·75	2·00
		a. Recut "2½"	32·00	
78	18	3d. black and yellow-green	65	4·50
79	20	6d. red	3·50	2·25
80	26	1s. black and red-brown	3·75	3·50
		a. Retouched (small) hyphen	38·00	38·00
81	22	2s.6d. deep purple (1943)	32·00	24·00
82	23	5s. black and brown-red (1943)	16·00	55·00
74/82		Set of 9	55·00	90·00
74s/82s		Perf "Specimen" Set of 9		£170

In Die III the foot of the "2" is longer than in Die II and extends towards the right beyond the curve of the loop; the letters of "PENI-E-UA are taller and differently shaped.

Damage to the "2" on R. 4/9 of No. 77 was frequently corrected by hand-painting.

For illustration of No. 75a see above No. 38 and of No. 77a see above No. 55.

The ½d. 1d., 3d. and 1s. exist perforated from either line or comb machines. The other values only come line perforated.

30

(Recess D.L.R.)

1944 (25 Jan). Silver Jubilee of Queen Salote's Accession. As T **29**, but inscr "1918–1943" at foot, as T **30**. Wmk Mult Script CA. P 14.

83		1d. black and carmine	15	1·25
84		2d. black and purple	15	1·25
85		3d. black and green	15	1·25
86		6d. black and orange	1·00	2·00
87		1s. black and brown.....................	75	7·00
83/7		Set of 5	2·00	7·00
83s/7s		Perf "Specimen" Set of 5	75·00	

1949 (10 Oct). 75th Anniv of U.P.U. As Nos. 114/17 of Antigua.

88		2½d. ultramarine	20	1·00
89		3d. olive	1·60	3·25
90		6d. carmine-red	20	50
91		1s. red-brown	25	50
88/91		Set of 4	2·00	4·75

31 Queen Salote	**33** Queen Salote

32 Queen Salote

(Photo Waterlow)

1950 (1 Nov). Queen Salote's Fiftieth Birthday. Wmk Mult Script CA. P 12½.

92	31	1d. carmine	70	2·25
93	32	5d. green	70	2·50
94	33	1s. violet	70	2·75
92/4		Set of 3	1·90	6·75

34 Map	**35** Palace, Nuku'alofa

(Recess Waterlow)

1951 (2 July). 50th Anniv of Treaty of Friendship between Great Britain and Tonga. T **34/5** and similar designs. Wmk Mult Script CA. P 12½ (3d.), 13×13½ (½d.), 13½×13 (others).

95		½d. green	20	2·75
96		1d. black and carmine	15	3·00
97		2½d. green and brown	30	2·75
98		3d. yellow and bright blue	2·50	3·00
99		5d. carmine and green	2·00	1·00
100		1s. yellow-orange and violet	1·75	1·25
95/100		Set of 6	6·25	12·00

Designs: Horiz—2½d. Beach scene; 5d. Flag; 1s. Arms of Tonga and G.B. Vert—3d. H.M.N.Z.S. Bellona.

OFFICIAL STAMPS

G.F.B.

(O 1)	(O 2)

(G.F.B. = Gaue Faka Buleaga = On Government Service)

1893 (13 Feb). Optd with Type O **1** by Govt Printing Office, Wellington, N.Z. W **2**. P 12×11½.

O1	5	1d. ultramarine (C.)....................	13·00	50·00
		a. Bisected diagonally (½d.) (on		
		cover)		
O2	6	2d. ultramarine (C.)....................	29·00	55·00
O3	5	4d. ultramarine (C.)....................	48·00	£100
O4	6	8d. ultramarine (C.)....................	90·00	£170
O5		1s. ultramarine (C.)....................	£110	£200
O1/5		Set of 5	£250	£500

Above prices are for stamps in good condition and colour. Faded and stained stamps from the remainders are worth much less.

1893 (Dec). Nos. O1 to O5 variously surch with new value, sideways as Type O 2.

O6	5	½d. on 1d. ultramarine	21·00	50·00
O7	6	2½d. on 2d. ultramarine	26·00	45·00
O8	5	5d. on 4d. ultramarine	26·00	45·00
O9	6	7½d. on 8d. ultramarine	26·00	80·00
		a. "D" of "7½D." omitted	£1200	
		b. Surch double	£2000	
O10		10d. on 1s. ultramarine	29·00	85·00
O6/10		Set of 5	£110	£275

Transjordan

Transjordan was part of the Turkish Empire from 1516 to 1918.

Turkish post offices are known to have existed at Ajlun ("Adjiloun"), Amman ("Omman"), Amman Station, Kerak ("Kerek"), Ma'an ("Mohan" or "Maan"), Qatrana, Salt and Tafila ("Tafile"). Stamps cancelled "Ibin" may have been used at Ibbin.

The area was overrun by British and Arab forces, organised by Colonel T. E. Lawrence, in September 1918, and as Occupied Enemy Territory (East), became part of the Syrian state under the Emir Faisal, who was king of Syria from 11 March to 24 July 1920. During 1920 the stamps of the Arab Kingdom of Syria were in use. On 25 April 1920 the Supreme Council of the Allies assigned to the United Kingdom a mandate to administer both Palestine and Transjordan, as the area to the east of the Jordan was called. The mandate came into operation on 29 September 1923.

E.E.F. post offices, using the stamps of Palestine, operated in the area from September 1918.

BRITISH MANDATED TERRITORY

(Currency. 1000 milliemes = 100 piastres = £1 Egyptian)

"EAST". Where the word "East" appears in Arabic overprints it is not used in its widest sense but as implying the land or government "East of Jordan".

شرقي الاردن	شرقي الاردن
(1) ("East of Jordan")	(1a)

(Optd at Greek Orthodox Convent, Jerusalem)

1920 (Nov). T **3** of Palestine optd with T **1**.

		(a) P 15×14.		
1	1	1m. sepia	1·25	2·25
		a. Opt inverted	£130	£250
2		2m. blue-green	12·00	13·00
		a. Silver opt	£2000	
3		3m. yellow-brown	1·50	1·75
		a. Opt Type 1a	£1100	
4		4m. scarlet	1·75	1·75
5		5m. yellow-orange	3·25	1·75
5a		1p. deep indigo (Silver)	£2000	
6		2p. olive	5·50	8·50
		a. Opt Type 1a	£850	
7		5p. deep purple	30·00	42·00
		a. Opt Type 1a	£1400	
8		9p. ochre	£800	£1400
1/7	(ex 5a)	Set of 7	50·00	65·00

		(b) P 14.		
9	1	1m. sepia	1·25	2·25
		a. Opt inverted	£160	
10		2m. blue-green	60	1·50
		a. Silver opt	£550	£600
11		3m. yellow-brown	16·00	19·00
12		4m. scarlet	15·00	25·00
13		5m. orange	2·00	1·50
14		1p. deep indigo (Silver)	1·50	2·25
15		2p. deep olive	4·50	4·50
16		5p. purple	2·75	7·50
17		9p. ochre	3·50	26·00
18		10p. ultramarine	8·00	26·00
19		20p. pale grey	10·00	45·00
9/19		Set of 11	60·00	£140

Nos. 1/9 were surcharged from five different settings of 120 (12×10) which produced eight sub-types of Type **1**. Type **1a** occurred on R. 8/12 from one setting. The 9p. also exists with this overprint, but no example appears to have survived without further overprint or surcharge.

1b Moab District Seal (full size)

1920 (Nov). Issued at Kerak. Handstamped. Manuscript initials "AK" in violet. Imperf.

19a	1b	(1p.) pale blue	£3500	£4000

No. 19a was issued in November 1920 by the political officer for Moab District, Captain (later Sir) Alex Kirkbride, and was used until supplies of Nos. 1/19 reached the area in March 1921. The local Turkish canceller was used as a postmark.

Emir Abdullah, 1 April 1921–22 May 1946

Abdullah, a son of the King of the Hejaz, was made Emir of Transjordan in 1921. On 26 May 1923 Transjordan was recognised as an autonomous state and on 20 February 1928 it was accorded a degree of independence.

غيرالقرش العرب لبنان

(2) ("Tenth of a piastre") | **(3)** ("Piastre") | **(4)** ("Arab Government of the East, April 1921")

1922 (Nov). *Nos. 1/19 additionally handstamped with steel dies at Amman as T* **2** *or* **3**.

(a) P 15×14.

20	2	⅒p. on 1m. sepia		25·00	45·00
		a. Red surch		70·00	70·00
		b. Violet surch		70·00	70·00
21		³⁄₁₀p. on 2m. blue-green		28·00	28·00
		a. Error. Surch "³⁄₁₀" for "³⁄₁₀"		£110	£100
		b. Red surch		80·00	80·00
		c. Violet surch		£100	£100
		ca. Error. "³⁄₁₀" for "³⁄₁₀"			
22		³⁄₁₀p. on 3m. yellow-brown		10·00	10·00
		a. Pair, one without surch		£750	
		b. Opt Type **1a**		£1200	£1200
		c. Error. "³⁄₁₀" for "³⁄₁₀"		£150	£150
		d. Violet surch		£150	£150
		da. Opt Type **1a**		£2750	
23		⁵⁄₁₀p. on 4m. scarlet		50·00	50·00
24		⁵⁄₁₀p. on 5m. yellow-orange		£180	£100
		a. Pair, one without surch		£250	£225
		b. Violet surch		£250	£225
25	3	2p. on 2p. olive		£250	75·00
		a. Opt Type **1a**		£1300	
		b. Red surch		£325	80·00
		ba. Opt Type **1a**			
		c. Violet surch		£300	90·00
26		5p. on 5p. deep purple		50·00	70·00
		a. Opt Type **1a**		£1500	
		b. Violet surch			
27		9p. on 9p. ochre		£300	£350
		a. Red surch		£130	£140
		b. Violet surch			

(b) P 14.

28	2	⅒p. on 1m. sepia		20·00	25·00
		a. Pair, one without surch		£1500	
		b. Red surch		60·00	60·00
		c. Violet surch		£250	£300
29		³⁄₁₀p. on 2m. blue-green		25·00	25·00
		a. Pair, one without surch		£1500	
		b. Error. Surch "³⁄₁₀" for "³⁄₁₀"		£100	£100
		c. Red surch		80·00	80·00
		ca. Error. Surch "³⁄₁₀" for "³⁄₁₀"			
		d. Violet surch		80·00	80·00
30		⁵⁄₁₀p. on 5m. orange		£225	£100
		a. Pair, one without surch		†	£2000
		b. Violet surch		£275	
31	3	1p. on 1p. deep indigo (R.)		£200	60·00
		a. Pair, one without surch		£1800	
		b. Violet surch		£400	
32		9p. on 9p. ochre (R.)		£500	£500
		a. Violet surch			
33		10p. on 10p. ultramarine		£850	£1000
		a. Violet surch inverted			
34		20p. on 20p. pale grey		£650	£850
		a. Violet surch		£900	£950

T **3** *of Palestine (perf 15×14) similarly surch.*

35	3	10p. on 10p. ultramarine		£1800	£2500
36		20p. on 20p. pale grey		£2500	£3000

T **2** reads "tenths of a piastre" and *T* **3** "the piastre", both with Arabic figures below. These surcharges were applied in order to translate the Egyptian face values of the stamps into the currency of the Arab Kingdom of Syria, but the actual face value of the stamps remained unchanged.

Being handstamped the surcharge may be found either at the top or bottom of the stamp, and exists double on most values.

1922 (Dec). *Stamps of 1920 handstamped with a steel die as T* **4** *in red-purple, violet or black**.

(a) P 15×14.

37	4	1m. sepia (R.P.)		25·00	25·00
		a. Violet opt		28·00	28·00
		b. Black opt		22·00	22·00
38		2m. blue-green (R.P.)		22·00	22·00
		a. Violet opt		20·00	20·00
		b. Black opt		18·00	18·00
39		3m. yellow-brown (R.P.)		40·00	40·00
		a. Opt Type **1a**		£1600	
		b. Violet opt		7·00	7·00
		ba. Pair, one without opt		£1200	
		bb. Opt Type **1a**		£1500	£2000
		c. Black opt		8·00	8·00
		ca. Opt Type **1a**			
40		4m. scarlet (R.P.)		45·00	50·00
		a. Violet opt		45·00	50·00
		b. Black opt		45·00	50·00
41		5m. yellow-orange (R.P.)		35·00	10·00
		a. Violet opt		15·00	10·00
42		2p. olive (R.P.)		55·00	40·00
		a. Opt Type **1a**		£1500	
		b. Violet opt		20·00	15·00
		ba. Opt Type **1a**		£1500	£1300
		c. Black opt		12·00	10·00
43		5p. deep purple (R.P.)		£100	£120
		a. Pair, one without opt		£1500	
		b. Violet opt		60·00	80·00
		c. Black opt			
44		9p. ochre (R.P.)		£400	£450
		a. Violet opt		£200	£250
		ab. Opt Type **1a**		£2250	
		b. Black opt		65·00	80·00

(b) P 14.

45	4	1m. sepia (R.P.)		12·00	15·00
		a. Pair, one without opt		£1200	
		b. Violet opt		22·00	20·00
		c. Black opt		18·00	18·00
46		2m. blue-green (R.P.)		25·00	25·00
		a. Violet opt		8·00	8·00

46c		b. Black opt		10·00	10·00
47		3m. yellow-brown (V.)		£800	£350
		5m. orange (R.P.)		£300	75·00
48		a. Violet opt		25·00	20·00
		1p. deep indigo (R.P.)		25·00	15·00
49		a. Violet opt		15·00	9·00
		2p. deep olive (V.)		75·00	80·00
50		5p. purple (R.P.)		90·00	£100
		a. Violet opt		£100	£110
		b. Black opt			
51		9p. ochre (V.)		£900	£1000
52		10p. ultramarine (R.P.)		£1800	£1900
		a. Violet opt		£1100	£1600
		b. Black opt			
53		20p. pale grey (R.P.)		£1600	£2000
		a. Violet opt		£1100	£1800
		b. Black opt			

*The ink of the "black" overprint is not a true black, but is caused by a mixture of inks from different ink-pads. The colour is, however, very distinct from either of the others.

Most values are known with inverted and/or double overprints.

حكومةالشرق
العربية
يسانـسنة ٩٢١

(5) ("Arab Government of the East, April 1921")

1923 (1 Mar). *Stamps of 1920, with typographed overprint, T* **5** *applied by Govt Printing Press, Amman.*

(a) P 15×14.

54	5	1m. sepia (Gold)		£1500	£1800
55		2m. blue-green (Gold)		20·00	22·00
56		3m. yellow-brown (Gold)		12·00	15·00
		a. Opt double		£500	
		b. Opt inverted		£550	
		c. Black opt		75·00	85·00
57		4m. scarlet		10·00	12·00
58		5m. yellow-orange		50·00	45·00
		a. Opt Type **1** albino		£1200	£1400
59		2p. olive (Gold)		15·00	15·00
		a. Opt Type **1a**		£1200	£1000
		b. Black opt		£250	£250
		ba. Opt Type **1a**			
60		5p. deep purple (Gold)		60·00	80·00
		a. Opt inverted		£225	
		b. Opt Type **1a**		£2000	
		ba. Opt inverted		£2500	
		c. Black opt inverted		£1500	

(b) P 14.

62	5	1m. sepia (Gold)		16·00	24·00
		a. Opt inverted		£600	
63		2m. blue-green (Gold)		14·00	18·00
		a. Opt inverted		£350	£350
		b. Opt double		£300	
		c. Black opt		£300	
		ca. Opt double		£1500	
64		5m. orange		10·00	12·00
65		1p. deep indigo (Gold)		10·00	14·00
		a. Opt double		£450	£475
		b. Black opt		£800	£850
66		9p. ochre		75·00	£100
		a. Gold opt		£3000	
67		10p. ultramarine (Gold)		70·00	£100
68		20p. pale grey (Gold)		70·00	£100
		a. Opt inverted		£375	
		b. Opt double		£450	
		c. Opt double, one inverted		£450	
		e. Opt double, one gold, one black, latter inverted		£750	
		f. Opt treble, one inverted		£1100	
		g. Black opt		£850	
		ga. Opt inverted		£1100	
		gb. Opt double, one inverted		£1300	

The gold overprints were created by sprinkling gold dust on wet black ink.

There are numerous constant minor varieties in this overprint in all values.

The 9p. perforated 15×14 was also prepared with this overprint, but the entire stock was used for No. 85.

The 20p. exists with top line of overprint only or with the lines transposed, both due to misplacement.

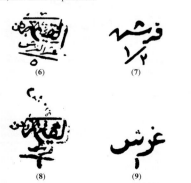

(6)		(7)
(8)		(9)

1923 (Apr–Oct). *Stamps of the preceding issues further surch by means of handstamps.*

(a) Issue of Nov 1920.

70	–	2½/10thsp. on 5m. (13) (B.–Blk.)		£160	£160
		a. Black surch		£160	£160
		b. Violet surch		£160	£160
70c	6	⁵⁄₁₀p. on 3m. (3)		†	£5000
70d		⁵⁄₁₀p. on 5m. (3)			
70e	9	2p. on 20p. (19)			

(b) Stamp of Palestine.

71	6	⁵⁄₁₀p. on 3m. (P 15×14)		£3000	

(c) Issue of Nov 1922.

72	6	⁵⁄₁₀p. on 3m. (22)		£7000	
		a. Pair, one without surch		£7500	
73		⁵⁄₁₀p. on 5p. (26) (V.)		70·00	80·00
		a. Black surch		£1200	
		ab. Opt Type **3** omitted		£1200	
73b		⁵⁄₁₀p. on 9p. (27a)		£1200	
74	7	½p. on 5p. (26)		70·00	80·00
		a. Pair, one without surch		£750	
75		½p. on 9p. (27)		£3500	
		a. On No. 27a		£350	£400
		ab. Opt Type **1a**		£3500	
76		½p. on 9p. (32)			£8000
77	8	1p. on 5p. (26)		80·00	£100

(d) Issue of Dec 1922.

78	6	⁵⁄₁₀p. on 3m. (39) (V.)		85·00	£100
		a. Black surch		£750	
		ab. Opt Type **1a**			
		b. On No. 39v		40·00	50·00
		ba. Pair, one without surch		£1400	
		bb. Without numeral of value			
		bc. Black surch		£750	
79		⁵⁄₁₀p. on 5p. (43b) (Blk.)		8·00	14·00
		a. Opt Type **1a**		£2000	
		b. Pair, one without surch		£500	
		c. Violet surch			
79d		⁵⁄₁₀p. on 9p. (44b)		—	£1200
		da. On No. 44a. Violet surch		—	£1300
80	7	½p. on 2p. (42)		£100	£120
		a. Opt Type **1a**		£2000	
		b. On No. 42b		80·00	£110
		c. On No. 42c		60·00	£110
		ca. Pair, one without surch		£1000	
		w. Wmk inverted			
81		½p. on 5p. (43)		£3000	
		a. On No. 43b		£1000	
82		½p. on 5p. (50)		£2000	
		a. On No. 50a		£2500	
83	8	1p. on 5p. (43)		£3750	
		a. On No. 43b		£2250	£2250
83c		1p. on 5p. (50)		£2500	

(e) Issue of 1 March 1923.

84	6	⁵⁄₁₀p. on 3m. (56)		25·00	30·00
		a. On No. 56c		£700	
85	7	½p. on 9p. (P 15×14)		90·00	£150
		a. Pair, one without surch		£5000	
86		½p. on 9p. (66)		£150	
87	9	1p. on 10p. (67)		£2250	£2500
		a. Violet surch		£2750	
88		2p. on 20p. (68)		60·00	80·00
88a		2p. on 20p. (68g)		£2000	

The handstamp on Nos. 70c, 88 and 88a has an Arabic "2" in place of the "1" shown in the illustration of Type **9**. Being handstamped many of the above exist inverted or double.

TYPES OF SAUDI ARABIA. The following illustrations are repeated here for convenience from Saudi Arabia.

11	20
21	22

حكومة
الشرق العربية
٩ شعبان ١٣٤١

(10) ("Arab Government of the East, 9 Sha'ban 1341")

الشرق العربية
٢٥ مايو استقلال ٩

(11) ("Arab Government of the East. Commemoration of Independence, 25 May 1923")

It should be noted that as Arabic is read from right to left, the overprint described as reading downwards appears to the English reader as though reading upwards. Our illustration of Type **11** shows the overprint reading downwards

1923 (April). *Stamps of Saudi Arabia. T* **11**, *with typographed opt, T* **10**.

89	10	⅛p. chestnut		2·75	2·50
		a. Opt double		£200	
		b. Opt inverted		£110	
90		½p. scarlet		2·75	2·50
		a. Opt inverted			
91		1p. blue		2·00	1·00
		a. Opt inverted		£120	£140

92		1½p. lilac	2·25	2·00
	a.	Opt double	£150	
	b.	Top line omitted	—	£250
	c.	Pair, one without opt	£250	
	d.	Imperf between (horiz pair)	£150	
93		2p. orange	2·75	6·50
94		3p. brown	4·50	12·00
	a.	Opt inverted	£225	
	b.	Opt double	£225	£250
	c.	Pair, one without opt	£375	
95		5p. olive	9·00	20·00
	89/95 Set of 7		23·00	42·00

On same stamps, surcharged with new values (Saudi Arabia, Nos. 47 and 49).

96	10	¼p. on ⅛p. chestnut	6·00	6·50
	a.	Opt and surch double	£150	
	b.	Ditto but 2nd and 3rd lines of opt omitted	£200	
	c.	Opt double	†	£200
97		10p. on 5p. olive	17·00	25·00
	a.	Top line omitted	£350	

In this setting the third line of the overprint measures 19–21 mm. On 35 stamps out of the setting of 36 the Arabic "9" (right-hand character in bottom line) is widely spaced from the rest of the inscription. Minor varieties of this setting exist on all values. For later setting, varying from the above, see Nos. 121/4.

Normal. "923"   Error. "933"

An error reading "933" instead of "923" occurs as No. 3 in the setting of 24 on all values. Only 24 stamps are believed to have been overprinted for each of Nos. 103A, 108A, 105B and 107B so that for these stamps only one example of the error can exist. No example has yet been confirmed for Nos. 103A or 105B.

1923 (25 May). *T 3 of Palestine optd with T 11, reading up or down, in black or gold by Govt Press, Amman, in a setting of 24 (12×2).*

A. Reading downwards.

98A		1m. (Blk)	17·00	17·00
	a.	Opt double, one inverted (Blk.)	£650	£650
	b.	Arabic "933"	85·00	
	c.	Gold opt	£150	£160
	ca.	Opt double, one inverted (Gold)	£900	£900
	cb.	Opt double (Blk.+Gold)	£900	
	cc.	Arabic "933"	£300	
99A		2m. (Blk)	29·00	35·00
	a.	Arabic "933"	£160	
100A		3m. (Blk.)	10·00	12·00
	a.	Arabic "933"	70·00	
101A		4m. (Blk.)	10·00	12·00
	a.	Arabic "933"	70·00	
102A		5m. (Blk.)	50·00	60·00
	a.	Arabic "933"	£300	
103A		1p. (Gold)	£650	£750
	a.	Opt double	£750	£850
104A		2p. (Blk.)	50·00	70·00
	a.	Arabic "933"	£275	
105A		5p. (Gold)	60·00	70·00
	a.	Opt double (Gold)	£650	
	b.	Arabic "933"	£300	
	c.	Opt double (Blk.)	£1500	
106A		9p. (Blk.)	70·00	90·00
	a.	Arabic "933"	£325	
107A		10p. (Blk.)	60·00	80·00
	a.	Arabic "933"	£300	
108A		20p. (Blk.)	90·00	
	a.	Arabic "933"	£2750	

B. Reading upwards.

98B		1m. (Blk)	90·00	£110
	b.	Arabic "933"	£250	
	c.	Gold opt	£150	£160
	cc.	Arabic "933"	£350	
99B		2m. (Blk)	45·00	50·00
	a.	Arabic "933"	£250	
100B		3m. (Blk.)	90·00	£110
	a.	Arabic "933"	£250	
101B		4m. (Blk.)	26·00	32·00
	a.	Arabic "933"	£130	
103B		1p. (Gold)	50·00	60·00
	a.	Opt double	£600	
	b.	Black opt	—	
	c.	Arabic "933"	£300	
105B		5p. (Gold)	£750	£600
	a.	Opt double	—	
	c.	Arabic "933"	£300	
106B		9p. (Blk.)	50·00	60·00
	a.	Arabic "933"	£275	
107B		10p. (Blk.)	£600	
	a.	Arabic "933"	£2500	
108B		20p. (Blk.)	70·00	90·00
	a.	Arabic "933"	£325	

The 9 and 10p. are perf 14, all the other values being perf 15×14.

No. 107A surch with T 9.

109	1p. on 10p. ultramarine	£6000	

نصف قرش

(12)

1923 (Sept). *No. 92 surch with T 12.*

(a) Handstamped.

110	12	½p. on 1½p. lilac	8·00	8·50
	a.	Surch and opt inverted	55·00	
	b.	Opt double	75·00	
	c.	Opt double, one inverted	90·00	£100
	d.	Pair, one without surch	£150	

This handstamp is known inverted, double and double, one inverted.

(b) Typographed.

111	12	½p. on 1½p. lilac	50·00	50·00
	a.	Surch inverted	£150	
	b.	Surch double	£180	
	c.	Pair, one without surch	£500	

حكمة   حكمة

الشرق العربية   الشرق العربية

٩ شبان ١٣٦١   ٩ شبان ١٣٦١

(13a)   (13b)

("Arab Government of the East, 9 Sha'ban, 1341")

These two types differ in the spacing of the characters and in the position of the bottom line which is to the left of the middle line in T 13a and centrally placed in T 13b.

1923 (Oct). *T 11 of Saudi Arabia handstamped as T 13a or 13b.*

112	13a	½p. scarlet	8·50	9·50
113	13b	½p. scarlet	8·50	9·50

No. 112 exists with handstamp inverted.

د · ق · ج

ملك العرب

يحيى ابن الفيصل   ١١ اج ٣ ٢٤٢٥

(15)   (16)

(15) ("Arab Government of the East")

(16) ("Commemorating the coming of His Majesty the King of the Arabs" and date)

1924 (Jan). *T 11 of Saudi Arabia with typographed opt T 15.*

114	15	½p. scarlet	10·00	11·00
	a.	Opt inverted	£180	
115		1p. blue	£300	£200
116		1½p. lilac	£350	
	a.	Pair, one without opt	£1500	

The ½p. exists with thick, brown gum, which tints the paper, and with white gum and paper.

The 2p. in the same design was also overprinted, but was not issued without the subsequent Type 16 overprint.

1924 (18 Jan). *Visit of King Hussein of Hejaz. Nos. 114/16 and unissued 2p. with further typographed opt T 16 in black.*

117	16	½p. scarlet	1·75	2·25
	a.	Type 15 omitted	£150	
	b.	Type 16 inverted	£150	
	c.	Imperf between (pair)	£110	
	d.	Type 16 in gold	2·25	2·50
	dc.	Imperf between (pair)	£250	
118		1p. blue	2·00	2·75
	a.	Type 15 omitted	£150	
	b.	Both opts inverted	£200	
	c.	Imperf between (pair)		
	d.	Type 16 in gold	2·25	2·75
	db.	Both opts inverted	£300	
	dc.	Imperf between (pair)	£225	
119		1½p. lilac	2·50	3·50
	a.	Type 15 omitted		
	b.	Type 15 inverted	£130	
	d.	Type 16 in gold	3·00	3·50
	da.	Type 15 inverted	£150	
120		2p. orange	4·75	6·00
	d.	Type 16 in gold	6·00	6·50

The spacing of the lines of the overprint varies considerably, and a variety dated "432" for "342" occurs on the twelfth stamp in each sheet (*Price £75 un*).

حكومة

الشرق العربية

٩ شعبان ١٣٤١

(16a)

شعبان   شبال   شعبن

"Shaban"   "Shabal"   "Shabn"

(normal)   (R. 4/6)   (R. 5/3)

1924 (Mar–May). *T 11 of Saudi Arabia optd with T 16a (new setting of Type 10).*

121		¼p. chestnut	18·00	12·00
	a.	Opt inverted	£100	
122		½p. scarlet	5·00	3·75
	a.	"Shabal"	50·00	
	b.	"Shabn"	50·00	
	c.	Opt inverted	£120	
123		1p. blue	9·00	2·00
	a.	"Shabal"	75·00	
	b.	"Shabn"	75·00	
	c.	Opt double	£120	
	d.	Imperf between (horiz pair) with opt double	£500	
124		1½p. lilac	14·00	15·00
	a.	"Shabal"	90·00	
	b.	"Shabn"	90·00	

This setting is from fresh type with the third line measuring 18¼ mm.

On all stamps in this setting (except Nos. 1, 9, 32 and 33) the Arabic "9" is close to the rest of the inscription.

The dots on the character "Y" (the second character from the left in the second line) are on many stamps vertical (:) instead of horizontal (..).

On some sheets of the ⅛p. and ½p. the right-hand character, "H", in the first line, was omitted from the second stamp in the first row of the sheet.

حكومة الشرق العربي   حكومة الشرق العربي

سنة   ١٣٤٢   ١٣٤٣

(17) ("Government of the Arab East, 1342")   (18) ("Government of the Arab East, 1343")

حكومة   جكرمة

"Hukumat" (normal)   "Jakramat" (R. 2/1)

١٣٤٢   ١٣٤٣   ١٢٤٢

"1342" (normal)   "1343" (R. 4/2)   "1242" (R. 6/1)

1924 (Sept–Nov). *T 11 of Saudi Arabia with type-set opt as T 17 by Govt Press, Amman.*

125	17	⅛p. chestnut	60	60
	a.	Opt inverted	£130	
	b.	"Jakramat"	25·00	
	c.	"1242"	25·00	
126		¼p. green	60	60
	a.	Tête-bêche (pair, both opts normal)	7·50	10·00
	b.	Opt inverted	85·00	
	c.	Tête-bêche (pair, one with opt inverted)	£300	
	d.	"Jakramat"	25·00	
	e.	"1242"	25·00	
127		½p. bright scarlet	60	60
	a.	Deep rose-red		
	b.	"1343"	25·00	
129		1p. blue	4·00	1·50
	a.	Imperf between (horiz pair)	£130	
	b.	Opt inverted		
	c.	"Jakramat"	35·00	
	d.	"1242"	35·00	
130		1½p. lilac	3·25	4·00
	a.	"1343"	50·00	
131		2p. orange	2·75	2·75
	a.	Opt double		
	b.	"1343"	50·00	
132		3p. brown-red	2·50	2·75
	a.	Opt double	£100	
	b.	Opt double	£100	
	c.	"1343"	75·00	
133		5p. olive	3·25	3·75
	a.	"Jakramat"	60·00	
	b.	"1242"	60·00	
134		10p. brown-purple and mauve (R.)	6·50	8·50
	a.	Centre inverted	£2000	
	b.	Black opt	£200	
	c.	"Jakramat"	90·00	
	d.	"1242"	90·00	
	125/34 Set of 9		22·00	24·00

Type 11 of Saudi Arabia was printed in sheets of 36 (6×6). The ¼p. value had the bottom three rows inverted, giving six vertical tête-bêche pairs. A few sheets were overprinted with the normal setting of Type 17, with the result that the overprints on the bottom rows were inverted in relation to the stamp, including on one of the stamps in the tête-bêche pair (No. 126c). A corrected setting with the overprint inverted on the lower rows was used for the majority of the printing giving tête-bêche pairs with the overprints both normal in relation to the stamps (No. 126a).

1925 (2 Aug). *T 20/2 of Saudi Arabia with lithographed opt T 18 applied in Cairo.*

135	18	⅛p. chocolate	50	1·25
	a.	Imperf between (horiz pair)	£120	£140
	b.	Opt inverted	60·00	
136		¼p. ultramarine	75	1·75
	a.	Opt inverted	60·00	
137		½p. carmine	60	50
	a.	Opt inverted	60·00	
138		1p. green	60	1·00
139		1½p. orange	1·50	2·75
	a.	Opt inverted	60·00	
140		2p. blue	2·00	3·50
	a.	Opt treble	£150	£200
141		3p. sage-green (R.)	2·50	4·50
	a.	Imperf between (horiz pair)	£120	£160
	b.	Opt inverted	80·00	
	c.	Black opt	£120	£150
142		5p. chestnut	3·25	8·50
	a.	Opt inverted	80·00	
	135/42 Set of 8		10·50	21·00

All values exist imperforate.

No. 141 imperforate with gold overprint comes from a presentation sheet for the Emir.

شرق الاردن

(19) ("East of the Jordan")

 22 Emir Abdullah

 23 Emir Abdullah

(Opt typo by Waterlow)

1925 (1 Nov)–**26**. *Stamps of Palestine, 1922 (without the three-line Palestine opt), optd with T 19. Wmk Mult Script CA. P 14.*

143	19	1m. deep brown	20	1·75
144		2m. yellow	20	40
145		3m. greenish blue	80	80

146		4m. carmine-pink	75	1·75
147		5m. orange	1·50	50
		a. Yellow-orange	35·00	20·00
148		6m. blue-green	1·00	1·50
149		7m. yellow-brown	1·00	1·50
150		8m. scarlet	1·00	70
151		1p. grey	1·00	50
152		13m. ultramarine	1·25	1·50
153		2p. olive	2·25	2·50
		a. Olive-green	£100	25·00
154		5p. deep purple	3·50	6·00
155		9p. ochre	7·00	12·00
		a. Perf 15×14 (1926)	£850	£1200
156		10p. light blue	16·00	21·00
		a. Error. "E.F.F." in bottom panel (R.10/3)	£750	£800
		b. Perf 15×14 (1926)	75·00	85·00
157		20p. light violet	24·00	38·00
		a. Perf 15×14 (1926)	£850	£850
143/57 Set of 15			55·00	80·00
143s/57s Optd "Specimen" Set of 15			£200	

(New Currency. 1000 milliemes = £1 Palestinian)

(Recess Perkins, Bacon & Co)

1927 (1 Nov)–**29.** *New Currency.* Wmk Mult Script CA. P 14.

159	22	2m. greenish blue	30	30
160		3m. carmine-pink	2·00	1·50
161		4m. green	3·00	2·75
162		5m. orange	65	30
163		10m. scarlet	2·00	2·50
164		15m. ultramarine	1·25	30
165		20m. olive-green	1·25	2·00
166	23	50m. purple	2·50	4·00
167		90m. bistre	7·00	18·00
168		100m. blue	8·00	14·00
169		200m. violet	17·00	30·00
170		500m. brown (5.29)	60·00	85·00
171		1000m. slate-grey (5.29)	£100	£140
159/71 Set of 13			£180	£275
159s/71s Optd or Perf (500, 1000m.) "Specimen" Set of 13			£225	

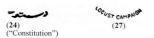

(24)	(27)
("Constitution")	("LOCUST CAMPAIGN")

1928 (1 Sept). *New Constitution of 20 February 1928.* Optd with T **24** by Atwood, Morris & Co., Cairo.

172	22	2m. greenish blue	2·25	3·25
173		3m. carmine-pink	2·50	5·00
174		4m. green	2·50	6·00
175		5m. orange	2·50	3·00
176		10m. scarlet	2·75	4·50
177		15m. ultramarine	2·75	3·25
178		20m. olive-green	5·50	12·00
179	23	50m. purple	8·00	12·00
180		90m. bistre	20·00	65·00
181		100m. blue	22·00	65·00
182		200m. violet	70·00	£150
172/82 Set of 11			£130	£300

1930 (1 Apr). *Locust Campaign.* Optd as T **27** by Whitehead, Morris & Co, Alexandria.

183	22	2m. greenish blue	2·25	5·50
		a. Opt inverted	£225	£500
184		3m. carmine-pink	2·00	6·50
185		4m. green	2·50	9·00
186		5m. orange	19·00	14·00
		a. Opt double	£325	£500
		b. Vert pair, top stamp opt double. Lower stamp without bottom line of opt	£1100	
187		10m. scarlet	2·00	4·00
188		15m. ultramarine	2·00	2·25
		a. Opt inverted	£200	£350
189		20m. olive-green	2·75	4·00
190	23	50m. purple	5·00	11·00
191		90m. bistre	10·00	45·00
192		100m. blue	12·00	45·00
193		200m. violet	32·00	85·00
194		500m. brown	75·00	£200
		a. "C" of "LOCUST" omitted (R. 5/3)	£700	£900
183/94 Set of 12			£150	£375

No. 186a was sold at Kerak.

28	29

(Re-engraved with figures of value at left only. Recess Perkins, Bacon)

1930 (1 June)–**39.** Wmk Mult Script CA. P 14.

194b	28	1m. red-brown (6.2.34)	1·75	1·00
		c. Perf 13½×13 (1939)	6·50	3·75
195		2m. greenish blue	50	50
		a. Perf 13½×13. Bluish grn (1939)	9·50	2·25
196		3m. carmine-pink	1·00	70
196a		3m. green (6.2.34)	3·00	85
		b. Perf 13½×13 (1939)	16·00	4·25
197		4m. green	70	50
197a		4m. carmine-pink (6.2.34)	2·75	1·00
		b. Perf 13½×13 (1939)	80·00	25·00
198		5m. orange	50	40
		a. Coil stamp. Perf 13½×14 (29.2.36)	22·00	17·00
		b. Perf 13½×13 (1939)	65·00	3·00

199		10m. scarlet	1·25	15
		a. Perf 13½×13 (1939)	£110	4·25
200		15m. ultramarine	1·50	20
		a. Coil stamp. Perf 13½×14 (29.2.36)	21·00	16·00
		b. Perf 13½×13 (1939)	40·00	4·50
201		20m. olive-green	1·75	35
		a. Perf 13½×13 (1939)	65·00	12·00
202	29	50m. purple	2·50	1·25
203		90m. bistre	2·50	4·25
204		100m. blue	3·75	4·25
205		200m. violet	11·00	14·00
206		500m. brown	23·00	45·00
207		£P1 slate-grey	50·00	80·00
194b/207 Set of 16			95·00	£140
194bs/207s Perf "Specimen" Set of 16			£225	

For stamps perf 12 see Nos. 230/43, and for T **28** lithographed, perf 13½, see Nos. 222/9.

30 Mushetta	32b Threshing Scene

32 The Khazneh at Petra	33 Emir Abdullah

(Vignettes from photographs; frames des Yacoub Sukker. Recess Bradbury, Wilkinson)

1933 (1 Feb). As T **30**/3. Wmk Mult Script CA. P 12.

208		1m. black and maroon	1·00	1·40
209		2m. black and claret	2·00	1·00
210		3m. blue-green	2·50	1·60
211		4m. black and brown	3·50	3·00
212		5m. black and orange	3·50	4·25
213		10m. carmine	4·50	3·75
214		15m. blue	3·25	1·25
215		20m. black and sage-green	4·25	5·00
216		50m. black and purple	17·00	14·00
217		90m. black and yellow	18·00	35·00
218		100m. black and blue	18·00	35·00
219		200m. black and violet	48·00	75·00
220		500m. scarlet and red-brown	£150	£190
221		£P1 black and yellow-green	£375	£600
208/21 Set of 14			£600	£850
208s/21s Perf "Specimen" Set of 14			£550	

Designs: As T30—2m. Nymphaeum, Jerash; 3m. Kasr Kharana; 4m. Kerak castles; 5m. Temple of Artemis, Jerash; 10m. Ajlun Castle; 20m. Allenby Bridge over the Jordan.

The 90m., 100m. and 200m. are similar to the 3-, 5m. and 10m. respectively, but are larger (33½×23½ mm). The 500m. is similar to T **32**, but larger (23½×33½ mm).

34

(Litho Survey Dept, Cairo)

1942 (18 May). T **28**, but with Arabic characters above portrait and in top left circle modified as in T **34**. No wmk. P 13½.

222	34	1m. red-brown	1·00	3·75
223		2m. green	2·00	1·50
224		3m. yellow-green	2·75	3·25
225		4m. carmine-pink	2·75	3·50
226		5m. yellow-orange	3·50	1·00
227		10m. scarlet	4·50	2·75
228		15m. blue	10·00	1·75
229		20m. olive-green	22·00	16·00
222/9 Set of 8			45·00	30·00

Forgeries of the above exist on whiter paper with rough perforations.

(Recess Bradbury, Wilkinson)

1943 (1 Jan)–**46.** Wmk Mult Script CA. P 12.

230	28	1m. red-brown	20	75
231		2m. bluish green	2·25	1·00
232		3m. green	2·00	1·25
233		4m. carmine-pink	1·75	1·25
234		5m. orange	1·75	20
235		10m. red	3·00	1·25
236		15m. blue	3·00	50
237		20m. olive-green (26.8.46)	3·00	1·00
238	29	50m. purple (26.8.46)	3·00	1·00
239		90m. bistre (26.8.46)	4·75	4·25
240		100m. blue (26.8.46)	5·00	1·75
241		200m. violet (26.8.46)	10·00	8·00
242		500m. brown (26.8.46)	13·00	12·00
243		£P1 slate-grey (26.8.46)	24·00	22·00
230/43 Set of 14			65·00	48·00

Nos. 237/43 were released in London by the Crown Agents in May 1944, but were not put on sale in Transjordan until 26 August 1946. Printings of the 3, 4, 10, 15 and 20m. in changed colours, together with a new 12m. value, were released on 12 May 1947.

POSTAGE DUE STAMPS

(D **12** "Due")	(D **13**)

1923 (Sept). *Issue of April, 1923, with opt T **10** with further typographed opt Type D **12** (the 3p. with handstamped surch as T **12** at top).*

D112	½p. on 3p. brown		21·00	24·00
	a. "Due" inverted		50·00	55·00
	b. "Due" double		50·00	60·00
	ba. "Due" double, one inverted		£150	
	c. Arabic "t" & "h" transposed (R. 1/2)		£100	
	ca. As c, inverted		£350	
	d. Surch at foot of stamp		26·00	
	da. Ditto, but with var. c.		£120	
	e. Surch omitted		£200	
D113	1p. blue		12·00	14·00
	a. Type **10** inverted		80·00	
	b. "Due" inverted		45·00	40·00
	c. "Due" double		50·00	
	d. "Due" double, one inverted		£150	
	e. Arabic "t" & "h" transposed (R. 1/2)		70·00	
	f. "Due" omitted (in vertical pair with normal)		£200	
D114	1½p. lilac		16·00	17·00
	a. "Due" inverted		45·00	45·00
	b. "Due" double		50·00	
	ba. "Due" double, one diagonal		75·00	
	c. Arabic "t" & "h" transposed (R. 1/2)		70·00	
	ca. As c, inverted		£275	
	d. "Due" omitted (in pair with normal)		£200	
D115	2p. orange		18·00	19·00
	a. "Due" inverted		60·00	60·00
	b. "Due" double		65·00	
	ba. "Due" double, one diagonal		£100	
	c. "Due" treble		£150	
	d. Arabic "t" & "h" transposed		70·00	
	e. Arabic "h" omitted		90·00	

The variety, Arabic "t" and "h" transposed, occurred on R. 1/2 of all values in the first batch of sheets printed. The variety, Arabic "h" omitted, occurred on every stamp in the first three rows of at least three sheets of the 2p.

*Handstamped in four lines as Type D **13** and surch as on No. D112*

D116	½p. on 3p. brown		50·00	55·00
	a. Opt and surch inverted		£200	
	b. Opt double		£200	
	c. Surch omitted		£225	
	d. Opt inverted. Surch normal, but at foot of stamp		£150	
	e. Opt omitted and opt inverted (pair)		£300	
	f. "Due" double, one inverted		£160	
	h. Surch double		£250	

(D **14**)	(D **20**) ("Due. East of the Jordan")

1923 (Oct). T **11** of Saudi Arabia handstamped with Type D **14**.

D117	½p. scarlet		1·75	4·00
D118	1p. blue		4·00	4·25
	a. Pair, one without handstamp			
D119	1½p. lilac		3·00	5·00
D120	2p. orange		4·50	6·00
D121	3p. brown		9·00	12·00
	a. Pair, one without handstamp		£500	
D122	5p. olive		9·50	18·00
D117/22 Set of 6			29·00	45·00

There are three types of this handstamp, differing in some of the Arabic characters. They occur inverted, double etc.

1923 (Nov). T **11** of Saudi Arabia with opt similar to Type D **14** but first three lines typo and fourth handstruck.

D123	1p. blue		60·00	
D124	5p. olive		15·00	
	a. Imperf between (vert pair)			

(Opt typo by Waterlow)

1925 (Nov). *Stamps of Palestine 1922 (without the three-line Palestine opt), optd with Type D **20**. P 14.*

D159	1m. deep brown		1·40	7·50
D160	2m. yellow		2·50	5·00
D161	4m. carmine-pink		3·00	10·00
D162	8m. scarlet		4·00	13·00
D163	13m. ultramarine		5·50	13·00
D164	5p. deep purple		6·50	17·00
	a. Perf 15×14		45·00	60·00
D159/64 Set of 6			20·00	60·00
D159s/64s Optd "Specimen" Set of 6			70·00	

Stamps as No. D164, but with a different top line to overprint Type D **20**, were for revenue purposes.

| (D **21**) (1m.) | (2m.) | (4m.) |

| (8m.) | (13m.) | (5p.) |

(Surch typo at Jerusalem)

1926 (Feb–May). *Postage stamps of 1 November 1925, surch "Due" and new value as Type D* **21** *by Greek Orthodox Printing Press, Jerusalem. Bottom line of surcharge differs for each value as illustrated.*

D165	1m. on 1m. deep brown..........................	7·00	8·00
	a. Red opt..	£100	
D166	2m. on 1m. deep brown..........................	5·50	8·00
D167	4m. on 3m. greenish blue.......................	6·00	9·00
D168	8m. on 3m. greenish blue.......................	6·00	9·00
D169	13m. on 13m. ultramarine.......................	9·50	10·00
D170	5p. on 13m. ultramarine.........................	10·00	15·00
D165/70 *Set of 6*...		40·00	55·00

| (D **25** "Due") | Extra Arabic character in opt (R. 4/10) |

1929 (1 Jan). *Nos. 159 etc. optd only or surch in addition as Type D* **25** *by Whitehead, Morris & Co, Alexandria.*

D183	**22**	1m. on 3m. carmine-pink	1·00	7·00
		a. Extra Arabic character ...	25·00	
D184		2m. greenish blue	1·50	7·00
		a. Pair, one without opt......	£325	
D185		4m. on 15m. ultramarine	1·50	8·00
		a. Surch inverted................	£130	£190
D186		10m. scarlet	3·25	8·00
D187	**23**	20m. on 100m. blue.........................	4·00	19·00
		a. Vert pair, one without surch..............................	£400	
D188		50m. purple	4·75	21·00
		a. Horiz pair, one without opt...............................	£425	
D183/8 *Set of 6*...			14·50	65·00

| D **26** | D **35** |

(Recess Perkins, Bacon)

1929 (1 Apr)–**39**. Wmk Mult Script CA. P 14.

D189	D **26**	1m. red-brown	1·50	5·50
		a. Perf 13½×13 (1939)..................	80·00	55·00
D190		2m. orange-yellow	2·00	5·00
D191		4m. green	2·75	7·00
D192		10m. scarlet	5·00	7·00
D193		20m. olive-green	8·50	14·00
D194		50m. blue.....................................	12·00	22·00
D189/94 *Set of 6*			28·00	55·00
D189s/94s Perf "Specimen" *Set of 6*			85·00	

(Litho Survey Dept, Cairo)

1942 (22 Dec). *Redrawn. Top line of Arabic in taller lettering. No wmk. P 13½.*

D230	D **35**	1m. red-brown	3·00	17·00
D231		2m. orange-yellow	12·00	9·50
D232		10m. scarlet	17·00	6·50
D230/2 *Set of 3*..			29·00	30·00

Forgeries of the above exist on whiter paper with rough perforations.

(Recess Bradbury, Wilkinson)

1944–49. Wmk Mult Script CA. P 12.

D244	D **26**	1m. red-brown	80	3·25
D245		2m. orange-yellow	80	3·75
D246		4m. green	80	5·00
D247		10m. carmine..............................	2·50	7·00
D248		20m. olive-green (1949)	55·00	60·00
D244/8 *Set of 5*..			55·00	70·00

OFFICIAL STAMP

(O **16**) ("Arab Government of the East, 1342" = 1924)

1924. *T* **11** *of Saudi Arabia with typographed opt, Type O* **16**.

| O117 | ½p. scarlet .... | 24·00 | £100 |
| | a. Arabic "1242" (R. 2/2, 3/6, 4/5, 4/6) | £150 | |

By treaty of 22 March 1946 with the United Kingdom, Transjordan was proclaimed an independent kingdom on 25 May 1946. Later issues are listed under JORDAN in Part 19 (*Middle East*) of this catalogue.

Transvaal *see* South Africa

Trinidad and Tobago

TRINIDAD

CROWN COLONY

The first post office was established at Port of Spain in 1800 to deal with overseas mail. Before 1851 there was no post office inland service, although a privately-operated one along the coast did exist, for which rates were officially fixed (see No. 1). During 1851 the colonial authorities established an inland postal system which commenced operation on 14 August. Responsibility for the overseas mails passed to the local post authorities in 1858.

No. CC1 is recorded in the G.P.O. Record Book on 21 March 1852, but no examples have been recorded used on cover before February 1858. The prepayment of postage on mail to Great Britain was made compulsory from 9 October 1858. From March 1859 1d. was used with the early Britannia 1d. stamps to indicate prepayment of the additional overseas rate in cash or, later, to show that letters were fully franked with adhesive stamps. This is the normal usage of the handstamp and commands little, if any premium over the cover price quoted below for the stamps involved. The use of the handstamp without an adhesive is rare.

PORT OF SPAIN

CROWNED-CIRCLE HANDSTAMPS

CC 1

| CC1 | CC **1** TRINIDAD (R.) (without additional adhesive stamp) (21.3.52).................... *Price on cover* £2750 |

PRICES FOR STAMPS ON COVER

No.	1	
Nos.	2/12	*from* × 10
Nos.	13/20	*from* × 4
Nos.	25/9	*from* × 10
No.	30	
Nos.	31/44	*from* × 4
No.	45	
Nos.	46/59	*from* × 4
Nos.	60/3	*from* × 5
Nos.	64/8	*from* × 4
Nos.	69/74	*from* × 20
Nos.	75/8	*from* × 50
No.	79	
No.	87	*from* × 20
Nos.	98/102	*from* × 6
No.	103	
Nos.	104/5	*from* × 20
Nos.	106/12	*from* × 12
No.	113	
Nos.	114/21	*from* × 4
Nos.	122/4	
No.	125	*from* × 10
Nos.	126/30	*from* × 5
No.	131	
Nos.	132/43	*from* × 3
Nos.	144/5	*from* × 3
Nos.	146/8	*from* × 3
Nos.	D1/17	*from* × 15

| 1 | 2 Britannia |

1847 (16 Apr). Litho. Imperf.

| 1 | **1** | (5c.) blue.................................... | £25000 | £10000 |

The "LADY McLEOD" stamps were issued in April 1847, by David Bryce, owner of the S.S. *Lady McLeod*, and sold at five cents each for the prepayment of the carriage of letters by his vessel between Port of Spain and San Fernando.

The price quoted for used examples of No. 1 is for pen-cancelled. Stamps cancelled by having a corner skimmed-off are worth less.

(Recess P.B.)

1851 (14 Aug)–**56**. *No value expressed. Imperf. Blued paper.*

2	**2**	(1d.) purple-brown (1851)..................	15·00	75·00
3		(1d.) blue *to* deep blue (12.51).........	15·00	60·00
4		(1d.) deep blue (1852)*	£150	80·00
5		(1d.) grey (11.52)...............................	75·00	65·00
6		(1d.) brownish grey (1853)..................	48·00	65·00
7		(1d.) brownish red (1853)....................	£300	65·00
8		(1d.) brick-red (1856)..........................	£300	70·00

No. 2 is known on paper bearing the sheet watermark "STACEY WISE/RUSH MILLS".

*No. 4 shows the paper deeply and evenly blued, especially on the back. It has more the appearance of having been printed on blue paper

---

1854–57. Imperf. *White paper.*

9	**2**	(1d.) deep purple (1854)...................	26·00	85·00
10		(1d.) dark grey (1854).......................	42·00	80·00
12		(1d.) rose-red (1857).........................	£2500	65·00

PRICES. Prices quoted for the unused of most of the above issues and Nos. 25 and 29 are for "remainders" with original gum, found in London. Old colours that have been out to Trinidad are of much greater value.

| 3 Britannia | 4 Britannia |

The following provisional issues were lithographed in the Colony (from die engraved by Charles Petit), and brought into use to meet shortages of the Perkins Bacon stamps during the following periods:
(1) Sept 1852–May 1853; (2) March 1855–June 1855; (3) Dec 1856–Jan 1857; (4) Oct 1858–Jan 1859; (5) March 1860–June 1860.

1852–60. *No value expressed.* Imperf.

A. First Issue (Sept 1852). Fine impression; lines of background clear and distinct.

(i) Yellowish paper.

| 13 | **3** | (1d.) blue.. | £8500 | £1600 |

(ii) Bluish cartridge paper (Feb 1853).

| 14 | **3** | (1d.) blue.. | — | £1800 |

B. Second issue (March 1855). Thinner paper. Impression less distinct than before.

| 15 | **3** | (1d.) pale blue *to* greenish blue.......... | — | £900 |

C. Third issue (August 1856). Background often of solid colour, but with clear lines in places.

| 16 | **3** | (1d.) bright blue *to* deep blue............. | £4500 | £1000 |

D. Fourth issue (October 1858). Impression less distinct, and rarely showing more than traces of background lines.

| 17 | **3** | (1d.) very deep greenish blue.............. | — | £650 |
| 18 | | (1d.) slate-blue .... | £4000 | £650 |

E. Fifth issue (March 1860). Impression shows no (or hardly any) background lines.

| 19 | **3** | (1d.) grey *to* bluish grey.................... | £4000 | £400 |
| 20 | | (1d.) red (*shades*).............................. | 14·00 | £600 |

In the worn impression of the fourth and fifth issues, the impression varies according to the position on the stone. Generally speaking, stamps of the fifth issue have a flatter appearance and cancellations are less well defined. The paper of both these issues is thin or very thin. In all issues except 1853 (Feb) the gum tends to give the paper a toned appearance.

Stamps in the slate-blue shade (No. 18) also occur in the fifth issue, but are not readily distinguishable.

PERKINS BACON "CANCELLED". For notes on these handstamps, showing "CANCELLED" between horizontal bars forming an oval, see Catalogue Introduction.

(Recess P.B.)

1859 (9 May). Imperf.

25	**4**	4d. grey-lilac (H/S "CANCELLED" in oval £8000)...................	£110	£325
28		6d. deep green (H/S "CANCELLED" in oval £8000)...................	£12000	£425
29		1s. indigo	£100	£350
30		1s. purple-slate.................................	£7000	

"CANCELLED" examples of No. 25 are in lilac rather than grey-lilac.

No. 30 may be of unissued status.

1859 (Sept).

(a) Pin-perf 12½.

31	**2**	(1d.) rose-red	£1500	55·00
32		(1d.) carmine-lake	£1800	50·00
33	**4**	4d. dull lilac	—	£900
34		4d. dull lilac	£6000	£900
35		6d. yellow-green	£2750	£200
36		6d. deep green	£2750	£200
37		1s. purple-slate.................................	£6500	£1300

(b) Pin-perf 13½–14.

38	**2**	(1d.) rose-red	£200	26·00
39		(1d.) carmine-lake	£325	25·00
40	**4**	4d. dull lilac	£1200	80·00
40a		4d. brownish purple	£180	£110
41		4d. dull purple	£475	£110
42		6d. yellow-green	£600	75·00
43		6d. deep green	£600	70·00
43a		6d. bright yellow-green......................	£150	£110
		b. Imperf between (vert pair)............	£6000	
44		1s. purple-slate.................................	£6500	£800

(c) Compound pin-perf 13½–14×12½.

| 45 | **2** | (1d.) carmine-lake .... | † | £3750 |
| 45a | **4** | 4d. dull purple .... | † | |

PRICES. The Pin-perf stamps are very scarce with perforations on all sides and the prices quoted above are for good average specimens.

The note after No. 12 also applies to Nos. 38, 40a, 43a, 46, 47 and 50.

1860 (Aug). Clean-cut perf 14–16½.

46	**2**	(1d.) rose-red	£150	55·00
		a. Imperf vert (horiz pair)................	£1100	
47	**4**	4d. brownish lilac	£170	80·00
48		4d. dull lilac	—	£300
49		6d. bright yellow-green......................	£400	90·00
50		6d. deep green	£250	£150

1861 (June). Rough perf 14–16½.

| 52 | **2** | (1d.) rose-red (H/S "CANCELLED" in oval £8000)................... | £140 | 29·00 |
| 53 | | (1d.) rose... | £140 | 26·00 |

54	**4**	4d. brownish lilac.............................	£275	70·00	
55		4d. lilac..	£600	85·00	
		a. Imperf.....................................			
56		6d. yellow-green..............................	£275	80·00	
57		6d. deep green................................	£400	70·00	
58		1s. indigo..	£850	£275	
59		1s. dp bluish purple (H/S "CANCELLED" in oval £8000)...	£1300	£425	

(Recess D.L.R.)

1862–63. *Thick paper.*

(a) P 11½, 12.

60	**2**	(1d.) crimson-lake............................	£130	20·00
61	**4**	4d. deep purple................................	£180	60·00
62		6d. deep green................................	£1100	85·00
63		1s. bluish slate................................	£2250	90·00

(b) P 11½, 12, compound with 11.

63*a*	**2**	(1d.) crimson-lake............................	£1600	£500
63*b*	**4**	6d. deep green................................	—	£6500

(c) P 13 (1863).

64	**2**	(1d.) lake..	42·00	20·00
65	**4**	6d. emerald-green............................	£500	55·00
67		1s. bright mauve..............................	£4000	£275

(d) P 12½ (1863).

68	**2**	(1d.) lake..	48·00	20·00

1863–80.

(a) Wmk Crown CC. P 12½.

69	**2**	(1d.) lake..	55·00	6·00
		a. Wmk sideways..........................	£120	16·00
		b. *Rose*..	55·00	2·50
		ba. Imperf (pair)............................		
		c. *Scarlet*.....................................	55·00	2·50
		d. *Carmine*...................................	55·00	2·75
		w. Wmk inverted...........................	†	55·00
		x. Wmk reversed...........................	60·00	3·00
		y. Wmk inverted and reversed......		65·00
70	**4**	4d. bright violet..............................	£120	12·00
		a. Pale mauve...............................	£200	16·00
		b. Dull lilac.................................	£160	16·00
		w. Wmk inverted...........................	£275	60·00
		x. Wmk reversed...........................	£130	14·00
71		4d. grey (1872)..............................	£130	5·50
		a. Bluish grey...............................	£120	6·00
		ax. Wmk reversed...........................	£120	8·00
		w. Wmk inverted...........................	—	65·00
72		6d. emerald-green............................	90·00	14·00
		a. Deep green...............................	£400	7·50
		b. Yellow-green............................	85·00	4·50
		c. Apple-green..............................	80·00	5·50
		d. Blue-green................................	£140	7·50
		x. Wmk reversed...........................	£100	6·00
73		1s. bright deep mauve.....................	£160	8·00
		a. Lilac-rose.................................	£130	8·00
		b. Mauve (aniline)........................	£110	5·00
		bw. Wmk inverted...........................		6·50
		bx. Wmk reversed...........................		6·50
74		1s. chrome-yellow (1872)...............	£150	1·50
		x. Wmk reversed...........................	—	6·50

(b) P 14 (1876).

75	**2**	(1d.) lake..	27·00	1·50
		a. Bisected (½d.) (on cover).........	†	£600
		b. Rose-carmine............................	27·00	1·50
		c. Scarlet.....................................	48·00	1·50
		x. Wmk reversed...........................	30·00	1·50
76	**4**	4d. bluish grey................................	£120	70
		y. Wmk inverted and reversed......	†	80·00
77		6d. bright yellow-green....................	£100	1·75
		a. Deep yellow-green....................	£130	1·75
		w. Wmk inverted...........................	†	70·00
		x. Wmk reversed...........................	£110	3·00
78		1s. chrome-yellow..........................	£130	3·25

(c) P 14×12½ (1880).

79	**4**	6d. yellow-green..............................	†	£5500

The 1s. perforated 12½ in purple-slate is a colour changeling.

(Typo D.L.R.)

1869. Wmk Crown CC. P 12½.

87	**5**	5s. rose-lake....................................	£170	75·00

HALFPENNY   ONE PENNY
(6)   (7)

1879–82. *Surch with T 6 or 7.* P 14.

(a) Wmk Crown CC (June 1879).

98	**2**	½d. lilac..	12·00	8·50
		w. Wmk inverted...........................	£100	32·00
		x. Wmk reversed...........................	12·00	8·50
99		½d. mauve.......................................	12·00	8·50
		a. Wmk sideways..........................	50·00	50·00
		w. Wmk inverted...........................	†	—

(b) Wmk Crown CA (1882).

100	**2**	½d. lilac (wmk reversed).................	£180	75·00
101		1d. rosy carmine............................	35·00	1·50
		a. Bisected (½d.) (on cover).........	†	£550
		x. Wmk reversed...........................	35·00	1·75

1882. Wmk Crown CA. P 14.

102	**4**	4d. bluish grey................................	£180	8·50
		x. Wmk reversed...........................		

(8) Various styles

1882 (9 May). *Surch by hand in various styles as T 8 in red or black ink and the original value obliterated by a thick or thin bar or bars, of the same colour.*

103		1d. on 6d. (No. 77) (Bk.)...............	—	£1500
104		1d. on 6d. (No. 77) (R.).................	9·00	5·50
		x. Wmk reversed...........................	13·00	6·00
105		1d. on 6d. (No. 77*a*) (R.)..............	9·00	5·50
		a. Bisected (½d.) (on cover).........	†	£300

10	**11** Britannia	**12** Britannia

(Typo D.L.R.)

1883–94. P 14.

(a) Wmk Crown CA.

106	**10**	½d. dull green.................................	5·00	1·25
107		1d. carmine....................................	10·00	50
		a. Bisected (½d.) (on cover).........	†	£800
		w. Wmk inverted...........................	†	£140
108		2½d. bright blue..............................	13·00	60
110		4d. grey..	2·50	60
		w. Wmk inverted...........................	†	£160
111		6d. olive-black (1884)....................	4·00	4·50
112		1s. orange-brown (1884)................	4·75	3·00

(b) Wmk Crown CC.

113	**5**	5s. maroon (1894)..........................	55·00	85·00
106/13 Set of 7..			85·00	90·00
106s/12s Optd "Specimen" Set of 6..........				£550

Two types of 1d. value:

ONE PENNY   ONE PENNY
(I) (round "o")   (II) (oval "o")

(Typo D.L.R.)

1896 (17 Aug)–**1906.** P 14.

(a) Wmk Crown CA.

114	**11**	½d. dull purple and green...............	3·25	30
115		1d. dull purple and rose (I)...........	3·50	10
116		1d. dull purple and rose (II) (1900).	£325	4·00
117		2½d. dull purple and blue................	6·00	20
118		4d. dull purple and orange.............	6·50	18·00
119		5d. dull purple and mauve..............	8·00	14·00
120		6d. dull purple and black...............	7·50	5·50
121		1s. green and brown.......................	7·00	6·50

(b) Wmk CA over Crown. *Ordinary paper.*

122	**12**	5s. green and brown.......................	45·00	75·00
123		10s. green and ultramarine.............	£180	£325
124		£1 green and carmine....................	£150	£200
		a. Chalk-surfaced paper (1906)...	£250	
114/24 Set of 10......................................			£375	£600
114s/24s Optd "Specimen" Set of 10......				£180

No. 119, surcharged "3d." was prepared for use in 1899 but not issued (*Price £3000 unused*). It also exists overprinted "Specimen" (*Price £75*). Collectors are warned against apparently postally used copies of this issue which bear "REGISTRAR-GENERAL" obliterations and are of very little value.

13 Landing of Columbus

(Recess D.L.R.)

1898 (31 July). *400th Anniv of Discovery of Trinidad.* Wmk Crown CC. P 14.

125	**13**	2d. brown and dull violet...............	2·50	1·25
		s. Optd "Specimen"....................	50·00	

1901–06. *Colours changed. Ordinary paper.* Wmk Crown CA or CA over Crown (5s.). P 14.

126	**11**	½d. grey-green (1902)....................	65	2·00
127		1d. black/*red* (II).........................	1·25	10
		a. Value omitted...........................	£30000	
		w. Wmk inverted...........................	†	£180
128		2½d. purple and blue/*blue* (1902)...	17·00	25
129		4d. green and blue/*buff* (1902).....	1·75	16·00
		a. Chalk-surfaced paper..............	3·50	14·00
130		1s. black and red/*yellow* (1903)...	19·00	5·50
131	**12**	5s. lilac and mauve........................	50·00	65·00
		a. Chalk-surfaced paper. *Deep purple and mauve* (1906)....	75·00	85·00
126/31 Set of 6......................................			80·00	80·00
126s/31s Optd "Specimen" Set of 6........				£120

A pane of sixty of No. 127a was found at the San Fernando post office of which fifty-one were subsequently returned to London and destroyed. Only three mint examples, one of which is in the Royal Collection, are now thought to survive.

1904–09. *Ordinary paper (½d., 1d., 2½d. (No. 137)) or chalk-surfaced paper (others).* Wmk Mult Crown CA. P 14.

132	**11**	½d. grey-green................................	3·50	1·00
		a. Chalk-surfaced paper..............	5·50	2·25
133		½d. blue-green (1906).....................	9·00	2·50
134		1d. black/*red* (II).........................	5·00	10
		a. Chalk-surfaced paper..............	6·50	10
135		1d. rose-red (1907)........................	1·50	10
136		2½d. purple and blue/*blue*.............	23·00	90
137		2½d. blue (1906).............................	3·75	15
138		4d. grey and red/*yellow* (1906).....	1·75	8·50
		a. Black and red/yellow...............	9·00	21·00
139		6d. dull purple and black (1905)...	16·00	15·00
140		6d. dull and bright purple (1906)...	7·00	10·00
141		1s. black and blue/*green*...............	20·00	8·00
142		1s. purple and blue/*golden yellow*...	11·00	16·00
143		1s. black/*green* (1906).................	1·75	1·25
144	**12**	5s. deep purple and mauve (1907)..	45·00	90·00
145		£1 green and carmine (1907)........	£150	£250
132/45 Set of 13.....................................			£250	£350
135s/43s (*ex Nos. 136, 139, 141*) Optd "Specimen" Set of 6..........				£120

No. 135 is from a new die, the letters of "ONE PENNY" being short and thick, while the point of Britannia's spear breaks the uppermost horizontal line of shading in the background.

14	**15**	**16**

(Typo D.L.R.)

1909. Wmk Mult Crown CA. P 14.

146	**14**	½d. green.......................................	4·25	10
147	**15**	1d. rose-red...................................	4·25	10
148	**16**	2½d. blue...	14·00	3·25
146/8 Set of 3..			20·00	3·25
146s/8s Optd "Specimen" Set of 3..........			70·00	

TOBAGO

Although a Colonial Postmaster was appointed in January 1765 it was not until 1841 that the British G.P.O established a branch office at Scarborough, the island capital, to handle the overseas mail.

The stamps of Great Britain were in use from May 1858 to the end of April 1860 when the control of the postal service passed to the local authorities.

From April 1860 Nos. CC1/2 were again used on overseas mail, pending the introduction of Tobago stamps in 1879.

SCARBOROUGH

CROWNED-CIRCLE HANDSTAMPS

CC 1	CC 2

CC1	CC 1 TOBAGO (R.) (31.10.1851)...	*Price on cover*	£900
CC2	CC 2 TOBAGO (R.) (1875).............	*Price on cover*	£3750

Stamps of GREAT BRITAIN *cancelled* "A 14" *as Type Z* **1** *of Jamaica.*

1858–60.

Z1	1d. rose-red (1857), perf 14.................................	£800
Z2	4d. rose (1857)...	£350
Z3	6d. lilac (1856)...	£250
Z4	1s. green (1856)...	£1500

PRICES FOR STAMPS ON COVER	
Nos. 1/4	*from* × 25
Nos. 5/7	
Nos. 8/12	*from* × 10
Nos. 13/19	*from* × 6
Nos. 20/4	*from* × 40
Nos. 26/33	*from* × 25

CANCELLATIONS. Beware of early stamps of Tobago with fiscal endorsements removed and forged wide "A 14" postmarks added.

    2½ PENCE

1	**2**	**(3)**

(T **1** and **2** Typo D.L.R.)

1879 (1 Aug). *Fiscal stamps issued provisionally pending the arrival of stamps inscr "POSTAGE".* Wmk Crown CC. P 14.

1	**1**	1d. rose..	95·00	75·00
2		3d. blue..	95·00	60·00
3		6d. orange.......................................	45·00	60·00
		w. Wmk inverted...........................	£100	£120
4		1s. green...	£400	70·00
		a. Bisected (6d.) (on cover).........	†	—
5		5s. slate..	£750	£700
6		1s. mauve..	£4250	

The stamps were introduced for fiscal purposes on 1 July 1879.

Stamps of T **1**, watermark Crown CA, are fiscals which were never admitted to postal use.

1880 (Nov). *No. 3 bisected vertically and surch with pen and ink.*
7	**1**	1d. on half of 6d. orange	£4750	£800
		w. Wmk inverted		

1880 (20 Dec). Wmk Crown CC. P 14.
8	**2**	½d. purple-brown	45·00	70·00
9		1d. Venetian red	£120	60·00
		a. Bisected (½d.) (on cover)	†	£2000
10		4d. yellow-green	£120	28·00
		a. Bisected (2d.) (on cover)	†	£2000
		b. Malformed "CE" in "PENCE"	£1700	£400
		w. Wmk inverted	—	£150
11		6d. stone	£375	£120
12		1s. yellow-ochre	75·00	85·00
		w. Wmk inverted		£180

For illustration of Nos. 10b, 18a, 22b, 30a, 31a and 33b see above No. 4 of Dominica.

1883 (Apr). *No. 11 surch with T* **3**.
13	**2**	2½d. on 6d. stone	60·00	60·00
		a. Surch double	£3250	£1600
		b. Large "2" with long tail	£140	£150

"SLASH" FLAW. Stamps as Type **2** were produced from Key and Duty plates. On the Key plate used for consignments between 2 October 1892 and 16 December 1896, damage in the form of a large cut or "slash" shows after the "E" of "POSTAGE" on R. 1/4.

After 1896 an attempt was made to repair the "slash". This resulted in its disappearance, but left an incomplete edge to the circular frame at right.

1882–84. Wmk Crown CA. P 14.
14	**2**	½d. purple-brown (1882)	2·00	14·00
15		1d. Venetian red (1882)	4·50	2·25
		a. Bisected diag (½d.) (on cover)		
16		2½d. dull blue (1883)	38·00	2·00
		a. Bright blue	8·00	1·00
		b. Ultramarine	8·00	1·00
		c. "Slash" flaw	60·00	42·00
		ca. "Slash" flaw repaired	£110	
18		4d. yellow-green (1882)	£180	90·00
		a. Malformed "CE" in "PENCE"	£1400	£475
19		6d. stone (1884)	£550	£475

1885–96. *Colours changed and new value.* Wmk Crown CA. P 14.
20	**2**	½d. dull green (1886)	2·50	1·25
		a. "Slash" flaw	35·00	40·00
		ab. "Slash" flaw repaired	65·00	
		w. Wmk inverted		
21		1d. carmine (1889)	3·25	1·25
		a. "Slash" flaw	45·00	42·00
		ab. "Slash" flaw repaired	80·00	
22		4d. grey (1885)	3·00	2·00
		a. Imperf (pair)	£2000	
		b. Malformed "CE" in "PENCE"	65·00	90·00
		c. "Slash" flaw	£110	£140
		ca. "Slash" flaw repaired	£140	
23		6d. orange-brown (1886)	2·50	5·50
		a. "Slash" flaw	£120	£170
		ab. "Slash" flaw repaired	£150	
24		1s. olive-yellow (1894)	3·00	19·00
		a. Pale olive-yellow	7·00	
		b. "Slash" flaw	£130	£275
		ba. "Slash" flaw repaired	£160	
24c		1s. orange-brown (1896)	10·00	75·00
		ca. "Slash" flaw	£180	
		20s/3s (ex 4d.) Optd "Specimen" Set of 3	£170	

No. 24c was printed in the colour of the 6d. by mistake.

½ PENNY	2½ PENCE	POSTAGE
(4)	**(5)**	**(6)**

1886–89. *Nos. 16, 19 and 23 surch as T* **4**.
26		½d. on 2½d. dull blue (4.86)	6·00	15·00
		a. Figure further from word	28·00	65·00
		b. Surch double	£2250	£1800
		c. Surch omitted. Vert pair with No. 26	£13000	
		d. Ditto with No. 26a	£22000	
27		½d. on 6d. stone (1.86)	3·25	21·00
		a. Figure further from word	26·00	£110
		b. Surch inverted	£2500	
		c. Surch double	£3000	
28		½d. on 6d. orange-brown (8.87)	£100	£140
		a. Figure further from word	£300	£350
		b. Surch double	—	£2500
29		1d. on 2½d. dull blue (7.89)	75·00	18·00
		a. Figure further from word	£190	85·00

The surcharge is in a setting of 12 (two rows of 6) repeated five times in the pane. On Nos. 26/9a the "½" is 6mm from the "P" (stamp 10 in the setting). The normal spacing is 3.75 mm. Stamps 7,9 and 10 in the setting have a raised "P" in PENNY.

1891–92. *No. 22 surch with T* **4** *or* **5**.
30		½d. on 4d. grey (3.92)	20·00	60·00
		a. Malformed "CE" in "PENCE"	£275	£475
		b. Surch double	£2750	
31		2½d. on 4d. grey (8.91)	9·50	8·00
		a. Malformed "CE" in "PENCE"	£160	£200
		b. Surch double	£3000	£3000

1896. *Fiscal stamp (T* **1**, *value in second colour,* wmk Crown CA, P 14), *surch with T* **6**.
33		½d. on 4d. lilac and carmine	70·00	38·00
		a. Space between "½" and "d"	£140	80·00
		b. Malformed "CE" in "PENCE"	£750	£550

Tobago became a ward of Trinidad on 1 January 1899. Stamps of Trinidad were used until issues inscribed "TRINIDAD AND TOBAGO" appeared in 1913.

TRINIDAD AND TOBAGO

PRICES FOR STAMPS ON COVER	
Nos. 149/55	*from* × 3
Nos. 156/7	—
Nos. 174/89	*from* × 10
Nos. 206/56	*from* × 2
Nos. D18/25	*from* × 12

17   **18**

(Typo D.L.R.)

1913–23. *Ordinary paper (½d. to 4d. and 1s.) or chalk-surfaced paper (others).* Wmk Mult Crown CA. P 14.
149	**17**	½d. green	3·00	10
		a. Yellow-green (1915)	3·50	20
		b. Blue-green (thick paper) (1917)	7·00	1·00
		ba. Wmk sideways	†	£1500
		c. Blue-green/bluish (3.18)	14·00	12·00
		w. Wmk inverted		
150		1d. bright red	1·50	10
		a. Red (thick paper) (1916)	3·25	30
		b. Pink (1918)	23·00	3·25
		c. Carmine-red (5.18)	2·50	10
		w. Wmk inverted		
151		2½d. ultramarine	7·00	50
		a. Bright blue (thick paper) (1916)	6·50	50
		b. Bright blue (thin paper) (1918)	8·00	50
152		4d. black and red/yellow	70	6·00
		a. Chalk-surfaced paper	1·75	10·00
		b. White back (12.13)		
		bs. Optd "Specimen"	24·00	
		c. On lemon (1917)	10·00	
		d. On pale yellow (1923)	5·00	9·00
		ds. Optd "Specimen"	28·00	
153		6d. dull and reddish purple	9·50	7·50
		a. Dull and deep purple (1918)	10·00	4·50
		b. Dull purple and mauve (2.18)	10·00	8·00
154		1s. black/green	1·75	4·50
		a. White back	1·00	
		as. Optd "Specimen"	24·00	
		b. On blue-green, olive back	8·50	9·00
		c. On emerald back	1·50	3·00
		cs. Optd "Specimen"	28·00	
155	**18**	5s. dull purple and mauve (1914)	60·00	95·00
		a. Deep purple and mauve (1918)	60·00	95·00
		b. Lilac and violet	90·00	£130
		c. Dull purple and violet	95·00	£140
		d. Brown-purple and violet	55·00	95·00
156		£1 grey-green and carmine (1914)	£160	£200
		a. Deep yellow-green & carmine (1918)	£140	£190
		149/56 Set of 8	£200	£275
		149s/56s Optd "Specimen" Set of 8	£180	

No. 156a is from a plate showing background lines very worn.

18a

1914 (18 Sept). *Red Cross Label authorised for use as ½d. stamp.* Typo. P 11–12.
157	**18a**	(½d.) Red	14·00	£225

The above was authorised for internal postal use on one day only, to frank circular letters appealing for funds for the Red Cross.

The used price is for stamp on cover cancelled on 18 Sep 1914. Labels affixed to earlier or later items of mail had no postal validity.

(19)

(19a)

1915 (21 Oct). *Optd with T* **19**. *Cross in red with outline and date in black.*
174	**17**	1d. red	1·50	2·00
		a. Cross 2 mm to right	20·00	30·00
		b. "1" of "15" forked foot	11·00	19·00
		c. Broken "0" in "10"	12·00	19·00

The varieties occur in the following positions on the pane of 60: a. No. 11. b. No. 42. c. No. 45. Variety a. is only found on the right-hand pane.

1916 (19 Oct). *Optd with T* **19a**. *Cross in red with outline and date in black.*
175	**17**	1d. scarlet	50	2·00
		a. No stop after "16"	9·50	27·00
		b. "19.10.16" omitted		
		c. Red shading on cross omitted		

No. 175a appears on stamp No. 36 on the right-hand pane only.

FORGERIES. Beware of forgeries of the "War Tax" errors listed below. There are also other unlisted errors which are purely fakes.

WAR TAX	WAR TAX	WAR TAX	WAR TAX
(19b)	**(20)**	**(21)**	**(22)**

1917 (2 Apr). *Optd with T* **19b**.
176	**17**	1d. red	2·25	2·75
		a. Opt inverted	£225	£300
		b. Scarlet	2·25	2·75
		w. Wmk inverted		

1917 (May). *Optd with T* **20**.
177	**17**	½d. green	10	20
		a. Pair, one without opt	£650	
178		1d. red	1·00	1·75
		a. Pair, one without opt	£650	£1200
		b. Scarlet	3·25	80
		ba. Opt double	£140	

The varieties without overprint were caused by the type being shifted over towards the left so that one stamp in the lowest row of each pane escaped.

1917 (21 June). *Optd with T* **21**.
179	**17**	½d. yellow-green	1·40	9·50
		a. Pale green	10	8·50
		b. Deep green	1·25	8·50
180		1d. red	10	75
		a. Pair, one without opt		

No. 180a was caused by a shifting of the type to the left-hand side, but only a few stamps on the right-hand vertical row escaped the overprint and such pairs are very rare.

1917 (21 July–Sept). *Optd with T* **22**.
181	**17**	½d. yellow-green	4·00	6·00
		a. Deep green	10	3·50
		aw. Wmk inverted	£100	
182		1d. red (Sept)	3·50	1·00

WAR TAX	WAR TAX	WAR TAX
(23)	**(24)**	**(25)**

1917 (1 Sept). *Optd with T* **23** (*closer spacing between lines of opt*).
183	**17**	½d. deep green	10	2·50
		a. Pale yellow-green		
184		1d. red	40·00	35·00

1917 (31 Oct). *Optd with T* **24**.
185	**17**	1d. scarlet	60	1·00
		a. Opt inverted	£130	

1918 (7 Jan). *Optd with T* **25**.
186	**17**	1d. scarlet	1·50	15
		a. Opt double	£200	£200
		b. Opt inverted	£130	£130

War Tax	War Tax
(26)	**(26a)**

27

1918 (13 Feb–May). *Optd with T* **26**.
187	**17**	½d. bluish green	10	2·00
		a. Pair, one without opt	£1200	
188		1d. scarlet	1·50	1·25
		a. Opt double	£130	
		b. Rose-red (1.5.18)	10	60

The ½d. exists with "TAX" omitted caused by a paper fold.

1918 (14 Sept). *New printing as T* **26**, *but 19 stamps on each sheet have the letters of the word "Tax" wider spaced, the "x" being to the right of "r" of "War" as T* **26a**. *Thick bluish paper.*
189	**17**	1d. scarlet ("Tax" spaced)	1·50	8·00
		a. Opt double	£200	
		b. Pair, one without opt	£1100	
		c. Opt inverted on back	£1100	

The varieties 189b and 189c are caused by a paper fold.

1921–22. *Chalk-surfaced paper (6d. to £1).* Wmk Mult Script CA. P 14.
206	**17**	½d. green	2·75	2·25
207		1d. scarlet	60	30
208		1d. brown (17.2.22)	60	60
209		2d. grey (17.2.22)	1·00	1·25
210		2½d. bright blue	80	16·00
211		3d. bright blue (17.2.22)	3·50	3·00
212		4d. dull and bright purple	2·00	16·00
213	**18**	5s. dull purple and purple (1921)	50·00	£150
214		5s. deep purple and purple (1922)	60·00	£150

215	£1 green and carmine	£100	£250
206/15 *Set of 9*		£140	£400
206/15s Optd "Specimen" *Set of 9*			£225

(Typo D.L.R.)

1922–28. *Chalk-surfaced paper (4d. to £1). P 14.*

(a) Wmk Mult Crown CA.

216	27	4d. black and red/*pale yellow*	3·25	9·50
217		1s. black/*emerald*	3·50	9·50

(b) Wmk Mult Script CA.

218	27	½d. green	50	10
219		1d. brown	50	10
		w. Wmk inverted	32·00	
220		1½d. bright rose	2·25	20
		aw. Wmk inverted	65·00	65·00
		b. Scarlet	1·75	
		bw. Wmk inverted		
222		2d. grey	50	1·25
223		3d. blue	50	1·25
224		4d. black and red/*pale yellow* (1928)	3·25	3·25
225		6d. dull purple and bright magenta .	2·25	25·00
226		6d. green and red/*emerald* (1924) ...	1·25	60
227		1s. black/*emerald*	5·50	1·75
228		5s. dull purple and mauve	22·00	38·00
229		£1 green and bright rose	£110	£200
216/29 *Set of 13*			£140	£250
216s/29s Optd "Specimen" *Set of 13*			£275

(New Currency. 100 cents = 1 West Indian dollar)

28 First Boca

29 Imperial College of Tropical Agriculture

30 Mt. Irvine Bay, Tobago

31 Discovery of Lake Asphalt

32 Queen's Park, Savannah

33 Town Hall, San Fernando

34 Government House

35 Memorial Park

36 Blue Basin

(Recess B.W.)

1935 (1 Feb)–37. *T* 28/36. *Wmk Mult Script CA (sideways). P 12.*

230	28	1c. blue and green	40	85
		a. Perf 13×12½ (1936)	30	10
231	29	2c. ultramarine and yellow-brown	75	1·00
		a. Perf 13×12½ (1936)	1·00	10
232	30	3c. black and scarlet	1·25	30
		a. Perf 13×12½ (1936)	2·75	30
233	31	6c. sepia and blue	4·25	2·50
		a. Perf 13×12½ (1937)	8·00	4·50
234	32	8c. sage-green and vermilion	3·75	3·50
235	33	12c. black and violet	3·25	1·75
		a. Perf 13×12½ (1937)	8·00	6·00
236	34	24c. black and olive-green	3·25	1·50
		a. Perf 13×12½ (1937)	13·00	10·00
237	35	48c. deep green	9·00	15·00
238	36	72c. myrtle-green and carmine	29·00	30·00
230/8 *Set of 9*			50·00	48·00
230s/8s Perf "Specimen" *Set of 9*			£150	

1935 (6 May). *Silver Jubilee. As Nos. 91/4 of Antigua, but ptd by B.W. P 11×12.*

239	2c. ultramarine and grey-black	30	75
	a. Extra flagstaff	35·00	55·00
	b. Short extra flagstaff	55·00	
	c. Lightning conductor	45·00	
	d. Flagstaff on right-hand turret	75·00	

240	3c. deep blue and scarlet	30	1·50
	a. Extra flagstaff	60·00	
	c. Lightning conductor	65·00	
241	6c. brown and deep blue	1·50	2·50
	a. Extra flagstaff	90·00	
	b. Short extra flagstaff	£140	
	c. Lightning conductor	£100	
242	24c. slate and purple	6·00	16·00
	a. Extra flagstaff	£150	
	c. Lightning conductor	£160	
	d. Flagstaff on right-hand turret	£200	
	e. Double flagstaff	£200	
239/42 *Set of 4*		7·50	19·00
239s/42s Perf "Specimen" *Set of 4*		95·00	

For illustrations of plate varieties see Omnibus section following Zanzibar.

1937 (12 May). *Coronation. As Nos. 95/7 of Antigua, but ptd by D.L.R. P 14.*

243	1c. green	15	60
244	2c. yellow-brown	35	15
245	8c. orange	90	2·25
243/5 *Set of 3*		1·25	2·75
243s/5s Perf "Specimen" *Set of 3*		85·00	

37 First Boca

38 Imperial College of Tropical Agriculture

39 Mt. Irvine Bay, Tobago

40 Memorial Park

41 G.P.O. and Treasury

42 Discovery of Lake Asphalt

43 Queen's Park, Savannah

44 Town Hall, San Fernando

45 Government House

46 Blue Basin

47 King George VI

(Recess B.W.)

1938 (2 May)–44. *T* 37/47. *Wmk Mult Script CA (sideways on 1c. to 60c.).*

(a) P 11½×11.

246	37	1c. blue and green	1·00	30
247	38	2c. blue and yellow-brown	1·25	20
248	39	3c. black and scarlet	11·00	1·00
248a		3c. green and purple-brown (1941)	30	20
		ab. "A" of "CA" missing from wmk.		
249	40	4c. chocolate	25·00	1·50
249a		4c. scarlet (1941)	50	1·00
249b	41	5c. magenta (1.5.41)	50	15
250	42	6c. sepia and blue	2·75	80
251	43	8c. sage-green and vermilion	2·75	1·00
252	44	12c. black and purple	20·00	2·00
		a. Black and slate-purple (1944)	2·75	10
253	45	24c. black and olive-green	2·50	10
254	46	60c. myrtle-green and carmine	8·50	1·50

(b) T 47. *P 12.*

255	47	$1.20 blue-green (1.40)	12·00	1·50
256		$4.80 rose-carmine (1.40)	24·00	38·00
246/56 *Set of 14*			85·00	42·00
246s/56s (ex 5c.) Perf "Specimen" *Set of 13*			£275	

1946 (1 Oct). *Victory. As Nos. 110/11 of Antigua.*

257	3c. chocolate	10	10
258	6c. blue	10	1·50
257s/8s Perf "Specimen" *Set of 2*		70·00	

1948 (22 Nov). *Royal Silver Wedding. As Nos. 112/13 of Antigua, but $4.80 in recess.*

259	3c. red-brown	10	10

260	$4.80 carmine	20·00	28·00

1949 (10 Oct). *75th Anniv of U.P.U. As Nos. 114/17 of Antigua.*

261	5c. bright reddish purple	35	1·00
262	6c. deep blue	1·75	1·75
263	12c. violet	40	1·50
264	24c. olive	45	1·25
261/4 *Set of 4*		2·75	5·00

1951 (16 Feb). *Inauguration of B.W.I. University College. As Nos. 118/19 of Antigua.*

265	3c. green and red-brown	20	1·25
266	12c. black and red-brown	30	1·25

Nos. 265/6 are inscribed "TRINIDAD".

STAMP BOOKLETS

1925.

SB1 2s. booklet containing eight ½d., 1d. and 1½d. (Nos. 218/20) in blocks of 4 ...

1931–32. *Black on pink covers.*

SB2 1s.8d. booklet containing eight ½d. and sixteen 1d. (Nos. 218/19) in blocks of 8 ...

SB3 2s. booklet containing eight ½d., 1d. and 1½d. (Nos. 218/20) in blocks of 8 (1932) ...

1935.

SB4 48c. booklet containing eight 1, 2 and 3c. (Nos. 230/2) in blocks of 4 ...

POSTAGE DUE STAMPS

D 1

Row 4 Row 5

The degree of inclination of the stroke on the 1s. value varies for each vertical column of the sheet: Columns 1, 2 and 6 104°, Column 3 108°, Column 4 107° and Column 5 (Nos. D9a, D17a, D25a) 100°.

(Typo D.L.R.)

1885 (1 Jan). *Wmk Crown CA. P 14.*

D1	D 1	½d. slate-black	15·00	45·00
D2		1d. slate-black	6·50	20
D3		2d. slate-black	29·00	20
		w. Wmk inverted	†	£300
D4		3d. slate-black	50·00	40
D5		4d. slate-black	35·00	4·00
D6		5d. slate-black	23·00	60
D7		6d. slate-black	38·00	5·50
D8		8d. slate-black	75·00	3·25
D9		1s. slate-black	65·00	5·00
		a. Upright stroke	£120	15·00
D1/9 *Set of 9*			£275	55·00

1905–06. *Wmk Mult Crown CA. P 14.*

D10	D 1	1d. slate-black	4·50	20
D11		2d. slate-black	26·00	20
		w. Wmk inverted	†	£200
D12		3d. slate-black	13·00	2·75
		w. Wmk inverted	—	£140
D13		4d. slate-black	13·00	14·00
		w. Wmk inverted		
D14		5d. slate-black	13·00	14·00
D15		6d. slate-black	10·00	6·00
D16		8d. slate-black	12·00	14·00
D17		1s. slate-black	13·00	35·00
		a. Upright stroke	25·00	75·00
D10/17 *Set of 8*			90·00	80·00

1923–45. *Wmk Mult Script CA. P 14.*

D18	D 1	1d. black	1·60	2·50
D19		2d. black	3·50	1·50
D20		3d. black (1925)	3·50	3·50
D21		4d. black (1929)	3·75	23·00
D22		5d. black (1944)	35·00	£100
D23		6d. black (1945)	55·00	42·00
D24		8d. black (1945)	45·00	£160
D25		1s. black (1945)	65·00	£120
		a. Upright stroke	£130	£200
D18/25 *Set of 8*			£190	£400
D18s/25s Optd or Perf (5d. to 1s.) "Specimen" *Set of 8*			£150	

1947 (1 Sept)–61. *Values in cents. Ordinary paper. Wmk Mult Script CA. P 14.*

D26	D 1	2c. black	3·00	4·25
		a. Chalk-surfaced paper (20.1.53).	20	3·75
		ab. Error. Crown missing. W 9a ...	95·00	
		ac. Error. St. Edward's Crown. W 9b	28·00	
D27		4c. black	1·00	3·00
		a. Chalk-surfaced paper (10.8.55).	3·75	4·50
D28		6c. black	2·50	1·50
		a. Chalk-surfaced paper (20.1.53).	30	7·50
		ab. Error. Crown missing. W 9a ...	£300	
		ac. Error. St. Edward's Crown. W 9b	75·00	

D29	8c. black		1·10	26·00
	a. Chalk-surfaced paper (10.9.58)		35	25·00
D30	10c. black		1·25	4·75
	a. Chalk-surfaced paper (10.8.55)		4·00	14·00
D31	12c. black		1·50	21·00
	a. Chalk-surfaced paper (20.1.53)		40	19·00
	ab. Error. Crown missing. W 9a		£400	
	ac. Error. St. Edward's Crown. W 9b		£130	
D32	16c. black		2·00	42·00
	a. Chalk-surfaced paper (22.8.61)		10·00	55·00
D33	24c. black		7·50	8·50
	a. Chalk-surfaced paper (10.8.55)		5·00	42·00
D26/33 *Set of 8*			18·00	£100
D26a/33a *Set of 8*			22·00	£150
D26s/33s Perf "Specimen" *Set of 8*			£140	

"TOO LATE" STAMPS

A handstamp with the words "TOO LATE" was used upon letters on which a too-late fee had been paid, and was sometimes used for cancelling the stamps on such letters.

OFFICIAL STAMPS

O S (O 1) **OFFICIAL** (O 2) **OFFICIAL** (O 3)

1894. Optd with Type O **1**.

(a) On Nos. 106/12. Wmk Crown CA. P 14.

O1	**10**	½d. dull green	35·00	55·00
O2		1d. carmine	38·00	60·00
O3		2½d. bright blue	45·00	90·00
O4		4d. grey	48·00	95·00
O5		6d. olive-black	48·00	95·00
O6		1s. orange-brown	65·00	£130

(b) On No. 87. Wmk Crown CC. P 12½.

O7	**5**	5s. rose-lake	£160	£475

1909. Nos. 133 *and* 135 optd with Type O **2**. Wmk Mult Crown CA. P 14.

O8	**11**	½d. blue-green	1·00	7·50
O9		1d. rose-red	1·00	7·50
		a. Opt double	—	£300
		b. Opt vertical	£110	£130
		c. Opt inverted	£750	£225

1910. No. 146 optd with Type O **2**. Wmk Mult Crown CA. P 14.

O10	**14**	½d. green	5·50	7·50
		w. Wmk inverted	£150	

1913. No. 149 optd with Type O **3** by lithography.

O11	**17**	½d. green	1·25	8·00
		a. Opt vertical		

OFFICIAL (O 4) **OFFICIAL** (O 5) **OFFICIAL** (O 6)

1914. No. 149 optd with Type O **4**.

O12	**17**	½d. green	2·00	15·00

1914–17. No. 149 optd with Type O **5** *(without stop).*

O13	**17**	½d. green	3·50	14·00
		a. Blue-green (thick paper) (1917)	50	6·50

1916. No. 149a optd with Type O **5** *(with stop).*

O14	**17**	½d. yellow-green	2·00	3·75
		a. Opt double	35·00	

1917 (22 Aug). No. 149 optd with Type O **6**.

O15	**17**	½d. green	3·25	18·00
		a. Yellow-green	3·75	21·00
		b. Blue-green (thick paper)	1·50	19·00

Tristan Da Cunha

Although first settled in 1817 no surviving mail is known from Tristan da Cunha until two whaler's letters written in 1836 and 1843, these being carried home in other whaling ships. Then there is a long gap until the late 1800's when other letters are known—surprisingly only some seven in number, up to 1908 when the first of the island cachet handstamps came into use.

The collecting of postal history material from 1908 to 1952, when Tristan's first stamps were issued, revolves around the numerous cachets of origin which were struck on mail from the island during these 44 years. The handstamps producing these cachets were supplied over the years by various people particularly interested in the island and the islanders, and were mostly used by the clergymen who volunteered to go and serve as the community's ministers.

The postal cachets are illustrated below. The use of the different cachets on mail frequently overlapped, at one period in 1930 there were five different types of handstamp in use. As there was no official source for providing them they appeared on the island from various donors; then disappeared without trace once they became worn out. Only one of these early rubber handstamps has apparently survived, Cachet Va.

Covers bearing the cachets are recognised collector's items, but are difficult to value in general terms. As elsewhere the value is discounted by poor condition of the cover, and may be increased by use on a scarce date or with additional postal markings.

Cachet Types V and VII are the commonest, Type Va, used only for three months, and Type IVa are the scarcest, equalling the scarcest use of Type I examples. All cacheted covers, particularly if non-philatelic, are desirable forerunner items. Even a philatelic cover of Type V is, at present, worth in the region of £35.

Dates given are of the first recorded use.

Cachet I   Cachet II

Cat. No			
C1	**1908** (May). Cachet I	*from*	£4000
C2	**1919** (31 July). Cachet II	*from*	£425

Cachet III

C3	**1921** (8 Feb). Cachet III	*from*	£275

Cachet IVa

C4	**1927** (1 Oct). Cachet IV (as IVa, *but without centre label*)	*from*	£800
C5	**1928** (28 Oct). Cachet IVa	*from*	£5500

Cachet V   Cachet VI

C6	**1929** (24 Feb). Cachet V	*from*	35·00
C7	**1929** (15 May). Cachet Va (as V, *but without break in inner ring. Shows* "T" "C" and "N" *damaged*)	*from*	£6500
C8	**1936** (Aug). Cachet VI	*from*	60·00

Cachet VII

C9	**1936** (1 Feb). Cachet VII	*from*	22·00

During World War II there was little mail from the island as its function as a meteorological station was cloaked by security. Such covers as are known are generally struck with the "tombstone" naval censor mark and postmarked "maritime mail" or have South African postal markings. A few philatelic items from early in the war bearing cachets exist, but this usage was soon stopped by the military commander and the handstamps were put away until peace returned. Covers from the period would be worth from £75 to, at least, £350.

Cachet VIII

C10	**1946** (8 May). Cachet VIII	*from*	85·00

Cachet IX

C11	**1948** (2 Feb). Cachet IX	*from*	45·00

This cachet with "A.B.C." below the date was in private use between 1942 and 1946.

Cachet X

C12	**1948** (29 Feb). Cachet X	*from*	55·00

TRISTAN DA CUNHA (1)

1952 (1 Jan). Nos. 131, 135a/40 and 149/51 of St. Helena optd with T **1**.

1	½d. violet		15	2·75
2	1d. black and green		1·00	1·50
3	1½d. black and carmine		1·00	1·50
4	2d. black and scarlet		1·00	1·50
5	3d. grey		1·00	1·50
6	4d. ultramarine		4·25	2·50
7	6d. light blue		4·25	2·50
8	8d. olive-green		4·25	7·00
9	1s. sepia		4·25	2·00
10	2s.6d. maroon		20·00	13·00
11	5s. chocolate		22·00	20·00
12	10s. purple		42·00	30·00
1/12 *Set of 12*			95·00	75·00

Turks and Caicos Islands

TURKS ISLANDS

DEPENDENCY OF JAMAICA

A branch of the British Post Office opened at Grand Turk on 11 December 1854 replacing an earlier arrangement under which mail for the islands was sorted by local R.M.S.P. agents.

No. CC 1 is known used between 22 October 1857 and 20 April 1862.

GRAND TURK

CROWNED-CIRCLE HANDSTAMPS

CC 1

CC1	CC **1** TURKS-ISLANDS (Oct 1857)		
	Price on cover		£5500

PRICES FOR STAMPS ON COVER TO 1945

Nos. 1/5	*from* × 30
No. 6	—
Nos. 7/20	*from* × 50
Nos. 20a/48	—
Nos. 49/52	*from* × 12
Nos. 53/7	*from* × 10
Nos. 58/65	*from* × 20
Nos. 66/9	*from* × 5
Nos. 70/2	*from* × 10
Nos. 101/9	*from* × 8
Nos. 110/26	*from* × 6
Nos. 129/39	*from* × 4
Nos. 140/53	*from* × 12
Nos. 154/90	*from* × 3
Nos. 191/3	*from* × 10
Nos. 194/205	*from* × 2

1

Throat flaw (R. 3/4)

(Recess P.B.)

1867 (4 Apr). No wmk. P 11–12.

1	**1**	1d. dull rose	60·00	60·00
		a. Throat flaw	£200	£225
2		6d. black	95·00	£120
3		1s. dull blue	90·00	60·00

1873–79. Wmk Small Star. W **w 2** (sideways on Nos. 5 and 6). P 11–12×14½–15½.

4	**1**	1d. dull rose-lake (7.73)	50·00	50·00
		a. Throat flaw	£180	£200
		b. Wmk sideways	90·00	90·00
		ba. Throat flaw	£325	£350
5		1d. dull red (1.79)	55·00	60·00
		a. Imperf between (horiz pair)	£18000	
		b. Throat flaw	£200	£225
		c. Wmk upright		
6		1s. lilac (1.79)	£5000	£2000

1881 (1 Jan). Stamps of the preceding issues surcharged locally, in black. Sheets of 30 (10×3).

There are twelve different settings of the ½d., nine settings of the 2½d., and six settings of the 4d.

(2)   (3)

Setting 1. T **2**. *Long fraction bar. Two varieties in a horizontal pair repeated fifteen times in the sheet.*

7	½ on 6d. black	75·00	£120

Setting 2. T **3**. *Short fraction bar. Three varieties in a vertical strip repeated ten times in sheet.*

Setting 3. Similar to setting 2, but the middle stamp of the three varieties has a longer bar.

8	½ on 6d. black (*setting 2 only*)	70·00	£100
9	½ on 1s. dull blue	95·00	£160
	a. Surch double	£5500	

(4)   (5)   (6)

Three varieties in a vertical strip repeated ten times in sheet.

Setting 4. Types **4, 5, 6**.
Setting 5. Types **4** *(without bar)*, **5, 6**.
Setting 6. Types **4, 5, 6** *(without bar)*.
Setting 7. Types **4** *(shorter thick bar)*, **6, 6**.

10	½ on 1d. dull red (*setting 7 only*) (T **6**)		
	a. Type **4** (shorter thick bar)	£1100	
11	½ on 1s. dull blue (*setting 6 and 7*) (T **4**)	£1600	
	a. Type **4** (shorter thick bar)	£2000	
	b. Type **5**	£1100	
	c. Type **6**	£900	
	d. Type **6** (without bar)	£1700	
	e. Surch double (T **4**)	£7500	
	f. Surch double (T **5**)	£7500	
	g. Surch double (T **6** without bar)		

12	½ on 1s. lilac (T **4**)	£250	£375
	a. Without bar	£500	
	b. With short thick bar	£475	
	c. Surch double	£3250	
	cb. Surch double and short thick bar	£7500	
13	½ on 1s. lilac (T **5**)	£120	£200
	a. Surch double	£3000	
14	½ on 1s. lilac (T **6**)	£120	£200
	a. Without bar	£550	
	b. Surch double	£5500	
	ba. Surch double and without bar	£7500	

Care should be taken in the identification of Types **6** and **7** which are very similar. For the 1s. value some varieties of No. 9 are often confused with Nos. 11b/c.

(7)   (8)   (9)   (10)

Setting 8. T **7**. *Three varieties in a vertical strip. All have a very short bar.*

15	½ on 1d. dull red	60·00	£100
	a. Throat flaw	£250	
	b. Surch double	£5000	

Setting 9. T **8**. *Three varieties in a vertical strip. Bars long and thick and "1" leaning a little to left.*

16	½ on 1d. dull red	£180	£250
	a. Surch double	£4000	
	b. Throat flaw	£550	

Setting 10. T **9** *and* **10**. *Fifteen varieties repeated twice in a sheet. Ten are of T* **9** *(Rows 1 and 2), five of T* **10** *(Row 3).*

17	½ on 1d. dull red (T **9**)	50·00	£110
	a. Surch double	£5000	
18	½ on 1d. dull red (T **10**)	80·00	£160
	a. Surch double	£7500	
	b. Throat flaw	£275	
19	½ on 1s. lilac (T **9**)	90·00	£170
20	½ on 1s. lilac (T **10**)	£160	£325
20a	½ on 1s. dull blue (T **9**)	£9000	
20b	½ on 1s. dull blue (T **10**)	£15000	

Types **9** and **11**. The difference is in the position of the "2" in relation to the "1". In setting 10 the "2" is to the left of the "1" except on No. 10 (where it is directly below the "1") and in setting 11 it is to the right except on No. 2 (where it is to the left, as in setting 10).

(11)   (12)   (13)   (14)

Setting 11. T **9** *and* **11** *to* **14**. *Fifteen varieties repeated twice in a sheet. Nine of T* **11**, *three of T* **12**, *and one each of T* **9**, **13** *and* **14**.

21	½ on 1d. dull red (T **11**)	£100	£180
22	½ on 1d. dull red (T **12**)	£225	
	a. Throat flaw	£1100	
23	½ on 1d. dull red (T **13**)	£1100	
	a. Throat flaw	£1100	
24	½ on 1d. dull red (T **14**)	£600	
24a	½ on 1s. dull blue (T **11**)	£14000	

Type **9** from these settings, where it occurs on position 2, can only be distinguished from similar stamps from setting 10 when *se-tenant* with Type **11**.

In setting 11 Type **13** occurred at R. 3/4 in the setting (5×3), corresponding to the position of the "Throat flaw" on the left half of each sheet of 30 (10×3). Nos. 23 and 23a therefore exist in equal quantities.

(15)   (16)

Setting 1. T **15**. *Fraction in very small type.*

25	2½ on 6d. black	£9500	

Setting 2. T **16**. *Two varieties repeated fifteen times in a sheet. Large "2" on level with top of the "1", long thin bar.*

26	2½ on 6d. black	£350	£425
	a. Imperf between (horiz pair)	£19000	
	b. Surch double	£9500	

(17)   (18)   (19)

Setting 3. T **17**. *As T* **16**, *but large "2" not so high up.*

27	2½ on 1s. lilac	£2500	

Setting 4. T **18**. *Three varieties in a vertical strip repeated ten times in sheet. Large "2" placed lower and small bar.*

28	2½ on 6d. black	£160	£300
	a. Surch double	£9500	

Setting 5. T **19**. *Three varieties in a vertical strip repeated ten times in sheet "2" further from "½", small fraction bar.*

29	2½ on 1s. lilac	£550	£850

(20)   (21)

(22)   (23)   (24)

Setting 6. T **20** *and* **21**. *Fifteen varieties. Ten of T* **20** *and five of T* **21**, *repeated twice in a sheet.*

30	2½ on 1s. lilac (T **20**)	£9500	
31	2½ on 1s. lilac (T **21**)	£15000	

Setting 7. T **22**. *Three varieties in a vertical strip, repeated ten times in a sheet.*

32	2½ on 6d. black	£7500	
33	2½ on 1s. dull blue	£15000	

Setting 8. T **23** *and* **24**. *Fifteen varieties. Ten of T* **23** *and five of T* **24** *repeated twice in a sheet.*

34	2½ on 1d. dull red (T **23**)	£650	
35	2½ on 1d. dull red (T **24**)	£1400	
	a. Throat flaw	£3500	
36	2½ on 1s. lilac (T **23**)	£550	£700
	a. Surch "½" double	£3500	
37	2½ on 1s. lilac (T **24**)	£1200	
	a. Surch "½" double	£6000	

(25)   (26)   (27)

Setting 9. T **25**, **26**, *and* **27**. *Fifteen varieties. Ten of T* **25**, *three of T* **26** *one of T* **26** *without bar, and one of T* **27**, *repeated twice in a sheet.*

38	2½ on 1s. dull blue (T **25**)	£800	
39	2½ on 1s. dull blue (T **26**)	£2500	
40	2½ on 1s. dull blue (T **26**) (without bar)	£8000	
41	2½ on 1s. dull blue (T **27**)	£8000	

(28)   (29)   (30)

Setting 1. T **28**. *"4" 8 mm high, pointed top.*

42	4 on 6d. black	£475	£300

Settings 2-6. T **29** *and* **30**.

43	4 on 6d. black (T **29**)	75·00	£100
44	4 on 6d. black (T **30**)	£325	£450
45	4 on 1s. lilac (T **29**)	£400	£550
	a. Surch double		
46	4 on 1s. lilac (T **30**)	£2500	
	a. Surch double		
47	4 on 1d. dull red (T **29**)	£750	£475
48	4 on 1d. dull red (T **28**)	£850	£550

The components of these settings can only be distinguished when in blocks. Details are given in the handbook by John J. Challis.

31

One Penny

(32)

(Typo D.L.R.)

1881. Wmk Crown CC (sideways* on T **1**). P 14.

49	**1**	1d. brown-red (Oct)	65·00	90·00
		a. Throat flaw	£250	£300
50	**31**	4d. ultramarine (Die I) (Aug)	£130	60·00
51		6d. olive-black (Oct)	£100	£150
52		1s. slate-green (Oct)	£160	£120

*The normal sideways watermark shows Crown to right of CC, *as seen from the back of the stamp*.

Nos. 49 and 51/2 also exist showing Crown to left of CC, but due to the position of the watermark such varieties are difficult to detect on single stamps.

1882–85. Wmk Crown CA (reversed on 1d.). P 14.

53	**31**	½d. blue-green (Die I) (2.82)	11·00	23·00
		a. Pale green (12.85)	3·00	4·00
		b. Top left triangle detached	£200	
55	**1**	1d. orange-brown (10.83)	75·00	30·00
		a. Bisected (½d.) (on cover)	†	£4500
		b. Throat flaw	£275	£130
		x. Wmk normal (not reversed)	£120	
56	**31**	2½d. red-brown (Die I) (2.82)	24·00	12·00
57		4d. grey (Die I) (10.84)	21·00	9·00
		a. Bisected (2d.) (on cover)	†	£4500

For illustration of "top left triangle detached" variety see above No. 7 of Montserrat.

1887 (July)**–89**. Wmk Crown CA.

		(a) P 12.		
58	**1**	1d. crimson-lake	20·00	4·75
		a. Imperf between (horiz pair)	£18000	
		b. Throat flaw	55·00	13·00
		x. Wmk reversed	14·00	3·00
		(b) P 14.		
59	**1**	6d. yellow-brown (2.89)	3·50	3·75
		s. Optd "Specimen"	50·00	
60		1s. sepia	5·00	3·50

TURKS AND CAICOS ISLANDS

During a shortage of 1d. stamps a supply of JAMAICA . No. 27 was sent to the Turks and Caicos Islands in April 1889 and used until replaced by No. 61. Price from £250 used.

1889 (May). *Surch at Grand Turk with T* **32**.

61	31	1d. on 2½d. red-brown	9·00	11·00
		a. "One" omitted	£1600	
		b. Bisected (½d.) (on cover)	†	£5000

No. 61a was caused by misplacement of the surcharge. Stamps from the same sheet can be found with the surcharge reading "Penny One".

Neck flaw (R. 3/2)

1889–93. Wmk Crown CA. P 14.

62	1	1d. crimson-lake (7.89)	4·25	4·50
		a. Bisected (½d.) (on cover)	†	£4500
		b. Throat flaw	18·00	20·00
		c. Neck flaw	25·00	27·00
		x. Wmk reversed	50·00	
63		1d. lake	3·25	3·25
		a. Bisected (½d.) (on cover)	†	£4500
		b. Throat flaw	13·00	13·00
		c. Neck flaw	19·00	20·00
64		1d. pale rosy lake	3·25	5·00
		b. Throat flaw	13·00	22·00
		c. Neck flaw	19·00	28·00
65	31	2½d. ultramarine (Die II) (4.93)	3·50	3·00
		s. Optd "Specimen"	50·00	

(33) 34

1893 (10 June). *No. 57 surch at Grand Turk with T* **33**.

Setting 1. Bars between "1d." and "2" separate, instead of continuous across the rows of stamps.

66		½d. on 4d. grey	£2750	£1200

Setting 2. Continuous bars. Thin and thick bar 10¾ mm apart. "2" under the "1".

67		½d. on 4d. grey	£190	£140

Setting 3. As last, but bars 11¾ mm apart.

68		½d. on 4d. grey	£150	£180

Setting 4. Bars 11 mm apart. Five out of the six varieties in the strip have the "2" below the space between the "1" and "d".

69		½d. on 4d. grey	£190	£170

There is a fifth setting, but the variation is slight.

(Typo D.L.R.)

1893–95. Wmk Crown CA. P 14.

70	31	½d. dull green (Die II) (12.93)	3·00	2·25
71		4d. dull purple & ultram (Die II) (5.95)	12·00	15·00
72	34	5d. olive-green and carmine (6.94)	5·00	15·00
		a. Bisected (2½d.) (on cover)	†	£4000
70/2 *Set of 3*			18·00	29·00
71s/2s Optd "Specimen" *Set of 2*			£100	

TURKS AND CAICOS ISLANDS

35 Badge of the Islands 36 Badge of the Islands

The dates on the stamps have reference to the political separation from Bahamas.

(Recess D.L.R.)

1900 (10 Nov)–**04**. Wmk Crown CA (½d. to 1s.) or Wmk Crown CC (2s., 3s.). P 14.

101	35	½d. green	2·75	4·00
		w. Wmk reversed		
102		1d. red	3·50	75
		w. Wmk inverted	85·00	
103		2d. sepia	1·00	1·25
		w. Wmk inverted		
		w. Wmk reversed	£100	
104		2½d. blue	7·50	16·00
		a. Greyish blue (1904)	1·75	1·00
		aw. Wmk inverted	85·00	
		ay. Wmk inverted and reversed		£140
105		4d. orange	3·75	7·00
106		6d. dull mauve	2·50	6·50

107		1s. purple-brown	3·25	18·00
108	36	2s. purple	40·00	55·00
109		3s. lake	55·00	75·00
101/9 *Set of 9*			£100	£150
101s/9s Optd "Specimen" *Set of 9*			£225	

1905–08. Wmk Mult Crown CA. P 14.

110	35	½d. green	5·00	15
111		1d. red	16·00	50
		w. Wmk inverted		
112		3d. purple/yellow (1908)	2·25	6·00
		s. Optd "Specimen"	50·00	
110/12 *Set of 3*			21·00	6·00

37 Turk's-head Cactus 38

(Recess D.L.R.)

1909 (2 Sept)–**11**. Wmk Mult Crown CA. P 14.

115	37	¼d. rosy mauve (1910)	1·75	1·00
		w. Wmk inverted		
116		¼d. red (1911)	60	40
		w. Wmk inverted		
117	38	½d. yellow-green	75	40
		w. Wmk inverted		
		w. Wmk reversed	55·00	
		y. Wmk inverted and reversed		
118		1d. red	1·25	40
119		2d. greyish slate	3·00	1·40
120		2½d. blue	3·75	3·75
		w. Wmk inverted		
		x. Wmk reversed	65·00	70·00
121		3d. purple/yellow	2·50	2·00
122		4d. red/yellow	3·25	6·00
123		6d. purple	7·00	6·00
124		1s. black/green	7·00	8·50
		w. Wmk inverted		
125		2s. red/green	35·00	48·00
126		3s. black/red	35·00	40·00
115/26 *Set of 12*			90·00	£110
115s/26s Optd "Specimen" *Set of 12*			£225	

See also Nos. 154 and 162.

WAR TAX

39 (40)

1913 (1 Apr)–**21**. Wmk Mult Crown CA. P 14.

129	39	½d. green	50	1·75
		w. Wmk inverted		
130		1d. red	1·00	2·25
		a. Bright rose-scarlet	1·10	2·00
		ax. Wmk reversed	55·00	
		b. Rose-carmine (1918)	3·75	6·00
131		2d. greyish slate	2·25	3·50
132		2½d. ultramarine	2·25	3·00
		aw. Wmk inverted		
		b. Bright blue (1918)	4·00	2·75
133		3d. purple/yellow	2·25	11·00
		a. On lemon	16·00	
		b. On yellow-buff	4·00	9·50
		c. On orange-buff	1·75	
		cx. Wmk reversed	75·00	
		d. On pale yellow	2·25	8·50
134		4d. red/yellow	1·00	9·50
		a. On orange-buff	1·60	7·50
		ab. "A" of "CA" missing from wmk		
		as. Optd "Specimen"	48·00	
		b. Carmine on pale yellow	7·50	16·00
135		5d. pale olive-green (18.5.16)	6·50	22·00
136		6d. dull purple	2·50	3·50
		w. Wmk inverted		
		x. Wmk reversed		
137		1s. brown-orange	1·50	5·00
		w. Wmk inverted		
138		2s. red/blue-green	7·50	26·00
		a. On greenish white (1919)	24·00	70·00
		b. On emerald (3.21)	48·00	70·00
		bs. Optd "Specimen"	48·00	
		bx. Wmk reversed	£150	
139		3s. black/red	15·00	26·00
129/39 *Set of 11*			35·00	95·00
129s/39s Optd "Specimen" *Set of 11*			£180	

1917 (3 Jan). *Optd with T* **40** *at bottom of stamp.*

140	39	1d. red	10	1·50
		a. Opt double	£180	£250
		ab. Opt double (in horiz pair with normal)	£400	
		b. "TAX" omitted		
		c. "WAR TAX" omitted in vert pair with normal	£550	
		d. Opt inverted at top	65·00	85·00
		e. Opt double, one inverted	£110	
		f. Opt inverted only, in pair with No. 140e	£550	
141		3d. purple/yellow-buff	1·25	5·00
		a. Opt double	95·00	
		b. Purple/lemon	2·25	7·00
		ba. Opt double	95·00	£120
		bb. Opt double, one inverted		

The overprint was in a setting of 60, applied twice to the sheets of 120. One sheet of the 1d. exists with the right-hand impression of the setting misplaced one row to the left so that stamps in vertical row 6 show a double overprint (No. 140ab). It appears that the right-hand vertical row

---

on this sheet had the overprint applied at a third operation.

In Nos. 140e/f the inverted overprint is at foot and reads "TAX WAR" owing to displacement. No. 140e also exists with "WAR" omitted from the inverted overprint.

In both values of the first printings the stamp in the bottom left-hand corner of the sheet has a long "T" in "TAX", and on the first stamp of the sixth row the "X" is damaged and looks like a reversed "K". The long "T" was subsequently converted.

1917 (Oct). *Second printing with overprint at top or in middle of stamp.*

143	39	1d. red	10	1·25
		a. Inverted opt at bottom or centre	48·00	
		c. Opt omitted (in pair with normal)	£550	
		d. Opt double, one at top, one at bottom	60·00	
		e. As d., but additional opt in top margin	£120	
		f. Horiz pair, one as d., the other normal	£300	
		g. Pair, one opt inverted, one normal	£550	
		h. Double opt at top (in pair with normal)	£275	
		i. Opt double	45·00	55·00
144		3d. purple/yellow	60	1·75
		a. Opt double	45·00	
		b. Opt double, one inverted	£325	
		c. Purple/lemon	3·50	

1918. *Overprinted with T* **40**.

145	39	3d. purple/yellow (R.)	10·00	27·00
		a. Opt double	£325	

WAR

WAR WAR TAX

TAX TAX
(41) (42) (43)

1918. *Optd with T* **41** *in London by D.L.R.*

146	39	1d. rose-carmine	20	1·25
		a. Bright rose-scarlet	15	1·25
		aw. Wmk inverted	65·00	
147		3d. purple/yellow	2·50	3·75
146/7 Optd "Specimen" *Set of 2*			80·00	

1919. *Optd with T* **41** *in London by D.L.R.*

148	39	3d. purple/orange-buff (R.)	10	2·50
		s. Optd "Specimen"	40·00	

1919. *Local overprint. T* **40**, *in violet.*

149	39	1d. bright rose-scarlet	30	3·25
		a. "WAR" omitted	£150	
		b. Opt double	21·00	
		c. Opt double in pair with normal	£120	
		d. Opt double, one inverted		
		e. Rose-carmine	6·50	14·00
		ea. Opt double		
		w. Wmk inverted	32·00	

1919. *Optd with T* **42**.

150	39	1d. scarlet	10	1·00
		a. Opt double	£140	£170
		b. Opt double, one albino and reversed		
151		3d. purple/orange-buff	30	2·75
		w. Wmk inverted	32·00	
		x. Wmk reversed	32·00	

1919 (17 Dec). *Optd with T* **43**.

152	39	1d. scarlet	20	2·50
		a. Opt inverted		
153		3d. purple/orange-buff	50	2·75
		w. Wmk inverted	30·00	
		x. Wmk reversed	25·00	
		y. Wmk inverted and reversed	12·00	

The two bottom rows of this setting have the words "WAR" and "TAX" about 1 mm further apart.

1921 (23 Apr). Wmk Mult Script CA. P 14.

154	37	¼d. rose-red	2·50	15·00
155	39	½d. green	2·75	5·50
156		1d. carmine-red	1·00	5·50
157		2d. slate-grey	1·00	19·00
		y. Wmk inverted and reversed	65·00	
158		2½d. bright blue	1·75	7·50
		x. Wmk reversed	90·00	
159		5d. sage-green	8·00	50·00
160		6d. purple	6·50	50·00
		w. Wmk inverted		
		x. Wmk reversed	70·00	
161		1s. brown-orange	6·50	28·00
154/61 *Set of 8*			26·00	£160
154s/61s Optd "Specimen" *Set of 8*			£140	

44 45

(Recess D.L.R.)

1922 (20 Nov)–**26**. P 14.

(a) Wmk Mult Script CA.

162	37	¼d. black (11.10.26)	80	1·00
163	44	½d. yellow-green	2·25	3·25
		a. Bright green	2·25	3·25
		b. Apple-green	5·50	10·00
164		1d. brown	50	3·25
165		1½d. scarlet (24.11.25)	6·50	16·00
166		2d. slate	50	5·00

167		2½d. purple/*pale yellow*	50	1·75
168		3d. bright blue	50	5·00
169		4d. red/*pale yellow*	1·25	16·00
		ax. Wmk reversed	65·00	
		b. Carmine/*pale yellow*	4·50	16·00
170		5d. sage-green	85	22·00
		y. Wmk inverted and reversed	70·00	
171		6d. purple	70	6·00
		x. Wmk reversed	75·00	
172		1s. brown-orange	80	19·00
173		2s. red/*emerald*	2·00	9·00

(b) Wmk Mult Crown CA.

174	44	2s. red/*emerald* (24.11.25)	25·00	70·00
175		3s. black/*red* (24.11.25)	5·00	28·00
162/75 *Set of 14*			42·00	£180
162s/75s Optd "Specimen" *Set of 14*			£200	

1928 (1 Mar). Inscr "POSTAGE & REVENUE". Wmk Mult Script CA. P 14.

176	45	½d. green	75	50
177		1d. brown	75	70
178		1½d. scarlet	75	3·25
179		2d. grey	75	50
180		2½d. purple/*yellow*	75	5·00
181		3d. bright blue	75	7·00
182		6d. purple	75	7·50
183		1s. brown-orange	3·75	7·50
184		2s. red/*emerald*	6·00	35·00
185		5s. green/*yellow*	11·00	35·00
186		10s. purple/*blue*	50·00	£100
176/86 *Set of 11*			70·00	£180
176s/86s Optd "Specimen" *Set of 11*			£160	

1935 (6 May). *Silver Jubilee. As Nos. 91/4 of Antigua, but ptd by Waterlow. P 11×12.*

187		½d. black and green	30	75
		k. Kite and vertical log	38·00	
		l. Kite and horizontal log	30·00	40·00
188		3d. brown and deep blue	2·75	4·50
		k. Kite and vertical log	80·00	£110
189		6d. light blue and olive-green	1·75	4·75
		k. Kite and vertical log	80·00	£110
190		1s. slate and purple	1·75	3·25
		k. Kite and vertical log	80·00	£120
187/90 *Set of 4*			6·00	12·00
187s/90s Perf "Specimen" *Set of 4*			90·00	

For illustrations of plate varieties see Omnibus section following Zanzibar.

1937 (12 May). *Coronation. As Nos. 95/7 of Antigua, but ptd by D.L.R. P 14.*

191		½d. myrtle-green	10	10
		a. Deep green	40·00	
192		2d. grey-black	65	50
193		3d. bright blue	65	50
191/3 *Set of 3*			1·25	1·00
191s/3s Perf "Specimen" *Set of 3*			75·00	

46 Raking Salt   **47** Salt Industry

(Recess Waterlow)

1938 (18 June)–**45**. Wmk Mult Script CA. P 12½.

194	46	¼d. black	20	10
195		½d. yellowish green	4·00	15
		a. Deep green (6.11.44)	1·75	70
196		1d. red-brown	75	10
197		1½d. scarlet	75	15
198		2d. grey	1·00	30
199		2½d. yellow-orange	4·75	80
		a. Orange (6.11.44)	2·50	1·75
200		3d. bright blue	70	30
201		6d. mauve	16·00	2·25
201a		6d. sepia (9.2.45)	50	20
202		1s. yellow-bistre	4·75	9·00
202a		1s. grey-olive (9.2.45)	50	20
203	47	2s. deep rose-carmine	42·00	14·00
		a. Bright rose-carmine (6.11.44)	17·00	18·00
204		5s. yellowish green	48·00	20·00
		a. Deep green (6.11.44)	38·00	22·00
205		10s. bright violet	14·00	7·50
194/205 *Set of 14*			90·00	48·00
194s/205s Perf "Specimen" *Set of 14*			£225	

1946 (4 Nov). *Victory. As Nos. 110/11 of Antigua.*

206		2d. black	10	10
207		3d. blue	15	10
206s/7s Perf "Specimen" *Set of 2*			70·00	

1948 (13 Sept). *Royal Silver Wedding. As Nos. 112/13 of Antigua.*

208		1d. red-brown	15	10
209		10s. mauve	8·00	12·00

50 Badge of the Islands   **51** Flag of Turks and Caicos Islands

52 Map of islands   **53** Queen Victoria and King George VI

(Recess Waterlow)

1948 (14 Dec). *Centenary of Separation from Bahamas. T* **50**/**53**. Wmk Mult Script CA. P 12½.

210	50	½d. blue-green	1·25	15
211		2d. carmine	1·25	15
212	51	3d. blue	1·75	15
213	52	6d. violet	1·00	30
214	53	2s. black and bright blue	1·25	1·50
215		5s. black and green	1·50	4·25
216		10s. black and brown	1·50	4·25
210/16 *Set of 7*			8·50	9·75

1949 (10 Oct). *75th Anniv of U.P.U. As Nos. 114/17 of Antigua.*

217		2½d. red-orange	20	1·60
218		3d. deep blue	2·00	60
219		6d. brown	20	75
220		1s. olive	20	35
217/20 *Set of 4*			2·40	3·00

54 Bulk Salt Loading   **55** Salt City

56 Caicos Mail   **57** Grand Turk

58 Sponge diving   **59** South Creek

60 Map   **61** Grand Turk Light

62 Government House   **63** Cockburn Harbour

64 Government offices   **65** Loading salt

66 Dependency's Badge

(Recess Waterlow)

1950 (1 Aug). *T* **54**/**66**. Wmk Mult Script CA. P 12½.

221	54	½d. green	85	40
222	55	1d. red-brown	80	75
223	56	1½d. deep carmine	1·25	55
224	57	2d. red-orange	1·00	40
225	58	2½d. grey-olive	1·25	50
226	59	3d. bright blue	60	40
227	60	4d. black and rose	2·75	70
228	61	6d. black and blue	2·00	50
229	62	1s. black and blue-green	1·25	40
230	63	1s.6d. black and scarlet	8·50	3·25
231	64	2s. emerald and ultramarine	3·00	4·50
232	65	5s. blue and black	18·00	8·50
233	66	10s. black and violet	18·00	18·00
221/33 *Set of 13*			50·00	35·00

Uganda

PRICES FOR STAMPS ON COVER TO 1945

The type-written stamps of Uganda, Nos. 1/53, are very rare used on cover.

Nos. 54/60	*from* × 20	
No. 61	—	
Nos. 70/5	*from* × 12	
No. 76	—	
Nos. 84/90	*from* × 20	
No. 91	—	
Nos. 92/3	*from* × 40	

PROTECTORATE

Following a period of conflict between Islamic, Protestant and Roman Catholic factions, Uganda was declared to be in the British sphere of influence by the Anglo-German Agreement of July 1890. The British East Africa Company exercised a variable degree of control until 27 August 1894 when the country was declared a British Protectorate.

Before the introduction of Nos. 84/91 the stamps of Uganda were only valid for internal postage. Letters for overseas were franked with British East Africa issues on arrival at Mombasa.

(Currency. 200 cowries = 1 rupee)

```
 ┌ ─ ─ ─ ─ ┐      ┌ ─ ─ ─ ─ ┐
 ¦ U     G ¦      ¦ U     G ¦
 ¦         ¦      ¦         ¦
 ¦   50    ¦      ¦   20    ¦
 ¦         ¦      ¦         ¦
 └ ─ ─ ─ ─ ┘      └ ─ ─ ─ ─ ┘
       1                2
```

TYPE-WRITTEN STAMPS. Nos. 2/53 were type-written by the Revd. E. Millar at Mengo for the Uganda administration. For all "printings" a thin laid paper was used, and all issues were imperforate and ungummed. The laid lines are invariably horizontal, with the exception of No. 20a.

The original typewriter used had wide letters, but in late April, 1895 Millar obtained a new machine on which the type face was in a narrower fount.

Each sheet was made up of whatever values were required at the time, so that different values can be found se-tenant or tête-bêche. These last were caused by the paper being inverted in the machine so that space at the foot could be utilised.

For the first issue the sheets were of 117 (9×13), but with the introduction of the narrower width (Nos. 17 onwards) a larger number of stamps per sheet, 143 (11×13), was adopted.

The manuscript provisionals, Nos. 9a/16 come from the Mission at Ngogwe, most of the manuscript surcharges including the initials of the Revd. G. R. Blackledge stationed there.

1895 (20 Mar). *Wide letters. Wide stamps, 20 to 26 mm wide.*

2	1	10 (c.) black	£3000	£1200
4		20 (c.) black	£5000	£1200
		a. "U A" for "U G"	†	£3000
6		30 (c.) black	£1400	£1400
7		40 (c.) black	£2750	£1200
8		50 (c.) black	£1200	£1000
		a. "U A" for "U G"	†	£4750
9		60 (c.) black	£1800	£1800

It is now believed that the 5, 15 and 25 cowries values in this width, previously Nos. 1, 3 and 5, do not exist.

A strip of three of No. 2 is known on cover of which one stamp has the value "10" altered to "5" in manuscript and initialled "E.M.".

1895 (May). *Wide stamps with pen-written surcharges, in black.*

9a	1	10 on 30 (c.) black	†	£38000
10		10 on 50 (c.) black	†	£38000
11		15 on 10 (c.) black	†	£25000
12		15 on 40 (c.) black	†	£30000
13		15 on 50 (c.) black	†	£38000
14		15 on 50 (c.) black	†	£38000
15		25 on 50 (c.) black	†	£38000
16		50 on 50 (c.) black	†	£38000

1895 (April). *Wide letters. Narrow stamps, 16 to 18 mm wide.*

17	1	5 (c.) black	£1700	£1000
18		10 (c.) black	£1700	£1100
19		15 (c.) black	£1000	£1000
20		20 (c.) black	£1700	£650
		a. Vertically laid paper	†	£2500
21		25 (c.) black	£950	£950
22		30 (c.) black	£8000	£8000
23		40 (c.) black	£7500	£7500
24		50 (c.) black	£3250	
25		60 (c.) black	£7000	

A single used example of No. 20a has been seen. Nos. 2/53 otherwise show the laid lines horizontal.

1895 (May). *Narrow letters. Narrow stamps 16 to 18 mm wide.*

26	2	5 (c.) black	£950	
27		10 (c.) black	£950	
28		15 (c.) black	£950	
29		20 (c.) black	£700	
30		25 (c.) black	£950	
31		30 (c.) black	£1000	
32		40 (c.) black	£1000	
33		50 (c.) black	£850	
34		60 (c.) black	£1700	

1895 (Nov). *Narrow letters. Narrow stamps, 16–18 mm wide. Change of colour.*

35	2	5 (c.) violet	£500	£500
36		10 (c.) violet	£475	£475
37		15 (c.) violet	£600	£425
38		20 (c.) violet	£375	£275
		a. "G U" for "U G"		
39		25 (c.) violet	£750	£750
40		30 (c.) violet	£1000	£750
41		40 (c.) violet	£900	£900

42		50 (c.)	violet	£850	£900
43		100 (c.)	violet	£2500	£2500

Stamps of 35 (c.) and 45 (c.) have been recorded in violet, on vertically laid paper. They were never prepared for postal use, and did not represent a postal rate, but were type-written to oblige a local official. (*Price* £2500 *each, unused*)

'V.9G.R'

25

'Uganda'

3

1896 (June).

44	3	5 (c.)	violet	£475	£500
45		10 (c.)	violet	£425	£400
46		15 (c.)	violet	£475	£500
47		20 (c.)	violet	£275	£200
48		25 (c.)	violet	£450	
49		30 (c.)	violet	£500	£650
50		40 (c.)	violet	£550	£650
51		50 (c.)	violet	£600	£650
52		60 (c.)	violet	£1500	
53		100 (c.)	violet	£1400	£1500

(New Currency. 16 annas = 1 rupee)

UGANDA
POSTAGE
V†R
1 ANNA
PROTECTORATE
4 (Thin "1")

UGANDA
POSTAGE
V†R
1 ANNA
PROTECTORATE
5 (Thick "1")

UGANDA
POSTAGE
V†R
4 ANNAS
PROTECTORATE
6

UGANDA
POSTAGE
VLR
4 ANNAS
PROTECTORATE
7

In the 2a. and 3a. the dagger points upwards; the stars in the 2a. are level with the top of "VR". The 8a. is as T **6** but with left star at top and right star at foot. The 1r. has three stars at foot. The 5r. has central star raised and the others at foot.

(Type-set by the Revd. F. Rowling at Lubwa's, in Usoga)

1896 (7 Nov). *Thick white wove paper (Nos. 54/8) or thin yellowish paper ruled with vertical lines 9 mm apart (Nos. 59/61)*.

(a) Types **4/6**.

54	4	1a.	black	£110	95·00
		a.	Small "o" in "POSTAGE"	£600	£550
55	5	1a.	black	19·00	24·00
		a.	Small "o" in "POSTAGE"	80·00	95·00
56	6	2a.	black	25·00	29·00
		a.	Small "o" in "POSTAGE"	£100	£120
57		3a.	black	27·00	32·00
		a.	Small "o" in "POSTAGE"	£110	£140
58		4a.	black	26·00	30·00
		a.	Small "o" in "POSTAGE"	£100	£120
59		8a.	black	29·00	32·00
		a.	Small 'o' in "POSTAGE"	£120	£140
60		1r.	black	75·00	95·00
		a.	Small "o" in "POSTAGE"	£300	£400
61		5r.	black	£225	£350
		a.	Small "o" in "POSTAGE"	£750	£950

(b) Optd "L", in black as in T **7** *for local use, by a postal official, R. R. Racey, at Kampala.*

70	4	1a.	black	£190	£170
		a.	Small "o" in "POSTAGE"	£1200	£900
71	6	2a.	black	£100	£120
		a.	Small "o" in "POSTAGE"	£425	£475
72		3a.	black	£250	£300
		a.	Small "o" in "POSTAGE"	£1300	£1600
73		4a.	black	£100	£160
		a.	Small "o" in "POSTAGE"	£475	
74		8a.	black	£190	£225
		a.	Small "o" in "POSTAGE"	£1100	£1300
75		1r.	black	£375	£425
		a.	Small "o" in "POSTAGE"	£1500	
76		5r.	black	£15000	£15000

Tête-bêche pairs of all values may be found owing to the settings of 16 (4×4) being printed side by side or above one another. They are worth a premium. The variety with small "O" occurs on R. 3/1.

8   9   **UGANDA**
(10)

(Recess D.L.R.)

1898 (Nov)–**1902**. P 14.

(a) Wmk Crown CA.

84	8	1a.	scarlet	2·00	2·25
		a.	Carmine-rose (1902)	2·00	1·00

86		2a.	red-brown	3·50	7·00
87		3a.	pale grey	12·00	27·00
		a.	Bluish grey	13·00	13·00
88		4a.	deep green	6·00	6·50
89		8a.	pale olive	8·00	24·00
		a.	Grey-green	13·00	32·00

(b) Wmk Crown CC.

90	9	1r.	dull blue	40·00	42·00
		a.	Bright blue	45·00	50·00
91		5r.	brown	70·00	£100
84/91 *Set of 7*				£120	£180
84s/91s Optd "Specimen" *Set of 7*				£160	

On 1 April 1901 the postal administrations of British East Africa and Uganda were merged. Subsequent issues to 1962 are listed under KENYA, UGANDA and TANGANYIKA.

1902 (Feb). *T* **11** *of British East Africa (Kenya, Uganda, and Tanganyika) optd with T* **10**.

92		½a.	yellow-green	2·00	1·40
		a.	Opt omitted (in pair with normal)	£4250	
		b.	Opt inverted (at foot)	£1800	
		c.	Opt double	£2000	
		x.	Wmk reversed		
93		2½a.	deep blue (R.)	2·75	3·00
		a.	Opt double	£600	
		b.	Inverted "S" (R. 1/1)	65·00	80·00

The Eastern Province of Uganda was transferred to British East Africa on 1 April 1902.

Victoria *see* Australia

Virgin Islands

CROWN COLONY

Apart from the 1951 Legislative Council issue, the word "BRITISH" did not appear regularly on the stamps until 1968 when it was introduced to avoid confusion with the nearby Virgin Islands of the United States (the former Danish West Indies).

Most mail from the early years of the islands' history was sent via the Danish island of St. Thomas.

It is not known exactly when the first post office, or agency, was established on Tortola, but an entry in a G.P.O. account book suggest that it was operating by 1787 and the earliest letter postmarked "TORTOLA" dates from June of that year. The stamps of Great Britain were used from 1858 to May 1860, when the colonial authorities assumed responsibility for the overseas mails from the British G.P.O.

For illustrations of the handstamp and postmark types see BRITISH POST OFFICES ABROAD notes, following GREAT BRITAIN.

TORTOLA

CROWNED-CIRCLE HANDSTAMPS

CC1	CC **1** TORTOLA (R.) (15.12.1842).	*Price on cover*	£5500
CC2	CC **5** TORTOLA (R.) (21.6.1854)...	*Price on cover*	£10000

No. CC2 is known used as an Official Paid mark during the years 1900 to 1918. *Price on cover* £950.

Stamps of GREAT BRITAIN *cancelled "A 13" as Type* **2**.

1858–60.

Z1	1d. rose-red (1857), perf 14		£3750
Z2	4d. rose (1857)		£4000
Z3	6d. lilac (1856)		£1400
Z4	1s. green (1856)		

PRICES FOR STAMPS ON COVER TO 1945	
Nos. 1/7	*from* × 30
Nos. 8/9	*from* × 40
No. 10	—
No. 11	*from* × 10
No. 12	*from* × 30
No. 13	—
Nos. 14/b	*from* × 10
Nos. 15/17	*from* × 30
Nos. 18/19	*from* × 40
No. 20	—
Nos. 21/b	*from* × 20
Nos. 22/b	*from* × 30
Nos. 24/31	*from* × 25
Nos. 32/4	*from* × 50
Nos. 35/7	*from* × 30
Nos. 38/41	*from* × 15
No. 42	*from* × 20
Nos. 43/50	*from* × 8
Nos. 54/77	*from* × 6
Nos. 78/81	*from* × 6
Nos. 82/101	*from* × 3
Nos. 103/6	*from* × 4
Nos. 107/9	*from* × 6
Nos. 110/21	*from* × 2

1 St. Ursula   2 St. Ursula

(Litho Nissen & Parker from original dies by Waterlow)

1866 (Dec). No wmk. P 12.

(a) White wove paper.

1	1	1d.	green	45·00	60·00
2		1d.	deep green	55·00	65·00
3	2	6d.	rose	90·00	£110
		a.	Large "V" in "VIRGIN" (R. 2/1)	£375	£475
4		6d.	deep rose	£130	£140
		a.	Large "V" in "VIRGIN" (R. 2/1)	£425	£500

(b) Toned paper.

5	1	1d.	green	48·00	60·00
		a.	Perf 15×12	£5500	£7000
6		1d.	deep green	£100	£120
7	2	6d.	rose-red	60·00	90·00
		a.	Large "V" in "VIRGIN" (R. 2/1)	£275	£375

The above were printed in sheets of 25.

6d. stamps showing part of the papermaker's watermark ("A. Cowan & Sons Extra Superfine A. C. & S.") are worth 50% more.

Beware of fakes of No. 5a made from perf 12 stamps.

3   4

Normal   Variety

1s. Long-tailed "S" in "ISLANDS" (R. 3/1)

(Litho and typo (figure of the Virgin) (1s.) or litho (others) Nissen and Parker from original dies by Waterlow)

1867–70. No wmk. P 15. *1s. with double-lined frame.*

(a) White wove paper.

8	1	1d. yellow-green (1868)	80·00	80·00
9	1	1d. blue-green (1870)	65·00	70·00
10	2	6d. pale rose	£600	£600
11	4	1s. black and rose-carmine	£275	£375
		a. Long-tailed "S"	£850	£1100

(b) Greyish (No. 14) or toned paper (others).

12	1	1d. yellow-green (1868)	85·00	80·00
13	2	6d. dull rose (1868)	£300	£350
14	4	1s. black & rose-carmine (*greyish paper*)	£275	£375
		a. Long-tailed "S"	£850	£1100
14b		1s. black and rose-carmine (*toned paper*)	£325	£375
		ba. Long-tailed "S"	£900	£1100

(c) Pale rose paper.

15	3	4d. lake-red	50·00	70·00

(d) Buff paper.

16	3	4d. lake-red	40·00	60·00
17		4d. lake-brown	40·00	60·00

The thin lines of the frame on the 1s. are close together and sometimes merge into one.

The 1d. from the 1868 printing was in sheets of 20 (5×4) with narrow margins between the stamps. Later printings were in sheets of 12 (3×4) with wider margins. The 4d. was in sheets of 25; and the remaining two values in sheets of 20 (5×4).

The greyish paper used for Nos. 14 and 20 often shows traces of blue.

1867. *Nos.* 11 *and* 14/b *with crimson frames superimposed extending into margins.* P 15.

18	4	1s. black and rose-carmine (*white paper*)	65·00	75·00
		a. Long-tailed "S"	£200	£250
		b. Figure of Virgin omitted	£85000	
19		1s. black and rose-carmine (*toned paper*)	65·00	75·00
		a. Long-tailed "S"	£200	£250
20		1s. black and rose-carmine (*greyish paper*)	£750	£900
		a. Long-tailed "S"	£1900	£2250

1868. *Nos.* 11 *and* 14b *with frame lines retouched so as to make them single lines. Margins remain white.* P 15.

21	4	1s. black and rose-carmine (*white paper*)	£140	£170
		a. Long-tailed "S"	£450	£550
21b		1s. black and rose-carmine (*toned paper*)	£140	£170
		ba. Long-tailed "S"	£450	£550

(Litho D.L.R.)

1878. Wmk Crown CC (sideways). P 14.

22	1	1d. green	80·00	£100
		a. Yellow-green	£170	£130
		b. Wmk upright	90·00	£120

6 (Die I)   (7)

(Typo D.L.R.)

1879–80. Wmk Crown CC. P 14.

24	6	1d. emerald-green (1880)	70·00	85·00
25		2½d. red-brown	95·00	£120

1883 (June)–84. Wmk Crown CA. P 14.

26	6	½d. yellow-buff	85·00	85·00
27		½d. dull green (*shades*) (11.83)	5·50	10·00
		b. Top left triangle detached	£225	£300
29		1d. pale rose (15.9.83)	25·00	29·00
		a. Deep rose (1884)	55·00	60·00
31		2½d. ultramarine (9.84)	2·75	16·00
		b. Top left triangle detached	£250	
		w. Wmk inverted	£160	

For illustration of "top left triangle detached" variety see above No. 21 of Antigua.

(Litho D.L.R.)

1887–89. Wmk Crown CA. P 14.

32	1	1d. red (5.89)	2·75	8·00
		x. Wmk reversed	£130	
33		1d. rose-red	2·50	7·50
34		1d. rose	5·00	14·00
35	3	4d. chestnut	35·00	65·00
		x. Wmk reversed	£180	
36		4d. pale chestnut	35·00	65·00
37		4d. brown-red	45·00	70·00
38	2	6d. dull violet	17·00	48·00
39		6d. deep violet	16·00	45·00
40	4	1s. sepia (2.89)	80·00	£100
41		1s. brown *to* deep brown	45·00	90·00
34s/40s		Optd "Specimen" *Set of 4*	£300	

The De La Rue transfers of T **1** to **4** are new transfers and differ from those of Messrs. Nissen and Parker, particularly T **4**.

1888 (July). *Nos.* 18/19. *Surch with T* **7**, *in violet, in Antigua.*

42		4 4d. on 1s. black & rose-car (*toned paper*)	£130	£160
		a. Surch double	£6500	
		b. Surch inverted (in pair with normal)	£42000	
		c. Long-tailed "S"	£450	£550
42d		4d. on 1s. black & rose-car (*white paper*)	£180	£225
		dc. Long-tailed "S"	£550	£700

The special issues for Virgin Islands were superseded on 31 October 1890, by the general issue for Leeward Islands. In 1899, however, a new special issue, Nos. 43/50, appeared; it did not supersede the general issue for Leeward Islands, but was used concurrently, as were all subsequent issues, until 1 July 1956 when the general Leeward Islands stamps were withdrawn.

8   9   10

(Recess D.L.R.)

1899 (Jan). Wmk Crown CA. P 14.

43	8	½d. yellow-green	2·50	55
		a. Error. "HALFPFNNY" (R. 10/1)	85·00	£120
		b. Error. "HALTPENNY" (R. 8/2)	85·00	£120
		c. Imperf between (horiz pair)	£8500	
44		1d. brick-red	3·00	2·50
45		2½d. ultramarine	12·00	2·75
46		4d. brown	4·00	8·00
		a. Error "FOURPENCF" (R.10/3)	£750	£1100
47		6d. dull violet	4·50	3·00
48		7d. deep green	8·50	6·00
49		1s. brown-yellow	22·00	35·00
50		5s. indigo	70·00	85·00
43/50		Set of 8	£110	£140
43s/50s		Optd "Specimen" Set of 8	£160	

Nos. 43a/b and 46a were corrected after the first printing.

(Typo D.L.R.)

1904 (1 June). Wmk Mult Crown CA. P 14.

54	9	½d. dull purple and green	75	40
55		1d. dull purple and scarlet	2·50	35
56	10	2d. dull purple and ochre	6·00	3·50
57	9	2½d. dull purple and ultramarine	2·00	2·00
58	10	3d. dull purple and black	3·50	2·50
59	9	6d. dull purple and brown	2·75	5·00
60	10	1s. green and scarlet	4·00	5·00
61		2s.6d. green and black	25·00	55·00
62		5s. green and blue	48·00	65·00
54/62		Set of 9	85·00	£120
54s/62s		Optd "Specimen" Set of 9	£140	

11   12

(Typo D.L.R.)

1913 (Feb)–19. Die I. *Chalk-surfaced paper (3d. to 5s.).* Wmk Mult Crown CA. P 14.

69	11	½d. green	1·50	4·00
		a. Yellow-green (8.16)	2·75	12·00
		b. Blue-green and deep green (3.19)	1·25	6·00
70		1d. deep red	8·50	11·00
		a. Deep red and carmine (10.17)	2·25	14·00
		b. Scarlet (10.17)	2·25	14·00
		c. Carmine-red (3.19)	48·00	27·00
71	12	2d. grey	4·00	25·00
		a. Slate-grey (1919)	4·25	29·00
72	11	2½d. bright blue	5·50	9·00
73	12	3d. purple/yellow	2·75	6·50
74	11	6d. dull and bright purple	5·00	11·00
75	12	1s. black/blue-green	3·25	9·00
76		2s.6d. black and red/blue	48·00	50·00
77	11	5s. green and red/yellow	35·00	£110
69/77		Set of 9	95·00	£200
69s/77s		Optd "Specimen" Set of 9	£180	

Stock of the original printing of the ½d., No. 69 was exhausted by January 1916 and Leeward Islands ½d. stamps were used until the yellow-green printing, No. 69a, arrived in August 1916.

WAR STAMP

(13)   14

1916 (20 Oct)–19. Optd with T **13**.

78	11	1d. carmine	1·75	18·00
		a. Watermark sideways	£1100	
		b. Pale red/bluish	50	7·00
		bw. Wmk inverted	55·00	
		by. Wmk inverted and reversed		
		c. Scarlet (11.3.19)	30	3·75
		d. Short opt (right pane R.10/1)	21·00	
79	12	3d. purple/yellow	3·00	17·00
		a. Purple/lemon (12.3.17)	3·25	14·00
		b. Purple/buff-yellow (11.3.19)	3·50	19·00
		bw. Wmk inverted	10·00	45·00
		by. Wmk inverted and reversed		
		c. Short opt (right pane R. 10/1)	42·00	
78s/9s		Optd "Specimen" Set of 2	70·00	

Nos. 78d and 79c show the overprint 2 mm high instead of 2½ mm.

No. 78c is known with the "A" of the "CA" watermark sideways.

1921 (18 Nov). As 1913–19, but Die II and wmk Mult Script CA.

80	11	½d. green	4·50	30·00
		w. Wmk inverted		
81		1d. scarlet and deep carmine	3·50	25·00
80s/1s		Optd "Specimen" Set of 2	70·00	

(Typo D.L.R.)

1922 (Mar)–28. P 14.

(a) Wmk Mult Crown CA. Chalk surfaced paper.

82	14	3d. purple/pale yellow (15.6.22)	65	17·00
83		1s. black/emerald (15.6.22)	75	14·00
84		2s.6d. black and red/blue (15.6.22)	5·50	11·00
85		5s. green and red/pale yellow (15.6.22)	30·00	£100
82/5		Set of 4	32·00	£130
82s/5s		Optd "Specimen" Set of 4	90·00	

(b) Wmk Mult Script CA. Chalk-surfaced paper (5d. to 5s.).

86	14	½d. dull green	85	2·75
87		1d. rose-carmine	60	60
88		1d. bright violet (1.27)	1·00	3·50
89		1d. scarlet (12.28)	15·00	14·00
90		1½d. carmine-red (1.27)	1·50	2·50
91		1½d. Venetian red (11.28)	1·75	1·50
92		2d. grey	1·00	6·00
93		2½d. pale bright blue	2·00	18·00
94		2½d. dull orange (1.9.23)	1·25	1·50
95		2½d. bright blue (1.27)	4·50	3·50
96		3d. purple/pale yellow (2.28)	2·25	11·00
97		5d. dull purple and olive (6.22)	5·50	45·00
98		6d. dull and bright purple (6.22)	1·50	6·50
99		1s. black/emerald (2.28)	2·50	14·00
100		2s.6d. black and red/blue (2.28)	19·00	48·00
101		5s. green and red/yellow (1.9.23)	19·00	70·00
86/101		Set of 16	70·00	£225
86s/101s		Optd or Perf (Nos. 89, 91) "Specimen" Set of 16	£275	

In the 1½d. stamps the value is in colour on a white ground.

1935 (6 May). *Silver Jubilee. As Nos.* 91/4 *of Antigua but printed by Waterlow.*

103		1d. deep blue and scarlet	1·25	4·25
		k. Kite and vertical log	85·00	
		l. Kite and horizontal log	90·00	£160
104		1½d. ultramarine and grey	1·25	4·00
		k. Kite and vertical log	90·00	
		l. Kite and horizontal log	£100	£170
		m. "Bird" by turret	£140	£160
105		2½d. brown and deep blue	1·75	4·00
		k. Kite and vertical log	£120	
		l. Kite and horizontal log	£130	£180
106		1s. slate and purple	10·00	19·00
		k. Kite and vertical log	£225	
		l. Kite and horizontal log	£200	£300
103/6		Set of 4	13·00	28·00
103s/6s		Perf "Specimen" Set of 4	£110	

For illustrations of plate varieties see Omnibus section following Zanzibar.

1937 (12 May). *Coronation. As Nos.* 95/7 *of Antigua.* P 11×11½.

107		1d. carmine	20	2·25
108		1½d. yellow-brown	50	50
109		2½d. blue	45	1·50
107/9		Set of 3	1·10	6·00
107s/9s		Perf "Specimen" Set of 3	75·00	

15 King George VI and Badge of Colony   16 Map

(Photo Harrison)

1938 (1 Aug)–47. *Chalk-surfaced paper.* Wmk Mult Script CA. P 14.

110	15	½d. green	2·50	2·50
		a. Ordinary paper (10.43)	30	1·00
111		1d. scarlet	3·25	1·25
		a. Ordinary paper (10.43)	75	60
112		1½d. red-brown	5·50	6·00
		a. Ordinary paper (10.43)	1·00	1·00
		w. Wmk inverted	†	£1100
113		2d. grey	4·75	2·25
		a. Ordinary paper (10.43)	1·75	90
114		2½d. ultramarine	4·00	1·25
		a. Ordinary paper (10.43)	1·00	2·50
115		3d. orange	5·50	70
		a. Ordinary paper (10.43)	70	80
116		6d. mauve	4·50	1·00
		a. Ordinary paper (10.43)	2·75	80
117		1s. olive-brown	13·00	3·25
		a. Ordinary paper (8.42)	1·50	70
118		2s.6d. sepia	42·00	7·00
		a. Ordinary paper (8.42)	17·00	3·00
119		5s. carmine	50·00	7·00
		a. Ordinary paper (8.42)	14·00	4·00
120		10s. blue (1.12.47)	6·00	8·00
121		£1 black (1.12.47)	8·00	20·00
110a/21		Set of 12	50·00	38·00
110s/21s		Perf "Specimen" Set of 12	£250	

The ordinary paper, used as a substitute for the chalk-surfaced for printings between 1942 and 1945, is thick, smooth and opaque.

1946 (1 Nov). *Victory. As Nos.* 110/11 *of Antigua.*

122		½d. lake-brown	10	10
123		3d. orange	10	30
122s/3s		Perf "Specimen" Set of 2	70·00	

1949 (3 Jan). *Royal Silver Wedding. As Nos. 112/13 of Antigua.*

124	2½d. ultramarine		10	10
125	£1 black		13·00	16·00

1949 (10 Oct). *75th Anniv of U.P.U. As Nos. 114/17 of Antigua.*

126	2½d. ultramarine		30	55
127	3d. orange		1·25	2·50
128	6d. magenta		35	40
129	1s. olive		35	50
126/9	Set of 4		2·00	3·50

(New Currency. 100 cents = 1 B.W.I. dollar)

1951 (16 Feb–10 Apr). *Inauguration of B.W.I. University College. As Nos. 118/19 of Antigua.*

130	3c. black and brown-red (10 Apr)		40	2·00
131	12c. black and reddish violet		60	1·75

Issue of the 3c. value was delayed when the supplies were sent to Puerto Rico by mistake.

(Recess Waterlow)

1951 (2 Apr). *Restoration of Legislative Council.* Wmk Mult Script CA. P 14½×14.

132	**16**	6c. orange		40	1·50
133		12c. purple		40	50
134		24c. olive		40	50
135		$1.20 carmine		1·00	1·00
132/5		Set of 4		2·00	3·25

17 Sombrero Lighthouse

18 Map of Jost Van Dyke

19 Sheep industry

20 Map of Anegada

21 Cattle industry

22 Map of Virgin Gorda

23 Map of Tortola

24 Badge of the Presidency

25 Dead Man's Chest

26 Sir Francis Drake Channel

27 Road Town

28 Map of Virgin Islands

(Recess D.L.R.)

1952 (15 Apr). *T* **17/28**. Wmk Mult Script CA. P 12½×13 (vert) or 13×12½ (horiz).

136	**17**	1c. black	80	2·00
137	**18**	2c. deep green	70	30
138	**19**	3c. black and brown	80	1·25
139	**20**	4c. carmine-red	70	1·50
140	**21**	5c. claret and black	1·50	50
141	**22**	8c. bright blue	70	1·25
142	**23**	12c. dull violet	80	1·40
143	**24**	24c. deep brown	70	50
144	**25**	60c. yellow-green and blue	4·50	11·00
145	**26**	$1.20 black and bright blue	5·00	12·00
146	**27**	$2.40 yellowish green and red-brown	11·00	16·00
147	**28**	$4.80 bright blue and carmine	12·00	17·00
136/47		Set of 12	35·00	60·00

Western Australia
see **Australia**

Western Samoa
see after **New Zealand**

Zanzibar

An Indian post office opened in Zanzibar in November 1868, but was closed for political reasons on 1 April of the following year. Little has survived from this period. Subsequently mail was forwarded via Seychelles or, later, Aden.

Stamps of INDIA were used in Zanzibar from 1 October 1875 until 10 November 1895, when the administration of the postal service was transferred from India to British East Africa. Seperate cancellations for Zanzibar are known from 1 June 1878.

Z 1   Z 1a

Stamps of INDIA *cancelled with Type Z* **1** (1878–79)

1865. *(Nos. 54/65).*

Z1	1a. deep brown	£180
Z2	2a. orange	£180

1866–78. *(Nos. 69/72).*

Z3	4a. blue-green (Die II)	£170

1865. *(Nos. 54/65).*

Z4	½a. blue (Die II)	£160

Surviving covers show that Type Z **1** was normally used as a datestamp, struck clear of the stamps which were obliterated by a rhomboid of bars, but examples of the c.d.s. used as a cancel are known.

Stamps of INDIA *cancelled with Type Z* **1a**.

1873. *(Nos. 75/6).*

Z7	2a. orange	£180

In Type Z **1a** the word "ZANZIBAR" is shorter than in Types Z **1** and Z **3**. It was generally used as an arrival mark but cancellations on adhesives are known.

Z 2

Stamps of INDIA *cancelled with Type Z* **2** (1879–82).

1865. *(Nos. 54/65).*

Z10	8p. mauve	£180
Z11	1a. deep brown	18·00
Z12	2a. orange	18·00

1866–78. *(Nos. 69/72).*

Z13	4a. green (Die I)	£100
Z14	4a. blue-green (Die II)	27·00

1868. *(Nos. 73/4).*

Z15	8a. rose (Die II)	70·00

1873. *(Nos. 75/6).*

Z16	½a. blue (Die II)	18·00

1874. *(Nos. 77/9).*

Z17	1r. slate	£190

1876. *(Nos. 80/2).*

Z18	6a. pale brown	85·00
Z19	12a. Venetian red	£130

1882. *(No. 90).*

Z19a	1a.6p. sepia	£120

OFFICIAL STAMPS

1874–82. *(Nos. O31/7).*

Z19b	1a. brown	£190

Z20	2a. orange	£180
Z21	4a. green (Die I)	£200
Z22	8a. rose (Die II)	£200

Z 3

Stamps of INDIA *cancelled with Type Z* **3** (1882–84)

1865. *(Nos. 54/65).*

Z25	1a. deep brown	38·00
Z26	2a. brown-orange	30·00

1866–78. *(Nos. 69/72).*

Z26a	4a. green (Die I)	£100
Z27	4a. blue-green (Die II)	38·00

1868. *(Nos. 73/4).*

Z28	8a. rose (Die II)	55·00

1873. *(Nos. 75/6).*

Z29	½a. blue (Die II)	28·00

1874. *(Nos. 77/9).*

Z29a	1r. slate	£130

1876. *(Nos. 80/2).*

Z30	6a. pale brown	48·00
Z31	12a. Venetian red	£110

1882–83. *(Nos. 84/101).*

Z32	1a. brown-purple	32·00
Z33	1a.6p. sepia	35·00
Z34	3a. orange	40·00

OFFICIAL STAMPS

1867–73. *(Nos. O20/30a).*

Z35	2a. orange	£200
Z36	8a. rose	£225

Z 4   Z 5

Stamps of INDIA *cancelled with Type Z* **4** (June 1884–May 1887) (*between* January *and* September 1885 *the postmark was used without year numerals*).

1865. *(Nos. 54/65).*

Z39	1a. deep brown	85·00
Z40	2a. brown-orange	35·00

1866–78. *(Nos. 69/72).*

Z41	4a. green (Die I)	£120
Z41a	4a. blue-green (Die II)	32·00

1868. *(Nos. 73/4).*

Z42	8a. rose (Die II)	35·00

1873. *(Nos. 75/6).*

Z43	½a. blue (Die II)	30·00

1874. *(Nos. 77/9).*

Z44	1r. slate	£140

1876. *(Nos. 80/2).*

Z45	6a. pale brown	70·00
Z45a	12a. Venetian red	£130

1882–86. *(Nos. 84/101).*

Z46	½a. blue-green	15·00
Z47	1a. brown-purple	26·00
Z48	1a.6p. sepia	21·00
Z49	2a. blue	48·00
Z50	3a. orange	15·00
Z51	4a. olive-green	45·00
Z52	4a.6p. yellow-green	20·00
Z53	8a. dull mauve	42·00
Z54	1r. slate	42·00

OFFICIAL STAMPS

1867–73. *(Nos. O20/30a).*

Z55	2a. orange	£160

1874–82. *(Nos. O31/7).*

Z55a	½a. blue	£110
Z56	1a. brown	90·00
Z56a	2a. orange	£190

1883–95. *(Nos. O37a/48).*

Z57	1a. brown-purple	£100

Stamps of INDIA *cancelled with Type Z* **5** (1887–94).

1876. *(Nos. 80/2).*

Z60		6a. pale brown	18·00
Z61		12a. Venetian red	55·00

1882–90. *(Nos. 84/101).*

Z62		½a. blue-green	6·50
Z63		9p. aniline carmine	48·00
Z64		1a. brown-purple	6·00
Z65		1a.6p. sepia	9·00
Z66		2a. blue	7·00
Z67		3a. orange	9·00
Z68		3a. brown-orange	7·50
Z69		4a. olive-green	38·00
Z70		4a.6p. yellow-green	12·00
Z71		8a. dull mauve	20·00
Z72		12a. purple/*red*	48·00
Z73		1r. slate	16·00

1891. *(No. 102).*

Z74		2½a. on 4a.6p. yellow-green	8·00

1892–95. *(Nos. 103/6).*

Z75		2a.6p. yellow-green	6·00

OFFICIAL STAMPS

1867–73. *(Nos. O20/30a).*

Z75a		4a. green	£225

1874–82. *(Nos. O31/71).*

Z76		½a. blue	85·00
Z77		1a. brown	90·00
Z78		2a. yellow	£150

Z 6   Z 7

Stamps of INDIA *cancelled with Type* Z 6 (1888–95).

1876. *(Nos. 80/2).*

Z80		6a. pale brown	19·00
Z80a		12a. venetian red	£130

1882–90. *(Nos. 84/101).*

Z81		½a. blue-green	30·00
Z82		9p. aniline carmine	55·00
Z83		1a. brown-purple	9·00
Z84		1a.6p. sepia	8·50
Z85		2a. blue	9·50
Z86		3a. orange	22·00
Z87		3a. brown-orange	16·00
Z88		4a. olive-green	16·00
Z89		4a.6p. yellow-green	17·00
Z90		8a. dull mauve	21·00
Z91		12a. purple/*red*	50·00
Z92		1r. slate	18·00

1891. *(No. 102).*

Z93		2½a. on 4a.6p. yellow-green	24·00

1892–95. *(Nos. 103/6).*

Z94		2a.6p. yellow-green	19·00

Stamps of INDIA *cancelled with Type* Z 7 (1894–95).

1876. *(Nos. 80/2).*

Z95		6a. pale brown	60·00

1882–90. *(Nos. 84/101).*

Z100		½a. blue-green	20·00
Z101		9p. aniline carmine	70·00
Z102		1a. brown-purple	28·00
Z103		1a.6p. sepia	45·00
Z104		2a.	20·00
Z105		3a. brown-orange	48·00
Z106		4a. olive-green	45·00
Z107		8a. dull mauve	60·00
Z108		12a. purple/*red*	65·00
Z109		1r. slate	60·00

1892–95. *(Nos. 103/6).*

Z110		2a.6p. yellow-green	12·00

1895. *(Nos. 107/9).*

Z111		2r. carmine and yellow-brown	£300

A French post office was opened on the island in January 1889 and this service used the stamps of FRANCE until 1894 when specific stamps for this office were provided. The French postal service on the island closed on 31 July 1904 and it is known that French stamps were again utilised during the final month.

A German postal agency operated in Zanzibar between 27 August 1890 and 31 July 1891, using stamps of GERMANY.

PRICES FOR STAMPS ON COVER TO 1945

Nos. 1/2		—
Nos. 3/16	*from* × 30	
No. 17	*from* × 8	
No. 18	*from* × 25	
Nos. 19/21		—
No. 22	*from* × 40	
Nos. 23/5	*from* × 25	
No. 26	*from* × 40	
Nos. 27/40		—
Nos. 41/6	*from* × 25	
Nos. 156/68	*from* × 15	
Nos. 169/77		—

PRICES FOR STAMPS ON COVER TO 1945

Nos. 178/87	*from* × 20	
Nos. 188/204	*from* × 15	
Nos. 205/9	*from* × 20	
Nos. 210/38	*from* × 15	
Nos. 239/45		—
Nos. 246/59	*from* × 8	
Nos. 260/f		—
Nos. 261/330	*from* × 4	
No. D1/3	*from* × 8	
No. D4	*from* × 1	
No. D5	*from* × 15	
No. D6		—
No. D7		—
No. D8/12	*from* × 15	
No. D13	*from* × 1	
No. D14		—
Nos. D15/16	*from* × 6	
No. D17	*from* × 4	
Nos. D18/24	*from* × 15	
Nos. D25/30	*from* × 30	

PROTECTORATE

(Currency. 12 pies = 1 anna. 16 annas = 1 rupee)

Zanzibar

(1)

1895 (14 Nov)–96. Nos. 81, 85, 90/6, 98/101, 103 and 106/9 of India (Queen Victoria) optd with T 1 by Zanzibar Gazette.

(a) In blue.

1		½a. blue-green	£15000	£4500
2		1a. plum	£2500	£500
		j. "Zanzidar" (R. 4/6, 8/5)	†	£20000

(b) In black.

3		½a. blue-green	4·25	3·75
		j. "Zanzidar" (R. 4/6, 8/5)	£1200	£650
		k. "Zanibar" (R. 7/2)	£1200	£1600
		l. Diaeresis over last "a" (R. 10/5)	£1600	£1600
		m. Opt double, one albino	£225	
4		1a. plum	4·50	3·75
		j. "Zanzidar" (R. 4/6, 8/5)	—	£3000
		k. "Zanibar" (R. 7/2)	£1600	£1800
		l. Diaeresis over last "a" (R. 10/5)	£3500	
5		1a.6p. sepia	4·75	3·50
		j. "Zanzidar" (R. 4/6, 8/5)	£3500	£1000
		k. "Zanibar" (R. 7/2)	£1500	£1600
		l. "Zanzibar" (R. 1/9)		
		m. Diaeresis over last "a" (R. 10/5)	£1400	
6		2a. pale blue	5·00	5·00
7		2a. blue	5·50	5·00
		j. "Zanzidar" (R. 4/6, 8/5)	£4750	£2250
		k. "Zanibar" (R. 7/2)	£4750	£2250
		l. Diaeresis over last "a" (R. 10/5)	£2000	
		m. Opt double	£250	
		n. Opt double, one albino	£250	
8		2½a. yellow-green	8·00	5·00
		j. "Zanzidar" (R. 4/6, 8/5)	£4250	£1600
		k. "Zanibar" (R. 7/2)	£600	£1200
		l. "Zapzibar"		
		n. Diaeresis over last "a" (R. 10/5)	£190	£1600
		o. Second "z" italic (R. 10/1)	£275	£400
		p. Opt double, one albino	£250	
10		3a. brown-orange	12·00	11·00
		j. "Zanzidar" (R. 4/6, 8/5)	£750	£1500
		k. "Zanibar" (R. 1/9)	£4500	£5000
11		4a. olive-green	20·00	17·00
		j. "Zanzidar" (R. 4/6, 8/5)	£8000	£4000
12		4a. slate-green	13·00	15·00
		l. Diaeresis over last "a" (R. 10/5)	£3500	
13		6a. pale brown	19·00	11·00
		j. "Zanzidar" (R. 4/6, 8/5)	£8500	£3750
		k. "Zanibar" (R. 7/2)	£650	£1200
		l. "Zanzibarr"	£4750	£4000
		m. Opt double		
		n. Opt double, one albino	£140	
		o. Opt triple, two albino	£190	
14		8a. dull mauve	27·00	21·00
		j. "Zanzidar" (R 4/6, 8/5)	£8000	£7000
15		8a. magenta (6.96)	18·00	23·00
		l. Diaeresis over last "a" (R. 10/5)	£5000	
16		12a. purple/*red*	17·00	10·00
		j. "Zanzidar" (R.4/6, 8/5)	£8000	£4000
17		1r. slate	80·00	75·00
		j. "Zanzidar" (R. 4/6, 8/5)	£7500	£4500
18		1r. green and aniline carmine (7.96)	18·00	26·00
		j. Opt vert downwards	£425	
19		2r. carmine and yellow-brown	60·00	85·00
		j. "r" omitted	£20000	
		k. "r" inverted	£3750	£4250
20		3r. brown and green	55·00	65·00
		j. "r" omitted	£20000	
		k. "r" inverted	£4250	£4500
		l. Opt double, one albino	£900	
21		5r. ultramarine and violet	65·00	85·00
		j. "r" omitted	£20000	
		k. "r" inverted	£3500	£4750
		l. Opt double, one inverted	£850	
		m. Opt double, one albino	£900	
3/21 *Set of 15*			£350	£375

There were a number of different settings for this overprint. Values to 1r. were initially overprinted from settings of 120 (12×10) including one which showed "Zanzidar" on R. 4/6 and R. 8/5 (soon corrected) and "Zanzibar" on R. 1/9 (also soon corrected). Later supplies of these values were overprinted from settings of 80 (8×10) for the 6a. only or 60 (6×10) for the others. One of these settings included "Zanzibar" on R. 7/2. Another late setting, size unknown, showed a diaeresis over last "a" on R. 10/5.

Many forgeries of this overprint exist and also bogus errors.

Forged examples of the blue overprints, Nos. 1/2, can be found on piece with genuine cancellations as type Z 7, dated "13 FE 97".

MINOR VARIETIES. The following minor varieties of type exist on Nos. 1/21:

A. First "Z" antique (all values)

B. Broken "p" for "n" (all values to 1r.)

C. Tall second "z" (all values)

D. Small second "z" (all values)

E. Small second "z" and inverted "q" for "b" (all values)

F. Second "z" Gothic (½a. to 12a. and 1r.) (No. 18) (black opts only)

G. No dot over "i" (all values to 1r.)

H. Inverted "q" for "b" (all values to 1r.)

I. Arabic "2" for "r" (all values to 1r.) (black opts only)

Varieties D and E are worth the same as normal examples, A (2, 3, 5r.) and C normal plus 50%, G and I from 3 times normal, A (values to 1r.) F and H from 4 times normal and B from 5 times normal.

2½	2½	2½	2½
(2)	(3)	(4)	(5)

1895–98. *Provisionals. I. Stamps used for postal purposes.*

(a) No. 5 surch in red (30.11.95).

22	2	2½ on 1½a. sepia	50·00	42·00
		j. "Zanzibar"	£1300	£1200
		k. "Zanzibar"	£3750	£1900
		l. Inverted "1" in "½"	£1100	£900

(b) No. 4 surch in black (11.5.96).

23	3	2½ on 1a. plum	£150	£100
24	4	2½ on 1a. plum	£400	£275
		j. Inverted "1" in "½"	£2250	
25	5	2½ on 1a. plum	£160	£110

2½	2½	2½
(6)	(7)	(8)

(c) No. 6 surch in red (15.8.96).

26	6	2½ on 2a. pale blue	50·00	30·00
		j. Inverted "1" in "½"	£425	£275
		k. Roman "I" in "½"	£225	£150
		l. "Zanzibar" double, one albino	£140	
		m. "Zanzibar" triple, two albino	£300	
27	7	2½ on 2a. pale blue	£150	90·00
		j. "2" of "½" omitted	£10000	
		k. "2" for "2½"	£14000	
		l. "1" in "½" omitted	£10000	£5000
		m. Inverted "1" in "½"	£2250	£1500
		n. "Zanzibar" double, one albino	£350	
28	8	2½ on 2a. pale blue	£4500	£2000

No. 28 only exists with small "z" and occurs on R. 2/2 in the setting of 60.

(d) No. 5 surch in red (15.11.96).

29	6	2½ on 1½a. sepia	£130	£100
		j. Inverted "1" in "½"	£1200	£1000
		k. Roman "I" in "½"	£850	£800
		l. Surch double, one albino	£250	
30	7	2½ on 1½a. sepia	£375	£325
		l. Surch double, one albino	£700	
31	8	2½ on 1½a. sepia	£15000	£9000

No. 31 only exists with small "z" and occurs on R. 2/2 in the setting of 60.

II. Stamps prepared for official purposes. Nos. 4, 5 and 7 surch as before in red (1.98).

32	3	2½ on 1a. plum	£225	£600
33	4	2½ on 1a. plum	£425	£900
34	5	2½ on 1a. plum	£250	£600
35	3	2½ on 1½a. sepia	75·00	£190
		j. Diaeresis over last "a"	£5500	
36	4	2½ on 1½a. sepia	£180	£450
37	5	2½ on 1½a. sepia	£110	£275
38	3	2½ on 2a. dull blue	95·00	£275
39	4	2½ on 2a. dull blue	£190	£475
40	5	2½ on 2a. dull blue	£110	£325

It is doubtful whether Nos. 32/40 were issued to the public.

1896. *Nos. 65/6, 68 and 71/3 of British East Africa (Queen Victoria), optd with T 1.*

41		½a. yellow-green (23 May)	32·00	18·00
42		1a. carmine-rose (1 June)	28·00	17·00
		j. Opt double	£750	£850
		k. Opt double, one albino	£300	
43		2½a. deep blue (R.) (24 May)	75·00	45·00
44		4½a. orange-yellow (12 Aug)	45·00	50·00
45		5a. yellow-bistre (12 Aug)	50·00	32·00
		j. "r" omitted	—	£2750
46		7½a. mauve (12 Aug)	40·00	50·00
41/6 *Set of 6*			£225	£190

MINOR VARIETIES. The various minor varieties of type detailed in the note below No. 21 also occur on Nos. 22 to 46 as indicated below:

A. Nos. 23, 25, 27, 30, 35, 38, 41/6

B. Nos. 22/3, 26, 29/30, 32/3, 36, 39, 44/6

C. Nos. 22, 25/6, 32, 36, 38, 40/6

D. Nos. 22/46

E. Nos. 22/46

F. Nos. 25/6, 29, 41/6

G. Nos. 25/6, 29, 35, 37/8, 40/6

H. Nos. 22, 41/6 (on the British East Africa stamps this variety occurs in the same position as variety C)

I. Nos. 26, 29, 35, 38, 41/6

The scarcity of these varieties on the surcharges (Nos. 22/40) is similar to those on the basic stamps, but examples on the British East Africa values (Nos. 41/6) are more common.

PRINTERS. All Zanzibar stamps up to Type **37** were printed by De La Rue & Co.

12   **13**

14 Sultan Seyyid   No right serif to left-hand "4"
Hamed-bin-Thwain   (R. 1/1)

1896 (Dec). *Recess. Flags in red on all values.* W **12**. P 14.

156	**13**	½a. yellow-green	4·00	1·75
157		1a. indigo	3·25	1·50
158		1a. violet-blue	5·00	4·25
159		2a. red-brown	2·75	75
160		2½a. bright blue	12·00	1·50
161		2½a. pale blue	13·00	1·50
162		3a. grey	11·00	6·00
163		3a. bluish grey	12·00	8·00
164		4a. myrtle-green	7·00	3·00
165		4½a. orange	5·00	5·50
		a. No right serif to left-hand "4"	£120	£130
		b. No fraction bar at right (R. 2/1)	£120	£130
166		5a. bistre	4·75	2·50
		b. Bisected (2½a.) (on cover)	†	£3500
167		7½a. mauve	3·50	3·00
168		8a. grey-olive	10·00	7·00
169	**14**	1r. blue	16·00	9·00
170		1r. deep blue	20·00	13·00
171		2r. green	24·00	9·50
172		3r. dull purple	25·00	9·50
173		4r. lake	20·00	13·00
174		5r. sepia	26·00	13·00
156/74 *Set of 15*			£160	75·00
156s/74s Optd "Specimen" *Set of 15*			£200	

The ½, 1, 2, 2½, 3 and 8a. are known without wmk, these being from edges of the sheets.

1897 (5 Jan). *No. 164 surch as before, in red.*

175	**3**	2½ on 4a. myrtle-green	60·00	40·00
176	**4**	2½ on 4a. myrtle-green	£190	£170
177	**5**	2½ on 4a. myrtle-green	75·00	50·00
175/7 *Set of 3*			£300	£225

18

1898 (May). *Recess.* W **18**. P 14.

178	**13**	½a. yellow-green	1·50	35
179		1a. indigo	2·50	55
		a. Greenish black	4·25	1·50
180		2a. red-brown	4·50	1·00
		a. Deep brown	6·00	1·75
181		2½a. bright blue	3·00	30
182		3a. grey	5·50	60
183		4a. myrtle-green	3·25	1·00
184		4½a. orange	8·00	1·00
		a. No right serif to left-hand "4"	£170	60·00
		b. No fraction bar at right (R. 2/1)	£170	60·00
185		5a. bistre	15·00	1·75
		a. Pale bistre	15·00	2·00
186		7½a. mauve	10·00	2·75
187		8a. grey-olive	13·00	2·25
178/87 *Set of 10*			60·00	10·00

19   **20** Sultan Seyyid
Hamoud-bin-Mohammed
bin Said

1899 (June)–**1901**. *Recess. Flags in red.* W **18** (Nos. 188/99) or W **12** (others). P 14.

188	**19**	½a. yellow-green	2·00	60
		a. Wmk sideways	12·00	4·75
189		1a. indigo	4·50	20
		a. Wmk sideways	26·00	1·25
190		1a. carmine (1901)	2·00	20
191		2a. red-brown	2·50	50
192		2½a. bright blue	2·25	60
193		3a. grey	3·00	2·25
194		4a. myrtle-green	3·25	1·50
195		4½a. orange	13·00	4·75
196		4½a. blue-black (1901)	15·00	12·00
197		5a. bistre	3·00	1·25
198		7½a. mauve	3·25	4·00
199		8a. grey-olive	3·25	4·50
200	**20**	1r. blue	18·00	15·00
201		2r. green	18·00	18·00
202		3r. dull purple	30·00	35·00
203		4r. lake	48·00	55·00

204		5r. sepia	55·00	70·00
188/204 *Set of 17*			£200	£200
188s/204s Optd "Specimen" *Set of 17*			£200	

Two & One	Two & Half	Two & Half	Two & Half
(21)	(22)	(22a) Thin open "w" (R. 2/2, 3/4)	(22b) Serif to foot of "f" (R. 3/1)

1904. *Nos. 194/6 and 198/9 surch as T* **21** *and* **22**, *in black or lake (L.) by Zanzibar Gazette in setting of 30 (6×5).*

205	**19**	1 on 4½a. orange	4·00	5·50
206		1 on 4½a. blue/black (L.)	4·50	18·00
207		2 on 4a. myrtle-green (L.)	14·00	18·00
208		2½ on 7½a. mauve	13·00	20·00
		a. Opt Type **22a**	80·00	£100
		b. Opt Type **22b**	£130	£180
		c. "Hlaf" for "Half"	£13000	
209		2½ on 8a. grey-olive	19·00	30·00
		a. Opt Type **22a**	£120	£160
		b. Opt Type **22b**	£190	£275
		c. "Hlaf" for "Half"	£12000	£9000
205/9 *Set of 5*			50·00	80·00

23   **24**

Monogram of Sultan Seyyid Ali bin Hamoud bin Naherud

1904 (8 June). *Typo. Background of centre in second colour.* W **18**. P 14.

210	**23**	½a. green	2·00	90
211		1a. rose-red	2·00	10
212		2a. brown	2·00	45
213		2½a. blue	2·75	35
214		3a. grey	2·50	2·25
215		4a. deep green	2·25	1·60
216		4½a. black	3·00	2·50
217		5a. yellow-brown	4·00	1·25
218		7½a. purple	4·75	7·00
219		8a. olive-green	3·75	3·00
220	**24**	1r. blue and red	22·00	14·00
		a. Wmk sideways	85·00	35·00
221		2r. green and red	27·00	40·00
		a. Wmk sideways	£170	£200
222		3r. violet and red	40·00	75·00
223		4r. claret and red	48·00	90·00
224		5r. olive-brown and red	48·00	95·00
210/24 *Set of 15*			£180	£275
210s/24s Optd "Specimen" *Set of 15*			£140	

25   **26**

27 Sultan Ali bin   **28** View of Port
Hamoud

1908 (May)–**09**. *Recess.* W **18** (sideways on 10r. to 30r.). P 14.

225	**25**	1c. pearl-grey (10.09)	2·25	30
226		3c. yellow-green	6·50	10
		a. Wmk sideways	6·50	1·25
227		6c. rose-carmine	9·50	10
		a. Wmk sideways	9·50	2·25
228		10c. brown (10.09)	3·25	2·00
229		12c. violet	16·00	3·25
		a. Wmk sideways	13·00	1·25
230	**26**	15c. ultramarine	13·00	40
		a. Wmk sideways	11·00	6·00
231		25c. sepia	4·00	1·00
232		50c. blue-green	6·50	4·50
233		75c. grey-black (10.09)	12·00	12·00
234	**27**	1r. yellow-green	26·00	12·00
		a. Wmk sideways	60·00	10·00
235		2r. violet	18·00	14·00
		a. Wmk sideways	£160	65·00
236		3r. orange-bistre	25·00	48·00
237		4r. vermilion	48·00	75·00
238		5r. steel-blue	42·00	55·00
239	**28**	10r. blue-green and brown	£150	£250
		s. Optd "Specimen"	40·00	

240		20r. black and yellow-green	£325	£475
		s. Optd "Specimen"	50·00	
241		30r. black and sepia	£375	£650
		s. Optd "Specimen"	65·00	
242		40r. black and orange-brown	£500	
		s. Optd "Specimen"	85·00	
243		50r. black and mauve	£450	
		s. Optd "Specimen"	85·00	
244		100r. black and steel-blue	£700	
		s. Optd "Specimen"	£140	
245		200r. brown and greenish black	£1100	
		s. Optd "Specimen"	£180	
225/38 *Set of 14*			£200	£200
225s/38s Optd "Specimen" *Set of 14*			£180	

29 Sultan Kalif   **30** Sailing Canoe
bin Harub

31 Dhow

1913. *Recess.* W **18** (sideways on 75c. and 10r. to 200r.). P 14.

246	**29**	1c. grey	40	20
247		3c. yellow-green	50	30
248		6c. rose-carmine	1·50	20
249		10c. brown	1·10	2·25
250		12c. violet	1·00	30
251		15c. blue	1·40	30
252		25c. sepia	1·00	1·25
253		50c. blue-green	2·00	4·50
254		75c. grey-black	2·00	3·25
		a. Wmk upright	£150	
		as. Optd "Specimen"	95·00	
255	**30**	1r. yellow-green	8·50	10·00
256		2r. violet	11·00	26·00
257		3r. orange-bistre	13·00	42·00
258		4r. scarlet	26·00	70·00
259		5r. steel-blue	35·00	40·00
260	**31**	10r. green and brown	£130	£225
260b		20r. black and green	£180	£400
		bs. Optd "Specimen"	40·00	
260c		30r. black and brown	£190	£475
		cs. Optd "Specimen"	50·00	
260d		40r. black and vermilion	£375	£650
		ds. Optd "Specimen"	80·00	
260e		50r. black and purple	£350	£700
		es. Optd "Specimen"	80·00	
260f		100r. black and blue	£450	
		fs. Optd "Specimen"	£100	
260g		200r. brown and black	£700	
		gs. Optd "Specimen"	£140	
246/60 *Set of 15*			£200	£375
246s/60as Optd "Specimen" *Set of 15*			£200	

1914–22. Wmk Mult Crown CA (sideways on 10r.). P 14.

261	**29**	1c. grey	80	25
262		3c. yellow-green	1·25	10
		a. Dull green	5·50	15
		w. Wmk inverted	†	£130
263		6c. deep carmine	85	10
		a. Bright rose-carmine	85	10
		aw. Wmk inverted	†	£130
264		8c. purple/pale yellow (1922)	75	4·00
265		10c. myrtle/pale yellow (1922)	75	30
266		15c. deep ultramarine	1·10	5·00
268		50c. blue-green	4·50	4·00
269		75c. grey-black	3·00	23·00
270	**30**	1r. yellow-green	4·00	3·50
271		2r. violet	5·50	8·00
272		3r. orange-bistre	16·00	35·00
273		4r. scarlet	16·00	85·00
		y. Wmk inverted and reversed	£130	
274		5r. steel-blue	16·00	65·00
		w. Wmk inverted	£130	
275	**31**	10r. green and brown	£130	£450
261/75 *Set of 14*			£180	£600
261s/75s Optd "Specimen" *Set of 14*			£200	

1921–29. Wmk Mult Script CA (sideways on 10r. to 30r.). P 14.

276	**29**	1c. slate-grey	20	7·50
277		3c. yellow-green	75	3·50
278		3c. yellow (1922)	30	10
		w. Wmk inverted		
279		4c. green (1922)	50	1·00
280		6c. carmine-red	30	50
281		6c. purple/blue (1922)	35	10
		w. Wmk inverted	†	£200
282		10c. brown	70	9·50
283		12c. violet	40	30
284		12c. carmine-red (1922)	40	40
285		15c. blue	55	9·00
286		20c. indigo (1922)	1·00	30
287		25c. sepia	75	12·00
288		50c. myrtle-green	1·25	4·00
		y. Wmk inverted and reversed	£130	
289		75c. slate	2·50	50·00
290	**30**	1r. yellow-green	4·25	3·50
291		2r. deep violet	3·75	9·50
292		3r. orange-bistre	4·25	7·50
293		4r. scarlet	12·00	35·00
294		5r. Prussian blue	19·00	65·00
		w. Wmk inverted	£180	
295	**31**	10r. green and brown	£110	£300

296		20r. black and green	£225	£450
		s. Optd "Specimen"	90·00	
297		30r. black and brown (1929)	£190	£550
		s. Perf "Specimen"	85·00	
276/95 *Set of 20*			£150	£475
276s/95s Optd "Specimen" *Set of 20*			£250	

32 Sultan Kalif **33**
bin Harub

1926–27. T **32** ("CENTS" *in serifed capitals*). Recess. Wmk Mult
Script CA. P 14.

299	**32**	1c. brown	50	10
300		3c. yellow-orange	20	15
301		4c. deep dull green	20	30
302		6c. violet	20	10
303		8c. slate	1·00	4·50
304		10c. olive-green	1·00	40
305		12c. carmine-red	1·50	10
306		20c. bright blue	50	30
307		25c. purple/*yellow* (1927)	4·25	2·50
308		50c. claret	2·25	35
309		75c. sepia (1927)	18·00	24·00
299/309 *Set of 11*			26·00	29·00
299s/309s Optd "Specimen" *Set of 11*			£120	

(New Currency. 100 cents = 1 shilling)

1936 (1 Jan). T **33** ("CENTS" *in sans-serif capitals*),
and T **30**/1, *but values in shillings.* Recess. Wmk Mult Script
CA. P 14×13½–14.

310	**33**	5c. green	10	10
311		10c. black	10	10
312		15c. carmine-red	10	1·25
313		20c. orange	10	10
314		25c. purple/*yellow*	10	10
315		30c. ultramarine	10	10
316		40c. sepia	15	10
317		50c. claret	30	10
318	**30**	1s. yellow-green	50	10
319		2s. slate-violet	1·00	1·75
320		5s. scarlet	15·00	6·00
321		7s.50 light blue	25·00	26·00
322	**31**	10s. green and brown	27·00	22·00
310/22 *Set of 13*			60·00	50·00
310s/22s Perf "Specimen" *Set of 13*			£130	

Nos. 310/22 remained current until 1952 and the unused prices are
therefore for unmounted examples.

36 Sultan Kalif bin Harub

1936 (9 Dec). *Silver Jubilee of Sultan.* Recess. Wmk Mult Script
CA. P 14.

323	**36**	10c. black and olive-green	2·50	30
324		20c. black and bright purple	4·50	1·00
325		30c. black and deep ultramarine	12·00	35
326		50c. black and orange-vermilion	12·00	4·00
323/6 *Set of 4*			28·00	5·00
323s/6s Perf "Specimen" *Set of 4*			80·00	

37 *Sham Alam* (Sultan's **(38)**
dhow)

1944 (20 Nov). *Bicentenary of Al Busaid Dynasty.* Recess. Wmk
Mult Script CA. P 14.

327	**37**	10c. ultramarine	85	2·75
		a. "C" of "CA" missing from wmk	£500	
328		20c. red	85	3·25
		a. "C" of "CA" missing from wmk	£500	
329		50c. blue-green	85	30
330		1s. dull purple	85	65
		a. "A" of "CA" missing from wmk	£500	
327/30 *Set of 4*			3·00	6·25
327s/30s Perf "Specimen" *Set of 4*			85·00	

1946 (11 Nov). *Victory. Nos. 311 and 315 optd with* T **38**.

331	**33**	10c. black (R.)	20	50
332		30c. ultramarine (R.)	20	50
331s/2s Perf "Specimen" *Set of 2*			55·00	

1949 (10 Jan). *Royal Silver Wedding. As Nos. 112/13 of Antigua.*

333		20c. orange	30	1·50
334		10s. brown	19·00	30·00

1949 (10–13 Oct). *75th Anniv of UPU. As Nos. 114/17 of Antigua.*

335		20c. red-orange (13 Oct)	30	3·00
336		30c. deep blue	1·75	1·25
		a. "C" of "CA" missing from wmk	£750	
337		50c. magenta	1·00	2·75
338		1s. blue-green (13 Oct)	1·00	4·50

335/8 *Set of 4*		3·50	10·50

POSTAGE DUE STAMPS

D **1**   D **2**

(Types D **1** and D **2** typo by the Government Printer)

1926–30. *Rouletted 10, with imperf sheet edges. No gum.*

D1	D **1**	1c. black/*orange*	11·00	£130
D2		2c. black/*orange*	4·50	60·00
D3		3c. black/*orange*	5·00	48·00
		a. "cent.s" for "cents."	£140	£325
D4		6c. black/*orange*	—	£7000
		a. "cent.s" for "cents."	—	£18000
D5		9c. black/*orange*	2·75	25·00
		a. "cent.s" for "cents."	23·00	£120
D6		12c. black/*orange*	£10000	£9000
D7		12c. black/*green*	£1400	£600
		a. "cent.s" for "cents."	£3750	£1700
D8		15c. black/*orange*	2·75	27·00
		a. "cent.s" for "cents."	23·00	£120
D9		18c. black/*salmon*	4·25	45·00
		a. "cent.s" for "cents."	42·00	£180
D10		18c. black/*orange*	20·00	75·00
		a. "cent.s" for "cents."	75·00	£250
D11		20c. black/*orange*	4·00	65·00
		a. "cent.s" for "cents."	42·00	£180
D12		21c. black/*orange*	3·50	38·00
		a. "cent.s" for "cents."	38·00	£130
D13		25c. black/*magenta*	£2750	£1300
		a. "cent.s" for "cents."	£6500	£3750
D14		25c. black/*orange*	£12000	£12000
D15		31c. black/*orange*	9·50	85·00
		a. "cent.s" for "cents."	50·00	
D16		50c. black/*orange*	21·00	£200
		a. "cent.s" for "cents."	95·00	
D17		75c. black/*orange*	65·00	£500
		a. "cent.s" for "cents."	£250	

Initial printings, except the 1c. and 2c., contained the error "cent.s"
for "cents" on R. 4/1 in the sheets of 10 (2×5). The error was corrected
on subsequent supplies of the 3c., 9c. and 15c.

It is known that examples of these stamps used before early 1929
were left uncancelled on the covers. Uncancelled examples of Nos.
D4, D6/7 and D13/14 which are not in very fine condition, must be
assumed to have been used.

1930–33. *Rouletted 5. No gum.*

D18	D **2**	2c. black/*salmon*	16·00	30·00
D19		3c. black/*rose*	3·25	50·00
D21		6c. black/*yellow*	3·25	35·00
D22		12c. black/*blue*	4·50	28·00
D23		25c. black/*rose*	9·00	80·00
D24		25c. black/*lilac*	16·00	55·00
D18/24 *Set of 6*			48·00	£250

D **3**

(Typo D.L.R.)

1936 (1 Jan)–**62.** Wmk Mult Script CA. P 14.

D25	D **3**	5c. violet	5·50	9·50
		a. Chalk-surfaced paper (18.7.56)	35	16·00
D26		10c. scarlet	4·50	2·75
		a. Chalk-surfaced paper (6.3.62)	35	7·50
D27		20c. green	2·25	4·75
		a. Chalk-surfaced paper (6.3.62)	35	21·00
D28		30c. brown	11·00	20·00
		a. Chalk-surfaced paper (18.7.56)	35	13·00
D29		40c. ultramarine	9·50	26·00
		a. Chalk-surfaced paper (18.7.56)	75	35·00
D30		1s. grey	10·00	29·00
		a. Chalk-surfaced paper (18.7.56)	1·00	22·00
D25/30 *Set of 6*			38·00	80·00
D25a/30a *Set of 6*			2·75	£100
D25s/30s Perf "Specimen" *Set of 6*			80·00	

Zululand *see* South Africa

Set Prices for British Empire Omnibus Issues

The composition of these sets is in accordance with the tables on the following pages. Only such items considered basic stamps are included; varieties such as shades, perforation changes and watermark changes are excluded.

1935 SILVER JUBILEE

1935. *Silver Jubilee. Complete set of 250 stamps*

	PRICE	
	Un	Used
	£1000	£1500

Country	Catalogue Nos.	Stamps
Great Britain	453/6	4
Antigua	91/4	4
Ascension	31/4	4
Australia	156/8	3
Nauru	40/3	4
New Guinea	206/7	2
Papua	150/3	4
Bahamas	141/4	4
Barbados	241/4	4
Basutoland	11/14	4
Bechuanaland	111/14	4
Bermuda	94/7	4
British Guiana	301/4	4
British Honduras	143/6	4
British Solomon Islands	53/6	4
Canada	335/40	6
Newfoundland	250/3	4
Cayman Islands	108/11	4
Ceylon	379/82	4
Cyprus	144/7	4
Dominica	92/5	4
Egypt-British Forces	A10	1
Falkland Islands	139/42	4
Fiji	242/5	4
Gambia	143/6	4
Gibraltar	114/17	4
Gilbert and Ellice Islands	36/9	4
Gold Coast	113/16	4
Grenada	145/8	4
Hong Kong	133/6	4
India	240/6	7
Jamaica	114/17	4
Kenya, Uganda and Tanganyika	124/7	4
Leeward Islands	88/91	4
Malaya-Straits Settlements	256/9	4
Malta	210/13	4
Mauritius	245/8	4
Montserrat	94/7	4
Morocco Agencies		
British Currency	62/5	4
Spanish Currency	149/52	4
French Currency	212/15	4
Tangier	238/40	3
New Zealand	573/5	3
Cook Islands	113/15	3
Niue	69/71	3
Western Samoa	177/9	3
Nigeria	30/3	4
Northern Rhodesia	18/21	4
Nyasaland	123/6	4
St. Helena	124/7	4
St. Kitts-Nevis	61/4	4
St. Lucia	109/12	4
St. Vincent	142/5	4
Seychelles	128/31	4
Sierra Leone	181/4	4
Somaliland Protectorate	86/9	4
South Africa	65/8	4×2
Southern Rhodesia	31/4	4
South West Africa	88/91	4
Swaziland	21/4	4
Trinidad and Tobago	239/42	4
Turks and Caicos Islands	187/9	4
Virgin Islands	103/6	4
Total		**250**

The concept initiated by the 1935 Silver Jubilee omnibus issue has provided a pattern for a series of Royal commemoratives over the past 50 years which have introduced countless collectors to the hobby.

The Crown Colony Windsor Castle design by Harold Fleury is, surely, one of the most impressive produced to the 20th-century and its reproduction in the recess process by three of the leading stamp-printing firms of the era has provided a subject for philatelic research which has yet to be exhausted.

Each of the three, Bradbury, Wilkinson & Co. and Waterlow and Sons, who both produced fifteen issues, together with De La Rue & Co. who printed fourteen, used a series of vignette (centre) plates coupled with individual frame plates for each value. All were taken from dies made by Waterlow. Several worthwhile varieties exist on the frame plates but most interest has been concentrated on the centre plates, each of which was used to print a considerable number of different stamps.

Sheets printed by Bradbury, Wilkinson were without printed plate numbers, but research has now identified eleven centre plates which were probably used in permanent pairings. A twelfth plate awaits confirmation. Stamps from some of these centre plates have revealed a number of prominent plate flaws, the most famous of which, the extra flagstaff, has been eagerly sought by collectors for many years.

Extra flagstaff (Plate "1" R. 9/1)

Short extra flagstaff (Plate "2" R. 2/1)

Lightning conductor (Plate "3" R. 2/5)

Flagstaff on right-hand turret (Plate "5" R. 7/1)

Double flagstaff (Plate "6" R. 5/2)

De La Rue sheets were initially printed with plate numbers, but in many instances these were subsequently trimmed off. Surviving examples do, however, enable a positive identification of six centre plates, 2A, 2B, (2A), (2B), 4 and 4/ to be made. The evidence of sheet markings and plate flaws clearly demonstrates that there were two different pairs of plates numbered 2A 2B. The second pair is designated (2A) (2B) by specialist collectors to avoid further confusion. The number of major plate flaws is not so great as on the Bradbury, Wilkinson sheets, but four examples are included in the catalogue.

Diagonal line by turret (Plate 2A R. 10/1 and 10/2)

Dot to left of chapel (Plate 2B R. 8/3)

Dot by flagstaff (Plate 4 R. 8/4)

Dash by turret (Plate 4/ R. 3/6)

Much less is known concerning the Waterlow centre plate system as the sheets did not show plate numbers. Ten individual plates have, so far, been identified and it is believed that these were used in pairs. The two versions of the kite and log flaw from plate "2" show that this plate exists in two states.

Damaged turret (Plate "1" R. 5/6)

Kite and vertical log (Plate "2A" R. 10/6)

Kite and horizontal log (Plate "2B" R. 10/6)

Bird by turret (Plate "7" R. 1/5)

1937 CORONATION

1937. *Coronation.*.........Complete set of 202 stamps £120 £180

Country	Catalogue Nos	Stamps
Great Britain	461	1
Aden	13/15	3
Antigua	95/7	3
Ascension	35/7	3
Australia		
Nauru	44/7	4
New Guinea	208/11	4
Papua	154/7	4
Bahamas	146/8	3
Barbados	245/7	3
Basutoland	15/17	3
Bechuanaland	115/17	3
Bermuda	107/9	3
British Guiana	305/7	3
British Honduras	147/9	3
British Solomon Islands	57/9	3
Canada	356	1
Newfoundland	254/6, 257/67	14
Cayman Islands	112/14	3
Ceylon	383/5	3
Cyprus	148/50	3
Dominica	96/8	3
Falkland Islands	143/5	3
Fiji	246/8	3
Gambia	147/9	3
Gibraltar	118/20	3
Gilbert and Ellice Islands	40/2	3
Gold Coast	117/19	3
Grenada	149/51	3
Hong Kong	137/9	3
Jamaica	118/20	3
Kenya, Uganda and Tanganyika	128/30	3
Leeward Islands	92/4	3
Malaya-Straits Settlements	275/7	3
Malta	214/16	3
Mauritius	249/51	3
Montserrat	98/100	3
Morocco Agencies		
Spanish Currency	164	1
French Currency	229	1
Tangier	244	1
New Zealand	599/601	3
Cook Islands	124/6	3
Niue	72/4	3
Nigeria	46/8	3
Northern Rhodesia	22/4	3
Nyasaland	127/9	3
St. Helena	128/30	3
St. Kitts-Nevis	65/7	3
St. Lucia	125/7	3
St. Vincent	146/8	3
Seychelles	132/4	3
Sierra Leone	185/7	3
Somaliland Protectorate	911/2	3
South Africa	71/5	5×2
Southern Rhodesia	36/9	4
South West Africa	97/104	8×2
Swaziland	25/7	3
Trinidad and Tobago	243/5	3
Turks and Caicos Islands	191/3	3
Virgin Islands	107/9	3
Total		**202**

1945–46 VICTORY

1945–46. *Victory.*.........Complete set of 164 stamps 48·00 75·00

Country	Catalogue Nos.	Stamps
Great Britain	491/2	2
Aden	28/9	2
Seiyun	12/13	2
Shihr and Mukalla	12/13	2
Antigua	110/11	2
Ascension	48/9	2
Australia	213/15	3

Country	Catalogue Nos.	Stamps
Bahamas	176/7	2
Barbados	262/3	2
Basutoland	29/31	3×2
Bechuanaland	129/31	3×2
Bermuda	123/4	2
British Guiana	320/1	2
British Honduras	162/3	2
British Solomon Islands	73/4	2
Burma	64/7	4
Cayman Islands	127/8	2
Ceylon	400/1	2
Cyprus	164/5	2
Dominica	110/11	2
Falkland Islands	164/5	2
Falkland Islands Dependencies	G17/18	2
Fiji	268/9	2
Gambia	162/3	2
Gibraltar	132/3	2
Gilbert and Ellice Islands	55/6	2
Gold Coast	133/4	2
Grenada	164/5	2
Hong Kong	169/70	2
India	278/81	4
Hyderabad	53	1
Jamaica	141/2	2
Kenya, Uganda and Tanganyika	155/6	2
Leeward Islands	115/16	2
Malta	232/3	2
Mauritius	264/5	2
Montserrat	113/14	2
Morocco Agencies		
Tangier	253/4	2
New Zealand	667/77	11
Cook Islands	146/9	4
Niue	98/101	4
Western Samoa	215/18	4
Nigeria	60/1	2
Northern Rhodesia	46/7	2
Nyasaland	158/9	2
Pakistan		
Bahawalpur	O19	1
Pitcairn Islands	9/10	2
St. Helena	141/2	2
St. Kitts-Nevis	78/9	2
St. Lucia	142/3	2
St. Vincent	160/1	2
Seychelles	150/1	2
Sierra Leone	201/2	2
Somaliland Protectorate	117/18	2
South Africa	108/10	3×2
Southern Rhodesia	64/7	4
South West Africa	131/3	3×2
Swaziland	39/41	3×2
Trinidad and Tobago	257/8	2
Turks and Caicos Islands	206/7	2
Virgin Islands	122/3	2
Zanzibar	331/2	2
Total		**164**

1948 ROYAL SILVER WEDDING

1948–49. *Royal Silver Wedding.* ....
....Complete set of 138 stamps   £1700   £1900

Country	Catalogue Nos.	Stamps
Great Britain	493/4	2
Aden	30/1	2
Seiyun	14/15	2
Shihr and Mukalla	14/15	2
Antigua	112/13	2
Ascension	50/1	2
Bahamas	194/5	2
Bahrain	61/2	2
Barbados	265/62	2
Basutoland	36/7	2
Bechuanaland	136/7	2
Bermuda	125/6	2
British Guiana	322/3	2
British Honduras	164/5	2
British Postal Agencies in Eastern Arabia	25/6	2
British Solomon Islands	75/6	2
Cayman Islands	129/30	2
Cyprus	166/7	2
Dominica	112/13	2
Falkland Islands	166/7	2
Falkland Islands Dependencies	G19/20	2
Fiji	270/1	2
Gambia	164/5	2
Gibraltar	134/5	2
Gilbert and Ellice Islands	57/8	2
Gold Coast	147/8	2
Grenada	166/7	2
Hong Kong	171/2	2
Jamaica	143/4	2
Kenya, Uganda and Tanganyika	157/8	2
Kuwait	74/5	2
Leeward Islands	117/18	2
Malaya		
Johore	131/2	2
Kedah	70/1	2
Kelantan	55/6	2
Malacca	1/2	2
Negri Sembilan	40/1	2
Pahang	47/8	2
Penang	1/2	2

Country	Catalogue Nos.	Stamps
Perak	122/3	2
Perlis	1/2	2
Selangor	88/9	2
Trengganu	61/2	2
Malta	249/50	2
Mauritius	270/1	2
Montserrat	115/16	2
Morocco Agencies		
Spanish Currency	176/7	2
Tangier	255/6	2
Nigeria	62/3	2
North Borneo	350/1	2
Northern Rhodesia	48/9	2
Nyasaland	161/2	2
Pitcairn Islands	11/12	2
St. Helena	143/4	2
St. Kitts-Nevis	80/1	2
St. Lucia	144/5	2
St. Vincent	162/3	2
Sarawak	165/6	2
Seychelles	152/3	2
Sierra Leone	203/4	2
Singapore	31/2	2
Somaliland Protectorate	119/20	2
South Africa	125	1×2
South West Africa	137	1×2
Swaziland	46/7	2
Trinidad and Tobago	259/60	2
Turks and Caicos Islands	208/9	2
Virgin Islands	124/5	2
Zanzibar	333/4	2
Total		**138**

1949 75th ANNIVERSARY OF U.P.U.

1949. *U.P.U. 75th Anniversary*
  Complete set of 310 stamps   £275   £425

Country	Catalogue Nos.	Stamps
Great Britain	449/502	4
Aden	32/5	4
Seiyun	16/19	4
Shihr and Mukalla	16/19	4
Antigua	114/17	4
Ascension	52/5	4
Australia	232	1
Bahamas	196/9	4
Bahrain	67/70	4
Barbados	267/70	4
Basutoland	38/41	4
Bechuanaland	138/41	4
Bermuda	130/3	4
British Guiana	324/7	4
British Honduras	172/5	4
British Postal Agencies in Eastern Arabia	31/4	4
British Solomon Islands	77/80	4
Brunei	96/9	4
Cayman Islands	131/4	4
Ceylon	410/12	3
Cyprus	168/71	4
Dominica	114/17	4
Falkland Islands	168/71	4
Falkland Islands Dependencies	G31/4	4
Fiji	272/5	4
Gambia	166/9	4
Gibraltar	136/9	4
Gilbert and Ellice Islands	59/62	4
Gold Coast	149/52	4
Grenada	168/71	4
Hong Kong	173/6	4
India	325/8	4
Jamaica	145/8	4
Kenya, Uganda and Tanganyika	159/62	4
Kuwait	80/3	4
Leeward Islands	119/22	4
Malaya		
Johore	148/51	4
Kedah	72/5	4
Kelantan	57/60	4
Malacca	18/21	4
Negri Sembilan	63/6	4
Pahang	49/52	4
Penang	23/6	4
Perak	124/7	4
Perlis	3/6	4
Selangor	111/14	4
Trengganu	63/6	4
Malta	251/4	4
Mauritius	272/5	4
Montserrat	117/20	4
Morocco Agencies		
Tangier	276/9	4
New Hebrides	64/7, F77/80	4+4
Nigeria	64/7	4
North Borneo	352/5	4
Northern Rhodesia	50/3	4
Nyasaland	163/6	4

Country	Catalogue Nos.	Stamps
Pakistan		
Bahawalpur	43/6, O28/31	4+4
Pitcairn Islands	13/16	4
St. Helena	145/8	4
St. Kitts-Nevis	82/5	4
St. Lucia	160/3	4
St. Vincent	178/81	4
Sarawak	167/70	4
Seychelles	154/7	4
Sierra Leone	205/8	4
Singapore	33/6	4
Somaliland Protectorate	121/4	4
South Africa	128/30	3×2
Southern Rhodesia	68/9	2
South West Africa	138/40	3×2
Swaziland	48/51	4
Tonga	88/91	4
Trinidad and Tobago	261/4	4
Turks and Caicos Islands	217/20	4
Virgin Islands	126/9	4
Zanzibar	335/8	4
Total		**310**

1951 INAUGURATION OF B.W.I. UNIVERSITY COLLEGE

1951. *B.W.I. University College*
  Complete set of 28 stamps   10·00   25·00

Country	Catalogue Nos.	Stamps
Antigua	118/19	2
Barbados	283/4	2
British Guiana	328/9	2
British Honduras	176/7	2
Dominica	118/19	2
Grenada	185/6	2
Jamaica	149/50	2
Leeward Islands	123/4	2
Montserrat	121/2	2
St. Kitts-Nevis	92/3	2
St. Lucia	164/5	2
St. Vincent	182/3	2
Trinidad and Tobago	265/6	2
Virgin Islands	130/1	2
Total		**28**

Index

Thrillseekers need not apply...

If you want risk, shocks and high blood pressure, play the stock market.
If you want a guaranteed minimum return of up to 6% per annum*, read on.

Rare Stamp & Autograph Investment

Up to 6% guaranteed MINIMUM return per annum*

Contract Length	Guaranteed Minimum Annual Return	Min value at end of term £5,000 Invested	Min value at end of term £25,000 Invested	Min value at end of term £100,000 Invested	Min value at end of term £250,000 Invested
4 Years	4%	£5,800	£29,000	£116,000	£290,000
5 Years	5%	£6,250	£31,250	£125,000	£312,500
10 Years	6%	£8,000	£40,000	£160,000	£400,000

*Subject to terms and conditions

For more information about Stanley Gibbons Ltd and investing in rare
stamps or autographs, call us on 020 7836 8444

www.stanleygibbons.com/investment

STANLEY GIBBONS
Celebrating 150 Years

Stanley Gibbons, 399 Strand, London. WC2R 0LX

405

Stanley Gibbons
Commonwealth Country Catalogues
Build your Commonwealth Country Catalogue Collection

Introducing our popular range:

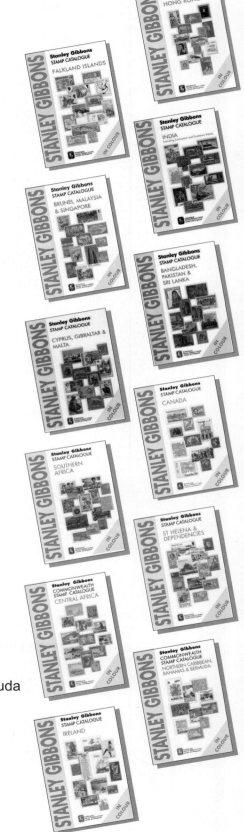

Stanley Gibbons Hong Kong
Item R2877-04   **£9.95**

Stanley Gibbons Falkland Islands
Item R2872-04   **£9.95**

Stanley Gibbons India (inc Feudatory States)
Item R2873-04   **£19.95**

Stanley Gibbons Brunei, Malaysia & Singapore
Item R2879-04   **£19.95**

Stanley Gibbons Bangladesh, Pakistan & Sri Lanka
Item R2977-05   **£14.95**

Stanley Gibbons Cyprus, Gibraltar & Malta
Item R2976-05   **£14.95**

Stanley Gibbons Canada
Item R2874-05   **£14.95**

Stanley Gibbons Southern Africa
Item R2978-05   **£19.95**

Stanley Gibbons St Helena
Item R2875-05   **£12.95**

Stanley Gibbons Central Africa
Item R2979-06   **£14.95**

Stanley Gibbons Northern Caribbean, Bahamas & Bermuda
Item R2980-06   **£16.95**

Stanley Gibbons Ireland
Item R2975-06   **£9.95**

www.stanleygibbons.com

Stanley Gibbons
7 Parkside, Christchurch Road, Ringwood, BH24 3SH
Tel: +44 (0)1425 472363 Fax: +44 (0)1425 470247 Email: sales@stanleygibbons.co.uk

COLLECT
COMMONWEALTH STAMPS
Priority order form
Four easy ways to order

Phone:
020 7836 8444
Overseas: +44 (0)20 7836 8444

Fax:
020 7557 4499
Overseas: +44 (0)20 7557 4499

Email:
stampsales@stanleygibbons.com

Post:
Stamp Mail Order Department
Stanley Gibbons Ltd, 399 Strand
London, WC2R 0LX, England

Customer details

Account Number _____

Name _____

Address _____

_____ Postcode _____

Country _____ Email _____

Tel no _____ Fax no _____

Payment details

Registered Postage & Packing   £3.60

I enclose my cheque/postal order for £............. in full payment. Please make cheques/postal orders payable to Stanley Gibbons Ltd. Cheques must be in £ sterling and drawn on a UK bank

Please debit my credit card for £.............. in full payment. I have completed the Credit Card section below.

Card Number

☐☐☐☐ ☐☐☐☐ ☐☐☐☐ ☐☐☐☐ ☐☐☐☐

Start Date (Switch & Amex) Expiry Date   Issue No (switch)

☐☐☐☐   ☐☐☐☐   ☐☐

Signature _____ Date _____

COLLECT
COMMONWEALTH STAMPS

Condition (mint/UM/used)	Country	SG No.	Description	Price	Office use only
			POSTAGE & PACKAGING	£3.60	
			GRAND TOTAL	£	

Please complete payment, name and address details overleaf

Interested in investment?

"If you're looking for the best place to put your money over the next three years, forget the stock market. Instead, I want to tell you about an investment vehicle that hardly anyone pays attention to, yet it has been used by the ultra-rich to grow and protect their wealth for decades."
Sjuggerud Confidential, Issue 10, November 2005.

What is he talking about?
Not the property market, not spread betting, but **investment in stamps**. If you would like to learn how you could achieve a guaranteed minimum return of up to 6% per annum*, with the potential for triple digit returns, please visit:
www.stanleygibbons.com/investment

For your *Free Guide to Investing in Rare Stamps and Autographs* simply fill out the form below and return it to us at your earliest convenience.

Name (Mr/Mrs/Miss/Ms) _____
Address _____

Post/Zip code _____
Tel _____
Email _____

Tel: +44(0)1481 708 270 Fax: +44(0) 1481 708 279
Email: investment@stanleygibbons.co.uk
Website: www.stanleygibbons.com/investment

* Subject to terms and conditions

STANLEY GIBBONS
Investment

Stanley Gibbons Stamp Mail Order Department
One of the world's largest stamp stocks

- Expertise in building collections
- Personal service
- Fast 48 hour despatch
- Free telephone advice
- We stock Aden to Zimbabwe
- Free monthly newsletter with exclusive special offers

Receive the latest Stanley Gibbons Great Britain Mail Order Brochure **FREE**.

Simply return the voucher below and we will send you the brochure(s) as and when they are ready.

Name (Mr/Mrs/Miss/Ms) _____
Address _____
_____
Post/Zip code _____
Tel _____
Email _____

Tel: +44(0) 20 7836 8444 Fax: +44(0) 20 7836 7342
Email: stampsales@stanleygibbons.co.uk
Website: www.stanleygibbons.com

STANLEY GIBBONS
Mail Order

Would you like the opportunity to discuss the sale of your collection?

Some reasons why you should sell to Stanley Gibbons:

- Immediate payment with £2 million available
- Unrivalled expertise in the field of philately
- Opportunity to sell at Auction boasting exceptional clearance rates
- Excellent prices paid for Great Britain & Commonwealth
- The largest philatelic audience in the UK

Name (Mr/Mrs/Miss/Ms) _____
Address _____
_____
Post/Zip code _____
Tel _____
Email _____

Tel: +44(0) 20 7836 8444 Fax: +44(0) 20 7836 7342
Email: buyers@stanleygibbons.co.uk
Website: www.stanleygibbons.com

Let us know more

For fast settlement (in any currency) please indicate what you have:

All World ☐
One Country ☐
....
Europe ☐
Foreign ☐
Postal History ☐
First Day Covers ☐
No of albums ....

STANLEY GIBBONS
A & A Department

Stanley Gibbons (Guernsey) Limited
18 Le Bordage
St Peter Port
Guernsey
Channel Islands
United Kingdom
GY1 1DE

Stanley Gibbons Mail Order
399 Strand
London
England
WC2R 0LX

Stanley Gibbons A & A Department
399 Strand
London
England
WC2R 0LX

A A C E

Authenticity   Choice   Expertise

Everything you can expect when visiting the Strand

Serving collectors for over 100 years, our showroom at 399 Strand is the world's largest stamp shop, covering everything philatelic from the highest quality Penny Blacks to the latest in watermark detection technology. Whether you are an experienced collector or just starting out, our friendly team of staff is happy to help with any query you may have.

Come to the Strand and lose yourself in the breathtaking array of philatelic material.

- over 1200 stockbooks containing stamps from 1840 to the latest issue
- catalogues, albums and accessories from Stanley Gibbons and other leading names
- our bookshelf section contains hundreds of rare philatelic titles from around the world
- valuations available by appointment from our dedicated team of experts

We cannot begin to do 399 Strand any justice in print so please take the time to visit our shop to judge for yourself – you will not be disappointed.

Stanley Gibbons
399 Strand, London, WC2R 0LX
The ace of stamps

Telephone: +44 (0)20 7836 8444 Fax: +44 (0)20 7836 7342
Email: shop@stanleygibbons.co.uk

We are open six days a week –
Monday to Friday, 9.00am to 5.30pm and Saturday, 9.30am to 5.30pm.